The Naval Institute Guide to

COMBAT FLEETS OF THE WORLD 1993

Their Ships, Aircraft, and Armament

Edited by
BERNARD PRÉZELIN

English-language version prepared by
A. D. BAKER III

NAVAL INSTITUTE PRESS
Annapolis, Maryland

In memory and admiration
Desmond Wettern
12 July 1934–8 December 1991

This ninth English-language edition is published by arrangement with Éditions Maritime et d'Outre-Mer, a division of Éditions Ouest-France.

Library of Congress Catalog Card Number: 78-50192

ISBN 1-55750-104-1

Printed in the United States of America on acid-free paper ∞

CONTENTS

TERMS AND ABBREVIATIONS

Most ship's characteristics are given as in the following sample:

Bldr	Laid down	L	In serv.
Lorient	12-62	15-5-65	1967

D: 5,090 tons (6,090 fl) **S:** 34 kts
Dim: 157.6 (148.0 pp) × 15.54 × 7.25 (max.)
A: 1/Masurca system (II × 1)—4/MM 38 Exocet—2/100-mm, Model 1953 (I × 2)—4/20-mm AA (I × 4)—1/Malafon system (13 missiles)—2/catapults for L-5 torpedoes (10 torpedoes)
Electron Equipt: Radar: 1/DRBI-23, 1/DRBV-50, 2/DRBR-51, 1/DRBC-32A, 1/DRBN-32
Sonar: 1/DUBV-23, 1/DUBV-43—SENIT-1, 2/Syllex systems
M: 2 Rateau double-reduction GT; 2 props; 72,500 shp
Boilers: 4 multitube, automatic-control; 45 kg/cm^2, 450°C
Electric: 3,440 kw (2 × 1,900-kw turbogenerators, 3 × 480-kw diesel alternators)
Range: 2,900/30; 2,400/29; 5,100/18
Crew: 23 officers, 164 petty officers, 168 men

Ship's hull numbers and names are in capitals and small capitals. Hull dimensions are in meters, calibers in millimeters, speeds in knots, ranges in nautical miles.

Dates: Dates are given in sequence: day-month-year.

D: Displacement. In most cases, standard displacement, as defined by the Treaty of Washington (1922), is given. Where possible, full load (fl) is given; otherwise, normal displacement or trial displacement is given. In the case of most submarines, two displacements are given: the first figure is surfaced displacement; the second is submerged displacement. When available, the figure for standard displacement precedes the surfaced and submerged figures.

S: Speed. This is given in knots and generally refers to maximum speed; in some cases trial speed is given. For submarines, surfaced speed is given first and is followed by submerged speed.

Dim: Hull dimensions are given as follows: length overall × beam × draft (full load, unless otherwise stated). Length between perpendiculars is given as "pp"; length at the waterline as "wl." In cases where two figures are given for one of the dimensions, e.g., the beam of the flight deck and of the hull of an aircraft carrier, the hull measurement is given as "hull."

A: Armament. Number of guns/bore diameter; or number of torpedo tubes or launchers with diameter. Figures in parentheses show the number of mounts and whether they are single, double, triple, etc.; e.g., (III × 2) indicates two triple mounts.

M: Machinery. Geared turbine is shown as GT; in some cases, the type or manufacturer of turbine is given, e.g., Parsons, etc. COSAG, CODAG/CODOG, COGAG/COGOG are used when such combinations of machinery have to be shown. "Props" indicates propellers. "CP" indicates controllable pitch.

Boilers: In most cases, number and type are shown. Steam pressure is expressed in kilograms/square centimeter and steam temperature in degrees centigrade.

Electric: Electric generating power, in kilowatts (kw) or kilovolt-amperes (kVA).

Armor: Armor protection, thickness given in millimeters.

Range: Cited in nautical miles at the speed given after the diagonal.

Man: Ship's company. Where not broken down into "officers" and "men" (i.e., noncommissioned personnel), a total complement figure is given as "tot."

A	Armament
AA	Antiaircraft
A & C, AT & Ch	Shipbuilding yard (*Atelier & Chantier*)
AAW	Anti-air warfare
ADAWS	Action Data Automation Weapon System
AEW	Airborne early warning
ARM	Anti-radiation missile
ASM	Anti-ship missile
ASROC	Antisubmarine Rocket
Ast Nav	Shipyard (*Astilleros Navales*)
ASW	Antisubmarine warfare
Author.	Authorized
avg	Average, normal
BB	Boatbuilding
bhp	brake horsepower (diesel engines)
Bldr	Builder
BPDMS	Basic Point Defense Missile System
BW	Boat Works
BY	Boat Yard
CAAIS	Computer-Assisted Action Information System
CH, Ch. Nav.	Builder, shipyard (*Chantier, Chantier Naval*)
CIWS	Close-In Weapon System (U.S.)
CN, Cant. Nav.	Naval shipyard (*Cantière Navale*)
COD	Carrier Onboard Delivery
COGAG/CODAG/ COSAG/COGOG/ CODOG	Combined propulsive machinery systems, gas turbine, diesel, steam. *CO* means *combined, A* means *and, O* means *or.* For example, CODOG means *combined diesel or gas turbine*
CP	Controllable-pitch
D	Displacement
d.c.	Depth charge
d.c.t.	Depth-charge thrower
DD, DDM	Dry dock, dry dock company (Dutch)
DECM	Deceptive Electronic Countermeasures
Dim	Dimensions
DP	Dual-purpose
DSRV	Deep Submergence Rescue Vessel
dwt	Deadweight tonnage
DY	Dockyard
ECM	Electronic countermeasures
ECCM	Electronic counter-countermeasures
Electron Equipt	Electronic equipment
ELINT	Electronic intelligence
Eng.	Engineering
E/O	Electro-Optical
ESM	Electronic support measures (i.e., passive EW)
EW	Electronic Warfare
FF, FFG	Frigate, guided-missile frigate
FLIR	Forward Looking Infrared Radar
f.c.s.	Fire-control system
fl	Full load
freq.	Frequency
FRAM	Fleet Rehabilitation and Modernization (U.S.)
fwd	Forward
G.E.	General Electric Company
GFCS	Gunfire-control system
G.M.	General Motors Corp.
grt	Gross registered tons
GT	Geared turbine
GWS	Guided Weapon System (U.K.)
HF	High frequency
HMDY	His/Her Majesty's Dockyard
H.S.A.	Hollandse Signaal Apparaaten
hp	Horsepower
IFF	Identification Friend or Foe
ihp	Indicated horsepower (reciprocating steam engines)
kg	Kilogram
Kon. Mij.	Royal Company (Dutch)
KT	Kiloton
kts	Knots
kVA	Kilovolt-ampere
kw	Kilowatt
L	Launched
LAMPS	Light Airborne Multi-purpose System (U.S.N. helicopter)
LF	Low frequency
loa	Length overall
LRMP	Long-Range Maritime Patrol (U.S.)
M	Machinery
MAD	Magnetic Anomaly Detection
Man	Manpower on board ship, crew, ship's company
MAP	Military Assistance Program (U.S. and allies)
MCM	Mine Countermeasures
MF	Medium frequency
mg	Machine gun
mm	Millimeters
MSC	Military Sealift Command
MTU	Motoren and Turbinen Union
N.B.	New Brunswick
NBC	Nuclear, biological, and chemical
NDY	Naval Dockyard
n.m.	Nautical miles
nrt	Net registered tons
N.S.	Nova Scotia
NTDS	Naval Tactical Data System
NY	Navy Yard
o.a.	Overall
PADLOC	Passive/Active Detection and Location

PDMS — Point-Defense Missile System
pp — Between perpendiculars
PUFFS — Passive Underwater Fire-Control System
RAS — Replenishment-At-Sea
RBOC — Rapid Blooming Overboard Chaff
RDY — Royal dockyard
RL — Rocket launcher
rpm — Revolutions per minute or rounds per minute
S — Speed
SAM — Surface-to-air missile
SAR — Search and rescue
SB — Shipbuilding
S.F.C.N. — Société Française de Construction Navale
shp — shaft horsepower (turbine engines)
SINS — Ships' Inertial Navigational System
SLBM — Submarine-Launched Ballistic Missile
SLEP — Service Life Extension Program
SSBN — Nuclear-powered fleet ballistic-m
SSM — Surface-to-surface missile
STIR — Separate Track and Illumination I
SURTASS — Surface Towed Array Surveillance
SY — Shipyard
syst — System
TACAN — Tactical Air Navigation beacon
TACTASS — Tactical Towed Acoustic Sensor System
TAS — Target Acquisition System
TASS — Towed-Array Surveillance System
TT — Torpedo tubes/launchers
tot. — Total
VDS — Variable-depth sonar
VLS — Vertical-Launch System
Wks. — Works
wl — Waterline

CONVERSION TABLES

◆ METERS (m.) to FEET (ft.)
based on 1 inch = 25.4 millimeters

m	0	1	2	3	4	5	6	7	8
	ft.	ft.	ft.	ft.	ft.	ft.	ft.	ft.	ft.
—	—	3.28084	6.5617	9.8425	13.1234	16.4042	19.6850	22.9659	26.2467
10	32.8084	36.0892	39.3701	42.6509	45.9317	49.2126	52.493	55.774	59.005
20	65.617	68.898	72.178	75.459	78.740	82.021	85.302	88.583	91.863
30	98.425	101.706	104.987	108.268	111.549	114.829	118.110	121.391	124.672
40	131.234	134.514	137.795	141.076	144.357	147.638	150.919	154.199	157.480
50	164.042	167.323	170.604	173.884	177.165	180.446	183.727	187.008	190.289
60	196.850	200.131	203.412	206.693	209.974	213.255	216.535	219.816	223.097
70	229.659	232.940	236.220	239.501	242.782	246.063	249.344	252.625	255.905
80	262.467	265.748	269.029	272.310	275.590	278.871	282.152	285.433	288.714
90	295.276	298.556	301.837	305.118	308.399	311.680	314.961	318.241	321.522
100	328.084	331.365	334.646	337.926	341.207	344.488	347.769	351.050	354.331
10	360.892	364.173	367.454	370.735	374.016	377.296	380.577	383.858	387.139
20	393.701	396.982	400.262	403.543	406.824	410.105	413.386	416.667	419.947
30	426.509	429.790	433.071	436.352	439.632	442.913	446.194	449.475	452.756
40	459.317	462.598	465.879	469.160	472.441	475.722	479.002	482.283	485.564
50	492.126	495.407	498.688	501.97	505.25	508.53	511.81	515.09	518.37
60	524.93	528.22	531.50	534.78	538.06	541.34	544.62	547.90	551.18
70	557.74	561.02	564.30	567.59	570.87	574.15	577.43	580.71	583.99
80	590.55	593.83	597.11	600.39	603.67	606.96	610.24	613.52	616.80
90	623.36	626.64	629.92	633.20	636.48	639.76	643.04	646.33	649.61
200	656.17	659.45	662.73	666.01	669.29	672.57	675.85	679.13	682.41
10	688.98	692.26	695.54	698.82	702.10	705.38	708.66	711.94	715.22
20	721.78	725.07	728.35	731.63	734.91	738.19	741.47	744.75	748.03
30	754.59	757.87	761.15	764.44	767.72	771.00	774.28	777.56	780.84
40	747.40	790.68	793.96	797.24	800.52	803.81	807.09	810.37	813.65
50	820.21	823.49	826.77	830.05	833.33	836.61	839.89	843.18	846.46
60	853.02	856.30	859.58	862.86	866.14	869.42	872.70	875.98	879.26
70	885.83	889.11	892.39	895.67	898.95	902.23	905.51	908.79	912.07
80	918.63	921.92	925.20	928.48	931.76	935.04	938.32	941.60	944.88
90	951.44	954.72	958.00	961.29	964.57	967.85	971.13	974.41	977.69
300	984.25	987.53	990.81	994.09	997.38	1000.66	1003.94	1007.22	1010.50
10	1017.06	1020.34	1023.62	1026.90	1030.18	1033.46	1036.75	1040.03	1043.31
20	1049.87	1053.15	1056.43	1059.71	1062.99	1066.27	1069.55	1072.83	1076.12
30	1082.68	1085.96	1089.24	1092.52	1095.80	1099.08	1102.36	1105.64	1108.92
40	1115.49	1118.77	1122.05	1125.33	1128.61	1131.89	1135.17	1138.45	1141.73
50	1118.29	1151.57	1154.86	1158.14	1161.42	1164.70	1167.98	1171.26	1174.54

◆ MILLIMETERS (mm.) to INCHES (in.)
based on 1 inch = 25.4 millimeters

mm	0	1	2	3	4	5	6	7	8
	in.	in.	in.	in.	in.	in.	in.	in.	in.
—	—	0.03937	0.07874	0.11811	0.15748	0.19685	0.23622	0.27559	0.31496
10	0.39370	0.43307	0.47244	0.51181	0.55118	0.59055	0.62992	0.66929	0.70866
20	0.78740	0.82677	0.86614	0.90551	0.94488	0.98425	1.02362	1.06299	1.10236
30	1.18110	1.22047	1.25984	1.29921	1.33858	1.37795	1.41732	1.45669	1.49606
40	1.57480	1.61417	1.65354	1.69291	1.73228	1.77165	1.81102	1.85039	1.88976

◆ MILLIMETERS (mm.) to INCHES (in.)
based on 1 inch = 25.4 millimeters (*continued*)

mm	0	1	2	3	4	5	6	7	8
	in.	in.	in.	in.	in.	in.	in.	in.	in.
50	1.96850	2.00787	2.04724	2.08661	2.12598	2.16535	2.20472	2.24409	2.28346
60	2.36220	2.40157	2.44094	2.48031	2.51969	2.55906	2.59843	2.63780	2.67717
70	2.75591	2.79528	2.83465	2.87402	2.91339	2.95276	2.99213	3.03150	3.07087
80	3.14961	3.18898	3.22835	3.26772	3.30709	3.34646	3.38583	3.42520	3.46457
90	3.54331	3.58268	3.62205	3.66142	3.70079	3.74016	3.77953	3.81890	3.85827
100	3.93701								

CONVERSION FACTORS

Meter	Yard	Foot	Inch	Centimeter	Millimeter
1	1.093 61	3.280 84	39.370 1	100	1 000
0.914 4	1	3	36	91.44	914.4
0.304 8	0.333 333	1	12	30.48	304.8
0.254	0.027 777 8	0.083 333	1	2.54	25.4 j
0.01	0.010 936 1	0.032 808 4	0.393 701	1	10
0.001	0.001 093 61	0.003 280 84	0.039 370 4	0.1	1

Nautical mile		Statute mile		Meters
1	=	1.151 52	=	1 853.18

◆ Boiler working pressure

Kilogram per square centimeter (atmosphere)		*Pounds per square inch*
1	equivalent →	14.223 3
0.070 307	← equivalent	1

◆ Conversion for Fahrenheit and centigrade scales

1 degree centigrade = 1.8 degrees Fahrenheit
1 degree Fahrenheit = 5/9 degree centigrade
t°F = 5/9(t − 32)°C.
t°C = (1.8t + 32)°F.

◆ Weights

1 kilogram = 2.204 62 *pounds* (av)
1 *pound* = 0.453 592 *kilograms*
1 ton (metric) = 0.984 21 *ton*
1 *ton* = 1.016 05 *metric ton*

◆ Power

1 CV = 0.986 32 *horsepower* (HP) 0.735 88 kilowatt (Greenwich) (75 kgm s)
1 *horsepower* (HP) = 1.013 87 (CV) 0.746 08 kilowatt (Greenwich)

PREFACE TO THE ENGLISH-LANGUAGE EDITION

It has always been something of a cliche that the editors of naval reference books make mention of an unusual number of changes since the last edition. In this instance, the cliche is nonetheless valid, for there can have been few times in modern naval history when the compositions of the fleets of the world have been so radically altered—and without major conflict being the cause. The breakup of the Soviet empire has spawned at least seven new fleets (Azerbaijan, Estonia, Georgia, Latvia, Lithuania, Turkmenistan, and Ukraine), and the dissolution of Yugoslavia has created three (Croatia, Slovenia, and the Yugoslav Federation of Montenegro and Serbia). The unifications of Germany and Yemen have reduced the number of navies by two, and the foolhardiness of Saddam Hussein has caused the near-disappearance of the navy of Iraq. Even as they modernize, the major navies are reducing their fleets by ridding them of older units, but many of those older but still useful ships are now flying new flags in other fleets. Altogether, the fleets of 171 separate political entities are described in the data pages that follow.

In addition to the unusually large number of changes in naval order of battle that have occurred over the two years since the last edition, there have also been major developments in naval technology. On the one hand, exotic new concepts such as Sweden's "stealth" trials craft *Smyge*, the U.S. and Japanese navies' SWATH ocean reconnaissance ships, and Norway's rigid sidewall air-cushion vehicle minesweeper/minehunters are beginning to enter service; on the other, the last of the battleships have been placed in reserve, leaving Peru with the dubious (and probably short-lived) honor of having the ship with the largest guns in commission. Thus, the compilers of *Flottes de Combat* and *Combat Fleets* have been unusually busy!

The new edition of *Combat Fleets* is some six months late in appearing, largely because the compiler decided to modernize the production process and employ a computer. The labor of manipulating what turned out to be well over 2,000 pages of manuscript proved more than bargained for—but it is hoped that the time lost on this edition will be recouped in future years. In addition to improving the speed with which new data can be assimilated into the *Combat Fleets* database, the computer has also allowed for greater accuracy and has provided the opportunity to revise completely and better organize the entire text. Many apologies to those who ordered the book months ago and have had to wait, but the compiler believes the delay will have proven worthwhile.

A brief study of the Terms and Abbreviations sections on the preceding pages will help the user understand the condensed data format used in the book. Conversion tables between the English measurements system and the metric system employed here are also given. One deviation, however, has been made from the metric system because so many of the users are U.S. citizens: *displacements for U.S. Navy ships have been retained in long tons of 2,240 lbs.* For those seeking to make "exact" comparisons between a U.S. Navy ship and a similar foreign vessel, convert the U.S. displacement to metric by multiplying it by 1.01605 or convert the metric displacement to English long tons by multiplying it by 0.98421. Major naval weapons systems, sensors, and naval aircraft are described at the beginning of each country-of-origin entry, after the entries on numbers of personnel, naval aviation forces, and, for the major fleets, naval construction programs. For more comprehensive data on naval weapons systems and sensors, see the Naval Institute's companion volume, the *Naval Institute Guide to World Naval Weapons Systems*, edited by Dr. Norman Friedman. A comprehensive index of all ship names (and also NATO's class nicknames for the navies of the People's Republic of China, the former U.S.S.R., and other ex–Warsaw Pact fleets) is included, and there is also an addenda for late-arriving information received through July 1992.

Because of the late appearance of this edition, the addenda is longer than usual; users are urged to consult it when studying the individual national entries throughout the book. In the addenda will also be found the entries for some of the newer navies mentioned in the opening paragraph.

All information in *Combat Fleets* has been derived from unclassified, open publications and correspondence received from around the world. The official publications of many navies have been consulted. Nonetheless, some data, particularly that on the submarines and major surface combatants of the former Soviet Union, China, and North Korea, is estimative in nature, based on the study of photography and reasonable engineering and naval architectural estimates. Particularly valuable as sources for and checks on information have been the following periodicals: *Air International, Alle Hens, Aviation Week, Flight, International Defense Review, Jane's Defence Weekly, Maritime Defence, Naval Aviation News, The Navy, Navint, Navy International, Revista Maritima, Ships of the World, Soldat und Technik, Surface Warfare, Undersea Technology,* and *Warship International.* Our sister references, *Almanacco Navale, Jane's Fighting Ships,* and *Weyers Flottentaschenbuch,* edited by Giorgio Giorgerini, Richard Sharpe, and Gerhard Albrecht, respectively, were frequently consulted as well.

As usual, many friends, manufacturers, and officials have assisted with this edition, some with only a single photograph or item of information and others with a large amount of invaluable information or photography. Some of these more than helpful individuals have been professionals in the offices of shipbuilders or various government agencies, while the majority have been "amateurs" in name only but in reality individuals with an intense interest in the navies of the world and, thank goodness, the knack of taking ship photographs from just the right angle to catch the details so necessary for illustration and to allow the editors to extract data on minute changes in equipment. All information and photography sent to *Combat Fleets* is carefully studied and employed in the preparation of the final manuscript.

One contributor who must be singled out for special mention is Leo Van Ginderen, indefatigable collector of ship images from around the world and a superb photographer in his own right. Leo's work is heavily represented in the following pages and constitutes perhaps a full one quarter of the over 4,300 photographs used to illustrate this edition. Almost every week come several packages of prints from his studio, providing a rich store of information as well as a great variety of views of thousands of naval vessels from which to choose illustrations; I wish we could have printed them all.

Those who have given invaluable help with this edition include: Robert G. Allen, president, Robert G. Allen Ltd., Vancouver, Canada; Dr. Giorgio Arra, one of the world's leading ship portrait photographers, who lent many hundreds of his excellent photographs for the U.S. Navy section and elsewhere; Victor M. Baca, for excellent photos of U.S. Navy and Coast Guard units; George I. Baldwin, Director, Communications Services, Bath Iron Works; Kapt. Lt. F. K. Bergmann, M.O.D. Bonn, for supplying superb photos of ships in the Baltic; J. H. Bih, editor, *Defense Technology,* for sharing photos and information; John Bouvia, for photos of U.S. Navy ships and craft; Mary Breig, editor of the Canadian Coast Guard's excellent quarterly, *Fleet News;* Nancy Breen, of the Military Sealift Command's Legislative and Public Affairs Office; Maurizio Brescia; David Broecker, for excellent photos of U.S. Navy ships and aircraft; Dr. Robert M. Browning, Jr., U.S. Coast Guard historian, for data about changes in the composition of that force; Peder W. Cappelen, senior executive officer, Press and Information Division, Defense Command, Norway; Commander Pete Bulkeley, USN; Rolland Campbell, for photos and data about *Hiddensee;* Fred Cassaday, of NAVSEA; Christopher P. Cavas, for several very useful photos; Raymond Cheung, for invaluable information and photography on the R.O.C.N.; Ronald P. Chiason, general manager, Conrad Industries; Dr. Chien Chung, Director, Nuclear Science & Development Center, National Tsing Hua University, Taiwan, for sharing photos and data; P. C. Clift; Gary Davies, of Maritime Photographic, whose expertly handled camera has ranged from the Baltic to the South Atlantic; Malcolm R. Dippy, for beautifully crisp photos from "down under"; Fred Dittmer, for data on former merchant ships; Wilhelm Donko, correspondent, intrepid photographer of the U.S. Navy, and now author of books on the U.S. fleet; Leslie M. Dury, faithful correspondent on Royal Navy and European developments; Russell D. Egnor and Pat Toombs of the News Photo Division, CHINFO, for unfailing assistance; Dipl.-Ing. Hartmut Ehlers, prolific photographer and correspondent on the Turkish Navy and the navies of Africa and elsewhere; Ron Elias, of Ingalls Shipbuilding, whose color photographs dramatize his company's ships so well; Lieutenant Arild Engelsen, R. Nor. N.; John R. Forster, for wide-ranging knowledge of small combatant developments; Dr. Norman Friedman, incredibly prolific and always authoritative author on naval and strategic subjects—and always a faithful friend; Roger J. L. Fry, who provided great assistance in understanding R. N. developments; Giorgio Ghiglione; Ross Gillett, editor of the Australian Navy League's *The Navy,* author of authoritative works on the R.A.N., and provider of much useful photography; Luciano Grazioli, for sending not only his own excellent photos, but also those of his colleagues; CDR Alvin H. Grobmeier, USN (Ret.), who provided valued assistance; Eric Grove, for photos and data on the fleets of Hungary and the Gambia; Gilbert Gyssels; Kpt. Lt. A. D. Heinsdorf, M.O.D. Bonn; Carlos Hernandez Gonzales, for invaluable help with the Venezuelan Navy and for a number of unique photos; David A. Hilty, of Newport News Shipbuilding and Dry Dock; R. Vanden Hoek; Percy Hunt; Kohji Ishiwata, editor of the world's leading magazine on contemporary warships, *Ships of the World;* Vic Jeffery, command public relations officer, R.A.N., Rockingham, for supplying useful information on the R.A.N. and the superb photography taken by the R.A.N.'s staff photographers in Western Australia; Florian Jentsch, for unusual and well-documented ship photos; Ulf Jönsson, of Kockums, Sweden; CDR Heinz Dieter Jopp, F.G.N.; Leif Jungestad, of Kockums Marine AB; Al Kamhi, manager, Public Relations, Martin Marietta Aero and Naval Systems; Teddy Kilbourne, of Ingalls Shipbuilding; Gerhard Koop, faithful chronicler of the *Bundesmarine* and its many developments; Jürg Kürsener, for photos from his interesting travels; Mike Louagie, a professional photographer whose camera knows no peer; Capitão de Fragata Henrique Alexandre Machado da Silva Fonseca, P.N., for photos of his fine new command, *Corte Real*; Paul J. Martineau, of Ingalls Shipbuilding; Carlo Martinelli, for a large number of excellent photos from the Mediterranean area; Fu S. Mei, for thoughts and data on the R.O.C.N.; Stafford Menard, McDermott, Inc.; Ted Minter, faithful correspondent on the U.S. Navy; Kevin E. Moak, of Gibbs & Cox, for the illustration of the DDG 51 Flight IIA destroyer; A. Molinari; Dennis P. Moore, for photos from Canada; Samuel L. Morison; John Mortimer; George Nassiopoulos, for photos of U.S. Navy units on the East Coast; Peter Noble, of Wärtsilä Marine, Vancouver, Canada; Jurrien S. Noot; Ronald E. Parkinson, for photography of U.S.N. ships; Maurizio de Pelligrini, of Fincantieri; J. Perrichet; Julie E. Phillips, Bath Iron Works; Norman Polmar, editor of *Ships and Aircraft of the U.S. Fleet* and *Guide to the Soviet Navy,* who cheerfully supplied many unique photos and much useful guidance; Antony Preston, editor (with Gillian Wettern) of the indispensable naval newsletter, *Navint;* Jasper Van Raemdonck, for useful data about the Belgian Navy; Anil Raj, vice president, Trinity Marine Group, for data and photos of his company's diverse and excellent ships; G. Rex; Pablo Peiro Riesco, of Bazán; Bram Risseeuw, correspondent on the Netherlands and South American navies, especially Uruguay, without whose constant help this book would have been considerably less comprehensive and accurate; A. J. Rizzo, of Anderson and Rizzo; Fouad Sadek, for unusual photos from unusual places; Walter Sartori, for excellent views from the Portsmouth, U.K., area; Dr. Robert L. Scheina, official historian, U.S. Coast Guard, for information in the U.S. Coast Guard section, and for providing advice and guidance on South American navies; Herbert H. Schenck, of Underseas Cable Engineers, Inc., for data on cable ships; George R. Schneider, Jr., for a large number of excellent photos of U.S., South American, and other naval ships and craft; Antonio Scrimali; Alexandre Sheldon-Duplaix; Piet Sinke; Harold D. Sisson, Jr., executive director, Marketing, Textron Marine Systems; Stuart Slade for data otherwise unobtainable; Adam Smigielski, for conveying a great deal of data on Baltic fleets; David Smith; W. D. Souter, for photos from the Marshall Islands; David Steigman; Ben Sullivan, for generously going well out of his way to obtain very useful photos and information; P-A. Stenberg, of Kockums, Canada; K-A. Sundin, managing director, Dockstavarvet, Sweden, for data and photos of his company's fine new assault craft; Arne Ingar Tandberg, for photos and data on Norwegian ships; Rev. Albert T. Tappman, for spiritual guidance; Dipl.-Ing. Stefan Terzibaschitsch, Germany's leading expert on the U.S. Navy, prolific photographer, and faithful correspondent on all manner of things; Ray Turner, NAVSEA, for obtaining photos of the YTT 9-class torpedo trials ships; LT L. R. Tye, R.N.Z.N., public relations officer, Royal New Zealand Navy; Giuseppe Valentini; Christophe Van Oyen; Hans J. Vanhöfen, for sharing his comprehensive new ship information database; Dr. Michael Vlahos, for much useful data on the Indian Navy and developments in the Middle East; Bill A. Warner, McDermott, Inc.; Peter C. Westdijk, for excellent photos from his wide travels; Armin Wetterhahn, for sharing his data and cogent observations on the former Soviet Navy; Mrs. E. Ureel-Deus for information about the fleet of Zimbabwe; Mike Waldschmidt; Mark Willis, of Maritime Photographic; Christopher C. Wright III, editor *Warship International* and expert on U.S. Navy programs; Thomas W. Wright, vice president, Intermarine, U.S.A.; Captain David Yaeger, NOAA Corps, for photos and data about the NOAA fleet. To all those others who helped as well, my deepest thanks; my apologies to anyone who has not gotten a letter of thanks from me lately.

The editor of our parent publication, *Flottes de Combat,* Bernard Prézelin, was generous, as always, with his advice and assistance. *Flottes de Combat* has its own stable of photography contributors and has been generous in sharing their work with *Combat Fleets.*

Computer geniuses Larry Bond, Dwin Craig, and John Gresham are especially to be thanked for setting up the Macintosh equipment and programs that allowed *Combat Fleets* to transition into the modern age; their patience with panicky telephone calls was exemplary. Special thanks go also to Rear Admiral Thomas A. Brooks, USN (Ret.), Rear Admiral Edward D. Sheafer, Jr., USN, and William H. J. Manthorpe for encouraging the continuation of this project.

Carol Swartz, senior manuscript editor at the Naval Institute Press, performed her usual miracles of organization and in addition typed the over 4,300 captions to the illustrations. Carol has contributed her knowledge and patience selflessly to this edition, listening sympathetically to the compiler's many woes (real and imagined) and always bringing her own special expertise to bear. Without her, the book would truly not have been possible.

Many others at the U.S. Naval Institute deserve grateful mention for their assistance and encouragement. Jim Barber, the executive director of the Naval Institute, Tom Epley, the director of the Naval Institute Press, and Fred Rainbow, editor of the *Proceedings,* offered constant support, as did *Proceedings* Associate Editor Fred Schultz. Photo editor/archivist Linda Cullen and her associate Mary Beth Straight were ever-generous with their time and energy in tracking down obscure illustration sources. Mary Medland worked with Carol Swartz in the difficult task of compiling the thousands of entries in the index, and Mary Lou Kenney acted as a pinch-hit editor every bit as careful as Carol. John Cronin and Eddie Vance kept track of the complex production effort, Pamela Schnitter provided the book's design, and Suzanne Peake and Roy Carson acted as the eagle-eyed proofreaders. For his excellent translation of the French preface and introduction to the major navies, I am again most grateful to Professor Kendall Lappin. Jim Sutton, Tom Harnish, and Susan Artigiani dreamed up innovative ways to get more copies into the hands of more users. The typesetters for this edition, Bi-Comp Incorporated, of York, Pennsylvania, did a superb job of transposing the lengthy manuscript and numerous illustrations into finished and pleasing pages. My sincere thanks to all who participated.

Work on *Combat Fleets* has been carried on during evenings, weekends, and vacations from the compiler's regular employment. For their understanding and patience at putting up with the even more than usually time-consuming work needed to revise and automate the 1993 edition, my wife, Anne-marie, and daughter Alexandra have my deepest gratitude. Both cheerfully delivered numerous packages to the post office and took down complicated messages from people with unusual accents. Both also put up with no summer vacation for two years in a row, which is well beyond the call of duty. Thank you both from the bottom of my heart.

This edition of *Combat Fleets* is dedicated to the memory of Desmond Robert French Wettern. For over thirty years, Desmond Wettern was the consummate professional reporter of naval matters in the British press, where his authoritative writing was always tempered by a deep knowledge of all aspects of things naval. Several years ago, Desmond started with Antony Preston the bi-weekly newsletter *Navint,* which quickly established itself as the most complete and knowledgeable periodical on technical, political, and operational developments in the fleets of the world. No one who has a need to be up-to-date on naval matters can afford to be without access to *Navint.* Desmond Wettern passed away on 8 December 1991 at an unfortunately young age, but the consummate standards of inquiry and reporting that he set will remain as a guide to all who work in the field of naval and military journalism. As Desmond's memorial, his wife Gillian and Antony Preston are carrying on with *Navint,* which continues unabated the fine work he began.

Combat Fleets and *Flottes de Combat* are published every two years, but the work of revision is continuous (especially now that the compiler is hard-wired to his Macintosh). Anyone with information to update or correct the book or who has photographs that could be used to illustrate the next edition is urged to contact the editors via the Naval Institute Press, 118 Maryland Ave., Annapolis, Md. 21402-5035. Dates and locations for all photographs are highly desirable, and all illustrations used will be credited to the contributors. With your help, we can make *Combat Fleets* and *Flottes de Combat* as accurate, thorough, and timely as possible.

A. D. Baker III
31 July 1992

PREFACE TO THE FRENCH EDITION

The 1992 edition of *Flottes de Combat* numbers 958 pages, 33 more than in 1990, partially because of a more complete description of paramilitary forces and in part because of greater graphic documentation (2,430 photographs, 1,330 of them new, as compared with 2,100 in 1990, and 130 sketch-plans, of which 23 are new).

For this 47th edition of the work, I am indebted to the following persons for aid and assistance furnished me in one form or another.

—Admiral Coatanéa, Chief of the General Staff of the French Navy, and the officers of his staff;

—Captain Bied-Charreton, Director of the Armed Forces Public Relations Service (navy section), and the public relations officers of the ports of Brest, Toulon, Lorient, and Cherbourg;

—Captain David de Drézigué, director, and Mme. Arnaudies, general secretary of the editorial staff of *Cols Bleus* [Blue Collars], the weekly magazine of the navy and naval dockyards; Captain (R) Dannery, editor-in-chief of *Marine*, the quarterly journal of ACORAM;

—Captains Max Moulin and Gheerbrant; Commander (R) Martin-Prével; Steward 1st Class Garapin;

—the naval attachés of South Africa, Brazil, Canada, Chile, and Sweden, and more particularly those of Germany (Captain Porrio), Denmark (Captain Fage-Pedersen), Spain (Commander De Ugarte de la Azuela), and Portugal (Commander Alves Correia), posted to Paris or London;

—the Designers of the volume, Commander Gassier and M. Robert Dumas, who is to be succeeded by M. Jean Moulin;

—the following photographers and ship-lovers faithful to *Flottes de Combat:* Messrs. Giorgio Arra, Marius Bar, Siegfried Breyer, Maurizio del Prete, Wilhelm Donko, James W. Goss, Gerhard Koop, Boris Lemachko, Pierre-Yves Léo, Mike Louagie, Carlo Martinelli, Jacques Pradignac, Alexandre Sheldon-Duplaix, Stefan Terzibaschitsch, Louis Van Cant, Maurice Voss, and Peter Voss;

—Mr. Tohru Kizu, editor-in-chief of the famous Japanese publication *Ships of the World*, from which come the great majority of photographs in the "Japan" section;

—the publishers of analogous foreign works: Captain Sharpe of *Jane's Fighting Ships*, Mr. Albrecht of *Weyers Flotten Taschenbuch*, Messrs. Giorgerini and Nani of *Almanacco Navale;*

—Mr. Arthur D. Baker III, who adapts *Flottes de Combat* in the United States under the title *Combat Fleets of the World* for the U.S. Naval Institute and who has sent me photos by Messrs. Behling, Bouvia, Broecker, Dippy, Ehlers, Engelsen, Gillett, Groves, Gyssels, Jedrlinic, Kornefeldt, Sadek, Schneider, Souter, Sullivan, and Van Ginderen;

—Monsieur Jean Labayle-Couhat of the Academie de Marine, my illustrious predecessor who, from 1974 to 1988, succeeded in giving new impetus to *Flottes de Combat* and whose advice has been of great assistance to me;

—finally, the personnel of the Maury printing establishments and of Ouest-France/EMOM Publications, who have been responsible for the book: Mesdames Colette Gaspais, Anne-Marie Séchet, Maryse Herbert, and M. Jean-Marc Lebreton.

May they all be assured of my profound gratitude.

Bernard Prézelin

THE MAJOR FLEETS AT A TIME OF CHANGE

EVOLUTION OF THE THREAT

A multitude of major events have taken place in the course of the past two years; these have profoundly changed all geo-strategic assumptions and the worldwide balances of power. Nevertheless, the dangers of crisis or war have by no means disappeared. Precisely because of the tremendous changes it is undergoing, the world remains a dangerous place with an uncertain future. The principal sources of danger are the perenniality of Russian military power, the violent resurgence of nationalism in Eastern Europe, the religious fanaticism of certain Arab countries, the authoritarianism of many third-world regimes, and the economic, social, and demographic problems confronting developing countries.

The reunification of Germany, the emancipation of eastern European countries, the dissolution of the Warsaw Pact, and the Baltic States' accession to independence are some of the events that have punctuated the crumbling of communism in Europe and have therefore contributed to a certain diminution of the Russian threat. A diminution, yes, but not disappearance; for the armed forces of the ex-Soviet states will remain powerful for many years. It behooves us, therefore, to remain vigilant and not to lower our guard too quickly, as certain Western nations seem to be doing by seizing upon military budgets as the most tempting targets for reducing their expenditures. Events such as the attempted coup in Moscow in August 1991 (fortunately unsuccessful) should counsel prudence; for individuals trained and indoctrinated under the old régime, especially in the military, are still in place, and it will probably be several decades before any profound changes take place in their mentality. Conflicts of nationality within such mosaics as the Commonwealth of Independent States and Yugoslavia, the presence of nuclear weapons in several ex-Soviet republics that are now proclaiming their independence, and the catastrophic economic condition of all Eastern Europe may lead to civil wars—already to be seen in Yugoslavia—with a possible maritime overspill (should the navies of these states come to the point of splitting into rival factions or to political blackmail). There are so many instability factors that it behooves us to keep things under control by maintaining a strong defense, and more precisely to keep our nuclear deterrent force at a high level of efficiency by adapting it to foreseeable technological developments, despite the START agreements and the recent proposals of Presidents Bush and Gorbachev.

In addition to the risks of uncertainty in the East, we must also be able to control insecurity factors throughout the world. Resorting to force in border disputes as in the Iraq-Kuwait affair, military nuclear research in certain non-aligned countries such as North Korea, Pakistan, and Iraq (the magnitude of which is now being revealed), the greatly increasing populations and economic and social degradation in southern countries (particularly in some capital cities surrounded by shantytowns), and the ethnic confrontations that are shaking the African continent demand that the Western nations maintain and even increase, as the Gulf War demonstrated, their capacity to intervene anywhere in the world. This is mandatory for France, not only in order to assert our authority over our overseas departments and territories and to ensure freedom of the seas—notably for passage of energy sources on which we all depend—but also to ensure the safety or the evacuation of our nationals and associates trapped in countries where there is a quasi-insurrectional situation, to fulfill our obligations wherever we have signed agreements on defense, and even to provide humanitarian aid to local populations under stress.

For the [French] Navy—"whose role is constantly increasing within our defense establishment by virtue of the global dimensions of its sphere of influence," as Admiral Coatanéa, Chief of General Staff of the Navy, pointed out to the graduating class of the École Navale on 12 October—these objectives can be achieved only if we are able to keep in a constant state of readiness a carrier task force including its own antiair and antisubmarine force, its operational transport and logistic support ships, and a component of nuclear-powered attack submarines [SSN] for advance protection. Moreover, the Gulf War has just shown once again that the "mine" threat is within the financial means of any state; so we must not neglect the anti-mine component. Finally, to an ever greater extent, space is going to become a fourth dimension that naval forces will require, not only for communications but also for intelligence information, which has become of capital interest in the conduct of operations.

As Admiral Lanxade, Chief of Staff of the Armed Forces, emphasized during the Seminar on Military Doctrine in Vienna on 8 October, "Our defense in the course of past decades has been designed to confront a violent, sudden, massive, but clearly defined and identified threat. Henceforth, it must enable us to deal with perils that are numerous, diversified, unclear, geographically widespread, and consequently more difficult to identify and come to grips with."

UNITED STATES NAVY

The United States Navy demonstrated at the time of the Gulf War its capacity to intervene massively and immediately, far from its bases. Six aircraft carriers with their embarked air groups—which performed, we must emphasize, almost one-third of the air missions of that war—and their escort and logistic forces participated in Desert Shield and Desert Storm. Counting all units present in the theater between the preparatory phase (August 1990) and the end of the fighting (March 1991), no less than 9 aircraft carriers, 2 battleships, 21 missile cruisers, 20 destroyers, 21 frigates, 4 minesweepers, 12 nuclear-powered attack submarines [SSN], 38 amphibious ships, and 23 logistic-support ships participated in the operations. To this gigantic armada must be added 9 vehicle-transport ships of the Military Sealift Command, 13 transports of the Afloat Prepositioning Force, and 64 ships of the Ready Reserve Force reactivated for the occasion.

Despite the victorious outcome of the war, the Bush administration has decided on a substantial reduction of its military forces in general and its naval forces in particular, to resorb a portion of their enormous budget deficit. The plan for a navy comprising 600 combatant ships, envisaged by the Reagan administration in the early 1980s, has been definitively abandoned as a result of the attenuation of the Soviet threat; the current objective of the U.S. Navy is to possess 450 combatant ships by 1995. But the reductions now in progress and those foreseeable will have little effect on the intervention capabilities of the U.S. Navy, which remains, and will continue in future years to be, the foremost in the world. Its personnel, which in 1991 numbered 570,000 in the navy and 194,000 in the Marine Corps, will be reduced by 1998 to 535,000 and 159,000, so its manpower will remain quite substantial.

The number of nuclear-powered aircraft carriers in service now stands at six units, since the commissioning of the *Abraham Lincoln* in late 1989; it will increase to seven with the forthcoming arrival of the *George Washington;* two others are under construction and two more are envisaged for delivery in the years 2001 and 2003. On the other hand, the number of classic aircraft carriers has diminished with the retirement of the *Midway* and *Coral Sea.* The *Forrestal* class will soon begin to be withdrawn from service: the *Ranger,* the only one of this series not to have undergone SLEP remodeling, will have done so by 1993; then it will be the *Saratoga*'s turn in 1995. The *Forrestal* is to become a training carrier in 1992. The navy plans by 1995 to have 12 aircraft carriers with 11 air groups (Carrier Air Wings) instead of the present 14 with 13 CAW; in both these cases, the missing CAW is that of an aircraft carrier undergoing SLEP. This remodeling is now in progress on the *Constellation* and has been completed on the *Kitty Hawk.*

The eleventh strategic submarine of the *Ohio* class joined the fleet in 1990, which entailed *ipso facto* the decommissioning of four *Lafayette*-class boats armed with Poseidon missiles in order to comply with the START agreements; another will become operational during fiscal 1992.

The number of nuclear-powered attack submarines [SSN] has fallen (from 97 to 85) as a result of the withdrawal of *Permit-* and *Sturgeon*-class boats in numbers not compensated by commissionings of the *Los Angeles* class; nevertheless, operational efficacy has thereby increased considerably, for the *Los Angeles*-class boats are far superior to the *Permits.* Construction of the one *Sea Wolf* continues, but commissioning may be considerably delayed since some flaws in welding were discovered in it last August. In any case, the number of these big SSNs will probably be limited to one because of their prohibitive cost. For the future, the U.S. Navy envisages building some smaller boats (6,000 tons vice 9,150); this is the *Centurion* project. The navy no longer has any classic diesel-powered submarines, (except for the *Dolphin,* used for experimentation).

The four ships of the line of the *Iowa* class were all in reserve by March of 1992. In case of need, these ships can be put back into service within four to six months. The number of nuclear-powered missile cruisers is to be reduced from nine to seven in the near future with the decommissioning of the *Truxtun* and *Bainbridge* for budgetary reasons. The number of ships of this type with conventional propulsion, on the other hand, is being increased by the commissioning of six new *Ticonderogas* equipped with Aegis; eight others are to join the fleet in the next two years.

The category of destroyers is the one undergoing the most changes, with the withdrawal from active service of DDGs of the *Coontz* and *Charles Adams* classes; the last four *Coontz* DDGs and the last eight of the *Charles Adams* class will all have been decommissioned by 1994. The commissioning of the *Arleigh Burke*s equipped with the Aegis system falls far short of compensating these losses, since only the first of that series is now in service; 16 more are under construction or financed, and they will be completed more rapidly than was the *Arleigh Burke.* A total of 40 destroyers will probably be delivered to the U.S. Navy in the next 20 years; furthermore, they will be the only large combat surface ships, with the exception of aircraft carriers, to be built in the course of that period of time. The two other classes of destroyers now in service continue to benefit from renovation and improvement: NTU modernization on the 4 *Kidds* and new armament on 24 of the 31 *Spruances.* Also, the number of frigates is to be greatly reduced in 1992–93 with the transfer of 32 of the 46 *Knox*es to reserve status, the transfer of 6 others to foreign countries, and the remaining 8 being taken over by the Naval Reserve Force. Reactivation of these frigates would require six months.

Mine warfare remains the Achilles heel of the U.S. Navy; this is all the more surprising since during the Iran–Iraq War the frigate *Samuel B. Roberts* was almost lost and two combat ships were victimized by Iraqi mines during the Gulf War, the missile cruiser *Princeton* being heavily damaged and the helicopter carrier *Tripoli* more lightly. Five additional *Avenger*-class minehunter-sweepers have been put into active service in the past two years, bringing their total to eight, and six more are under construction; the first *Osprey*-class minehunter, derived from the Italian *Lerici* class, was launched in March, and 11 others are financed. Certainly the navy's anti-mine forces are being replenished, but the number of ships of this type is glaringly insufficient, and the fact that most are manned in part by Naval Reserve Force personnel makes it clear that mine warfare is not a major concern of the American command.

The amphibious component has been strengthened by the entry into service of the last four LSDs of the *Whidbey Island* class, bringing their total to eight; three others (*Harper's Ferry* class), slightly different, are under construction, as are four *Wasp*-class helicopter carriers. For the future, the navy has under study a new type of amphibious ship, the LX, which will begin to replace all LPDs, LSDs and LSTs around the year 2000; of these, 27 are envisaged.

In the field of support vessels, only one ship has been launched: the fleet oiler-storeship *Supply.* Two others are on the ways. Jumboization has been completed on two of the five *Cimarron*-class oilers and is in progress on the other three. The scientific fleet of the Military Sealift Command is undergoing a complete rejuvenation with the construction or commissioning of five new hydrographic and oceanographic ships. The first acoustic-surveillance ship with SWATH hull was accepted for service in March; 3 others are under construction and will be added to the 18 *Stalwart*-class monohulls in service; the latter, however, are to begin withdrawal from service beginning in 1992. Finally, the series of 18 large oiler-storeships of the *Kaiser* class is progressing: 10 are operational and 8 in various stages of construction, which has made it possible to decommission older ships dating from World War II or shortly thereafter.

Most of the current carrier-borne aircraft types will continue to be manufactured or modernized. For instance, two new versions of the Hornet F/A-18, the -E and -F versions, will be built; the same is true of the Marine Corps's AV-8B Harrier, with the Harrier Plus version. As for other categories of aircraft, they will be undergoing partial transformations: re-engining on the F-14 Tomcat and the EA-6B Prowler; re-engining and wing-rebuilding on the A-6E Intruder; modification of equipment on the S-3A/B Viking and the E-2C Hawkeye. Several projected aircraft have fallen victim to budgetary pressure and have been abandoned: namely the A-12 Avenger, a very "stealthy" airplane that was to replace the Intruder; the Navy Advanced Tactical Fighter, which was to replace the Tomcat; and lastly the P-7 LRCAA, a successor to the maritime-patrol Orion. On the other hand, the V-22 Osprey, which figured among the administration's prime targets, has been well supported by Congress. To compensate for the abandoned projects, presently envisioned are an AX assault plane less costly than the A-12, and a P-3C Plus version to replace the P-7. In the category of helicopters, the SH-60F Ocean Hawk, a purely ASW version of the SH-60B Sea Hawk, is progressively replacing the SH-3 Sea King aboard aircraft carriers, and the large helicopters CH-53E Super Stallion and MH-53E Sea Dragon are joining marine corps and navy units, respectively.

In the field of weapons, the major development is the success achieved by Tomahawk cruise missiles in the Gulf War, which constituted a baptism of fire for this weapons system; 291 were launched, some from battleships and cruisers deployed in the Arabian–Persian Gulf, some from *Los Angeles*-class SSNs deployed in the Red Sea, with an estimated success rate of 80 percent. All the missiles utilized, of course, were armed with conventional warheads. All Tomahawks with nuclear warheads are to be withdrawn from the arsenal, in accordance with the decision taken by President Bush on 27 September 1991, to suppress all tactical nuclear weapons. In addition to its Tomahawk TLAM-Ns, the U.S. Navy will have to divest itself of its B47, B57, and W80 nuclear bombs. On the other hand, Trident missiles are not affected by this decision, since it applies only to land-based missiles, insofar as strategic missiles with multiple warheads are concerned. Existing weapons systems are constantly being perfected, whether it be the Harpoon antiship missile, the SM-2 and Sea Sparrow surface-to-air missiles, or the Phalanx multitube anti-missile artillery system. The administration has told the U.S. Navy to abandon its studies relating to two new missiles, the Sea Lance antisubmarine and the NAAWS antiair, because of their high cost.

RUSSIAN NAVY

Economic and social difficulties in the now-dissolved U.S.S.R, cuts in the defense budget, and changes in the armament industry to support the economy obliged the Russian Navy to reorganize itself and to make better use of its available resources. During the past two years, it has continued to modernize itself, despite a reduction in its overall tonnage. This reduction is due essentially to the decommissioning of many old combat ships whose military value had become negligible and which required for their crews a great deal of manpower. For these considerations, the Russian Navy has partially or totally divested itself of its nuclear-powered submarines of the Hotel, November, and Echo-I classes, its conventional submarines of the Golf, Romeo, and Whiskey classes, its *Sverdlov*-class cruisers, its destroyers of the Kanin, Kotlin, Kotlin-SAM, Kildin, and *Skoryy* classes, and its Riga-class frigates. All the equivalents to these vessels had disappeared from Western navies more than ten years ago. A modest beginning seems to be being made in the decommissioning of some more recent vessels: for instance, in 1990–91, by virtue of the SALT 1 accords, several Yankee-class SSBNs have been withdrawn from service at regular intervals; the only Yankee-II-class SSBN, the Papa-class SSN, certain units of the Echo-II class, a few conventional submarines of the Foxtrot class, and the Alfa-class SSNs have likewise been decommissioned. Three cruisers of the Kresta-I class, three of the Kresta-IIs, all four Kyndas, and one of the Kashin class have suffered the same fate.

On the other hand, some new ships have appeared: in the course of the year 1990, ten submarines were launched (a figure not reached since 1982), as well as nine large combat ships, while in 1991 six submarines were launched. So we are witnessing a continued modernization of the Russian fleet, despite the numerous decommissionings in recent years. It is likely, however, that the pace of new construction will be slowing down in the years to come because of the sorry state of the Russian economy. Still, by the end of the decade the Russian Navy will probably be smaller and more compact, but more efficient.

The strategic submarine component has been reinforced by the commissioning of the sixth and last Typhoon-class SSBN and the seventh (and also, apparently last) Delta-IV. Since our last edition, the SSN force was also being modernized by the delivery or construction of additional Oscar-II-class nuclear-powered, aerodynamic-missile-carrying submarines, bringing their total to 7; 3 Akula-class SSNs (7 now in service); the third submarine of the Sierra class; and the last 4 of the 26 Victor-III class. Four conventional submarines of the Kilo class have also been put into service, and 2 or 3 more are ready to join the fleet, which will bring their total to 19 or 20.

As for large surface ships, construction of the fifth *Kirov*-class missile cruiser was discontinued soon after it had begun. Work on the fourth is still in progress. It is now expected to be commissioned in 1993–94, to be followed a year later by the long-delayed fourth *Slava*-class cruiser, the last of that series, which like the third will have some electronic gear different from that of the first two. The eleventh *Udaloy*-class missile destroyer has been put into service, and the twelfth and last will be very soon. A thirteenth is well known to be under construction, but its armament will be different: notably a twin 130-mm turret instead of two 100-mm and the CADS-N-1 anti-missile systems instead of the multitube 30-mm antiaircraft guns of the first 12. The *Sovremennyy* series is also being continued, with four units having been commissioned in 1990–91 and the fifteenth expected in 1992; the sixteenth has been launched, and it is estimated that this series may eventually number 22 ships, far superior in capabilities to the Kanins and Kashins they have replaced.

The first Bal-Com 8–type frigate was sighted at sea for the first time in December 1990. It is the first of a series of ASW ships that were expected to replace the Riga class in the short term and the Krivaks in the future, but it is likely that only a few will be built. A special effort has been made to keep this ship, christened *Neustrashimyy,* "stealthy" (raked superstructures, lowered stacks). It has six tubes in its superstructures aft, from which it may or may not be capable of launching not only torpedoes but also antisubmarine SS-N-15 and SS-N-16 missiles. The KGB, before its recent reorganization, took delivery of a seventh Krivak-III-class frigate, and an eighth is scheduled for delivery in 1992.

In the field of small combat ships, commissioning of the following should be mentioned: nine Grisha-V and six Parchim-II corvettes; the surface-effect missile air-cushion vehicle of the Dergach class, which is the largest vessel of its kind in the world (750 tons); seven Tarantul-III missile boats, two Mukha-class patrol ships, ten Pauk-class antisubmarine patrol boats, and two Svetlyak-class and ten Muravey-class patrol boats. As for mine warfare, a second Gorya-class minehunter-sweeper is nearing completion, and a new series of small minesweepers, the Lida class, is under construction. Other small units may be under development.

The third and final *Ivan Rogov*-class transport for landing craft joined the Northern Fleet in 1990. The 26th Ropucha tank-landing ship, with armament and electronic gear different from that of earlier units, was delivered from Poland. The category of auxiliary support ships has been enriched only by a third Malina-class repair ship.

With respect to naval aviation, we should mention the delivery of a dozen or so Flanker interceptors, which were to constitute the first elements of *Kuznetsov*'s air group, and especially the transfer of more than 270 Fencer, Fitter, Flogger, and Frogfoot airplanes from the air force to the navy, to circumvent the terms of the treaty on reduction of conventional forces in Europe now being negotiated, since the aircraft of naval forces will not be taken into account by this treaty as will those of air forces. A new maritime patrol aircraft may be put into service in the mid-1990s, the Albatross Be-44, which will replace May and Mail, but the Yak-141 Freestyle V/STOL fighter has been canceled, leaving the Russian Navy with no fighter aircraft for its four *Kiev*-class carriers. While the first true carrier, *Admiral Flota Sovetskogo Kuznetsov*, deployed to the Northern Fleet in December 1991, it had no air wing, and work on the second carrier has been suspended. In February 1992 came word that the third carrier was being scrapped on the ways.

In the field of weapons and equipment, the Russians are developing a new generation of missiles. A new strategic ballistic missile will be carried by Typhoon-class SSBNs, modernization of which has begun. The SS-NX-25 is an antiship missile, seemingly equivalent to the Western nations' Harpoon and Exocet. Mr. Gorbachev having accepted President Bush's proposals to suppress tactical nuclear weaspons, the Russian Navy will be obliged to divest itself of nuclear warheads with which its weapons (notably several types of torpedoes and missiles) can be armed.

With regard to personnel, the current reorganization of the armed forces is resulting, within the Russian Navy, in a manpower diminution, due to the elimination of old ships, reduced length of enlistments (from 3 to 2 years, and now to only 18 months), with the "professionalization" of some enlisted volunteers to begin in 1992 if funds can be found.

This navy is continuing many activities within its preferred exercise areas, but at a greatly reduced pace, due to lack of fuel: the Barents Sea, the northern part of the Norwegian Sea, and the Sea of Japan, although there has been no large-scale, major exercise in the past three years. For the sake of economy but also because of the political trend toward military disengagement, the Russian Navy has reduced its long-distance deployments. For two years the number of units present in the Mediterranean had been reduced, the maintenance of a permanent combatant force ended in December 1991; in the Atlantic, the fisheries-protection force along the coasts of Africa to support Russian fishing has been withdrawn; in 1991, we witnessed a total withdrawal of the units customarily deployed in the Indian Ocean, which explains the quasi-absence of Russian ships in that theater of operations during the Gulf War, and early in 1992 it became apparent that the Cam Ranh Bay base was being abandoned.

ROYAL NAVY

The years 1990 and 1991 were not auspicious for the Royal Navy because of the adoption by the British government and Parliament of the "Option for Changes" program. Established since the events in Eastern Europe and the attenuation of the Soviet threat, this program is intended to reduce both the manpower potential and the material means of the Royal Navy, out of concern for budgetary economy. This is the more surprising since the Gulf War demonstrated, as indicated above, the imperative necessity of having naval forces available, since they alone can be deployed with minimal delay to theaters of operations throughout the world; as a matter of fact, the Royal Navy contributed substantially to the operations conducted in the Middle East from August 1990 to June 1991: two conventional submarines, five missile destroyers, six frigates, eight minesweepers, four amphibious landing ships, and nine logistic support ships were dispatched there at various times.

The Royal Navy's reduction in personnel is quite severe, its total strength, formerly 67,000, having fallen to 62,000 in 1991; and it may fall soon to 55,000, according to an announcement made in July 1991. Paradoxically, the British navy is experiencing difficulty, despite these numbers, in manning all its ships, because of resignations and poor enlistment rates, so that it must now appeal for volunteers, including women; thus one finds women serving aboard a dozen or more combat ships and constituting overall some 10 percent of active-duty personnel.

In the field of materiel, the "Option for Changes" program provides for a substantial reduction in numbers of ships, principally in the categories of submarines, escort ships, and mine-warfare vessels. Specifically, the total number of attack submarines, nuclear and conventional, which was 27 in 1990, will be cut to 16: escort ships (destroyers and frigates) from 50 to 40, and mine-warfare ships from 40 to 30. To these programmed reductions have been added some premature decommissionings (included in the above figures) resulting from technical reactor problems aboard the nuclear-powered SSNs *Conqueror, Warspite,* and *Churchill.* Three of the four missile submarines [SSBM] have experienced similar difficulties, but because of their strategic importance, they have only been temporarily immobilized, not decommissioned.

Naval air strength is not affected by these cutbacks, except for the number of Nimrod maritime-patrol aircraft operated by the R.A.F., which will be reduced from 30 to 25. For a time it was feared that the aircraft carrier *Illustrious* might be sold, but it will now be retained by the Royal Navy, and its refitting to bring it up to the level of the *Invincible* was begun in November 1991. The installation of Sea Wolf short-range surface-to-air missiles initially planned, however, will not be realized, for financial reasons. The same may be said of the two sister ships of *Illustrious* and the four *Manchester*-class missile destroyers, all of which were to have received this weapons system.

Construction of the first three *Vanguard*-class missile-firing submarines is proceeding according to plan; the fourth and last of this series should be ordered very soon, but actually its construction has already begun. So it is now certain that the program of updating the strategic submarine force will be carried through to its conclusion. The arrival of these SSBNs is being awaited with impatience, especially since the problems cited above with the *Renown, Repulse,* and *Revenge.*

The commissioning of the nuclear-powered SSNs *Talent* and *Triumph,* the seventh and last unit of the *Trafalgar* class, will not suffice to compensate for the withdrawal of three *Valiant*-class SSNs already effected and that of the last two boats of the series, plus that of the first two *Swiftsures*, which have encountered similar problems since they have the same model nuclear reactor as the *Valiants*. The Royal Navy, however, envisages construction of four to six SSNs derived from the *Trafalgar* design for the second half of the decade (*Trafalgar Batch 2*).

The number of conventional submarines is inexorably diminishing, the number of *Oberons* having been reduced by more than half in two years; in

October 1991 there were only four left, and these will all be gone by 1995. The advent of the first two *Upholders* in 1990 and 1991 and that of the following pair, which will occur in 1992 and 1993, is likewise insufficient to counterbalance the decommissioning of these large oceangoing submarines, especially since the eventual construction of four more *Upholders* (which would have constituted the *Upholder Batch 2* class) has been definitively abandoned.

In the category of missile-firing destroyers, two salient facts are to be noted. Firstly, the *Bristol* has been withdrawn from active service after only 18 years and despite its recent modernization, effected between 1984 and 1986; its fate has not yet been determined: sale to a foreign navy, demolition, or conversion into a quayside school ship to replace the *Kent* at Portsmouth. Secondly, on 1 March 1991, the Chiefs of Staff of the British and French navies signed in London a protocol of agreement on a joint study of a new antiaircraft ship equipped with the FSAF/LAMS medium-rage surface-to-air system; this ship of about 5,500 tons is to replace the *Sheffield* and *Manchester* classes in the Royal Navy. One after another, the destroyers of these classes are receiving new electronics gear; but contrary to expectations, their antiair self-defense will not be augmented by a downsized Sea Wolf system.

Type 23 frigates are beginning to make their appearance: three are already in service, two are being fitted out, and five are under construction. Three more were ordered in February 1992. These are very good ASW vessels, very silent because of their propulsion mode, which combines a diesel-electric system with a gas turbine. Unfortunately, the first five suffer from the handicap of lacking a data-processing system. The system initially envisaged, the CACS-4, has in fact been abandoned because of poor performance, and its replacement, the SSCS, will not be available until the sixth unit; but the first five will get it in the course of subsequent refittings. These frigates, of which 16 are planned for the present, are replacing those of the *Leander* class, which the Royal Navy is decommissioning or selling to foreign navies; two were sold to Ecuador in 1991 and one to Chile in 1990. There is no change in the status of Type 22 frigates of Batch 1, 2, or 3, except for rumors that those of Batch 1 may be put up for sale by 1992.

As far as mine warfare is concerned, the only noteworthy event is the commissioning of the second *Sandown*-class minesweeper, *Inverness*. The next three should be operational some time in 1992. Unfortunately, the flotilla of seven additional units of the same class that was supposed to be ready by 1991 has been rescheduled for a later, still undetermined date. This ship class is doing rather well in the export market: it has been adopted by the Saudi Arabian and Spanish navies, although the latter has yet to place a firm order. As for minehunters and sweepers of the "Ton" class, they are gradually disappearing, only one sweeper and five hunters now remaining.

No change has occurred in the category of amphibious ships. Studies relating to two landing-craft transports destined to replace the *Fearless* and *Intrepid* are continuing and will result in orders in 1994–95, and an aviation support ship will also be built. It is now certain that the three still-unmodified amphibious landing ships of the *Sir Lancelot* class will be brought up to the standard of the *Sir Tristram,* thus extending their service life to the year 2000. As for logistic support ships, the multipurpose supply ship *Fort Victoria* should soon be ready to replace the oiler-storeship *Tidespring,* which has just been decommissioned.

Worthy of mention in naval aeronautics are the first orders for FRS2 Sea Harrier airplanes (10 in 1990, for delivery in 1994) and a forthcoming order for EH-101 Merlin ASW helicopters, of which the Royal Navy expects to acquire 44. The Royal Air Force, which operates maritime-patrol aircraft, finds itself confronted anew by the problem of supplanting its Nimrods; adoption of the American P-7 has been envisaged, but with the abandonment of that aircraft by the U.S. Navy, the problem remains unsolved.

Finally, in the field of weapons, the major development in these past two years is Great Britain's participation in the Franco-Italian project, the FSAF-FAMS surface-to-air missile with the LAMS system, which meets the requirements of the British concept of antiaircraft warfare and which the Spanish Navy also has found suitable for its future antiaircraft frigates. The abandonment of the downsized Sea Wolf systems, initially destined for 3 aircraft carriers and 12 missile destroyers, is a crushing blow to the Royal Navy as well as to the manufacturer (British Aerospace); once again, the budget axe has fallen.

The austerity measures now being inflicted on the Royal Navy (as on the army and air force), which one might reasonably have expected to be eased after the Gulf War, demonstrate a certain degree of ingratitude on the part of the British government toward its navy after the brilliant performance of its naval air forces off the coast of Kuwait: the almost total destruction of the Iraqi fleet by carrier-based Lynx helicopters with their Sea Skua missiles, the interception by British Sea Dart missiles of an Iraqi Silkworm missile fired at the American battleship *Missouri,* and the mine-clearing operations. Be that as it may, these measures should present no obstacle to the modernization of the British fleet and to its qualitative improvement.

FRENCH NAVY

The objectives of new construction for the next few years will be established in future military programming legislation, which will cover the period 1992–97 and will take into account what has been learned from the Gulf War. The French Navy's participation in recent events in the Middle East was substantial, effective, and many-faceted: introduction of the first combat helicopters with the "Salamandre" group; embargo control in the straits of Tiran, Bab-el-Mandeb, and Hormuz with Artimon missions to the west, south, and east; escorting the carrier task forces and amphibious ships of the U.S. Navy; transporting army materiel and troops with landing ships, medical support at Yanbu, and logistic support at Djibouti; and finally, mine-clearing off the coast of Kuwait. Taking part successively were one aircraft carrier, one missile cruiser, six ASW frigates, two destroyer escorts, three aviso-escorts, three landing-barge transports, five minehunters, three oiler-storeships, four logistic support ships, a number of navy maritime-patrol planes and commandos, and also a number of merchant ships (principally roll-on/roll-off vehicle ramp and container ships).

Despite its stretching-out in time, construction of the nuclear-powered aircraft carrier *Charles de Gaulle* is proceeding at Brest. The hull is almost finished; launching will come in 1994 and commissioning in 1998. *Clémenceau* may then be decommissioned; it is hoped at present that a second ship of the same type to replace *Foch* by 2004 will be provided for in the programming legislation; the need for two such ships is obvious, taking into account periods of unavailability for maintenance and repair.

The favorable evolution of the threat in the East is not affecting construction of the first two nuclear-powered missile-firing submarines of the *Le Triomphant* class, which will be operational in 1995 and 1997. Their arrival is impatiently awaited, for with the decommissioning of *Redoutable* last year and the immobilization of *Foudroyant* by its remodeling, the task of keeping three SSBNs constantly at sea with only four boats available is becoming a day-to-day concern of our navy. *Terrible* has been returned to active service after having undergone the M4 remodeling from which *Tonnant* and *Indomptable* had benefited before her; that of *Foudroyant* will be finished early in 1993. Our flotilla of nuclear-powered attack submarines was enlarged in December with the arrival of *Améthyste,* the first boat of the improved *Rubis* series; the second, *Perle,* is being fitted out. The next two, unfortunately, have been canceled due to budgetary restrictions. The first four *Rubis*es will be brought up to the standard of *Améthyste;* this has already been begun on *Saphir* (June 1991). The number of conventional submarines has decreased: only four *Daphnés* are still in service (three having been decommissioned in the past two years) together with the four *Agostas*.

The situation in the category of antiaircraft escort ships is becoming problematical with the decommissioning last year of the missile cruiser *Colbert* and the squadron escort *Du Chayla*. These withdrawals are partially compensated by the commissioning of the *Jean Bart* and the modernization of the *Suffren* and *Duquesne;* the latter two ships will thus be able to remain in service until the advent of the new antiaircraft ships that France is going to develop jointly with Great Britain, according to an agreement signed in London on 1 March 1991 by Admiral Coatanéa and his British opposite number. The frigate *Cassard* will be brought up to the standard of *Jean Bart,* mainly by replacement of the DRBV 15 radar by the DRBJ 11. While falling short of numerical replacement of our antiaircraft ships, whose number has decreased from seven in the late 1970s to four, we are witnessing *per contra* a qualitative improvement in the replacements.

The category of ASW escort ships is in a more favorable position, having just been bolstered by the commissioning of the *Latouche-Tréville,* a superior replacement for the retired *La Galissonnière*. Only a single ship of the 18-unit *Surcout* series, *Duperré,* remains in service, but not for long, for it will be decommissioned in July 1992. Two destroyers of the *Tourville* class are to be modernized in the near future, including installation of the SLASM ASW system, which is based on a new very low frequency active sonar.

Replacement of the aviso-escorts has begun with the commissioning late in 1991 of the first surveillance frigate, *Floréal,* to be followed at six-month intervals by five more. These frigates are being delivered without armament by Chantiers de l'Atlantique of Saint-Nazaire to the Director of Naval Construction at Lorient, who sees to its installation; constructed to "merchant marine" standards, these sturdy, inexpensive ships are destined to perform missions of presence and sovereignty off the coasts of our overseas departments and territories. For high-risk areas, three *La Fayette*-class frigates are under construction; a second set of three ships was ordered early in 1992. Unlike the surveillance frigates, the *La Fayette*s will have a much more sophisticated armament and will be very stealthy. They will have, however, no ASW capability (neither sensors nor weapons), at least initially; but during construction, precautionary arrangements are made for the possible subsequent installation of new weapons systems.

In the area of mine warfare, no changes have taken place. The hull of our first oceangoing anti-mine ship, *Narvik,* has been constructed; but this already-funded ship and the five others whose construction had been planned have become the first victims of budgetary austerity.

The landing-craft transport *Foudre,* newly commissioned, was plunged into the thick of the action during the Gulf War, carrying army troops, vehicles, and helicopters to Saudi Arabia. This event demonstrates the usefulness of such a ship, and now it is essential that the construction of two other ships of the same class be financed immediately, as future replacements for *Ouragan* and *Orage,* which also were in great demand.

In the category of auxiliaries, we should mention the delivery by Chantiers de l'Atlantique of the test-and-measurement ship *Monge,* destined to replace *Henri Poincaré;* installation of its scientific equipment is under way at Brest. Also, the fifth and last oiler-storeship of the *Durance* class, *Somme,* has been commissioned for active service; like *Var* and *Marne,* it is configured as a command ship.

The Rafale-Marine airplanes should be ready as scheduled for embarkation in 1998 on *Charles de Gaulle,* a first 15-plane flotilla (flotilla 14F, temporarily disbanded last July) being constituted for July 1998; in the meantime, the F-8F Crusaders must continue to fly, and this is why 14 of them are to be renovated to last until 1997; everyone knows that this option was not the one preferred by the navy's general staff. Successors must also be found for two other carrier planes, the photoreconnaissance Étendard IVP and the venerable search-and-rescue Alizé. The mission of the former may be accomplished by a version of the Rafale-Marine; to replace the latter, purchase of a small number of American E-2C Hawkeye aerial lookout planes is envisioned. In the field of helicopters, a new aircraft, the Dauphin, is being used more and more for aircraft carrier rescue missions and aboard *Floréal-* and *La Fayette*-class frigates. The Super Frélons will be flying until 2000, to be relieved at that time by the new European NFH-90 helicopter. Finally, to complete our panorama of naval aviation, we salute the arrival of the Atlantique 2, which has replaced the Atlantic in Flotilla 23F; seven aircraft are in service. Deliveries are to continue at the rate of three aircraft per year, but the total of 42 initially planned has been reduced to about 30, for budgetary reasons.

As far as weapons and equipment are concerned, we must note the success achieved by the new SAAM antiair weapons system with its Aster 15 missile, developed jointly by France and Italy: Great Britain and Spain (temporarily) have also associated themselves with this program via their LAMS project, which is more specifically responsive to the British concept of antiaircraft warfare. An improved Crotale system, the CN2, with the hypervelocity VTI missile is being fabricated for *La Fayette*-class frigates. Development is to begin again soon on the Franco-German ANS antiship missile, successor to the Exocet, and an airborne version is now planned for naval aviation use. The AS30 Laser missile utilized successfully in the Gulf War by the French Air Force is now to be employed by the modernized Super-Étendards. Finally, France has decided to fuse its Murène light torpedo program with the analogous Italian A-290 torpedo program; the new weapon, christened the MU-90, will be operational in 1996. In the field of sensors, we should mention the advent of a new air-search radar, the DRBV 21 or MARS, on surveillance frigates, and the studies relative to the Arabel radars linked to Aster 15 and Astral missiles, to a long-range air-search radar associated with the Aster 30 missile, and to the very low frequency active sonar that is the principal element in the SLASM system.

GERMAN NAVY

As a direct consequence of the fall of the Berlin Wall in November 1989 and of German reunification on 3 October 1990, the navy of the former East Germany has been abolished. A number of units were integrated temporarily into the *Bundesmarine,* both to keep their personnel (3,500 men out of a total of 16,500) employed and to evaluate the Soviet materiel constituting the framework of the *Volksmarine.* After more than a year of operating these units, the Federal Navy decided to dispose of most of them by demolition or by putting them up for sale or donation, along with all the rest of the *Volksmarine* ships they had not incorporated, on 1 January 1992, with the exception of five barracks ships, three tugs, and one small oiler. Nations such as Poland, Algeria, Uruguay, and Malta have shown some interest in acquiring some of these ships: for instance, Poland had already purchased three incomplete *Sassnitz-* class patrol boats just prior to the German unification.

Taking into account the diminution of the threat on its eastern border, the German government has decided to reduce its armed forces; between now and 1994, the date when the last Russian troops are to leave the territory of the former East Germany, the Federal Navy will be obliged to reduce its personnel from 37,500 to 30,000, then to 25,000, and to decommission some 60 ships. By the end of the decade, its composition is to be as follows: 18 submarines, 16 frigates, 26 missile-firing patrol boats, 26 anti-mine ships, and 10 logistic-support ships.

Construction of four Type 212 submarines will not be affected by these cutbacks. The first one, supposedly to be laid down in the near future, will be ready for service in 1996; these four boats will replace numerically the four of the 205 type still in service. Modernization of 12 of the 18 Type 206 units is proceeding normally and should be completed in 1992.

Escort forces have changed very little. One destroyer of the *Hamburg* class, however, has been decommissioned. Construction of the first of four Brandenburg (Type 123) frigates, destined to replace these destroyers, began in February 1991; they will be the largest units in the German fleet. The eighth and last Type 122 frigate, *Lübeck,* is now in active service. Type 420 (*Thetis*-class) corvettes will soon be disappearing from the German inventory: two were transferred to Greece in September, and the other three will follow in 1992.

Types 143 and 143A missile-firing patrol ships have not yet received the RAM missile mounts they have been awaiting for more than ten years, because of the complexity of this German-American weapons system and the great amount of labor required to install it. On the other hand, the 20 units of Type 148 are gradually being fitted with new electronic gear.

The composition of the anti-mine forces has been considerably modified. The ten Type 343 minesweepers are now all in service. At the behest of German legislators, three of these are to receive a mine-hunting sonar; this is one of the lessons learned by the *Bundesmarine* during the Gulf War. Early on, the German contingent was limited to sending to the eastern Mediterranean two minesweepers and three minehunters, accompanied by two support ships, the German constitution not permitting deployment of national forces outside the NATO sphere of influence; once hostilities were over, two sweepers, also accompanied by two support ships, were sent to the Kuwait area to be integrated into the multi-national force charged with neutralizing the minefields sown by the Iraqis. Ten more ships of Type 332, which constitutes the "minehunter version" of Type 343, are being built to replace the Type 331 class.

The amphibious component has greatly shrunk, and is destined to disappear completely within five years' time. Auxiliary ships likewise are diminishing in number: nine logistic-supply ships have been decommissioned in the past two years; conversely, six multipurpose supply ships of Type 404 have been ordered; these will be delivered in 1993–94 but will be without armament, which has made it possible, via extensive automatization, to reduce the size of their crews and to lessen their cost.

Finally naval aviation, like the fleet, is undergoing some reductions; 40 of the 105 Tornado pursuit planes of the *Bundesmarine* are to be transferred to the *Luftwaffe.* There is also a crucial problem with regard to the replacement of the maritime-patrol Atlantics, the U.S. Navy having abandoned its P-7 program while the German Navy was actively involved therein. The French Atlantique Mk 2 might have been substituted as a replacement, but Germany does not seem to consider this a proper solution.

NETHERLANDS NAVY

The Netherlands Navy will find itself affected in the near future by budgetary restrictions. At the end of the century it will have to decommission its two *Zwaardvis*-class submarines, which will not be replaced, for only four *Walrus*-class are to be built; the first of these is in service; the second soon will be, and the two others will commission within the next two years. The Netherlands general staff has been unable to secure authorization to build two more units.

The two *Tromp*-class missile destroyers will be replaced late in the decade by two new AA ships, whose design is now being studied jointly with Spain. Three *Kortenaer*-class frigates will be sold in 1994, three will be placed in reserve in 1996, and the last four will be modernized. These withdrawals will be mitigated by the commissioning of the *Karel Doorman* frigates, of which the first two are operational; four others are being fitted out; the last two are under construction. But the advent of these eight large units will not suffice to compensate numerically for the withdrawal of the aforementioned *Kortenaer*s, for the *Karel Doorman*s are also replacing the six *Van Speijk*-class frigates, which were all sold to Indonesia.

Retirement into reserve of about half of the Tripartite-type minehunters is also envisaged, as is decommissioning of the ten *Dokkum*-class minesweepers, which will be replaced in principle by ten new ships being planned jointly with Belgium. A positive element for the *Koninklijke Marine* lies in the fact that an assault transport of 9,500 tons may be built by 1995, after completion of studies being undertaken jointly with Spain, which is also interested in a ship of this type. Hispano-Dutch cooperation is also going to take concrete form with the construction of a 17,000-ton oiler-storeship destined to replace *Poolster.*

The Netherlands Navy's contribution to the Gulf War consisted of the dispatching of four frigates (two of them missile-firing), one oiler-storeship, and three minehunters.

OTHER NAVIES OF NORTHERN EUROPE

The Danish Navy has been enriched by three ex-Norwegian submarines of the *Kobben* class, transferred after modernization. The frigates *Peder Skram* and *Herluf Trolle* have been definitively crossed off the active list after removal of their Harpoon missiles, which will be used for coastal defense. The first frigate of the Stanflex 2000 class was commissioned in 1991, and three others are under construction to replace the *Hvidbjörnen*-class fishery-protection ships; emplacements are being reserved aboard these four ships for subsequent installation of additional armament. Thirteen patrol ships of the Stanflex 300 class are also joining the fleet to replace old patrol ships and minesweepers, and five are now operational. Modernization of several ships is envisaged: submarines of Type 205, the fisheries-protection frigate *Beskytteren, Bille*-class missile patrol boats, and *Falster*-class minelayers. The Danish Navy made its contribution to the Gulf War by sending the frigate *Olfert Fischer* to participate in embargo control in the Red Sea.

This was also the case for the Norwegian Navy, which sent the coast guard cutter *Andenes* into the embargo zone. This navy has received the first three Type 210 submarines built in Germany; three more will follow in 1992. The *Oslo*-class frigates have all been recently modernized. There remains the problem of finding a successor to the old missile patrol ships of the *Snögg* and *Storm* classes. The problem of replacement has been solved for the old ex-American minesweepers with the ordering of nine surface-effect anti-mine ships, construction of which has just begun.

With respect to the Swedish Navy, we must note the commissioning of the fourth and last submarine of the *Västergötland* class; she is to be followed by three units of the *Gotland* class, which will have a Stirling closed-circuit auxiliary propulsion system. The surface forces have received three *Göteborg*-class missile corvettes (with a fourth to be delivered in 1992) and an experimental surface-effect patrol ship, *Smyge*, which is noteworthy for its "stealth" signature-reduction features.

The Finnish Navy has just received its first two *Rauma*-class missile patrol ships; two others are under construction, as well as two *Hameenmaa* minelayers and several smaller ships.

In conclusion, the Belgian Navy has taken delivery of its last three Tripartite minehunters, bringing the total to ten. Two of them, accompanied by the support ship *Zinnia*, took part in mine-clearance operations off the coast of Kuwait, while two frigates were integrated into the Union of Western Europe forces charged with enforcing the embargo. For the future, the Belgian Naval Force is going to build several coastal minesweepers, being designed jointly with the Netherlands and Portugal, to replace the former American minesweepers still listed on the fleet's active list.

ITALIAN NAVY

The composition of the Italian Navy has not undergone the aftereffects of the recent events in the Mid-East, since its tonnage has increased slightly since 1989. Like other European navies, it was solicited for help in the Gulf War: one missile destroyer, six frigates, two corvettes, four minehunters, one assault transport, and two oiler-storeships took part at various times in war-zone operations.

After obtaining from Parliament authorization to acquire short-takeoff aircraft for embarkation on the aircraft carrier *Garibaldi*, the navy ordered 16 Harrier II AV-8B Plus planes from the United States and 2 TAV-8B two-seater training planes, to be delivered between June 1991 and 1996. A second ship of the same type, to be ordered in good time as a medium-term replacement for the cruiser-helicopter-carrier *Vittorio Veneto*, remains in prospect.

Replenishment of submarine forces is well under way; after the construction of the two *Pelosi*-class units that replaced in 1989 two former American submarines, the general staff decided to order two improved *Pelosis*, the *Longobardos*, which will replace the remaining *Totis* in 1993. This will all be done before undertaking the construction of four larger units of the S90 type. The situation is similar for the escort forces, with two missile destroyers of the *Animoso* class (launched in 1989 and 1991, respectively) to be operational in 1992 and 1994 to replace the two *Impavidos*, which were stricken in August 1991; furthermore, construction of four additional *Minerva*-class corvettes, of which eight units now figure on the Italian active list, is being seriously considered to replace the old *Cristofaro* and *Albatros* classes; finally, the first four oceangoing patrol ships of the *Cassiopea* class have joined the fleet, and a fifth is still planned. The four completed but never delivered *Lupo*-class frigates built for Iraq will be incorporated into the Italian Navy, but the fates of the six undelivered missile corvettes, an oiler, and a floating dry dock have not been determined.

Anti-mine forces are to be modernized and improved, with the replacement of American-designed coastal minesweepers by *Lerici II*-class minehunters, of which six units were ordered in 1988 and two more in 1991. A third *San Giorgio*-class assault ship has been ordered, destined to play the role of a seagoing school ship to replace the missile cruiser *Caio Duilio*, decommissioned late in 1989 and temporarily relieved by *San Giorgio*. On the other hand, the oiler-storeship *Etna*, in the planning stage for several years, has not yet been ordered.

Italian firms occupy a privileged position in the field of weapons and equipment, but they have understood that collaboration with other European nations is the wave of the future; thus the firm Alenia has abandoned development of the Idra surface-to-air missile, which was supposed to replace the Aspide system, to associate itself with the French firms Thomson/CSF and Aérospatiale in the FSAF/FAMS missile programs. Similarly, the A290 light torpedo program of Whitehead-Motofides has been merged with the French Murène program of our DCN; these now constitute the MU90 torpedo program. Finally, we cite the long-continuing cooperation of OTO Melara and Matra on development of the new Milas ASW missile, which was derived from the Franco-Italian Otomat surface-to-surface missile.

SPANISH NAVY

The Spanish Navy has been pursuing its modernization program for the past two years. It has proceeded with modifications on the aircraft carrier *Principe de Asturias*, notably to increase her capacity to carry Matador (AV-8A) and Harrier (AV-8B) airplanes, the latter of which she is to acquire 7 additional units, and to modernize concurrently 11 of the 20 planes already available, as well as to take account of the lessons learned from two years' utilization of this big ship. Pending construction by the end of the decade of new submarines to replace the *Daphné* class, the *Agosta* class is being modernized.

The fourth missile frigate of the U.S. FFG 7 type has been delivered, thus permitting retirement of the old *Gearing*-class American destroyers, of which only two remain; two more FFG 7s have been ordered, but no work has begun. The five *Baleares*-class missile frigates have now all been refitted with Harpoon missiles, Meroka multi-barrel anti-missile systems, and new electronic gear. Four new corvettes of the *Serviola* class are replacing the four *Atrevidas* for surveillance of the exclusive economic zone; they can each carry a helicopter. Finally, the Spanish Navy will soon have available its first true oiler-storeship, *Mar del Norte*, which will make possible longer deployments of Naval Air Group Alfa, consisting of the aircraft carrier *Principe de Asturias* and the four type FFG 7-class frigates.

For the future, the *Alta Mar* [High Seas] plan adopted in 1989–90 has set the objectives for new construction: four ASW frigates of type F100, five AA frigates of type F110, four submarines of type S90, eight minehunters of the British *Sandown* class, four coastal minesweepers, one assault transport, four tank-landing transports, and one multipurpose supply ship. Several of these units will be studied jointly by the Spanish firm Bazán and the Netherland's Nevesbu: the ASW frigates, the AA frigates, the assault transport and the multipurpose supply ship, which the Netherlands Navy also has ordered. So, in the Spanish Navy, bilateral cooperation is the order of the day.

Like many navies of the Union of Western Europe, the Spanish Navy participated in embargo control during the Gulf War, deploying three missile frigates, six conventional frigates, and one assault transport at various times.

OTHER NAVIES OF SOUTHERN EUROPE

The Portuguese Navy is gradually being renovated, thanks to the commissioning of three Meko 200-class frigates built in Germany with partial NATO financing; these replace three *Dealey*-class American frigates. Construction of six new small patrol craft (five *Argoses* and one *Rio Minho*) has been completed. Along with these new construction projects, some work on electronic modernization will be undertaken on *Daphné*-class submarines and *Commandant Rivière* frigates. Portugal's NATO obligations in the Atlantic did not permit her navy to participate substantially in naval operations connected with the Gulf War, but the transport *São Miguel* performed several logistic round trips to the Middle East, and one frigate was integrated into NAVOCFORMED in the eastern Mediterranean.

The Greek Navy is to be rejuvenated in the next four years by the transfer of four *Charles Adams*-class missile destroyers from the U.S. Navy in exchange for the maintenance of American bases on Greek soil, and especially by the commissioning of four Meko-class frigates, the first building in Germany and the other three in Greece. During 1992, three *Knox*-class ASW frigates are to be transferred from the U.S. Navy. These eleven ships will more than replace the old American destroyers which, although they have been modernized several times, are now reaching a very advanced age (50 years). The same sort of rejuvenation will occur in the amphibious component with the delivery of five much-delayed *Jason*-class LSTs. We should cite Greek participation during the Gulf War: two *Kortenaer*-class frigates were dispatched to the war zone; these were *Elli* and *Limnos*, both equipped with Phalanx point-defense systems for the occasion.

No major change has occurred in the composition of the Greek Navy's rival, the Turkish Navy, since our last edition. Plans for the future, on the other hand, are numerous: six submarines of the German Type 209/1400 (*Preveze* class); two Meko 200-class frigates to be added to the four already in service, equipped like their predecessors with Sea Sparrow missiles but this time with a vertical launching system and a different propulsion plant; ten missile patrol ships of type FPB 57; and two minelayer/landing ships of the *Osman Paşa* class are in various stages of delivery or planning.

JAPANESE NAVY

The Japanese Navy (Maritime Self-Defense Force) is certainly the world's most fortunate, for that nation's good economic health enables it in large measure to disregard budgetary restrictions. At the most, Japan's contribution to the Gulf War may have delayed the programmed construction of two surface-effect missile patrol ships and a cadet-training vessel; that contribution was essentially financial, for the Japanese constitution does not authorize distant deployments of Japanese self-defense forces; four minehunters, one support ship, and one oiler-storeship, however, did take part in mine-clearing operations off Kuwait City in the second and third quarters of 1991.

The possible construction of a 20,000-ton aircraft carrier has not yet materialized in the programming legislation, despite certain calculations and proposals. The second *Harushio*-class submarine entered service in 1991, which permitted the reclassification as an auxiliary of a third unit of the *Uzushio* class, commissioned in 1975; this means that Japanese submarines are remaining in active operational status for no longer than 16 years and being replaced one-for-one after that interval, which may leave Western navies dreaming.

The last four *Asagiri*-class ASW destroyers were commissioned in 1990–91; this series of eight ships of 4,250 tons, which followed a series of twelve ships of 3,700 tons, will itself be followed by a planned series of eight units of 4,400 tons, the first of which was financed in the 1991 budget; these ships will employ vertical-launch systems for Sea Sparrow antiaircraft and antisubmarine ASROC missiles and will have a smaller crew (160 men instead of 230 for the *Asagiri*), thanks to some very advanced automatization. Construction of missile destroyers with the American Aegis system is continuing: the first, *Kongo*, was launched in August 1991; the second was financed in the 1990 budget, and the third in that of 1991; five others are planned. Commissioning of *Kongo* will permit retirement of *Amatsuzake*, which dates from 1965 and is the oldest of all Japanese combatant ships.

Also newly operational since our last edition are four frigates of 2,500 tons of the *Abukuma* class; a fifth was launched in December 1991 and the sixth in January 1992, ending the series.

In the field of anti-mine forces, the first *Yaeyama*-class deep-water minesweeper was launched in September 1991, and two others are under construction; these ships seem to have been inspired by the American *Avengers*. Four *Awashima*-class minehunters were commissioned in 1990–91 and a fifth has been launched; these 5 units are an improved version of the 21 *Hatsushima*-class minehunters.

In the field of auxiliaries, noteworthy is the doubling of the number of oiler-storeships in four years; from two units in 1987, the number has risen to four in 1991 with the commissioning of *Tokiwa* and *Hamana*, which enables the Japanese fleet to make more frequent and longer high-seas deployments. Let us note also the acceptance for active service of the first acoustic-surveillance ship, *Hibiki*, which has a SWATH hull; like its American counterparts, this ship is charged with surveillance of the movements of Russian submarines based in the Pacific; the data collected is transmitted at once by satellite to an on-shore processing center located at Yokosuka; the personnel responsible for its exploitation are in part American.

All these new units have brought the Japanese Navy's total tonnage from 220,000 to 260,000 tons, solidifying its position as the fifth largest in the world and bringing it considerably closer to fourth position, now occupied by our French Navy (Japan's fleet even surpasses ours, when one counts not by total tonnage but by the number of ships of more than 2,000 tons). This explains why the United States, which assumes partial responsibility for the security of Japan, has asked that nation to assume a greater role in its own protection.

Japanese naval aviation is as well off as the maritime component: 72 Orion P-3C maritime-patrol planes are now operational (compared to 50 in 1989), and a total of 104 are planned, to replace the old Neptune P-2Js, of which only 6 are still flying. SH-60J Seahawk helicopters are making their appearance; another hundred or so of these are envisaged. The case is similar for the large S-80M1 minesweeping helicopters, which constitute the Japanese version of the American MH-53E; the first units of a series of 12 were delivered between 1989 and 1991.

Finally, in the field of equipment, we are witnessing more and more the designing and fabrication of national materiel, whether it be missiles (such as Mitsubishi's SSM-1 antiship missile), torpedoes, radars, sonars, or electronic-warfare equipment, whereas for many years the Japanese Navy has contented itself with importing or adapting American materiel.

CHINESE NAVY

The People's Republic of China is trying to develop its influence in the East China and South China Seas and to equip itself with oceangoing ships that will enable it to maintain greater control over the southern seas, and in particular over the islands of the Spratley and Paracels archipelagoes, claimed by several nations in their vicinity. The naval arm of the People's Liberation Army is gradually increasing in strength and is beginning to be modernized.

It now has at its disposal only one missile-firing nuclear submarine of the *Xia* class; but four other SSBNs of an improved design may be built in the course of this decade. The fifth SSN of the Han class was completed in 1991. Two missile destroyers of the Luhu type are under construction in Shanghai; they may be equipped in part with armament of Western origin. Several of the 16 Luda-class destroyers are to be modernized; notably, some of them may receive Chinese C801 antiship missiles to replace the old HY-2s. In the category of frigates, we must mention the successful exportation of the Jianghu class, which seem to be of simple, sturdy construction: after delivery of two units of this class to Egypt in 1984, we have witnessed in the past two years the sale of one used unit to Bangladesh (a second is planned) and the building of four modified ships for Thailand. Two larger frigates have also recently been built for the Chinese Navy itself. Some new types of patrol boats and picket boats, such as the Haijui and Huzhou, are making their appearance among the multitude of small craft that still constitute the framework of the Chinese naval forces.

For the future, this navy wishes to modernize and extend the action radius of its naval aviation, which presently consists of shore-based interceptors and bombers, a few maritime-patrol planes, and some helicopters.

OTHER ASIAN NAVIES

The Taiwanese Navy is being completely modernized. After delivery of the two *Hai Lung*-class submarines in 1988, it envisages ordering four units of the German Type 209 and is also attempting to order more Dutch-designed submarines. To replace ex-American destroyers of the *Sumner*, *Gearing*, and *Fletcher* classes, some of which have been completely transformed, it is having built locally eight missile frigates derived from the American *Oliver Hazard Perry* (FFG 7) class. Moreover, the French government has just recently rescinded the veto it had imposed on Taiwan's order for six *La Fayette*-class frigates, a veto due to pressure exerted by the People's Republic of China; these will be delivered without armament, and ten more may be built under license in Taiwan. Delivery of four minehunters by a German shipyard has been completed, although the builder claims that these are only supply ships for oil-drilling platforms. In closing, let us cite the commissioning of a large 17,000-ton oiler-storeship, *Wu Yi*, in 1990.

Although less spectacular, a considerable renovation is also taking place in the Thai Navy. Four *Jianghu*-series frigates have been delivered or are about to be; they have armament nearly identical to that of their Chinese counterparts, despite the desire of the Thais to see them equipped with Western weaponry. On the other hand, China has agreed that two other frigates of a larger type (25T), also built in China, may be equipped originally with Western electronic gear. Two of the four *Kamronsin*-class corvettes being built locally are in service; they constitute an improved version of the Vosper Thornycroft–designed *Province* class already in service in the navies of Egypt, Kenya, and Oman. A helicopter-carrying assault ship is in the planning stage; but the construction contract signed with Bremer Vulkan was canceled in July 1991, and the Bazán shipyard in Spain has now been selected. Thailand has definitively renounced the Romeo-class submarines it had discussed ordering from China.

South Korea is no exception to the trend toward renovation and growth in Asian fleets. Six submarines of Type 209 are under order, the first in Germany, the other five in Korea. Twelve new destroyers (type HDF 3500) are expected to replace the old ex-American destroyers still in service. Seven *Ulsan*-class frigates and 22 *Dong Hae*-class corvettes of South Korean design and construction are now in service, and others are under construction. Some minehunters derived from the Italian *Lerici* class but built in Korea, some tank-landing ships, and an oiler-storeship (the first of a series of three) are also being finished or are under construction.

Creation of a submarine force was seriously considered in Malaysia; Sweden was to deliver two submarines of Type 196 (export version of the Swedish *Gotland*) and to furnish without charge two *Dräken*-class units for the training of crews. The Malaysian Navy's chief of general staff ultimately abandoned this plan in favor of construction of two corvettes, which will be built by the British Yarrow shipyard. As for the Indonesian Navy, it has incorporated the last two Netherlands *Van Speijk*-class frigates; it now envisages construction of a score of 3,000-ton frigates to replace in the not-too-distant future some ships of the various types that make up the bulk of its fleet: Netherlands *Van Speijk*-class frigates, British *Tribal*-class frigates and American *Claud Jones*-class frigates. Instead, however, it may acquire used ships from various European navies.

NAVIES OF THE SOUTH PACIFIC

The Australian Navy is showing interest in the Indian Ocean; it is now deploying ships on the continent's west coast. Furthermore, it took part in the Gulf War despite its distance from the theater of operations: one missile destroyer, three missile frigates, and two oiler-storeships, divided into two successive combat groups of three ships each, were sent to the war zone. Construction of the first two submarines of the Swedish Type 471 has begun; six boats are scheduled, to replace the *Oberons*. Work on the last of six *Oliver Hazard Perry*-class missile frigates is continuing; and construction of eight Meko 200 Anzac-class frigates is to begin in 1992, to compensate for the anticipated decommissioning of the remaining three "River" class units. An order for additional minehunters with catamaran hulls has been definitively canceled, the Australian Navy being disappointed not only by the poor performance of the DSQS-11H sonar but also by the mediocre seakeeping qualities of the two ships of this type now in service; it envisages ordering instead some ships currently available on the world market (principally European) that have already proven themselves. The Ikara ASW weapons system has been removed from the several ships that still employed it because of its now-superseded performance and the economy of crew manpower thus effected.

The Australian Navy's neighbor, the New Zealand Navy, has also ordered two frigates of the Meko 200 Anzac class, confirming once again the export success being achieved by these ships of German design, since the Meko 200 has been adopted successively by Turkey, Portugal, Greece, Australia, and finally New Zealand. The two units ordered by the latter nation will replace the two oldest *Leander*-class frigates, and two more Mekos are being considered to replace the two remaining more recent *Leanders*. Authorization for construction of an assault transport envisaged for several years, however, has not been forthcoming.

NAVIES OF THE INDIAN OCEAN

The strongest force on the shores of the Indian Ocean, the Indian Navy, continues its ascendancy, but is now confronted by budgetary and technical problems that are slowing down certain major programs. For instance, study of an aircraft carrier in collaboration with some French firms was postponed in 1991. Also, the nuclear-powered submarine *Chakra* of the Soviet Charlie I class has been returned to Russia at the end of her three-year charter. Henceforth, India will build most of its new units in its own shipyards (under license, or using its own plans).

Two more Kilo-class conventional submarines were delivered in 1990 and 1991 respectively, which now brings the number of these boats to eight; a new series may be transferred to replace the aging Foxtrots. The first Indian-built Type 209/1500 submarine was finally commissioned early in 1992, and the second should be launched soon.

The first Type 15 6,500-ton destroyer, *Delhi,* was launched last year; this is the largest combatant ship ever built in Indian naval dockyards. A second was immediately laid down, and three more are projected. Three new frigates derived from the *Godavari* are in progress. Also now in service are six *Sukanya*-class corvettes, initially destined for the coast guard (for whom three others are being built) but finally commissioned by the navy, and four *Khukri*-class corvettes (four more ordered); these ships will replace the seven Petya II-class corvettes still in service. Six Tarantul missile corvettes are in service, and a total of 20 are projected, the remainder of which are building in Indian yards. Four modified Pauk-class patrol ships were delivered from 1989 to 1991. A second *Magar*-class landing ship has been launched. Finally, construction of a third oiler-storeship derived from *Deepak* has begun. In addition to the navy, the coast guard has also been strengthened, with the arrival of three new *Vikram*-class frigates since the last edition.

The Indian Navy's competitor, the Pakistani Navy, which in 1988–89 had been considerably reinforced by the lease of four American *Brooke*-class missile frigates and four *Garcia*-class ASW frigates, the purchase of two *Leander*-class frigates from Great Britain, and the delivery of an oiler-storeship by People's China, received no new ships at all in 1990 and 1991. Only the Maritime Security Agency took delivery of four patrol boats of Chinese construction. Naval aviation was to receive three American P-3C Orion maritime-patrol planes to replace the Bréguet Atlantics, but their delivery has been held up by the suspension of American aid.

CANADIAN NAVY

The Canadian Navy's program of renovation and modernization is making very slow progress. The first "City"-class frigate, *Halifax,* was only recently admitted to active service, instead of in late 1989 as originally planned. Commissioning of the 11 others is to be spread out at the rate of 2 per year until 1996; the last 6 were to have been 10 meters longer to increase carrying capacity for Sea Sparrow missiles, but budgetary constraints have thwarted this project. Delay is even more flagrant in the case of the TRUMP remodeling of *Iroquois*-class frigates: construction work initially expected to take 18 months will in fact take almost four years. The two frigates of this class on which work had not been started were considerably modified (as were two *Restigouche*-class frigates and an oiler-storeship) for their deployment to the Middle East at the time of the Gulf War. All these ships received additional electronic gear and armament, notably Phalanx and Harpoon missiles.

Budgetary restrictions did not prevent the ordering of the first MCDV-type anti-mine ships. To compensate for the abandonment of the acquisition of new nuclear-powered submarines, the plan is to modernize once again the three *Oberon*-class submarines so that they will remain operational until 2000–2005. As for naval aviation, an order for three Arcturus maritime-patrol planes—Arcturus being derived from Aurora, which in turn is derived from the American Orion—was placed in 1989, and the purchase of 35 EH-101 Merlin helicopters is still envisaged, to relieve the Sea King CH-124s.

SOUTH AMERICAN NAVIES

The Brazilian Navy is rejuvenating its submarine component with a series of four boats of the German 209 type; the first, built in Germany, has been operational since 1989, but construction of the three others in Brazil is progressing very slowly. For this reason, actual realization of the nuclear attack submarine force envisaged for several years seems hardly possible before 2010. The first two *Inhaúma*-class frigates are now in service after having spent nearly seven years in the builder's hands. The United States delivered a number of ships to Brazil in the course of the past two years: first, four *Garcia*-class frigates in 1989, then two *Thomaston*-class landing-barge transports in 1990. One oiler-storeship of Brazilian construction was completed late in 1991.

Not much has changed in the Argentine Navy in the past two years because of that country's economic difficulties; these are delaying the project of re-engining the aircraft carrier *Veintecinco de Mayo* (which will probably be abandoned), the remodeling of Type 209 submarines, and the finishing of the last two Meko 140-class frigates. We should mention the contribution of this navy to operations in the Gulf by sending two frigates for embargo control; Argentina is thus the only Latin American nation to have joined the international coalition.

The Chilean Navy has acquired a *Leander*-class frigate, *Achilles,* from Great Britain; likewise the Ecuadorean Navy, to which the Royal Navy has ceded the frigates *Penelope* and *Danae* of the *Leander* Exocet class to replace two old ex-American units. The Uruguayan Navy, for its part, has turned to France, purchasing from us the frigates *Commandant Bourdais* and *Amiral Charner,* bringing to three the number of ships of this type in service in Uruguay since the acquisition of *Victor Schoelcher* in 1988. The composition of the Colombian, Peruvian, and Venezuelan navies has not significantly changed, except for the recent arrival in Venezuela of a hydrographic vessel built in Spain.

Bernard Prézelin
October 1991/revised June 1992
Translated by Kendall Lappin

ALBANIA

People's Socialist Republic of Albania

Personnel (1991): about 1,900 total, including about 400 Coast Guard troops

Note: Neither the U.S.S.R. nor China is now supporting Albania, and the material condition of the ships listed below must be suffering. All former Soviet equipment was transferred prior to 1961.

◆ **2 Soviet Whiskey-class submarines**

422 442

D: 1,049/1,349 tons **S:** 17/13.5 kts **Dim:** 76.0 × 6.3 × 4.8
A: 6/533-mm TT (4 fwd, 2 aft)—12 torpedoes or 24 mines
Electron Equipt: Radar: 1/Snoop Plate—Sonar: Tamir-5 MF active
M: 2 Type 37-D, 2,000-bhp diesels, electric motors; 2 props; 2,500 shp (sub.); 2/50-shp electric creep motors
Range: 6,000/5 (snorkel) **Endurance:** 40–45 days **Crew:** 50 tot.

Remarks: Of the four acquired 1960–61, all reported out of service in 1980, but two have reportedly been made operational. A third survives as a battery-charging hulk, and the other has been stricken. Original diving depth: 170 meters.

◆ **6 Chinese Shanghai-II-class patrol boats**

150 151 152 650 651 652

D: 122.5 tons (134.8 fl) **S:** 28 kts **Dim:** 38.78 × 5.41 × 1.55 (props)
A: 4/37-mm AA (II × 2)—4/25-mm AA (II × 2)
Electron Equipt: Radar: 1/Pot Head
M: 2/1,200-hp M50F-4 diesels, 2/910-hp 12D6 diesels; 4 props; 4,220 bhp
Crew: 36 tot. **Electric:** 39 kw **Endurance:** 7 days
Range: 750/16.5

Remarks: Transferred 1974–75; probably operational.

Note: The last two Kronshtadt-class patrol boats, 350 and 351, are no longer operational.

◆ **29 Chinese Huchuan-class hydrofoil torpedo boats**

121–129 320–325 427–432 522–533

Huchuan-class in Albanian service 1976

D: 39 tons (45.8 fl) **S:** 50 kts
Dim: 22.30 × 3.80 (6.26 over fenders) × 1.15
A: 2/533-mm TT—4/14.5-mm mg (II × 2)
Electron Equipt: Radar: 1/Skin Head
M: 3 M50F-4 diesels; 3 props; 3,600 bhp **Electric:** 5.6 kw
Range: 500/30 **Crew:** 11 tot.

Remarks: Bow foils only; stern planes on surface. Transferred 1974–1975. One other defected 5-91 to Italy, where the crew requested asylum.

◆ **1 Soviet T-43-class ocean minesweeper**

D: 500 tons (570 fl) **S:** 14 kts **Dim:** 58.0 × 8.6 × 2.3 (3.5 sonar)
A: 4/37-mm AA (II × 2)—8/12.7-mm mg (II × 4)—2/d.c.t.—mines
Electron Equipt: Radar: 1/Ball End—Sonar: Tamir-11
M: 2 Type 9-D diesels; 2 props; 2,200 bhp
Range: 3,200/10 **Crew:** 65 tot.

◆ **4 Soviet T-301-class coastal minesweepers**

D: 145.8 tons (160 fl) **S:** 12.5 kts **Dim:** 38.0 × 5.1 × 1.6
A: 1/45-mm AA—4/12.7-mm mg (II × 2)—mines
M: 3/6-cyl. diesels; 3 props; 1,440 bhp **Range:** 2,500/8
Crew: 32 tot.

Remarks: Two others have been discarded.

◆ **2 Soviet Khobi-class small oilers**

Patos (ex-Sov. *Linda*) Semani

D: 1,525 tons (fl) **S:** 12.7 kts **Dim:** 67.4 (63.7 pp) × 10.0 × 4.4
M: 2 diesels; 2 props; 1,600 bhp **Range:** 2,500/12.5

Remarks: 795 grt/834 dwt. Transferred 2-59. *Semani* defected to Italy mid-1991; will probably be returned.

◆ **1 Soviet Toplivo-1-class fuel lighter**

771 Tomb (In serv. late 1950s)

Semani Giuseppe Valentini, 1991

D: 450 tons (fl) **S:** 10 kts **Dim:** 34.5 × 6.5 × 3.0
M: 1 diesel; 1 prop; 150 bhp

◆ **1 Soviet Sekstan-class degaussing tender**

354 Shenjin

D: 408 tons (fl) **S:** 10.5 kts **Dim:** 41.0 × 9.3 × 4.2.
M: 1 diesel; 1 prop; 400 bhp **Range:** 1,200/10

Remarks: Wooden construction.

◆ **2 Soviet Tuger-class coastal tugs**

Mujoulqinaku . . .

D: 300 tons (fl) **S:** 12 kts **Dim:** 30.7 × 7.7 × 2.3
M: 1 set reciprocating steam; 1 prop; 500 bhp **Boilers:** 2

◆ **1 Soviet Nyryat-1-class diving tender**

Sqipetari

D: 120 tons (fl) **S:** 12 kts **Dim:** 29.0 × 5.0 × 1.7
M: 1 diesel; 1 prop; 450 bhp **Range:** 1,600/10 **Crew:** 15 tot.

◆ **1 Soviet Poluchat-I-class torpedo retriever**

663 Skenderbeu

D: 90 tons (fl) **S:** 18 kts **Dim:** 29.6 × 6.1 × 1.9
A: 2/14.5-mm mg (II × 1) **M:** 2 M50 diesels; 2 props; 2,400 bhp
Range: 450/17; 900/10 **Crew:** 20 tot.

Remarks: Primarily employed as patrol craft.

◆ **1 Soviet Duna-class power barge**

Remarks: Employed as a battery-charging station for the submarines.

ALGERIA

Democratic and Popular Republic of Algeria

Personnel (1991): 6,500 total with about 350 to 400 officers (includes Coast Guard)

Naval Aviation: The Algerian Air Force uses 3 Fokker F-27 (Maritime) Mk 400 and 2 Beech Super King Air 200T patrol aircraft for maritime surveillance.

SUBMARINES

◆ **2 Soviet Kilo class** Bldr: United Admiralty SY, Leningrad

Algerian Navy Kilo 23 Flot., French Navy, 9-88

SUBMARINES *(continued)*

D: 2,325/3,076 tons **S:** 10/17 kts **Dim:** 74.3 (70.0 wl) × 10.0 × 6.6
A: 6/533-mm TT (18 torpedoes)—possible SA-N-5 Grail SAM system (hand-held launcher)
Electron Equipt:
Radar: 1/Snoop Tray—Sonar: LF suite, HF active
EW: Brick Pulp or Squid Head intercept; Quad Loop DF
M: 3/1,825-bhp diesel generator sets, electric drive; 1/6-bladed prop; 5,900 shp
Crew: 12 officers, 41 enlisted **Range:** 6,000/7 surf.; 400/3 sub.

Remarks: First unit left the Baltic on 15-9-87; the second during 1-88. The possible Grail SAM launch position is at the aft end of the sail.

Note: The two Romeo-class submarines transferred from the U.S.S.R. became non-operational by 1989 but remain in Algeria.

FRIGATES

◆ **3 Soviet Koni class** Bldr: Zelenodolsk SY

901 Mourad Raïs (In serv. 20-12-80) 903 Raïs Korfu (In serv. 10-84)
902 Raïs Kellik (In serv. 24-3-82)

Mourad Raïs (901) VS-22/U.S. Navy, 1986

D: 1,440 tons normal (1,596 fl) **S:** 30 kts
Dim: 96.40 × 12.55 × 3.48 (4.90 sonar)
A: 1/SAN-4 SAM syst. (II × 1; 20 Gecko missiles)—4/76.2-mm DP (II × 2)—4/30-mm AA (II × 2)—2/RBU-6000—2/d.c. racks—mines
Electron Equipt:
Radar: 1/Don-2 nav., 1/Strut Curve air/surf. search, 1/Pop Group missile f.c., 1/Hawk Screech 76-mm gun f.c., 1/Drum Tilt 30-mm gun f.c.
Sonar: 1/MF, hull-mounted
EW: 2/Watch Dog intercept; 1/Cross Loop-A D/F; 2/chaff RL (XVI × 2)
IFF: 2/Square Head interrogators, 1/High Pole B transponder (Salt Pot C on 902)
M: CODAG: 1/19,000-shp gas turbine, 2 Type 68-B, 8,000-bhp diesels; 3 props; 35,000 hp
Range: 1,800/14 **Crew:** 130 tot.

Remarks: In-service dates reflect delivery dates. Have two chaff launchers, deckhouse abaft stack, unlike earlier examples. D.C. racks bolt to mine rails. Believed to be the 5th, 7th, and 10th units of the class.

GUIDED-MISSILE CORVETTES

◆ **3 Soviet Nanuchka-II class** Bldr: Petrovskiy SY, Leningrad

801 Raïs Hamidou 802 Salah Raïs 803 Raïs Ali

Raïs Ali (803) French Navy, 1988

D: 675 tons (fl) **S:** 30 kts **Dim:** 59.3 × 12.6 × 2.4
A: 4/SS-N-2C Styx SSM (II × 2)—1/SA-N-4 SAM syst. (II × 1; 20 Gecko missiles)—2/57-mm AK-57 DP (II × 1)
Electron Equipt:
Radar: 1/Mius nav., 1/Square Tie surf. search/missile target desig., 1/Pop Group SA-N-4 f.c., 1/Muff Cob gun f.c.
EW: 1/Bell Tap intercept, 1/Cross Loop MF D/F, 2/chaff RL (XVI × 2)
IFF: 2/Square Head interrogators, 1/Salt Pot B transponder
M: 3 M517 diesels; 3 props; 30,000 bhp **Range:** 900/30; 2,500/12
Crew: 60 tot.

Remarks: 801 arrived in Algeria 4-7-80, 802 in 2-81, 803 in 5-82. The Square Tie surface target tracking radar antenna is mounted within the Band Stand radome atop the bridge.

GUIDED-MISSILE PATROL BOATS

◆ **9 Soviet Osa-II class**

644 645 646 647 648 649 650 651 974

Algerian Osa-II 650 French Navy, 1988

D: 215 tons (240 fl) **S:** 36 kts **Dim:** 38.6 × 7.6 × 1.9 (3.0 props)
A: 4/SS-N-2B Styx SSM (I × 4)—4/30-mm AK-230 AA (II × 2)
Electron Equipt:
Radar: 1/Square Tie surf. search/missile target desig., 1/Drum Tilt gun f.c.
IFF: 2/Square Head interrogators, 1/High Pole B transponder
M: 3 M504 diesels; 3 props; 15,000 bhp **Range:** 500/34; 750/25
Crew: 30 tot.

Remarks: Transferred 1976–78, except for 974: 12-80. A shortage of parts for the M504 diesels, which require frequent overhauls, has kept them from being fully effective.

◆ **2 Soviet Osa-I class**

641 642

D: 185 tons (209 fl) **S:** 36 kts **Dim:** 38.6 × 7.6 × 1.8 (2.9 props)
A: 4/SS-N-2A Styx SSM (I × 4)—4/30-mm AK-230 AA (II × 2)
Electron Equipt:
Radar: 1/Square Tie surf. search/missile target desig., 1/Drum Tilt gun f.c.
IFF: 2/Square Head interrogators, 1/High Pole B transponder
M: 3 M503A diesels; 3 props; 12,000 bhp **Range:** 500/34; 750/25
Crew: 30 tot.

Remarks: Transferred 1967. No. 643 lost in explosion 1981.

PATROL BOATS

◆ **2 (+1) C-58 design** Bldr: ONCN/CNE, Mers el-Kébir

351 (L: 3-2-85) 352 (L: 1990) 353 (L: . . .)

D: 496 tons (540 fl) **S:** 35 kts **Dim:** 58.40 (54.00 pp) × 8.40 × . . .
A: 351: 2/30-mm AK-230 AA (II × 1)—4/25-mm AA (II × 2); ultimate armament: 1/76-mm OTO Melara DP—2/40-mm Breda AA (II × 1)
Electron Equipt: Radar: 1/Decca . . . nav.
M: 2 MTU 20V538 TB92 diesels; 2 props; 9,800 bhp
Range: . . ./. . . **Crew:** . . .

Remarks: Reportedly of Bulgarian design. Ordered 7-83; difficulties in fitting out the prototype forced suspension of work on the other pair prior to launch. Were to have optronic director for the 76-mm gun, optical director for the twin 40-mm. Trials for first, mid-1987.

C-58 patrol boat 351 on trials—with provisional armament French Navy, 11-88

AMPHIBIOUS WARFARE SHIPS

◆ **2 medium landing ships**

	Bldr	Laid down	L	In serv.
472 KALAAT BENI HAMMED	Brooke Marine, Lowestoft	. . .	18-4-84	4-84
473 KALAAT BENI RACHED	Vosper Thornycroft, Woolston	20-12-82	15-5-84	10-84

Kalaat Beni Rached (473) Leo Van Ginderen, 9-84

Kalaat Beni Hammed (472) Leo Van Ginderen, 1984

D: 2,130 tons (fl) **S:** 16 kts **Dim:** 93.0 (80.00 pp) × 15.0 × 2.5
A: 2/40-mm Breda AA (II × 1)—2/20-mm AA (I × 2)
Electron Equipt: Radar: 1/Decca TM 1229 nav., 1/Marconi S800 f.c.
M: 2 MTU 12V1163 TB92 diesels; 2 props; 6,000 bhp
Range: 3,000/12 **Endurance:** 28 days (10 with troops)
Crew: 81 tot. + 240 troops

Remarks: 472 ordered 10-81; 473 sub-contracted to Vosper Thornycroft 18-10-82. Naja optronic gun director. Helicopter deck aft. Pontoon sections stowed on deck forward. The vehicle deck is 75 m long by 7.4 m wide and is served by a 30-m by 7-m hatch. The bow ramp extends to 18 m and is 4–5 m wide, while the stern ramp measures 5 m by 4 m. The traveling crane has a 16-ton capacity. Minimum beaching gradient is 1:40. Can carry 650 tons of cargo, but beaching limit is 450.

◆ **1 Soviet Polnocny-B-class medium landing ship** (Transferred 9-76)

471 . . . . . .

D: 740 tons (800 fl) **S:** 18 kts **Dim:** 74.0 × 8.6 × 2.0
A: 2/30-mm AK-230 AA (II × 1)—2/140-mm barrage RL (XVIII × 2)
Electron Equipt:
Radar: 1/Don-2 nav., 1/Drum Tilt gun f.c.
IFF: 1/Square Head, 1/High Pole A
M: 2 Type 40D diesels; 2 props; 5,000 bhp **Range:** 1,500/14
Crew: 40 tot.
Cargo: 180 tons vehicles (130 troops for short voyage also)

Algerian Polnocny-B (471) Leo Van Ginderen, 1990

MISCELLANEOUS

◆ **1 Chinese-built salvage ship**

261 . . . . . .

Salvage ship 261 French Navy, 7-90

D: approx. 1,000 tons (fl) **S:** . . . kts **Dim:** . . . × . . . × . . .
A: 2/12.7-mm mg (I × 2) **Electron Equipt:** Radar: 1/ . . . nav.
M: 2 diesels; 2 props; approx. 2,000 bhp
Crew: . . . tot.

Remarks: In Algeria by 9-90. Has large quadrantial gantry at stern, fire-fighting monitor atop pilothouse.

◆ **1 Soviet Poluchat-1-class torpedo retriever**

A 641

D: 90 tons (fl) **S:** 18 kts **Dim:** 29.6 × 5.8 × 1.5
M: 2 M50 diesels; 2 props; 2,400 bhp **Crew:** 20 tot.
Range: 450/17; 900/10

◆ **1 Soviet Nyryat-1-class diving tender** (Transferred 1965)

VP 650 YAUDEZAN

D: 120 tons (fl) **S:** 12 kts **Dim:** 29.0 × 5.0 × 1.7
Electron Equipt: Radar: Spin Trough nav. **Endurance:** 10 days
M: 1 diesel; 1 prop; 450 bhp **Range:** 1,600/10 **Crew:** 15 tot.

◆ **1 250-grt survey craft** Bldr: Matsukara, Hirao, Japan (L: 17-4-80)

A 673 EL IDRISSI

COAST GUARD

◆ **3 (+4) modified Chinese Hainan-class patrol boats**

251–257 EL MOUDERRIB-I–VII

El Mouderrib-I (251) French Navy, 7-90

El Mouderrib-I (251) Leo Van Ginderen, 8-90

D: 363 tons (388 fl) **S:** 24 kts **Dim:** 58.77 × 7.60 × 2.50 (hull)
A: 2/14.5-mm mg (II × 1) **Electron Equipt:** Radar: 1/ . . . nav.
M: 4 diesels; 4 props; 8,800 bhp **Range:** 2,000/14 **Crew:** 60 tot.

Remarks: First three arrived 3-90. Simplified version of Chinese antisubmarine patrol boat with enlarged superstructure, boats stowed on fantail. An additional twin 14.5-mm mg mount can be mounted on a ring on the fantail.

ALGERIA *(continued)*
COAST GUARD *(continued)*

◆ **13 (+ 5) Brooke Marine 37.5-meter patrol boats** Bldr: 341–343: Brooke Marine, Lowestoft; others: ONCN/CNE, Mers el-Kébir

	In serv.		In serv.
341 El Yadekh	12-82	350	1988?
342 El Morakeb	12-6-83	351	1989?
343 El Kechef	5-84	352	1990?
344 El Moutarid	1985	353	1991?
345 El Rassed	10-11-85	354	. . . . . .
346 El Djari	1986	355	. . . . . .
347 El	1986?	356	. . . . . .
348 El	1987?	357	. . . . . .
349 El	1988?	358	. . . . . .

El Morakeb (342) Skyfotos, 1983

D: 166 tons (250 fl) **S:** 27 kts **Dim:** 37.50 (34.74 pp) × 6.86 × 1.78
A: 2/25-mm Soviet 2M-8 AA (II × 1) (341, 342: 1/76-mm OTO Melara DP)—2/14.5-mm Soviet 2M-7 mg (I × 2)
Electron Equipt: Radar: 1/Decca 1226 nav.
Crew: 3 officers, 24 enlisted
M: 2 MTU 12V538 TB92 diesels; 2 props; 6,000 bhp **Range:** 2,500/15

Remarks: Also known as "Kebir" class. Total numbers listed are suspect; reported that 353–358 were ordered 9-89. Nos. 347–349 ordered 1984, three more in 1986. Laurence Scott optronic GFCS on first three. Based at Algiers, Annaba, Oran, Ghazaouet, and Djidjeli. First two began refit at Vosper Thornycroft, Portsmouth, late 1990.

◆ **6 Mangusta-class patrol boats** Bldr: Baglietto, Italy (In serv. 1977–78)

GC 323 Ombrine GC 324 Dorade GC 331 Requin
GC 332 Espadon GC 333 Marsouin GC 334 Murene

D: 91 tons (fl) **S:** 32 kts **Dim:** 30.0 × 5.84 × 2.1
A: 2/25-mm Soviet 2M-8 AA (II × 2)—2/23-mm AA (II × 1)
Electron Equipt: Radar: 1/3RM 20 SMA nav.
M: 3 diesels; 3 props; 4,050 bhp **Range:** 800/24; 1,400/12.5
Crew: 3 officers, 11 men

Requin (now renumbered and armed) Carlo Martinelli, 1977

◆ **9 coastal patrol craft** Bldr: . . . , China (In serv. 1990–91)

231 232 233 234 235 236 237 238 239

Remarks: No details available.

◆ **10 Type 20-GC-class patrol craft** Bldr: Baglietto, Italy (In serv. 8-76 to 12-76)

100 112 113 114 221 222 235 236 237 325

Baglietto 20-GC class Carlo Martinelli, 1977

D: 44 tons (fl) **S:** 36 kts **Dim:** 20.4 × 5.2 × 1.7 **A:** 1/20-mm AA
M: 2 CM 18DS diesels; 2 props; 2,700 bhp **Range:** 445/20
Crew: 11 tot.

CUSTOMS SERVICE

◆ **3 P 1200 Mk II-class patrol craft** Bldr: Watercraft, Shoreham, U.K. (In serv. 21-11-85)

Bouzagza Djurdjura Hodna

D: 38.5 tons (fl) **S:** 35 kts **Dim:** 20.80 (18.00 wl) × 5.59 × 1.52
A: 2/7.62-mm mg (1 × 2) **Electron Equipt:** Radar: 1/Decca 170
M: 2 M.A.N. V10 D2450 MLE diesels; 2 props; 1,300 bhp
Range: 300/21 **Crew:** 4 tot.

Remarks: Glass-reinforced plastic construction.

◆ **2 P 802-class patrol craft** Bldr: Watercraft, Shoreham, U.K. (In serv. 21-11-85)

Aures Hoggar

Remarks: 8.00 m overall, powered by two Volvo AQAD 40 inboard/outboard diesels for 30+ kts. GRP construction.

◆ **12 18-ton patrol craft** Bldr: ONCN/CNE, Mers el-Kébir (In serv. 1982–83)

Djebel Antar Djebel Handa 10 others

ANGOLA

People's Republic of Angola

Personnel (1991): about 1,250 total

Naval Aviation: One Fokker F-27 Maritime and two EMB 111 patrol aircraft. Two CASA C-218-300N to deliver 1993–94, and four more ordered 21-5-91—all for maritime surveillance.

Note: The ex-Portuguese craft were located in Angola in 1975 and were transferred on independence.

GUIDED MISSILE PATROL BOATS

◆ **5 Soviet Osa-II class**

Angolan Navy Osa-II (57) French Navy, 1988

ANGOLA *(continued)*
GUIDED MISSILE PATROL BOATS *(continued)*

D: 215 tons (245 fl) **S:** 36 kts **Dim:** 39.0 × 7.7 × 1.8
A: 4/SS-N-2 Styx (I × 4)—4/30-mm AK-230 (II × 2)
Electron Equipt:
Radar: 1/Square Tie surf. search/missile target desig., 1/Drum Tilt gun f.c.
IFF: 2/Square Head interrogators, 1/High Pole B transponder
M: 3 Type M504 diesels; 3 props; 15,000 bhp
Range: 430/34; 790/20 **Crew:** 30 tot.

Remarks: Delivered in pairs, 10-82, 12-82, and 11-83 by RO/FLO cargo ship *Stakhanovets Petrash*. Sister *4 Feveiro* lost 2-6-88 in a collision.

TORPEDO BOATS

♦ **4 Soviet Shershen class**

D: 145 tons (170 fl) **S:** 45 kts **Dim:** 34.0 × 6.8 × 1.5
A: 4/30-mm AK-230 AA (II × 2)—4/533-mm TT
Electron Equipt:
Radar: 1/Pot Drum surf. search, 1/Drum Tilt f.c.
IFF: 1/Square Head interrogator, 1/High Pole A transponder
M: 3 M503A diesels; 3 props; 12,000 bhp **Range:** 450/34; 700/20
Crew: 15 tot.

Remarks: Delivered 12-77 to 11-79. Unlike many transfers of this class, all retained torpedo tubes.

PATROL BOATS

♦ **0 (+ 4) Spanish 26.5-m class** Bldr: Bazán, La Carraca, Cadiz

D: . . . tons **S:** . . . kts **Dim:** . . . × . . . × . . . **A:** . . .
M: . . . diesels; 2 props; . . . bhp

Remarks: Ordered 27-3-91 for fisheries patrol duties. Larger program to order three Cormoran-class patrol boats, six smaller patrol boats, and two landing craft from Bazán did not reach fruition.

♦ **1 Soviet Zhuk class** (Transferred 23-1-77)

D: 50 tons (60 fl) **S:** 34 kts **Dim:** 26.0 × 4.9 × 1.5
A: 4/14.5-mm mg (II × 2)
Electron Equipt: Radar: 1/Spin Trough nav.
M: 2 M50 diesels; 2 props; 2,400 bhp **Range:** 700/28; 1,100/15
Crew: 12 tot. **Fuel:** 10 tons

Remarks: One sister transferred to São Tome 4-90.

♦ **2 Soviet Poluchat-I class** (Transferred 12-79)

D: 90 tons (fl) **S:** 18 kts **Dim:** 29.6 × 5.8 × 1.5
A: 2/14.5-mm mg (II × 1) **M:** 2 M50 diesels; 2 props; 2,400 bhp
Range: 450/17; 900/10 **Crew:** 20 tot.

MINE COUNTERMEASURES VESSELS

♦ **2 Soviet Yevgenya-class inshore minehunters** Bldr: Sredniy Neva SY, Kolpino

D: 80 tons (90 fl) **S:** 11 kts **Dim:** 26.2 × 6.1 × 1.5
A: 2/14.5-mm mg (II × 1) **M:** 2 diesels; 2 props; 600 bhp
Electron Equipt: Radar: 1/Spin Trough navigational
Range: 300/10 **Crew:** 10 tot. (plus 2 or 3 mine-clearance divers)

Remarks: Transferred 9-87. May have twin 25-mm AA vice listed 14.5-mm mg. GRP hull and superstructure. Employ a television minehunting system that dispenses marker buoys to permit later disposal of mines; useful in depths to 30 m.

AMPHIBIOUS WARFARE SHIPS

♦ **3 Soviet Polnocny-B-class medium landing ships** Bldr: Stocznia Północna, Gdańsk, Poland

D: 800 tons (fl) **S:** 19 kts **Dim:** 74.0 × 8.6 × 2.0
A: 2/30-mm AK-230 AA (II × 1)—2/140-mm barrage RL (XVIII × 2)
Electron Equipt:
Radar: 1/Don 2 navigational, 1/Drum Tilt f.c.
IFF: 1/Square Head interrogator, 1/High Pole A transponder
M: 2 Type 40D diesels; 2 props; 5,000 bhp
Range: 1,500/14 **Crew:** 40 tot.

Remarks: First transferred 16-12-77, second 16-12-78, third 1-12-79.

Note: Landing ships *10 Diciembre* and *11 Novembre*, listed as naval in previous edition, are in fact in commercial service.

♦ **1 Soviet T-4-class landing craft** (Transferred 1976)

D: 70 tons (fl) **S:** 10 kts **Dim:** 19.0 × 4.3 × 1.0
M: 2 diesels; 2 props; 600 bhp **Crew:** 5 tot.

Remarks: Four others transferred at the same time have been retired.

♦ **4 Portuguese LDM-400-class landing craft**

D: 56 tons (fl) **S:** 9 kts **Dim:** 17.0 × 5.0 × 1.2 **A:** 1/20-mm AA
M: 2 Cummins diesels; 2 props; 450 bhp

Remarks: Five sisters have been discarded.

ANGUILLA

MARINE POLICE

PATROL CRAFT

♦ **1 British-built** Bldr: Halmatic, U.K.

DOLPHIN (In serv. 30-12-89)

D: 17.3 tons (fl) **S:** 27+ kts **Dim:** 15.40 (12.20 pp) × 3.86 × 1.15
A: 1/7.62-mm mg **Electron Equipt:** Radar: 1/ Decca 370BT nav.
M: 2 G.M. 6V92 TA diesels; 2 props; 1,100 bhp (770 sust.)
Range: 300/20 **Fuel:** 2,700 liters **Crew:** 6 tot.

Remarks: Provided by U.K. government; sisters in several other Caribbean island countries. Has davits aft for inflatable inspection boat.

♦ **1 "Huntsman" patrol craft** Bldr: Fairey Marine, U.K.

LAPWING (In serv. 1984)

Remarks: GRP construction; 8.50 m o.a. Employed for fisheries protection, police, and search-and-rescue duties.

♦ **1 "Interceptor" rescue launch** Bldr: Fairey Marine, U.K. (In serv. 1978)

Remarks: Two 280-bhp outboard motors, 560 bhp. Carries eight 25-person liferafts; used as rescue launch for Coolidge Airport.

♦ **2 patrol launches**

ANGUILLETTA (1984): 9.75 m, 2 Evinrude outboards, 370 bhp
MAPLELEAF (1982): 8.23 m, 1 Perkins diesel, 185 bhp

ANTIGUA-BARBUDA

COAST GUARD

PATROL CRAFT

♦ **1 U.S. 65-ft Commercial Cruiser class** Bldr: Swiftships, Inc., Morgan City, Louisiana

P-01 LIBERTA (In serv. 30-4-84)

Liberta (P-01) PH2 Pixier, USN, 1987

D: 36 tons (fl) **S:** 23 kts **Dim:** 19.96 × 5.59 × 1.52
A: 1/12.7-mm mg **Electron Equipt:** Radar: 1/Raytheon 1210 nav.
M: 2 G.M. 12V71 TI diesels; 2 props; 1,350 bhp
Electric: 20 kw **Range:** 500/18 **Crew:** 6 tot.

Remarks: Aluminum construction. U.S. Grant-Aid. U.S. Coast Guard-trained. Also in use are two U.S.-supplied Boston Whaler outboards: 2 tons (fl), 6.81 × 2.26 × . . . , 40 kts.

ARGENTINA

Argentine Republic

Personnel (1991): approx. 14,000 men, including 2,500 officers and 3,000 Marines

Note: Fiscal constraints have forced the cutting of new programs, the disposal of older ships, the reduction of manpower by 7,500 (including 500 officers and 3,000 Marines), and a severe restriction in annual steaming days to 20 days per ship. Half of all career personnel were to be rotated through 8 months "leave," beginning in 3-91.

Naval Aviation: In 1991, the aircraft for shipboard service included: 13 Super Étendard (3 in storage, remainder now flown from land), 4 A-4Q Skyhawk fighter-bombers, and 6 S-2E ASW aircraft. Helicopters: 5 SH-3D, 2 SH-3H, 6 Hughes 500M Cayuse, 2 Sikorsky S-61NR, and 7 Alouette-III.

For land-based duties: 3 Aeromacchi MB-339AA and 8 MB-326GB attack/trainers; 3 Fokker F-28-3000, 1 BAe 125 Series 400 A, 12 Lockheed L-188 Electra (2 with Exocet capability, 2 with maritime search radars and EW gear), and 12 EMB-326GB Xavante transports; 8 Beech Super King Air 200, 5 Beech B80 Queen Air, and 3 Fairchild Porter light transports; 11 Beech T-34 C-1 trainers; 2 AS-332 Super Puma and 2 Puma helicopters.

The Prefectura Marine operates 5 CASA C-212 Series 200 light transports and 6 Brazilian-built HB-350 Esquilo helicopters.

The six S-2E Trackers are being converted in Israel to S-2UP configuration with Garrett TPE-331-15 AW turbines in place of the original reciprocating engines and other improvements to give them 20 years' additional service. Helicopters for service aboard combatants are still being sought. Recent losses include 1 Super Étendard on 11-20-89 and 1 Alouette-III lost 1-11-90.

Argentine S-2E Tracker U.S. Navy, 10-90

AIRCRAFT CARRIER

Note: A 30,000-ton replacement for *Veinticinco de Mayo* is planned, finances permitting, but construction is unlikely to commence before the late 1990s, if ever.

◆ **1 British Colossus-class** Bldr: Cammell Laird, Birkenhead (Non-operational)

	Laid down	L	In serv.
VEINTICINCO DE MAYO (ex-*Karel Doorman*, ex-*Venerable*)	3-12-42	30-12-43	17-1-45

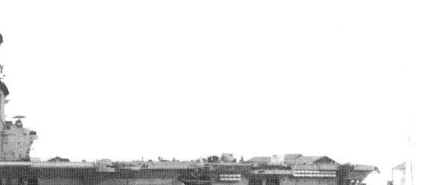

Veinticinco De Mayo Robert L. Scheina, 1982

D: 15,892 tons (19,896 fl) **S:** 24.5 kts (limited to 18.0)
Dim: 212.67 (192.04 pp) × 24.49 (40.66 flight deck) × 7.5
A: 9/40-mm AA (I × 10)
Aircraft: 4 A-4Q Skyhawk, 5 S-2UP Tracker, 3–4 SH-3D or H helo, 1–2 Alouette III helo
Electron Equipt:
Radar: 2/LW-02 air search, 1/SGR-109 height-finding, 1/SGR-105 (DA-05) surf. search, 1/SGR-103 (ZW-01) nav., 1/SMA MM/SPN-720 air control
TACAN: URN-20
M: *see* Remarks **Electric:** 2,500 kw (before re-engining)
Fuel: 3,200 tons **Range:** 6,200/23; 12,000/14 **Crew:** 1,509 tot.

Remarks: Purchased by the Netherlands from the Royal Navy in 1948. Rebuilt from 1955 to 1958 by Wilton-Fijenoord; 165.80-meter angled flight deck, steam catapult, mirror optical landing equipment, new antiaircraft guns, and new radar equipment of Dutch conception and construction. Modified for service in the tropics. Partially air-conditioned. In 1967 new boilers were installed from the British aircraft carrier *Leviathan*, which was never completed. Purchased in 1968 by Argentina and again refitted, recommissioning 22-8-69. She is equipped with the British C.A.A.I.S. combat data system, compatible with the ADAWS-4 data system on the *Sheffield*-class destroyers. 1980 refit enlarged flight deck to permit deck-parking three additional aircraft. Altered 1982–83 to permit operating Super Étendard fighter-bombers and received new communications and other electronic equipment compatible with the MEKO frigate classes; 1/40-mm AA removed. Post–Falklands War trials proved Super Étendards to be incompatible with the ship, which can only operate the handful of remaining naval A-4Q Skyhawks and S-2 Trackers.

Persistent engineering problems left her inactive from 6-86, and she entered AFNE, Rio Santiago SY, 10-1988 for what was to have been a two-year refit to include new boilers and turbines and new diesel generators; instead, after the original plant was removed, she lay unattended until a contract was let 6-7-90 with Fincantieri of Italy for design work to install two GE/Fiat LM-2500 gas turbines for main propulsion, although some sources say that the main propulsion plant is to employ diesels. New boilers would still be required for the steam catapult, but diesel generators will probably be installed also, if the work ever commences. As of 12-90, it was hoped to complete the re-engining by mid-1992, after which the ship might operate only helicopters; no work had commenced by 12-91, however, and the ship may never operate again.

SUBMARINES

◆ **2 (+ 4) TR-1700-class diesel-electric attack submarines**

	Bldr	Laid down	L	In serv.
S 41 SANTA CRUZ	Thyssen Nordseewerke, Emden	6-12-80	28-9-82	14-12-84
S 42 SAN JUAN	Thyssen Nordseewerke, Emden	18-3-82	20-6-83	18-11-85
S 43 SANTA FE	Manuel Domecq Garcia, Buenos Aires	14-10-83	. . .	. . .
S 44 SANTIAGO DEL ESTERO	Manuel Domecq Garcia, Buenos Aires	8-85	. . .	. . .
S 45	Manuel Domecq Garcia, Buenos Aires	. . .	. . .	. . .
S 46	Manuel Domecq Garcia, Buenos Aires	. . .	. . .	. . .

D: 1,770 tons (2,150 surf./2,356 sub. fl)
S: 25 kts (sub.)—13 snorkel, 15 kts (surf.) **Dim:** 65.90 × 7.30 × 6.50
A: 6/533-mm TT (22 SST-4 wire-guided torpedoes)
Electron Equipt: Radar: 1/MM/BPS-704—Sonar: Krupp Atlas . . .
M: diesel-electric: 4/MTU 16V652 MB80 1,100-kw generator sets; 1/6,600-kw motor; 1 prop; 8,970 shp (8,000 sust.)
Fuel: 319 tons **Endurance:** 30 days **Crew:** 30 tot.
Range: 20/25, 50/20, 110/15, 460/6 sub.—12,000/8 surf.

Remarks: Ordered 30-11-77. Originally only *Santa Cruz* to be built in Germany. Two smaller Type TR-1400 replaced by two TR-1700 in the 2-82 change to order. 300-m depth. Battery has eight groups of 120 cells, 5,858-amp/10-hr, and weighs 500 tons. H.S.A. SINBADS (Submarine Integrated Battle and Data System) weapons control system, SAGEM plotting table. Pressure hull 48.0 m long. Torpedoes auto-reload in 50 seconds. Range also given as 15,000/5 snorkeling; 300/10, 70/20 submerged.

San Juan (S 42)—*Murature*-class training frigate in background
Leo Van Ginderen, 4-87

SUBMARINES *(continued)*

TR-1700 class Leo Van Ginderen, 5-87

Permission to sell all of these submarines to a third country was given in 6-86 by West Germany; the Argentine-built ships have been for sale since 1984. No work seems to have been done on the planned 5th and 6th units, and progress has been very slow on the others, with S 43 only about 80 percent ready for launch by the end of 1990.

◆ **2 German Type 209/1200-class diesel-electric submarines**

	Bldr	Laid down	L	In serv.
S 31 SALTA	Howaldtswerke, Kiel	3-4-70	9-11-72	7-3-74
S 32 SAN LUIS	Howaldtswerke, Kiel	1-10-70	3-4-73	24-5-74

Salta (S 31) Argentine Navy, 1982

D: 1,000 tons standard, 1,180 surf., 1,285 sub.
Dim: 55.9 × 6.30 × 5.50 **S:** 22 max. sub., 12 snorkel, 11.5 surf.
A: 8/533-mm TT (14 German SST-4 and U.S. Mk 37 torpedoes)
M: 4 MTU 12V493 TY60 600-bhp diesels, 4/405-kw generators, Siemens electric motor; 1 prop; 5,000 shp
Endurance: 40 days **Fuel:** 63 tons
Range: 230/8; 400/4 sub.; 6,000/8 snorkel
Crew: 5 officers, 26 enlisted

Remarks: Built in four sections at Kiel and assembled at the Rio Santiago Navy Yard. *San Luis* fired six torpedoes, without success, in the Falklands War; *Salta* did not take part. H.S.A. M8 fire-control system. Have four 120-cell, 11,500-amp/hr batteries; weight 257 tons.

Salta reported for sale 1986, but entered Domecq Garcia SY 1988 for new engines and a new electronics suite; work still incomplete 1991, with ship remaining in two sections. S 32 also to be refitted.

DESTROYERS

◆ **2 British Sheffield-class guided-missile destroyers**

	Bldr	Laid down	L	In serv.
D 1 HERCULES	Vickers, Barrow	1971	24-10-72	10-5-76
D 2 SANTISIMA TRINIDAD	Ast. Nav., Rio Santiago	2-72	9-11-74	-81

D: 3,150 tons (4,100 fl) **S:** 28 kts
Dim: 125.0 (119.5 pp) × 14.34 × 4.2 (hull)
A: 4/Exocet MM 38 SSM (I × 4)—1/Sea Dart Mk 30 Mod. 2 SAM syst. (II × 1, 20 missiles)—1/114-mm DP Mk 8—2/20-mm AA—6/324-mm ASW TT (III × 2, A-224S torpedoes)—1/. . . helicopter
Electron Equipt:
Radar: 1/1006 nav., 1/965M early warning, 1/992Q surf./air search, 2/909 f.c.
Sonar: 1/184M LF hull-mounted, 1/162M bottomed target detection
EW: intercept array
M: COGOG 2 Olympus TM 3B gas turbines, 27,200 shp each for boost; 2 Tyne RM 1A gas turbines, 4,100 shp each for cruising; 2 CP, 5-bladed props
Electric: 4,000 kw **Range:** 4,000/18 **Crew:** 270 tot.

Remarks: Ordered 18-5-70. D 2 was sabotaged on 22-8-75 and completion was delayed; initial trials on 7-3-80. D 1, refitted 1980, had MM 38 Exocet missiles added atop the hangar; these were relocated in place of the boats abreast the stack in both, early 1982, when EW gear was also fitted. Have ADAWS-4 data system and NATO Link 10 data link. Both reported to be for sale in 9-84, due to inability to obtain spares from Britain; offered to Turkey mid-1986, but both were operational in mid-1988.

Hercules (D 1)—note Exocets abreast stack Argentine Navy, 1984

FRIGATES

◆ **4 MEKO 360 H2 class** Bldr: Blohm + Voss, Hamburg

	Laid down	L	In serv.
D 10 ALMIRANTE BROWN	8-9-80	28-3-81	2-2-83
D 11 LA ARGENTINA	31-3-81	25-9-81	19-7-83
D 12 HEROINA	24-8-81	17-2-82	7-11-83
D 13 SARANDI	9-3-82	31-8-82	27-4-84

D: 2,900 tons (3,360 fl) **S:** 30.5 kts
Dim: 125.9 (119.0 pp) × 15.0 × 4.32 (5.80 sonar)

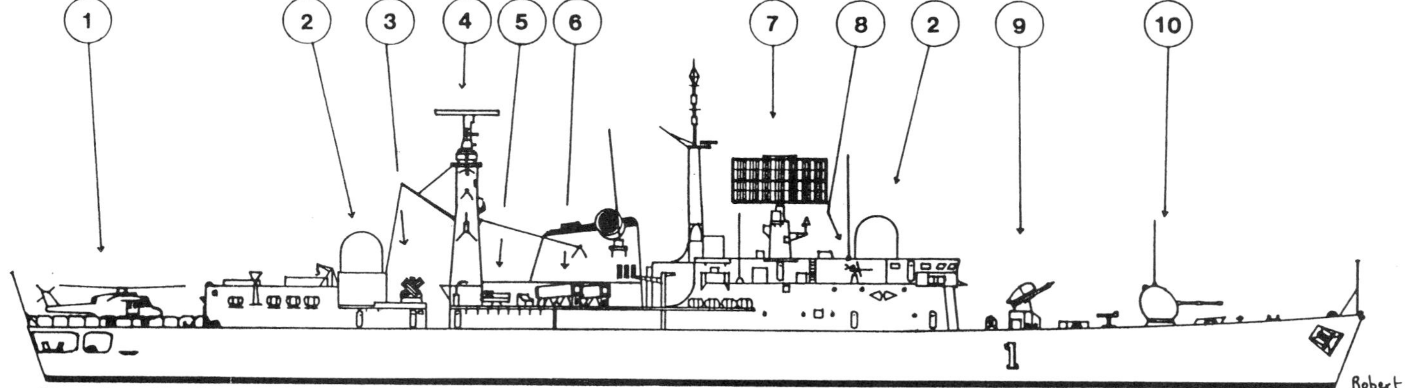

Hercules (D 1) 1. helicopter 2. Type 909 radar director 3. Corvus decoy rocket launchers 4. Type 992Q air/surface search radar 5. ASW torpedo tubes (III × 2) 6. MM 38 Exocet launchers 7. Type 965M early warning radar 8. 20-mm Oerlikon AA 9. Sea Dart launcher 10. Mk 8 114-mm dual-purpose gun
Drawing by Robert Dumas

FRIGATES *(continued)*

Sarandi (D 13) PH2 Tracy Didas, U.S. Navy, 10-90

Sarandi (D 13) PH2 Tracy Didas, U.S. Navy, 10-90

A: 8/MM 40 Exocet SSM (IV × 2)—1 Albatros SAM syst. (VII × 1; 24 Aspide missiles)—1/27-mm OTO Melara DP—8/40-mm Breda AA (II × 4)—6/324-mm ILAS-3 ASW TT (III × 2; 18 torp.)—1 or 2 Alouette-III helicopters

Electron Equipt:
Radar: 1/H.S.A. ZW-06 nav., 1/H.S.A. DA-08A air/surf. search, 1/H.S.A. WM-25 track-while-scan f.c., 1/STIR f.c., 1/H.S.A. LIROD f.c.
Sonar: 1/Krupp Atlas KAE 80, hull-mounted
EW: Scimitar jammer, Rapids intercept., 2/SCLAR chaff (XX × 2), G738 towed torpedo decoy

M: COGOG: 2 Olympus TM 3B gas turbines, 25,800 hp each; 2 Tyne RM 1C, 5,100 hp each for cruise; 2 Escher-Wyss CP props; 51,600 shp max.

Electric: 2,600 kw (2/940-kw sets, 2/360-kw) **Range:** 4,500/18
Crew: 26 officers, 84 petty officers, 90 enlisted

Remarks: Considered to be destroyers by Argentine Navy. Ordered 11-12-78 as a class of six, four of which were to be built in Argentina, but altered to four when MEKO 140-series frigate program was introduced. Albatros system has a 16-missile Aspide SAM rapid-reload magazine nearby. SEWACO weapons data/control system. The two H.S.A. LIROD radar/optronic GFCS each control two twin 40-mm AA, for which 10,752 rounds can be carried. Graseby G1738 towed torpedo decoy system. Four Lynx helicopters for these ships canceled by U.K., 1982; one Alouette-III is normally carried. Can carry up to 10 ASW torpedoes for the helicopters. The MEKO concept calls for modularized weapons and electronics systems, to permit rapid modernization and repair. Nigeria's *Aradu* is very similar. D 10 participated in the UN Coalition fleet in the Iraqi War, 1990–91, losing her Alouette-III helicopter on 1-11-90.

◆ **4 (+2) MEKO 140 A16 class** Bldr: AFNE, Rio Santiago, Ensenada

	Laid down	L	In serv.
41 Espora	10-3-80	23-1-82	5-7-85
42 Rosales	7-1-81	4-3-83	14-11-86
43 Spiro	1-4-82	24-6-83	24-11-87
44 Parker	9-2-82	31-3-84	17-4-90
45 Robinson	6-6-83	2-85	. . .
46 Gomez Roca (ex-*Seaver*)	1-12-83	14-11-86	1-92

D: 1,560 tons (1,790 fl) **S:** 27 kts
Dim: 91.2 (86.4 pp) × 11.0 × 3.33 (hull)
A: 4/MM 40 Exocet SSM (II × 2)—1/76-mm OTO Melara DP—4/40-mm AA Breda (II × 2), 2/12.7-mm mg (I × 2)—6/324-mm ASW TT (III × 2)—1/helo

Electron Equipt:
Radar: 1/Decca TM 1226 nav., 1/H.S.A. DA-05/2 surf./air search, 1/H.S.A. WM-28 track-while-scan f.c., 2/H.S.A. LIROD f.c.
Sonar: 1/Krupp Atlas AQS-1 hull-mounted
EW: RDC-2ABC and RCM-2 systems, 2/Dagaie chaff RL

M: 2 SEMT-Pielstick 16 PC2-5V400 diesels; 2/5-bladed props; 22,600 bhp
Electric: 1,410 kVA (3 × 470 kVA diesel sets) **Range:** 4,000/18
Fuel: 230 tons **Crew:** 11 officers, 46 petty officers, 36 enlisted

Remarks: All reported to be available for sale late 1984. Ordered 8-79. Blohm + Voss design, based on Portuguese *João Coutinho* class. Have fin stabilizers. LIROD radar/electro-optical system controls 40-mm AA. Carry Whitehead A244S ASW torpedoes. Carry 5 tons aviation fuel, 70 tons fresh water. H.S.A. DAISY data system. Telescoping helo hangar on F 44–F 46 only. F 44 flooded out 2-10-86, delaying completion. New hull numbers assigned 1988 (originally F10–F15). Work on fitting out last two progressing very slowly. 43 accompanied D 10 to Mideast to assist UN Coalition, 1990–91; relieved by 42 during 3-91. Fitting out on 46 was more advanced than on 45 as of early 1991.

Parker (44) PH2 Tracy Didas, U.S. Navy, 10-90

Espora (41) on trials Blohm + Voss, 1984

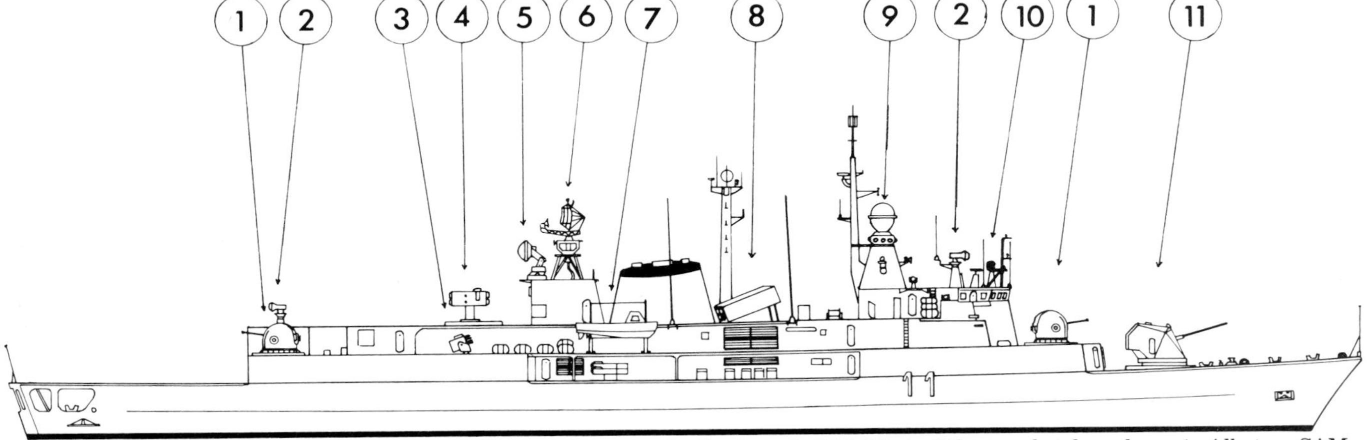

MEKO 360 H2 class 1. twin 40-mm AA 2. LIROD radar/optronic director 3. SCLAR chaff/flare rocket launcher 4. Albatros SAM launcher 5. STIR missile director 6. DA-08 long-range radar antenna 7. triple ASW torpedo tubes 8. quadruple MM 40 Exocet ramps (under shield) 9. WM-25 track-while-scan radar 10. ZW-06 navigational radar 11. 127-mm dual-purpose gun mount
Drawing by Robert Dumas

FRIGATES *(continued)*

♦ **3 French Type A-69 class** Bldr: Lorient DY

	Laid down	L	In serv.
31 Drummond (ex-*Good Hope*, F 432, ex-*Lieutenant de Vaisseau le Henaff*, F 784)	12-3-76	5-3-77	10-78
32 Guerrico (ex-*Transvaal*, F 102, ex-*Commandant l'Herminier*, F 791)	11-10-76	9-77	10-78
33 Granville	end-78	28-6-80	22-6-81

Guerrico (32) PH2 Tracy Didas, U.S. Navy, 10-90

D: 1,100 tons (1,250 fl) **S:** 23.3 kts
Dim: 80.5 (76.0 pp) × 10.3 × 3.0 (5.2 sonar)
A: 4/MM 38 Exocet (II × 2)—1/100-mm DP Mod. 1968—2/40-mm Breda AA (II × 1)—2/20-mm AA (I × 2)—6/324-mm ASW TT (III × 2)
Electron Equipt:
Radar: 1/Decca RM 1226 nav., 1/DRBV-51A air/surf. search, 1/DRBC-32E f.c.
Sonar: Thomson-Sintra Diodon MF hull-mounted
EW: DR 2000 S3 intercept, Alligator 51 jammer, 2 chaff RL
M: 2 SEMT-Pielstick 12 PC 2 V400 diesels; 2 CP props; 12,000 bhp
Electric: 840 kw **Range:** 3,000/18; 4,500/15 **Endurance:** 15 days
Crew: 5 officers, 79 enlisted

Remarks: The first two were originally ordered by South Africa, but delivery was embargoed. Purchased by Argentina, 25-9-78, to augment fleet in case of war with Chile. Armament and some electronic gear differ from French Navy version. All now have Breda twin 40-mm AA controlled by a CSEE Naja optronic GFCS; the first two originally had older Bofors L60 mountings. Have fin stabilizers. 33 has Dagaie chaff rocket system; the other two have British Corvus rocket launchers. 32 damaged on 7-4-82 during the Argentine invasion of South Georgia; repaired.

CORVETTES

♦ **1 former U.S. oilfield supply vessel** Bldr: Quality SY, Houma, Louisiana (In serv. 1981; acquired 15-11-87)

A 2 Teniente Olivieri (ex-*Marsea 10*)

D: 1,640 tons (fl) **S:** 12 kts **Dim:** 56.29 × 12.20 × 3.66
A: 2/12.7-mm mg (I × 2) **Electron Equipt:** Radar: . . .
M: 2 G.M. EMD 16-645-EZ diesels; 2 props; 3,700 bhp—300 shp bow-thruster
Electric: 198 kw **Range:** 2800/12 **Crew:** 4 officers, 11 enlisted

Remarks: 293 grt/992 dwt. Purchased from the U.S. Maritime Administration 12-87 and delivered 5-88 as a "dispatch boat," i.e., a patrol vessel. Cargo capacity on 35.06 × 9.33-m open deck aft: 610 tons. Can also carry 315 tons cargo fuel, 514 tons drilling water (tanks probably altered to carry other liquids), 44 tons potable water, and 113 tons drilling mud. Replaced discarded patrol tug *Alfarez Sobral.*

♦ **2 U.S. Achomawi class** Bldr: Charleston SB & DD Co., Charleston, S.C.

	Laid down	L	In serv.
A 1 Comandante General Irigoyen (ex-*Cahuilla*, ATF 152)	16-6-44	2-11-44	10-3-45
A 3 Francisco de Churruca (ex-*Luiseno*, ATF 156)	7-11-44	17-3-45	16-6-45

D: 1,235 tons (1,675 fl) **S:** 16.5 kts
Dim: 62.48 (59.44 wl) × 11.73 × 4.67
A: 4/40-mm AA (II × 2, I × 2)—2/20-mm AA (I × 2) **Crew:** 85 tot.
Electron Equipt: Radar: 1/. . . navigational
M: 4 G.M. 12-278A diesels, electric drive; 1 prop; 3,000 shp
Fuel: 363 tons **Electric:** 400 kw **Range:** 7,000/15; 15,000/8

Remarks: A 1 transferred 1961 as an ocean tug; rerated a patrol ship in 1966. A 3 purchased 1-7-75. Retain tug and salvage facilities. A 3: 2/40-mm AA (II × 1) only. Were to be discarded on completion of MEKO 140 class.

Comandante General Irigoyen (A 1) Robert L. Scheina, 1980

♦ **2 Murature class** Bldr: Ars. de Rio Santiago

	Laid down	L	In serv.
P 20 Murature	3-40	7-43	4-45
P 21 King	6-38	11-43	11-46

King (P 21)—with *Murature* (P 22) inboard Leo Van Ginderen, 3-87

D: 913 tons (1,032 fl) **S:** 18 kts **Dim:** 77.0 × 8.8 × 2.3
A: 3/105-mm DP (I × 3)—4/40-mm AA (II × 1, I × 2)—5/12.7-mm mg (I × 5)
Electron Equipt: Radar: 1/. . . navigational
M: 2 Werkspoor 4-cycle diesels; 2 props; 2,500 bhp
Range: 6,000/12 **Fuel:** 90 tons **Crew:** 100 tot.

Remarks: Riveted construction patrol gunboats now limited to sheltered waters and used primarily as cadet training ships. Scheduled to be replaced by MEKO 140-class frigates. Guns are obsolete German weapons. See photo of *San Juan* (S 42) for appearance.

PATROL BOATS

♦ **2 TNC 45 class** Bldr: Friedrich Lürssen Werft, Vegesack, Germany

	L	In serv.		L	In serv.
P 85 Intrepida	2-12-73	20-7-74	P 86 Indomita	8-4-74	12-74

Indomita (P 86) Leo Van Ginderen, 1986

PATROL BOATS *(continued)*

D: 240 tons (265 fl) **S:** 37.8 kts
Dim: 44.9 (42.3 pp) × 7.4 × 2.28 (prop.)
A: 1/76-mm DP OTO Melara—2/40-mm AA (I × 2)—2/533-mm TT (German SST-4 wire-guided torp.)
Electron Equipt:
Radar: 1/Decca 101 nav., 1/H.S.A. WM-22 track-while-scan f.c.
EW: Decca RDL-1 intercept
M: 4 MTU MD872 diesels; 4 props; 14,400 bhp **Electric:** 330 kw
Range: 640/36; 1,700/16 **Crew:** 5 officers, 37 enlisted

Remarks: Anti-rolling fin stabilizers. Plans to acquire two more canceled.

◆ **4 Israeli Dabur class** Bldr: Israeli Aircraft Industries, Israel (In serv. 1978)

P 61 Baradero P 62 Barranqueras P 63 Clorinda
P 64 Concepción del Uruguay

D: 26.8 tons (34.2 fl) **S:** 22 kts **Dim:** 19.8 × 5.4 × 1.75
A: 2/20-mm AA (I × 2)—4/12.7-mm mg (II × 2)
Electron Equipt: Radar: Decca 101 navigational **Crew:** 8 tot.
M: 2 G.M. 12V71 T diesels; 2 props; 1,200 bhp **Range:** 700/16

Remarks: Deployed to Golfo de Fonseca, west coast of Central America, 1990, for UN peacekeeping force duties.

MINE WARFARE SHIPS

◆ **6 British "Ton"-class minesweepers/minehunters**

	L
M 1 Neuquen (ex-*Hickleton*)	26-1-55
M 2 Rio Negro (ex-*Tarlton*)	10-11-54
M 3 Chubut (ex-*Santon*)	18-8-55
M 4 Tierra del Fuego (ex-*Bevington*)	17-3-53
M 5 Chaco (ex- *Rennington*)	27-11-58
M 6 Formosa (ex-*Ilmington*)	8-3-54

Three Argentine "Tons"—minehunter at left Leo Van Ginderen, 4-84

D: 370 tons (425 fl) **S:** 15 kts **Dim:** 46.33 (42.68 pp) × 8.76 × 2.50
A: 1/40-mm AA **Electron Equipt:** Radar: 1/Type 978 navigational
M: 2 Paxman Deltic 18A-7A diesels; 2 props; 3,000 hp **Fuel:** 45 tons
Range: 2,300/13; 3,000/8 **Crew:** 27 tot. (M 5, M 6: 36 tot.)

Remarks: M 5 and M 6 refitted as minehunters in 1968, with Plessey Type 193M sonar. The others may retain Mirrlees JVSS-12 diesels, totaling 2,500 hp. In poor condition; may soon be stricken.

AMPHIBIOUS WARFARE SHIPS

◆ **1 Modified U.S. DeSoto County-class tank landing ship**

	Bldr	L	In serv.
Q 42 Cabo San Antonio	AFNE, Rio Santiago	1968	2-11-78

Cabo San Antonio (Q 42) 7-88

D: 4,300 tons (8,000 fl) **S:** 16 kts
Dim: 134.72 (129.8 wl) × 18.9 × 5.5
A: 12/40-mm AA (IV × 3)—2/20-mm AA (I × 2)
Electron Equipt: Radar: 1/ . . . navigational, 1/SPS-10 surface search
M: 6 diesels; 2 CP props; 13,700 bhp **Electric:** 900 kw
Crew: 124 tot.

Remarks: Differs from U.S. Navy version primarily in armament and in having a 60-ton Stülcken heavy-lift king post set amidships. Carries 4 LCVP. Tank deck 88 m long can stow 23 medium tanks. 700 troops can be carried. Three U.S. Mk 51 Mod. 2 optical lead-computing GFCS. The Plessey AWS-1 air-search radar originally fitted was replaced by a U.S. SPS-10 surface-search set by 1988.

◆ **4 U.S. LCM(6)-class landing craft** (In serv. 6-71)

EDM 1 EDM 2 EDM 3 EDM 4

D: 24 tons (56 fl) **S:** 10 kts **Dim:** 17.07 × 4.37 × 1.17 (aft)
A: 2/12.7-mm mg **Range:** 130/10 **Cargo:** 30 tons
M: 2 Gray Marine 64 HN9 diesels; 2 props; 330–450 bhp

◆ **8 U.S. LCVP-class landing craft**

EDVP 30–37

D: 13 tons (fl) **S:** 9 kts **Dim:** 10.90 × 3.21 × 1.04 (aft)
M: 1 Gray Marine 64 HN9 diesel; 225 bhp **Range:** 110/9

Remarks: It is not known whether the above list includes the four LCVPs carried by *Cabo San Antonio*. Cargo: 36 troops or 3.5 tons. Five others discarded post-1982.

Note: The Argentine Marine Corps operates 18 LVTP-7 amphibious armored troop carriers, one LVTC-1 amphibious command vehicle, and one LVTR-1 amphibious vehicle recovery vehicle.

HYDROGRAPHIC SHIPS

◆ **1 Puerto Deseado class** Bldr: ASTARSA, San Fernando

	Laid down	L	In serv.
Q 20 Puerto Deseado	17-3-76	4-12-77	26-2-79 (trials)

D: 2,133 tons **S:** 15 kts **Dim:** 70.81 (67.0 pp) × 13.2 × 4.5
M: 2 Fiat-GMT diesels; 2 props; 2,700 bhp **Electric:** 1,280 kVA
Range: 12,000/12
Crew: 12 officers, 53 enlisted, 9 scientists, 10 technicians

Remarks: Used for hydrometeorological reporting. Four Hewlett-Packard 2108-A computers for data analysis/storage. Has seismic, gravimetric, and magnetometer equipment. Omega- and NAVSAT-equipped. Has geology laboratory. Ice-reinforced. The previously listed *Alvaro Alberto*, completed 1983, is subordinate to the Ministry of Marine, as is the *Capitan Oca Balda* (598 dwt), completed 1983.

◆ **1 Comodoro Rivadavia class** Bldr: Mestrina, el Tigre

	L	In serv.
Q 11 Comodoro Rivadavia	29-11-73	6-12-76

Comodoro Rivadavia (Q 11) Leo Van Ginderen, 8-88

D: 655 tons (830 fl) **S:** 12 kts **Dim:** 52.2 × 8.8 × 2.6
M: 2 Werkspoor Stork RHO-218K diesels; 1,160 bhp
Range: 6,000/12 **Crew:** 27 tot.

◆ **1 inshore survey craft** Bldr: Cadenazzi, el Tigre

Q 16 Petrel (In serv. 1965)

D: 52 tons (fl) **S:** 9 kts **Dim:** 19.7 × 4.5 × 1.7
M: 2 diesels; . . . props; 340 hp **Crew:** 9 tot.

◆ **1 inshore survey craft** Bldr: AFNE, Rio Santiago

Q 15 Cormoran (In serv. 20-2-64)

D: 82 tons (102 fl) **S:** 11 kts **Dim:** 25.3 × 5.0 × 1.8
M: 2 diesels; 2 props; 440 bhp **Crew:** 19 tot.

HYDROGRAPHIC SHIPS *(continued)*

Petrel (Q 16) Leo Van Ginderen, 1986

AUXILIARY SHIPS

◆ **1 antarctic support ship icebreaker** Bldr: Wärtsilä, Helsinki, Finland

	Laid down	L	In serv.
Q 5 Almirante Irizar	4-7-77	3-2-78	15-12-78

Almirante Irizar (Q 5) Leo Van Ginderen, 1-87

D: 11,811 (14,900 fl) **S:** 16.5 kts **Dim:** 119.3 × 25.0 × 9.5
A: 2/40-mm AA (I × 2)—2/helicopters
Electron Equipt: Radar: 2/ . . . nav., 1 Plessey AWS-2 air search
M: diesel-electric; 4 SEMT-Pielstick 8 PC 2.5 L/400 diesels; 2 Stromberg motors; 2 props; 16,200 shp
Electric: 2,640 kw **Crew:** 123 ship's company + 100 scientists

Remarks: Ordered 17-12-75. Canadian RAST helicopter downhaul winch system, 2 helicopters. Wärtsilä bubbler system to keep ice from hull bottom. Sixty-ton towing winch. Two 16-ton cranes. Used as a hospital ship during Falklands War. Red hull, white upperworks.

Note: There are long-range plans to replace the antarctic supply transport *Bahia Paraiso* (Q 6), which went aground at Palmer Land on 28-1-89 and sank on 31-1-89, with a new ship, possibly a variant of the Italian Navy's helicopter-carrying disaster relief ship/transport *San Marco*.

◆ **3 "Costa Sur"-class transports** Bldr: Principe & Menghe SY, Maciel Isl.

	Laid down	L	In serv.
B 3 Canal Beagle	10-1-77	14-10-77	28-4-78
B 4 Bahia San Blas	11-4-77	29-4-78	27-11-78
B 5 Cabo de Hornos (ex-*Bahia Camarones*)	29-4-78	4-11-78	18-7-79

Bahia San Blas (B 4) George R. Schneider, Jr., 4-89

D: 7,640 tons (fl) **S:** 15 kts **Dim:** 119.9 × 17.5 × 6.4 **A:** none
M: 2 AFNE-Sulzer diesels; 2 props; 6,400 bhp **Crew:** . . . tot.

Remarks: To supply remote stations. 4,600 grt/5,800 dwt. 9,700 cubic meters cargo. Also carry passengers and cargo in commercial service.

◆ **2 merchant tankers** Bldr: Italcantiere, Castellamare

Note: The Argentine Navy no longer has any underway replenishment oilers of its own, but, as was done during the Falklands War, it has access to two state-owned merchant tankers that have been equipped with alongside refueling capabilities.

Puerto Rosales Campo Duran

D: approx. 37,000 tons (fl) **S:** 16.5 kts
Dim: 170.2 (161.53 pp) × 25.94 × 11.02
M: 2 GMT diesels; 1 CP prop; 14,400 hp **Electric:** 7,000 kw

Remarks: 18,012 grt/30,884 dwt.

Note: The lighthouse supply ship *San Julian* (B 7, ex-U.S. Army FS 281) was stricken during 1989–90.

◆ **2 auxiliary ocean tugs** Bldr: Ast. Vicente Forte, Buenos Aires

R 2 Querandi (In serv. 22-8-78) R 3 Tehuelche (In serv. 2-11-78)

Querandi (R 2) and Tehuelche (R 3) Leo Van Ginderen, 4-84

D: 370 tons (fl) **S:** 12 kts **Dim:** 33.6 × 8.4 × 3.0
M: 2 M.A.N. 6V 23.5/33 diesels; 1,200 bhp
Range: 1,200/12 **Crew:** 30 tot.

◆ **1 training ship** Bldr: Union Naval de la Levante, Valencia, Spain

Q 31 Piloto Alsina (ex-*Ciudad de Formosa*) (In serv. 1963)

Piloto Alsina (Q 31) Leo Van Ginderen, 3-87

D: 2,800 tons (fl) **S:** 14 kts **Dim:** 105.60 (99.98 pp) × 17.89 × 2.52
M: 3 Maquinista-Burmeister & Wain 8-cyl. diesels; 1 prop; 4,800 bhp
Electric: 480 kw **Fuel:** 224 tons **Crew:** . . . tot.

Remarks: 3,986 grt/720 dwt. Former passenger ferry purchased and commissioned 17-3-81 for training duties.

◆ **1 sail-training vessel**

	Bldr	L	In serv.
Q 2 Libertad	AFNE, Rio Santiago	30-5-56	1962

AUXILIARY SHIPS *(continued)*

Libertad (Q 2) Leo Van Ginderen, 8-90

D: 3,025 tons (3,625 fl) **S:** 12 kts
Dim: 94.25 (79.9 pp) × 13.75 × 6.75
M: diesels; 2 props; 2,400 bhp **Range:** 12,000
Crew: 222 ship's company and 140 cadets

Note: The former sail-training ship *Presidente Sarmiento* (1898) and the sail corvette *Uruguay* (1874) are maintained by the navy as museums at Buenos Aires.

♦ **4 small sail-training yachts**

Q 25 Fortuna I	Bldr: Tandanor, Buenos Aires	D: 17 tons
Q 26 Fortuna II	Bldr: Tandanor, Buenos Aires	D: 31.5 tons
Q 72 Tequara	Bldr: . . .	
Q 73 Ilati II	Bldr: Cadenazzi SY, 1979	D: 80 tons (fl) S: 15 kts

YARD AND SERVICE CRAFT

♦ **6 U.S. YTL-422-class small harbor tugs** (In serv. 1944–45)
Bldrs: R 5, 16, 18: Robt. Jacobs, City Isl., NY; R 6, 19: H.C. Grebe Co.; R 10: Everett Pacific BY, Everett, Wash.

R 5 Mocovi (ex-YTL 441)
R 10 Chulupi (ex-YTL 426)
R 18 Chiquillan (ex-YTL 444)
R 6 Calchaqu (ex-YTL 445)
R 16 Capayan (ex-YTL 443)
R 19 Morcoyan (ex-YTL 448)

Mocovi (R 5) Leo Van Ginderen, 4-81

D: 70 tons (80 fl) **S:** 10 kts **Dim:** 20.16 × 5.18 × 2.44
M: 1 Hoover-Owens-Rentschler diesel; 300 hp **Electric:** 40 kw
Fuel: 7 tons **Crew:** 5 tot.

Remarks: R 16, 18, 19 leased 3-65; others, 3-69; all purchased outright 16-6-77.

♦ **6 floating dry docks**

Y 1 (ex-U.S. ARD 23): 3,500-ton capacity; 149.0 × 24.7 × 7.3 (light) (In serv. 1944)
Y 2: 1,500-ton capacity; 91.5 × 18.3 (In serv. 1913)
Y 3, Y 4: 750-ton capacity; 65.8 × 14
A: 12,000-ton capacity; 172.5 × 26 (In serv. 1958)
B: 2,800-ton capacity; 110.0 × 18.0 (In serv. 1956)

♦ **4 floating cranes**

PREFECTURA NAVAL ARGENTINA

Personnel (1988): 1,200 officers, 12,000 men

Note: Ships and craft painted white. Attached aircraft include 2 Puma and 6 Hughes H500 helicopters. The former Skyvan light transports are being replaced by 5 CASA C-212 series 200 transports, and it is planned to acquire 4 Helibras HB-350 Esquilo helicopters to replace the Hughes H500s. The *Prefectura Naval* was transferred from naval control to the Ministry of Defense in 10-84; it may, however, be returned to naval subordination in the near future. Most personnel serve ashore.

PATROL SHIPS AND BOATS

♦ **5 "Halcon"-class ocean patrol ships** Bldr: Bazán, El Ferrol, Spain

	Laid down	L	In serv.
GC 24 Doctor Manuel Mantilla	16-2-81	29-6-81	15-5-82
GC 25 Azopardo	1-4-81	14-10-81	1-83
GC 26 Thompson	2-81	7-12-81	20-6-83
GC 27 Prefecto Fique	9-81	24-2-82	29-7-83
GC 28 Prefecto Derbes	11-81	16-6-82	16-11-83

Doctor Manuel Mantilla (GC 24) Bazán, 1982

D: 767 tons normal (900 fl) **S:** 21.5 kts
Dim: 67.0 (63.0 pp) × 10.0 × 3.06
A: 1/40-mm AA Breda-Bofors—2/12.7-mm mg (I × 2)—1 Alouette-III helo
Electron Equipt: Radar: 1 Decca AC 1226 nav. **Electric:** 710 kw
M: 2 Bazán-MTU 16V956 TB91 diesels; 2 props; 9,000 hp (7,500 sust.)
Range: 5,000/18 **Crew:** 9 officers, 24 enlisted, 4 cadets

Remarks: Ordered 3-79 to patrol 200-nautical-mile economic zone. Endurance 20 days. Carry 144 rounds 40-mm. Same class built for Mexico. Helicopters, when aboard, would be on loan from navy.

♦ **1 former whaler, used for ocean patrol**

	Bldr.	In serv.	In Arg. C.G.
GC 13 Delfin (ex-R1)	NV IJsselwerf, Rotterdam	4-57	23-1-70

Delfin (GC 13) George R. Schneider, Jr., 8-89

D: 700 tons (1,000 fl) **S:** 15 kts **Dim:** 60.0 × 9.0 × 4.7
A: 1/20-mm AA—2/12.7-mm mg (I × 2) **Crew:** 27 tot.
M: 2 M.A.N. 10-cyl. diesels; 1 prop; 2,300 bhp **Range:** 6,720/10

Remarks: Purchased 1969 from Calpe Shipping Co., Gibraltar, and converted for patrol duties. Three sisters formerly served in the Norwegian Coast Guard.

♦ **1 Dorado class** Bldr: Rio Santiago Naval Base

GC 43 Mandubi (In serv. 1940)

ARGENTINA *(continued)*
PATROL SHIPS AND BOATS *(continued)*

D: 208 tons (270 fl) **S:** 11 kts **Dim:** 33.2 × 4.0 × 1.9
A: 2/12.7-mm mg (I × 2)
M: 2 M.A.N. G6V 23.5/33 diesels; 2 props; 880 bhp
Range: 800/14; 3,400/10 **Crew:** 12 crew + 20 trainees

Remarks: Sister *Dorado* (GC 34) and the similar *Robalo* (GC 45) stricken 1985–86. Used as a training craft for cadets.

PATROL CRAFT

♦ **18 Z-28 class** Bldr: Blohm + Voss, Hamburg (All in serv. 9-79/1-80)

GC 64 Mar Del Plata
GC 65 Martin Garcia
GC 66 Rio Lujan
GC 67 Rio Uruguay
GC 68 Rio Paraguay
GC 69 Rio Parana
GC 70 Rio Plata
GC 71 La Plata
GC 72 Buenos Aires
GC 73 Cabo Corrientes
GC 74 Quequen
GC 75 Bahia Blanca
GC 76 Ingeniero White
GC 77 Golfo San Matias
GC 78 Madryn
GC 79 Rio Deseado
GC 80 Ushuaia
GC 81 Canal De Beagle

Buenos Aires (GC 72) Leo Van Ginderen, 1984

D: 81 tons (fl) **S:** 22 kts **Dim:** 27.65 (26.0) × 5.30 × 1.65
A: 1/20-mm AA—2/12.7-mm mg (I × 2)
Electron Equipt: Radar: 1/Decca 1226 navigational
M: 2 MTU 8V331 TC92 diesels; 2 props; 2,100 bhp (1,770 sust.)
Electric: 90 kVA **Range:** 780/18; 1,200/12
Crew: 3 officers, 11 enlisted

Remarks: Ordered 24-11-78. Fin stabilizers fitted. During the Falklands War, *Rio Iguaza* (GC 83) was lost and *Islas Malvinas* (GC 82) was captured and renamed *Tiger Bay* by British forces. Not all units have the 20-mm gun.

♦ **2 Lynch class** Bldr: AFNE, Rio Santiago (In serv. 1964–67)

GC 21 Lynch GC 22 Toll

D: 100 tons (117 fl) **S:** 22 kts **Dim:** 27.44 × 5.80 × 1.85
A: 1/20-mm AA **M:** 2 Maybach diesels; 2 props; 2,700 hp
Crew: 16 tot.

Remarks: Sister *Erezcano* (GC 23) stricken 1986.

♦ **34 GC 48-class patrol craft** Bldr: Cadenazzi SY, Tigre (except GC 88–114; Ast. Belen de Escobar)

GC 48–GC 61 (In serv. 1978–79)
GC 88–GC 95, GC 102–GC 114 (In serv. 1984–86)

D: 13 tons (15 fl) **S:** 25 kts **Dim:** 12.54 × 3.57 × 1.10
A: 1/12.7-mm mg **Range:** 400/20
M: 2 G.M. 6V71N diesels; 2 props; 514 bhp **Crew:** 3 tot.

♦ **1 salvage tug** Bldr: Sanym SA, San Fernando

GC 47 Tonina (In serv. 21-10-77)

D: 103 tons (153 fl) **S:** 11 kts **Dim:** 25.5 × 5.3 × 2.1
A: 1/20-mm AA—2/12.7-mm mg **Range:** 2,800/10
Electron Equipt: Radar: 1 Decca 1226 nav. **Crew:** 11 tot.
M: 2 G.M. 16V71N 162-2000 diesels; 2 props; 1,500 hp

Remarks: Used as training ship until 1986. Has divers' facilities, including a decompression chamber.

♦ **1 patrol craft** Bldr: Rio Santiago Naval Base (In serv. 17-12-39)

GC 101 Dorado (ex- . . .)

D: 43 tons (fl) **S:** 12 kts **Dim:** 21.2 × 4.3 × 1.5
A: . . . **M:** 2 G.M. 6071-6A diesels; 2 props; 360 hp
Range: 1550/12 **Crew:** 1 officer, 6 enlisted

♦ **6 miscellaneous tugboats**

SB 8 Canal Emilio Mitre
SB 2–SB 5, SB 9

Remarks: SB 8: 53 tons (fl); 10 kts; Damen "Pushy-Cat 1500" design, built 1982.

♦ **17 pilot boats**—no data available

SP 14 Lago Alumine
SP 15 Lago Traful
SP 16 Lago Colhue
SP 17 Lago Mascardi
SP 18 Lago Argentino
SP 19 Lago Nahuel Huapi
SP 20 Lago Viedma
SP 21 Lago San Martin
SP 22 Lago Buenos Aires
SP 23 Lago Faviano
SP 24 Lago Lacar
SP 25 Lago Cardial
SP 26 Lago Musters
SP 27 Lago Quillen
SP 28 Lago Roca
SP 29 Lago Puelo
SP 30 Lago Futalaufquen

Remarks: SP 14 and SP 15 displace 33.7 tons; SP 16–SP 18 displace 42 tons; SP 19–SP 23 displace 51 tons; SP 24–SP 29 displace 5 tons. SP 30, 16.5 m overall, was built by Damen, the Netherlands, in 1983; the others were completed in 1981. Also in use as pilot craft are SP 3, SP 6, SP 7, SP 9, and SP 13.

♦ **1 pilot station ship** Bldr: Brodogradiliste i Tvornia Dizel Motora Split, Yugoslavia

Recalada (ex-*Lago Lacar*)

Recalada George R. Schneider, Jr., 4-89

D: approx. 14,000 tons (fl) **S:** 16.75 kts
Dim: 157.23 (144.02 pp) × 20.35 × 8.23
M: 1 Fiat 9-cyl. diesel; 1 prop; 10,300 bhp
Electric: 654 kw **Fuel:** 993.5 tons heavy oil/217 tons diesel

Remarks: Former six-hold cargo vessel of 8.486 grt/10,458 dwt acquired from Empresa Lineas Maritimas Argentina S.A. (ELMA) for conversion and use as a pilot station vessel in the Rio Plata. Helicopter flight deck added aft. Retains eight 10-ton and two 5-ton cargo booms. Incorrectly identified and described in previous editions.

♦ **1 sail-training yacht** (L: 12–68)

Esperanza

D: 32 tons **S:** 15 kts (6 power) **Dim:** 19.0 × 4.3 × 2.7
M: 1 G.M. diesel; 90 bhp **Crew:** 6 crew + 6 cadets

Remarks: Also in use is the yacht *Adhara II* (ex-*Gloria*, ex-*Cormoran*, GC 36) of 30 tons, with 1 G.M. auxiliary diesel, 10–15 kts.

Note: Also in use are some 450 smaller launches, semi-rigid inflatable boats, and service craft such as floating cranes.

AUSTRALIA

Commonwealth of Australia

Personnel (2-90): 15,492 total (including 2,438 women); 1,436 reserves (172 women); approximately 5,000 civilians (some of whom operate service craft). Women are being introduced into service aboard many naval-manned ships.

Naval Aviation: Helicopters in service include: 16 Sikorsky S-70B2 shipboard ASW helicopters (U.S. Navy LAMPS-III-equivalent, with MEL "Super Searcher" radar in place of LN-66), 7 Mk 56 Sea King ASW helicopters (upgraded from 2 Mk 50A and 5 Mk 50), 6 AS-350B Écureuil light helicopters, and 3 Bell 206B Kiowa ultility helicopters. Two HS-748 fixed-wing transports have been retained for EW training. Six Royal New Zealand Air Force A-4K Skyhawk fighter-bombers were transferred to R.A.N. control during 1990 for a five-year period for training.

The R.A.A.F. operates 20 P-3C Orion with AQS-901 receiver/processors for the Australian-developed "Barra" S5Q-801 sonobuoy; all P-3Cs are scheduled to receive ELTA EW intercept equipment.

S-70B2 Seahawk in R.A.N. service R.A.N., 1990

HS-748 EW training aircraft R.A.N., 8-87

Weapons and Systems: The Royal Australian Navy uses U.S. equipment and systems on its U.S.-built warships and British weapons and systems on its older ships, but some of its air-search and fire-control radars have been purchased in the Netherlands (LW-02, M-20, etc.). U.S. Mk 48 torpedoes have been purchased for use by submarines. U.S. Harpoon antiship missiles are to be carried by the submarines, FFG 7-class frigates, and R.A.A.F. P-3C, F-18, and F-111 aircraft. The 37 ships with Magnavox MX1100 SATNAV systems are being updated to use the Global Positioning System.

Except for the U.S.-built ships, the sonars are of British or Australian (Mulloka) origin. Mulloka is a high-frequency set tailored to Australian coastal water-sound propagation conditions. The "Karrawarra" towed passive sonar array entered service in 1985 for submarines and is being further developed as the "ASSTASS" (Australian Surface Ship Towed Array Surveillance System). The "Winnin" countermeasures system with "Hoveroc" chaff/IR decoy rockets that began trials in 1985 uses the same Mk 137 6-tubed launcher as the U.S. Mk 36 SRBOC system, with the Winnin tubes added. The Ikara ASW cruise missile system is to be retired by 1992. All ASW torpedoes are to be upgraded to Mk 46 Mod. 5.

SUBMARINES

◆ **0 (+6) Collins class (Kockums Type 471)** Bldr: Australian Submarine Corporation, Port Adelaide

	Laid down	L	In serv.
S . . . Collins	14-2-90	1994	1-95
S . . . Farncomb	3-3-91	1995	. . .
S . . . Waller	. . .	. . .	. . .
S . . . Dechaineux	. . .	. . .	. . .
S . . . Sheehan	. . .	. . .	. . .
S . . . Rankin	. . .	. . .	1999

Collins class (Kockums Type 471) Kockums, 1987

D: 2,450 surfaced/2,700 submerged **S:** 21 kts (sub.); 10.5 kts (surf.)
Dim: 75.0 × 7.8 × 6.8
A: 6/533-mm TT fwd. (23 Harpoon SSM and Mk 48 torpedoes)

Collins class SS R.A.N., 1991

Electron Equipt:
Radar: . . .— EW: Argo AR-700-US or MEL UAH (Manta) intercept
Sonar: Thomson-Sintra Scylla hull array; Karrawarra TASS
M: diesel-electric: 4 Garden Isl.-HedemoraVB210-18 diesel generator sets (6,900 bhp tot.), . . . Jeumont-Schneider motors; 1 prop; 5,000 shp
Range: 11,500/ . . . (*see* Remarks); 9,000/10 (snorkel); 32.6/21 (sub.); 480/4 (sub.)
Endurance: 70 days **Crew:** 42 tot. + 5 trainees

Remarks: Contract announced 18-5-87 for six, with option for two more, later dropped. Kockums, Sweden, design. Australian Submarine Corp. is a consortium of Kockums, Hardie, Ltd., and the government-owned Australian Industrial Development Co. Bow and stern of first two to build at Malmö, Sweden. Electronics/weapons control is to be by a consortium of Rockwell International, Singer Librascope, Computer Science (Aust.), and Thompson-CSF. They will have the Singer Librascope SCCS Mk 2 f.c.s., and Marconi SDG-1802 degaussing gear. Will have a receive-only interface with the LINK-11 combat information system data-link.

To be the quietest, most shock-resistant diesel-electric submarines in the world. Modular construction. Intended to meet a mission requirement of 3,500 n.m. radius at 10 kts submerged, plus 47 days on station at 4 kts. Battery capacity gives 120 hours at 4 kts. Provision may be made in the fifth and sixth units to accommodate a Stirling engine air-independent propulsion system. One Stirling engine ordered for trials.

The sonar system is derived from Thomson-Sintra's Eledone and will include a bow-mounted passive, an intercept, flank, towed (the Australian Karrawarra, with 1,000-m array, 40-mm in diameter), passive ranging, active (5 kHz) and mine-avoidance arrays. There will also be an 8–11 kHz underwater telephone. The Australian "Bunny" strap-on minelaying system may be procured for this class. The British Strachan & Henshaw submerged signal and decoy ejector system will be installed.

◆ **6 British Oberon class** Bldr: Scotts' SB & Eng., Greenock

	Laid down	L	In serv.
S 57 Oxley	2-7-64	24-9-65	27-3-67
S 59 Otway	29-6-65	29-11-66	22-4-68
S 60 Onslow	26-5-67	29-8-68	22-12-69
S 61 Orion	6-10-72	16-9-74	15-6-77
S 62 Otama	28-5-73	3-12-75	27-4-78
S 70 Ovens	17-6-66	5-12-67	18-4-69

Ovens (S 70) Leo Van Ginderen, 8-91

Otama (S 62) Leo Van Ginderen, 10-90

SUBMARINES *(continued)*

D: 1,610/2,196/2,417 tons **S:** 17.5/15 kts
Dim: 89.92 (87.45 pp) × 8.07 × 5.48
A: 6/533-mm TT for Sub-Harpoon and U.S. Mk 48 Mod. 3 torpedoes (fwd)—12 reloads
Electron Equipt:
Radar: 1/1006—EW: Elbit TIMNEX 4CHV2 (2–18 gHz) (*see* Remarks)
Sonar: Krupp Atlas CSU-3-41 system, 1/2007, "Micro-Puffs," 1/Karrawarra TASS
M: two 1,840-bhp Admiralty Standard Range 16 VVS-ASR1 diesel engines; diesel-electric propulsion; 2 props; 6,000 hp
Endurance: 56 days **Fuel:** 298 m^3 (446 m^3 emergency)
Crew: 6 officers, 57 enlisted

Remarks: All six R.A.N. *Oberons* received mid-life modernization: S 59 from 1-79 to 1981, S 70 from 3-80 to mid-1983, S 60 from 8-82 to 12-84, S 61 from 11-81 to 8-83, and S 62 from 1984 to 11-85. S 57, the prototype for the modernization, completed long refit 8-5-87 to bring her up to the definitive standard. *Oxley* recommissioned 22-2-80 with U.S. Singer/Librascope SFCS Mk 1 digital computer fire-control system with a UYK-20 computer, and a new sonar suit incorporating a Krupp Atlas CSU-3-41 active/passive system (active transducer in sail, passive array in enlarged dome on bow), U.K. Type 2007 LF passive array, and Type 2004 sound velocity meter. The two short 533-mm torpedo tubes aft are no longer used. 448 battery cells deliver 5,000 amp/hr. at 1-hr. rate, 7,420 amp/hr. at 5-hr. rate. Maximum operating depth: 200 m.

All received Sub-Harpoon antiship missile capability under the 1985–89 Defense Program, and U.S. Mk 48 Mod. 3 torpedoes have replaced all the Mk 37 type formerly carried. S 70 first R.A.N. sub to launch Sub-Harpoon, 12-85. S 62 began trials with the "Karrawarra" towed linear passive hydrophone array in 1984, and S 59 received the first definitive version of this "clip-on" array in 4-85. The apparently unsatisfactory EW suite may be replaced with the MEL UAH (Manta) suite. As of 1990, were to receive PIPRS—Ping Intercept Passive Ranging Sonar adaptation. Have U.K. Mk 2 submerged signal and decoy ejector forward, Mk 4 Mod 1B aft; both launch 102-mm devices.

S 59 operating experimentally with two crews; S 60, to perform trials with equipment for *Collins* class, was late completing a further refit, 1991. S 70 recommissioned 4-7-90 after fourth and last refit, with upgraded communications and rehabilitated machinery. S 57, based in Western Australia, was restricted from diving as of early 1991; all to strike 1993–1998. S 62 in refit 2-92 to 8-93.

DESTROYERS

◆ **3 U.S. Charles F. Adams class** Bldr: Defoe SB, Bay City, Michigan

	Laid down	L	In serv.
D 38 PERTH (ex-U.S. DDG 25)	21-9-62	26-9-63	17-7-65
D 39 HOBART (ex-U.S. DDG 26)	26-10-62	9-1-64	18-12-65
D 41 BRISBANE (ex-U.S. DDG 27)	15-2-65	5-5-66	16-12-67

Perth (D 38)—after modernization R.A.N., 10-90

D: 3,472 tons (4,720 fl) **S:** 35 kts
Dim: 134.18 (128.0 pp) × 14.32 × 6.0
A: 1/Mk 13 system for Harpoon SSM and Standard SM-1A SAM (40 missiles)—2/127-mm DP Mk 42 (I × 2)—2/12.7-mm mg (I × 2)—16/324-mm ASW TT Mk 32 (III × 2)
Electron Equipt:
Radar: 1 /978 nav., 1/SPS-67(V) surface search, 1/SPS-40C air search, 1/SPS-52C 3-D air search, 2/SPG-51C missile f.c., 1/SPG-53A gun f.c., 1 Ikara control
Sonar: 1/SQS-23F—TACAN: 1/URN-20 (D 41: URN-25)
EW: WLR-1F and WLR-6 intercept; URD-4 UHFD/F; 2/Mk 136 decoy RL (VI × 2)
M: 2 sets GT; 2 props; 70,000 shp **Fuel:** 900 tons
Electric: 2,200 kw
Boilers: 4 Babcock & Wilcox; 84 kg/cm; 520-deg. C superheat
Range: 1,600/30; 4,500/15 **Crew:** 21 officers, 312 enlisted

Brisbane (D 41)—with Mk. 15 Phalanx CIWS R.A.N., 10-90

DESTROYERS *(continued)*

Remarks: D 38 modernized in the U.S. 3-9-74 to 2-1-75 with SM-1A Standard missiles, NTDS, and Mk 42 Mod. 10 guns. The other two were refitted to the same standard in Australia. Missile fire control is Mk 74 Mod. 8 with two radar directors; guns are controlled by one Mk 68 radar director (optical range-finder removed). Further modernization began mid-1985, with D 41. The Mk 13 missile system was updated to handle Harpoon missiles. Sonars update with solid-state transmitters. D 41 completed modernization 12-87; D 38 began 1-88 and completed 11-89; D 39 began 9-89. The two Ikara ASW missile launchers were deactivated in all by end 1991. Modernization of D 41 was also to have included replacing the Mk 68 director with the U.S. Mk 86 GFCS and substituting the SLQ-32(V)2 EW system for the original array, but the work was not done.

For service with the UN Coalition during Desert Shield/Desert Storm in 1990–91, D 41 was fitted with two U.S. 20-mm Mk 15 Phalanx CIWS port and starboard on deckhouses abreast the after stack in place of the boats; davit-handled rigid inflatable boats were substituted. The sonars may be updated by substituting the Raytheon solid-state DE 1191 processor.

FRIGATES

◆ **0 (+ 8) ANZAC frigate (MEKO 200 variant) class** Bldr: Australian Marine Engineering Consolidated, Ltd. (AMECON), Williamstown and Newcastle

	Laid down	L	In serv.
F	. . .	. . .	6-96
F	. . .	. . .	6-98
F	. . .	. . .	6-99
F	. . .	. . .	6-00
F	. . .	. . .	6-01
F	. . .	. . .	6-02
F	. . .	. . .	6-03
F	. . .	. . .	6-04

ANZAC (MEKO 200 ANZ) frigate Blohm + Voss

ANZAC (MEKO 200 ANZ) frigate—launching Sea Sparrow missile Jeff Isaacs/R.A.N., 1991

D: 3,195 tons (3,495 fl) **S:** 31.75 kts (20 kts on diesel)
Dim: 117.50 (109.50 pp) × 14.80 (13.80 wl) × 5.99 (4.12 hull)
A: Mk 41 VLS (VIII × 1; 8 Sea Sparrow missiles)—1/127-mm U.S. Mk 45 Mod. 2 DP—6/324-mm Mk 32 ASW TT (III × 2)— 1/Seahawk helicopter
Electron Equipt:
Radar: 1/Krupp-Atlas ARPA 8600 nav., 1/ Ericsson 150 HC Sea Giraffe search, 1/H.S.A. LW-08 early warning, 1/BEAB 9LV200 f.c.
Sonar: Thomson-CSF Spherion B hull-mounted; ASSTASS towed array
EW: MEL Sceptre XL intercept (1 to 7.5 gHz); 4 Mk 36 SRBOC RL with Winnin decoys
M: CODOG: 2 MTU 12V1163 TB83 diesels (4,420 bhp each), 2 G.E. LM-2500-30 gas turbines (30,000 shp each); 2 CP props
Electric: 2,600 kw (4 × 650 kw MTU TB 396 series diesel sets)
Fuel: 300 tons **Range:** 900/31.75; 4,100/18 (2 diesels); 6,000/. . .
Crew: 22 officers, 41 petty officers, 100 ratings

Remarks: Contract awarded 14-8-89, with options for two or four more for New Zealand, which decided in 9-89 to order only two. All to be launched at Williamstown, in part using modules built at Newcastle. Construction, however, may be delayed by the failure of Carrington Slipways at Newcastle, which was to have built hull modules. Blohm + Voss, Hamburg, the design agent, is a 25 percent owner of AMECON, with the remainder owned by Transfield Pty Ltd., which may sell the Williamstown Dockyard portion of its holdings to the Australian government-owned Australian Defence Industries (ADI). Australian and New Zealand manufacturers will get 80 percent of the work by value, but European companies will be major suppliers, including Thorn EMI, Siemens AG, Bofors Electronics, and Sweden's Ericsson. Additional units may be ordered later to replace the three U.S. *Charles F. Adams*-class guided-missile destroyers.

Will have Bofors 9LV453 Mk 3 combat data/fire-control system, with only one Sea Viking (9LV 200-derivative) director (although space for a second is present). The ASW TT are to recycled from the "River" class as they are retired. ASSTASS (Australian Surface Ship Towed Array Surveillance System) is a variant of the Karriwara submarine TASS. The design is based on the version of the MEKO 200 being built for Portugal. Space and weight are reserved for eight Harpoon SSM (IV × 2), a second 8-cell VLS group, and a Mk 15 Phalanx CIWS, a towed sonar array, a helicopter data-link, and extending the EW coverage to 18 gHz.

◆ **4 (+2) U.S. Oliver Hazard Perry-class guided-missile frigates**

	Bldr	Laid down	L	In serv.
F 01 Adelaide (ex-FFG 17)	Todd, Seattle	29-7-77	21-6-78	6-11-80
F 02 Canberra (ex-FFG 18)	Todd, Seattle	1-3-78	1-12-78	21-3-81
F 03 Sydney (ex-FFG 35)	Todd, Seattle	16-1-80	26-9-80	29-1-83
F 04 Darwin (ex-FFG 44)	Todd, Seattle	2-7-81	26-3-82	21-7-84
F 05 Melbourne	AMECON, Melbourne	12-7-85	5-5-89	15-2-92
F 06 Newcastle	AMECON, Melbourne	11-88	3-92	21-2-92

Adelaide (FFG 01)—returning from Mideast Leo Van Ginderen, 12-90

Canberra (FFG 02) Mike Louagie, 5-9

FRIGATES *(continued)*

Sydney (F 03)—during the Iraq war; note radar-absorbent matting (RAM) on superstructure sides R.A.N., 11-90

Darwin (F 04)—launching Standard SM-1 MR missile R.A.N., 1990

D: 3,073 tons (3,962 fl) **S:** 29 kts
Dim: 138.80 (126.0 wl) × 13.72 × 4.52 (7.47 max.)
A: 1/Mk 13 Mod. 4 launcher for Standard SM-1A SAM and Harpoon (40 missiles)—1/76-mm DP OTO Melara Compact (U.S.Mk75)—1/20-mm Mk 15 CIWS—6/324-mm ASW TT Mk 32 for Mk 46 torpedoes (III × 2)—2/helicopters (*see* Remarks)
Electron Equipt:
Radar: 1/SPS-55 surf. search, 1/SPS-49(V)2 air search, 1/Mk 92 Mod. 2 track-while-scan gun/missile f.c., 1/SPG-60 STIR missile f.c.
Sonar: SQS-56 (F 05, 06: Mulloka)—TACAN: URN-25
EW: SLQ-32(V)2, Elbit EA 2118 intercept (2-40 gHz), modified Mk 36 SRBOC R2 (VIII × 2—with Winnin), SLQ-25 Nixie torpedo decoy
M: 2 G.E. LM-2500 gas turbines; 1 CP prop; 41,000 shp; 2/350-hp aux. propulsors
Electric: 3,000 kw **Fuel:** 587 tons (plus 64 tons helo fuel)
Range: 4,200/20; 5,000/18
Crew: 15 officers, 172 enlisted (plus air group)

Remarks: First two ordered 27-2-76 in lieu of Australian DDL design. The third was ordered 23-1-79 and the fourth on 28-4-80. In 1980 two more were authorized for construction in Australia. The first two Australian-built ships were ordered 12-10-83. Two drop-down, diesel-electric-driven propellers are located forward beneath the hull for emergency propulsion and maneuvering. F 04 arrived Australia 25-10-85. The former Williamstown Dockyard, plagued by labor troubles, was sold private as AMECON (Australian Marine Engineering, Consolidated), in 1988 to complete F 05 and F 06. The selection of the Sikorsky S-70B2 helicopter for these ships required that the first three be lengthened 9 feet and have fin stabilization systems added at Garden Island Dockyard; the RAST helicopter downhaul and traversing system also had to be added. The S-70B2 will be able to carry two antiship missiles (Penguin Mk 2 Mod. 7 or Sea Skua). F 03 completed lengthening 1-89, F 01 in 8-89; F 02 to complete by end-1991. The ships normally carry one S-70B2 and one Écureuil helicopter.

The Australian-built units have Mulloka sonars in place of SQS-56, the Australian-developed ASSTASS towed-array sonar, and the Winnin countermeasures system, with Hoveroc decoys. F 01 and 02 had their two Mk 24 target designators atop the pilothouse and EW systems added after delivery; their Mk 15 Vulcan-Phalanx Close-in Weapon Systems were ordered during 1984. All carry the SLQ-25 towed torpedo decoy and WSC-3 SATCOMM. Israeli intercept equipment added 1989–90.

During service with UN Coalition forces in Operation Desert Shield/Desert Storm in 1990–91, F 01 and F 04 had 2/12.7-mm mg added and radar-absorbent matting (RAM) added around the superstructure and masts. Trials for F 06 began 10-9-91.

◆ **3 "River"-class frigates**

	Bldr	Laid down	L	In serv.
DE 49 Derwent	Williamstown Nav. DY	16-6-58	17-4-61	30-4-64
DE 50 Swan	Williamstown Nav. DY	18-8-65	16-12-67	20-1-70
DE 53 Torrens	Cockatoo D. & Eng. Co.	18-8-65	28-9-68	19-1-71

Derwent (DE 49) Malcolm Dippy, 11-89

Derwent (DE 49)—Sea Cat removed LSPH S. Connolly, 5-91

Swan (DE 50)—with Ihara and Sea Cat removed LS P. Steele, R.A.N., 8-91

Torrens (DE 53) Leo Van Ginderen, 8-91

FRIGATES *(continued)*

D: 2,100 tons (2,750 fl) **S:** 30 kts
Dim: 112.75 (109.75 pp) × 12.50 × 3.90 (hull)
A: 2/114-mm DP Mk 6 (II × 1)—2/12.7-mm mg (I × 2)—6/324-mm Mk 32 ASW TT (II × 2)
Electron Equipt:
Radar: 1/Krupp-Atlas 8600 ARPA nav. (DE 49: 1/978) nav., 1/LW-02 early warning, 1/WM-22 track-while-scan f.c.
Sonar: 1/Mulloka, 1/Type 162—EW: intercept arrays
M: 2 sets geared steam turbines; 2 props; 34,000 shp
Electric: 1,140 kw (DE 46: 1,500 kw) **Crew:** 15 officers, 217 enlisted
Boilers: 2 Babcock & Wilcox, 38.7 kg/cm, 450-deg. C
Range: 4,500/12 **Fuel:** 400 tons

Remarks: Sister *Yarra* (DE 45) was stricken 22-11-85 and hulked as a spares source. *Parramatta* (DE 46) stricken 11-1-91; *Stuart* (DE 48) stricken 26-6-91. Improved versions of the British *Rothesay* class. Profiles of the DE 50 and DE 53 differed from those of earlier units, resembling more the British *Leander* class. DE 49 given an extensive mid-life overhaul 7-81 to 3-86, receiving two triple Mk 32 ASW torpedo tubes in place of the Limbo mortar, Mulloka sonar in place of part of the original suite, H.S.A. M 22 gunfire-control systems with LIROD optronic backup director, boilers converted to use diesel fuel, and accommodations improved. Sea Cat SAM system and Ikara ASW missile system were removed spring 1991, limiting their use to basic patrol functions. DE 49 had optical GWS 20 Sea Cat system, while DE 50 and 53 had an H.S.A. M4 radar director with an M 45 radar. All three now based at Cockburn Sound, Western Australia. DE 45, 46 sold for scrap 8-91.

PATROL BOATS

◆ **15 Fremantle class** Bldr: North Queensland Eng. and Agents, Cairns (P 203: Brooke Marine, Lowestoft)

	L	In serv.
P 203 Fremantle	15-2-79	8-10-79
P 204 Warrnambool	25-10-80	14-3-81
P 205 Townsville	16-5-81	18-7-81
P 206 Wollongong	17-10-81	28-11-81
P 207 Launceton	23-1-82	1-3-82
P 208 Whyalla	22-5-82	3-7-82
P 209 Ipswich	25-9-82	13-11-82
P 210 Cessnock	15-1-83	5-3-83
P 211 Bendigo	9-4-83	28-5-83
P 212 Gawler	9-7-83	30-8-83
P 213 Geraldton	22-10-83	10-12-83
P 214 Dubbo	21-1-84	10-3-84
P 215 Geelong	14-4-84	2-6-84
P 216 Gladstone	28-7-84	8-9-84
P 217 Bunbury	3-11-84	15-12-84

Warrnambool (P 204)—Naval Reserve training unit
Malcolm Dippy, 9-89

Geraldton (P 213) Leo Van Ginderen, 1990

Bendigo (P 211) R.A.N., 1990

D: 200 tons (230 fl) **S:** 30 kts **Dim:** 42.0 × 7.15 × 1.8
A: 1/40-mm AA—1/81-mm mortar—212.7-mm mg (II × 2)
Electron Equipt: Radar: 1/Kelvin-Hughes 1006 navigational
M: 2 MTU 16V538 TB91 diesels; 2 CP props; 7,200 bhp—1 Dorman 12JTM diesel; 1 prop; . . . hp for cruising (removed from P 206)
Range: 1,450/28; 4,800/8 **Crew:** 4–5 officers, 18 enlisted

Remarks: Brooke Marine PCF-420 design. Ordered 9-77. Five more (*Ballarat, Mildura, Armidale, Bundaberg, Pirie*) authorized 1980, but canceled 1982. P 203 was built as pattern craft. The 40-mm AA was to be replaced with newer weapons, but will now be retained for reasons of economy; all 40-mm guns modernized during the late 1980s by the Government Ordnance Factory to improve firing rate and elevation and train speeds. P 203: 26 tons overweight (246 fl), later reduced to 20 tons overweight; all later units 10 tons over original 220-ton design fl. P 206 aground 31-5-85, later salved; cruise engine removed during repairs. P 203 became Reserve training ship at Sydney 6-2-88, P 204 at Melbourne in 6-88. At least ten are planned to be refitted to extend their lives into the next century.

Note: Plans for a successor class to have been ordered 1993 or 1994 have been shelved; the new units would have had the same obsolescent armament.

◆ **3 Attack-class coastal-patrol boats** (R.A.N. Reserve Training)

	Bldr	Laid down	L	In serv.
P 82 Adroit	Evans Deakin	8-67	3-2-68	17-8-68
P 87 Ardent	Evans Deakin	10-67	27-4-68	26-10-68
P 91 Aware	Walkers, Ltd.	7-67	7-10-67	21-6-68

Aware (P 91) Leo Van Ginderen, 1990

D: 149 tons (fl) **S:** 24 kts **Dim:** 32.76 (30.48 pp) × 6.2 × 1.9
A: 1/40-mm Mk 7 AA—2/7.62-mm mg (I × 2)
Electron Equipt: Radar: 1/Decca RM 916 navigational
M: 2 Davey-Paxman Ventura 16 YJCM diesels; 2 props; 3,500 bhp (2,460 sust.)
Range: 1,220/13 **Crew:** 3–4 officers, 19–20 enlisted

Remarks: Steel hull; light-alloy superstructure; air-conditioned. All assigned to R.A.N. Reserve training, P 82 at Fremantle, P 87 at Hobart, and P 91 at Adelaide. Sisters P 84 *Aitape*, P 92 *Ladava*, P 93 *Lae*, P 94 *Madang*, P 85 *Samarai* transferred to Papua New Guinea in 1974. P 86 *Archer* and P 95 *Bandolier* sold in 1973 to Indonesia

PATROL BOATS *(continued)*

and transferred in 1973 and 1974, respectively. P 88 *Arrow* sank 25-12-74 in cyclone Tracey. Transferred to Indonesia were *Barricade* (P 98) on 22-4-82, *Bombard* (P 99) in 11-83, and *Acute* (P 81) on 6-5-83. *Barbette* (P 97) stricken 15-6-84; *Buccaneer* (P 100) decommissioned to material reserve 27-7-84; *Attack* (P 90) stricken 21-2-85; *Barbette* (P 97) transferred to Indonesia 22-2-85, *Buccaneer* (P 100) in 5-85, and *Attack* (P 90) in 1-86; Assail (P 89) stricken 18-10-85 and transferred to Indonesia 30-1-86. *Advance* (P 83) stricken 6-2-88, became a museum exhibit. *Bayonet* (P 101) stricken 6-88.

MINE COUNTERMEASURES SHIPS

Note: With the evident failure of the "Bay" program and the closure of its builders, the R.A.N. is considering the possibility of constructing four to six larger coastal mine countermeasures vessels in Australia, possibly of the Swedish *Landsort*, Italian Lerici, or U.S. *Osprey* class.

◆ 2 "Bay"-class catamaran minehunters Bldr: Carrington Slipway, Tomago

	Laid down	L	In serv.
M 80 RUSHCUTTER	31-5-84	8-5-86	1-11-86
M 81 SHOALWATER	17-9-85	26-6-87	10-10-87

Rushcutter (M 80) Leo Van Ginderen, 10-90

Shoalwater (M 81) James W. Goss, 10-88

D: 100 tons (170 fl) **S:** 10 kts **Dim:** 31.00 (28.00 wl) × 9.0 × 1.90
A: 2/12.7-mm mg (I × 2)
Electron Equipt:
Radar: 1/Kelvin-Hughes Type 1006(4) navigational
Sonar: M 80: KAE DSQS-11H; M 81: Thomson-Sintra TSM 2022
M: 2 SACM-Poyaud 520-V8-S2 325-hp diesels, hydraulic drive; 2 Schottel azimuthal props; 340 shp
Range: 1,200/10 **Crew:** 2 officers, 12 enlisted

Remarks: First two ordered late 1981. Glass-reinforced plastic construction; each of the two hulls is of 3.00 m beam. If first pair successful, had planned construction of four (originally to have been six) more, beginning in mid-1988, for delivery by mid-91. The building yard went into receivership in 12-90, leaving the status of the program in doubt, although it had been planned possibly to order four more in 1993 (including the abortive M 82, which had been laid down on speculation on 22-9-87); the Australian government bought the GRP fabrication facility in 10-90 and will lease it to shipbuilders if more of the craft are ordered.

Sonar transducer beneath port hull. Sonar/mine-countermeasures control room in dismountable deckhouse. Trials with the original mine detection system have proven unsatisfactory, delaying the program; a Thomson-CSF IBISV sonar system was substituted in M 81 for trials, completing 18-11-91, and was to be compared with a modified KAE system in M 80. If either system is successful, two more units of this class may be ordered. Main engines drive propulsion generators and ship's service generators. Carry two PAP-104 remote-controlled, tethered minehunting submersibles.

Note: In addition to the class listed above, the R.A.N. has a "COOP" (Craft-of-Opportunity) program for employing fishing craft as auxiliary mine-countermeasures craft. To equip the craft, a number of 100–500-kHz U.S. Klein Type 590 sidescan sonars have been ordered, each equipped with a Klein 595 transceiver/graphic recorder. Also to be carried will be the DYAU, a 6.4 × 0.53-m, hollow, two-section mild steel pipe with two strontium-ferrite inserts for countering magnetic mines. A "HOOP" (Helicopter-of-Opportunity) program is also under way.

The last R.A.N. "Ton"-class coastal minehunter, *Curlew* (M 1121, ex-*Chediston*) was stricken 30-4-90. If further trials with the *Rushcutter* class are unsatisfactory, a new, larger coastal minehunter class may be ordered.

◆ 2 Craft-of-Opportunity (COOP) auxiliary minehunter/tugs
Bldr: . . . (In serv.: . . .)

WALLAROO (ex-*Greenville V*) BANDICOOT (ex- *Greenville VII*)

Wallaroo Leo Van Ginderen, 10-90

D: 520 tons (fl) **S:** 11 kts **Dim:** 29.34 (26.83 pp) × 8.54 × 3.43
Electron Equipt: Radar: 1/ . . . navigational
M: 2 Stork-Werkspoor diesels; 2/Kort-nozzle props; 2,160 bhp
Electric: 150 kw (2 × 75 kw); 2 G.M. 4-71 diesels **Crew:** 12 tot.
Range: 6,300/11 **Endurance:** 24 days

Remarks: Acquired 3-8-90 and 8-8-90, respectively, from Maritime Pvt., Singapore, for use as COOP minehunters and as tugs to handle visiting foreign warships at Sydney. 242.37 grt. Hull moulded depth: 4.42m. Originally had 30-ton bollard pull, but towing capability removed as part of COOP conversion. Arrived Australia in 9-90 and completed conversion mid-1991.

◆ 2 Craft-of-Opportunity (COOP) auxiliary minehunters Bldr: Kall Boatyard, . . .

KORAAGA (ex-*Grozdana A.*) (In serv. 1974) SALVATORE V (In serv. . . .)

Koraaga James W. Goss, 7-89

D: around 150 tons (fl) **S:** 10.5 kts **Dim:** 22.0 × . . . × 3.0
Electron Equipt: Radar: 1/ . . . navigational **Crew:** 9 tot.
M: 1 Caterpillar D346 (*Salvatore V*: D353) diesel; 1 prop; 450–470 bhp

MINE COUNTERMEASURES SHIPS *(continued)*

Salvatore V Leo Van Ginderen, 10-90

Remarks: *Koraaga*, a former tuna boat, was purchased from Australian Fishing Enterprises and delivered to R.A.N. 16-2-89. *Salvatore V* is a former fishing trawler leased from the Campese family and delivered 21-2-89. *Wave Rider*, another former trawler, was leased and delivered 2-89 and returned to owners 19-4-91. Both are similar, 119–120 grt wooden-hulled craft and are operated from HMAS *Waterhen*, Sydney, to develop tactics and doctrine for newly developed auxiliary mine countermeasures equipment. Both are equipped with NAVSAT receivers, HFD/F, and a winch suitable for streaming mine countermeasures gear. Four Meridian Ocean Systems QUILS-II (Q-route Underwater Identification and Location System) were ordered during 1990 for use in these and other COOP vessels. *Salvatore V* to be returned to owners 2-92.

♦ **1 auxiliary minesweeper** Bldr: Australian SB Industries, Fremantle

BROLGA (ex-*Lumen*) (In serv.: 12-78)

Brolga Leo Van Ginderen, 10-90

D: . . . tons (fl) **S:** 11 kts **Dim:** 28.35 (26.37 pp) × 8.62 × 3.10
Electron Equipt: Radar: 2/ . . . navigational
M: 2 Mirrlees Blackstone ESL 8 Mk 2 diesels; 2 props; 1,080 bhp
Crew: . . . tot.

Remarks: 264 grt. Former steel-hulled government lighthouse maintenance vessel at Brisbane, laid up 4-87 and transferred 2-2-88 to R.A.N. for use in mine countermeasures trials. Not a commissioned ship.

AMPHIBIOUS WARFARE SHIPS

Note: The R.A.N. is studying the possibility of ordering a helicopter carrier to accommodate one battalion of troops and 8–12 Sikorsky S-70 Blackhawk helicopters. Competitors for the contract included Australian Defence Industries (ADI), with a plan to convert a bulk-carrier; Italy's Fincantieri, with a modified *San Giorgio*; and Bremer-Vulkan of Germany, as of early 1991. The ship would also be used for training (to replace *Jervis Bay*) and for disaster relief work.

♦ **1 modified British Sir Bedivere class**

	Bldr	Laid down	L	In serv.
L 50 TOBRUK	Carrington Slipways, Tomago	7-2-79	1-3-80	23-4-81

Tobruk (L 50) Leo Van Ginderen, 10-90

D: 3,600 tons (6,000 fl) **S:** 17 kts **Dim:** 129.50 × 19.60 × 4.30
A: 2/40-mm AA (I × 2)
Electron Equipt: Radar: 1/Decca RM 916 nav., 1/Decca 1226 nav.
M: 2 Mirrlees-Blackstone KDM8 diesels; 2 props; 9,600 bhp
Electric: 1,990 kw **Crew:** approx. 18 officers, 50 enlisted

Remarks: Announced 8-76 as a replacement for the *Sydney*, a former light carrier used as a troopship. Can carry troop helicopters operating from platform amidships and aft, and can carry 300–500 troops, Leopard tanks, and other military vehicles. Bow and stern ramps fitted. Two LCVP carried. Can carry two LCM 8 on deck. Two 4.5-ton cranes fwd.; 60-ton heavy lift boom before bridge. Home-ported at Sydney, 1986. Announced 1990 that she is to be equipped with an air-search radar and IFF equipment.

♦ **6 Balikpapan-class heavy landing craft** Bldr: Walkers Ltd., Maryborough

	Laid down	L	In serv.
L 126 BALIKPAPAN	5-71	15-8-71	27-9-74
L 127 BRUNEI	7-71	15-10-71	5-1-73
L 128 LABUAN	10-71	29-12-71	9-3-73
L 129 TARAKAN	12-71	16-3-71	15-6-73
L 130 WEWAK	3-72	18-5-72	10-8-74
L 133 BETANO	9-72	5-12-72	8-2-74

Tarakan (L 129) foreground, with Balikpapan (L 126), Labuan (L 128), Betano (L 133), and Brunei (L 127) beyond. R.A.N., 5-91

D: 316 tons (503 fl) **S:** 10 kts (9 sust.) **Dim:** 44.5 × 10.1 × 1.9
A: 2/7.62-mm mg (I × 2)
Electron Equipt: Radar: 1/Decca RM 916 nav.
M: 2 G.M. 6-71 diesels; 2 props; 675 bhp **Range:** 3,000/10
Crew: 2 officers, 11 enlisted

Remarks: Can carry three Leopard tanks. Sisters *Salamaua* (L 131) and *Buna* (L 132) were transferred to Papua New Guinea in 1974. Originally were to be army-subordinated. L 127 and L 133, used for many years as inshore survey craft, became diving training vessels at the Mine Warfare and Patrol Boat Base, HMAS *Waterhen*, Sydney, on 27-10-88 and 16-12-88, respectively. L 126, L 129, and L 130 placed in storage ashore at Cairns in 1985, but L 129 reactivated 1988 as naval reserve research and training vessel at Cairns and L 126 reactivated for same purpose at Darwin in 2-90.

♦ **3 Sea-Truck-type small landing craft** Bldr: Rotork, U.K.

LCVP 1301–1303 (In serv.: 12-80 to 2-81)

D: 9.75 tons (fl) **S:** 15.5 kts (sust.) **Dim:** 12.70 × 3.20 × 2.81
M: 3 diesels; 3 waterjet pumps; 345 bhp

Remarks: Aluminum construction. Two carried by *Tobruk*, one aboard *Success*.

[H]YDROGRAPHIC SHIPS

1 Moresby class Bldr: State Dockyard, Newcastle, NSW

	Laid down	L	In serv.
[A 5]73 Moresby	1-7-62	7-9-63	6-3-64

[M]oresby (A 573)—Écureuil helo on deck Malcolm Dippy, 11-88

[M]oresby (A 573)—with stricken *Cook* (A 291) beyond R.A.N., 1990

D: 1,725 tons (2,351 fl) **S:** 19 kts **Dim:** 95.7 (86.7 pp) × 12.8 × 4.6
Electron Equipt:
Radar: 1/Decca TM 916 nav.—
Sonar: 1/Simrad SU-2
M: diesel-electric propulsion: 3/1,330-hp diesels; 3 CSVM generator sets, each 1,330 kw/800 rpm; 2 electric motors, 2 props; 5,000 shp
Crew: 13 officers, 133 enlisted

[R]emarks: A small helicopter can be carried. Ship is air-conditioned. 2/40-mm AA [re]moved, exhaust pipe added on foredeck, stack heightened 1973–74. Three inshore [su]rvey launches carried. Has Qubit CHART(VM) automatic data-logger.

[N]ote: The larger and newer (completed 1980) survey ship *Cook* (A 291) was stricken [3]1-10-90; she had never been satisfactory and had seen only limited use.

1 Flinders-class coastal survey ship Bldr: Williamstown Naval DY

	Laid down	L	In serv.
[A] 312 Flinders	11-6-71	29-7-72	27-4-73

[F]linders (A 312) Leo Van Ginderen, 9-86

D: 765 tons (fl) **S:** 13.5 kts **Dim:** 49.1 × 10.05 × 3.7
Electron Equipt: Radar: Decca TM 916 nav.—Sonar: Simrad SU-2
M: 2 Paxman Ventura diesels; 2 props; 1,680 bhp **Range:** 5,000/9
Crew: 4 officers, 34 enlisted

Remarks: Similar to the Philippine ship *Atyimba*. Operates along Barrier Reef, based at Cairns. Received new survey launch named *Bramble* in 1982. Has Qubit CHART(VM) automatic data-logger.

♦ **4 Paluma-class inshore survey craft** Bldr: EGLO Eng., Port Adelaide

	Laid down	L	In serv.
AGSC 01 Paluma	21-3-88	6-2-89	27-2-89
AGSC 02 Mermaid	19-7-88	24-11-89	4-12-89
AGSC 03 Shepparton	21-9-88	5-12-89	24-1-90
AGSC 04 Benalla	25-11-88	6-3-90	. . .-5-90

Benalla (AGSC 04) Malcolm Dippy, 3-90

Paluma (AGSC 01) R.A.N., 1989

D: 310 tons (fl) **S:** 12 kts (10 sust.)
Dim: 36.7 (33.0 pp) × 13.7 × 1.90
Electron Equipt: Radar: 1/. . . nav.—Sonar: . . .
M: 2 G.M. 12V92A TA diesels; 2 props; 1,290 bhp **Range:** 1,800/10
Endurance: 14 days **Fuel:** 41,000 liters
Crew: 2 officers, 10 enlisted

Remarks: Catamaran hulls. Based at Cairns on northeast Queensland coast to conduct Great Barrier Reef surveys. Work in pairs. Have Racal HYDLAPS (Hydrographic Data Logging and Processing System).

AUXILIARIES

♦ **1 modified French Durance-class replenishment oiler**

	Bldr	Laid down	L	In serv.
AOR 304 Success	Vickers, Cockatoo DY	9-8-80	3-3-84	23-4-86

D: 17,933 tons (fl) **S:** 18 kts **Dim:** 157.3 (149.0 pp) × 21.2 × 10.8
A: 3/40-mm AA (I × 3)—4/12.7-mm mg (I × 4)
Electron Equipt: Radar: 3 navigational sets
M: 2 SEMT-Pielstick 16 PC 2.5 diesels; 1 CP prop; 20,000 bhp
Electric: 5,440 kw **Range:** 9,000/15 **Fuel:** 750 tons
Crew: 16 officers, 12 CPO, 22 PO, 127 enlisted

AUXILIARIES *(continued)*

Success (AOR 304) R.A.N., 8-90

Success (AOR 304) R.A.N., 1990

Remarks: Ordered 9-79 from design prepared by DTCN, France. Second proposed 1980, but was not built. Carries 8,220 tons distillate fuel, 1,131 tons aviation fuel, 170 tons munitions, 183 tons provisions, 259 tons water, and 45 tons of spare parts. Carries 2 stores-handling landing craft in davits and is able to refuel three ships simultaneously. Helicopter platform. Construction progress was slow and costs tripled. Carried Bofors RBS-70 shoulder-launched surface-to-air missiles during 13-8-90 to 7-3-91 Operation Desert Shield/Desert Storm deployment.

◆ **1 British Appleleaf-class replenishment oiler** Bldr: Cammell Laird, Birkenhead

	L	In serv.
AO 195 Westralia (ex-*Appleleaf,* ex-*Hudson Cavalier*)	24-7-75	11-79

Westralian (AO 195) Vic Jeffery, R.A.N., 1-91

D: 40,870 tons (fl) **S:** 16.4 kts
Dim: 170.69 (163.51 pp) × 25.94 × 11.56
A: 2/20-mm AA (I × 2) **Electron Equipt:** Radar: 2/ . . . nav.
M: 2 Crossley-Pielstick 14 PC2V-400 diesels; 1 CP prop; 14,000 hp
Fuel: 2,498 tons **Crew:** 60 tot.

Remarks: 20,440 grt/33,750 dwt. Agreement reached 3-89 to lease to Australia for 5 years, then to be purchased; transferred 9-10-89. Intended to support Indian Ocean squadron based at Fremantle. Refitted 12-78 to 11-79 for Royal Fleet Auxiliary service: stack raised 3.5 m, dry-cargo hold added forward, replenishment-at-sea working deck added amidships, and superstructure enlarged aft. Has one fueling station per side, plus astern refueling position. Cargo: 22,000 tons distillate fuel, 3,800 tons JP-5. Helicopter vertical replenishment (but not landing) platform and superstructure mounting for refrigerated provisions containers added for *Westralia's* service in support of Operation Desert Storm 1-91 through 5-91.

Note: The destroyer tender *Stalwart* (AD 215) was paid off 8-12-89 and stricken 9-3-90; she was sold commercial for conversion as an Aegean-area cruise liner.

◆ **1 training ship** Bldr: State Dockyard, Newcastle, NSW

	Laid down	L	In serv.
AGT 203 Jervis Bay (ex-*Australian Trader*)	18-8-67	17-2-69	17-6-69

Jervis Bay (AGT 203) R.A.N., 11-8

D: 8,915 tons (fl) **S:** 17 kts **Dim:** 135.7 (123.5 pp) × 21.5 × 6.1
A: none
Electron Equipt:
Radar: 1/Decca RM 916 nav., 1/Krupp-Atlas 8600 ARPA
M: 2 Crossley-Pielstick 16 PC 2V400 diesels; 2 props; 13,000 bhp
Fuel: 820 tons **Electric:** 2,000 kw **Crew:** 111 tot. plus 40 trainees

Remarks: A former roll-on/roll-off cargo ferry converted to a training ship to repla the destroyer *Duchess*. Commissioned 25-8-77. Name commemorates a Royal Na armed merchant cruiser of World War II. Can also serve as a transport and vehic cargo ship. U.S. WSC-3 SATCOMM equipment added in 1984 and helicopter deck 6-87. Plans to further modify to accept Sea King or Seahawk helicopters have be canceled. The ship may be stricken 1991–92.

◆ **1 submarine trials support ship** Bldr: Elder-Prince Marine Services Fremantle (In serv.: 20-3-91–in R.A.N.)

ASR 241 Protector (ex-*Blue Nabilla*)

Protector (ASR 241) Leo Van Ginderen, 4-

D: 650 tons (fl) **S:** 12 kts **Dim:** 42.10 (38.99 pp) × 9.50 × 3.00
Electron Equipt: Radar: 2/Decca . . . nav. **Crew:** 20 tot.
M: 2 G.M. 12V-92A diesels; 2 CP props; 1,240 bhp—bow and stern thrusters
Electric: 192 kw (2 × 96 kw sets) **Range:** 1,600/12 **Fuel:** 28 ton

Remarks: 282 grt. Acquired 9-90 from Victorian Division of the National Safe Council, which had used her as a pollution control ship. Commissioned 20-3-91. H been lengthened 8.00 m by Queensland Engineering in 1988 and a helicopter platfor added. Can carry a PC 1804 salvage submersible, and is equipped with a SATCOM system. The ship is intended to support trials for the *Collins*-class submarines and w initially be used for mine countermeasures and mining trials, as a diving tender, and a base craft for remotely operated vehicles; she is based at HMAS *Waterhen,* Sydn and is painted orange, with yellow upperworks.

◆ **2 general-purpose tenders** Bldr: Walkers, Ltd., Maryborough

	Laid down	L	In serv.
AG 244 Banks	11-58	15-12-59	16-2-60
AG 247 Bass	11-58	26-3-60	15-11-60

Banks (AG 244) Leo Van Ginderen, 10-

AUXILIARIES *(continued)*

D: 207 tons (255 fl) **S:** 10 kts **Dim:** 30.8 (27.5 pp) × 6.7 × 2.5
Electron Equipt: Radar: 1/978 navigational
M: diesels; 2 props; . . . bhp **Crew:** 2 officers, 12 enlisted

Remarks: AG 247 was originally equipped as a hydrographic ship and AG 244 for fisheries protection, but both have been used primarily for reserve training. AG 247: 160 tons fl. AG 247 to Darwin 18-10-85 for reserve training. Both due to be stricken 1993, but may be extended to 1995.

◆ **1 sail-training ship** Bldr: . . .

YOUNG ENDEAVOUR (In serv. 3-8-87)

Young Endeavour

D: 200 tons (fl) **S:** 14 kts (sail)/10 (diesel)
Dim: 44.00 (31.00 hull, 28.30 wl) × 7.80 × 4.00
Electron Equipt: Radar: 1/. . . navigational
M: 2 diesels; 1 prop; . . . bhp; 110-m sail area
Crew: 8 officers, 24 trainees

Remarks: Gift of the U.K. government on Australia's 200th anniversary. Left U.K. -8-87 and arrived Sydney 25-1-88. R.A.N. supplies officer/instructors for youth trainees.

◆ **5 Swarbrick III-class small training yachts** Bldr: Swarbrick Bros., Osbourne Park, Western Australia (In serv. 1984)

3807 ALEXANDER OF CRESSWELL	3810 CHARLOTTE OF CERBERUS
3808 FRIENDSHIP OF LEEUWIN	3811 SCARBOROUGH OF CERBERUS
3809 LADY PERYHYN OF NIRIMBA	

D: 4.35 tons (fl) **S:** . . . kts **Dim:** 11.10 × 3.20 × 1.95
M: 1 Yanmar diesel; 22 bhp **Crew:** 8 to 10

Remarks: Also in use are 70 Tasar 4.57-m sailing dinghies acquired 1970. The 13.11-m sailboat *Franklin* (1937) was due for disposal in 1991.

YARD AND SERVICE CRAFT

Note: Letters in the pendant numbers ceased to be painted on the hulls in 1984–85 when the units were named. Landing craft *Brunei* (L 127) and *Betano* (L 133) are employed as diving tenders.

◆ **1 coastal tug** Bldr: Australian SB Industries, South Coogee, Western Australia

	Laid down	L	In serv.
OT 2601 TAMMAR	20-4-83	10-3-84	15-3-84

D: 265 tons (300 fl) **S:** 11.5 kts
Dim: 25.68 (23.63 pp) × 8.42 × 2.00
Electron Equipt: Radar: 1/Furuno . . . navigational
M: 2 G.M. 16V149 TI diesels; . . . props; 2,560 bhp
Range: 1400/10 **Crew:** 6 tot. (civilian)

Remarks: Ordered 30-3-83 for use at HMAS *Stirling*, Cockburn Sound, Western Australia. 160 grt. Bollard pull 40 tons.

◆ **1 medium harbor tug** Bldr: Shoreline Eng., Portland, Victoria

OT 1801 QUOKKA (L: 10-83)

D: 110 tons (fl) **S:** 9 kts **Dim:** 18.17 (16.84 pp) × 5.91 × 2.55
Electron Equipt: Radar: 1/Furuno . . . navigational
M: 2 G.M. 8V53 diesels; 633 bhp **Crew:** 5 tot. (civilian)

Remarks: Used at Cockburn Sound, Western Australia. Bollard pull 8.5 tons.

Royal Australian Navy sail-training yacht Friendship of Leeuwin LSPH S. Connolly, R.A.N., 4-91

Tammar (OT 2601) James W. Goss, 8-89

YARD AND SERVICE CRAFT *(continued)*

Quokka (OT 1801) Vic Jeffery, R.A.N., 3-91

◆ **3 501-class harbor tug** Bldr: Stannard Bros., Sydney (504: Perrin Eng., Brisbane)

HTS 501 Bronzewing (In serv. 12-68)
HTS 502 Currawong (In serv. 1969)
HTS 504 Mollymawk (In serv. 1972)

Mollymawk (HTS 504) Leo Van Ginderen, 2-86

D: 34 tons (47.5 fl) **S:** 9 kts **Dim:** 19.4 × 4.6 × . . .
M: 2 G.M. diesels; 2 props; 340 bhp **Range:** 710/9.5
Crew: 3 tot. (civilian)

Remarks: Sister 503 to Papua New Guinea 1974. Civilian-manned. Named 1983. HTS 504 in collision with *Tobruk* (L 50) during 1990, nearly sank.

Note: The wooden-hulled tug *Cerberus V* (TB 1536) was stricken during 1991. COOP minehunters *Wallaroo* and *Bandicoot* are also intended to act as tugs to assist foreign warships visiting at Sydney.

◆ **3 torpedo-recovery craft** Bldr: Williamstown DY (In serv. 1970–71)

TRV 801 Tuna TRV 802 Trevally TRV 803 Tailor

Tailor (TRV 803) R.A.N., 1990

D: 91.6 tons **S:** 13 kts **Dim:** 27.0 × 6.4 × 1.4
M: 3 G.M. 6-71 diesels; 3 props; 684 bhp **Range:** 500/8
Crew: 1 officer, 8 enlisted

Remarks: TRV 802 previously used as a diving tender. Named 1982. All to be stricken 1995.

Note: The last World War II-era Seaward Defense Boat, SDB 1325, was put up for sale in 1990; there is hope of preserving her as a museum exhibit.

◆ **4 liquid-cargo lighters** Bldr: Williamstown DY

WFL 8001 Warrigal (In serv. 10-84)
WFL 8002 Wallaby (In serv.3-2-83)
WFL 8003 Wombat (In serv. 10-2-83)
WFL 8004 Wyulda (In serv. 10-84)

Wyulda (WFL 8004) Leo Van Ginderen, 9-9

D: 265 tons light (1,206 fl) **S:** 9 kts **Dim:** 38.0 × 10.2 × 3.98
M: 2 G.E.C. diesels; 1 Harbormaster outdrive prop fwd., 1 aft; 564 bhp
Range: 100/9 **Crew:** 5 tot. (civilian)

Remarks: Cargo 564 tons diesel fuel, 107 tons feedwater, 104 tons distilled water, 9 tons waste, and 73 tons ballast. Designation "WFL" means Water-Fuel Lighter.

◆ **3 crane stores lighters** Bldr: Cockatoo DY, Sydney

CSL 01 Wattle (In serv. 15-8-72)
CSL 02 Boronia (In serv. 25-9-72)
CSL 03 Telopea (In serv. 31-10-72)

Boronia (CSL 02) Gilbert Gyssels, 1-8

D: 145.1 tons (fl) **S:** 8 kts **Dim:** 23.7 × 9.75 × 2.0
M: 2 G.M. 6-71 diesels; 2 props; 600 bhp **Range:** 320/8
Crew: 4 tot. (civil.)

Remarks: Catamarans. One 3-ton electric crane. Based on AWL 304 design, but wit pilothouse aft.

◆ **1 pollution-control craft** Bldr: Cockatoo DY, Sydney

AWL 304 (In serv. 16-1-67)

D: 175 tons (fl) **S:** 8.8 kts **Dim:** 23.7 × 9.75 × 2.0
M: 2 G.M. 6-71 diesels; 2 props; 600 bhp **Range:** 320/8
Man: 3 tot. (civil.)

Remarks: Built as an aircraft transport to service the carrier *Melbourne*. General similar to the CSL 01 class. Used in recent years as a general stores lighter un converted 1990 to act as a pollution and oil-spill control craft.

◆ **15 Naval Work Boats** Bldr: North Queensland Engineers, Cairns

NWB 1280–1294 (In serv. 1980–81)
Known names: NWB 1281, *Otter*; NWB 1282, *Walrus*; NWB 1283, *Beaver*; NWB 1285, *Grampus*; NWB 1286, *Dolphin*; NWB 1287, *Dugong*; NWB 1292, *Turtle*

YARD AND SERVICE CRAFT *(continued)*

Beaver (NWB 1283) Leo Van Ginderen, 10-88

D: 12.5 tons **S:** 12 kts **Dim:** 12.0 × . . . × . . .
M: 2 diesels; 2 props; . . . hp

Remarks: Army operates 7 additional. Some (including NWB 1288) are configured as diving tenders. Aluminum construction. To be replaced beginning 1995.

◆ **27 wooden-hulled work boats** (In serv. 1944–46)

AWB 418–424, 426, 428, 430, 433–436, 440–442, 444, 445, 1658, 4001–4003, 4006, 4007, 4010, 4011

AWB 4003 Ross Gillett, 1985

D: 10 tons light (22 fl) **S:** 8 kts **Dim:** 12.2 × 3.81 × 1.37
M: 1 Gray Marine 64 HN 9 diesel; 175 bhp **Range:** 600/8

Remarks: Superstructures vary. "AWB" means Australian Work Boat. Some have names (AWB 420, *Amethyst*). To be replaced by 21 new-construction work boats, to be ordered during the early 1990s.

Other self-propelled service craft include (dates of construction in parentheses, where known):

1 11.89-m Miscellaneous Motor Boat (1939)
1 10.0-m Admiral's Barge (1969)
1 7-m Range Clearance Boat: RCV 0701
1 8-m "Shark Cat" Diving Tender: DV 0801
10 10.0-m Fleet Utility Boats: FUB 3310–3319 (1974)
7 10.0-m Harbor Personnel Boats: HPB 3350–3356 (1974)
7 7.9-m Harbor Personnel Boats: HPB 2620–2626 (1973)
1 7.6-m Harbor Personnel Boat: HPB 25101
72 5.0-m Light Utility Boats in 3 types: LUB 20 . . . series (1981–84)
4 Firefish Radio-Controlled Surface Targets: RCST 02–05
4 General Surface Targets (1980)
10 10.0-m Sea Boats: SB 3330–3339 (1974)
7 10.36-m Survey Motor Boats: SMB 3401 (*Fantome*), 3405, 3411 (1966–70; other 4: 1981)

Non-self-propelled service craft include:

3 100-ton Concrete Ammunition Lighters: CAL 101 series
4 50-ton Concrete Ammunition Lighters: CAL 501 series
3 Dry Dock Caissons: DCI 1, 2; DC 219
21 60-ton Flat-Top Lighters: FTL 60101–60121
1 Flat-Top Lighter: FTL 764
1 1,000-ton-capacity Floating Dock: FD 1002
5 5.0-m Diving Demolition Boats (DDB) (1983)
4 4.3-m Aluminum Dinghies (AD) (1970)
26 4.0-m Aluminum Dinghies (AD) (1981–84)
13 3.6-m Aluminum Dinghies (AD) (1980)
7 2.6-m Pram Dinghies
67 General-Purpose Inflatable Boats

Note: Aboard the various ships of the R.A.N. are 2 4.6-m Rigid-Inflatable Boats; 6 7.9-m Fleet Utility Boats (1968); 5 7.92-m Motor Whale Boats; 3 7.92-m Personnel Boats; and 2 7.31-m lifeboats. All other utility craft listed in the previous edition (including Harbor Personnel Launches 38101 and 38102) have been discarded.

Survey Motor Boat SMB 3405 Ross Gillett, 1984

Harbour Personnel Boat HPB 3352 Leo Van Ginderen, 7-85

ROYAL AUSTRALIAN ARMY CORPS OF ENGINEERS

Personnel: Approx. 300

◆ **16 U.S. LCM (8)-class landing craft** Bldrs: AB 1050–1061: North Queensland Engineers, Cairns; others: Dillingham SY, Fremantle (In serv. 1967)

AB 1050–1053, 1055, 1056, 1058–1067

AB 1067—green-painted Gilbert Gyssels, 1-88

D: 34 tons light (116 fl) **S:** 12 kts (9 loaded)
Dim: 22.70 × 6.41 × 1.37
M: 2 G.M. 12V71 diesels; 2 props; 600 bhp **Range:** 200/9
Crew: 5 tot.

AUSTRALIA *(continued)*
ROYAL AUSTRALIAN ARMY CORPS OF ENGINEERS *(continued)*

Remarks: Cargo: 55 tons. Some kept in land storage. Sister AB 1057 transferred to Tonga in 1982; AB 1054 stricken 1984. LCVPs 752, 755–757: stricken 1984. The army plans to replace the LCMs with a larger type of utility landing craft, and four 6.5-ton landing craft are also to be acquired. 1050 named *Cocoanut Queen*, 1052 *Reluctant Lady*, 1053 *Sea Widow*.

♦ **2 harbor tugs** (In serv. 1963)

AT 2700 Joe Mann   AT 2701 The Luke

Joe Mann (AT 2700) Gilbert Gyssels, 1-88

D: 54.5 tons (60 fl) **S:** 10 kts **Dim:** 17.06 × 5.20 × 1.60
M: 2 G.M. 6-71 diesels; 1 prop; 333 bhp **Range:** 5,700/8
Crew: 3 tot.

Remarks: AT 2700 based at Sydney, AT 2701 at Brisbane. AT 2701 has smaller pilothouse. Both fitted for firefighting.

♦ **2 NLE (Naval Lighterage Equipment) self-propelled pontoons**

201 Castor   202 Pollux

D: 32.6 tons **S:** 4 kts **Dim:** 25.5 × 6.4 × . . .
M: 2 portable diesel outdrives

♦ **7 Navy Work Boats** Bldr: North Queensland Engineers, Cairns (In serv. 1979–80)

AM 417 Oolah   AM 420 Boongaree   AM 422 Akuna
AM 418 Kewal   AM 421 Mena II   AM 423 Gabinga
AM 419 Sea Horse One

Oolah (AM 417)—with portable cover over passenger deck
Ross Gillett, 1984

Remarks: Data as for naval version. Crew: 2.

♦ **2 Shark Cat launches** Bldr: Shark Cat, Queensland (In serv. 1980)

AM 215   AM 216

Remarks: Glass-reinforced plastic, 30-knot, radar-equipped catamarans, for landing craft command and control.

D: About 4 tons. Several sisters are operated by the R.A.A.F. Marine Section.

♦ **2 diving tender/survey craft** (In serv. 1979)

AB 251 African Queen   AB 252

♦ **70 U.S. Army LARC V Design 8005 amphibious craft**

D: 8.9 tons light (13.4 fl) **S:** 9 kts (25 mph on land)
Dim: 10.67 × 3.05 × 3.10 high **M:** 1 diesel; 1 prop; 300 bhp
Range: 40/8.7 loaded (in water) **Cargo:** 5 tons

♦ **159 Assault Boats** Bldr: Australian Boat Mfgrs., Ltd., Perth (In serv. 1990–91)

D: 210 kg light (1500 kg fl) **S:** 10 kts **Dim:** 5.0 × 2.0 × . . .
M: 1 outboard; 40 bhp **Cargo:** 1,200 kg or 12 troops

Remarks: Intended to replace earlier craft of this type. Aluminum construction; wil float while loaded if flooded-out.

ROYAL AUSTRALIAN AIR FORCE

♦ **1 search-and-rescue craft** Bldr: Stebercraft, Taree

Sea Hawk (In serv. 2-10-89)

D: 11.75 tons (fl) **S:** 26 kts **Dim:** 11.0 × 3.5 × 1.0
Electron Equipt: Radar: 1/RMC Rasterscan nav. **Crew:** 8 max.
M: 2 Caterpillar 3208TA diesels; 2 props; 750 bhp
Range: 350/30; 400/20

Note: The following craft are in service for search-and-rescue duties:
016-100 *Warana*—49 tons, 23 m, range 400/18
. . . *Max Eise* II—14.7 m, 18.4 kt, waterjet-propelled
3 Shark Cat catamarans:
07-001—7.0 m, 2 × 175-hp outboards, 35 kts
08-001, 08-002, 08-003—8.3 m, 2 × 135-hp outboards, 35 kts

Remarks: One of the Shark Cats listed above was lost during 1988.

AUSTRIA

Republic of Austria

AUSTRIAN ARMY DANUBE FLOTILLA

Personnel (1988): 1 officer, 26 men

♦ **1 large patrol craft for Danube service** Bldr: Korneuberg Werft AG

	Laid down	L	In serv.
A 604 Niederösterreich	31-3-69	26-7-69	16-4-70

Niederösterreich (A 604) Erwin Sieche, 4-85

D: 73 tons (fl) **S:** 22 kts **Dim:** 29.67 × 5.41 × 1.10
A: 1/20-mm AA—2/12.7-mm mg—2/7.62-mm mg—1/84-mm Carl Gustav M2 mortar
M: 2 MWM V-16 diesels; 1,620 bhp **Fuel:** 9.3 tons
Range: 900/. . . **Crew:** 1 officer, 11 enlisted

Remarks: Re-engined 1985.

♦ **1 patrol craft for Danube service** Bldr: Korneuberg Werft AG

601 Oberst Brecht (In serv. 14-1-58)

USTRIA *(continued)*
USTRIAN ARMY DANUBE FLOTILLA *(continued)*

D: 10 tons **S:** 14 kts **Dim:** 12.30 × 2.51 × 0.75
A: 1/12.7-mm mg—1/84-mm mortar
M: 2 Graf & Stift 6-cyl. diesels; 290 bhp
Range: 160/10 **Crew:** 5 tot.

1 small patrol craft for Danube service Bldr: OSWAG, Korneuberg

4 Greif (In serv. 3-87)

D: . . . **S:** . . . **Dim:** 9.50 × . . . × . . .
A: . . . **M:** . . . **Crew:** . . .

10 M-boot 80-class launches Bldr: Schottel Werft, West Germany (In serv. 1984)

D: 4.7 tons (fl) **S:** 14 kts **Dim:** 7.5 × 2.5 × 0.6
M: 1 Klockner-Humboldt-Deutz V-12 diesel; . . . bhp

marks: Push-boat/personnel launches. Replaced 10 U.S. Army M-3 Series nches discarded 1984.

several motorized pontoons

D: 8.5 to 40 tons (fl) **Dim:** 19.0 × 1.70 (some 3.00) × 0.7

te: For police duty, 4 aluminum patrol craft were ordered 1989 from Österreichse iiffswerften AG: 15.46 × 3.74 × 1.10; M: 2 Volvo Penta TMD.70c diesels; Schottel lder props; 17.25 kts.

THE BAHAMAS

mmonwealth of the Bahamas

POLICE MARINE DIVISION

rsonnel (1991): approximately 850 total

ATROL BOATS

3 "Protector" class Bldr: Fairey Marine, Cowes, U.K. (In serv. 20-11-

03 Yellow Elder P 04 Port Nelson P 05 Samana

ellow Elder (P 03) Mike Louagie, 8-86

D: 100 tons (fl) **S:** 30 kts (26 sust.)
Dim: 33.00 (28.96 wl) × 6.73 × 1.95 (props)
A: 1/20-mm Oerlikon Mk 7A AA—2/7.62-mm mg (I × II)
Electron Equipt: Radar: 1/Furuno FR-701
M: 3 G.M. Detroit Diesel 16V149 TIB diesels; 3 props; 5,400 bhp
Fuel: 16 tons **Range:** 300/24; 1,400/14
Crew: 2 officers, 18 enlisted

marks: Ordered 1985. Steel construction. All delivered by ship 6-10-86. Racal MNS 00 navigation system. P 03 completed 14-7-86; all commissioned in country.

1 103-foot patrol boat Bldr: Vosper Thornycroft

	Laid down	L	In serv.
01 Marlin	22-11-76	20-6-77	23-5-78

D: 100 tons (125 fl) **S:** 24 kts **Dim:** 31.5 × 5.9 × 1.6
A: 1/20-mm AA **M:** 2 Paxman Ventura diesels; 2 props; 2,900 bhp
Range: 2,000/13 **Crew:** 3 officers, 16 enlisted

marks: Fin stabilizers, steel hulls. Two 50-mm flare launchers. Sister *Flamingo* nk 11-5-80 by Cuban MiG-21 aircraft.

Marlin (P 01) Dr. Giorgio Arra, 2-89

◆ **6 ex-U.S. Coast Guard Cape class** Bldr: U.S. Coast Guard Yard, Curtis Bay, Maryland

	In serv.	Modernized	Transferred
P 06 Fenrick Sturrup (ex-*Cape Shoalwater*, WPB 95324)	17-10-58	13-7-79	9-12-88
P 07 David Tucker (ex-*Cape Upright*, WPB 95303)	2-7-53	20-11-77	6-1-89
P 08 Austin Smith (ex-*Cape York*, WPB 95332)	6-9-59	15-7-81	26-5-89
P 09 Edward Williams (ex-*Cape Current*, WPB 95307)	24-8-53	3-10-78	1-5-89
P 10 San Salvador II (ex-*Cape Fox*, WPB 95316)	22-8-55	8-9-80	30-6-89
P 11 Fort Fincastle (ex-*Cape Morgan*,WPB 95313)	5-7-55	21-4-80	20-10-89

Austin Smith (P 08) Dr. Giorgio Arra, 12-89

D: 87–90 tons (106 fl) **S:** 20 kts **Dim:** 28.96 × 6.10 × 1.55
A: 2/12.7-mm mg (I × 2)—2/40-mm Mk 64 grenade launchers (I × 2)
Electron Equipt: Radar: 1/SPS-64(V) **Electric:** 60 kw
M: 2 G.M. 16V149 TI diesels; 2 props; 2,470 bhp
Endurance: 5 days **Range:** 1,900/11.5
Crew: 2 officers, 16 enlisted

Remarks: The original four Cummins VT-12-M-700 diesels were replaced during modernization; theoretical max. speed is 24 kts, but it cannot be achieved without straining the hulls, hence speed restriction. Transferred for use in antidrug patrol work; were to have been scrapped by USCG 1989–90. P 06, P 07, P 09, and P 10 commissioned in Bahamian service 2-89, other two in 11-89.

PATROL CRAFT

◆ **5 Keith Nelson patrol craft** Bldr: Vosper Thornycroft (First four in serv. 5-3-71, last three 10-12-77)

P 22 Andros P 25 Exuma P 27 Inagua
P 23 Eleuthera P 26 Abaco

D: 30 tons (37 fl) **S:** 19.5 kts **Dim:** 18.29 (17.07 pp) × 5.03 × 1.53
A: 2/7.62-mm mg (I × 2) **Electron Equipt:** Radar: 1/Decca 110
M: 2 Caterpillar 3408 TA diesels; 2 props; 950 bhp
Fuel: 4 tons **Electric:** 29 kVA **Range:** 650/16 **Crew:** 11 tot.

Remarks: GRP construction, air-conditioned. First unit, *Acklins* (P 21), destroyed by fire, 1980. *San Salvador* (P 24) stricken 1982.

THE BAHAMAS *(continued)*
PATROL CRAFT *(continued)*

◆ **1 Standard Arctic-24-class rigid inflatable rescue craft**
Bldr: Osbourne, Littlehampton (In serv. 10-86)

Remarks: 7 m o.a., two Yamaha ABTL outboards, 180 bhp, 3-man crew; has self-righting buoyancy bag.

◆ **4 small GRP patrol craft** Bldr: Phoenix Marine, Florida, U.S.A.

P 30, P 31 (In serv. 6-81) P 32, P 33 (In serv. 12-81)

D: 8 tons (fl) **S:** 24 kts **Dim:** 8.8 × 3.0 × 0.7
A: 2/7.62-mm mg (I × 2) **Range:** 350/21
M: 2 Volvo TAMD 40 diesel outdrives; . . . bhp **Crew:** 4 tot.

◆ **1 support craft, former fishing boat** (Purchased 6-8-80)

AO 1 Fort Montague (ex-. . .)

D: 90 tons (fl) **S:** 10 kts **Dim:** 28.6 × 7.0 × 1.8
A: 2/7.62-mm mg (I × 2) **Range:** 3,000/10
M: 1 G.M. 12-71 diesel; 1 prop; . . . hp **Crew:** 16 tot.

Note: Support craft *Fort Charlotte* (A 02) discarded 1990.

◆ **6 miscellaneous launches**

P 101—8.53 m o.a., 2/235-hp Johnson outboards
P 102—8.64 m o.a., 2/235-hp Mercury outboards
P 103—9.14 m o.a., 2/350-hp Mercury outboards
P 104—11.68 m o.a., 2/235-hp Mercury outboards
P 105—. . .
P 106—. . .

◆ **3 former fishing boats—**about 15 m o.a., 12 kts

P 35 (ex-*Carey*)
P 36 (ex-. . .)
P 37 (ex-*Maria Mercedes II*)

BAHRAIN

State of Bahrain

DEFENSE FORCES

Personnel (1991): About 1,000 Navy; 280 Coast Guard

CORVETTES

◆ **2 Type FPB 62-001** Bldr: Lürssen, Vegesack, Germany

50 Al Manama (In serv. 3-2-88) 51 Al Muharraq (In serv. 3-2-88)

Al Manama (50) Leo Van Ginderen, 2-91

Al Muharraq (51) French Navy, 1989

D: 632 tons (fl) **S:** 34.7 kts (32.25 sust.)
Dim: 62.95 (59.90 pp) × 9.30 × 2.90
A: 4/MM 40 Exocet SSM (II × 2)—1/76-mm OTO Melara Compact C Mod. 6 DP—2/40-mm Breda L70B AA (II × 1)—2/20-mm Oerlikon GAM B01 AA (I × 2)—1/Dauphin helo (AST-15 missiles)
Electron Equipt:
Radar: 1/Decca 1226, 1/Philips 9LV200, 1/Ericcson Sea Giraffe
EW: Cygnus jammer, RDL-2 intercept, 2/Dagaie RL
M: 4 MTU 20V538 TB93 diesels; 4 props; 19,600 bhp **Fuel:** 120 tons
Range: 4,000/16 **Electric:** 408 kw (3 × 136 kw)
Crew: 7 officers, 18 petty officers, 18 ratings

Remarks: Ordered 2-84. The raised helicopter platform incorporates an elevator to lower the helicopter to the hangar below. Eight AST-15 antiship missiles are carried for the helicopter. Philips 9LV-331 weapons-control system with one I/J-band air/surface-search radar, one J-band tracking radar (with t.v./laser/infrared backup), one helicopter control and navigational radar and two Panda Mk 2 optronic directors. Carry 900 rds 76-mm, 4,400 rds 40-mm, 5,000 rds 20-mm. EW system is Racal 242, with SADIE processor.

PATROL BOATS

◆ **4 TNC 45-class guided-missile boats** Bldr: Lürssen, Vegesack, Germany

20 Ahmed Al Fateh (In serv. 5-2-84) 21 Al Jaberi (In serv. 5-84)
22 Abdul Rahman Al-Fadel (In serv. 5-1-86) 23 Sabah (In serv. . . .-89)

Abdul Rahman Al-Fadel (22)—note Cygnus jammer aft
French Navy, 198[illegible]

D: 203 tons light (259 fl) **S:** 40.5 kts
Dim: 44.9 (42.3 fl) × 7.3 × 2.05 (2.31 props)
A: 4/MM 40 Exocet SSM (II × 2)—1/76-mm OTO Melara DP— 2/40-mm Breda AA (II × 1)—2/12.7-mm M3 mg (I × 2)
Electron Equipt:
Radar: 1/Decca . . . nav.; 1/. . . search radar; 1/PEAB 9 LV223 f.c.s.
EW: Decca RDL-2 ABC passive warning, 1/Dagaie chaff RL
M: 4 MTU 16V538 TB92 diesels; 4 props; 15,600 bhp (13,460 sust.)
Fuel: 45 tons **Electric:** 405 kVA
Range: 500/38.5; 1,500/16 **Crew:** 6 officers, 30 enlisted

Remarks: First pair ordered 1979, second pair in 5-85; no third pair yet on order. Very similar to TNC 45 class for the United Arab Emirates. CSEE Panda backup director for 40-mm guns. Carry 250 rds 76-mm, 1,800 rds 40-mm, 6,000 rds 12.7-mm ammunition. Second pair have Racal Cygnus jammers. Also carry a Bofors 57-mm rocket flare launcher.

◆ **2 FPB 38-class patrol boats** Bldr: Lürssen, Vegesack, Germany

	L	In serv.		L	In serv.
10 Al Riffa	4-81	3-3-82	11 Hawar	. . .	3-3-8[illegible]

D: 188 tons normal (205 fl) **S:** 34 kts
Dim: 38.5 (36.0 pp) × 7.0 × 2.2 (props)
A: 2/40-mm AA Breda AA (II × 1)—2/mine rails
Electron Equipt: Radar: 1/Decca . . . nav.; 1/9GR 600
Electric: 130 kVA **M:** 2 MTU diesels; 2 props; 9,000 bhp
Range: 550/31.5; 1,100/16 **Crew:** 3 officers, 24 enlisted

Hawar (11) Pieter Sinke, 11-8[illegible]

PATROL BOATS *(continued)*

Remarks: Ordered 1979. 2/3-pdr. saluting cannon. CSEE Lynx optical GFCS. Bofors 57-mm flare rocket/chaff launcher abaft mast.

◆ **2 65-ft Commercial Cruiser class** Bldr: Swiftships, Morgan City, La., U.S.A.

30 Al Jarim (In serv. 9-2-82) 31 Al Jasrah (In serv. 26-2-82)

Al Jarim (30) John Bouvia, 1987

D: 33 tons (fl) **S:** 30 kts **Dim:** 19.17 × 5.56 × 1.98
A: 1/20-mm Oerlikon GAM B01 AA
Electron Equipt: Radar: 1/Decca 110
M: 2 G.M. 12V71 TI diesels; 2 props; 1,200 bhp **Range:** 1,200/18

Remarks: Aluminum construction.

MINE COUNTERMEASURES SHIPS

Note: During 1988, it was announced that Bahrain was considering the acquisition of three minehunters; none had been ordered as of 12-91.

MINISTRY OF THE INTERIOR COAST GUARD

PATROL BOATS AND CRAFT

◆ **1 30-meter Wasp class** Bldr: Souter, Cowes, U.K.

Al Yusrah (Laid down: 15-11-84; in serv. 12-8-85)

Al Yusrah John Bouvia, 1987

D: 10.5 tons (fl) **S:** 23.6 kts **Dim:** 30.0 (26.75 wl) × 6.40 × 1.60
A: 1/20-mm AA, 1/7.62-mm mg
M: 2 G.M. 16V149 TI diesels; 2 props; 3,100 bhp **Fuel:** 17 tons
Electric: 47 kVA **Range:** 500/22; 1,000/12 **Crew:** 16 tot.

Remarks: Enlarged version of standard 20-m Wasp, ordered 3-8-84. GRP construction. A VIP lounge is built over the stern. Outfitted as a yacht.

◆ **2 20-meter Wasp class fiberglass-hulled** Bldr: Souter, Cowes, U.K. (Ord. 1-83; in serv. 1983)

Dera'a 4 Dera'a 5

D: 34 tons (fl) **S:** 21 kts **Dim:** 20.0 (16.0 wl) × 5.0 × 1.5
A: 2/7.62-mm mg (I × 2) **Electron Equipt:** Radar: 1/Decca . . .
M: 2 G.M. 12V71 TI diesels; 2 props; 1,200 bhp **Crew:** 8 tot.

Dera'a 4 John Bouvia, 1987

◆ **3 11-meter Wasp class fiberglass-hulled** Bldr: Souter, Cowes, U.K. (Ord. 20-8-82; in serv. 1983)

Sahem 1 Sahem 2 Sahem 3

D: 7.25 tons (fl) **S:** 24 kts **Dim:** 11.0 × 3.2 × 0.56
A: 1/7.62-mm mg
M: 2 Perkins TV8.450 diesels; 2 waterjets; 612 bhp

◆ **4 Sword class fiberglass-hulled** Bldr: Fairey Marine, Cowes, U.K. (In serv. 1980)

Saif 1 Saif 2 Saif 3 Saif 4

Saif 2 John Bouvia, 1987

D: 15.2 tons **S:** 28 kts **Dim:** 13.7 × 4.1 × 1.32 **Crew:** 6 tot.
M: 2 G.M. 8V71 TI diesels; 2 props; 850 bhp **Range:** 500/. . .

◆ **3 patrol craft** Bldr: Vosper, Singapore (In serv. 1977)

Al Bayneh Junnan Quaimas

D: 6.3 tons (fl) **S:** 27 kts **Dim:** 11.1 × 3.3 × 0.9
M: 1 Sabre diesel; 210 bhp

◆ **1 Tracker class** Bldr: Fairey Marine, U.K.

Dera'a 1 (In serv. 1975) Dera'a 3 (In serv. 1980)

Dera'a 2 John Bouvia, 1987

D: 26 tons (fl) **S:** 28 kts **Dim:** 19.6 × 4.9 × 1.5 **A:** 1/20-mm AA
M: 2 G.M. diesels; 2 props; 1,120 bhp **Range:** 500

Remarks: *Dera'a 3* is a later-model Tracker Mk II with larger superstructure. Sister *Dera'a 2* discarded 1990.

◆ **2 Spear class fiberglass-hulled** Bldr: Fairey Marine, U.K. (In serv. 1975)

Sahem 4 5 Khataf

BAHRAIN *(continued)*
PATROL BOATS AND CRAFT *(continued)*

D: 4.5 tons (10 fl) **S:** 26 kts **Dim:** 9.1 × 2.75 × 0.84
A: 2/7.62-mm mg **M:** 2 Perkins diesels; 2 props; 290 bhp
Range: 220/26 **Crew:** 3 tot.

◆ **3 27-foot launches** Bldr: Cheverton, Cowes, U.K. (In serv. 1977)

15 Noon 16 Askar 17 Suwad

D: 3.3 tons **S:** 15 kts **Dim:** 8.23 × 2.44 × 0.81
M: 2 diesels; 1 prop; 150 bhp

◆ **1 50-foot launch** Bldr: Cheverton, Cowes, U.K. (In serv. 1976)

6 Mashtan

D: 9 tons **S:** 22 kts **Dim:** 15.2 × 4.3 × 1.4
M: 2 G.M. 8V TI diesels; 2 props; 900 bhp **Range:** 660/12

AMPHIBIOUS WARFARE CRAFT

◆ **1 utility landing craft** Bldr: Swiftships, Inc., Morgan City, La.

41 Ajirah (In serv. 21-10-82)

Ajirah (41) John Bouvia, 1987

D: 428 tons (fl) **S:** 12 kts **Dim:** 39.62 × 10.97 × 1.30
A: none **Electron Equipt:** Radar: 1/Decca . . . nav.
M: 2 G.M. Detroit Diesel 16V71N diesels; 2 props; 1,800 bhp
Fuel: 20 tons **Range:** 1,500/10 **Crew:** 2 officers, 6 enlisted

Remarks: Aluminum construction. Cargo: vehicles, supplies, up to 100 tons cargo fuel and 88 tons water. Bow ramp. 15-ton crane. Turning radius: 77 m. Two sisters in Venezuelan Navy.

◆ **1 Loadmaster II-class landing craft** Bldr: Fairey Marine, Cowes, U.K.

40 Safra II (In serv. 1981)

Safra II (40) John Bouvia, 1987

D: 150 tons (fl) **S:** 8 kts **Dim:** 22.5 × 7.5 × 1.2 **Crew:** 6 tot.
M: 2 G.M. 8V92N diesels; 2 props; 776 bhp **Range:** 500/. . .

◆ **1 Loadmaster-class landing craft** Bldr: Cheverton, Cowes, U.K.

7 Safra I (In serv. 1976)

D: 90 tons (fl) **S:** 10 kts **Dim:** 18.23 × 6.1 × 1.0
M: 2 diesels; 2 props; 240 bhp **Range:** 600/9 **Crew:** 13 tot.

Remarks: Can carry 40 tons of vehicles or dry cargo, or 60 tons of liquid cargo.

MISCELLANEOUS

◆ **10 wooden motor dhows for logistics and patrol duties**

◆ **1 utility hovercraft** Bldr: Tropimere, U.K. (In serv. 1977)

D: 4.23 tons (fl) **S:** 45 kts **Dim:** 8.9 × 4.5 × 3.6 high

◆ **1 tug** (In serv. 1981)

. . . . . .

D: 12 tons (fl) **S:** . . . kts **Dim:** 11.0 × . . . × . . .
M: 1 G.M. 6V71 diesel; 300 bhp

BANGLADESH

People's Republic of Bangladesh

Personnel (1991): About 7,650 total (650 officers)

Note: A number of Bangladeshi naval units were damaged and possibly destroyed during the cyclone that devastated the country during late April 1991. The units described below are those in service prior to the storm.

FRIGATES

◆ **1 Chinese Jiangnan-II class** Bldr: Jiangnan SY, Shanghai

	L	To Bangladesh
F 18 Osman (ex-556)	1986	8-11-89

Osman (F 18) U.S. Navy, 1991

D: 1,568 tons (1,900 fl) **S:** 25.5 kts **Dim:** 103.2 × 10.2 × 3.05 (hull)
A: 4/HY-2 SSM (II × 2)—4/ 100-mm DP (II × 2)—8d/37-mm AA (II × 4)—2/RBU-1200 ASW RL (V × 2)—4/ BMB-2 d.c. mortars—2/ d.c. racks (internal)
Electron Equipt:
Radar: 1/Type 756 nav., 1/Eye Shield (MX-902) air-search, 1/Square Tie target desig., 1/Sun Visor gun f.c.
Sonar: 1/medium-freq. hull-mounted
EW: probable Jug Pair intercept
IFF: 2/Square Head interrogators, 1/High Pole A transponder
M: 2/SEMT-Pielstick 12 PA6 diesels; 2 props; 16,000 bhp
Range: 4,000/15; 1,750/25 **Endurance:** 15 days
Crew: approx. 195 tot.
Electric: 1,320 kw (3 × 400-kw, 1 × 120-kw diesel sets)

Remarks: Transfer of a second unit was to have taken place in 1990 but did not and may have been canceled. Apparently taken from Chinese Navy inventory and not built new for Bangladesh.

◆ **2 British Leopard-class (Type 41) frigates**

	Bldr	Laid down	L	In serv.
F 15 Abu Bakr (ex-*Lynx*, F 27)	John Brown, Clydebank	13-8-53	12-1-55	14-3-57
F 17 Ali Haider (ex-*Jaguar*, F 37)	Wm. Denny, Dumbarton	2-11-53	30-7-57	12-12-59

D: 2,300 tons (2,520 fl) **S:** 23 kts
Dim: 103.63 (100.58 pp) × 12.19 × 4.8 (fl)
A: 4/114-mm Mk 6 DP (II × 2)—1/40-mm Mk 9 AA
Electron Equipt:
Radar: 1/978 nav., 1/965 early warning, 1/993 air/surf. search, 1/275 fire-control
M: 8 Admiralty 16 VVS ASR 1 diesels; 2 CP props; 12,400 bhp
Range: 2,300/23; 7,500/16 **Crew:** 15 officers, 220 enlisted

FRIGATES *(continued)*

Ali Haider (F 17) R.A.N., 5-90

Ali Haider (F 17) Leo Van Ginderen, 5-90

Remarks: F 17 purchased 6-7-78; arrived Bangladesh 11-78 after overhaul. F 15 purchased 12-3-82, commissioned 19-3-82. Squid ASW mortar and sonars removed while in Royal Navy. Fin stabilizers. 1/Mk 6 GFCS with Type 275 radar for 114-mm guns; 40-mm, local control only.

◆ **1 ex-British Salisbury-class (Type 61) aircraft direction frigate**

	Bldr	Laid down	L	In serv.
F 16 Umar Farooq (ex-*Llandaff*, F 61)	Hawthorn Leslie	27-8-53	30-11-55	11-4-58

Umar Farooq (F 16) James W. Goss, 5-90

D: 2,170 tons (2,408 fl) **S:** 24 kts
Dim: 103.6 (100.58 pp) × 12.19 × 4.8
A: 2/114-mm Mk 6 DP (II × 1)—2/40-mm Mk 5 AA (II × 1)—1/Mk 4 Squid ASW mortar (III × 1)
Electron Equipt:
Radar: 1/975 nav., 1/965 early warning, 1/993 air/surf. search, 1/277Q height-finder, 1/982 air search, 1/275 f.c.
Sonar: 1/174, 1/170B
M: 8 Admiralty 16 VVS ASR 1 diesels; 2 props; 12,400 bhp
Range: 2,300/24; 7,500/16 **Crew:** 14 officers, 223 enlisted

Remarks: Transferred 10-12-76. Mk 6 GFCS for 114-mm mount. Major machinery casualty during 1985; may be nonoperational.

PATROL BOATS AND CRAFT

◆ **4 Chinese Huangfeng (Type 021)-class guided-missile patrol boats** Bldr: Jiangnan SY, Shanghai

P 8125 Durdharsha P 8127 Durnibar
P 8126 Durdanta P 8128Durdanda

D: 175 tons, 186.5 normal (205 fl) **S:** 35 kts
Dim: 38.75 × 7.60 × 1.70 (mean)
A: 4/HY-1 SSM (I × 4)—4/30-mm Sov. AK-230 AA (II × 2)
Electron Equipt:
Radar: 1/Square Tie surface search/target desig.
IFF: 2/Square Head interrogators, 1/High Pole A transponder
M: 3 M503A diesels; 3 props; 12,000 bhp **Electric:** 65 kw
Range: 800/30 **Crew:** 5 officers, 60 enlisted

Remarks: All four commissioned in Bangladesh fleet on 10 November 1988. Lack fire-control radar director for the 30-mm guns. Chinese copy of the Soviet Osa-I design. Reported crew size seems excessive.

◆ **4 Chinese Hoku-class guided-missile patrol boats**

P 8111 Duranta P 8112 Durbar P 8113 Duruedya
P 8114 Durdam

D: 68 tons (79 fl) **S:** 37 kts **Dim:** 27.00 × 6.50 × 1.80 (1.3 hull)
A: 2/CSS-N-1 SSM (I × 2)—2/25-mm AA (II × 1)
Electron Equipt: Radar: 1/Square Tie **Electric:** 65 kw
M: 4 M50F-4 diesels; 4 props; 4,800 bhp **Range:** 500/24
Crew: 16 tot.

Remarks: First two delivered 6-4-83; others in 10-83. Steel construction. Have 5-day endurance.

◆ **4 Huchuan-class hydrofoil torpedo boats** Bldr: Hudong SY, Shanghai (In serv. 1-3-88)

T 8235 T 8236 T 8237 T 8238

Huchuan class T 8235 French Navy, 4-89

D: 39 tons (45.8 fl) **S:** 50 kts
Dim: 22.50 × 3.80 (6.26 over foils) × 1.146
A: 2/533-mm TT—4/14.5-mm mg (II × 2)
Electron Equipt: Radar: 1/Type 756 nav.
M: 3 M50 diesels; 3 props; 3,600 bhp **Electric:** 5.6 kw
Range: 500/30 **Crew:** 3 officer, 20 enlisted

Remarks: Built prior to 1980. Are from among the later-built units of the class, which had gun mounts fore and aft. Have forward foils only (aft small foil intended to assist getting boat up "on foil"); stern planes on the surface. Replaced four P-4 class torpedo boats transferred 1983 and discarded 1989.

◆ **2 fisheries protection patrol boats** Bldr: Vosper Pty, Tanjong Rhu, Singapore

P 211 Meghna (L: 19-1-84) P 212 Jamuna (L: 19-3-84)

Megna (P 211)—fitting out outboard *Jamuna* (P 212)
Gilbert Gyssels, 1987

PATROL BOATS AND CRAFT *(continued)*

D: 410 (fl) **S:** 20 kts **Dim:** 46.5 × 7.5 × 2.0 (hull)
A: 4/40-mm AA (II × 2)—2/7.62-mm mg (I × 2)
Electron Equipt: Radar: 1/Decca 1229 nav.
M: 2 Paxman Valenta 12 CM diesels; 2 props; 6,000 bhp
Crew: 3 officers, 45 enlisted **Range:** 2,000/16

Remarks: Operated for the Ministry of Agriculture by the navy for 200-nautical-mile economic zone patrol. P 211 originally fitted with a mockup of a Bofors 57-mm DP forward. Both have Selenia NA 18B optronic director. May instead have been fitted with MTU diesels for a maximum speed of 24 kts.

◆ 2 Chinese Hainan-class submarine chasers

P 811 Durjoy (In serv. 10-9-82) P 812 Nirbhoy (In serv. 1-12-85)

D: 375 tons normal (400 fl) **S:** 30.5 kts
Dim: 58.77 × 7.20 × 2.20 (hull)
A: 4/57-mm AA (II × 2)—4/25-mm AA (II × 2)—4/RBU-1200 ASW RL (V × 4)—2/BMB-2 d.c. mortars—2/d.c. racks—mines
Electron Equipt:
Radar: 1/Pot Head surf. search Sonar: 1/Tamir-11 HF
M: 4 diesels; 4 props; 8,800 bhp **Range:** 2,000/14 **Crew:** 70 tot

Remarks: Previous reports that there had been six of this class transferred seem to have been in error.

◆ 8 Chinese Shanghai-II-class patrol boats

P 411 Shaheed Daulat
P 412 Shaheed Farid
P 413 Shaheed Mohibullah
P 414 Shaheed Akhtaruddin
P 415 Towheed
P 416 Towfiq
P 417 Tamjeed
P 418 Tanveer

Shaheed Farid (old number) and sister 1980

D: 122 tons (135 fl) **S:** 28.5 kts **Dim:** 38.78 × 5.41 × 1.55 (max.)
A: 4/37-mm AA (II × 2)—4/25-mm AA (II × 2) **Crew:** 36 tot.
Electron Equipt: Radar: 1/Pot Head **Electric:** 39 kw
M: 2 M50F-4/1,200-bhp and 2/910-bhp diesels; 4 props; 4,220 bhp
Range: 750/16.5

Remarks: 411–414 delivered 6-7-80. 415–418 delivered 5-82. Two earlier units, delivered 1974, now stricken.

◆ 1 salvaged Pakistani patrol boat
Bldr: Brooke Marine, Lowestoft, U.K.

P 311 Bishkali (ex-*Jessore*)—In serv. 20-5-65

D: 115 tons (143 fl) **S:** 24 kts **Dim:** 32.62 (30.48 pp) × 6.10 × 1.55
A: 2/40-mm AA (I × 2) **Electron Equipt:** Radar: 1/ Decca . . . nav.
M: 2 MTU 12V538 diesels; 2 props; 3,400 bhp **Crew:** 303 tot.

Remarks: Sunk in 1971 War of Independence; salvaged and repaired, Khulna SY; recommissioned 23-11-78.

◆ 2 ex-Indian Ajay-class patrol boats
Bldr: Hooghly D & E, Calcutta (In serv. 1-62)

P 312 Padma (ex-*Akshay*, P 3136) P 313 Surma (ex-*Ajay*, P 3135)

D: 120 tons (151 fl) **S:** 18 kts **Dim:** 35.75 (33.52 pp) × 6.1 × 1.9
A: 8/20-mm AA (IV × 2) **Electron Equipt:** Radar: 1/ . . . nav.
M: 2 Paxman YHAXM diesels; 2 props; 1,000 bhp—1 Foden FD-6 cruise diesel; 100 bhp
Range: 500/12; 1,000/8 **Crew:** 3 officers, 32 men

Remarks: Indian version of British "Ford" class, donated by India and commissioned 12-4-73 and 26-7-74, respectively. Rearmed late 1980s with Yugoslav weapons.

◆ 1 ex-Yugoslav Kraljevica-class patrol boat (In serv. 1956)

P 315 Tistna (ex-Yugoslav PBR 505)

D: 190 tons (202 fl) **S:** 18 kts **Dim:** 41.0 × 6.3 × 2.2
A: 2/40-mm AA (I × 2)—4/20-mm AA (I × 4)—2/Mk 6 d.c. mortars—2/d.c. racks—2/128-mm RL (V × 2)
Electron Equipt:
Radar: 1/Decca 1229 nav. Sonar: QCU-2 hull-mounted
M: 2 M.A.N. W8V 30/38 diesels; 2 props; 3,300 bhp
Range: 1,000/12 **Crew:** 4 officers, 40 men

Remarks: Transferred 6-6-75. New navigational radar. In poor condition; sister *Karnaphuli* (P 314, ex-Yugoslav PBR 502) reduced to reserve 1988 and may have been stricken.

◆ 5 river patrol boats
Bldr: DEW Narayengonj, Dacca

P 111 Pabna (In serv. 6-72)
P 112 Noakhali (In serv. 7-72)
P 113 Patuakhali (In serv. 11-74)
P 114 Bogra (In serv. 6-77)
P 115 Rangamati (In serv. 6-77)

D: 69.5 tons (fl) **S:** 10 kts **Dim:** 22.9 × 6.1 × 1.9
A: 1/40-mm AA **M:** 2 Cummins diesels; 2 props
Range: 700/8 **Crew:** 3 officers, 30 men

Remarks: Last two differ in configuration, gun forward. Form River Patrol Squadron 11, based at Mongla. No radar fitted.

◆ 1 former Thai fishing boat
Bldr: . . . , Japan

A 513 Shah Jalal (ex-*Gold 4*)

D: 600 tons (fl) **S:** 12 kts **Dim:** 40.2 × 9.1 × 2.5
A: 2/20-mm Oerlikon AA (I × 2) **Crew:** 3 officers, 52 enlisted
M: 1 16-cyl. diesel; . . . bhp **Range:** 7,000/12

Remarks: Confiscated and commissioned 15-1-87 for fisheries patrol duties, the "A"-series pendant number notwithstanding.

AMPHIBIOUS WARFARE CRAFT

Note: Six U.S. Navy LCM(6) landing craft are to be donated, arriving in 1-92.

◆ 4 Chinese Yuchai (Type 068)-class landing craft

LCT 101 LCT 102 LCT 103 LCT 104

D: 85 tons (fl) **S:** 11.5 kts **Dim:** 24.8 × 5.2 × 1.3
A: 4/14.5-mm mg (II × 2)
M: 2 Type 12V150 diesels; 2 props; 600 bhp **Range:** 450/11.5
Crew: 23 tot. (including vehicle crew)

Remarks: Two transferred 4-5-86, two on 1-7-86.

◆ 3 Bangladesh-design
Bldr: LCVP 011, 012: Khulna SY; LCVP 013: DEW Narayangong

LCVP 011 LCVP 012 LCVP 013

D: 83 tons (fl) **S:** 12 kts (light) **Dim:** 21.3 × 5.2 × 1.5 **A:** none
M: 2 Cummins diesels; 2 props; 730 bhp **Crew:** 1 officer, 9 enlisted

AUXILIARIES

◆ 2 Chinese Yuchin (Type 069)-class landing craft employed as inshore survey craft (In serv. 1983)

A 581 Darshak A 582 Talleshi

Talleshi (A 582)—outboard *Darshak* (A 581) French Navy, 4-89

Khan Jahan Ali (A 515) Gilbert Gyssels, 6-87

BANGLADESH *(continued)*
AUXILIARIES *(continued)*

D: 83 tons (fl) **S:** 11.5 kts **Dim:** 24.1 × 5.2 × 1.1
M: 2 Type 12V150 diesels; 2 props; 600 bhp
Range: 700/11.5 **Crew:** 1 officer, 25 enlisted

◆ **1 small underway-replenishment ship** Bldr: . . . SY, Japan

515 Khan Jahan Ali (In serv. 1983)

D: 2,900 tons (fl) **S:** 12 kts **Dim:** 76.1 × 11.4 × 5.3
M: 1 6-cyl. diesel; 1 prop; 1,350 bhp **Crew:** 3 officers, 23 enlisted

Remarks: Transferred 1983 from state-owned shipping line and equipped for underway refueling. 1,342 grt. Cargo: 1,500 tons.

◆ **1 small repair ship**

512 Shahayak

D: 477 tons (fl) **S:** 11.5 kts **Dim:** 44.7 × 8.0 × 2.0
A: 1/20-mm Oerlikon AA **Electron Equipt:** Radar: 1/ . . . nav.
M: 1 Cummins 12 VTS diesel; 1 prop; . . . bhp **Range:** 3,800/11.5
Crew: 1 officer, 44 enlisted

Remarks: Former riverine passenger ship. Purchased, re-engined, and refitted at Khulna Shipyard, and commissioned as a tender in 1978.

◆ **1 training ship** Bldr: Atlantic SB, Montreal, Canada (In serv. 3-57)

511 Shaheed Ruhul Amin (ex-Canadian *Anticosti*)

D: 710 tons (fl) **S:** 11.50 kts **Dim:** 47.5 × 11.1 × 3.1
A: 1/40-mm AA **Electron Equipt:** Radar: 1/ . . . nav.
M: 1 Caterpillar diesel
Range: 4,000/10 **Crew:** 8 officers, 72 enlisted

Remarks: Transferred 1972 from Indian relief agency; recommissioned after conversion to training ship at Khulna Shipyard, 10-12-74.

◆ **1 Chinese Dinghai-class seagoing tug** Bldr: Wuhu SY

721 Khadem (In serv. 6-5-84)

Khadem (A 721) Gilbert Gyssels, 6-87

D: 1,472 tons (fl) **S:** 14 kts **Dim:** 60.22 × 11.60 × 4.44
A: 2/12.7-mm mg (I × 2) **Electron Equipt:** Radar: 2/. . . nav.
M: 2 diesels; 2 props; 2,640 bhp **Crew:** 7 officers, 49 men
Range: 7,200/14

Remarks: 980.28 grt.

◆ **1 general-purpose harbor tender** Bldr: . . .

. . . Sanket (Acquired 1989)

D: 80 tons (fl) **S:** 18 kts **Dim:** 29.4 × 6.1 × 1.8
A: 1/20-mm Oerlikon AA
M: 2 Deutz Sea 16M diesels; 2 props; 2,430 bhp
Range: 1,000/16 **Crew:** 1 officer, 23 enlisted

◆ **1 general-purpose tender, ex-Thai fishing boat**

FV 66 (In serv. . . .)

D: 96 tons (fl) **S:** 8 kts **Dim:** 28.0 × 6.0 × 1.8
A: 1/20-mm Oerlikon AA **Electron Equipt:** Radar: 1/ . . . nav.
M: 1 8-cyl. diesel; . . . bhp **Range:** 750/8
Crew: 1 officer, 23 enlisted

◆ **1 floating dry dock** Bldr: Tito SY, Trogir, Yugoslavia

701 Sundarban (In serv. 15-8-80)

Lift capacity: 3,500 tons **Dim:** 117.0 × 27.6 × 0.3 loaded.

Remarks: Self-docking type with 7 sectional pontoons. 17.6 m between dock walls, which are 101.4 m long. A second, commercial floating dry dock, 16,500 tons capacity, 12.9 m o.a., delivered 1981, is also available.

◆ **1 self-propelled floating crane** Bldr: Khulna SY

Balaban (In serv. 18-5-88)

D: . . . tons **S:** 9 kts **Dim:** . . . × . . . × . . . **M:** . . .

Remarks: Lift capacity: 70 tons.

BARBADOS

COAST GUARD

Personnel (1990): 90 total (12 officers, 78 men); to increase to 120 total

◆ **1 patrol boat** Bldr: Brooke Marine, Lowestoft, U.K.

	L	In serv.
P 01 Trident	14-4-81	11-81

Trident (P 01) C.&L. Cavas, 6-89

D: 165 tons (200 fl) **S:** 25 kts **Dim:** 37.50 × 6.86 × 1.78
A: 1/40-mm Mk 3 AA—1/20-mm Rheinmetall AA
Electron Equipt: Radar: 1/Decca TM 1226C
M: 2 Paxman Valenta 12 RP 200 diesels; 2 props; 4,000 bhp
Range: 3,000/12 **Crew:** 27 tot.

Remarks: Refitted Bender SB & Repair, Mobile, Alabama, 6-6-90 to 14-9-90.

Note: Converted shrimp-boat *Excellence*, used for patrol duties, was sold 9-90.

◆ **1 Halmatic Guardian-class patrol craft** Bldr: Aquarius Boat, Christchurch, U.K.

P 04 George Ferguson (In serv. 12-74)

George Ferguson (P 04) C.&L. Cavas, 6-89

D: 30 tons (fl) **S:** 24 kts **Dim:** 20.00 × 5.25 × 1.53 **Crew:** 10 tot.
M: 2 G.M. 12V71 TI diesels; 2 props; 1,300 bhp **Range:** 650/12

Remarks: Reported stricken 1986, but was refitted and placed back in service by mid-1989. Used for search-and-rescue duties and can carry 2/7.62-mm mg (I × 2). Glass-reinforced plastic hull by Halmatic.

◆ **2 Halmatic 12-meter Guardian-II-class patrol craft** Bldr: Aquarius Boat, Christchurch, U.K.

P 05 Commander Marshall (In serv. 12-73)
P 06 J.T.C. Ramsey (In serv. 11-74)

BARBADOS *(continued)*
COAST GUARD *(continued)*

D: 11.5 tons **S:** 21 kts **Dim:** 12.0 × 3.7 × 1.0 **A:** 1/7.62-mm mg
M: 2 Caterpillar Mk 334 TA diesels; 2 props; 580 bhp **Crew:** 4 tot.

Remarks: Used for search and rescue. Can carry 1/7.62-mm mg. Glass-reinforced plastic hull by Halmatic. Sister *T. T. Lewis* (P 07) stricken. Resemble *George Ferguson* (P 04), above.

Note: Also in service are one Arctic 6.7-m rigid inflatable boat (in serv. 11-85) for search-and-rescue duties and 6.7-m, 40-kt Boston Whaler patrol launches P 08 and P 09 (in serv. 1989).

BELGIUM

Kingdom of Belgium

Personnel (1991): 4,418 total (including 1,193 draftees)

Naval Aviation: Three Alouette-IIIB helicopters. The Air Force uses 5 Westland Sea King Mk 48 helicopters for search-and-rescue duties.

FRIGATES

◆ **4 Wielingen class, Type E 71**

	Bldr	Laid down	L	In serv.
F 910 Wielingen	Boelwerf, Temse	5-3-74	30-3-76	20-1-78
F 911 Westdiep	Cockerill, Hoboken	2-9-74	8-12-75	20-1-78
F 912 Wandelaar	Boelwerf, Temse	5-3-75	21-6-77	27-10-78
F 913 Westhinder	Cockerill, Hoboken	8-12-75	31-7-77	27-10-78

Wielingen (F 910) Leo Van Ginderen, 3-90

Westdiep (F 911) Gilbert Gyssels, 12-90

Wandelaar (F 912) Bernard Prézelin, 5-90

D: 1,880 tons (2,283 fl) **S:** 25 kts on gas turbine
Dim: 106.38 (103.0 pp) × 12.3 × 5.3 (over sonar)
A: 4 MM 38 (II × 2) Exocet—1/100-mm Model 1968 DP—1/NATO Sea Sparrow SAM syst. (8 AIM-7M missiles)—1/375-mm Bofors ASW RL (VI × 1)—2 launching racks for L-5 Mod 4 ASW torpedoes
Electron Equipt:
Radar: 1/Raytheon TM 1645/9X nav., 1/DA-05 air search, 1/H.S.A. WM-25 f.c.
Sonar: 1/Westinghouse SQS-505A MF hull-mounted
EW: Elcos-1 intercept, 2 Mk 36 SRBOC chaff (VI × 2), SLQ-25 Nixie torpedo decoy system
M: CODOG: 2 Cockerill CO-240V-12 diesels, each 3,000 bhp; 1 Rolls-Royce Olympus TM 3B gas turbine, 28,000 shp; 2 CP props
Fuel: 250 tons diesel **Electric:** 2,000 kw (4 × 500-kw diesel sets)
Range: 4,500/18; 6,000/16 **Crew:** 15 officers, 145 enlisted

Remarks: Vosper fin stabilizers. 15 knots max. on one diesel, 20 knots on two. Hav SEWACO-IV automatic tactical data system and NATO Link-11 datalink. Two Pand optical gun directors. The ASW rocket launcher carries six 103-mm rocket flare rail Have lost 3 kts below original 28-kt trial speeds after modifications. Are equipped wit fin stabilizers. Plan to add 30-mm Goalkeeper AA system in abeyance due to shortag of funds. Plans to modernize all four deferred 1989; did receive new ASW torpedoes i 1987.

MINE WARFARE SHIPS

◆ **0 (+ 10) deep-sea minehunter/sweepers** Béliard, Ostend

	Laid down	L	In serv.
M	late-1992	. . .	. . .
M	. . .	. . .	. . .
M	. . .	. . .	. . .
M	. . .	. . .	. . .

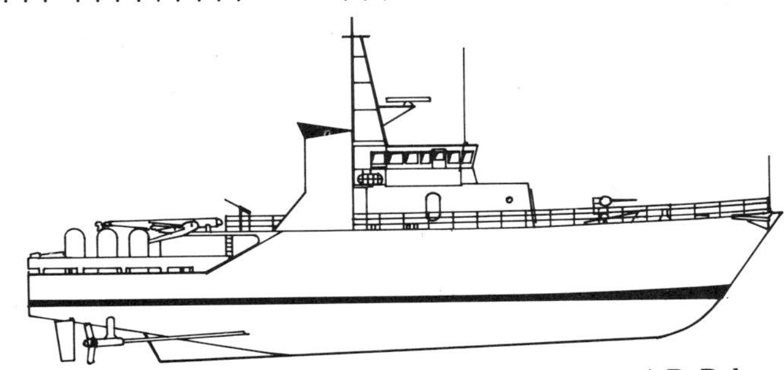
Dutch-Belgian minehunter/sweeper A.D. Baker, 19

D: 610 tons (fl) **S:** 15 kts (10 kts sweeping)
Dim: 47.0 (43.0 pp) × 9.6 × 3.6
A: 1/20-mm AA—2/12.7-mm mg (I × 2, for mine disposal)
Electron Equipt: Radar: 1/ . . . . nav.—Sonar: . . . . . .
M: 2 . . . . diesels; 2 props; 2,200 bhp **Range:** 3,000/1
Crew: 25 tot. + 5 mine-disposal divers

Remarks: Although a consortium of Boelwerf, Béliard Mercantile, and ACEC h been formed to study a minehunter design to follow the "Tripartite" program, this w superseded in a 12-9-86 announcement that Belgium would join the Netherlands a Norway in a study of a plan to produce a joint minehunter program for 17 ships. In 4- it was announced that Belgium would proceed alone, but in 5-89, the program w revised to one of cooperation with van der Giessen du Noord, the Netherlands, and 1991, it was announced that Portugal had joined the program.

◆ **10 Tripartite-class minehunters** Bldr: Béliard, Ostend and Antwer

	Laid down	L	In serv.
M 915 Aster	26-4-83	29-6-84	18-12-85
M 916 Bellis	9-2-83	22-2-85	18-9-86
M 917 Crocus	9-10-84	2-10-85	5-2-87
M 918 Dianthus	4-4-85	16-4-86	18-8-87
M 919 Fuchsia	31-10-85	27-11-86	20-3-88
M 920 Iris	23-5-86	19-6-87	3-10-88
M 921 Lobelia	4-12-86	3-2-88	10-5-89
M 922 Myosotis	6-7-87	4-10-88	14-12-89
M 923 Narcis	25-2-88	20-6-89	27-9-90
M 924 Primula	10-11-88	8-7-90	18-5-91

Iris (M 920)—in the Persian Gulf, note added machine guns
Leo Van Ginderen, 1

INE WARFARE SHIPS *(continued)*

yosotis (M 922)—in the Persian Gulf, note SATCOMM antenna
Leo Van Ginderen, 1991

:imula (M 924)—on builder's trials Leo Van Ginderen, 4-91

ırcis (M 923)—diver's chamber deckhouse not aboard
Leo Van Ginderen, 9-90

): 511 tons (595 fl) **S:** 15 kts
)im: 51.6 (47.1 pp) × 8.96 × 2.49 (hull)
\: 1/20-mm AA—on units deployed to Persian Gulf: 2/12.7-mm mg (I × 2)
Electron Equipt: Radar: Decca 1229 nav.—Sonar: DUBM-21B
M: 1 Brons/Werkspoor A-RUB 215X 12 diesel; 1 CP prop; 1,900 bhp (1,200 rpm); 2 120-hp maneuvering props (active rudder); bow-thruster
Electric: 880 kw **Range:** 3,000/12
Crew: 34 tot. (49 accommodations)

marks: Same as French and Dutch versions of the class. Original construction sortium, Polyship, dissolved. Ships reordered 12-2-81 from Béliard; hulls launched Ostend and fitted out by Béliard Mercantile at Rupelmonde, Antwerp. Three azou-IV, 320-kw gas-turbine generators; 1 140-kw diesel set. Two PAP-104 remote-trolled mine locators; automatic pilot; automatic track-plotter; TORAN and Sydelis igation systems; conventional wire sweep also. Glass-reinforced plastic construc-ı. Carry portable divers' decompression van aft on 01 deck just above forecastle ak. Crew sizes on all minehunters were to be reduced during 1989. Can be equipped h 2/12.7-mm mg (I × 2), as on M 917 on Mideast deployment during 1987–88, 0–91. M 918, M 920, and M 922 participated in mine-clearance operations in the sian Gulf during 1991.

6 U.S. Dash-class oceangoing minesweeper/minehunters
Bldrs: M 902: Peterson Bldrs, Sturgeon Bay, Wisc.; M 903, 904: Bellingham BY, Bellingham, Wash.; M 906: Tacoma BY, Tacoma, Wash.; M 908, 909: Tampa SB, Tampa, Fla.

	L	In serv.
M 902 J. E. Van Haverbeke (ex-MSO 522)	29-10-59	7-11-60
M 903 A. F. Dufour (ex-*Lagen*, ex-MSO 498)	13-8-54	27-9-55
M 904 De Brouwer (ex-*Nansen*, ex-MSO 499)	15-10-54	1-11-55
M 906 Breydel (ex-AM 504)	25-3-55	24-1-56
M 908 Georges Truffaut (ex-AM 515)	1-11-55	21-9-56
M 909 François Bovesse (ex-AM 516)	28-2-56	21-12-56

Breydel (M 906) Leo Van Ginderen, 3-91

François Bovesse (M 909) Leo Van Ginderen, 3-91

D: 720 tons (780 fl) **S:** 14 kts **Dim:** 52.42 (50.3 pp) × 10.97 × 4.20
A: 2/12.7-mm mg (II × 1)
Electron Equipt: Radar: 1/Decca 1229 nav.—Sonar: SQQ-14
M: 4 G.M. 8-268A diesels; 2 CP props; 1,520 bhp **Fuel:** 53 tons
Range: 3,000/10; 2,400/12 **Crew:** 5 officers, 67 enlisted

Remarks: Transferred 1955–60, except M 903 and M 904 transferred from Norway in 1966. Equipped as minehunters, with PAP-104 remote-control minehunting submersibles. Wooden hulls. *Artevelde* (M 907) stricken 1-2-85. M 906 and M 907 carried two extra 12.7-mm mg (I × 2) and MARISAT SATCOMM on 1987–88 Mideast deployment.

♦ **4 U.S. Adjutant-class coastal minesweepers** Bldr: Béliard, Ostend

	L	In serv.
M 929 Heist	. . .	4-4-56
M 930 Rochefort	5-6-54	28-11-55
M 932 Nieuwpoort	12-3-55	9-1-56
M 933 Koksijde	4-6-55	29-11-55

Rochefort (M 930)—with *Libération* (P 902) alongside
Leo Van Ginderen, 10-90

MINE WARFARE SHIPS *(continued)*

D: 330 tons (390 fl) **S:** 13.5/12 kts **Dim:** 44.0 (42.1 pp) × 8.3 × 2.6
A: 1/40-mm U.S. Mk 3 AA
Electron Equipt: Radar: 1/Decca 1229 nav.—Sonar: AN/UQS-1
M: 2 G.M. 8-268A diesels; 2 props; 880 bhp **Fuel:** 28 tons
Range: 2,700/10.5 **Crew:** 4 officers, 17 petty officers, 19 non-rated

Remarks: M 929, converted to degaussing tender (A 964) in 1978, restored as a minesweeper 6-85. Two minehunter conversions, *Verviers* (M 934, ex-U.S. AMS 259) and *Veurne* (M 935, ex-U.S. AMS 260) stricken 6-85. Sister *Stavelot* (M 928) stricken 31-12-87. M 932 has a lengthened forward deckhouse. All based at Zeebrugge are to be retired during 1992.

◆ 7 Herstal-class inshore minesweepers Bldr: Mercantile Marine Yard, Kruibeke

	L	In serv.
M 474 Turnhout	7-9-57	29-9-58
M 475 Tongeren	16-11-57	9-12-58
M 476 Merksem	5-4-58	6-2-59
M 478 Herstal (ex-MSI 90)	6-8-56	14-10-57
M 482 Vise (ex-MSI 94)	7-9-57	11-9-58
M 483 Ougrée (ex-MSI 95)	16-11-57	10-11-58
M 484 Dinant (ex-MSI 96)	5-4-58	14-1-59

Merksem (M 476) Mike Louagie, 10-91

D: 160 tons (190 fl) **S:** 15 kts **Dim:** 34.5 (32.5 pp) × 6.7 × 2.1
A: 2/12.7-mm mg (II × 1)
Electron Equipt: Radar: 1/Decca 1229 nav.
M: 2 Fiat-Mercedes Benz MB 820 diesels; 2 props; 1,260 bhp
Fuel: 24 tons **Range:** 2,300/10
Crew: 1 officer, 7 petty officers, 9 non-rated

Remarks: Wooden hulls. Intended to sweep the Schelde River. Fitted for magnetic, acoustic, and mechanical sweeping to a depth of 4.50 to 10 m. M 471, 472, 478 were designated RDS-Ready Duty Ship, sweep gear removed, deckhouse in place of cable reel, and pollution cleanup gear and special cranes added aft; M 471, 478 restored as minesweepers, 1983, but without large cable drum. Modified version of British "Ham" class. M 478 to M 485 were built with U.S. funds. Sister *Hasselt* (M 471) towed away for scrap, 11-9-86; *Lokeren* (M 473) stricken 1987. *Kortrijk* (M 472) stricken 1-8-89, *Oudenaarde* (M 477), *Huy* (M 479, ex-MSI 91), and *Seraing* (M 480, ex-MSI 92) stricken 1990; and *Andenne* (M 485, ex-MSI 97) in 1991. Planned transfer of M 475 to Zaire in 1988 did not go through. M 478 is used for hydrographic survey work. All are likely to be discarded soon.

◆ 1 command and logistic support ship for mine countermeasures

	Bldr	Laid down	L	In serv.
A 961 Zinnia	Cockerill, Hoboken	8-11-66	6-5-67	5-9-67

D: 1,705 tons (2,685 fl) **S:** 18 kts (20 on trials)
Dim: 99.5 (94.2 wl) × 14.0 × 3.6 **A:** 3/40-mm (I × 3)—1/Alouette-IIIB helicopter
Electron Equipt: Radar: 2/Decca 1229 nav.
M: 2 Cockerill-Ougree V 12 TR 240 CO diesels; 1 CP prop; 5,000 bhp
Fuel: 150 m^3 diesel; 300 m^3 for supply to minesweepers
Crew: 13 officers, 46 petty officers, 64 non-rated
Range: 14,000/12.5

Remarks: Fin stabilizers, telescoping helicopter hangar. Led Belgian deployment to Persian Gulf, 1987–88 and again in 1990–91, with INTELSAT commercial SATCOMM added.

Zinnia (A 961) Leo Van Ginderen, 10-

◆ 1 command and logistic support ship for mine countermeasure

	Bldr	Laid down	L	In serv.
A 960 Godetia	Boelwerf, Temse	15-2-65	7-12-65	23-5-66

Godetia (A 960) Gilbert Gyssels, 9-

D: 1,700 tons (2,500 fl) **S:** 18 kts
Dim: 91.83 (87.85 pp) × 14.0 × 3.5
A: 1/40-mm AA—6/12.7-mm mg (II × 2, I × 1)
Electron Equipt: Radar: 2/ Decca 1229 nav.
M: 4 ACEC-M.A.N. diesels; 2 CP props; 5,400 bhp **Fuel:** 294 tons
Range: 2,250/15; 8,700/12
Crew: 10 officers, 37 petty officers, 48 non-rated

Remarks: 15 knots on one diesel. Passive tank stabilization. Protected closed-circ ventilation. Can accommodate oceanographic research personnel and has space laboratory. Minesweeping cables are stowed on reels on the helicopter deck, which been extended aft to continue to permit one Alouette-III to land. Formerly could a serve as royal yacht. Received major mid-life overhaul 1981–82.

AUXILIARIES

◆ 1 oceanographic research ship

	Bldr	Laid down	L	In serv.
A 962 Belgica	Boelwerf, Temse	17-10-83	6-1-84	5-7-84

Belgica (A 962) Leo Van Ginderen, 1

D: 835 tons (fl) **S:** 12 kts **Dim:** 50.90 (44.95 pp) × 10.00 × 4.40
M: 1 ABC 6M DZC-1000-150 diesel; 1 Kort-nozzle prop; 1,570 bhp
Fuel: 158 tons **Electron Equipt:** Radar: 1/Decca . . . nav.
Electric: 640 kw **Range:** 20,000/12 **Crew:** 15 crew + 11 scientis

AUXILIARIES *(continued)*

Remarks: For use in North and Irish seas or for fisheries or hydrographic research. Can carry two laboratory containers on deck. 150-hp thrusters fore and aft. Very bluff hull lines, bulbous bow.

Note: The 80-grt research ship *Ter Streep,* launched 28-6-85 by Langerbragge, Ghent, is not naval.

◆ 1 U.S. Adjutant-class munitions transport, former minesweeper

	Bldr	L	In serv.
A 963 SPA (ex-M 927)	Boelwerf, Temse	21-6-54	1-1-56

Spa (A 963) Ben Sullivan, 8-89

Remarks: Carries missiles, torpedoes, and gun ammunition in support of frigates. Data as for minesweeper sisters. Retains 1/40-mm AA. Crew: 3 officers, 8 petty officers, 19 non-rated.

◆ 1 sail-training craft

	Bldr	Laid down	L	In serv.
A 958 ZENOBE GRAMME	Boelwerf, Temse	7-10-60	23-10-61	1962

Zenobe Gramme (A 958) Leo Van Ginderen, 8-90

D: 149 tons **S:** 10 kts
Dim: 28.15 (23.10 wl × 6.85 × 2.64
Electron Equipt: Radar: 1/. . . . . . nav.
M: 1 MWM 518A diesel; 232 bhp **Crew:** 14 tot.

Remarks: Fitted out as Bermudian ketch (240 m² sail area). Formerly also used for oceanographic research.

◆ 1 seagoing tug Bldr: Ch. Navals & Atelier Const. de Hemixem

A 954 ZEEMEEUW (In serv. 1971)

D: 400 tons (fl) **S:** 10 kts **Dim:** 27.94 (26.60 pp) × 7.29 × 3.37
Electron Equipt: Radar: 1/Decca 1229 nav. **Crew:** 6 tot.
M: 2 ABC 6-cyl. diesels; 2 props; 1,040 bhp **Electric:** 96 kw

Remarks: 146 grt/24 nrt. Acquired from another Belgian government agency, 17-8-81. Based at Zeebrugge and used on pollution-control duties.

Zeemeeuw (A 954) Leo Van Ginderen, 9-91

◆ 2 seagoing tugs Bldr: H. Bodewes, Millengen a/d Ryn

A 950 VALCKE (ex-*Astroloos,* ex-*Steenbank*) (In serv. 14-12-60)
A 998 EKSTER (ex-*Astronoom,* ex-*Schouwenbank*) (In serv. 6-10-60)

Valcke (A 950) Leo Van Ginderen, 12-90

D: 420 tons (fl) **S:** 13 kts **Dim:** 30.08 × 7.55 × 2.99
Electron Equipt: Radar: 1/Decca 1229 **Crew:** 12 tot.
M: 2 4-cycle, single-acting 8-cyl. diesels, electric drive; 1 prop; 1,250 shp

Remarks: 183 grt. Purchased 1980 from A. Smit. Based at Zeebrugge. A 950 in collision 1985, out of service for many months.

YARD AND SERVICE CRAFT

◆ 1 river patrol craft Bldr: Hitzler, Regensburg (In serv. 4-8-54)

P 902 LIBÉRATION

Libération (P 902) Leo Van Ginderen, 6-91

D: 30 tons (fl) **S:** 19 kts **Dim:** 26.00 × 4.00 × 0.90
A: 2/12.7-mm mg (I × 2) **Crew:** 1 officer, 6 enlisted
M: 2 MWM diesels; 2 props; 440 bhp

Remarks: Stricken 12-6-87 but returned to service 15-9-89. Survivor of a class of six.

◆ 2 Bij-class small harbor tugs

	Bldr	In serv.
A 953 BIJ	Akerboom, Lisse	1959
A 956 KREKEL	Rupelmonde SY	1961

BELGIUM *(continued)*
YARD AND SERVICE CRAFT *(continued)*

Bij (A 953) Leo Van Ginderen, 10-90

D: 60 tons (71 fl) **S:** 10 kts
Dim: 17.65 (16.0) × 5.2 × 2.0 **Crew:** 5 tot.
M: 2 MWM RHS 518A diesels; 2 Voith-Schneider vertical cycloidal props; 300 bhp

♦ **1 Hommel-class harbor tug** Bldr: Voith, Heidenheim

A 951 Hommel (In serv. 1953)

D: 22 tons **S:** . . . kts **Dim:** . . . × . . . × . . .
M: 2 diesels; 2 Voith-Schneider vertical cycloidal props; 300 bhp

Remarks: Used on pollution-control duties at Ostend. Sister *Wesp* (A 952) stricken 1982.

Hommel (A 951) Mike Louagie, 4-87

♦ **1 personnel launch/tug**

Spin (In serv. 1958)

D: 32 tons **S:** 8 kts **Dim:** 14.6 × . . . × . . .
M: 1 diesel; 1 Voith-Schneider vertical cycloidal prop; 250 bhp

Spin Leo Van Ginderen, 8-85

♦ **2 small royal yachts**

A 981 Avila (In serv. 1963) A 982 Trefogliu (In serv. . . .)

Remarks: A 981, a small cabin cruiser, is normally kept at Motril, Spain.

Avila Mike Louagie, 1991

BELIZE

Personnel (1991): 8 officers, 42 enlisted

Aviation: 2 Pilatus-Britten-Norman BN 2B Defender.

♦ **2 20-meter Wasp-class patrol craft** Bldr: Souter, Cowes, U.K. (In serv. 19-9-84)

PB 01 Dangriga PB 02 Toledo

Dangriga (PB 01) Leo Van Ginderen, 8-83

D: 36.25 tons (fl) **S:** 18 kts **Dim:** 20.00 (16.00 pp) × 5.00 × 1.50
A: 1/12.7-mm mg—4/7.62-mm mg (I × 4)
Electron Equipt: Radar: 1/Decca 150 nav.
M: 2 G.M. 16V71 TI diesels; 2 props; 2,400 bhp
Range: 430/18 **Electric:** 37 kw (2 × 18.5 kw) **Fuel:** 5 tons
Crew: 2 officers, 6 enlisted

Remarks: GRP construction. Can carry up to 30 troops. Completed 8-84, but not commissioned in-country until 19-9-84. Could make 23 kts when new. In 1989 it was announced that one of these craft would be sold to raise funds to acquire 3 Cougar Cat 900 catamaran patrol craft (40 kts, A: 1/12.7-mm mg, 2/7.62-mm mg, 4.5 tons), but as of mid-1991, that had not been done.

Note: Also in service are small GRP-hulled patrol launches P-1 through P-3, two Avon and two Gemini rigid-inflatable boats, and a 10.7-m personnel launch.

BENIN

People's Republic of Benin

Personnel (1991): About 200

♦ **1 PR-362T-class patrol boat**

	Bldr	Laid down	L	In serv.
Patriote	SBCN, Loctudy	10-86	1-88	15-5-88

Patriote Bernard Prézelin, 6-88

BENIN *(continued)*

D: 70 tons (fl) **S:** 36 kts **Dim:** 38.00 (36.20 pp) × 6.80 × 1.30
A: 1/20-mm M 621 AA—2/12.7-mm mg (I × 2) **Crew:** 23 tot.
Electron Equipt: Radar: 1/Decca . . . nav. **Range:** 1,500/16
M: 3 Baudouin 12P15-2SR7 diesels; 3 waterjets; 3,600 bhp

Remarks: Composite wood/epoxy hull. Damaged during delivery voyage and remained at Carena Shipyard, Abidjan, until 28-5-91 before being returned to France for repairs that were completed 10-91.

♦ **4 Soviet Zhuk-class patrol boats**

Four Zhuks at Cotonou 1-84

D: 48 tons (60 fl) **S:** 34 kts **Dim:** 24.0 × 5.0 × 1.2 (1.5 props)
A: 4/14.5-mm mg (II × 2) **Electron Equipt:** Radar: 1/Spin Trough
M: 2 M50F-4 diesels; 2 props; 2,400 bhp **Crew:** 12 tot.
Range: 700/28; 1,100/15 **Fuel:** 10 tons

Remarks: Transferred: 2 in 1979, 1 in 5-80, 1 in 9-80. Have twin mg in side-by-side, enclosed mountings. All reported to be in very poor condition by end-1990, and may have been discarded.

Note: The two torpedo boats donated by North Korea in 1979 had been stricken by late 1990, and the tug *Kondo* listed in the previous edition is not naval.

BERMUDA

The Crown Colony of Bermuda

BERMUDIAN POLICE

♦ **1 former commercial craft** Bldr: . . . , Mystic, Connecticut, U.S.A.

The Heron (In serv. 1970)

D: . . . tons **S:** . . . kts **Dim:** 19.8 × 6.2 × . . .
M: 2 Cummins diesels; 2 props; 640 bhp **Crew:** 5 tot.

Remarks: Acquired 8-85. Carries 5-m rigid inflatable inspection boat with 70-bhp outboard motor.

♦ **1 sport cruiser** Bldr: Harris Boat, Newburyport, Mass., U.S.A.

Blue Heron (In serv. 22-5-78)

D: 7 tons **S:** . . . **Dim:** 10.9 × . . . × . . .
M: 2 G.M. diesels; 2 props; 260 bhp **Crew:** 3

♦ **1 Boston Whaler patrol and rescue craft** Bldr: Boston Whaler, U.S.A.

Heron II (In serv. 12-88)

D: 1.5 tons (2 fl) **S:** 30 kts **Dim:** 6.81 × 2.26 × . . .
M: 2 Yamaha outboards; 230 bhp **Crew:** 2 tot.

Remarks: "Unsinkable" GRP foam-core construction. Replaced craft with same name delivered 7-81.

♦ **2 Arctic-class rigid inflatable boats** Bldr: Osbourne, U.K.

Rescue 1 (In serv. 9-86) Rescue II (In serv. 5-88)

D: 1.45 tons (fl) **S:** . . . kts **Dim:** 7.30 × . . . × . . .
M: 1 Yanmar diesel; 90 bhp **Crew:** 3 tot.

Note: The Bermuda Customs Service also operates patrol craft, including at least one Fairey "Protector" patrol boat.

BOLIVIA

Republic of Bolivia

Personnel (1990): 5,000, including 600 Almirante Grau Battalion marines

Naval Aviation: 1 Cessna U206 light transport, 8 Helibras SA 315B Gavião helicopters.

PATROL BOATS AND CRAFT

♦ **6 (+ 4) U.S. Boston Whaler GRP-hulled** Bldr: Boston Whaler, U.S.A.

LP-01 Comando LP-02 Tactica LP-04 Inti LP-05 Mallcu
LP-08 Auxiliar LP-. . . . . LP-. . . . .

D: 1.5 tons (2 fl) **S:** 40 kts **Dim:** 6.81 × 2.26 × . . .
A: 2/12.7-mm mg (I × 2)—small arms **Crew:** 3 tot.
M: 2 outboard motors; 360 bhp **Range:** 167/40; 750/ . . .

Remarks: Four delivered late 1989, two in 12-90, four more to deliver in 1991.

♦ **1 local-design** Bldr: Guayaramerin Boatyard

LP- . . . General Banzer (L: 9-90)

Remarks: 16.75-m overall; no other data available.

♦ **1 aluminum-hulled patrol boat** Bldr: Hope/Progressive Shipbuilders, Houma, Louisiana, U.S.A.

PR 51 Santa Cruz de la Sierra (In serv. 1985)

Santa Cruz de la Sierra (PR 51) Hope, 1985

D: . . . **S:** . . . **Dim:** 20.4 × . . . × . . .
A: 2/12.7-mm mg (I × 2)
Electron Equipt: Radar: 1/Furuno . . . nav.
M: 2 G.M. diesels; 2 props; . . . bhp

♦ **1 or more Brown-class patrol launches** (In serv. 1978– . . .)

Almirante Guillermo Brown

D: 4 tons **S:** 12 kts **Dim:** 7.0 × 2.3 × 1.0

♦ **3 ex-U.S. PBR Mk-II patrol boats**

LP-502 Tamengo LP-510 Suarez Arana
LP-512 Mariscal Santa Cruz

D: 8.9 tons **S:** 24 kts **Dim:** 9.73 × 3.53 × 0.81
A: 3/12.7-mm mg (II × 1, I × 1)—1/60-mm mortar
Electron Equipt: Radar: 1/Raytheon 1900 **Crew:** 4 tot.
M: 2 G.M. 6V53N diesels; 2 water jets; 430 bhp **Range:** 150/23

Remarks: On Lake Titicaca. GRP construction. Transferred 4-74.

AUXILIARIES

♦ **1 seagoing cargo ship** Bldr: Fairfield, U.K., 1951

TM-01 Libertador Bolívar (ex-*Simon Bolívar*, ex-*Ciudad de Barquisimeto*)

D: 9,000 tons **S:** 14.5 kts **Dim:** 128.3 (120.4 pp) × 16.76 × 6.7
M: 1 Doxford diesel; 4,350 bhp **Range:** 7,000/14

Remarks: Donated by Venezuela, 1977. Home-ported in Argentina. Used to generate revenue and for training in preparation for possible ceding to Bolivia of a "corridor to the sea" between Peru and Chile. 4,214 grt/6,390 dwt/2,352 nrt.

♦ **11 miscellaneous river launches for patrol and logistic support**

M-18 Litoral M-223 Libertador
M-101 Almirante Grau M-224 Trinidad
M-103 Comandante Arandia M-225 J. Chavez Suarez

BOLIVIA *(continued)*
AUXILIARIES *(continued)*

M-315 Ing. Palacios
M-322 Itenez
M-329 Bruno Racua
M-331 TF. R. Rios
M-341 Ing. Gumucio

Remarks: All of 20 tons except M-341: 70 tons. Iron or wooden hulls.

◆ **6 fuel lighters**

BTL-01 General Pando
BTL-02 Nicolas Suarez
BTL-03 Mariscal Cruz
BTL-04 Max Paredes
BTL-06 V.A.H. Ugartche
BTL-07 Manuripi

Remarks: All of 40–45 tons; no other data available.

◆ **1 hospital launch**

AH-01 Julian Apaza

Remarks: Launched 1977–78; 17 tons; a gift of the U.S.A.

◆ **2 30-ton hydrographic survey craft**

LH-01 Pionera   LH-03 Centauro

◆ **1 30-ton river transport**

LT-01 General Belgrano

BOTSWANA

◆ **2 U.S. "Raider"-class patrol craft**   Bldr: Napco, Hopkins, Minnesota

D: 2.95 tons (fl) **S:** 40 kts **Dim:** 6.80 (6.40 wl) × 2.26 × 0.86
A: 2/12.7-mm mg (I × 2)
M: 2 gasoline outboard motors; 2 props; 310 bhp
Range: 167/40; 220/30; 750/. . . **Crew:** 3 tot.

Remarks: Provided under Fiscal Year 1988 Military Aid Program funds. Additional units have been requested. Use "Boston Whaler" GRP hulls.

BRAZIL

Federative Republic of Brazil

Personnel (1990): 50,000 total (5,700 officers, 44,000 enlisted, including 14,600 *Fuzileiros Navais* officers and men).

Naval Aviation: 6 AS.332F (UH-14) Super Puma with AM-39 Exocet missiles (delivered 8-87; 9 more planned), 7 SH-3D/H Sea King, 16 Bell 206B JetRanger (SAH-11), 7 Westland Mk 21 Lynx with Sea Skua missiles, 12 SA-350B Esquilo (UH-12) 10 Helibras AS-355F Esquilo II (UH-13), and 8 Westland Wasp Mk 21 and 23 (UH-2). Eight Helibras SA-315B Gaviao (Aerospatiale Lama) are on order, and 5 additional WG-13 Lynx with Super Searcher radar and Rolls-Royce Gem 42 engines were ordered late 1991; the 7 Mk 21 Lynx are to be upgraded to "Super Lynx" standard with Seaspray radars.

The Air Force makes available to the Navy: 3 RC-130E Hercules and 20 EMB 111 (P-95) Bandeirante in a sea-surveillance version; 10 more EMB 111 were ordered during 1990. Eight Grumman S-2E (P-16H) Tracker aircraft are available for use on *Minas Gerais,* and 4 S-2A are used for training and transport, all being re-engined with Pratt & Whitney, Canada PT6A-67AF turboprops and equipped with Varian radar, and new FLIR and MAD equipment under 1989 contract with Embraer and Thomson-CSF to be completed 1992. To support the Navy, the Air Force also operates 2 Piper/Embraer Seneca II, 15 Neiva T-25 Universal aircraft, and 6 AS-332F (UH-14) Super Puma helicopters for search-and-rescue purposes.

UH-14 Super Puma M.R. Vaz Carneiro

Mk 21 Sea Lynx U.S. Navy

Weapons and Sensors: In late 1988 it was announced that the indigenous Barracuda antiship missile and SSA-N-1 surface-to-air missile system development programs had been canceled. During U.S. Fiscal Year 1990 (1-10-89 to 30-9-90), 18 Harpoon missiles were ordered. Existing U.S. Mk 46 Mod. 2 ASW torpedoes are to be upgraded to Mod. 5, and additional Mk 46 Mod. 5 are to be acquired. A number of Danish Terma navigational radars were ordered 1991 to equip patrol and service craft. AM-39 Exocet missiles are being acquired for the Sea King helicopters.

LIGHT ANTISUBMARINE AIRCRAFT CARRIER

Note: Long-range plans for replacing *Minas Gerais* with one or two small carriers have been canceled.

◆ **1 British Colossus class**

	Bldr	Laid down	L	In serv.
A 11 Minas Gerais (ex-*Vengeance*)	Swan Hunter, Wallsend-on-Tyne	16-11-42	23-3-44	15-1-45

Minas Gerais (A 11) PH2 Tracy Didas, USN, 10-90

Minas Gerais (A 11) Don S. Montgomery, 10-9

D: 15,890 tons (19,890 fl) **S:** 24 kts
Dim: 211.25 × 36.44 (24.50 hull) × 7.15
A: 10/40-mm AA (IV × 2, II × 1)—6/S-2E aircraft—4-6/SH-3, 2/UH-11, 3/UH-12 helicopters
Electron Equipt:
Radar: 1/Terma Scanter MIL nav., 1/SPS-4 surface search ,1/SPS-40B air search, 2/SPG-34 fire control, 1/Terma landing control
EW: WLR-1 intercept, . . . D/F
M: Parsons GT; 2 props; 42,000 shp **Range:** 12,000/14; 6,200/23
Boilers: 4 Admiralty 3-drum; 28 kg/cm, 371° C **Fuel:** 3,200 tons
Electric: 2,500 kw (4 × 500-kw turbogenerators, 1 × 500-kw diesel set)
Crew: 1,000 ship's company plus 300 aviation personnel

Remarks: Purchased from Great Britain in 12-56; refitted in Rotterdam, completin in 1960 with new weapons, steam catapult, angled flight deck (8.5-deg.), mirror optica landing equipment, new radars, and two new elevators. GFCS for the 40-mm A include 2 Mk 63 (with SPG-34 radar on the quadruple mounts) and 1 Mk 51 Mod.

LIGHT ANTISUBMARINE AIRCRAFT CARRIER *(continued)*

Hangar 135.6 × 15.8 × 5.3 high; 2 elevators 13.7 × 10.4. When operational, catapult can launch 15-ton aircraft. A data link system for cooperation with the *Niteroi* class has been installed, and U.S. SPS-40B radar has replaced SPS-12. Plans to purchase 12 A-4 Skyhawk fighter-bombers for use from this ship were announced in 1984 and canceled early in 1985. The SPS-8B height-finding radar was removed during 1984. Laid up in 1987 with catapult problems, and in 1989 it was announced that a refit was to be postponed. Although nominally operational, can only make about 17 knots and the catapult is out of service, leaving her capable only of operating helicopters. New Danish Terma navigational and landing control radars fitted 1991.

SUBMARINES

◆ **0 (+6) NAC-1 class** Bldr: Ast. Ilha das Cobras, Rio

	Laid down	L	In serv.
S.	. . .	. . .	2000
S.	. . .	. . .	. . .
S.	. . .	. . .	. . .
S.	. . .	. . .	. . .
S.	. . .	. . .	. . .
S.	. . .	. . .	. . .

D: 2,500 tons (sub.) **S:** 25–30 kts **Dim:** . . . × . . . × . . .
A: 6/533-mm TT (12 total torpedoes)
M: diesel-electric; 1 prop; . . . bhp **Crew:** . . .

Remarks: A follow-on program to the Type 1400 effort. To have 280-m working depth. A 2,700-ton nuclear-powered variant with a 12-megawatt reactor is planned, but would not enter service before circa 2010; two turboalternators would drive one motor for 30-kt submerged speeds. Due to the difficulties being encountered in assembling Type 209 submarines in Brazil, this program is likely to be delayed or canceled.

◆ **1 (+ 4 + 2) German Type 209/1400 Mod. 3 class**

	Bldr	Laid down	L	In serv.
S 30 Tupi	Howaldtswerke, Kiel	8-3-85	28-4-87	20-8-88
S 31 Tamoio	Ast. Ilha das Cobras, Rio	15-7-86	1994	1995
S 32 Timbira	Ast. Ilha das Cobras, Rio	15-9-87	. . .	. . .
S 33 Tapajós	Ast. Ilha das Cobras, Rio	. . .	. . .	. . .
S 34 Tocantins	Ast. Ilha das Cobras, Rio	. . .	. . .	. . .
S 35	Ast. Ilha das Cobras, Rio	. . .	. . .	. . .

Tupi (S 30) Brazilian Navy, 1988

Tupi (S 30) Brazilian Navy, 6-89

D: 1,150 tons surf./1,440 sub. **S:** 11 surf., 21.5 sub.
Dim: 61.20 × 6.25 × 5.50
A: 8/533-mm TT fwd.–16 Mk 24 Mod. 1 Tigerfish torpedoes
Electron Equipt:
Radar: . . .
Sonar: Krupp-Atlas CSU-83/1 suite (DBSQS-21 active, . . . flank arrays)
EW: Thomson-CSF DR-4000W
M: 4 MTU 12V493 TY60, 600 bhp diesels, 4 AEG 420-kw generators, electric drive; 1 prop; 5,000 shp
Range: 8,200/8 snorkel; 50/16; 230/8; 400/4 submerged
Fuel: 116 tons **Crew:** 33 tot.

Remarks: Order placed 8-82. Have Ferranti KAFS A10 action data system, 2 Kollmorgen periscopes, Sperry Mk 29 Mod. 2 Ships Inertial Navigation System (SINS). Can make 25 knots for brief period. Diving depth: 250 m. Endurance: 50 days. 480-cell battery. By 1991, the program was about three years behind schedule. S 34 and S 35 may be of an enlarged design, of which two further units are planned. S 30 arrived at Rio on 27-6-89.

◆ **3 British Oberon class** Bldr: Vickers, Barrow

	Laid down	L	In serv.
S 20 Humaitá	3-11-70	5-10-71	18-6-73
S 21 Tonelero	18-21-70	22-11-72	8-9-78
S 22 Riachuelo	26-5-73	6-9-75	12-3-77

Tonelero (S 21) Don S. Montgomery, 10-90

D: 1,620 tons standard, 2,040 surf., 2,410 sub. **S:** 17.5/15 kts
Dim: 89.9 × 8.07 × 5.48
A: 8/533-mm TT (6 long fwd. with 18 U.K. Mk 24 Tigerfish; 2 short aft with 4 U.S. Mk 37 torpedoes)
Electron Equipt:
Radar: Kelvin Hughes 1006 nav.
Sonar: Type 187 MF active/passive, Type 2007 passive flank array, DUUG-1 underwater telephone, AUUD-1 intercept
M: 2 Admiralty Standard Range 16 VVS-ASR1 diesels; 2 electric generators, each 1,280 kw; 2 electric motors; 2 props; 6,000 shp
Range: 11,000/11 snorkel **Endurance:** 56 days
Crew: 5 officers, 57 men

Remarks: S 21 several years late entering active service due to a fire on board during construction. Batteries made up of 224 elements in two sections, with a 7,240-ampere capacity for five hours. "One-man control" system for immersion and diving. Satellite navigation receiver installed. Have U.K. Mk 2 submerged signal and decoy ejector forward, Mk 4 Mod. 1B aft; both launch 102-mm devices. Were to receive U.K. DCH torpedo f.c.s., but badly needed modernizations canceled 1989 for lack of funds.

◆ **1 ex-U.S. Guppy III class** Bldr: Electric Boat Co., Groton, Connecticut

	Laid down	L	In serv.
S 16 Amazonas (ex-*Greenfish,* SS 351)	29-1-44	21-12-45	7-6-46

D: 1,650 tons standard, 1,975 surf., 2,450 sub.
S: 17.2/14.5 kts (9.4 snorkel)
Dim: 99.52 × 8.23 × 5.18
A: 10/533-mm TT (6 fwd, 4 aft; 24 U.S. Mk 37 torpedoes)
Electron Equipt: Radar: 1/SS-2A
Sonar: BQG-4 PUFFS, BQR-2B passive
M: diesel-electric propulsion: 4 G.M. 16-278A diesel generator sets (6,400 bhp); 2 electric motors; 2 props; 5,400 shp
Range: 12,000/10 surf., 95/5 sub. **Crew:** 86 tot.

Remarks: Purchased19-12-73. S 16 converted to Guppy II in 1948, lengthened to Guppy III in 1961. Two 126-cell batteries. Sister *Goías* (S 15, ex-*Trumpetfish,* SS 425) stricken 16-4-90. To strike on completion of Type 1400-class replacements, and is reported to be limited to shallow diving.

◆ **1 U.S. Guppy II class** Bldr: Portsmouth Naval Shipyard, Portsmouth, N.H.

	Laid down	L	In serv.
S 12 Bahia (ex-*Sea Leopard,* SS 483)	7-11-44	2-3-45	11-6-45

D: 1,525 tons standard, 1,848 surf., 2,440 sub.
S: 17.4/14 kts (9.4 snorkel)
Dim: 93.36 × 8.18 × 5.04
A: 10/533-mm TT (6 fwd.,4 aft; 24 Mk 37 torpedoes)

SUBMARINES *(continued)*

Electron Equipt: Radar: 1/SS-2A
Sonar: BQR-2B passive, BQS-4 active
M: diesel-electric propulsion: 3 Fairbanks-Morse 38D 8 ⅛ × 10 generator sets (4,800 bhp); 2 electric motors; 2 props; 5,400 shp
Fuel: 330 tons **Range:** 10,000/10 surf., 95/5 sub. **Crew:** 86 tot.

Remarks: Purchased 27-3-73. Was reported to be stricken for use as pierside trainer during 1989, but was still seagoing at end 1990. Four sisters stricken: *Rio Grande do Sul* (S 11, ex-*Grampus*, SS 523) and *Rio de Janeiro* (S 13, ex-*Odax*, SS 484) in 1978; *Guanabara* (S 10, ex-*Dogfish*, SS 350) in 1983, and *Ceara* (S 12, ex-*Amberjack*, SS 522), sold for scrap 24-7-90 after having been laid up since 1987. *Bahia* is probably limited to shallow diving depths.

DESTROYERS

Note: Plans to acquire retired units of the U.S. *Charles F. Adams* (DDG 2) class were canceled during 1990 due to the projected cost of overhauling and operating the ships; in 7-91, however, it was reported that four may be acquired in 1993.

◆ **2 ex-U.S. Gearing class, FRAM I** Bldr: Consolidated Steel, Orange, Texas

	Laid down	L	In serv.
D 25 MARCILIO DIAZ (ex-*Henry W. Tucker*, DD 875)	29-5-44	8-11-44	10-3-45
D 26 MARIZ E BARROS (ex-*Brinkley Bass*, DD 887)	20-6-44	26-5-45	1-10-45

Marcilio Diaz (D 26) Don S. Montgomery, 10-90

D: 2,425 tons (3,600 fl) **S:** 30 kts
Dim: 119.17 × 12.52 × 4.61 (6.4 over sonar)
A: 4/127-mm, 38-cal. DP (II x 2)—1/ Mk 116 ASROC ASW launcher (VIII × 1; 12 total missiles)—6/324-mm Mk 32 ASW TT (III × 2; U.S. Mk 46 torpedoes)—1/Wasp helicopter
Electron Equipt:
Radar: 1/SPS-10 surf. search, 1/SPS-40 air search, 1/Mk 25 fire control, 1/. . . nav.-air control
Sonar: 1/SQS-23 hull-mounted—EW: WLR-1 intercept, ULQ-6 jammer
M: 2 sets General Electric GT; 2 props, 60,000 shp
Boilers: 4 Babcock & Wilcox, 43.3 kg, 454° C
Electric: 1,200 kw tot.
Fuel: 750 tons **Range:** 2,400/25; 4,800/15
Crew: 14 officers, 260 enlisted

Remarks: Purchased 3-12-73 and reached Brazil in 6-74. Mk 37 GFCS for 127-mm guns. Former DASH drone ASW helicopter hangar used for Westland Wasp.

◆ **4 ex-U.S. Allen M. Sumner class** Bldr: Bethlehem SY, San Pedro, Cal. (D 36, D 37: San Francisco, Cal.)

	Laid down	L	In serv.
D 35 SERGIPE (ex-*James C. Owens*, DD 776)	9-4-44	1-10-44	7-2-45
D 36 ALAGAOS (ex-*Buck*, DD 761)	1-2-44	11-3-44	28-6-46
D 37 RIO GRANDE DO NORTE (ex-*Strong*, DD 758)	25-7-43	23-4-44	8-3-45
D 38 ESPIRITO SANTO (ex-*Lowry*, DD 770)	1-8-43	6-2-44	28-7-44

D: 2,200 tons (3,320 fl) **S:** 30 kts **Dim:** 114.75 × 12.45 × 5.8
A: 6/127-mm, 38-cal. DP (II × 3)—2/Hedgehog ASW RL (XXIV × 2)—6/324-mm Mk 32 ASW TT (III × 2)—1/Wasp helicopter
Electron Equipt:
Radar: 1/SPS-10 surf. search, 1/SPS-40 (D38: 1/SPS-29) air search, 1 Mk 25 fire-control
Sonar: 1/SQS-44 hull mounted; D 35 also: SQA-10 VDS
EW: WRL-1 or 3 intercept (D 38 also: ULQ-6 jammers)
M: 2 sets GT; 2 props; 60,000 shp **Electric:** 1,200 kw
Boilers: 4 Babcock & Wilcox, 43.3 kg/cm, 454° C **Fuel:** 460 tons
Range: 1,260/30; 4,600/15 **Crew:** 15 officers, 260 enlisted

Remarks: Transferred in D 35 and D 36 on 16-7-73; D 37 on 30-11-73; and D 38 on 29-10-73. Mk 37 GFCS for 127-mm, 38-cal. guns. Drone helicopter facilities adapted for manned Wasp helicopters. D 35 collided with a merchant ship 11-84, out of service for 8 months or more. Unmodified sister *Mato Grosso* (D 34, ex-*Compton*, DD 705) was stricken 7-90, and her hulk is retained as a source of spare parts.

Rio Grande do Norte (D 37) PH1 Michael D. P. Flynn, USN, 10-90

Sergipe (D 35)—outboard dry dock *Afonso Peña* (G 25) Don S. Montgomery, 10-90

Espirito Santo (D 38)—and a sister Leo Van Ginderen, 10-85

Note: U.S. *Fletcher*-class destroyer *Santa Catarina* (D 32, ex-*Irwin*, DD 794) was stricken 1-89. Sister *Piaui* (D 31, ex-*Lewis Hancock*, DD 675) stricken 2-6-89 and *Maranhao* (D 33, ex-*Shields*, DD 596) during 7-90; all three had been in reserve for several years, and their hulks will likely be retained for a while longer as sources of spare parts.

FRIGATES

◆ **2 (+2) Inhaúma class** Bldr: First two: Ast. Ilha das Cobras, Rio; others: Verolme do Brasil, Puerto Alegre

	Laid down	L	In serv.
V 30 INHAÚMA	23-9-83	3-12-86	12-12-89 (accepted)
V 31 JACEGUARI	15-10-84	8-6-87	12-90 (accepted)
V 32 JULIO DE NORONHA	15-11-87	. . .	1993
V 33 FRONTIN	15-12-87	. . .	1994

D: 1,670 tons (1,970 fl) **S:** 26 kts
Dim: 95.77 (90.00 pp) × 11.40 × 3.64
A: 4/MM 40 Exocet SSM (II × 2)–1/114-mm Vickers Mk 8 DP—1/20-mm U.S. Mk 15 CIWS (provision for)—2/40-mm Bofors L 70 AA (I ×2)–6/324-mm ASW TT for Mk 46 torpedoes (III × 2)—1/ Lynx helicopter
Electron Equipt:
Radar: 1/. . . navigational, 1/Plessey AWS-4 air search,1/Orion RTN-10X f.c.

FRIGATES *(continued)*

Inhaúma (V 30)—on trials Brazilian Navy, 1989

Inhaúma (V 30)—as completed Brazilian Navy, 1990

Sonar: Krupp Atlas ASO-4-2
EW: . . . passive, Cygnus jammer, 2/Plessey Shield chaff RL (VI × 2)
M: CODOG: 1 G.E. LM 2500 gas turbine, 27,000 shp; 2 MTU 16V956 TB91 diesels, 7,880 bhp; 2 CP props
Electric: 2,000 kw (4 Siemens 500-kw alternators)
Range: 4,000/15. **Crew:** 14 officers, 33 petty officers, 79 enlisted

Remarks: Originally to have been a program of 12 smaller "corvettes," intended for Coast Guard service. Four were authorized 11-81, with the possibility of more later, and the first two were ordered 15-2-82; second pair ordered 9-6-86, originally for delivery 1989, but now delayed indefinitely due to shipyard labor problems and bankruptcy (completion dates above estimated). Have Ferranti CAAIS 2-50 (Computer-Assisted Information System). U.S. Mk 15 "Vulcan/Phalanx" CIWS selected 1988 for installation on stern. Reported to suffer from topweight problems, which has helped to delay the entry into full active service of the first two. The projected 5th–16th units would have had the now-canceled Avibras Barracuda SSM and SSA-N-1 SAM systems.

♦ **6 British Vosper Thornycroft Mk 10 class** Bldrs: F 40–F 43: Vosper Thornycroft, Woolston; others: Ast. Ilha das Cobras, Rio de Janeiro

	Laid down	L	In serv.
F 40 Niteroi	8-6-72	8-2-74	20-11-76
F 41 Defensora	14-12-72	27-3-75	5-3-77
F 42 Constituição	13-3-74	15-4-76	31-3-78
F 43 Liberal	2-5-75	7-2-77	18-11-78
F 44 Independência	11-6-72	2-9-74	3-9-79
F 45 União	11-6-72	14-3-75	12-9-80

D: 3,200 tons (3,800 fl)
S: 30.5 kts (28 cruising on gas turbines, 22 on diesels)
Dim: 129.24 (121.92 pp) × 13.52 × 4.20 (5.94 sonar)
A: F 42, 43: 4/MM 38 Exocet SSM; others: MM 40 Exocet (II × 2)—1(F 42, 43: 2)/114-mm Mk 8 Vickers automatic DP—2/40-mm Bofors AA (I × 2)—2/Sea Cat SAM systems (III × 2)—Branik ASW system (not on F 42, 43)—1/375-mm, Bofors ASW RL (II × 1)—6/324-mm ASW TT (III × 2)—1/Lynx helicopter—/d.c. rack (5 charges)
Electron Equipt:
Radar: 1/H.S.A. ZW-06 surf. search, 1/Plessey AWS-2 air search, 2/Orion RTN-10 × f.c.–1/Ikara tracker (not in F 42, 43)
Sonar: 1/EDO 610 E; ASW ships also have 1/EDO 700 VDS
EW: Decca RDL-2/3 intercept–2/Plessey Shield RL (VI × 2)

Niteroi (F 40)—general-purpose version Leo Van Ginderen, 3-89

Independência (F 44)—ASW version French Navy, 1987

Defensora (F 41)—ASW version Don S. Montgomery, 10-90

M: CODOG: 2 Rolls-Royce Olympus TM3B gas turbines, 28,000 shp each; 4 MTU 16V956 TB91 diesels, 3,940 bhp each; 2 Escher-Wyss CP props; 56,000 shp max.
Range: 1,300/29; 5,300/17 **Crew:** 22 officers, 187 enlisted

Remarks: Ordered 20-9-70. Fitted with retractable fin stabilizers. Branik is the name of the system devised for handling the Australian Ikara ASW missile in these ships. All have CAAIS action data system (Ferranti 1600B computers). The Brazilian-built units experienced considerable delays in fitting out. F 40, 41, 44, 45 received 4 MM 40 Exocet SSM ordered 1986; the others retain MM 38 Exocet originally installed. Plan to install U.S. Mk 15 Phalanx CIWS on F 40, 41, 44, and 45, if funds permit. All are to be given a mid-life modernization in the mid-1990s, with a SAM system to be added in place of Sea Cat.

♦ **4 U.S. Garcia class** Bldrs: D 27, D 29: Lockheed SB, Seattle; D 28: Avondale SY, New Orleans; D 30: Bethlehem SB, San Francisco

	Laid down	L	In serv.
D 27 Pará (ex-*Albert David,* FF 1050)	29-4-64	19-12-64	19-10-68
D 28 Paraíba (ex-*Davidson,* FF 1045)	20-9-63	3-10-64	7-12-65
D 29 Paraná (ex-*Sample,* F 1048)	19-7-63	28-4-64	23-3-68
D 30 Pernambuco (ex-*Bradley,* FF 1041)	17-1-63	26-3-64	15-5-65

D: 2,624 tons (3,560 fl) **S:** 27 kts
Dim: 126.33 (121.90 wl) × 13.47 × 7.90 (over sonar)
A: 2/127-mm 38-cal. DP (I × 2)—1/Mk 116 ASROC ASW RL (VIII × 1; *see* Remarks)—6/324-mm Mk 32 ASW TT (III × 2)—1/ . . . helicopter
Electron Equipt:
Radar: 1/LN-66 nav., 1/SPS-10 surf. search, 1/SPS-40 air search, 1/Mk 35 f.c. (on Mk 56 GFCS)
Sonar: first two: SQS-26 BX; others: SQS-26 AXR

FRIGATES *(continued)*

Paraná (D 29)—with small fixed hangar, but with ASROC reload magazine PH3 Catherine T. Hogan, USN, 11-89

EW: WLR-1, WLR-3 intercept, ULQ-6 jammer, 2/Mk 33 RBOC RL (VI × 2)
TACAN: SRN-15
M: 1 set G.E. GT; 1 prop; 35,000 shp **Electric:** 2,000 kw
Range: 4,000/20 **Boilers:** 2 Foster-Wheeler; 83.4 kg/cm, 510° C
Fuel: 600 tons **Crew:** 18 officers, 250 enlisted (in U.S.N. service)

Remarks: Considered to be "destroyers" by the Brazilian Navy. Commissioned into Brazilian service on 18-9-89, 25-7-89, 24-8-89, and 25-9-89, having been decommissioned from U.S. Navy on 18-9-89, 8-12-88, 23-9-88, and 30-9-88, respectively. Antirolling fin stabilizers fitted. The boilers are vertical, have turbo-pressurized combustion, and are difficult to maintain. D 27 and D 29 carried SQR-15 TASS prior to transfer and retain the original small DASH drone helicopter hangar. The other two had the hangar enlarged to 14.6 × 5.4 m to accommodate the SH-2F LAMPS-I helicopter. Ex-FF 1048 and FF 1050 have a reload magazine with 8 missiles for the ASROC system; the others do not. All have the Mk 56 GFCS for the 127-mm guns and the Mk 114 ASW fire-control system.

CORVETTES

◆ **9 Imperial Marinheiro class** Bldr: L. Smit, Kinderdijk, Netherlands

	L	In serv.
V 15 Imperial Marinheiro	24-11-54	8-6-55
V 16 Iguatemi	1954	17-9-55
V 18 Forte de Coimbra	11-6-54	26-7-55
V 19 Caboclo	28-8-54	-4-55
V 20 Angostura	1955	1955
V 21 Bahiana	11-54	26-6-55
V 22 Mearim	8-54	3-8-55
V 23 Purus	6-11-54	-4-55
V 24 Solimões	24-11-54	1955

Forte de Coimbra (V 18)

D: 911 tons (960 fl) **S:** 15 kts **Dim:** 55.72 × 9.55 × 3.6
A: 1/76.2-mm DP—4/20-mm AA (I × 4)
Electron Equipt: Radar: 1/ . . . nav. **Crew:** 60 tot.
M: 2 Sulzer diesels; 2 props; 2,160 bhp **Fuel:** 135 tons

Remarks: Oceangoing tug design. Were intended to be convertible for minesweeping or minelaying. V 15 is used as a submarine tender. Officially designated "vedettes" and used in district patrols and in support of the 200-mile economic zone. Sister *Iparanga* (V 17) stricken 1983.

PATROL BOATS AND CRAFT

◆ **0 (+2 + 6) Graúna class** Bldr: Estaleiro Mauá, Rio de Janeiro

	Laid down	L	In serv.
P 40 Graúna	1988	. . .	1991 (?)
P 41 Goiana	24-10-89	. . .	1991(?)
P 42 Grajaú	. . .	. . .	. . .
P 43 Guaiba	. . .	. . .	. . .
P 44 Guajará	. . .	. . .	. . .
P 45 Guaporé	. . .	. . .	. . .
P 46 Gurupá	. . .	. . .	. . .
P 47 Gurupi	. . .	. . .	. . .

D: 410 tons (fl) **S:** 24.5 kts **Dim:** 46.50 (42.50 pp) × 7.50 × 2.29
A: 1/40-mm Bofors AA—2/20-mm Oerlikon AA (I × 2)
Electron Equipt: Radar: 1/ Decca 1290A navigational
M: 2 MTU 16V 396 TB94 diesels; 2 props; 2,780 bhp
Range: 2,200/12 **Fuel:** 23.25 tons **Crew:** 4 officers, 21 enlisted
Electric: 300 kw (3 × 100 kw diesel sets)

Paraíba (D 28)—with telescoping hangar, no ASROC reload magazine PH3 Catherine T. Hogan, USN, 11-89

PATROL BOATS AND CRAFT *(continued)*

6.5-meter design Vosper QAF, 1988

Remarks: The original program, announced 2-86, envisioned construction of 8 patrol boats of 450 tons and four of 1,000 tons for use in 200-n.m.-economic-zone patrol and in SAR duties. The first two of a much more modest design were ordered late 1987 to a design by Vosper QAF, Singapore, with actual work beginning late in 1988. To date, no additional orders have been placed, but it is hoped to order six more, for which names have already been announced.

6 Piratini-class patrol boats Bldr: Ast. Ilha das Cobras, Rio de Janeiro

	In serv.
10 Piratini (ex-PGM 109)	30-11-70
11 Pirajá (ex-PGM 110)	3-71
12 Pampeiro (ex-PGM 118)	6-71
13 Parati (ex-PGM 119)	7-71
14 Penedo (ex-PGM 120)	9-71
15 Poti (ex-PGM 121)	10-71

Penedo (P 14) 1985

D: 105 tons (fl) **S:** 18.0 kts (15.5 sust.) **Dim:** 28.95 × 6.10 × 1.55
A: 1/20-mm Oerlikon AA—2/12.7-mm mg (I × 2)
Electron Equipt: Radar: 1/ Decca RM 1070A navigational
M: 4 Cummins VT-12M diesels; 2 props; 1,100 bhp
Electric: 40 kw **Range:** 1,000/15; 1,700/12
Crew: 2 officers, 14 enlisted

Remarks: These patrol craft are based on the 95-foot WPBs of the U.S. Coast Guard and were funded by the United States.

4 Tracker-20-class patrol craft Bldr: Asteleiros du Sud, Porto Alegre

LP.01 (In serv. 20-10-88) LP.03 (In serv. . . . -. . . -90)
LP.02 (In serv. 20-2-89) LP.04 (In serv. 22-2-90)

D: 31 tons (37 fl) **S:** 27 kts **Dim:** 20.0 (19.3 pp) × 5.18 × 1.45
A: 1/20-mm Oerlikon AA—2/12.7-mm mg (I × 2)
Electron equipt: Radar: 1/. . . navigational
M: 2 MTU 8V396 TB83 diesels; 2 props; 2,000 bhp **Range:** 600/15
Electric: 40 kw (2 × 20 kw) **Crew:** 8 tot. **Fuel:** 14.5 tons

Remarks: Licensed construction GRP craft designed by Fairey Marinteknik, Cowes, U.K. License agreed 4-87. Shipyard also known as "Ebin So." Further construction of up to a dozen more is envisioned.

10 U.S. Swift Mk II patrol craft Bldr: R 61–64: Swiftships, Morgan City, La.; others: DM-Commercio, Importacao & Maintencao de Producto Nauticas

R 61 through R 76

D: 22.5 tons (fl) **S:** 22 kts **Dim:** 15.66 × 4.55 × 1.1
A: 1/12.7-mm mg **Electron Equipt:** Radar: 1/. . . navigational
M: 2 G.M. Detroit 12V71 TI diesels; 2 props; 850 bhp
Electric: 6 kw **Range:** 400/22 **Crew:** 6 tot

Cacao (5002) and 5001 George R. Schneider, Jr., 5-89

Remarks: Employed by naval police and port captains. Six ordered 16-1-81 in Brazil. Four earlier units built in U.S. transferred under AID program in 1972–73. Port captain–subordinated units bear names and have hull numbers in the 5000-series.

RIVER PATROL SHIPS

◆ **0 (+1) new-construction river patrol ship**

	Bldr	Laid down	L	In serv.
P 8 Porto Esperança	Ars. de Marinha, Rio	14-1-85	. . .	1992

D: 270 tons (380 fl) **S:** 12 kts **Dim:** 49.33 (45.57 pp) × 8.45 × 1.40
A: 2/40-mm AA (I × 2)—6/12.7-mm mg (I × 6)—2/81-mm mortars (I × 2)
Electron Equipt: Radar: 3/ . . . navigational
M: 2 MEP-M.A.N. V6V 16/18 TL diesels; 2 props; 1,824 bhp
Crew: 8 officers, 54 enlisted (accommodations)

Remarks: Replaced canceled program for ships to be named *Cascaval* and *Jararaca,* announced 1981. For use on Paraguay River as replacement for *Parnaiba.* Will have a helo deck for one Bell 206 JetRanger and carry 2 LCVP. Program delayed by financial problems, and two planned sisters, to have been built at private yards, canceled. Appearance will be generally similar to the *Roraima* class, and *Itaipu,* in the Paraguayan Navy, is a sister.

◆ **3 Roraima class** Bldr: MacLaren, Niteroi

	L	In serv.		L	In serv.
P 30 Roraima	9-11-72	21-2-75	P 32 Amapá	9-3-73	1-76
P 31 Rondônia	10-1-73	3-12-75			

Amapá (P 32) Brazilian Navy, 1985

D: 340 tons (365 fl) **S:** 14.5 kts **Dim:** 46.3 × 8.45 × 1.37
A: 1/40-mm AA—6/12.7-mm mg (I × 6)—2/81-mm mortars (I × 2)
Electron Equipt: Radar: 3/ . . . navigational
M: 2 MEP-M.A.N. V6V16/18 TL diesels; 2 props; 1,824 bhp
Range: 6,000/11 **Crew:** 9 officers, 31 enlisted **Range:** 6,000/12

Remarks: In Amazon Flotilla. Carry one armed LCVP on fantail, handled by crane.

◆ **2 Pedro Teixeira class** Bldr: Ilha das Cobras, Rio de Janeiro

	L	In serv.
P 20 Pedro Teixeira	11-6-72	17-12-73
P 21 Raposo Tavares	11-6-72	17-12-73

D: 690 tons (fl) **S:** 16 kts **Dim:** 63.55 × 9.71 × 1.70
A: 1/40-mm AA—6/12.7-mm mg (I × 6)—2/81-mm mortars (I × 2)—1/SAH-11 helicopter
Electron Equipt: Radar: 2/Decca . . . navigational
M: 2 MEP-M.A.N. V6V16/18 TLS diesels; 2 props; 1,824 bhp
Range: 6,800/10 **Crew:** 6 officers, 72 enlisted

Remarks: In Amazon Flotilla. Carry two armed LCVP on fantail.

RIVER PATROL SHIPS *(continued)*

Pedro Teixeira (P 20) Brazilian Navy, 1990

◆ **1 old river monitor** Bldr: Arsenal de Marinha, Rio de Janeiro

	Laid down	L	In serv.
U 17 Parnaiba	11-6-36	2-9-37	11-37

Parnaiba (U 17) 1976

D: 620 tons (720 fl) **S:** 12 kts **Dim:** 55.0 × 10.1 × 1.6
A: 1/76.2-mm DP—2/47-mm—2/40-mm AA (I × 2)—6/20-mm AA (I × 6)
M: 2 sets Thornycroft triple-expansion reciprocating steam; 2 props; 1,300 shp
Boilers: 2/3-drum **Fuel:** 90 tons
Range: 1,350/10 **Crew:** 90 tot.

Remarks: In Mato Grosso Flotilla. To be replaced by *Porto Esperança.* Does not have a radar. Has some side and deck armor protection.

MINE WARFARE SHIPS

◆ **6 German Schütze-class (Type 340a) patrol minesweepers**
Bldr: Abeking and Rasmussen, Lemwerder, West Germany

	L	In serv.
M 15 Aratú	27-5-70	5-5-71
M 16 Anhatomirim	4-11-70	30-11-71
M 17 Atalaia	14-4-71	13-12-72
M 18 Araçatuba	1971	13-12-72
M 19 Abrolhos	7-5-74	16-4-75
M 20 Albardão	9-74	21-7-75

Araçatuba (M 18)—outboard *Anhatomirim* (M 16) and *Aratú* (M 15)
Don S. Montgomery, 10-90

D: 241 tons (280 fl) **S:** 24 kts **Dim:** 47.44 × 7.16 × 2.4
A: 1/40-mm Bofors AA
Electron Equipt: Radar: 1/. . . navigational
M: 4 Maybach diesels; 2 Escher-Wyss vertical cycloidal props; 4,500 bhp
Electric: 120-kw plus 340-kw sweep generator **Fuel:** 22 tons
Range: 710/20 **Crew:** 4 officers, 32 enlisted

Remarks: Four ordered 4-69, two 11-73. Fitted for magnetic, mechanical, and acoustic minesweeping. Wooden hulls. A new series of minesweepers is planned, but it is more likely that this sextet will be refitted and modernized instead. They are supported by *Gastão Moutinho* (A 10).

◆ **1 mine countermeasures support ship** Bldr: Charleston SB & DD, Charleston, South Carolina

	Laid down	L	In serv.
A 10 Gastão Moutinho (ex-K 10; ex-*Skylark,* ASR 20; ex-*Yustaga,* ATF 165)	23-7-45	19-3-46	19-7-4

D: 1,780 tons (2,140 fl) **S:** 14.5 kts
Dim: 62.48 (59.44 wl) × 11.96 × 4.72
A: 2/20-mm Oerlikon AA (I × 2)
Electron Equipt: Radar: 1/. . . nav.
M: 4 G.M.12-278A diesels, electric drive; 1 prop; 3,000 shp
Electric: 400 kw **Fuel:** 301 tons **Range:** 15,000/8
Crew: . . . tot.

Remarks: Begun as a U.S. Navy *Achomawi*-class fleet tug, but completed as *Penguin*-class submarine rescue ship.. Purchased 30-6-73 and employed as a diving tender, hydrographic survey ship, and submarine rescue ship until replaced by *Felinto Perry* (K 11) in 1988. Converted 1990–91 to serve as support ship for mine countermeasures vessels, with most salvage equipment deleted and now carrying spare cable cutters, and sweep gear, as well as fuel for transfer.

AMPHIBIOUS WARFARE SHIPS

◆ **2 U.S. Thomaston-class dock landing ships** Bldr: Ingalls SB, Pascagoula, Mississippi

	Laid down	L	In serv.
G 30 Ceará (ex-*Hermitage,* LSD 34)	11-4-55	12-6-56	14-12-5
G 31 Rio de Janeiro (ex-*Alamo,* LSD 33)	11-10-54	20-1-56	24-8-5

Ceará (G 30) Brazilian Navy, 19

Ceará (G 30) Brazilian Navy, 19

D: 6,880 tons (12,150 fl) **S:** 22.5 kts
Dim: 155.45 × 25.60 × 5.40 (5.80 max.)
A: 6/76.2-mm Mk 34 DP (II × 3)
Electron Equipt:
Radar: 1/CRP-3100 nav., 1/SPS-10 surf. search; 1/SPS-6 air-search
M: 2 sets G.E. GT; 2 props; 24,000 shp **Fuel:** 1,390 tons
Boilers: 2 Babcock & Wilcox, 40.8 kg/cm pressure
Range: 5,300/22.5; 10,000/20; 13,000/10
Crew: 20 officers, 325 enlisted + troops: 29 officers, 312 enlisted (in U.S.N.)

MPHIBIOUS WARFARE SHIPS *(continued)*

emarks: G 30 acquired upon decommissioning 2-10-89 from U.S. Navy; arrived azil in 12-89. G 31 decommissioned 30-9-90 and commissioned 18-1-91 in Brazilian avy. Both are on 5-year lease. Can carry 2 LCU or 18 LCM (6) or 6 LCM (8) in 119.2 × .6 m well deck, with 975 m² of vehicle parking space forward of the docking well. arry 2 LCVP, 2 LCPL in davits. Maximum cargo capacity: 7,400 tons. Have two -ton cranes. Helicopter deck. Two Mk 56 and two Mk 63 GFCS removed in 1977, aving gun mounts with local control only. Air search radar is obsolete and may not be erational.

1 U.S. De Soto County-class tank landing ship Bldr: Avondale, New Orleans

	L	In serv.
26 Duque de Caxias (ex-*Grant County,* LST 1174)	12-10-56	8-11-57

uque de Caxias (G 26) Don S. Montgomery, 10-90

D: 4,164 tons (7,800 fl) **S:** 16 kts
Dim: 135.7 (129.8 wl) × 18.9 × 5.3
A: 6/76.2-mm DP (II × 3) **Electron Equipt:** Radar: 1/. . . nav.
M: 4 Fairbanks-Morse 38D 8⅛ × 12 diesels; 2 CP props; 13,900 bhp
Electric: 900 kw **Range:** 13,000/10
Crew: 11 officers, 164 enlisted + 700 troops

marks: Transferred 15-1-73; purchased 12-17-78. Air-conditioned. Tank deck 88 m g. Four LCVP in davits; can carry four causeways (pontoon sections). Platform for licopter. Three Mk 51 Mod. 2 GFCS for guns.

te: The U.S. LST 542-class tank landing ship *Garcia D'Avila* (G 28, ex-*Outagamie unty,* LST 1073) was sold 24-7-90 for scrap.

0 U.S. LCU 1610-type landing craft Bldr: Arsenal de Marinha, Rio de Janeiro

	L	In serv.
10 Guarapari	16-6-77	27-3-78
11 Timbaú	14-9-77	27-3-78
12 Camboriú	. . .	1989(?)

uarapari (L 10) Brazilian Navy, 1978

D: 200 tons (396 fl) **S:** 11 kts **Dim:** 41.0 × 8.42 × 2.0
A: 3/12.7-mm mg (I × 3) **Electron Equipt:** Radar: 1/. . . nav.
M: 2 G.M. Detroit Diesel 12V71 diesels; 2 props; 1,000 bhp
Range: 1,200/8 **Crew:** 6 tot. + 120 troops for short distances

marks: Typed EDCG–"*Embarcacao de Desembarque de Carga Generales.*" Can rry 143 tons cargo; cargo space: 30.5 × 5.5 m. Uncompleted sister *Tramandai* (L 13) apped in 1983. Late note: All reported stricken 14-9-90.

te: The necessary plans and data to construct units of the U.S. LCM(8)-class land- g craft were acquired from the United States in 1991; when construction will com- ence has not been announced.

3 LCM(6)-class landing craft Bldr: . . . , Brazil

DVM 301–303

D: 24 tons (56 fl) **S:** 10 kts **Dim:** 17.07 × 4.37 × 1.17 (aft)
M: 2 G.M. Detroit Diesel 6-71 diesels; 2 props; 330 bhp
Range: 130/10
Crew: 3 tot. + 80 troops for short distances

emarks: Can carry 29 tons cargo.

30 EDVP class Bldr: . . . , Japan (In serv. 1959–60) and . . . , Brazil (In serv. 1971)

DVP 501–530

D: 13 tons (fl) **S:** 9 kts **Dim:** 10.90 × 3.21 × 1.04 (aft)
M: 1 Yanmar diesel; 1 prop; 180 bhp **Range:** 110/9
Crew: 3 tot. + 36 troops

Remarks: EDVP 501–521 are wooden construction version of standard U.S. Navy LCVP design; others, built 1971 in Brazil, have GRP hulls and are powered by a 153-bhp Saab Scania diesel. Can carry 36 troops or 3.5 tons cargo in 5.24 × 2.29-m cargo space with 2.0-m wide access through the bow ramp. Several (armed with 2/ 12.7-mm mg) are carried by Amazon Flotilla gunboats and others aboard landing ship *Duque de Caxias* (G 26).

♦ **16 U.S. LVTP-7 amphibious tracked armored personnel carriers**

Remarks: Employed by the Brazilian Marine Corps.

HYDROGRAPHIC AND OCEANOGRAPHIC SHIPS

♦ **0 (+1) projected polar icebreaker/research ship** Bldr: Caneco SY, Rio de Janeiro

D: 6,000 tons (fl) **S:** 17 kts (3 kts on electric quiet-running motors)
Dim: 100.0 (93.0 pp) × 20.0 × 7.0 **A:** probably none
Electron Equipt: Radar: . . .
M: 2 . . . diesels; . . . props; 10,000 bhp; 2/ 880 shp electric pumpjets
Range: 20,000/13 **Crew:** 22 officers, 73 enlisted + 40 scientists

Remarks: Ordered in 1988 to be laid down 2-89, but funds were not available for construction. Canadian design. Would have seismic, meteorology, oceanography, geology, geophysical, and marine biology laboratories. Would have facilities for two small helicopters. Was to have replaced *Barao de Teffe* (H 42) in 1991, but there is no indication as to when building may begin.

♦ **1 seismic survey vessel** Bldr: Burton SY, Port Arthur, Texas (In serv. 1973)

H 43 Almirante Alberto Alvaro (ex-*Grant Mariner,* ex-*Polar 903*)

D: 1,517 tons light (2,400 fl) **S:** 13.5 kts
Dim: 64.02 (61.02 pp) × 13.81 × 4.75
A: none **Electron Equipt:** Radar: 2/Decca . . . nav.
M: 3 Fairbanks-Morse 12-38D8⅛ diesels; 3 props; 7,200 bhp—bow-thruster
Range: . . . **Fuel:** 1,231 tons **Electric:** 500 kw (2 × 250 kw)
Crew: 10 officers, 38 enlisted

Remarks: 652 grt/496 dwt. Acquired 7-10-87 from the U.S. Maritime Administration and commissioned 6-6-88. Former oilfield supply vessel converted 1982 by Atlantic Drydock & SB, Mobile, Ala., to a petroleum seismic survey vessel. Has a large helicopter platform, MARISAT SATCOMM gear.

♦ **1 seismic survey ship** Bldr: Mjellem & Karlsen A/S, Bergen (In serv. 1984)

H 40 Antares (ex-*Lady Hamilton*)

D: 855 tons light (1,400 fl) **S:** 13.5 kts **Dim:** 55.0 × 10.3 × 4.3
Electron Equipt: Radar: 2/Decca . . . nav.
M: 1 Burmeister & Wain Alpha diesel; 1 CP prop; 1,860 bhp—bow-thruster
Range: 10,000/12 **Crew:** 10 officers, 35 enlisted

Remarks: 1,076 grt. Acquired from Racal Energy Resources and commissioned 6-6-88. Painted white with red upperworks, as are all Brazilian Navy oceanographic and hydrographic survey ships. Small helicopter platform at stern.

♦ **1 U.S. Robert D. Conrad-class oceanographic ship** Bldr: Marietta Co., Pt. Pleasant, West Virginia (In serv. 8-2-65)

H 41 Almirante Câmara (ex-*Sands,* T-AGOR 6)

Almirante Câmara (H 41) Brazilian Navy, 1974

HYDROGRAPHIC AND OCEANOGRAPHIC SHIPS *(continued)*

D: 1,030 tons light (1,380 fl) **S:** 13.5 kts
Dim: 63.7 (59.7 pp) × 12.2 × 4.9 mean
Electron Equipt: Radar: 1/RCA CRM-N1A-75 nav., 1/ . . . nav.
M: 2 Caterpillar D-378 diesels, electric drive; 1 prop; 1,000 shp
Electric: 1,470 kw **Fuel:** 211 tons **Range:** 10,000/12
Crew: 8 officers, 18 enlisted + 15 oceanographers

Remarks: Loaned 1-7-74; purchased outright 1991. An auxiliary 620-hp gas turbine powers a small electric maneuvering propeller for stationkeeping purposes at extremely low rpm; also has bow-thruster. Equipped for gravimetric, magnetic, and geological research. Has echo-sounders capable of measuring 11,000-meter depths.

◆ **1 antarctic exploration support ship** Bldr: Aalborg Vaerft, Denmark

H 42 Barão de Teffé (ex-*Thala Dan*) (In serv. 10-57)

Barão de Teffé (H 42) Don S. Montgomery, 10-90

D: approx. 5,500 tons (fl) **S:** 12 kts
Dim: 75.14 (65.54 pp) × 13.77 × 6.30
Electron Equipt: Radar: 2/ . . . nav.
M: 1 Burmeister & Wain 7-cyl. diesel; 1 CP prop; 1,970 bhp
Electric: 680 kw **Fuel:** 457 tons
Crew: 90 tot. (including scientific party)

Remarks: 2,183 grt/2,164 dwt. Purchased 5-82 from J. Lauritzen in lieu of the Royal Navy ice-patrol ship, *Endurance.* Conversion completed 28-9-82 as antarctic support ship, including helicopter deck over stern (added overall length not included above). Ice-reinforced former cargo ship. Was to be replaced by a Brazilian-built polar oceanographic ship due for completion in 1991, but will now have to serve indefinitely.

◆ **2 Sirius class** Bldr: Ishikawajima-Harima Heavy Industries, Tokyo

	Laid down	L	In serv.
H 21 Sirius	12-56	30-7-57	1-1-58
H 22 Canopus	12-56	20-11-57	15-3-58

Canopus (H 22)

D: 1,463 tons (1,900 fl) **S:** 15 kts **Dim:** 77.90 × 12.03 × 3.70
Electron Equipt: Radar: 2/ . . . nav.
M: 2 Sulzer 7T6-36 diesels; 2 CP props; 2,700 bhp
Range: 12,000/11 **Fuel:** 343 tons
Crew: 102 tot. + 14 scientific party

Remarks: 1 SAH-11 helicopter, 1 LCVP, 3 small survey craft.

Note: Oceanographic ship *Almirante Saldanha* (H 10) was stricken 6-8-90. Stricken 14-9-90 were the fisheries research ship *Suboficial Oliveira* (U 15) and the *Paraibano*-class hydrographic survey craft *Paraibano* (H 11), *Rio Branco* (H 12), *Nogueira da Gama* (H 14), *Itacurussa* (H 15), *Camocim* (H 16), and *Caravelas* (H 17); all may have been transferred to another government agency.

◆ **3 Argus-class coastal survey ships** Bldr: Ars. de Marinha, Rio de Janeiro

	L	In serv.
H 31 Argus	6-12-57	29-1-59
H 32 Orion	5-2-58	11-6-59
H 33 Taurus	7-1-58	23-4-59

Taurus (H 33) Brazilian Navy, 198

D: 250 tons (350 fl) **S:** 15 kts **Dim:** 44.67 (41.14 pp) × 6.50 × 2.80
Electron Equipt: Radar: 1/Decca 1226 nav.
M: 2 Caterpillar DT 379 diesels; 2 props; 1,200 bhp **Fuel:** 35 tons
Range: 3,000/15 **Endurance:** 20 days **Crew:** 34 tot.

Remarks: Based on the Portuguese *Azevia*-class gunboat. H 32 modernized in 197. 74, with new propulsion machinery, auxiliaries, and electronic equipment. In need replacement.

AUXILIARY SHIPS

◆ **1 cadet training ship, modified Mk 10 frigate**

	Bldr	Laid down	L	In ser
U 27 Brasil	Ast. Ilha das Cobras, Rio	18-9-81	23-9-83	21-8-8

Brasil (U 27) Leo Van Ginderen, 9-9

Brasil (U 27) Leo Van Ginderen, 9-

D: 2,380 tons (3,400 fl) **S:** 18 kts
Dim: 131.25 × 13.52 × 4.21 mean (fl)
A: 2/40-mm Bofors L70 AA (I × 2)–4/3-pdr saluting cannon (I × 4)
Electron Equipt: Radar: 2/Decca . . . navigational
M: 2 Ishikawajima Brasil-Pielstick 6 PC. 2 L400 diesels; 2 props; 7,800 bhp
Range: 7,000/15 **Endurance:** 30 days
Crew: 20 officers,186 enlisted + 200 cadets

Remarks: Uses hull of the Mk 10 frigate design, but has less powerful propulsi plant and far simpler weapons and electronics. Electro-optical GFCS only. Fin s bilizers. Replaced transport *Custodio de Mello* (U 26) for training cadets from Na

AUXILIARY SHIPS *(continued)*

and Merchant Marine academies. Master CIC with 3 satellite training CICs, navigational training compartment for 40 trainees, 2 other classrooms. A planned 76-mm OTO Melara Compact mount forward has not been installed, nor was the planned helicopter hangar, although the helo platform can accommodate 1 light helicopter.

◆ **4 Custodio de Mello-class transports** Bldr: Ishikawajima, Tokyo

	Laid down	L	In serv.
G 16 Barroso Pereira	12-53	7-8-54	1-12-54
G 20 Custódio de Mello	12-53	10-6-54	1-12-54
G 21 Ary Parreiras	12-55	24-8-56	29-12-56
G 22 Soares Dutra	12-55	13-12-56	23-3-57

Custódio de Mello (G 20) Don S. Montgomery, 10-90

D: 4,800 tons (8,600 fl) **S:** 16 kts
Dim: 119.2 (110.4 pp) × 16.0 × 6.1
A: 2/76.2-mm 50-cal. U.S. Mk 26 DP (I × 2)—2/20-mm AA (I × 2)
Electron Equipt: Radar: 2/ . . . navigational
M: 1 set double-reduction GT; 2 props; 4,800 shp
Boilers: 2 Foster-Wheeler 2-drum water-tube; 350° C **Fuel:** 880 tons
Crew: 127 tot. + up to 1,972 troops (497 normal)

Remarks: 4,879 grt/4,200 dwt. Living spaces mechanically ventilated and partially air-conditioned. All have a helicopter platform aft except *Custódio de Mello,* formerly used as training ship until replaced in that role by *Brasil* (U 27). Are occasionally used in commercial service; all have 425-m^3 refrigerated cargo space and can carry about 4,000 tons general cargo.

◆ **1 U.S. Aristaeus-class small repair ship** Bldr: Maryland DD, Baltimore

	Laid down	L	In serv.
G 24 Belmonte (ex-*Helios,* ARB 12, ex-LST 1127)	23-11-44	14-2-45	26-2-45

Belmonte (G 24)

D: 2,030 tons (4,100 fl) **S:** 9 kts
Dim: 100.0 (96.3 wl) × 15.25 × 3.36 **A:** 8/40-mm 60-cal. AA (IV × 2)
Electron Equipt: Radar: 1/. . . nav.
M: 2 G.M. 12-567A diesels; 2 props; 1,800 bhp **Electric:** 600 kw
Fuel: 584 tons **Range:** 6,000/9 **Crew:** . . . tot.

Remarks: Loaned in 1-62; purchased 28-12-67. 1/60-ton winch crane, 2/10-ton booms. Used mainly as a transport and not likely to be in use much longer.

◆ **1 replenishment oiler** Bldr: Ishikawajima do Brasil, Rio de Janeiro

	Laid down	L	In serv.
G 23 Almirante Gastão Motta	11-12-89	1-6-90	7-91

D: 10,300 tons (fl) **S:** 20.5 kts
Dim: 135.00 (128.00 pp) × 19.00 × 7.50
A: none **Electron Equipt:** Radar: 2/. . . nav.
M: 2 Wärtsilä Vasa 12V52 diesels; 1 CP prop; 11,700 bhp
Electric: 3,600 kw (2 × 900-kw shaft generators; 3 × 600-kw alternators, 3 Ishibras-Wärtsilä 4-R22 diesels driving)
Fuel: 600 tons **Range:** 10,000/15 **Crew:** 120 tot. + 12 spare berths
Electric: 3,000 kw (2 × 900-kw shaft alternators, 2 × 600-kw diesel sets)

Almirante Gastão Motta (G 23)—artist's rendering Braz. Navy, 1988

Remarks: 6,000 dwt. Cargo fuel capacity: 4,400 tons. Single replenishment station each side amidships; no astern refueling. No helicopter facilities. Ordered 15-12-87. Replaces the uncompleted conversion of the former Lloyd Brasileiro Steamship Co. tanker *Itatinga* (also to have been named *Almirante Gastão Motta,* G 29; sold 1987) as a replacement for *Marajó* (G 27).

◆ **1 river oiler** Bldr: Papendrecht, Holland

G 17 Potengi (L: 16-3-38)

D: 600 tons **S:** 10 kts **Dim:** 54.5 × 7.5 × 1.8
M: 2 diesels; 2 props; 550 bhp **Range:** 600/8 **Crew:** 20 tot.

Remarks: In Mato Grosso Flotilla. Cargo capacity: 450 tons

◆ **1 submarine rescue and general salvage ship** Bldr: Stord Vaerft A/S, Stord, Norway (In serv. 1979)

K 11 Felinto Perry (ex-*Holger Dane,* ex-*Wildrake*)

Felinto Perry (K 11) Leo Van Ginderen, 11-88

D: 1,380 tons light (approx 3,900 fl) **S:** 14.5 kts
Dim: 77.78 × 17.48 × 4.66
A: none **Electron Equipt:** Radar: 2/Raytheon . . . nav.
M: 2 Bergen Mek. Verksteder KVGB 12 diesels (4,880 bhp tot.); 2 Bergen Mek. Verksteder KVGB 16 diesels (6,520 bhp tot.); 2 Daimler-Benz OM414 diesels (910 hp); 2 × 1,712-kw generators, electric drive; 2 CP props; 7,000 shp; 4 × 550-shp side-thrusters
Electric: 6,160 kw (2 × 2,280 kw, 2 × 300 kw)
Crew: 9 officers, 56 enlisted

Remarks: 1,769 grt/496 dwt. Former North Sea oilfield rescue ship purchased 11-88 from Rederiet H. H. Faddersbjell A/S for use as a submarine rescue and general salvage ship replacement for the U.S. *Penguin*-class submarine rescue ship *Gastão Moutinho* (K 10). Very lavishly equipped for salvage and fire-fighting duties. Has a 19.0-m octagonal helicopter deck mounted above the pilothouse. Equipped with centerline "moonpool" and capable of conducting saturation diving to 300 m. Has an 8-man pressurized divers' lifeboat. Working deck is 238 m^2. Has one 30-ton, one 7-ton, and two 3-ton electrohydraulic cranes. Equipped with Kongsberg AOP 503 Mk II dynamic positioning system and has 4-point mooring system. Three water and two foam fire monitors, with 200-m water/60-m foam range.

◆ **2 Tritão-class oceangoing tugs** Bldr: ESTENAVE, Manaus

	In serv.		In serv.
R 21 Tritão (ex-*Sarandi*)	23-7-86	R 23 Triunfo (ex-*Sorocaba*)	8-10-87

AUXILIARY SHIPS *(continued)*

Triunfo (R 23) Leo Van Ginderen, 7-87

D: 819 tons (1,680 fl) **S:** 15 kts
Dim: 53.52 (50.02 pp) × 11.61 × 3.35
A: 2/20-mm AA (I × 2) **Electron Equipt:** Radar: 2/. . . nav.
M: 2 Burmeister & Wain Alpha diesels; 2 props; 2,480 bhp
Endurance: 45 days **Crew:** 49 tot.

Remarks: Begun as oilfield supply tugs for PETROBRAZ but purchased 5-86 while still under construction as replacements for the three former U.S. Navy *Sotoyomo*-class ocean tugs. Intended for 200-n.m. economic zone patrol and SAR duties. Have bow-thrusters. 23.5-ton bollard pull. Sister *Tridente* (R 22, ex-*Sambaiba*) reported stricken 24-7-90 for scrap, apparently as a result of damage.

◆ **2 oceangoing tugs** Bldr: Sumitomo Heavy Industries, Japan (Both L: 1976)

R 24 Almirante Guilhem (ex-*Superpesa 4*)
R 25 Almirante Guillobel (ex-*Superpesa 5*)

Almirante Guilhem (R 24) Brazilian Navy, 1989

D: 2,400 tons (fl) **S:** 14 kts **Dim:** 63.15 × 13.40 × 4.50
A: 2/20-mm AA (I × 2) **Electron Equipt:** Radar: 2/. . . nav.
M: 2 G.M. 20-645 ET diesels; 2 CP props; 7,200 bhp
Electric: 550 kw **Fuel:** 670 tons **Crew:** 40 tot.

Almirante Graça Aranha (H 34) Brazilian Navy, 1989

Remarks: Purchased 1980 from Superpesa Maritime Transport, Ltd., and commissioned 22-1-81. Former oilfield supply tugs. 84-ton bollard pull. 525-bhp bow-thruster.

◆ **1 lighthouse and buoy tender** Bldr: Elbin, Niteroi

	Laid down	L	In serv.
H 34 Almirante Graça Aranha	end-1970	23-6-74	9-9-76

D: 1,343 tons (2,390 fl) **S:** 13 kts **Dim:** 75.57 × 13.0 × 3.71
A: none **Electron Equipt:** Radar: 2/Decca . . . nav.
M: diesel; 1 CP prop; 2,000 bhp; 1 bow-thruster **Crew:** 80 tot.

Remarks: Telescoping hangar for one Bell 206 JetRanger (UH-11) helicopter. Two LCVP carried as supply lighters. Has one electrohydraulic buoy-handling crane.

YARD AND SERVICE CRAFT

Note: R- and U-series pendant numbers removed from most yard and service craft 1989.

◆ **4 Comandante Marriog-class yard tugs** Bldr: Turn-Ship Ltd., U.S.A. (In serv. 1981)

Comandante Didier (ex-R 14) Tenente Magalhaes (ex-R 17)
Comandante Marriog (ex-R 15) Cabo Schram (ex-R 18)

D: 115 tons (fl) **S:** 10 kts **Dim:** 19.8 × 7.0 × 2.0
M: 2 G.M. diesels; 2 props; 900 bhp **Crew:** 6 tot.

Remarks: Sisters *Audaz* (R 31) and *Guarani* (R 33) stricken 1986. Have no radar.

◆ **2 Isaias de Noronha-class tugs** (In serv. 1972–74)

Tenente Lahmeyer D.N.O.G.

D: 100 tons (fl) **Dim:** 32.0 × . . . × . . . **M:** . . .

Remarks: Name "D.N.O.G." refers to the Brazilian naval contingent in Europe during World War I.

◆ **1 personnel and stores transport** Bldr: Embrasa, Itajai, Santa Catarina (L: 29-8-74)

Sargento Borges (ex-R 47)

D: 108.5 tons (fl) **S:** 10 kts **Dim:** 28.0 × 6.5 × 1.5
M: 2 diesels; 2 props; 480 bhp **Crew:** 10 tot. + 106 passengers
Range: 400/10

◆ **4 Rio Pardo-class harbor passenger ferries** Bldr: Inconav Niteroi Shipbuilders (In serv. 1975–76)

Rio Pardo (ex- U 40) Rio Chui (ex-R 42)
Rio Negro (ex-R 41) Rio Oiapoque (ex-R 43)

D: 150 tons **S:** 14 kts **Dim:** 35.38 × 6.5 × 1.9
M: 2 diesels; 2 props; 1,096 bhp **Crew:** . . . tot. + 400 passengers

◆ **6 Rio Doce-class river transports** Bldr: G. deVries Leutsch, Amsterdam

	In serv.		In serv.
Rio Doce (ex-U 20)	12-5-54	Rio Real (ex-U 23)	1955
Rio das Contas (ex-U 21)	15-9-54	Rio Turvo (ex-U 24)	16-12-54
Rio Formoso (ex-U 22)	10-54	Rio Verde (ex-U 25)	12-8-54

D: 150 tons (200 fl) **S:** 14 kts **Dim:** 36.6 × 6.5 × 2.1
M: 2 Sulzer diesels; 2 props; 450 bhp **Cargo:** 600 passengers
Range: 700/14 **Crew:** 10 tot. + 600 passengers

◆ **1 river transport/despatch boat for the Mato Grosso Flotilla** Bldr: Estaliero SNBP, Mato Grosso

U 29 Piraim (In serv. 1982)

D: 73.3 tons (91.5 fl) **S:** 7 kts **Dim:** 25.0 × 5.5 × 0.97
M: 2 MWM diesels; 2 props; 400 bhp **Range:** 700/7
Electric: 60 kVA **Crew:** 2 officers, 13 enlisted, 2 civilian pilots

◆ **2 small service transports**

Tenente Fabio Tenente Raul

D: 55 tons **S:** 10 kts **Dim:** 20.28 × 5.1 × 1.2
M: 1 diesel; 135 bhp
Cargo Capacity: 22 tons **Range:** 350

◆ **6 munitions lighters**

São Francisco dos Santos (1964), Ubirajara dos Santos (1968), Operatio Luis Leal (1968), Miguel dos Santos (1968), Aprendiz Lédio Conceição (1968), U 30 Almirante Hess (In serv. 27-10-83)

D: 88.2 tons (fl) **S:** 13.5 kts **Dim:** 23.6 × 6.0 × 2.0 **M:** . . .

Remarks: Last three for torpedoes.

◆ **2 water tankers** (L: 1957)

Itapura (ex-R 42) Paulo Afonso (ex-R 43)

D: 485.3 tons **Dim:** 42.8 × 7.0 × 2.5 **M:** 1 diesel **Cargo:** 389 tons

◆ **3 miscellaneous small water tankers**

Doctor Gondim (ex-R 38) Guairia (ex-R 40)
Iguaçu (ex-R 41)

YARD AND SERVICE CRAFT *(continued)*

Iguaçu (R 41) George R. Schneider, Jr., 1989

Remarks: R 38 is 485 tons (fl), 42.8 × 7.0 × 2.5. Capacity: 380 tons.

♦ **4 Comandante Varella-class navigational aid tenders** Bldr: São João de Nilo SY (H 18: Ast. Ilha das Cobras, Rio de Janeiro)

	Laid down	L	In serv.
H 18 Comandante Varella	1-8-78	18-9-81	30-9-82
H 19 Comandante Menhães	. . .	. . .	. . .
H 20 Tenente Castelho	. . .	. . .	15-12-83
H 25 Tenente Boanerges	. . .	. . .	1985

Comandante Varella (H 18) Brazilian Navy, 1985

D: 300 tons light (440 fl) **S:** 12 kts
Dim: 37.51 (34.5 pp) × 8.60 × 2.56
M: 2 8-cyl. diesels; 2 props; 1,300 bhp **Range:** 2,880/12
Crew: 22 tot.

♦ **5 130-ton navigational aid tenders**

H 13 Mestro João dos Santos
H 24 Castelhanos
H 26 Faroleiro Mario Seixas
H 27 Faroleiro Areas
H 30 Faroleiro Nascimento

Remarks: No data available. H 26 acquired 21-1-84. Also in use as buoy tenders are H 21 *Sirius* and captured U.S. fishing poachers *Sea Horse* and *Condor*.

♦ **2 river hospital ships** Bldr: Arsenal de Marinha, Rio de Janeiro

	Laid down	L	In serv.
U 18 Oswaldo Cruz	1981	11-7-83	31-5-84
U 19 Carlos Chagas	1982	16-4-84	12-84

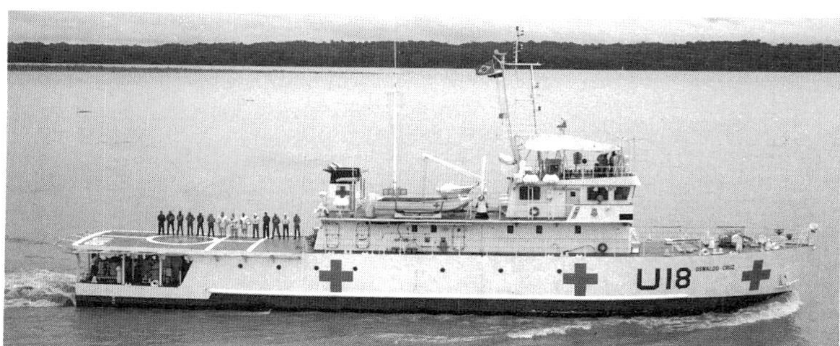

Oswaldo Cruz (U 18) Brazilian Navy, 1990

D: 500 tons (fl) **S:** 9 kts **Dim:** 47.18 (45.0 pp) × 8.45 × 1.75
Electron Equipt: Radar: 1/Decca . . . nav.
M: 2 diesels; 2 props; 714 bhp **Range:** 4,000/9 **Electric:** 420 kVA
Crew: 4 officers, 21 enlisted + 6 doctors/dentists, 15 health personnel

Remarks: Intended to serve in Amazon Flotilla with the similar *Roraima*-class gunboats. Helo deck for one UH-12 Esquilo. Two sick bays (6 total beds), operating theater, two clinics, dental laboratory, X-ray facilities.

♦ **3 Voga Picada-class training craft** Bldr: CARBRASMAR, Rio de Janeiro (All in serv. 17-1-84)

Voga Picada (ex-U 31)
Rosca Fina (ex-U 32)
Leva Ariba (ex-U 33)

Rosca Fina (U 32) Brazilian Navy, 1985

D: 50 tons (fl) **S:** 11 kts **Dim:** 18.60 × 4.70 × 1.20
Electron Equipt: Radar: 1/ . . . nav. **Range:** 200/11
M: 1 MWM diesel; 1 prop; 650 bhp
Crew: 5 tot. + 11 trainees

Remarks: Used for maneuvering training at the Centro de Instruçao Almirante Braz de Aguiar along with the captured ex-U.S.-registry fishing vessel *Night Hawk*.

♦ **3 Aspirante Nascimento-class training craft** Bldr: Embrassa Itajai, Santa Catarina (In serv. 1980–81)

U 10 Aspirante Nascimento
U 11 Guardia Marinha Jansen
U 12 Guardia Marinha Brito

Aspirante Nascimento (U 10) Brazilian Navy, 1985

D: 130 tons (fl) **S:** 10 kts **Dim:** 28.0 (25.0 pp) × 6.50 × 1.80
A: 1/12.7-mm mg **Electron Equipt:** Radar: 1/Decca . . . nav.
M: 2 MWM D232V12 diesels; 2 props; 650 bhp
Range: 700/10 **Crew:** 2 officers, 10 enlisted + 24 midshipmen

Remarks: Used for navigation and seamanship training at the Naval Academy. Also used for training at the Naval Academy are the 24-m sail yacht *Cisne Branco* (ex-U.S. *Ondine*, built 1974), two other sailboats of 23.2 m and 16.5 m o.a., and two other racing yachts.

FLOATING DRY DOCKS

♦ **1 U.S. AFDL 34 class** Bldr: V.P. Loftis (In serv. 10-44)

G 27 Cidade de Natal (ex-U.S. AFDL 39, ex-ARDC 6)

Lift capacity: 2,800 tons **Dim:** 118.6 × 25.6 × 2.84 (light)

Remarks: Loaned 10-11-66; purchased 28-12-77. Concrete construction. 17.7-m clear width inside, 105.2-m length on blocks.

♦ **1 U.S. AFDL 1 class** Bldr: Chicago Bridge & Iron (In serv. 12-43)

G 26 Almirante Jeronimo Gonçalves (ex-*Goiaz*, ex-AFDL 4, ex-AFD 4)

Lift capacity: 1,000 tons **Dim:** 60.96 × 19.51 × 1.04 (light)

Remarks: Loaned 10-11-66; purchased 28-7-77. Steel construction. 13.7-m clear width inside, 56.4-m length on blocks.

♦ **1 U.S. ARD 12 class** Bldr: Pacific Bridge, Alameda, Cal. (In serv. 11-43)

G 25 Afonso Peña (ex-*Ceara*, ex-ARD 14)

Lift capacity: 3,500 tons **Dim:** 149.86 × 24.69 × 1.73 (light)

Remarks: Loaned 1963; purchased 28-12-77. Steel construction, pointed ship-type bow. 18.0-m clear width inside, 118.6-m length on blocks.

BRAZIL *(continued)*
FLOATING DRY DOCKS *(continued)*

◆ **1 U.S. dry dock companion craft** Bldr: Bushell Lyons Ironwks, Tampa, Fla. (In serv. 22-3-45)

. . . (ex-YFN 903)

D: 170 tons (590 fl) **Dim:** 33.53 × 10.36 × 2.74

Remarks: Converted non-self-propelled cargo barge. Loaned 1963; purchased 28-12-77.

BRUNEI DARUSSALEM

Personnel (1990): 570 (including 50 officers and "Special Combat Squadron" of 6 officers and 114 men for river duties)

FLOTILLA OF THE ROYAL BRUNEI ARMED FORCES

Naval Aviation: Three IPTN Indonesia-built CN 235 light maritime patrol aircraft.

CORVETTES

Note: Although it had been announced in 11-89 that the Vosper Thornycroft "Vigilance" class had been selected for a 3-ship order, the Sultan of Brunei canceled the arrangement in 1990 prior to any order being placed. In addition to the Vosper Thornycroft design, also under consideration are a 100-m design from Todd Shipyards, U.S., and a 78.6-m, 955-ton design from Bremer-Vulkan of Germany. Armament is to include U.S. Harpoon missiles (24 of which were ordered in 1990), a 76-mm OTO Melara DP gun, and a twin 40-mm Breda AA mounting.

PATROL BOATS AND CRAFT

◆ **3 Waspada-class missile patrol boats** Bldr: Vosper Pty, Singapore

	L	In serv.		L	In serv.
P 02 Waspada	3-8-77	7-78	P 04 Seteria	22-6-78	1979
P 03 Pejuang	3-78	1979			

Waspada (P 02) R.A.N., 5-90

Seteria (P 04)—note open bridge U.S. Navy, 1988

D: 150 tons (206 fl) **S:** 30 kts **Dim:** 36.88 (33.53 pp) × 7.16 × 1.8
A: 2/MM 38 Exocet SSM—2/30-mm AA (II × 1)—4/7.62-mm mg (II × 2)
Electron Equipt:
Radar: 1/Decca AC 1229
EW: Decca RDL intercept
M: 2 MTU 20V538 TB91 diesels; 2 props; 9,000 bhp (7,500 sust.)
Fuel: 16 tons **Range:** 1,200/14 **Crew:** 4 officers, 30 enlisted

Remarks: P 02 has enclosed upper bridge (open on other two) and facilities for training. All have Sperry Sea Archer electro-optical fire-control system and two 50-mm rocket-flare launchers. The 30-mm mount is a BMARC/Oerlikon GCM-B01. Modernized with new EW suite, twin mg; planned 2-m stretch canceled.

◆ **2 Periwa-class patrol craft** Bldr: Vosper Pty, Singapore

	L	In serv.
P 14 Periwa	5-74	9-9-74
P 15 Pemburu	30-1-75	17-6-75

Periwa (P 14) 1974

D: 30 tons (38.5 fl) **S:** 32 kts **Dim:** 21.7 × 6.1 × 1.2
A: 2/20-mm AA (I × 2)—2/7.62-mm mg
Electron Equipt: Radar: Decca RM 1290 nav.
Range: 600/20; 1,000/16 **M:** 2 MTU 12V331 TC81 diesels; 2,700 bhp
Crew: 2 officers, 12 enlisted

Remarks: Sister *Penyarang* (P 16) stricken 1991 and cannibalized.

AMPHIBIOUS WARFARE CRAFT

◆ **2 Loadmaster-class landing craft** Bldr: Cheverton, Cowes, U.K.

L 31 Damuan (In serv. 5-76) L 32 Puni (In serv. 2-77)

D: 64.3 tons (light) **S:** 8.5 kts **Dim:** 22.86 × 6.1 × 1.07
Electron Equipt: Radar: Decca RM 1216 nav.
M: 2 G.M. Detroit Diesel 6-71 diesels; 2 props; 348 bhp
Range: 300/8.5; 1,000/6 **Crew:** 8 tot. **Cargo:** 30 tons

Remarks: L 31: 19.8 m overall, 60 tons light.

◆ **3 FPB 512-class landing craft** Bldr: Rotork Marine, U.K.

S 24 (In serv. 11-80) S 25 (In serv. 5-81) S 26 (In serv. 5-81)

S 24 U.S. Navy, 10-90

RUNEI DARUSSALEM *(continued)*
MPHIBIOUS WARFARE CRAFT *(continued)*

D: 8.8 tons (fl) **S:** 27 kts **Dim:** 12.7 × 3.2 × . . .
A: 3/7.62-mm mg (I × 3) **Electron Equipt:** Radar: 1/Decca 060
M: 2 Ford Mermaid diesels; 2 Castoldi Type 06 waterjets; 430 bhp
Range: 100/12 **Crew:** 3 tot.

marks: GRP hulls, bow ramps. For patrol and transport duties.

25 small armed river craft for the Special Combat Squadron

: 1/7.62-mm mg **M:** 100 bhp

ERVICE CRAFT

1 support tender Bldr: Cheverton, Cowes, U.K. (In serv. 1982)

JRONG NURI

D: 23 tons (fl) **S:** 12 kts **Dim:** 17.8 × 4.3 × 1.5
Electron Equipt: Radar: 1/Decca 060 nav.
M: 2 G.M. diesels, 2 props; 400 bhp **Crew:** 5 tot.

marks: Used as tug, target tug, diving tender, or for anti-pollution duties. GRP nstruction.

1 support launch

ORAIN

D: 25 tons (fl) **S:** 26 kts **Dim:** 18.9 × 4.8 × 1.4
Electron Equipt: Radar: 1/ Decca . . . nav.
M: 2 diesels; 2 props; 1,250 bhp **Crew:** 5 tot.

marks: Used for search-and-rescue duties and as a general-purpose launch.

MARINE POLICE

7 14.5-m patrol craft Bldr: Singapore SB & Eng. (In serv. 6-87 to 12-87)

DB 12 through PDB 18

DB 13 Singapore SB & Eng., 10-87

D: 20 tons (fl) **S:** 30 kts **Dim:** 14.54 × 4.23 × 1.20 (props)
A: 1/7.62-mm mg **Electron Equipt:** Radar: 1/. . . nav.
M: 2 M.A.N. D2840 diesels; 2 props; 1,270 bhp
Range: 310/22 **Fuel:** 2,600 liters **Crew:** 7 tot.

marks: Aluminum construction craft similar to Singapore Marine Police Force's 1 class. Ordered 28-10-86. First 3 delivered 5-10-87.

2 GRP-hulled patrol craft Bldr: Vosper Pty, Singapore (In serv. 1979)

ENANG ABADI

D: 14 tons (fl) **S:** 28 kts **Dim:** 18.0 × 4.88 × 0.79
A: 1/7.62-mm mg **M:** 2 MTU diesels; 2 water jets **Crew:** 5 tot.

BULGARIA

eople's Republic of Bulgaria

rsonnel (1991): approx. 8,800 men, including 2,200 coast defense troops

aval Aviation: Up to 12 Mi-14 Haze A, land-based ASW helicopters may be in rvice.

UBMARINES

3 Soviet Romeo class

POBIEDA 82 . . . . . . 83 . . . . . .

Sails of Bulgarian Romeos 81 and 84 Siegfried Breyer Collection

D: 1,319/1,712 tons **S:** 15.2/13 kts **Dim:** 76.60 × 6.70 × 4.95
A: 8/533-mm TT (6 fwd, 2 aft; 14 torpedoes or 24 mines)
Electron Equipt:
Radar: 1/Snoop Plate surf. search
Sonar: MF active; passive array
M: 2/2,000-bhp Type 37D diesels, electric drive; 2 shrouded props; 3,000 shp—2/50-shp electric creep motors
Range: 7,000/5 (snorkel) **Endurance:** 45 days **Crew:** 60 tot.

Remarks: Of an initial pair, transferred 1971–72 to replace two Whiskey class with same names, *Slava* was stricken 9-90. Third unit transferred 1985, fourth in 1986. Can dive to 300 meters. Only the two most recently transferred are active.

FRIGATES

♦ **1 Soviet Koni class** Bldr: Zelenodolsk SY (In serv. circa 1978)

12 SMELI (ex-Soviet *Del'fin*)

D: 1,440 tons normal (1,596 fl) **S:** 30 kts
Dim: 96.40 × 12.55 × 3.48 (4.90 sonar)
A: 1/SAN-4 SAM syst. (II × 1; 20 Gecko missiles)—4/76.2-mm DP (II × 2)—4/30-mm AA(II × 2)—2/RBU-6000 ASW RL (XII × 2)—2/d.c. racks—mines
Electron Equipt:
Radar: 1/Don-2 nav., 1/Strut Curve air/surf. search, 1/Pop Group missile f.c, 1/Hawk Screech 76-mm gun f.c., 1/Drum Tilt 30-mm gun f.c.
Sonar: 1/ MF, hull-mounted
EW: 2/Watch Dog intercept; 1/Cross Loop-A DF; 2/chaff RL (XVI × 2)
IFF: 2/Square Head interrogators, 1/High Pole B transponder
M: CODAG: 1/19,000-shp gas turbine, 2 Type 68-B, 9,000-bhp diesels; 3 props; 35,000 hp
Range: 1,800/14 **Crew:** 130 tot.

Remarks: Transferred 6-90 after having been used by the Soviet Navy for training foreign crews for export units of the class. Depth-charge racks bolt to mine rails.

♦ **1 Soviet Riga class**

11 DRUZKI (ex-Soviet *Kobchik*)

D: 1,168 tons (1,393 fl) **S:** 30 kts
Dim: 91.58 (88.00 wl) × 10.20 × 3.15 hull (4.40 max.)
A: 3/100-mm (I × 3) DP—4/37-mm AA (II × 2)—4/25-mm AA (II × 2)—2/533-mm TT (II × 1)—2/RBU-2500 ASW RL (V × 2)—2/d.c. racks (internal)
Electron Equipt:
Radar: 2/Spin Trough nav., 1/Slim Net air/surf. search, 1/Sun Visor 100-mm gun f.c.
Sonar: 1/ Herkules HF hull-mounted
EW: 2/Watch Dog intercept, 1 MFD/F loop
IFF: 2/Square Head interrogators, 1/High Pole B transponder
M: 2 sets Type TB9 GT; 2 props; 20,000 shp
Boilers: 2; 27 kg/cm, 370° C **Range:** 550/28; 2,000/15
Electric: 450 kw **Fuel:** 230 tons **Crew:** 180 tot.

Remarks: Two earlier units, the original *Smeli* and the *Bodri,* were stricken 1990. The surviving unit was transferred from the Soviet Black Sea Fleet in 11-85 and will probably be discarded soon as well.

CORVETTES

♦ **2 Soviet Grisha-II class**

13 . . . . . . 14 . . . . . .

D: 850 tons (1,100 fl) **S:** 30 kts
Dim: 71.6 (66.9 wl) × 9.8 × 3.5 (hull)
A: 4/57-mm AK-72 DP (II × 2)—2/RBU-6000 ASW RL (XII × 2)—4/533-mm ASW TT (II × 2)—2/d.c. racks (12 d.c.) or mines

CORVETTES *(continued)*

Electron Equipt:
Radar: 1/Don-2 nav., 1/Strut Curve surf./air search, 1/Muff cob f.c.
Sonar: Bull Nose MF hull-mounted, Elk Tail MF dipping
EW: 2/Watch Dog intercept
IFF: High Pole B transponder (interrogation by Strut Curve)
M: CODAG: 1/15,000-shp gas turbine on center shaft, 2 M517 diesels (8,000 bhp each) on outboard shafts; 3 props; 31,000 hp
Range: 450/30; 4,000/18 **Crew:** 60 tot.

Remarks: Transferred 1990 from Black Sea area KGB Maritime Border Guard assets to replace the two stricken Bulgarian Riga-class frigates. Were probably early-construction Grisha-IIs, which had a lower output propulsion plant, as listed. In Grisha-IIs, a second 57-mm AK-57 mount replaced the SA-N-4 Gecko SAM system on the forecastle.

GUIDED-MISSILE, PATROL, AND TORPEDO BOATS

◆ **2 (+ ...) Soviet Tarantul-I class**

101 102

D: 480 tons (550 fl) **S:** 41 kts
Dim: 56.5 (52.3 wl) × 10.2 (9.5 wl) × 3.8 (2.5 hull)
A: 4/ SS-N-2C Styx SSM (II × 2)—1/76-mm AK-76 DP—1/SA-N-5/8 SAM syst. (IV × 1, . . . SA-7/14 Grail missiles)—2/30-mm AK-630 gatling AA (I × 2)
Electron Equipt:
Radar: 1/Spin Trough nav., 1/Plank Shave missile target designation, 1/Bass Tilt gun f.c.
EW: . . . intercept, 2/decoy RL (XVI × 2)
IFF: 1/Square Head interrogator, 1/High Pole B transponder
M: COGOG: 2 M15 boost gas turbines (15,610 shp each), 2 cruise gas turbines (2–3,000 shp each); 2 props; 31,220 shp
Range: 400/36; 2,000/14 **Fuel:** 50 tons
Crew: 5 officers, 29 enlisted

Remarks: Transferred 6-90 to begin replacement of the obsolete Osa-I and Osa-II missile boats.

◆ **3 Soviet Osa-II-class guided-missile patrol boats**

102 104 111

D: 190 tons (240 fl) **S:** 35 kts **Dim:** 38.6 × 7.6 × 2.0 mean
A: 4/SS-N-2B Styx SSM—4/30-mm AK-230 AA (II × 2)
Electron Equipt:
Radar: 1/Square Tie surf. search/missile target desig., 1/Drum Tilt gun f.c.
IFF: 2/Square Head, 1/High Pole B
M: 3 Type M504 diesels; 3 props; 15,000 bhp
Range: 500/34; 750/25 **Crew:** 30 tot.

Remarks: Transferred in 1978, 1982, and 1984.

◆ **3 Soviet Osa-I-class guided-missile patrol boats**

103 105 112

D: 175 tons (215 fl) **S:** 36 kts **Dim:** 38.6 × 7.6 × 1.8
A: 4/SS-N-2A Styx SSM—4/30-mm AK-230 AA (II × 2)
Electron Equipt:
Radar: 1/Square Tie surf. search/missile target desig., 1/Drum Tilt gun f.c.
IFF: 2/Square Head interrogators, 1/High Pole B transponder
M: 3 Type M503A diesels; 3 props; 12,000 bhp
Range: 500/34; 750/25 **Crew:** 30 tot.

Remarks: Transferred 1970–71 and likely to be stricken soon.

◆ **4 Soviet Shershen-class torpedo boats**

113 114 115 116

D: 150 tons (170 fl) **S:** 45 kts **Dim:** 34.7 × 6.7 × 1.5
A: 4/533-mm TT—4/30-mm AK-230 AA (II × 2)
Electron Equipt:
Radar: 1/Pot Drum surf. search, 1/Drum Tilt f.c.
IFF: 1/Square Head interrogator, 1/High Pole A transponder
M: 3 Type M503A diesels; 3 props; 12,000 bhp
Range: 460/42; 850/30 **Crew:** 20 tot.

Remarks: Transferred 1970. Two stricken 1990, and others likely to follow soon.

◆ **7 Soviet Zhuk-class patrol boats**

510 511 512 513 514 515 516

D: 48 tons (60 fl) **S:** 34 kts **Dim:** 24.0 × 5.0 × 1.8 (props)
A: 4/14.5-mm mg (II × 2)
Electron Equipt: Radar: 1/Spin Trough nav.
M: 2 Type M50F diesels; 2 props; 2,400 bhp **Fuel:** 10 tons
Range: 700/30; 1,100/15 **Crew:** 12 tot.

Bulgarian Zhuk 511 Siegfried Breyer Collecti

Remarks: Transferred 1980–81.

MINE WARFARE SHIPS

◆ **4 Soviet Sonya-class coastal minesweepers**
Bldr: Petrozavodsk SY

61 62 63 64

D: 380 tons (450 fl) **S:** 15 kts **Dim:** 48.8 × 8.8 × 2.1
A: 2/30-mm AK-230 AA (II × 1)—2/25-mm 2M-8 AA (II × 1)
Electron Equipt:
Radar: 1/Spin Trough nav.
IFF: 2/Square Head interrogators, 1/High Pole A transponder
M: 2 diesels; 2 props; 2,400 bhp
Range: 1,600/14; 3,000/10 **Crew:** 40 tot.

Remarks: Wooden hull with plastic sheathing. First unit transferred 1983, others 1986.

◆ **6 Soviet Vanya-class minesweepers** Bldr: Petrozavodsk SY

31 32 33 34 35 36

Bulgarian Vanya 31 Siegfried Breyer Collect

D: 220 tons (245 fl) **S:** 12 kts **Dim:** 40.2 × 7.9 × 1.7
A: 2/30-mm AK-230 AA (II × 1)—mines
Electron Equipt:
Radar: 1/Don-2 nav.—IFF: High Pole A transponder
M: 1 diesel; 1 prop; 1,100 bhp **Range:** 10/2,400 **Crew:** 30 tot.

Remarks: Wooden construction. Transferred 2 in 1970, 2 in 1971, and 2 in 1985.

◆ **4 Soviet Yevgenya-class inshore minesweepers** Bldr: Sredniy Neva SY, Kolpino

65 66 67 68

D: 80 tons (90 fl) **S:** 11 kts **Dim:** 26.2 × 6.1 × 1.5
A: 2/14.5-mm 2M-7 AA (II × 1)
Electron Equipt: Radar: 1/Spin Trough nav.—IFF: 1/High Pole B
M: 2 diesels; 2 props; 600 bhp **Range:** 300/10 **Crew:** 12 tot.

Remarks: All transferred 1977. GRP construction. Equipped with towed televi minehunting and marking system effective to 30-meter depths. Probably replaced 2-class minesweeping boats, which are now employed by the Frontier Police.

AMPHIBIOUS WARFARE SHIPS

◆ **2 ex-Soviet Polnocny-A-class medium landing ships** Bldr: Stocznia Północna, Gdańsk, Poland

701 Ivan Zagubanski 702 . . . .

ULGARIA *(continued)*
MPHIBIOUS WARFARE SHIPS *(continued)*

an Zagubanski (701) Siegfried Breyer Collection

D: 770 tons (fl) **S:** 19 kts **Dim:** 73.0 × 8.6 × 1.9 (aft)
A: 2/30-mm AK-230 AA (II × 2)—2/140-mm barrage RL (XVIII × 2)
Electron Equipt:
Radar: 1/Spin Trough navigational
IFF: 1/Square Head interrogator, 1/High Pole A transponder
M: 2 Type 40D diesels; 2 props; 5,000 bhp
Range: 900/18; 1,500/14 **Crew:** 35 tot.

emarks: Transferred 1986–87. Cargo: about 180 tons vehicles.

ote: The remaining Vydra-class landing craft are believed to have been assigned to ilian transportation duties.

UXILIARIES AND SERVICE CRAFT

2 Mesar-class replenishment oilers Bldr: . . . , Bulgaria (?)

1 ANLENE (In serv. 1979) 202 DIMITRI A. DIMITROV (In serv. 1987)

mitri A. Dimitrov 6-80

D: 3,500 (fl) **S:** 20 kts **Dim:** 97.5 × 13.2 × 5.0
A: 4/30-mm AK-230 AA (II × 2)
Electron Equipt: Radar: 1/Don-2 nav.
M: 2 diesels; 2 props; 12,000 bhp **Crew:** . . . tot.

marks: First ship deployed to Mediterranean 1980 with two Rigas. Over-the-stern lerway refueling; also have dry stores cargo. Unusually fine hull lines for an oiler ign. "Mesar" is NATO nickname.

1 Soviet Moma-class survey ship/buoy tender Bldr: Stocznia Pólnocna, Gdańsk, Poland

ADMIRAL BRANIMIR ORMANOV (In serv. 1977)

D: 1,260 tons (1,540 fl) **S:** 17 kts **Dim:** 73.3 × 10.8 × 3.8
Electron Equipt:
Radar: 2/Don-2 nav.—IFF: 1/High Pole A transponder
M: 2 Sgoda-Sulzer 6 TD 48 diesels; 2 CP props; 3,600 bhp
Endurance: 35 days **Range:** 8,700/11 **Crew:** 56 tot.

1 Soviet Bereza-class (Type 130) deperming tender Bldr: Stocznia Pólnocna, Gdańsk, Poland

KAPITAN I RANG DIMITRI DOBREV (In serv. 7-89)

D: 2,094 tons (fl) **S:** 15.5 kts **Dim:** 69.50 × 13.80 × 4.00
Electron Equipt: Radar: 1/Kivach navigational
M: 2 Cegielski-Sulzer 8TD48 diesels; 2 CP props; 4,400 bhp (3,600 sust.)
Electric: . . . kw **Range:** . . ./. . . **Crew:** 50 tot.

marks: Numerous sisters in Soviet service. A large crane is fitted aft to handle erming arrays. Has bow-thruster. Moulded depth of hull is 5.60 m.

1 Soviet Sorum-class seagoing tug Bldr: Yaroslavl SY

2 PERUN (In serv. 1977)

D: 1,210 tons (1,656 fl) **S:** 14 kts **Dim:** 58.30 × 12.60 × 4.60
Electron Equipt:
Radar: 2/Don-2 nav.—IFF: 1/High Pole B transponder
M: 2 Type 5-2D42 diesels, electric drive; 1 prop; 1,500 shp
Range: 6,720/13 **Fuel:** 322 tons **Crew:** 35 tot.

◆ **1 East German Type-700 salvage tug** Bldr: Peenewerft, Wolgast

201 JUPITER (In serv. 20-3-64)

D: 700 tons (791 fl) **S:** 12 kts **Dim:** 44.7 × 10.7 × 3.9
M: 2 Type 12 KVD 21 diesels, electric drive; 2 props; 1,680 shp
Range: 3,000/12 **Crew:** 39 tot.

SERVICE CRAFT

◆ **2 inshore survey craft** (In serv. 1973)

350 GENERAL VLADIMIR ZAIMOV
351 KAPITAN KIRIL KHALACHEV

D: 600 tons (fl) **S:** 12 kts **Dim:** 48.0 × . . . × . . . **M:** diesel

◆ **2 Type 024 yard oilers** (In serv. 1956)

D: 450 tons (fl) **S:** 9 kts **Dim:** 46.0 × 6.1 × 2.5

◆ **2 small tugs**

◆ **2 diving tenders:** 333, 337: no data available.

◆ **1 Soviet Bolva-class barracks barge** Bldr: Valmet Oy, Helsinki, Finland

SALGIR

D: 6,500 tons (fl) **Dim:** 113.5 (110.9 pp) × 13.8 × 2.8
Crew: 374–394 berthing

Remarks: Used to accommodate visiting Soviet warship crews. There are about five smaller barracks barges used by the Bulgarian Navy.

FRONTIER POLICE

◆ **12 Soviet PO-2-class patrol boats**

D: 50 tons (fl) **S:** 9 kts **Dim:** 21.0 × 4.5 × 1.0
A: 1/12.7-mm mg **Electron Equipt:** Radar: . . .
M: 1 Type 3D6 diesel; 1 prop; 150 bhp **Crew:** 10 tot.

Remarks: Built in the 1950s; transferred from the Bulgarian Navy, where they had been used as minesweeping boats. There are two 25-kt launches with a range of 350 n.m. in service as well.

BURUNDI

NAVAL SECTION OF THE BURUNDIAN GENDARMERIE

PATROL CRAFT

◆ **2 steel-hulled locally designed** Bldr: CN de Tanganyika, Bujumbura

. . . . . . (In serv. 3-91) . . . . . . (In serv. 6-91)

D: . . . tons (fl) **S:** 25 kts **Dim:** 11.6 × . . . × . . .
A: 1/12.7-mm mg—1/7.62-mm mg
M: 2 Caterpillar . . . diesels; 2 props; 750 bhp
Electric: 16 kVA (2 shaft generators) **Crew:** 6 tot. + 12 passengers

CAMBODIA

Democratic Kampuchea

Note: The units listed below were delivered to forces subservient to the Vietnamese government. A few craft left behind in 1975 by fleeing forces may still exist, but no reliable details are available.

PATROL BOATS

◆ **2 Soviet Stenka class**

D: 170 tons (210 fl) **S:** 36 kts **Dim:** 39.5 × 7.6 × 1.8
A: 4/30-mm AK-230 AA (II × 2) **Crew:** 22 tot.
Electron Equipt:
Radar: 1/Pot Drum nav./surf. search, 1/Drum Tilt f.c.
IFF: 1/High Pole B transponder, 2/Square Head interrogators
M: 3 M503A diesels; 3 props; 12,000 bhp **Range:** 550/34; 750/25

Remarks: Delivered 10-87 without standard fit of four 400-mm ASW torpedo tubes and a helicopter-type dipping sonar. Two others, one delivered 10-85, are used as cannibalization spares. Use Osa-I hull and propulsion. Built in U.S.S.R. 1967 to present.

CAMBODIA *(continued)*
PATROL BOATS *(continued)*

◆ **3 Soviet Turya-class hydrofoils**

D: 215 tons (250 fl) **S:** 40 kts
Dim: 39.0 × 7.6 (12.5 over foils) × 2.0 (4.0 over foils)
A: 2/57-mm AK-257 AA aft (II × 1)—2/25-mm 2M-8 AA fwd (II × 1)
Electron Equipt:
Radar: 1/Pot Drum nav./surf. search, 1/Muff Cob f.c.
IFF: 1/High Pole B transponder, 1/Square Head interrogator
M: 3 M504 diesels; 3 props; 15,000 bhp
Range: 400/38; 650/25 **Crew:** 24 tot.

Remarks: One unit delivered 3-84, two on 23-2-85 to Kompong Son without torpedo tubes and helicopter-type dipping sonar. Fixed hydrofoils forward, with stern planing on surface. Use Osa-II hull and propulsion.

RIVER PATROL BOATS

◆ **4 Soviet Shmel-class monitors—**Delivered: 2 in 3-84, 2 in 1-85

D: 60 tons (fl) **S:** 22 kts **Dim:** 28.3 × 4.6 × 0.9
A: 1/76.2-mm, 48-cal. gun fwd. in tank turret (with one coaxial 7.62-mm mg)—2/25-mm AA aft (II × 1)—1/122-mm RL (XVIII × 1)—2/mine rails
Electron Equipt: Radar: 1/Spin Trough nav. **Crew:** 15–20 tot.
M: 2 M50F-4 diesels; 2 props; 2,400 bhp **Range:** 240/20; 600/10

◆ **1 Soviet PO-2 class launch—**Delivered 3-2-86

D: 50 tons (fl) **S:** 9 kts **Dim:** 21.0 × 4.5 × 1.0
A: 1/12.7-mm mg **M:** 1 Type 3D6 diesel; 1 prop; 150 bhp

AMPHIBIOUS CRAFT

◆ **2 Soviet T-4 class landing craft**–Delivered 1984–85

D: 70 tons (fl) **S:** 10 kts **Dim:** 19.0 × 4.3 × 1.0
M: 2 diesels; 2 props; 600 bhp **Crew:** 5 tot.

CAMEROON

United Republic of Cameroon

Personnel (1991): 1,450 total, including one company paracommandos.

Naval Aviation: Three Dornier 128-6 Maritime Patrol aircraft with MEL Marec radar.

GUIDED-MISSILE PATROL BOAT

◆ **1 French P 48S class** Bldr: Soc. Française Constructions Navales (SFCN), Villeneuve-la-Garenne

	Laid down	L	In serv.
P 104 Bakassi	12-81	22-10-82	8-10-83

Bakassi SFCN, 1983

D: 270 tons (308 fl) **S:** 26 kts **Dim:** 50.0 (47.0 pp) × 7.45 × 2.35
A: 8/MM 40 Exocet (IV × 2)—2/40-mm Bofors AA (I × 2)
Electron Equipt: Radar: 2/Decca 1226 nav.
M: 2 SACM 195V16 CZSHR diesels; 2 props; 6,400 bhp
Electric: 280 kw **Range:** 2,000/16
Crew: 6 officers, 21 petty officers, 12 non-rated

Remarks: Ordered 14-12-80; enlarged version of P 48 class. Two CSEE Naja optronic sights for 40-mm AA, with RADOP ranging system using the navigation radars. Racal CANE 100 (Command and Navigation Equipment) fitted. One radar has true-motion (TM) display, the other relative-motion(RM).

PATROL BOATS AND CRAFT

Note: A planned program to construct three 55-meter patrol boats in the U.S. had to b canceled for lack of U.S. aid funds. A single 15.2-m patrol boat included in the U.S Foreign Military Sales budget request for Fiscal Year 1990 was also not procured. Th P 48 class patrol boat *L'Audacieux* was inoperable by 1991 and has been hulked.

◆ **20 38-ft. patrol craft** Bldr: Swiftships, Morgan City, La.

38-foot patrol craft on trials Linda Turgeon, 19

D: 11.7 tons (fl) **S:** 33 kts **Dim:** 11.58 × 3.81 × 1.00
A: 2/12.7-mm mg (I × 2)—2/7.62-mm mg (I × 2)
Electron Equipt: Radar: 1/. . . navigational
M: 2 Stewart & Stevenson-G.M. 6V92 MTA diesels; 2 props; 1,100 bh
Range: 216/20 **Crew:** 4 tot.

Remarks: A contract for thirty of these craft (10 for the Gendarmerie) was sign 29-8-86, with all deliveries to be made by end 1987. For use on the Chad River, based Douala. Aluminum construction. Hull of 1.90-m moulded depth. The first 10 arrived Cameroon 3-87, the second 10 in 9-87.

◆ **3 U.S. "Raider"-class patrol craft** Bldr: NAPCO, Hopkins, Minnesota (In serv. 1987)

D: 2.95 tons (fl) **S:** 40 kts **Dim:** 6.81 (6.40 wl) × 2.26 × 0.86
A: 2/12.7-mm mg (I × 2) **Range:** 167/40; 222/30
M: 2 outboard engines; 2 props; 310 bhp **Crew:** 3 tot.

Remarks: Ordered 2-87. Use well-known "Boston Whaler" GRP hull. Thirty more planned.

Note: The locally built patrol craft *Quartier Maitre Alfred Motto* has been hulked.

AMPHIBIOUS WARFARE CRAFT

◆ **2 small landing craft** (In serv. 1973)

Betika (ex-*Bakassi*) Bibundi

D: 57 tons (fl) **S:** 9 kts **Dim:** 17.5 × 4.28 × 1.3
M: 2 Baudouin diesels; 490 bhp

Remarks: First unit built by Tanguy Marine, France; the second by Carena, Abidj Ivory Coast, with French assistance. Refitted 1987.

◆ **5 LCVP-type landing craft** Bldr: A.C.R.E., Libreville, Gabon

Souellaba Indépendance Réunification Manoka Machtiga

D: 11 tons **S:** 10 kts

SERVICE CRAFT

◆ **1 buoy tender** Bldr: Cossens, Emden (In serv. 12-90)

Nyong

Nyong A.A. de Kruif & P. Sinke, 2

AMEROON *(continued)*
ERVICE CRAFT *(continued)*

D: 218 grt **S:** 11.5 kts **Dim:** . . . (41.40 pp) × 11.50 × 3.00
M: 2 MWM TBD-440-6K diesels; 2 props; 2,200 bhp **Crew:** 15 tot.

2 10-ton harbor launches
SANAGA BIMBIA

1 floating dry dock Bldr: Flenderwerft, Lübeck

AMUSSO (In serv. 23-7-87)

emarks: Government-owned, for repair of commercial and government vessels. Capacity: 10,000 tons.

GENDARMERIE

ATROL CRAFT

4 French-built (In serv. 3-91)

D: . . . tons **S:** . . . kts **Dim:** 12.2 × 4.1 × . . . **A:** small arms
M: 2 . . . diesels; 2 props; 930 bhp **Crew:** 1 officer, 10 enlisted

emarks: Transferred from the Navy during 10-91.

10 38-ft. patrol boats Bldr: Swiftships, Morgan City, La. (In serv. 3-88)

emarks: For characteristics, see above under naval entry.

6 harbor patrol craft Bldr: Société Africaine d'Étude de la Réalisation Industrielle (SAERI), Douala (In serv. 1986–87)

D: . . . **S:** . . . **Dim:** 9.1 × . . . × . . . **M:** diesels

ote: Police forces also operate 12 Type 650 and Type 800 launches of 3.5 tons elivered 1977–1982 by Chantiers Plascoa, Cannes; dim: 8.50 × 3.00 × 0.72.

CANADA

ersonnel (1991): About 17,100 active, plus 4,011 in the Naval Reserve and 7,400 civil nployees.

aval Aviation: Made up of ship-based ASW helicopters, maritime patrol aircraft, and SW aircraft, formerly carrier-based but now maintained at land bases.
Aircraft include:
—31 ASW CH-124A Sea King helicopters (see U.S.A. section for data), armed with Mk or Mk 46 torpedoes and AQS-13 sonar. Several are used in logistics service aboard the plenishment oilers. All were based on the East Coast, at Shearwater, Nova Scotia, until 87, when 4 transferred to West Coast. Six were modified for possible Persian Gulf service the fall of 1990 with FLIR-2000G forward-looking IR sensor, APR-39, ALE-37, and LQ-144 EW equipment; five actually went, and all six are to retain the alterations. All are being fitted with Calypso acoustic processors, and some may be updated to CH-124B od. 6 status if the order for 35 new EH.101 helicopters (which was to be placed in 1992) is elayed. As of early 1991, it was hoped to deliver the first Canadian EH.101 from Italy in 95; 15 are to be in search-and-rescue configuration, and all are to be powered by three E. 2,000-shp CT7-6A1 turbines.

P-140 Aurora C.A.F., 1990

H-124A Sea King ASW helicopter Bernard Prézelin, 5-90

—18 CP-140 Aurora maritime patrol aircraft, based on the U.S. Navy's P-3 Orion. The first plane was delivered 28-5-80, with the remaining arriving by 3-81. The Aurora is fitted not only for reconnaissance, ASW, and electronic warfare, but also for detecting atmospheric and maritime pollution and for analyzing oil spills at sea. It has a crew of twelve. The Aurora has the Orion's A-NEW system, based on the miniaturized Univac ASQ-114 computer, which can store 65,000 words of 30 bits and has a retrieval time of 4 microseconds. There are 36 launching chutes for dropping active and passive sonobuoys and racks for 120 reserve sonobuoys. Other principal systems are: 2ASN-84 inertial navigation computers; doppler radar; tactical recorder flight-control director; tactical data link system: FLIR (Forward-Looking Infrared); SLAR (Side-Looking Airborne Radar) antennas; detectors for lasers; a low-light television pod. Three simplified CP-140A Arcturus ordered 3-7-89 for Arctic patrol and training; to enter service 12-92 to . . . -93. Will have APS-137 radar; no ASW equipment. Nine coastal-patrol aircraft are planned.
Eight Canadian Challenger 600/601 corporate jets were ordered 1985 to supply naval and land forces as the EC-144 for EW training and as the CC-144 for transport duties; 2 CC-144 and 1 EC-144 were converting 1990–92 to perform maritime surveillance in place of the CP-121 (CS-2F) Tracker piston-engined aircraft, which were all retired on 1-4-90. Three CH-113A Labrador helicopters (rehabilitated CH-76) entered service 1986 for SAR duties, and several CT-33A Silver Star jet trainers are still in use for target service duties.

WEAPONS AND SYSTEMS

A. MISSILES

♦ **NATO Sea Sparrow surface-to-air missiles.**
Designed to attack aircraft or missiles flying at a low altitude at a transonic speed.

Length: 3.660 m **Diameter:** 0.200 m
Wingspan: .020 m **Weight:** 204 kg
Speed: Mach 3.5 **Practical antiaircraft range:** 8,000 to 10,000 m

The Raytheon vertical-launch system for Sea Sparrow underwent trials aboard *Huron* in 2-81 at Roosevelt Roads, Puerto Rico, and is being used on the *Halifax* class. Vertically launched Standard SM-2 MR will replace Sea Sparrow in the *Iroquois* ("Tribal") class.
Canada has purchased the U.S. AGM-84 Harpoon missile for use by CP-140 Aurora aircraft. In 1984, 34 RGM-84D shipboard versions were ordered.

B. GUNS

The following guns are currently in use:
57-mm Bofors SAK Mk 2. Single mount on the *Halifax* class. See Swedish section for data.
76.2-mm Mk 22. Twin DP (U.S. Mk 34 mount) mounted within a GRP gunhouse. See U.S. section for data. Fitted on *St. Laurent, Restigouche, Mackenzie,* and *Annapolis* class of frigates.
76.2-mm Mk 6. Twin barrel, automatic (British model).

Length: 70 calibers **Muzzle velocity:** . . . m/s
Maximum firing rate: 60 rounds per minute per barrel
Maximum effective antiaircraft range: 5,000 m

Installed forward on *Restigouche* and *Mackenzie* classes of frigates.
127-mm OTO-Melara. Installed on the Iroquois-class destroyers, being replaced by the OTO Melara 76-mm DP gun. See Italian section for data.
40-mm Bofors AA on Mk 5C "Boffin" mounting. Standard 60-cal. gun on powered mount originally designed for twin 20-mm Oerlikon AA during World War II; used on ships sent to Mideast during Operation Desert Shield and on auxiliaries; thoroughly obsolescent.

C. ASW WEAPONS

♦ **Depth-charge and torpedo launchers**

—British Mk 10 Limbo triple-barreled mortar on frigates.
—U.S. ASROC on 4 *Restigouche*-class frigates.
—U.S. Mk 32 ASW triple torpedo tubes on all destroyers and frigates.

♦ **Torpedoes**

—U.S. Mk 46 ASW torpedoes aboard ships, and on Sea King heli-copters and maritime patrol aircraft.
—U.S. Alliant NT37C for submarines.
—U.S. Mk 48 Mod. 4 on submarines; 48 ordered 1985; 13 in 1988; 26 Mk 48 Mod. 4 ordered 23-6-89 to deliver by 6-91.

D. ELECTRONICS

♦ **Radars:**

—Mk 127E and its successor, Mk 340, Canadian Sperry-made navigational radars on frigates and destroyers.
—Model 1629C, Raytheon navigational radar on *Halifax*-class frigates.
—SPG-515 gun fire control radar (Norden); Canadian designation for U.S. SPG-48.
—SPS-12 long-range air search.
—SPS-49(V), Raytheon 2-D air-search radar on *Halifax* class.
—SPS-501 long-range air search (version of Dutch LWO-3) installed in *Iroquois*-class destroyers. Uses LWO-3 antenna, SPS-12 transmitter.
—SPS-502, Cardoen SPS-10D surface search, on older frigates.
—SPS-503, Canadian-made Marconi S1820 air-search radar using the Plessey AWS-4 antenna, for 8 modernized frigates.
—SPQ-2D combination search (Italian radar) installed in the unmodified *Iroquois*-class destroyers.
—Sea Giraffe HC 150, Swedish Ericsson surface search on the *Halifax* class.

♦ **Sonars:**

—BQG-501, U.S. Sperry "Micropuffs" passive ranging, on *Oberon* class.
—SQS-501, for detection of submarines lying on the sea bottom (U.K. Type 162).
—SQS-502, (U.K. Type 170B) for Limbo control.

WEAPONS AND SYSTEMS *(continued)*

—SQS-503, hull-mounted MF.
—SQS-504, MF variable-depth sonar with Type 503 transducer.
—SQS-505, hull-mounted and towed LF installed in the *Iroquois* class (SQA-502 hoist). SQS-505 TASP with digital acoustic processing and SHINPADS display tested in an *Iroquois*-class ship in 1984. Will be carried by *Halifax* class vice planned SQS-510.
—SQR-501 CANTASS towed passive linear hydrophone array for the *Halifax* class; uses "wet end" of U.S. AN/SQR-19A system with Canadian UYS-501 receiver/processor and UYQ-501 displays; 15 sets ordered.

◆ Countermeasures:

—SLQ-25, U.S. Nixie towed acoustic homing torpedo decoy.
—SLQ-501, MEL CANEWS (Canadian Electronic Warfare System) intercept for frigates and destroyers.
—SLQ-503 MEL RAMSES (Reprogrammable Advanced Multimode Shipboard ECM system) jammer for the *Halifax* class.
—WLR-1, U.S.-supplied intercept array, being replaced by SLQ-501.
—Antimissile decoy launchers include the British Knebworth/Corvus eight-tubed rocket launcher and the U.S. Hycor Mk 137 six-tubed fixed launcher, the latter capable of launching the NATO Sea Gnat decoy rocket.

SUBMARINES

Note: What had originally been planned as a program for four diesel-electric submarines to replace the present *Oberon*-class in the mid-1990s, possibly employing some form of closed-cycle auxiliary propulsion, was vastly expanded into a program to construct from eight to twelve nuclear-powered submarines, to cost some $400–500 million (Can.) each. These ships were intended to defend Canada's Arctic sovereignty. The program was canceled in 4-89, but in 7-89, authorization to begin a program to acquire 8 new diesel-electric submarines was granted. Britain's VSEL offered to coproduce 4 *Upholder*-class submarines in Canada, with the first to deliver in 1998, and a variant of the Swedish-Australian *Collins* class was also proposed for construction in Canada. The trio are to be retained until 2002–2004 and will receive the U.K. Type 2051 (Plessey Triton) sonar and a towed array in 1993-on. SS 73 is being used for towed-array trials.

◆ 3 British Oberon class

Bldr: H.M. Dockyard, Chatham

	Laid down	L	In serv.
SS 72 OJIBWA (ex-*Onyx*)	27-9-62	29-2-64	23-9-65
SS 73 ONANDAGA	18-6-64	25-9-65	22-6-67
SS 74 OKANAGAN	25-3-65	17-9-66	22-6-68

Okanagan (SS 74) Dr. Giorgio Arra, 2-89

Ojibwa (SS 72) PO Wayne Loane, CF, 1990

D: 1,645/2,105/2,445 tons
Dim: 17.5/15 kts **Dim:** 89.92(87.45 pp) × 8.80 × 5.48
A: 8/533-mm TT (6 long fwd, 2 short aft; 18 Mk 48 and 4 NT37C torpedoes)
Electron Equipt:
Radar: 1/1006—EW . . .
Sonar: British 2007 passive, Krupp-Atlas CSU3-41 passive suite, BQG-501 passive range-finding (*see* Remarks)
M: 2 Admiralty Standard Range 16VVS-AS21 diesels, diesel-electric drive; 2 props; 6,000 shp
Endurance: 56 days **Fuel:** 298 m (446 m emergency)
Crew: 6 officers, 62 enlisted

Remarks: *Ojibwa* was begun as *Onyx* for the Royal Navy and transferred while s under construction. Diving depth: 200 m. The living spaces have been modified Canadian weather conditions. Modernized under "SOUP" (Submarine Operatio Update Program), beginning in 1980 with SS 72 getting Singer-Librascope Mk 1 Mo fire-control system using Sperry UYK-20 computer and new sonar suit with the Kru Atlas CSU3-41 active-passive system and an active transducer in the sail replacing original Type 187, 197, and 719 sets. The Type 2007 long-range passive search ar was retained. SS 72 completed 6-82, SS 73 in 4-84, and SS 74 in 5-86. Two Thorn-E Petrel low light-level t.v. periscopes in each. Have U.K. Mk 7 submerged signal a decoy ejector forward, Mk 4 Mod 1B aft; both launch 102-mm devices.

In 1989, the Plessey Triton (U.K. Type 2051) sonar was ordered to update the so suite further; installation was completed in S 73 during a 20-month refit ending 4 and is being installed in S 74 during a refit scheduled to end in 1993. Able to emp Sub-Harpoon missiles, but none have been ordered. U.S. Mk 48 torpedoes now carr forward in all, with SS 74 firing first Canadian Mk 48 shot in 11-90. The aft tubes only be employed for NT37C torpedoes.

In 5-91, it was announced that all three will receive one more major refit, with S 7 be refitted 1993–95 and stricken 2000; S 73 to refit 1996–98 and stricken 2002, and S to refit 1998–2000 and stricken 2004, at which point she will be thoroughly obsol Royal Navy sister *Olympus* (S 12) purchased 12-7-89 for use as a dockside trai arrived Halifax 18-9-89 and is not capable of getting under way or diving.

DESTROYERS

◆ 4 Iroquois (DDH 280) class

	Bldr	Laid down	L	In ser
DDH 280 IROQUOIS	Marine Ind., Sorel	15-1-69	28-11-70	29-7-7
DDH 281 HURON	Marine Ind., Sorel	15-1-69	3-4-71	16-12-7
DDH 282 ATHABASCAN	Davie S.B., Lauzon	1-6-69	27-11-70	30-11-7
DDH 283 ALGONQUIN	Davie S.B., Lauzon	1-9-69	23-4-71	30-9-7

Athabascan (DDH 282) modified for Mideast duty Henry H. Hill, 9-

Iroquois (DDH 280) prior to modernization WO Al Clarke, CF, 1

STROYERS (continued)

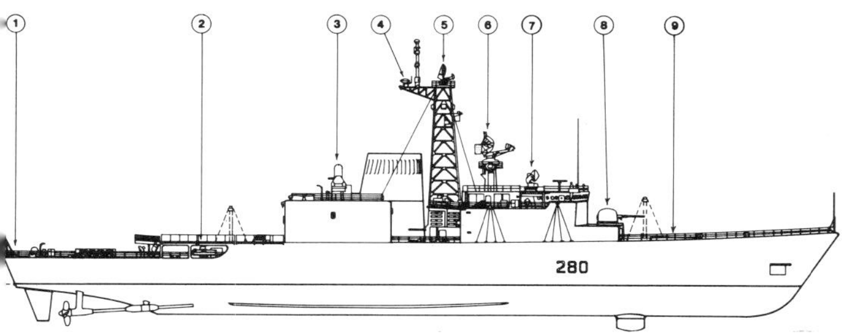

quois class as modernized: A.D. Baker III
VDS housing 2. triple Mk 32 ASW TT 3. Mk 15 CIWS 20-mm ling AA 4. URN-25 TACAN 5. DA-08 radar 6. LW-08 long-range rch radar 7. 2 STIR 1.8 fire-control tracker/illuminator radars 76-mm OTO Melara Compact DP 9. Standard SM-2 Mk 41 VLS launcher

gonquin (DDH 283) as modernized Martin-Marietta, 2-91

gonquin (DDH 283) as modernized Martin-Marietta, 2-91

D: 3,551 tons (4,200 fl; post-mod.: 4,860 fl)
S: 30 kts (29 after modernization)
Dim: 128.92 (121.31 pp) × 15.24 × 4.42 (hull, prior to modernization)
A: DDH 280, 283: 2/Canadian Sea Sparrow SAM syst. (IV × 2; 32 AIM-7M missiles)—1/127-mm OTO Melara DP—1/Mk 10 Limbo ASW mortar (III × 1)—6/324-mm Mk 32 ASW TT (III × 2)—2/Sea King ASW helicopters (*see* Remarks)
DDH 281, 282: 1/Mk 41 VLS (32 Standard SM 2 Block II missiles) —1/76-mm OTO Melara Compact DP—1/20-mm U.S. Mk 15 Phalanx CIWS gatling AA—6/324-mm Mk 32 ASW TT (III × 2)—2/Sea King helicopters
Electron Equipt:
DDH 280, 283:
Radar: 1/Sperry Mk 340 nav.,1/ H.S.A. DA-08 surf./air search, 1/H.S.A. LW-08 early warning, 2/STIR 1.8 f.c. tracker/ illuminator, 1/Phalanx f.c.
Sonar: 1/SQS-505, 1/SQS-505 VDS—TACAN: URN-25
EW: SLQ-503 (M.E.L. CANEWS) intercept, SLQ-503 (Ramses) jammer, 2/Plessey Shield decoy RL (VI × 2), SLQ-25 Nixie torpedo decoy syst.
DDH 281, 282:
Radar: 1/ Sperry Mk 340 nav., 1/SPS-501 air search, 1/SPQ-2D air/ surf. search; 2/WM-22 dir.
Sonar: 1/SQS-505, 1/SQS-505 VDS, 1/SQS-501—TACAN: URN-25
EW: DDH 281: as on DDH 280, 283; DDH 282: WLR-1 intercept, ULQ-6 jammer, 1/6-rail flare and chaff RL, 2/Corvus decoy RL (VIII × 2)

M: COGOG: DDH 280, 283: 2 G.E. LM-2500-30 boost gas turbines (23,747 shp each), 2 G.M. Allison 570KF cruise gas turbines (6,394 shp each); DDH 281, 282: 2 FT 4A2 Pratt & Whitney boost gas turbines (25,000 shp each), 2 Solar Mk FT 12H cruise gas turbines (3,700 shp each); 2 five-bladed CP props; 47,494 shp max. (DDH 281, 282: 50,000 shp max.)
Electric: 2,750 kw (DDH 280, 283: 3,750 kw) **Range:** 4,500/20
Crew: 27 officers, 258 enlisted (prior to modernization)

Remarks: These ships are being updated under the TRUMP (Tribal Update and Modernization Program) under a design prepared by Litton Systems Canada. DDH 283 began a scheduled 18-month conversion period in 10-87 at MIL-Davie, Lauzon, Quebec, but the conversion was delayed by two fires and other problems, and the ship was not back in service until 7-91. DDH 280 began conversion 25-10-88 at the same facility, and the work is now expected to complete in 5-92. DDH 281 was scheduled to begin TRUMP modernization in the summer of 1991 after returning from the Mideast, but has been delayed to 5-92. Because of the continuing delays, the Canadian government took over the contract in 7-91. ASW systems in the modernized ships are basically unchanged, except for removal of the Limbo mortar and its depth-finding sonar. The U.S. Mk 41 VLS (Vertical Launch System) for 32 Standard SM-2 MR Block II SAMs replaced the 127-mm forward, while an OTO Melara 76-mm DP gun was installed in the former Sea Sparrow magazine area. A Mk 15 CIWS (Vulcan/Phalanx) was placed atop the hangar, and ASW torpedo stowage and handling was improved. The 76-mm gun and Standard missiles will be controlled by two H.S.A. STIR 1.8 fire-control illuminator/trackers. The LW-08 long-range air-search radar is supplemented by a DA-06 medium-range radar atop the mast. Harpoon antiship missiles are no longer planned to be carried. Plessey's Shield decoy RL (VI × 2) replaced Knebworth/Corvus, and the CANEWS EW system (with Ramses jammer) replaced WLR-1 (which was installed for trials in the mid-1980s in DDH 281). The SHINPADS command-and-control system has been added, as has the U.S. SLQ-25 Nixie torpedo decoy. A new G.M. 1,000-kw diesel generator has been fitted. Water ballast compensation has been fitted for the fuel tanks. An inertial navigation system is planned. Ships to remain active to post-2004.

DDH 282, 283 retain two paired stacks, angled to avoid corrosion of the antennas by stack gases, and have H.S.A. ASWDS computerized data display system. All have the Bear Trap positive-control helicopter landing system. Passive-tank anti-rolling system fitted to improve stability at low speeds. *Huron* tested the Raytheon vertical-launch Sea Sparrow SAM system in 2-81. U.S. WSC-3 SATCOMM with 2 OE-82 antennas added 1982. DDH 283 tested the AN/SAR-8 IRSTD (Infrared Search and Target Designation) system atop her pilothouse in 1984. *Huron* to West Coast 7-87 but returned to Halifax 2-91 to prepare for TRUMP modernization.

DDH 282 deployed to the Mideast 8-90 after modifications including the replacement of the Limbo mortar by a Mk 15 Phalanx CIWS; removal of the ASW TT and their replacement by 2 single 40-mm AA in "Boffin" mountings; the addition of six single 12.7-mm mg and Blowpipe and Javelin shoulder-launched point-defense SAMS; the addition of 2 Shield decoy RL and the ALR-76 airborne EW system; installation of the C-Tech mine-avoidance sonar; and the installation of INMARSAT NAVSAT and HY-PERFIX radio-navigation gear. Much of the equipment came from gear delivered for the *Halifax* program. DDH 282 was relieved by the similarly modified DDH 281 in 5-91.

FRIGATES

Note: In 7-89, authorization was given for two new antiaircraft frigates in lieu of the planned four additional "City"-class units, but it does not seem likely now that these will be built either.

◆ **1 (+11) Halifax or "City" class** Bldr: A: St. John SB, New Brunswick; B: MIL Group Davie SY, Lauzon, Quebec (sterns by MIL, Tracy)

	Bldr	Laid down	L	In serv.
FFH 330 Halifax	A	19-3-87	30-4-88	3-7-91
FFH 331 Vancouver	A	19-5-88	8-7-89	. . . . .
FFH 332 Ville de Québec	B	16-12-88	16-5-91	4-93
FFH 333 Toronto	A	. . . . .	. . . . .	. . . . .
FFH 334 Regina	B	6-10-89	25-10-91	. . . . .
FFH 335 Calgary	B	15-6-91	5-92	. . . . .
FFH 336 Montreal	A	2-91	. . . . .	. . . . .
FFH 337 St. Johns	A	. . . . .	. . . . .	. . . . .
FFH 338 Charlottetown	A	. . . . .	. . . . .	. . . . .
FFH 339 Winnipeg	A	. . . . .	. . . . .	. . . . .
FFH 340 Fredericton	A	. . . . .	. . . . .	. . . . .
FFH 341 Ottawa	A	. . . . .	. . . . .	-97

D: 4,362 tons (4,750 fl) **S:** 29.2 kts (27 sust.)
Dim: 135.5 (124.50 pp) × 16.40 (14.80 wl) × 4.94 mean hull (6.15 max.)
A: 8/Harpoon SSM (IV × 2)—Sea Sparrow VLS SAM system (II × 8 RIM-7M missiles)— 1/57-mm Bofors SAK Mk 2 DP—1/20-mm Mk 15 Mod. 0 Block 1 gatling CIWS—6/324-mm Mk 32 ASW TT (III × 2)—1/CH-124A helicopter
Electron Equipt:
Radar: 1/Raytheon 1629C nav., 1/Ericsson Sea Giraffe 150HC search, 1/SPS-49(V) long-range air search, 2/H.S.A. STIR 1.8 f.c.
Sonar: SQS-505(V)6 hull-mounted, SQR-501 CANTASS towed array
EW: SLQ-501 (M.E.L. CANEWS) intercept, SLQ-503 (Ramses) jammer, 4/Shield RL (VI × 4), SLQ-25 Nixie torpedo decoy syst.
TACAN: URN-25
M: CODOG: 2 G.E. LM-2500-30 gas turbines (23,747 shp each K 3,600 rpm), 1 S.E.M.T.-Pielstick 20PA6-V280-BTC diesel (11,780 bhp); 2 CP props; 47,494 shp
Electric: 4,488 kVA (4 MWM TBO-602 V-16K diesel generator sets)
Fuel: 479 tons **Range:** 4,500/20; 5,700/15
Crew: 180 tot. (accommodations for 225)

FRIGATES *(continued)*

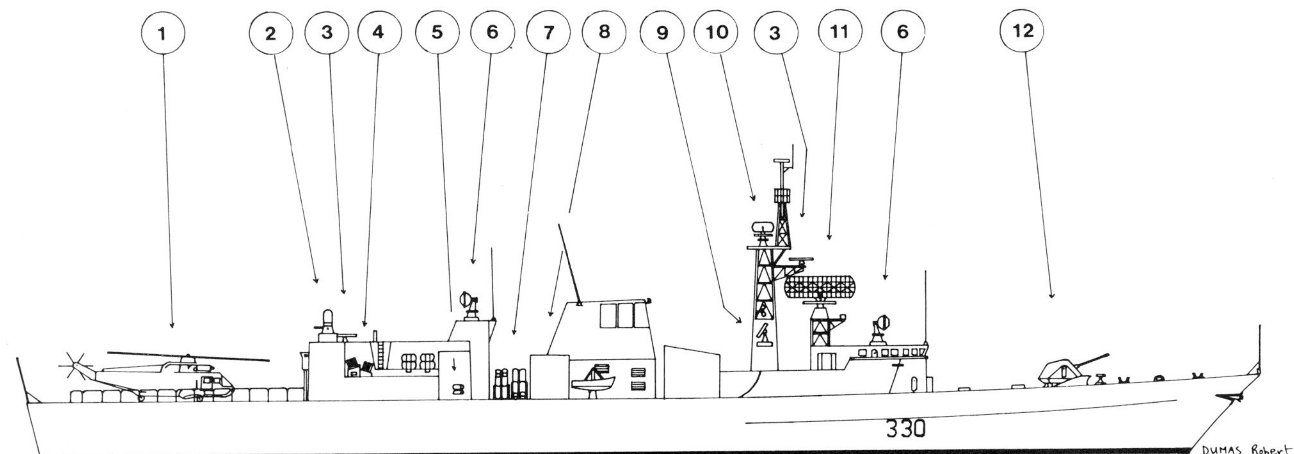

Halifax class 1. helicopter 2. Mk 15 CIWS 3. helicopter hangar 4. STIR weapon-control radars 5. Harpoon antiship missiles (IV × 2) 6. OE-82 SATCOMM antennas 7. Sea Sparrow vertical launchers 8. Shield decoy RL 9. Sea Giraffe radar 10. Racal-Decca 1629C nav. radar 11. SPS-49 air-search radar 12. 57-mm SAK Mk 2 DP mount

Halifax (FFH 330) Dr. Giorgio Arra, 8-91

Halifax (FFH 330) Dr. Giorgio Arra, 8-91

Halifax (FFH 330) Dr. Giorgio Arra, 8-91

Remarks: Program announced 22-12-77. First six ordered 29-7-83 from consortium of St. John Shipbuilding and Dry Dock, Paramax Electronics, and Sperry, with three subcontracted to Marine Industries (now MIL Group). Second flight of six ordered 18-12-87, all from St. John. A planned third flight will probably not now be built. T second flight were to have been 10 m longer, in part to provide accommodations female crew, but the plan has been canceled. Full-load displacement has grown by tons since construction began; limiting displacement is 5,100 tons. FFH 330 was have been laid down 12-84, but program encountered delays and was suspended 3-8 5-86 when inferior steels were discovered being used in construction; she conduc builder's sea trials (at 4,717 tons) 6 to 21-8-90, but further delays with the com systems pushed acceptance into mid-1991, and further developmental trials w postpone operational debut until 1-93. Construction on the three ships under contr to MIL was declared to be in default by St. John as of 7-90.

Were to have had new SQS-510 hull-mounted sonar, since canceled. SQR-501 C TASS towed tactical passive hydrophone array system uses the "wet end" of the U SQR-19A TACTASS. The U.S./Canadian AN/SAR-8 IRSTD (Infrared Search and T get Designation) system is to be carried. The ships have a bubbler noise-reduct system and fin stabilizers. The H.S.A. SHINPADS (Shipboard Integrated Process And Display System) data system with the UYS-503 sonobuoy processor is fitted planned additional 12 VLS Sea Sparrow reload SAMs will not now be carried. A further money-saving move, the ships will not have the latest version of the Harp missile weapons-control system, being fitted with SWG-1(V) vice SWG-1A.

Note: A "Destroyer Life Extension Program" (DELEX) was approved 7-8-80. All o frigates received: ADLIPS (Automated Data Link Processing System), hull and chinery overhaul and repair, new underwater telephones, the Mk 12 IFF syst secure UHF communications, and a new navigational radar. Additional features w added to the various ships in proportion to their future value, with $22 million per s spent on the 1964-vintage *Annapolis* class, down to only $5 million for the *St. Laur* class ships, which, as the oldest, were the first to be worked on. Individual class DEL features are listed in the Remarks sections.

♦ 2 Annapolis class

	Bldr	Laid down	L	In serv.
DDE 265 Annapolis	Halifax Shipyards, Ltd	7-60	27-4-63	19-12-64
DDE 266 Nipigon	Marine Industries, Sorel	4-60	10-12-61	30-5-64

Nipigon (DDE 266)—note tall lattice mast Cpl Gerry Kean, CF, 1

FRIGATES *(continued)*

D: 2,600 tons (3,420 fl) **S:** 28 kts
Dim: 111.56 × 12.80 × 4.40 (6.93 sonar)
A: 2/76.2-mm DP Mk 33 (II × 1)—6/324-mm ASW TT (III × 2) Mk 32—1/CH-124A Sea King helicopter
Electron Equipt:
Radar: 1/Sperry Mk 127E nav., 1/SPS-503 air search, 1/502 surf. search, 1/Norden SPG-515 f.c.
Sonar: SQS-505(V), SQR-501 CANTASS (*see* Remarks)
EW: SLQ-501 (CANEWS) intercept, 2/Mk 36 SRBOC RL (VI × 2), SLQ-25 Nixie torpedo decoy
TACAN: URN-25
M: 2 sets English-Electric GT; 2 props; 30,000 shp
Boilers: 2 Babcock & Wilcox; 43.3 kg/cm, 454° C
Electric: 1,400 kw **Range:** 4,750/14
Crew: 18 officers, 210 enlisted

Remarks: Made 32 knots on trials. Both have two sets non-retractable fin stabilizers, Litton CCS-280 data system, and U.S. UQC-2B underwater telephones. DELEX conversion 23-6-83 to 24-8-84 for DDE 265, 8-85 to 1-87 for DDE 266; received SPS-503 (CMR-1820) air-search radar with Plessey AWS-4 antenna, new EW system, fire-control syst., and navigational radar; SQS-503 sonar replaced by SQS-505; SLQ-25 Nixie torpedo decoys added. DDE 266 also got SQR-501 CANTASS in 1988 in place of SQS-504 VDS. DDE 265 received CANEWS, lengthened stern for SQR-501 during DELEX. The Mk 60 GFCS for the 76.2-mm mount is a digital version of the U.S. Mk 69. Both have two Litton ADLIPS data displays. New masts in both. DDE 265 transferred to Pacific Coast, arriving 28-8-89. DDE 266, based at Halifax, had over 50 women in crew as of 1991. Planned to upgrade SQS-505 (V) hull-mounted sonar to SQS-510 with TASP (Team Architecture Signal Processor), but system has been canceled; DDE 266 performed trials for SQS-510 in 1983–87. To remain in service until at least 1994–96. One is to be fitted with Dowty rubber/polymer anechoic tiles below the waterline to reduce the radiated noise signature, under a 1991 contract. To strike by 2000.

♦ 4 Mackenzie-class frigates

	Bldr	Laid down	L	In serv.
DDE 261 Mackenzie	Canadian-Vickers, Montreal	15-12-58	25-5-61	6-10-62
DDE 262 Saskatchewan	Victoria Machinery, Victoria, B.C.	16-7-59	1-2-61	16-2-63
DDE 263 Yukon	Burrard SY, Vancouver, B.C.	25-10-59	27-7-61	25-5-63
DDE 264 Qu'appelle	Davie S.B., Lauzon, Quebec	14-1-60	2-5-62	14-19-63

Saskatchewan (DDE 262) Ross Gillett, 10-91

MacKenzie(DDE 261) WO Vic Johnson, CF, 1990

D: 2,380 tons (2,890 fl) **S:** 28 kts
Dim: 111.56 × 12.80 × 4.11 (6.93 sonar)
A: 4/76.2-mm DP (II × 2—*see* Remarks)—2/Mk 10 Limbo mortars (III × 2)—6/324-mm ASW TT Mk 32 (III × 2)
Electron Equipt:
Radar: 1/Sperry Mk 127E nav., 1/SPS-502 surf. search, SPS-12B air search, 2/ Norden SPG-48 f.c.
Sonar: 1/SQS-501 depth-determining, 1/SQS-505 hull-mounted
EW: WLR-1C, UPD-501 broadband intercept, SLQ-25 Nixie torpedo decoy
M: 2 sets English-Electric GT; 2 props; 30,000 shp
Boilers: 2 Babcock & Wilcox; 43 kg/cm, 454° C
Range: 4,750/14 **Crew:** 14 officers, 210 enlisted

Remarks: All based at Esquimault in the Pacific. Mk 60 gunfire control. Do not have fin stabilizers. DDE 264 has had British Mk 6, 76.2-mm/70-cal. gun mount forward replaced by U.S. Mk 34, 76.2-mm/50-cal. mount, which is mounted aft on all. Under DELEX received SQS-505 in place of SQS-503, Sperry Mk 127E navigational radar in place of Mk 2, 2 ADLIPS displays, LINK 11, and the SLQ-25 Nixie torpedo decoy. DELEX refit of DDE 264 completed 1-84, DDE 263 in 1-85, DDE 262 in 2-86, and DDE 261 in 1987, all by Burrard Yarrows, Victoria. Were to be retired 1990–1993, but will remain in service longer due to delays in *Halifax* program.

♦ 4 modified Restigouche-class ASW frigates

	Bldr	Laid down	L	In serv.
DDE 236 Gatineau	Davie SB, Lauzon, Quebec	30-4-53	3-6-57	17-2-59
DDE 257 Restigouche	Canadian-Vickers, Montreal, Quebec	15-7-53	22-11-54	7-6-58
DDE 258 Kootenay	Burrard, Vancouver, B.C.	21-8-52	15-6-54	7-3-59
DDE 259 Terra Nova	Victoria Machinery, Victoria, B.C.	14-11-52	21-6-55	6-6-59

Terra Nova (DDE 259) modified for Mideast duty R.A.N., 3-91

Gatineau (DDE 236) Maritime Photographic, 10-90

FRIGATES *(continued)*

Restigouche (DDE 257)—with Harpoon, Phalanx, and other alterations for Mideast service (*see* Remarks in text) Ben Sullivan, 5-91

D: 2,714 tons (3,007 fl) **S:** 28 kts
Dim: 113.16 × 12.80 × 4.11 (6.04 sonar)
A: 2/76.2-mm DP Mk 6 (II × 1) fwd—1/U.S. ASROC Mk 116 ASW RL syst. (VIII × 1, 8 reloads)—1/Mk 10 Limbo mortar (III × 1)—6/324-mm ASW TT (III × 2)(*see* Remarks for DDE 257 and 259)
Electron Equipt:
Radar: 1/Sperry Mk 127E nav., 1/SPS-502 surf. search, 1/SPS-503 air search, 1/Norden SPG-515 f.c.
Sonar: 1/SQS-501depth-determining, 1/SQS-503 hull-mounted, 1/SQS-505 VDS
EW: SLQ-501 (CANEWS) passive, UPD-501 broadband intercept, SLR-503 comms intercept, WLR-1C analyzer, ULQ-6 jammer, Mk 36 SRBOC RL syst. (VI × 4), SLQ-25 Nixie torpedo decoy
M: 2 sets English-Electric GT; 2 props; 30,000 shp
Boilers: 2 Babcock & Wilcox, 43.3 kg/cm, 454° C
Electric: 1,800 kw **Range:** 4,750/14
Crew: 13 officers, 201 enlisted

Remarks: DDE 236, 259 on Pacific Coast, based at Esquimault; DDE 236 transferred home port to Halifax in 7-87, DDE 259 late in 1989. Reconstruction with lengthened hull for VDS and ASROC in place of aft 76.2-mm mount and one Limbo completed 1968–73. Do not have fin stabilizers. Unmodified sisters *Chaudière* (DDE 235), *Columbia* (DDE 260), and *St. Croix* (DDE 256) were reduced to disposal reserve in 1974; DDE 235 and 256 were discarded in 1988–89, while DDE 260 is used as a stationary training ship at Esquimault. DDE 258 completed DELEX modernization 11-83, DDE 259 in 1984. SPS-503 radar replaced SPS-12, Mk 127E navigational radar replaced Mk 2, U.S. WSC-3 SATCOMM gear (two OE-82 antennas) was added, Mk 32 ASW TT replaced the Knebworth/Corvus chaff RL on the upper deck aft, and two Mk 137 launchers for the U.S. Mk 36 SRBOC chaff system replaced the flare rocket launcher atop the ASROC reload magazine. The GFCS was updated to GFCS Mk 60, data-link capability improved, SLQ-25 Nixie torpedo decoys and a 400-kw generator were added. To be retained until at least 1994–96.

DDE 258 collided with MV *Nordpol* 1-6-89 and received new bow from hulk of *Chaudière*; repairs completed 25-7-89.

DDE 259 deployed to Mideast 8-90 with 8 Harpoon missiles (IV × 2) in place of the ASROC launcher, 2 single 40-mm AA in Mk 5C Boffin mountings, and a Mk 15 Phalanx CIWS in place of the Limbo. Added were six 12.7-mm mg, Blowpipe and Javelin shoulder-launched SAMS, 4 U.K. DLF-2 Rubber Duck floating radar decoys, C-Tech mine-avoidance sonar, ALR-76 intercept gear, WSC-3 SATCOMM, INMARSAT SATCOMM, and Hyperfix radio navigation equipment. DDE 257 received the same update in anticipation of relieving DDE 259 in 7-91, but DDE 259 returned to Halifax on 7-4-91 at the conclusion of Desert Storm hostilities; both ships will retain the alterations until the equipment is required for installation in later units of the *Halifax* class.

◆ **3 St. Laurent-class helicopter-carrying frigates**

	Bldr	Laid down	L	In serv.
DDE 207 SKEENA	Burrard, Vancouver	1-6-51	19-8-52	30-3-57
DDE 230 MARGAREE	Halifax Shipyards	12-9-51	29-3-56	5-10-57
DDE 233 FRASER	Burrard, Vancouver	11-12-51	19-2-53	28-6-57

D: 2,550 tons (2,858 fl) **S:** 28 kts
Dim: 111.56 × 12.80 × 4.11 (6.04 sonar)
A: 2/76.2-mm DP Mk 33—1/Mk 10 Limbo mortar (III × 1)—6/324-mm Mk 32 ASW TT (III × 2)—1/Sea King helicopter
Electron Equipt:
Radar: 1/ Sperry Mk 127E nav., 1/SPS-12B air search, 1/SPS-10D surf. search, 1/SPG-48 (GUNAR II) f.c.
Sonar: 1/SQS-503 hull-mounted, 1/SQS-501 depth-determining, 1/SQS-505 VDS

Skeena (DDE 207) Bernard Prézelin, 5-90

Margaree (DDE 230) Hartmut Ehlers, 3-91

EW: SLQ-501 (CANEWS) intercept, SRD-501 HFD/F, SLQ-25 Nixie torpedo decoy
TACAN: URN-22A (not on DDE 233)
M: 2 sets English-Electric GT; 2 props; 30,000 shp
Boilers: 2 Babcock & Wilcox; 43.3 kg/cm, 454° C
Electric: 1,400 kw **Range:** 4,750/14
Crew: 18 officers, 210 enlisted

Remarks: Sisters *St. Laurent* (DDE 205) stricken in 1974 and sold 6-79 for scrap; *Assiniboine* (DDE 234) laid up 2-7-88, decommissioned 14-12-89, and replaced *St. Croix* (DDE 256) as non-operational engineering trials ship at Halifax; *Saguenay* (DDE 206) was decommissioned 31-8-90; and *Ottawa* (DDE 229) decommissioned . . .-. . -91. *Fraser,* which was completed by Yarrow, Ltd., has a lattice mast between her funnels to support the TACAN dome; the others carry their TACAN atop a pole mast. DDE 207 and 233 given major overhauls 1977-78. DELEX overhaul began 1980 on the survivors. DDE 207, 229, 233 were to refit again 1986–87, losing Limbo and VDS to a towed array sonar system, but work was not done. All have 2 sets non-retractable fin stabilizers. Helo deck is 23.8 m long by 12.2 m wide. The survivors will be decommissioned soon, although DDE 230 was extended in service from planned 11-91 strike date to 6-92.

MINE WARFARE SHIPS

Note: The planned new construction mine countermeasures ships listed in the previous edition are now to be configured as offshore patrol vessels with only a vestigial mine countermeasures capability in the form of route-survey sonars in some or all; the ships are listed under Reserve Training Ships and Craft, below.

◆ **2 mine countermeasures trials and training ships** Bldr: Allied SB, North Vancouver

	In serv.	Comm.
MSA 110 ANTICOSTI (ex-*Jean Tide,* ex-*Lady Jean*)	4-73	7-5-89
MSA 112 MORESBY (ex-*Joyce Tide,* ex-*Lady Joyce*)	9-73	7-5-89

D: approx. 2,200 tons (fl) **S:** 13.5 kts
Dim: 58.27 (51.74 pp) × 13.14 × 5.12 (moulded depth) **A:** none
Electron Equipt: Radar: 2/Decca . . . nav.—Sonar: PINS Towfish
M: 4 Nohab SF16RS diesels; 2 CP Kort-nozzle props; 4,200 bhp; bow-thruster
Electric: 752.5 kw (3 × 230 kw, 1 × 62.5 kw) **Fuel:** 313 tons
Crew: . . . tot.

Remarks: Two 1,075-grt/1,196-dwt commercial offshore supply vessels purchased from Tidewater Liberia, Inc., 12-88 for delivery 3-89 for naval reserve training in mine countermeasures and for trials with equipment to be employed in the new ships to be built. Both commissioned 7-5-89 and then underwent refit for naval service with wire sweep Mk 9, BAJ sweep monitors, and Algerine team sweep gear capable of operating in up to 200-m depths. Have PINS 9000 precision navigation system, Hyperfix, and Loran-C radio navaids, and Shipmate RS 5000TS SATNAV receiver.

OCEANOGRAPHIC AND HYDROGRAPHIC SHIPS

◆ **1 converted oilfield supply tug** Bldr: de Waal, Zaltbomme, Netherlands (In serv. 1975; comm. in RCN: . . . .)

AGOR . . . RIVERTON (ex-*Smit-Lloyd 112*)

OCEANOGRAPHIC AND HYDROGRAPHIC SHIPS *(continued)*

D: 2,563 tons (fl) **S:** 15.5 kts **Dim:** 63.91 (60.56 pp) × 13.29 × 5.06
Electron Equipt: Radar: . . . .
M: 2 Stork-Werkspoor TM-4106 diesels; 2 Kort-nozzle CP props; 8,000 bhp
Electric: 544 kw (4 × 136 kw) **Range:** 13,000/12
Crew: 5 officers, 5 enlisted, 16 technicians

Remarks: 1,293-grt oilfield tug/anchor-handling vessel purchased 3-3-89 for conversion as replacement for *Bluethroat* (AGOR 114). Was to become operational mid-1990 and to be used for trials in support of the *Halifax* class. Has bow-thrusters.

♦ 1 Quest-class oceanographic research ship

	Bldr	Laid down	L	In serv.
AGOR 172 Quest	Burrard DD, Vancouver	1967	9-7-68	21-8-69

Quest (AGOR 172) — Cpl Gerry Kean, CF, 1986

D: 2,130 tons (fl) **S:** 15 kts **Dim:** 77.2 (71.62 pp) × 12.8 × 4.6
Electron Equipt: Radar: 1/Decca 838, 1/Decca 929
M: 2 Fairbanks-Morse 38D8⅛-9 diesels, G.E. electric drive; 2 props; 2,960 shp
Fuel: 256 tons **Range:** 10,000/12 **Crew:** 55 tot.

Remarks: A modification of the *Endeavour* (AGOR 171) with the same machinery. Ice-reinforced hull. Two electrohydraulic 5- and 9-ton cranes. Fin and pitch stabilization system. Small helicopter deck now used for equipment stowage. Performs towed linear hydrophone array research for the Naval Research Establishment, Defence Research Board, operating from Halifax.

♦ 1 Endeavour-class oceanographic ship

	Bldr	L	In serv.
AGOR 171 Endeavour	Yarrow, Ltd., Victoria, B.C.	17-8-61	9-3-65

Endeavour (AGOR 171) — Canadian Forces, 1985

D: 1,560 tons (fl) **S:** 16 kts **Dim:** 71.85 (65.53 wl) × 11.73 × 4.0
Electron Equipt:
Radar: 1/Decca 838, 1/Decca 929
Sonar: SQR-501 CANTASS
M: 2 Fairbanks-Morse 38D8Q, 9-cylinder diesels, G.E. electric drive; 2 props; 2,960 bhp
Fuel: 256 tons **Range:** 10,000/12
Crew: 10 officers, 40 enlisted, 13 technicians, 2 aircrew

Remarks: Reinforced hull for navigation in icefields. Two electrohydraulic 5- and 9-ton cranes. Bulbous bows. Anti-rolling and anti-pitching devices. Civilian crew. Conducts trials with the SQR-501 CANTASS towed hydrophone array; she has a 14.6 × 9.4-m helicopter deck. Sound-quiet engineering plant.

Note: Trials ship, former minelayer *Bluethroat* (AGOR 114), was stricken 8-3-90.

DEEP SUBMERGENCE EXPERIMENTAL SHIP

♦ 1 former Italian stern-haul trawler — Bldr: Marelli, Italy

ASXL 20 Cormorant (ex-*Aspa Quarto*) (In RCN serv. 10-11-78)

Cormorant (ASXL 20) — Leo Van Ginderen, 10-89

D: 2,350 tons (fl) **S:** 15 kts **Dim:** 74.6 (72.0 pp) × 11.9 × 5.5
Electron Equipt: Radar: 1/Decca TM 1229, 1/RM 1229 nav.
M: 3 Marelli-Deutz ACR 12456 CV, 950-bhp diesels, electric drive; 1 CP prop; 2,100 shp
Electric: 730 kVA + 250 kw **Range:** 11,800/15; 13,000/12
Crew: 10 officers, 70 enlisted

Remarks: Ex-Italian stern-haul trawler bought in 1975 and adapted by Davie Shipbuilding, Lauzon, to handle and service the SDL-1 submersible, which can dive to 600 m. A large hangar for submersibles and a gallows crane have been built on the stern. The ship can also support conventional and saturation divers and has extensive compressor facilities, decompression chambers, etc. Numerous specialized echo-sounders fitted.

MULTI-PURPOSE UNDERWAY REPLENISHMENT SHIPS

♦ 2 Protecteur class — Bldr: St John SB & DD, St. John, New Brunswick

	Laid down	L	In serv.
AOR 509 Protecteur	17-10-67	18-7-68	30-8-89
AOR 510 Preserver	17-10-67	29-5-69	30-7-70

Protecteur (AOR 509) returning from Persian Gulf — Henry H. Hill, 4-91

D: 8,380 tons light (24,700 fl) **S:** 21 kts
Dim: 172.0 (166.42 pp) × 23.16 × 9.15
A: *see* Remarks—3/CH-124A Sea King helicopters
Electron Equipt:
Radar: 1/Decca . . . nav., 1/Decca TM 969 nav.—TACAN: URN-20
Sonar: 1/SQS-505 hull-mounted MF
M: 1 set Canadian G.E. geared turbines; 1 prop; 21,000 shp
Boilers: 2 watertube **Electric:** 3,500 kw
Range: 4,100/20; 7,500/11.5
Crew: 15 officers, 212 enlisted + up to 57 passengers

Remarks: Four replenishment-at-sea stations, one elevator abaft the navigation bridge, two 15-ton cranes on the afterdeck. One bow-thruster. Daily freshwater distillation capacity is 80 tons. Cargo capacity: 13,250 tons total, with 12,000 tons distillate fuel, 600 tons diesel oil, 400 tons jet fuel, frozen and dry foods, spare parts, munitions, etc. Twin 76.2-mm gun mount, formerly carried at the extreme bow, was removed in both in 1983; locally controlled, it was of little use and had several times been washed overboard. Can be used to carry military vehicles and troops for commando purposes. Carry four LCVPs. Both operate from Halifax in the Atlantic.

For service in the Mideast during 1990–91, AOR 509 was equipped in a very short time with the bow-mounted twin 76.2-mm gun mount, 2 single 40-mm AA in Mk 5C "Boffin" mountings, 2/20-mm U.S. Mk 15 Phalanx CIWS, 6/12.7-mm mg, Blowpipe and Javelin shoulder-launched SAMS, the ADLIPS (Automated Data Link Plotting System) for NATO Link 11, U.S. WSC-3 UHF SATCOMM and commercial INMARSAT SATCOMM, an SPS-502 navigational radar, Mk 12 IFF equipment, Racal Kestrel broadband intercept EW equipment, ALR-76 intercept gear, a C-Tech mine-avoidance sonar, and Plessey Shield and U.S. Mk 137 RBOC decoy launchers. On her return to Halifax on 7-4-91, it was announced that the alterations would be retained on board indefinitely. AOR 510 in refit 19-7-90 to 7-91 and received U.S. Mk 15 Phalanx 20-mm gatling CIWS, and Mk 137 decoy RL; the ship was stripped of asbestos, and a new sewage treatment system was installed. Both to receive Racal Kestrel 242 (SLQ-504) EW intercept gear in 1992 and will later be modernized for service past 2004.

MULTI-PURPOSE UNDERWAY REPLENISHMENT SHIPS
(continued)

◆ **1 Provider class** Bldr: Davie Shipbuilding, Lauzon, Quebec

	Laid down	L	In serv.
AOR 508 Provider	1-5-61	5-7-62	28-9-63

Provider (AOR 508) Ross Gillett, 10-91

D: 7,300 tons (22,000 fl) **S:** 20 kts
Dim: 168.00(159.40 pp) × 23.17 × 9.15
A: none **Electron Equipt:** Radar: 2/. . . nav.
M: 2 sets double-reduction geared turbines; 1 prop; 21,000 shp
Range: 3,600/20 **Boilers:** 2 watertube **Electric:** 2,140 kw
Crew: 15 officers, 151 enlisted

Remarks: 14,054 grt. Platform and hangar for two CH-124A Sea King helicopters. Cargo: 12,000 tons distillate fuel, 1,200 tons diesel, 1,000 tons aviation fuel, 250 tons provisions, ammunition, and spares. Has U.S. SLQ-25 Nixie towed torpedo decoy system. Based at Esquimault in the Pacific.

RESERVE TRAINING SHIPS AND CRAFT

Note: In addition to the ships and craft listed below, the four *Mackenzie*-class frigates are used primarily for training. The new offshore patrol vessels are intended to replace the *Bay*- and *Porte*-class training ships. The smaller training craft were to be replaced by 30-m, 244-ton "harbor-class" craft with a diving tender capability; the first 10 of these ships were to be requested in 1985-86, but the program was delayed for lack of funds.

◆ **0 (+12) new-construction offshore patrol vessels** Bldr: Halifax-Dartmouth Industries, Halifax, N.S. (In serv. 1994 through 1998)

D: 962 tons (fl) **S:** 15 kts **Dim:** 55.0 × . . . × . . .
A: 1/40-mm Mk 3 AA in Mk 5 Boffin mounting—2/12.7-mm mg (1 × 2)
Electron Equipt:
Radar: 1/. . . X-band nav., 1/. . . S-band surf. search
Sonar: Towfish towed array
M: 2 . . . diesels, electric drive; 2 props; 3,000 shp **Range:** 4,000 / . . .
Endurance: 20 days **Electric:** . . . . . . **Crew:** 32 tot.

Remarks: Were originally to have been steel-hulled mine countermeasures ships to replace the *Bay*-class former minesweepers and *Porte*-class ships used as training ships for naval reservists, but will now be primarily intended for offshore patrol duties and based at Halifax and Esquimault. Design contracts to CSE and Fenco Engineers (with Halifax-Dartmouth Ind.) 7-89. Original plan was for the order to be placed in 3-91 and deliveries to occur from 1992–1997, but program has slipped considerably. The Fenco consortium design was selected on 2-10-91 and was expected to cost 440 million U.S. dollars. The ships are to have a 25-year service life.

The 40-mm AA will be refurbished World War II mountings returned from Europe where they have been used by the Canadian Army for airfield defense. The maximum speed may be increased to 18 kts. Will be capable of route survey work in support of mine countermeasures and will carry a remote-controlled drone submersible for examining undersea objects. See illustration in addenda.

◆ **1 ex-Royal Canadian Mounted Police patrol boat**
Bldr: Canadian SB & Eng. Co. (L: 18-7-59; in serv. 11-59)

PB 140 Fort Steele

Fort Steele (PB 140) George Nassiopoulos, 7-91

D: 85 tons (110 fl) **S:** 18 kts **Dim:** 35.97 × 6.4 × 2.1
A: none **Electron Equipt:** Radar: 1/Decca . . . navigational
M: Paxman Ventura 12 YJCM diesels; 2 CP props; 2,800 bhp
Range: 1,200/16 **Crew:** 16 tot.

Remarks: Transferred 1973 from RCMP. Although designated a research ship, primarily acts as training ship for Reserves at Halifax. Originally had Napier Deltic diesels. Refitted 1986.

◆ **6 Bay-class former minesweepers**

	Bldr	Laid down	L	In serv.
PB 159 Fundy	Davie SB, Lauzon, Que.	3-55	14-6-56	27-11-56
PB 160 Chignecto	Davie SB, Lauzon, Que.	10-55	26-2-57	1-8-57
PB 161 Thunder	Port Arthur SB, Ont.	9-55	27-10-56	3-10-57
PB 162 Cowichan	Yarrows SB, Victoria, B.C.	7-56	26-2-57	19-12-57
PB 163 Miramichi	Victoria Machinery, B.C.	2-56	22-2-57	28-10-57
PB 164 Chaleur	Marine Industries, Sorel, Que.	2-56	17-11-56	12-9-57

Thunder (PB 161) Leo Van Ginderen, 7-87

D: 370 tons (415 fl) **S:** 15 kts **Dim:** 50.0 (46.05 pp) × 9.21 × 2.8
A: none **Electron Equipt:** Radar: 1/Sperry Mk 2 nav.
M: 2 12-278A G.M. diesels; 2 props; 2,500 bhp **Electric:** 690 kw
Fuel: 53 tons **Range:** 4,500/11 **Crew:** 3 officers, 35 enlisted

Remarks: Reclassified as patrol escorts in 1972 and used for training reserve personnel. They took the names of minesweepers transferred to France in 1954. The *Gaspé* (143), *Comox* (146), *Ungava* (148), and *Trinity* (157) were transferred to Turkey in 1958. Hull of composite construction. One 40-mm AA removed, deckhouse added in place of former sweep winch.

◆ **5 Porte class** Bldrs: 180, 183: Davie SB, Lauzon; 184: Victoria Mach. & DD; 185: Burrard DD; 186: Pictou Foundry

	In serv.
YNG 180 Porte St. Jean	4-6-52
YNG 183 Porte St. Louis	28-8-52
YNG 184 Porte de la Reine	19-9-52
YNG 185 Porte Quebec	28-8-52
YNG 186 Porte Dauphine	10-12-52

Porte de la Reine (YNG 184) Leo Van Ginderen, 198

D: 300 tons (429 fl) **S:** 12 kts **Dim:** 38.0 × 8.5 × 3.9
A: none **Electron Equipt:** Radar: 1/Decca . . . nav.
M: 1 Fairbanks-Morse 6-cyl. diesel, electric drive; 1 prop; 600 bhp
Fuel: 47 tons **Range:** 4,100/10 **Crew:** 3 officers, 20 enlisted

Remarks: Launched 1950–52. Built as auxiliary minesweepers and net tende YNG 186, reacquired 1974 from Department of Transportation, is on West Coast wi YNG 184 and YNG 185; others operate from Halifax.

◆ **2 ex-Canadian Coast Guard R-class patrol craft**

PB 141 Rally (In serv. 1963) PB 142 Rapid (In serv. 1963)

ESERVE TRAINING SHIPS AND CRAFT *(continued)*

apid (PB 142) George Nassiopoulus, 7-91

D: 105 tons (fl) **S:** 13.5 kts **Dim:** 29.03(27.34 pp) × 6.10 × 1.96
A: none **Electron Equipt:** Radar: 2/Decca . . . nav.
M: 4 Cummins VT-12-M-700 diesels; 2 props; 2,400 bhp
Electric: 76 kw **Fuel:** 12 tons **Range:** 1,050/16; 1,500/12.5 **Crew:** 12 tot.

emarks: Transferred 1983 from Coast Guard for $1 each. Sisters in Coast Guard.

4 former Mounted Police patrol craft Bldr: Smith & Rhulorel, Lunenburg, N.S. (In serv. 1957–59)

B 191 ADVERSUS PB 193 CAPTOR
B 194 ACADIAN PB 195 SIDNEY

aptor (PB 193) Leo Van Ginderen, 1991

D: 48 tons **S:** 12 kts **Dim:** 19.8 × 4.6 × 1.2
M: 1 Cummins diesel; 410 bhp **Range:** 1,000/10.5 **Crew:** 18 tot.

emarks: Transferred from RCMP 1975. Sister *Detector* stricken 1988.

1 former Mounted Police patrol craft Bldr: Smith & Rhulorel, Lunenburg, N.S. (In serv. 1968; transferred from RCMP, 1976)

B 196 NICHOLSON

D: 85 tons (fl) **S:** 16 kts **Dim:** 36.0 × 6.4 × 2.1 **Crew:** 18 tot.
M: 2 Paxman YJCM diesels; 2 CP props; 2,800 bhp **Range:** 900/13

6 Ville-class former tugs Bldr: Russell Bros.

	In serv.
TL 578 CAVALIER (ex-*Listerville*)	12-10-44
TL 582 BURRARD (ex-*Lawrenceville*)	8-1-44
TL 586 QUEENSVILLE	5-12-44
TL 587 PLAINSVILLE	23-11-44
TL 588 YOUVILLE	5-12-44
TL 589 LOGANVILLE	13-12-44

D: 25 tons **S:** . . . **Dim:** 12.2 × 3.2 × 1.5 **M:** 1 diesel; 150 bhp

emarks: Sister *Beamsville* (YTL 583) remains in use as a tug.

4 miscellaneous reserve training craft

AG 116 (18 tons) YAG 651 PEGASUS
FL 104 (102 tons) YDT 2 CARIBOU (70 tons)

1 sailing ketch for cadet training

AC 3 ORIOLE (In serv. 1920)

D: 78.2 tons **S:** 8 kts (power) **Dim:** 31.1 × 5.8 × 2.7
M: 1 Cummins diesel; 1 prop; 165 hp **Crew:** 24 tot.

emarks: Based at Esquimault. Also in use are the 11.0-m Class CS 36S GRP sloops *ına*, at the Fleet Training School, Halifax, and *Goldcrest*, at Esquimault, both bought 85.

SEAGOING TUGS

♦ **2 Saint class** Bldr: St. John DD, St. John, New Brunswick

ATA 531 SAINT ANTHONY (In serv. 22-2-57)
ATA 533 SAINT CHARLES (In serv. 7-6-57)

Saint Charles (ATA 533) C. P. Cavas, 9-90

D: 840 tons (1,017 fl) **S:** 14 kts **Dim:** 46.2 (40.7 pp) × 10.0 × 5.2
M: 1 Fairbanks-Morse diesel; 1 prop; 1,920 bhp **Crew:** 21 tot.

HARBOR TUGS

♦ **5 Glen-class harbor tugs** Bldrs: 640, 641: Yarrow, Esquimault; others: Georgetown SY, Prince Edward Isl. (In serv. 1975–77)

YTB 644 GLENSIDE YTB 640 GLENDYNE
YTB 642 GLENEVIS YTB 641 GLENDALE
YTB 643 GLENBROOK

Glenside (YTB 644)—*Margaree* (DDE 230) beyond C. P. Cavas, 9-90

D: 255 tons (400 fl) **S:** 11.5 kts **Dim:** 28.2 × 8.5 × 3.8
Electron Equipt: Radar: 1/Decca . . . nav. **Crew:** 6 tot.
M: 2 Ruston AP-3 diesels; 2 vertical cycloidal props; 1,750 bhp

♦ **5 new Ville-class harbor tugs** Bldrs: YTL 590, 591: Vito Steel & Barge Co.; others: Georgetown SY, Prince Edward Isl. (In serv. 1974)

YTL 590 LAWRENCEVILLE YTL 593 MERRICKVILLE
YTL 591 PARKSVILLE YTL 594 MARYSVILLE
YTL 592 LISTERVILLE

Parksville (YTL 591) C. P. Cavas, 9-90

HARBOR TUGS *(continued)*

D: 70 tons (fl) **S:** 9.8 kts **Dim:** 13.6 × 4.5 × 2.4
M: 1 diesel; 370 bhp **Crew:** 3 tot.

Note: The "Wood"-class *Wildwood* was stricken 1990.

◆ **1 old Ville-class tug** Bldr: Russell Bros. (In serv. 16-1-44)

YTL 583 Beamsville

Remarks: Rest of class used for reserve training; see earlier entry for data.

DIVING TENDERS

◆ **2 steel-hulled** Bldr: Ferguson, Pictou, N.S.

YDT 11 (In serv. 1-62) YDT 12 (In serv. 7-8-63)

YDT 12 1980

D: 70 tons (132 fl) **S:** 11 kts **Dim:** 38.3 × 8.0 × . . .
M: 1 G.M. 6-71 diesel; 288 bhp
Crew: 3 officers, 20 men

◆ **2 or more small**

YDT 650 YDT 651

YDT 650 and 651 at Halifax C. P. Cavas, 9-90

Remarks: No data available. YDT 650 and 651 are based at Halifax.

FIREBOATS

◆ **2 130-ton**

YTR 561 Firebird YTR 562 Firebrand

◆ **2 48-ton**

YFB 556 Fire Tug 1 YFB 557 Fire Tug 2

TORPEDO RETRIEVERS

◆ **4 Experimental and Test Range Support Vessels** Bldr: West Coast Manly SY, Vancouver, B.C. (All launched 10-11-90)

TSRV 610 Sechelt TSRV 611 Sikanni
TSRV 612 Sooke TSRV 613 Stikine

D: 220 tons (300 fl) **S:** 12.5 kts **Dim:** 33.0 (30.0 pp) × . . . × . . .
Electron Equipt: Radar: . . .—Sonar: . . .
M: 2 diesels; 2 props; . . . bhp **Range:** . . ./. . .
Crew: 4–6 tot.

Remarks: Ordered 9-88 and delivered 6-90 to 8-91 to serve the Maritime Experimental and Test Range, Vancouver, as torpedo retrievers, range safety craft, etc.

Firebird (YTR 561)—red superstructure, black hull C. P. Cavas, 9-

MISCELLANEOUS SERVICE CRAFT

Note: Approximately 12 self-propelled units in the categories of fuel-oil lighter, wa tanker, degaussing tender, water tender, floating crane, etc., plus a number of non-s propelled cargo and fuel barges, power barges, sludge-removal craft, etc. Kno names/numbers: *Tayut* (YAG 1), *Guillemot* (YAG 2), *Egret* (YAG 3), . . . (YAG *Admiral's Lady* (YFL 100), . . . (YFL 101), *Pogo* (YFL 104), *Flamingo* (YFL 8 *Black Duck* (YFL 872), and *Gannet* (YFL 873).

Self-propelled ammunition lighter YE 218 (sister is YFNL 220)

Small cargo lighter 207 at Halifax C. P. Cavas, 9-

COAST GUARD

Created in 1972 from a number of government agencies, the Canadian Coast Gu is a civilian organization in the Department of Transportation. It operates some ships, 20 icebreakers, and 35 helicopters. During 1988–1993, it was planned to order replacement ships, 115 small craft, 3 air-cushion vehicles, 1 transport aircraft, and helicopters.

Aviation: The Canadian Coast Guard operates one Douglas DC-3 transport and helicopters: 1 Sikorsky S-61N, 5 Bell 212, 6 Bell 206B, 7 Bell 206L, and 16 M BO-105CBS; 12 of the latter delivered 1986–87. Helicopters are painted red wit white stripe. The 13 oldest Bell 206 are to be replaced with twin-engined craft. Helic ter operations may be privatized.

Note: The 88,000-shp Type 1500 Polar Icebreaker ("Polar 8" Project) was canc during 2-90. The commercial icebreaker *Terry Fox* was chartered 8-91; *see addend*

HEAVY GULF ICEBREAKERS (Type 1300)

◆ **1 modernized** Bldr: Canadian Vickers, Montreal, Quebec

	Region	L	In serv.
Louis S. St. Laurent	Maritimes	3-6-66	8-69

EAVY GULF ICEBREAKERS *(continued)*

ouis S. St. Laurent—before modernization Can. C.G., 1985

D: 14,509 tons (fl) **S:** 17.7 kts
Dim: 111.70 (101.80 pp) × 24.38 × 9.45
Electron Equipt: Radar: 2/Kelvin-Hughes 14-12, 1/Kelvin-Hughes 14-9 nav.
M: 5 Krupp MaK 16M453C diesels (8,000 bhp each), electric drive; 3 props; 42,940 shp
Electric: . . . . . . kw (main generators + 2 Krupp MaK 6M282 diesel sets, 1,000 kw each)
Fuel: 3,632 tons **Range:** 16,000/13 **Crew:** 77 tot.

emarks: 10,907 grt. Had serious fire 3-82 and again 30-12-85. In modernization 87–91, with new bow (dimensions and displacement may be altered from listing ove). Original geared turbine steam plant with four Babcock & Wilcox boilers placed, bubbler underhull de-icing system added. Original hangar for two Bell-206-ed helicopters below flight deck replaced by telescoping hangar on deck. Has accom-odations for 216 crew total. Flume passive stabilization tanks.

VER ICEBREAKERS (Type 1200)

1 improved Radisson class Bldr: Versatile Pacific, North Vancouver, B.C.

	Region	Laid down	L	In serv.
ENRY LARSEN	Maritimes	15-8-85	3-1-87	1-7-88

enry Larsen Can. C.G., 1990

D: 5,798 light, 6,172 tons normal (6,600 Gt. Lakes load, 8,290 fl)
S: 16.5 kts (13.5 cruise) **Dim:** 99.90 (93.00 pp) × 19.77 × 7.24
Electron Equipt: Radar: 2/Racal-Decca . . . nav.
M: 3 Wärtsilä Vasa 16V32 diesels (8,160 bhp each), 3 G.E. 5,000-kw generators, electric drive; 2 props; 16,300 shp
Electric: . . . kw (main engine generators + 1/625-kw emergency set)
Fuel: 1,900 tons; 20 tons for helo **Range:** 15,000/13.5
Crew: 15 officers, 37 nonrated (72 accom.)

emarks: 6,172 grt/2,490 dwt (1,860 dwt Gt. Lakes, 2,490 dwt Arctic). Ordered -5-84. Design based on *Pierre Radisson* class, but with improved bow form. Delayed a ar in completion by damage to shaft couplings and main transformers during dock als, summer 1987. Has Wärtsilä bubbler underwater de-icing system, with two 0-kw generators associated. Has 100-ton cargo hold, 20 tons refrigerated cargo wage. Based at Dartmouth, Nova Scotia.

3 Pierre Radisson-class river icebreakers Burrard DD Co., Ltd., Vancouver, B.C. (*Des Groseilliers:* Port Weller DD Co., Ltd., Ontario)

	Region	L	In serv.
ERRE RADISSON	Laurentian	3-6-77	6-78
R JOHN FRANKLIN	Newfoundland	10-3-78	3-79
ES GROSEILLIERS	Laurentian	20-2-82	7-8-82

Pierre Radisson Leo Van Ginderen, 1990

D: 6,400 tons (7,721 fl) **S:** 16.2 kts
Dim: 98.15 (87.90 pp) × 19.50 × 7.16
Electron Equipt: Radar: 1/TR-611-1 nav., 1/TR-311-S1 nav.
M: diesel-electric: 6 Montreal Loco MLW 251V-16F diesels (17,580 bhp total); 6 G.E.C. alternators (11,100 kw); 2 G.E.C. motors; 2 props; 13,600 shp
Range: 15,000/13.5 **Fuel:** 2,215 tons **Electric:** 2,250 kw
Crew: 59 tot. (76 accom.)

Remarks: 5,910 grt/2,820 dwt; 440 m³ cargo capacity. *Franklin:* 6,100 grt, range: 16,500/13.5, 55 crew. Bow-thruster-equipped. Telescopic hangar and flight deck for one Bell-212 helicopter. Passive-tank stabilization. Used on St. Lawrence River and Great Lakes in winter, in Arctic in summer. *Radisson* to refit and modernize 6-92 to 11-93.

♦ **1 river icebreaker** Bldr: Vickers, Montreal (In serv. 6-69)
NORMAN MCLEOD ROGERS

Norman McLeod Rogers—hangar extended Leo Van Ginderen, 3-88

D: 6,506 tons (fl) **S:** 15.0 kts **Dim:** 89.92 (81.10 pp) × 19.05 × 6.10
Electron Equipt: Radar: 2/Kelvin-Hughes 14/12 nav.
M: 2 Ruston-Paxman HP 16 RKC diesels, electric drive; 2 props; 8,000 shp
Electric: 1,615 kw **Fuel:** 1,095 tons **Range:** 12,000/12
Crew: 56 tot. (78 accom.)

Remarks: 4,179 grt/2,320 dwt. Cargo: 900 tons. Also navigation tender. One helicopter, telescoping hangar. Operates in Laurentian Region. Re-engined during refit 7-11-83 to 14-9-84.

♦ **1 cable-laying river icebreaker** Bldr: Vickers, Montreal (In serv. 31-5-65)
JOHN CABOT

John Cabot Leo Van Ginderen, 11-89

D: 4,180 tons light (6,502 fl) **S:** 15 kts
Dim: 95.50 (84.13 pp) × 18.29 × 6.73
Electron Equipt: Radar: 1/Decca 969 nav., 1/Decca 2400 nav.
M: 4 Fairbanks-Morse 38D8$^{1}/_{8}$-12 diesels, electric drive; 2 props; 9,000 shp
Electric: 1,060 kw **Fuel:** 719 tons **Range:** 10,000/12
Crew: 76 tot.

RIVER ICEBREAKERS (Type 1200) *(continued)*

Remarks: 5,097 grt/2,220 dwt. Carries 400 miles of cable in 3 tanks. Flume passive stabilization and heeling tanks, telescoping helo hangar, 1,000-bhp bow-thruster, 70-ton towing winch (50-ton bollard pull). Operates in Newfoundland Region. Received new bow sheaves in refit ending mid-1987, to handle transatlantic fiberoptic cable, with Dowty-Boulton Paul 30-ton cable capstan. Refitted 1-89 to 4-89.

◆ **1 river icebreaker** Bldr: Davie SB, Lauzon, Que. (In serv. 9-60)

JOHN A. MACDONALD

John A. MacDonald—before modernization Leo Van Ginderen, 10-82

D: 9,307 tons (fl) **S:** 15.5 kts **Dim:** 96.01 (88.40 pp) × 21.30 × 8.58
Electron Equipt: Radar: 2/. . . nav.
M: 9 Fairbanks-Morse 38D8$^1/_8$ diesels, electric drive; 3 props; 15,000 shp
Fuel: 2,245 tons **Range:** 20,000/10 **Crew:** 70 tot.

Remarks: 6,186 grt/3,380 dwt. Three helicopters, fixed hangar. 221-m cargo space. Carries four stores landing craft. Operates in Maritimes Region. Modernization commenced 9-87.

LIGHT ICEBREAKER/NAVIGATIONAL AIDS TENDERS (Type 1100)

◆ **6 Martha L. Black class**

	Bldr	Laid down	L	In serv.
MARTHA L. BLACK	Versatile Pacific, Vancouver, B.C.	-3-84	6-9-85	3-4-86
GEORGE R. PEARKES	Versatile Pacific Victoria, B.C.	-3-84	30-11-85	17-4-86
ANN HARVEY	Halifax Ind., N.S.	1984	12-12-85	29-6-87
SIR WILLIAM ALEXANDER	Marine Industries, Tracy, Que.	4-2-86	23-10-86	13-2-87
EDWARD CORNWALLIS	Marine Industries, Tracy, Que.	5-7-84	22-2-86	14-8-86
SIR WILFRID LAURIER	Canadian SB, Collingwood, Ont.	14-5-85	6-12-85	15-11-86

Sir Wilfrid Laurier—derrick stepped at bridge face, telescoping hangar extended Leo Van Ginderen, 11-89

Sir William Alexander—king posts forward, lower superstructure Leo Van Ginderen, 2-87

D: 3,287 tons light (4,861 fl) **S:** 15.3 kts
Dim: 83.00 (75.00 pp) × 16.20 × 5.75
Electron Equipt: Radars: 2/. . . nav.
M: diesel-electric: 3 Bombardier/Alco 12V-251 diesels (2,950-bhp each), 3 Can. G.E. generators, 2,000 kw each, 2 Can. G.E. motors; 2 props; 8,000 shp—bow-thruster
Fuel: 693 tons **Range:** 6,500+/15; 18,250/10
Crew: 40 (+10 spare accom.)

Remarks: 1,950 grt/1,522 dwt. Carry one Bell 212 helicopter. Cargo capacity is 40 tons in forward hold, 50 tons aft. Carry 670 tons water ballast. Construction of pai assigned to Marine Industries delayed by strike; both have lower superstructure derricks on king posts, while on the others the derricks are stepped on the bridge fac First two operate from Prince Rupert on the Pacific coast; *Ann Harvey* (with crew only 28) from Newfoundland; next two from St. John and Dartmouth; and *Laurier* fro Quebec City.

◆ **GRIFFON** Bldr: Davie SB, Lauzon, Que. (In serv. 12-70)

Griffon Leo Van Ginderen, 5-

D: 2,959 tons (fl) **S:** 14.0 kts **Dim:** 71.32 × 14.94 × 4.73
Electron Equipt: Radar: 2/Kelvin-Hughes 14-12 nav.
M: 4 Fairbanks-Morse 38D8$^1/_8$-8 diesels, electric drive; 2 props; 4,000 shp
Electric: 422 kw **Fuel:** 345 tons **Range:** 5,500/11 **Crew:** 38 tot.

Remarks: 160-ton cargo capacity. Flume passive tank stabilization. Helicopter lan ing platform, no hangar; 10- and 20-ton buoy derricks. Operates in Central Regio (Great Lakes). Refitted 8-89 to 5-90 and to refit again 1991.

◆ **J.E. BERNIER** Bldr: Davie SB, Lauzon, Que. (In serv. 8-67)

J.E. Bernier—with hangar extended Leo Van Ginderen, 12-

D: 3,150 tons (fl) **S:** 13.5 kts **Dim:** 70.48 (64.62 pp) × 14.94 × 4.91
Electron Equipt: Radar: Kelvin-Hughes; 1/14-12 nav., 1/14-9 nav.
M: 2 diesels, electric drive; 2 props; 4,250 shp
Fuel: 450 tons **Range:** 8,000/11 **Crew:** 38 tot.

Remarks: Similar to *Griffon* and *Montcalm* classes, but thinner plating. Has te scoping helo hangar. Flume passive stabilization tanks. Operates in Laurentian gion. Refitted 5-89 to 7-90 and to refit again 1992–93.

◆ **NARWHAL** Bldr: Canadian Vickers, Montreal (In serv. 7-63)

D: 2,222 tons (fl) **S:** 12 kts **Dim:** 76.66 (69.80 pp) × 12.80 × 3.75
M: 2 Cooper-Bessemer direct-drive diesels, fluid couplings; 2 props; 2,000 bhp
Electric: 796 kw **Fuel:** 399 tons **Range:** 9,200/11 **Crew:** 38 tot

GHT ICEBREAKER/NAVIGATIONAL AIDS TENDERS ype 1100) *(continued)*

rwhal—with single-sweep oil-recovery gear Can. C.G., 1990

marks: 2,064 grt/697 dwt. Originally typed "Depot Ship/Lighthouse and Buoy nder" and intended for summer use as an Arctic supply ship carrying 60 stevedores, stores landing craft crew, and 20 administrators. During rest of year, based at rtmouth, N.S. Has 40-ton buoy derrick. Mid-life refit at Halifax Shipyard, 1984 to 6: helicopter deck and telescoping hangar added, new engines.

Sir Humphrey Gilbert Bldr: Davie SB, Lauzon, Que. (In serv. 6-59)

D: 3,053 tons (fl) **S:** 13 kts **Dim:** 67.06 (61.53 pp) × 14.63 × 4.98
M: 2 2,400 bhp diesels, electric drive; 4,250 shp **Fuel:** 552 tons
Range: 10,000/11 **Crew:** 28 tot.

marks: 1,931 grt. Home-ported at Quebec City. Telescoping helicopter hangar. No ding craft. Refitted 1983 to 1-86 at Halifax SY, with new bow, Wärtsilä bubbler tem, new 20-ton crane.

AVIGATIONAL AIDS TENDERS (Type 1050)

2 Samuel Risley class

	Bldr	L	In serv.	Region
muel Risley	VITO Corp., Vancouver	. . .	-6-85	Central
rl Grey	Ferguson Ind., Pictou, N.S.	21-10-85	30-5-86	Maritimes

muel Risley Leo Van Ginderen, 5-90

D: 2,186 tons light (2,861fl) **S:** 12 kts **Dim:** 69.73 × 13.70 × 5.20
Electron Equipt: Radar: 2/ Decca . . . nav.
M: 4 Bombardier/Wärtsilä diesels; 2 Kort-nozzle CP props; 8,500 bhp—750-bhp bow-thruster—400-bhp stern-thruster
Fuel: . . . tons **Range:** 21,650/10 **Crew:** 24 tot. (accom. for 31)

marks: Design based on offshore supply vessel technology. Able to break 0.6-m ice. nputerized steering control. Buoy crane capacity 15 tons at 8.0-m radius, 8.5 tons at n. Two fire monitors produce 600 m/hr to 75-m range. *Risley* based at Thunder Bay, y at Charlottetown.

E-STRENGTHENED NAVIGATIONAL AIDS TENDERS pe 1000)

0 (+1) programmed new construction Bldr: . . . . . .

D: . . . tons **S:** . . . kts **Dim:** . . . × . . . × . . .
Electron Equipt: Radar: . . .
M: . . . diesels: . . . props; . . . bhp
Range: . . ./. . . **Fuel:** . . . tons **Crew:** . . .

Remarks: One (formerly to have been two) to build 2-91 to 2-93 for Maritimes Region. To break 3-m ice, handle 5.4-ton buoys.

◆ **2 Provo Wallis class** Bldr: Marine Industries, Sorel, Que.

Provo Wallis (In serv. 10-69) Bartlett (In serv. 12-69)

Bartlett Leo Van Ginderen, 5-90

D: *P. Wallis:* . . . tons (fl); *Bartlett:* 1,722 tons (fl) **S:** 12.5 kts
Dim: *P. Wallis:* 63.7 × 12.95 × 4.60; *Bartlett:* 57.68 × 12.95 × 3.66
Electron Equipt: Radar: 2/Kelvin-Hughes 14-12 nav.
M: 2 direct-drive diesels; 2 CP props; 1,760 bhp **Fuel:** 102 tons
Range: 3,300/11 **Crew:** 27 tot.

Remarks: 1,317 grt (*Provo Wallis:* 1,313). *Bartlett* to Central Region 1987 after refit with bow-thruster, flush 'tween decks hatches to cargo hold, new winches, modifications to the navigation bridge, a new sewage system, and other improvements; refitted again 6-91 to 4-92. *Provo Wallis,* lengthened during refit 5-89 to 5-90 at Marystown Shipyards, is 6 m longer and is based at St. John, New Brunswick, operating with alternating crews; also fitted with bow- and stern-thrusters, new generators, a modified Liebherr boom crane, and a Miranda davit to handle an RI 22 fast rescue RIB. Both have 15-ton derrick, one 9.1-m landing craft.

◆ **Tracy** Bldr: Port Weller DD, Ltd. (In serv. 17-4-68)

Tracy Can C.G., 1990

D: 1,320 tons (fl) **S:** 13 kts **Dim:** 55.17 (50.29 pp) × 11.58 × 3.66
Electron Equipt: Radar: 1/Kelvin-Hughes 14-12 nav.
M: 2 Fairbanks-Morse 38D8$^1/_8$-8 diesels, electric drive; 2 props; 2,000 bhp
Electric: 402 kw **Fuel:** 131 tons **Range:** 5,000/11.5
Crew: 30 tot.

Remarks: 960 grt. Based at Sorel, Quebec, in the Laurentian Region.

◆ **Montmagny** Bldr: Russell Bros., Owen Sound, Ont. (In serv. 5-63)

D: 565 tons (625 fl) **S:** 12 kts **Dim:** 45.11 × 8.84 × 2.59
Electron Equipt: Radar: 1/Kelvin-Hughes 14-9 nav.
M: 2 Werkspoor diesels; 2 props; 1,048 bhp **Fuel:** 48 tons
Range: 4,000/10 **Crew:** 23 tot.

Remarks: 497 grt. Based at Sorel, Quebec, Laurentian Region. One 7-ton derrick.

ICE-STRENGTHENED NAVIGATIONAL AIDS TENDERS (Type 1000) *(continued)*

Montmagny Leo Van Ginderen, 6-86

◆ **Nicolet** Bldr: Collingwood SY, Collingwood, Ont. (In serv. 12-66)

Nicolet Leo Van Ginderen, 6-84

D: 565 tons light (901 fl) **S:** 13 kts **Dim:** 51.74 × 11.10 × 3.05
Electron Equipt: Radar: 1/Kelvin-Hughes 14-9 nav.
M: 2 diesels; 2 props; 1,350 bhp
Range: 3,000/10 **Fuel:** 76 tons **Crew:** 27 tot.

Remarks: 887 grt. Based at Sorel, Que., for use as a hydraulic survey and soundings ship on the St. Lawrence Ship Channel, Laurentides Region. Refitted/modernized 12-90 to 12-91.

◆ **Simcoe** Bldr: Canadian Vickers, Montreal (In serv. 1962)

Simcoe Leo Van Ginderen, 10-89

D: 1,392 tons (fl) **S:** 13 kts **Dim:** 54.62 × 11.58 × 3.83
Electron Equipt: Radar: 2/Kelvin-Hughes 14-9 nav.
M: 2 diesels, electric drive; 2 props; 2,000 shp
Range: 5,000/10 **Fuel:** 156 tons **Crew:** 32 tot.

Remarks: 961 grt. Based on Lake Ontario at Prescott, in Central Region.

Note: The buoy tender *Thomas Carleton* was decommissioned 11-90.

◆ **Tupper** Bldr: Marine Ind., Sorel, Que. (In serv. 12-59)

D: 1,380 tons (fl) **S:** 13.5 kts **Dim:** 62.36 × 12.80 × 4.23
M: 2 diesels, electric drive; 2 props; 2,900 bhp
Range: 5,000/11 **Fuel:** 206 tons **Crew:** 37 tot.

Remarks: 1,358 grt. Based at Charlottetown, Prince Edward Isl., in Maritimes Region. Helicopter deck, no hangar. 15-ton buoy derrick. Design for a replacement began 1988.

Note: The buoy tender *Montmorency* was stricken 11-90.

◆ **1 Alexander McKenzie class** Bldr: Burrard DD, Vancouver, B.C.

Sir James Douglas (In serv. 11-56)

D: 768 tons (fl) **S:** 11.5 kts **Dim:** 45.87 × 9.45 × 3.17
M: 2 diesels; 2 props; 1,000 bhp
Range: 5,500/10.5 **Fuel:** 89 tons **Crew:** 31 tot.

Remarks: 564 grt; based at Prince Rupert, British Columbia. 10-ton buoy boom. Sister *Alexander McKenzie* stricken 1987, *Douglas* soon to follow.

SMALL NON-ICE-STRENGTHENED NAVIGATIONAL AIDS TENDERS (Type 900)

◆ **0 (+4) new construction** Bldr: . . . . . .

	Laid down	L	In serv.	Region
. . . .	12-89	. . . . . .	9-91	Central
. . . .	4-90	. . . . . .	1-92	Western
. . . .	12-91	. . . . . .	9-93	Laurentians
. . . .	1-93	. . . . . .	10-93	Laurentians

D: . . . tons **S:** . . . kts **Dim:** . . . × . . . × . . .
Electron Equipt: Radar: . . .
M: . . . . . . diesels; . . . props; . . . bhp **Crew:** 12 to 15 tot.

Remarks: Will be able to handle 428-kg buoys. Program delayed?

◆ **Namao** Bldr: Riverton Boatworks, Manitoba (In serv. 1975)

Namao Can. C.G., 19

D: 386 tons (fl) **S:** 12 kts **Dim:** 33.53 × 8.53 × 2.13
M: 2 diesels; 2 props; 1,350 bhp
Range: 2,000/11 **Fuel:** 34.5 tons **Crew:** 11 tot.

Remarks: Employed as buoy tender on Lake Winnipeg. Refitted 6-90 to 4-91.

◆ **Robert Foulis** Bldr: St. John DD, N.B. (In serv. 24-11-69)

Robert Foulis Can. C.G., 1

MALL NON-ICE-STRENGTHENED NAVIGATIONAL AIDS ENDERS (Type 900) *(continued)*

D: 332 tons (fl) **S:** 11 kts **Dim:** 31.70 × 7.62 × 2.44
M: 2 diesels; 2 props; 960 bhp **Range:** 1,500/10
Fuel: 21 tons **Crew:** 12 tot.

emarks: 258 grt. Employed on St. John River, New Brunswick.

KENOKI Bldr: Erieu Dry Dock, Erieu, Ont. (In serv. 5-64)

enoki—as modified Can C.G., 1991

D: 274 tons (438 fl) **S:** 8 kts **Dim:** 37.41 × 10.97 × 2.13
Electron Equipt: Radar: 1/Kelvin-Hughes 14-9 nav.
M: 2 diesels; 2 props; 900 bhp
Range: 1,000/10 **Fuel:** 40 tons **Crew:** 12 tot.

emarks: 375.2 grt. Built with barge-like hull with four hydraulic spuds for precise sitioning while working as a shallow-water buoy tender on the St. Lawrence Seaway. efitted 1973 as an aids-to-navigation tender with a more conventional pointed bow, e spuds deleted, and the original two 5-ton cranes replaced with a single 10-ton crane. ased at Amherstburg, Ontario, in Central Region, where she serves 190 floating and 1 fixed navaids on Lake Erie, Lake St. Clair, and the lower Lake Huron region.

MALL NAVIGATIONAL AIDS TENDERS (Type 800)

ote: One new Type 800 is projected to be built 2-92 through 3-93 for service in the aritimes Region.

4 Partridge Island class Bldr: Breton Industrial & Marine, Hawkesbury, N.S.

	Laid down	L	In serv.
ARTRIDGE ISLAND	1-11-84	2-7-85	31-10-85
E DES BARQUES	1-11-84	3-7-85	26-11-85
E SAINT OURS	7-5-85	25-4-86	15-5-86
ARIBOU ISLE	7-5-85	7-5-86	16-6-86

artridge Island Can C.G., 1990

D: 133 tons (fl) **S:** 10 kts **Dim:** 23.00 (22.50 wl) × 6.00 × 1.35
Electron Equip: Radar: 1/Sperry Mk 1270 nav.
M: 2 G.M. 8V92 diesels; 2 props; 640 bhp **Endurance:** 7–10 days
Electric: 70 kw (2 gen.) **Range:** 1,800/8 **Fuel:** 26,000 l
Crew: 5 tot.

emarks: The first pair, ordered 23-7-84, are considered to be Type 800 tenders and erate at St. John, New Brunswick, and the Laurentian Region, respectively. The her pair, ordered 23-11-84, are considered to be "day boats." Cargo capacity is 20 tons. ave a fire monitor with 2,500-l/min. capacity to 60-m range.

◆ **2 Cove Isle class** Bldr: Canadian Dredge & Dock, Kingston, Ont.

COVE ISLE (In serv. 1980) GULL ISLE (In serv. 1980)

D: 116 tons (fl) **S:** 10 kts **Dim:** 20.00 × 6.00 × 1.35 **Crew:** 5 tot.
M: 2 diesels; 2 props; 470 bhp **Range:** 2,500/8 **Fuel:** 20.5 tons

Remarks: Both operate on Great Lakes, in Central Region.

SPECIAL RIVER NAVIGATIONAL AIDS TENDERS (Type 700)

Note: All Type 700 tenders serve in the Hay River Region, Northwest Territories.

◆ ECKALOO Bldr: Vancouver SY Ltd., North Vancouver (L: 9-7-88)

Eckaloo Can. C.G., 1988

D: 534 tons (fl) **S:** 13 kts **Dim:** 49.10 × 13.40 × 1.22
Electron Equipt: Radar: 2/. . . nav.
M: 2 Caterpillar diesels; 2 props; 2,116 bhp
Range: 1,500/. . . **Fuel:** . . . **Crew:** 9 tot. (10 accom.)

Remarks: 661.13 grt. Replaced 1961-built ship with same name. Flat hull bottom; tunnel-mounted propellers.

◆ DUMIT Bldr: Allied SB, Vancouver, B.C. (In serv. 7-79)

Dumit Can. C.G., 1985

D: 628 tons (fl) **S:** 12 kts **Dim:** 49.40 × 12.40 × 1.30
M: diesel-electric; 2 props; 1,140 bhp
Fuel: 175 tons **Range:** 9,000/10 **Crew:** 10 tot.

◆ NAHIDIK Bldr: Allied SB, North Vancouver, B.C. (In serv. 1974)

Nahidik Can. C.G., 1990

D: 1,122 tons (fl) **S:** 14 kts **Dim:** 53.35 × 15.24 × 1.98
M: diesel-electric: 2 diesels; 2 props; 4,360 bhp
Fuel: 331 tons **Range:** 1,000/11 **Crew:** 15 tot.

SPECIAL RIVER NAVIGATIONAL AIDS TENDERS (Type 700) *(continued)*

◆ **Tembah** Bldr: Allied SB, Vancouver, B.C. (In serv. 9-63)

Tembah Can. C.G.

D: 181 tons (fl) **S:** 13 kts **Dim:** 37.51 × 7.92 × 0.91 **Crew:** 9 tot.
M: 2 diesels; 2 props; 680 bhp **Fuel:** 21 tons **Range:** 1,000/11

◆ **Miskanaw** Bldr: Allied SB, Vancouver, B.C. (In serv. 1958)

D: 99.6 tons (fl) **S:** 10 kts **Dim:** 20.30 x 7.90 × 1.10 **Crew:** 8 tot.
M: 2 diesels; 2 props; 300 bhp **Fuel:** 9.9 tons **Range:** 300/9.5

Remarks: Operates on the Athabaska River.

LARGE SEARCH-AND-RESCUE CUTTERS (Type 600)

Note: One new Type 600 was to be ordered, for construction 7-90 to 3-92, but program has been delayed.

◆ **1 offshore supply vessel type** Bldr: Marystown SY, Marystown, Nfld.

Sir Wilfred Grenfell (In serv. 1987)

Sir Wilfred Grenfell Can. C.G., 1988

D: 3,753 tons (fl) **S:** 16 kts **Dim:** 68.48 × 15.00 × 5.97
Electron Equipt: Radar: . . .
M: 2 . . . diesels; 2 CP props; 12,860 bhp—bow- and stern-thrusters
Range: . . ./. . . **Fuel:** . . . tons **Crew:** 20 tot.

Remarks: Ice-strengthened hull, based at St. John's, Newfoundland. Has six fire monitors, two fast rescue craft, 70-ton electrohydraulic crane. Replaces unsatisfactory earlier unit with same name.

◆ **1 modified offshore anchor-handling vessel** Bldr: Marystown SY, Marystown, Newfoundland

	Laid down	L	In serv.
Mary Hitchens (ex-*Beau Bois*)	23-5-83	5-11-83	19-4-85

D: 3,262 tons (fl) **S:** 15 kts **Dim:** 64.40 (56.40 pp) × 13.80 × 5.91
M: 2 B & W Alpha 14-U28L-VO diesels; 2 Kort-nozzle CP props; 7,420 bhp— 2 bow-thrusters; 1,000 hp
Fuel: . . . tons **Range:** 8,000/15
Crew: 7 officers, 2 cadets, 11 nonrated, and up to 85 survivors

Mary Hitchens Can. C.G., 19[illegible]

Remarks: Ulstein Type 704 oilfield supply-tug design purchased on completion, 3[illegible] 84. Based at Dartmouth, N.S. Carries 8,000 liters foam concentrate and fire monit[illegible] Can pump 5,000 lit./min. Two 6.7-m rigid inflatable rescue boats. Passive tank stab[illegible]zation.

◆ **1 former oilfield supply tug** Bldr: Bel-Aire SY, North Vancouver, B.C. (In serv. 1972)

Georges E. Darby (ex-. . .)

D: 2,204 tons (fl) **Dim:** 56.08 × 13.72 × 4.72 **Crew:** 16 tot.
M: 2 Ruston diesels; 2 props; 4,380 bhp **Range:** 6,500/11.5

Remarks: Purchased 1-82 and refitted for Coast Guard at Vancouver for Pa[illegible] service. 885 grt. Was to be replaced in 1992, but replacement program delayed.

◆ **1 former oilfield supply ship** Bldr: Bel-Aire SY, North Vancouver, B.[illegible]

Jackman (ex-M/V *Hudson Service,* ex-*Nordic IV*) (In serv. 8-73)

D: 2,106 tons (fl) **S:** 13 kts **Dim:** 56.10 (51.94 pp) × 13.70 × 4.42
M: 4 G.M. 16-565C diesels; 2 props; 6,400 bhp **Electric:** 360 kw
Fuel: 587 tons **Range:** 6,500/12 **Crew:** 16 tot.

Remarks: 877 grt/452 dwt. Acquired from Nordic Offshore Services in 1979 and ba[illegible] at St. John's, Newfoundland. Typical oilfield supply tug with long, low, open clea[illegible] fantail. Main engines built 1950 for railroad use, rebuilt in 1972 for shipboard [illegible] Ice-strengthened hull. Sister *Grenfell* replaced by new *Sir Wilfred Grenfell,* 1987.

◆ **Alert** Bldr: Davie SB, Lauzon, Que. (In serv. 20-11-69)

Alert Can. C.G., 1[illegible]

D: 2,164 tons (fl) **S:** 18.7 kts **Dim:** 71.40 × 12.12 × 4.94
Fuel: 275 tons **M:** 2 diesels, electric drive; 2 props; 9,716 shp
Range: 6,000/14.5 **Crew:** 25 tot.

Remarks: 1,752 grt. Was to have been first of a class of six. Telescoping hangar [illegible] helicopter. Operates in Maritimes Region. To be given life-extension modernizatio[illegible]

◆ **Simon Fraser** Bldr: Burrard DD, Vancouver (In serv. 2-60)

D: 1,375 tons (fl) **S:** 13.5 kts **Dim:** 62.26 × 12.80 × 4.27
Range: 5,000/10 **M:** 2 diesels, electric drive; 2 props; 2,900 shp
Fuel: 178 tons **Crew:** 25 tot.

ARGE SEARCH-AND-RESCUE CUTTERS (Type 600) *(continued)*

mon Fraser Can. C.G., 1988

marks: 1,352 grt. Based at Quebec City, Laurentian Region. Helicopter deck and escoping hangar. Very similar to *Tupper*. Refitted at Versatile Vickers SY, Mon-al, 1985 to 4-86; hangar removed, extra lifeboats added for search-and-rescue duties; typed from Type 1000 navigational aids tender.

NTERMEDIATE SEARCH-AND-RESCUE CUTTER (Type 500)

2 Gordon Reid class Bldr: Versatile Pacific SY, Vancouver

GORDON REID (In serv. 7-91) JOHN JACOBSON (In serv. 7-91)

D: . . . tons (fl) **S:** 17 kts **Dim:** 49.95 × 11.00 × 4.00
Electron Equipt: Radar: . . .
M: 4 Deutz-MWM SBV6M628 diesels; 2 CP props; 4,980 bhp—500-shp tunnel thruster
Crew: . . . tot. **Range:** 2,500/12

marks: Ordered late 1988 as replacement in the Western Region for the Type 400 *cer* and *Ready*. Have two 600-ton/hr. capacity pumps, 7-m rigid inflatable rescue aft.

IALL SEARCH-AND-RESCUE CUTTERS (Type 400)

4 Point Henry class Bldr: Breton Industry & Machinery, Point Hawkesbury, N.S.

	In serv.		In serv.
G 123 POINT HENRY	1980	CG 125 POINT RACE	4-82
G 124 ÎLE ROUGE	1980	CG 126 CAPE HURD	4-82

e Rouge Can. C.G., 1988

D: 77 tons (97 fl) **S:** 24 kts **Dim:** 21.30 × 5.50 × 1.70
M: 2 MTU 8V396 TC2 diesels; 2 props; 1,300 bhp
Fuel: 7 tons **Range:** 1,000/12 **Crew:** 5 tot.

emarks: CG 123, 125 proceeded from Nova Scotia to the Pacific Coast under own ower. CG 126 based in Central Region, CG 124 in Laurentian Region.

◆ **2 R class**

	Bldr	In serv.
G 140 RACER	Yarrow, Esquimault, B.C.	1963
G 143 READY (ex-*Hunter Point*)	Burrard DD, Vancouver, B.C.	1963

D: 105 tons (fl) **S:** 16 kts **Dim:** 29.03 (27.34 pp) × 6.10 × 1.96
M: 2 KHD Deutz SBA 8M8-16CR diesels; 2 props; 1,480 bhp
Electric: 76 kw **Fuel:** 12 tons **Range:** 1,050/16; 1,500/12.5
Crew: 12 tot.

Remarks: Based on U.S. Coast Guard 95-ft. design. Sisters *Rally* (CG 141), *Rapid* (CG 142), and *Relay* (CG 144) to Navy, 1983. CG 140, 143 re-engined in refits 9-84 to 12-2-85 and 11-84 to 29-3-85. See photo of *Rally* in Navy section. Sister *Rider*, unmodified and in reserve, deleted 1986.

◆ **2 S class—for Great Lakes service**

	Bldr	In serv.
SPRAY	J.J. Taylor & Son, Toronto, Ont.	1964
SPINDRIFT	Cliff Richardson BY, Medford, Ont.	1964

D: 57 tons (fl) **S:** 14 kts **Dim:** 21.88 × 5.11 × 1.40
M: 2 diesels; 2 props; 1,050 bhp
Fuel: 5.3 tons **Range:** 500/13.5 **Crew:** 4 tot.

Remarks: Sister *Spume* stricken 7-87; others to strike soon. Both in Central Region.

LARGE SEARCH-AND-RESCUE LIFEBOATS (Type 310)

◆ **1 (+1+4) Halmatic "Arun" class** Bldr: AMT Marine, ...

BICKERTON (In serv. 8-89) . . . . (In serv. 1992)

Bickerton Can C.G., 1989

D: 34 tons (fl) **S:** 18 kts **Dim:** 15.85 × 5.34 × 1.50
Electron Equipt: Radar: 1/ Furuno 1510 raster-scan nav.
M: 2 Caterpillar 3412 diesels; 2 props; 1,000 bhp **Crew:** 5 tot.

Remarks: 34 grt. Kevlar construction hull. Have Furuno Loran C90 radio navaid, Anschutz gyrocompass, integrated communication system on bridge. Low freeboard aids in picking up survivors. First unit based at Port Bickerton, Nova Scotia. Second unit approved 1990. Four more are planned to be constructed 1991–94.

SEARCH-AND-RESCUE LIFEBOATS (Type 300)

Note: Five Type 300 search-and-rescue lifeboats are planned for construction 1991–93.

◆ **2 ice-strengthened rescue craft** Bldr: Georgetown SY

	Laid down	L	In serv.
HARP	15-12-85	20-9-86	12-12-86
HOOD	15-12-85	5-11-86	12-12-86

Harp Can. C.G., 1988

SEARCH-AND-RESCUE LIFEBOATS (Type 300) *(continued)*

D: 225 tons (fl) **S:** 11 kts **Dim:** 24.5 (21.50 pp) × 7.50 × 2.40
Electron Equipt:
Radar: 1/Sperry Mk 1270E nav.—EW: Taiyo MF/DF, Raytheon VHF/DF
M: 2 Caterpillar 3408-BDITA diesels; 2 CP, Kort-nozzle props; 850 bhp
Range: 500/10 **Fuel:** 50,000 liters **Crew:** 7 (10 spare accom.)
Electric: 80 kw (2/40-kw sets, Perkins 635A diesels)

Remarks: Ordered 26-4-85. Steel rescue ships to operate up to 100 n.m. from land. Have towing, fire-fighting, and medical evacuation capability. Red hull, yellow superstructure.

◆ **1 rigid inflatable rescue boat** Bldr: Hurricane Rescue Craft, Vancouver

CGR-100 (In serv. 1986)

D: 10.5 tons (fl) **S:** 30 kts **Dim:** 12.40 × . . . × . . .
M: 2 Caterpillar 3208 diesels; 2 P.P. 140 waterjets; . . . bhp

Remarks: World's largest rigid-hull inflatable craft when delivered; has deep-vee hull. Additional units planned.

◆ **2 self-righting motor lifeboats** Bldr: Hike Metal, Wheatly, Ont. (In serv. 1985)

Cap Goelands Souris

D: . . . **S:** 14.5 kts **Dim:** 13.5 × 3.9 × 1.0
Electron Equipt: Radar: 1/. . .
M: 2 diesels; 2 props; 462 bhp **Crew:** 3 tot.

◆ **14 U.S. Coast Guard 44-ft. motor lifeboat class**

	In serv.	Region
CG 102 Westport	1969	Maritimes
CG 104 Bamfield	1970	Western
CG 105 Tofino	1970	Western
CG 106 Bull Harbour	1970	Western
CG 107 Burin	1974	Newfoundland
CG 108 Tobermory	1974	Central
CG 109 Westfort (ex-*Thunder Bay*)	1974	Central
CG 114 Burgeo	1973	Newfoundland
CG 115 Shippegan	1975	Maritimes
CG 116 Clark's Harbour	1975	Maritimes
CG 117 Sambro	1975	Maritimes
CG 118 Louisburg	1975	Maritimes
CG 140 Port Mouton	1982	Maritimes
CG 141 Cap Aux Meules	1982	Maritimes

44-foot lifeboat in Canadian Coast Guard service Can. C.G.

D: 17.9 tons (fl) **S:** 14 kts **Dim:** 13.45 × 3.86 × 1.01
Electron Equipt: Radar: 1/Raytheon 1900 nav.
M: 2 G.M. 6-71 diesels; 2 props; 360 bhp (294 bhp sust.)
Fuel: 1.2 tons **Range:** 150/10.5 **Crew:** 3 tot.

Remarks: First unit built U.S.C.G. Yard, Curtis Bay, Md., in 1967; remainder built in Canada, CG 140 and 141 by Georgetown SY, Prince Edward Isl. CG 107 and later are 485 bhp. Some are to be replaced by additional CGR-100-type rigid inflatables, others by new "Arun"-class lifeboats.

SMALL RESCUE CRAFT (Type 100)

◆ **4 U.S. Coast Guard 41-ft. Utility Boat Class** Bldr: Matsumoto, Vancouver

CG . . . Mallard (In serv. 28-2-86) CG . . . Sterne (In serv. 1987)
CG 156 Osprey (In serv. 3-5-86) CG . . . Skua (In serv. 14-3-86)

Skua Leo Van Ginderen, 7-8

D: 12.8 tons (15 fl) **S:** 26 kts **Dim:** 12.40 × 4.11 × 1.24
Range: 312/26 **M:** 2 Mitsubishi S6B diesels: 2 props; 640 bhp
Crew: 3 tot.

Remarks: 207 built for U.S. Coast Guard 1973–82. Canadian units all on West Coast

◆ **5 miscellaneous**

CG . . . Swift (In serv. 1981)
CG . . . Avocet (ex-*Sterne;* in serv. 1975)
CG 119 (ex-*Grebe;* in serv. 1973)
CG 121 Sora (In serv. 1982)
CG . . . Bittern (In serv. 1982)

Remarks: All in Central Region, with three- or four-person crews. Also in use f search-and-rescue purposes are four 7.0-m and eight 4.0-m launches, all powered b one Cummins 100-bhp diesel, driving a Parker waterjet.

AIR-CUSHION VEHICLES

Note: Three additional air-cushion vehicles are planned for construction 1991–94.

◆ **1 AP-1-99-class rigid sidewall air-cushion vehicle** Bldr: BHC, Cowes, U.K.

Waban-Aki (In serv. 15-7-87)

Waban-Aki Can. C.G., 198

D: 47.6 tons light **S:** 50 kts (35 cruise) **Dim:** 11.2 × . . . × . . .
Electron Equipt: Radar: 1/Decca RM 914C nav. **Crew:** 6 tot.
M: 4 Deutz BF 12L 513CP diesels; 2 Hoffman air-screws; 6 lift fans; 2,400 bhp

Remarks: Ordered 26-2-86; laid down 23-7-86; launched 1-5-87. Name means "Peop of the Dawn," the Indians living in the region of Quebec. Cargo capacity: 12 ton Replaced Bell-built *Voyageur* at Montreal; transferred to Laurentian Region, 8-89.

◆ **3 British Hovercraft SRN-6 class (all on West Coast)**

CG 045 CG 039 CG 086

D: 10 tons (fl) **S:** 58 kts **Dim:** 14.8 × 7.7 × 4.8 (high)
M: 1 Rolls-Royce Gnome gas turbine; 1 airscrew prop/2 lift fans; 900 shp
Crew: 3 tot.

TRAINING SHIP

◆ **1 former lightship** (L: 1959)

Mikula (ex-*Lurcher,* ex-*Catarque*)

:RAINING SHIP *(continued)*

ikula Can C.G., 1990

emarks: Retired as lightship 1969. Employed as training ship for the Coast Guard ›llege. Carries 5 officers and 22 cadets; operates in the Gulf of St. Lawrence. The llowing are also used at the Coast Guard College: *Westmount* (ex-*Souris,* U.S. Coast uard lifeboat type), a lifeboat, a Zodiac boat, the 10.7-m launches *Mink, Muskrat,* and *artin* (all built 1983 as buoy tenders but found to be defective and rebuilt as training nders by the students at the College), 3 8.2-m workboats, 3 Boston Whalers, 2 lf-propelled barges, and a 5.5-m Crockett McConnell launch.

ote: The following small craft were also in use in 1991: 19 Type A1 workboat/ 'eboats (8–9 m o.a.), 2 Type A2 workboats (8–9 m), 3 Type B workboats (10–14 m), 2 ›pe C self-propelled barges (7–8 m), 23 Type D self-propelled barges (9–12 m), 3 Type landing craft (15–17 m), and 2 Type F utility craft.

DEPARTMENT OF FISHERIES AND OCEANS

ISHERIES PATROL SHIPS

1 seagoing patrol ship Bldr: West Coast Manly SY, Vancouver

	Laid down	L	In serv.
EONARD J. COWLEY	15-1-84	24-10-84	4-85

eonard J. Cowley West Coast Manly, 1985

D: 1,470 tons light (2,080 fl) **S:** 12.25 kts
Dim: 72.00 (67.60 pp) × 14.00 × 4.50 (4.90 max.)
M: 2 Nohab Polar F312A diesels; 1 Kort-nozzle CP prop; 3,140 bhp
Fuel: 400 tons **Range:** 12,000/12 **Crew:** 30 crew + 10 spare

emarks: 1,730 grt. Helo deck. Bow-thruster. For Pacific Region. Ordered 8-11-83.

1 research vessel Bldr: Bel-Aire SY, Vancouver

	Laid down	L	In serv.
)HN P. TULLY	30-1-84	27-10-84	5-85

ohn P. Tully Fisheries & Oceans, 1988

D: 2,200 tons (fl) **S:** 14 kts **Dim:** 68.90 (60.00 pp) × 14.00 × 4.50
M: 2 Deutz SBV-628 diesels; 1 CP prop; 3,120 bhp
Fuel: 400 tons **Range:** 12,000/12 **Crew:** 25 crew + 15 scientists

:emarks: 1,750 grt. For oceanographic/fisheries research and hydrographic survey.

♦ **1 aluminum construction patrol boat** Bldr: John Manly SY, Vancouver

JAMES SINCLAIR (In serv. 4-81)—Pacific Region

James Sinclair Manly SY, 1981

D: 430 tons (fl) **S:** 16.5 kts **Dim:** 37.8 × 8.4 × 3.0
Electron Equipt: Radar: 2/Sperry navigational
M: 2 MTU 12V538 TB91 diesels; 2 props; 4,600 bhp

♦ **1 seagoing patrol ship** Bldr: Marystown SY, Newfoundland

CYGNUS (In serv. 1981)—Newfoundland Region

Cygnus 1981

D: 1,461 tons (fl) **S:** 16 kts **Dim:** 62.5 × 12.2 × . . .
M: 2 Nohab diesels; 1 prop; . . bhp

♦ **1 1,255 grt seagoing patrol ship** Bldr: Ferguson, Pictou, N.S.

CAPE ROGER (In serv. 1977)—Maritime Region

Cape Roger—note telescoping helo hangar Pictou SB, 1979

FISHERIES PATROL SHIPS *(continued)*

D: approx. 1,500 tons **S:** 15 kts
Dim: 62.49 (57.31 pp) × 12.22 × 4.13
M: 2 Bofors Nohab diesels; 2 CP props; 4,410 bhp—bow-thrusters
Electric: 575 kw (1 × 250 kw, 1 × 75 kw) **Crew:** 42 tot.

◆ **2 fisheries research boats** Bldr: Ferguson, Pictou (In serv. 1981)

ALFRED NEEDLER WILFRED TEMPLEMAN

Alfred Needler C.&L. Cavas, 9-90

D: approx. 1,300 tons (fl) **S:** 15 kts **Dim:** 50.3 × 11.0 × 4.3
M: . . . diesels; 1 prop; . . . bhp **Crew:** . . .

Remarks: 925-grt stern-haul trawlers. *Needler* based at Halifax, in Scotia/Fundy Region; *Templeman* based at St. John's, Newfoundland.

◆ **2 Louisbourg-class patrol/survey ships** Bldr: . . . (In serv. 1977)

LOUISBOURG LOUIS M. LAUZIER (ex-*Cape Harrison*)

Louisbourg Leo Van Ginderen, 10-82

D: 450 tons (fl) **S:** 20 kts **Dim:** 38.1 (36.6 pp) × 8.2 × 2.5
M: 2 MTU 12V538 TB91 diesels; 2 props; 4,500 bhp

Remarks: *Louisbourg* patrols the Maritime Region, *Lauzier* was renamed 1984 after conversion as a survey boat by Breton Industrial & Marine, Port Hawkesbury, N.S.

◆ **1 seagoing patrol ship** Bldr: Yarrow, Esquimault (In serv. 7-9-68)

TANU

Tanu Leo Van Ginderen, 1990

D: 880 tons (925 fl) **S:** 15 kts
Dim: 54.69 (50.06 pp) × 32.00 × 3.35 mean
M: 2 Fairbanks-Morse 38D8Q-8 diesels; 1 CP prop; 2,400 bhp
Range: 5,000/12 **Electric:** 500 kw **Crew:** 34 tot.

Remarks: Has 125-hp Pleuger active auxiliary propulsion rudder. Aluminum sup structure. In Pacific Region.

◆ **1 seagoing patrol ship** Bldr: Ferguson, Pictou, N.S.

CHEBUCTO (In serv. 1966)—Maritime Region

Chebucto Fisheries & Oceans, 19

D: 865 tons normal **S:** 15 kts **Dim:** 54.6 × 9.45 × . . .
M: 2 Fairbanks-Morse 38D8Q-8 diesels; 1 CP prop; 2,560 bhp
Range: 6,000/12 **Electric:** 300 kw **Crew:** 35 tot.

Note: The following oceanographic and hydrographic survey vessels are operated the Department of Fisheries and Oceans for other Canadian government agencies:

	Blt.	grt.	Dim.	Kts.	Regio
HUDSON	1963	3,721	90.5 × 15.2 × 6.4	12	Sco/F
BAFFIN	1956	3,480	87.2 × 14.9 × 5.7	11	Sco/F
DAWSON	1967	1,311	64.6 × 12.2 × 4.9	12	Sco/F
PARIZEAU	1967	1,314	64.6 × 12.2 × 4.6	13	Pacifi
W.E. RICKER	1978	1,105	54.3 × 9.5 × 4.4	12.9	Pacifi
MATTHEW	1990	886	. . × . . . × . . .	. . .	Pacifi
MEAFORD	1989	808	51.2 × 10.5 × . . .	. . .	Pacifi
G.B. READ	1962	759	51.2 × 9.8 × 4.0	11.5	Pacifi
LIMNOS	1968	460	44.8 × 9.8 × 2.6	10	Centr
E.E. PRINCE	1966	406	39.6 × 8.2 × 4.6	10	Sco/F
VECTOR	1967	516	39.6 × 9.5 × 3.0	10.5	Pacifi
MAXWELL	1961	262	35.0 × 7.6 × 2.4	10	Newf
R.B. YOUNG	1990	172	19.9 × 6.9 × 2.8	9.5	Pacifi
BAYFIELD	1960	177	32.0 × 6.4 × 2.6	10	Centr
PIERRE FORTIN	1975	136	30.5 × 5.5 × 2.3	15	Quebe

Hudson Leo Van Ginderen, 4

Dawson C. P. Cavas, 9-

'ISHERIES PATROL SHIPS *(continued)*

imnos Leo Van Ginderen, 5-78

Operating Regions: Sco/Fun: Nova Scotia/Bay of Fundy; Newfdl.: Newoundland; Central: Central and Arctic, etc.

Remarks: *Hudson* and *Baffin* have icebreaking hulls. *Meaford* launched 29-12-89: 18 tons (fl), powered by two Caterpillar 3412-DITA diesels, 950 bhp tot. *Mathew* aunched 29-4-90 by Versatile SB, Vancouver. *R.B. Young* delivered 21-3-90 by Allied B, Vancouver: 1 Caterpillar 3412 diesel; 503 bhp; range: 2,000/9.5; crew: 4 tot.

DEPARTMENT OF FISHERIES AND OCEANS CRAFT UNDER 100-FT. LENGTH

(Arranged by descending order of length)

Name	Yr. Blt.	Gross Tons	Dimensions	Speed (kts.)	Region*
ENDER (Barge)	75	588	29.6 × 13.1 × 0.9	0	Pacific
.P. LE QUEBECOIS	68	186	28.4 × 7.0 × 3.1	10.5	Quebec
. PACIFICA (Barge)	73	324	26.5 × 8.8 × 1.2	0	Pacific
DVENT	72	72	23.5 × 5.5 × 1.7	19	Central
UMELLA	83	80	23.2 × 4.9 × 1.5	14	Sco/Fun
ELELLA (Barge)	63	259	23.2 × 7.3 × 1.5	0	Pacific
RROW POST	56	114	22.0 × 6.7 × 2.7	10.5	Pacific
ARINUS	77	120	21.6 × 6.7 × 3.7	9	Newfdl.
HAMOOK	75	120	21.6 × 6.6 × 2.7	10	Newfdl.
ROSWATER BAY	83	80	21.5 × 5.1 × 2.7	13.5	Newfdl.
OBEQUID BAY	67	76	21.3 × 5.5 × 2.4	10	Sco/Fun
ELLE BAY	57	57	21.0 × 4.9 × 2.4	10	Newfdl.
L. HART	74	90	19.8 × 6.1 × 2.4	10	Sco/Fun
AVICULA	68	78	19.8 × 5.5 × 3.1	9	Sco/Fun
TLIN POST	75	57	19.2 × 5.2 × 1.2	16	Pacific
HILCO POST	75	57	19.2 × 5.2 × 1.2	16	Pacific
AMP POST	75	57	19.2 × 5.2 × 1.2	16	Pacific
ITIMAT II	74	57	19.2 × 5.2 × 1.2	15	Pacific
OOKE POST	73	59	19.2 × 5.2 × 1.2	15	Pacific
STOLET BAY	65	63	18.5 × 4.9 × 2.4	9	Newfdl.
OOSE BAY	69	62	18.5 × 4.9 × 2.4	9	Newfdl.
ANDER BAY	69	63	18.5 × 4.9 × 2.4	10	Gulf
URIN BAY	67	62	18.5 × 4.9 × 2.4	9	Newfdl.
RATENA	53	56	18.0 × 4.9 × 1.8	10.5	Newfdl.
ADGER BAY	54	48	17.4 × 4.7 × 2.4	8	Newfdl.
ICHARDSON	62	59	16.8 × 5.2 × 2.1	10	Pacific
HARK	71	29	16.5 × 4.6 × 1.2	15	Cen/Arc
UTTER ROCK	67	36	16.2 × 4.3 × 1.8	10.5	Pacific
AJO REEF	84	50	16.1 × 5.1 × 2.3	12	Pacific
HRISTIE BAY NO. 1	73	35	15.9 × 4.3 × 1.5	20	Cen/Arc
ALIGUS	67	41	15.6 × 4.6 × 1.8	10	Pacific
ABINE POST	73	37	15.6 × 4.3 × 1.2	15	Pacific
TUART POST	73	37	15.6 × 4.3 × 1.2	15	Pacific
ORTH ROCK	75	31	14.6 × 4.6 × 1.2	15	Pacific
URGE ROCK	64	33	14.6 × 4.3 × 1.5	9.5	Pacific
EAVER ROCK	61	31	14.3 × 4.3 × 1.5	9.5	Pacific
ONILLA ROCK	71	41	14.3 × 4.3 × 1.5	13.5	Pacific
ALCON ROCK	60	26	14.3 × 4.3 × 1.5	10	Pacific
LLAR ROCK	61	31	14.3 × 4.3 × 1.5	10	Pacific
REBE	70	32	14.3 × 4.9 × 2.1	11	Quebec
GMA-T	63	33	14.0 × 4.6 × 2.0	8	Sco/Fun
GAC	86	117	13.7 × 4.6 × 1.5	. . .	Central
UEBOR	87	. . .	13.7 × . . . ×	10	Sco/Fun
IGILANCE	87	. . .	13.7 × . . . ×	. . .	Sco/Fun
GILE	69	22	13.4 × 3.7 × 1.2	15	Pacific
EAL ROCK	59	24	13.4 × 3.7 × 1.5	10	Pacific
EMPLE ROCK	60	23	13.1 × 3.7 × 1.5	9	Pacific
QUARIEL	86	31	12.8 × 4.6 × 1.5	12	Sco/Fun
. . . (No Name)	69	15	12.8 × 4.7 × 1.5	10	Sco/Fun
ANDULUS III	86	31	12.8 × 4.7 × 1.8	10	Sco/Fun
C-4827	86	7	12.8 × 3.9 × 1.1	15	Gulf
C-4829	86	7	12.8 × 3.9 × 1.1	15	Gulf
B-1452	79	12	12.8 × 4.0 × 1.0	20	Gulf
. . .	87	. . .	12.8 × . . . ×	. . .	Gulf
COLONEL BARRY	83	11	12.8 × 3.9 × 1.1	19	Gulf
J. WILLIE DERASPE	86	16	12.5 × 5.4 × 1.1	15	Quebec
BRAMA	55	20	12.5 × 3.7 × 1.5	9	Pacific
DENIS RIVERIN	84	15	12.5 × 4.0 × 1.1	15	Quebec
F.X. ROSS	84	15	12.5 × 4.0 × 1.1	15	Quebec
JOHANN BEETZ	84	15	12.5 × 4.0 × 1.1	15	Quebec
LOUIS BERUBE	84	15	12.5 × 4.0 × 1.1	15	Quebec
KETA	75	23	12.2 × 4.0 × 1.5	9	Pacific
LEMOYNE	59	20	12.2 × 3.4 × 1.5	10	Cen/Arc
GULL II	82	. . .	12.2 × 4.6 × 1.2	. . .	Cen/Arc
NITINAT QUEEN	68	37	12.2 × 4.9 × 1.2	8	Pacific
STAR ROCK	57	18	12.2 × 3.4 × 1.5	9	Pacific
ROSMARUS	85	19	11.9 × 4.3 × 2.4	10	Quebec
GOOSE II	85	. . .	11.9 × 3.1 × 0.6	8	Cen/Arc
F.D. 202	46	18	11.6 × 3.1 × 1.5	10	Pacific
SURF	74	12	11.6 × 3.7 × 1.4	9	Cen/Arc
20A-1139	74	10	11.6 × 3.4 × 1.2	20	Gulf
20A-1141	74	10	11.6 × 3.4 × 1.2	20	Gulf
20A-1138	74	10	11.6 × 3.4 × 1.2	20	Gulf
20A-1142	74	10	11.6 × 3.4 × 1.2	20	Gulf
20A-1152	74	10	11.6 × 3.4 × 1.2	20	Gulf
20A-1153	74	10	11.6 × 3.4 × 1.2	20	Gulf
TUOLIK	64	. . .	11.3 × 3.1 × 2.3	7.5	Sco/Fun
REVISOR	69	11	11.0 × 3.7 × 1.8	14	Pacific
WALKER ROCK	76	15	11.0 × 4.0 × 1.5	9	Pacific
ACTIVE LASS	60	15	10.7 × 3.7 × 1.2	7.5	Pacific
BEC SCIE	83	8	10.4 × 2.7 × 1.8	18	Quebec
DECIBAR	66	18	10.4 × 3.7 × 0.9	15	Pacific
DUMB BARGE	77	. . .	10.4 × 2.9 × 6.1	20 (sic)	Cen/Arc
MACREUSE	83	8	10.4 × 2.7 × 1.8	18	Quebec
NAUTILUS	77	10	10.4 × 2.7 × 1.2	19	Cen/Arc
NAVIGATOR	82	10	10.4 × 2.7 × 1.2	19	Cen/Arc
NIMBUS	77	10	10.4 × 2.7 × 1.2	19	Cen/Arc
NIOBE	82	10	10.4 × 2.7 × 1.2	19	Cen/Arc
NUCLEUS	. . .	10	10.4 × 2.7 × 0.9	14	Pacific
PETREL ROCK	69	15	10.4 × 3.7 × 0.9	18	Pacific
HAGDON	82	. . .	10.3 × 2.8 × 0.9	16	Sco/Fun
HERON	82	. . .	10.3 × 2.8 × 0.9	16	Sco/Fun
NAIS	75	10	10.1 × 3.0 × 0.9	25	Sco/Fun
ROANNA	71	. . .	10.1 × 2.7 × 1.2	9	Pacific
TAHLOK	66	10	9.8 × 3.2 × 1.1	10	Pacific
SANDPIPER	73	. . .	9.8 × 3.0 × 1.2	14	Cen/Arc
KINGFISHER	73	. . .	9.5 × 2.7 × 1.5	13	Sco/Fun
. . . (Landing Barge)	62	. . .	9.5 × 3.0 × 1.7	7	Sco/Fun
FALCON	75	. . .	9.5 × 2.7 × 1.7	11	Sco/Fun
FINCH	75	. . .	9.5 × 2.7 × 1.7	11	Sco/Fun
FLAMINGO	75	. . .	9.5 × 2.7 × 1.7	11	Sco/Fun
FRIGATE	74	. . .	9.5 × 2.7 × 1.7	11	Sco/Fun
GOOSE	78	. . .	9.5 × 2.7 × 1.7	10	Sco/Fun
GOSHAWK	78	. . .	9.5 × 2.7 × 1.7	10	Sco/Fun
GREBE	77	. . .	9.5 × 2.7 × 1.7	9	Sco/Fun
GUILLEMOT	77	. . .	9.5 × 2.7 × 1.7	9	Sco/Fun
OSPREY	85	. . .	9.5 × 2.9 × 1.4	20	Sco/Fun
PROTO	70	. . .	9.5 × 2.4 × 1.5	9	Sco/Fun
SCAUP	59	. . .	9.5 × 2.7 × 1.4	9	Sco/Fun
SHOVELLER II	61	. . .	9.5 × 2.7 × 1.4	9	Sco/Fun
RESSAC	79	10	9.5 × 2.7 × 0.9	11	Quebec
ROSA DES VENTS	79	10	9.5 × 2.7 × 0.9	11	Quebec
TALTHEILEI	71	. . .	9.5 × 4.1 × 0.8	. . .	Cen/Arc
21C-2630	72	5	9.5 × 2.1 × 0.9	10	Quebec
IBIS	83	. . .	9.4 × 3.0 × 1.2	9	Sco/Fun
RESSAC	79	6	9.4 × 2.4 × 1.5	39	Quebec
ROSE DE VENTS	79	6	9.4 × 2.4 × 1.5	39	Quebec
ANCHOR ROCK	74	10	9.1 × 3.4 × 0.9	10	Pacific
CRESCENT ROCK	65	11	9.1 × 3.1 × 0.9	10	Pacific
GALE ROCK	67	11	9.1 × 3.1 × 1.2	16	Pacific
GULL ROCK	65	12	9.1 × 3.1 × 1.2	10	Pacific
HERON ROCK	74	10	9.1 × 3.4 × 0.9	10	Pacific
HERON	70	4	9.1 × 2.4 × 0.8	30	Cen/Arc
VEDDER ROCK	66	12	9.1 × 3.1 × 1.5	10	Pacific
WARRIOR ROCK	65	11	9.1 × 3.1 × 1.2	16	Pacific
JAEGER	74	5	8.8 × 3.1 × 1.5	19	Pacific
STORM	83	6	8.7 × 3.3 × 1.1	15	Pacific
SURGE	83	6	8.7 × 3.3 × 1.1	15	Pacific
WAVE	82	6	8.7 × 3.3 × 1.1	15	Pacific
WIND	82	6	8.7 × 3.3 × 1.1	15	Pacific
TEMPEST	84	6	8.7 × 3.2 × 1.0	15	Pacific
TORNADO	84	6	8.7 × 3.2 × 1.0	15	Pacific
HOOD	56	. . .	8.5 × 2.4 × 1.4	5	Sco/Fun
PLUVIER	85	5	8.2 × 2.7 × 1.5	14	Quebec
RAYMONT (Barge)	. . .	. . .	8.2 × 2.4 × 0.3	0	Pacific
SARCELLE	85	5	8.2 × 2.7 × 1.5	14	Quebec

CANADA *(continued)*
FISHERIES PATROL SHIPS *(continued)*

Name	Yr. Blt.	Gross Tons	Dimensions	Speed (kts.)	Region*
Squamish	74	3	8.2 × 2.4 × 1.2	20	Pacific
The Barge	77	. . .	8.2 × 2.9 × 0.6	0	Cen/Arc
Alfie	83	4	8.2 × 2.4 × 1.2	8	Pacific
Mallard	85	. . .	8.1 × 2.7 × 1.4	14	Newfdl.
Merganser	85	. . .	8.1 × 2.7 × 1.4	14	Newfdl.
Cormorant	70	. . .	7.9 × 2.4 × 0.9	8	Sco/Fun
Curlew	70	. . .	7.9 × 2.4 × 0.9	8	Sco/Fun
Gull	61	. . .	7.9 × 2.7 × 1.5	8	Sco/Fun
Penguin	65	3	7.9 × 2.4 × 0.9	8	Pacific
Mirage	80	4	7.9 × 2.7 × 0.7	35	Cen/Arc
Sea Turtle	85	2	7.9 × 2.6 × 0.9	10.5	Cen/Arc
Beacon Point	82	. . .	7.7 × 2.4 × 0.8	. . .	Cen/Arc
Frontier	82	. . .	7.7 × 2.4 × 0.8	. . .	Cen/Arc
Barracuda	69	5	7.6 × 2.4 × 1.2	14	Pacific
Bold	70	5	7.6 × 2.4 × 0.9	14	Pacific
Brave	70	5	7.6 × 2.4 × 0.9	14	Pacific
Bright	70	5	7.6 × 2.4 × 0.9	14	Pacific
Brisk	70	5	7.6 × 2.4 × 0.9	14	Pacific
Beluga	85	5	7.6 × 2.4 × 0.3	20	Quebec
Brion	85	5	7.6 × 2.4 × 0.3	20	Quebec
Brock	70	. . .	7.6 × 3.0 × 0.9	22	Cen/Arc
Dunlin	66	. . .	7.6 × 3.0 × 1.4	28	Sco/Fun
Gibor	85	5	7.6 × 2.4 × 0.6	20	Quebec
Hydro IV	71	6	7.6 × 2.7 × 0.9	16	Quebec
L'Istorlet	87	5	7.6 × 2.4 × 0.3	20	Quebec
Jaeger	66	. . .	7.6 × 3.0 × 1.4	28	Sco/Fun
Sea Truck	71	. . .	7.6 × 3.0 × 0.5	25	Cen/Arc
Willet	66	. . .	7.6 × 3.0 × 1.4	20	Sco/Fun
Godwit (Also known as *La Bradelle*)	66	. . .	7.6 × 3.0 × 1.4	28	Sco/Fun
R.D. 104	69	5	7.3 × 3.0 × 0.9	9	Pacific
7C-1528	84	2	7.1 × 2.6 × 0.8	40	Gulf
Cormorant	86	. . .	7.0 × . . . × . . .	. . .	Cen/Arc
Melibe	63	5	7.0 × 3.0 × 0.6	8	Pacific
Morillon	82	5	7.0 × 2.5 × 0.9	20	Quebec
Penguin	87	. . .	7.0 × 2.4 × 0.9	. . .	Cen/Arc
Petrel	87	. . .	7.0 × 2.4 × 0.9	. . .	Cen/Arc
Pewee	87	. . .	7.0 × 2.4 × 0.9	. . .	Cen/Arc
Pintail	87	. . .	7.0 × 2.4 × 0.9	. . .	Cen/Arc
Plover	87	. . .	7.0 × 2.4 × 0.9	. . .	Cen/Arc
Puffin	86	. . .	7.0 × 2.4 × 0.6	. . .	Cen/Arc
Raven	86	2	7.0 × 2.7 × 0.9	20	Pacific
Robin	85	2	7.0 × 2.7 × 0.9	20	Pacific
Slicker I (Barge)	77	. . .	7.0 × 2.4 × 0.6	8 (sic)	Pacific
Wagtail	84	2	7.0 × 2.7 × 0.9	30	Cen/Arc
Warbler	86	2	7.0 × 2.7 × 0.9	30	Cen/Arc
Waxwing	84	2	7.0 × 2.7 × 0.9	30	Cen/Arc
Weaver	83	2	7.0 × 2.7 × 0.9	30	Cen/Arc
Whistler	84	2	7.0 × 2.7 × 0.9	30	Cen/Arc
Willet	83	2	7.0 × 2.7 × 0.9	30	Cen/Arc
Woodcock	83	2	7.0 × 2.7 × 0.9	30	Cen/Arc
Woodpecker	84	2	7.0 × 2.7 × 0.9	30	Cen/Arc
Wren	83	2	7.0 × 2.7 × 0.9	30	Cen/Arc
Gate	82	. . .	7.0 × 2.5 × 0.8	20	Quebec
Gode	82	5	7.0 × 2.5 × 0.8	20	Quebec
Gold	82	5	7.0 × 2.5 × 0.8	20	Quebec
Kihao	82	. . .	6.7 × 2.1 × 0.7	. . .	Cen/Arc
Loks Land	80	. . .	6.7 × 2.1 × 0.7	. . .	Cen/Arc
Midge	77	. . .	6.7 × 2.1 × 0.7	. . .	Cen/Arc
Pitsiulak	81	. . .	6.7 × 2.1 × 0.7	. . .	Cen/Arc
Revenge	82	. . .	6.7 × 2.1 × 0.7	. . .	Cen/Arc
Strider	78	. . .	6.7 × 2.1 × 0.7	. . .	Cen/Arc
Windy Bay	82	. . .	6.7 × 2.4 × 0.8	. . .	Cen/Arc
Bonne Esperance	85	5	6.7 × 2.4 × 0.3	20	Quebec
Heron	81	5	6.7 × 2.4 × 0.6	30	Quebec
La Grande Basque	84	5	6.7 × 2.6 × 0.3	18	Quebec
La Mouvee	84	5	6.7 × 2.6 × 0.3	18	Quebec
Manicomeau	84	5	6.7 × 2.6 × 0.3	18	Quebec
Le Foulon	85	5	6.7 × 2.4 × 0.3	20	Quebec
Mecatina	82	5	6.7 × 2.4 × 0.3	20	Quebec
Mysis	74	5	6.7 × 2.4 × 1.5	7	Sco/Fun
Orca	84	3	6.7 × 2.4 × 0.9	18	Pacific
Fish Point	72	. . .	6.4 × 2.1 × 0.5	. . .	Cen/Arc
Murph I	83	. . .	6.4 × 2.0 × 0.7	. . .	Cen/Arc
Murph II	83	. . .	6.4 × 2.0 × 0.7	. . .	Cen/Arc
Outrage	82	. . .	6.4 × 2.1 × 0.5	. . .	Cen/Arc
Parlaiyut	73	. . .	6.4 × 2.1 × 0.5	. . .	Cen/Arc
Penquis	72	. . .	6.4 × 2.1 × 0.5	. . .	Cen/Arc
Sculpin	72	. . .	6.4 × 2.1 × 0.5	. . .	Cen/Arc
Barachois	86	5	6.4 × 2.4 × 0.9	20	Quebec
Demon 1	83	. . .	6.4 × 2.4 × 0.9	36	Quebec
Demon 2	84	. . .	6.4 × 2.4 × 0.9	36	Quebec
Harpie	70	4	6.4 × 2.4 × 1.2	28	Gulf
Hornet	70	4	6.4 × 2.4 × 0.8	28	Cen/Arc
Hydra	70	4	6.4 × 2.4 × 0.8	28	Cen/Arc
Lab 1 through 3	72	. . .	6.4 × 2.1 × 0.8	22	Cen/Arc
Marsoin	85	5	6.4 × 2.4 × 0.9	20	Quebec
Wasp	72	. . .	6.4 × 2.1 × 0.8	14	Quebec
Dauphin	79	5	6.4 × 1.9 × 0.6	30	Quebec
Defi	79	5	6.4 × 1.9 × 0.6	30	Quebec
Pisces IV (Submersible)	71	5	6.1 × 3.0 × . . .	2 (sub)	Pacific

* Regions: Newfdl.—Newfoundland; Cen/Arc—Central & Arctic; Sco/Fun—Nova Scotia & Bay of Fundy

Note: There are also 22 craft in the "Procor" series built 1982–86: 6 grt; 6.7 × 2.1 × 1 meters; 30 knots; 14 operating in the Newfoundland Region, three in the Gulf Region, four in the Nova Scotia-Bay of Fundy Region, and one in the Quebec Region. The Department of Fisheries and Oceans also operates approximately 500 craft of less than 6.0-m. length.

CAPE VERDE

Republic of Cape Verde

COAST GUARD

Personnel: Approx. 160 total

Naval Aviation: An EMB-111 Bandeirante was acquired early 1989 for maritime surveillance duties.

PATROL BOATS

Note: The acquisition of Brazilian-built patrol boats was under study in 1989. All surviving units are in poor condition and require replacement.

♦ **2 Soviet Shershen-class former torpedo boats**

451 452

Shershen 451, outboard 452 19

D: 145 tons (170 fl) **S:** 45 kts **Dim:** 34.0 × 6.8 × 1.5
A: 4/30-mm AK-230 AA (II × 2)
Electron Equipt: Radar: 1/Pot Head surf. search, 1/Drum Tilt f.c.
M: 3 M503A diesels; 3 props; 12,000 bhp
Range: 460/42; 850/30 **Crew:** 18 tot.

Remarks: Transferred 3- and 7-79. Torpedo tubes removed prior to transfer.

♦ **3 Soviet Zhuk class**—transferred 1980

D: 48 tons (60 fl) **S:** 34 kts **Dim:** 24.0 × 5.0 × 1.2 (1.8 props)
A: 4/14.5-mm mg (II × 2)
Electron Equipt: Radar: 1/Spin Trough nav.
M: 2 M50 diesels; 2 props; 2,400 bhp **Range:** 700/28; 1,100/15
Crew: 12 tot.

APE VERDE *(continued)*

JXILIARIES

1 logistics landing craft Bldr: Stülcken , West Germany

HEU RASO (In serv. 11-88)

D: . . . **S:** . . . **Dim:** 28.50 × . . . × . . . **M:** . . .

1 Biya-class survey ship Bldr: Stocznia Pólnocna, Gdańsk, Poland

450 5 DE JULIO (In serv. 1968–72)

le Julio (A 450) 1982

D: 750 tons (fl) **S:** 13 kts **Dim:** 55.0 × 9.2 × 2.6
Electron Equipt: Radar: 1/Don-2 nav.
M: 2 diesels; 2 CP props; 1,200 bhp
Range: 4,700/11 **Endurance:** 15 days **Crew:** 25 tot.

marks: Transferred from U.S.S.R. 1980 for use as a training ship. Also capable of ing as a navigational buoy tender. One 5-ton crane.

1 oceanographic and fisheries research ship

. . . . . . (ex-*Fengus*)

D: . . . **S:** 11 kts **Dim:** 27.32 × 7.40 × 3.60
M: 2 Caterpillar 3508 DITA diesels; 1 prop; 565 bhp

marks: 157 grt/60 dwt. Transferred 6-5-84 by Icelandic Government Agency for reign Aid.

CHILE

public of Chile

rsonnel (1991): 24,700 total (2,000 officers; 22,700 men); 5,200 naval infantry. il Service personnel number about 6,600.

val Aviation: Fixed-wing aircraft include 3 Falcon Guardian, 6 Embraer EMB 111 ndeirante, and 3 EMB 110 Bandeirante maritime surveillance aircraft, 10 A-36 cón strike/trainers equipped for (but not with) Sea Skua antiship missiles (trans- red from the air force in 1988), 5 CASA 212 Aviocar light transports, and several atus PC-7 trainers. Helicopters include 4 NAS.332 F and 4 AS.332 Super Puma (one d as a trainer), 4 AS.365F Dauphin light ASW, 10 Alouette-III, and 6 Bell 206A Ranger. There are plans to acquire up to 11 Beech 99A maritime surveillance craft to replace the Bandeirantes.

ilean Navy Falcon Guardian 200 Chilean Navy, 1990

ilean Navy EMB 111 Bandeirante Chilean Navy, 1990

Chilean Navy CASA 212 Aviocar Chilean Navy, 1990

Chilean Navy Alouette-III Gary Davies/Maritime Photographic, 2-90

Chilean Navy PC-7 trainer Chilean Navy, 1990

Weapons: In 1989, 20 Murène torpedoes were ordered from France for use by the ASW helicopters. Chile obtained a license to build the Marconi Tigerfish homing torpedo in 1991 and also plans to export the weapon. The four NAS-532F Super Puma helicopters delivered 3-90 can launch AM 39 Exocet missiles, as can the Falcon Guardian maritime surveillance aircraft. Most other equipment is of U.S. or British origin.

Note: Although pendant numbers are given below for reference, the Chilean Navy has not had them painted on ships' sides for some years.

SUBMARINES

Note: Chile desires to acquire three to four additional submarines, possibly of the Dutch Moray design, with some to be built at ASMAR, Talcahuano.

◆ **2 IKL Type 209/1400** Bldr: Howaldtswerke, Kiel, West Germany

	Laid down	L	In serv.
S 20 THOMSON	1-11-80	28-2-82	31-8-84
S 21 SIMPSON	15-2-81	29-7-83	18-9-84

Simpson (S 21) Chilean Navy, 1990

SUBMARINES *(continued)*

Simpson (S 21) Gary Davies/Maritime Photographic, 2-90

Simpson (S 21) Leo Van Ginderen, 1991

D: 1,158 tons light (1,285 tons surf./1,395 sub. fl) **S:** 11/22 kts
Dim: 61.00 × 6.30 × 5.50 (surf.)
A: 8/533-mm TT fwd (16 German SST-4 torpedoes)
Electron Equipt:
Radar: 1/Calypso II—Sonar: Krupp Atlas CSU-3 system
M: 4 MTU 12V-493 AZ-80 diesels; 4/450-kw AEG generators; 1 Siemens electric motor; 5,000 bhp
Fuel: 116 tons **Range:** 400/4; 16/21.5 sub.; 8,200/8 snorkel
Endurance: 50 days **Crew:** 5 officers, 26 enlisted

Remarks: Ordered 12-80; construction encountered political opposition in West Germany. Used components from canceled Iranian order. Maximum snorkel speed is 12 kts. S 21, damaged in collision 29-3-84 on trials, was completed 18-9-84. S 20 was completed 7-5-84. Have larger casing than earlier IKL-designed submarines. Sail and masting .5 m higher than on other ships of this class, to cope with heavy seas in Chilean operating areas. S 20 began 10-month overhaul at ASMAR, Talcahuano, in 10-90, to be followed by S 21 and prompting claim by ASMAR that it can now build submarines in Chile.

♦ 2 British Oberon class Bldr: Scott-Lithgow SB & Eng., Greenock

	Laid down	L	In serv.
S 22 O'Brien	17-1-71	21-12-72	4-76
S 23 Hyatt	16-1-72	26-9-73	27-9-76

O'Brien (S 22) Dr. Giorgio Arra, 1977

D: 1,650/2,070/2,450 tons **S:** 15/17.5 kts
Dim: 89.92 (87.45 pp) × 8.07 × 5.48
A: 8/533-mm TT (6 long fwd, 2 short aft)—22 SST-4 torpedoes
Electron Equipt:
Radar: 1/Kelvin-Hughes Type 1006 nav.
Sonar: 1/Type 2007 passive LF, 1/187 active/passive, 1/197 Velox sound intercept, 1/719 underwater telephone
M: 2 1,840-hp Admiralty Standard Range 16 VVS-AS21 diesels, diesel-electric drive; 2 props; 6,000 shp
Endurance: 56 days **Fuel:** 298 m^3 (446 m^3 emergency)
Crew: 6 officers, 62 enlisted

Remarks: Delivery of these submarines was a year late because of a number of malfunctions in the electrical equipment. The after two "short" torpedo tubes were for countermeasures weapons and are no longer in use. Have U.K. Mk 2 submerged signal and decoy ejector forward, Mk 4 Mod 1B aft; both launch 102-mm devices. Collided with each other on surface, 4-87; repaired.

Note: The *Brooklyn*-class cruiser *O'Higgins* (ex-*Brooklyn*, CL 40) was stricken 12-91 and sold for scrap.

Almirante Latorre (14), Capitan Prat (11), destroyer Almirante Riveros (18), and submarine Simpson (S 21) at Valparaiso Maritim Photographic, 2-90

DESTROYERS

♦ 4 British "County" class

	Bldr	Laid down	L	In serv
11 Capitan Prat (ex-*Norfolk*)	Swan Hunter, Wallsend-on-Tyne	15-3-66	16-11-67	7-3-7
12 Almirante Cochrane (ex-*Antrim*)	Fairfield SB & Eng., Govan	20-1-66	19-10-67	14-7-7
14 Almirante Latorre (ex-*Glamorgan*)	Vickers-Armstrong, Newcastle-on-Tyne	13-9-62	9-7-64	11-10-6
15 Blanco Encalada (ex-*Fife*)	Fairfield SB & Eng., Govan	1-6-62	9-7-64	21-6-6

Blanco Encalada (15)—helo carrier Capt. Gustavo Marin Watkins, C.N., 198

Blanco Encalada (15)—helo carrier conversion Chilean Navy, 198

Almirante Cochrane (12)—Sea Slug-equipped Chilean Navy, 19

DESTROYERS *(continued)*

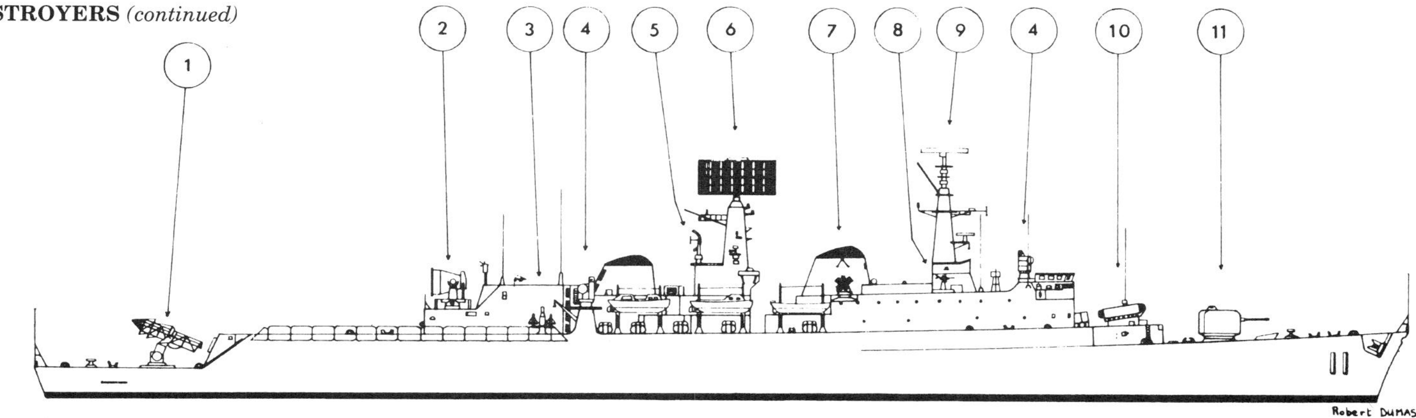

Capitan Prat (11) 1. Sea Slug launcher 2. Type 901 radar director 3. Sea Cat launcher 4. MRS.3 radar director for Sea Cat 5. Type 278 height-finding radar 6. Type 965M air early-warning radar 7. Knebworth/Corvus chaff RL 8. 20-mm AA 9. Type 9920 search radar 10. Exocet launchers 11. 114-mm Mk 6 gun mounts

D: 5,440 tons (6,200 fl) **S:** 32.5 kts (30 sust.)
Dim: 158.55 (153.9 pp) × 16.46 × 6.3 (max.)
A: D 11, 12: 4/MM 38 Exocet—1/Sea Slug Mk 2 syst. (II × 1; 30 missiles)—2/Sea Cat GWS 22 SAM syst. (IV × 2, . . . missiles)—2/114-mm Mk 6 DP (II × 1)—2/20-mm AA (I × 2)—1/Alouette-III helicopter; D 13, 14: 4/MM 38 Exocet—14 only: 2/Sea Cat GWS 22 syst. (IV × 2)—2/114-mm Mk 6 DP (II × 1)—2/20-mm AA (I × 2)—2/AS.365F Dauphin or NAS.332F Super Puma helicopters
Electron Equipt:
Radar: 1/978 nav., 1/965M early warning , 1/992Q air search, 1/277 height-finder, 1/901 Sea Slug f.c.(not in 13, 14), 1/903 gun f.c., 2/904 Sea Cat f.c. (not in 13)
Sonar: 1/184 MF hull-mounted, 1/162 depth-determining
EW: UA-8/9 passive, . . . jammers, 2 Corvus chaff RL (VIII × 2)
M: COSAG: 2 sets A.E.I. GT (15,000 shp each) and 4 English Electric G6 gas turbines (7,500 shp each); 2 props; 60,000 shp
Boilers: 2 Babcock & Wilcox; 49.2 kg/cm, 510° C **Fuel:** 600 tons
Electric: 4,750 kw **Range:** 3,500/28 **Crew:** 36 officers, 434 men

Remarks: *Prat* purchased by Chile, left U.K. 17-2-82, transferred 6-4-82 in Chile; *Cochrane* purchased 22-6-84, commissioned 25-6-84. *Latorre* transferred by sale 3-10-86, arriving 12-86. *Blanco Encalada* purchased and transferred 12-8-87. *Prat* damaged by fire early 1986, but returned to service by 9-87. Four pair fin stabilizers. Twin rudders. Sea Slug magazine runs 80 m long through ship, with two parallel rows of 15 missiles. SCOT SATCOMM equipment deleted. Have ADAWS-1 data system.

Blanco Encalada had the Sea Slug facilities deleted and replaced with a larger helicopter hangar and flight deck to handle two helicopters each at ASMAR, Talcahuano, completing 10-88. Similar conversion of *Almirante Latorre* to complete 1992. Future plans include installation of an Israeli Barak point-defense SAM system and a towed sonar array (TACTASS) in all.

In this class, each propeller is driven by one steam turbine for cruise, adding one or two gas turbines for boost. There are 3 steam turbo-alternators and 3 gas-turbine generators.

The Sea Slug Mk 2 SAM system, which can also be used against surface targets, is now used only by Chile, which bought all remaining missiles during 1986.

Weight: 900 kg (2,000 kg with boosters)
Length: 5.94 m
Diameter: 0.41 m
Wingspan: 1.42 m
Guidance: Beam-rider, using the one Type 901 radar
Altitude: 500 to 50,000 ft.
Speed: Mach 1.8
Range: 15 n.m.
Propulsion: Solid fuel, with four solid-fuel boosters

◆ **2 Almirante Williams class** Bldr: Vickers-Armstrong, Ltd., Barrow-in-Furness

	Laid down	L	In serv.
D 18 Almirante Riveros	12-4-57	12-12-58	31-12-60
D 19 Almirante Williams	20-6-56	5-5-58	26-3-60

Almirante Riveros (18)—with new EW equipment, all 102-mm guns aboard Gary Davies/Maritime Photographic, 2-90

Almirante Williams (19)—with "B" 102-mount landed, inboard *Ministro Portales* (17) and the submarine *O'Brien* (S 22) Gary Davies/Maritime Photographic, 2-90

D: 2,730 tons (3,300 fl) **S:** 34.5 kts
Dim: 122.5 (113.99 pp) × 13.1 × 3.9
A: 4/MM 38 Exocet (see Remarks)—2/Sea Cat SAM systems (IV × 2) — 4/102-mm DP (I × 4) (see Remarks)—4/40-mm AA (I × 4)—6/324-mm Mk 32 ASW TT (III × 2)—2/Squid Mk 4 ASW mortars (III × 2)
Electron Equipt:
Radar: 1/Decca 1629 nav., 1 Plessey AWS-1 early warning, 1 Marconi SNW-10 air/surf. search, 2/H.S.A. SGR-102 gun f.c., 2/H.S.A. SNG-20 Sea Cat f.c.
Sonar: 1/184B MF hull-mounted, 1/170 HF attack/depth-determining
EW: WLR-1 intercept
M: 2 sets Parsons-Pamatreda GT; 2 props; 50,000 shp
Boilers: 4 Babcock & Wilcox; 43.3 kg/cm, 454° C
Range: 6,000/16
Crew: 17 officers, 249 enlisted

Remarks: Refitted in Great Britain, D 18 in 1973–75 and D 19 in 1971–74. Dutch M-4 radar directors for Sea Cat. Exocet replaced four 533-mm TT (IV × 1); 2 Exocet removed from each and placed on *Allen M. Sumner* class, 1980, and they did not appear to have the missiles aboard in recent sightings. The 114-mm guns are unique to this class; gunhouse weight is 26 tons, muzzle velocity is 900 m/sec., firing rate is 46 rpm, range is 18,500 m, and maximum altitude is 12,000 m. The gun mounts were progressively rehabilitated on both during their refits in 1986–88, two mounts being maintained operational on each ship; the aft superfiring position was used as an interim helicopter deck on *Almirante Williams*. The manually loaded Squid mortars have a maximum range of 800 m and carry a 52-kg warhead. If funds are available, the Israeli Barak SAM system will replace the obsolete and ineffective Sea Cat.

Note: The U.S. *Allen M. Sumner*-class destroyers *Ministro Zenteno* (D 16, ex-*Charles S. Sperry,* DD 697) and *Ministro Portales* (D 17, ex-*Douglas H. Fox,* DD 779) were stricken at the end of 1990.

FRIGATES

◆ **3 (+ 1) British Leander class** Bldr: Yarrow & Co., Scotstoun, Glasgow

	Laid down	L	In serv.
PF 06 Condell	5-6-71	12-6-72	21-12-73
PF 07 Lynch	6-12-72	6-12-73	25-5-74
PF 08 Ministro Zenteno (ex-*Achilles*)	1-12-67	21-11-68	9-7-70

FRIGATES *(continued)*

Lynch (PF 07)—as modernized
Gary Davies/Maritime Photographic, 2-90

Lynch (PF 07)—note MM 40 Exocet tubes flanking hangar, cleared fantail, new EW suite Gary Davies/Maritime Photographic, 2-90

D: 2,500 tons (2,962 fl), except PF 08: 2,660 tons (3,120 fl) **S:** 27 kts
Dim: 113.38 (109.73 pp) × 13.12 × 4.50 (5.49 props)
A: 4/MM 40 Exocet SSM (II × 2)—2/114-mm Mk VI DP (II × 1)—1/Sea Cat GWS.22 SAM syst. (IV × 1)—2/20-mm AA (I × 2)—PF 06, 07: 6/324-mm ASW TT (III × 2)—PF 08: 1/Limbo Mk 10 ASW mortar (III × 1)—1/Alouette-III or Bell 206A JetRanger helicopter
Electron Equipt:
Radar: 1/978 (PF 08: 1006) nav., 1/965 early warning, 1/992Q (PF 08: 994) air/surf. search, 1/903 gun f.c., 1/904 Sea Cat f.c.
Sonar: 1/177 MF hull-mounted (PF 08: 184), 1/170B HF attack, 1/162 depth-determining
EW: Elta NS-9003 intercept, 4 decoy RL (II × 2), 2/Corvus (DLC) decoy RL (VI × 2)
M: 2 sets geared turbines; 2 props; 30,000 shp
Boilers: 2 Babcock & Wilcox; 38.7 kg/cm, 450° C
Electric: 2,500 kw **Range:** 4,500/12 **Fuel:** 500 tons
Crew: 19–20 officers, 241 enlisted

Remarks: PF 06 and 07 ordered 14-1-70. PF 08 paid off from Royal Navy at end March 1990 and was sold to Chile later in the year, leaving as deck cargo aboard the heavy-lift ship *Super Servant 4* on 27-11-90. MRS 3 GFCS for 114-mm. PF 06 and 07 originally had MM 38 Exocet missiles at stern in lieu of Limbo ASW mortar; the missiles were exchanged for the later MM 40 and were relocated flanking the hangar in refits at the end of the 1980s, at which time the EW suite was updated with Israeli-supplied equipment. PF 08 will be updated to the same standard at a future date but will initially be employed unaltered for EEZ patrol duties. All three are to be equipped with the Israeli Barak SAM system when it becomes available. Chile still hopes to acquire one more *Leander,* probably *Achilles,* which is scheduled to be retired from the Royal Navy in the spring of 1992; the ship would be named *O'Higgins.*

◆ **1 U.S. Charles Lawrence class** Bldr: Bethlehem SY, Hingham, Mass.

	Laid down	L	In serv.
29 Virgilio Uribe (ex-*Daniel Griffin,* APD 38, ex-DE 54)	7-9-42	25-2-43	9-6-43

Virgilio Uribe (29)—note SPS-6 radar antenna aft Chilean Navy, 1989

D: 1,691 tons (2,130 fl) **S:** 23 kts **Dim:** 93.27 × 11.25 × 4.80
A: 1/127-mm 38-cal Mk 30 DP—6/40-mm AA (II × 3)—2/Mk 11 Hedgehog ASW mortars (XXIV × 2)—2/Mk 9 d.c. racks (12 d.c.)
Electron Equipt:
Radar: 1/. . . nav., 1/SPS-4 surf. search, 1/SPS-6 air search
Sonar: . . .
M: 2 G.E. turbines, turboelectric drive; 2 props; 12,000 shp
Boilers: 2 Foster-Wheeler: 30.6 kg/cm, 399° C **Electric:** 680 kw
Range: 1,750/23; 4,800/12 **Crew:** . . . . . .

Remarks: Transferred 12-66, the survivor of four transferred to Chile. Had been out of service for several years but was reactivated during the late 1980s for service as training ship for the Second Naval Zone. Can carry two LCVP landing craft in quadrantial davits amidships. The antenna for the SPS-6 radar is located atop the lattice mast aft—an unusual location for a ship of this class.

CORVETTES

Note: There are plans to construct five 70-meter fisheries-protection ships at ASMAR, Talcahuano, using plans prepared by NEVESBU, the Netherlands. They would be armed with one light gun and have helicopter facilities.

◆ **1 U.S. Abnaki-class former fleet tug** Bldr: Charleston SB & DD Co., S.C.

	Laid down	L	In serv.
63 Sergente Aldea (ex-*Arikara,* ATF 98)	28-11-42	22-4-43	15-11-43

Sergente Aldea (63) Chilean Nav

D: 1,235 tons (1,675 fl) **S:** 15 kts
Dim: 62.48 (59.44 wl) × 11.73 × 4.67
A: 1/76.2-mm DP Mk 26—2/20-mm AA (I × 2)
Electron Equipt: Radar: 1/SPS-5 surf. search **Crew:** 85 tot.
M: diesel-electric: 4 Busch-Sulzer BS539 diesels; 1 prop; 3,000 shp
Electric: 400 kw **Fuel:** 363 tons **Range:** 7,000/15; 15,000/8

Remarks: Transferred 1-7-71 on lease, later purchased. Sister *Yelcho* (AGS 64) is used as a survey vessel (see below). May now also have a navigational radar set.

Note: U.S. Sotoyomo-class tug *Lautaro* (62), long used on patrol duties, was transferred to Uruguay 5-91.

GUIDED-MISSILE BOATS

◆ **2 Israeli Reshev (Sa'ar IV) class** Bldr: Israeli SY, Haifa

	L	In serv.	Transferred
LM 30 Casma (ex-*Romach*)	1-74	3-74	12-79
LM 31 Chipana (ex-*Keshet*)	23-8-73	10-73	1-81

Reshev class in Chilean service Chilean Navy, 198

GUIDED-MISSILE BOATS *(continued)*

D: 415 tons (450 fl) **S:** 32 kts **Dim:** 58.10 × 7.60 × 2.40
A: 4/Gabriel SSM (I × 4)—2/76-mm DP OTO Melara (I × 2)—2/20-mm AA (I × 2)—2/12.7-mm mg (I × 2)
Electron Equipt:
Radar: 1/Thomson-CSF THD 1040 Neptune search, 1/Elta M-2221 (Orion RTN-10X) f.c.
EW: Elta MN-53 or NS 9000 passive intercept syst.—4 large/72 small chaff RL
M: 4 MTU MD 871 diesels; 4 props; 14,000 bhp
Range: 1,500/30; 4,000/17 **Crew:** 45 tot.

Remarks: Harpoon SSM removed prior to transfer. Transfer of four additional units canceled.

◆ **2 Israeli Sa'ar II class** Bldr: CMN, Cherbourg, France

LM 32 Iquique (ex-*Hanit*) (L: 1969)
LM 33 Covadonga (ex-*Hetz*) (L: 14-12-69)

Sa'ar II class in Chilean service Chilean Navy, 1990

Iquique (LM 32) Chilean Navy, 1990

D: 220 tons (250 fl) **S:** 40 kts
Dim: 45.00 × 7.00 × 1.80 (2.50 props)
A: 6/Gabriel SSM (III × 2)—1/76-mm OTO Melara DP—2/12.7-mm mg (1 × 2)
Electron Equipt:
Radar: 1/Thomson-CSF THD 1040 Neptune search, 1/Elta M 2221 (Orion RTN-10X) f.c.
EW: VHFD/F, Elta MN-53 or NS 9000 intercept, . . ./RL
M: 4 MTU MD871 diesels; 4 props; 14,000 bhp **Fuel:** 30 tons
Range: 1,000/30; 1,600/20; 2,500/15
Crew: 5–6 officers, 30–35 men

Remarks: Purchased 12-88, transferred 1-89, and commissioned 3-5-89. U.S. Harpoon missiles removed prior to transfer, and a second triple, trainable Gabriel launcher installed on the aft mounting ring, which can also accommodate a single 40-mm AA gun. Acquired in lieu of a once-planned indigenous missile boat construction program and in lieu of additional units of the larger Sa'ar IV class.

TORPEDO BOATS

◆ **4 Guacolda class (Lürssen 36-m design)** Bldr: Bazán, Cadiz, Spain (In serv. 1965–66)

81 Frescia 82 Guacolda 83 Quidora 84 Tehualda

Frescia (81) Chilean Navy, 1989

D: 134 tons (fl) **S:** 30 kts **Dim:** 36.2 (34.0 wl) × 5.6 × 1.68
A: 2/40 mm AA—4/533-mm TT (British Mk IV)
Electron Equipt: Radar: 1/Decca 505 nav.
M: 2 Mercedes-Benz MB839Bb diesels; 2 props; 4,800 bhp
Electric: 90 kVA **Range:** 1,500/15 **Crew:** 20 tot.

PATROL BOATS

◆ **1 U.S. PC 1638-class submarine chaser** Bldr: ASMAR, Talcahuano

	In serv.
P 37 Papudo (ex-U.S. PC 1646)	27-11-71

Papudo (P 37) Chilean Navy, 1977

D: 313 tons (417 fl) **S:** 20 kts **Dim:** 52.9 × 7.0 × 3.1
A: 1/40-mm AA—4/20-mm AA (II × 2)—1/Mk 15 Hedgehog trainable ASW mortar (XXIV × 1)—4/Mk 6 d.c. throwers—1 d.c. rack
Electron Equipt:
Radar: 1/ . . . nav.—Sonar: SQS-17 MF hull-mounted
M: 2 G.M. 16-567 diesels; 2 props; 2,800 bhp **Fuel:** 60 tons
Range: 5,000/10 **Crew:** 4 officers, 65 enlisted

Remarks: The construction of two additional units of this class, to have been named *Abtao* (P 36) and *Pisaqua* (P 38), was canceled. Based on U.S. PC 461 design. Sisters in Turkish Navy.

◆ **6 Israeli Dabur class** Bldr: Israeli Aircraft Industries, Be'er Sheva (In serv. 1973–77)

Bolados Bravo Camos Diaz Saunas Tellez

D: 25 tons (35 fl) **S:** 25 kts **Dim:** 19.8 × 5.8 × 0.8
A: 2/20-mm (I × 2)—2/12.7-mm mg (I × 2)
Electron Equipt: Radar: 1/Decca 926 navigational
M: 2 G.M. 12V71 TI diesels; 2 props; 960 bhp
Electric: 20 kw **Range:** 1,200/17 **Crew:** 1 officer, 5 enlisted

Remarks: Purchased at the end of 1990. Quarters air-conditioned and spacious.

HYDROGRAPHIC SURVEY AND RESEARCH SHIPS

◆ **1 Antarctic patrol, transport, and research ship**

	Bldr	Laid down	L	In serv.
AP 45 Piloto Pardo	Haarlemsche Scheepsbouw	1957	1958	8-58

Piloto Pardo (AP 45) Chilean Navy, 1977

D: 1,250 tons (2,545 fl) **S:** 14 kts **Dim:** 83.0 × 11.9 × 7.4 (fl)
M: diesel-electric propulsion; 1 prop; 2,000 shp **Range:** 6,000/10
Crew: 56 ship's company + 24 passengers

Remarks: Ice-reinforced hull. U.S. Mk 26 76.2-mm single-fire gun on forecastle removed mid-1980s. Helicopter platform can accommodate one Bell 206 JetRanger or Alouette-III.

◆ **1 U.S. Cherokee-class former fleet tug** Bldr: Commercial Iron Wks, Portland, Ore.

	Laid down	L	In serv.
AGS 64 Yelcho (ex-USS *Tekesta*, ATF 93)	7-9-42	20-3-43	16-8-43

HYDROGRAPHIC SURVEY AND RESEARCH SHIPS *(continued)*

Yelcho (AGS 64) Chilean Navy, 1987

D: 1,235 tons (1,675 fl) **S:** 15 kts
Dim: 62.48 (59.44 wl) × 11.73 × 4.67
A: 1/76.2-mm Mk 26 DP—2/20-mm AA
Electron Equipt: Radar: 2/. . . nav. **Crew:** 5 officers, 67 enlisted
M: 4 G.M. 12-278 diesels, electric drive; 1 prop; 3,000 shp
Fuel: 363 tons **Range:** 7,000/15; 15,000/8 **Electric:** 260 kw

Remarks: Used for oceanographic and Antarctic research. Loaned 15-5-60. Carries survey launch on fantail.

AUXILIARY SHIPS AND SERVICE CRAFT

♦ **1 replenishment oiler** Bldr: Burmeister & Wain, Copenhagen

	L	In serv.
AO 53 Araucano	21-6-66	10-1-67

Araucano (AO 53) Chilean Navy, 1989

D: 23,000 tons (fl) **S:** 17 kts **Dim:** 160.93 × 21.95 × 8.80
A: 8/40-mm Bofors AA (II × 4)
Electron Equipt: Radar: 2/. . . nav.
M: 1 Burmeister & Wain 62 VT 2 BF 140, 9-cyl. diesel; 1 prop; 10,800 bhp
Range: 12,000/14.5 **Crew:** 13 officers, 117 enlisted

Remarks: Can replenish two ships alongside under way simultaneously. Carries 21,126 cu. meters liquid and 1,444 cu. meters dry cargo. Has four U.S. Mk 51 lead-computing directors for the 40-mm AA mounts.

♦ **1 U.K. "Later Tide"-class replenishment oiler** Bldr: Hawthorn Leslie, Hebburn-on-Tyne

	Laid down	L	In serv.
AO 52 Almirante Montt (ex-*Tidepool*)	4-12-61	11-12-62	28-6-63

Almirante Montt (AO 52) Chilean Navy, 1990

D: 8,531 tons light (27,400 fl) **S:** 18.3 kts (17 sust.)
Dim: 177.60 (167.65 pp) × 21.64 × 9.75
A: 4/20-mm Oerlikon Mk 9 AA (I × 4)—4/12.7-mm mg (II × 2)
Electron Equipt:
Radar: 1/Kelvin-Hughes 14/12, 1 Kelvin-Hughes 14/16
M: 1 set Pametrada GT; 1 prop; 15,000 shp **Range:** 15,000/17
Boilers: 2 Babcock & Wilcox, 60 kg/cm, 510° C **Crew:** 110 tot.

Remarks: 14,130 grt/18,900 dwt. Sold to Chile and was to have been transferred 2-4-82 at Valparaiso; repossessed because of Argentine invasion of Falklands, returned and commissioned in Chilean Navy 8-82. Cargo: approx. 18,000 tons liquid. Hangar and flight deck for one NAS 332F Super Puma or three Alouette-III helicopters. Can replenish liquids from three stations to port, two to starboard and solids at one station to starboard.

♦ **1 small tanker** Bldr: Marco Chilena SA, Iquique (In serv. 1966)

AO 55 Guardian Brito (ex-*Silvia*)

Guardian Brito (AO 55) Chilean Navy, 1989

D: 482 tons (fl) **S:** 10 kts **Dim:** 39.60 × 7.44 × 3.30 (max.)
M: MWM diesel; 400 bhp **Range:** 3,000/8
Crew: 1 officer, 7 enlisted

Remarks: Acquired 13-1-83 from the Ultramar Co. Based at Punta Arenas.

♦ **1 coastal fuel lighter** Bldr: Svendborg, Denmark (In serv. . . .)

AP 48 Aguila (ex-*Australgas*)

D: 735 tons (fl) **S:** 10 kts **Dim:** 51.3 × 8.7 × 3.6 **Crew:** 13 tot.
A: 3/20-mm AA (I × 3)
Electron Equipt: Radar: 1/ Decca . . . nav.
M: 1 Burmeister & Wain Alpha diesel; 480 bhp
Range: 6,000/10

Remarks: 397 dwt. Former commercial tanker acquired 1984 and commissioned 1985.

♦ **2 Norwegian-built tug/supply vessels** (In serv. 1974)

	Bldr.
ATF 65 Janequeo (ex-*Maersk Transporter*)	L.H. Salthammer Båtbyggeri A/S, Vestnes
ATF 66 Galvarina (ex-*Maersk Traveller*)	Aukra Bruk A/S, Aukra

Janequeo (ATF 65) Chilean Navy, 19[illegible]

D: 941 tons light (2,380 fl) **S:** 15 kts (14 sust.)
Dim: 58.32 (52.20 pp) × 12.63 × 3.97
Electron Equipt:
Radar: 1/Furuno FR 240 nav., 1/ Terma Pilot 7T-48 nav.
M: 2 Atlas-MAK 8M 553AK diesels, 2 CP props; 6,400 bhp—bow-thruster
Range: . . ./. . . **Crew:** 5 officers, 15 enlisted

Remarks: ATF 65 was fitted out by Aukra Bruk A/S. Both purchased 1987, l[illegible] Europe 14-12-87, and commissioned 26-1-88 for use as patrol and search-and-resc[illegible] ships and logistics transports in Chile's southern regions. Cargo capacity: 1,400 to[illegible] Ice-strengthened hulls. 65-ton bollard pull, 100-ton towing winch.

AUXILIARY SHIPS AND SERVICE CRAFT *(continued)*

1 Dutch-built tug/supply vessel Bldr: Scheepswerf De Waal, Zaltbommerl (In serv. 1972)

ATF . . . LEUCOTON (ex-*Lilen*, ex-*Smit Lloydd 44*)

D: 1,750 tons (fl) **S:** 13 kts **Dim:** 53.14 (49.31 pp) × 12.30 × 4.44
Electron Equipt: Radar: . . .
M: . . . diesels; 2 props; 4,000 bhp **Crew:** . . . tot.

Remarks: 743 grt. Acquired 6-8-90 from commercial service.

♦ **3 French BATRAL-class landing ship/transports** Bldr: ASMAR, Talcahuano

	L	In serv.
91 MAIPO	26-9-81	12-82
92 RANCAGUA	26-3-82	1-7-83
93 CHACABUCO	16-7-85	1-4-86

Maipo (R 91) Chilean Navy, 1990

D: 770 tons (1,330 fl) **S:** 16 kts
Dim: 80.0 (68.0 pp) × 13.0 × 3.0 (max.)
A: 1/40-mm Bofors AA—1/20-mm AA—2/81-mm mortar (I × 2)
Electron Equipt: Radar: 1/Decca 1229 nav.
M: 2 SACM V-12 diesels; 2 props; 3,600 bhp **Range:** 4,500/13
Electric: 360 kw **Crew:** 49 ship's company + 138 troops.

Remarks: Constructed with French technical assistance. Cargo: 350 tons. Bow ramp has 40-ton capacity. Helicopter platform can accommodate up to a Super Puma. Cargo: 50 tons vehicles and/or dry cargo, 208 tons potable water or ballast.

♦ **1 transport and disaster-relief ship** Bldr: ASMAR, Talcahuano

	Laid down	L	In serv.
AP 47 AQUILES	27-5-86	4-12-87	15-7-88

Aquiles (AP 47) Chilean Navy, 1990

D: 2,767 tons light (4,550 fl) **S:** 18 kts (15 sust.)
Dim: 103.00 (97.00 pp) × 17.00 × 5.50 **A:** none
Electron Equipt: Radar: 2/. . . nav.
M: 2 MaK 8M453B diesels; 1 CP prop; 7,200 bhp—bow-thruster
Electric: 1,375 kw (1 × 500 kw, 2 × 400 kw, 1 × 75 kw)
Crew: 80 ship's company + 250 troops

Remarks: 1,550 dwt. Replaced an earlier *Aquiles* (also AP 47). Has two cargo holds, one 20-ton electric crane. Helicopter deck large enough to accept a Super Puma.

♦ **2 Orompello-class logistics landing ships**

	Bldr	In serv.
AP 94 OROMPELLO	Dade DD Co., Miami, Fla.	15-9-64
AP 95 ELICURA	ASMAR, Talcahuano	10-12-63

D: 290 tons (750 fl) **S:** 12 kts **Dim:** 43.9 (42.05 pp) × 10.3 × 6.9
A: 3/20-mm AA (I × 3)
Electron Equipt: Radar: 1/Raytheon 1500B nav.
M: 2 Cummins VT-17-700M diesels; 2 props; 900 bhp **Electric:** 120 kw
Range: 2,900/10.5 **Fuel:** 71 tons **Crew:** 20 tot.

Remarks: Two near-sisters operated by a Chilean commercial firm. Cargo: 350 tons maximum. Have bow ramp, one 10-ton capacity cargo boom.

♦ **1 Meteoro-class coastal ferry** Bldr: ASMAR, Talcahuano

AP 110 METEORO (In serv. 1967)

D: 205 tons (fl) **S:** 8 kts **Dim:** 24.4 × 6.7 × . . .
M: diesel; . . . bhp **Crew:** . . . tot. + 220 passengers

Remarks: Sister *Grumete Perez Huemel* (AF 112) has been stricken. Attached to the Seaman's School as harbor transport.

♦ **1 submarine tender** Bldr: Orenstein & Koppel, Germany (In serv. 1966)

70 ANGAMOS (ex-*Puerto Montt*, ex-*Pres. Aguirre*, ex-*Cerda*, ex-*København*)

Angamos (70) Gary Davies/Maritime Photographic, 2-90

D: 3,560 tons **S:** 16 kts **Dim:** 93.92 × 16.2 × 4.5
A: none **Electron Equipt:** Radar: . . .
M: 2 Lind-Pielstick V-8 diesels; 2 props; 6,500 bhp **Crew:** . . . tot.

Remarks: 4,616 grt. Former car and passenger ferry, purchased from Empresa Maritime del Estado 4-77 and in service in 1979. Now fitted with workshops, spare parts stores, and ammunition and torpedo magazines. Also used as a transport.

♦ **1 sail-training ship** Bldr: Bazán, Cadiz

	L	In serv.
BE 43 ESMERALDA (ex-*Don Juan de Austria*)	12-5-53	9-54

Esmeralda (BE 43) Maritime Photographic, 7-90

D: 3,673 tons **S:** 11 kts (under power)
Dim: 109.8 (94.1 pp) × 13.1 × 8.7
A: 4/47-mm saluting cannon **Electron Equipt:** Radar: 1/ . . . nav.
M: 1 Fiat diesel; 1,400 bhp **Range:** 8,000/8
Crew: 271 ship's company + 80 midshipmen

Remarks: Four-masted schooner, ordered by Spain, sold to Chile in 1953. Similar to the Spanish *Juan Sebastian de Elcano*. Sail area: . . . Refitted in South Africa, 1977. Was used as a prison ship during the more repressive period of the Pinochet regime. The small yacht *Blanco Estella* (14 crew) is also used for training.

♦ **1 tug** Bldr: Southern Shipbuilders, Faversham, U.K. (In serv. 6-75)

YT 115 GALVEZ

AUXILIARY SHIPS AND SERVICE CRAFT *(continued)*

D: 112 grt **S:** . . . kts **Dim:** 25.5 × 7.3 × 2.8

Remarks: Subordinated to ASMAR, Talcahuano, which also has three small tugs of 200 hp and 500 hp, *Caupolican, Reyes,* and *Cortes.*

◆ **1 1,200-ton-capacity floating dry dock** Bldr: ASMAR, Talcahuano

Marinero Gutierrez (In serv. 10-91)

Remarks: Length overall: 80 m. Replaced 1908-built *Manterola.*

◆ **1 10,000-ton-capacity floating dry dock** Bldr: ASMAR, Talcahuano

Valparaiso III (L: 8-10-83)

D: 4,150 tons (light)
Dim: 167.0 (151.2 on blocks) × 32.1 (26.1 interior width) × 3.95

Remarks: Built for shipyard, rather than naval service, but available to the navy.

◆ **2 U.S. ARD 24-class floating dry docks** (In serv. 1944)

131 Ingeniero Mery (ex-ARD 25) 132 Mutilla (ex-ARD 32)

Ingeniero Mery (131) 1974

Capacity: 3,500 tons **Dim:** 149.86 × 24.69 × 1.73 (light)

Remarks: 131 leased 15-12-60; 132 transferred 20-8-73. Both at Talcahuano. Dock inside dimensions: 118.6 m on blocks, 18.0 m clear width, 6.3 m draft over blocks. Bow end closed and pointed.

Note: There are also two floating cranes, one of 30-ton and one of 180-ton capacity.

CHILEAN COAST GUARD—GENERAL DIRECTORATE OF THE MARITIME TERRITORY

Founded 1848 and now responsible for regulating the Chilean merchant marine, water sports, coastal and port patrol, and for navigational aid maintenance. Also intended to organize the merchant marine as a potential naval reserve. In addition to the units listed below, there are also a large number of very small launches, rigid inflatable boats, etc. The Coast Guard operates several navy-manned MBB-105 helicopters acquired 1991.

PATROL BOATS

◆ **2 "Protector" class** Bldr: Fairey Marintechnik, Cowes, U.K. (Both in serv. 24-6-89)

Hallef Alacalufe

Alacalufe FBM, 1989

D: 107 tons (fl) **S:** 20 kts **Dim:** 33.00 (28.96 wl) × 6.73 × 1.95
A: . . . **Electron Equipt:** Radar: 1/Decca . . . nav.
M: 2 MTU diesels; 2 props; 5,200 bhp **Range:** 1,000/15
Crew: 16 tot.

Remarks: Although initially announced as being intended for the Customs Servi when ordered in 1987, they are labeled as "pilot boats" and are assigned to patrol ar search-and-rescue duties in the Straits of Magellan area. Up to six more may b ordered.

◆ **2 small trawler-type** Bldr: ASMAR, Talcahuano (In serv. 1966–67)

PC 75 Marinheiro Fuentalbas PC 76 Cabo Odger

D: 215 tons **S:** 9 kts **Dim:** 24.4 × 6.4 × 2.75
A: 1/20-mm AA—3/12.7-mm mg (I × 3)
Electron Equipt: Radar: . . . **M:** 1 Cummins diesel; 340 bhp
Range: 2,600/9 **Crew:** 3 officers, 14 enlisted

Remarks: Purchased 1966, used primarily as buoy tenders.

PATROL CRAFT

◆ **10 "Anchova"-class** Bldr: MacLaren, Niteroi, Brazil

	In serv.		In serv
GC 1801 Pillan	8-79	GC 1806 Llaina	10-4-8
GC 1802 Troncador	8-80	GC 1807 Antuco	16-4-8
GC 1803 Rano-Kau	11-80	GC1808 Osorno	16-4-8
GC 1804 Villarrica	11-80	GC 1809 Choshuenco	16-11-8
GC 1805 Corcovado	6-3-81	GC 1810 Copahue	16-11-8

D: 31 tons (43 fl) **S:** 31 kts **Dim:** 18.60 × 5.25 × 1.62
A: 1/20 mm AA—1/12.7-mm mg—2/d.c. racks
Electron Equipt: Radar: 1/Decca 110 nav.
M: 2 MTU 8V331 TC81 diesels; 2 props; 1,800 bhp
Range: 700/15 **Electric:** 10 kw **Crew:** 1 officer, 5 enlisted

Remarks: Ordered 1977. Wooden construction. Named for volcanoes. ("Anchova" the builder's class name.)

◆ **2 Ona class** Bldr: ASENAV, Valdivia (In serv. 1980)

LEP 1601 Ona LEP 1602 Yagan

D: 79 tons (fl) **S:** 22 kts **Dim:** 24.6 × 5.3 × 2.9 **Crew:** 5 tot.
A: 2/12.7-mm mg (I × 2) **M:** 2 MTU 6V331 TC82 diesels; 2 props; 1,320 bhp

Remarks: One based at Puerto Montt, the other at Chiloé.

MISCELLANEOUS CRAFT

◆ **1 buoy tender/patrol boat** Bldr: . . . (In serv. 1968)

WPC 113 Castor

D: 80 tons (149 fl) **S:** 8 kts **Dim:** 21.6 × 6.3 × 3.2
A: 2/20-mm AA (I × 2)—2/12.7-mm mg (I × 2)
M: 1 Cummins diesel; 1 prop; 365 bhp **Crew:** 14 tot.

Remarks: Acquired for Coast Guard service 1975.

◆ **1 hospital craft** Bldr: ASMAR, Talcahuano (In serv. 1964)

CG 111 Cirujano Videla

D: 140 tons (fl) **S:** 14 kts **Dim:** 31.0 × 6.5 × 2.0
M: 2 Cummins VT-12-700M diesels; 2 props; 1,400 bhp
Electric: 60 kw

Remarks: Modified U.S. PGM 59 gunboat design, with enlarged superstructure. Or inally used by navy for civil assistance programs but later transferred to Coast Gu for same function.

◆ **10 search-and-rescue craft** Bldr: ASENAV, Valdivia (In serv. 1982–83)

LPM 1901 Maule LPM 1905 Isluga LPM 1909 Cau-Ca
LPM 1902 Lauca LPM 1906 Loa LPM 1910 Pudeto
LPM 1903 Aconcagua LPM 1907 Maullin
LPM 1904 Rapel LPM 1908 Copiapo

D: 14 tons (fl) **S:** 18 kts **Dim:** 13.3 × 3.5 × 1.0
A: 1/12.7-mm mg **Electron Equipt:** Radar: 1/ . . . nav.
M: 2 MTU 6V331 TC82 diesels; 2 props; 1,320 bhp

◆ **1 service launch for search and rescue at Easter Island**

LSR 1701 Kimitahi (In serv. 1981)

D: 14 tons **S:** 20 kts **Dim:** 19.5 × . . . × . . .
Crew: 1 officer, 6 enlisted, 50 passengers

◆ **1 service launch** (In serv. 1986)

LPM 1916 Petrohue

D: . . . tons **S:** 10 kts **Dim:** 9.7 × 3.1 × 0.9
M: 1 Perkins diesel: 85 bhp

◆ **1 fast launch** (In serv. 1953)

Bellatrix

D: . . . tons **S:** 24 kts **Dim:** 9.7 × 3.1 × 0.9
M: 2 Volvo diesels; 2 props; 500 bhp

Note: Also in service are small craft *Guale* (LAM . . .), *Millalobo* (LPR . . .), a *Pincoy* (LPR . . .).

HINA

ople's Republic of China

PEOPLE'S LIBERATION ARMY NAVY (PLAN)

rsonnel: 176,500 (regular naval: 24,000 afloat/80,000 ashore; naval air arm: 000; marine corps: 42,500). There are also about 1,000,000 paramilitary personnel the naval militia.

val Aviation: Under the operational control of the PLAN, the naval air arm sists of a force of 840 or more aircraft, including:
er 760 fixed-wing:
bout 120 Shenyang J-5 interceptors (MiG-17F Fresco copy)
bout 250 Shenyang J-6 interceptors (MiG-19 Farmer copy)
bout 200 Xian J-7 interceptors (a modified version of the MiG-21F)
bout 75 Nanchang Q-5 Fantan strike aircraft
bout 80 H-5 bombers (copy of the Soviet Il-28 Beagle)
bout 35 H-6 bombers (copy of the Tu-16 Badger), some equipped to carry two HY-4 iship missiles (version B-6D)
bout 10 Soviet Be-6 Madge amphibians
Hanzhong Y-8 maritime patrol aircraft (modified copy of An-12 Cub)
or more Harbin SH-5 amphibians, powered by four 3,150-hp turboprops for a ising speed of 300 kts and a 2,850-n.m. range (1,200-n.m. patrol radius at 45 tons x. takeoff weight); 10-ton payload (including 6 tons depth bombs). Equipped with D boom, guns, and radar. First flight 3-4-76. Can operate 12 hours on 4 engines or on 2 at 6,000-ft altitude.

ui Hong 5 (SH 5) ASW amphibian China Features, 1986

i-8 (SA 321 Super Frélon) PLAN

er 80 helicopters:
bout 40 Harbin Z-5 land-based patrol/ASW (copy of Mi-4 Hound)
13 French-supplied Super Frélon heavy shipboard helicopters (2 or 3 equipped with omson-Sintra HS 3125 dipping sonars), with additional Zhi-8 copies being built ce 1985
26 or more Zhi-9 (copy of SA-375 Dauphin) light shipboard helicopters out of 50 ensed for production
China continues to study acquisition of improved ASW helicopters for shipboard use, luding the Sikorsky S 76, Kaman SH-2F LAMPS I, Dauphin variants, and the Super ma. However, the possible sale of 100 Sikorsky S 76 helicopters to China was bargoed 6-89.

WEAPONS AND SENSORS

The ballistic missiles on the Xia-class SSBN and the majority of the other weapons on inese ships are of Chinese manufacture, with many being copies of or derivations of viet systems.

RATEGIC BALLISTIC MISSILES:

Ju Lang (C-SS-N-3). Became operational 7-88 after proof launch from a Xia-class omarine. Single stage, solid fuel.

Length: 10.0 m **Weight:** 14,000 kg **Diameter:** 1.5 m
Range: 2,700–3,600 km

. . . . . (CSS-NX-4). Successor to CSS-N-3, in development.

ANTISHIP CRUISE MISSILES:

—Hai Ying-1 ("Sea Eagle-1")—a direct copy of the Soviet SS-N-2a Styx (P-15)
—Hai Ying-2 (CSS-N-2)—improved Styx

Length: 7.36 m **Weight:** 2,998 kg **Range:** 90 km
Wingspan: 2.75 m **Speed:** Mach 0.9 **Altitude:** 90—100 m

♦ **Hai Ying-2 (HY-2) is used aboard Luda destroyers and Jianghu-class frigates and uses a jettisonable solid rocket booster. Guidance is by gyro autopilot, with radar terminal homing. A land-launched version (Western nickname "Silk Worm") is also available. All have a 513-kg warhead. Other versions include:**

—Hai Ying-2A—infrared, vice radar, terminal homing
—Hai Ying-2G—radar altimeter-equipped, with 20-m cruise altitude, descending to 8 m during radar terminal homing
—Hai Ying-4—air-launched version, carried two per B-6D (Badger) bomber. Turbojet engine 7.36 m long, 0.76 m diameter, speed: Mach 0.85

♦ **C 801 Yinji-6 or Shui Ying-2 ("Hawk Attack")—wholly Chinese weapon, using a box launcher similar to that of Exocet MM 38. Land-based version is Fei Lung-7. Propelled by solid rocket, with two solid boosters.**

Length: 5.2 m **Diameter:** 0.5 m **Range:** 32 km
Speed: Mach 1.4 **Wingspan:** 1.0 m **Weight:** 1,800 kg

♦ **C 802—C 801 variant with turbojet engine, Mach 0.8–0.9; cruises at 20–30-m altitude, with 5–7-m altitude final approach. Length: 5.8 m. Employs active radar and incorporates ECCM features.**

♦ **C 601—air-launched, rocket-powered weapon with 110-km range at Mach 0.9, with 500-kg warhead.**

♦ **C 611—air-launched, turbojet variant of C 601 with same warhead and speed, 220-km range.**

SURFACE-TO-AIR MISSILES:

♦ **Hong Qian-61 (CSA-N-1)—naval version of land-based SAM in development since 1960s and used only aboard the two Jiangdong frigates.**

Length: 3.99 m **Range:** 10 km max./3 km min.
Diameter: 0.286 m **Altitude:** 8 km **Wingspan:** 1.66 m
Guidance: command, using Fog Lamp radar tracker/ illuminator,semi-active homing
Speed: Mach 3.0 **Propulsion:** single-stage, solid-fuel rocket

♦ **Hong Qian 2J((HQ-2J)—Two-stage coast-defense SAM. Range: 34 km.**

♦ **Hong Nu 5(HN-5)—Land-based derivative of Soviet SA-7. Weight: 16 kg; range: 4 km.**

♦ **French Crotale modulaire (described in French section) aboard two Luda-class destroyers.**

AIR-TO-AIR MISSILES:

♦ **Pen Lung-2—Weight: 11 kg; range: 8 km; infrared-homing.**

♦ **Pen Lung-5—Speed: Mach 4.5; range: 16 km; infrared-homing.**

♦ **Pen Lung-7—Weight: 12 kg; range: 14 km; infrared-homing.**

♦ **Pen Lung-9—Weight: 120 kg; range: 5 km**

SHIPBOARD CONVENTIONAL WEAPONS

♦ **Guns are all versions of Soviet equipment of 130-mm, 100-mm, 57-mm, 37-mm, and 25-mm caliber, except for French Creusot-Loire 100-mm mount on the Jianghu-III frigate 544. Torpedoes and mines are of Soviet or local design, with negotiations ongoing to manufacture the Italian Whitehead A-244 lightweight ASW torpedo, and several U.S. Mk 46 lightweight ASW torpedoes transferred prior to the 1989 embargo. The China State Shipbuilding Corporation, No. 105 Research Institute, reported successful development of a new torpedo, the "Chinese Sturgeon II," in 1-91. Plans for China to acquire the U.S. Mk 15 20-mm CIWS for air defense have been put in abeyance.**

♦ **CY-1—An antisubmarine weapon launched from the Hai Ying 2 launchers on Luda-class destroyers. Still in development.**

Length: 5.5 m **Weight:** 700 kg **Diameter:** 0.41 m **Range:** 18 km

SHIPBOARD CONVENTIONAL WEAPONS *(continued)*

- ♦ **Rocket launchers include the Soviet RBU-1200 and a larger, 12-tubed weapon used on the Luda-class destroyers. Also used are copies of the Soviet BMB-1 and BMB-2 depth-charge mortars.**

- ♦ **A new 122-mm, 40-tubed rocket launcher has been anounced; the rockets weigh 66.6 kg, and the warhead weight is 18.4 kg. Presumably, the launcher is intended for amphibious warfare ships and craft.**

ELECTRONIC SYSTEMS

Radars are, with a few exceptions, known by their Western nicknames:

Name:	*Origin:*	*Band:*	*Function:*
Ball End	U.S.S.R.	E/F	Surface search
Bean Sticks	China	S	Early warning
Eye Shield	China	E/F	Surface search (Chinese name: MX-902)
Fin Curve	U.K.	I	Nav. (Decca 707 copy)
Fog Lamp	China	H/I	SAM f.c.
Neptun	U.S.S.R.	I	Nav.
Pot Head	U.S.S.R.	I	Nav./surface search
Rice Lamp	China	I	Gun control
Rice Screen	China	G	3-D phased-array air search (Chinese "Sea Eagle")—in two versions
Skin Head	U.S.S.R.	I	Surface search
Slim Net	U.S.S.R.	E/F	Air/surface search
Square Tie	U.S.S.R.	. . .	Surface search (Chinese name: Type 331)
Sun Visor	U.S.S.R.	I	Gun f.c.
Type 756	China	S	Nav.
Type 354	China	C	Low-altitude air search

IFF systems have only come into general use since the early 1980s and are still not universally fitted. The equipment includes the Soviet Square Head interrogation antenna and the High Pole A transponder. Sonars are of Soviet design, with an active program under way to acquire modern Western systems. Japanese electronic systems, including Oki navigational radars, are widely used.

CLASS NAMES AND PENDANTS

The class names used below are generally those assigned by Western intelligence services; the Chinese Navy uses a numbered system, for which few of the designations are known, and there is also a project number system employed in foreign sales efforts.

For combatants, three-digit hull numbers are assigned. Small combatants have a four-digit pendant, the first number of which signifies area subordination. Until recently, auxiliaries had three-digit numbers preceded by a letter signifying function, but that system has now been superseded by one employing two or more Chinese ideographs describing the ship's function. In addition, the numerous ships subordinated to the various districts of the Maritime Border Defense Force have four-digit pendants preceded by a letter signifying the district; known prefixes include "S" for Shenyang, "N" for Nanjing (commonly seen in the Shanghai area), and "G" for Guangzhou.

BALLISTIC-MISSILE SUBMARINES

♦ **1 Xia class nuclear powered** Bldr: Huludao SY

	L	In serv.
406	30-4-81	1988

D: 7,000 tons submerged **S:** 20 kts sub. **Dim:** 120.0 × 10.0 × . . .
A: 12 Ju Lang-1 (CSS-N-3) strategic missiles—6/533-mm TT (fwd)
M: 1 90-megawatt pressurized-water nuclear reactor, turboelectric drive; 1 prop; 15,000 shp

Remarks: The "Xia" (Western nickname)-class submarine was launched from the same facility that builds the Han-class nuclear-powered attack submarine, 200 km northeast of Beijing in Liao Ning province. The design is essentially that of the Han, lengthened to accommodate the missile tubes. At least two additional units were expected, but no second ship has appeared. The first CSS-NX-3 submerged launch took place on 12-10-82 to a range of 1,600 km from the Golf-class trials submarine. The missile is believed to have 2 solid-propulsion stages and to have a range of 1,500 n.m. (2,795 km). The first Xia missile launch took place between 14- and 27-7-88, and no further launches have been announced.

♦ **1 Soviet Golf-class diesel-powered missile trials submarine**
Bldr: Dalien SY

200 (L: 1964)

D: 2,500 surf./2,900 sub. tons **S:** 14 kts submerged
Dim: 99.00 × 8.50 × 6.50
A: 2 ballistic missiles—10/533-mm TT (6 fwd, 4 aft)
M: 3 YType 37D diesels, electric drive; 3 props; 6,000 shp
Range: 9,000/5

Remarks: Plans furnished by the Soviet Union at a time when relations between the two countries were good. One tube removed around 1974 when altered for Ju Lang-1 missile trials. Launched first Chinese SLBM on 12-10-82. Probably not considered a first-line submarine.

Xia 406 *Ships of the World, 19*

Xia 406 Siegfried Breyer Collecti

NUCLEAR-POWERED ATTACK SUBMARINES

♦ **5 Han class** Bldr: Huludao SY

	Laid down	L	In serv.
401	1965–68	1972	1974
402	. . .	1977	1980
403	. . .	1983	21-9-84
404	. . .	. . .	1988
405	. . .	6-90	1991

D: 4,500 tons sub. **S:** 25 kts surf./30 kts sub.
Dim: 90.0 × 10.0 × . . .
A: 6/533-mm TT (fwd) **Crew:** 75 tot.
M: 1 90-megawatt pressurized-water nuclear reactor, turboelectric drive; 1 prop; 15,000 shp

UCLEAR-POWERED ATTACK SUBMARINES *(continued)*

an 402, the second unit China Features

emarks: The trials series for the first unit was very protracted, and at least the rlier units have not proven reliable. All believed to be assigned to the North Sea eet. May have Thomson-Sintra DUUX-5 passive sonar array. Believed that only five ll be built, although design of a follow-on is likely to be underway.

RUISE MISSILE SUBMARINES

0 (+ . . .) Project E5SG Bldr: . . .

D: 1,650 tons surf./2,100 sub. **S:** 15/17 kts
Dim: 74.00 × 7.60 × 5.30
A: 6 C 801 SSM (I × 6)—8/533-mm TT (6 fwd, 2 aft; 18 torpedoes or 28 mines)
Electron Equip:
Radar: Snoop Plate surf. search
Sonar: Herkules active/passive, Feniks or DUUX-5 passive
M: diesel-electric, 2 diesels; 2 props; 2,500 shp
Range: 8,000/8 (snorkel); 330/4 (sub.) **Endurance:** 60 days
Crew: 10 officers, enlisted

emarks: A *surface*-launched cruise-missile-carrying version of the Ming (Project 5SE) attack submarine, offered for foreign sale but, apparently, not constructed as t. Arrangement based on the converted Romeo-class cruise missile trials submarine 1. Each of the six tubes elevates separately to fire one C 801 Yinji missile. Diving pth: 300 m.

1 Wuhan (converted Romeo) cruise missile trials submarine Bldr: . . .

51 (In serv. 1987)

onverted Romeo launching C 801 missile CPMIEC, 1987

D: 1,400/1,790 tons **S:** 15/12 kts **Dim:** 76.60 × 7.60 × 4.95
A: 6 C 801 SSM (I × 6)—8/533-mm TT (6 fwd/2 aft)—14 torpedoes or 28 mines
Electron Equipt:
Radar: 1/Snoop Plate
Sonar: Tamir 5 L active, Feniks passive
M: diesel-electric: 2 Type 1Z38 diesels, 2,400 bhp each; 2 props; 2,700 shp—2 electric creep motors: 100 shp
Endurance: 60 days **Range:** 14,000/9 surf.; 350/9 sub. **Crew:** . . .

Remarks: Converted from a standard Romeo (Project 33)-class attack submarine to test the concept of surface-launching short-range antiship cruise missiles. Would be quite vulnerable during attacks, especially if no means of over-the-horizon targeting is provided. Characteristics, where differing from those of the Romeo, are estimated.

DIESEL-POWERED ATTACK SUBMARINES

◆ **6 (+ . . .) Ming class (Project ES5E)** Bldr: Wuhan SY (?)

232 233 341 342 343 353 . . .

Ming class 342 *Ships of the World,* 1988

D: 1,584 tons surf./2,113 tons sub. **S:** 15 surf./10 snorkel/18 sub.
Dim: 76.00 × 7.6 × 5.10
A: 8/533-mm TT (6 fwd, 2 aft; 16 torpedoes or 32 mines)
Electron Equipt:
Radar: 1/Snoop Plate
Sonar: Herkules active/passive, Feniks passive
M: diesel-electric, 2 diesels; 2 props; 2,500 shp—2/75-shp creep motors
Range: 8,000 (8 snorkel; 330/4 sub.) **Endurance:** 60 days
Crew: 12 officers, 48 enlisted

Remarks: First two launched 1975, third in 1982; series construction then commenced again around 1988. One reported lost after a fire. Based on Romeo design, but with different propulsion plant (possibly of foreign origin) and fuller hull form. Design offered for export. Diving depth: 300 m.

◆ **84 Soviet Romeo (Chinese ES3B) class** Bldr: Wuzhang SY, Guangzhou SY, Jiangnan SY, Huludao SY (In serv. 1960–84)

Romeo 256 7-89

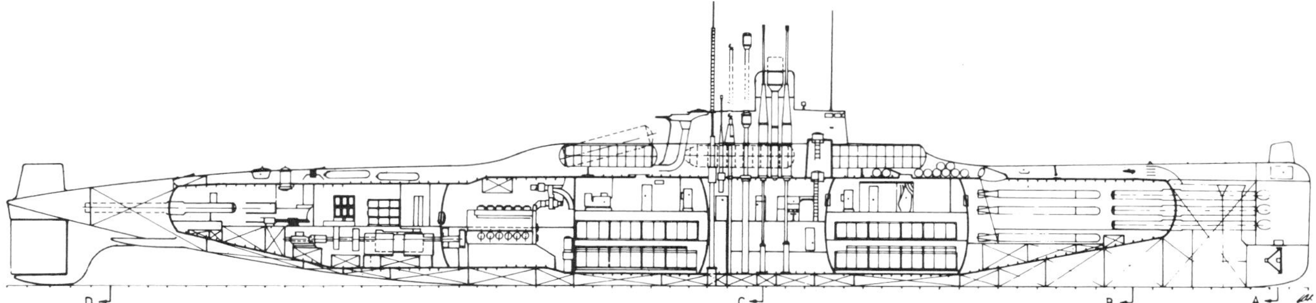

Project E5SG

DIESEL-POWERED ATTACK SUBMARINES *(continued)*

Romeo 240 *Ships of the World*

D: 1,319/1,712 tons **S:** 15.2/13 kts **Dim:** 76.60 × 6.70 × 4.95
A: 8/533-mm TT (6 fwd/2 aft)—14 torpedoes or 28 mines
Electron Equipt:
Radar: 1/Snoop Plate
Sonar: Tamir 5 L active, Feniks passive (see Remarks)
M: diesel-electric: 2 Type 1Z38 diesels, 2,400 bhp each; 2 props; 2,700 shp—2 electric creep motors: 100 shp
Endurance: 60 days **Range:** 14,000/9 surf.; 350/9 sub.
Crew: 8 officers, 43 enlisted

Remarks: Also called Project 33. Generally similar to the Soviet version built in the late 1950s, but with numerous changes in equipment and detail. Diving depth: 300 meters. Foreign transfers include 4 to North Korea between 1973 and 1975 and 4 to Egypt in 1982–83. 224-cell battery: 6,600 amp hr. One unit has one of two Thomson-Sintra DUUX-5 passive sonar suites delivered in 1983, and export version is offered with that gear plus an enlarged chin sonar dome. Up to 50 may be modernized with new batteries and sensors, but as of 1991, only about 34 were operational.

DESTROYERS

◆ **0 (+2) Project EF5 class** Bldr: Qiuxin SY, Shanghai

	Laid down	L	In serv.
. . . .	24-5-90	. . .	. . .
. . . .	. . .	. . .	. . .

D: 4,200 tons (fl) **S:** 32 kts (20 on diesel) **Dim:** 132.0 × 12.8 × . . .
A: 8/C.801 SSM (IV × 2)—1/Crotale Modulaire SAM system—medium-caliber gun mount—. . . /. . .-mm AA—1/. . . ASW missile system—6/324-mm ASW TT (III × 2)—2/Zhi-9 helicopters
Electron Equipt:
Radar: . . .
Sonar: . . .
EW: . . .
M: CODOG: 2 G.E. LM-2500 gas turbines/2 SEMT-Pielstick . . . . . . diesels; 2 CP props; 48,000 shp max.
Range: 4,000/18 **Crew:** 220 tot.

Remarks: Also known as Project 053HT. Design based on that of the Luda class. U.S. weapons and other systems were originally to have been fitted, but their delivery is now unlikely.

◆ **17 Luda (Project EF4) class** Bldr: Hongqi SY, Luda SY, Donglang SY, Guangzhou and Zhonghua SY, Shanghai (In serv., 1972–19. . .)

105 Jinan	110 Dalian	161 Changsha	. . . .
106 Xian	131 Nanjing	162 Nanning	. . . .
107 Yinchuan	132 Hefei	163 Nanchang	
108 Xining	133 Chongqing	164 Guilin	
109 Kaifeng	134 Zunyi	165	

Dalian (110)—with Rice Screen 3-D radar 1989

Jinan (105)—with Jiangdong-class *Yingtan* (531) and two now-stricken *Gordyy*-class destroyers in the background *Ships of the World,* 1983

Dalian (110)—with Rice Screen 3-D radar, but no f.c. radars R.A.N., 1‍[illegible]

Hefei (132)—with 8 57-mm AA, two f.c. radars, Rice Screen and Pea Sti[illegible] search radars R.A.N., 1[illegible]

D: 3,250 tons (3,960 fl) **S:** 34 kts (32 sust.)
Dim: 132.0 (127.5 pp) × 12.8 × 4.0 (5.2 sonar)
A: 6/HY-2 SSM (III × 2)—4/130-mm DP (II × 2)—8/57-mm (on 105, 108, 132) or 37-mm AA (II × 4)—4/25-mm AA (II × 2)—2 12-tube ASW RL— 4/BMB-2 d.c. mortars—2/d.c. racks—mines (see Remarks)
Electron Equipt:
Radar: 1/Fin Curve or Type 756 navigational, 1/Eye Shield (MX-902) short-range air-search, 1 Bean Sticks or Pea Sticks (antenna variant) long-range air-search, 1/Square Tie, 1/Su[n] Visor (not on all), 2/Rice Lamp for 57-mm f.c. (not on all); 108, 110, 132: Rice Screen also
Sonar: . . . . . . MF hull-mounted—EW: 2/Jug Pair intercept
IFF: 3/Square Head interrogators, 1/High Pole A transponder
M: 2 sets GT; 2 props; 60,000 shp **Boilers:** 4
Range: 1,100/32; 3,475/18; 5,000/14 **Crew:** 27 officers, 275 enliste[d]

Remarks: Also known as Project 051. Superficially resemble Soviet Kotlin, but larger and have a flat transom stern, larger superstructure, etc. Ships in 100 se[ries] built at Luda and based in North Sea Fleet; 130 series at Shanghai and based in E[ast] Sea Fleet; 160 series at Guangzhou and based in South Sea Fleet. Some system[s of] Soviet design; the ASW rocket launchers are derived from the Soviet RBU-1200 desi[gn] but have more tubes. Equipment varies greatly from ship to ship, with only a sm[all] number having fire-control radar systems, even on the Soviet Wasp Head ("Wok Wa[n"]) 130-mm GFCS. The SSM used is derived from the Soviet SS-N-2 Styx, but is lon[ger]. One ship of this class (probably 162) lost 8-78 near Zanjiang through explosion. [...] equipped for underway fueling.

Ludas 108 and 132 are the only units confirmed to mount twin 57-mm vice 37-[mm] AA; they also carry the Rice Lamp AA fire-control radars not mounted on the oth[ers]. Pea Sticks long-range air search is carried by 107, 131, 132, and 162; the remain[der] have Bean Sticks. 108, 132, and 110 have a larger variant of the Rice Screen ([...] Eagle) 3-D phased-array air-search radar atop the after mast. Sun Visor fire-con[trol] radars are mounted on the Wasp Head ("Wok Wan") directors for the 130-mm DP g[uns] only on 105, 108, 131, 161, and 162. Plans to modernize the entire class with Bri[tish] equipment fell through in 1983.

In 1985 it was announced that U.S. Mk 15 CIWS (Vulcan/Phalanx) would be ad[ded] along with U.S. Mk 46 ASW torpedoes and, possibly, ASW helicopters (Kaman SH[-2] LAMPS I) in a few; U.S. weapons deliveries were, however, embargoed 1989. The[y] may have a bow-mounted sonar. The 105 completed a refit in 5-87 with a helico[pter] flight deck and hangar in place of the after twin 130-mm DP mount, after twin 37-[mm] AA, and the 4 d.c. mortars; she also has a new sonar and satellite navigation gear.

Two are being modernized 1991–92 with French assistance to carry the Cro[tale] Modulaire SAM system (VIII × 1), Thomson-CSF Sea Tiger air-search radar, and TAVITAC weapons control/combat data system. Construction of additional unit[s] apparently continuing, despite the overall obsolescence of the basic platform.

Note: All units of the 1930s-vintage Soviet Gordyy class (Project 07) are now belie[ved] to have been retired; hull 103, *Chang Chun* (ex-Soviet *Retivyy*), incorrectly identifie[d as] *"Ji Lin"* in previous editions, is a museum exhibit.

FRIGATES

◆ **0 (+ 2 + . . .) EF 30 design** Bldr: Hudong SY, Shanghai
539 . . . . . . (L: 1991) 540 . . . . . . (L: 25-10-91)

FRIGATES *(continued)*

D: 1,700 tons **S:** 28 kts
Dim: 110.0 × 11.5 × . . . (8.0 moulded depth)
A: 4/C 801 SSM (II × 2)—2/100-mm DP (II × 1)—8/30-mm (II × 2)—2/RBU-1200 ASW RL (V × 2)—6/324-mm ASW TT (III × 2)— 1/Zhi-9 (SA-365N Dauphin) helicopter
Electron Equipt:
Radar: 1/Type 956 nav., 1/Eye Shield air search, 1/Square Tie f.c., 1/Rice Lamp f.c., 1/Sun Visor f.c.
Sonar: 1/MF bow-mounted
EW: . . . intercept, 2 chaff RL
M: 2 diesels; 2 props; 24,000 bhp **Crew:** approx. 180 tot.
Range: 2,500/18 **Electric:** 1,720 kw (4 × 400 kw, 1 × 120 kw)

Remarks: To have China's first computerized weapons data and control system. Two units to this basic design, but with different propulsion systems and equipment, are being built for Thailand for delivery 1995–96.

◆ **1 Jianghu IV class** Bldr: Hudong SY, Shanghai

	L	In serv.
544 Siping	9-85	11-86

Siping (544) 4-88

Siping (544) 1991

D: 1,600 tons (1,820 fl) **S:** 25.5 kts **Dim:** 103.2 × 10.2 × 3.05 (hull)
A: 2/HY-2 SSM (II × 1)—1/100-mm Creusot-Loire Compact DP— 8/37-mm AA (II × 4)—6/324-mm ILAS-3 ASW TT (III × 2)—2/RBU-1200 ASW RL (V × 2)—1/Zhi-9 (SA-365N Dauphin) helicopter
Electron Equipt:
Radar: 1/Type 956 nav., 1/Eye Shield air search,1/Square Tie missile f.c.
Sonar: 1/MF hull-mounted
EW: 2/ Jug Pair intercept, 2/U.S. Mk 33 RBOC Decoy RL (VI × 2)
IFF: 2/Square Head interrogators, 1/High Pole A transponder
M: 2 SEMT-Pielstick 12 PA6 diesels; 2 props; 16,000 bhp
Electric: 1,320 kw (3 × 400 kw, 1 × 120 kw)
Range: 4,000/15; 1,750/25
Endurance: 15 days **Crew:** 25 officers, 160 enlisted

Remarks: Pendant 544, launched 9-85, was the first Chinese combatant to incorporate a helicopter. Adding the helicopter facility to the Jianghu design cost the after medium-caliber gun and twin SSM positions. The 100-mm gun, which can fire at 90 rounds per minute, is controlled by a CSEE Naja laser-electro-optical director. First PLAN ship to be equipped with modern Western ASW torpedoes. To date, no second unit has been reported under construction.

◆ **2 Jianghu III class** Bldr: Hudong SY, Shanghai

535 Huangshi (In serv. 1986) 536 Wuhu (In serv. 1987)

D: 1,865 tons (approx 2,100 fl) **S:** 25.5 kts
Dim: 103.2 × 10.2 × 3.05 (hull)
A: 8/C 801 SSM (II × 4)—4/100-mm DP (II × 2)—8/37-mm V-47M AA (II × 4)—2/RBU-1200 ASW RL (V × 2)—2/BMB-2 d.c. mortars
Electron Equipt:
Radar: 1/Type 756 nav., 1/Eye Shield (MX-902) air search, 1/Rice Lamp f.c. (aft), 1/Square Tie, 1/Sun Visor f.c.
Sonar: bow-mounted MF—EW: 4 intercept arrays (see Remarks)
IFF: 2/Square Head interrogators, 1/High Pole transponder
M: 2 SEMT-Pielstick 12 PA6 diesels; 2 props; 16,000 bhp
Electric: 1,720 kw (4 × 400 kw, 1 × 120 kw)
Endurance: 15 days **Range:** 4,000/15; 1,750/25
Crew: approx. 200 tot.

Huangshi (535)—outboard *Wuhu* (536) 7-89

Huangshi (535) 1991

Remarks: An improved version of the Jianghu I/II series, apparently on the same hull and propulsion plant, but with a full shelter deck amidships supporting four pairs of SSM launchers. Wasp Head (known as "Wok Wan" in China) optical GFCS forward (with Sun Visor radar) for surface gunfire, and Rice Lamp radar director aft for AA. The 100-mm mounts are auto-loading. Equipped with fin stabilizers. The EW intercept system is reportedly based on the Italian Elettronica Newton Beta system. Four very similar ships delivered to Thailand 1991–92, two with helicopter facilities in place of the after 100-mm gun mount.

◆ **25 (+ . . .) Jianghu I and II* classes** Bldr: Jianghu I: Jiangnan SY, Shanghai; Jianghu II: Hudong SY, Shanghai (1975–. . .)

509 Chang De	518 Jian	534 Jinhua*	557 . . . . . .*
510 Shaoxing	519 Changzhi	543 Dandong*	
511 Nantong	522	545 . . . . . .*	
512 Wuxi	525 Chanshao	551 Maoming	
513 Huayin	526 Xian	552 Yibin*	
514 Zhenjiang	527	553 Shaoguan*	
515 Xiamen	532 . . . . . .*	555	
516 Jiujiang	533 Ningbo*	556 Xiangtan	

Chang De (509)—a Jianghu I 1989

Wuxi (512)—outboard Yukan-class landing ship 927 Ross Gillett, 9-84

FRIGATES *(continued)*

Zhenjiang (514)—outboard *Huayin* (513), both with single 100-mm mounts 1984

Jianghu II 557—with twin 100-mm mounts, rounded stack 1989

D: 1,586 tons (1,900 fl) **S:** 25.5 kts **Dim:** 103.2 × 10.2 × 3.05 (hull)
A: 4/HY-2 SSM (II × 2)—2 or 4/100-mm DP (I or II × 2)—8 or 12/37-mm V-47M AA (II × 4 or 6)—2 or 4/RBU-1200 (V × 2 or 4)—4/BMB-2 d.c. mortars— 2/d.c. racks—mines (533, 534 have 2 twin 100, only 4 twin 37-mm)
Electron Equipt:
Radar: 1/Type 756 nav.,1/Eye shield (MX-902) air search, 1/Square Tie f.c.
Sonar: 1/medium-freq.—EW: none or 2/Jug Pair intercept
IFF: 2/Square Head interrogators, 1/High Pole A transponder
M: 2/SEMT-Pielstick 12 PA6 diesels; 2 props; 16,000 bhp
Electric: 1,320 kw (3 × 400 kw, 1 × 120 kw)
Range: 4,000/15; 1,750/25 **Endurance:** 15 days **Crew:** 195 tot.

Remarks: First launched 1975. Chinese Project EF3H, or *Changsha* class. Units with square stacks built by Jiangnan SY; the others have rounded stacks. Ships with twin 100-mm mounts (531, 533, 534, 543, 553, 557, etc.) are referred to as Jianghu II; they omitted two twin 37-mm AA as partial weight compensation. Most have only two RBU-1200, while 515, 516, and five ships in the 521 series have four. 100-mm fire control is by a simple stereoscopic rangefinder. The twin 100-mm mounts are auto-loading. Two sisters with twin 57-mm guns vice 100-mm were delivered to Egypt in 1984–85, and sister *Anshun* (554) was transferred to Bangladesh in 1990.

◆ **2 Jiangdong-class, guided missile** Bldrs: 531: Hudong SY, Shanghai; 532: Chiuhsin SY, Shanghai

531 Yingtan (In serv. 1972) 532 . . . . . . (In serv. 1975)

Yingtan (531) *Ships of the World,* 1983

D: 1,568 tons (1,900 fl) **S:** 25.5 kts
Dim: 103.2 × 10.2 × 3.05 (hull)
A: 2/HQ-61 SAM systems—4/100-mm DP (II × 2)—8/37-mm V-47M AA (II × 4)—2/RBU-1200 (V × 2)—2/BMB-2 d.c. mortars—2/d.c. racks
Electron Equipt:
Radar: 1/Type 756 nav., 1/Rice Screen 3-D air search, 2/Fog Lamp missile f.c., 1/Rice Lamp AA f.c. , 1/Sun Visor surf. f.c.
Sonar: 1/MF hull-mounted—EW: 2 Jug Pair intercept
IFF: 1/High Pole A transponder
M: 2 SEMT-Pielstick 12 PA6 diesels; 2 props; 16,000 bhp
Range: 4,000/15; 1,750/25 **Endurance:** 15 days
Crew: 195 tot. **Electric:** 1,720 kw (4 × 400 kw, 1 × 120 kw)

Remarks: SAM system, of Chinese design, only achieved operational status in th mid-1980s after 20 years of development. A Fog Lamp missile f.c. radar is mounted o the foremast, with a second aft. A Rice Screen ("Sea Eagle") phased-array 3-D ai search radar antenna surmounts the foremast, and a Rice Lamp AA gun f.c. radar atop the aftermast. Wasp Head (Chinese "Wok Wan") director is atop bridge. Hull ar propulsion plant are the same as the Jianghu series. 532 sighted 1982 without SA system and may not yet be fully operational.

◆ **5 Jiangnan class (Project 65)** Bldr: Shantou SY and Jiangnan SY, Shanghai (In serv. 1964–68)

501 Xiaguan 502 Nanchong 503 Kaiyuan
504 Dongchuan 529 Haikou

Nanchong (502) Boris Lemachko Collectio

D: 1,350 tons (1,600 fl) **S:** 28 kts **Dim:** 92.0 × 10.2 × 3.15 (hull)
A: 3/100-mm Sov. BU-34 DP (I × 3, 1 fwd, 2 aft)—8/37-mm Sov. V-47M AA (II × 4)—4/14.5-mm mg (II × 2)—2/RBU-1200 (V × 2)—4/BMB-2 d.c. mortars—2/d.c. racks—mines
Electron Equipt:
Radar: 1/Fin Curve nav., 1/Ball End surf. search
Sonar: MF hull-mounted
M: 2 diesels; 2 props; 16,000 bhp **Crew:** 15 officers, 165 enlisted

Remarks: Chinese variant of the Soviet Riga class, with diesel propulsion. One bui at Shanghai 1968, the others at Shantou. Lack sensors and radar f.c., but do ha Chinese-designed "Twin Eyes" optical director for 100-mm guns. One in East Sea Flee others (including 502 and 503) in South Sea Fleet.

◆ **4 Soviet Riga class (Project 01)**

	Bldr	L	In serv.
505 Guiyang	Hudong SY, Shanghai	26-9-56	1958
506 Kunming	Guangzhou SY	1957	1959
507 Chengdu	Hudong SY, Shanghai	28-4-56	1958
509 Guilin	Guangzhou SY	1957	1959

Kunming (506) 198

Chengdu (507) 198

[FR]IGATES *(continued)*

[D]: 1,186 tons (1,415 fl) **S:** 28 kts
[D]im: 91.58 (88.00 wl) × 10.20 × 3.15 (4.40 sonar)
[A]: 2/ HY-2 SSM (II × 1)—3/100-mm Sov. BU-34 DP (I × 3)—4/37-mm Sov. V-47 AA (II × 2)—4/14.5-mm mg (II × 2)—4/BMB-2 d.c.mortars— 2/d.c. racks—mines
[E]lectron Equipt:
Radar: 1/Type 756 nav., 1/Slim Net air search, 1/Square Tie missile target acq., 1/Sun Visor gun f.c.
Sonar: Pegas-2M MF hull-mounted—EW: none
IFF: 2/Square Head interrogators, 1/High Pole A transponder
[M]: 2 sets GT; 2 props; 20,000 hp **Boilers:** 2: 27 kg/cm, 360° C
[F]uel: 230 tons **Electric:** 450 kw **Range:** 550/28; 2,000/13
[C]rew: 16 officers, 154 enlisted

[Re]marks: Built with Soviet assistance and with Soviet-supplied components. Origi[nal]ly had higher bridge and light tripod mast, as in early-construction Soviet Navy [Ri]gas. Twin, trainable antiship missile launcher replaced torpedo tube mount during [ear]ly 1970s. Very limited endurance. No longer considered first-line ships.

[GU]IDED-MISSILE PATROL BOATS

0 (+ . . .) Type 343M "multi-role corvette"

[No]te: The boat in the drawing below has been offered for export sale by the China [Sh]ipbuilding Trading Co., in conjunction with Racal Marine. There has been no indica[tio]n to date of any under construction. See addenda for other new classes.

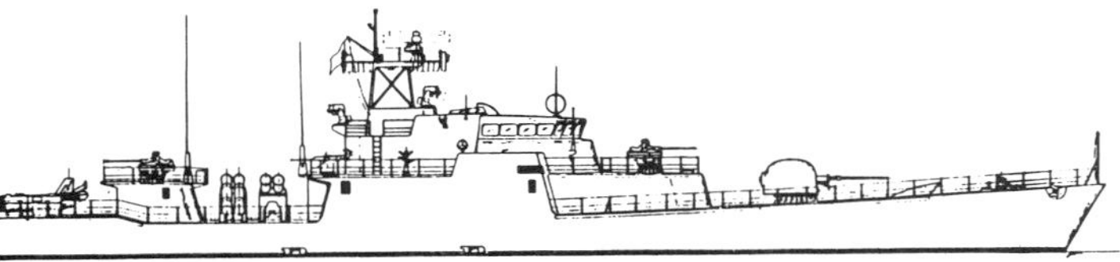

[Ty]pe 343M CSSC/Racal

[D]: 430 tons (fl) **S:** 32 kts **Dim:** 58.77 × 7.20 × 2.20 (hull)
[A]: 4/C.801 SSM (II × 2)—1/76-mm OTO Melara DP—4/30-mm GCM-A02 AA (II × 2)—2/20-mm GAM-B01 (I × 2)—6/324-mm ASW TT (III × 2)
[E]lectron Equipt:
Radar: 1/Decca . . . nav./surf. search, 2/. . . f.c.
Sonar: HF hull-mounted— EW: . . .
[M]: 4 diesels; 4 props; 8,800 bhp **Range:** 2,000/14; 750/18

[Re]marks: Design based on the Hainan subchaser/patrol boat.

1 Hola class (In serv. 1970)

[D]: 300 tons **S:** . . . kts **Dim:** 43.0 × . . . × . . .
[A]: 2/HY-2 SSM (I × 2)—2/37-mm AA V-47M (II × 2)

[Re]marks: An enlarged version of Osa-I, and at one time equipped with a large [ra]dome. Apparently unsuccessful. Two additional SSM also removed by 1980s.

112 Huangfeng (Project 21; Soviet Osa-I) class Bldr: Jiangnan SY, Shanghai, 1960–. . .

[Hu]angfeng No. 6106 4-88

[No]. 3101—with 25-mm AA, no IFF or gun f.c. radar PLAN, 1983

D: 175 tons, 186.5 normal (205 fl) **S:** 35 kts
Dim: 38.75 × 7.60 × 1.7 (mean)
A: 4/HY-1 SSM—4/25-mm 2M-8 or 30-mm AK-230 AA (II × 2)
Electron Equipt:
Radar: 1/Square Tie surf. search/target desig., some: Round Ball gun f.c.
IFF: 2/Square Head, 1/High Pole A
M: 3 M503A diesels; 3 props; 12,000 bhp
Electric: 65 kw **Range:** 800/30 **Crew:** 28 tot.

Remarks: At least four were transferred by the U.S.S.R. circa 1960 and had 4/30-mm AA (II × 2) but no Drum Tilt gun fire-control radar. Most Chinese-built units had two twin 25-mm AA until early 1980s, when increasing numbers with a Chinese-built version of the Soviet AK-230, 30-mm AA began to appear; more recently, several have had a "Round Ball" radome installed aft for a probable f.c. radar for the 30-mm AA. The 1980s have also seen the introduction of IFF equipment. Considerable numbers of the craft have been seen in an incomplete state in the Shanghai area in recent years, and not all of the listed total are operational. Some reported receiving four C.801 missiles in 1988. Four each transferred to Pakistan and Bangladesh. Soviet-made M503A multi-row radial diesels are difficult to maintain and offer only about 600 hours between overhauls; it is likely that the Chinese-made version is even less reliable.

♦ **1 Homa (Project EM1B) class** (In serv. circa 1970)

D: 85 tons (fl) **S:** 38 kts
Dim: 28.00 × 6.60 × . . . (3.10 moulded depth)
A: 2/HY-1 SSM (I × 2)—4/25-mm 2M-8 AA (II × 2)
Electron Equipt:
Radar: 1/Square Tie surf. search/missile target desig.
M: 4 M50 series diesels; 4 props; 5,600 bhp
Range: 500/25 **Crew:** 20 tot.

Remarks: A single, apparently unsuccessful prototype with lengthened hull over the Houku design, an extra twin 25-mm AA mount aft and uprated engines. Design offered for foreign sale 1986.

♦ **100+ Houku (Project EM1A or Project 24) class** (In serv. circa 1968–. . .)

Houku-class guided-missile patrol boats Poly Technologies, 1986

D: 68 tons (74 normal/79.19 fl) **S:** 37 kts
Dim: 27.0 × 6.50 (6.30 wl) × 1.8 (1.295 mean hull)
A: 2/HY-1 SSM—2/25-mm 2M-8 AA (II × 1)
Electron Equipt:
Radar: 1/Square Tie surf. search/missile target desig.
IFF: High Pole A transponder
M: 4 M50 diesels; 4 props; 4,800 bhp **Electric:** 65 kw
Endurance: 5 days **Range:** 500/24 **Crew:** 2 officers, 15 enlisted

Remarks: Steel-hulled improvement on Soviet-supplied Komar, which is no longer operational in the PLAN. Also referred to as "Hegu" class. Most are now fitted with a High Pole A IFF transponder. Offered for export with 4 C-801 missiles, which may also have been backfitted into some Chinese Navy units. Exported to Pakistan (4), Bangladesh (4), and Egypt (6).

TORPEDO BOATS

♦ **1 Huzhou class** Bldr: . . . . . . SY, China (In serv. late 1980s?)

Remarks: A new design apparently intended to begin replacement of the obsolescent P-6 class. No data available.

♦ **120 Huchuan-class (Project 25) semi-hydrofoils** Bldr: Hudong SY, Shanghai (In serv. 1966–1980)

Chinese Huchuan class—unit in foreground (3214) has no hydrofoils; craft in background to left does

TORPEDO BOATS *(continued)*

Late Huchuan class—at speed on foils; note mg mounts fore and aft 1983

D: 39 tons (45.8 fl) **S:** 50 kts
Dim: 22.50 × 3.80 (6.26 over foils) × 1.146
A: 2/533-mm TT—4/14.5-mm mg (II × 2)
Electron Equipt: Radar: 1/Type 756 nav. **Crew:** 11 tot.
M: 3 M50 diesels; 3 props; 3,600 bhp
Electric: 5.6 kw **Range:** 500/30

Remarks: Identical to the hydrofoils delivered to Albania, Bangladesh, Pakistan, and Tanzania. Also built in Romania. Not all units have the foils fitted. No foils aft, as stern planes on surface, but there are auxiliary foils forward to assist in getting the boat "on foil." In most, both gun mounts are aft, but in late-construction units, one mount is forward. Early units had Skin Head radar, while later ships have a Type 756 slotted-waveguide radar antenna.

♦ **40 Soviet P 6-class (Project 26) wooden-hulled** Bldr: China (In ser. 1960–66)

D: 56 tons (67.5 fl) **S:** 45 kts **Dim:** 25.40 × 6.24 × 1.24 (1.70 props)
A: 2/533-mm TT—4/25-mm 2M-8 AA (II × 2)
Electron Equipt: Radar: 1/Skin Head surf. search **Crew:** 20 tot.
M: 4 M50 diesels; 4 props; 4,800 bhp **Range:** 450/30, 600/15

Remarks: Wooden-hull construction copies of an early 1950s Soviet design. A number have been retired, and the remainder are of dubious utility.

♦ **20–30 Soviet P 4-class aluminum-hulled hydroplanes** (In serv. 1950s)

D: 19.3 tons (22.4 fl) **S:** 55 kts **Dim:** 19.3 × 3.7 × 1.0
A: 2/14.5-mm mg (II × 1)—2/450-mm TT **Crew:** 12 tot.
Electron Equipt: Radar: 1/Skin Head surf. search
M: 2 M50 diesels; 2 props; 2,400 hp **Range:** 400/30

Remarks: Survivors believed to be in land storage reserve. Four transferred to Bangladesh, 1983. Single-step planing-hull hydroplanes, with aluminum-alloy hulls. Very difficult to maneuver at high speeds.

PATROL BOATS

♦ **3 (+ . . .) seagoing** Bldr: Wuxi SY (In serv. 1991– . . .)

D: 300 tons (fl) **S:** 17 kts **Dim:** 45.0 × 7.6 × . . .
A: . . . **Electron Equipt:** Radar: . . .
M: 2 Deutz-MWM TBD-234 diesels; 2 props; 2,448 bhp
Crew: . . . tot.

Remarks: Ordered 12-89. Probably intended for customs/anti-smuggling patrol and may be under Customs rather than PLAN control.

♦ **3 search-and-rescue/patrol boats** Bldr: Guan Bee SY, Singapore (In serv. 1990–91)

Yan Jiu Sheng 1 Hu Jiu Sheng 1 Sui Jiu Sheng 1

D: 365 tons (fl) **S:** 28 kts **Dim:** 49.97 × 8.00 × 1.80
A: prob. 2/14.5-mm mg (II × 1)
Electron Equipt: Radar: 1 or 2/ . . . nav.
M: 3 MTU . . . . . . diesels; 3 props; 6,600 bhp **Crew:** 8 tot.

Remarks: 290 grt. Intended for search-and-rescue work, oil-spill patrol, etc. All three launched 30-6-90. Probably subordinated to regional governments rather than to the PLAN.

♦ **2 Hai Guan 901-class Customs patrol** Bldr: Huangpu SY, Guangzhou (In serv. 1989)

Hai Guan 901 Hai Guan 902

D: 400 tons (fl) **S:** 30 kts **Dim:** 58.0 × 7.6 × . . .
A: 2/14.5-mm mg (II × 1) **Electron Equipt:** Radar: 1 or 2/ . . . nav.
M: . . . diesels; . . . props; . . . bhp **Crew:** . . . tot.

Remarks: Serve as Customs Force flagships in South China area.

♦ **3 (+ . . .) Haijui class** Bldr: . . . . . . (In serv. 1987– . . .)

688 693 697

Haijui class 693—with twin 57-mm gun mounts fore and aft Boris Lemachko Co

Haijui class 688—with VDS in place of aft 57-mm mount 7-

D: 450 tons (fl) **S:** . . . kts **Dim:** 64.0 × . . . × 2.20 (hull)
A: 4/57-mm AA (II × 2)—4/30-mm 65-cal. AK-230 AA (II × 2)—4/RBU-1200 ASW RL (V × 4)—2/BMB-2 d.c. mortars—2/d.c. racks—mine rails
Electron Equipt:
Radar: 1/Pot Head surf. search, 1 Round Ball f.c.
Sonar: HF hull-mounted
M: 4 diesels; 2 props; 8,800 bhp **Crew:** 70 tot.

Remarks: A lengthened version of the Hainan class, with newer AA weapons. Has optical f.c. director. Hulls 688 and 697 have French Thomson-Sintra SS 12 variab depth sonar in lieu of aft twin 57-mm mount.

♦ **76 (+ . . .) Hainan class (Project 037)** (In serv. 1964– . . .)

Hainan-class patrol boat 642 Ross Gillett, 9-

Hainan-class patrol boat 703 Boris Lemachko collecti

ATROL BOATS *(continued)*

ainan-class patrol boat 680 1986

D: 375 tons (400 fl) **S:** 30.5 kts **Dim:** 58.77 × 7.20 × 2.20 (hull)
A: 4/57-mm AA (II × 2)—4/25-mm 2M-8AA (II × 2)—4/RBU-1200 (V × 4)—2/BMB-2 d.c. mortars—2/d.c. racks—mines
Electron Equipt:
Radar: 1/Pot Head surf. search
Sonar: Tamir-11 HF hull-mounted—IFF: 1/High Pole A transponder
M: 4 diesels; 4 props; 8,800 bhp **Range:** 2,000/14 **Crew:** 70 tot.

emarks: Hull numbers in 200s, 300s, 600s, and 800s. Early units (which are beginng to be retired) had 2/76.2-mm DP U.S. Mk 26 vice 4/57-mm AA and Skin Head dars. Two were transferred to Pakistan, 1976, and two more in 1980; eight delivered Egypt 1983–85; eight to Bangladesh 1982–85; and six to Myanmar in 1991.

320 Shanghai-II class (Project 62) (In serv. 1962–. . .)

ıanghai-II 107—late version 1986

anghai-II class 3314—with two RBU-1200 ASW RL 1988

D: 122.5 tons (134.8 fl) **S:** 28.5 kts
Dim: 38.78 × 5.41 × 1.49 (hull; 1.554 full load)
A: 4/37-mm V-47M AA (II × 2)—4/25-mm 2M-8 AA (II × 2)— depth charges—mines (some also: 2 RBU-1200 ASW RL (V × 2))
Electron Equipt:
Radar: Pot Head or Skin Head surf. search
Sonar: HF on some—IFF: High Pole A transponder
M: 2 M50F-4, 1,200-bhp, and 2/12D6, 910-bhp diesels; 4 props; 4,200 bhp
Endurance: 7 days **Electric:** 39 kw **Range:** 750/16.5
Crew: 36 tot.

emarks: No longer being constructed, and numbers are slowly declining through ansfers abroad and attrition. At least 72 others have been transferred to foreign vies, and Romania also built the design. Very unsophisticated and sparsely uipped. Shanghai-I class was smaller and had 2/57-mm (II × 1) forward; a few of the built 1959–60 may remain in service: 125 tons (fl); 36.0 × 5.5 × 1.4; propulsion as for anghai-II. The 12D6 diesels are used during cruising, with the high-speed M50F esels being cut in for maximum speeds.

ATROL CRAFT

ote: In addition to the classes listed below, there are probably additional classes of ıall patrol boats for which no information is available. Most patrol craft are not bordinated to the PLAN but rather to various military districts and police forces, as ell as to the Customs Service.

Customs Patrol 301 at Shanghai Ross Gillett, 9-84

The above craft, armed with 4/14.5-mm mg (II × 2), is one of a number operated by customs and piloting agencies. This particular unit displaces 245 tons (fl), has a max. speed of 28 knots (27 continuous), an endurance of 2,000 n.m. at 16 kts, and has dimensions of 44.50 × 7.00 × 1.85.

♦ **1 (+ . . .) Cougar catamarans** Bldr: . . .

D: 5 tons **S:** 35 kts **Dim:** 14.0 (13.50 wl) × 5.15 × 1.30 **A:** . . .
M: 2 MWM diesels; 2 props; 1,230 bhp **Range:** 500/35
Crew: 3–5 tot.

Remarks: Prototype and moulds for this GRP design delivered 2-87 by Cougar Holdings, Hamble, U.K., for license production in China. Program status uncertain.

♦ **1 (+ . . .) 25-meter class** Bldr: . . . (In serv. 1980s)

D: 53.5 tons normal (55.77 fl) **S:** 38 kts **Dim:** 25.0 × 5.0 × . . .
A: 4/25-mm AA (II × 2) **Electron Equipt:** Radar: 1/Pot Head
M: 3 M50-series diesels; 3 props; 3,600 bhp **Electric:** 12 kw
Endurance: 5–7 days **Range:** 300/27; 490/. . . **Crew:** 20 tot.

Remarks: Official data for a class of patrol craft that has yet to receive a Western nickname. Apparently a production successor to the now-stricken Beihai class.

♦ **. . . Yulin-class patrol craft** Bldr: . . . (In serv. 1964–68)

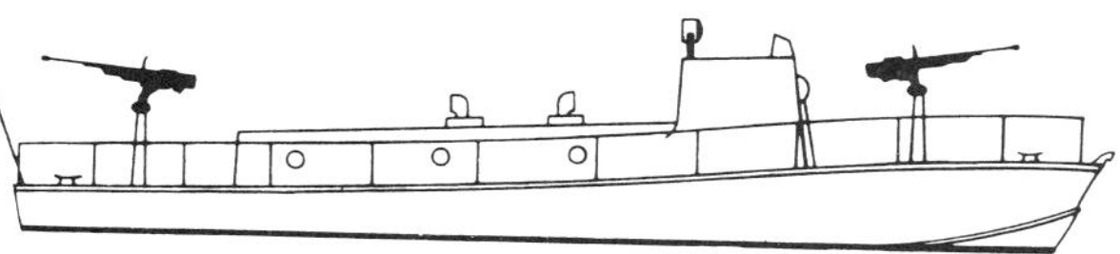
Yulin-class patrol craft

D: 9.8 tons (fl) **S:** 20 kts **Dim:** 13.0 × 2.9 × 1.1 **Crew:** 4–6 tot.
A: 2/12.7-mm mg (I × 2) **M:** 1 3D6 diesel; 1 prop; 300 bhp

Remarks: Craft of this class also transferred to Kampuchea, Congo, and Tanzania.

MINE WARFARE SHIPS

Note: In the late 1980s, China was reported to be planning to construct 20 to 40 GRP-hulled minehunters, possibly of the Italian *Lerici* class, with the first one or two to build in Italy. Financial constraints and international outrage at internal events in China have apparently delayed the program.

♦ **1 or more Wolei-class minelayers** (In serv. late 1980s)

Remarks: No details available.

♦ **1 or more Bulieijian-class minelayer** (In serv. 1988)

Remarks: No details available; may in fact be the "Wolei" class listed above.

♦ **41 Soviet T-43-class (Project 010) fleet minesweepers** Bldrs: Wuzhang SY, Guangzhou SY (In serv. 1956–1970s, mid-1980s–. . .)

D: 500 tons (590 fl) **S:** 14 kts **Dim:** 60.0 × 8.6 × 2.16
A: 4/37-mm V-47M AA (II × 2)—4/25-mm 2M-8 AA (II × 2)— 4/12.7-mm mg (II × 2)—2/d.c. mortars—12–16 mines
Electron Equipt:
Radar: 1/Ball End surf. search or Type 756 nav.
Sonar: Tamir-11 HF
IFF: 1/Square Head interrogator, 1/High Pole A transponder
M: 2/Type 9D diesels; 2 props; 2,200 bhp
Fuel: 70 tons **Range:** 3,200/10
Electric: 550 kw **Crew:** 10 officers, 60 enlisted

Remarks: A few shorter-hulled, 58-meter, 570-ton units were transferred from the U.S.S.R.; the majority are long-hulled ships and were built in China. Production began again in the mid-1980s at Guangzhou. Several others were built or converted as surveying ships, civilian research ships, and submarine rescue ships (J 124). At least three minesweepers had an 85-mm DP gun forward. Current hull numbers in the 800s.

MINE WARFARE SHIPS *(continued)*

Chinese T-43-class minesweeper Ross Gillett, 9-84

T-43-class 830 Leo Van Ginderen, 1-87

♦ **1 or more Wosao-class inshore minesweepers** Bldr: Wusung SY, Shanghai (In serv. 1988–. . .)

4422

Wosao-class minesweeper 4422 U.S. Navy photo, 1989

D: 310 tons (fl) **S:** 15.5 kts **Dim:** 44.7 × 6.2 × 2.1
A: 4/25-mm 2M-8 AA (II × 2)—mine rails
Electron Equipt: Radar: 1/Type 756 nav.—Sonar: probably none
M: 2 diesels; 2 props; . . . bhp **Crew:** 3 officers, 14 enlisted

Remarks: 4422, noted at Shanghai 1988, is equipped only to sweep moored mechanical mines. Steel-hulled.

♦ **20 Fushun-class coastal minesweepers** (In serv. 1976–. . .)

D: 275 tons (fl) **S:** 25 kts **Dim:** 40.0 (37.00 pp) × 5.5 × 3.0
A: 2/37-mm V-47M AA (II × 1)
M: 2 M50F-4 diesels, 2 12D6 diesels; 4 props; 4,220 bhp

♦ **. . . Yenkuan and Wochang classes**

Remarks: Shanghai II-class patrol boats adapted as minesweepers. Class differentiation not available.

♦ **up to 80 auxiliary Lienyun-class minesweepers converted from fishing boats**

♦ **60 Futi-class (Type 312) drone minesweepers** (In serv. 1984–. . .)

D: 46.95 tons (fl) **S:** 12 kts **Dim:** 20.94 × 4.20 × 1.30
M: 1 Type 3D12 diesel; 1 CP prop; 300 hp **Crew:** 3 tot. (for ferrying)

Auxiliary minesweepers—subordinated to the Shanghai area Milita Maritime District. Sometimes referred to as the "Lienyun class," these sh displace about 400 tons, are armed with 12.7-mm machine guns, and a based on a steel-hulled trawler design. 19

Futi-class (Type 312) drone minesweeper PLAN, 19

Remarks: Normally operated by radio control to a range of 3 n.m., but can be mann Electric propulsion for sweeping at 1 to 5 kts. Diesel generator amidships pow integral electromagnet for magnetic sweeping and a noisemaker for actuating acou mines. All equipment shock-mounted. Laser precision navigation system. Offici stated not to be good sea boats; large numbers have been built, however. Class has b exported to Thailand.

AMPHIBIOUS WARFARE SHIPS

♦ **4 Yukan-class landing ships** Bldr: Zhonghua SY, Shanghai (In serv 1978–80)

927 928 929 934

Yukan No. 927 19

Yukan No. 929 *Ships of the Wo*

D: 3,110 tons (fl) **S:** 17 kts **Dim:** 119.5 × 15.6 × 2.9
A: 8/57-mm AA (II × 4)—8/25-mm 2M-8 AA (II × 4)
Electron Equipt: Radar: 2/nav.—IFF: 1/High Pole A
M: 2 SEMT-Pielstick 12 PA6 diesels; 2 props; 16,000 bhp

Remarks: Evidently built to replace aging World War II-built U.S. LSTs, these s are larger and considerably faster than their predecessors. Carry two U.S.-de LCVPs. Bow and stern ramps.

♦ **13 ex-U.S. LST 1- and LST 542-class tank landing ships** (In serv 1943–45)

355, 361, 901, 902, 903, 906, 907, 921, 922, 923, 924, 925, 926

D: 1,625 tons (4,080 fl) **S:** 11 kts **Dim:** 99.98 × 15.24 × 4.36
A: 2–3/76.2-mm DP (I × 2 or 3)—6, 8, or 12/37-mm AA (II × 3, 4, or 6)
Electron Equipt: Radar: 2/ Type 756/Fin Curve nav.
M: 2 G.M. 12-278A or 12-567A diesels; 2 props; 1,800 bhp

IPHIBIOUS WARFARE SHIPS *(continued)*

T 1-class 903—76.2-mm guns fore and aft, one radar
Ships of the World, 1986

T 1-class 901—two twin 37-mm on bow, two radars
Ships of the World, 1986

narks: Cargo capacity: 2,100 tons. Some are immobile as accommodations ships or lers for submarines. Most rearmed during late 1950s with U.S. 76.2-mm guns and iet twin 37-mm AA.

4 Yudao-class (Type 073) medium landing ships (In serv. 1980–. . .)

dao 985 Boris Lemachko Collection

D: 1,460 tons (fl) **S:** . . . **Dim:** 82.07 (78.00 pp) × 12.60 × 3.10 max.
A: 8/25-mm 2M-8AA (II × 4) **M:** diesels

marks: Probably intended as replacements for World War II-era U.S. LSM 1 class. semble a smaller version of the LST 1 design.

14 ex-U.S. LSM 1-class medium landing ships (In serv. 1944–45)
2, 353, 354, 393, 511, 809, 810, 811, 931, 932, 933, 934, 935, 936

M 1-class 936—showing mine port aft Ross Gillett, 9-84

LSM 1-class 932—and two sisters Ross Gillett, 9-84

D: 743 tons (1,095 fl) **S:** 12.5 kts **Dim:** 62.03 × 10.52 × 2.54
A: 6/37-mm AA (II × 3)—4/25-mm AA (II × 2)—mines
Electron Equipt: Radar: 1/Fin Curve nav.
M: 2 Fairbanks-Morse 38D8Q-10 or G.M. 16-278A diesels; 2 props; 2,800 bhp
Range: 2,500/12 **Crew:** 60 tot.

Remarks: Rearmed with Soviet weapons late 1950s. Most have two minelaying ports in the stern. Several have superstructure built over the open tank deck.

♦ **23 Yuling-class utility landing craft** (In serv. 1971–75)

Yuling-class N 1122—of the Nanjing Maritime Border Defense Force 1983

D: 600 tons (fl) **S:** 12 kts **Dim:** 50.0 × 7.0 × 2.0
A: 8/14.5-mm mg (II × 4) **Electron Equipt:** Radar: 1/Type 756 nav.
M: 2 diesels; 2 props; . . . bhp

♦ **300 Yunnan-class (Project 067) landing craft** Bldr: Huangzhou SY (In serv. 1968–72)

Yunnan-class J1206—employed as a cargo lighter
Boris Lemachko Coll.

D: 133.2 tons (fl) **S:** 10.5 kts **Dim:** 27.50 (24.07 pp) × 5.40 × 1.40
A: 2–4/14.5-mm mg (I or II × 2) **M:** 2 diesels; 2 props; 600 bhp
Range: 500/10 **Crew:** 6 tot.

Remarks: Cargo: 46 tons (1 tank). Cargo deck 15.0 × 4.0 m.

♦ **40–50 Yuqin-class landing craft** (In serv. 1962–72)

Yuqin-class 7575 1980

AMPHIBIOUS WARFARE SHIPS *(continued)*

D: 58 tons light (110 fl) **S:** 11.5 (9 loaded) kts
Dim: 24.1 × 5.2 × 1.1 **A:** 2/14.5-mm mg (I × 2)
M: 2 diesels; 2 Type 12V50 props; 600 bhp

Remarks: Two transferred to Bangladesh in 1984 as survey craft. Can carry up to 110 troops over short distances.

♦ **20–30 Yuchai-class landing craft** (In serv. 1960s)

Yuchai-class Y 761 Ross Gillett, 9-84

D: 70 tons (fl) **S:** 10 kts **Dim:** 20.0 × 4.3 × 1.0
A: 4/14.5-mm mg (II × 2) **M:** 2 diesels; 2 props; 600 bhp

Remarks: Some, including unit shown above, have "Y"-pendants, indicating service as "transports" rather than as landing craft per se.

♦ **1 Dagu-A-class air-cushion landing craft prototype**

Dagu-A air-cushion vehicle—note bow door 1981

D: 61 tons (fl) **S:** 55 kts **Dim:** 27.2 × 13.8 × 9.6 (high)
M: 2 turboprop propulsion engines; 1 gas-turbine lift engine, geared also to 2 auxiliary propellers

Remarks: Cargo: 16.8 tons. Designed by Shanghai SB Research and Development Institute. The function of the small airscrews amidships is uncertain; they may aid in maneuvering. There are six centrifugal lift-fans. Appears to be an engineering prototype rather than an operational combatant. Other hovercraft designs reported include the 15-meter Payi and 70-ton Jingoah designs.

AUXILIARY SHIPS

There is no authoritative, comprehensive information on the PLAN's logistic support fleet, but China has designated and built large numbers of auxiliary vessels, running the spectrum of logistics support, repair, hydrographic survey, and research types, including a great many tugs and small oilers. Known types and classes are listed below.

ICEBREAKERS

♦ **1 Yanbing class** Bldr: . . .

Haiping 723 (In serv. late 1970s)

Haiping 723—note radomes forward JMSDF/*Ships of the World,*

D: approx. 5,000 tons (fl) **S:** 16 kts **Dim:** . . . × . . . × . . .
A: 8/37-mm V-47M AA (II × 4)
Electron Equipt: 1 Fin Curve nav., 1/Type 756 nav.
M: 2 or 4 diesels; 2 props; . . . bhp **Crew:** approx. 100 tot.

Remarks: An enlarged variant of the Haiping 721 class, most recently equipped intelligence-collection duties, with two radomes centerline forward of the bridge. also be used for ocean towing.

♦ **2 Haiping class** Bldr: Jiu Shin SY, Shanghai

Haiping 721 (L: 26-12-69) Haiping 722 (L: 1972)

D: 3,200 tons **S:** 16 kts **Dim:** 84.0 × 15.0 × 5.0
A: 8/37-mm V-47M AA (II × 4)—8/25-mm 2M-8 AA (II × 4)
Electron Equipt:
Radar: 2/Fin Curve nav.— IFF: High Pole A transponder
M: 2 diesels; 2 props; 5,200 bhp **Crew:** 90 tot.

Remarks: Differ in details of superstructure. Can break 1.2-m ice, can also be use ocean tugs, and have been employed as intelligence collectors on occasion. Resemb slightly smaller version of Haiping 723 above, with one less level of superstruc above the bridge and no after mast.

HYDROGRAPHIC SURVEY SHIPS

♦ **1 Ganzhu class** Bldr: Zhu Zhiang SY (In serv. 1975)

K 420

Ganzhu-class K 420 1

D: 1,000 tons (fl) **S:** 20 kts **Dim:** 65.0 × 9.0 × 3.0
A: 4/37-mm AA V-47M (II × 2)—4/25-mm 2M-8 AA (II × 2)— 4/14 mm mg (II × 2)
M: 4 diesels; 2 props; 4,400 bhp **Crew:** 120 tot.

Remarks: Operates in South China waters.

♦ **4 Yanlai class** (In serv. early 1970s)

K 200 K 427 K 512 K 629

Yanlai Class K 200—with armament temporarily removed JMSDF,

DROGRAPHIC SURVEY SHIPS *(continued)*

): 1,100 tons (fl) **S:** 16 kts **Dim:** 72.0 × 9.8 × 3.0
A: 4/37-mm AA (II × 2)—4/25-mm AA (II × 2)
M: 2 diesels; 2 props; 2,200 bhp

marks: Funnel amidships; large crane aft.

2 modified T-43-class minesweepers (In serv. late 1960s)

94 S . . .

3-class research ship S 994 Ross Gillett, 9-84

): 500 tons (590 fl) **S:** 14 kts **Dim:** 60.0 × 8.6 × 2.16
A: 2/37-mm V-47M AA (II × 1)—4/14.5-mm AA (II × 2)
lectron Equipt: Radar: 1/Fin Curve nav. **Range:** 3,200/10
M: 2 Type 9D diesels; 2 props; 2,200 bhp **Fuel:** 70 tons

narks: "S" pendant indicates research rather than hydrographic survey role. Exded after deckhouse, no minesweeping equipment. Four-point mooring capability.

2 Hace-class coastal survey ships (In serv. 1960s)

): 400 tons **S:** 12 kts **Dim:** 38.0 × 7.6 × 3.4
A: 4/14.5-mm mg (II × 2) **M:** 1 diesel; 1 prop; 400 bhp

narks: Design derived from that of a coastal cargo ship.

1 Yanlun class (In serv. 1965)—no data available

up to 10 additional naval survey ships

TELLIGENCE-COLLECTION SHIP

te: The Haiping and Yanbing classes of icebreakers have also performed elligence-collection missions; see entries above.

1 Dadie class Bldr: Wuhan SY, Wuchang

DIAO 841 (In serv. 1987)

diao 841—note intercept arrays JMSDF/*Ships of the World,* 1991

): 2,500 tons (fl) **S:** 17 kts **Dim:** 94.0 × 11.3 × 4.0
A: 4/14.5-mm mg (II × 2)
lectron Equipt: Radar: 2/type 756 nav.—EW: see Remarks
M: 2 diesels; 2 props; . . . bhp **Crew:** 15 officers, 145 enlisted

marks: Has been deployed as far as the Japanese coast. Has bow centerline anchor sharply raked bow, and therefore may be equipped with a bow-mounted sonar ay. Intercept arrays are mounted on the lattice masts and atop the pilothouse.

EANOGRAPHIC RESEARCH SHIPS

e: The *Xiang Yang Hong* ("East is Red," the title of the Chinese national anthem) es ships are mainly disparate in size and characteristics; all are capable of a variety xperimental duties (including general oceanography), particularly in support of sile and satellite research and hydrometeorology. All are under the general subortion of the Academy of Sciences.

1 Huanghai 11 class Bldr: Zhejiang SY, Hutoudu

ANGHAI 11 (L: 1990)

): 300 tons (fl) **S:** 17 kts **Dim:** 45.0 × 7.6 × . . . **M:** diesels

◆ **1 ocean surveillance ship** Bldr: Wuchang SY

	Laid down	L	In serv.
72	6-87	26-10-88	3-89

D: 899 tons (fl) **S:** 19.2 kts **Dim:** 70.0 (65.0 pp) × 9.4 × 3.0
M: 2 M.A.N.-Burmeister & Wain 6L28/32 diesels; 1 CP prop; 3,600 bhp
Electron Equipt: Radar: 2/Decca RM 1290A nav.
Range: 2,500/16 **Electric:** 560 kw **Crew:** 45 tot.

Remarks: Operated for the National Bureau of Oceanography for environmental research and patrol. Equipage includes 120-shp bow-thruster, MX 5102 SATCOMM receiver, two 50-m^2 laboratories, and pollution control equipment.

◆ **1 Antarctic research and support ship** Bldr: . . . , Finland

XIANG YANG HONG . . . (ex-*Ji Di,* ex-*Rhea*) (In serv. 1971)

D: 15,000 tons (fl) **S:** . . . **Dim:** . . . × . . . × . . .
M: . . .

Remarks: 7,890 grt/10,000 dwt. Acquired 10-85. Has helicopter deck and hangar. Carried 126 scientists to Antarctica 12-86, traveling 26,700 n.m. on a 200-day journey.

◆ **1 weather-reporting ship**

XIANG YANG HONG 14

Remarks: No data available; participated in joint U.S.–Chinese Western Pacific research cruise 12-85 to 2-86.

◆ **1 Xiang Yang Hong 10 class** Bldr: Hudong SY, Shanghai (In serv. 1980)

XIANG YANG HONG 10

Xiang Yang Hong 10 1983

D: 10,975 tons **S:** 20 kts **Dim:** 156.2 × 20.6 × 6.8
M: 2 Xin Zhong-M.A.N. K9Z60/105E diesels; 2 props; . . . bhp

Remarks: Operated by the East China Sea Branch, State Oceanographic Bureau. Referred to by China as a "blue-water survey ship." Uses same hull and propulsion as the Dajiang-class submarine tenders, but has twin, side-by-side funnels; the crane forward is smaller, and the king posts abaft the stacks and the heavy foremast support large log-periodic HF antennas. Has hangar space for two French Super Frélon helicopters and retractable fin stabilizers. Conducted 150-day Antarctic expedition 20-11-84 to 10-4-85 with submarine tender J 121 and a landing ship named *Great Wall 2.*

◆ **3 Xiang Yang Hong 9 class** Bldr: Hudong SY, Shanghai (In serv. 1979–. . .)

XIANG YANG HONG 9 XIANG YANG HONG 14
XIAN YANG HONG 16

Xiang Yang Hong 9 JMSDF, 8-90

Xiang Yang Hong 16 JMSDF, 7-90

D: 4,400 tons **S:** 18 kts **Dim:** 122.0 × . . . × . . .
M: diesels; 4,000 bhp **Range:** 11,000/. . . **Crew:** 145 tot.

Remarks: Operated for the National Bureau of Oceanography.

OCEANOGRAPHIC RESEARCH SHIPS *(continued)*

♦ **1 Polish Francesco Nullo-class (Type B-41) former cargo ship** Bldr: Paris Commune SY, Gdynia, Poland (In serv. 1967)

Xiang Yang Hong 5 (ex-*Chang Niy*)

Xiang Yang Hong 5 R.N.Z.N., 1980

D: 14,500 tons (fl) **S:** 16 kts **Dim:** 152.6 (141.6 pp) × 19.5 × 8.75
M: 1 Cegielski-Sulzer 6RD68 diesel; 1 prop; 7,200 bhp
Range: 15,000/16

Remarks: Extensively rebuilt as a hydrometeorological-research and radiosonde-balloon-tracking ship at Canton in 1970–72, and altered again after 1976, with a two-level superstructure replacing the after two hatches. Has one large log-periodic HF antenna forward. One of her four Chinese-operated merchant sisters briefly served as an unaltered support ship under the name *Xiang Yang Hong 11* in the late 1970s.

♦ **1 Xiang Yang Hong 2 class** (In serv. 1971)

Xiang Yang Hong 2

D: 1,000 tons (fl) **S:** . . . kts **Dim:** 72.5 × 8.7 × . . .
M: 2 diesels; 2 props; . . . bhp

♦ **3 Xiang Yang Hong 1 class** (In serv. 1972–74)

Xiang Yang Hong 1 Xiang Yang Hong 4 Xiang Yang Hong 6

Xiang Yang Hong 6 U.S. Navy, 1979

D: approx. 1,000 tons (fl) **S:** . . . kts **Dim:** 67.0 × 10.0 × . . .
M: 2 diesels; 2 props; . . . bhp

Remarks: Carried 2/37-mm AA (II × 1), 8/14.5-mm mg (II × 4) as completed.

♦ **1 Shihjian 3 class** Bldr: . . .

Shihjian 3 (In serv. 1982)

D: 3,300 tons (fl) **S:** 22.5 kts **Dim:** 104.0 × 13.7 × 5.2
Electron Equipt: Radar: . . .
M: 2 diesels; 2 props; 9,600 bhp
Crew: 8 officers, 45 men, plus 94 scientists

Remarks: Laid down 1979, launched 4-81. Name means "Experiment." Operated for the South China Sea Institute of Oceanology, Guangzhou. Has Magnavox 1102 NAVSAT receiver, 10-km-depth echo-sounder, Endeco 1074 towed submersible.

♦ **2 Haiyang class** (In serv. 1972–73)

Haiyang 01 Haiyang 02

D: 3,295 tons **S:** 20 kts **Dim:** 104.0 × 13.8 × 5.0
A: 6/37-mm V-47M AA (II × 3) **M:** 2 diesels; 2 props; 9,000 bhp

Remarks: Resemble passenger liners; white-painted.

♦ **3 Shukuang 01 class** (In serv. late 1960s)

Shukuang 01 Shukuang 02 Shukuang 03

D: 500 tons (590 fl) **S:** 14 kts **Dim:** 60.0 × 8.4 × 2.15
A: 1/37-mm AA **Electron Equipt:** Radar: 1/Fin Curve nav.
M: 2 Type 9D diesels; 2 props; 2,200 bhp **Fuel:** 70 tons
Range: 3,200/10

Remarks: Design closely derived from T-43-class minesweeper. White-painted. There is also *Shukuang* 04, a more modern-appearing ship about the same size.

♦ **2 Shihjian 1 class** Bldr: Hudong SY, Shanghai (In serv. 1968–69)

Shihjian 1 Shihjian 2

D: 2,955 tons **S:** 16.2 kts **Dim:** 94.73 (87.00 pp) × 14.04 × 4.75
A: 8/14.5-mm mg (II × 4) **Electric:** 1,065 kw
M: 2 Type 6 ESD(2) 48/82 diesels; 2 props; 4,000 bhp
Range: 7,500/14.5

Remarks: 2,500 grt/1,000 dwt. Enlarged version of *Dong Fang Hong* class.

♦ **2 Dong Fang Hong class** Bldr: Hudong SY, Shanghai (In serv. 1964–66)

Dong Fang Hong . . . . . .

Dong Fang Hong 1!

D: 2,900 tons **S:** 14 kts **Dim:** 86.00 × 11.50 × 4.75 **A:** none
M: 2 diesels; 2 props; 4,000 hp

Remarks: Subordinated to the Shandong Oceanographic College. There are also l numbers of civilian-agency-subordinated research vessels for oil exploration, fishe research, etc.

EXPERIMENTAL SHIPS

♦ **2 Yuanwang-class space-event support ships** Bldr: Hudong SY Shanghai (In serv. 1980)

Yuanwang 1 Yuanwang 2

Yuanwang 1 U.S. Navy photo, 4

D: 17,100 tons (21,000 fl) **S:** 20 kts **Dim:** 190.0 × 22.6 × 7.5
M: 1 Dalian-Sulzer 8LRB66 diesel; 1 prop; 17,400 bhp
Range: 18,000/20 **Endurance:** 100 days

Remarks: First observed during the 5-80 Chinese ICBM tests in the Central Pac Among the 54 research-associated antennas are one large parabolic tracking ante two log-periodic HF ("fish-spine") antennas, several precision theodolite optical tr ing stations, and two smaller missile-tracking radars, as well as positions for l installation of equipment. Large helicopter deck, but no hangar. Have a bow-thru and retractable fin stabilizers. Navigational equipment includes SINS (Ship's Iner Navigation System) and NAVSAT receiver. Equipped with satellite communicat gear; both were refitted 1990 with improved communications and data-handling g

♦ **1 Yen Hsi-class weapons trials support ship** Bldr: . . . SY, Shanghai

Hsun 701 (In serv. 1970)

D: 1,200 tons (fl) **S:** 16 kts **Dim:** 60.0 × 11.0 × 3.5
A: 2/37-mm V-47M AA (II × 1)—4/14.5-mm mg (II × 2)
Electron Equipt: Radar: 1/Fin Curve nav.
M: 2 Type 8300Z diesels; 2 props; 2,200 bhp **Range:** 4,500/11

Remarks: Apparently intended to support antiship cruise missile trials.

SUBMARINE SUPPORT SHIPS

♦ **3 Dajiang class** Bldr: Hudong SY, Shanghai (In serv. 1976–80)

J 121 Chang Xing Dao J 302 Chong Ming Dao
J 506 Yong Xing Dao

JBMARINE SUPPORT SHIPS *(continued)*

ıong Ming Dao (J 302) Ross Gillett, 9-84

ng Xing Dao (J 506)—in refit at Shanghai 7-89

D: 10,087 tons (fl) **S:** 20 kts **Dim:** 156.2 × 20.6 × 6.8 **A:** none
Electron Equipt: Radar: 2/Fin Curve, 1/Eye Shield (MX-902)
M: 2 Xin Zhong-M.A.N. K9Z60/105E diesels; 2 props; . . . bhp

marks: Also capable of employment as general salvage vessels. Carry two Zhi-8 per Frèlon) heavy helicopters in a double hangar. J 121 differs in not having the p anchor recesses at the stern (evidently intended to permit a 4-point moor). The e crane forward tends two trainable cradles just forward of the bridge; the cradles semicircular in section and support salvage-and-rescue submersibles. The sub- rsibles first appeared in 1986, are 15 m overall by 2.6 m diameter and can reportedly e to 600 m; carrying a crew of 3–4, they can rescue up to 22 personnel or can be used underwater salvage work, being equipped with a sonar, t.v., and a manipulator arm. The ships share the hull and propulsion of the research ship *Xiang Yang Hong 10* and bably also have fin stabilizers. Former J 506 transferred to Academy of Sciences, 3, and renumbered R 327; large log-periodic antenna added, and the ship is/was dently employed for some research purpose; by 1989, the ship had been returned to al service.

◆ **3 Dalang class** Bldr: Guangzhou SY (U 911: Wuhu SY)

03 (In serv. 11-75) J 504 (In serv. 1986) U 911 (In serv. 1986)

alang J 503 1980

D: 4,000 tons (fl) **S:** 16 kts **Dim:** 130.0 × 14.0 × 4.0
A: 8/37-mm V-47M AA (II × 4)—4/14.5-mm mg (II × 2)
Electron Equipt: Radar: 1/Fin Curve nav.
M: 2 diesels; 2 props; 4,000 bhp

marks: Primarily intended for general salvage and towing duties in support of marines. U 911 may be somewhat larger, and the "U" in the hull number is mally associated with repair ships rather than with submarine-associated vessels.

◆ **1 Hudong class** Bldr: Hudong SY, Shanghai (In serv. 1969)

301

Hudong-class submarine tender J 301 Ross Gillett, 9-84

D: 5,000 tons (fl) **S:** 15 kts **Dim:** 95.0 × 17.0 × 4.5
A: 6/37-mm AA V-47M (II × 3)—4/14.5-mm mg (II × 2)
Electron Equipt: Radar: 1/Fin Curve nav.
M: 1 diesel; 1 prop; 3,600 bhp **Range:** 5,000/12

Remarks: Has large gantry over stern for lowering a submarine rescue chamber, and is equipped with stern-quarter anchors to permit a 4-point moor.

◆ **1 Dazhi class** Bldr: Hudong SY, Shanghai (In serv. mid-1960s)

U 920

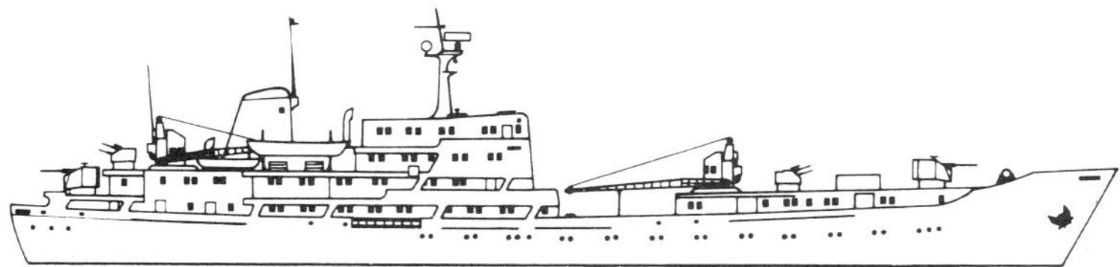

Dazhi class

D: 5,800 tons (fl) **S:** 14 kts **Dim:** 106.7 × 15.3 × 6.1
A: 4/37-mm AA V-47M (II × 2)—8/25-mm 2M-8 AA (II × 4)
Electron Equipt: Radar: 1/Fin Curve nav.
M: 1 diesel; 1 prop; . . . bhp

Remarks: The only PLAN submarine tender equipped on the Soviet scheme with spare torpedoes, battery-charging station, command and control facilities, and for light repair duties, the others being primarily intended for submarine rescue and salvage.

Note: There are several other small submarine support classes, including the 1,100-ton Dazhou class (J 502) and the 2,800-ton, 82-meter Dadong class (J 304, . . .). At least one T-43 minesweeper (J 124) is used in a submarine support role.

REPAIR SHIPS

◆ **1 Romanian Galati class** Bldr: Galati SY (In serv. early 1970s)

D: 5,200 tons (fl) **S:** 12.5 kts
Dim: 100.60 (93.70 pp) × 13.92 × 6.60 **A:** . . .
M: 1 Sulzer 5TAD56 diesel; 1 prop; . . . bhp **Electric:** 345 kw
Fuel: 250 tons **Range:** 5,000/12.5

Remarks: Converted from a cargo ship with minimal external alterations. Of nine sisters purchased by China, two others serve the navy as cargo ships.

◆ **1 U.S. Achelous class** Bldr: Kaiser Co., Vancouver, Wash.

	Laid down	L	In serv.
U 891 Takushan (ex-*Hsing An*, ex-*Achilles*, ARL 41, ex-LST 455)	3-8-42	17-10-42	30-1-43

Takushan (U 891) Ross Gillett, 9-84

REPAIR SHIPS *(continued)*

D: 4,100 tons (fl) **S:** 11 kts **Dim:** 99.98 × 15.24 × 3.40
A: 12/37-mm AA V-47M (II × 6)—4/14.5-mm mg (II × 2)
Electron Equipt: Radar: 1/Fin Curve nav.
M: 2 G.M. 12-567A diesels; 2 props; 1,800 bhp **Electric:** 350 kw
Range: 9,000/9 **Crew:** 290 tot.

Remarks: Acquired 1949. Has 60-ton A-frame gantry, plus several cranes. Generally immobile at Shanghai. Bow doors still functional.

SALVAGE SHIPS

◆ **1 Kansha class** Bldr: Chunghua SY, Shanghai (In serv. 7-81)

Hai Lao . . .

D: 1,400 tons (fl) **S:** 13.5 kts **Dim:** 69.9 × 10.5 × 3.6
A: . . . **Electron Equipt:** Radar: . . .
M: 2 Type 8300ZC diesels; 2 props; 2,200 bhp **Range:** 2,400/13.5

Remarks: Carries French-supplied SM-358-S salvage submersible, 7 m overall, with 300-m working depth. Has one 5-ton crane forward and a 2-ton crane aft. Operates in East Sea Fleet.

◆ **3 Yenting class** (In serv. 1972–74)

Hai Lao 456 Hai Lao 520 Hai Lao 523

D: 320 tons (fl) **S:** 10 kts **Dim:** 31.5 × 7.0 × 2.5
A: 4/14.5-mm mg (II × 2) **Electron Equipt:** Radar: . . .
M: 1 Type 3D12 diesel; 1 prop; 300 bhp **Crew:** 18 tot.

Remarks: Trawler hulls adapted for salvage duties.

◆ **3 Ding Hai class** Bldr: . . . (In serv. 1964–65)

Hai Lao 446 Hai Lao 447 Hai Lao 511

D: 400 tons (fl) **S:** 11 kts **Dim:** 37.5 × 7.0 × 3.5
A: 4/14.5-mm mg (II × 2)
Electron Equipt: Radar: 1/ Fin Curve nav.
M: 1 Type 3D12 diesel; 1 prop; 300 bhp **Crew:** 30 tot.

Remarks: Design adapted from a small cargo ship class; one hatch tended by 2-ton boom aft. Probably equipped as diving tenders.

CABLE SHIPS/BUOY TENDERS

◆ **3 or more Youzhong class** Bldr: Zhonghua SY, Shanghai (In serv. 1982–. . .)

G 2693 N 2304 N 2404

Youzhong-class cable layer N 2304 Ross Gillett, 9-84

D: 750 tons (fl) **S:** 14.5 kts **Dim:** 59.0 × 10.50 × 2.8
A: 4/14.5-mm mg (II × 2)
Electron Equipt: Radar: 1/Fin Curve nav.
M: 2 Type 8300Z diesels; 2 props; 2,200 hp

Remarks: Smaller version of Youdian class, shallower draft, with only 50 m³ of cable stowage.

◆ **4 or more Youdian class** Bldr: Zhonghua SY, Shanghai (In serv. late 1970s)

Beilan 765 Beilan 873 H 263 N . . .

Cable layer Beilan 765—note fixed gantry aft Boris Lemachko Coll.

Buoy tender H 263—note lack of bow sheaves, buoy crane, and handling deck, with reinforced hull sides Ross Gillett, 9-8

D: 1,550 tons (fl) **S:** 14 kts (sust.)
Dim: 71.40 (63.00 pp) × 10.50 × 3.60
A: 4/37-mm AA (II × 2)—4/14.5-mm mg *or* 8/14.5-mm mg (II × 2) *or* none
M: 2 Type 8300Z diesels; 2 props; 2,200 bhp
Electron Equipt: Radar: 1/Fin Curve

Remarks: Design built for both military and civil use. Cable tank has 187-m³ capa ity; ship can lay cable up to 100 mm thick. Those with "B" pendants serve as cab layers; those with "H" pendants are used as mooring buoy tenders. Several ("I pendants) also serve the Nanjing Maritime Border Defense Force.

REPLENISHMENT OILERS

◆ **2 Fuqing class** Bldr: Dalien SY (In serv. 1980–82)

X 575 Taikang X 615 Fencang

Fencang (X 615) Leo Van Ginderen, 1-

Taikang (X 575) U.S. Navy, 19

D: 14,600 tons (21,740 fl) **S:** 18.6 kts **Dim:** 160.82 × 21.80 × 9.40
A: none
Electron Equipt:
Radar: 2/Fin Curve nav.—IFF: 1/High Pole A transponder
M: 1/Dalian-Sulzer 8RLB 66 diesel; 1 prop; 17,400 hp
Electric: 2,480 kw **Range:** 18,000/14.6
Crew: 26 officers, 120 enlisted

Remarks: Equipment similar to U.S. Navy transfer systems. Two liquid repleni ment stations per side, with constant-tension solid transfer stations each side j forward of the stack. Helo deck, but no hangar. Provision for four twin 37-mm AA g mounts. Have 4 small electric cranes for stores handling. Carry 11,000 tons fuel 1,000 tons diesel fuel, 200 tons feedwater, 200 tons potable water, and 50 tons lube A sister, *Nasr* (A 47), was delivered to Pakistan in 1988, and in 1989, the third PL ship of the class, *Hongcang* (X 950), was placed in merchant service.

TRANSPORT OILERS

◆ **3 Jinyou class** Bldr: Kanashashi SY, Japan (In serv. 1989–90)

Dongyun 625 Dongyun 675 Dongyun . . .

D: 2,500 tons light (4,800 fl) **S:** 15 kts **Dim:** 99.0 × 31.8 × 5.7
A: none **Electron Equipt:** Radar: 2/Type 756 nav.
M: 1 SEMT-Pielstick 8PC2.2L diesel; 1 prop; 3,000 bhp
Range: 4,000/9

◆ **2 or more Shengli class** Bldr: Hudong SY, Shanghai (In serv. 1981–. . .)

Dongyun 620 Dongyun 621

D: 4,940 tons (fl) **S:** 14 kts **Dim:** 101.0 (92.0 pp) × 13.8 × 5.5
A: none **Electron Equipt:** Radar: 2/Type 756 nav.
M: 1 Type 6 ESDZ 43 diesel; 1 prop; 2,600 bhp **Range:** 2,400/14

Remarks: 3,318.5 dwt. Cargo: 3,002 tons fuel oil (4,240 m³). Most are for commer service, but at least two also employed by the PLAN.

RANSPORT OILERS *(continued)*

7 or more Fulin class Bldr: Hudong SY, Shanghai (In serv. 1972–. . .)

ongyun 583 Dongyun 607 Dongyun 609 Dongyun 628
ongyun 629 Dongyun 633 N 1104

D: 2,200 tons (fl) **S:** 10 kts **Dim:** 66.0 × 10.0 × 4.0
A: 4/25-mm AA (II × 2) **Electron Equipt:** Radar: 1/Fin Curve nav.
M: 1 diesel; 1 prop; 600 bhp **Range:** 1,500/8 **Crew:** 30 tot.

emarks: Part of a series of 20, most of which went into merchant service. Several ported to have a single underway replenishment rig. At least one (N 1104) is subordi-ted to the Nanjing Maritime Border Defense Force. Resemble an enlarged Fuzhou.

14 or more Fuzhou class Bldr: Hudong SY, Shanghai (In serv. 1964–70)

ongyun 573 Dongyun 580 Dongyun 606 Dongyun 629
1101 etc.

uzhou Dongyun 606 7-89

uzhou Dongyun 582—early version Boris Lemachko Coll.

D: 1,200 tons (fl) **S:** 10–12 kts **Dim:** 60.0 (55.0 pp) × 9.0 × 3.5
A: 4/25-mm AA (II × 2)—4/14.5-mm mg (II × 2)
Electron Equipt: Radar: 1/Fin Curve or Type 756 nav.
M: 1 diesel; 1 prop; 600 bhp **Crew:** 30 tot.

emarks: Cargo: 600 tons. Five also built in a water-tanker version. Some of the ers (including N 1101) are subordinated to Maritime Border Defense Force. Some are t armed.

5 Leizhou class (In serv. early 1960s)

D: 900 tons **S:** 10–12 kts **Dim:** 53.0 (48.0 pp) × 9.8 × 3.0
A: 4/37-mm V-47M AA (II × 2)—2/14.5-mm mg (I × 2)
M: 1 diesel; 1 prop; 600 bhp **Crew:** 30 tot.

emarks: Four also built in a water-tanker version, and another was built as a cargo ip (Y 737) with a single king post and two cargo holds amidships.

ATER TANKERS

9 Fuzhou class Bldr: Hudong SY, Shanghai (In serv. 1964–70)

ai Shui 416 Hai Shui 557
ai Shui 419 Hai Shui 608 etc.
ai Shui 556

uzhou-class water tanker X 629—no armament Ross Gillett, 9-84

D: 1,200 tons (fl) **S:** 10–12 kts **Dim:** 60.0 (55.0 pp) × 9.0 × 3.5
A: none **Electron Equipt:** Radar: 1/Fin Curve or Type 756 nav.
M: 1 diesel; 1 prop; 600 bhp **Crew:** 30 tot.

Remarks: Also used by the PLAN in a transport oiler version. Lack raised cargo expansion tank top amidships. Formerly armed with 4/25-mm AA (II × 2), 4/14.5-mm mg (II × 2). Cargo: approx. 600 tons.

♦ **4 Leizhou class** (In serv. early 1960s)

Hai Shui 412 Hai Shui 555 Hai Shui 558 Hai Shui . . .

D: 900 tons **S:** 10–12 kts **Dim:** 53.0 (48.0 pp) × 9.8 × 3.0
A: 4/37-mm V-47M AA (II × 2)—2/14.5-mm mg (I × 2)
M: 1 diesel; 1 prop; 600 bhp **Crew:** 30 tot.

Remarks: Five sisters serve as fuel tankers and can be distinguished by their raised cargo expansion trunks down the centerline of the well deck.

♦ **. . . harbor tankers** (In serv. . . .)

N 1143 N 11 . . .

Harbor tanker N 1112 and sisters N 1111, N 1113 7-89

Remarks: Two small liquid cargo transports subordinated to the Nanjing District of the Maritime Border Defense Force. Capacity is about 50–70 tons. The total number of craft of this design and the Western nickname are unavailable.

TRANSPORTS

♦ **7 Qiongsha class** Bldr: Guangzhou SY (In serv. 1980–. . .)

Y 831 Y 832 Y 833 Y . . . Y . . . Y . . . Y . . .

Qiongsha-class transport Y 832 U.S. Navy, 5-83

D: 2,150 tons (fl) **S:** 16.2 kts **Dim:** 86.0 (76.0 pp) × 13.4 × 3.9
A: 8/14.5-mm mg (II × 4)
Electron Equipt: Radar: 2/Fin Curve nav.
M: 3 8NVD48A-2U diesels; 3 props; 3,960 bhp
Fuel: 195 tons **Electric:** 575 kw **Crew:** 59 tot.

Remarks: Built for South Seas Fleet service. Carry about 400 troops. Cargo holds fore and aft, each tended by two 1-ton derricks, can accommodate 350 tons. Two sisters, painted white and unarmed, serve as hospital ships.

CARGO SHIPS

♦ **4 Danlin class** (In serv. circa 1980)

Hai Leng 191 Hai Leng 201 Hai Leng 790 Hai Leng 795

Danlin-class cargo ship Hai Leng 201 1980

CARGO SHIPS *(continued)*

D: 1,290 tons (fl) **S:** 14 kts **Dim:** 60.5 × 9.0 × 4.0
A: 2/37-mm V-47M AA (II × 1)—4/14.5-mm mg (II × 2)
Electron Equipt: Radar: 1/Fin Curve or Type 756 nav.
M: 1 Type 6DRN 30/50 diesel; 1 prop; 750 bhp **Crew:** 30 tot.

Remarks: Three holds, served by two electrohydraulic cranes; cargo about 750 dwt, including refrigerated stores. Two or more others are in civilian service.

◆ **6 Hongqi 081 class** Bldr: . . . (In serv. 1970s)

Y 433 Y 443 Y 528 Y 755 Y 756 Y 771

D: 1,950 tons (fl) **S:** 14 kts **Dim:** 62.0 (58.0 wl) × 12.0 × 4.5
A: 4/25-mm 2M-8 AA (II × 2) **Electron Equipt:** Radar: 1/. . . nav.
M: 1 diesel; . . . bhp **Range:** 2,500/11 **Crew:** 30 tot.

Remarks: 875 grt/1,100 dwt. Sisters in commercial service.

◆ **2 Romanian Galati class** Bldr: Santieral SY, Galati (In serv. early 1970s)

Hai Yun 318 Hai Jiu 600

D: 5,200 tons (fl) **S:** 12.5 kts **Dim:** 100.60 (93.70 pp) × 13.92 × 6.60
A: . . . **Electron Equipt:** Radar: 2/ . . . nav.
M: 1 Sulzer 5TAD56 diesel; 1 prop; . . . bhp **Electric:** 345 kw
Fuel: 250 tons **Range:** 5,000/12.5

Remarks: One sister serves as a repair ship (see above), and six others are in merchant service under the Chinese flag. Cargo capacity: 3,750 dwt.

◆ **1 Zhandou 59 class** (In serv. 1959–65)

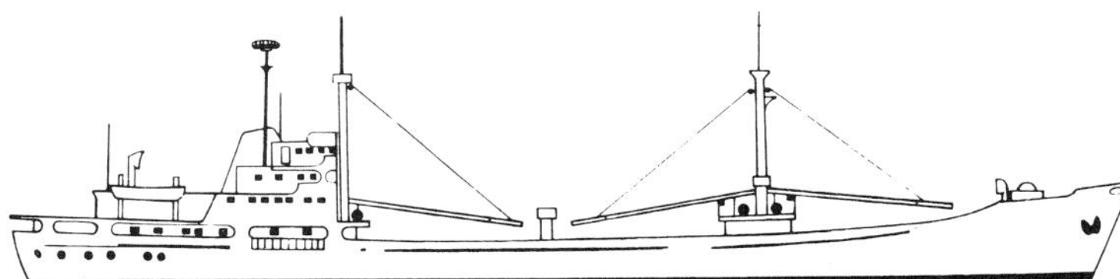

Zhandou 59 class

D: 4,735 tons (fl) **S:** 12.5 kts **Dim:** 99.4 × 13.0 × 5.5 **A:** . . .
M: 1 diesel; 1 prop; . . . bhp **Crew:** 50 tot.

Remarks: 2,798 grt/3,200 dwt. One of a class of 20 built for merchant marine service; two were combined to produce an oil-drilling platform in the mid-1970s.

◆ **7 or more Danlin class** (In serv. 1960–62)

Hai Leng 191 Hai Leng 201 Hai Leng 202 Hai Yun 795
Hai Yun 591 Hai Yun 790 Hai Yun 794

Danlin-class cargo ship Hai Yun 794 7-89

D: 1,150 tons (fl) **S:** 14 kts **Dim:** 60.0 × 9.1 × 3.5
A: 2/37-mm V-47A AA (I × 2) or 4/25-mm 2M-8 AA (II × 2)
Electron Equipt: Radar: 1/Type 756 nav.
M: 1 Type 6DRN 30/50diesel; 1 prop; 750 bhp **Crew:** approx. 30 tot.

Remarks: *Hai Yun* series in East Sea Fleet; *Hai Leng* series in South Sea Fleet. Cargo: approx. 600 tons; have refrigerated cargo capacity. Others are in civilian service.

◆ **. . . trawler-type coastal cargo ships**

Small cargo transport N 3215 Ross Gillett, 9-84

Remarks: One of a number of units of this design (including N 1121 and N 3215), mo of which seem to be subordinated to the Maritime Border Defense Force districts. about 450 tons (fl) displacement, they have a single cargo hold amidships, are equipp with a Type 756 navigational radar, and are armed with two twin side-by-side 14. mm mg mounts. Maximum speed is about 9 kts on a single 300-hp diesel.

TRAINING SHIP

◆ **1 Dakin-class naval cadet training ship**

	Bldr	L	In serv.
81 Zheng He	Qiuxin SY, Shanghai	12-7-86	27-4-87

Zheng He (81) U.S. Air Force, 4-

Zheng He (81) U.S. Air Force, 4-

D: 5,500 tons (fl) **S:** 15 kts **Dim:** 142.0 (132.0 pp) × 16.0 × . . .
A: 4/57-mm AA (II × 2)—4/30-mm AK-230 AA (II × 2)—2/RBU-120 ASW RL (I × 2)
Electron Equipt:
Radar: 2/Type 756 nav., 1/Eye Shield air search, 1/Round Ball f.c.
Sonar: HF hull-mounted
M: 2 diesels; 2 props; . . . bhp
Crew: 170 ship's company, 30 instructors, 200 cadets

Remarks: As completed, bore pendant V 856. Resembles a coastal passenger sh Helicopter deck aft. Officially stated to employ British navigation and radar syste Subordinated to the Naval Academy and has made voyages to Hawaii (1989) and Indian Ocean. Named for Emperor Yungli's eunuch admiral, who led seven gr exploration voyages between 1405 and 1453, traveling as far as Africa; his first voy carried 27,000 men in 317 ships.

DEGAUSSING/DEPERMING TENDERS

◆ **2 Yen Pai class** (In serv. . . .)

Hai Dzu 746 Dong Qin 863

D: 1,100 tons (fl) **S:** 14 kts **Dim:** 74.0 × 9.6 × 3.0
A: 4/37-mm V-47M AA (II × 2)—4/25-mm 2M-8 AA (II × 2)
Electron Equipt: Radar: 1/Type 756 or Fin Curve nav.
M: 2 Type 9D diesels; 2 props; 2,200 bhp **Crew:** approx. 60 tot.

Remarks: Resemble enlarged T-43-class minesweepers.

◆ **2 Yen Ka class** (In serv. 1966–68)

Hai Dzu 745 Hai Dzu . . .

D: approx. 460 tons (fl) **S:** 10–12 kts **Dim:** 47.0 × 7.5 × 2.2
A: 2/37-mm V-47M AA (II × 1)—4/14.5-mm mg (II × 2)
Electron Equipt: Radar: 1/ Type 756 or Fin Curve nav.
M: . . . diesels; 1 prop; . . . bhp **Crew:** approx. 40 tot.

Note: Several earlier degaussing/deperming tenders may still be in service, includ the two Yen Fang-class converted trawlers, *Hai Dzu* 950 and 951, converted aro 1965 and of only about 150 tons (fl), and four former U.S. Navy LSIL-type landing c which bore *Hai Dzu* 741, 742, 804, and 821.

HINA (continued)

EAGOING TUGS

3 or more Hujiu-class seagoing Bldr: . . . (In serv. 1980s)

155 T 854 T 867

ujiu-class tug T 867 Ross Gillett, 9-84

D: 750 tons (fl) S: 13.5 kts Dim: 49.0 (44.5 pp) × 9.5 × 3.7
A: . . . M: 2 LVP 24 diesels; 2 CP props; 1,800 bhp Fuel: 135 tons
Electric: 336 kVA Range: 2,200/13.5; 1,100/9 (towing)

4 Tuzhong-class salvage tugs Bldr: Zhonghua SY, Shanghai (In serv. late 1970s)

154 T 710 T 830 T 890

uzhong-class salvage tug T 710 Boris Lemachko Coll.

D: 3,600 tons (fl) S: 18.5 kts Dim: 84.90 (77.00 pp) × 14.00 × 5.50
A: none Electron Equipt: Radar: 1/Fin Curve nav. (*see* Remarks)
M: 2/9 ESDZ 43/82B diesels; 2 CP props; 9,000 bhp
Range: 18,000/. . . Crew: approx 60 tot.

emarks: Powerful salvage tugs equipped for firefighting, emergency repairs, and th high-capacity pumps. Have 35-ton-capacity towing winch. T 710 has Square Tie ssile fire-control radar on foremast, possibly for weapons trials purposes. There is ovision to mount at least two twin 37-mm AA.

2 Dinghai class Bldr: Wuhu SY (In serv. late 1970s)

837 T 717

nghai-class tug T 717 Leo Van Ginderen, 1-87

D: 1,472 tons (fl) S: 14 kts Dim: 60.22 × 11.60 × 4.44
A: . . . Electron Equipt: Radar: 1/ Type 756 nav.
M: 2 diesels; 2 props; 2,460 hp Range: 7,200/14
Crew: 7 officers, 49 enlisted

emarks: 980.28 grt. Also built for civil use. 25-ton-capacity towing winch. Equipped firefighting. One sister transferred to Bangladesh Navy, 5-84.

16 Soviet Gromovoy class Bldr: China (early 1960s)

AI TO 210, 221, 230, 231, 235, 319
147 T 716 T 802 T 814 + 6 more

Gromovoy-class tug T 802—in refit at Shanghai 7-89

D: 900 tons (fl) S: 11 kts Dim: 45.7 (41.5 pp) × 9.45 × 4.6
A: 4/12.7-mm or 14.5-mm mg (II × 2)
Electron Equipt:
Radar: 1/Fin Curve, Type 756, or Oki X-NE-12 nav.
M: 2 diesels; 2 props; 1,200 bhp
Range: 7,000/7 Crew: 30 tot.

Remarks: Soviet commercial tug design, built under license.

◆ **4 Soviet Roslavl class** Bldr: *See* Remarks (In serv. 1958–65)

HAI TO 302 HAI TO 403 HAI TO . . . J 120

D: 750 tons (fl) S: 11 kts Dim: 44.5 × 9.5 × 3.5 Crew: 30 tot.
A: 4/14.5-mm mg (II × 2) Electron Equipt: Radar: 1/. . . nav.
M: 2 diesels, electric drive; 2 props; 1,200 bhp Range: 6,000/11

Remarks: One transferred from the U.S.S.R.; the others built circa 1964–65 in China.

YARD AND SERVICE CRAFT

There are a reported 380 units in this category, but the true total number is probably far larger and would include yard oilers, tugs, barges, floating dry docks, dredges, and the like. No details are available.

Two Chinese Navy harbor tugs Ross Gillett, 9-84

COLOMBIA

Republic of Colombia

Personnel (1991): Approximately 16,500 total (including 6,879 marines)

Naval Aviation: Four Cessna A-37B Dragonfly light attack aircraft, four MBB-105CB helicopters (4 more planned).

SUBMARINES

◆ **2 German Type 209/1200 class** Bldr: Howaldtswerke, Kiel

	L	In serv.
S 28 PIJAO	10-4-74	17-4-75
S 29 TAYRONA	16-7-74	18-7-75

Pijao (S 28) French Navy, 4-91

SUBMARINES *(continued)*

Tayrona (S 29) Leo Van Ginderen, 1990

D: 1,000 tons std./1,180 surf./1,285 sub. **S:** 11.5/22 kts (1 hr.)
Dim: 56.10 × 6.20 × 5.50 (surf.)
A: 8/533-mm TT fwd (6 reloads, 14 tot. SUT SST-4 torpedoes)
Electron Equipt:
Radar: 1/Calypso II
Sonar: Krupp-Atlas CSU 3-2 active/PRS 3-4 passive
M: 4 MTU 12V493 TY60 diesels, 600 bhp each; 4 A.E.G. 405-kw generators; 1 Siemens motor, 5,000 shp (3,670 kw)
Range: 8,000/8 (snorkel), 11,300/4 (snorkel), 460/4 (sub.)
Fuel: 85 tons **Endurance:** 30 days **Crew:** 5 officers, 26 enlisted

Remarks: Ordered 1971. Both refitted beginning 11-90 in Germany at Howaldtswerke (HDW) facility at Gaarden, with S 28 completing 5-91 and S 29 in 9-91. Have Type AS C18 attack periscope, Type BS 19 search 'scope. The four 120-cell batteries weigh a total of 257 tons and produce 11,500 amp/hr. H.S.A. Mk 8 Mod. 24 torpedo f.c.s. Diving depth: 250 m.

◆ **2 Italian S.X. 506 midgets** Bldr: Cosmos, Livorno, Italy (1972–74)

S 20 Intrepido S 21 Indomable

Indomable (S 21) Hartmut Ehlers, 10-90

D: 58 tons (70 sub.) **S:** 8.5/7 kts **Dim:** 23.0 × 2.0 × 4.0
M: 1 diesel generator set, electric drive; 1 prop; 300 shp
Range: 1,200/7 **Crew:** 5 tot. + 8 frogmen

Remarks: Sisters *Roncador* (S 23) and *Quita Sueno* (S 24) were out of service by the mid-1980s. Cargo capacity: 2,050 kg of explosives; 8 frogmen fully equipped; 2 submarine vehicles (for the frogmen) supported by a fixed system on lower part of the hull, one on each side. Of little practical use except for training, due to short range and meager performance. They are served by the special floating dry dock/tender *Mayor Jaime Arias* (DF 170).

FRIGATES

◆ **4 FS 1500 class** Bldr: Howaldtswerke, Kiel, W. Germany

	Laid down	L	In serv.
CM 51 Almirante Padilla	3-81	8-1-82	31-10-83
CM 52 Caldas	6-81	14-6-82	14-2-84
CM 53 Antioquia	22-6-81	28-8-82	30-4-84
CM 54 Independiente	22-6-81	21-1-83	27-7-84

Independiente (CM 54) Hartmut Ehlers, 11-9

Antioquia (CM 53) Hartmut Ehlers, 11-

Caldas (CM 52)—with four MM 40 Exocet aboard Hartmut Ehlers, 11-

D: 1,600 tons (1,850 fl) **S:** 27 kts
Dim: 95.3 (90.0 pp) × 11.3 × 3.5 (hull)
A: 8/MM 40 Exocet SSM (IV × 2)—1/76-mm OTO Melara DP—2/40-mm Breda AA (II × 1)—6/324-mm Mk 32 ASW TT(III × 2)—1/MBB-105CB helicopter
Electron Equipt:
Radar: 1/. . . nav., 1/Sea Tiger air search, 1/Castor IIB f.c.
Sonar: Krupp Atlas ASO 4-2 hull-mounted
EW: Phillips/EMI Scimitar deception jammer; Argo Phoenix-II intercept, SUSIE intercept; 2/Dagaie chaff RL
M: 4 MTU 20V1163 TB82 diesels; 2 CP props; 23,000 bhp (21,000 sust.)
Fuel: 200 tons **Range:** 5,000/14 **Electric:** 2,120 kw
Crew: 92 tot.

Remarks: Ordered 1980, with the first originally scheduled for delivery 20-7-82. I stabilizers, helicopter hangar. Engines were a new model not previously installed i ship. Thomson-CSF Vega II f.c.s. for the 76-mm gun, with 2 Canopus optronic directc Torpedo tubes, Exocet, 30-mm AA, and Dagaie chaff were not mounted at time commissioning. The Israeli Barak SAM system is planned for later installation forw of the bridge and atop the hangar.

◆ **1 U.S. Courtney class** Bldr: New York SB, Camden, New Jersey

	Laid down	L	In serv.
16 Boyaca (ex-*Hartley*, DE 1029)	10-55	24-11-56	26-1-57

Boyaca (16) Hartmut Ehlers, 11-

RIGATES *(continued)*

D: 1,450 tons (1,914 fl) **S:** 25 kts
Dim: 95.86 × 11.26 × 4.30 (5.30 sonar)
A: 2/76.2-mm 50-cal. DP (II × 1)—6/324-mm Mk 32 ASW TT (III × 2)—1/MBB-105 helicopter (not normally carried)
Electron Equipt:
Radar: 3/. . . nav., 1/SPS-5D surf. search, 1/SPS-6E air search
Sonar: SQS-23—EW: WLR-1 intercept
M: 1 set Delaval geared turbines; 1 5-bladed prop; 20,000 shp
Boilers: 2 Foster-Wheeler; 42 kg/cm, 510° C. **Fuel:** 400 tons
Range: 4,400/11 **Crew:** 11 officers, 150 enlisted

emarks: Transferred from the U.S. 8-7-72. Placed in reserve 1983, but was reac- vated 1988, primarily as a stationary headquarters ship. Twin rudders. Flight deck d hangar for small helicopter (originally for U.S. DASH drone ASW helo) used imarily for ceremonial spaces. Mk 63 GFCS (with SPG-34 radar) for the Mk 33 twin .2-mm gun mount removed 1988, leaving local control only option. One half-sister rvives in the Uruguayan Navy.

ATROL SHIPS

2 U.S. Cherokee and Abnaki*-class former fleet tugs Bldr: Charleston SB & DD, Charleston, S.C.

	Laid down	L	In serv.
M 72 Pedro de Heredia (ex-*Choctaw*, ATF 70)	4-4-42	18-11-42	21-4-43
M 74 Rodrigo de Bastedas (ex-*Hidatsa*, ATF 102)*	8-8-43	29-12-43	25-4-44

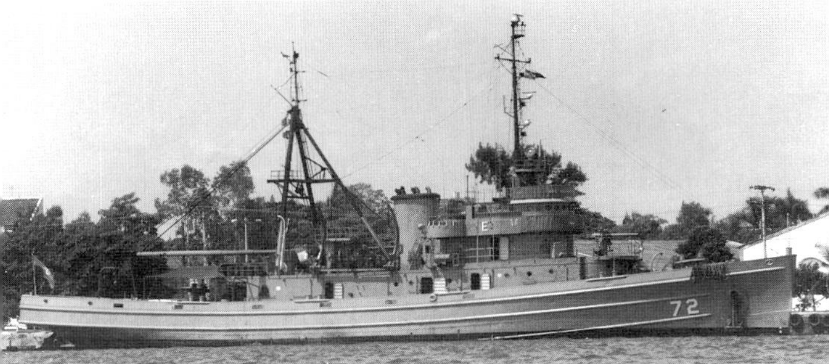

edro de Heredia (RM 72)—with stack Hartmut Ehlers, 11-90

odrigo de Bastidas (RM 74)—without stack Hartmut Ehlers, 10-90

D: 1,235 tons (1,675 fl) **S:** 15 kts
Dim: 62.48 (59.44 wl) × 11.73 × 4.67
A: 1/76.2-mm DP Mk 26 **Electron Equipt:** Radar: 1/. . . nav.
M: diesel-electric: 4 G.M. 12-278 (RM 74: Busch-Sulzer BS-539) diesels; 1 prop; 3,000 shp
Electric: 300 kw **Fuel:** 363 tons
Range: 7,000/15; 15,000/8 **Crew:** 75 tot.

emarks: Although reported stricken 1987 along with sisters *Sebastian de Belalzar* (RM 73, ex-*Carib*, ATF 82) and *Bahia Solano* (RM 76, ex-*Jacarilla*, ATF 104), th were in service during 1990. RM 72 originally transferred on loan 1961 and rchased 31-3-78; RM 74 reactivated from U.S. Maritime Administration National efense Reserve Fleet and transferred 15-3-79. Used as patrol and rescue ships.

ATROL BOATS

2 U.S. Asheville class

	Bldr	Laid down	L	In serv.
111 Albuquerque (ex-*Welch*, PG 93)	Peterson SB, Sturgeon Bay, Wisc.	8-8-67	25-7-68	8-9-69
112 Quito Sueño (ex-*Tacoma*, PG 92)	Tacoma Boat Tacoma, Wash.	24-7-67	13-4-68	14-7-69

Quito Sueño (P 112)—in dock Hartmut Ehlers, 10-90

D: 225 tons (245 fl) **S:** 40 kts (16 cruising)
Dim: 50.14 (46.94 wl) × 7.28 × 2.9
A: 1/76.2-mm 50-cal. Mk 34 DP—4/12.7-mm mg (II × 2)
Electron Equipt: Radar: 1/LN-66 nav., 1/Raytheon 1900 nav.
M: CODOG: 1 G.E. 7LM-1500-PE 102 gas turbine; 13,300 shp (12,500 sust.); 2 Cummins VT 12-875M diesels, 1,650 bhp (1,450 sust.); 2 CP props
Range: 325/35; 1,700/16 **Fuel:** 50 tons
Electric: 100 kw **Crew:** 25 tot.

Remarks: Leased 16-5-83, towed to Jonathan Corp., Norfolk, Va., for reactivation for use on anti-drug patrol. Offer of two more not taken up due to difficulty of maintaining engineering plants on this pair, which are generally inoperative. The Mk 63 g.f.c.s., with SPG-50 f.c. radar, have been removed, leaving the 76.2-mm gun with local control capability only.

PATROL CRAFT

◆ **2 U.S. 110-ft. Commercial Cruiser class** Bldr: Swiftships, Inc., Morgan City, La.

José Maria Palas (PB 103) (In serv. 10-89)
Medardo Monzon (PB 104) (In serv. 4-90)

PB 103 Hartmut Ehlers, 11-90

D: 99.8 tons **S:** 24 kts (22 cruise) **Dim:** 33.53 × 7.62 × 2.13
A: 1/40-mm Mk 3 AA (aft)—2/12.7-mm mg (I × 2)
Electron Equipt: Radar: 1/. . . nav.
M: 4 G.M. 12V71 TI diesels; 4 props; 2,400 bhp
Range: 1,800/15 **Fuel:** 31,608 liters **Crew:** 11 tot.

Remarks: Procured via the U.S. Foreign Military Sales program. Aluminum construction.

◆ **2 U.S. Sea Spectre PB Mk-III class** Bldr: Peterson Bldrs. (In serv. 1975–79)

PB 105 Jaime Gomez PB 106 Nepomuceno Peña

Jaime Gomez (PB 105) Hartmut Ehlers, 10-90

PATROL CRAFT *(continued)*

D: 28 tons (36.7 fl) **S:** 30 kts (now less)
Dim: 19.78 × 5.50 × 1.80 (props)
A: 1/20-mm—2/12.7-mm mg (I × 2)—2/7.62-mm mg (I × 2)
Electron Equipt: Radar: 1 or 2/. . . nav.
M: 3 G.M. 8V71 TI diesels; 3 props; 1,800 bhp **Endurance:** 3 days
Range: 450/26; 2,000/. . . **Crew:** 1 officer, 8 men

Remarks: Transferred to Colombia 1990. Aluminum construction. The 40-mm weapon is in a special stabilized Mk 3 Mod. 9 mounting with a removable reload magazine. Not as heavily armed as when in U.S. Navy service.

◆ **2 U.S. 105-ft Commercial Cruiser class** Bldr: Swiftships Inc., Berwick, La.

PB 101 Olaya Herrera (In serv. 16-10-81)
PB 102 Rafael del Castillo y Rada (In serv. 2-83)

Rafael del Castillo y Rada (PB 102) 1983

D: 103 tons (fl) **S:** 25 kts **Dim:** 31.5 × 6.6 × 2.1
A: 1/40-mm AA—2/12.7-mm mg
M: 2 MTU 12V331 TC92 diesels; 2 props; 7,000 bhp
Range: 1,600/25; 2,400/15 **Electric:** 113 kw
Crew: 3 officers, 16 enlisted

Remarks: PB 102 transferred to navy from Coast Guard 1990. PB 101 had been stricken 1986 but was reactivated at Cartagena during 1990–91.

RIVER PATROL BOATS AND CRAFT

◆ **2 Rio Hacha class** Bldr: Unial, Barranquilla (In serv. 1955)

CF 135 Rio Hacha CF 137 Arauca

Arauca (CF 137)—with old hull number

D: 170 tons (184 fl) **S:** 13 kts **Dim:** 47.25 × 8.23 × 1.0
A: 2/76.2-mm 50-cal. DP (I × 2)—4/20-mm AA (I × 4)
M: 2 Caterpillar diesels; 2 props; 800 bhp **Range:** 1,000/12
Crew: 27–43 tot.

Remarks: Sister *Leticia* disarmed and equipped as a hospital boat.

◆ **5 U.S. PBR MK II patrol craft** Bldr: Uniflite, Bellingham, Washington (In serv. 1968, 1971)

Rio Magdalena Rio San Jorge
Rio Atrato Rio Sinu
Rio Cauca

D: 8.9 tons (fl) **S:** 30 kts **Dim:** 9.73 × 3.53 × 0.81
A: 2/12.7-mm mg (II × 1)—1/60-mm mortar
Electron Equipt: Radar: 1/Raytheon 1900 (SPS-66) nav.
M: 2 G.M. 6V53T diesels; 2 Jacuzzi waterjets; 550 bhp
Range: 150/23 **Crew:** 6 tot.

Rio San Jorge Hartmut Ehlers, 11-9

Remarks: Glass-reinforced plastic construction, plastic armor. Transferred 11-8 Are ex-U.S. Navy hulls 31 RP6886, 31 RP7121, 31 RP7128–30.

◆ **5 (+ 3) U.S. 22-ft. Boston Whalers** Bldr: Boston Whaler, Rockland, Mass.

Dim: 1.5 tons light (2 fl) **S:** 40 kts **Dim:** 6.81 × 2.26 × . . .
A: 2/12.7-mm mg (I × 2) **M:** 2 outboard motors; 360 bhp
Range: 167/40 **Crew:** 3–4 tot.

Remarks: Glass-reinforced plastic construction, for riverine patrol use; transferr 1990. Three more ordered 12-91.

◆ **2 Rotork class** Bldr: Rotork, U.K. (In serv. 1989–90)

Manuela Saenz Jamie Rook

D: 9 tons (fl) **S:** 25 kts **Dim:** 12.7 × 3.2 × 0.7
A: 1/12.7-mm mg—2/7.62-mm mg
M: 2 Caterpillar diesels; 240 bhp; 2 props **Crew:** 4

Remarks: Can transport 8 fully equipped marines.

AMPHIBIOUS WARFARE CRAFT

Note: Four ex-U.S. Army LCU 1466-class utility landing craft transferred 10-91 riverine troop transport duties; four other ex-U.S. Army landing craft to transfer 19 See addenda.

OCEANOGRAPHIC RESEARCH SHIPS

◆ **2 Malpelo class** Bldr: Martin Jansen Werft, Leer, Germany (In serv. 24-7-81)

BO 155 Providencia BO 156 Malpelo

Providencia (BO 155) 19

D: 1,090 tons (fl) **S:** 13 kts **Dim:** 50.3 (44.0 pp) × 10.0 × 4.0
M: 2 M.A.N. 6-cyl. diesels; 1 Kort-nozzle prop; 1,570 bhp
Range: 16,000/11.5 **Crew:** 9 officers, 18 enlisted, 6 scientists

Remarks: Operated for DIMAR (*Dirección General Maritima Portuario*), one for g physical research, one for fisheries. White-painted. Naval manned. Bow-thrust flapped Becker rudder. Prime contractor: Ferrostaal, Kiel.

◆ **1 former lighthouse tender** Bldr: Lindigoverken, Lindigo, Sweden

BO . . . Gorgona (L: 28-5-54)

D: 560 tons **S:** 13 kts **Dim:** 41.15 × 9.00 × 2.83
A: 2/12.7-mm mg (I × 2) **Electron Equipt:** Radar: 1/ . . . nav.
M: 2 Nohab diesels; 2 props; 900 bhp **Crew:** . . . tot.

Remarks: Laid up early 1980s but began reactivation late 1990 for further servic a survey ship. May have been re-engined.

◆ **1 U.S. former refrigerated stores lighter** Bldr: Niagara SB, Buffalo, N.Y.

BO 153 Quindio (ex-U.S. YFR 433) (In serv. 11-11-43)

EANOGRAPHIC RESEARCH SHIPS *(continued)*

indio (BO 153) Hartmut Ehlers, 11-90

D: 380 tons (600 fl) **Dim:** 40.4 × 9.10 × 2.5
M: 1 Union diesel; 600 bhp **Crew:** 17 tot.

marks: Leased 7-64; purchased 31-3-78. Used on coastal survey duties.

XILIARY SHIPS

1 coastal transport Bldr: Schiffswerft H. Rancke, Hamburg (In serv. 1956)

60 San Andres (ex-*Philip P.*, ex-*Marga B.*, ex-*Margaret Oltmann*, ex-*uth*, ex-*Nadir*, ex-*Elbstrjm*)

n Andres (TM 60) Hartmut Ehlers, 10-90

): approx. 900 tons (fl) **S:** 9 kts
)im: 51.85 (46.18 pp) × 8.41 × 3.46
1: 1 diesel; 1 prop; 300 bhp

narks: 432 grt/680 dwt. Former Honduran coaster detained for smuggling and en over for navy 1986 for use as a coastal survey vessel (with pendant BO 154) but ssigned to transportation duties by 1990.

1 small transport ship Bldr: Sander, Delfzijl, Netherlands (In serv. 3-53)

43 Ciudad De Quibdo (ex-M/V *Shamrock*)

): 633 tons **S:** 11 kts **Dim:** 50.3 × 7.2 × 2.8
1: 1 M.A.N. diesel; 1 prop; 390 bhp **Fuel:** 32 tons **Crew:** 11 tot.

te: The coastal cargo ship *Jurado* was scrapped during 1990.

1 sail training ship Bldr: Celaya, Bilbao, Spain

oria (In serv. 7-9-68)

oria Hartmut Ehlers, 10-90

D: 1,150 tons (1,300 fl) **S:** 10.5 kts (power)
Dim: 76.00 (64.7wl) × 10.6 × 6.6
M: 1 diesel; 530 bhp **Sail area:** 1,400 m² (bark-rigged)
Crew: 10 Officers, 41 enlisted, 88 cadets **Endurance:** 60 days

SERVICE CRAFT

◆ **2 riverine hospital craft** Bldr: Cartagena Naval DY (In serv. 1956)

BD 33 Socorro (ex-*Alberto Gomez*, TF 53)
BD 35 Teniente Hernando Gutierrez (ex-TF 52)

Teniente Hernando Gutierrez (BD 35) Hartmut Ehlers, 10-90

D: 70 tons **S:** 9 kts **Dim:** 25.00 × 5.50 × 0.75 **Crew:** 10 tot.
A: 2/12.7-mm mg (I × 2) **M:** 2 G.M. diesels; 2 props; 270 bhp

Remarks: Originally built as riverine transports for 56 troops; now used as mobile surgeries. Another hospital craft, *Mayor Mario Serpa*, was derelict at Cartagena in 11-90.

◆ **1 Rio Hacha-class riverine hospital ship, former gunboat**
Bldr: Unial, Barranquilla (In serv. 1955)

BD 36 Leticia

D: 170 tons (184 fl) **S:** 13 kts **Dim:** 47.25 × 8.23 × 1.00
A: 2/12.7-mm mg **M:** 2 Caterpillar diesels; 2 props; 800 bhp
Range: 1,000/12 **Crew:** 40 tot.

Remarks: Disarmed and converted sister to the two *Rio Hacha*-class river gunboats. Has 6-bed ward, surgery facilities, etc.

◆ **8 miscellaneous captured drug runners**

TM 42 Turbu, TM 44 Tolu, TM 45 Serranilla (ex-*Tropic Ace*), TM 47 Bahia Cupica, TM . . . Teniente De Navio Jose Maria Palas, TM . . . Teniente De Navio Alejandro Bal Domero Salgado, TM . . . Teniente Primo Alcala, Teniente Luis Guillermo Alcala (ex-*Joanna*)

Turbu (TM 42) Hartmut Ehlers, 10-90

Tolu (TM 44) Hartmut Ehlers, 10-90

Remarks: Characteristics unknown; placed in service 1981 to help combat drug traffic in the Caribbean. Most are ex-drug runners. TM 42, TM 45, and TM 47 now used as stores transports, TM 44 as a diving tender, others in similar support rôles.

COLOMBIA *(continued)*
SERVICE CRAFT *(continued)*

♦ **1 ex-U.S. small harbor tug** Bldr: Henry C. Grebe (In serv. 2-9-43)

RM 73 Teniente Ricardo Sorzano (ex-YTL 231)

D: 70 tons (80 fl) **S:** 9 kts **Dim:** 20.2 × 5.2 × 1.5 **Electric:** 15 kw
M: 1 Cooper-Bessemer diesel; 240 bhp **Fuel:** 7 tons **Crew:** 10 tot.

Remarks: Loaned 1963; purchased 31-3-78. On more-or-less permanent loan to Compañía Colombiana de Astilleros Limitada (CONASTIL) dockyard, Cartagena, but also available to support naval operations.

♦ **2 river tug/transports** Bldr: Servicio Naviero Armada R. de Colombia, Puerto Leguizamo

RR 92 Igaraparaña (In serv. 6-85)
RR 95 Mana Casias (In serv. 6-86)

D: 104 grt **S:** 7 kts **Dim:** 31.2 × 7.2 × 0.9
Crew: 1 officer, 6 enlisted **M:** 2 G.M. 4-71 diesels; 2 props; 230 bhp
Range: 1,600/7

♦ **5 Capitan Castro-class riverine tugs**

RR 81 Capitan Castro
RR 84 Capitan Alvaro Ruis
RR 86 Capitan Rigoberto Giraldo
RR 87 Capitan Vladimir Valek
RR 88 Teniente Luis Bernal

D: 50 tons **S:** 9 kts **Dim:** 19.20 × 4.25 × 0.75
M: 2 G.M. diesels; 260 bhp

Remarks: Sister *Candido Leguizamo* (RR 82) stricken 1987.

Note: Also in use are river tug *Mitu* and Swedish-built seagoing tug *Calima.*

♦ **1 admiral's yacht**

Contralmirante Bell Salter

Contralmirante Bell Salter Hartmut Ehlers, 10-90

Remarks: No characterisitic data available. Based at Cartagena.

♦ **1 floating dry dock/midget submarine tender**

DF 170 Mayor Jaime Arias—D: 700 tons (fl) Capacity: 165 tons

Mayor Jaime Arias (DF 170) Hartmut Ehlers, 10-90

Note: On loan to the Compañía Colombiana de Astilleros Limitada (CONASTIL) are the former Colombian Navy service craft *Rodriguez Zamora* (ex-U.S. Navy floating dry dock ARD 28), *Victor Cabillos* (ex-U.S. dry-dock service craft YFND 16), and *Mantilla* (ex-U.S. floating repair shop YR 66).

COAST GUARD
(Cuerpo del Guardacosta)

Established 1981. The surviving craft of the former Customs Service fleet have been refitted and incorporated. A major function is anti-drug patrol. In 1990–91, the trend was to transfer patrol craft from the Coast Guard to the navy, and the organization's future is in doubt.

PATROL BOATS

♦ **1 Jorge Soto de Corval class** Bldr: Rauma Repola SY, Rauma, Finland

AN 208 Carlos Alban (In serv. 1971)

D: 100 tons (130 fl) **S:** 18 kts **Dim:** 34.0 × 6.0 × 1.9
A: 1/20-mm AA **M:** 2 MTU diesels; 2 CP props; 2,500 bhp

Remarks: AN 208 recommissioned 1980 after several years in reserve. Sister *J.S Corval* hulked early 1980s, while *Nito Restropo* (AN 209) was discarded and strippe 1990.

Note: Also in use is the launch AN 214. The 12.2-m launch *Rodriguez* has t discarded.

AN 214 Hartmut Ehlers, 1

COMOROS

Republic of the Comoros

PATROL CRAFT

♦ **2 Japanese Yamayuri class** Bldr: Ishihara DY, Takasago (In serv. 10-81)

Kasthala Ntringhui

D: 27 tons (40.3 fl) **S:** 20.7 kts **Dim:** 18.0 × 4.3 × 0.82 (1.1 prop)
A: 2/12.7-mm mg (II × 1) **Electron Equipt:** Radar: 1/ . . . nav.
M: 2 Nissan Type RD 10TA 06 diesels; 2 props; 900 bhp **Crew:** 6 t

Remarks: Identical to craft in the Japanese Maritime Safety Agency.

AUXILIARIES

♦ **1 former French transport** Bldr: Toulon DY (In serv. 1957)

Ville de Nimachova (ex-*Issole*)

D: 600 tons (fl) **S:** 12 kts **Dim:** 49.0 × 7.0 × 2.2
M: 2 diesels; 2 props; 1,000 bhp **Fuel:** 36 tons **Range:** 2,600/10.

Remarks: Stricken from French Navy and acquired by Comoros in 1981. For "regional transport" with bow doors and beaching ramp for vehicle cargo. Cargo: tons plus 60 tons on deck.

CONGO

People's Republic of the Congo

Personnel (1991): 300 total

COASTAL NAVY

The naval forces are divided into the coastal navy and the river navy. Pla acquire three additional seagoing patrol boats began during 1985; under consider are three 357-ton Spanish "Cormoran"-class gunboats. Most of the craft listed b are in poor condition.

PATROL BOATS AND CRAFT

♦ **3 Spanish "Piraña"-class patrol boats** Bldr: Bazán, Cadiz

	In serv.
P 601 Marien Ngouabi (ex-*L'Intrápide*)	10-11-82
P 602 Les Trois Glorieuses (ex-*Le Vaillant*)	1-83
P 603 Les Maloango (ex-*Le Terrible*)	3-83

NGO (continued)
TROL BOATS AND CRAFT (continued)

Maloango (P-603) French Navy, 12-90

: 125 tons (138 fl) **S:** 34 (29 sust.)
im: 32.70 (30.60 pp) × 6.15 × 1.55
: 1/40-mm—1/20-mm AA—2/12.7-mm mg (I × 2)
lectron Equipt: Radar: 1/Raytheon RM 1220/6X8 nav.
: 2 MTU 12V538 TB92 diesels; 2 props; 6,120 bhp (5,110 sust.)
lectric: 210 kw **Range:** 1,000/17 **Crew:** 3 officers, 16 enlisted

arks: Ordered 1980. CSEE Panda optronic GFCS. Renamed on delivery; arrived ongo 1-6-83; by 8-84 badly needed overhaul, which began at builders in 1985. By 3, P 601 was inoperable, P 602 was in use, and P 603 was barely serviceable.

6 Soviet Zhuk-class patrol craft (3 transferred 1982, 3 in 2-84)

01 V 302 V 303 V 304 V 305 V 306

: 48 tons (60 fl) **S:** 34 kts **Dim:** 24.0 × 5.0 × 1.2 (1.8 props)
: 4/14.5-mm mg (II × 2) **Fuel:** 10 tons **Crew:** 12 tot.
: 2 M50F-4 diesels; 2 props; 2,400 bhp **Range:** 700/28; 1,100/15

e: The Soviet Shershen-class torpedo boat transferred in 1979 without torpedo s had been discarded by 1989. Three Chinese Shanghai-II-class patrol boats transed in 1975 are also out of service.

RIVER NAVY

2 ARCOR-43-class GRP patrol craft Bldr: ARCOR, France (In serv. 1982)

ORE MATSOUA MAÎTRE CHRISTIAN MALONGGA MOKOKO

: 12 tons (fl) **S:** 25 kts **Dim:** 13.00 (11.60 pp) × 4.0 × 1.5
: 1/7.62-mm mg **M:** 2 diesels; 2 props; 450 bhp

2 ARCOR-38-class GRP patrol craft Bldr: ARCOR, France (In serv. 1982)

SEIGNE DE VAISSEAU YAMBA LAMASS . . . .

: 7.5 tons (fl) **S:** 28 kts **Dim:** 11.40 (9.90 pp) × 3.60 × 1.10
: 1/7.62-mm mg **M:** 2 diesels; 2 props; 250 bhp

Up to 10 locally built outboard-powered craft

arks: Also in use are one Norwegian-built "Smuggler-28," one Norwegian uggler 21," and one Soviet-supplied BMK-150 launches.

COOK ISLANDS

TROL BOAT

1 Australian ASI 315 class Bldr: Australian SB Ind. (WA), South Coogie

	Laid down	L	In serv.
KUKUPA	5-6-88	27-1-89	1-9-89

: 165 tons (fl) **S:** 20 kt (sust.) **Dim:** 31.50 (28.60 wl) × 8.10 × 2.12
: small arms
lectron Equipt:
Radar: 1/Furuno 1011 nav.
EW: 1 Furuno 120 MF-HFD/F,1 Furuno 525 VHFD/F

M: 2 Caterpillar 3516 diesels; 2 props; 2,820 bhp (2,400 sust.)
Range: 2,500/12 **Fuel:** 27.9 tons **Endurance:** 8–10 days
Electric: 116 kw (2 × 50 kw, 1 × 16 kw)
Crew: 3 officers, 14 enlisted

Te Kukupa Leo Van Ginderen, 9-89

Remarks: A unit of the Australian "Pacific Patrol Boat" foreign aid program. Extremely well equipped with navaids: SATNAV receiver, doppler log, etc. Carries a 5-m Stressl aluminum boarding boat with a 40-hp outboard.

COSTA RICA

Republic of Costa Rica

Personnel (1991): 200 total

Naval Aviation: The Civil Guard has 2 Cessna 337 Skymasters for maritime patrol. The Air Section has 4 Cessna 206 and 3 Cessna O-2A aircraft and 2 Hughes 500 E helicopters for similar duties, SAR, etc.

CIVIL GUARD

PATROL BOATS AND CRAFT

◆ **1 U.S. 105-foot Commercial Cruiser class** Bldr: Swiftships, Morgan City, Louisiana

SP 1055 ISLA DEL COCO (In serv. 2-78)

Isla del Coco (SP 1055) Swiftships 4-85

D: 118 tons (fl) **S:** 33 kts (30 sust.) **Dim:** 31.73 × 7.1 × 2.16
A: 3/12.7-mm mg (I × 3)—1/60-mm mortar
Electron Equipt: Radar: 1/Decca RM 916 nav.
M: 3 MTU 12V331 TC92 diesels; 3 props; 10,500 bhp
Range: 1,200/18 **Fuel:** 21 tons **Electric:** 80 kw (2 × 40 kw)
Crew: 3 officers, 11 enlisted

Remarks: Refitted 1984 to 3-85 by builders. Aluminum construction.

COSTA RICA *(continued)*
PATROL BOATS AND CRAFT *(continued)*

♦ **1 ex-U.S. Coast Guard Cape class** Bldr: Coast Guard Yard, Curtis Bay, Md.

	In serv.	Transferred
SP 951 Astronauta Franklin Chang (ex-*Cape Henlopen,* WPB 45328)	5-12-58	28-9-89

D: 90 tons (fl) **S:** 20 kts **Dim:** 28.96 × 6.10 × 1.55
A: 2/12.7-mm mg
Electron Equipt: Radar: 1/Raytheon SPS-64(V)1 nav.
M: 2 G.M. 16V149 TI diesels; 2 props; 2,470 bhp **Electric:** 60 kw
Range: 550/20; 1,900/11.5 **Endurance:** 5 days **Crew:** . . .

♦ **4 U.S. 65-foot Commercial Cruiser class** Bldr: Swiftships, Morgan City, Louisiana (In serv. 1978)

SP 656 Cabo Velas SP 658 Cabo Blanco
SP 657 Isla Uvita SP 659 Punta Burica

65-ft. patrol boat SP 657 Swiftships, 4-85

D: 24.9 tons (35 fl) **S:** 23 kts (19 sust.)
Dim: 19.77 (17.90 wl) × 5.56 × 1.98
A: 3/12.7-mm mg (I × 3)—1/60-mm mortar
Electron Equipt: Radar: 1/Decca RM 916
M: 2 MTU 8V331 diesels; 2 props; 1,400 bhp **Fuel:** 4.8 tons
Range: 1,300/18 **Electric:** 20 kw **Crew:** 2 officers, 7 enlisted

Remarks: Aluminum construction. Refitted by builder, 1985.

♦ **1 U.S. 42-ft. aluminum patrol craft** Bldr: Swiftships, Morgan City, Louisiana

SP 421 Donna Margarita (ex-*Puntarena*) (In serv. 9-86)

D: 11 tons (16.2 fl) **S:** 34 kts **Dim:** 12.80 × 4.26 × . . .
A: 1/12.7-mm mg—1/60-mm mortar—2/7.62-mm mg (I × 2)
M: 2 G.M. 8V92 TI diesels; 2 props; . . . bhp **Range:** 450/18
Crew: 1 officer, 3 enlisted

Remarks: Employed as a hospital launch.

♦ **2 U.S. 36-ft. aluminum patrol craft** Bldr: Swiftships, Morgan City, Louisiana (Both in serv. 3-86)

SP 361 Telamanca SP 362 Cariari

D: 9 tons (10.7 fl) **S:** 24 kts **Dim:** 10.97 × 3.05 × . . .
A: 1/12.7-mm mg—1/60-mm mortar **Crew:** 1 officer, 3 enlisted
Electron Equipt: Radar: 1/Raytheon 1900 nav.
M: 2 G.M. DD8240 MT diesels; 2 props; . . . bhp **Range:** 248/18

♦ **8 GRP outboard-propelled craft** Bldr: Boston Whaler, U.S.A.

181-188

Remarks: 5.49 m o.a., one 70-hp outboard motor. Survivors of 13 delivered 1983.

CUBA

Republic of Cuba

Personnel (1991): Approx. 9,000 men, including 1,000 naval infantry

Naval Aviation: 4–6 Kamov KA-28 Helix-A and 4 Mi-14 Haze-A ASW helicopter

SUBMARINES

♦ **3 Soviet Foxtrot class**

D: 1,950/2,400 tons **S:** 16/15.5 kts **Dim:** 92.0 × 7.0 × 6.0
A: 10/533-mm TT (6 fwd, 4 aft)—22 torpedoes or 44 mines
Electron Equipt:
Radar: 1/Snoop Tray
EW: Stop Light intercept, Quad Loop MFD/F
Sonar: MF active, passive arrays
M: 3/2,000-bhp Type 37D diesels, 3 electric motors; 3 props; 5,300 shp
Endurance: 70 days **Range:** 11,000/8 (snorkel); 350/2 (sub.)
Fuel: 360 tons **Crew:** 9 officers, 50 enlisted

Remarks: Transferred 1-79, 1-80, and 2-84. A non-operational Whiskey-class submarine was transferred 4-79 for use as a battery-charging barge. Not believed to be very active and likely to deteriorate further in the immediate future.

FRIGATES

♦ **3 Soviet Koni class (Project 1159)** Bldr: Zelenodolsk SY

350 Mariel 353 . . . . 356 . . . .

Cuba's third Koni (353) R. Neth. N., 4

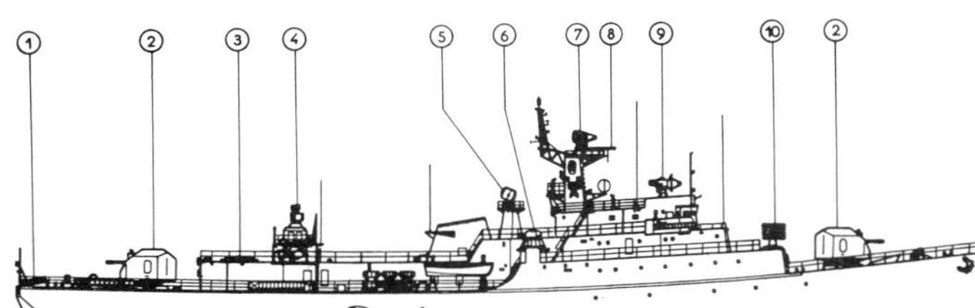

Cuban Koni Louis Gas

1. depth charge racks 2. twin 76-mm AK-276 DP gunmounts 3. SA-N-4 missile system 4. Pop Group radar director for SA-N-4 system 5. Drum Tilt radar director for 30-mm AA 6. twin AK-230 30-mm AA guns port and starboard 7. Strut Curve air/surface search radar 8. Don navigational radar 9. Hawk Screech radar director for 76-mm guns 10. two RBU 6000 ASW rocket launchers.

Cuba's third Koni (353) U.S. Navy, 4

RIGATES *(continued)*

D: 1,440 tons (1,900 fl) **S:** 30 kts **Dim:** 96.40 × 12.55 × 3.48 (hull)
A: 1/SAN-4 SAM syst. (II × 1; 20 missiles)—4/76-mm AK-276 DP (II × 2)— 4/30-mm AK-230 AA (II × 2)—2/RBU-6000 ASW RL (XII × 2)—mines
Electron Equipt:
Radar: 1/Don-2 nav., 1/Strut Curve air/surf. search, 1/Pop Group missile f.c., 1/Hawk Screech 76.2-mm f.c., 1/Drum Tilt 30-mm f.c.
Sonar: 1/MF hull-mounted
EW: 2 Watch Dog intercept, 2/chaff RL (XVI × 2)
IFF: 2/Square Head interrogators, 1/High Pole A transponder
M: CODAG: 1 19,000-shp M8G gas turbine, 2 Type 68D, 8,000-bhp diesels; 3 props (CP on outboard, diesel-powered shafts)
Range: 1,800/14 **Crew:** 120 tot.

marks: 350 delivered 23-9-81; 356 arrived 2-84; 353 in 4-88. Name *Mariel* is certain; all may be unnamed. Like the Algerian units, have a continuous deckhouse idships, probably to incorporate additional air-conditioning equipment. Normal splacement is 1,596 tons.

UIDED-MISSILE PATROL BOATS

13 Soviet Osa-II class

ban Osa-II—note man with Grail missile amidships U.S. Navy, 7-84

D: 215 tons (245 fl) **S:** 35 kts **Dim:** 38.60 × 7.60 × 2.0
Crew: 30 tot.
A: 4/SS-N-2 Styx (I × 4)—4/30-mm AK-230 AA (II × 2)
Electron Equipt:
Radar: 1/Square Tie surf. search/target desig., 1/Drum Tilt gun f.c.
IFF: 2/Square Head interrogators, 1/High Pole A transponder
M: 3 M504 diesels; 3 props; 15,000 bhp **Range:** 500/34; 750/25

emarks: Transferred: 2 in 1977, 3 in 1978, 2 in 1979, 2 in 11-81, 2 in 1-82, 2 in 2-82. rry SA-7 Grail (Strela) surface-to-air missiles in hand-held launchers.

4 Soviet Osa-I-class

D: 175 tons (210 fl) **S:** 36 kts **Dim:** 38.60 × 7.60 × 1.80
A: 4/SS-N-2 Styx (I × 4)—4/30-mm AK-230 AA (II × 2)
Electron Equipt:
Radar: 1/Square Tie surf. search/target desig., 1/Drum Tilt gun f.c.
IFF: 2/Square Head interrogators, 1/High Pole A transponder
M: 3 M503A diesels; 3 props; 12,000 bhp **Range:** 500/34; 750/25
Crew: 30 tot.

emarks: Two were delivered in 1972, two in 1973, and two in 1974; one deleted in 81 and another in 1990. Rest probably in poor condition.

ATROL BOATS

1 (+ . . .) Soviet Modified Pauk class Bldr: Volodarskiy SY, Rybinsk

uban Modified Pauh French Navy, 5-90

D: 385 tons (455 fl) **S:** 32 kts
Dim: 58.50 (52.30 wl) × 9.80 (9.40 wl) × 2.14 hull (3.59 props)
A: 1/76.2-mm AK-176 DP—1/SA-N-5 SAM syst. (IV × 1, SA-7 Grail missiles)—1/30-mm AK-630 gatling AA—4/533-mm ASW TT— 2/RBU-1200 ASW RL (V × 2)—2/d.c. racks (12 d.c.)
Electron Equipt:
Radar: 1/Spin Trough nav., 1/Cross Dome air/surf. search, 1/Bass Tilt f.c.
Sonar: MF hull-mounted, MF dipping sonar at stern
EW: . . .—IFF: 2/Square Head interrogators
M: 2 M 517-series multi-row radial diesels; 2 props; 20,000 bhp
Range: 2,000/20 **Fuel:** 50 tons **Crew:** 7 officers, 32 enlisted

Remarks: Delivered 22-5-90. Prospects for additional deliveries uncertain, given state of Soviet-Cuban relations and the Soviet economy. Four virtually identical units built for India. Differs from Soviet Navy version in having larger pilothouse, incorporating Cross Dome radar, and using 533-mm vice 400-mm ASW TT. Housing for dipping sonar projects well beyond the transom stern.

Note: The last two Soviet SO-1-class patrol boats are believed to have been discarded by mid-1990. The four Soviet-supplied Stenka-class patrol boats are in the Ministry of the Interior's Border Guard (see below).

TORPEDO BOATS

♦ **9 Soviet Turya-class semi-hydrofoils**

Cuban Navy Turya 193 U.S. Navy, 7-84

Two Turyas en route to Cuba—note foil configuration 12-82

D: 215 tons (250 fl) **S:** 40 kts **Crew:** 24 tot.
Dim: 39.0 × 7.6 (12.5 over foils) × 2.0 (4.0 over foils)
A: 2/57-mm AK-257 DP aft (II × 1)—2/25-mm 2M-8 AA (II × 1)—4/533-mm TT (I × 4)—see Remarks
Electron Equipt:
Radar: 1/Pot Drum surf. search, 1/Muff Cob f.c.
IFF: 1/Square Head interrogator, 1/High Pole B transponder
M: 3 M504 diesels; 3 props; 15,000 bhp **Range:** 400/38; 650/25

Remarks: First two delivered 2-79, the first foreign transfer of this class; 2 more followed in 2-80, 2 in 1-81, 2 in 1-83, and 1 in 11-83. ASW capability omitted. Semi-retractable forward hydrofoils; stern planes on surface. Uses Osa-II hull and propulsion. Hand-held SA-7 Grail ("Strela") surface-to-air missiles were carried by mid-1984. The Muff Cob radar director (equipped with a t.v. camera also) controls only the 57-mm mount; the 25-mm mount is locally controlled.

MINE WARFARE SHIPS

♦ **4 Soviet Sonya-class coastal minesweepers**
Bldr: Petrozavodsk SY

MINE WARFARE SHIPS *(continued)*

Cuban Sonya U.S. Navy, 1-85

D: 380 tons (450 fl) **S:** 14 kts **Dim:** 48.8 × 8.8 × 2.1
Crew: 40 tot.
A: 2/30-mm AK-230 AA (II × 1)—2/25-mm 2M-8 AA (II × 1)
Electron Equipt:
Radar: 1/Spin Trough nav.—Sonar: none
IFF: 1/High Pole B transponder, 1/Square Head interrogator
M: 2 diesels; 2 props; 2,400 bhp **Range:** 1,600/14; 3,000/10

Remarks: Delivered 8-80, 10-80, 1-85, and 12-85—all by tow. Wooden hulls, sheathed in glass-reinforced plastic. There is a "Kolonka-1" remote ringsight director for the 30-mm gun mount; the 25-mm mount is locally controlled.

◆ **9 Soviet Yevgenya-class inshore minesweepers**
Bldr: Srednyy Neva SY, Kolpino

D: 80 tons (90 fl) **S:** 11 kts **Dim:** 26.2 × 6.1 × 1.5
A: 2/25-mm 2M-8 AA (II × 1)
Electron Equipt:
Radar: 1/Spin Trough
IFF: 1/High Pole B transponder
M: 2 diesels; 2 props; 600 bhp **Range:** 300/10 **Crew:** 12 tot.

Remarks: Two transferred 1978, two in 1979, two in 12-80, one in 11-82, and two in 11-84; two others, delivered 9-84, were transferred to Nicaragua. Equipped to search for mines in depths of up to 30 m using towed television, marker buoys, and standard wire cable gear. Glass-reinforced plastic construction.

AMPHIBIOUS WARFARE SHIPS AND CRAFT

◆ **2 Soviet Polnocny B class** Bldr: Stocznia Północna, Gdańsk (In serv. circa 1968)

Cuban Polnocny B Skyfotos, 10-82

D: 800 tons (fl) **S:** 19 kts **Dim:** 74.0 × 8.9 × 1.9 (aft)
A: 4/30-mm AK-230 AA (II × 2)—2/140-mm artillery RL (XVIII × 2)
Electron Equipt:
Radar: 1/Spin Trough nav., 1/Drum Tilt gun f.c.
IFF: 1/Square Head interrogator, 1/High Pole B transponder
M: 2 Type 40D diesels; 2 props; 5,000 bhp **Range:** 900/18; 1,500/14
Fuel: 36 tons **Crew:** 30 tot. plus 200 troops

Remarks: The first, wearing transfer pendant, arrived in 9-82; the second, number 442, arrived 4-12-82. These particular units are configured for troop carrying, as evidenced by the large number (23) of 10-man life rafts carried. Cargo: 180 tons (5 tanks).

HYDROGRAPHIC SURVEY SHIPS

◆ **1 Soviet Biya class** Bldr: Stocznia Północna, Gdańsk, Poland (1972–76)

H 103 Guama (ex-GS 186)

D: 750 tons (fl) **S:** 13 kts **Dim:** 55.0 × 9.2 × 2.6
Electron Equipt: Radar: 1/Don-2 nav.
M: 2 diesels; 2 CP props; 1,200 bhp **Endurance:** 15 days
Range: 4,700/11 **Fuel:** 90 tons **Crew:** 25 tot.

Remarks: Transferred 11-80. Carries one survey launch. Also useful as a buoy tender: one 5-ton crane.

◆ **1 Spanish-built** Bldr: Maritime del Musel, Gijon (In serv. 1979)

H 102 Taino

D: 1,100 tons **S:** 12 kts **Dim:** 53.0 (42.0 pp) × 10.4 × 3.5
M: 2 diesels; 2 props; 1,550 bhp **Electric:** 360 kw **Crew:** . . . tot.

Remarks: 669 grt/572 dwt. Primarily a buoy tender.

◆ **1 converted trawler** Bldr: Ast. Talleres de Celaya, Bilbao, Spain

H 101 Siboney (In serv. 1968)

D: 600 tons (fl) **S:** 11.4 kts **Dim:** 40.2 × 8.3 × 2.6
M: 2 Stork-Werkspoor RHD-216K diesels; 1 prop; 910 bhp
Electric: 160 kw **Crew:** . . . tot.

◆ **3 Lamda-class converted wooden fishing boats** (In serv. 1960s)

H 76 H 77 H 78

D: 150 tons (fl) **S:** 10 kts **Dim:** 29.0 × 6.0 × 2.1
M: 1 diesel; 1 prop; 250 bhp

◆ **6 Soviet Nyryat-1 class** (In serv. 1962–69)

H 91 H 92 H 93 H 94 H 95 H 96

D: 120 tons (fl) **S:** 12 kts **Dim:** 29.0 × 5.0 × 1.7
Electron Equipt: Radar: 1/Spin Trough nav.
M: 1 diesel; 2 props; 450 bhp **Range:** 1,600/10 **Crew:** 15 tot.

Remarks: Dates of transfer not known. Known in U.S.S.R. as GPB 480 class. Some with different equipment, also used as diving tenders.

AUXILIARIES

◆ **1 replenishment oiler** Bldr: Niigata Iron Wks., Japan

Las Guasimas (In serv. 1978)

D: 8,300 tons (fl) **S:** 12.75 kts
Dim: 106.99 (100.01 pp) × 14.84 × 6.99
M: 1 diesel; 1 CP prop; 4,000 bhp **Fuel:** 862 tons **Electric:** 900 kw

Remarks: 3,600 grt/5,631 dwt. Ostensibly for the fishing fleet, but can refuel under way alongside or astern.

◆ **1 cargo ship** Bldr: . . . . . .

Arenal (In serv. 1965)

Remarks: 763 grt. Acquired 12-82. No other data available.

◆ **1 Soviet Pelym-class degaussing tender**

Cuban Pelym-class degaussing tender 2-8

D: 1,300 tons (fl) **S:** 16 kts **Dim:** 65.5 × 11.6 × 3.4
A: none **Electron Equipt:** Radar: 1/Don-2 nav.
M: 2 diesels; 2 props; . . . bhp **Range:** 4,500/12 **Crew:** 70 tot.

Remarks: Arrived in Cuba 2-82 under tow. Equipped to deploy, operate, and recover deperming cable array.

◆ **1 intelligence collector, former fishing boat** Bldr: Sociedad Española de Construcción Naval, Bilbao (In serv. 1967)

Isla de la Juventud (ex-*Arminza*)

UBA (continued)
UXILIARIES (continued)

la de la Juventud U.S. Navy, 7-84

D: 1,556 grt **S:** 13 kts **Dim:** 70.0 × 12.6 × 5.4
M: 1 MWM diesel; 1 prop; 2,200 bhp

emarks: Equipped with a variety of electronic collection antennas. Converted ound 1980.

1 yacht

11 GRANMA

marks: Small cabin cruiser in which Fidel Castro returned to Cuba in 1956. Maintned by the navy as a museum.

1 Soviet Okhtenskiy-class seagoing tug (In serv. 1960s)

ARIBE

D: 663 tons (926 fl) **S:** 13.3 kts
Dim: 47.3 (43.0 pp) × 10.3 × 5.5 (4.1 mean)
M: electric drive: 2 Type 5D50 diesels; 1 prop; 1,500 bhp
Range: 7,800/7 **Fuel:** 197 tons **Electric:** 340 kw **Crew:** 40 tot.

emarks: Transferred 1976.

3 Soviet Prometey-class large harbor tugs

D: 319 tons (fl) **S:** 12 kts **Dim:** 29.8 (28.2 pp) × 8.30 × 3.20
A: 3/12.7-mm mg (I × 3)
Electric Equipt: Radar: 1/Spin Trough nav.
M: 2 Type 6D30/50.4 diesels; 2 CP props; 1,200 bhp
Electric: 50 kw (2 × 25 kw) **Crew:** 8 tot.

emarks: Two transferred 1967, one in 1972. Bollard pull: 14 tons.

2 Soviet Yelva-class diving tenders

D: 295 tons (fl) **S:** 12.4 kts **Dim:** 40.9 (37.0 pp) × 8.0 × 2.1
Electron Equipt: Radar: 1/Spin Trough nav. **Electric:** 200 kw
M: 2 3D12A diesels; 2 props; 600 bhp **Crew:** 20 tot.

emarks: Transferred 1978. Can support 7 divers to 60-m depths.

1 or more Soviet Poluchat-I-class torpedo retrievers

uban Poluchat-I 1983

D: 90 tons (fl) **S:** 18 kts **Dim:** 29.6 × 6.1 × 1.9
A: 4/14.5-mm mg (II × 2)
Electron Equipt: Radar: 1/Spin Trough nav.
M: 2 M50F-1 diesels; 2 props; 1,800 bhp
Range: 450/17; 900/10 **Electric:** 14 kw **Crew:** 20 tot.

emarks: Transfer data uncertain. Equipped for patrol boat duties as well as for etrieving torpedoes via a stern ramp.

♦ **1 Soviet Whiskey-class battery-charging barge**

D: 1,050 tons **Dim:** 75.0 × 6.3 × 4.8 **Electric:** 3,000 kw

Remarks: Former submarine, transferred under tow 4-79 with propellers removed, torpedo tubes sealed, and periscopes removed, for use as a charging station for the Foxtrot-class submarines.

MINISTRY OF THE INTERIOR BORDER GUARD

PATROL BOATS AND CRAFT

♦ **4 Soviet Stenka-class patrol boats**

D: 170 tons (210 fl) **S:** 36 kts **Dim:** 39.50 × 7.0 × 1.80
A: 4/30-mm AA AK-230 (II × 2) **Crew:** 20 tot.
Electron Equipt:
Radar: 1/Pot Drum surf. search, 1/Drum Tilt f.c.
EW: 2/chaff RL (XVI × 2)
IFF: 1/Square Head interrogator, 1/High Pole B transponder
M: 3 M503A diesels; 3 props; 12,000 bhp **Range:** 550/34; 750/25

Remarks: Transferred two in 2-85, two in 9-85. Do not have the 4/400-mm ASW TT and stern-mounted dipping sonar found on standard Soviet Navy version and presumably have no antisubmarine capability.

♦ **27 Soviet Zhuk-class patrol craft**

Cuban Zhuk U.S. Navy, 7-84

D: 48 tons (60 fl) **S:** 34 kts **Dim:** 24.0 × 5.0 × 1.2 (1.8 props)
A: 4/14.5-mm mg (II × 2)
Electron Equipt: Radar: 1/Spin Trough nav.
M: 2 M50F-4 diesels; 2 props; 2,400 bhp **Range:** 700/28; 1,100/15
Fuel: 10 tons **Crew:** 10–12 tot.

Remarks: Transferred 1 in 12-71, 1 in 7-74, 4 in 10-75, 2 in 12-76, 4 in 1977–79, 6 in 1980 (including 3 in 12-80), 3 in 1984, 4 in 9-85, 2 in 9-89. At least eight others have been passed onward to Nicaragua.

♦ **1 22-knot patrol craft** Bldr: Cadiz, Spain (L: . . .)

GUANABACOA

♦ **6 fast launches** Bldr: . . . SY, Spain (In serv. 1971–72)

CAMILO CIENFUEGOS	MACEO	MARTI
ESCAMBRAY	CUARTEL MONCADA	FINLAY

Remarks: No other information available.

CYPRUS

Republic of Cyprus

Naval Aviation: Three Agusta-Bell 47G helicopters are assigned coastal patrol duties, as is one Britten-Norman Defender.

♦ **2 Type 32L patrol boats** Bldr: Ch. Navals de l'Estérel, Cannes

APHRODITE (In serv. 12-82) SALAMIS (In serv. 24-5-83)

D: 96 tons (fl) **S:** 32 kts **Dim:** 32.1 × 6.45 × 1.9
A: 1/40-mm AA—1/20-mm AA
M: 2 MTU diesels; 2 props; 4,000 bhp **Range:** 1,500/15

Remarks: Wooden construction. First unit ordered 9-81. *Salamis* powered by SACM diesels producing 4,640 bhp. *Aphrodite* operated by the Maritime Police, *Salamis* by the Naval Command of the National Guard.

NORTH CYPRUS

Turkish Republic of North Cyprus

PATROL CRAFT

Note: 57-ton patrol boat *Sergey Krstanovic* delivered 1991; see addenda for details.

♦ **1 Turkish-built** Bldr: Profilo Holding Proteksan SY, Tuzla, Istanbul

74 Raif Denktas (L: 23-9-88)

Raif Denktas (74) Selçuk Emre, 9-88

D: 10 tons (fl) **S:** 28 kts **Dim:** 11.9 × 3.5 × . . . **Crew:** 6 tot.
A: 1/12.7-mm mg **Electron Equipt:** Radar: 1/Raytheon . . . nav.
M: 2 Volvo Aquamatic diesels; 2 propos; 400 bhp **Range:** 250/. . .

CZECHO-SLOVAKIA

Note: The 1,200-man Army River Force operates some 16 river craft; no data available.

DENMARK

Kingdom of Denmark

Personnel (1991): 5,240 total (1,150 officers, 3,050 enlisted, 1,040 conscripts), plus 2,460 civilians. There are 5,900 Naval Reservists and 4,100 members of the Home Guard.

Naval Aviation: Eight Mk 80 Lynx helicopters, the first of which was delivered 15-5-80; these are being updated to Mk 80/90 with the Racal data system and Kestrel ESM; two Sea Lynx Mk 90 (ex-Argentine order) were acquired in 5-87 and 5-88 from the U.K. and a third direct from Argentina in 1989. The air force took delivery of three U.S. Gulfstream G-111 Maritime Patrol Aircraft during 1981–82 and also operates 8 Sikorsky S-61A-1 helicopters in 772 Squadron for search-and-rescue duties.

Weapons and Sensors: Most equipment is of European origin, except for the U.S. Sea Sparrow and Harpoon missile systems. A lightweight, 10-cell launcher for the U.S. RAM (Rolling Airframe Missile) RIM-116A SAM is being developed by the Per Udsen Co. for use on the *Flyvefisken*-class convertible boats and, possibly, the *Nils Juel*-class frigates; weight: 3 tons. The French Mistral SAM has been selected for use by small combatants. The SM.2G sea mine is being developed with West Germany; some 3,000 were to be delivered 1990–93.

In 1991, two mobile Harpoon coast-defense batteries were ordered from McDonnell-Douglas in the United States; the batteries, each consisting of two trucks with four missiles each and a third command center vehicle, will employ RGM-84A missiles removed from the stricken frigates of the *Peder Skram* class and are to be operational by the end of 1994.

SUBMARINES

♦ **2 German Type 205** Bldr: Royal Dockyard, Copenhagen

	Laid down	L	In serv.
S 320 Narhvalen	16-2-65	10-9-68	27-2-70
S 321 Nordkaperen	20-1-66	18-12-69	22-12-70

Narhvalen (S 320) Maritime Photographic, 10-9

D: 370 light/430 surf./480 tons **S:** 10/17 kts
Dim: 45.41 × 4.60 × 3.80 (surf.)
A: 8/533-mm TT fwd (. . . Swedish TP 61 torpedoes)
Electron Equipt:
Radar: 1/Thomson-CSF Calypso
Sonar: Krupp Atlas CSU 3/2 syst., 1/SRS-M1H, 1/GHG AN5039A1
M: 2 MTU 820 Db, 600-hp diesels; 2/405-kw generators, 1/2,300-shp motor
Crew: 4 officers, 17 enlisted

Remarks: Modeled on the German Type 205 and Norwegian Type 207 (*Kobben* clas[s]). To be updated beginning 1992 to the same standard as the ex-Norwegian boats.

♦ **3 ex-Norwegian Kobben class** Bldr: Rheinstahl Nordseewerke, Emden

	Laid down	L	In serv.
S 322 Tumleren (ex-*Utvaer,* S 303)	24-3-65	30-7-65	1-12-65
S 323 Sælen (ex-*Uthaug,* S 304)	31-5-65	3-10-65	16-2-66
S 324 Springeren (ex-*Kya,* S 317)	26-5-63	20-2-64	15-1-64

Springeren (S 324) Hartmut Ehlers, 11-

D: 412/524 tons **S:** 13.5/17 kts **Dim:** 46.61 × 4.60 × 3.80
A: 8/533-mm TT, fwd (8 Swedish TP 613 torpedoes)
Electron Equipt:
Radar: Thomson-CSF Calypso—Sonar: Krupp-Atlas . . .
EW: Racal Sealion intercept
M: 2 MTU 12V493 AZ, 600-bhp diesels, 2/405-kw generators, 1/1,100 kw motor; 1 prop (2.3 m dia.); 1,700 shp max.
Crew: 5 officers, 13 enlisted

Remarks: West German IKL Type 207 design, based on Type 205 but deeper divi[ng]: 190 m max. Purchased by Denmark 1986. Refitted at Urivale SY, Bergen, 1987– with new Thorn-EMI D3 fire-control system, sonar, and a propulsion overhaul; leng[th]ened 1.60 m. Danish Navy desired to acquire two more, but funding was lacking. T[he] three Danish boats are the second, fourth, and sixth to be modernized in the seri[es]. Norway's *Stadt* (S 307) was to have been the third boat transferred but was damag[ed] beyond economic repair in the spring of 1987; replaced by *Kya* mid-1989. S 322 co[m]pleted modernization 10-89, S 232 on 9-7-90, and S 324 in 5-91 (delivered 7-91). S 3[..] sank 3-12-90 while under tow without crew; raised 17-12-90, she was to be repaired, the damage, despite flooding of the pressure hull, was found to be minimal. A succes[sor] class for this trio is planned to be ordered after 1997.

FRIGATES

♦ **3 Nils Juel (Type KV 72) class** Bldr: Aalborg Vaerft, Aalborg

	Laid down	L	In serv.
F 354 Nils Juel	20-10-76	27-9-78	22-8-80
F 355 Olfert Fischer	6-12-78	15-1-80	16-10-81
F 356 Peter Tordenskjold	3-12-79	2-81	2-4-82

Nils Juel (F 354) Danish Navy, 19

IGATES *(continued)*

fert Fischer (F 355)—in the Mideast Leo Van Ginderen, 1-91

ter Tordenskjold (F 356) Danish Navy, 1990

: 1,100 tons (1,320 fl) **S:** 30 kts (20 on diesel)
im: 84.0 (80.0 pp) × 10.3 × 3.1
: 8/Harpoon SSM (IV × 2)—1 NATO Sea Sparrow SAM syst. (VIII × 1, no reloads)—1/76-mm OTO Melara Compact DP—4/20-mm AA (I × 4)— 1 d.c. rack
lectron Equipt:
Radar: 2/Skanter 009 nav., 1/Plessey AWS-5 air search, 1/Phillips 9GR 600 surf. search., 1/Phillips 9 LV 200 gun f.c. (with Type 771 low-light t.v. tracker); 1/U.S. Mk 91 Mod. 1 missile f.c. (2 directors)
Sonar: Plessey PMS-26—EW: Decca-Racal Cutlass intercept
1: CODOG: 1 G.E. LM-2500 gas turbine (26,600 shp), 1 MTU 20V956 TB82 diesel (4,800 bhp); 2 CP props
ange: 800/28; 2,500/18 **Electric:** 1,500 kw (3,500-kw diesel sets)
uel: 130 tons **Crew:** 18 officers, 9 CPOs, 63 enlisted

narks: Ordered 5-12-75. Planned ASW torpedo system not installed, and, as a ılt, they have little ASW capability. Two Breda SCLAR chaff/flare RL not yet ed. NATO Sea Sparrow system, with no reloads, has two radar directors. aSAAB CEPLO data system. F 355 commissioning delayed by fire 5-81. Planned to ive U.S. RAM (Rolling Airframe Missile) SAM system, using two lightweight, nissile launchers per ship; under 1991 request for proposals, however, the program opened up to competing systems, including the French Sadral (with Mistral mis-s) and the British VISRAD (with Starstreak missiles). Major modernization of all e has been deferred, but they are to receive an integrated action information em. F 355 in collision 6-4-88 with ferry. F 354 deployed to the Mideast with United ions forces 1990–91. The RIM-7M Sea Sparrow missiles are to be replaced by the r RIM-7P.

te: The frigates *Peder Skram* (F 352) and *Herlof Trolle* (F 353) were placed in ntained reserve in 12-87 and formally decommissioned on 4-6-88. They are to be cken for scrap by 1991. Their Harpoon missiles will be employed by shore batteries, their Sea Sparrow systems will be used for naval base defense.

SHERIES PROTECTION FRIGATES

1 (+3) Stanflex 2000 class Bldr: Svendborg Skibsværft, Svendborg

	Laid down	L	In serv.
57 THETIS	10-10-88	23-6-89	4-3-91
58 TRITON	27-6-89	16-3-90	1-92
59 HVIDBJØRNEN	19-3-90	21-12-90	5-92
60 VÆDDEREN	2-1-91	11-10-91	3-93

): 2,600 tons (3,500 fl) **S:** 21.5 kts
im: 112.50 (99.75 pp) × 14.40 × 6.00
: 1/76-mm OTO Melara DP—1/20-mm AA—2/d.c. racks—1/Lynx Mk 90 helicopter
lectron Equipt:
Radar: 1/Terma Scanter Mil . . . nav., 1/Plessey AWS-6 air search
Sonar: 1/ C-Tech CTS-36 hull-mounted,1/Thomson-Sintra Salmon HF VDS

M: 3 M.A.N. Burmeister & Wain 12V 28/32 diesels; 1 KaMeWa CP prop; 12,000 bhp (6,366 sust.)—800-shp bow-thruster, 1,090-shp retractable azimuthal thruster (for 8 kts)
Electric: 1,440 kw (3 × 480 kw , G.M. 16-cyl. diesel sets, see Remarks)
Range: 8,500/15.5 **Endurance:** 21+ days
Crew: 65 ship's company + 11 passengers

Thetis (F 357) Danish Navy, 1990

Thetis (F 357) Danish Navy, 1990

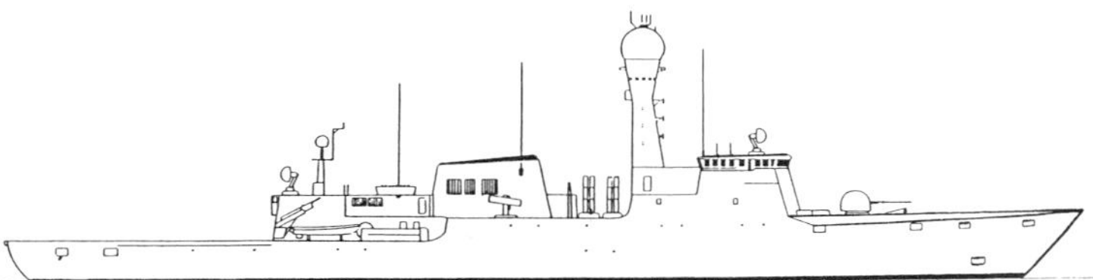

Thetis class—proposed weapons system upgrade Danish Navy, 1991

Remarks: Designed with Y-ARD assistance. Ordered 10-87 to replace the *Hvidbjørnen* class. Engines on resilient mountings to reduce radiated noise. Ice-reinforced hulls. Have Philips 9LV 200 Mk 3 weapons direction system for the 76-mm gun, with t.v. tracker/director. Helicopter deck 28 × 14 m. At a later date, these ships may be fitted with two 8-cell vertical-launch Sea Sparrow SAMs modules (with three target illuminators), two triple ASW TT, eight Harpoon missiles (IV × 2), two point-defense SAM launchers, and two decoy rocket launchers; in addition, the combat system would be improved by adding two radar directors, a towed passive linear hydrophone array, and the U.S. SLQ-25 Nixie towed torpedo decoy system may be added, with completion of the alterations to occur between 1998 and 2001.

Thetis was equipped with a towed array of six pneumatic seismic survey "guns" during the spring of 1991 at Aarhus SY for use in oil exploration along the eastern coast of Greenland under charter to the Nunaoil; her first survey voyage began 12-7-91.

◆ **1 modified Hvidbjørnen class** Bldr: Aalborg Værft, Aalborg

	Laid down	L	In serv.
F 340 BESKYTERREN	15-12-74	27-5-75	27-2-76

Beskyterren (F 340) Danish Navy, 1990

FISHERIES PROTECTION FRIGATES *(continued)*

D: 1,970 tons (fl) **S:** 18 kts **Dim:** 74.4 × 11.8 × 4.5
A: 1/76.2-mm 50-cal. DP—1/Lynx Mk 80/90 helicopter
Electron Equipt:
Radar: 1/Skanter Mil 009 nav., 1/Plessey AWS-6 air search
Sonar: 1/Plessey PMS-26 MF hull-mounted
M: 4 Burmeister & Wain Alpha diesels; 1 CP prop; 7,440 bhp
Range: 6,000/13 (one engine) **Crew:** 8 officers, 59 enlisted

Remarks: Ice-reinforced hull. At one time, an OTO Melara Compact 76-mm gun was to have been fitted in place of the locally controlled U.S. Mk 26 mount currently fitted. To be refitted and modernized for further service.

♦ 4 Hvidbjørnen class

	Bldr	Laid down	L	In serv.
F 348 Hvidbjørnen	Aarhus Flydedok	6-61	23-11-61	12-62
F 349 Vædderen	Aalborg Værft	10-61	6-4-62	3-63
F 350 Ingolf	Svendborg Skibsværft	12-61	27-7-62	6-63
F 351 Fylla	Aalborg Værft	6-62	18-12-62	7-63

Hvidbjørnen (F 348)—with radome for SATCOMM aft Danish Navy, 1990

D: 1,345 tons (1,650 fl) **S:** 18 kts **Dim:** 72.6 × 11.6 × 4.9
A: 1/76.2-mm 50-cal.DP—1/Lynx helicopter
Electron Equipt:
Radar: 1/Skanter Mil 009, 1/Plessey AWS-6 air search
Sonar: 1 Plessey PMS-26 MF hull-mounted
M: 4 G.M. 16-567C diesels; 1 CP prop; 6,400 bhp **Range:** 6,000/13
Crew: 10 officers, 60 enlisted

Remarks: Ice-reinforced hull. Plessey AWS-6 replaced CWS-1 radar in all 1985–87. All four to be replaced by the new *Triton* class 1992–93. F 348 could be equipped for survey duties, carrying four survey launches and an enhanced crew of 10 officers and 75 enlisted at the expense of the helicopter capability. Can also be equipped with two depth-charge racks.

GUIDED-MISSILE BOATS

♦ 10 Willemoes class Bldr: Frederikshavn Værft, Fredrikshavn

Hammer (P 542)—with Harpoon SSM Danish Navy, 1990

Rodsteen (P 546) Danish Navy, 1

	In serv.		In serv.
P 540 Bille	10-76	P 545 Norby	22-11-77
P 541 Bredal	21-1-77	P 546 Rodsteen	16-2-78
P 542 Hammer	1-4-77	P 547 Sehested	19-5-78
P 543 Huitfeldt	15-6-77	P 548 Suenson	10-8-78
P 544 Krieger	22-9-77	P 549 Willemoes	7-10-76

D: 232 tons (265 fl) **S:** 40 kts (36 normal)—diesels: 12 kts
Dim: 46.1 (42.4 pp) × 7.4 × 2.1 (2.7 over props)
A: 4/Harpoon SSM—1/76-mm OTO Melara Compact—2/533-mm T (I × 2)
Electron Equipt:
Radar: 1/Terma 20T48 nav., 1/ Philips 9GA-208 air/surf. search, Philips 9LV 200 fire-control
EW: Racal Cutlass intercept, 6/chaff/flare rocket rails
M: CODOG: 3 Rolls-Royce Proteus 52M/544 gas turbines; 2 G.M. 8V-71 diesels; 3 Liaan CP props; 12,750 shp/800 bhp
Electric: 420 kw **Range:** 400/36 **Crew:** 5 officers, 21 enlisted

Remarks: Based on the Swedish Lürssen-designed Spica class and ordered in The torpedoes are Swedish Type 61, wire-guided, with a range of 20,000 me Endurance is normally 36 hours. Two triple 103-mm flare rocket rails on piloth sides. Have TORCI torpedo f.c.s. and CEPLO tactical data system. Normally ope with only two Harpoon aboard. Can carry 20 mines in lieu of SSM and torpedoes torpedo tubes and no SSM. Five are to receive a new Terma tactical data system, an are to get a point-defense SAM system: Stinger, RBS 70, SADRAL (Mistral), or Short Starstreak; trials were conducted on P 545 in 1989 with a SINBAD laun (Mistral missiles) atop the superstructure aft. All are to receive one more major re extend their operational lives.

Note: The six *Søløven*-class torpedo boats, *Søløven* (P 510), *Søridderen* (P 511), *bjornen* (P 512), *Søhesten* (P 513), *Søhunden* (P 514), and *Søulven* (P 515) were carded 1990–91 on completion of the initial group of STANFLEX 300 patrol boat

MULTI-PURPOSE GUIDED-MISSILE PATROL BOATS

♦ 6 (+7) "Stanflex 300"-class multifunctional Bldr: Aalborg Vaer

	Laid down	L	In serv.
P 550 Flyvefisken	15-8-85	26-4-86	19-12-89
P 551 Hajen	16-6-88	6-12-88	22-9-89
P 552 Havkatten	16-12-88	30-5-89	1-11-90
P 553 Laxen	18-5-89	17-10-89	23-3-91
P 554 Makrelen	13-10-89	7-3-90	7-91
P 555 Støren	5-2-90	14-12-90	12-91
P 556 Sværdfisken	. . .	1-91	-92
P 557 Glenten	1-91	. . .	1993
P 558 Gribben	. . .	. . .	. . .
P 559 Lommen	. . .	. . .	. . .
P 560 Ravnen	. . .	. . .	. . .
P 561 Skaden	. . .	. . .	. . .
P 562 Viben	. . .	. . .	1993

D: 320 tons (fl; 400 fl as minelayer)
S: 35 kts (30 sust./19 diesel/6 hydraulic)
Dim: 54.00 (50.00 pp) × 9.00 × 3.00 max. hull

Hajen (P 551)—with eight Harpoon missiles Danish Navy, 1

LTI-PURPOSE GUIDED-MISSILE PATROL BOATS *(continued)*

: Gunboat and mine countermeasures: 1/76-mm OTO Melara Super Rapid DP—2/12.7-mm mg (I × 2)
Guided-missile boat: 4 Harpoon SSM (II × 2)—1/76-mm OTO Melara Super Rapid DP—later also: 1/point-defense SAM launcher— optional: 2/533-mm TT (wire-guided)
lectron Equipt:
Radar: 1/Terma Pilot nav., 1/Plessey AWS-6 air search (see Remarks)
Sonar: Thomson-Sintra TSM 2640 MF hull-mounted (ordered)
EW: Racal SABRE intercept (0.6-40 gHz), Cygnus jammer
I: CODAG: 1 G.E.-Fiat LM-500 gas turbine (5,680 shp) centerline (not in P 561 and P 562), 2 MTU 16V396 TB94 diesels (3,480 bhp each), 1 G.M. 12V71 diesel (500 bhp) to windmill centerline prop and to power hydraulic drive slow-speed system; 3 props (CP outboard)— bow-thruster
lectric: 600 kw (3 G.M. 6-71 diesels driving) **Range:** . . ./. . .
rew: 4 officers, 13 enlisted as patrol boat; 4 officers, 15 enlisted as missile boat (28 tot. accom.)

en (P 551)—in patrol boat configuration 5-91

vefisken (P 550) Gilbert Gyssels, 8-89

arks: Prototype and first six production models (completed in gunboat configu-n) ordered 27-7-85 to a Karlskrona design. Second group of six units ordered 6-90, nally without the gas turbines, guns, and other equipment; complete outfitting of irst four plus sonar systems and torpedo modules for all was funded in 1991, and s to complete the outfitting of the other two will be sought later. Authorization for ird group of three was denied under the 1991 Budget and again in 1992; instead, ition-control modules will be ordered for use by earlier units.

e boats are intended to be convertible to replace the *Daphne*-class patrol boats, the *ven*-class torpedo boats, and the existing minesweepers, as well as to be able to act st minelayers (and, possibly, later as survey ships, oceanographic research ships, tenders, fishery protection ships, and other semi-combatant and auxiliary mis-s).

550 began trials 27-10-87; she was initially fitted with a standard OTO Melara pact DP, but the 120-rpm "Super Rapid" mounting is to be substituted later. It now not appear that the twin 30-mm guns initially specified for use when in the mine fare configurations will be acquired, although point-defense missile systems will be ured.

o outfit the class, it is planned to acquire the following portable modules: 16 76-mm , 16 crane, 16 minelaying, 16 air defense, 12 antiship, 12 torpedo, 5 mine clearance, and 16 electronics warfare; later it is hoped to add 6 ASW modules. The final equipment modules are to be delivered in 2000. Hull for P 550 built in Sweden by Karlskronavarvet. Foam-core glass-reinforced plastic hull construction; due to weight-saving measures, the eighth and later boats will displace about 15 tons less. The first seven were completed with the 76-mm gun and electrohydraulic crane modules. The Plessey AWS-6 radar is to be replaced in all by a three-dimensional search set. As of 1991, 7 sonar sets and 3 towed linear hydrophone arrays had been ordered for use on the class.

The boats employ passive tank stabilization at low speeds, when they are powered by hydraulic drive for noise suppression; at high speeds, rudder roll control is employed. The outboard, diesel-driven props are controllable pitch; the centerline screw is windmilled by the auxiliary diesels when the gas turbine is not operating, in order to reduce drag. Have the U.S. WSC-3 UHF communications suite.

The modular mine countermeasures suite consists of two Danyard-built, remote-controlled minehunting drones (17.7-m overall, 38 tons full load, 12–15 knots on waterjet propulsion), a Thomson-Sintra towed TSM 2054 sidescan sonar, with the IBIS 43 minehunting system and Thomson-Sintra 2061 tactical mine countermeasures data system. The first drone, MRF 1, was completed 3-91, and seven more are planned.

MRF 1—drone minehunter for Stanflex 300 class Danyard, 1991

Note: Of the ten *Daphne*-class patrol boats, *Havmanden* (P 532) was stricken in 1978; *Neptun* (P 536) and *Rota* (P 538) in 1989; and *Daphne* (P 530), *Dryaden* (P 531), *Havfruen* (P 533), *Najaden* (P 534), *Nymfen* (P 535), and *Ran* (P 537) in 1990–91.

FISHERIES PROTECTION PATROL BOATS

◆ **3 Agdlek class** Bldr: Svendborg Værft, Svendborg

Y 386 AGDLEK (In serv. 12-3-74) Y 387 AGPA (In serv. 14-5-74)
Y 388 TULUGAQ (In serv. 26-6-79)

Agpa (Y 387) Gunnar Olsen, 6-87

D: 330 tons (fl) **S:** 12 kts **Dim:** 31.4 × 7.7 × 3.3
A: 2/20-mm AA (I × 2)
Electron Equipt:
Radar: 1/Terma 20T48 (NWS-3) nav., 1/Skanter 009 nav.
M: 1 Burmeister & Wain Alpha diesel; 800 bhp **Crew:** 15 tot.

Remarks: For fisheries patrol service in Greenland waters. Can carry two survey launches. Y 388 has only one navigational radar, is .3 m longer, and can make 14 kts.

◆ **9 Barsø class** Bldr: Svendborg Værft, Svendborg

	In serv.		In serv.
Y 300 BARSØ	13-6-69	Y 305 VEJRØ	17-10-69
Y 301 DREJØ	1-7-69	Y 306 FARØ	17-5-73
Y 302 ROMSØ	21-7-69	Y 307 LÆSØ	23-7-73
Y 303 SAMSØ	15-8-69	Y 308 ROMØ	3-9-73
Y 304 THURØ	12-9-69		

FISHERIES PROTECTION PATROL BOATS *(continued)*

Farø (Y 306) Danish Navy, 1990

D: 155 tons (fl) **S:** 11 kts **Dim:** 25.5 × 6.0 × 2.8
A: 2/20-mm AA (I × 2)—1/12.7-mm mg
Electron Equipt: Radar: 1/Skanter 009 nav.
M: 1 diesel; 1 prop; 385 bhp **Crew:** 4 officers, 16 enlisted

Remarks: Y 307, with decompression chamber forward, is used as a diving tender. Y 306–308 have broader pilothouses.

◆ **2 Maagen-class fisheries patrol boats** Bldr: Helsingør DY

Y 384 Maagen (In serv. 19-5-60)
Y 385 Mallemukken (In serv. 19-5-60)

Maagen (Y 384) Leo Van Ginderen, 6-85

D: 175 tons (190 fl) **S:** 10 kts **Dim:** 27.0 × 7.2 × 2.75
A: 2/20-mm AA (I × 2)
Electron Equipt:
Radar: 1/Terma 20T48 (NWS-3) nav., 1/Skanter 009 nav.
M: diesel; 1 prop; 350 bhp **Crew:** 14 tot.

Remarks: Operate in Greenland waters. Guns not normally mounted.

NAVAL PATROL CRAFT

◆ **2 Y 375 class** Bldr: Botved (In serv. 1974)

Y 375 Y 376

D: 12 tons (fl) **S:** 26 kts **Dim:** 13.3 × 4.5 × 1.1 **A:** 1/7.62-mm mg
Electron Equipt: Radar: 1/NWS-3 nav.
M: 2 diesels; 2 props; 680 hp

Remarks: Have facilities for combat swimmers.

Y 376

◆ **1 small patrol craft** Bldr: Skagen (In serv. 1941)

Y 343 Lunden

D: 71.5 tons **S:** 8 kts **Dim:** 19.7 × 5.4 × 2.8
A: 1/7.62-mm mg **Electron Equipt:** Radar: 1/NWS-3 nav.
M: 1 diesel; 1 prop; . . . bhp **Crew:** 4 tot.

Remarks: Sister to Home Guard craft MHV 51 and MHV 76. Wooden trawler hu

PATROL CRAFT MANNED BY THE HOME GUARD

Note: The Home Guard is responsible for coastal waters surveillance, harbor tr control, guarding naval installations, and search-and-rescue operations. The p military organization had about 4,500 personnel in 1991.

◆ **0 (+6+19) MHV 800 class** Bldr: Søby SY, Ærø

	In serv.		In serv
MHV 800	5-92	MHV 803	11-9
MHV 801	11-92	MHV 804	5-9
MHV 802	5-93	MHV 805	11-9

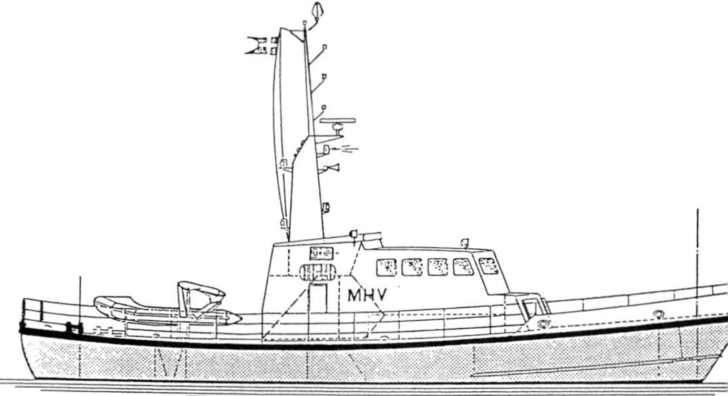

MHV 800 class Danish Navy, 1

D: 80 tons (83 fl) **S:** 13 kts **Dim:** 23.70 (20.26 pp) × 5.60 × 2.0
A: 2/7.62-mm mg (I × 2)—provision for 1/20-mm AA
Electron Equipt: Radar: 1/. . . . . . nav. **Endurance:** 3 days
M: 2 diesels; 2 props; 900 bhp **Crew:** 4 officers, 4 enlisted
Range: 790/11

Remarks: Steel construction. Intended as the long-overdue replacements for the merous Home Guard patrol craft, some of which date to the 1920s. First 12 author under 1987 budget. Six more authorized under 1989 budget. First six ordered with the intent to order six per year henceforth through the planned total of 25 nee

◆ **6 MHV 20 class** Bldr: Eivinds Plasticjolle & Bådeverft, Plastikbodervaerft Svendborg (In serv. 1974–81)

MHV 20 Baunen MHV 22 Kureren MHV 24 Patrioten
MHV 21 Budstikken MHV 23 Partisan MHV 25 Sabatøren

D: 60 tons (fl) **S:** 15 kts **Dim:** 16.5 × 4.2 × 2.0
A: 2/7.62-mm mg (I × 2) **Electron Equipt:** Radar: 1/NWS-3 na
M: 2 MTU diesels; 2 props; 500 bhp **Crew:** 9 tot.

Remarks: Additional units of these craft were intended to replace the older M units, but no further units were authorized. Glass-reinforced plastic hulls.

TROL CRAFT MANNED BY THE HOME GUARD *(continued)*

dstikken (MHV 21) Danish Navy, 1990

◆ 6 MHV-90 class, steel-hulled Bldr: A: Svendborg Værft; B: Sakskijbing

	Bldr	In serv.
V 90 Bopa	A	1975
V 91 Brigaden	B	1974
V 92 Holger Danske	B	1975
V 93 Hvidsten	B	1975
V 94 Ringen	A	1974
V 95 Speditøren	A	1975

pa (MHV 90) Danish Navy, 1990

D: 85 tons (130 fl) **S:** 10.7 kts **Dim:** 19.8 × 5.7 × 1.6
A: 2/7.62-mm mg (I × 2)
Electron Equipt: Radar: 1/Raytheon 1290S nav.
M: 1 Burmeister & Wain diesel; 400 bhp

◆ **3 MHV 70 class** Bldr: Royal Dockyard, Copenhagen (In serv. 1958)

V 70 Saturn MHV 71 Scorpius MHV 72 Sirius

turn (MHV 70) Hartmut Ehlers, 5-90

D: 78 tons (130 fl) **S:** 10 kts **Dim:** 20.1 × 5.1 × 2.5
A: 2/7.62-mm mg (I × 2)
Electron Equipt: Radar: 1/Raytheon 1290S nav.
M: 1 diesel; 200 bhp

◆ **7 MHV 80 class**

	Bldr	In serv.
MHV 80 Fænø (ex-MHV 69, ex-MS 6)	Svendborg	7-41
MHV 81 Askø (ex-Y 386, ex-M 560, ex-MS 2)	Holbæk	1-8-41
MHV 82 Enø (ex-Y 388, ex-M 562, ex-MS 5)	Holbæk	18-8-41
MHV 83 Manø (ex-Y 391, ex-M 566, ex-MS 9)	Fredrikssund	30-10-41
MHV 84 Baagø (ex-Y 387, ex-M 561, ex-MS 3)	Korsør	9-8-41
MHV 85 Hjortø (ex-Y 389, ex-M 564, ex-MS 7)	Korsør	24-9-41
MHV 86 Lyø (ex-Y 390, ex-M 565, ex-MS 8)	Korsør	22-10-41

Enø (MHV 82) Leo Van Ginderen, 1991

D: 74 tons (fl) **S:** 11 kts **Dim:** 24.4 × 4.9 × 1.6
A: 2/7.62-mm mg (I × 2)
Electron Equipt: Radar: 1/Raytheon 1290S nav.
M: 1 diesel; 350 bhp

Remarks: In Home Guard service 1958. Former inshore minesweepers. Wooden hulls. The machine guns have replaced the single 20-mm AA formerly carried.

◆ **14 smaller craft**

	Bldr	In serv.
MHV 51 Antares	Nyborg	1933
MHV 56 Apollo	Gilleleje	1941
MHV 60 Aries	Søby	1937
MHV 61 Betelgeuse	Skagen	1929
MHV 62 Covina	Bogense	1941
MHV 63 Cassiopeia	Fredrikssund	1938
MHV 64 Crux	Skagen	1929
MHV 66 Dubhe	Bildøsund	1928
MHV 67 Gemini	Frederikshavn	1932
MHV 73 Hercules	Hundested	1944
MHV 74 Jupiter	Gilleleje	1940
MHV 75 Luna	Gilleleje	1938
MHV 76 Lyra	Frederikshavn	1932

Luna (MHV 75) Hartmut Ehlers, 7-89

PATROL CRAFT MANNED BY THE HOME GUARD *(continued)*

Hercules (MHV 73) Hartmut Ehlers, 7-87

D: 20–30 tons **S:** 8–10 kts **Dim:** 13.0–17.0 × 3.9–6.0 × 1.9–2.2
A: 1/7.62-mm mg **Electron Equipt:** Radar: 1/Raytheon 1290S nav.
M: 1 Alpha or Grenå diesel; 1 prop; 100–165 bhp

Remarks: Wooden-hulled fishing boats, all built for the Danish Navy Home Guard, except MHV 66, acquired in 1958, and MHV 73, acquired in 1959. To be replaced by new-construction, MHV 800-class craft. MHV 51 and MHV 76 are sisters to the naval *Lunden* (Y 343).

MINE WARFARE SHIPS

Note: The minimal current Danish Navy mine countermeasures capability is to be enhanced through the use of STANFLEX-300-class convertible gunboat/mine warfare units, which are to be equipped with a modular mine countermeasures suite; see listing above.

♦ 4 Falster-class minelayers

	Bldr	Laid down	L	In serv.
N 80 Falster	Nakskov Skibsværft	4-62	19-9-62	7-11-63
N 81 Fyen	Frederikshavn Værft	4-62	3-10-62	18-9-63
N 82 Møen	Frederikshavn Værft	10-62	6-6-63	20-4-64
N 83 Sjælland	Nakskov Skibsværft	1-63	14-6-63	7-7-64

Møen (N 82) Gilbert Gyssels, 3-90

Falster (N 80)—original mast height aft Danish Navy, 1990

D: 1,880 tons (fl) **S:** 16.5 kts **Dim:** 77.0 (72.5 pp) × 12.8 × 3.4
A: 4/76.2-mm DP U.S. Mk 33 (II × 2)—400 mines (4 minelaying tracks)
Electron Equipt:
Radar: 1/Terma Pilot nav., 1/CWS-2 air/surf. search, 1/NWS-2 su search, 1/M-46 f.c,
EW: . . . intercept, 2/57-mm rocket flare/decoy launchers
M: 2 G.M. 16-567D3 diesels; 2 CP props; 4,800 bhp **Fuel:** 130 tons
Crew: 10 officers, 123 men

Remarks: NATO design. The Turkish ship *Nusret* is identical. N 82 is training for naval cadets. N 83 converted to submarine tender in 1976, to replace *Henrik Ge* (can still lay mines). N 80 and N 82 built with U.S. "Offshore" funds as MMC 14 MMC 15. All to be refitted for service through 2010; to receive point-defense systems and updated combat data systems. N 82 (and on occasion N 81) can act as training ship, with 66 cadets berthed in temporary accommodations on the mine d

♦ 2 Lindormen-class coastal minelayers Bldr: Svendborg Værft

	Laid down	L	In serv.
N 43 Lindormen	2-2-77	7-6-77	16-2-78
N 44 Lossen	9-7-77	11-10-77	14-6-78

Lindormen (N 43) Leo Van Ginderen,

D: 575 tons (fl) **S:** 14 kts **Dim:** 43.3 (40.0 pp) × 9.0 × 2.65
A: 2/20-mm AA (I × 2)—50 to 60 mines
Electron Equipt: Radar: 1/NWS-3 nav. **Crew:** 27 tot.
M: 2 Wichmann 7AX diesels; 2 props; 4,200 bhp **Electric:** 192 kw

Remarks: Built to replace the *Lougen* class. Controlled minefield planters.

♦ 3 ex-U.S. Adjutant-class coastal minesweepers

	Bldr	In serv.
M 574 Grønsund (ex-MSC 256)	Stephen Bros. SY	21-9-56
M 575 Guldborgsund (ex-MSC 257)	Stephen Bros. SY	11-11-56
M 578 Vilsund (ex-MSC 264)	Harbor BY, Terminal Isl., Cal.	15-11-56

Grønsund (M 574) Hartmut Ehlers, 1

D: 350 tons (376 fl) **S:** 13 kts (8 sweeping)
Dim: 43.89 (41.50 pp) × 7.95 × 2.55 **A:** 1/40-mm AA
Electron Equipt: Radar: 1/NWS-3—Sonar: 1/UQS-1
M: 2 G.M. 8-268A diesels; 2 props; 1,000 bhp
Fuel: 40 tons **Range:** 2,500/10 **Crew:** 38 tot.

Remarks: Survivors of seven. Sisters *Aarøsund* (M 571) stricken 1981, *Omøsun* 576) placed in reserve 1981 as spare parts source; *Alssund* (M 572), *Egernsund* (M and *Ulvsund* (M 577) stricken 1988. Have all had their charthouses enlarged so they can act as hydrographic survey ships. Wooden construction.

XILIARY SHIPS AND CRAFT

6 SKA 11-class inshore survey launches Bldr: Rantsausminde

	In serv.		In serv.		In serv.
A 11	1980	SKA 13	1982	SKA 15	1984
A 12	1981	SKA 14	1982	SKA 16	1985

A 13—and a sister Hartmut Ehlers, 5-88

D: 52 tons (fl) **S:** 12 kts **Dim:** 20.0 × 5.2 × 2.1
Electron Equipt: Radar: 1/Skanter Mil 009 nav.
M: 1 G.M. diesel; 1 prop; 540 bhp **Crew:** . . . tot.

2 U.S. YO 65-class coastal oilers Bldr: Jeffersonville Boat & Machine, Indiana

	Laid down	L	In serv.
68 Rimfaxe (ex-YO 226)	21-4-45	20-7-45	22-10-45
69 Skinfaxe (ex-YO 229)	25-5-45	28-8-45	7-12-45

nfaxe (A 568) Piet Sinke, 5-89

D: 440 tons (1,390 fl) **S:** 10 kts **Dim:** 53.0 × 9.75 × 4.0
A: 1/20-mm AA **Electron Equipt:** Radar: 1/NWS-3 nav.
M: 1 G.M. 8-278A diesel; 1 prop; 640 bhp **Electric:** 40 kw
Range: 2,000/8 **Fuel:** 25 tons **Crew:** 23 tot.

Remarks: Transferred 2-8-62. Cargo: 900 tons. Used as tenders to missile/torpedo t.

1 torpedo transport/retriever Bldr: Åbenrå Skibsværft, Åbenrå

59 Sleipner (In serv. 18-7-86)

ipner (A 559) Danish Navy, 1986

D: 450 tons (fl) **S:** 11 kts **Dim:** 36.50 (34.00 pp) × 7.60 × 2.70
Electron Equipt: Radar: 1/Skanter Mil 009 nav. **Crew:** 6 tot.
M: 1 Callesen 427 EOT diesel; 1 prop; 575 bhp

Remarks: Replaced earlier former coastal freighter of the same name. Cargo capacity: 150 tons.

◆ **3 small torpedo retrievers** Bldr: Eivinds Plasticjolle & Bødeverft, Svendborg (In serv. . . . . . .)

TO 8 Hugin TO 9 Munin TO 10 Mimer

D: 23 tons (fl) **S:** 15 kts **Dim:** 16.15 × 4.15 × 1.25
Electron Equipt: Radar: 1/ . . . nav.
M: 1 MWM diesel; 1 prop; 450 bhp **Crew:** . . .

◆ **1 royal yacht** Bldr: Royal Dockyard, Copenhagen

	L	In serv.
A 540 Dannebrog	10-10-31	1932

Dannebrog (A 540) Leo Van Ginderen, 8-90

D: 1,130 tons (fl) **S:** 14 kts **Dim:** 74.9 × 10.4 × 3.7
A: 2/37-mm saluting cannon (I × 2)
Electron Equipt: Radar: 1/Skanter Mil 009 nav.
M: 2 Burmeister & Wain Alpha 6 T23L-KVO diesels; 2 CP props; 1,600 bhp
Crew: 55 tot. including passengers **Electric:** 507 kVA

Remarks: Re-engined, new electrical generating plant winter 1980–81. Does not wear pendant number assigned.

◆ **2 20-grt dockyard tugs** Bldr: Assens Skibsværft (In serv. 1983)

Hermod Balder

Hermod Gunnar Olsen, 10-86

D: . . . . . . tons **S:** 8.7 kts **Dim:** 11.85 × 4.00 × 1.65
M: 1 G.M. 6-71 series diesel; 1 prop; 300 bhp

AUXILIARY SHIPS AND CRAFT *(continued)*

◆ **3 training craft, former inshore survey launches**

	Bldr	In serv.
SKB 1 GRASPURVEN (ex-*SKA 5*)	Rantsausminde Værft	1961
SKB 2 SNESPURVEN (ex-*SKA 6*)	Rantsausminde Værft	1961
SKB 4 JERNSPURVEN (ex-*SKA 8*)	Holbak Værft	1969

Graspurven (SKB 1) Leo Van Ginderen, 6-91

D: 27 tons (fl) **S:** 9 kts **Dim:** 14.05 (13.00 pp) × 4.0 × . . .
Electron Equipt: Radar: 1/Skanter Mil 009 nav.
M: 1 Volvo Penta diesel; 1 prop; 100 bhp **Crew:** . . .

Remarks: Replaced by SKA 11–16 as inshore survey craft and now employed as navigational training craft. Wooden hulls. Sister *Gulspurven* (SKB 3, ex-SKA 7) stricken 1990.

◆ **2 small sail-training yawls** Bldr: Molich, Hundested (In serv. 1960)

Y 101 SVANEN Y 102 THYRA

Thyra Stafan Terzibaschitsch, 6-90

D: 32 tons (fl) **S:** 7.5 kts (power) **Dim:** 19.2 × 4.8 × 2.4
M: 1 Volvo Penta diesel; 1 prop; 72 bhp (sail area: 500 m)

MINISTRY OF FISHERIES

◆ **1 "Osprey" FV 710-class patrol ship** Bldr: Frederikshavn SY

HAVØRNEN (In serv. 7-79)

D: 320 tons (506 fl) **S:** 18 kts **Dim:** 49.98 (45.8 pp) × 10.50 × 2.75
Electron Equipt: Radar: 1/Skanter Mil 009 nav., 1/NWS-3 nav.
M: 2 Burmeister & Wain Alpha 16V23L-VO diesels; 2 CP props; 4,640 bhp
Range: 4,500/16 **Crew:** 15 tot. (accommodations for 35)

Havørnen Leo Van Ginderen, 6-

Remarks: Has small stern ramp for a 6.5-m rubber inspection dinghy. Built to m cantile specifications, a modified British "Osprey" design. Helicopter deck and har facilities not used.

◆ **1 fisheries research ship** Bldr: Dannebrog, Aarhus

DANA (In serv. 1982)

Dana Danish Navy, 1

D: 2,483 grt **S:** 15.5 kts **Dim:** 78.43 × 14.7 × . . .
M: 2 diesels; 1 CP prop; 4,600 bhp **Crew:** 27 crew, plus 12 scientist

◆ **1 fisheries oceanographic ship**

JENS VAEVER (In serv. 1960)

D: 280 tons (fl) **S:** 11.5 kts **Dim:** 30.53 × 6.35 × 3.15
M: 1 Burmeister & Wain 406 VD diesel; 1 prop; 420 bhp
Fuel: 20 tons **Range:** 2,600/9 **Crew:** 10 tot.

◆ **1 fisheries research boat** Bldr: Hantsholm Aluminium

LEDA (In serv. 4-90)

D: 70 tons (fl) **S:** 9.5 kts **Dim:** 17.7 (pp) × 4.8 × 1.9
M: 1 diesel; 1 prop; 760 bhp **Crew:** 4 tot. **Electric:** 8 kw

◆ **1 Vestkysten-class rescue and salvage tug** Bldr: Marstal Stålskibsværft & Maskinfabrikk, Marstal

VESTKYSTEN (In serv. 3-87)

D: 657 grt **S:** 17 kts **Dim:** 49.30 × 10.00 × 4.20
M: 2 M.A.N. Alpha 6L23/30 diesels; . . . props; 2,200 bhp

◆ **2 Nordsøen-class salvage & rescue tugs** Bldr: Frederikshavn D (In serv. 1968)

NORDJYLLAND NORDSØEN

D: 900 tons (fl) **S:** 14.5 kts **Dim:** 52.35 (45.75 pp) × 10.00 × 3.35
M: 2 Burmeister & Wain 8-23MTBF-308G diesels; 1 CP prop; 1,960 bhp
Electric: 472 kw **Crew:** 12 tot.

MINISTRY OF TRADE AND SHIPPING

ICEBREAKERS

Note: Danish icebreakers are all civilian-manned and subordinate to the Ministr Trade and Shipping. During summer months they are maintained by the Danish N at Frederikshavn.

EBREAKERS *(continued)*

1 Thorbjørn class Bldr: Svendborg Værft, Svendborg

ORBJØRN (L: 6-80)

orbjørn Danish Navy, 1990

D: 2,250 tons (fl) **S:** 16.5 kts **Dim:** 67.5 × 15.3 × 4.70
M: 4 Burmeister & Wain Alpha diesels, electric drive; 2 props; 6,800 shp

marks: Can be used for hydrographic surveys by the navy when not needed for reaking, and can also act as a tug.

2 Danbjørn class Bldr: Lindø Værft, Odense

NBJØRN (In serv. 1965) ISBJØRN (In serv. 1966)

jørn Leo Van Ginderen, 6-90

D: 3,685 tons (fl) **S:** 14 kts **Dim:** 76.8 × 16.8 × 6.0
M: diesel-electric; 2 props; 11,880 shp **Crew:** 34 tot.

1 Elbjorn class Bldr: Frederikshavn Værft

BJØRN (In serv. 1953)

bjørn Leo Van Ginderen, 6-90

D: 898 tons (1,400 fl) **S:** 12 kts **Dim:** 47.0 × 12.1 × 4.35
M: diesel-electric; 2 props; 3,600 shp

marks: Used by Danish Navy for survey work in the summer.

MINISTRY OF THE ENVIRONMENT

(These units are manned by naval and civil personnel)

LLUTION-CONTROL SHIPS AND CRAFT

2 Gunnar Thorson class Bldr: Ørnskov SY, Frederikshavn

NNAR THORSON (In serv. 8-5-81)
NNAR SEIDENFADEN (In serv. 2-7-81)

Gunnar Thorson Danish Navy, 1981

D: 672 tons (750 fl) **S:** 14.5 kts **Dim:** 55.6 (47.9 pp) × 12.3 × 3.9
M: 2 Burmeister & Wain Alpha 8V-23L-VO diesels; 2 CP props; 2,320 bhp

◆ **2 "Sea Truck" design**

	Bldr	In serv.
METTE MILJØ	Carl B. Hoffman SY, Esbjerg	22-2-80
MARIE MILJØ	Søren Larsen SY, Nykøbing Mors	22-2-80

Mette Miljø Danish Navy, 1990

D: 157 tons **S:** 10 kts **Dim:** 29.8 × 8.0 × 1.6
M: 2 Grena GF 24 diesels; 2 props; 660 bhp **Crew:** 8 tot.

◆ **2 Miljø 101 class** Bldr: Eivinds, Svendborg

MILJØ 101 (In serv. 1-11-77) MILJØ 102 (In serv. 1-12-77)

Miljø 102 Danish Navy, 1990

D: 16 tons **S:** 15 kts **Dim:** 16.2 × 4.2 × 2.2
M: 1 MWM TBD232 V12 diesel; 1 prop; 454 bhp
Range: 350/8 **Crew:** 3 tot. (naval crew)

Remarks: Glass-reinforced plastic construction. Carry spill containment gear.

DJIBOUTI

Republic of Djibouti

Personnel (1991): 90 total

◆ **2 patrol craft** Bldr: Plascoa, Cannes

P 10 Moussa Ali (In serv. 8-6-85)
P 11 Mont Arreh (In serv. 16-2-86)

Moussa Ali (P 10) Plascoa, 6-85

D: 30 tons (35 fl) **S:** 24.5 kts **Dim:** 23.30 × 5.50 × 1.50
A: 1/20-mm GIAT AA—1/12.7-mm mg
Electron Equipt: Radar: 1/Decca 36 MN
M: 2 UNI Diesel V12-520 M25 diesels; 2 props; 1,700 bhp
Range: 750/12; 460/15 **Crew:** 15 tot.

Remarks: GRP construction. Ordered 10-84 as a gift from France. Used for coastal surveillance.

◆ **5 Iraqi Swari-class patrol craft** (Transferred 1989–90)

D: 7 tons (fl) **S:** 25 kts **Dim:** 11.0 × 2.5 × 0.6
A: . . . **M:** 2 diesels; 2 props; . . . bhp

Remarks: Gift of the Iraqi government. GRP-construction open launches of the type encountered by UN forces during the 1991 Mideast conflict.

◆ **1 ex-French patrol craft** Bldr: Tecimar (In serv. 1974)

Zena (ex-P 771)

D: 30 tons (fl) **S:** 25 kts **Dim:** 13.3 × 4.1 × 1.1
A: 1/12.7-mm and 1/7.5-mm mg
M: 2 G.M. 6-71 diesels; 2 props; 480 bhp

Remarks: Transferred 1977 from the French colonial police at Djibouti. Glass-reinforced plastic construction.

◆ **3 U.K. Searaider rigid inflatable launches** Bldr: Avon

Remarks: Transferred 25-10-88. Characteristics not available, but probably about 4–6 m overall.

DOMINICA

COAST GUARD

Personnel (1991): 20 total

◆ **1 U.S. 65-ft Commercial Cruiser-class patrol boat**
Bldr: Swiftships, Inc., Morgan City, Louisiana, U.S.A.

D-4 Melville (In serv. 2-5-84)

Melville (D-4) Swiftships, 5-84

D: 34 tons (fl) **S:** 23 kts **Dim:** 19.96 × 5.58 × 1.52
A: small arms **Electron Equipt:** Radar: 1/Raytheon 1210 nav.
M: 2 G.M. 12V71 TI diesels; 2 props; 1,350 bhp
Range: 500/18 **Electric:** 20 kw **Crew:** 6 tot.

Remarks: One of three sisters presented to Caribbean island republics by the U government, the others going to Antigua-Barbuda (see photo) and St. Lucia. Alum num construction. Blue hull, white upperworks.

◆ **2 U.S. Boston Whaler utility craft**
Bldr: Boston Whaler, Rockland, Mass.

Observer Vigilance

D: 2.4 tons (fl) **S:** 35 kts **Dim:** 8.2 × 2.6 × 0.3
M: 2 Johnson gasoline outboards; 310 bhp **Crew:** 2 tot.

Remarks: Glass-reinforced, foam-core construction. Employed for patrol and SA duties.

DOMINICAN REPUBLIC

Personnel (1991): 4,600 officers and men (including marines)

FRIGATE

◆ **1 Canadian "River" class** Bldr: Davie SB, Lauzon, Quebec

	L	In ser
451 Mella (ex-*Presidente Trujillo*, ex-*Carlplace*)	6-7-44	13-12-

Mella (F 451) Hartmut Ehlers, 11-

D: 1,445 tons (2,300 fl) **S:** 19 kts **Dim:** 92.35 × 11.45 × 4.3
A: 1/76.2-mm Mk 26 DP—2/40-mm AA (II × 1)—4/20-mm AA (I × 4)— 2/47-mm saluting guns
Electron Equipt: Radar: 1/SPS-64(V)6 nav./surf. search
M: 2 sets triple-expansion reciprocating steam; 2 props; 5,500 ihp
Boilers: 2 (3-drum) **Fuel:** 645 tons **Range:** 7,700/12
Crew: 15 officers, 130 men, 50 midshipmen

Remarks: Bought in 1947. Serves as fleet flagship and as a training ship.

CORVETTES

◆ **3 ex-U.S. Cohoes-class former net tenders**

	Bldr	L	In ser
P 207 Cambiaso (ex-*Etlah*, AN 79)	Marietta Mfg., W. Va.	16-12-44	16-4-
P 208 Separación (ex-*Passaconaway*, AN 86)	Marine Iron & Ry, Duluth, Minn.	30-6-44	27-4-
P 209 Calderas (ex-*Passaic*, AN 87)	Leatham D. Smith, Sturgeon Bay, Wisc.	29-6-44	6-3-

D: 650 tons (785 fl) **S:** 12.3 kts **Dim:** 51.36 (44.5 pp) × 10.31 × 3.
A: 2/76.2-mm Mk 26 DP (I × 2)—3/20-mm AA (I × 3)
Electron Equipt: Radar: 1/SPS-64(V)6 nav./surf. search
M: diesel-electric: 2 Busch-Sulzer B5-539 diesels, 1 motor; 1 prop; 1,200 bhp
Electric: 120 kw **Fuel:** 88 tons **Crew:** 48 tot.

Remarks: Recommissioned from the U.S. Maritime Commission's reserve fl where they had been laid up since 1963, and transferred 9-76. Despite low speed general unsuitability, they are employed as patrol ships and tugs. Also used in gen support, navigational tender, and hydrographic survey duties. They have had net-tender "horns" at the bow removed and a new, curved stem added; they received a second 76.2-mm gun on the forecastle and new radars.

)RVETTES *(continued)*

paración (P 208) Hartmut Ehlers, 6-89

2 ex-U.S. Admirable-class former minesweepers
Bldr: Associated SB, Seattle, Washington

	Laid down	L	In serv.
(454 Prestol Botello (ex-Separación, ex-*Skirmish*, MSF 303)	8-4-43	16-8-43	30-6-44
(455 Tortugero (ex-*Signet*, MSF 302)	8-4-43	16-8-43	20-8-44

estol Botello (BM 454) Hartmut Ehlers, 11-90

D: 600 tons (903 fl) **S:** 15 kts **Dim:** 54.24 × 10.06 × 4.4
A: 1/76.2-mm Mk 26 DP—2/40-mm Mk 3 AA (I × 2)—4/20-mm AA (I × 4)
Electron Equipt: Radar: 1/SPS-64(V)9 nav.
M: 2 Cooper-Bessemer GSB-8 diesels; 2 props; 1,710 bhp
Electric: 240 kw **Fuel:** 260 tons **Range:** 5,600/9
Crew: 8 officers, 82 enlisted

marks: Transferred 13-1-65. BM 454 renamed 1976. All minesweeping equipment d ASW armament removed from both.

TROL BOATS AND CRAFT

te: The three early-1930s-vintage former U.S. Coast Guard *Argo*-class patrol boats ve been placed "in reserve" and are unlikely to see further service: *Independencia* (P , ex-*Icarus*), *Libertad* (P 205, ex-*Rafael Atoa*, ex-*Thetis*), and *Restauración* (P 206, *Galatea*).

3 110-ft Commercial Cruiser class Bldr: Swiftships, Inc., Morgan City, Louisiana

108 Canopus (In serv. 6-84)	GC 110 Luperon (In serv. . . .-88)
109 Orion (In serv. 8-84)	

Orion (GC 109)—40-mm gun aft Hartmut Ehlers, 6-89

D: 93.5 tons (fl) **S:** 23 kts (20 sust.) **Dim:** 33.53 × 7.32 × 1.83
A: 1/40-mm Mk 3 AA (aft)—2/12.7-mm mg (I × 2)
Electron Equipt: Radar: 1/. . . nav.
M: 3 G.M. 12V92 TI diesels; 3 props; 2,700 bhp
Range: 1,500/12 **Crew:** . . .

Remarks: Aluminum construction. The 40-mm gun is mounted aft.

◆ **1 ex-U.S. PGM 71 class** Bldr: Peterson SB, Sturgeon Bay, Wisc.

GC 102 Betelgeuse (ex-PGM 77)

D: 130 tons (145.5 fl) **S:** 16 kts
Dim: 30.8 (30.2 pp) × 6.4 × 1.85 **Crew:** 20 tot.
A: 1/20-mm AA—2/12.7-mm mg (I × 2)
Electron Equipt: Radar: 1/. . . nav.
M: 2 Caterpillar D-348TA diesels; 2 props; 1,450 bhp
Range: 1,000/12

Remarks: Transferred 14-1-66. One of many gunboats of this class transferred to smaller navies by the United States. Re-engined and armament reduced, 1980.

◆ **4 U.S. 85-ft Commercial Cruiser-class patrol craft** Bldr: Sewart Seacraft, Berwick, La.

	In serv.		In serv.
GC 103 Procion	1972	GC 106 Bellatrix	1967
GC 104 Aldebarán	1967	GC 108 Capella	1968

Aldebarán (GC 104) Hartmut Ehlers, 6-89

D: 60 tons (fl) **S:** 21.7 kts **Dim:** 25.9 × 5.7 × 2.1 **Crew:** 9 tot.
A: 3/12.7-mm mg (I × 3) **Electron Equipt:** Radar: 1/. . . nav.
M: 2 G.M. 16V71N diesels; 2 props; 1,400 bhp **Range:** 800/20

◆ **1 former U.S. Army aircraft-rescue launch**

GC 105 Capitán Alsina (L: 1944)

D: 100 tons (fl) **S:** 17 kts **Dim:** 31.5 × 5.8 × 1.75
A: 2/20-mm AA (I × 2)
M: 2 G.M. diesels; 2 props; 1,000 bhp **Crew:** 20 tot.

Remarks: Wooden hull. Used as Naval Academy training craft, refitted 1977.

AUXILIARY SHIPS AND CRAFT

◆ **1 utility landing craft** Bldr: Ast. Navales Dominicanos (In serv. 1958)

LDM 302 Samana

D: 128 tons (310 fl) **S:** 8 kts **Dim:** 36.4 × 11.0 × 1.15
A: 1/12.7-mm mg **M:** 3 G.M. 64HN9 diesels; 3 props; 450 bhp
Fuel: 80 tons **Crew:** 17 tot.

DOMINICAN REPUBLIC *(continued)*
AUXILIARY SHIPS AND CRAFT *(continued)*

Remarks: U.S. LCT(5) design, used for logistics duties. Sister *Enriquillo* discarded 1979.

Note: Buoy tender *Neptuno* was stricken 1989.

♦ **1 U.S. YO 153-class small oiler** Bldr: Ira S. Bushey, Brooklyn, N.Y.

	Laid down	L	In serv.
BT 5 Capitan Beotegui (ex-U.S. YO 215)	23-4-45	30-8-45	17-12-45

Capitan Beotegui—with launch BA-1 Hartmut Ehlers, 6-89

D: 370 tons (1,076 fl) **S:** 8 kts
Dim: 47.63 × 9.32 × 3.66
A: 2/20-mm AA (I × 2) **M:** 1 Union diesel; 1 prop; 525 bhp
Electric: 39 kw **Crew:** 23 tot.

Remarks: Loaned 4-64; lease extended 31-12-80. Cargo: 6,071 barrels fuel (660 tons). Sister *Capitan W. Arvelo* (BT 4) sank at sea during 2-89.

Note: Small survey launch *Atlantida* (BA 8) stricken 1990.

♦ **1 U.S. Cherokee-class fleet tug** Bldr: Charleston SB & DD, S. Carolina

	Laid down	L	In serv.
RM 21 Macorix (ex-*Kiowa,* ATF 72)	22-6-42	5-11-42	7-6-43

D: 1,235 tons (1,675 fl) **S:** 15 kts
Dim: 62.48 (59.44 wl) × 11.73 × 4.67
A: 1/76.2-mm Mk 26 DP—2/20-mm AA (I × 2)
Electron Equipt: Radar: 1/SPS-64(V)9 nav.
M: 4 G.M. 12-278 diesels, electric drive; 1 prop; 3,000 shp
Electric: 260 kw **Fuel:** 295 tons **Crew:** 85 tot.

Remarks: Transferred 16-10-72; lease extended 31-12-80.

♦ **2 U.S. Sotoyomo-class auxiliary ocean tugs**

	Bldr	Laid down	L	In serv.
RM 18 Caonabo (ex-*Sagamore,* ATA 208)	Gulfport Boiler, Port Arthur, Tex.	27-11-44	19-1-45	19-3-45
RM 22 Enriquillo (ex-*Stallion,* ATA 193)	Levingston SB, Orange, Tex.	26-10-44	24-11-44	1-2-45

Enriquillo (RM 22) Hartmut Ehlers, 11-90

D: 534 tons (860 fl) **S:** 13 kts **Dim:** 43.59 × 10.31 × 3.96
A: 1/76.2-mm DP—2/20-mm AA (I × 2)
Electron Equipt: Radar: 1/Raytheon 1500B nav., 1/. . . nav.
M: 2 G.M. 12-278A diesels, electric drive; 1 prop; 1,500 shp
Electric: 120 kw **Fuel:** 160 tons **Range:** 8,000/8 **Crew:** 45 tot.

Remarks: RM 18 leased 1-2-72, extended 31-12-80. RM 22 purchased 30-10-80.

♦ **2 Hercules-class harbor tugs** Bldr: Ast. Navales Dominicanos (In serv. 1960)

RP 12 Hercules RP 13 Guacanagarix

D: 200 tons (fl) **S:** . . . kts **Dim:** 21.4 × 4.8 × 2.7
M: 1 Caterpillar diesel; 1 prop; 500 bhp **Crew:** 8 tot.

♦ **1 harbor tug, former LCM(6)-class landing craft**

RDM 303 Ocoa

D: 50 tons (fl) **S:** 9 kts **Dim:** 17.1 × 4.3 × 1.2 **Crew:** 5 tot.
M: 2 G.M. 6-71 diesels; 2 props; 450 bhp **Range:** 130/9

Remarks: Modified for use as a tug about 1976. Retains bow ramp.

♦ **1 U.S. YTL 422-class small tug** Bldr: Robt. Jacob, City Isl., NY

RP 16 Bohechio (ex-*Mercedes,* ex-YTL 600) (In serv. 25-7-45)

D: 70 tons (80 fl) **S:** 10 kts **Dim:** 20.1 × 5.5 × 2.4 **Crew:** 6 tot.
M: 1 Hoover-Owens-Rentschler diesel; 1 prop; 375 bhp **Fuel:** 7 tons

Remarks: Transferred 1-71.

♦ **1 sail-training ship for Naval Academy** (In serv. 1979)

BA 7 Nube Del Mar (ex-*Catuan)*

D: 40 tons (fl) **S:** 12 kts **Dim:** 12.8 × 3.6 × . . .
M: 1 Volvo Penta 21A diesel; 1 prop; 75 bhp

♦ **1 ex-U.S. Navy floating dry dock** Bldr: Chicago Bridge & Iron

DF-1 (ex-*Endeavor,* AFDL 1) (In serv. 1943)

Lift Capacity: 1,000 tons **Dim:** 60.96 × 19.51 × 1.07 (light)

Remarks: Leased from U.S. 8-3-86. Length on blocks: 56.39 m; clear width: 13.7 draft over blocks: 4.42 m; max. draft: 8.23 m.

DUBAI

Note: In addition to Dubai's participation in the federated naval force of the Un Arab Emirates (U.A.E.), Dubai also operates four patrol boats for customs enforcem purposes:

♦ **2 13FC-class GRP-hulled** Bldr: Baglietto, Varazze, Italy (In serv. 10-88)

D: 11 tons (fl) **S:** 43 kts **Dim:** 13.10 × 3.30 × 0.80
A: 2/7.62-mm mg (I × 2) **Crew:** 4 tot.
M: 2 M.A.N. D2848 LE diesels; 2 props; 1,020 bhp **Range:** 180/30

♦ **2 U.S. 65-ft Commercial Cruisers** Bldr: Swiftships, Morgan City, Louisiana (In serv. 12-12-77)

D: 24.9 tons (36.3 fl) **S:** 24 kts **Dim:** 19.77 (17.9 wl) × 5.56 × 1.9
M: 2 MTU 8V331 diesels; 2 props; 1,400 bhp
Range: 1,200/18 **Fuel:** 4.8 tons **Electric:** 20 kw **Crew:** 7 tot.

♦ **2 Modified Arun-class lifeboats** Bldr: Halmatic, Havant, U.K.

Naseem (In serv. 16-10-90) . . . . (In serv. 1991)

D: 37 tons (fl) **S:** 21 kts **Dim:** 18.30 (16.37 pp) × 5.57 × 1.45
Electron Equipt: Radar: 1/ . . . nav.
M: 2 Caterpillar 3412TA diesels; 2 props; 1,720 bhp
Range: 250/21 **Fuel:** 4,783 liters. **Crew:** 4 tot.

Remarks: GRP construction. Second unit ordered 16-10-90. Can also be employe patrol duties.

ECUADOR

Republic of Ecuador

Personnel (1991): 3,800 total (300 off., 3,500 men), 1,900 naval infantry

Naval Aviation: A small detachment with 5 Bell 206 JetRanger helicopters, 1 235, 4 Cessna T-37, 1 Cessna 320E, one Cessna 177 Citation, 3 Beech T-34C-1 trai and one Beech Super King Air light transport.

AVAL AVIATION *(continued)*

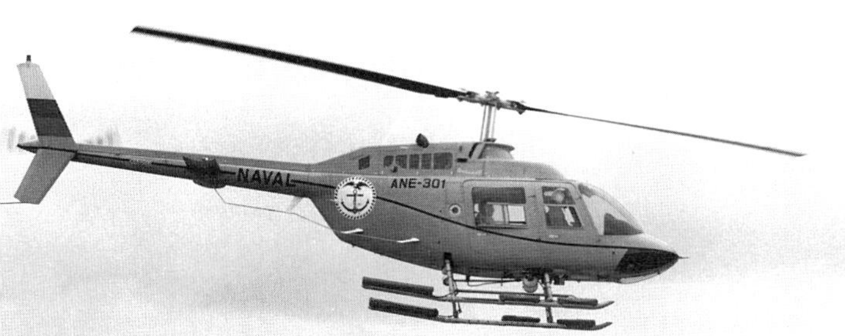

:uadorian Navy Bell 206 JetRanger helicopter — Ecuadorian Navy, 1990

›te: Pendant numbers on Ecuadorian ships are changed every few years; there has ›n an extensive series of changes since the last edition.

JBMARINES

2 German Type 209/1300 Bldr: Howaldtswerke, Kiel

	Laid down	L	In serv.
101 SHYRI	5-8-74	6-10-76	6-11-77
102 HUANCAVILCA	20-1-75	15-3-77	16-3-78

›rman Type 209/1300 — Ecuadorian Navy, 1990

pe 209/1300 submarine — Ecuadorian Navy, 1990

): 1,100 tons light/1,265 surf./1,395 sub.
;: 11 surf./21.4 kts sub. (1 hr.)
)im: 59.50 × 6.30 × 5.50
\: 8/533-mm TT fwd. (14 Seeal and Mk 37 wire-guided torpedoes)
:lectron Equipt:
Radar: 1 Thomson-CSF Calypso
Sonar: Krupp Atlas CSU-3 suite: A526 passive, CSU AN407 A9 active, DUUX-2 passive hull array
/I: 4 MTU 12V493 TY60 diesels, 4 Siemens 405-kw generators, electric drive: 1 Siemens motor; 1 prop; 5,000 shp
:ndurance: 45 days
Range: 8,400/8, 11,200/4 snorkel; 25/20, 445/4 sub.
'uel: 87 tons normal/106 max. **Crew:** 5 officers, 28 enlisted

marks: Ordered 1974. Hollandse Signaal M8 Mod. 24 torpedo f.c.s. S 101 refitted at builders, 1983, S 102 in 1984. The 257-ton battery installation includes four sets of cells and is rated at 11,500 amp./hr. Both based at Guayaquil.

IGATES

2 British "Exocet Leander" Batch 2B conversions

	Bldr	Laid down	L	In serv.
:-01 PRESIDENTE :LOY ALFARO ›x-*Penelope,* F 27, ex-*:oventry)*	Vickers-Armstrong, Barrow-in-Furness	14-3-61	17-8-62	31-10-63
:-02 MORAN 'ALVERDE (ex-*)anae,* F 47)	HM Dockyard, Devonport	16-12-64	31-10-65	7-9-67

Moran Valverde (FM-02)—departing the U.K. — Ben Sullivan, 7-91

Presidente Eloy Alfaro (FM-01) — Ben Sullivan, 5-91

D: 2,650 tons (3,200 fl) **S:** 28 kts
Dim: 113.38 (109.73 pp) × 12.50 × 4.80 (6.20 props)
A: 3/Sea Cat GWS.22B SAM syst. (IV × 3—2 directors)—2/40-mm AA (I × 2)—1/Bell 206 helicopter
Electron Equipt:
Radar: 1/Type 1006 nav., 1/Type 994 air/surf. search, 1/Type 965 early warning, 2/904 f.c.
Sonar: Type 184P (7.5 kHz hull-mounted), Type 162M (HF classification), Type 185 (underwater telephone)
EW: UA-8/9 passive, Type 668 or 669 jammer, 2/DLC chaff RL (VIII × 2), 2 DLD decoy RL (VI × 2), FH-12 HFD/F
M: 2 sets White-English Electric geared steam turbines; 2 props; 30,000 shp
Boilers: 2 Babcock & Wilcox 3-drum; 38.7 kg/cm^2, 450° C
Electric: 1,900 kw **Fuel:** 460 tons **Range:** approx. 4,000/12
Crew: 20 officers, 228 enlisted (in Royal Navy service)

Remarks: FM-01 paid off from Royal Navy service 31-3-91, was sold with FM-02 to Ecuador 25-4-91, and commissioned on 25-5-91. FM-2 transferred at the end of 7-91 on completion of Royal Navy service. Have twin rudders and one pair of fin stabilizers, set well aft of amidships.

FM-01 converted from Sea Wolf missile system trials ship, recommissioning 22-1-82. FM-02 completed conversion 9-80 from standard *Leander* configuration. A Sea Cat launcher and four Exocets replaced the twin 114-mm gun forward, the former single Sea Cat launcher atop the enlarged helicopter hangar was augmented by a second launcher, and the Limbo ASW mortar was replaced by two sets ASW TT. Have CAAIS combat data system. F 45 is, technically speaking, a "Batch 2A" conversion unit. Neither ship was equipped with Exocet missiles at time of transfer to Ecuador; the two triple STWS.1 ASW TT and three single 20-mm AA had also been removed.

Note: The two frigates above replaced the former U.S. Navy *Gearing* FRAM I-class destroyer *Presidente Eloy Alfaro* (DD 01, ex-*Holder,* DD 819), stricken 1991, and the *Charles Lawrence*-class former fast transport *Moran Valverde* (DD 03, ex-*26 de Julio,* ex-*Enright,* APD 66), stricken 1989.

CORVETTES

◆ **6 Italian modified Wadi M'ragh class**

	Bldr	Laid down	L	In serv.
CM 11 ESMERALDAS	CNR, Muggiano	27-9-79	5-10-80	7-8-82
CM 12 MANABI	CNR, Ancona	1-2-80	5-2-81	21-6-83
CM 13 LOS RIOS	CNR, Muggiano	1-9-79	28-2-81	1-10-83
CM 14 EL ORO	CNR, Ancona	1-3-80	5-2-81	10-12-83
CM 15 GALAPAGOS	CNR, Muggiano	20-10-80	5-7-81	26-5-84
CM 16 LOJA	CNR, Ancona	6-2-81	27-2-82	26-5-84

Manabi (CM 12) — Ecuadorian Navy, 1990

CORVETTES *(continued)*

Los Rios (CM 13) Ecuadorian Navy, 1990

Galapagos (CM 15) Ecuadorian Navy, 1990

D: 620 tons (700 fl) **S:** 37 kts **Dim:** 62.3 (57.8 pp) × 9.3 × 2.8
A: 6/MM 40 Exocet SSM (III × 2)—1 Albatros SAM system (IV × 1; Aspide missiles)—1/76-mm OTO Melara DP—2/40-mm Breda AA (II × 1)—6/324-mm ILAS-3 ASW TT (III × 2; A-244 torpedoes)—1/Bell 206 helicopter
Electron Equipt:
Radar: 1/Decca TM1226 nav., 1/RAN-10S air/surf. search, 1/Orion 10X f.c., 1/Orion 20X f.c.
Sonar: Thomson-Sintra Diodon MF hull-mounted
EW: Elettronica ELT-318 Newton intercept, 1/105-mm Breda SCLAR decoy RL (XX × 1)
M: 4 MTU 20V956 TB92 diesels; 4 props; 24,400 bhp (20,400 sust.)
Electric: 750 kw **Fuel:** 126 tons
Range: 1,200/31; 4,000/18 **Crew:** 51 tot.

Remarks: Ordered 1978 from CNR del Tirreno. More powerful engines than earlier Libyan units of class, helicopter platform added. Selenia IPN-10 data system, with NA 21 Mod. 0 radar f.c.s. and two CO3 directors for guns and SAM system. Have a helicopter platform, but no hangar. CM 14 badly damaged by fire, 18-4-85; repaired by 1987.

GUIDED-MISSILE PATROL BOATS

◆ **3 FPB 45 class** Bldr: Friedrich Lürssen Werft, Vegesack, Germany

	L	In serv.
LM 21 Quito	20-11-75	13-7-76
LM 22 Guayaquil	5-4-76	22-12-77
LM 24 Cuenca	12-76	17-7-77

FPB 45 class Ecuadorian Navy, 1990

D: 250 tons (265 fl) **S:** 35 kts **Dim:** 47.0 × 7.0 × 2.4
A: 4/MM 38 Exocet SSM (II × 2)—1/76-mm 62-cal. OTO Melara DP—2/35-mm 90-cal. Oerlikon AA (II × 1)
Electron Equipt: Radar: 1/Decca TM 1226 nav., 1/Thomson-CSF Triton air/surf. search, 1/Thomson-CFS Pollux f.c.
M: 4 MTU 16V538 diesels; 4 props; 14,000 bhp **Electric:** 330 kw
Fuel: 39 tons **Range:** 600/30 **Crew:** 34 tot.

Remarks: Carry 250 rounds of 76-mm and 1,100 rounds of 35-mm ammunition. Thomson-CSF Vega fire-control system. Also have electronic intercept array.

◆ **3 Manta class** Bldr: Friedrich Lürssen Werft, Vegesack, Germany

LM 25 Manta (In serv. 11-6-71)
LM 26 Tulcan (In serv. 2-4-71)
LM 27 Nueva Rocafuerte (ex-*Tena*) (In serv. 23-6-71)

Manta (LM 25) U.S. Navy, 19

D: 119 tons (134 fl) **S:** 35 kts **Dim:** 36.2 × 5.8 × 1.7
A: 4/Gabriel II SSM (I × 4)—2/30-mm AA Emerlec (II × 1)
Electron Equipt: Radar: 1/. . . nav., 1/Thomson-CSF Pollux f.c.
M: 3 Mercedes-Benz diesels; 3 props; 9,000 bhp **Fuel:** 21 tons
Range: 700/30; 1,500/15 **Crew:** 19 tot.

Remarks: Similar to Chilean *Guacolda* class, but faster. New guns added 19 Gabriel missiles and Thomson-CSF Vega fire-control system (without Triton sea radar) replaced 2/533-mm TT 1980–81. Replacements for these three units were be sought in 1987, with the Spanish "Piraña" class under consideration.

AMPHIBIOUS WARFARE SHIPS AND CRAFT

◆ **1 ex-U.S. LST 542-class tank landing ship** Bldr: Chicago Bridge & Iron

	Laid down	L	In serv.
T 55 Hualcopo (ex-*Summit County*, LST 1146)	15-2-45	23-5-45	1-6-45

D: 1,650 tons (4,080 fl) **S:** 11.6 kts **Dim:** 100.04 × 15.24 × 4.3
A: 8/40-mm (II × 2, I × 4)—2/20-mm AA (I × 2)
Electron Equipt: Radar: 1/. . . nav.
M: 2 G.M. 12-567A diesels; 2 props; 1,700 bhp **Electric:** 300 kw
Range: 7,200/10 **Crew:** 119 ship's company + 147 troops

Remarks: Bought 14-2-77. Used as transport. Has ice-reinforced waterline, an as of limited value in tropical waters. May be replaced by a new transport to be built ASTINAVE.

◆ **6 river launches** Bldr: ASTINAVE, Guayaquil

D: . . . tons **S:** 20 kts **Dim:** 6.70 × . . . × . . .
A: 1/7.62-mm mg **M:** 2 gasoline outboards; 200 bhp
Crew: 2 + 21 troops

Remarks: Ordered 1991. Kevlar plastic construction. May order additional u later. Same class operated by Coast Guard and Army.

◆ **6 "Sea Trucks"** Bldr: Rotork, U.K. (In serv. 1979)

LF 91 LF 92 LF 93 LF 94 LF 95 LF 96

D: 5 tons (9 fl) **S:** 26 kts (light) **Dim:** 12.65 × 3.20 × . . .
M: 2 Volvo AQD 40A diesels; 2 outdrive props; 240 bhp
Cargo: 4 tons

AUXILIARY SHIPS

◆ **1 oceanographic research ship** Bldr: Ishikawajima Harima, Toky

HI-91 Orion (ex-*Dometer*) (In serv. 21-10-81)

Orion (HI-91) Ecuadorian Navy, 1

UXILIARY SHIPS *(continued)*

D: 1,105 grt **S:** 12.6 kts
Dim: 70.17 (64.20 pp) × 10.70 × 3.6 (5.40 max.)
Electron Equipt: Radar: 2/Decca 1226 nav. **Electric:** 700 kw
M: 3 G.M. 16V92 TI diesels, electric drive (2 motors); 1 prop; 950 shp
Range: 6,000/12 **Crew:** 6 officers, 25 enlisted, 19 scientists

marks: *Dometer* was delivery name, changed to *Orion* on arrival for commissioning. Equipped to conduct physical and biological oceanography, geophysical re-rch, and hydrographic surveys.

1 coastal tanker Bldr: ASTINAVE, Guayaquil

66 TAURUS (In serv. 1985)

D: approx. 1,800 tons (fl) **S:** 11 kts **Dim:** 53.1 × 11.0 × 4.4
A: . . . . . . **M:** 2 G.M. 6-71 diesels; 1 prop; 750 bhp

marks: 1,110 grt/1,175 dwt. Transferred to naval service in 1987.

1 ex-U.S. water tanker Bldr: Leatham D. Smith, Sturgeon Bay, Wisconsin

63 ATAHUALPA (ex-YW 131) (In serv. 17-9-45)

D: 440 tons (1,390 fl) **S:** 7 kts **Dim:** 53.1 × 9.8 × 4.6
M: 1 G.M. diesel; 1 prop; 640 bhp **Fuel:** 25 tons **Crew:** 20 tot.

marks: Transferred 2-5-63; purchased 1-12-77. Stricken 1988 but restored to ser-e in 1990. Cargo: 930 tons water.

1 ex-British cargo ship Bldr: Cleland SB, Wallsend

	Laid down	L	In serv.
727 CALICUCHIMA (ex-*Throsk*, A 379)	25-8-76	31-3-77	20-9-77

D: 2,193 tons (fl) **S:** 14 kts
Dim: 70.57 (64.31 pp) × 11.90 × 4.57
Electron Equipt: Radar: 1/Decca Type 1006 nav.
M: 2 Mirrlees-Blackstone diesels; 1 prop; 3,000 bhp
Range: 1,500/14; 5,000/10 **Crew:** 32 tot.

marks: 1,150-dwt former ammunition transport purchased 11-91. Can carry 760 s in two holds totaling 750 m³, plus 25 tons on deck; has two cranes. Formerly erated by Royal Corps of Transport. Left for Ecuador 2-92.

2 U.S. Abnaki*- and Achomawi-class fleet tugs Bldr: Charleston SB & DD, Charleston, S.C.

	Laid down	L	In serv.
711 CAYAMBE* (ex-*Los Rios*, ex-*Cusabo*, ATF 155)	18-9-44	26-2-45	19-5-45
710 CHIMBORAZO (ex-*Chowanoc*, ATF 100)	24-4-43	20-8-43	21-2-44

imborazo (R 710)—with old number Ecuadorian Navy

D: 1,235 tons (1,675 fl) **S:** 16.5 kts
Dim: 62.48 (59.44 wl) × 11.73 × 4.67
A: 1/76.2-mm Mk 26 DP—2/40-mm Mk 3 AA (I × 2)—2/20-mm AA (I × 2)
Electron Equipt: Radar: 1/Decca 916 nav.
M: 4 G.M. 12-278A diesels, electric drive; 1 prop; 3,000 shp
Electric: 400 kw **Fuel:** 376 tons
Range: 16,000/8; 7,000/15 **Crew:** 85 tot.

marks: R 710: **A:** 2/12.7-mm mg; **M:** 4 Busch-Sulzer B5-539 diesels; pipe ex-ust *vice* stack. *Cayambe* leased 2-11-60, purchased 30-8-78. *Chimborazo* purchased 0-77.

1 sail-training barque Bldr: Ast. Celaya , Bilbao, Spain

	L	In serv.
51 GUAYAS	23-9-76	23-7-77

Guayas (BE 51) Ecuadorian Navy, 1990

D: 934 grt **S:** 10.5 kts **Dim:** 76.2 × 10.6 × 4.2
M: 1 G.M. 12V149 diesel; 1 prop; 700 bhp **Crew:** 180 berths

SERVICE CRAFT

♦ **1 ex-British water lighter** Bldr: Drypool, Hull

R . . . QUISQUIS (ex-*Waterside*, Y 20) (In serv. 1968)

D: 344 tons (fl) **S:** 11 kts
Dim: 40.02 (37.50 pp) × 7.50 × 2.44
M: 1 Lister-Blackstone ERS-8MGR diesel; 1 prop; 600 bhp
Electric: 155 kw **Range:** 1,500/11 **Crew:** 11 tot.

Remarks: Purchased 11-91; delivered 2-92.
Cargo: 150 tons water.

♦ **1 inshore oceanographic research craft** Bldr: Halter Marine, New Orleans

LH-92 RIGEL (In serv. 1975)

D: 50 tons **S:** 10 kts **Dim:** 19.7 × 5.2 × 1.1
M: 2 diesels; . . . bhp **Crew:** 10 tot.

♦ **5 Tungurahua-class tugs** Bldr: . . . . . .

R 722 TUNGURAHUA R 724 SIRIUS R 726 QUILOTOA
R 723 ANTIZANA R 725 ALTAR

D: 490 grt **S:** 8 kts **Dim:** 30.6 × . . . × 2.5
M: . . . diesels; 1 prop; . . . bhp

♦ **1 medium harbor tug** (In serv. 1952; acquired 1952)

R 720 SANGAY (ex-*Losa*)

D: 295 tons (390 fl) **S:** 12 kts **Dim:** 32.6 × 7.9 × 4.25
M: 1 Fairbanks-Morse diesel; 1 prop; . . . bhp

♦ **1 former U.S. Army tug** Bldr: Equitable Bldg., New Orleans (In serv. 1945; acquired 1947)

R 721 COTOPAXI (ex-*R. T. Ellis*)

D: 150 tons **S:** 9 kts **Dim:** 25.0 × 6.62 × 2.9
M: diesel; 1 prop; 650 bhp

♦ **1 ex-U.S. YR 24-class repair barge** Bldr: New York Navy Yard

BT 84 PUTAMAYO (ex-YR 34) (In serv. 1944)

D: 520 tons (770 fl) **Dim:** 45.7 × 10.4 × 1.8 **Electric:** 330 kw

Remarks: Transferred 7-62; purchased 1-12-77. Supports the floating dry dock.

♦ **1 ex-U.S. dry dock companion craft** (In serv. 1944)

DF 82 NAPO (ex-YFND 20)

D: 590 tons (fl) **Dim:** 33.53 × 9.75 × . . .

Remarks: Leased 2-11-61 to support *Amazonas* and purchased 1988. Rectangular barge hull.

♦ **1 ex-U.S. auxiliary repair dock** (In serv. 1944)

DF 81 AMAZONAS (ex-ARD 17)

Capacity: 3,500 tons **Dim:** 149.9 × 24.7 × 1.7 (light)

Remarks: Transferred 7-1-61. Pointed bow. Length over blocks: 118.6 m; 18.0-m clear width.

COAST GUARD
Established 1980

Personnel (1991): 13 officers, 257 enlisted men

Note: It is planned to acquire additional small patrol craft from the United States, including two 40-ft (12.19-m) riverine patrol craft funded under U.S. Fiscal Year 1987 and 1989 but not ordered as of 6-91.

ECUADOR *(continued)*
COAST GUARD *(continued)*

♦ **0 (+2) U.S. Espada-class patrol boats** Bldr: Equitable Builders, New Orleans

LGC 31 5 de Agosto (In serv. 5-91) LGC 32 27 de Febrero (In serv. 11-91)

D: 120 tons (fl) **S:** 27 kts **Dim:** 34.14 (31.62 pp) × 6.86 × 2.14
A: 1/40-mm Mk 3 AA—2/12.7-mm mg(I × 2)
Electron Equipt: Radar: 1/. . . nav.
M: 2 G.M. 16V-149 TI diesels (1,280 bhp each), 1 G.M. 16V92 TAB diesel (860 bhp); 3 props; 3,420 bhp
Range: 1,500/13 **Crew:** 5 officers, 14 enlisted

Remarks: Built under U.S. Foreign Military Sales program for Galapagos Islands service. Carry a Zodiac rigid inflatable inspection boat. Photo in addenda.

♦ **2 U.S. PGM 71-class patrol boats** Bldr: Peterson Bldrs, Sturgeon Bay, Wisconsin (In serv. 30-11-65)

LGC 31 25 de Julio (ex-*Quito*)
LGC 32 24 de Mayo (ex-*Guayaquil*)

24 de Mayo (LGC 32) Ecuadorian Navy, 1990

D: 130 tons (147 fl) **S:** 17 kts **Dim:** 30.81 (30.20 pp) × 6.45 × 2.3
A: 1/40-mm AA—4/20-mm AA (II × 2)—1/12.7-mm mg (I × 2)
Electron Equipt: Radar: 1/. . . nav.
M: 2 Mercedes-Benz MB 820D diesels; 2 props; 2,200 bhp (1,900 sust.)
Electric: 30 kw **Fuel:** 16 tons **Range:** 1,000/12 **Crew:** 15 tot.

Remarks: Built as U.S. PGM 75 and PGM 76 for foreign aid. Transferred from Ecuadorian Navy to Coast Guard in 1980 and discarded 1983. Refitted 1988–89 for further service.

♦ **6 Puyango-class patrol craft** Bldr: First two: Halter Marine, New Orleans; others: ASTINAVE, Guayaquil

	In serv.		In serv.
LGC 40 Rio Puyango	6-86	LGC 43 Rio Chone	11-3-88
LGC 41 Rio Matege	6-86	LGC 44 Rio Daule	17-6-88
LGC 42 Rio Zarumilla	11-3-88	LGC 45 Rio Babhoyo	17-6-88

"Puyango" class Halter, 1987

D: 17 tons (fl) **S:** 26 kts **Dim:** 13.41 (12.39 pp) × 4.12 × 0.76
A: 1/12.7-mm mg—1/7.62-mm mg
Electron Equipt: Radar: 1/Furuno 2400 nav. **Range:** 500/18
M: 2 G.M. 8V71 TI diesels; 2 props; 850 bhp **Fuel:** 1.6 tons
Electric: 12 kw **Crew:** 1 officer, 4 enlisted

Remarks: First two, purchased for service in the Galapagos Islands, were in service by 1986. Second pair built in U.S., followed by four built in Ecuador from U.S.-supplied kits. Have a 250-gal./min. fire monitor to starboard and two fire pumps to port. Aluminum construction.

♦ **6 river patrol craft** Bldr: ASTINAVE, Guayaquil (In serv. 1991)

D: . . . tons **S:** 20 kts **Dim:** 6.70 × . . . × . . .
A: 1/7.62-mm mg **M:** 2 gasoline outboards; 200 bhp
Crew: 2 + 21 troops

Remarks: Ordered 1991. Kevlar plastic construction. May order additional uni[ts] later. Same class operated by Naval Infantry and Army.

♦ **14 U.S. Baycraft 40-ft. patrol craft** (In serv. 1979–80)

Remarks: Glass-reinforced plastic hulls; modified sport-fishing boat design. In add[i]tion, six 22-ft. Boston Whaler patrol craft were delivered 12-90.

ECUADORIAN ARMY

♦ **0(+40) river patrol craft** Bldr: ASTINAVE, Guayaquil

D: . . . tons **S:** 20 kts **Dim:** 6.70 × . . . × . . .
A: 1/7.62-mm mg **M:** 2 gasoline outboards; 200 bhp
Crew: 2 + 21 troops

Remarks: Ordered 1991. Kevlar plastic construction. May order additional un[its] later. Same class operated by Coast Guard and Naval Infantry.

EGYPT

Arab Republic of Egypt

Personnel (1991): Approx. 19,500 total, plus 15,000 reserves

Naval Aviation: The navy operates 18 Westland Sea King Mk 47 helicopters and Aerospatiale SA 342 L Gazelle helicopters. The Sea Kings are to be fitted to gui[de] Otomat antiship missiles, and the Gazelles can carry AS.12 wire-guided missiles. T[he] air force has six Beech 1900C light coastal surveillance aircraft with Litton radar.

Coast Defenses: The navy is responsible for coastal defenses. Fifty coast-defen[se] truck-mounted versions of the Otomat missile were purchased 1983. Targeting p[er]formed by land-based Sea King helicopters. Some Soviet Samlet coast-defense missi[les] remain in service also.

SUBMARINES

Note: A contract to acquire two former Royal Navy submarines, *Walrus* and *Ober[on]* was not consummated and is now unlikely to be signed. Egypt continues to seek m[ore] modern submarines and hopes to acquire two German Type 209, possibly to be built [in] the United States.

♦ **4 Chinese Romeo class**

831 842 852 858

Chinese-built Egyptian Romeo (old number) Leo Van Ginderen, 2-

Egyptian Navy Romeo in dry dock U.S. Navy, 1[9]

BMARINES *(continued)*

D: 1,320/1,712 tons **S:** 15.2/13 kts **Dim:** 77.60 × 6.70 × 4.95
A: 8/533-mm TT (6 fwd, 2 aft)—14 torpedoes or 28 mines
Electron Equipt:
Radar: 1/Snoop Plate nav./surf. search—EW: . . .
Sonar: Tamir-5L active, Feniks passive
M: diesel-electric, 2 Type 37D diesels, 2,000 bhp each; 2 props; 2,700 shp—2/50-shp creep motors
Range: 350/4 sub.; 14,000/9 surf.; 7,000/5 (snorkel)
Endurance: 60 days **Crew:** 8 officers, 43 enlisted

marks: Six Soviet-built units were transferred—5 in 1966, 1 in 1969—and began tting with European equipment in 1981. They had been constructed between 1957 1960 at Baltic Shipyard, Leningrad; two were discarded by the mid-1980s, and others during 1989. Two units, launched in 1980, were delivered from China on 3-83; the second Chinese pair were delivered 3-1-84 and commissioned 21-5-84. ve 224 battery cells, producing 6,000 amp/hr. Operating depth is 270 m (300 max.). he four Chinese-built units were to be refitted in Egypt with assistance from oma Boatyard, U.S., and China between 10-88 and 10-93, but delays were encoun- ed, and the U.S. Congress granted permission only in late 7-89; the effort was ther slowed by the bankruptcy of the U.S. contractor, Tacoma Boat, in 11-90. gram reinstated late 1991, with completion by 1995 planned. Will receive U.S. -37F wire-guided torpedo and Sub-Harpoon missile capability and Singer Libra- be fire-control system.

STROYER

1 U.K. Z-class Bldr: William Denny & Bros., Dumbarton, Scotland

	Laid down	L	In serv.
. El Fateh (ex-*Zenith*, ex-*Wessex*)	19-5-42	5-6-44	22-12-44

Fateh (921) French Navy, 7-88

D: 1,730 tons (2,575 fl) **S:** 31 kts (new)
Dim: 110.6 × 10.9 × 4.9 (5.2 props)
A: 4/114-mm 45-cal. Mk 6 DP (I × 4)—6/40-mm AA (II × 1; I × 4)—4/533-mm TT (IV × 1)
Electron Equipt:
Radar: 1/Decca 916 nav., 1/Marconi SNW-1 air/surf. search, 1/Type 275 f.c.
Sonar: none—EW: none
IFF: 1/Square Head interrogator, 1/High Pole A transponder
M: 2 sets Parsons geared steam turbines; 2 props; 40,000 shp
Boilers: 2 Admiralty 3-drum
Range: 2,800/20 **Crew:** 186 crew + . . . cadets

marks: Employed on midshipman training duties. Thoroughly obsolescent. Pur- ed from U.K. in 1955, refitted in U.K., completing 7-56; modernized with new earch radar 1964. Uses single Fly 4 director with World War II-era Type 275 radar ntrol 114-mm guns. Sonar and ASW ordnance removed.

GATES

2 Chinese Jianghu class Bldr: Jiangnan SY, Shanghai

Najim al Zafir (In serv. 27-10-84)
El Nasser (In serv. 16-4-85)

im al Zafir (951) Leo Van Ginderen, 9-91

El Nasser (956) French Navy, 1990

D: 1,586 tons (1,900 fl) **S:** 25.5 kts
Dim: 103.20 × 10.20 × 3.05 (hull)
A: 4/HY-2 SSM (II × 2)—4/57-mm DP (II × 2)—12/37-mm V-47M AA (II × 6)—4/RBU-1200 ASW RL (V × 4)—4/BMB-2 d.c. mortars—2/d.c. racks—mines
Electron Equipt:
Radar: 1/Decca . . . nav. , 1/Type 756 nav. , 1/Eye Shield air/surf. search, 1/Square Tie missile target designation
Sonar: MF, hull-mounted—EW: Elettronica Beta intercept
IFF: 2/Square Head interrogators, 1/High Pole A transponder
M: 2 SEMT-Pielstick 12 PA 6 diesels; 2 props; 16,000 bhp
Electric: 1,320 kw **Range:** 1,750/25; 4,000/15
Endurance: 15 days **Crew:** 195 tot.

Remarks: Ordered 1982. 951 completed 7-84, arriving in Egypt in 10-84. 952 completed 12-84, arriving in Egypt 3-85. Differ from Chinese Navy units in having twin 57-mm guns vice single or twin 100-mm mounts fore and aft, and in having an enclosed housing for the optical rangefinder atop the bridge. There is no radar fire-control equipment for the eight gun mounts, all of which are locally controlled via on-mount sights. Elettronica EW equipment added after delivery, also a second navigational radar. 951 visited West Germany in 6-88, in part to determine modernization possibilities, but to date no contracts have been placed to modernize the vessels to make them capable of combat under modern conditions.

♦ **2 Spanish Descubierta class** Bldr: Bazán, Cartagena

	Laid down	L	In serv.
941 El Suez (ex-*Centinela*)	31-10-78	6-10-79	21-5-84
946 El Aboukir (ex-*Serviola*)	28-2-79	20-12-79	27-10-84

El Aboukir (946) Peter Voss, 7-87

El Suez (941) Carlo Martinelli, 10-89

D: 1,363 tons (1,575 fl) **S:** 26 kts
Dim: 88.88 (85.80 pp) × 10.40 × 3.70
A: 8/Harpoon SSM (IV × 2)—1/Mk 29 SAM launcher (VIII; 24 NATO Sea Sparrow missiles)—1/76-mm OTO Melara Compact—2/40-mm AA (I × 2)—1/375-mm Bofors ASW RL (II × 1)—6/324-mm Mk 32 ASW TT (III × 2, Stingray torpedoes)
Electron Equipt:
Radar: 1/H.S.A. ZW-06/Z nav./surf. search, 1/H.S.A. DA-05/2 air/surf. search, 1/H.S.A. WM-25 f.c.
Sonar: Raytheon DE 1167LF hull-mounted and VDS
EW: Elettronica Beta intercept
M: 4 MTU-Bazán 16 MA656 TB91 diesels; 2 CP props; 18,000 bhp
Electric: 1,810 kw **Fuel:** 250 tons **Range:** 6,000/18
Crew: 10 officers, 106 enlisted (146 accom.)

FRIGATES *(continued)*

Remarks: Originally ordered 25-5-76 for the Spanish Navy, but sold to Egypt 1982. 946 completed 28-2-84 and 941 on 6-9-84. Have fin stabilizers, plus U.S. "Prairie/Masker" bubbler system to reduce sound radiation below the waterline. Carry 600 rds. 76-mm ammunition. H.S.A. SEWACO weapons-control system. The U.S. supplied the Harpoon missiles in 1984.

Note: The British *Black Swan*-class frigate *Tariq* (ex-*Malek Farouk,* ex-HMS *Whimbrel*) was retired at the end of 1989 but is still afloat at Alexandria, along with the hulk of the British "Hunt-1" escort destroyer *Port Said* (ex-*Mohammed Ali el Kebit,* ex-HMS *Cottesmore*).

GUIDED-MISSILE PATROL BOATS

Note: Still planned is the acquisition of a further six Western-designed guided-missile patrol boats. Funds to order these ships are still lacking, however.

◆ **6 Chinese Houku class** Bldr: . . . (In serv. 27-10-84)

611 612 613 614 615 616

Houku 615 Alexander Sheldon-Duplaix, 4-88

D: 68 tons, 73.88 normal (79.19 fl) **S:** 37 kts
Dim: 27.0 × 6.50 × 1.80 (1.295 hull)
A: 2/HY-2 SSM (I × 2)—2/25-mm AA (II × 1)
Electron Equipt: Radar: 1/Square Tie search/target desig.
M: 4 M50F-4 diesels; 4 props; 4,800 bhp **Electric:** 65 kw
Endurance: 5 days **Range:** 500/24 **Crew:** 16 tot.

Remarks: Delivered 9-84 and commissioned together the following month. Steel construction. Two reported non-operational by 1989. Former hull numbers 401–406.

◆ **6 Ramadan class** Bldr: Vosper Thornycroft, Portchester, U.K.

	Laid down	L	In serv.
670 Ramadan	22-9-78	6-9-79	20-7-81
672 Khyber	23-2-79	31-1-80	15-9-81
674 El Kadesseya	23-4-79	19-2-80	6-4-82
676 El Yarmouk	15-5-79	12-6-80	18-5-82
678 Badr	29-9-79	17-6-81	17-6-82
680 Hettein	29-2-80	25-11-80	28-10-82

El Yarmouk (676) and El Kadesseya (674) 1990

D: 262 tons (312 fl) **S:** 35 kts **Dim:** 52.0 (48.0 pp) × 7.6 × 2.0 (hull)
A: 4/Otomat SSM (II × 2)—1/76-mm OTO Melara Compact DP—2/40-mm Breda AA (II × 1)
Electron Equipt:
Radar: Marconi: 1/S810 nav., 1/S820 air/surf. search, 2/ST802 f.c.
EW: Decca-Racal Cutlass , Decca-Racal Cygnus jammer, MEL Protean chaff RL (VI × 2)
M: 4 MTU 20V538 TB91 diesels; 4 props; 16,000 bhp **Fuel:** 43 tons
Electric: 420 kw **Range:** 2,000/15 **Crew:** 4 officers, 27 enlisted

Remarks: Ordered 4-9-77. Have Marconi Sapphire fire-control system with two ST 802 radar/t.v. directors, two Lawrence Scott optical directors. Ferranti CAAIS automated data system. First pair arrived Egypt 13-11-81, second 23-7-82, third in 12-82.

◆ **4 6 October class** Bldr: Egypt/Vosper Thornycroft (In serv. 1980–81)

785 787 789 791

6 October class (791)—Otomat racks empty Leo Van Ginderen, 7-

D: 71 tons (82 fl) **S:** 40 kts **Dim:** 25.3 × 6.0 × 1.8
A: 2/Otomat SSM—4/30-mm AA Type A32 (II × 2)
Electron Equipt:
Radar: Marconi: 1/S810 nav./surf. search, 1/ST802 f.c.
EW: MEL Matilda passive, MEL Protean chaff RL (VI × 2)
M: 4 CRM 18V-12D/55 YE diesels; 4 props; 5,400 bhp
Range: 400/30 **Crew:** 20 tot.

Remarks: Wooden hulls, built at Alexandria DY, Egypt, 1969–75. Completed Vosper Thornycroft at Portchester, Portsmouth, 1979–81, with Italian-French missi and British guns; diesels are Italian. Basic design is that of the Soviet Komar class. Marconi Sapphire radar/t.v. fire-control system. 791 was lost overboard during de ery 16-12-80, salvaged, returned to U.K. 30-6-81, and completed repairs 13-8-82. ters 781 and 783 retired 1989.

◆ **3 ex-Soviet Osa-I class**

633 641 643

Egyptian Osa-I 1

D: 175 tons (209 fl) **S:** 35 kts **Dim:** 38.6 × 7.6 × 1.8
A: 4/SS-N-2A Styx SSM (I × 4)—1/SA-7 Grail position— 4/30-mm AAAK-230 (II × 2)—2/12.7-mm mg (I × 2)
Electron Equipt:
Radar: 1/Decca 916 nav., 1/Square Tie surf. search/target desig., 1/Drum Tilt gun f.c.
EW: MEL Matilda intercept/warning
IFF: 2/Square Head interrogators, 1/High Pole A transponder
M: 3 M503A diesels; 3 props; 12,000 bhp **Range:** 500/34; 750/25
Crew: 30 tot.

Remarks: Survivors of 13 transferred 1966–68. All carry shoulder-launched S Grail (SA-N-5) SAMs, launched from a tub amidships. Four others, 631, 635, 637, 639, were inoperable by end-1989.

PATROL BOATS

◆ **8 Chinese Hainan class**

	In serv.		In serv.
430 Al Nour	23-10-83	442 Al Gatar	21-5-84
433 Al Hadi	23-10-83	445 Al Saddam	6-84
436 Al Hakim	21-5-84	448 Al Salam	6-84
439 Al Wakil	21-5-84	451 Al Rafia	6-84

ATROL BOATS *(continued)*

Nour (430) French Navy, 5-89

D: 375 tons normal (400 fl) **S:** 30.5 kts
Dim: 58.77 × 7.20 × 2.20 (hull)
A: 4/57-mm AA (II × 2)—4/23-mm AA (II × 2)—4/RBU-1200 ASW RL (V × 4)—2/BMB-2 d.c. mortars—2/d.c. racks—mines
Electron Equipt:
Radar: 1/Pot Head
Sonar: Tamir-11 HF (25-31 kHz)
M: 4 diesels; 4 props; 8,800 bhp **Crew:** 70 tot. **Range:** 2,000/14

marks: First pair arrived 10-83, next three in 2-84, and final trio in 6-84. All were livered aboard the Chinese float-on cargo ship *Shamekou.* Four have received 6 4-mm ASW TT (III × 2) and Stingray torpedoes, along with a U.S. Librascope e-control system and a new sonar. Reportedly, the original 25-mm AA guns were placed with Egyptian-made 23-mm weapons on the same 2M-8 mountings. May now rry a commercial navigational radar in addition to the not very effective Pot Head.

4 Chinese Shanghai-II class

3 795 797 799

yptian Navy Shanghai-II 799 1984

D: 122.5 tons normal (134.8 fl) **S:** 28.5 kts
Dim: 38.78 × 5.41 × 1.55
A: 4/37-mm AA (II × 2)—4/23-mm AA (II × 2)
Electron Equipt: Radar: 1/Pot Head surf. search
M: 2 M50F-4, 1,200-bhp diesels; 2/12D6, 910-bhp diesels; 4 props; 4,220 bhp
Electric: 39 kw **Range:** 750/16.5 **Crew:** 36 tot.
Endurance: 7 days

marks: Transferred 1984 with transfer numbers E 601–604. Do not have depth arges, as on Chinese Navy examples. The original 25-mm guns have reportedly been changed for Egyptian-made 23-mm weapons on the same 2M-8 mountings.

RPEDO BOATS

6 Soviet Shershen class

1 753 755 757 759 761

ershen 757—with no 122-mm rocket launchers or torpedoes. U.S. Navy, 1989

D: 145 tons (170 fl) **S:** 45 kts **Dim:** 34.0 × 6.8 × 1.5
Crew: 22 tot.
A: 4/30-mm AA (II × 2)—1/SA-7 Grail SAM position—4/533-mm TT (I × 4) or none
Electron Equipt: 1/Pot Drum surf. search, 1/Drum Tilt f.c.
M: 3 M503A diesels; 3 props; 12,000 bhp **Range:** 460/42; 850/30

Remarks: Survivors of seven transferred 1967–68. Three were armed with two 20-tubed 122-mm artillery rocket launchers instead of torpedoes; the launchers have subsequently been removed. Carry shoulder-launched SA-7 Grail (SA-N-5) missiles. Former hull numbers 310, 321, 332, 343, 354, and 365.

MINE WARFARE SHIPS

◆ **4 ex-Soviet Yurka-class minesweepers**

530 Aswan 533 Giza 536 Qena 539 Sohag

Aswan (530) Carlo Martinelli, 10-89

D: 400 tons (460 fl) **S:** 16 kts **Dim:** 52.0 × 9.3 × 2.0
Crew: 50 tot.
A: 4/30-mm AK-230 AA (II × 2)—10 mines
Electron Equipt: Radar: 1/Don-2 nav.—Sonar: HF, hull-mounted
M: 2 diesels; 2 props; 4,000 bhp **Range:** 2,000/14; 3,200/10

Remarks: Delivered new 1969. Do not have Drum Tilt radar fire-control system. Low-magnetic alloy steel construction. May be modernized with new MTU diesels, new sonar, etc. It is hoped to equip these obsolescent ships with a towed side-scan sonar and remotely operated minehunting vehicles.

◆ **3 Soviet T-43-class minesweepers**

516 Assiout 522 Bahaira 533 Gharbia

Assiout (516) Wilhelm Donko, 10-87

D: 569 tons (fl) **S:** 14 kts **Dim:** 58.0 × 8.6 × 2.3
A: 4/37-mm V-47M AA (II × 2)—8/12.7-mm mg (II × 4)—2/BMB-1 d.c. mortars—mines
Electron Equipt:
Radar: 1/Decca . . . nav.—Sonar: Tamir-11
IFF: 1/Square Head interrogator, 1/High Pole A transponder
M: 2 Type 9D diesels; 2 props; 2,200 bhp **Electric:** 550 kw
Range: 3,200/10 **Fuel:** 70 tons **Crew:** 65 tot.

Remarks: Survivors from a group delivered in the early 1970s; all early 1950s-built "short-hull" version. Reportedly, to be modernized with new engines, Gayrobot Pluto remote-controlled submersibles, and towed sidescan sonars.

◆ **2 Soviet T-301-class minesweepers** (In serv. circa 1950)

El Fayoud El Manufieh

D: 145.8 tons (160 fl) **S:** 12.5 kts **Dim:** 38.0 × 5.1 × 1.6
A: 2/45-mm AA (I × 2)—2/12.7-mm mg (I × 2)
M: 3 6-cyl. diesels; 3 props; 1,440 bhp
Range: 2,500/8 **Fuel:** 20 tons **Crew:** 30 tot.

Remarks: Transferred 1962–63. No radars. Steel-hulled craft with no compound curves to the hull plating. Used in harbor service only.

◆ **0 (+6) U.S. inshore minesweepers** Bldr: Swiftships, Inc., Morgan City, Louisiana (In serv. 1992)

D: 178 tons (fl) **S:** 12.4 kts **Dim:** 33.53 (31.09 pp) × 8.23 × 1.53
A: . . .
Electron Equipt:
Radar: 1/ . . . nav.
Sonar: Thomson-Sintra TSM 7022
M: 2 MTU 12V183 TC82diesels; 2 props; 1,034 bhp—1 White Gill 300-shp thruster (4 kts)
Range: . . ./. . . **Crew:** 17 total

MINE WARFARE SHIPS *(continued)*

Remarks: Ordered 12-90. GRP construction. Also for use as route survey craft in peacetime. Have Thomson-Sintra Ibis V mine-countermeasures control system.

♦ **2 U.S. route survey craft** Bldr: Swiftships, Inc., Morgan City, Louisiana (In serv. 1991)

D: . . . tons (fl) **S:** . . . kts **Dim:** 26.82 × . . . × . . .
M: . . . **Crew:** . . .

Remarks: Ordered 11-90. GRP construction. Intended to survey harbor and coastal navigational channels during peacetime to chart bottom obstructions.

AMPHIBIOUS WARFARE SHIPS

♦ **3 Soviet Polnocny A-class medium landing ships** Bldr: Stocznia, Pólnocna, Gdańsk, Poland

301 303 305

Egyptian Polnocny-A 303 George R. Schneider, Jr., 5-90

Egyptian Polnocny-A 305 Carlo Martinelli, 10-89

D: 770 tons (fl) **S:** 19 kts **Dim:** 73.0 × 8.6 × 2.0
A: 2/30-mm AK-230 AA (II × 1)—2/140-mm artillery RL (XVIII × 2)
Electron Equipt: Radar: 1/Don-2 nav., 1/Drum Tilt gun f.c.
M: 2 Type 40D diesels; 2 props; 4,000 bhp
Range: 900/18; 1,500/14 **Crew:** 40 tot.

Remarks: Transferred 1974. Cargo: 3 tanks or 180 tons.

♦ **9 ex-Soviet Vydra-class LCUs**

330 332 334 336 338 340 342 344 346

Egyptian Vydra 346 George R. Schneider, Jr., 5-90

D: 425 tons (600 fl) **S:** 11 kts **Dim:** 54.9 × 7.6 × 2.0
A: 4/40-mm AA (II × 2)
Electron Equipt: Radar: 1/Decca . . . nav.
M: 2 Type 3D12 diesels; 2 props; 600 bhp
Range: 2,700/10 **Crew:** 20, plus 200 troops

Remarks: Transferred 1967–69. Some had 37-mm AA vice 40-mm; guns removed altogether in others. Cargo: 200 tons.

♦ **2 ex-Soviet SMB-I-class LCUs**

374 376

D: 180 tons (335 fl) **S:** 10 kts **Dim:** 48.2 × 6.5 × 2.0
A: none **Electron Equipt:** Radar: none
M: 2 Type 3D12 diesels; 2 props; 600 bhp
Range: 400/8 **Crew:** 16 tot.

Remarks: Transferred 1965. Cargo: 180 tons. Two others discarded.

♦ **8 U.S. "Seafox"-class swimmer delivery craft** Bldr: Uniflite, Bellingham, Wash. (In serv. 1982–83)

D: 11.3 tons (fl) **S:** 30+kts **Dim:** 11.0 × 3.0 × 0.84
A: small arms **Electron Equipt:** Radar: 1/LN-66
M: 2 G.M. 6V92 TA diesels; 2 props; 900 bhp **Crew:** 3 tot.

Remarks: Ordered 1982. Glass-reinforced plastic construction.

AUXILIARY SHIPS AND CRAFT

♦ **6 Soviet Toplivo-2-class coastal tankers** Bldr: Alexandria SY, Egypt

214 216 218 etc.

D: 466 tons (1,180 fl) **S:** 10 kts
Dim: 54.26 (49.40 pp) × 9.40 × 3.40 max.
Electron Equipt: Radar: 1/Spin Trough nav.
M: 1 Russkiy Dizel 6 DR 30/50-5-2 diesel; 1 prop; 600 bhp
Electric: 250 kw **Fuel:** 19 tons **Range:** 1,500/10 **Crew:** 16 tot.

Remarks: 308 grt/508 dwt. Part of a series of 26 ordered in Egypt for the U.S.S prior to that country's expulsion. Cargo: 606 m³ (500 tons diesel oil); some are used water tankers.

♦ **4 Soviet Okhtenskiy-class tugs** Bldr: Okhtenskiy SY, Leningrad

105 Al Agami 109 Al Dikhila 107 Antar
111 Al Iskandarani

D: 700 tons (950 fl) **S:** 13.3 kts **Dim:** 47.3 × 10.3 × 5.5
Electron Equipt: Radar: 1/Don-2 or Spin Trough nav.
M: 2 diesels, electric drive; 1 prop; 1,500 shp
Range: 7,800/7 **Crew:** 40 tot.

Remarks: Two transferred complete in 1966; two assembled in Egypt.

Note: The British "River"-class former frigate *Rachid* (936, ex-*Spey*), used for ma years as a submarine support vessel, was discarded 1990.

♦ **2 Soviet Nyryat-I-class diving tenders** (Transferred 1964)

D: 120 tons (fl) **S:** 12 kts **Dim:** 29.0 × 5.0 × 1.7
Electron Equipt: Radar: 1/Spin Trough nav.
M: 1 diesel; 1 prop; 450 bhp **Range:** 1,600/10 **Crew:** 15 tot.

♦ **2 Soviet Poluchat-I-class torpedo retrievers**

D: 80 tons (90 fl) **S:** 18 kts **Dim:** 29.6 × 5.8 × 1.5 **Crew:** 20 tot.
Electron Equipt: Radar: 1/Spin Trough nav.
M: 2 M50 diesels; 2 props; 2,400 bhp **Range:** 450/17; 900/10

♦ **2 Soviet PO-2-class general-purpose launches**

D: 50 tons (fl) **S:** 9 kts **Dim:** 21.0 × 4.5 × 1.0
M: 1 diesel; 1 prop; 150 bhp

Note: Also reported in service are the 20-ton survey craft *Safaga* and *Abu el Ghos* and the former trawler *Amira Rama,* also used on survey duties since 1987.

TRAINING SHIPS

♦ **1 1,000-ton Naval Academy navigational training ship**

El Kousser (ex- *El Emir Fawzia*)

♦ **1 Soviet Sekstan-class former degaussing tender**

160

D: 408 tons (fl) **S:** 10.5 kts **Dim:** 41.0 × 9.3 × 4.2
M: 1 diesel; 1 prop; 400 bhp **Range:** 1,200/10

Remarks: Wooden construction. Used as a training craft at the Naval Academy.

♦ **1 500-ton former yacht, attached to the Naval Academy**

Intisar (ex-*Fakr el Bihar*)

COAST GUARD

Note: The Coast Guard is a branch of the naval service in Egypt.

PATROL BOATS

♦ **9 U.S. Commercial Cruiser design** Bldr: 1st 3: Swiftships, Inc., Morgan City, La.; others: Osman Ahmed Osman & Co., Ismailia, Egypt. (In serv.: first 3: 15-1-85; 338: 9-9-85; 339: 24-10-85; 340: 24-11-85; others: 1986)

335 336 337 338 339 340 341 342 343

D: 102 tons (fl) **S:** 27 kts **Dim:** 28.30 × 5.66 × 1.60
A: 1/20-mm AA (aft)—1/12.7-mm mg (fwd)
Electron Equipt: Radar: 1/Furuno . . .
M: 2 MTU 12V331 TC92 diesels; 2 props; 2,660 bhp
Range: 1,000/12 **Fuel:** 11.7 tons **Crew:** 2 officers, 12 men

EGYPT *(continued)*
PATROL BOATS *(continued)*

Commercial Cruiser 338 French Navy, 5-88

Remarks: Ordered 11-83. First three built in U.S.; remainder assembled in Egypt from U.S.-supplied components. Steel construction.

♦ **6 Timsah-II class** Bldr: Timsah SY, Ismailia (In serv. 1988–89)

imsah-II class George R. Schneider, Jr., 5-90

D: 99 tons **S:** 24 kts **Dim:** 29.0 × 5.2 × 1.48
A: 2/20-mm Oerlikon GAM-B01 AA (I × 2)
Electron Equipt: Radar: . . .
M: 2 MTU 12V331 TC92 diesels; 2 props; 2,660 bhp
Range: 600/. . . **Fuel:** 10 tons **Crew:** 13 tot.

emarks: Revised version of Timsah class, with different engines, waterline ex-usts vice stack. Ordered 1-85.

6 Timsah class Bldr: Timsah SY, Alexandria (In serv. 1981–84)

D: 100 tons (fl) **S:** 25 kts **Dim:** 29.0 × 5.2 × 1.48
A: 1/20-mm AA **Electron Equipt:** radar: 1/. . . nav.
M: 2 MTU 8V331 diesels; 2 props; 2,960 bhp
Fuel: 10 tons **Range:** 600/. . . **Crew:** 13 tot.

marks: Based on *Nisr*-class design. First unit laid down 1-1-80, launched 11-81, livered 12-81.

te: The patrol boats *Nimr, Nisr,* and *Thar* were stricken 1990.

ATROL CRAFT

4 small patrol craft Bldr: Canal Naval Const., Port Fuad, Egypt

D: 10 tons **S:** . . . **Dim:** 10.49 × . . . × . . .
M: 1 Thornycroft diesel

marks: Ordered 12-12-83. No further data available. Last two delivered 1986.

♦ **6 MV70 class GRP-hulled** Bldr: Crestitalia, Ameglia (La Spezia), Italy (In serv. 1981–82)

D: 33 tons (41.5 fl) **S:** 35 kts **Dim:** 21.0 × 5.2 × 0.9
A: 2/30-mm Oerlikon A32 (II × 1)—1/20-mm AA—2/12.7-mm mg
M: 2 MTU 12V331 TC92 diesels; 2 props; 2,800 bhp **Range:** 500/32

♦ **30 DC-35 class** Bldr: Dawncraft, Wroxham, U.K. (In serv. 1977)

D: 4 tons (fl) **S:** 25 kts **Dim:** 10.7 × 3.5 × 0.8
M: 2 Perkins T6-354 diesels; 2 props; 390 bhp **Crew:** 4 tot.

Remarks: GRP construction. For harbor police duties.

♦ **20 28-ft. "Enforcer" class** Bldr: Bertram Yacht, Miami, Fla. (In serv. 1973)

D: 8 tons (fl) **S:** 24 kts **Dim:** 8.5 × . . . × . . .
A: 2/12.7-mm mg (I × 2) **M:** 2 diesels; 2 props; 300 bhp

Remarks: Formerly naval, had 4/122-mm RL on sides of hull. GRP construction.

Note: Also reported to be in service are four patrol craft delivered 1982 by Damen, Gorinchem, the Netherlands: *Khafra, Khoufou, Krier,* and *Ramses.*

CUSTOMS SERVICE

PATROL CRAFT

♦ **12 U.S. Sea Spectre PB Mk III class** Bldr: Peterson Builders, Sturgeon Bay, Wisconsin (In serv. 1980–81)

D: 28 tons (36.7 fl) **S:** 30 kts **Dim:** 19.78 × 5.50 × 1.80 (props)
A: 2/12.7-mm mg (I × 2) **Electron Equipt:** Radar: 1/. . . nav.
M: 3 G.M. 8V71 TI diesels; 3 props; 1,800 bhp
Endurance: 3 days **Range:** 450/26; 2,000/. . .
Crew: 1 officer, 8 enlisted

EL SALVADOR

Republic of El Salvador

Personnel (1991): 2,450 total including 1,300-man marine battalion and 450 commandos

PATROL BOATS

♦ **1 U.S. 77-ft Commercial Cruiser class** Bldr: Swiftships, Inc., Morgan City, Louisiana.

GC 11 (In serv. 6-5-85)

GC 11 Swiftships, 6-85

D: 48 tons (fl) **S:** 26 kts **Dim:** 23.47 × 6.10 × 1.52
A: 2/12.7-mm mg (I × 2)
Electron Equipt: Radar: 1/Furuno . . . nav.
Range: . . . **M:** 3 G.M. 12V71 TI diesels; 3 props; 1,200 bhp

Remarks: Aluminum construction.

Note: Patrol boat GC 10 discarded by 1989; patrol boat GC 5 grounded and lost 1-90.

♦ **3 aluminum-hulled** Bldr: Camcraft, Crown Point, Louisiana

GC 6 (In serv. 24-10-75) GC 7 (In serv. 3-12-75)
GC 8 (In serv. 11-75)

EL SALVADOR *(continued)*
PATROL BOATS *(continued)*

GC 6 John Forster, 1986

D: 100 tons (fl) **S:** 25 kts **Dim:** 30.5 × 6.4 × 1.5 **Crew:** 10 tot.
A: 3/12.7-mm mg (I × 3) **Electron Equipt:** Radar: 1/Furuno . . .
M: 3 G.M. 12V71 TI diesels; 3 props; 1,200 bhp **Range:** 780/24

Remarks: Rebuilt 1985–86 by Lantana Boatyard, Lantana, Florida; deckhouse extended 6 m, new radar, new radios.

PATROL CRAFT

♦ **5 coastal-patrol craft** Bldr: Mercougar, North Miami, Fla. (In serv. 1988)

D: . . . tons (fl) **S:** . . . kts **Dim:** 12.2 × . . . × . . . **A:** . . .
M: 2 Ford Merlin 6-cyl. diesels; 2 Arneson outdrives; 600 bhp
Range: 300/. . . **Crew:** . . .

Remarks: Built under U.S. FY 87 Military Aid Program; ordered 18-12-87. Plans to acquire 20 more did not reach fruition.

♦ **5 catamaran river-patrol craft** Bldr: Mercougar, North Miami, Fla. (In serv. 1988)

LDF 7 LDF 8 LDF 9 LDF 10 LDF 11

D: . . . tons (fl) **S:** . . . kts **Dim:** 9.1 × . . . × . . . **A:** . . .
M: 2 Ford Merlin 6-cyl. diesels; 2 Arneson outdrives; 600 bhp
Range: 400/ . . . **Crew:** . . .

Remarks: First five (one of which is configured as an ambulance craft) built under U.S. FY 87 Military Aid Program; ordered 18-12-87. Plans to acquire ten more (five in ambulance configuration) did not reach fruition. "LDF" stands for *Lanchas de Operaciones Fluviale*.

♦ **10 "Protector"-class aluminum patrol craft** Bldr: SeaArk, Monticello, Arkansas

"Protector" class for El Salvador SeaArk, 1988

D: 15 tons (fl) **S:** 28 kts **Dim:** 12.19 (11.13 wl) × 3.86 × 0.69 (hull)
A: 2/12.7-mm mg (I × 2)—2/7.62-mm mg (I × 2)—6/M16 rifles
Electron Equipt: Radar: 1/Furuno 2400 nav. **Crew:** 5 tot.
M: 2 Caterpillar 3208 TA diesels; 2 props; 690 bhp **Range:** 350/20

Remarks: Completed 1988–89.

♦ **6 "Piranha"class river patrol craft** Bldr: Lantana Boatyard, Lantana, Fla. (In serv. 2-87)

LDF 1 LDF 2 LDF 3 LDF 4 LDF 5 LDF 6

"Pirhana" class for El Salvador Lantana, 2-87

D: 9 tons (fl) **S:** 26 kts (22 sust.) **Dim:** 12.19 × 3.05 × 0.53
A: 2/12.7-mm mg (I × 2)—2/7.62-mm mg (I × 2)
Electron Equipt: Radar: 1/Furuno 3600 nav.
M: 2 Caterpillar 3208 TA diesels; 2 props; 630 bhp
Endurance: 5 days **Crew:** 5 tot.

Remarks: Aluminum construction with Kevlar plastic armor. Lengthened version of 8-unit class built for Honduras, 1986.

♦ **1 "Outrage"-class patrol craft** Bldr: Boston Whaler, U.S.A. (In serv. 1983)

D: 2.2 tons (fl) **S:** 35 kts **Dim:** 7.62 × 2.40 × 0.40
A: 1/12.7-mm mg—1/7.62-mm mg **Crew:** 4 tot.
M: 2 outboard motors; 2 props; 300 hp **Range:** 200/35

Remarks: GRP foam sandwich construction. Five others discarded.

♦ **25 small launches with outboard motors**

Remarks: Locally built and typically armed with 1/12.7-mm and 1/7.62-mm mg.

AMPHIBIOUS CRAFT

♦ **4 U.S. LCM(8)-class landing craft** (Transferred 1987–88)

LD 2 LD 3 LD 4 LD 5

D: 34 tons light (121 fl) **S:** 12 kts **Dim:** 22.43 × 6.40 × 1.40 (aft)
M: 4 G.M. 6-71 diesels; 2 props; 590 bhp
Range: 150/12 **Crew:** 3 tot. **Cargo:** 58 tons or 120 troops

♦ **1 U.S. LCM(6)-class landing craft** (Transferred 11-86)

LD 1

D: 24 tons light (56 fl) **S:** 10 kts **Dim:** 17.07 × 4.37 × 1.17 (aft)
M: 2 G.M. 6V71 diesels; 2 props; 330 bhp
Range: 130/10 **Crew:** 3 tot. **Cargo:** 34 tons or 80 troops

EQUATORIAL GUINEA

Republic of Equatorial Guinea

Personnel (1991): Approx. 120 tot.

PATROL BOATS AND CRAFT

♦ **1 68-ft. U.S. patrol boat** Bldr: Lantana Boatyard, Lantana, Fla.

	Laid down	L	In serv.
037 Isla de Bioko	3-87	3-88	5-88

QUATORIAL GUINEA (*continued*)
ATROL BOATS AND CRAFT (*continued*)

la de Bioko (037) Lantana, 5-88

D: 33 tons (fl) **S:** 24 kts (28 trials) **Dim:** 20.73 × 5.50 × 1.50
A: 1/12.7-mm mg—2/7.62-mm mg (I × 2)
Electron Equipt: Radar: 1/Furuno 3600 nav.
M: 2 G.M. 8V92 TI diesels; 2 props; 1,170 bhp **Range:** 800/15
Crew: 2 officers, 10 enlisted

marks: Aluminum construction; delivered unpainted. Paid for by U.S. Grant Aid ogram. A planned, larger ship from the same builder was not funded.

1 ex-Nigerian P/20-class patrol craft Bldr: Van Mill Marine Service, Hardinxveld-Giessendam, the Netherlands

o Wele (ex-P 220) (In serv. 17-1-86)

D: 45 tons (fl) **S:** 32.5 kts **Dim:** 20.26 (18.00 wl) × 5.30 × 1.75
A: 1/20-mm Rheinmetall AA—2/7.62-mm mg (I × 2)
Electron Equipt: Radar: 1/Decca . . . nav.
M: 2 MTU 6V331 TC82 diesels; 2 props; 2,250 bhp
Range: 950/25; 1,200/11 **Crew:** 2 officers, 10 enlisted

marks: Transferred as a gift from Nigeria 27-6-86. GRP construction.

ETHIOPIA

ote: Precise information as to the losses to the Ethiopian Navy during the successful rean revolution in 1991 are not available; a number of ships and craft were said to ve been destroyed during 3-90 at Massawa. The class totals below are based on the st available information and are in part estimates; some units apparently escaped to en or Djibouti, and their status is as yet uncertain. Eritrean rebels controlled most of e Ethiopian coastline and the Dahlak Islands by the end of 1991; they are known to erate a number of small motorboats and motor-dhows and have intercepted passing rchant vessels.

rsonnel (1991): 1,600 men, including about 200 officers

val Aviation: Several Soviet Mi-14 Haze A ASW helicopters reported in service, 87.

ORVETTES

2 Soviet Petya-II class

1616 (ex-*Zerai Deres*) (In serv. 20-7-83) F 1617 (In serv. 20-3-84)

D: 950 tons light, 1,020 tons std (1,160 fl) **S:** 29 kts (16 on diesel)
Dim: 81.8 (78.00 pp) × 9.20 × 2.97
A: 4/76.2-mm AK-276 DP (II × 2)—2/RBU-6000 ASW RL (XII × 2)—10/400-mm ASW TT (V × 2)—2/d.c. racks—mines
Electron Equipt:
Radar: 1/Don-2 nav., 1/Strut Curve air/surf. search, 1/Hawk Screech f.c.
Sonar: 1/HF hull-mounted
EW: 2/Watch Dog intercept—IFF: High Pole B transponder
M: CODAG: 2/15,000-shp gas turbines, 1 Type 61-V3, 6,000-bhp diesel; 3 props (CP on centerline); 36,000 hp—2 active rudders; 100 hp
Range: 450/29; 1,800/16 (diesel); 4,800/10 **Crew:** 8 off., 84 enlisted

emarks: In service dates above are those of arrival at Massawa. Believed to be andard Petya-IIs, i.e., not "export model" with 3/533-mm TT and 4/RBU-2500. Hawk reech gunfire-control radar has two associated target designators on the open bridge. ame deleted from F 1616 in 1990. At least one escaped destruction.

GUIDED-MISSILE PATROL BOATS

♦ **4 Soviet Osa-II class**

FMB 160 FMB 161 FMB 162 FMB 163

D: 210 tons (240 fl) **S:** 35 kts **Dim:** 38.6 × 7.6 × 2.0
A: 4/SS-N-2B Styx SSM—4/30-mm AK-230 AA (II × 2)
Electron Equipt:
Radar: 1/Square Tie target desig./surf. search, 1/Drum Tilt gun f.c.
IFF: 2/Square Head interrogators, 1/High Pole B transponder
M: 3 M504 diesels; 3 props; 15,000 bhp **Range:** 500/34; 750/25
Crew: 30 tot.

Remarks: First unit transferred 1978, second 10-80, third 13-1-81, the fourth in 1982.

TORPEDO BOATS

♦ **2 Soviet Turya-class semi-hydrofoils**

HTB 112 HTB 113

HTB 112 1988

D: 215 tons (250 fl) **S:** 38 kts **Crew:** 24 tot.
Dim: 39.0 × 7.6 (12.5 over foils) × 2.0 (4.0 over foils)
A: 2/57-mm AK-257 DP aft (II × 1)—2/25-mm 2M-8 AA (II × 1)—4/533-mm TT (I × 4)
Electron Equipt:
Radar: 1/Pot Drum surf. search, 1/Muff Cob f.c.
IFF: 1/Square Head interrogator, 1/High Pole B transponder
M: 3 M504 diesels; 3 props; 15,000 bhp **Range:** 400/38; 650/25

Remarks: First transferred 3-85, second in 3-86. Do not have the normal helicopter-type dipping sonar. The Mugg Cob radar/electro-optical director controls only the 57-mm gun mount; the 25-mm mount is locally controlled. Hydrofoils forward only; the stern planes on the surface.

♦ **2 Soviet Mol class**

FTB 110 FTB 111

D: 175 tons (220 fl) **S:** 36 kts **Dim:** 38.6 × 7.6 × 1.9
A: 4/30-mm AK-230 AA (II × 2)—4/533-mm TT (I × 4)
Electron Equipt:
Radar: 1/Pot Head surf. search, 1/Drum Tilt f.c.
IFF: 1/Square Head interrogator, 1/High Pole B transponder
Crew: 30 tot.

Remarks: Transferred 1-78. Hull and propulsion plant essentially the same as those of the Turya and Osa classes.

PATROL BOATS

♦ **4 Soviet Zhuk class**

P-205 (ex-PC 16) P-206 (ex-PC 17) P-207 P-208

D: 48 tons (60 fl) **S:** 34 kts **Dim:** 24.0 × 5.0 × 1.2 (1.8 props)
A: 4/14.5-mm (II × 2) **Electron Equipt:** Radar: 1/Spin Trough nav.
M: 2 M50F-4 diesels; 2 props; 2,400 bhp **Fuel:** 10 tons
Range: 700/28; 1,100/15 **Crew:** 12 tot.

Remarks: First two delivered 18-10-82; other pair delivered 1990, possibly as replacements.

♦ **3 U.S. 104-ft Commercial Cruiser class** Bldr: Swiftships, Morgan City, La. (In serv. 4-77)

P 201 P 203 P 204

D: 118 tons (fl) **S:** 32 kts **Dim:** 31.73 × 7.1 × 2.16
A: 4/30-mm Emerlec AA (II × 2)
Electron Equipt: Radar: Decca RM 916
M: 2 MTU MB 16V538 TB90 diesels; 2 props; 7,000 bhp
Range: 1,200/18 **Man:** 21 tot.

Remarks: Ordered 1976; two additional units were canceled by the U.S. arms embargo. P 203 and P 204 have four 23-mm AA (II × 2) and two 12.7-mm machine guns (II × 1). P 202 defected to Somalia, 1984.

ETHIOPIA *(continued)*
PATROL BOATS *(continued)*

P-204—with twin 23-mm AA aft, single 14.5-mm mg fwd. 1988

Note: The Dutch *Wildervank*-class former minesweeper acquired in 1971 and long employed as a patrol boat was discarded during 1990. The four Sewart-built 13.1-m patrol craft, GB 21 through 24, were discarded or lost during 1990–91.

MINE COUNTERMEASURES SHIPS

Note: One Soviet Natya class delivered 4-91 and one Soviet Sonya-class minesweeper delivered 1-91 are believed to be in Yemeni custody.

AMPHIBIOUS SHIPS

♦ **2 Soviet Polnocny-B class** Bldr: Stocznia Pólnocna, Gdańsk, Poland

LTC 1037 LTC 1038

D: 800 tons (fl) **S:** 19 kts **Dim:** 74.0 × 8.6 × 2.0
A: 4/30-mm AK-230 AA—2/140-mm RL (XVIII × 2)
Electron Equipt:
Radar: 1/Spin Trough nav., 1/Drum Tilt gun f.c.
IFF: 1/Square Head interrogator, 1/High Pole transponder
M: 2 Type 40D diesels; 2 props; 4,000 bhp **Range:** 900/18; 1,500/14
Crew: 40 tot.

Remarks: Transferred 11-81 and 1-83. Cargo: 180 tons.

Note: Logistic landing craft *Chamo* and *Ziway,* delivered by early 1991, are/were subordinated to the Ministry of Transport, not the navy.

♦ **1 French EDIC-class logistics landing craft** Bldr: SFCN, Villeneuve la Garonne (L: 5-77)

LTC 1036

D: 250 tons (670 fl) **S:** 8 kts **Dim:** 59.0 × 11.95 × 1.3
A: 2/20-mm AA (I × 2) **M:** 2 MGO diesels; 2 props; 1,000 bhp
Range: 1,800/8 **Crew:** 1 officer, 15 enlisted

Remarks: Cargo: 11 trucks or 5 light armored vehicles. Sister LTC 1035 lost 1990.

♦ **2 Soviet T-4-class landing craft**

D: 70 tons (fl) **S:** 10 kts **Dim:** 19.0 × 4.3 × 1.0
M: 2 diesels; 2 props; 600 bhp **Crew:** 5 tot.

Remarks: Transferred 1984. Four transferred 1977–78 are believed to have been discarded by 1990.

AUXILIARIES

Note: In service at end 1990 were a tug, AO 2, transferred from the U.S.S.R. in 1979, and a small service launch, TR 74. Training ship *Ethiopia* (A 01, ex-U.S. *Orca,* AVP 49) remained in service into 1990 but was apparently lost during 1991. Cargo ship/training vessel *Ras Dedgen* (A 03) was lost during 1990.

FÆROE ISLANDS

Semi-Autonomous Danish Dependency

COAST GUARD AND FISHERY PROTECTION SERVICE

♦ **1 fisheries protection ship and rescue tug** Bldr: Svolvær Værft, Norway

TJALDUR (In serv. 1976)

D: 650 tons (fl) **S:** 14.5 kts **Dim:** 44.50 × 10.10 × 4.02
A: 1/57-mm single-fire **Electron Equipt:** Radar: 3/. . . nav.
M: 2 MWM 6-cyl. diesels; 1 prop; 2,400 bhp **Crew:** . . .

Remarks: Acquired 1987. 437 grt. Gun manufactured 1896 at Royal Dockyard, Co enhagen. Equipped for fire fighting and ocean towing. Based at Tórhavn, Streym Island.

Note: The former trawler *Olavur Halgi* has been stricken.

FALKLAND ISLANDS

(British Colony)

Aviation: In addition to R.A.F. assets stationed in the Falklands, the local gover ment has acquired a Dornier Do. 228–200 maritime surveillance aircraft with Sper Primus radar.

FISHERIES PATROL SHIPS

Note: Ships involved in fisheries protection duties for the Falkland Islands are ch tered from commercial operators and are retained for one or two years only. Plans w announced 1-3-91 to charter another vessel, which probably means that one of the un listed below will be off-charter by 1992. Of the ships listed in the previous edition, t former German fisheries protection ship *Falklands Right* (ex-*Lancella,* ex-*Ant Dohrn,* ex-*Walter Herwig*) was sold in 1991; the former Argentine oilfield supply t *Falklands Sound* (ex-*Yehuin,* ex-*Millern Tor*) is employed in commercial service; and the two former Royal Navy tenders, *Beaulieu* was sold to Chile in 1990 and *Blaker* sank in 1990.

♦ **1 former stern haul trawler** Bldr: Stocznia Gdynia, Poland (In serv. . . .)

FALKLANDS PROTECTOR (Ex-*Eastella,* ex-*Falklands Right,* ex-*G.A. Reay,* ex-*Arctic Privateer*)

D: approx. 2,000 tons (fl) **S:** 14.5 kts
Dim: 69.15 (60.30 pp) × 11.99 × 4.99
A: none **Electron Equipt:** Radar: . . .
M: 1 diesel; 1 prop; 2,500 bhp **Range:** . . .
Fuel: 329 tons **Crew:** 23 tot.

Remarks: 1,878 grt. Chartered 3-90 after refit in Poland 1988–89. Had previou been chartered 1-2-87 by Falklands government after serving in the South Atlantic British government charter since 26-9-84. Has accommodations for 6 spare personn

♦ **1 former seismic survey vessel** Bldr: Hall-Russell, Aberdeen

FALKLANDS DESIRE (ex-*Seisella,* ex-*Southella*) (In serv. 2-69)

D: approx. 2,400 tons (fl) **S:** 15 kts
Dim: 74.50 (64.32 pp) × 12.68 × 4.57
A: none **Electron Equipt:** Radar: . . .
M: 1 Mirrlees-National diesel; 1 prop; 2,880 bhp **Fuel:** 400 tons
Range: 15,000/15 **Electric:** 750 kw (3 × 250 kw) **Crew:** 32 tot.

Remarks: 1,496 grt. Chartered from J. Marr 1-2-87 for fisheries patrol; off-charter 1990 but rehired 1991. Former stern-haul trawler, converted 1986 as seismic surv and oilfield-standby vessel. Has helicopter deck and accommodations for 15 sp personnel.

Note: Trawler *Mount Kent* (ex-*St. Jason*) was briefly under charter 1990–91 duri the absence of *Falklands Desire.*

FIJI

Dominion of Fiji

Personnel (1991): 260 total

Naval Aviation: One Aérospatiale AS-355 Écureuil helicopter purchased 198 supplement the Bell 206 JetRanger on lease from a private company in Fiji.

PATROL BOATS AND CRAFT

Note: With the change in Fiji's government, the order placed on 3-10-85 for Australian "Pacific Forum" ASI-315-class patrol boats was canceled, and the b were earmarked for Tonga.

♦ **2 former oilfield support craft** Bldr: Beaux's Baycraft, Louisiana (In serv. 1979–80)

101 LEVUKA (ex-*Maranatha*) 102 LAUTOKA (ex-*Rapture*)

'JI *(continued)*
ATROL BOATS *(continued)*

he crewboat Rapture, just prior to conversion for Fiji as a patrol oat (present appearance very similar) George F. Schneider, Jr., 9-87

D: 97 tons (fl) **S:** 27 kts **Dim:** 33.80 × 7.40 × 1.50
A: 1/12.7-mm mg **Electron Equipt:** Radar: 2/. . . nav.
M: 4 G.M. 12V71 TI diesels; 4 props; 2,156 bhp **Crew:** . . .

marks: Aluminum craft purchased 9-87 and commissioned 22-10-87 and 28-10-87, spectively. Correlation of former names to Fijian names uncertain.

4 ex-Israeli Dabur-class patrol craft
Bldr:

1 302 303 304

D: 25 tons (35 fl) **S:** 25 kts **Dim:** 19.80 × 5.80 × 0.80
A: 2/20-mm Oerlikon AA (I × 2)—2/12.7 mm mg (I × 2)
Electron Equipt: Radar: 1/Decca 101 or Decca 926 nav.
M: 2 G.M. 12V71 TI diesels; 2 props; 960 bhp
Electric: 20 kw **Range:** 1,200/17 **Crew:** 6 tot.

marks: Purchased 8-91 and commissioned in Fiji 22-11-91.

te: The last two U.S. *Redwing*-class former minesweepers, *Kikau* (204, ex-*odpecker,* MSC 209) and *Kula* (205, ex-*Vireo,* MSC 205), were decommissioned ring 7-90.

UXILIARIES

1 hydrographic survey ship Bldr: Carrington Slipway, Tomago, Australia

ABELE (ex-*Eugene McDermott II*) (In serv. . . .)

D: 1,200 tons (fl) **S:** 12 kts **Dim:** 52.6 × 11.7 × 3.4
Electron Equipt: Radar: 2/. . . nav. **Crew:** 31 tot.
M: 2 Caterpillar D 399 diesels; 2 props; 2,500 bhp **Range:** 9,400/10

marks: Former oilfield seismic survey ship purchased 4-87 for the Marine Department of the Ministry of Transport and passed to the navy in early 1989. Has a small licopter platform aft.

1 presidential yacht Bldr: Government Yd., Suva

AGIDONU (In serv. 1979)

marks: 33-meter, 2-masted motor yacht acquired 6-91 and operated by navy. Crew 18.

-INLAND

public of Finland

val Aviation: The navy has no aircraft of its own. The Frontier Guard operates a mber of helicopters and fixed-wing aircraft; see below.

rsonnel (1991): 1,800 total (200 officers, 500 petty officers, 1,000 conscripts) plus 0 Frontier Guards

EAPONS

The *Turunmaa*-class corvettes and the minelayer *Pohjanmaa* have a single-barrel tomatic Bofors 120-mm gun with the following characteristics:

ight without munitions: 28.5 ons	arc of elevation: -10 deg. to +80 deg.
gth: 46 calibers	maximum rate of fire: 80 rounds/min
zzle velocity: 800 m/sec	projectile weight: 35 kg
ining speed: 40 deg./sec	maximum effective range, surface
vation speed: 30 deg./sec	fire: 12,000 m

The other major weapons employed are Soviet SS-N-2 Styx missiles, Bofors 40-mm 0 AA guns, Soviet twin 30-mm AA guns, and 23-mm AA in twin mountings. Swedish S-15 antiship missiles were ordered in 1983 to equip the *Helsinki* class and also for ore-based defense, using Sisu trucks, with four missiles per vehicle.

CORVETTES

♦ **2 Turunmaa class** Bldr: Wärtsilä, Helsinki

	L	In serv.		L	In serv.
03 TURUNMAA	11-7-67	29-8-68	04 KARJALA	16-8-67	21-10-68

Turunmaa (03) Finnish Navy, 1990

Karjala (04) Hartmut Ehlers, 9-90

D: 605 tons (770 fl) **S:** 35 kts **Dim:** 74.1 × 7.8 × 2.83
A: 1/120-mm 46-cal. Bofors DP—2/40-mm Bofors L70 AA (I × 2)—4/23-mm Soviet AA (II × 2)—2/RBU-1200 ASW RL (V × 2)—2/d.c. racks
Electron Equipt:
Radar: 1/. . . nav., 1/. . . surf. search, 1/H.S.A. M22
Sonar: . . .—EW: . . .
M: CODOG propulsion: 1 Bristol-Siddeley Olympus TM1A, 22,000-shp gas turbine; 3 Mercedes-Benz 1,100-bhp diesels; 3 CP props
Electric: 880 kVA **Fuel:** 120 tons **Range:** 2,500/14
Crew: 70 tot.

Remarks: Both laid down 3-67. Cruise on the diesels at 17 knots. Have Vosper fin stabilizers. Soviet ASW rocket launchers are behind doors in main-deck superstructure, abreast the mast; the d.c. racks are internal, at the stern. The exhaust from the gas turbine is trunked down either side of the fantail. Six 103-mm flare RL rails on 120-mm mount. Both refitted 1984–86 by Wärtsilä, Turku; received Data Saab EOS-400 optronic f.c.s, new radars, EW gear, and sonar.

GUIDED-MISSILE PATROL BOATS

♦ **1 (+3) Helsinki-II class** Bldr: Hollming, Rauma

	L	In serv.
70 RAUMA	. . .	18-5-90
71 RAAHE	8-91	2-92
72	11-91	. . .
73	. . .	. . .

Rauma (70)—on trials Hollming, 1990

D: 215 tons (fl) **S:** 30 kts **Dim:** 48.00 (41.00 pp) × 8.00 × 0.87
A: 6/RBS-15SF SSM (II × 2, I × 2)—1/40-mm Bofors L 70-600E AA—1/ SAM launcher (VI × 1, Mistral missiles) SAM syst.—2/12.7-mm mg (I × 2)—4/Saab Elma LLS. 920 ASW RL (IX × 4)—mines
Electron Equipt:
Radar: 1/. . . nav.; 1/9GA208 surface search; 1/9LV225 f.c.
Sonar: Simrad ST 240 "Towfish" VDS (24 kHz)
EW: MEL Matilda-E (9EW 300) passive, 2/Wallop Barricade decoy RL (XXXII × 2)
M: 2 MTU 16V538 TB93 diesels; 2 Riva Calzone waterjets; 8,000 bhp
Electric: 386 kw (2 × 193 kw; 2 Saab Scania DS11 diesel driving)
Crew: 19 tot.

Remarks: Construction approved 2-87, with the first laid down fall 1987. Shorter and shallower in draft than *Helsinki* class. Name of first unit originally to have been *Luokka*. Second unit laid down 3-8-89. A second group of four is planned. Have PEAB 9LV200 Mk 3 optronic fire control system and 9EW300 EW system. The surface-to-air missile launcher is a Finnish-designed converted 23-mm AA gun mount equipped with infrared and t.v. cameras for fire control.

GUIDED-MISSILE PATROL BOATS *(continued)*

◆ **4 Helsinki (PB 80) class** Bldr: Wärtsilä, Helsinki

	Laid down	L	In serv.
60 Helsinki	3-9-80	5-11-80	1-9-81
61 Turku	1-1-84	1985	1-6-85
62 Oulu	. . .	. . .	1-10-85
63 Kotka	. . .	. . .	16-6-86

Oulu (62)—with four RBS-15SF missiles Hartmut Ehlers, 9-90

Kotka (63) Hartmut Ehlers, 9-90

D: 250 tons (280 fl) **S:** 30 kts **Dim:** 45.0 × 8.9 × 3.0 (props)
A: 4/RBS-15SF SSM (II × 2)—1/57-mm Bofors Mk 1 DP—4/23-mm AA (II × 2)—mines
Electron Equipt:
Radar: 1/navigational, 1/9GA208, 1/9L V225 f.c.
Sonar: Simrad SS 304 hull-mounted
M: 3 MTU 16V538 TB92 diesels; 3 props; 12,000 bhp
Range: . . . **Crew:** 30 tot.

Remarks: Prototype ordered 5-10-78. Three additional ordered 13-1-83. Aluminum hull. Data Saab EOS-400 optronic f.c.s. on 61–63, which had a revised pilothouse shape; 60 later brought up to same standard. Can carry up to 8 RBS-15SF missiles. Further construction deferred in favor of "Helsinki-II" class above.

◆ **4 Soviet Osa-II class**

11 Tuima 12 Tuisku 14 Tuuli 15 Tyrsky

Tuuli (14) Finnish Navy, 1990

D: 210 tons (240 fl) **S:** 35 kts **Dim:** 38.6 × 7.6 × 2.0
Crew: 30 tot.
A: 4/SS-N-2B Styx—4/30-mm AA (II × 2)
Electron Equipt:
Radar: 1/Decca 1626 nav., 1/Square Tie missile target desig., 1/Drum Tilt gun f.c.
M: 3 M504 diesels; 3 props; 15,000 bhp **Range:** 500/34; 750/25

Remarks: Transferred in 1975. Some Western electronic equipment has been added, including a navigational radar. Engines reported to be unreliable.

PATROL BOATS

◆ **1 prototype** Bldr: Fiskar's Turan, Veneveistamo SY/Laivateollisuus

30 Hurja

D: 54 tons (60 fl) **S:** 42 kts **Dim:** 21.7 × 5.0 × 2.0
A: 2/23-mm AA (II × 1) **Electron Equipt:** Radar: 1/. . . nav.
M: 3 diesels; waterjets; 3,800 bhp **Crew:** 10 tot.

Remarks: Glass-reinforced plastic prototype hull delivered 1-7-80 to Laivateollisu for fitting out. The gun mount is aft. This class was intended to replace at least seven the *Nuoli* class during the 1980s, but no further orders have materialized. A "Nuoli 9 class is still in the planning stages.

◆ **6 Nuoli class** Bldr: Laivateollisuus, Turku

	In serv.		In serv.
35 Nuoli 5	6-7-62	41 Nuoli 11	5-5-64
38 Nuoli 8	10-10-62	42 Nuoli 12	30-11-64
40 Nuoli 10	5-5-64	43 Nuoli 13	12-10-66

Nuoli 5 (35) Finnish Navy, 19

D: 40 tons (64 fl) **S:** 40 kts **Dim:** 22.0 × 6.65 × 1.5
A: 2/23-mm AA (II × 1)—1/12.7-mm mg—4 depth charges
Electron Equipt: Radar: Decca 707 nav.
M: 3 Soviet M50 diesels; 3,600 bhp **Crew:** 15 tot.

Remarks: Sisters *Nuoli 1–3, 6,* and *9* discarded by 1984; survivors refitted, w new weapons replacing the single 40-mm and 20-mm AA weapons originally installe

◆ **5 Ruissalo and Rihtniemi classes**

	Bldr	L	In serv.
51 Rihtniemi	Rauma-Repola, Rauma	. . .	21-2-57
52 Rymattyla	Rauma-Repola, Rauma	. . .	20-5-57
53 Ruissalo	Laivateollisuus, Turku	16-6-59	11-8-59
54 Raisio	Laivateollisuus, Turku	2-7-59	12-9-59
55 Röytta	Laivateollisuus, Turku	2-6-59	14-10-59

Rihtniemi (51) Leo Van Ginderen, 19

Ruissalo (53) Finnish Navy, 1

D: 115 tons (135 fl) **S:** 18 kts **Dim:** 34.0 × 6.0 × 1.8
A: 4/23-mm AA (II × 2)—2/RBU-1200 ASW RL (V × 2)—mines
M: 2 Mercedes-Benz diesels; 2 CP props; 2,500 bhp **Crew:** 20 tot.

Remarks: Former convertible minesweeper/gunboats, modernized 1977–80. 51 52 originally only 31 meters overall and are 5.7 meters in beam. All five now have bulwarks.

INE WARFARE SHIPS

ote: In addition to the ships and craft listed in this section as having minelaying pabilities, most other classes of Finnish combatants, auxiliaries, and service craft are so equipped for minelaying.

0 (+2) seagoing minelayer Bldr: Hollming, Rauma

	Laid down	L	In serv.
. HAMEENMAA	. . .	11-91	1992
. . . .	. . .	. . .	1993

ameenmaa—artist's rendering — Finnish Navy

D: 1,000 tons (fl) **S:** 19 kts **Dim:** 75.00 × 11.60 × 3.0
A: 2/40-mm Bofors AA (I × 2)—1/ SAM launcher (VI × 1, Mistral missiles)— 4/23-mm AA (II × 2)—100–150 mines
Electron Equipt:
Radar: 2/. . . nav.
EW: . . . intercept; Super Barricade chaff RL (XXXII × 2)
M: 2 Wärtsilä-Vasa 16V 22MD diesels; 2 props; 6,400 bhp—bow-thruster
Crew: 70 tot.

marks: First ship authorized and originally ordered 7-89 from Wärtsilä, Helsinki, delivery 1991; re-ordered 29-12-89 after Wärtsilä's bankruptcy. Will have bow and ern ramps to permit use as logistics transports as well as minelayers, and will also ve side-loading ports. Intended to replace the aging *Keihässalmi.*

1 minelayer/training ship Bldr: Wärtsilä, Helsinki

	Laid down	L	In serv.
POHJANMAA	5-78	28-8-78	8-6-79

hjanmaa (01) — Leo Van Ginderen, 1991

D: 1,100 tons (fl) **S:** 20 kts **Dim:** 78.3 × 11.6 × 3.0
A: 1/120-mm Bofors DP—2/40-mm AA (I × 2)—8/23-mm AA (II × 4)—2/RBU-1200 ASW RL (II × 2)—mines
Electron Equipt:
Radar: 1/. . . nav., 1/H.S.A. DA 05 air search, 1/9GA 208, 1/9LV100 f.c.
Sonar: 2 hull-mounted sets
M: 2 Wärtsilä-Vasa 16V22 diesels; 2 CP props; 5,800 bhp—bow-thruster
Electric: 1,040 kVA **Range:** 3,500/17
Crew: 80 ship's company plus 70 cadets

marks: Training facilities fitted in portable containers mounted on the two inter-l mine rails, easily removable if the ship is required for combat. Six 102-mm flare RL ls mounted on 120-mm mount.

0 (+3) coastal minelayer/anti-pollution ships
Bldr: Olkiluoto Telakka

	Laid down	L	In serv.
kiluto	. . .	. . .	8-91
. . . .	. . .	. . .	. . .
. . . .	. . .	. . .	. . .

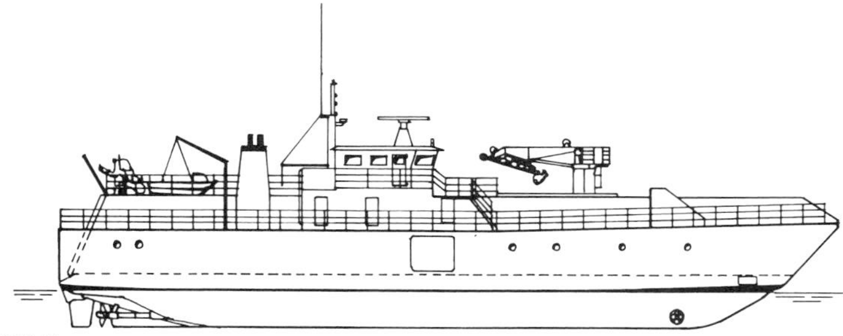

Olkiluto

D: . . . tons (fl) **S:** . . . kts **Dim:** 45.0 × . . . × . . .
A: 2/23-mm AA (II × 1)—. . . mines
Electron Equipt: Radar: 1/. . . nav.
M: 2 . . . . . . diesels; 2 props; . . . bhp—bow-thruster
Crew: . . . tot.

Remarks: Ordered 1990 for delivery 1991–92 as combination coastal minelayers, anti-pollution ships, and landing craft. Have bow and stern ramps as well as side-loading ports.

◆ **1 coastal minelayer** Bldr: Valmet Oy, Helsinki (L: 16-3-57)

05 KEIHÄSSALMI

Keihässalmi (05) — Leo Van Ginderen, 1982

D: 290 tons (360 fl) **S:** 15 kts **Dim:** 56.0 × 7.7 × 2.0
A: 4/30-mm AK-230AA (II × 2)—2/20-mm AA (I × 2)—100 mines
Electron Equipt: Radar: 1/. . . nav., 1/Drum Tilt f.c.
M: 2 Wärtsilä diesels; 2 props; 2,000 bhp **Crew:** 60 tot.

Remarks: Given Soviet guns 1972, Drum Tilt f.c. radar 1976. May remain in use after the new seagoing minelayer is completed.

◆ **2 minelaying barges** Bldr: Lehtinen, Rauma (In serv. 1987)

721 821

D: 130 tons (fl) **Dim:** 15.0 × 7.0 × 1.5 **A:** . . . mines

Remarks: Non-self-propelled craft intended primarily to transport mines but also capable of being used to lay mines.

◆ **6 Kuha-class inshore minesweepers** Bldr: Laivateollisuus, Turku

	In serv.		In serv.
KUHA 21	28-6-74	KUHA 24	7-3-75
KUHA 22	10-1-74	KUHA 25	17-6-75
KUHA 23	7-3-75	KUHA 26	13-11-75

D: 90 tons (fl) **S:** 12 kts **Dim:** 26.6 × 6.9 × 2.0
A: 2/23-mm AA (II × 1)—1/12.7-mm mg
Electron Equipt: Radar: 1/Decca . . . nav.
M: 2 Cummins NT-380M diesels; 2 outboard-drive props; 660 bhp
Crew: 2 officers, 12 enlisted

Remarks: Glass-reinforced plastic hulls. Plans for eight additional canceled. Engines, flexibly mounted, drive rudder/propellers through hydrostatic transmissions. Can tow Type F-82 electrode sweep.

MINE WARFARE SHIPS *(continued)*

Kuha 24 Finnish Navy, 1985

◆ **7 Kiskii-class drone minesweepers** Bldr: Fiskar's Turun, Turku

	Laid down	L	In serv.
521 Kiskii 1	. . .	. . .	1983
522 Kiskii 2	20-1-83	21-10-83	4-11-83
523 Kiskii 3	14-2-83	10-11-83	28-11-83
524 Kiskii 4	5-4-83	28-11-83	12-12-83
525 Kiskii 5	16-5-83	2-5-84	24-5-83
526 Kiskii 6	29-8-83	9-5-84	24-5-83
527 Kiskii 7	12-9-83	10-5-84	24-5-83

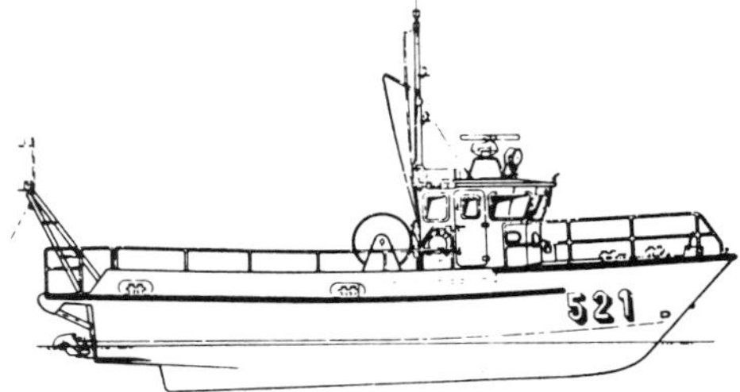

Kiskii class Finnish Navy, 1983

D: 17.7 tons (20 fl) **S:** 10.7 kts **Dim:** 15.18 (13.00 pp) × 4.10 × 1.20
A: 1/20-mm AA **Range:** 250/10 **Crew:** 4 tot. (for transits)
M: 2 Valmet 611 CSMP diesels; 2 Hamilton Model 1341 waterjets; 340 bhp

Remarks: Were to be operated by crews or under remote control by *Kuha*-class inshore minesweepers, but are now operated in manned mode only. Glass-reinforced plastic construction. Tow a Type F-82 electrode sweep to counter magnetic mines and can also counter acoustic mines. *Kiskii 1* was a trials prototype.

AMPHIBIOUS WARFARE SHIPS

◆ **3 Kampela-class utility landing craft** Bldr: Enso-Gutzeit, Savonlinna

Kampela 1 (In serv. 29-7-76) Kampela 3 (In serv. 23-10-79)
Kampela 2 (In serv. 21-10-76)

Kampela class Finnish Navy, 1984

D: 90 tons (260 fl) **S:** 9 kts **Dim:** 32.5 × 8.0 × 1.5
A: 4/23-mm AA (II × 2)—mines
Electron Equipt: Radar: 1/ . . . nav.
M: 2 Scania diesels; 2 props; 460 bhp **Crew:** 10 tot.

Remarks: *Kampela 3* built by Finnmekano, Teija.

◆ **6 Kala-class utility landing craft** Bldr: Rauma-Repola, Rauma (In serv. 1956–59)

Kala 1 Kala 2 Kala 3 Kala 4 Kala 5 Kala 6

Kala 6 Alexander Sheldon Duplaix, 7-8

D: 60 tons (200 fl) **S:** 9 kts **Dim:** 27.0 × 8.0 × 1.8
A: 1/20-mm AA—34 mines **Electron Equipt:** Radar: 1/ . . . nav.
M: 2 Valmet diesels; 2 props; 360 bhp **Crew:** 10 tot.

Note: The five *Kave*-class landing craft, *Kave 1* through *Kave 6,* were stricken 1990

◆ **2 Lohi-class personnel transports** Bldr: Savonlinna SY (In serv. 7-9-84)

251 Lohi 452 Lohm

Lohm (452) Alexander Sheldon Duplaix, 7-

D: 28 tons (38 fl) **S:** 24 kts **Dim:** 20.50 × 5.90 × 1.00
A: 2/23-mm AA (II × 1)—1/12.7-mm mg—mines
Electron Equipt: Radar: 1/Decca . . . nav.
M: 2 Wizeman-Mercedes-Benz diesels; 2 KaMeWa waterjets; 1,100 bhp
Range: 240/24 **Crew:** 4 tot.

Remarks: Have a near-vertical bow door and ramp for landing personnel embarke Ordered 17-1-83 and laid down 8-83 and 9-83. Aluminum construction. Used as V transports, patrol craft, hospital launches, etc. Guns not always mounted.

◆ **9 Meriusko-class assault boats** Bldr: Alumina Varvet, Kokkola

U-203–U-211 (In serv. 1986)

D: 8.5 tons (10.2 fl) **S:** 36 kts (30 loaded) **Dim:** 11.3 × 3.5 × 0.9
M: 2 Volvo TAMD70E diesels; 2 Hamilton 291 waterjets; 600 bhp
Crew: 48 troops

Remarks: Small bow ramp. U 203 and one other have cable-handling equipment enable them to act as boom-defense boats.

◆ **2 Vietivisko class** Bldr: Alumina Varvet, Kokkola (In serv. 1983)

U-201 U-202

D: 10.72 tons (fl) **S:** 25 kts **Dim:** . . . × . . . × . . .
M: 2 Volvo TAMD70E diesels; 2 props; 600 bhp

Remarks: Similar to Meriusko class.

AUXILIARY SHIPS

◆ **1 trials ship** Bldr: Reposaaron Konepaja, Pori

	Laid down	L	In serv.
826 Isku	11-68	4-12-69	1970

XILIARY SHIPS *(continued)*

:u (826) Finnish Navy, 1990

D: 180 tons (fl) **S:** 18 kts **Dim:** 33.35 × 8.70 × 1.80
A: . . . mines **Electron Equipt:** Radar: 1/Raytheon ARPA nav.
M: 4 Soviet M50-F4 diesels; 4 props; 4,800 bhp **Crew:** 25 tot.

Remarks: "Seasled" planing hull with rectangular planform. Built as a guided mis- patrol boat and armed with four Soviet SS-N-2a Styx missiles and a twin 30-mm 230 AA mount. Never made designed speed and in recent years was relegated to s duties. In 1989–90 was lengthened 7 m by Uusikaupunki Shipyard, deckhouse thened, minerails added, and an articulated crane added near the bow.

1 pollution-cleanup ship

	Bldr	Laid down	L	In serv.
HALLI	Hollming, Rauma	18-3-86	25-6-86	1-87

D: . . . . . . **S:** 11.3 kts
Dim: 60.50 × 12.40 × . . . (5.6 moulded depth)
Electron Equipt: Radar: . . .
M: 2 Wärtsilä Vasa 6R22 diesels; 2 Aquamaster swiveling props; 2,650 bhp
Range: 3,000/11.3 **Crew:** . . .

Remarks: 1,400 grt/1,200 dwt. Enlarged version of *Hylse.* Employs McGregor-Navire LORI pollution-collection system, sweeps 30-m path at 1.5 kts. Has 360-m^3 waste- ection tank. Can also be used as a landing ship and logistic support vessel; has 11-m ramp for 48-ton vehicles. Operated for the Ministry of the Environment by the istry of Navigation under navy control with a civilian crew.

1 pollution-cleanup ship Bldr: Laivateollisuus, Turku

HYLSE (In serv. 3-6-81)

D: 1,500 (fl) **S:** 7 kts **Dim:** 49.9 × 12.5 × 3.0
M: 2 Saab-Scania DSI-14 diesels; 2 retractable, steerable props; 680 bhp

Remarks: Operated for the Ministry of the Environment by the Ministry of Transpor- on under navy control with civilian crew. Can carry 100 tons of deck cargo. Storage ks can hold 550 m^3 of recovered seawater/oil slurry and 850 m^3 recovered oil. One n and one 13-m oil-skimming boat carried.

1 cable ship Bldr: Rauma-Repola, Rauma

PUTSAARI (L: 15-12-65)

D: 430 tons (fl) **S:** 10 kts **Dim:** 45.5 × 8.9 × 2.3
M: 1 Wärtsilä diesel; 1 prop; 450 bhp **Crew:** 20 tot.

Remarks: Refitted 1987 by Wärtsilä. Has two 10-ton cable winches and bow cable- ng sheaves. Capable of operating in light ice.

1 salvage ship Bldr: Laivateollisuus, Turku (In serv. 1960)

PARAINEN (ex-*Pellinki,* ex-*Meteor*)

rainen (420) Leo Van Ginderen, 1991

D: 700 tons (fl) **S:** 12 kts **Dim:** 38.50 × 9.25 × 4.10
A: 2/23-mm AA (II × 1)
Electron Equipt: Radar: 1/. . . . . . nav.
M: 2 Crossley diesels; 1 prop; 1,200 bhp **Crew:** 17 tot.

Remarks: Former tug, acquired 1978 from Oy Neptun Ab, then refitted and equipped for salvage duties by Teijon Telakka. Gun mount not always aboard.

♦ **2 headquarters ships** Bldr: Valmet, Turku

93 KEMIÖ (ex-*Valvoja II*) (In serv. 1958)
99 KUSTAANMIEKKA (ex-*Valvoja III*) (In serv. 1963)

Kemiö (93) Leo Van Ginderen, 1991

D: 340 tons (fl) **S:** 11 kts **Dim:** 36.70 × 9.40 × 3.20
A: 2/23-mm AA (II × 1) **Electron Equipt:** Radar: 1/. . . nav.
M: 1 Burmeister & Wain Alpha diesel; 1 prop; 480 bhp
Fuel: 38.5 tons **Electric:** 5 kw **Crew:** 10 tot.

Remarks: 406 grt. Former buoy tenders, acquired from Board of Navigation in 1983 and 1989, respectively, and refitted for naval service by Hollming, Rauma. Twin 23-mm replaced 40-mm Bofors AA on bow, 1988.

SERVICE CRAFT

♦ **1 modified Valas-class diving tender** Bldr: Hollming Oy, Rauma

. . . MERSU (In serv. 10-80)

D: 300 tons (fl) **S:** 12 kts **Dim:** 30.65 × 8.1 × 3.4
A: 2/23-mm AA (II × 1)—1/12.7-mm mg
Electron Equipt: Radar: 1/Decca . . . nav.
M: 1 Wärtsilä Vasa 22 diesel; 1 prop; 1,450 bhp
Crew: 1 officer, 6 enlisted + 20 divers

Remarks: Can also be used to transport 300 personnel. Appearance generally as the *Valas* class.

♦ **4 Valas-class general-service tenders** Bldr: Hollming Oy, Rauma (In serv. 1979–81)

220 VALAS 221 VAHAKARI 222 VAARLEHTI 223 VÄNÖ

Vaarlehti (222) Leo Van Ginderen, 10-90

D: 100 tons (275 fl) **S:** 12 kts **Dim:** 30.65 × 7.85 × 3.40
A: 2/23-mm AA (II × 1)—1/12.7-mm mg—20 mines
Electron Equipt: Radar: 1/Decca . . . nav.
M: 1 Wärtsilä Vasa 22 diesel; 1 prop; 1,300 bhp **Crew:** 11 tot.

Remarks: Ordered 1978. Can break .4-meter ice. Carry 30 tons of cargo or 150 passengers. Stern ramp for vehicle-loading or minelaying.

♦ **2 Pukkio-class general-service tenders** Bldr: Valmet, Turku (In serv. 1947–48)

420 PANSIO 421 PORKKALA

D: 162 tons **S:** 10 kts **Dim:** 28.5 × 6.0 × 2.7
A: mines **Electron Equipt:** Radar: 1/ . . . nav.
M: 1 Wärtsilä diesel; 1 prop; 300 bhp **Crew:** 10 tot.

Remarks: Used as tugs, transports, patrol boats, and minelayers. Sister *Pyharänta* (422) stricken 1990.

SERVICE CRAFT *(continued)*

◆ **6 Hauki-class personnel transports** Bldr: First three: Linnan Telakka, Turku; others: Valmet Oy, Kolka (In serv. 1978–80)

133 Havouri	232 Hauki	235 Hirsala
334 Hankoniemi	431 Hakuni	436 Houtskär

Hankoniemi (334) 1980

D: 46 tons (fl) **S:** 10 kts **Dim:** 14.4 × 4.6 × 2.2
M: 2 Valmet 611 CSM diesels; 1 prop; 280 bhp **Crew:** 2 tot.

Remarks: Cargo: 40 personnel or 6 tons supplies. Can break .2-meter ice. Operated for the Coast Artillery.

◆ **1 presidential yacht** Bldr: Uusikaupanki SY (In serv. 5-84)

Kultaranta VII

D: 15 tons (fl) **S:** 25 kts **Dim:** 12.5 × 4.0 × 1.4
M: 2 diesels; 2 props; 700 bhp

Remarks: Described as a "communications ship" and used as a presidential yacht in summer and for search and rescue and medical transport in winter.

◆ **1 GRP-hulled transport and command launch** Bldr: . . .

541 Vihuri (In serv. 1988)

D: 13 tons (fl) **S:** 30 kts **Dim:** 13.0 × 4.0 × 0.9
M: 2 diesels; 2 waterjets; 772 bhp

◆ **2 GRP-hulled personnel/command launches** Bldr: . . . . . .

241 Askeri 91 Viiri

D: 20 tons (fl) **S:** 20 kts **Dim:** 16.0 × 4.4 × 1.4
M: 2 diesels; 2 props; . . . bhp

◆ **7 RV 37-series patrol launches** Bldr: Hollming, Rauma (In serv. 1978–85)

RV 37–41 RV 142 RV 243

D: 20 tons (fl) **S:** 12 kts **Dim:** 14.3 × 3.6 × 1.6
M: 1 Mercedes-Benz diesel; 1 prop; 300 bhp

◆ **9 PV 11-class patrol launches** Bldr: Fiskar's, Turku (In serv. 9-84)

PV 11, 12, 104, 108, 205, 209, 210, 306, 307

D: 10 tons **S:** 29 kts **Dim:** . . . × . . . × . . .
M: 2 Volvo Penta diesels; . . . bhp

Note: Also in use for patrol and search-and-rescue duties by the Coastal Artillery are 29 older patrol craft: RV 1 class (1965): 17 tons; RV 8 (1958): 10 tons; 9 RV 9 series (1959–60): 12 tons; 11 RV 10 series (1961–63): 18 tons; and 7 RV 30 series (1973–74): 19 tons. All can make 10 kts. Two 6-ton, 13-kt launches were delivered in 1986.

◆ **2 harbor tugs** Bldr: Teijon Telakka (In serv. 12-85)

731 Haukipää 831 Kallanpää

D: 38 grt **S:** 9 kts **Dim:** 14.0 × 5.0 × 2.3
M: 2 diesels; 2 vertical cycloidal props; 360 bhp **Crew:** 2 tot.

◆ **1 fuel and water lighter**

PA 3 (In serv. 1979)

D: 540 tons (fl) **S:** 2 kts (normally towed) **Dim:** . . . × . . . × . . .

FRONTIER GUARD

Operated by the Ministry of the Interior. All ships now have black hulls with a red-white-red diagonal stripe, as on U.S. Coast Guard ships. Upperworks are white.

Aviation: Fixed-wing aircraft include two Fokker F-27 Mk 400M Maritime and two Piper PA-31 patrol aircraft. Helicopters include six Mi-8 Hip and two Aerospatiale AS 332B Super Puma helicopters, all equipped with French dipping sonars for ASW wo[rk]. Two more Super Puma ASW-capable helicopters were ordered in 1991. Also in serv[ice] are an Agusta-Bell AB 412 Griffin utility/transport helicopter and two Agusta-Bell 206B JetRanger utility helicopters.

PATROL SHIPS

◆ **2 improved Turva class** Bldr: Rauma-Repola Oy, Uusikaupunki

	Laid down	L	In serv.
Tursas	4-9-85	31-1-86	6-6-86
Uisko	4-4-86	19-6-86	27-1-87

Tursas Rauma-Repola, 1[…]

D: 750 tons (fl) **S:** 15.5 kts **Dim:** 49.00 (43.80 pp) × 10.40 × 4.00
A: 2/23-mm AA (II × 1)
Electron Equipt:
Radar: 2/ . . . nav.
Sonar: Simrad SS 105 (14 kHz)
M: 2 Wärtsilä Vasa 8-R22 diesels; 2 props; 3,200 bhp
Electric: 1,070 kw (1 × 750 kw, 2 × 160 kw)
Fuel: 73 tons **Crew:** 32 tot.

Remarks: First unit ordered 12-12-84, second on 20-3-86. Ice-strengthened hu[ll], equipped for towing and salvage duties. Sister ordered for Sweden, 1989.

◆ **3 (+ 1) Kiisla class** Bldr: Hollming Oy, Rauma

	Laid down	L	In serv.
Kiisla	12-2-86	18-9-86	25-5-87
Kurki	3-8-89	. . .	11-90
. . . . . .	. . .	. . .	1991
. . . . . .	. . .	. . .	1992

Kurki Hollming, 1[…]

D: 250 tons (270 fl) **S:** 25 kts **Dim:** 48.30 (41.80 pp) × 8.80 × 2.2[…]
A: 2/23-mm AA (II × 1)
Electron Equipt:
Radar: 2/ . . . nav. —Sonar: Simrad SS 304 hull-mounted and VD[…]
M: 2 MTU 16V538 TB93 diesels; 2 KaMeWa 90S62 waterjets; 4,500 bhp
Fuel: 53 tons **Electric:** 264 kw **Crew:** 22 tot.

Remarks: *Kiisla* ordered 21-11-84; the other three on 22-11-88. Aluminum const[ruc]tion. Can also act as minesweepers, minelayers, or ASW escorts; in the latter mode, [can] carry 2 Soviet RBU-1200 RL (V × 2). Equipped for fire fighting and carry a 5.7-m r[igid] inflatable inspection boat. Have Rademac 2100 E/C electro-optical surveillance de[vice] atop pilothouse.

TROL SHIPS *(continued)*

improved Valpas class Bldr: Laivateollisuus Oy, Turku

VA (In serv. 15-12-77)

va Leo Van Ginderen, 1990

: 550 tons (fl) **S:** 16 kts **Dim:** 48.5 × 8.6 × 3.9
: 1/20-mm Oerlikon AA
lectron Equipt:
Radar: 2/ . . . nav.
Sonar: Simrad SS 105 (14 kHz)
: 2 Wärtsilä diesels; 1 prop; 2,000 bhp **Crew:** 22 tot.

arks: Ordered 24-6-75. An improved *Valpas;* similar in appearance. Can be pped with a twin 23-mm AA gun mount on the forecastle.

1 Valpas class Bldr: Laivateollisuus Oy, Turku

	Laid down	L	In serv.
PAS	20-5-70	22-12-70	21-7-71

pas Leo Van Ginderen, 1-90

: 545 tons **S:** 15 kts **Dim:** 48.3 × 8.7 × 4.0
: 1/20-mm Oerlikon AA
lectron Equipt:
Radar: 2/ . . . nav.
Sonar: Simrad SS 105 (14 kHz)
: 1 Werkspoor TMABS-398 diesel; 1 CP prop; 2,000 bhp
rew: 22 tot.

arks: Ice-strengthened; equipped for towing, fire fighting, and salvage duties.

1 Silmä class Bldr: Laivateollisuus Oy, Turku

	Laid down	L	In serv.
MÄ	30-8-62	23-3-63	19-8-63

mä Leo Van Ginderen, 1990

D: 530 tons **S:** 15 kts **Dim:** 48.3 × 8.3 × 4.3
A: 1/20-mm Oerlikon AA
Electron Equipt: Radar: 2/ . . . nav.—Sonar: Simrad SS 105
M: 1 Werkspoor diesel; 1 prop; 1,800 bhp **Crew:** 22 tot.

Remarks: Equipped for fire fighting, towing, and salvage.

PATROL BOATS

♦ **3 Tiira class** Bldr: Valmet-Laivateollisuus, Turku

	Laid down	L	In serv.
Tiira	11-3-85	5-9-85	1-11-85
Kajava	25-11-85	25-3-86	28-8-86
Kihu	7-4-86	7-86	17-12-86

Kihu Leo Van Ginderen, 1990

D: 65 tons (fl) **S:** 25+ kts
Dim: 26.80 (24.20 pp) × 5.50 × 1.40 (1.85 props)
A: 1/20-mm AA
Electron Equipt: Radar: 1/. . . nav.—Sonar: Simrad SS-242
M: 2 MTU 8V396 TB82 diesels; 2 props; 2,286 bhp
Electric: 62 kVa **Fuel:** 8 tons **Crew:** 2 officers, 6 enlisted

Remarks: Development of *Lokki* design, with hard-chine vice round-bilged hull form. Aluminum construction. Can be fitted with a second 20-mm AA. Planned second trio not ordered.

♦ **1 Lokki class** Bldr: Valmet-Laivateollisuus, Turku

Lokki (In serv. 27-11-81)

Lokki Leo Van Ginderen, 1990

D: 53 tons (60 fl) **S:** 25 kts **Dim:** 26.80 × 5.20 × 1.40 (1.85 props)
A: 1/20-mm AA **Electron Equipt:** Radar: 1/ . . . nav.
M: MTU 8V396 TB83 diesels; 2 props; 2,040 bhp
Electric: 62 kVa **Crew:** 8 tot.

Remarks: Aluminum construction. Ordered 17-5-80.

♦ **1 Viima class** Bldr: Laivateollisuus Oy, Turku

	L	In serv.
Viima	20-7-64	12-10-64

D: 135 tons **S:** 23 kts **Dim:** 35.7 × 6.6 × 2.0
A: 1/20-mm Oerlikon AA **Electron Equipt:** Radar: 1/ . . . nav.
M: 3 Maybach diesels; 3 CP props; 4,050 bhp **Crew:** 12 tot.

Remarks: A variant of the Finnish Navy's *Ruissalo* class.

♦ **3 Koskelo class** Bldr: Valmet, Helsinki (In serv. 1955–60)

Telkkä Kuikka Tavi

D: 75 tons (97 fl) **S:** 23 kts **Dim:** 29.42 × 5.02 × 1.5
A: 1/20-mm Madsen AA **Electron Equipt:** Radar: 2/ . . . nav.
M: Mercedes-Benz diesels; 2 props; 2,700 bhp **Crew:** 11 tot.

Remarks: *Telkkä* used as training ship. Modernized and re-engined 1970–74 by Laivateollisuus, Turku. Sisters *Kaakkuri, Koskelo, Kuovi,* and *Kiisla* stricken 1986–87, *Kurki* in 1990.

PATROL BOATS *(continued)*

Telkkä Leo Van Ginderen, 1989

PATROL CRAFT

♦ **9 PV 11 class** Bldr: Fiskar's Oy, Turku (In serv. 1984–85)

PV 11 PV 12 PV 104
PV 108 PV 205 PV 209
PV 210 PV 306 PV 307

D: 10 tons (fl) **S:** 28 kts **Dim:** 10.0 × . . . × . . .
Electron Equipt: Radar: 1/ . . . nav.
M: 2 diesels; 2 waterjets; . . . bhp

♦ **7 RV 37 class** Bldr: Hollming Oy, Rauma (In serv. 1978–85)

RV 37 RV 38 RV 39 RV 40 RV 41 RV 142 RV 243

D: 20 tons (fl) **S:** 12 kts **Dim:** 14.3 × 3.6 × 1.6
Electron Equipt: Radar: 1/ . . . nav.
M: 1 Mercedes-Benz diesel; 300 bhp

Note: Also in Frontier Guard service are the following small patrol launches:
7 RV 30 class: 19 tons (fl), 10 kts, built 1973–74
11 RV 10 class: 18 tons (fl), 10 kts, built 1961–63
9 RV 9 class: 12 tons (fl), 10 kts, built 1959–60
RV 8: 10 tons (fl), 10 kts, built 1958
RV 1 (ex-RV 41): 17 tons (fl), 10 kts, built 1965
In addition, there are two 6-ton tenders, and a new class of five small patrol craft was ordered late in 1989 from Waterman Oy, Teijo.

BOARD OF NAVIGATION

ICEBREAKERS

♦ **2 Otso class** Bldr: Wärtsilä, Helsinki

	L	In serv.		L	In serv.
Otso	12-7-85	30-1-86	Kontio	30-7-86	29-1-87

Otso and Kontio Alexander Sheldon Duplaix, 7-88

D: 8,500 tons (fl) **S:** 18.5 kts
Dim: 99.0 (90.0 pp) × 24.20 (23.50 wl) × 8.00
Electron Equipt: Radar: 3/ . . . nav. **Crew:** 28 tot.
M: 4 Wärtsilä Vasa 16V32 diesels (7,425 bhp each); Kymi-Stromberg a.c. cyclo-converters; 2 props; 20,400 shp (17,700 sust.)

Remarks: *Otso* ordered 29-3-84, *Kontio* on 29-11-85. Have 2 transverse thrusters, bow-thruster, Wärtsilä "bubbler" system.

♦ **2 Urho class** Bldr: Wärtsilä, Helsinki

Urho (In serv. 5-3-75) Sisu (In serv. 28-1-76)

Sisu and Urho Florian Jentsch, 1989

D: 7,960 tons (9,500 fl) **S:** 18 kts **Dim:** 104.6 × 23.8 × 8.3
Electron Equipt: Radar: 3/ . . . nav. **Crew:** 45 tot.
M: 5 SEMT-Pielstick 5,000-bhp diesels, electric drive; 4 props; 22,000 shp

Remarks: Sisters to Swedish *Atle* class. One helicopter. Two props forward, two

♦ **3 Tarmo class** Bldr: Wärtsilä, Helsinki

Tarmo (In serv. 1963) Varma (In serv. 1968) Apu (In serv. 197

Apu, Tarmo, and Varma Florian Jentsch, 1

D: 4,890 tons **S:** 17 kts **Dim:** 85.7 × 21.7 × 6.8
Electron Equipt: Radar: 2/ . . . nav. **Crew:** 45–55 tot.
M: 4 Sulzer diesels, electric drive; 4 props; 10,000 shp

Remarks: Two props forward, two aft.

♦ **1 Voima class** Bldr: Wärtsilä, Helsinki

Voima (In serv. 1954)

Voima Leo Van Ginderen, 1

D: 4,415 tons **S:** 16.5 kts **Dim:** 83.6 × 19.4 × 6.8
Electron Equipt: Radar: 2/ . . . nav. **Crew:** . . . tot.
M: 6 Wärtsilä Vasa 16V22 diesels (17,460 bhp), electric drive; 4 pro 14,000 shp

Remarks: Reconstructed and re-engined 1978–79 by Wärtsilä; expected to serve 1994.

♦ **1 harbor icebreaker, ex-buoy tender** Bldr: Rauma-Repola Oy, Rauma

Letto (In serv. . . .)

Remarks: 735 grt. No other data available. Conversion by Hollming for service harbor icebreaker and pollution-control ship completed 11-5-89.

♦ **1 harbor icebreaker** Bldr: Rauma-Repola Oy, Rauma

Harun (In serv.: 14-5-86)

D: 115 grt **S:** 13 kts **Dim:** 35.0 × 8.2 × 3.0
M: 1 Wärtsilä Vasa diesel; 1 prop; 1,200 bhp

Remarks: Also intended as a general-purpose tender and support craft.

NLAND *(continued)*

LLUTION-CONTROL SHIPS

2 buoy tender/pollution-control craft Bldr: Rauma-Repola, Rauma

MMELI SEKTORI (Both in serv. 31-5-85)

: . . . tons (fl) **S:** 10 kts **Dim:** 28.2 × 7.9 × 2.5
1: 2 diesels; 1 prop; 700 bhp

3 pollution-control craft Bldr: . . . . . .

I 1 OILI 2 OILI 3

2 MacGregor-Navire, 1987

: . . . tons **S:** 10 kts **Dim:** 23.5 × . . . × . . .
1: 2 diesels; 2 Kort-nozzle props; . . .

arks: Lengthened 1987 by 5.5 m to incorporate the MacGregor-Navire MAC-I pollution-control system, which is also installed in *Kummeli* and *Sektori*. Have a ramp and can be used as logistics transports.

e: The larger pollution-control ships *Halli* (899) and *Hylse* (799) are operated by Finnish Navy for the Ministry of the Environment. The Board of Navigation also ates 9 other buoy tenders and pollution-control/cleanup craft (including the *Kum-*), and 14 transport ships.

RANCE

nch Republic

sonnel (1-1-91): 65,295 men and women on active duty, including 4,571 officers, 54 petty officers, 11,172 enlisted ratings and 19,098 conscripts.

al Aviation: Principal combat aircraft in service (numbers in parentheses indi- first-line units) include: 19 (12) F-8E Crusader interceptors, 59 (38) Super-dard fighter-bombers; 11 (8) Étendard IVP photoreconnaissance aircraft; 26 (18) ernized Alizé shipboard ASW aircraft; 7 Atlantique Mk 2 (7); 37 (21) Atlantic Mk 1, 5 (5) Gardian surveillance aircraft; 16 (12) Super-Frélon heavy helicopters; and 36 WG-13 Lynx light ASW helicopters. Also in naval service are 147 other support training aircraft and helicopters.

e: The French Navy was reorganized into two Maritime Regions on 6-9-90; the Maritime Region is headquartered at Brest and the Second at Toulon.

WEAPONS AND SYSTEMS

MISSILES

strategic ballistic

ntered service in 1985 aboard *L'Inflexible*. Characteristics include:

otal height: 11.05 m Diameter: 1.93 m Launch: powder charge
aunch weight: 36 tons (first stage: 20 tons; second stage: 8 tons; third stage: 1.5 tons)
hrust: First stage: 70 tons; second stage: 30 tons; third stage: 7 tons
uration of thrust: first stage 65 sec.; second stage: 75 sec.; third stage: 45 sec.
1ax. range: 4,000 km (M4B: 5,000) Payload: 6 × 150-kt warheads

reater precision and with improved penetration over the retired M20. The launch rval is shorter between missiles than with the M20 and is capable of being carried at greater depths. The first at-sea firings took place in early 3-82. M4 was back-d into all earlier submarines except *Le Redoutable* by replacing the existing mis- tubes. The six TN-70 warheads spread over a 150- × 350-km area at a range of 0 km.

M45

Weights and dimensions essentially the same as the M4. Uses the TN-75 reentry vehicle to a range of 5,000 km, although one was officially reported to have traveled 6,000 km on 4-3-86. To be operational in 1994 aboard *Le Triomphant*.

M5

A new weapon being developed for the "second-generation" ballistic-missile submarines and expected to enter service in 2002. To have a range of 7,000 km (3,240 n.m.), with 10 to 12 TN-75 independently targeted warheads (MIRV). The first to carry it will be the fifth ship of the *Le Triomphant* class, and it will be backfitted into earlier units of the class.

♦ surface-to-air

SAAM (Système Surface Anti-Air Missiles) Manufacturer: Aérospatiale

Intended to become operational in 1998 aboard the carrier *Charles de Gaulle*. It will be vertically launched from 8-missile modular cell groups. Guidance will be supported by the Thomson-CSF Arabel (*Antenne Radar à Balayage Électronique*) I/J-band missile-detection radar, which has a range of 100 km. The SAMP-T version is intended for land-based use. The 2-stage "Aster 15" missile, which will be highly maneuverable, will have the following characteristics:

Length: 4.20 m Speed: Mach 2.5
Diameter: 0.18 m Range: 15 km
Weight: 298 kg Maneuverability: 15 g

A 30-km range version, "Aster-30," is also in development in a system known as SAMP/N (*Surface-Air Moyenne Portée Naval*) to replace the SM-1 MR missile during the period 1998–2000 as part of the NATO project FSAF (*Famille de Systèmes Surface-Air Futurs*), which is also known as the LAMS (Local Area Missile System). The development is being shared by France's Aérospatiale (25%) and Thomson-CSF (25%), and Italy's Selenia (50%), with the United Kingdom, Germany, and Spain also involved. The system will incorporate the French Arabel and Astral radars. The following characteristics have been announced:

Length: 4.80 m Speed: Mach 3.5
Weight: 450 kg Range: 30 km
Altitude: 60 to 10,000 m

Masurca

A medium-range missile (30 nautical-mile range, intercept between 100 ft and 75,000 ft) launched by a solid-propellant booster, which in a few seconds brings it to a speed close to Mach 3; a slower-burning solid propellant maintains this speed throughout the flight. The missile and booster together are 8.6 m long and weigh 2,098 kg. Other characteristics are:

	Missile	Booster
Length	5.38 m	3.32 m
Diameter	0.406 m	0.57 m
Span of fins	—	1.5 m
Weight	950.0 kg	1,148.0 kg
Warhead	100.0 kg	—

Mod. 3, a semiactive homing missile, is the only version now in service. It follows a trajectory determined by proportional navigation, keeping its antenna pointed at the target, which is illuminated by the launching ship's radar transmitter.

Masurca, which is installed only in the *Suffren*-class guided-missile destroyers, consists of (1) a target-designator and weapon-assignment console, including a computer, which uses the shipboard search radar and the Senit automatic tactical data system, and (2) two guidance systems, each with: DRBC 51 tracking radar, a director carrying the rear-reference beam and illumination beam for the control system, an illumination beam, a twin launcher, storage and maintenance facilities, including two horizontal ready-service drums containing 18 missiles in addition to reserve missiles in the magazines, and IFF and control equipment.

The Masurca systems aboard the *Suffren* class were modernized 1983–85 to keep the system up-to-date to the end of its expected service life (1998–2000).

Standard SM-1 MR

A one-stage U.S.-designed and manufactured solid-fuel missile.

Length: 4.60 m Guidance: semiactive homing, proximity fuze
Diameter: .41 m Range: 50,000 m, max.
Weight: 590 kg Interception altitude: 60 ft to 80,000 ft

The complete system consists of, in addition to the missile: a Mk 13 launcher, vertical stowage-loader containing 40 missiles; various computers; DRBJ 11B height-finding radar; and 2 SPG-51C tracking radars. SM-1 MR is carried only by the two C-70 AAW-type destroyers. Thirty additional missiles were acquired from the U.S. in 1990.

Crotale/Crotale EDIR Manufacturer: Matra/Thomson-CSF

A French Air Force missile adapted for naval use. Electronics are by Thomson-CSF and the missile by Matra. Characteristics for the R440N missile are:

Length: 2.930 m Speed: Mach 2.4
Diameter: 0.156 m Range: 13,000 m
Span: 0.54 m with fins extended Warhead: 14 kg
Weight: 85.1 kg Launcher: octuple
Interception altitudes: 150 ft to 12,000 ft
Guidance: beam-riding, then detonation by infrared fuze incorporated in the missile

Installed on the F 67 and C 70 destroyer classes, the carriers *Clemenceau* and *Foch*, and four Saudi Arabian frigates and has been acquired by China. In French ships, it is used with DRBV 51C radar and has a Thomson Ku-band tracking radar. Eighteen reload missiles are carried in the magazine.

MISSILES *(continued)*

Crotale has been updated to enable it to handle Mach 2.0 targets at altitudes down to 4 m. The missiles, named Crotale EDIR *(Écartometrie Différentielle Infra Rouge)*, were equipped with a new proximity fuze, and an infrared tracker was added to the launcher/director; range was increased from 8,000 m to 13,000 m.

Crotale Modulaire is a lightweight system installed for trials in the private-venture patrol boat *Iris.* Crotale Modulaire employs an octuple launcher and any number of control systems. A further improvement of the basic missile, designated Crotale NG, will use a VT-1 hypervelocity, Mach 3.5 missile and will be installed in sextuple launchers aboard *La Fayette*-class frigates. One thousand ordered 7-91.

SADRAL *(Système d'Auto Défense Rapprochée Anti-aérienne Léger)*
Manufacturer: Matra

A point-defense, short-range system with a C.S.E.E. automatic director and employing the Mistral IR-homing missile, which has laser-backup proximity and impact fuzing. Characteristics for the missile itself are:

	Weight: 24 kg
Length: 1.80 m	Warhead: 3 kg (1,500 tungsten balls)
Diameter: 0.90 m	Speed: Mach 2.5

Range: under 500 to around 6,000 m, at altitudes down to 3 m.

The missiles are installed in a 950-kg, 6-missile, rapid-reload, lightweight launcher. The system became operational in 1988 in the antiaircraft destroyer *Cassard.* First "operational" firing 23-10-86 from *Île d'Oléron.* SADRAL is also to be installed in the carrier *Charles de Gaulle* and the landing ship *Foudre.*

A lightweight, twin launcher system for Mistral, SIMBAD *(Système Intégre de Mistral Bimunition pour l'Auto Défense)*, for smaller ships, began trials in 1989 aboard *Premier Maître L'Her* (F 792) and is being seriously considered by a number of foreign navies. In the French Navy, it will be employed aboard the *Floréal*-class frigates.

♦ Surface-to-surface

ANS *(Anti-Navire Supersonique)* Manufacturer: Aérospatiale and MBB (Germany)

Intended as the successor to Exocet. Single-stage weapon with integral booster. First launch 21-5-87. Originally intended to enter service around 1994, but withdrawal of German support from 1989 to 1991 contributed to delays, and the system is now expected to be available in 1999. Improved guidance system and countermeasures resistance over Exocet, and will have 10 to 15 g maneuverability. A total buy of 225 is planned.

Length: 5.78 m	Weight: 920 kg
Diameter: 0.35 m	Warhead weight: 180 kg
Speed: Mach 2.0	Range: 180 km

A lightweight, 30-km-ranged version is being developed as the ANL *(Anti-Navire Léger).*

MM 40 Exocet Manufacturer: Aérospatiale

An improved version of the MM 38 and the AM 39, the MM 40 is an over-the-horizon missile whose range is adapted to radar performance and is able to use fire-control data relayed by an outside source. It employs a cylindrical GRP launcher, which, because it is lighter and has fewer fittings than the rectangular metal launcher used by the MM 38, increases firepower by allowing more missiles to be carried. To employ fully the range of the missile, over-the-horizon targeting must be provided by helicopters or aircraft. The missile is initially under inertial guidance, switching to radar terminal homing at a preset distance from the target (usually 12 to 15 km), and the seeker incorporates a number of electronic counter-countermeasures features. It can cruise at preset altitudes between 3 and 15 m. MM 40 is employed by a number of countries worldwide.

Length: 5.80 m	Weight: 850 kg
Diameter: 0.35 m	Warhead weight: 165 kg
Wingspan: 1.135 m	Speed: Mach 1.0
Range: 65 km	

SM 39 Exocet Manufacturer: Aérospatiale

A submarine torpedo-tube-launched version of the Exocet concept, SM 39 began in 1981 aboard the *Narval*-class submarine *Requin.* With its solid-fueled launch/ejection capsule, the missile fits within a 533-mm torpedo tube. After broaching the surface, the missile rises to 50 m and then descends to cruising altitude. The system became operational 1985 on *Saphir* and is employed only by the French Navy, aboard ballistic missile submarines, nuclear-powered attack submarines, and the diesel submarines of the *Agosta* class. Thirty-six ordered 1986.

Length: 4.69 m (5.80 in capsule)	Warhead weight: 165 kg
Diameter: 0.35 m	Range: 50 km
Wingspan: 1.135 m	Speed: Mach 1.0
Weight: 652 kg (1,350 with capsule)	

MM 38 Exocet: Manufacturer: Aérospatiale

A fire-and-forget homing missile with solid-fuel propulsion. The fire-control solution requires a fix on the target provided by the surface radar of the firing ship and uses the necessary equipment for launching the missile and determining the correct range and height bearing of the target.

The missile is launched at a slight elevation (about 15°). After the boost phase, it reaches its flight altitude of between 3 and 15 meters. Altitude is maintained by a radar altimeter.

During the first part of the flight, the missile is automatically guided by an inertial system that has received the azimuth of the target. When within a certain distance from the target, an automatic homing radar begins to seek the target, picks it up, and directs the missile. Great effort has been made to protect the missile from countermeasures during this phase. A "Super ADAC" seeker, with improved anti-jamming features, is offered for backfit to earlier missiles.

Detonation takes place upon impact or by pseudo-proximity (time-to-target estimation) fuze, according to interception conditions, size of the target ship, and the condition of the sea.

Length: 5.20 m	Wingspan: 1.00 m
Diameter: 0.35 m	Warhead weight: 165 kg
Speed: Mach 1.0	Range: 42 km
Weight: 735 kg	

B. AVIATION MISSILES

♦ Air-to-ground

ASMP *(Air-Surface à Moyenne Porte)* Manufacturer: Aérospatiale

Entering service in 1990–91 on the Super-Étendard fighter-bombers attached to carrier *Foch,* the ASMP has a 300-kt nuclear warhead. It uses inertial guidance, h radar altimeter, and is very resistant to countermeasures. Range is dependen the altitude and speed of the launch aircraft. Operational 1-5-86 on the land-b Mirage IV.

Length: 5.30 m	Weight: 840 kg	Diameter: 0.35 m
Range: 100–350 km	Wingspan: 0.956 m	Speed: Mach 2.4

AM 39 Exocet Manufacturer: Aérospatiale

This is the air-to-sea version of the MM 38. After being launched, it has the s flight characteristics as the MM 38. Range is dependent on the altitude and speed o launch aircraft.

Length: 4.633 m	Weight: 650 kg (warhead: 165 kg)
Diameter: 0.348 m	Range: 50–70 km
Wingspan: 1.004 m	Speed: Mach 1.0

Operational since 1978, AM 39 is a "fire-and-forget" missile that permits an airc that has fired to renew its attack or to seek a new target. In the French Navy, it is with the Atlantique Mk 2 patrol aircraft, the Super-Étendard aircraft, and the Su Frélon helicopter.

AS 37 Martel Manufacturers: Matra and British Aerospace

Two types, television and anti-radar. Only the latter is used in the French Nav

Length: 4.122 m	Weight: 531 m	Diameter: 0.40 m
Range: over 20,000 m	Wingspan: 1.192 m	

The missile homes on the radar emissions of the enemy vessel. Immediately a being fired, the missile is on its own, permitting the launch aircraft to depart or ev Used with Atlantic Mk 1 aircraft.

AS 30 Manufacturer: Aérospatiale

Radio command or laser-designated (AS 30L) weapon for firing from a maneuve aircraft at middle, low, or very low altitude. Used by the Super-Étendard. Ra dependent on speed and altitude of launch aircraft.

Length: 3.785 m	Wingspan: 1.000 m
Diameter: 0.342 m	Weight: 528 kg

Range: maximum 9 to 12,000 m; minimum 1,500 m

AS 20 Manufacturer: Aérospatiale

Training missile for the AS 30. Radio command guidance. Range dependen launch aircraft speed and altitude.

Length: 2.60 m	Wingspan: 0.80 m	Weight: 140 kg
Diameter: 0.25 m	Range: 4,000 to 8,000 m	

AS 15 TT Manufacturer: Aérospatiale

For use by light helicopters (Dauphin, Lynx); developed under the Saudi Ara "Sawari" program. Export weapon; not employed by the French Navy. First produc deliveries 3-85. A surface-launched version, MM 15, is also offered.

Length: 2.16 m	Range: 15 km	Weight: 96 kg

AS 12 Manufacturer: Aérospatiale

A wire-guided system with optical aim. Used by WG-13 Lynx helicopter.

Length: 1.870 m	Wingspan: 0.650 m
Diameter: 0.210 m	Weight: 75 kg

Range: maximum 7,500 to 8,000 m; minimum 1,500 m

AS 11 Manufacturer: Aérospatiale

A wire-guided system with optical alignment on the target. Used for training by 175 aircraft.

Length: 1.210 m	Diameter: 0.164 m
Wingspan: 0.50 m	Weight: 29.9 kg

♦ Air-to-air

R 530 Manufacturer: Matra

There are two versions of this missile: infrared (IR) and semi-passive radar-hor (EMD). Used by Crusader interceptors.

Length: IR type: 3.198 m; EMD type: 3.284 m
Diameter: 0.263 m Wingspan: 1.103 m
Weight: IR type: 193.5 kg, EMD type: 192 kg
Range: maximum 10,000 m; minimum 5,000 m

R 550 Magic Manufacturer: Matra

Length: 2.900 m	Weight: 89 kg
Diameter: 0.157 m	Range: 300/8,000 m
Wingspan: 0.660 m	Guidance: infrared-homing

Mica Manufacturer: Matra

Active radar or infrared-homing being developed as the successor to Magic for u the Rafale fighter.

ATION MISSILES *(continued)*

ength: 10.00 m | Weight: 100 kg
iameter: 0.16 m | Warhead weight: 12 kg
ingspan: . . . m | Range: 50 km

ewinder Manufacturer: Ford Instrument and Raytheon

e French Navy uses this air-to-air American missile (*see* U.S.A. section).

UNS

mm Compact Manufacturer: USINOR/Creusot-Loire

ngle-barrel automatic, for export only. Standard installations have a 42-round azine, while those for Malaysia had 90-round magazines. Also used by Saudi ia and China.

eight of mount: 17.3 tons | Length of barrel: 55 calibers
ange: 17,200 m | Muzzle-velocity: 870 m/sec.
ax. effective range for surface fire: 12,000 m
ax. effective range for antiaircraft fire: 6,000 m
ax. rate of fire: 20, 45, or 90 rpm, or single file
rc of elevation: -15° to +80°
ax. speed: training 50°/sec, elevation 33°/sec

mm Models 1953, 1964, and 1968

ngle-barrel automatic, for use against aircraft, surface vessels, or land targets. el 1968 is a lighter version of Model 1953; Model 1964 is virtually identical to el 1953. The ammunition is the same for all three. Models 1953 and 1964 require operators on-mount, while Model 1968 can operate in full automatic. Characteris- f Model 1968:

eight of mount: 22 tons length of barrel: 55 calibers
ange at 40° elevation: 17,000 m
aximum effective range for surface fire: 15,000 m
aximum effective range for antiaircraft fire: 8,000 m
aximum rate of fire: 78 rounds/minute
rc of elevation: -15° to +80°
aximum speed: training 40°/sec, elevation 25°/sec

odel 1953 and Model 1964 use an analog fire-control system with electro- anical and electronic equipment for the fire-control solution. The director can be ated in optical and radar modes. Used in *Jeanne d'Arc,* the *Suffren* class, and the *Rivière* class.

odel 1968 uses a digital fire-control system, with central units, and memory disks agnetic tape for data storage. Light radar gun director. Optical direction equip- can be added. Used in the *Tourville* class and *Aconit.* The first four units of the *ges Leygues* class, *Duperré,* and the A-69-class frigates employ a hybrid system of al and analog computers. In *Primauguet* and later *Georges Leygues*-class frigates, *Cassard* class, and the *Suffren* class, control is effected by multiple sensors. the CADAM (*CAdence De tir AMéliorée*) program, the rate of fire of all three ons was increased from the original 60 rds/min to 78 rds/min.

nm L/60

ench-made, Bofors-design general-purpose weapon used aboard P 400-class gun- s and a number of amphibious warfare and auxiliary classes in single mountings.

ube length: 60 calibers | Muzzle velocity: 853 m/sec.
eight: 2 tons | Range: 3,600 m max. practical
ate of fire: 130 rds/min

nm CN MIT-20F2 Manufacturer: GIAT

general-purpose weapon on a DCAN-designed mounting, used aboard P 400-class oats and a number of amphibious warfare classes. Generally known as the "F2." two 300-rd ready-service magazines attached.

ength: 2.60 m overall | Muzzle velocity: . . .
eight: 322 kg empty | Rate of fire: 650–720 rds/min
rc of elevation: −15° to +65°

nm Oerlikon

eneral-purpose mounting still found on mine countermeasures ships, etc. Employs d ammunition canisters.

ength: 2.20 m overall | Muzzle velocity: . . .
Veight: 480 kg empty | Rate of fire: 450 rds/min
rc of elevation: −15° to +90°

e: Two point-defense gun systems are under private development: Satan omson-CSF and General Electric), using the Castor II fire-control radar, and Samos GEM and General Electric), with an optronic fire-control system.

ANTISUBMARINE WEAPONS

as (MIssile de Lutte ASM) Manufacturer: Matra and OTO Melara

combination of the new Murène MU-90 torpedo and the Otomat missile. To enter ice around 1996 as a replacement for Malafon in the *Tourville* class.

ength: 6.0 m | Weight: 800 kg Cruise altitude: 200 m
iameter: 0.46 m | Speed: 1,080 m/sec.
ingspan: 1.06 m | Range: 5–55 km

Malafon Manufacturer: Latécoère, with St. Tropez Arsenal

A glider that carries L 4 torpedoes and is launched with the assistance of twin solid-fuel booster rockets. It is stabilized by automatic pilot and guided by radio command. The Malafon is installed in the two *Suffren*-class destroyers, the *Aconit,* and the *Tourville*-class destroyers. Now considered obsolescent and is to be replaced by the Milas.

Length: 6.15 m | Glider speed: 830 m/sec
Diameter: 0.65 m | Range: 12,000 m
Span: 3.30 m | Weight, including torpedo: 1,500 kg

375-mm Rocket Launchers, Models 1964 and 1972

Sextuple mount. Automatic loading in vertical position. Firing rate, 1 rocket/second. Range: 1,600 m. Time or proximity fuze. Based on Bofors quadruple mounting. Normally has six illumination-flare rocket rails mounted also.

305-mm Mortar

Quadruple mount; automatic loading. ASW projectile weight: 230 kg; range: 400 to 3,000 m. Can also fire a 100-kg projectile against land targets; range: 6,000 m. Normally has four illumination-flare rocket rails mounted on the face of the rotating housing. Used only on the *Commandant Rivière* class (removed from *Aconit*).

E. TORPEDOES

	Length in m	Weight in kg	Diameter in mm	Range in km	Speed in kts	Depth in m
♦ For surface ships:						
L 3	—	900	550	5.5	25	—
L 5 Mod. 4	4.40	935	533	7.0	35	500
♦ For submarines:						
L 5, Mod. 1	—	1,000	533	—	35	—
L 5, Mod. 3	—	1,300	533	7.7	35	—
F 17 Mod. 1	—	1,300	533	—	35	—
F 17 Mod. 2	5.38	1,300	533	18	40	600
♦ For aircraft:						
L 4	3.03	525	533	6	30	300
U.S. Mk 46	2.59	232	324	11	—	—
Murène	2.96	285	324	10	50	1,000

Note: The French Thomson-Sintra Murène and Italian Whitehead A-290 torpedo programs were combined into one effort in 1991 as the MU-90; some 3,000 are expected to be produced, and the weapons should enter service in 1996. The E 15 Mod. 2 export torpedo employs L 3, E 14, and Z 16 torpedoes updated with AH 8 homing heads and silver-zinc batteries, and offers 2,000-m detection range, 300-m depth capability, 31-kt speed, and a range of 12 km with a 300-kg warhead.

F. SONARS

♦ For surface ships:

	Type	Frequency	Average range/Comments
DUBA 3	Hull	HF	3,000 m
DUBV 23	Bow	LF	*see* Remarks
DUBV 24	Hull	LF	6,000 m
DUBV 24C	Hull	LF (5 kHz)	*see* Remarks
DUBV 43C	Towed	LF (5 kHz)	*see* Remarks
DUBA 25	Hull	MF (9 kHz)	TSM 2400; *see* Remarks
DUBM 20B	Hull—on *Circé*-class minehunters		
DUBM 21	Hull—TSM 2022; on new Tripartite and modernized MSO minehunters		
DUBM 41	Towed—on modernized MSO; sidescan minehunting (500 kHz)		
DUBM 42	DUBM 41 with DUBM 60 forward-looking sonar		
DSBV 61B	A towed passive linear array system, VLF		
DSBV 62C	Towed linear array, VLF		
Diodon	A 12 kHz hull-mounted sonar developed for export. Is also available in 11 and 13 kHz models.		
SQS-503	Hull—Canadian set on aircraft carriers		
SQS-17	U.S. MF; on *Cdt. Rivière* class and *Ouragan*		

Remarks: DUBV 23 and DUBV 43 are used simultaneously and, under normal sound-propagation conditions, achieve ranges of 8,000 and 10,000 meters; the DUBV 43C operates at depths of up to 700 m; when used with DUBV 43C, hull-mounted sonar becomes DUBV 24. In certain bathymetric conditions, the range is 20,000 meters. The DUBM 41B can be towed at 10 kts and covers a 400-m swath, compared to the 4-kt/50-m capability of the DUBM 41. The 2-kHz SLASM (Système de Lutte Anti-Sous-Marine), a variable-depth towed linear array, is in trials on the sonar trials ship *Commandant Rivière.*

♦ For submarines:

Listening devices, active-passive sonars, and underwater telephone equipment, including:

DUUA 2	On modernized *Daphné, Agosta,* and *Rubis* classes (DUUA 2B in latter); active
DSUV 2	Hydrophone array on *Narval* and *Daphné* classes
DSUV 22	Hydrophone array on *Rubis* and *Agosta* classes
DUUV 23	Panoramic passive array on the ballistic-missile submarines

SONARS *(continued)*

DSUX 21	Multifunction system for *L'Inflexible* and earlier missile submarines
DSUV 61	Towed passive array for the ballistic-missile submarines
DSUV 62A	Towed passive array for the *Agosta* and *Rubis* classes
DSUV 62C	Towed passive array for the *Améthyste* class
DUUX 2	Passive hull array
DUUX 5	Passive hull array on ballistic-missile submarines

◆ **For helicopters:**

	Frequency	Remarks
AQS-13	HF	U.S. sonar (Bendix)
DUAV 1	HF	
DUAV 4	HF	In the WG-13 Lynx

◆ **Sonobuoys:**

DSTA 3	active-passive
DSTV 4M (TSM 8010)	passive
DSTV 7 (TSM 8030)	passive
TSM 8050	active

G. COMBAT INFORMATION SYSTEMS

SENIT (*Système d'Exploitation Naval des Informations Tactique*): This system serves four principal purposes:
• It establishes the combat situation from the manual collection of information derived from detection equipment on board and from the automatic or manual collection of information from external sources.
• It disseminates the above data to the ship and to other vessels by automatic means (Links 11 and 14).
• It assists in decision making and transmits to the target-designation console all the information it requires.
The several versions of the SENIT are similar in general concept but differ in construction and programming in order to ensure fulfillment of the various missions assigned to each type of ship:

SENIT 1: A system with one or two computers. Installed in the *Suffren* class.
SENIT 2: A one-computer system installed in the carriers *Clemenceau* and *Foch* and with two computers in the destroyer *Duperré*.
SENIT 3: A central system consisting of two computers and two memory banks, the entire group designed for the control of various weapons (guns, Malafon ASW system, torpedoes). Installed in the *Aconit,* and the three *Tourville*-class ships.
The above three systems are based on equipment of U.S. origin, some built in France under license.
SENIT 4: A system conceived by the French Navy's programming center and designed around the French Iris N 55 computer. Fitted in the *Georges Leygues* class.
SENIT 5: Also designed by the French Navy's programming center and intended for use on small ships. It uses the French M 15 minicomputer.
SENIT 6: Designed by the French Navy's programming center for the *Cassard* class. It combines a number of M 15 computers and a new generation of display devices particularly adapted for command purposes. Has 20 to 22 display consoles.

SACEIT (*Système Automatisé de Commandement et d'Exploitation des Informations Tactiques*): Derived from the Thomson-CSF TAVITAC 2000 commercial system; will be employed on the *La Fayette*-class frigates. Employs color video display consoles.

SISC (*Système d'Intégration du Système de Combat*): New data system being developed for the carrier *Charles de Gaulle*.

AIDCOMER (*Aide de Commandement à la Mer*): Decision-making system for installation in the carriers *Clemenceau* and *Foch* beginning at the end of 1991 to provide artificial intelligence assistance in situation assessment, decision making, and resource management of ships and aircraft within a task force, as well as to act with the land-based SYCOM NG command-and-control system. AIDCOMER interfaces with the SENIT data systems and with the Syracuse SATCOMM system and contains an extensive threat database.

ALTESSE (*Alerte et Ténue de Situation de Surface*): Decison aid system by Thomson-CSF to be carried by *La Fayette*-class frigates to improve ESM system performance and to provide an overview of the local surface situation.

DLT D3: All submarines use the *Direction de Lancement Torpilles,* DLT D3. There are three identical data displays for current and historical target data, and the system can be used to launch torpedoes and missiles.

H. RADARS

◆ **Navigational**

Decca RM 416, 1229, etc.:	Commercial radars used on smaller units.
DRBN 32:	French Navy designator for Decca 1226 navigational radar.

◆ **Air search:**

DRBV 22A:	Mounted in *Aconit, Duperré,* and A-69-class escorts.
DRBV 22C:	*Île d'Oléron* only.
DRBV 22D:	*Jeanne d'Arc* and *Henri Poincaré*.
DRBV 22E:	*Rance* only.
DRBV 23B:	On aircraft carriers *Clemenceau* and *Foch*.
DRBV 24:	For the *Floréal*-class frigates; uses a solid-st transmitter derived from that of the DRBV 26C a the antenna from the DRBV 22A. Range: o 100 km. Thomson-CSF's commercial name: M (TRS-3015).
DRBV 26A:	Mounted in the *Tourville* class, first four *Geor Leygues* class, and the *Cassard*. Range: 150-n Commercial name: Jupiter.
DRBV 26C:	Upgraded DRBV 26A with solid-state transmit Range: 360 km. Carried by *Jean Bart*.
DRBV 26D:	Further development of DRBV 26 for the *Charle Gaulle* and for future antiaircraft combata Thomson-CSF commercial Jupiter- III using H.S LW-08 antenna. Formerly known as DRBV 27.

◆ **Height-finding/three-dimensional**

DRBI 10:	Mounted in aircraft carriers and *Île d'Oléron*. "Noddir type antenna with "Robinson" feed.
DRBI 23:	Mounted in the *Duquesne* and *Suffren;* monopulse.
DRBJ 11B:	Pulse-coded radar for the C-70 AAW-class guided-mis destroyer *Jean Bart* and the carrier *Charles de Gaull*
ASTRAL:	L-band radar under study for use with the FAMS mis program. Range: 400 km.

◆ **Surface and low-altitude air search**

DRBV 15:	S-band pulse-doppler design, with pulse-compression frequency agility, intended to replace the DRBV Commercial name: Sea Tiger. In *Primauguet, La M Picquet,* and *Latouche-Tréville,* and, provisiona *Cassard*. Replaced DRBV 13 in *Aconit* and will rep DRBV 50 in the *Suffren* class. Range: 110 km.
DRBV 15C	Improved DRBV 15 with stabilized antenna. Range: km against an aircraft and 50 km against a mis Destined for the missile range instrumentation *Monge, La Fayette*-class frigates, and the carrier *Cha de Gaulle*.
DRBV 50:	Mounted on aircraft carriers, *Jeanne d'Arc,* and auxilia *Rhin* and *Île d'Oléron*.
DRBV 51A:	Mounted on A-69-class frigates and the *Ouragan*-c landing ships.
DRBV 51B:	Mounted on the *Tourville* class.
DRBV 51C:	Mounted on the *Georges Leygues* class.

◆ **Fire-control**

DRBC 32A:	For the 100-mm guns on the *Jeanne d'Arc*.
DRBC 32B:	For 100-mm guns on the *Aconit*.
DRBC 32C:	Mounted on carriers and the *Cdt. Rivière* class.
DRBC 32D:	Mounted on the *Tourville* class.
DRBC 32E:	Mounted on the A-69-class frigates. X-band.
DRBC 33A:	Monopulse, frequency-agile. On *Cassard* and *Suf* classes.
DRBC 51:	Tracking radar for the Masurca on *Suffren* and *Duque* C-band (5-cm) tracker, 7-cm command signal.
SPG-51C:	U.S. tracker/illuminator for the Standard system on *Cassard* class.
Arabel:	Multi-function control radar for the SAAM system.

Note: Also in use is the DIBV 1A Vampir, an infrared detection and fire-co system built by Thomson-CSF.

I. COUNTERMEASURES

◆ **Intercept systems**

ARBR/ARBA 10C/D, ARBR 16 (Thomson-CSF DR 2000 Mk 1), ARBI (Thomson-CSF DR 4000, C–G band) for surface ships; ARUR 11, ARUR and ARUX 1 for submarines; ARAR 10B, ALR-8, ARAR 12, and ARAI with DALIA for Atlantique Mk 2 aircraft. SAIGON (*Système Automa d'Interception et de GONiomètrie*) for interception of VHF through UHI

◆ **Jammers**

ARBB 32, ARBB 33: For surface ships; work against reception anten and jammers. Manufacturer: Électronique Serge Dassault.

◆ **Countermeasures launchers**

Syllex: Version of British Knebworth/Corvus, 8 tubes; being phased o

Dagaie (AMBL 1B): *Dispositif d'Auto-défense pour la Guerre A missiles Infra-rouge et Électro-magnétique*. Made by CSEE. Launches l IR and chaff-type decoys, relying on input from SENIT systems. launcher holds 10 "suitcases," each with 33 projectiles with four cha in the antiradar version or 34 projectiles in the infrared version. Wei 500 kg. Range: 750 m.

Sagaie (AMBL 2A): *Système d'Auto-défense pour la Guerre Anti-mis infra-rouge et Électro-magnétique*. Made by CSEE. Launches decoy roc

COUNTERMEASURES *(continued)*

for confusion, seduction, or distraction. The launcher is trainable and holds ten containers launching infrared or radar-jamming rockets 170-mm in diameter and weighing 45 kg. An antitorpedo round is being developed. Range: 3,000 m. Launcher weight: 1,600 kg.

♦ **Torpedo countermeasures**

SLAT: Système de Lutte Anti-Torpilles. A directional towed-array detector to be used in conjunction with an active decoy possibly to be launched by Sagaie; in development.

SLQ-25 Nixie: U.S.-made towed noisemaker in surface combatants.

SPDT-1A: Torpedo detector in development by Crozet-Safare.

J. COMMUNICATIONS

Recent construction or recently modified major ships are receiving radome-mounted antennas for the Syracuse-series satellite communications transmission system. The system became fully operational in 1987. Syracuse operates at 7–8 gHz, and transmission rate is 2400-bit voice/75-baud telemetry per second. Syracuse II, to enter service in 1992, employs a constellation of Télécom 2A (launched 1991), Télécom 2B (launched 1992), and Télécom 2C (kept in reserve) satellites. The reception antennas are 0.90 m in diameter on surface ships and 0.40 m in diameter on Atlantique Mk 2 aircraft.

To ensure communications with submerged ballistic-missile submarines, the ELF Astarte system is being developed, with a transmitter at Rosnay. Also being developed is an airborne system using U.S. VLF equipment mounted in four C 160 Transall aircraft. Astarte entered service 1988.

K. SPACE SURVEILLANCE

The first French-Italian-Spanish Hélios surveillance satellite is to be launched in 1994, using technology derived from the civilian Spot program. The Hélios constellation will employ four satellites with an operating duration of three years at an altitude of 450 km.

NUCLEAR-POWERED AIRCRAFT CARRIER

0 (+1+1) Charles de Gaulle class Bldr: DCN, Brest

	Laid down	L	In serv.
91 Charles de Gaulle (ex-*Richelieu*)	14-4-89	5-94	10-98

Charles de Gaulle (R 91)—artist's view, showing revised bridge, mast, SAAM, installation, and Rafale aircraft DCN, 1989

Charles de Gaulle (R 91)—under construction DCAN, Brest, 17-10-90

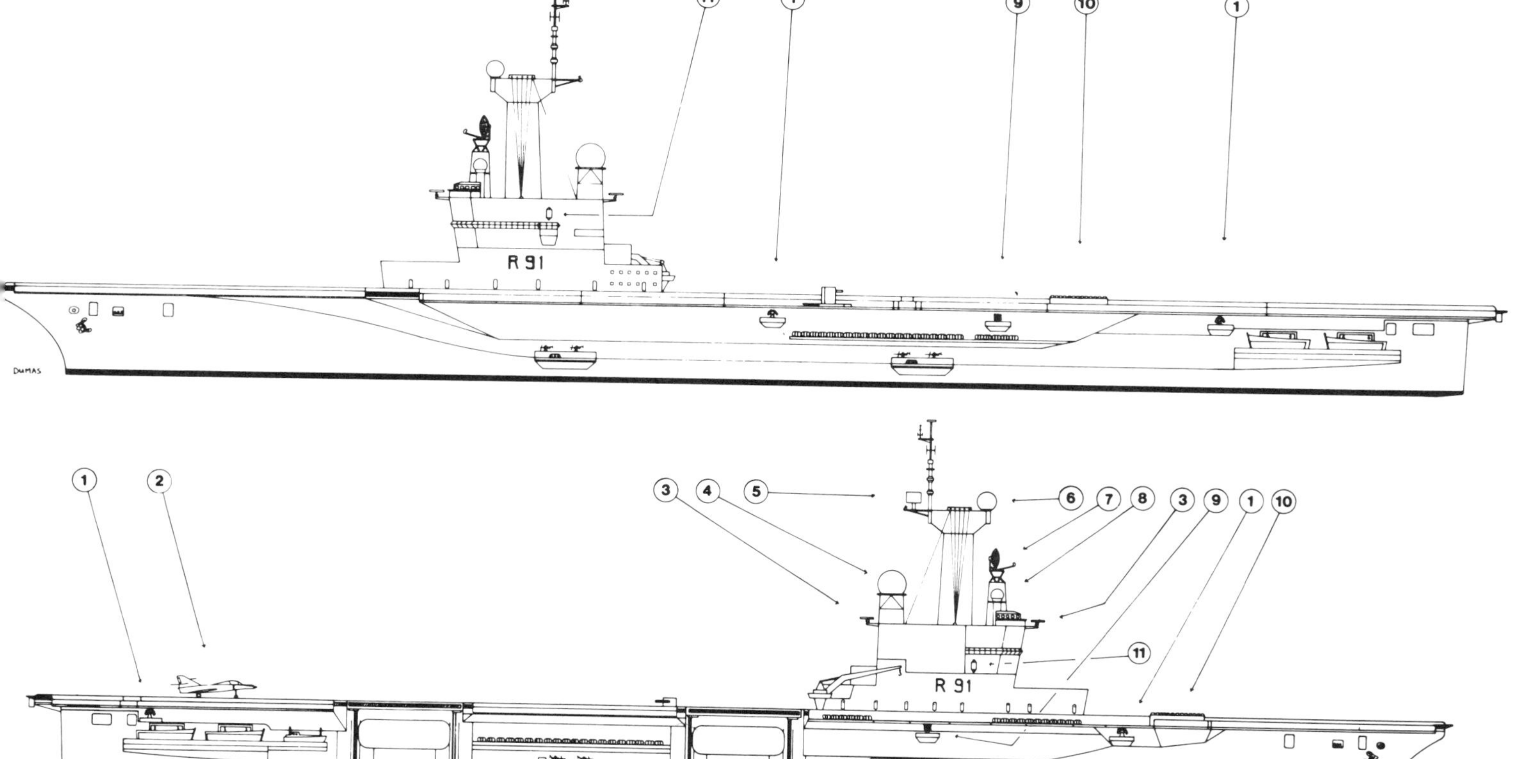

Charles de Gaulle (R 91) 1. Sagaie decoy launchers 2. Super-Étendard fighter-bomber 3. Decca 1226 nav. radar 4. DRBJ 11B radar 5. DRBV 15C radar 6. ARABEL radar 7. DRBV 26D radar 8. Syracuse SATCOMM antenna 9. SADRAL point-defense SAM 10. SAAM vertical launchers 11. ARBB 33 jammers Robert Dumas

NUCLEAR-POWERED AIRCRAFT CARRIER *(continued)*

D: 34,500 tons (36,000 fl) **S:** 27 kts
Dim: 261.50 (238.00 pp) × 64.36 (31.50 wl) × 8.50
Air Group: 35 to 40 aircraft (including fixed-wing fighters and helicopters)
A: 32 SAAM vertical-launch SAM (XVI × 2, 32 Aster missiles)—2/Sadral point-defense SAM (VI × 2)—8/20-mm F2 AA (I × 8)
Electron Equipt:
Radar: 2/Decca nav., 1/DRBJ 11B height-finder, 1/DRBV 15C air/surf. search, 1/DRBV 26D early warning, 1/Arabel f.c.
EW: ARBR 17 intercept, 2/ARBB 33 jammers, 4/Sagaie RL
IR: DIBV 10 Vampir
M: 2 150-megawatt, type K15 pressurized-water reactor plants; double-reduction-geared steam turbines; 2 5-bladed props; 83,000 shp
Electric: 20,000 kw (4 × 4,000 kw turbo alternators; 4 × 1,000-kw diesel sets; 1 × 800-kw diesel emergency set)
Crew: 1,950 total (177 officers, 890 petty officers, 833 non-rated including the 550-man air group; can also carry up to 800 troops)
Endurance: 45 days

Remarks:

General: The first ship was ordered 4-2-86 and was to have been launched 1-5-92; in 6-89, it was announced that the original 1996 date of operation would be delayed two years. The second ship, announced 21-11-88, is now expected to complete not earlier than 2005. *Charles de Gaulle* will replace *Clemenceau;* the second will replace *Foch.*

Hull: Design based on *Clemenceau,* but with more robust construction and protection systems. Four fin stabilizers, rudder roll stabilization, and an air-filtration system will be installed. In addition to being able to embark up to 800 troops, may receive a modular hospital installation.

Aviation installations: Will be able to handle aircraft of up to 22 tons. Aircraft will not be able to land and take off at the same time, due to the restricted size of the flight deck. The flight deck will be 261.5 m long, with a 195-m, 8.3-degree angled-deck portion. Maximum flight deck width is 64.36 m for an area of 12,300 m. There will be two 75-m U.S. Type C13 F steam catapults, one on the angled deck and the other on the port side of the bow, an arrangement that emphasizes parking arrangements over an ability to launch and land simultaneously. Three arrestor wires. There will be two 36-ton deck-edge elevators, both to starboard amidships. The nuclear propulsion arrangement allows the island to be mounted much farther forward than is standard practice, ahead of both elevators, and permits more efficient deck utilization. The 138-m-long by 29-m-broad by 6.1-m-high (4,600 m) hangar will be lower than on the *Clemenceau* class, but considerably larger in area and better protected; it will accommodate 23 fixed-wing aircraft and 2 helicopters at one time. The initial combat airc will be the Super-Étendard, but a new fighter-bomber, the ACM (*Avion de Cor Maritime*) may be developed to replace the Super-Étendard by 1999. Four U.S. E Hawkeye radar aircraft may be acquired, resulting in a fixed-wing air group c Rafale and 4 E-2C. Aviation fuel capacity: 3,000 m^3; munitions magazines: 4,900

Propulsion: The plant will be located in five compartments.

Electronics: Will have the SISC data system and the SLAT rocket-launched tor decoy system. Will have the NATO LINK II, LINK 14, and LINK 16 data links. Aster/Arabel missile-guidance system will be able to track 100 targets and co missiles aimed at 10. An inertial navigation system will be carried.

Note: As part of the development of this complex ship, a 20-ton, 19.83-m mod *Charles de Gaulle* was built by Le Perrière, Lorient. Ordered 22-4-86, it was laid d 3-8-86, launched 30-1-87, and delivered 2-87. Powered by two 50-kw electric moto has a crew of three.

AIRCRAFT CARRIERS

◆ 2 Clemenceau class

	Bldr	Laid down	L	In se
R 98 CLEMENCEAU	Brest Arsenal	11-55	21-12-57	22-11-
R 99 FOCH	Ch. Atlantique	2-57	28-7-60	15-7-

Clemenceau (R 98) Leo Van Ginderen,

Clemenceau (R 98)—with air group of Super-Étendard, Alizé, and Crusader aircraft on deck French Navy,

AIRCRAFT CARRIERS *(continued)*

Foch (R 99) Pradignac & Leo, 5-89

Clemenceau (R 98) Leo Van Ginderen, 6-91

D: 24,200 tons (32,700 fl) **S:** 32 kts
Dim: 265.0 (238.0 pp) × 31.72 beam (51.2 flight deck) × 7.8 light draft (8.6 fl)
Air Group: 15 Super-Étendard fighter-bombers, 8 F-8E Crusader interceptors, 4 Étendard IVP recce, 8 Alizé ASW, 2 SA-365N Dauphin helo, 2 Super-Frélon helo (as helicopter carriers: 30 to 40 Super Puma, Puma, and Gazelle)
A: 2/Crotale EDIR SAM syst. (VIII × 2; 36 missiles)—4/100-mm Model 1953 DP
Electron Equipt:
Radar: 1/Decca 1226 nav., 1/DRBV 23B air search, 1/DRBV 15 3-D height-finder, 2/DRBI 10 height-finder, 2/DRBC 32C f.c., 1/NRBA 51 air-control
Sonar: Canadian SQS-503—TACAN: U.S. SRN-6
EW: ARBR 16 intercept, ARBR 17 intercept, 2 Sagaie RL
M: 2 sets Parsons geared turbines; 2 props; 126,000 shp
Electric: 14,000 kw (2 × 2,000-kw turbo-alternators, 6 × 2,000-kw diesel sets)
Boilers: 6; 45 kg/cm^2, 450° C **Range:** 4,800/23; 7,500/18
Endurance: 60 days **Fuel:** 3,720 tons
Armor: Reinforced flight deck, armored bulkheads in engine room and magazines, reinforced-steel bridge superstructure
Crew: Peacetime: as aircraft carriers: 1,338 total (64 officers, 476 petty officers, 798 other enlisted) plus 582 air group; as helicopter carriers: 45 officers, 392 petty officers, 547 other enlisted. Total: 984, plus troops

Remarks: *Clemenceau* built under the 1953 Budget, *Foch* under 1955. *Foch,* built in a special dry dock at St. Nazaire, was towed to Brest for the installation of her armament.

Flight deck 257 m in length overall with 8° 165.5 × 29.5 angled portion; deck forward of the angled deck: 93 × 28; width of the deck abreast the island: 35 m. Hangar dimensions: 180 × 22 to 24 × 7 (height) m. Two elevators 16 m long, 11 m in width, one forward on the main flight deck, one slightly abaft the island, able to raise a 15-ton aircraft 8.50 m in 9 seconds. Two 50-meter Mitchell-Brown-type BS5 steam catapults, able to launch 15–20-ton aircraft at 110 knots, one forward, another on the angled deck. New catapult mechanisms installed in the mid-1980s. French-made OP 3 mirror landing equipment.

The propulsion machinery was built by the Chantiers de l'Atlantique. Living spaces are air-conditioned. Medium-sized island with three bridges: flag, navigation, aviation. Communication systems, especially with fighter aircraft, are a significant aspect of the ships' capabilities.

Aviation fuel: 1,800 m^3 of jet fuel and 109 m^3 of aviation gasoline carried by the *Foch;* 1,200 m^3 of jet fuel and 400 m^3 of aviation gasoline by the *Clemenceau.* Both carry about 3,000 m^3 of aviation ammunition.

Between September 1977 and November 1978, *Clemenceau* underwent a significant refit in the Toulon dockyard. The work consisted of a general overhaul of her installations and living spaces, modernization of the flight deck, reinforcement of the arresting gear, strengthening of the catapults, machinery overhaul, and the addition of two auxiliary boilers. Her electronic systems were modernized, and she was given the SENIT 2 combat data system removed from the inactivated destroyer *Jaurreguibery.* On the *Clemenceau,* this system has three main functions: to establish a situation based on information from external sources (land-based radars, aircraft, ships); to disseminate those data to the ship and to other ships; and to assist in decision making. The ship was equipped with a closed-circuit television system that displays needed information in interested parts of the ship: flight-deck control, the combat operations center, the ready rooms, the air operations office. To operate the Super-Étendard, the *Clemenceau* has been fitted with a central inertial guidance system that transfers information to the inertial guidance system in each plane. Her magazines have been modified to carry AN-52 tactical nuclear weapons. The *Foch* underwent a similar overhaul 15-7-80 to 4-12-81, receiving SENIT 2 from the inactivated destroyer *Tartu. Clemenceau* received the DALLAS laser landing aid early in 1988 as a prototype for *Charles de Gaulle.*

Foch received the prototype AIDCOMER (*Aide au Commandement à la Mer*) command-support aid in 9-89, and a second began trials in *Clemenceau* in the fall of 1990; production versions of the system were to be put aboard both beginning late in 1991, and the systems will be integrated with the new SYCOM NG shore-based command-and-control system. AIDCOMER provides help in tactical situation assessment, decision making, and resource management of ships and aircraft at the task-force level.

Clemenceau refitted 1-9-85 to 31-8-86 to improve sensor and defensive systems, including the substitution of two Crotale EDIR systems for four of the 100-mm guns and catapult overhaul. *Foch* began modernization to a similar standard in 2-87 and began post-refit trials 1-6-88. Both received Syracuse SATCOMM systems during refits ending in 1984. In 1989, the positions of the antennas for the DRBV 15 and DRBV 23B radars were reversed on the *Clemenceau*; on *Foch,* the DRBV 15 is before the mast and the DRBV 23B abaft.

Clemenceau to be replaced by *Charles de Gaulle* in 1998, *Foch* to strike in 2003.

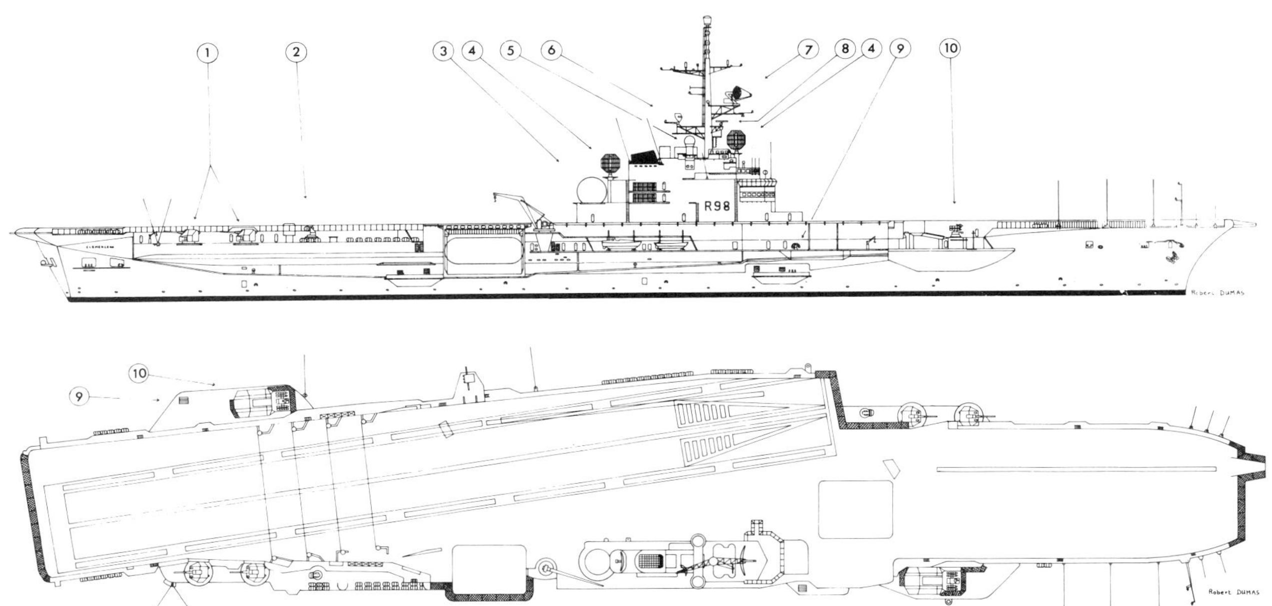

Clemenceau (R 98) 1. 100-mm Model 1953 DP 2. DRBC 32C f.c. radar directors 3. NRBA 51 aircraft landing-aid radar 4. DRBI 10 height-finding radar 5. Syracuse SATCOMM antenna radomes 6. DRBV 23B early warning radar 7. DRBV 15 search radar 8. DRBN 32 (Decca 1226) nav. radar 9. Sagaie decoy RL 10. Crotale EDIR SAM launchers

AIRCRAFT CARRIERS *(continued)*

♦ 1 helicopter-carrier and cadet training ship

	Bldr	Laid down	L	In serv.
R 97 JEANNE D'ARC (ex-*La Résolue*)	Brest Ars.	7-7-60	30-9-61	30-6-64

D: 10,575 tons (13,270 fl) **S:** 26.5 kts (cruising)
Dim: 182.0 (172.0 wl) × 24.0 (22.0 wl) × 7.30 aft max.
Air Group: up to 8 helicopters (Super Frélon, Dauphin, Lynx, etc.)
A: 6/MM 38 Exocet SSM—4/100-mm DP Model 1953 (I × 4)—4/12.7-mm mg (I × 4)
Electron Equipt:
Radar: 1/DRBN 32 nav., 1/DRBV 22D air search, 1/DRBV 50 surf./air search, 3/DRBC 32A f.c.
Sonar: DUBV 24—TACAN: U.S. SRN-6
EW: ARBR 16 intercept, 2 Syllex RL (VIII × 2)
M: 2 sets Rateau-Bretagne geared steam turbines; 2 props; 40,000 shp
Electric: 4,400 kw
Boilers: 4 asymmetric, multitube; 45 kg/cm^2, 450° C
Fuel: 1,360 tons **Range:** 3,000/26.5; 3,750/25; 5,500/20; 6,800/16
Crew: 31 officers, 182 petty officers, 414 other enlisted, 140 cadets

Remarks: Replaced the former cruiser *Jeanne d'Arc* as a training ship for officer cadets; when on that mission, she carries only a small number of utility helicopters. In wartime, she would be used for ASW missions, amphibious assault, or as a troop transport. The number of Super-Frélon heavy helicopters can be quickly augmented by simple structural changes. Aviation facilities include a 62 × 21-m flight deck aft of the island structure, which permits the simultaneous takeoff of two helicopters, while two machines can be stationed forward of the takeoff area and two others astern, one on each side of the elevator. An elevator (12-ton capacity) is located at the after end of the flight deck.

The hangar deck can, if some of the living quarters used by the cadets are removed, accommodate eight helicopters. At the after end of the hangar deck there are machine shops for maintenance and repair, including helicopter electronic equipment and an area for inspection. The compartments for handling weapons and ammunition (torpedoes, missiles, etc.) are there also.

In addition to the navigation bridge, the superstructure contains a helicopter-control bridge, a modular-type information-and-operations center, and a combined control center for amphibious operations. Two LCVP landing craft are carried.

The engineering spaces are divided into two compartments, each with two boilers and a turbine, separated by a bulkhead. The DRBI 10 height-finding radar was removed during a 1983–84 refit. A further refit from 12-88 to 12-89 made improvements to the propulsion plant and to the 100-mm gun system; MARISAT commercial SATCOMM equipment was added. The ship is expected to serve until 2005.

Jeanne d'Arc (R 97) Peter Voss, 6-91

NAVAL AVIATION

The Naval Air establishment is made up of combatant flotillas, maintenance squadrons or sections, bases, schools, and the special services necessary to ensure the efficient operation of the flight components. First aircraft received 26 December 1910. In 1991, there were 11,000 personnel involved in naval aviation, including about 700 pilots.

Administration is handled by the Aeronautical Division of the Naval General Staff and the Central Service Branch of Naval Air, both headed by flight officers. Operational and training matters are directed by the Navy Staff, whose various bureaus include aviation officers.

Primary training in fixed-wing planes is provided by the air force; helicopter pilots are given initial training by the army. Specialized training of pilots in multi-engine aircraft or in carrier-based fixed-wing and rotary aircraft is provided by Naval Air. The latter also trains navigators and maintenance crews at the Naval Air School, Rochefort.

The combat flotillas are:

(a) those embarked, which, flying from aircraft carriers or helicopter carriers, carry out intercept, attack, reconnaissance, or CAP missions and engage in antisubmarine warfare;

(b) maritime patrol flotillas and antisubmarine warfare flotillas that are land-based.

The service support squadrons and sections have various missions: schools, training exercises, transportation, logistical support for seagoing forces, experimental and salvage operations.

Authority over embarked flotillas and squadrons is assigned to a rear admiral commander, aircraft carriers and seagoing aviation (ALPA).

Maritime patrol squadrons are commanded by a rear admiral (ALPATMAR).

Shore-based flotillas, squadrons, and sections are commanded by the Préfets Mar[illegible] times (Naval District Commandants) through the regional aviation commanders.

Bases: Hyères and Landivisiau (shipboard fighters); Lann-Bihoué and Nîmes Garons (maritime patrol); Lanvéoc-Poulmic and Saint Mandrier (helicopters); Sair[illegible] Raphaël (experimental); Cuers-Pierrefeu (repair/rework); and Ajaccio-Asprett[illegible] (training).

Fixed-wing combat aircraft available in 1991 included: 19 F-8E Crusader intercep[illegible]tors, 59 Super-Étendard fighter-bombers, 11 Étendard IVP reconnaissance fighters, 2[illegible] Alizé ASW aircraft, 37 Atlantic Mk 1 land-based ASW aircraft, 7 Atlantique Mk 2, an[illegible] 5 Gardian patrol aircraft. Combat helicopters included 16 Super-Frélon heavy helico[illegible]ters and 36 WG-13 Lynx ASW helicopters. Support aircraft included: 12 CM-17[illegible] Magister jet trainers, 9 MS-760 Paris trainers, 6 Falcon X Mer communications jets, [illegible] Nord 23 trainer/transports, 17 EMB 121 Xingu light transports, 12 Piper Navajo lig[illegible] transports, 11 Socata 100 and 10 Robin HR 100 light communications, 6 CAP 10B a[illegible] experience aircraft, 3 SA-365F Dauphin SAR helicopters (out of a planned 18), and [illegible] Alouette-III and 7 Alouette-II training helicopters. Four C-160 Transall/ASTART[illegible] communications aircraft for SSBNs are air force-operated.

Jeanne d'Arc (R 97) LSPH W. McBride, RAN, [illegible]

'AL AVIATION *(continued)*

ne 40–50 AlphaJet M3 Marine may replace the current Magister trainers (would ve Agave radar, 2/20-mm cannon, 2 Magic R550 missiles). Four Grumman E-2C keye radar surveillance aircraft may be purchased from the United States for the *les de Gaulle*; they would be equipped with APS-145 radar, 4-color displays, and on T56A-147 turboshaft engines.

FIRST-LINE OPERATIONAL FLOTILLAS

lla	Subordination	Bases	Equipment	Missions
'	ALPA	Lann-Bihoué	**8 Alizé**	ASW
'	ALPA	Nîmes-Garons	**8 Alizé**	ASW
'	ALPA	Landivisiau	**12 Super-Étendard**	Attack
'	ALPA	Landivisiau	**12 Crusader (F-8E)**	Interception
'	ALPA	Landivisiau	**8 Étendard IVP**	Reconnaissance
'	ALPA	Hyères	**12 Super-Étendard**	Attack
'	ALPATMAR	Nîmes-Garons	**7 Atlantic Mk 1**	Maritime patrol
'	ALPATMAR	Nîmes-Garons	**7 Atlantic Mk 1**	Maritime patrol
'	ALPATMAR	Lann-Bihoué	**7 Atlantic Mk 1/ Atlantique Mk 2**	Maritime patrol
'	ALPATMAR	Lann-Bihoué	**7 Atlantic Mk 1**	Maritime patrol
'	ALPA	St. Mandrier	**14 WG-13 Lynx**	ASW
'	ALPA	Lanvéoc-Poulmic	**6 Super-Frélon**	Troop transport
'	ALPA	St. Mandrier	**6 Super-Frélon**	Troop transport
'	ALPA	Lanvéoc-Poulmic	**11 WG-13 Lynx**	ASW
'	ALPA	Lanvéoc-Poulmic	**9 Alouette-III, 3 Alouette-II**	Training

· aircraft assignments to training squadrons include: Nord 262 (2 S, 3 S, 11 S, 56 alcon X Mer (3 S, 57 S), PA 31 Navajo (2 S, 3 S), CM 175 Fouga Magister (59 S), MS 57 S), MS 880 (50 S, 51 S), unmodernized Super-Étendard (59 S), Alizé (10 S, 59 S), a (10 S, 11 S, 52 S), Alouette-II (22 S, 23 S), Alouette-III (12 S, 22 S, 23 S), Dauphin S). For overseas-based surveillance under ALPATMAR, squadron 12 S, based at Tahiti, operates 3 Gardian, and 9 S, at Tontouta, New Caledonia, operates 2 ian.

PRINCIPAL COMBAT AIRCRAFT

HIPBOARD FIXED-WING AIRCRAFT

afale-M interceptor/attack aircraft Manufacturer: Dassault

le protoype Dassault/Katsuhiko Tokunaga

ingspan: 11.00 m **Length:** 15.80 m **Height:** . . . m
eight: 14,000 kg **Speed:** Mach 2.0
opulsion: 2 SNECMA M-88-2 turbojets (7,500 kg thrust each)
ax. ceiling: . . . ft **Range:** . . . n.m.
eapons: Mica missiles; bombs and/or rockets in attack mode

arks: Plan to acquire 86 to replace first the Crusader and then the Étendard IV P. naval prototype flew 11-91, and the first series production aircraft is to deliver with the first operational flotilla of 15 aircraft to become operational in 7-98. 2 radar. Thirteen hardpoints. Considerable use of composite material in construc- First flight 12-12-91.

'-8E(FN) Crusader all-weather interceptor Manufacturer: LTV J.S.)

Crusader ECPA, 1987

Wingspan: 10.72 m **Length:** 16.61 m **Height:** 4.80 m
Weight: 13,000 kg **Speed:** Mach 1.8
Propulsion: 1 Pratt & Whitney J57 P20A turbojet, with afterburner
Max. ceiling: 50,000 ft **Range:** 1,500 n.m. (2 hr 30 min)
Weapons: 4/20-mm cannon, M 530 air-to-air missiles

Remarks: Announced 22-12-89 that F-8E Crusaders would be rehabilitated for service until Rafale is available, rather than the less expensive and more effective expedient of leasing U.S. F/A-18 Hornets; the first of 17 is to complete in 6-92, the last in 12-94, and 12 will be kept in first-line service.

◆ **Super-Étendard fighter-bomber** Manufacturer: Dassault

Super-Étendard—in new camouflage paint scheme French Navy, 1987

Wingspan: 9.60 m **Length:** 14.35 m **Height:** 3.85 m
Weight: 11,900 kg
Speed: Mach 1.0 at 11,000 m; Mach 0.97 at low altitude
Propulsion: 1 SNECMA 8 K 50 turbojet, 5,000 kg thrust
Max. ceiling: 35,000 ft
Range: 750 n.m. (1 hr 45 min or, with external fuel, 2 hr 15 min)
Weapons: 2/30-mm cannon, bombs, rockets, or 1 AM 39 Exocet

Remarks: Two flotillas have been modified to carry the ANT 52 nuclear bomb. During 1990–95, 48 Super-Étendard are to receive the Anémone radar, new EW equipment, and head-up display, and a S.A.G.E.M. UAT 90 computer in place of the UAT 10 and other improvements to extend their service by 15 years. Work on the first aircraft began 9-90.

◆ **Étendard IVP photoreconnaissance aircraft** Manufacturer: Dassault

Étendard IVP—in new camouflage Bernard Prézelin, 5-86

Wingspan: 9.60 m **Length:** 14.50 m **Height:** 3.85 m
Weight: 10,800 kg **Speed:** Mach 1.3
Propulsion: 1 SNECMA Atar 8 turbojet **Max. ceiling:** 35,000 ft
Range: 750 n.m. (1 hr 45 min or, with external tanks, 2 hr 15 min)
Weapons: 100 mm and 68 mm rockets, cameras

◆ **Alizé (BR 1050) ASW aircraft** Manufacturer: Bréguet

Wingspan: 15.60 m **Length:** 13.86 m **Height:** 4.75 m
Weight: 8,200 kg **Speed:** 240 kts max.
Propulsion: 1 Rolls-Royce Dart 21 turboprop (1,950 shp + 230 kg thrust)
Max. ceiling: 11,000 ft **Range:** 685 n.m. (4 hr 45 min)
Weapons: Mk 46 torpedoes, 100-mm rockets, depth charges, 50- and 250-kg bombs, sonobuoys, etc.

Alizé—in new paint scheme Carnets de vol, 1989

SHIPBOARD FIXED-WING AIRCRAFT *(continued)*

Alizé Bernard Prézelin, 4-90

Remarks: All surviving Alizés have been modernized with Iguane radar, Omega radio navigational aid, ARAR 12A radar detector, and other new EW gear. To be kept in service through 2000.

B. LAND-BASED MARITIME RECONNAISSANCE

◆ **Atlantique ATL 2** Manufacturer: Dassault-Bréguet

Atlantique ATL 2 Dassault, 1989

Wingspan: 37.30 m **Length:** 32.62 m **Height:** 10.80 m
Weight: 46,200 kg **Speed:** 300 kts
Propulsion: 2 Rolls-Royce Tyne 21 turboprops (6,000 shp each)
Max. ceiling: 30,000 ft. **Range:** 18 hrs
Weapons: 2 AM 39 Exocet missiles or 8 ASW torpedoes, depth charges, sonobuoys, etc. (3,000 kg total)

Remarks: Have Iguane radar, Crouzet MAD Mk 3, FLIR system, Tango thermal camera, DSAX 1 sonobuoy processor, ARAR 13 EW gear. Plan to acquire 30 at the rate of 3 per year. First operational aircraft entered service 7-89; by 12-91, 12 were to be in service. None were included in the 1992 budget.

◆ **Atlantic ATL 1 (BR 1150)** Manufacturer: Bréguet

Atlantic ATL 1—in old paint scheme Bernard Prézelin, 4-90

Atlantic ATL 1—in new paint scheme Bernard Prézelin, 4-90

Wingspan: 36.30 m **Length:** 31.75 m **Height:** 11.33 m
Weight: 43,500 kg **Speed:** 300 kts
Propulsion: 2 Rolls-Royce Tyne 20 turboprops (6,000 shp each)
Max. ceiling: 30,000 ft **Range:** 4,300 n.m. (18 hr)
Weapons: AS 37 Martel missiles, L4 and Mk 46 torpedoes, depth charges, sonobuoys, etc.

Remarks: Can be equipped with a photoreconnaissance pod. Being replaced by Atlantique Mk 2.

◆ **Gardian SAR and surveillance** Manufacturer: Bréguet

Gardian (Falcon 20) French Navy, 1

Wingspan: 16.3 m **Length:** 17.15 m **Height:** 5.32 m
Weight: 15,200 kg **Speed:** Mach 0.86
Propulsion: 2 Garrett ATF 3 turbojets **Max. ceiling:** 42,000 ft
Range: 2,200 n.m. (5 hr 30 min) **Weapons:** none

Remarks: Version of the Falcon 20 transport, with Varan radar. Ventral trapdo permit launching rescue equipment.

C. HELICOPTERS:

◆ **NH 90 antisubmarine** Manufacturer: Aérospatiale-MBB-Agusta-Fokker

Rotor diameter: 16.00 m **Length:** 19.50 m **Height:** 5.20 m
Weight: 9,100 kg **Speed:** 140 kts
Propulsion: 2 Rolls-Royce or Turbomeca 322 turboshafts
Max. ceiling: . . . ft **Range:** 4 hr
Weapons: Murène MU-90 torpedoes, . . .

Remarks: Cooperative European venture. Intended to replace the Super-Frél the French Navy, beginning in 1999. Composite materials employed in construc Late note: France quit the NH-90 program 8-91.

◆ **Super-Frélon heavy transport** Manufacturer: Aérospatiale

Super-Frélon Mike Louagie,

Rotor diameter: 18.90 m **Length:** 23.00 m **Height:** 6.70 m
Weight: 13,000 kg **Speed:** 145 kts
Propulsion: 3 Turbomeca III C3 turboshafts (1,500 shp each)
Max. ceiling: 10,000 ft **Range:** 420 n.m. (3 hr 30 min)
Weapons: none

Remarks: No longer equipped for ASW rôle.

◆ **Lynx antisubmarine/antiship** Manufacturer: Westland-Aérospati

WG-13 Lynx Bernard Prézelin,

.ICOPTERS *(continued)*

13 Lynx—with prototype Murène ASW torpedo DCN

otor diameter: 12.80 m **Length:** 15.2 m **Height:** 3.60 m
eight: 4,150 kg **Speed:** 150 kts
opulsion: 2 Rolls-Royce BS 360 turboshafts (900 shp each)
x. ceiling: 12,000 ft
nge: 2 hr 30 min, part in transit, part hovering
apons: Mk 46 torpedoes, AS 12 wire-guided missiles

arks: Have ORB 31 radar, DUAV 4 dipping sonar. Capable of localization, classi-on, and attack on submarine and surface targets.

auphin (SA-365F) SAR and transport Manufacturer: érospatiale

phin French Navy, 1990

otor diameter: 13.29 m. **Length:** 11.41 m **Height:** 4.00 m
eight: 4,100 kg **Speed:** 135 kts
ropulsion: 2 Turbomeca Aireil 1 MN turboshafts
ax. ceiling: . . . ft **Range:** 225 n.m. (4 hr) **Weapons:** none

arks: Five ordered 1989–90, with 15 more planned to replace the remaining ette-III helicopters for training and liaison duties.

ette-III Bernard Prézelin, 5-86

BALLISTIC-MISSILE SUBMARINES

General Note for Submarines: Names and pendant numbers ceased to be displayed on 1-1-83, to augment security.

♦ 0 (+2 +2 + . . .) SNLE-NG new design Bldr: DCN, Cherbourg

	Laid down	L	In serv.
S 616 Le Triomphant	9-6-89	1993	12-94
S 617 Le Téméraire	. . .	. . .	1996

Model of Le Triomphant (S 616) DCN/ Jean Biaugeaud

Model of Le Triomphant (S 616) STCAN

Model of Le Triomphant (S 616) DCAN

D: 12,640 tons/14,120 submerged **S:** over 25 kts (sub.)
Dim: 138.00 × 12.50 × . . .
A: 16/M 45 ballistic missiles—4/533-mm TT (SM 39 missiles, torpedoes)
Electron Equipt: Radar: . . .—EW: . . .—Sonar: . . .
M: 1 Type K15, 150-megawatt pressurized-water reactor; 1 pump-jet prop; 41,500 shp—diesel-electric emergency propulsion: 2 SEMT-Pielstick 8 PA4 V200 diesel generator sets; 5,000 n.m. range
Crew: 2 crews (red and blue), 110 total each

Remarks: A "new generation," first announced 1981. Will use new NLES 100, high-elasticity steel for pressure hull and a potential 500-m diving depth. Careful attention to radiated noise reduction, including "rafted" (isolated) propulsion plant and a pump-jet propulsor. Sail-mounted bow planes and vertical surfaces at ends of stern planes. Second ship in 1989 Budget. At least five are planned. The initial four will have the M 45 missile, with TN-71 warheads. The fifth ship will have the M 5 missile with TN-75 warheads, to be backfitted into the first four.

♦ 1 L'Inflexible class Bldr: DCAN, Cherbourg

	Laid down	L	In serv.
S 615 L'Inflexible	27-3-80	23-6-82	1-4-85

D: 8,080/8,920 tons **S:** over 20 kts (sub.)
Dim: 128.70 × 10.60 × 10.00
A: 16/M 4 ballistic missiles—4/533-mm TT fwd (12 torpedoes/SM 39 missiles)
Electron Equipt:
Radar: DRUA 33—EW: radar detector
Sonar: DSUX 21 multifunctional passive, DUUX 5 intercept, DSUV 61 towed array

BALLISTIC-MISSILE SUBMARINES *(continued)*

L'Inflexible (S 615) Jean Biaugeaud,

M: 1 pressurized-water reactor, 2 steam turbines; turbo-reduction drive; 1 prop; 16,000 shp—electric emergency propulsion with 5,000-n.m. range
Crew: 2 crews in rotation, each of 15 officers, 120 men

Remarks: Ordered 9-78, *L'Inflexible* has most characteristics in common with the five preceding SSBNs of *Le Redoutable* class, but takes advantage of many technological advances in propulsion, sonar systems, navigation systems, etc., and is able to dive 100 m deeper. The ship was equipped from the outset with the M 4 missile, which has six TN-70 150-kt Multiple Independent Re-entry Vehicle (MIRV) warheads. Sail planes higher on more streamlined sail than in *Le Redoutable* class. First patrol began 25-5-85.

◆ **4 Le Redoutable class** Bldr: DCAN, Cherbourg

	Laid down	L	Trials	In serv.
S 612 Le Terrible	24-6-67	12-12-69	1971	1-1-73
S 610 Le Foudroyant	12-12-69	4-12-71	5-73	6-6-74
S 613 L'Indomptable	4-12-71	17-9-74	12-75	23-12-76
S 614 Le Tonnant	19-10-74	17-9-77	4-79	3-5-80

Le Terrible (S 614) French Navy, 1989

D: 8,000/9,000 tons **S:** 20 kts max. **Dim:** 128.0 × 10.6 × 10.0
A: 16 M 4 ballistic missiles—4/550-mm TT fwd (18 SM 39 Exocet missiles and/or L 5 and F 17 torpedoes)
Electron Equipt:
Radar: 1/DRUA 33—EW: radar detector
Sonar: DSUX 21 multi-functional passive, DSUV 61 or 62 towed passive array, DUUX 5 intercept
M: 1 pressurized-water reactor, 2 steam turbines with 1 set turboreduction gears; 1 prop; 16,000 shp—1 SEMT-Pielstick 16 PA4, 850-kw diesel generator set; 1 electric motor (sufficient fuel for 5,000 n.m.)
Crew: 2 crews in rotation, each of 15 officers and 115 men

Remarks: *Le Redoutable* (authorized in March 1963) and other submarines of this class have been the principal elements of the French naval deterrent. They can dive more than 200 meters. All, with the exception of *Le Redoutable,* were backfitted to carry the M 4 missile. The substitution did not require replacing the existing missile tubes. The sonar suit was upgraded by the installation of DSUX 21, and other equipment has been modernized. The "turtle-deck" casing at the bow was reconfigured as in *L'Inflexible.* S 614 began modernization 1-2-85 at Cherbourg, completing 19-10-87. S 613 followed from 12-87 to 6-89. S 612 began 2-88 and completed 6-90. S 610 modernized at Cherbourg 7-90 to . . .-92. Sister *Le Redoutable* (S 612), unmodified, completed her last patrol early in 1991 and, after trials employment, was str 12-91.

NUCLEAR-POWERED ATTACK SUBMARINES

Note: A third generation of nuclear-powered attack submarines is planned to service in 2005. The design is still under consideration, and there may be a coope program with the United Kingdom.

◆ **1 (+2) Améthyste class** Bldr: DCN, Cherbourg

	Laid down	L	In serv.
S 605 Améthyste	31-10-83	14-5-88	9-91
S 606 Perle	3-85	22-9-90	4th quarter '94
S 607 Turquoise	. . .	1994	3rd quarter '97

Améthyste (S 605) APP Cherbourg,

D: 2,400 tons surf./2,660 tons sub. **S:** 28 kts sub. (25 sust.)
Dim: 73.60 × 7.60 × 6.40
A: 4/533-mm TT fwd, rapid-loading (14 weapons: F17 Mod. 2 and L Mod. 3 torpedoes, SM 39 Exocet, FG 29 mines)
Electron Equipt:
Radar: 1/. . . . .—EW: ARUR, ARUD intercept
Sonar: DMUX 20 multifunctional hull array, DSUV 62 towed passive
M: 1 SAS-48 48-megawatt natural-circulation, pressurized-water reactor, turboelectric drive with 2/3,150-kw turbo-alternators, electric motor; 1 7-bladed prop; 9,500 shp—emergency diesel-electric propulsion: 200 kw
Electric: 2/850-kw alternators **Endurance:** 90 days
Crew: two crews of 8 officers, 49 petty officers, 9 non-rated each

Remarks: "Améthyste" is both the name of the first unit and an acronym for "*A ration Tactique Transmission Écoute*" (Reduced Radiated Noise Transmission design is that of an improved *Rubis* and employs the same propulsion plant pressure hull is constructed of HLES 80, 100,000 psi steel, and the hull form emp lengthened body-of-revolution bow form tested on the trials submarine *Da* (S 633). The superstructure is built of GRP. Diving depth is over 300 m. The ships two SAGEM Minicin inertial navigation systems and two data bases. Endurar battery power alone will be about 15 hours. Two crews will be assigned to ea 30-year operating life is planned. Fourth unit, to have been named *Diamant*, ca 1991, and start of work on third delayed.

CLEAR-POWERED ATTACK SUBMARINES *(continued)*

Améthyste class—artist's rendering 1. secondary electric motor 2. main electric propulsion motor 3. propulsion control station 4. turbo-alternators 5. reactor/steam generator 6. officers' quarters 7. auxiliary engineering compartment 8. galley 9. operational control room 10. periscopes 11. storerooms 12. magazine 13. weapons-launch tubes

e first two were ordered on 17-10-84, and the fourth under the 1989 budget on -90. In 5-89 it was announced that S 605 and the units following would be delayed udgetary reasons.

éthyste (S 605) Leo Van Ginderen, 6-91

Rubis class, Type SNA 72 Bldr: DCAN, Cherbourg

	Laid down	L	Trials	In serv.
1 Rubis (ex-ovence)	11-12-76	7-7-79	1-4-81	23-2-83
2 Saphir (ex-etagne)	1-9-79	1-9-81	1-7-83	6-7-84
3 Casabianca x-Bourgogne)	9-81	22-12-84	4-86	21-4-87
4 Émeraude	10-82	12-4-86	10-87	15-9-88

is (S 601) Leo Van Ginderen, 6-90

hir (S 602) Pradignac & Léo, 5-91

: 2,265 std./2,385 surf./2,670 tons sub. **S:** 25 kts
im: 72.10 × 7.60 × 6.40
: 4/533-mm TT fwd (14 torpedoes and SM 39 missiles, or 32 mines)
ectron Equipt:
Radar: 1/DRUA 33—EW: ARUR, ARUD intercept
Sonar: DSUV 22 multi-functional passive array, DUUA 2B active, DUUX 5 intercept, TUUM underwater telephone, DSUV 62 towed passive array
: 1 CAS-48 48-megawatt pressurized-water reactor; two 3,950 kw turbo-alternator sets; 1 electric motor; 1 prop; 9,500 shp—1 electric motor driven by batteries powered by 1 SEMT-Pielstick 16PA4, 85-kw diesel generator set

Electric: 1,700-kw (2 × 850-kw alternators) **Endurance:** 60 days
Crew: two crews of 8 officers, 49 petty officers, 9 other enlisted

Remarks: Names for the first three changed 11-80. Fire-control, torpedo-launching, and submarine-detection systems are the same as for the *Agosta* class. *Rubis* was financed under the Third Military Equipment Plan. The second through the fourth came under the Fourth Plan (1977–82). *Rubis*'s reactor became operational early 2-81, and trials started 6-81. S 602 was the first to carry the SM 39 Exocet missile. All have the Pivair optronic periscope and employ the SADE automated combat data system. Diving depth: 300 m. Hull of HLES 80 steel.

S 602 began modernization to *Améthyste*-class standard in 10-89 and S 603 in 6-91; the others will be similarly modified by 1995.

ATTACK SUBMARINES

♦ **4 Agosta class** Bldr: DCAN, Cherbourg

	Laid down	L	In serv.
S 620 Agosta	10-11-72	19-10-74	28-7-77
S 621 Bévéziers	17-5-73	14-6-75	27-9-77
S 622 La Praya	1974	15-5-76	9-3-78
S 623 Ouessant	1974	23-10-76	27-7-78

Agosta (S 620) Bernard Prézelin, 5-90

Bévéziers (S 621) Bernard Prézelin, 5-90

D: 1,230 std./1,490 surf./1,740 tons sub. (fl)
S: 12.5 kts surf./20.5 kts for 5 min., 17.5 kts for 1 hr sub.
Dim: 67.57 × 6.80 × 5.40
A: 4/550-mm TT fwd (20 L5 Mod. 3 and F 17 torpedoes, SM 39 Exocet)
Electron Equipt:
Radar: 1/DRUA 33—EW: ARUR, ARUD intercept
Sonar: DUUA 2A or DUUA 2D active, DSUV 22 multi-functional passive, DUUX 2A intercept, DSUV 62 towed passive array
M: 2 SEMT-Pielstick 16 PA4 V 185 VO diesel generator sets (850 kw each); 1 × 3,500-kw propulsion motor; 1 prop; 4,600 shp—1 × 23-hp creep motor
Fuel: 185 tons **Endurance:** 45 days **Crew:** 7 officers, 47 men
Range: 8,500/9 (snorkel); 178/3.5 (creep motor), 7,900/. . . surf. (1 engine)

Remarks: Oceangoing submarines, authorized in the 1970–75 program. Weapons and equipment similar to the refitted *Daphné* class. DLA D3 fire control centralized in one computer bank. Air-conditioned. Retractable deck fittings on hull exterior. Advanced techniques for quiet operations both inboard and outboard. The torpedo tubes accept torpedoes of either 550-mm or 533-mm diameter. S 621 used in SM 39 Exocet trials. 320-cell battery with twice the capacity of the *Daphné* class. Diving depth 300 m. Spain built four of this class of submarine, and Pakistan has two—from an embargoed South African order. Planned to be retired between 2002 and 2005.

ATTACK SUBMARINES *(continued)*

◆ **4 Daphné class**

	Budget	Bldr	Laid down	L	In serv.
S 643 Doris	1955	Cherbourg Ars.	1-9-58	14-5-60	26-8-64
S 648 Junon	1960	Cherbourg Ars.	1-7-61	11-5-64	25-2-66
S 650 Psyché	1964	Brest Arsenal	1-5-65	28-6-67	1-7-69
S 651 Sirène	1964	Brest Arsenal	1-5-65	28-6-67	1-3-70

Galatée (S 646) Leo Van Ginderen, 6-91

Psyché (S 650) Bernard Prézelin, 4-91

D: 700 std./869 surf./1,043 tons sub. **S:** 13.5 kts surf./16 kts sub.
Dim: 57.75 × 6.76 × 5.25 (max.)
A: 12/550-mm TT, 8 fwd, 4 aft (no reloads)
Electron Equipt:
Radar: 1/DRUA 33—EW: . . . intercept
Sonar: DUUA 2B active, DSUV 2 passive, DUUX 2 intercept
M: 2 SEMT-Pielstick/Jeumont-Schneider 12 PA1 (S 650, 651:12 PA4-135) 450-kw diesel generator sets; 2 × 1,000-shp (1,300 for a brief period) electric motors; 2 props—*see* Remarks
Range: 4,300/7.5 (snorkel) **Endurance:** 30 days
Crew: 6 officers, 39 enlisted

Remarks: Development of the now-stricken *Aréthuse* class. Very quiet when submerged. Modernized, beginning in 1971, with special attention given to detection equipment and weapons. S 650 and S 651 were the last modernized, in 1981. Can submerge to 300 meters. Have DLT D3 torpedo fire-control system. The first three have Type 12 PA1 diesels, while S 650 and S 651 use Type 12 PA4-135. This class of submarine has been purchased by the following countries: Portugal, four in 1964; Pakistan, three in 1966 (and a fourth from Portugal in 1975); South Africa, three in 1967. Spain built four with French technical assistance. S 651 flooded and sank 11-10-72 but was salvaged; sisters *Minerve* (S 647) and *Eurydice* (S 644) lost 27-1-68 and 4-3-70, respectively. *Diane* (S 642) stricken 31-12-87, *Daphné* (S 641) stricken 16-10-89, *Vénus* (S 649) stricken 3-12-90, *Flore* (S 645) in 1989, and *Galatée* (S 646) in 11-91. Although originally planned for disposal in the late 1980s, the others are being kept active because of the slow delivery of the new nuclear-powered submarines, and are now planned to strike 1992-2000.

◆ **1 Narval-class trials submarine** Bldr: Cherbourg Arsenal

	Laid down	L	In serv.
S 633 Dauphin	5-52	17-9-55	1-8-58

Dauphin (S 633) Pradignac & Léo, 7-90

D: 1,320 std./1,635 surf./1,910 tons sub. **S:** 15 kts surf./18 kts sub.
Dim: 80.50 × 7.82 × 5.40 **A:** none
Electron Equipt:
Radar: 1/DRUA 33—EW: ARUR-ARUD intercept
Sonar: DUUA 2 active, DSUV 22 passive, DSUV 62 towed passive
M: 3 SEMT-Pielstick 12 PA4 diesel generator sets; 2 electric motors; props; 3,000 shp (2 × 40-shp creep motors)
Endurance: 45 days **Range:** 15,000/8 (snorkel)
Crew: 7 officers, 57 enlisted

Remarks: Of sisters, *Requin,* modified 1980 for trials with the SM 39 submer launch missile, discarded 11-85; *Marsouin* (S 632) decommissioned 8-11-82 for ca balization; *Narval* (S 631), which had a special swimmer-delivery vehicle housin deck aft, stricken spring 1983; *Espadon* (S 637) stricken 1985 as a museum exhibit; *Morse* (S 638) was discarded 9-86. S 633 is used in trials of materials and equipmen future submarines, having had the bow for the new "Améthyste" series nuc powered attack submarines grafted on in 1986, extending her length by 2.9 Refitted again 4-89 to 4-90. To be retired 1992.

GUIDED-MISSILE DESTROYERS

Note: Ships formerly typed officially as "corvettes" were redesignated as destroye 7-88. The guided-missile cruiser *Colbert* (C 611) was decommissioned 24-5-91, six y earlier than originally planned, to become a museum at Brest.

◆ **2 Cassard (C 70 AA) class**

	Bldr	Laid down	L	In serv.
D 614 Cassard	DCAN, Lorient	3-9-82	6-2-85	29-7-88
D 615 Jean Bart	DCAN, Lorient	12-3-86	19-3-88	1-9-91

Jean Bart (D 615)—with DRBJ 11B amidships Bernard Prézelin,

Jean Bart (D 615)—with DRBJ 11B amidships Bernard Prézelin,

D: 3,900 tons (4,500 fl) **S:** 29.5 kts
Dim: 139.00 (129.00 pp) × 14.00 × 5.60 (4.20 hull)
A: 8/MM 40 SSM (IV × 2)—1/Mk 13 launcher (40 Standard SM-1 M missiles)—2/Sadral systems (VI × 2; 39 Mistral missiles)— 1/10 mm Model 1968 DP—2/20-mm AA (I × 2)—4/12.7-mm mg (I × 4)—2 /KD-59E fixed torpedo catapults (10 L-5 Mod. 4 ASW torpedoes)— 1/WG-13 Lynx helicopter
Electron Equipt:
Radar: D 614: 2/Decca RM 1229 nav./helo control, 1/DRBV 15 su air search, 1/DRBV 26A early warning, 2/SPG-51C missi f.c., 1/DRBC 33A gun f.c.—D 615: 2/Decca RM 1229 nav./ helo control, 1/DRBJ 11B 3-D air search, 1/DRBV 26C ea warning, 2/SPG-51C missile f.c., 1/DRBC 33A gun f.c.

DED-MISSILE DESTROYERS *(continued)*

Sonar: 1/DUBA 25A (D 615: DUBA 24C) hull-mounted (D 615 also: U/RDT 1A torpedo-detection system)
IR: DIBV 1A Vampir surveillance, Piranha III IR/t.v./laser director
EW: ARBR 17 intercept, ARBB 33 jammer, Saigon VHFD/F, 2/Dagaie and 2/Sagaie countermeasures RL, SLQ-25 Nixie

: 4 SEMT-Pielstick 18 PA 6V 280 BTC diesels; 2 props; 42,300 bhp
lectric: 3,400 kw (4 × 850-kw diesel alternator sets)
uel: 600 tons **Range:** 4,800/24; 8,000/17 **Endurance:** 30 days
rew: 22 officers, 122 petty officers, 80 non-rated (251 accom.)

arks: 1977–82 program; the first was authorized under the 1978 budget, the 1d under the 1979 budget. A third and fourth were authorized in 1983 but were eled 27-2-84; they were to have been named *Chevalier Paul* (D 616) and *Courbet* (D D 615 sank the trawler *Rayou Vert* 30-5-90 in a collision.

ard (D 614)—with DRBV 15 radar amidships French Navy, 1990

ard (D 614) Leo Van Ginderen, 6-91

The Mk 13 launchers and missile fire-control systems were taken from the converted T-47-class destroyers *Kersaint* and *Bouvet*. The design has been recast, with a second 100-mm mount aft replaced by a hangar for a helicopter, flanked on either side by launchers for SADRAL system short-range point-defense missiles. The space beneath the helicopter deck may eventually accommodate the DSBV 61 towed linear passive hydrophone array. The ships have the SENIT 6 digital data system, and the new DRBC 33 radar fire-control director is aided by a Piranha III t.v./laser attachment. Also installed are 2 CSEE Lynx and 2 Naja optronic directors. A SAMAHE 210 deck traversing system is fitted for the helicopter. The Model 1968 CADEM gun has a 78 rd/min firing capability. Have 2 "Mini SINS" inertial navigation aids.

The intended DRBJ 11B radar in D 614 was replaced by DRBV 15 because of developmental problems; she is to be brought up to the same electronic standard as D 615 in 1992. The EW system is integrated by the "NEWSY" system, with a dedicated computer. LINK 11 and 14 data-link capability. Thomson-CSF "SPIN" jam-resistant HF radios fitted, as is the Syracuse SATCOMM. Also have TUUM-2D underwater telephone, NUBS-8A echo-sounder, Telegon 10 direction-finder. Weapons-control system employs 2 Type 88-DD00-ZA target designators and 1 Type DMaB optical director.

The main engines are rated at 10,800 bhp at 1,050 rpm. Four Jeumont-Schneider 850-kw generators are driven by 4 AGO 195-V12-CSHR diesels. The 5-bladed propellers are 4.2 m in diameter. There are 16 watertight bulkheads to the hull. Aluminum superstructure.

Ultimately, both are to receive the SAMP-N SAM system in place of Standard SM-1 MR.

♦ 7 Georges Leygues (C 70 ASW) class Bldr: Brest Arsenal

	Laid down	L	In serv.
D 640 Georges Leygues	16-9-74	17-12-76	10-12-79
D 641 Dupleix	17-10-75	2-12-78	16-6-81
D 642 Montcalm	5-12-75	31-5-80	28-5-82
D 643 Jean de Vienne	26-10-79	17-11-81	25-5-84
D 644 Primauguet	19-11-81	17-3-84	5-11-86
D 645 La Motte-Picquet	9-2-82	6-2-85	18-2-88
D 646 Latouche-Tréville	31-5-85	19-3-88	16-7-90

D: DD 640 to D 643: 3,550 tons (4,350 fl); D 644 to D 646: 3,680 tons (4,580 fl)
S: 30 kts (gas turbines), 21 kts (diesels)
Dim: 139.00 (129.00 pp) × 14.00 × 4.10 (hull); 5.73 (props); 4.10 hull (5.50 sonar)
A: 4/MM 38 Exocet (D 642 and later: 8 MM 40)—1/Crotale EDIR SAM system (VIII × 1; 26 missiles)—1/100-mm Model 1968 DP—2/20-mm AA (I × 2)—2/12.7-mm mg (I × 2)—2 /KD-59E fixed torpedo catapults (10 L-5 Mod.4 ASW torpedoes)—2/WG-13 Lynx helicopters
Electron Equipt:
Radar: D 640–643: 2/DRBN 32 (Decca RM 1226) nav., 1/DRBV 26 early warning, 1/DRBV 51C air/surf. search, 1/DRBC 32D gun f.c.; D 644–646: 2/DRBN 32 (Decca RM 1226) nav., 1/DRBV 15A surf./air search, 1/DRBC 33A f.c.with Piranha optronics
Sonar: D 640–643: DUBV 23 hull-mounted; DUBV 43B (D 643: DUBV 43C) VDS; D 644–646: DUBV 24C hull-mounted, DUBV 43C VDS, DSBV 61A towed array
EW: D 640–643: ARBR 16 intercept, ARBR 11B (D/F), ARBB 32 jammer, 2/Syllex (D 643: Dagaie) countermeasures RL, SLQ-25

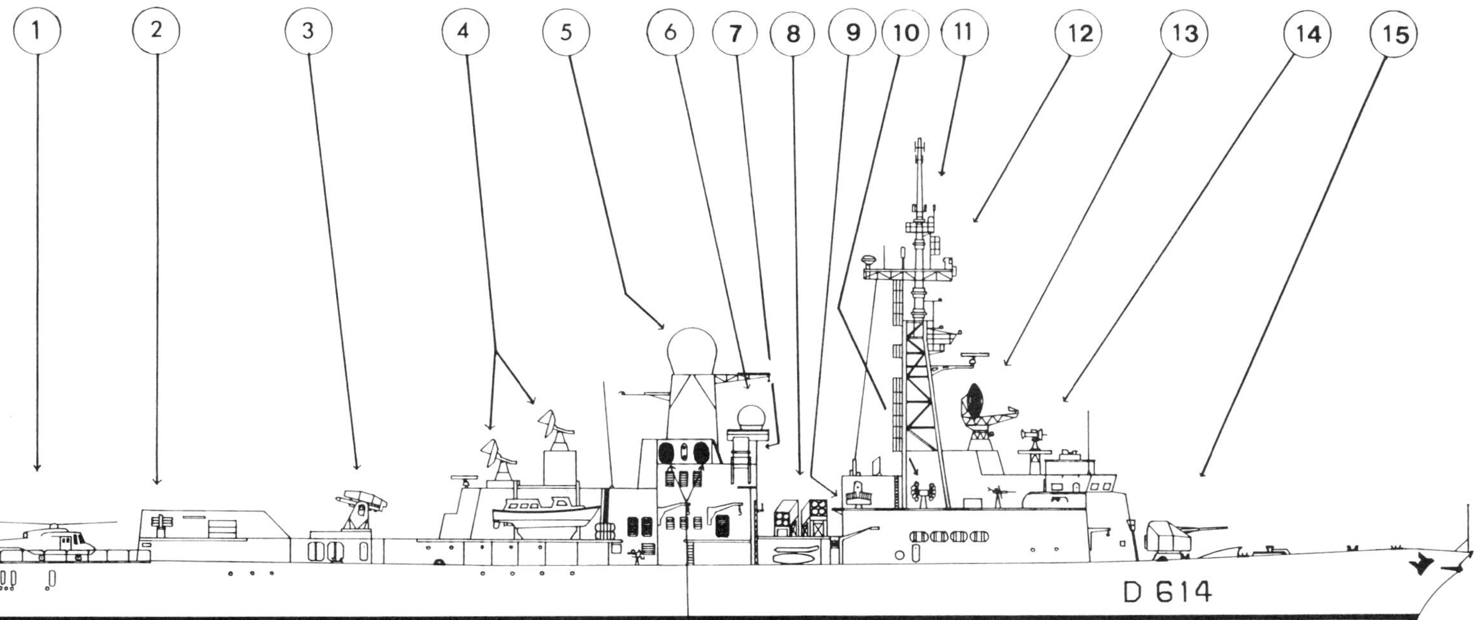

ard (D 614) 1. WG-13 Lynx helicopter 2. SADRAL launcher (VI × 2) 3. Mk 13 missile launcher for Standard SM-1 MR 4. SPG-51C tracker/ ninator radars 5. DRBJ 11B 3-D radar (DRBV 15 provisionally, as completed) 6. Syracuse SATCOMM antennas 7. ARBB 33 jammers 8. MM 40 et launch cells 9. Dagaie countermeasures launcher 10. Sagaie countermeasures launcher 11. ARBR 17 EW antenna 12. DIBV 1A Vampir IR eillance system 13. DRBV 26A radar 14. DRBC 33 f.c. radar director 15. 100-mm DP Model 1968 Robert Dumas

GUIDED-MISSILE DESTROYERS *(continued)*

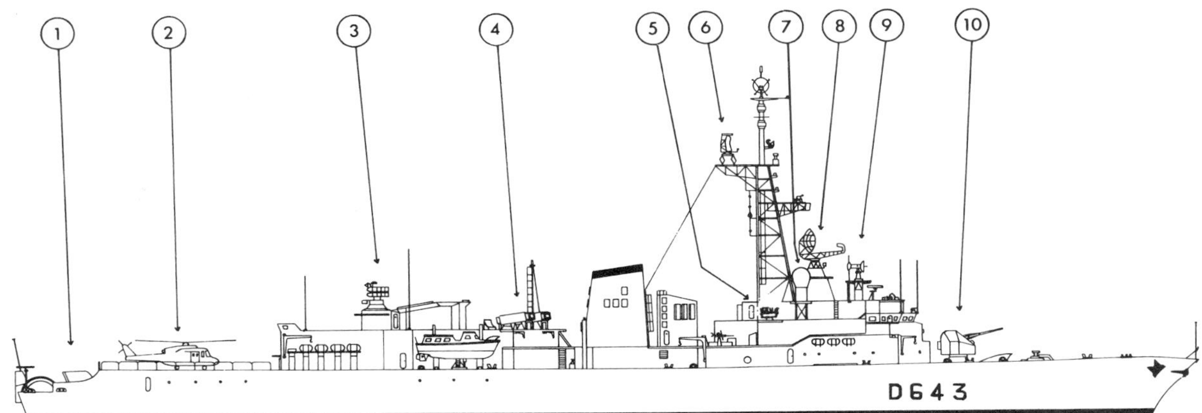

Jean de Vienne (D 643) 1. DUBV 43 towed sonar 2. WG-13 Lynx helicopter 3. Crotale SAM system 4. MM 40 Exocet 5. Dagaie decoy launcher 6. DRBV 51C radar 7. Syracuse SATCOMM radome 8. DRBC 33 f.c. radar 9. 100-mm Model 1968 DP — Robert Dumas

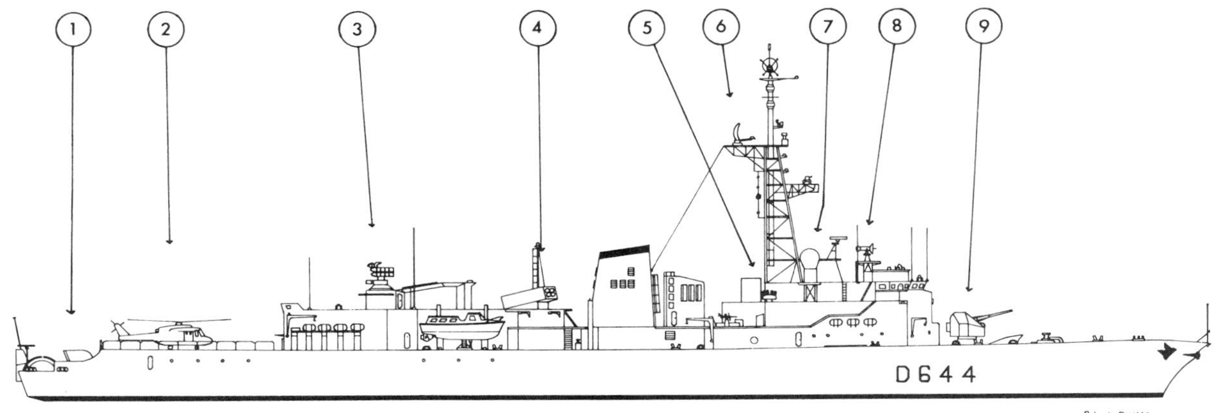

Primauguet (D 644) 1. DUBV 43 towed sonar 2. WG-13 Lynx helicopter 3. Crotale EDIR SAM system 4. MM 40 Exocet SSM 5. Dagaie decoy launcher 6. DRBV 15 surveillance radar 7. Syracuse SATCOMM radome 8. DRBC 33 f.c. radar 9. 100-mm Model 1969 DP — Robert Dumas

Latouche-Tréville (D 646) — Pradignac & Léo, 3-90

Dupleix (D 641)—with MM 38 missiles — French Navy,

La Motte-Picquet (D 645) — APP Brest, 6-90

Primauget (D 644)—with MM 40 missiles — APP Brest,

GUIDED-MISSILE DESTROYERS *(continued)*

Dupleix (D 641) Pradignac & Léo, 6-89

Nixie; D 644–646: ARBR 17 intercept, Saigon HF/VHF monitoring syst. (not in D 644), 2/Dagaie RL, SLQ-25 Nixie

M: CODOG: 2 Rolls-Royce Olympus TM3B gas turbines; 2 SEMT-Pielstick 16 PA 6 CV 280 diesels; 2 CP props; 52,000 shp (gas turbine), 10,400 bhp (diesel)

Electric: 3,400 kw (4 × 850-kw alternator sets)

Fuel: 600 tons distillate **Range:** 1,000/30; 9,500/17 diesels

Crew: D 640–643: 15 officers, 90 petty officers, 111 non-rated; D 644–646: 20 officers, 120 petty officers, 95 non-rated

Remarks: D 645 and D 646 built at Brest and fitted out at Lorient Dockyard. Main propulsion and auxiliary equipment is divided among four compartments, from forward to aft: forward auxiliary room, turbine room, diesel room with the reduction gears, and after auxiliary room. Full speed on the gas turbines can be reached in 3 minutes from a standing start. On diesel power and with the DUBV 43 sonar in the water, maximum speed is 19 knots, and the control system transfers power automatically from the diesels to the gas turbines. Centralized control of the propulsion machinery from the bridge greatly reduces the engineering staff required (3 officers, 23 petty officers, 24 men).

As in the *De Grasse,* much attention has been given to habitability, which caused the addition of 5 meters of length and 150 tons to the original plans. Denny Brown automatic stabilizers fitted. Have SENIT 4 data system and are equipped for NATO Link 11 and Link 14. Dagaie rocket launchers replace Syllex in D 643 and later ships. Have 1 CSEE Panda optronic backup director for the 100-mm gun. The helicopters can be used for ASW with Mk 46 torpedoes or Mk 54 depth bombs or for antiship duties with AS-12 missiles. All have the "Minicin" inertial navigation system.

The final three have a modified sensor suit and the pilothouse placed one deck higher. D 640–643 will eventually have their electronics suites brought up to the same standard as the final three. Beginning with D 644, the Crotale EDIR SAM system was installed during construction, and the others have had it backfitted since 1988. All have the SENIT 4 combat data system and Syracuse SATCOMM equipment. The DIBV 1A Vampir IR system is to be added, as is a new torpedo-detection and decoy system. All are to receive the Milas ASW missile system in the 1990s, and the SAAM/Aster 15 SAM system may replace Crotale.

3 Tourville class (Type F 67, ex-C 67A) Bldr: Lorient Arsenal

	Budget	Laid down	L	In serv.
610 Tourville	1967	3-70	13-5-72	21-6-74
611 Duguay-Trouin	1967	1-71	1-6-73	17-9-75
612 De Grasse	1970	1972	30-11-74	1-10-77

Duquay-Trouin (D 611) Bernard Prézelin, 7-91

Tourville (D 610) Leo Van Ginderen, 1-91

D: 4,650 tons (5,885 fl) **S:** 32 kts

Dim: 152.75 (142.0 pp) × 15.3 × 5.70 hull (6.48 props)

A: 6/MM 38 Exocet—1/Crotale EDIR SAM syst. (VIII × 1, 24 missiles)— 2/100-mm DP, Model 1968 (I × 2)—2/20-mm AA (I × 2)—1/Malafon ASW syst. (13 missiles)—2 /KD-59E fixed torpedo catapults (10 L-5 Mod.4 ASW torpedoes)—2/WG-13 Lynx helicopters

Electron Equipt:

Radar: 2/DRBN 32 (Decca RM 1226) nav., 1/DRBV 26 early warning, 1/DRBV 51B air/surf. search, 1/DRBC 32D f.c.

Sonar: DUBV 23 hull-mounted, DUBV 43 VDS, DSBV 62C towed array

E/O: DIBV 1A Vampir IR

EW: ARBR 16 intercept, ARBB 32 jammer, 2/Syllex countermeasures RL (VIII × 2), SLQ-25 Nixie torpedo decoy

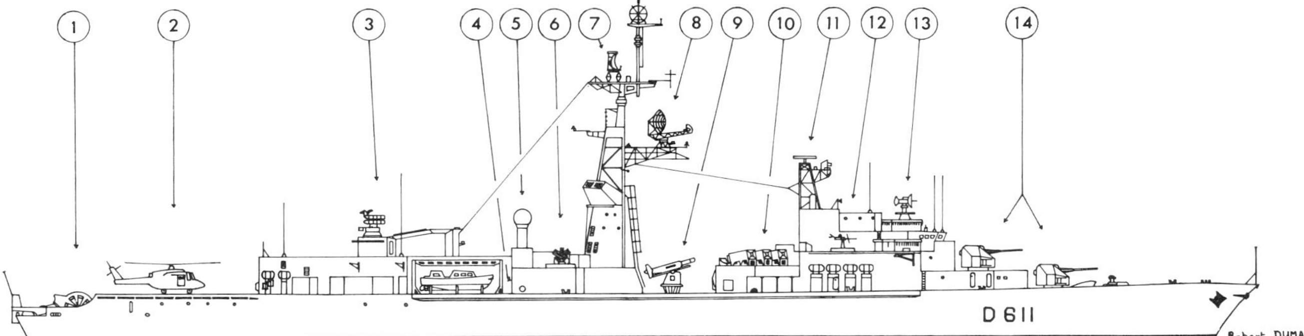

Duguay-Trouin (D 611) 1. DUBV 43 VDS 2. WG-13 Lynx helicopter 3. Crotale SAM system 4. catapults for L5 ASW torpedoes 5. Syracuse SATCOMM antenna radomes 6. Syllex chaff RL 7. DRBV 51B search radar 8. DRBV 26 early-warning radar 9. Malafon ASW system 10. MM 38 Exocet launchers 11. Decca 1226 nav. radar 12. 20-mm AA 13. DRBC 32D f.c. radar director 14. 100-mm Model 1968 DP Robert Dumas

GUIDED-MISSILE DESTROYERS *(continued)*

Tourville (D 610) APP Brest, 11-88

M: 2 sets Rateau double-reduction geared steam turbines; 2 props; 54,400 shp
Boilers: 4 asymmetric, multitube, automatic-control; 45 kg/cm^2, 450° C
Electric: 4,440 kw (2 × 1,500-kw turbogenerators, 3 × 480-kw diesel alternators)
Range: 1,900/30; 4,500/18
Crew: 17 officers, 122 petty officers, 143 non-rated

Remarks: SENIT 3 data system fitted. *Duguay-Trouin* was equipped with the Crotale antiaircraft missile system during 1979, *Tourville* in 1980, and *De Grasse* in 1981. In preparation for Crotale, the third 100-mm gun mount atop the helicopter hangar on *Tourville* and *Duguay-Trouin* was removed; it was never carried by *De Grasse*. During her Crotale installation refit, the *Tourville* had her boilers converted to burn distillate fuel, which had been burned by *De Grasse* from the outset. Fin stabilizers are fitted. These ships, particularly *De Grasse*, have a very high standard of habitability, and they have seakeeping qualities on a par with those of the *Suffren* class. The Crotale EDIR missile system was substituted in 1990. A prototype Thomson-Sintra DSBV 62 towed passive sonar array was added to D 610 in 1986. D 612 received DSBV 62C during her 1989–90 overhaul; in D 610, the array and processing equipment were added in 4-90 to the handling gear installed during 1989; D 611 received a complete system during her 3-90 to 9-90 overhaul. The VDS system thus has both MF and VLF transducers and a towed linear VLF array with a 3,000-m towing cable; in 1992, a computerized system will be installed to enable the ships to interpret the data produced by the array better. A spare towed array is stowed atop the helicopter hangar.

By 1995, a further modernization will be undertaken: Milas will replace Malafon, a new low-frequency sonar will replace DUBV 23, ARBB 33 jammers will be added, the Syllex countermeasures launchers will be replaced by two Sagaie systems, and the SLASM towed torpedo countermeasures system will be added. D 610 used for ALTESSE combat command system trials 1991–92.

◆ 2 Suffren class

	Bldr	Budget	Laid down	L	In serv.
D 602 SUFFREN	Lorient Ars.	1960	12-62	15-5-65	20-7-67
D 603 DUQUESNE	Brest Ars.	1960	11-64	11-2-66	1-4-70

Suffren (D 602) Pradignac & Léo, 11-89

Suffren (D 602) Leo Van Ginderen, 6-91

D: 5,335 tons (6,780 fl) **S:** 34 kts
Dim: 157.60 (148.00 pp) × 15.54 × 7.40 (max.)
A: 4/MM 38 Exocet SSM—1/Masurca SAM syst. (II × 1; 48 missiles)— 2/100-mm Model 1964 DP (I × 2)—4/20-mm AA (I × 4)—2/12.7-mm mg (I × 2)— 1/Malafon ASW syst. (13 missiles)—2 /KD-59E fixed torpedo catapults (10 L-5 Mod.4 ASW torpedoes)
Electron Equipt:
Radar: 1/DRBN 32 (Decca 1226) nav.,1/ DRBV 15 air/surf. search, 2/DRBR 51 missile f.c., 1/DRBC 33A gun f.c. with Piranha III
Sonar: 1/DUBV 23 hull-mounted, 1/DUBV 43 VDS
EW: ARBR 17 intercept, ARBB 33 jammer, 2 Sagaie countermeasures RL, SLQ-25 Nixie towed torpedo decoy
M: 2 sets Rateau double-reduction geared steam turbines; 2 props; 72,500 shp
Boilers: 4 multitube, automatic-control; 45 kg/cm^2, 450° C
Electric: 3,440 kw (2 × 1,000-kw turbogenerators, 3 × 480-kw diesel alternators)
Range: 2,000/30; 2,400/29; 5,100/18
Crew: 23 officers, 164 petty officers, 168 non-rated

Remarks: Built under the 1960–65 plan, these ships are extremely seaworthy; th roll and pitch only slightly and vibrate very little. Three pairs of nonretractab anti-rolling stabilizers. Living and operating spaces are air-conditioned. SENIT 1 da system and Syracuse SATCOMM equipment fitted.

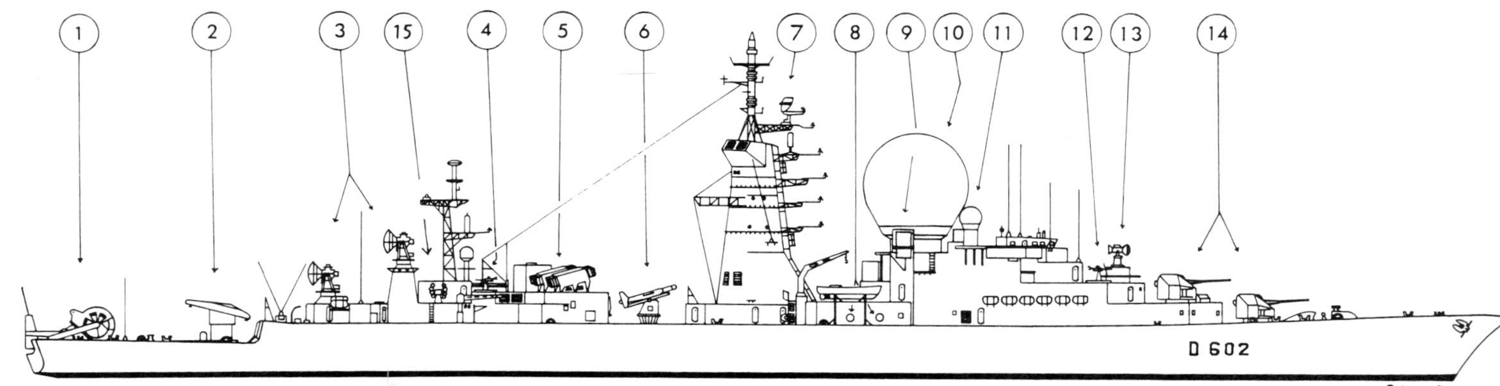

Suffren (D 602) 1. DUBV 43 VDS 2. Masurca twin SAM launcher 3. DRBR 51 f.c. radar directors 4. 20-mm AA 5. MM 38 Exo launchers 6. Malafon ASW system 7. DRBV 15 search radar 8. catapults for ASW torpedoes 9. Syllex chaff launcher 10. radome over DRBI 23 radar 11. Syracuse SATCOMM antenna radomes 12. 20-mm AA 13. DRBC 32A f.c. radar director 14. 100-mm Model 1964 DP Robert Dur

UIDED-MISSILE DESTROYERS *(continued)*

ıquesne (D 603) French Navy, 1988

:n a refit ending in D 602 in 1989 and during the 1990–91 refit of D 603, the DRBC 33 ɜ-control radar with Piranha III optronic (t.v., laser, infrared) attachment was sub-tuted for DRBC 32, the ARBR and ARBB 33 EW equipment was substituted for :lier equipment, the *Amélie* microcomputer-assisted data system was added, the ısurca system was updated, DRBV 15 radar replaced DRBV 50 in D 602, the SENIT nbat data system was updated, and the DUBV 43 variable-depth sonar was mod-ıized.

) 602 is to be retired in 1998 and D 603 in 2000.

1 F 65 (ex-C 65) class

	Bldr	Laid down	L	In serv.
509 Aconit	Lorient Arsenal	1967	7-3-70	30-3-73

ːonit (D 609) Leo Van Ginderen, 1990

Aconit (D 609) APP Brest, 1989

GUIDED-MISSILE DESTROYERS *(continued)*

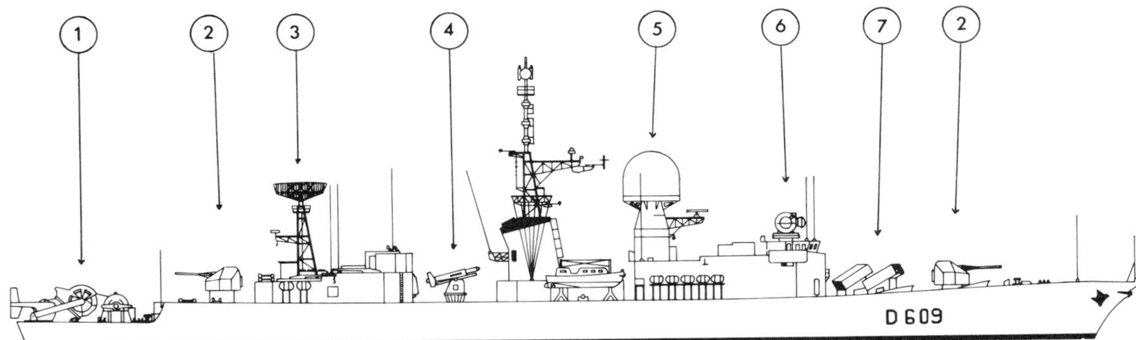

Aconit 1. DUBV 43 sonar 2. 100-mm DP mounts 3. DRBV 22A radar 4. Malafon launcher 5. DRBV 15 radar 6. 100-mm gun director with DRBC 32B radar 7. MM 40 Exocet launch cells Robert Dumas

D: 3,135 tons (3,870 fl) **S:** 27 kts
Dim: 127.00 × 13.40 × 4.05 (5.80 props)
A: 8/MM 40 Exocet SSM (IV × 2)—2/100-mm Model 1968 DP (I × 2)—1/Malafon ASW system (13 missiles)—2 /KD-59E fixed torpedo catapults (10 L-5 Mod. 4 ASW torpedoes)
Electron Equipt:
Radar: 1/DRBN 32 (Decca 1226) nav., 1/DRBV 15 air/surf. search, 1/DRBV 22A air search, 1/DRBC 32B f.c.
Sonar: 1/DUBV 23 hull-mounted, 1/DUBV 43 VDS, DSBV 62C towed array
EW: ARBR 16 intercept, ARBB 32 jammer, 2/Syllex countermeasures RL, SLQ-25 Nixie towed torpedo decoy
M: 1 set Rateau double-reduction geared steam turbines; 1 prop; 28,650 shp (31,500 shp for short periods)
Boilers: 2 asymmetric, multitube, automatic-control; 45 kg/cm^2, 450° C
Electric: 2,960 kw **Range:** 1,600/27; 5,000/18
Crew: 15 officers, 103 petty officers, 114 non-rated

Remarks: One computer controls the SENIT 3 data-system functions and the weapons. Propulsion machinery is very compact and produced 31,500 hp on trials. Equipped with fin stabilizers. During a major refit in 1984–85 she received 8/MM 40 Exocet positions in place of the 305-mm mortar and DRBV 15 in place of DRBV 13, but the radome was retained. A DSBV 62C towed linear hydrophone array during a refit to begin in 1992, and Dagaie will replace Syllex. Normally carries only 4/MM 40 Exocet. Received Thomson-Sintra DSBV 62C towed linear hydrophone array during 1991.

◆ **1 modified T-53 class, ASW** Bldr: Lorient Arsenal

	Laid down	L	In serv.
D 633 Duperré	11-54	23-6-56	8-10-57

Duperré (D 633) Bernard Prézelin, 10-90

Duperré (D 633) Pradignac & Léo, 1988

D: 2,900 tons (3,740 fl) **S:** 34 kts (32 fl)
Dim: 132.8 × 12.7 × 5.9 (props)
A: 4/MM 38 Exocet—1/100-mm Model 1968 DP—2/20-mm AA (I × 2)— 2 /KD-59E fixed torpedo catapults (8 L-5 Mod.4 ASW torpedoes)— 1/WG-13 Lynx helicopter
Electron Equipt:
Radar: 2/DRBN 32 (Decca 1226) nav., 1/DRBV 22A air search , 1/DRBV 51 air search, 1/DRBC 32E f.c.
Sonar: 1/DUBV 23 hull-mounted, 1/DUBV 43 VDS
EW: ARBR 16 intercept, 2/Syllex countermeasures RL
M: 2 sets Rateau geared steam turbines; 2 props; 64,000 shp
Boilers: 4/ACB-Indret; 35 kg/cm^2, 385° C **Fuel:** 800 tons
Electric: 1,640 kw **Range:** 1,500/30; 5,000/18
Crew: 15 officers, 102 petty officers, 142 non-rated

Remarks: From 1967 to 1971, the *Duperré* was unarmed and was used for tow sonar research, using the huge array later mounted in the auxiliary *Aunis*. Rec verted at Brest from 1972 to 21-5-74, as the final step in the long evolution of the T *Surcouf*-class destroyer design, of which she is the last example of 24 delivered 19 62. The hangar is fixed and has maintenance facilities, and the flight deck ha harpoon helicopter-recovery system similar to that on the *Tourville* and *Georges L gues* classes. SENIT 2 data system fitted. The ship ran aground 13-4-78 and was ba damaged, but was repaired using components cannibalized from the inactivated *Bourdonnais,* recommissioning 2-80. To be discarded 1992.

Note: The last T-47 ASW conversion destroyer, *Maille Brézé* (D 627), was stric 1-4-88 and is a museum at Nantes. The T-56 ASW destroyer *La Galissonnière* (D was stricken 29-6-90 to become part of the breakwater at the Naval Academy, and last Type T-47 guided-missile destroyer, *Du Chayla* (D 630), was stricken at the en July 1990.

FRIGATES

◆ **0 (+3+3) La Fayette-class frigates** Bldr: DCN, Lorient

	Laid down	L	In serv.
F 710 La Fayette	15-12-90	6-92	1-95
F 711 Surcouf	. . .	. . .	12-95
F 712 Courbet	. . .	. . .	1996
F	. . .	. . .	. . .
F	. . .	. . .	. . .
F	. . .	. . .	2000

D: 3,000 tons trials (3,280 fl) **S:** 25 kts
Dim: 125.00 (115.00 pp) × 15.40 (13.80 wl) × 4.10 (hull)
A: 8/MM 40 Exocet (IV × 2)—1/Modular Crotale SAM system (VIII 1; 16 tot. missiles)—1/100-mm Model 1968 DP—2/20-mm AA (I × 2)— 2/12.7-mm mg (I × 2)—1/NH-90 helicopter with AM 39 Exoc or AS 15 missiles
Electron Equipt:
Radar: 2/Decca RM 1229 nav., 1/DRBV 15 3-D air/surf. search, 1/ Castor f.c.
Sonar: none
EW: ARBR 17 intercept, SAIGON VLF-UHF/DF, 2/Dagaie decoy
M: 4 SEMT-Pielstick 12 PA 6 280 STC diesels; 2 CP props; 21,000 bh
Electric: 1,970 kw **Endurance:** 50 days
Range: 7,000/15; 9,000/12
Crew: 15 officers, 68 petty officers, 56 non-rated (+ 25 commandos)

Remarks: The first three of a planned six were in the 1989 budget and are intended overseas possessions patrol and a rôle in the protection of Europe in a crisis. Unusua having no ASW sensors or armament. The first was ordered on 14-3-88. The des permits the future addition or substitution of later weapon systems, including 8-cell SAAM installations for Aster 15 vertical-launch missiles, the associated Ar radar, and the SLAT anti-torpedo system. Normally, only 4 MM 40 missiles wi aboard. The helicopter will be able to be launched and recovered in up to Sea Sta and will carry antiship missiles.

The SACEIT combat data system with five display terminals and the Syracus SATCOMM system will be carried. The ships will be equipped with NATO Link 11 Link 14 capability. The Thomson-CSF Altesse (*Alerte et Ténue de Situation de Sur*

FRIGATES *(continued)*

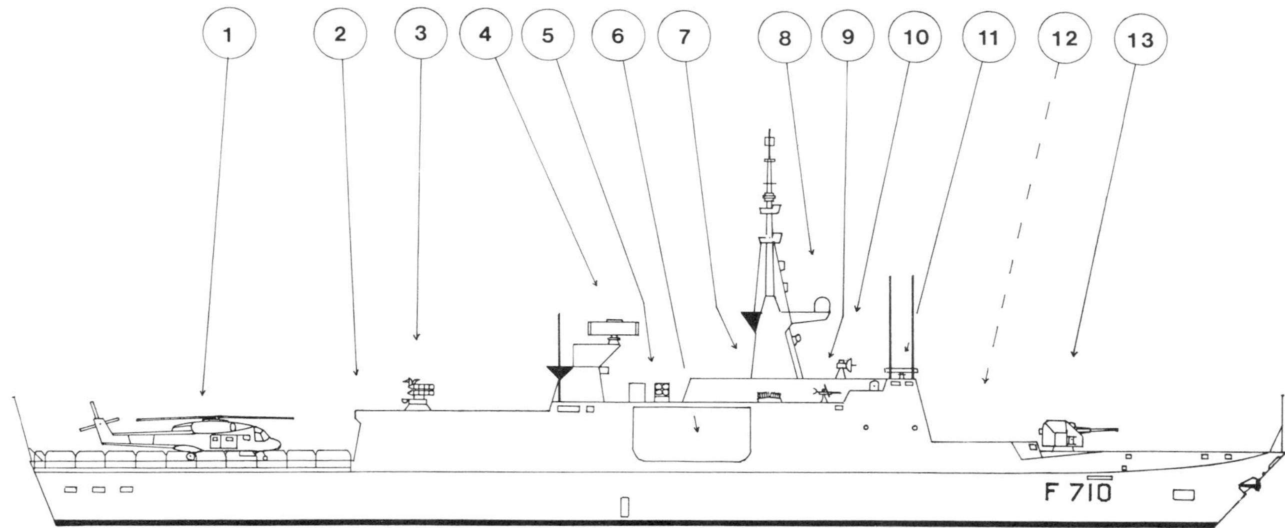

La Fayette (F 710) 1. NH 90 helicopter 2. helicopter hangar 3. Crotale NG SAM launcher 4. DRBV 15C search radar 5. MM 40 Exocet launch cells 6. moveable panel covering boat stowage 7. Dagaie countermeasures launcher 8. Syracuse-II SATCOMM antenna 9. 20-mm F2 AA 10. gun fire control radar 11. Racal-Decca navigational radar 12. position reserved for later installation of vertical-launch SAM system 13. 100-mm Model 1968 DP gun Robert Dumas

La Fayette (F 710)—artist's rendering 1990

La Fayette (F 710)—model DCN, 1990

La Fayette (F 710)—model DCN, 1990

warning and surface-situation data display system will be installed to provide artificial intelligence-aided assist to the ESM system and will provide direction finding of a signal within 500 m with an accuracy better than 0.5 degrees.

A particular effort has been made to reduce the ships' signatures; the diesel propulsion engines are mounted in pairs on isolation platforms, and the superstructure, masts, and forecastle are covered with radar-absorbant GRP-resin compound. Vertical hull and superstructure surfaces are slanted at plus or minus 10° to reduce radar reflectivity. Special armor is provided for the magazines. All chocks, bollards, and boat recesses are covered to reduce radar reflectivity. Employs modified deep-vee hull form, fin stabilizers, and rudder-controlled roll reduction to improve seaworthiness. Modular installation of weapons and sensors is employed, making it possible for foreign customers to specify different equipment suites and even propulsion plants.

◆ **1 (+5) Floréal-class surveillance frigates** Bldr: Chantiers de l'Atlantique, St. Nazaire

	Laid down	L	In serv.	Based
F 730 Floréal	2-4-90	6-10-90	12-91	La Réunion
F 731 Prairial	9-90	16-3-91	3-92	Papeete/Nouméa
F 732 Nivôse	4-91	10-91	9-92	Papeete/Nouméa
F 733 Ventôse	10-91	4-92	3-93	Papeete/Nouméa
F 734 Vendémiaire	4-92	10-92	9-93	Fort de France
F 735 Germinal	10-92	4-93	3-94	Brest

D: 2,600 tons (2,950 fl) **S:** 20 kts
Dim: 93.50 (85.20 pp) × 14.00 × 4.30
A: 2/MM 40 Exocet SSM (I × 2)—1/100-mm Model 1968 DP—2/SIMBAD point-defense SAM systems (II × 2; Mistral missiles) *or* 2/20-mm F2 AA (I × 2)—1/Dauphin helicopter
Electron Equipt:
Radar: 2/Decca RM 1229 nav., 1/DRBV 24 (Mars) air/surf. search
Sonar: none
EW: ARBR 17 intercept, SAIGON D/F, 2/Dagaie decoy RL
M: 4 SEMT-Pielstick 6PA6 L280 BTC diesels; 2 CP props; 8,800 bhp—250-kw bow-thruster
Electric: 1,770 kw (3 × 590-kw sets, 3 Baudouin 12 P15 2SR diesels driving)
Endurance: 50 days **Fuel:** 370 tons **Range:** 9,000/15
Crew: 10 officers, 30 petty officers, 40 ratings (*see* Remarks)

Floréal (F 730)—model as completed French Navy, 10-90

FRIGATES *(continued)*

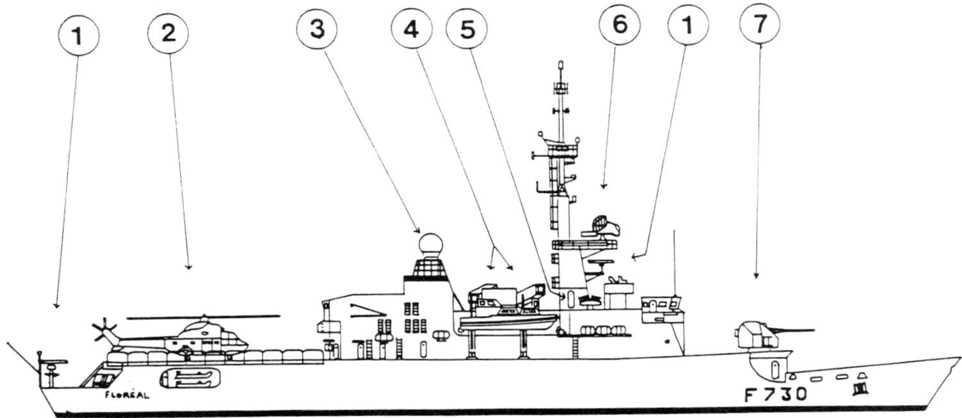

Floréal (F 730) 1. Racal-Decca navigational radar 2. NH-90 helicopter 3. Syracuse-II SATCOMM antenna 4. MM 38 Exocet missiles 5. Dagaie countermeasures launcher 6. DRBV 24 search radar 7. 100-mm Model 1968 DP gun Robert Dumas

Floréal (F 730) Bernard Prézelin, 8-91

Floréal (F 730) Bernard Prézelin, 8-91

Remarks: First two ordered 20-1-89 under the 1989 budget, next pair ordered 9-1-90 under the 1990 budget, and the other two ordered 2-91 under the 1991 budget. Military equipment added at the Lorient Arsenal after delivery by the builder; F 730 delivered by builders 8-3-91 for outfitting.

Intended for operations in low-risk areas for ocean surveillance, economic exclusion zone patrol, fisheries protection, and maritime policing duties. Constructed to Veritas commercial vice military standards. Emphasis on seaworthiness, with helicopter operations possible up to Sea State 5. The ships can accommodate a 9-ton helicopter and have a platform 23 × 14 meters. There is no SENIT combat data system. The 100-mm gun is controlled by a CSEE Najir optronic director. The Syracuse-II SATCOMM system is carried. Fin stabilizers are installed. Have accommodations for 123 personnel, including 24 commandos and 13 passengers.

♦ 17 D'Estienne d'Orves class, Type A-69 Bldr: Lorient Arsenal

	Laid down	L	In serv.
F 781 D'Estienne d'Orves	1-9-72	1-6-73	10-9-76
F 782 Amyot d'Inville	11-9-73	30-11-74	13-10-76
F 783 Drogou	1-10-73	30-11-74	30-9-76
F 784 Détroyat	15-12-74	31-1-76	4-5-77
F 785 Jean Moulin	15-1-75	31-1-76	11-5-77
F 786 Quartier-Maître Anquetil	1-8-75	7-8-76	4-2-78
F 787 Commandant de Pimodan	1-9-75	7-8-76	20-5-78
F 788 Second Maître le Bihan	1-11-76	13-8-77	7-7-79
F 789 Lieutenant de Vaisseau le Hénaff	11-13-77	16-9-78	13-2-80
F 790 Lieutenant de Vaisseau Lavallée	11-11-77	29-5-79	16-8-80
F 791 Commandant l'Herminier	7-5-79	7-3-81	19-1-86
F 792 Premier Maître l'Her	15-12-78	28-6-80	15-12-81
F 793 Commandant Blaison	15-11-79	7-3-81	28-4-82
F 794 Enseigne de Vaisseau Jacoubet	11-4-79	26-9-81	23-10-82
F 795 Commandant Ducuing	1-10-80	26-9-81	17-3-83
F 796 Commandant Birot	23-3-81	22-5-82	14-3-84
F 797 Commandant Bouan (ex-*Commandant Levasseur*)	12-10-81	23-4-83	11-5-84

D: 781–791: 1,100 tons (1,250 fl); 792, 793: 1,140 tons (1,290 fl); 794–797: 1,175 tons (1,330 fl)

S: 23.3 kts **Dim:** 80.00 (76.00 pp) × 10.30 × 3.00 (5.30 sonar)

A: F 792–797: 4/MM 40 Exocet (II × 2); others: 2/MM 38 Exocet (I × 2) or none (*see* Remarks)—1/100-mm DP, Model 1968—2/20-mm AA (I × 2)—2 or 4/12.7-mm mg (I × 2 or 4)—1/375-mm Model 1972 ASW rocket launcher (VI × 1)—4/TT for L-3 or L-5 ASW torpedoes (no reloads)

Commandant Bouan (F 797)—with 2 MM 40 Exocet Leo Van Ginderen, 6

FRIGATES *(continued)*

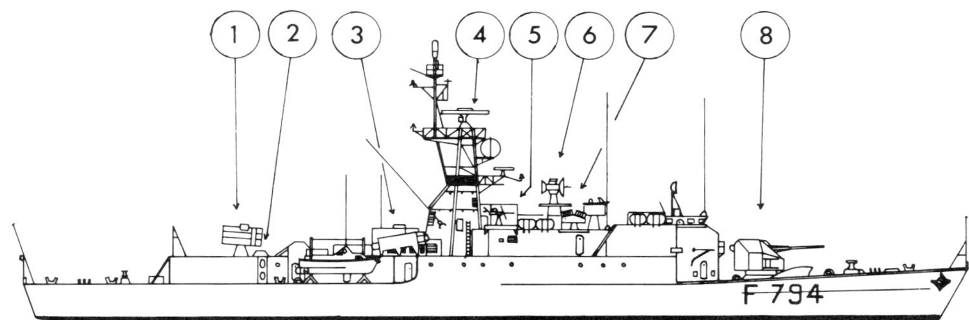

Enseigne de Vaisseau Jacoubet (F 794) 1. sextuple Bofors ASW RL, Model 1954 2. ASW torpedo tubes 3. MM 40 Exocet launchers 4. DRBV 51A search radar 5. 20-mm AA gun mounts 6. DRBC 32E f.c. radar 7. Dagaie countermeasures launcher 8. 100-mm Model 1968 DP gun mount Robert Dumas

Commandant Ducuing (F 795)—with 4 MM 40 Exocet, 4/12.7-mm mg RAN, 5-90

Amyot d'Inville (F 782)—with no Exocet missiles Bernard Prézelin, 3-90

Drogou (F 783)—with 2 MM 38 Exocet Hartmut Ehlers, 10-90

Lieutenant de Vaisseau Le Hénaff (F 789)—no Exocet Bernard Prézelin, 3-90

Lieutenant de Vaisseau Lavallée (F 790)—with 2 MM 38 Exocet OS2 John Bouvia, USN, 5-91

Electron Equipt:
Radar: 1/DRBN 32 (Decca 1226) nav., 1/DRBV 51A air/surf. search, 1/DRBC 32E f.c.
Sonar: 1/DUBA 25
EW: ARBR 16 intercept, 2/Dagaie RL , SLQ-25 Nixie torpedo decoy
M: 2 SEMT-Pielstick 12 PC 2 V400 diesels; 2 CP props; 12,000 bhp
Electric: 840 kw (2 × 320 kw, 1 × 200 kw) **Endurance:** 15 days
Range: 4,500/15 **Crew:** 7 officers, 42 petty officers, 43 ratings

Remarks: Very economical and seaworthy ships designed for coastal antisubmarine warfare, but available for scouting missions, training, and showing the flag. Can carry a troop detachment of one officer and seventeen men. All have fin stabilizers except F 795 and F 797, which have a "dynamic" stabilization system. Stacks and masts were modified from the *Jean Moulin* (F 785) onward; the heightened stack was backfitted in earlier units. Plans to add a helicopter facility to F 793 and F 794 were abandoned. All are to transition to a 60-month overhaul cycle, during which period they will spend 5 months in dockyard completely decommissioned.

F 791 has 2 SEMT-Pielstick 12 PA 6 BTC diesels totaling 14,400 hp, with infrared signature suppression features; protracted trials delayed commissioning. The original *Lieutenant de Vaisseau Le Hénaff* and *Commandant L'Herminier* were completed to a slightly modified design for South Africa and then sold to Argentina, which also ordered an additional unit.

F 782, F 785, F 788, and F 791 are equipped to receive MM 38 Exocet missiles but do not actually carry them. The control system for the 100-mm gun consists of a DRBC 32E monopulse, X-band radar, and a semi-analog, semi-digital computer; there is also a CSEE Naja optical director. F 782 completed refit 11-86 with new 100-mm gun, U.S. SLQ-25 Nixie torpedo decoy, upgraded sonar, Dagaie launchers, L-5 ASW torpedo capability, and waste-processing system; the others have been similarly upgraded during subsequent refits. Plans to add a towed array sonar have been canceled. Twin-launcher SIMBAD point-defense missile system trials conducted with F 792 in 1989; another ship tested the Modular Crotale launcher in place of the 100-mm gun in 1987–88.

♦ **1 Modified Commandant Rivière class** Bldr: Lorient Arsenal

	Laid down	L	In serv.
F 729 Balny	3-60	17-3-62	1-2-70

FRIGATES *(continued)*

D: 1,650 tons (2,150 fl) **S:** 26 kts **Dim:** 102.7 (98.0 pp) × 11.8 × 5.0 (prop)
A: 2/100-mm Model 1953 DP (I × 2)—2/40-mm AA (I × 2)—1/305-mm ASW mortar (IV × 1)—6/TT for L-3 ASW torpedoes (III × 2)
Electron Equipt:
Radar: 1/DRBN 32 (Decca 1226) nav., 1/DRBV 22A air search, 1/DRBC 32C f.c.
Sonar: 1/DUBA 3 depth-determining, 1/SQS 17 scanning
EW: ARBR 16 intercept
M: CODAG: 1 Turbomeca M 38 gas turbine (11,500 shp), 2 AGO V-16 diesels (3,600 bhp each); 1 CP prop; 18,700 hp
Electric: 1,280 kw (3 × 320 kw) **Range:** 13,000/10 **Fuel:** 310 tons
Crew: 9 officers, 67 petty officers, 93 ratings

Balny (F 729) OS2 John Bouvia, USN, 5-91

Remarks: Allocated for trials in 1964 with the French Navy's first combined gas-turbine *and* diesel plant (CODAG). The gas turbine is a version of the Atar-8 turbojet used in the Étendard fighter, reduced in rating from 15,000 shp to 11,500 hp. Both diesels and the gas turbine can be clutched together to drive the single propeller, which is 3.6 meters in diameter and extends 1 meter beneath the keel. The compactness of the *Balny*'s propulsion plant, compared with that of the all-diesel plants in her half-sisters of the *Commandant Rivière* class, permits her to carry approximately 100 more tons of fuel, which accounts for her great endurance on diesels alone. Because one of her 100-mm guns is mounted atop the lengthened after superstructure, it has not been possible to install Exocet antiship missiles. To be retired by 1995.

◆ **3 Commandant Rivière class** Bldr: Lorient Arsenal

	Laid down	L	In serv.
F 726 Commandant Bory	3-58	11-10-58	5-3-64
F 748 Protet	9-61	7-12-62	1-5-64
F 749 Enseigne de Vaisseau Henry	9-62	14-2-63	1-1-65

Protet (F 748) Pradignac & Léo, 1988

Commandant Bory (F 726) L. Rex, 10-88

Enseigne de Vaisseau Henry (F 749)—partially disarmed as training ship Peter Voss, 6-91

D: 1,960 tons (2,170 fl) **S:** 26 kts (26.6 on trials)
Dim: 102.7 (98.0 pp) × 11.8 × 4.35 (hull)
A: 4/MM 38 Exocet—2/100-mm DP, Model 1963 (I × 2)—2/40-mm AA—1/305-mm ASW mortar (IV × 1; not in F 749)—6/TT L-3 ASW torpedoes (III × 2; not in F 749)
Electron Equipt:
Radar: 1/DRBN 32 nav., 1/DRBV 22A air search, 1/DRBC 32C f.c.
Sonar: 1/DUBA 3 depth determining, 1/SQS-17 scanning
EW: ARBR 16 intercept, 2/Dagaie countermeasures RL
M: 4 SEMT-Pielstick 12 PC 1L 600 diesels; 2 props; 16,000 bhp
Electric: 1,280 kw (4 × 320 kw diesel sets) **Endurance:** 45 days
Range: 2,300/26; 7,500/16.5 **Fuel:** 210 tons
Crew: 9 officers, 66 petty officers, 91 ratings

Remarks: Designed for escort duty in various climates; air-conditioned. Can embark a flag officer and staff or an 80-man commando unit. F 726 originally had free-piston generators driving turbines, but these were replaced with a standard diesel plant in 1974–75. Beginning in the mid-1970s, four Exocet missiles replaced a 100-mm gun atop the after superstructure. F 726 was the first ship to carry the Dagaie countermeasures rocket-launching system. F 749, as tender to the training ship *Jeanne d'Arc,* has had her ASW mortar and torpedo tubes removed.

Sister *Commandant Rivière* (F 733) rerated as an auxiliary and converted 1985 as sonar trials ship. Sister *Victor Schoelcher* (F 725), stricken 22-7-88, was sold to Uruguay 19-12-88 after removal of MM 38 missiles and Dagaie decoy launchers; also sold to Uruguay were *Commandant Bourdais* (F 740), transferred 20-8-90, and *Amiral Charner* (F 727), transferred 18-1-91. Sister *Doudart de Lagrée* (F 728) was scheduled for disposal during 1991, F 748 is to be discarded during 1992, and the others by 1995 (F 749 last).

PATROL BOATS

◆ **1 Grèbe class** Bldr: SFCN, Villeneuve La Garenne

	Laid down	L	In serv.
P 679 Grèbe	. . .	16-11-89	8-90

Grèbe (p 679)—with stern ramp door open Bernard Prézelin, 10-

D: 260 tons (320 fl) **S:** 24 kts (23 sust.)
Dim: 52.00 (44.50 pp) × 9.80 × 2.75 (props)
A: 2/12.7-mm mg (I × 2)
Electron Equipt: Radar: 1/Decca 2690 nav.
M: 2 UNI-diesel UD 33V 12RVR diesels; 2 CP props; 4,800 bhp—2/90-kw electric auxiliary propulsion motors; 250 shp (8 kts)
Electric: 370 kw
Range: 1,400/23; 4,500/12; 14,000/8 (electric power)
Endurance: 30 days **Crew:** 4 officers, 9 petty officers, 6 ratings

Remarks: Commercial *Espadon 50* design employing deep-vee hull form. Orde 13-7-88 and was to begin trials 13-9-89. Has a stern embarkation ramp for an EDL 7-m rigid inflatable inspection boat capable of 30 kts. Can also carry 5 passengers an to be used primarily as a fisheries protection vessel in European waters.

Note: *Grèbe* replaced the former minesweeper *Mercure* (P 765), stricken 30-6-90.

PATROL BOATS *(continued)*

♦ **1 experimental patrol boat** Bldr: CN de L'Estérel, Cannes

	L	In serv.
P 696 Iris	21-12-88	11-89

Iris (P 696) Leo Van Ginderen, 6-91

D: 210 tons (230 fl) **S:** 23 kts **Dim:** 45.80 (43.00 pp) × 8.54 × 2.15
A: 1/Modular Crotale SAM system (VIII × 1; 8 missiles)— 2/35-mm Oerlikon AA (II × 1)
Electron Equipt: Radar: 1/Furuno. . . nav., 1/Triton-G air/surf. search, 1/ DRBC 32D Crotale f.c.
M: 2 MTU 16V396 TB83 diesels; 2 props; 4,160 bhp
Range: 1,500/15; 2,300/12 **Electric:** 270 kw **Endurance:** 5 days
Crew: 2 officers, 6 petty officers, 2 ratings

Remarks: Privately funded by Thomson-CSF to serve as a technology demonstrator like the Italian *Saetti* to show that even a small combatant can be equipped with a potent point-defense SAM system. Hull constructed of wood and epoxy resin. Highly automated; capable of unmanned operation of the navigation and propulsion systems. Has two pair Vosperfin stabilizers. *IRIS* is an acronym for "Intermediate Range Interceptor System." Controlled and operated by the French Navy.

♦ **10 P 400 (Super PATRA) class** Bldr: CMN, Cherbourg

	Laid down	L	In serv.	Op. Area/ base
P 682 L'Audacieuse	11-4-83	21-3-84	10-9-86	Cherbourg
P 683 La Boudeuse	15-6-83	21-5-84	25-7-86	Indian Ocean
P 684 La Capricieuse	12-9-83	31-10-84	26-9-86	Fr. Guyana
P 685 La Fougueuse	25-11-83	17-12-84	19-2-87	Fr. Guyana
P 686 La Glorieuse	21-2-84	25-1-85	25-3-87	Nouméa
P 687 La Gracieuse	26-4-84	26-3-85	17-7-87	Tahiti
P 688 La Moqueuse	4-10-84	8-4-86	25-3-87	Nouméa
P 689 La Railleuse	27-12-84	2-9-86	16-5-87	Tahiti
P 690 La Rieuse	14-3-85	17-10-86	13-6-87	Indian Ocean
P 691 La Tapageuse	13-8-85	16-2-87	24-2-88	Tahiti

Tapageuse (P 691) Leo Van Ginderen, 5-90

Audacieuse (P 682)—with twin stacks added APP Cherbourg, 1990

D: 373 tons (477 fl) **S:** 24 kts
Dim: 54.50 (50.00) × 8.00 (7.70 wl) × 2.54
A: 1/40-mm AA—1/20-mm F2 AA—1/7.62-mm mg
Electron Equipt: Radar: 1/DRBN 32 (Decca 1226) nav.
M: 2 Alsthom/SEMT-Pielstick 16 PA 4V200 VGDS diesels; 2 props; 8,000 bhp
Electric: 360 kw **Range:** 4,200/15 **Endurance:** 15 days
Crew: 3 officers, 21 enlisted + 20 passengers **Fuel:** 73 tons

Remarks: First six ordered 5-82, remainder on 6-3-84. Four were originally to have been part of the *Force de Service Public* (Public Service Force) under the designation SP 400 class; they were to have had fire-fighting, search-and-rescue, and anti-pollution equipment. Carry 840 rds 40-mm and 2,100 rds 20-mm ammunition; equipped for later addition of two Exocet missiles and a fire-control radar. P 686 carried Thomson-CSF VDS-12 small variable-depth sonar for trials in 1985. Propulsion problems with P 682 greatly delayed entire program, and the ships are well beyond their 422-ton designed displacement. P 682, P 683, and P 685 fitted with two exhaust stacks abaft the bridge during 1990 to replace unsuccessful underwater exhaust system; the others were to complete modification by end-1991.

♦ **1 Sterne class** Bldr: A & C. de la Perrière, Lorient

	Laid down	L	In serv.
P 680 Sterne (ex-PM 41)	18-5-79	31-10-79	18-7-80

Sterne (P 680) Bernard Prézelin, 11-87

D: 250 tons (340 fl) **S:** 20 kts **Dim:** 49.00 (43.60 pp) × 7.50 × 2.80
A: 2/12.7-mm mg (I × 2)
Electron Equipt: Radar: 1/DRBN-32 nav., 1/Decca . . . nav.
M: 2 SACM V12 CZSHR diesels; 2 props; 4,200 bhp
Electric: 240 kw (2 × 120 kw) **Endurance:** 15 days
Range: 1,500/19; 4,900/12 **Crew:** 16 tot.

Remarks: Constructed to merchant marine specifications for fisheries patrol duties within the 200-nautical-mile economic zone, including rescue services. Equipped with a large infirmary. Passive tank stabilization system. Can patrol at speeds up to 6.5 knots on an electrohydraulic drive system connected to the starboard propeller. Two rubber inspection dinghies are carried. Accommodations for 23 persons.

♦ **4 Trident ("PATRA") class**

	Bldr	L	In serv.
P 670 Trident	Auroux, Arcachon	31-5-76	17-12-76
P 671 Glaive	Auroux, Arcachon	25-8-76	3-77
P 672 Épée	CNM, Cherbourg	31-3-76	9-10-76
P 673 Pertuisane	CNM, Cherbourg	2-6-76	20-1-77

Épée (P 672) Gilbert Gyssels, 6-89

D: 120 tons (150 fl) **S:** 28 kts **Dim:** 40.70 (38.5 wl) × 5.90 × 1.60
A: 1/40-mm AA—2/12.7-mm mg (I × 2)
Electron Equipt: Radar: 1/DRBN 32 (Decca 1226) nav.
M: 2 AGO 195V12 CZSHR diesels; 2 CP props; 5,000 bhp (4,400 sust.)
Electric: 120 kw **Range:** 750/20; 1,500/15; 1,750/10
Crew: 1 officers, 5 petty officers, 12 ratings

Remarks: Thirty were planned, then fourteen, but only four were finally built. Two sisters have been built for the Ivory Coast, and another, initially commissioned as *Rapière* (P 674) in the French Navy, was sold to Mauritania in 1982. Tranferred to the the Gendarmerie Maritime in 1986-87; P 670 and P 672 serve at Lorient, P 671 and P 673 at Toulon. Carry 500 rounds of 40-mm, 2,000 rounds 12.7-mm ammunition. Six SS-12 wire-guided missile launchers atop the superstructure have been replaced by two 12.7-mm mg.

PATROL BOATS *(continued)*

◆ **1 former stern-haul trawler** Bldr: CN Le Trait, Le Havre (In serv. 1967)

P 681 ALBATROS (ex-*Nevé*)

Albatros (P 681)—with P 763 on deck Bernard Prézelin, 4-91

D: 1,940 tons (2,800 fl) **S:** 15 kts
Dim: 85.00 (75.00 pp) × 13.50 × 6.00
A: 1/40-mm AA—2/12.7-mm mg (I × 2)
Electron Equipt: Radar: 2/Decca . . . nav.—EW: ARUR intercept
M: 3 M.A.N. 1,700-bhp diesel generator sets, 1 AEG electric motor; 1 prop, 2,350 bhp—2/250-shp electric cruise motors
Electric: 750 kw (2 × 375-kw diesel sets) **Range:** 12,000/15
Crew: 6 officers, 22 petty officers, 19 ratings + 15 passengers

Remarks: Purchased 4-83 from Société Naval Caenaise for use in Antarctic-area fisheries-patrol duties, off Kerguelen, Crozet, St. Paul, and Amsterdam islands. Based at La Réunion. Commissioned in French naval service 23-3-84. Re-engined at Lorient during 7-90 to 3-91 refit. Has extensive hospital facilities, 200 tons cargo capacity, helicopter vertical replenishment area aft. Carries one launch and one small landing craft.

Note: The patrol boat *La Combattante* (P 730) was stricken during 1991.

◆ **1 Sirius-class former minesweeper** Bldr: CMN, Cherbourg

	L	In serv.
M 749 PHÉNIX	23-5-55	21-12-56

Phénix (M 749) Leo Van Ginderen, 10-90

D: 400 tons (440 fl) **S:** 15 kts **Dim:** 46.40 (42.70 pp) × 8.55 × 2.50
A: 1/20-mm Oerlikon AA
Electron Equipt: Radar: 1/DRBN 31 nav.
M: 2 SEMT-Pielstick 16 PA 1 175 diesels; 2 props; 2,000 bhp
Range: 3,000/10 **Crew:** 3 officers, 13 petty officers, 19 ratings

Remarks: Last surviving unit in French service of a once-numerous class; sisters in Yugoslav Navy. Wooden hull. Although still equipped for minesweeping, is used for patrol. To be stricken 1992.

PATROL CRAFT

◆ **16 VC 14 class** Bldr: CMN, Cherbourg (In serv. 1987–1990)

P 760 P 761 P 763 P 764 P 778 P 779 P 780 (*Guyane*)
P 781 (*Karukera*) P 789 P 790 P 791 P 792 Y 776 Y 777 Y 779
Y 781

D: 20 tons (30 fl) **S:** 24 kts **Dim:** 24.9 × 5.3 × . . .
A: 1 or 2/12.7-mm mg or 1/12.7-mm mg—1/7.62-mm mg (none in "Y" pendants)
Electron Equipt: Radar: 1/. . . nav.
M: 2 G.M. 6V71 diesels; 2 props; 480 bhp **Crew:** 4 tot.

P 781—first series Leo Van Ginderen, 6-91

Y 776—second series Leo Van Ginderen, 6-9

Remarks: GRP construction. Built in two series. P 779 at Réunion, P 780 at Fren Guyana, P 781 at Guadaloupe; names in parentheses are unofficial. Units with "P" pendants are manned by the Gendarmerie Maritime; those with "Y" pendants a naval-manned and are employed as pilot boats.

◆ **2 Volte 43 class** Bldr: Tecimar (In serv. 1975)

P 772 P 774

P 772 Tecimar, 1

D: 14 tons **S:** 21 kts **Dim:** 13.30 × 3.90 × 1.10
A: 1/12.7-mm mg—1/7.62-mm mg
M: 2 G.M. 8V71 diesels; 2 props; 670 bhp
Electron Equipt: Radar: 1/Decca 1229 nav.
Range: 400/20 **Crew:** 4 tot.

Remarks: Hull molded of glass-reinforced plastic. Manned by the Gendarmeri Brest. Sister P 771 transferred to Djibouti, and P 770 stricken 1990.

MINE WARFARE SHIPS

Note: The tender *Loire* (A 615) is, in effect, a mine countermeasures support However, because she has an auxiliary "A" pendant, and for convenience, she is li with her *Rhin*-class sisters under Support Tenders.

The *Narvik*-class BAMO (*Bâtiment Anti-Mines Océanique*) program was canc 9-91, despite the first ship of the series, *Narvik* (M 651), having been laun during 6-91. The ordering of five others in the class, *Autun* (M 652), *Bir Ha* (M 653), *Colmar* (M 654), *Garigliano* (M 655), and *Berlaimont* (M 656) had ea been deferred to post-1993. The first six were in the 1987–91 program as rep ments for the old U.S.-built ocean minesweepers, but orders for units two thr five have now been canceled. Three more, for a total of nine, were origi sought.

NE WARFARE SHIPS *(continued)*

10 Tripartite-class minehunters Bldr: Lorient Arsenal

	Laid down	L	In serv.
41 Éridan	20-12-77	2-2-79	16-4-84
42 Cassiopée	26-3-79	28-9-81	5-5-84
43 Andromède	6-3-80	22-5-82	19-10-84
44 Pégase	22-10-80	24-4-83	30-5-85
45 Orion	17-8-81	6-2-85	14-1-86
46 Croix du Sud	22-4-82	6-2-85	14-11-86
47 Aigle	2-12-82	8-3-86	1-7-87
48 Lyre	14-10-83	15-11-86	16-12-87
49 Persée	20-10-84	9-3-88	4-11-88
50 Sagittaire*	13-11-85	9-11-88	27-7-89

Pakistan 8-92.

: 535 tons (605 fl) **S:** 15 kts on main engine, 7 kts while hunting
im: 51.6 (47.1 pp) × 8.96 × 2.49 hull (3.50 max.)
: 1/20-mm AA—2/12.7-mm mg (I × 2)
lectron Equipt: Radar: 1/Decca 1229—Sonar: DUBM 21B
: 1 Brons-Werkspoor A RUB 215V12 diesel; 1 CP prop, 1,900 bhp—2 ACEC electric maneuvering props, 120 shp each; bow-thruster
lectric: 750 kw **Range:** 3,000/12
rew: 5 officers, 23 petty officers, 21 ratings

siopée (M 642) Bram Risseeuw, 3-91

dan (M 641) Sean Biaugeaud/DCN

ix du Sud (M 646) Bernard Prézelin, 10-90

Cassiopée (M 642)—with decompression chamber module Bernard Prézelin, 6-90

Lyre (M 648)—with 2/12.7-mm mg added abaft decompression chamber at the aft end of the forecastle deck Luciano Grazioli, 5-90

Remarks: Hull built of glass-reinforced polyester plastic. Program well behind schedule; last five canceled in favor of the BAMO class. Have one mechanical drag sweep. France, Belgium, and the Netherlands cooperated in building these ships for the requirements of the three countries. Have the EVEC 20 automatic plotting table and Decca HiFix and Syledis radio precision navigation equipment, and two PAP-104 remote-controlled minehunting submersibles. Have a 6-man portable decompression chamber module at the aft end of the forecastle deck. In 1985 began to receive the AP-4 acoustic sweep. The first six are based at Brest, the others at Toulon.

M 650 is to be transferred to Pakistan in 8-92 and replaced by a new-construction unit to be completed around 1997. M 642 was in collision with Dutch tanker *Anwya* at Rotterdam on 21-2-91.

♦ 5 Circé-class minehunters Bldr: CMN, Cherbourg

	Laid down	L	In serv.
M 712 Cybèle	15-9-70	2-3-72	28-9-72
M 713 Calliope	4-4-70	20-10-71	28-9-72
M 714 Clio	4-9-69	10-6-71	18-5-72
M 715 Circé	30-1-69	15-12-70	18-5-72
M 716 Cérès	2-2-71	10-8-72	8-3-73

Calliope (M 713) Maritime Photographic, 9-90

MINE WARFARE SHIPS *(continued)*

D: 423 tons (508 fl) **S:** 15 kts
Dim: 50.90 (46.50 pp) × 8.90 × 3.60 (max.)
A: 1/20-mm AA—2 PAP-104 remote-control mine-locators
Electron Equipt: Radar: Decca 1229 nav.—Sonar: DUBM 20B
M: 1 MTU diesel; 1 prop; 1,800 bhp—2/260-shp electric propulsors
Range: 3,000/12 **Crew:** 4 officers, 19 petty officers, 24 ratings

Remarks: Designed for the detection and destruction of mines laid as deep as 60 meters. Hull made of laminated wood. Design stressed low magnetic signature and silent operation. Two independent propulsion systems, one for transit, the other for minesweeping, both with remote control. Special rudders with small propellers mounted at the base of the rudder's after end and powered by a 260-hp electric motor, giving a speed of 7 knots and permitting exceptional maneuverability.

Mines are destroyed either by divers (six in each crew) or by the PAP-104 (*poisson auto-propulsé*) wire-guided sled device, which is 2.7 meters long, 1.1 meters in diameter, weighs 700 kg, is moved by two electric motors that drive it at 6 knots for a distance of up to 500 meters, and has a television camera that displays an image of the mine. It can deposit its explosive charge of 100 kg near the mine. When the sled has been recovered, the charge is detonated by ultrasonic waves. These ships do not have minesweeping gear. *Cérès* carried the prototype EVEC automatic plotting table, now aboard all. All received updated DUBM 20A sonar with coherent processing feature during mid-1980s refits; subsequently further updated to DUBM 20B.

♦ 3 ex-U.S. Agile-class ocean minesweepers

	Bldr	In serv.
M 610 Ouistreham (ex-MSO 513)	Peterson Bldrs., Sturgeon Bay, Wisc.	8-56
M 612 Alençon (ex-MSO 453)	Bellingham SY, Wash.	6-54
M 623 Baccarat (ex-MSO 505)	Tacoma Boat, Wash.	3-56

Ouistreham (M 610)—tall stack version Leo Van Ginderen, 2-91

Alençon (M 612)—short stack version Bernard Prézelin, 5-90

D: 710 tons (780 fl) **S:** 13.5 kts (14 kts on trials)
Dim: 50.29 × 10.67 × 3.15
A: 1/40-mm AA
Electron Equipt: Radar: Decca 1229 nav.—Sonar: DUBM 41B
M: 2 G.M. 8-268A diesels; 2 CP props; 1,600 bhp
Fuel: 47 tons **Range:** 3,000/10 **Crew:** 5 officers, 53 enlisted

Remarks: Full conversion of these ships to minehunters was canceled. They be receiving the new DUBM 41B sonar in 1978, however. M 612 recommissioned in 1 and M 610 on 1-7-81. M 612 has a very short stack. Sister *Narvik* (M 609) reclassified A 769 on 1-1-76 as trials ship for the AP-4 acoustic sweep and the DUBM sonar and was stricken in 1988. The survivors are now all equipped with the A sweep. Sister *Berneval* (M 613, ex-MSO 450) was stricken in 1988, and *Berlaimont* 520, ex-MSO 500) in 10-89. Five sisters converted as minehunters have been stric also: *Dompaire* (M 616) and *Mytho* (M 618) in 1987, *Vinh-Long* (M 619) and *Garigli* (M 617) in 1988, and *Cantho* (M 615) in 1989.

♦ 4 mine countermeasures divers' tenders

	Bldr	Laid down	L	In serv
M 611 Vulcain	La Perrière, Lorient	15-5-85	17-1-86	11-10-8
A 613 Achéron	CMN, Cherbourg	5-2-86	19-11-86	17-6-8
M 614 Styx	CMN, Cherbourg	20-5-86	3-3-87	22-7-8
M 622 Pluton	La Perrière, Lorient	11-10-85	13-5-86	12-12-8

Achéron (A 613)—mine clearance diver training ship Pradignac & Léo,

Styx (M 614) Bernard Prézelin,

D: 409 tons (490 fl) **S:** 13.7 kts
Dim: 41.60 (36.96 pp) × 7.50 × 3.20
A: 1/12.7-mm mg **Electron Equipt:** Radar: 1/Decca 1226 nav.
M: 2 SACM MGO V16 AFHR diesels, 2 Kort-nozzle CP props; 2,200 bhp—750-shp bow-thruster
Electric: 176 kw **Range:** 2,850/13.5; 7,400/9 **Fuel:** 92 m^3
Crew: 1 officer, 8 petty officers, 6 ratings

Remarks: Derived from the *Chamois*-class local support-tender design as placements for the U.S. *Adjutant*-class former minesweepers used as mine-clear diver-support tenders. M 611, M 622 ordered 11-10-84, other pair 7-85 on subcont Can support 12 divers. Hydraulic crane on fantail can lift 5 tons at 6-m radius, 3.5 at 10 m. Syledis automatic pilot fitted. There is a 2-man decompression chamber. A is training ship for the Diving School.

AMPHIBIOUS WARFARE SHIPS

♦ 1 TCD 90 dock landing ship

	Bldr	Laid down	L	In serv.
L 9011 Foudre	Brest Arsenal	26-3-86	19-11-88	7-12-90

AMPHIBIOUS WARFARE SHIPS *(continued)*

Foudre (L 9011) Bernard Prézelin, 4-90

Foudre (L 9011) Bernard Prézelin, 4-90

D: 9,300 tons (11,880 fl) **S:** 21 kts
Dim: 168.00 (160.00 pp) × 23.50 (22.00 wl) × 5.20 (9.10 flooded)
A: 2/Sadral SAM syst. (VI × 2, . . . Mistral missiles)—1/40-mm AA—2/20-mm F2 AA (I × 2)—4/12.7-mm mg (I × 4)—4/Super Puma helicopters (army)
Electron Equipt:
Radar: 1/Decca . . . nav., 1/DRBV 51 air/surf. search
M: 2 SEMT-Pielstick 16 PC 2.5-V400 diesels; 2 CP props; 21,600 bhp— 700-hp bow-thruster
Electric: 4,250 kw (5 × 850-kw diesel sets)
Range: 11,000/15 **Fuel:** . . .
Crew: 13 officers, 197 enlisted + troops: 35 officers, 435 enlisted

Remarks: TCD = *Transport de Chalands de Débarquement.* First ordered 5-11-84; wo others were to order 1986 and 1988 but were deferred; the second was to have been uilt at NORMED, La Seyne. Intended to carry one mechanized regiment plus 1,080 ns combat vehicles and cargo for the Rapid Action Force; also able to act as logistics ıpport ship.

Docking well 122.0 × 13.50 × 7.70 high for 2 CDIC (EDIC replacement), 1 large tug, r 10 CTM landing craft, or 1 P 400 patrol boat: 1,740 m². Helo platform 1,080 m² with vo spots equipped with SAMAHE hold-down systems, plus third spot on rolling ɔck-well cover; hangar for 4 helicopters. Vehicle cargo area of 1,360 m² can be xtended by using dock floor; 60-ton elevator (13.5 × 8m) connects dock floor and cargo ecks. To flood down for loading and unloading embarked craft, has 7,000-m³ ballast apacity. Side-loading doors. Has Syracuse SATCOMM system. Carries 2 LCVP-type nding craft.

Propulsion plant same as in *Meuse*-class replenishment ships. Trials 19-11-89. Has tensive command/communications facilities, 500-m² hospital. A passive roll stabilization system is to be installed during 1992–93.

1 BTMS small dock landing ship   Bldr: Dubigeon, Nantes

	Laid down	L	In serv.
9077 Bougainville	28-1-86	3-10-86	25-2-88

ugainville (L 9077) French Navy, 2-88

Bougainville (L 9077) Bernard Prézelin, 10-87

D: 3,310 tons light, 4,200 tons normal (4,870 fl) **S:** 15 kts (14.6 sust.)
Dim: 113.50 (105.00 pp) × 17.00 × 4.24
A: 2/12.7-mm mg (I × 2)—2/Super Puma helicopters (army)
Electron Equipt: Radar: 2/DRBN 32 (Decca 1226) nav.
M: UNI UD 33-V12-M5 diesels; 2 CP props; 4,800 bhp—1/400-hp side-thruster
Electric: 1,600 kw (2 × 480 kw, 2 × 320 kw) **Range:** 6,000/12
Fuel: . . . **Endurance:** 45 days
Crew: 6 officers, 18 petty officers, 29 ratings + 60 passengers

Remarks: BTMS—*Bâtiment de Transport Moyen et de Soutien;* intended for Directorate of Nuclear Experimentation for use between Papeete and the Muraroa Test Center. Ordered 22-11-84; completed after launch by Ch. de l'Atlantique, St. Nazaire, when building yard closed. Miniature LSD design with 78.0 × 11.8 (10.2 clear)-m docking well for landing craft or 40 20-ft containers. Draft aft 9.20 when flooded, providing 3.15 m clear over deck. 37-ton crane aft to starboard. Six-meter ramp to starboard can accommodate 53 tons. Has 70 m helicopter fuel. Can also act as a repair and stores ship.

♦ 2 Ouragan-class dock landing ships   Bldr: Brest Arsenal

	Laid down	L	In serv.
L 9021 Ouragan	6-62	9-11-63	1-6-65
L 9022 Orage	6-66	22-4-67	1-4-68

Orage (L 9022) Leo Van Ginderen, 6-91

Ouragan (L 9021) Pradignac & Léo, 2-89

AMPHIBIOUS WARFARE SHIPS *(continued)*

D: 5,965 tons (8,500 fl) **S:** 17.3 kts
Dim: 149.0 (144.5 pp) × 21.5 × 5.40 (8.70 max.)
A: 4/40-mm AA (I × 4)—2/120-mm mortars (on L 9021 only)
Electron Equipt: Radar: 2/DRBN 32 nav.—Sonar: SQS-17 on L 9021
M: 2 SEMT-Pielstick 12 PC 2V diesels; 2 CP props; 8,640 bhp
Electric: 2,650 kw **Range:** 9,000/15
Crew: 10 officers, 66 petty officers, 135 ratings + up to 470 troops

Remarks: Bridge to starboard of permanent helicopter deck. Both have repair facilities. Can carry 349 troops, including 14 officers, or 470 troops for a short distance. A 120-meter-long well with a 14-by-5.5-meter stern gate can be submerged by 3 meters. When ships are ballasted down, displacement reaches 14,400 tons. Movement of the sluices and valves is automatic, using pumps (3,000 m^3/h) controlled from a central position. A removable deck in six sections covers 36 meters of the after part of the well and allows the landing and takeoff of heavy helicopters. A 90-meter-long temporary deck in 15 sections can be used to stow cargo or vehicles, but its use reduces the number of landing craft that can be carried, because the well is then diminished by half.

If used as transports, they can embark either 2 EDIC landing craft for infantry and tanks, carrying 11 light tanks or trucks, or 8 LCM(8) with tanks or vehicles and, in addition, heavy helicopters on the landing platform. If used as cargo-carriers, they can embark 1,500 tons of material. Lifting equipment includes two 35-ton cranes. A combined command center permits the simultaneous direction of helicopter and amphibious operations. Were to be discarded in 1990 and 1993, respectively, but will now be retained for the foreseeable future. Both are attached to the First Maritime Region, Brest.

◆ 5 Champlain-class medium landing ships
Bldrs: L 9030, 9031: Brest Arsenal; others: At. Français de L'Ouest, Grand-Quevilly

	Laid down	L	In serv.
L 9030 Champlain	1973	17-11-73	5-10-74
L 9031 Francis Garnier	1973	17-11-73	21-6-74
L 9032 Dumont d'Urville	4-81	27-11-81	5-2-83
L 9033 Jacques Cartier	10-81	28-4-82	23-9-83
L 9034 La grandière	27-8-84	11-12-85	20-1-87

Champlain (L 9030)—low superstructure — Bernard Prézelin, 9-90

Jacques Cartier (L 9033)—high superstructure — 16 Flot., French Navy, 1984

D: 770 tons (1,330 fl; L 9032–9034: 1,386 fl) **S:** 16 kts (13 cruising)
Dim: 80.0 (68.0 pp) × 13.0 × 3.0 (2.50 hull)
A: L 9030, 9031: 2/40-mm AA (I × 2)—2/81-mm mortars (I × 2)—2/12.7-mm mg (I × 2)—others: 2/20-mm AA (I × 2)—2/81-mm mortars (I × 2)— 2/12.7-mm mg (I × 2)
Electron Equipt: Radar: 1/DRBN 32 (Decca 1226) nav.
M: 2 SACM 195 V-12 CSHR diesels; 2 CP props; 3,600 bhp
Range: 3,500/13
Electric: 360 kw **Crew:** 3 officers, 15 petty officers, 26 ratings

Remarks: Bow-door design, embarkation ramp and helicopter platform aft. Cargo: 350 tons. Living quarters for a landing team (5 officers, 15 noncommissioned officers, 118 men) and its 12 vehicles, including Leopard armored personnel carriers. L 9032 through L 9034 are able to transport 180 men; they have a 40-ton-capacity bow ramp, improved accommodations, and carry 1 LCVP and 1 LCP landing craft. Their superstructure is one deck higher, and they can carry a 330-ton vehicle cargo for beaching and 208 tons of potable water. All have a helicopter deck. A sister ship has been built for Gabon, Morocco has three, the Ivory Coast one, and Chile has built three. L 9034, built on speculation, then acquired for French Navy, has a longer helicopter deck.

◆ 2 CDIC tank landing craft
Bldr: SFCN, Villeneuve la Garenne

	L	In serv.		L	In serv.
L 9061	25-2-88	28-7-88	L 9062	3-11-88	17-2-89

L 9061—note simplified superstructure — Bernard Prézelin, 4-89

D: 250 tons (600 fl) **S:** 10 kts
Dim: 59.40 (55.45 pp) × 11.90 × 1.10 (1.76 max.)
A: 2/20-mm F2 AA (I × 2)—2/12.7-mm mg (I × 2)
Electron Equipt: Radar: 1/Decca RM 1229 nav.
M: 2 SACM UD30V12 M1 diesels; 2 props; 1,080 bhp **Fuel:** 20 tons
Electric: 156 kw **Range:** 1,000/10 **Crew:** 18 tot.

Remarks: Although intended for service with ships of the *Foudre* class, these ships have sufficient navigational equipment and accommodations to permit a coastal voy age of several days duration. CDIC = *Chalands de Débarquement d'Infanterie et de Chars* (landing ships for infantry and tanks). Cargo capacity: 336 tons. Plans to con struct three more deferred.

◆ 2 EDIC-700-class tank landing craft
Bldr: SFCN, Villeneuve-la-Garenne

	L	In serv.		L	In serv.
L 9051	3-3-87	13-6-87	L 9052	10-9-87	19-12-87

L 9051 — French Navy, 6-8

D: 326 tons light (736 fl) **S:** 12 kts
Dim: 59.40 (55.85 pp) × 11.90 × 1.76 (max.)
A: 2/20-mm F2 AA (I × 2)—2/12.7-mm mg (I × 2)
Electron Equipt: Radar: 1/Decca 1226 nav.
M: 2 SACM UD30V12 MB diesels; 2 props; 1,080 bhp
Fuel: 20 tons **Range:** 1,000/10 **Electric:** 156 kw
Crew: 7 petty officers, 9 ratings

Remarks: Financed by the French nuclear testing center (DIRCEN). L 9051 is ba at Muraroa, L 9052 at Djibouti. Cargo capacity: 340 tons in 28.5 × 8-m cargo deck w bow ramp.

◆ 4 EDIC-class tank landing craft
Bldr: SFCN, Villeneuve-la-Garen

	L		L
L 9070	30-3-97	L 9072	1968
L 9074	7-2-70	L 9096	11-10-58

D: 282 tons (670 fl) **S:** 8 kts **Dim:** 59.0 × 11.95 × 1.3 (1.62 fl)
A: 2/20-mm AA (I × 2) **M:** 2 MGO diesels; 2 props; 1,000 bhp
Range: 1,800/8 **Crew:** 5 petty officers, 12 ratings

AMPHIBIOUS WARFARE SHIPS *(continued)*

L 9096—prior to conversion Leo Van Ginderen, 9-90

Remarks: EDIC = *Engins de Débarquement pour Infanterie et Chars.* Can carry 11 trucks or 5 armored personnel carriers. Two each can be carried aboard the *Ouragan* and the *Orage.* L 9096 reconfigured as a pollution-control craft in 1990, with a 7-ton crane added. L 9095 transferred to Senegal, 1-7-74. L 9071 stricken 19-4-77, L 9092 and L 9082 stricken 1981. L 9084 reclassified BAME (repair barge). L 9096 was loaned to Lebanon 7-11-83 and returned in 1-85. L 9073, L 9083 stricken 1986; L 9091, L 9093 in 1988; L 9094 in 1990. The others will soon follow.

◆ **1 utility transport/ferry** Bldr: Ch. Serra, La Seyne

L 9090 GAPEAU (In serv. 2-10-87)

Gapeau (L 9090) Carlo Martinelli, 5-91

D: 509 tons light (1,058 fl) **S:** 10 kts
Dim: 64.00 × 12.20 × 3.30 max.
A: none **Electron Equipt:** Radar: 1/. . . nav.
M: 2 . . . . . . diesels; 2 props; . . . bhp **Crew:** 6 tot. + 30 passengers

Remarks: Replaced EDIC L 9092 and L 9093 as support craft for the *Centre d'Essais de la Méditerranée* missile range, Île du Levant. Cargo capacity: 460 tons on drive-through deck with bow and stern ramps.

◆ **22 U.S. LCM (8)-class landing craft** Bldr: CMN, Cherbourg (CTM 4, 5, 11: C.N. Auroux, Arcachon)

	In serv.		In serv.		In serv.
CTM 1	19-10-82	CTM 9	25-5-83	CTM 16	1985–86
CTM 2	27-10-82	CTM 10	22-6-83	CTM 17	13-8-86
CTM 3	12-82	CTM 11	20-7-83	CTM 18	27-4-88
CTM 4	2-12-82	CTM 12	11-8-83	CTM 19	22-6-88
CTM 5	21-12-82	CTM 13	11-4-84	CTM 20	8-88
CTM 6	16-2-83	CTM 14	8-8-84	CTM 21	1989
CTM 7	3-83	CTM 15	25-10-84	CTM 22	1989
CTM 8	1983				

CTM 18 Bernard Prézelin, 3-89

D: 56 tons light (150 fl) **S:** 9.5 kts **Dim:** 23.80 × 6.35 × 1.25
A: 2/12.7-mm mg (I × 2) **Electron Equipt:** Radar: 1/. . . nav.
M: 2 Poyaud 520 V8 diesels; 2 props; 480 bhp **Range:** 380/8
Endurance: 48 hours at half power **Fuel:** 3.4 tons **Crew:** 6 tot.

Remarks: Repeat version of earlier CTM 1–16. Cargo capacity: 90 tons. The machine guns are not always mounted. CTM=*Chalands de Transport de Matériel.*

◆ **2 U.S. LCM (3) class** Bldr: Ch. . . . , La Réunion (In serv. 3-83)

LCM 1057 LCM 1058

D: 26 tons (52 fl) **S:** 8 kts **Dim:** 15.25 × 4.3 × 1.2
M: 2 Gray Marine 64 HN9 diesels; 2 props; 450 bhp

Remarks: Employed in local service at Mayotte Naval Base, La Réunion. LCM 1031, 1045, 1052, 1074, and 1076 stricken 1984–85; LCM 1035 stricken 1987; LCM 1036 in 1989; L 1055, L 1056 in 1990. All except the two survivors had been built in the United States and transferred 6-58. Cargo: 30 tons.

◆ **. . . LCVP** Bldr: . . . . (In serv. . . .)

D: 13 tons (fl) **S:** 8 kts **Dim:** 10.90 × 3.21 × 1.09 (aft)
M: 1 diesel; 225 bhp **Range:** 110/8

Remarks: GRP construction, based on standard U.S. design. Can carry 36 troops or 3.5 tons cargo in 5.2 × 2.3-m cargo well. At least 20 are in service, aboard various landing ships and auxiliaries.

EXPERIMENTAL SHIPS

Note: For smaller experimental trials tenders with Y-series pendants, see Miscellaneous Service Craft entry at end of France section.

◆ **0 (+1) new construction missile-range tracking ship**

	Bldr	Laid down	L	In serv.
A 601 MONGE	Ch. de l'Atlantique, St. Nazaire	26-3-90	6-10-90	10-92

Monge (A 601)—model, showing appearance as completed, 1992
Ch. de l'Atlantique, 1990

Monge (A 601)—on trials Dr. Giorgio Arra, 5-91

D: 17,760 tons (21,040 fl) **S:** 15.8 kts
Dim: 225.60 (203.40 pp) × 24.84 × 7.66
A: 2/20-mm F2 AA (I × 2)—2/Super Frélon helicopters
Electron Equipt:
Radar: 2/Decca RM 1229 nav., 1/DRBV 15C air search, 1/Gascogne tracking, 2/Armor tracking, 1/Savoie tracking, 1/. . . (I-band) tracking
M: 2 SEMT-Pielstick 8PC 2.5 L400 diesels; 1 CP prop; 9,000 bhp—1,000 shp bow-thruster
Range: 15,000/15
Electric: 7,560 kw (6 × 1,200 kw, 1 × 360 kw diesel sets)
Endurance: 60 days
Crew: 10 officers, 94 enlisted + 184 scientific staff

Remarks: Replacement for the current *Henri Poincaré* (A 603). The Syracuse I, Syracuse II, and MARISAT SATCOMM systems will be fitted, along with NAVSTAR NAVSAT receivers. Extensive tracking equipment will be installed, as on her predecessor, including Lidar green-laser upper atmospheric analysis equipment. There will also be 14 telemetry antennas. Computer-controlled passive tank stabilization system to reduce roll to 9-degrees maximum at Sea State 6. Carries 160 tons aviation fuel. Accepted from builder 6-3-91 for trials. Tracking equipment to begin installation 3-6-91, with operational trials scheduled to begin 5-92.

EXPERIMENTAL SHIPS *(continued)*

♦ **1 NES 200 experimental surface effect ship** Bldr: CMN, Cherbourg

	Laid down	L	In serv.
A 786 AGNES 200	6-89	2-7-90	1991

Agnes 200 (A 786) CMN/DGA, 10-90

D: 229 tons (254 fl) **S:** 40 kts on cushion/15 kts hull-borne
Dim: 51.00 (45.00 pp) × 13.00 × 2.30 hullborne/1.00 on cushion
A: 2/20-mm F2 AA (I × 2)—1/Dauphin helicopter
Electron Equipt: Radar: 1/. . . nav.
M: 2 MTU 8V538 TB 83 diesels (2,000 bhp each) for lift fans, 2 MTU 16V538 TB93 diesels for propulsion; 2 KaMeWa waterjets; 8,000 bhp
Range: 1,200/14; 750/25
Crew: 1 officer, 7 enlisted + 46 passengers

Remarks: Ordered 18-2-88. Catamaran aluminum-construction hull, with helicopter platform aft. Capable of operating in State 4 seas. Intended as a technology demonstrator/prototype for the planned 1,000-ton EOLES *(Escorteur Océanique Léger à Effet de Surface)*. Helicopter deck 200 m^2.

♦ **1 mine countermeasures experimental ship** Bldr: DCN, Lorient

	Laid down	L	In serv.
A 785 THÉTIS (ex-*Néreide*)	8-3-86	15-11-86	9-11-88

Thétis (A 785) Pradignac & Léo, 11-89

D: 720 tons light (1,000 fl) **S:** 15 kts
Dim: 59.00 (53.00 pp) × 10.90 × 3.63
A: 2/12.7-mm mg (I × 2)—mines
Electron Equipt: Radar: 1/Decca 1226 nav.—Sonar: DUBM 42
M: 2 UNI UD30-V16-M7 diesels; 1 CP prop; 2,500 bhp—1 electric motor for low speeds; 120 shp—200-hp bow-thruster
Range: 6,000/12 **Crew:** 2 officers, 36 enlisted + 10 technicians

Remarks: Typed BEGM—*Bâtiment d'Expérimentation de la Guerre des Mines*. Ordered 11-10-84. Use same hull and machinery as the *La Pérouse*-class hydrographic survey ships. A second unit was in the 1984–88 Building Plan but was canceled. Performs trials with DUBM 42, new remotely operated mine-disposal vehicle, and AD-4 acoustic sweep. Replaced *Narvik* (A 769).

♦ **1 ASW weapons-trials support tender** Bldr: DCAN, Toulon

	L	In serv.
A 743 DENTI	7-10-75	15-7-76

D: 170 tons (fl) **S:** 12 kts **Dim:** 34.70 (30.00 pp) × 6.60 × 2.27
Electron Equipt: Radar: 1/Decca . . . nav.
M: 2 Baudouin DP 8 diesels; 2 props; 960 bhp
Range: 800/12 **Crew:** . . .

Remarks: Employed by DCAN Toulon in support of weapons trials. Essentially a recovery craft, with an overhead rail gantry aft. Carries divers also.

Denti (A 743) Leo Van Ginderen, 6-91

♦ **1 underwater-research ship** Bldr: Lorient Arsenal

	Laid down	L	In serv.
A 646 TRITON	1967	7-3-70	20-1-72

Triton (A 646) Maritime Photographic, 11-9

D: 1,410 tons (1,510 fl) **S:** 13 kts
Dim: 74.00 (68.00 pp) × 11.85 × 3.65
Electron Equipt: Radar: 1/Decca 1226—Sonar: . . .
M: 2 MGO V-12 ASHR diesels, electric drive; aft: 1/Voith-Schneider 3 G cycloidal propeller; 880 shp; forward: 2 electric motors, 1/Voith-Schneider 26 G cycloidal propeller; 530 shp
Electric: 640 kw **Range:** 4,000/13
Crew: 4 officers, 44 enlisted + divers: 5 officers, 12 enlisted

Remarks: Assigned to GISMER (*Groupe d'Intervention sous la Mer*) for deep-s diving and observation. Has a decompression chamber, laboratories, television, na gational radar, sonar for deep-water area search, etc. Helicopter platform. Good m neuverability at very slow speeds; capable of remaining positioned above a point 3 meters deep. Can be used in submarine-rescue operations. Her 15-ton crane can low and raise: (a) a 13.5-ton tethered bell that can be sunk to 250 meters and can carry t four-man diving teams; (b) the two-man submarine *Griffon*, which is capable of divi to 600 meters for underwater exploration; (c) diving devices, sleds (troika, automa cally guided). The *Griffon* has a manipulator arm, and other characteristics are:

D: 14.2 to 16.7 tons **Dim:** 7.8 × 2.3 × 3.1 (height)
M: 1 electric motor **Range:** 24 hours/4 kts

Note: The *Chamois*-class local support tender *Isard* is also subordinated to GISM and supports the ERIC (*Engin de Recherche et d'Intervention par Cable*) wire-gui submersible. For data, see the *Chamois* class under Miscellaneous Auxiliary Ships

♦ **1 missile-range tracking ship** Bldr: Cantieri Riuniti de Adriatico, Monfalcone, Italy

	L	In serv.
A 603 HENRI POINCARÉ (ex-*Maina Morasso*)	10-60	1-3-68

Henri Poincaré (A 603) Leo Van Ginderen,

EXPERIMENTAL SHIPS *(continued)*

D: 22,640 tons (23,430 fl) **S:** 15 kts
Dim: 180.00 (160.00 pp) × 22.20 × 9.40 **A:** 2/20-mm AA
Electron Equipt:
Radar: . . ./. . . nav., 1/DRBV 22D air search, 2/Gascogne tracking, 1/Savoie tracking
M: 1 set Parsons GT; 1 prop; 10,000 shp; bow-thruster
Boilers: 2 Foster-Wheeler; 48 kg/cm, 445°C **Range:** 11,800/13.5
Crew: 22 officers, 144 petty officers, 159 ratings, and several civilian technicians

Remarks: Flagship of Group M (the Naval Test and Measurement Group), which makes at-sea tests, takes measurements, and conducts experiments, as requested by the navy or any other organization, civilian or military. The chief mission of the *Henri Poincaré* is to measure the trajectory of ballistic missiles (MSBS and SSBS) fired from the experimental station at Landes or from missile-carrying nuclear submarines and to compute their flight characteristics, especially from re-entry to impact. Her secondary mission is to assist the flag officer in controlling the naval and air elements in the test area, particularly recovery and security.

A former Italian tanker, the ship was entirely rebuilt by DCAN at Brest between 1964 and 1967, during which time she was given three radars for tracking and trajectory-measuring in ballistic tests and a sonar dome. She also has an automatic tracking station; celestial position-fixing equipment; a camera-equipped theodolite; infrared equipment; a Transit navigational system; aerological, meteorological, and oceanographic equipment; excellent communications equipment; a programming and transcribing center for all experiments and installations; and a platform and hangar for two heavy or five light helicopters. Refitted 1-8-79 to 1-6-80 with Gascogne tracking radars in place of original two Bearn, as well as other alterations. Received Syracuse SATCOMM system in 1983. To strike 8-92 and be replaced by *Monge* (A 601).

♦ **1 Commandant Rivière-class sonar trials ship, former frigate** Bldr: Lorient Arsenal

	Laid down	L	In serv.
733 Commandant Rivière (ex-733)	4-57	11-10-58	4-12-62

Commandant Rivière (A 733) Leo Van Ginderen, 6-91

D: 1,750 tons (2,100 fl) **S:** 16 kts
Dim: 103.00 × 12.52 (11.80 wl) × 4.50
A: 1/40-mm AA—2/12.7-mm mg (I × 2)—1/550-mm ASW TT
Electron Equipt:
Radar: 1/DRBN 32 (Decca 1226) nav., 1/DRBV 22A air/surf. search
Sonar: . . . hull-mounted, DUBV 43B VDS, DSBV 61 towed array
M: 4 SEMT-Pielstick 12 PC 1 diesels; 2 props; 16,000 bhp
Electric: 1,280 kw
Crew: 9 officers, 48 petty officers, 58 ratings + 37 technicians

Remarks: Converted during 1985 as replacement for the former frigate *L'Agenais* (A) for sonar research for the *Centre d'Études Pratiques du Matériel et Armes Navales,* Toulon. The 100-mm guns and MM 38 Exocet missiles were removed, and a 40-mm gun replaced the 305-mm mortar. A single 550-mm torpedo tube was placed to port amidships, and a 2-ton capacity (at 10 m) telescoping hydraulic torpedo recovery crane mounted to starboard. The stern was widened at the main deck over a length of about 20 m to support the hoist and drum for the DUBV 43 variable-depth sonar equipment removed from the stricken destroyer *Casabianca* (D 631). The original hull-mounted sonar suite has been replaced by an installation for sonars under test. The original 26-knot speed has been restricted. Will be used to test a new Thomson-CSF active towed linear array during the 1990s.

♦ **1 guided-missile trials ship** Bldr: A. G. Weser, Bremen (L: 1939)

A 610 Île d'Oléron (ex-*München,* ex-*Sperrbrecher 32,* ex-*Mur*)

Île d'Oléron (A 610) Pradignac & Léo, 11-86

D: 5,085 tons (6,100 fl) **S:** 14.5 kts
Dim: 115.05 (107.00 pp) × 15.24 × 6.40
A: 1/SADRAL SAM system (VI × 1)
Electron Equipt:
Radar: 1/DRBN 32 nav., 1/DRBV 22C air search, 1/DRBV 50 surf. search, 1/DRBI 10 height-finder
M: 2 M.A.N. 6-cyl. diesels; 1 prop; 3,500 bhp **Electric:** 1,240 kw
Fuel: 340 tons **Range:** 5,900/14; 7,200/19
Crew: 9 officers, 46 petty officers, 113 ratings

Remarks: Taken from the Germans as a prize of war and commissioned in French Navy 29-8-45 as a transport until converted, 1957–58, to an experimental ship for missiles, operating for CEPAM: *Centre d'Études Pratiques du Matériel et Armes Navales,* Toulon. Besides the radars listed, she carries guidance radars for the systems under test. Previously used for Exocet, Crotale, Masurca, and Otomat trials. Trials with SADRAL SAM system began 5-86. Will conduct trials with the Milas antisubmarine missile. Helicopter deck aft. 100-mm Model 1968 gun (trials with 78-rpm loader) removed by 1988. To be retained in service to the end of the century.

♦ **1 chartered oilfield tug/supply ship** Bldr: Halter Marine, New Orleans

Langevin (ex-*Martin Fish*)

Langevin Bernard Prézelin, 7-90

D: . . . **S:** . . . kts **Dim:** . . . × . . . × . . .
Electron Equipt: Radar: 2/ . . . nav.
M: . . . **Range:** . . . **Crew:** . . .

Remarks: Chartered 5-90 for use by the *Direction des Constructions Navales* (DCN) for a variety of purposes connected with the new-generation nuclear-powered ballistic-missile submarine program.

Note: The electronics experimental ship *Berry* (A 644, ex-*Medoc*) was stricken during 1991. The chartered oilfield support ship *Abeille Supporter,* which had been employed as tender to the submersible *Licorne* at the Landes Test Center, was returned to her owners in 1990.

OCEANOGRAPHIC RESEARCH SHIP

♦ **1 expeditionary ship** Bldr: Brest Arsenal

	Laid down	L	In serv.
A 757 D'Entrecasteaux	7-69	30-5-70	10-10-70

D'Entrecasteaux (A 757) French Navy, 1987

D: 2,058 tons (2,450 fl) **S:** 15 kts
Dim: 95.65 (89.00 pp) × 13.00 × 4.20 (5.50 props)
Electron Equipt: Radar: 2/Decca 1226 nav.
M: 2 diesel engines, electric drive; 2 CP props; 2,720 shp—2 retractable Schottel propellers, 1 fwd, 1 aft
Range: 12,000/12
Crew: 6 officers, 31 petty officers, 41 ratings + 38 scientists/technicians

OCEANOGRAPHIC RESEARCH SHIP *(continued)*

Remarks: For oceanographic research and hydrographic duties. Has a dynamic mooring/maneuvering system permitting station-keeping in 5,000-m depths. Can take soundings and surveys to a depth of 5,000 meters. Helicopter platform and hangar. Electrohydraulic oceanographic equipment cranes, one landing craft, three hydrographic launches, hull-mounted scanning sonar. Painted white. Three echo-sounders (one stabilized). Has Trident, Syledis, Toran, Transit, Omega, and Global Positioning System navigation equipment, plus *Hydrac* and *Hydrai* automatic data systems.

Note: The underwater archeological research ship *Archéonaute* (A 789) was stricken during 1991.

HYDROGRAPHIC SURVEY SHIPS

◆ **4 La Pérouse class** Bldr: DCN, Lorient

	Laid down	L	In serv.
A 791 La Pérouse	11-6-85	15-11-86	20-4-88
A 792 Borda	2-9-85	15-11-86	16-6-88
A 793 La Place	1-9-87	9-11-88	5-10-89
A 795 Arago	26-6-89	6-9-90	9-91

Borda (L 792) Bernard Prézelin, 10-90

La Place (A 793) LSPH K. Degener, RAN, 5-91

D: 850 tons (980 fl) **S:** 15 kts **Dim:** 59.00 (53.00 pp) × 10.90 × 3.63
A: 2/12.7-mm mg (I × 2)
Electron Equipt: Radar: 1/Decca 1226—Sonar: *see* Remarks
M: 2 UNI UD30-V16-M7 diesels; 2 CP props; 2,500 bhp—200-hp bow-thruster
Range: 6,000/12 **Electric:** 620 kw
Crew: 2 officers, 11 petty officers, 14 enlisted (+11 survey party)

Remarks: First two ordered 24-7-84; second two, ordered 22-1-86, were originally to have been built by Ch. Normandie, Grand Quevilly, which closed. A 791, based at Brest with A 792, is equipped with the DUBM 21C minehunting sonar for trials, wreck identification, and channel certification. The other three have the Thomson-Sintra CSFTSM 5425 multifunction wreck identification/echo-sounder. A 793 is based at Nouméa and A 795 at Papeete. All carry one scientific and two data-reduction computers. All can carry two 8-m hydrographic survey launches and are equipped with the *Hydrac* and *Hydrai* survey systems. Painted white.

◆ **1 converted trawler** Bldr: Stocznia Gdynia, Poland (L: 1962)

A 756 L'Espérance (ex-*Jacques Coeur*)

L'Espérance (A 756) Leo Van Ginderen, 1-89

D: 1,045 tons (1,300 fl) **S:** 13.5 kts
Dim: 63.45 (59.75 pp) × 9.82 × 5.85 (fl)
Electron Equipt: Radar: 1/Decca 1226 nav.
M: 2 M.A.N. diesels; 1 prop; 1,870 bhp **Range:** 7,500/13
Crew: 3 officers, 11 petty officers, 29 ratings

Remarks: Former oceangoing fishing trawler, purchased 1968–69, converted for survey work, and commissioned 12-7-69. Carries two survey launches. Oceanographic winch on stern, articulated crane amidships. Painted white. Sister *L'Estafette* (A 766) stricken 1991 on completion of *Arago* (795).

Note: Survey ship *Boussole* (A 781) was sold into commercial service 15-1-90. Inshore survey ship *Corail* (A 794, ex-*Marc Joly*) was stricken 11-8-90.

SUPPORT TENDERS

◆ **1 multipurpose repair ship** Bldr: Brest Arsenal

	Laid down	L	In serv.
A 620 Jules Verne (ex-*Achéron*)	1969	30-5-70	1-6-76

Jules Verne (A 620) Bernard Prézelin, 5-

Jules Verne (A 620)—note double hangar Bernard Prézelin, 5

D: 7,815 tons (10,250 fl) **S:** 18 kts **Dim:** 147.0 × 21.56 × 6.5
A: 2/40-mm AA (I × 2) **Electron Equipt:** Radar: 1/Decca 1226 na
M: 2 SEMT-Pielstick 12 PC V400 diesels; 1 prop; 11,200 bhp
Electric: 3,800 kw **Range:** 9,500/18
Crew: 16 officers, 150 petty officers, 116 enlisted

Remarks: Six years after being launched as an ammunition ship, the uncompl *Jules Verne* completed conversion 1973–76 to a floating workshop to provide suppo a force of from three to six surface warships. Has significant capabilities for regular maintenance and battle-damage repair: mechanical, engine, electrical, sh metal, electronic workshops, etc. Has four 12-ton cranes. Carries a stock of torpe and other munitions. Has a platform and hangar for two helicopters. Operat support of the Indian Ocean Flotilla.

◆ **1 training and medical support ship** Bldr: Lorient Arsenal

	Laid down	L	In serv.
A 618 Rance	8-64	5-5-65	5-2-66

Rance (A 618) Pradignac & Léo

SUPPORT TENDERS *(continued)*

D: 2,510 tons (2,700 fl) **S:** 16.5 kts
Dim: 101.05 (92.05 pp) × 13.10 × 3.75 **A:** 2/12.7-mm mg (I × 2)
Electron Equipt:
Radar: 1/DRBN 32 nav., 1/DRBV 22E air search
EW: ARBR/ARBA 10 intercept
M: SEMT-Pielstick 12 PA 4 diesels; 3,600 bhp
Crew: 9 officers, 42 petty officers, 71 ratings

ₑmarks: Formerly served as general repair workshop and support ship for the ·acific nuclear weapons trials center at Muraroa. Has been converted to act as medical nd command tender to the *Force d'Assistance Rapide* and as flagship of the Mediterra-ₑean fleet training center. Has a hangar capable of accommodating three small helicop-ₑrs and two flight platforms, one above the hangar.

♦ **1 general-purpose repair ship** Bldr: Lorient Arsenal

	Laid down	L	In serv.
ₐ 617 Garonne	23-12-63	8-8-64	1-9-65

aronne (A 617) Malcolm Dippy, 2-90

D: 2,320 tons **S:** 15 kts **Dim:** 101.50 (92.05 pp) × 13.80 × 3.70
A: 1/40-mm AA—2/20-mm AA (I × 2)
Electron Equipt: Radar: 1/DRBN 32 (Decca 1226) nav.
M: 2 SEMT-Pielstick 12 PA 4 diesels; 1 prop; 3,600 bhp
Range: 13,000/13 **Crew:** 6 officers, 39 petty officers, 69 ratings

ₑmarks: Designed for overseas service and operates primarily in the Pacific and ıian oceans. Has metalworking, electronics repair, and carpentry shops, an extra ·k with lower overhead, and a 30-ton crane mounted in the center of the fantail; no ıicopter facilities.

3 Rhin-class tenders Bldr: Lorient Arsenal

	Purpose	Laid down	L	In serv.
315 Loire	Minesweepers	9-7-65	1-10-66	10-10-67
321 Rhin	Electronics	24-4-61	17-3-62	1-3-64
322 Rhône	Submarines	23-2-62	8-12-62	1-12-64

ıne (A 622) Dr. Giorgio Arra, 7-90

e (A 615) Bernard Prézelin, 5-90

A 615: 2,050 tons; A 621: 2,035 tons; A 622: 2,280 tons (all: 2,445 fl)
16.5 kts **Dim:** 101.05 (92.05 pp) × 13.10 × 3.65
3/40-mm AA (I × 3)—A 615 also: 3/12.7-mm mg (I × 3)
ectron Equipt: Radar: 1, 2, or 3/DRBN 32
2 SEMT-Pielstick 16 PA 2V diesels; 1 prop; 3,200 bhp
ectric: 920 kw **Range:** 13,000/13
ew: 11 officers, 67 petty officers, 78 ratings

Remarks: Generally similar but equipped for specific tasks listed above. All have helicopter platform, but only A 615 and A 622 have hangars. There are about 700 m^2 of workshop space and 1,700 m^3 of storeroom space. All have one 5-ton (at 12 m) crane. A 615 participated in the United Nations Mideast Coalition fleet in 1991.

FLEET REPLENISHMENT SHIPS

♦ **5 Durance-class fleet oilers** Bldr: Brest Arsenal (A 631: CNIM, La Seyne)

	Laid down	L	In serv.
A 629 Durance	10-12-73	6-9-75	1-12-76
A 607 Meuse	2-6-77	2-12-78	2-8-80
A 608 Var	12-78	9-5-81	29-1-83
A 630 Marne	4-8-82	6-2-85	16-1-87
A 631 Somme	3-5-85	3-10-87	7-3-90

Var (A 608) Leo Van Ginderen, 6-91

Marne (A 630) Mike Louagie, 5-90

Somme (A 631) Leo Van Ginderen, 5-91

D: A 629, 607: 7,600 tons (17,800 fl); others: 7,800 tons (17,900 fl)
S: 20 kts (19 sust.) **Dim:** 157.20 (149.00 pp) × 21.20 × 8.65 (10.8 fl)
A: A 629: 2/40-mm AA (I × 2); others: 1/40-mm AA—2/20-mm AA (I × 2)—2/12.7-mm mg (I × 2)
Electron Equipt: Radar: 2/DRBN 32 (Decca 1226) nav.
M: 2 SEMT-Pielstick 16 PC 2.5 V400 diesels; 2 CP props; 20,760 bhp
Electric: 5,400 kw **Fuel:** 750 tons **Range:** 9,000/15
Crew: A 629, A 607: 8 officers, 62 petty officers, 89 ratings; others: 10 officers, 58 petty officers, 74 ratings

Remarks: A 631 was ordered 3-84 from CNM, La Seyne, on speculation and purchased 10-87 for the French Navy; the ship is identical to A 608 and A 630. A near-sister was built in Australia for the R.A.N.

Two dual solid/liquids underway-replenishment stations per side. Can supply two ships alongside and one astern. *Durance:* 7,500 tons fuel oil, 1,500 tons diesel fuel, 500 tons JP-5, 130 tons distilled water, 170 tons fresh provisions, 150 tons munitions, 50 tons spare parts; *Meuse*: 5,090 tons fuel oil, 4,014 tons diesel, 1,140 tons JP-5, 250 tons distilled water, 180 tons provisions, 122 tons munitions, and 45 tons spare parts. *Var* and *Marne*: 5,090 tons fuel oil, 3,310 tons diesel, 1,090 tons JP-5, 260 tons distilled water, 170 tons ammunition, 180 tons provisions, 15 tons spares. *Somme*: 9,250 tons fuel oil, 250 tons water, 190 tons provisions, 45 tons spares.

Hangar for one Alouette-III or Lynx and flight deck for larger helicopters. Superstructure before the bridge one deck lower in A 629. In A 607 the 40-mm AA is aft; in A 608, 630, and 631 it is forward. *Var, Marne,* and *Somme* are equipped as flagships for a major area commander and can accommodate 257 persons, including 45 commandos; their forward superstructure blocks are extended aft by 8 meters to provide increased staff accommodations, and the two beam-mounted stores cranes immediately abaft the bridge are replaced by a single, centerline crane; the Syracuse-I SATCOMM system is fitted. A 630 also has MARISAT. All carry two LCVP landing craft.

TRANSPORT OILERS

◆ **2 Punaruu class** Bldr: Trosvik Verksted, Brevik, Norway

	In serv. (French Navy)
A 625 PAPENOO (ex-*Bow Queen*)	9-11-71
A 632 PUNARUU (ex-*Bow Cecil*)	16-11-71

Papenoo (A 625) Leo Van Ginderen, 1990

D: 1,195 tons light (4,050 fl)
S: 13 kts **Dim:** 83.00 (70.70 pp) × 13.85 × 5.50
Electron Equipt: Radar: 1/DRBN 32 (Decca 1226) nav.
M: 2 Normo LSMC-8 diesels; 1 CP prop; 2,050 bhp—720-shp bow-thruster
Electric: 290 kw **Range:** 8,000/11.5 **Fuel:** 174 tons
Crew: 2 officers, 20 enlisted

Remarks: 1,119 grt, 2,889 dwt. Former Norwegian solvent tankers purchased at the end of 1969. Highly automated ships. Capacity: 2,554 m^3. Ten washable "inox" cargo tanks that can accept any liquid. Astern fueling capability. Operate in the Pacific, and due to strike in 1994.

Note: The chartered transport tanker *Port Vendres* was returned to her owners in 3-90 in expectation of the completion of *Somme* (A 631); the 25,253-dwt ship retains her over-the-stern replenishment equipment, as do the larger commercial tankers *Penhors* and *Mascarin*. The small tanker *Aber Wrach* (A 619) was stricken at the end of 1989.

MULTI-PURPOSE SUPPORT AUXILIARIES

◆ **1 Type RR 2000 (modified Chamois)-class tug/supply vessel**

	Bldr	Laid down	L	In serv.
A 633 TAAPE	de la Perrière, Lorient	22-10-82	14-4-83	30-6-83

Taape (A 633) Leo Van Ginderen, 1990

D: 383 tons (505 fl) **S:** 14.2 kts **Dim:** 41.02 (38.50 pp) × 7.5 × 3.18
Electron Equipt: Radar: 1/DRBN 32 (Decca 1226) nav.
M: 2 SACM MGO V16 ASHR diesels; 2 CP Kort-nozzle props; 2,200 bhp
Range: 6,000/12 **Crew:** 2 officers, 10 enlisted + 6 passengers

Remarks: Ordered 11-10-82. Construction financed by the nuclear test center, DIRCEN. A variation of the FISH-class design, which was also used in the *Chamois*-class tenders. 24.8 bollard pull. Can carry 100 tons of cargo on the long, open afterdeck. Transported in the landing ship *Orage* in 4-84 to Muraroa for duty in the Pacific.

◆ **6 Chamois-class local support or diving tenders** Bldr: Ch. de la Perrière, Lorient

	Laid down	L	In serv.
A 767 CHAMOIS	. . .	30-4-76	24-9-76
A 768 ÉLAN	16-3-77	28-7-77	7-4-78
A 774 CHEVREUIL	15-9-76	8-5-77	7-10-77
A 775 GAZELLE	30-12-76	7-6-77	13-1-78
A 776 ISARD	2-11-77	2-5-78	15-12-78
A 779 TAPATAI (ex-*Silver Fish*)	. . .	1971	27-3-81

Élan (A 768) Bernard Prézelin, 4-9

Isard (A 776)—white-painted divers' support ship Leo Van Ginderen, 1

D: 305 tons light (505 fl) **S:** 14.5 kts
Dim: 41.60 (36.96 pp) × 7.5 × 3.20
Electron Equipt: Radar: 1/DRBN 32 (Decca 1226) nav.
M: 2 SACM MGO V16 AFHR diesels; 2 CP Kort-nozzle props; 2,200 b
Fuel: 92 m^3 **Range:** 7,200/12
Crew: 2 officers, 16 petty officers, 2 ratings

Remarks: Except for a 5.6-ton crane, the first four are identical to the 14 merc FISH (Feronica International Shipping) commercial class designed for the supp petroleum platforms. Hydraulic 50-ton stern crane mounted on A 767, A 774. All b 776 can carry 100 tons dry cargo on deck or 125 tons fuel and 40 tons water (or 65 fuel/125 tons water). A 768 and A 775 primarily used as water tankers. Can be use coastal towing and cleaning up oil spills. Two rudders and an 80-hp bow-thruster. winch with 28-ton bollard pull. Can be used as transports for 28 passengers, as m layers, or as torpedo retrievers. All except A 776 and A 779 have two crews.

Isard (A 776) is equipped as a divers' support ship and tender for the ERIC guided submersible (2 tons, 4 m overall, 600-m diving depth). She has a U decompression chamber capable of simulating pressures to a water depth of 150 m also has a longer aft structure, supporting divers' rubber dinghies, and a small he ter deck; the ship is subordinated to GISMER. A 779, a former merchant unit o class, was purchased at Nouméa in 1979 and commissioned for service in support Pacific Test Center.

NET TENDERS

◆ **1 seagoing net tender** Bldr: Brest Arsenal

	Laid down	L	In serv.
A 731 TIANÉE	1-4-73	1-11-73	8-7-75

D: 842 tons (905 fl) **S:** 12 kts **Dim:** 54.3 × 10.6 × 4.40
Electron Equipt: Radar: 1/DRBN 32 (Decca 1226) nav.
M: 2/480-kw diesel generator sets, 1/880-kw electric motor; 1 pro 1,200 shp—. . . shp bow-thruster
Range: 5,200/12 **Crew:** 1 officer, 15 petty officers, 25 ratings

Remarks: Living quarters air-conditioned. Used primarily as a mooring-buoy t Originally stationed at Papeete, but since 1985 refit, has been at Toulon.

NET TENDERS *(continued)*

'ianée (A 731) Pradignac & Léo, 1987

3 La Prudente-class port netlayers Bldr: Ateliers & Chantiers La Manche, St. Malo (Y 750: At. & Ch. La Rochelle-Pallice)

	L	In serv.
749 La Prudente	13-5-68	27-7-69
750 La Persévérante	14-5-68	3-3-69
751 La Fidèle	26-8-68	10-6-69

Prudente (Y 749) Leo Van Ginderen, 1989

): 446 tons (626 fl) **S:** 10 kts **Dim:** 43.5 (42.0 pp) × 10.0 × 2.8
:lectron Equipt: Radar: 1/ DRBN 32 (Decca 1226)
I: 2 Baudouin diesels, electric drive; 1 prop; 620 shp
:lectric: 440 kw **Range:** 4,000/10
:rew: 1 officer, 8 petty officers, 21 ratings

ıarks: Used as mooring-buoy tenders. Lifting power via pivoting gantry forward: ɔns. Y 749 based at Brest, Y 750 at Toulon, and Y 751 at Cherbourg.

1 small mooring-buoy tender Bldr: IMC, Rochefort sur Mer

	L	In serv.
92 Telenn Mor	4-4-85	16-1-86

': 518 tons (fl) **S:** 8 kts **Dim:** 41.40 (37.00 pp) × 9.10 × 1.88
I: 2 diesels; 2 props; 900 bhp **Electric:** 350 kw **Crew:** 10 tot.

ɪnn Mor (Y 692) Leo Van Ginderen, 1-89

◆ **1 Tupa-class mooring-buoy tender**

Y 667 Tupa (In serv. 16-3-74)

Tupa (Y 667) French Navy, 1983

D: 292 tons light **S:** 6 kts **Dim:** 28.5 × 8.3 × 0.85
M: 1 diesel; 1 prop; 210 bhp

Remarks: Based at Papeete.

◆ **1 Calmar-class small mooring-buoy tender**

Y 698 Calmar (In serv. 12-8-70)

D: 270 tons light **S:** 9.5 kts **Dim:** . . . × . . . × . . .
M: 1 Baudouin diesel; 1 prop; . . . bph

Remarks: Based at Lorient. Former tug.

CHARTERED MOORING TENDERS

◆ **1 oilfield supply tug** Bldr: Bréhéret, Couéron (In serv. 1983)

Albacore (ex-*Beryl Fish*)

Albacore Pradignac & Léo, 9-89

D: approx. 1,800 tons (fl) **S:** 14 kts
Dim: 56.98 (52.46 pp) × 14.30 × 3.80
Electron Equipt: Radar: 2/. . . . . . nav.
M: 3 SNMC 6-cyl. diesels; 3 CP props; 4,350 bhp—2/340-hp side-thrusters
Electric: 640 kw (2 diesel alternators of 320 kw)
Endurance: 30 days **Crew:** 4 officers, 4 unlicensed

Remarks: 1,217 grt. Chartered 1-10-87 from FISH (Feronica International Shipping) for service as seagoing mooring tender at Toulon in place of the stricken naval mooring tenders *Criquet* and *Scarabée* at Toulon. Bollard pull: 57 tons initial. One 20-ton portal crane and one 12-ton crane. Has 660 tons liquid cargo capacity, two fire-fighting water monitors.

◆ **2 Alcyon-class oilfield supply tugs** Bldr: At. et Ch. de la Manche, Dieppe

Alcyon (ex-*Bahram;* in serv. 1981) Ailette (ex-*Cyrus;* in serv. 1982)

Alcyon APP Brest, 1-88

CHARTERED MOORING TENDERS *(continued)*

D: 1,500 tons (fl) **S:** 13.5 kts **Dim:** 53.01 (51.01 pp) × 13.31 × 4.50
Electron Equipt: Radar: 2/. . . nav. **Crew:** 7 tot.
M: 2 12-cyl. diesels; 2 CP props; 5,200 bhp—. . . shp bow-thruster

Remarks: Bollard pull: 60 tons initial. Thirty-ton portal crane at stern. Chartered 1988 for service at Brest to replace naval mooring tenders *Cigale* and *Fourmi*. Have two fire-fighting water monitors. Hulls painted green, superstructures white.

DIVING TENDERS

◆ **2 (+8) Coralline class** Bldr: Lorient Arsenal (In serv. 1990–92)

A 790 Coralline Y790 Y 791 Y 792 Y 793 Y 794
Y 795 Y 796 Y 797 Y 798

Y 790 Leo Van Ginderen, 6-91

D: 44 tons (fl) **S:** 13 kts **Dim:** 21.00 × 4.50 × 1.10
Electron Equipt: Radar: 1/ Furuno . . . nav.
M: 2 diesels; 2 props; 264 bhp **Crew:** 4 tot. (A 790: 7 tot.)

Remarks: A 790 completed 2-90 to replace *Palangrin* (Y 743) as radiological monitoring craft at Cherbourg. Others employed as diving support craft and as tenders to the Diving School.

◆ **1 combat-swimmer support tender**

	Bldr	L	In serv.
A 722 Poseidon	SICCNAV, St.-Malo	5-12-74	14-1-77

Poseidon (A 722) Leo Van Ginderen, 6-91

D: 200 tons (239 fl) **S:** 13 kts **Dim:** 40.5 (38.5 pp) × 7.2 × 2.2
Electron Equipt: Radar: 1/DRBN 32 (Decca 1226) nav.
M: 1 diesel; 600 bhp **Endurance:** 8 days **Crew:** 42 tot.

Remarks: Used for training combat frogmen. Based at Toulon.

TORPEDO RETRIEVERS

◆ **2 small torpedo retrievers for use at the St. Tropez trials center**

Pégase (In serv. 1975) Sambracite (In serv. 1974)

Remarks: *Pégase*, a catamaran with one 550-mm torpedo tube aft, was built by SFCN and is powered by two 440-bhp diesels. No characteristics data available for *Sambracite*.

Note: The torpedo retriever *Pélican* (A 699) was stricken during 1989.

COASTAL TRANSPORT/PERSONNEL FERRIES

◆ **9 Ariel class** Bldr: SFCN, Franco-Belges (Y 700–702: DCAN, Brest)

	L		L
Y 604 Ariel	27-4-63	Y 700 Néréide	17-2-77
Y 613 Faune	8-9-71	Y 701 Ondine	4-10-79
Y 661 Korrigan	6-3-64	Y 702 Naiade	4-10-79
Y 662 Dryade	10-12-72	Y 741 Elfe	14-4-70
Y 696 Alphée	10-6-69		

Faune (Y 613) and Korrigan (Y 661) Ben Sullivan, 5-

D: 195 tons (225 fl) **S:** 15 kts **Dim:** 40.5 × 7.45 × 3.3 **Crew:** 9 tot.
Electron Equipt: Radar: 1/DRBN 32 (Decca 1226) nav.
M: 2 MGO (1,640 bhp tot.) or Poyaud (1,730 bhp tot.) diesels; 2 props

Remarks: Can carry 400 passengers (250 seated). All based at Brest, except *Ariel* a *Naiade* at Toulon.

◆ **1 small personnel transport**

Y . . . Trébéron (In serv. 26-11-79)

Remarks: Based at Brest; no data available. Appears to be about 18 m overall.

◆ **3 Merlin class** Bldr: C.N. Franco-Belges (Y 671: Toulon Arsenal)

Y 735 Merlin (L: 8-11-67) Y 736 Mélusine (L: 23-12-63)
Y 671 Morgane (L: 14-6-73)

Merlin (Y 735) Leo Van Ginderen,

D: 170 tons **S:** 11 kts **Dim:** 31.5 × 7.06 × 2.4
M: 2 MGO diesels; 2 props; 960 bhp **Crew:** . . . tot.

Remarks: All based at Toulon. No radar. Carry up to 400 passengers.

◆ **1 Sylphe class** Bldr: C.N. Franco-Belges (In serv. 1960)

Y 710 Sylphe

Sylphe (Y 710)

COASTAL TRANSPORT/PERSONNEL FERRIES *(continued)*

D: 142 tons (189 fl) **S:** 12 kts **Dim:** 38.5 (36.75 pp) × 6.9 × 2.5
M: 1 MGO diesel; 1 prop; 425 bhp **Crew:** 9 tot.

Remarks: Has operated from Brest since 1981.

CHARTERED SALVAGE AND RESCUE TUGS

Note: The French government leases salvage tugs as a result of the *Amoco Cadiz* disaster; *Abeille Normandie* and *Abeille Provence* were returned to the owners in 1986 and replaced by *Mérou* and *Girelle* in 1987. In addition to the units listed below, an agreement signed 19-3-90 between the French Navy and the Dunkerque Society for Towing and Salvage places at the disposal of the Cherbourg Maritime Prefecture the tugs *Robuste, Puissant,* and *Hardi* (all 2,600 bhp, 40-ton bollard pull), based at Dunkerque, to ensure safety in the area of Pas-de-Calais.

1 Mérou class Bldr: B.V. Scheepswerf Waterhuizen J. Pattje, Groningen (In serv. 1982)

MÉROU (ex-*King Fish*)

Mérou Leo Van Ginderen, 6-91

D: approx. 1,900 tons (fl) **S:** 14.2 kts **Dim:** 59.35 × 15.00 × 5.32
Electron Equipt: Radar: 2/. . . nav.
M: 4 Wichmann diesels; 2 CP props; 8,000 bhp—500-shp bow-thruster
Endurance: 50 days **Range:** 13,000/14.2
Crew: 8 officers, 18 unlicensed + 12 passengers

Remarks: 1,471 grt. Leased from FISH (Feronica International Shipping) in 1987 and based at Toulon. Bollard pull: 100 tons initial, up to 250 tons under way. One 1,200-m³/hr. fire pump; two water cannon with 120-m range. Equipped for anti-pollution duties. Hull and superstructure painted gray, pilothouse white.

1 Girelle class Bldr: B.V. Scheepswerf Waterhuizen J. Pattje, Groningen (In serv. 1981)

GIRELLE (ex-*Moon Fish*)

Girelle Leo Van Ginderen, 7-89

D: approx. 1,600 tons (fl) **S:** 13 kts **Dim:** 53.55 × 11.54 × 4.56
Electron Equipt: Radar: 2/. . . nav.
M: 2 Wichmann diesels; 2 CP props; 4,000 bhp—400-shp bow-thruster
Range: 13,248/13 **Crew:** 5 officers, 14 unlicensed + 12 passengers

Remarks: 851 grt. Bollard pull: 2 tons initial to 170 tons under way. One 600-m³/hr. pump; 2 water cannon with 90-m range. Chartered from FISH (Feronica International Shipping) in 1987 for towing and anti-pollution duties in the Mediterranean and at Toulon. Hull and superstructure painted gray, pilothouse white.

◆ **1 Abeille Bretagne class** Bldr: Ch. & At. de la Manche, Dieppe (In serv. 1979)

ABEILLE BRETAGNE

D: approx. 1,450 tons (fl) **S:** . . . kts
Dim: 43.74 (40.00 pp) × 11.82 × 4.71
Electron Equipt: Radar: . . .
M: 2 SEMT-Pielstick 6-cyl. diesels; 1 CP prop; . . . bhp—bow-thruster
Range: . . ./. . . **Crew:** . . . tot.

Remarks: Chartered 1990 to provide towing, search-and-rescue, and salvage services in the vicinity of Muraroa in the South Pacific.

◆ **2 Abeille Flandre-class oceangoing tugs** Bldr: Ulstein Hatlo A/S, Ulsteinvik, Norway (In serv. 1978)

ABEILLE FLANDRE (ex-*Neptun Suecia*)
ABEILLE LANGUEDOC (ex-*Neptun Gothia*)

Abeille Languedoc Mike Louagie, 3-87

D: approx. 3,800 tons (fl) **S:** 17 kts
Dim: 63.40 (58.60 pp) × 14.74 × 6.90
Electron Equipt: Radar: 2/. . . nav.
M: 4/8-cyl. Atlas diesels; 2 CP props; 23,000 bhp
Electric: 1,280 kw **Fuel:** 1,450 tons **Crew:** 2 officers, 10 unlicensed

Remarks: 1,577 grt. *A. Flandre* at Brest, *A. Languedoc* at Cherbourg. Ice-strengthened; have bow-thrusters. Among world's most powerful tugs. Bollard pull: 160 tons. Hull painted black, superstructure white.

SEAGOING TUGS

◆ **2 Type RR 4000 class tug/supply vessels** Bldr: Bréhéret, Couëron, Nantes

	L	In serv.		L	In serv.
A 634 RARI	16-4-84	5-2-85	A 635 REVI	15-5-84	6-2-85

Rari (A 634) Bernard Prézelin, 7-84

D: 1,057 tons light (1,557 fl) **S:** 14.5 kts
Dim: 51.00 (49.50 wl) × 12.60 × 4.10
Electron Equipt: Radar: 1/ DRBN 32 (Decca 1226) nav.
M: 2 SACM Type 195 V12 RVR; 2 CP props; 4,000 bhp—2/2.5-ton side-thrusters
Electric: 600 kw (2 × 300 kw) **Range:** 6,000/12 **Fuel:** 300 tons
Crew: 2 officers, 9 petty officers, 10 ratings + 18 passengers

Remarks: Bollard pull: 47 tons. Have a 14-ton quadrantial gantry at the extreme stern. Two water cannons for firefighting. Can carry fuel cargo or 400 tons of cargo on the open deck aft. Built for DIRCEN, the French Pacific nuclear testing center and based at Muraroa.

◆ **3 Tenace class**

	Bldr	L	In serv.
A 664 MALABAR	Oelkers, Hamburg	16-4-75	3-2-76
A 669 TENACE	Oelkers, Hamburg	12-71	15-11-73
A 674 CENTAURE	Ch. de la Rochelle-Pallice	8-1-74	15-11-74

SEAGOING TUGS *(continued)*

Tenace (A 669) APP Brest, 5-90

D: 970 tons (1,440 fl) **S:** 13.5 kts **Dim:** 51.0 × 11.5 × 5.7
Electron Equipt: 1/DRBN 32 (Decca 1226) nav.
M: 2 diesels; 1 Kort-nozzle CP prop; 4,600 bhp—*see* Remarks
Electric: 502 kw (A 674: 766 kw) **Fuel:** 500 tons **Range:** 9,500/13
Crew: 2 officers, 30 petty officers, 24 ratings

Remarks: Bollard pull: 60 tons. Living quarters air-conditioned. All based at Brest. A 664 and A 669 are powered by two MaK 9-cylinder diesels, while A 674 is powered by two SACM AGO 240 V12 diesels. A 674 has 3 × 227-kw and 1 × 85-kw generators; the others have 2 × 227-kw and 1 × 48-kw sets. Pumps include one of 350 m^3/hr. (serving two fire monitors with a range of 60 m) and one of 120 m^3/hr., plus numerous smaller salvage and fire-fighting pumps. Carry two semi-rigid boats.

COASTAL TUGS

♦ 2 (+4) Type RPC 12

Bldr: Ch. La Perrière, Lorient (A 677: Leroux & Loth, Lorient)

	L	In serv.
A 675 Fréhel	6-10-88	16-2-89
A 676 Saire	7-3-89	26-3-89
A 677 Armen	. . .	1991
A 678 La Houssaye	. . .	. . .
A 679 Sicie	. . .	. . .
A 680 Lardier	. . .	. . .

Saire (A 676) Bernard Prézelin, 10-90

D: 259 tons **S:** 11 kts (10 sust.) **Dim:** 25.00 (23.50 pp) × 8.40 × 2.20
M: 2 Uni UD 30 V12 M3 diesels; 2 Voith-Schneider 18 G2115 vertical cycloidal props: 1,350 bhp
Electric: 195 kw (3 × 65-kw diesel alternators)
Range: 800/10 **Crew:** 5–8 tot.

Remarks: Bollard pull: 12 tons. First unit ordered 14-8-87, second 27-3-88, third in 6-91; others planned to replace the earlier harbor tug classes. One water cannon for fire fighting, no radar.

♦ 3 Maito class

Bldr: SFCN, Villeneuve-la-Garenne

	Laid down	L	In serv.
A 636 Maito	24-6-83	6-1-84	27-2-84
A 637 Maroa	30-8-83	20-1-84	30-3-84
A 638 Manini	15-11-84	19-4-85	12-9-85

Maroa (A 637) 198

D: 245 tons (278 fl) **S:** 11 kts **Dim:** 27.60 (24.50 wl) × 8.90 × 3.50
Electron Equipt: Radar: 1/ DRBN 332 (Decca 1226) nav.
M: 2 SACM Type 175 6L RVR diesels; 2 Voith-Schneider vertical cycloidal props; 1,280 bhp
Range: 1,200/11 **Crew:** 6 tot. + 4 passengers

Remarks: Serve at Muraroa for DIRCEN. Bollard pull: 12 tons. Have a fire-fighti water cannon.

♦ 3 Bélier class

Bldr: Cherbourg Arsenal

	L	In serv.
A 695 Bélier	4-12-79	25-7-80
A 696 Buffle	18-1-80	19-7-80
A 697 Bison	20-11-80	16-4-81

Bélier (A 695) Leo Van Ginderen,

D: 500 tons (800 fl) **S:** 11 kts **Dim:** 32.0 × 8.8 × . . .
Electron Equipt: Radar: 1/DRBN 32 (Decca 1226) nav.
M: 2 SACM AGO 195 V8 CSHR diesels, electric drive; 2 Voith-Schneider vertical cycloidal props; 2,600 bhp
Crew: 1 officer, 7 petty officers, 4 ratings

Remarks: Bollard pull: 25 tons. Have one fire-fighting monitor atop pilothouse. at Toulon.

♦ 10 Actif group

	Bldr	D: light/fl	In
A 671 Le Fort	FCG, Bordeaux	248/311	12
A 672 Utile	FCG, Bordeaux	226/288	8
A 673 Lutteur	FCM, Le Havre	226/288	19
A 685 Robuste	Franco-Belges	194/239	4
A 686 Actif	FCM, Le Havre	226/288	11
A 687 Laborieux	FCM, Le Havre	226/287	14
A 688 Valeureux	Franco-Belges	196/247	17-
A 692 Travailleur	FCM, Le Havre	226/288	1
A 693 Acharné	La Perriere, Lorient	218/293	[illegible]
A 694 Efficace	La Perriere, Lorient	230/. . .	17-

COASTAL TUGS *(continued)*

Acharné (A 693) Mike Louagie, 6-90

D: see name list **S:** 11.8 kts **Dim:** 28.3 (25.3 pp) × 7.9 × 4.3
Electron Equipt: Radar: 1/DRBN 32 (Decca 1226) nav.
M: 1 MGO ASHR diesel; 1,100 to 1,450 bhp
Range: 2,400/1 **Crew:** 12 tot.

Remarks: Similar, but not identical, ships. Bollard pull: 17 tons. Sister *Hercule* (A 667) stricken 1991.

HARBOR TUGS

◆ **4 special push tugs for ballistic-missile submarines**
Bldr: . . .

–4

D: 44 tons light **S:** 6 kts **Dim:** . . . × . . . × . . .
M: 1 diesel; 1 prop; 456 bhp **Crew:** . . . tot.

◆ **4 P.19-class push-tugs** Bldr: La Perrière, Lorient (In serv. 1989)

19–P.22

D: 44 tons **S:** 6 kts **Dim:** . . . × . . . × . . .
M: 2 Poyaud 520 V8M diesels; 2 props; 456 bhp (440 sust.)
Crew: 2 tot.

Remarks: Similar to the P.1–P.18 series.

◆ **18 P.1-class push tugs** Bldr: La Perrière, Lorient (In serv. 1976–1983)

1–P.18

P.18—24-ton pusher tug Bernard Prézelin, 6-90

D: 24 tons (fl) **S:** 9.2 kts **Dim:** 11.50 (11.25 wl) × 4.30 × 1.45
M: 2 Poyaud 520 V8M diesels; 2 props; 440 bhp
Range: 191/9; 1,560/8 **Fuel:** 1.7 tons **Crew:** 2 tot.

Remarks: For dockyard use. Primarily for pushing, but have 4.1-ton bollard pull. No names or NATO pendant numbers assigned.

Note: The tugs listed below have two-letter contractions of names on bows instead of usual pendant numbers.

◆ **2 Bonite class** Bldr: SFCN, Châlon-sur-Seine

Y 630 Bonite (In serv. 1975) Y 634 Rouget (In serv. 1974)

D: 93 tons (fl) **S:** 11 kts **Dim:** . . . × . . . × . . .
M: 1 diesel; 1 prop; 380 bhp

Remarks: Bollard pull: 7 tons.

Bonite (Y 630) J.-C. Bellonne, 1975

◆ **26 Acajou Class** (alphabetical listing; pendant numbers not borne)

Y 601 Acajou	Y 654 Hètre	Y 686 Palétuvier
Y 607 Balsa	Y 655 Hévéa	Y 740 Papayer
Y 623 Charme	Y 663 Latanier	Y 688 Peuplier
Y 620 Chataigner	Y 666 Manguier	Y 689 Pin
Y 624 Chêne	Y 638 Marronnier	Y 695 Platane
Y 629 Cormier	Y 668 Mélèze	Y 720 Santal
Y 717 Ébène	Y 669 Merisier	Y 708 Saule
Y 618 Érable	Y 739 Noyer	Y 704 Sycomore
Y 644 Frêne	Y 719 Olivier	

Charme (Y 623) Leo Van Ginderen, 8-90

D: 105 tons **S:** 11 kts **Dim:** 21.0 (18.4 pp) × 6.9 × 3.2
M: 1 diesel; 1 prop; 700 bhp

Remarks: Bollard-pull capacity: 10 tons. *Bouleau* (Y 612) stricken 1980; *Equeurdreville* (Y 635) in 1986; *Okoumé* (Y 682) in 1990.

◆ **27 Oiseau class** (alphabetical listing, pendant numbers not borne)

Y 720 Alouette	Y 748 Gélinotte	Y 621 Mésange
Y 730 Ara	Y 648 Goéland	Y 673 Moineau
Y 611 Bengali	Y 728 Grand Duc	Y 617 Mouette
Y 625 Cigogne	Y 747 Loriot	Y 687 Passereau
Y 628 Colibri	Y 727 Macreuse	Y 691 Pinson
Y 632 Cygne	Y 725 Marabout	Y 694 Pivert
Y 729 Eider	Y 675 Martin Pêcheur	Y 724 Sarcelle
Y 723 Engoulevent	Y 636 Martinet	Y 726 Toucan
Y 687 Fauvette	Y 670 Merle	Y 722 Vanneau

Cygne (Y 632) Leo Van Ginderen, 9-90

D: 65 tons **S:** 9 kts **Dim:** 18.4 × 5.7 × 2.5
M: 1 Poyaud diesel; 250 bhp **Range:** 1,700/9

Remarks: Bollard-pull capacity: 3.5 tons. *Ibis* (Y 658) on loan to Senegal. *Aigrette* (Y 602) and *Héron* (Y 653) stricken in 1990.

TRAINING SHIPS AND CRAFT

Note: In addition to the designated ships and craft below, the French Navy operates a number of other units primarily in training roles. These include the helicopter carrier *Jeanne d'Arc* (R 97), frigate *Doudart de Lagrée* (F 728), and the diving tender *Poseidon* (A 722).

TRAINING SHIPS AND CRAFT *(continued)*

♦ **8 Léopard class**

	Bldr	Laid down	L	In serv.
A 748 Léopard	de la Manche, St.-Malo	6-4-81	4-6-81	4-12-82
A 749 Panthère	de la Manche, St.-Malo	9-6-81	3-9-81	4-12-82
A 750 Jaguar	de la Manche, St.-Malo	27-9-81	29-10-81	18-12-82
A 751 Lynx	La Perrière, Lorient	23-7-81	27-2-82	18-12-82
A 752 Guépard	de la Manche, St.-Malo	11-10-82	1-12-82	1-7-83
A 753 Chacal	de la Manche, St.-Malo	11-10-82	11-2-83	10-9-83
A 754 Tigre	La Perrière, Lorient	16-4-82	8-10-82	1-7-83
A 755 Lion	La Perrière, Lorient	21-2-82	13-12-82	10-9-83

Panthère (A 749) Leo Van Ginderen, 6-90

Léopard (A 749) Leo Van Ginderen, 5-90

D: 335 tons (460 fl) **S:** 15 kts **Dim:** 43.00 (40.15 pp) × 8.30 × 3.21
A: 2/20-mm AA (I × 2)
Electron Equipt: Radar: 1/DRBN 32 (Decca 1226) nav.
M: 2 SACM 75 V16 ASHR diesels; 2 props; 2,200 bhp
Range: 4,100/12 **Electric:** 160 kw
Crew: 1 officer, 7 petty officers, 6 ratings + 2 officer instructors, 2 petty officer instructors, 18 trainees

Remarks: First four authorized 1980, second group 1981. Replaced the minesweepers of the U.S. *Adjutant* class in training duties. Also for use as patrol vessels if required.

♦ **2 tenders** Bldr: Ch. Bayonne (In serv. 1971)

Y 706 Chimère Y 711 Farfadet

Farfadet (Y 711) Pradignac & Léo, 1983

D: 100 tons **S:** 11 kts **Dim:** 30.50 × 5.25 × 1.75
M: 1 diesel; 200 bhp

Remarks: Used by the Naval Academy for training in seamanship. No radar.

♦ **2 auxiliary barkentines** Bldr: Chantiers de Normandie, Fécamp (In serv. 1932)

A 649 L'Étoile A 650 La Belle Poule

La Belle Poule (A 650) L. Van Ginderen, 7-8

D: 225 tons (275 fl) **S:** 6 kts **Dim:** 40.45 (32.25 hull) × 7.0 × 3.2
M: Sulzer diesel; 125 bhp—425 m[2] sail area **Crew:** 16 + 20 trainees

Remarks: Assigned to the Naval Academy. The tallest mast is 28.30 m high. Whit hulls.

♦ **1 sail-training yawl** (L: 1932)

A 653 La Grande Hermine (ex-*La Route Est Belle,* ex-*Menéstrel*)

Remarks: Fourteen-meter yawl purchased in 1964 for the reserve officers' school. D: tons (13 fl).

♦ **1 sail-training craft** Bldr: C.N. de Vendée (L: 1927)

A 652 Mutin

Mutin (A 652) Bernard Prézelin,

TRAINING SHIPS AND CRAFT *(continued)*

D: 40 tons (55 fl) **S:** . . . **Dim:** 33.0 (22.0 hull) × 6.5 × 3.2 (1.5 fwd)
M: 1 Baudouin 6-cyl. diesel; 1 prop; 112 bhp—240 m² sail area.
Crew: 12 tot.

Remarks: Assigned to the annex of the Seamanship School.

Note: The training ships *Engageante* (A 772) and *Vigilante* (A 773) were stricken during 1991.

MISCELLANEOUS SERVICE CRAFT

◆ **1 ASW trials tender** Bldr: . . .

L'AVENTURIÈRE II (In serv. 1985)

D: . . . **S:** . . . **Dim:** 24.5 × 7.9 × 3.1
M: 1 Poyaud diesel; 1 prop; 650 bhp

Remarks: No hull number. Used by GESMA (*Group d'Études Sous Marines de l'At-'antique*) at Brest.

◆ **1 trials support tender**

DCAN 164 MÉROU

lérou (DCAN 164) Gilbert Gyssels, 6-85

emarks: A diving tender with bow-door arrangement for lowering test equipment. ased at Toulon and civilian-operated.

2 weapons range-safety boats Bldrs: C.N. de L'Estérel, Cannes

	L	In serv.		L	In serv.
712 ATHOS	20-11-79	22-11-79	A 713 ARAMIS	9-9-80	22-9-80

hos (A 712) and Aramis (A 713) Bernard Prézelin, 4-90

): 80 tons (99.5 fl) **S:** 28 kts **Dim:** 32.1 × 6.5 × 1.9
\: 1/20-mm AA
lectron Equipt: Radar: 1/DRBN 32 (Decca 1226) nav.
I: 2 SACM Type 195 V12 diesels; 2 props; 4,640 bhp
ange: 1,500/15
rew: 1 officer, 6 petty officers, 10–11 ratings (including 6 divers)

narks: Operate at the Landes Test Center, both as range-safety craft and for pons-recovery duties. Wooden hulls.

1 range-safety craft

02 GIRELLE

lle (A 702) Hartmut Ehlers, 5-86

D: 42 tons (45 fl) **S:** . . . **M:** . . .

Remarks: Wooden construction. Operates from St. Raphaël for the *Centre d'Essais de la Méditérranée.*

◆ **1 range-safety craft** Bldr: C.N. de L'Estérel, Cannes

A 714 TOURMALINE (In serv. 14-2-74)

Tourmaline (A 714) Pradignac & Léo, 6-88

D: 37 tons (45 fl) **S:** 15 kts **Dim:** 26.8 × 4.97 × 1.53
Electron Equipt: Radar: 1/DRBN 32 (Decca 1226) nav.
M: 2 diesels; 2 props; 480 bhp

Remarks: Wooden construction. Can carry 1/20-mm AA. Attached to the *Centre d'Essais de la Méditérranée.* Identical craft serve the French Customs Service.

◆ **6 fireboats**

Y 618 CASCADE	Y 645 GAVE	Y 646 GEYSER
Y 684 OUED	Y 745 AIGUIÈRE	Y 746 EMBRUN

Cascade (Y 618) Bernard Prézelin, 4-91

D: 70 tons (85 fl) **S:** 11.3 kts **Dim:** 23.8 × 5.3 × 1.7
M: 2 Poyaud 6 PZM diesels; 2 props; 405 bhp

◆ **1 degaussing (deperming) tender**

Y 732

Y 732 DCAN, 1970

D: 260 tons **S:** 10 kts **Dim:** 38.2 × 4.3 × 2.4
M: 1 diesel; 1 prop; 375 bhp **Crew:** 5 tot.

Note: The radiological monitoring craft *Palangrin* (Y 743) was stricken 1990.

◆ **18 motor lighters, converted from LCM (3)-class landing craft**

CHA 1, 2, 6, 7, 8, 9, 13, 14, 15, 16, 17, 18, 19, 22, 23, 24, 25, 26

D: 20 tons (50 fl) **S:** 7 kts **Dim:** 15.2 × 4.4 × 1.6
M: 1 diesel; 100 bhp (CHA 1, CHA 6: 115 bhp)

MISCELLANEOUS SERVICE CRAFT *(continued)*

CHA-series Bernard Prézelin, 4-91

◆ **18 non-self-propelled water lighters**

1–18

D: . . . **S:** 9 kts **Dim:** . . . × . . . × . . . **M:** 1 diesel; 430 bhp

Remarks: Nos. 5 and 6 in Tahiti, No. 2 at Brest, Nos. 1 and 11 at Toulon, No. 12 at Lorient, others at the CEP (*Centre d'Expérimentation Pacifique*).

◆ **5 self-propelled floating cranes**

GFA 1–5

GFA 2 Ben Sullivan, 5-91

Remarks: Lift capacity: 15 tons maximum. GFA—*Grue Flottante Automotrice.* Two each at Brest and Toulon, one at Cherbourg.

◆ **1 floating dry dock** (In serv. 1975)

Remarks: Capacity: 3,500 tons. Based at Papeete.

MARITIME POLICE

Administered by the Ministry of the Merchant Marine for the enforcement of maritime laws and regulations. Except for the officers (who serve on land and are commissioned), the personnel are civilians. Hull numbers begin with PM (*Police Maritime*). The patrol craft are at the disposition of the Maritime Prefectures.

REGIONAL SURVEILLANCE CRAFT (*Vedettes Régionales de Surveillance*)

◆ **1 Gabian class** Bldr: C.N. de l'Estérel, Cannes (In serv. 1986)

PM 30 Gabian (based at La Rochelle)

Gabian (PM 30) Bernard Prézelin, 10-90

D: 76 tons (fl) **S:** 23 kts **Dim:** 32.10 × 6.46 × 3.03 (moulded depth)
A: 1/12.7-mm mg **Electron Equipt:** Radar: 1/. . . nav.
M: 2 Baudouin diesels; 2 props; 900 bhp **Endurance:** 100 hours
Range: 1,280/15 **Crew:** 8 tot.

◆ **1 Arcor 56 class** Bldr: CNA, La Teste (In serv. 1991)

PM 64 Cap d'Ailly (based at Dieppe)

D: 75 tons (fl) **S:** . . . kts **Dim:** 17.00 × 4.85 × . . .
A: . . . **Electron Equipt:** Radar: 1/. . . nav.
M: 2 Baudouin diesels; 2 props; 1,400 bhp **Crew:** 5 tot.

◆ **2 A.E.C. Ancelle class** Bldr: C.N. de l'Estérel, Cannes (In serv. 1962, 1963)

PM 25 A.E.C. Ancelle (at Sète) PM 26 P.L. Renet (at Marseille)

Administrateur en Chef Ancelle (PM 25) Hartmut Ehlers, 8-8

D: 74 tons (fl) **S:** 21 kts **Dim:** 31.45 × 5.75 × 3.08 (moulded depth)
A: 1/7.5-mm mg **Electron Equipt:** Radar: 1/. . . nav.
Range: 1,380/15
M: 2 diesels; 2 props; 800–900 bhp **Endurance:** 72 hours
Crew: 8 tot.

Remarks: PM 25 has 400-bhp Poyaud diesels, PM 26 has 450-bhp Baudouin diese

◆ **1 Armoise class** Bldr: Sibiril, Carentec (In serv. 1968)

PM 27 Armoise (based at St. Nazaire)

Armoise (PM 27) Bernard Prézelin, 8

D: 74 tons (fl) **S:** 21 kts **Dim:** 30.50 × 6.00 × 3.10 moulded dept
A: 1/7.5-mm mg **Electron Equipt:** Radar: 1/. . . nav.
M: 2 Poyaud diesels; 2 props; 780 bhp **Endurance:** 92 hours
Range: 580/18 **Crew:** 8 tot.

◆ **1 Mauve class** Bldr: C.N. de L'Estérel, Cannes (In serv. 1984)

M 29 Mauve (based at Bayonne)

D: 65 tons (fl) **S:** 26 kts **Dim:** 30.50 × 5.70 × 2.78 moulded dept
A: 1/12.7 mm mg—1/7.5-mm mg
Electron Equipt: Radar: 1/. . . nav.
M: 2 MWM-Deutz diesels; 2 props; 2,120 bhp **Endurance:** 61 hou
Range: 900/15.5 **Crew:** . . . tot.

Remarks: Re-engined in 1990.

◆ **1 Tourne-Pierre class** Bldr: CMN, Cherbourg (In serv. 1984)

PM 28 Tourne-Pierre (based at Lorient)

D: 71 tons (fl) **S:** 22 kts **Dim:** 28.95 × . . . × . . .
A: 1/12.7-mm mg **Electron Equipt:** Radar: 1/. . . nav.
M: 2 MWM-Deutz diesels; 2 props; 2,120 bhp **Endurance:** 100 h
Range: 1,150/15 **Crew:** 8 tot.

Remarks: Re-engined 1990.

REGIONAL SURVEILLANCE CRAFT *(continued)*

Tourne-Pierre (PM 28) Bernard Prézelin, 5-90

♦ 2 Couriandre class Bldr: CMN, Cherbourg (In serv. 1974)

PM 12 COURIANDRE (at Cherbourg)
PM 13 MARJOLAINE (at Boulogne)

larjolaine (PM 13) Mike Louagie, 10-90

D: 84 tons (fl) **S:** 23 kts **Dim:** 27.90 × 5.80 × 2.45 moulded depth
A: 1/7.5-mm mg **Electron Equipt:** Radar: 1/. . . nav.
M: 2 MGO diesels; 2 props; 1,200 bhp **Endurance:** 87 hours
Range: 850/15 **Crew:** 9 tot.

emarks: German-style lifeboats, with stern ramps for rigid inflatable rescue craft. ster *Garance* (PM 11) stricken 1986.

ISHORE SURVEILLANCE CRAFT *(Vedettes de Surveillance approchée)*

1 Eider class Bldr: Polymer, Tregunc (In serv. 1988)

1 63 EIDER (based at Morlais)

er (PM 63) Ben Sullivan, 6-91

: 28 tons **S:** 20 kts **Dim:** 16.80 × 4.50 × 2.10 moulded depth
: none **Electron Equipt:** Radar: 1/. . . nav.
: 2 M.A.N. diesels; 2 props; 1,250 bhp **Crew:** . . .

Pétrel class Bldr: C.N. de l'Estérel, Cannes (In serv. 1985)

31 PÉTREL (based at Brest)

Pétrel (PM 61) Bernard Prézelin, 10-90

D: 26 tons (fl) **S:** 25 kts **Dim:** 17.10 × 4.58 × 2.24 moulded depth
A: none **Electron Equipt:** Radar . . . **Endurance:** 30 hours
M: 2 Poyaud diesels; 2 props; 450 bhp **Crew:** . . .

♦ 1 Tadorne class Bldr: Polymer, Tregunc (In serv. 1986)

PM 62 TADORNE (based at Bayonne)

D: 21.5 tons (fl) **S:** 20 kts **Dim:** 15.70 × 4.20 × 2.10 moulded depth
A: none **M:** 2 Baudouin diesels; 2 props; 400 bhp
Endurance: 40 hours **Crew:** . . .

♦ 3 Courlis class Bldr: ACMP, Dieppe (In serv. 1981)

PM 56 COURLIS (at Trinité) PM 57 AVOCETTE (at Les Sables)
PM 60 CAROUGE (at Fort de France)

Avocette (PM 57) Bernard Prézelin, 8-90

D: 13 tons (fl) **S:** 21 kts **Dim:** 13.30 × 4.20 × 1.90
A: none **M:** 2 Poyaud diesels; 2 props; 270 bhp
Endurance: 44 hours **Crew:** . . . tot.

Remarks: Sisters *Eider* (PM 58) stricken 1988, *Pluvier* (PM 59) in 1991.

♦ 3 Sorbier class Bldr: Yachting-France, Arcachon (In serv. 1976–1978)

PM 50 SORBIER (at St.-Malo) PM 54 VALÉRIANE (at Ajaccio)
PM 55 ROMARIN (at Bastia)

D: 13 tons (fl) **S:** 23 kts **Dim:** 13.05 × . . . × . . . **A:** none
M: 2 RMC diesels; 2 props; 290 bhp
Endurance: 40 hours **Crew:** . . . tot.

Remarks: PM 54 is 12.60 m o.a., 12 tons.

INSHORE SURVEILLANCE CRAFT *(Vedettes de Surveillance Littoral)*

♦ 13 miscellaneous units

PM 279 SARRIETTE (1988): 10.90 m o.a.; 250 bhp
PM 284 CAP DE NICE (1990): 10.30 m o.a.; 500 bhp; 26 kts
PM 282 OCÉANE, PM 283 GIRONDINE (1988): 9.15 m o.a.; 440 bhp; 17 kts
PM 285 SYNDIC VICTOR SALEZ (1990): 8.15 m o.a.; 250 bhp; 18 kts
PM 246 LA COURSIÈRE (1981): 8.25 m o.a.; 140 bhp
PM 268 PERTUISANE, PM 269 MOR BRAZ (ex-*La Cauchoise*), PM 270 KORRIGAN, PM 272 CAP D'AZUR (ex-*Cap de Nice*), PM 273 LOU LABECH (1981–82): 8.0 m o.a.; 140 bhp
PM 261 IBIS (1980): 7.50 m o.a.; 105 bhp
PM 245 LES EVENS (1970): 6.50 m o.a.; 175 bhp

CUSTOMS SERVICE

The French Customs Service, under the Ministry of Finance, also operates a number of patrol craft with hull numbers beginning with "DF" (*Douanes Françaises*). The Customs Service also operates the following aircraft: 6 Cessna 406 and 6 Cessna 404 light transports and 5 Écureuil helicopters.

PATROL BOATS AND CRAFT

♦ **2 Avel Gwalarn class** Bldr: C.N. de l'Estérel, Cannes

DF 41 Avel Gwalarn (In serv. 1984) DF 42 Suroît (In serv. 1988)

Avel Gwalarn (DF 41) Bernard Prézelin, 5-90

D: 67 tons (fl) **S:** 28 kts **Dim:** 30.35 × 5.80 × 1.83 **Crew:** 8 tot.
A: 1/12.7-mm mg **Electron Equipt:** Radar: 1/. . . nav.
M: 2 Poyaud UD 20 diesels; 2 props; 2,200 bhp **Range:** 1,200/15

♦ **1 Vent d'amont class** Bldr: CMN, Cherbourg (In serv. 1983)

DF 40 Vent d'amont

Vent d'amont (DF 40) Jürg Kürsener, 8-89

D: 61 tons (71 fl) **S:** 25 kts **Dim:** 28.95 × 5.70 × 1.65
Range: 750/21; 1,165/15 **Crew:** 8 tot.
A: 1/12.7-mm mg **Electron Equipt:** Radar: 1/. . . nav.
M: 2 Poyaud UD 20 diesels; 2 props; 2,200 bhp

♦ **2 Haize Hegoa class** Bldr: Plascoa (In serv. 1990–91)

DF 43 Haize Hegoa DF 44 Mervent

D: 64 tons (75 fl) **S:** 28 kts **Dim:** 28.70 × 6.41 × 1.60
A: 1/12.7-mm mg **Electron Equipt:** Radar: 1/. . . nav.
M: 2 G.M. Detroit Diesel 12V71 TI diesels; 2 props; 2,200 bhp—1 G.M. Detroit Diesel diesel; 1 waterjet; 550 bhp
Range: 1,200/15 **Crew:** 8 tot.

Mervent (DF 44) Bernard Prézelin, 8-91

♦ **8 Marinada class** Bldr: C.N. de l'Estérel, Cannes

DF 30 Marinada (1965) DF 36 Avel Sterenn (1968)
DF 33 Lissero (1966) DF 37 Rafale (1970)
DF 34 Alizé (1968) DF 38 Vent d'Aval (1977)
DF 35 Vent d'Autan (1968) DF 39 Aquilon (1978)

D: 37 tons (45 fl) **S:** 25 kts **Dim:** 26.80 × 4.97 × 1.53
Range: 900/18 (DF 38, 39: 800/15) **Crew:** 8 tot.
A: 1/12.7-mm mg **Electron Equipt:** 1/. . . nav.
M: 2 G.M. diesels; 2 props; 956 bhp

Remarks: DF 38 and DF 39 have MTU diesels totaling 900 bhp for 30 kts. Wooden construction. Sister *Tourmaline* (A 714) is in the French Navy. Sister *Haize Hegoa* (DF 31) scrapped 1990, *Mervent* (DF 32) in 1991.

♦ **1 Gregau class** Bldr: C.N. de l'Estérel, Cannes (In serv. 1990)

DF 16 Gregau

D: 41 tons (fl) **S:** 28 kts **Dim:** 23.00 × 5.55 × 1.65
A: 1/7.5-mm mg **Electron Equipt:** Radar: 1/. . . nav.
M: 2 G.M. Detroit Diesel 12V71 TI diesels; 2 props; 2,200 bhp—1 G.M. Detroit Diesel diesel; 1 waterjet; 550 bhp
Range: 500/25 **Crew:** 8 tot.

♦ **2 Libeccio class** Bldr: C.N. de l'Estérel, Cannes

DF 26 Libeccio (In serv. 1979) DF 27 Levant (In serv. 1985)

D: 30 tons (fl) **S:** 28 kts (DF 27: 29) **Dim:** 21.00 × 4.70 × 1.40
A: 1/7.7-mm mg **Electron Equipt:** Radar: 1/. . . nav.
M: 2 Poyaud diesels; 2 props; 1,400 bhp (DF 27: 1,900)
Range: 450/15 (DF 27: 420/16) **Crew:** 8 tot.

♦ **6 Noroit class** Bldr: Plascoa (In serv. 1988–89)

DF 12 Noroit DF 15 Norues DF 28 Orsuro
DF 14 Nordet DF 25 Lagarde DF 29 Muntese

Nordet (DF 14) Mike Louagie, 8-9

D: 35 tons (fl) **S:** 28 kts **Dim:** 21.00 × 5.55 × 1.50
A: 1/12.7-mm or 7.5-mm mg **Electron Equipt:** Radar: 1/. . . nav.
M: 2 Poyaud UD 20 V12 M5 diesels; 2 props; 2,000 bhp (*see* Remarks)
Range: 500/25 **Electric:** 27 kw **Crew:** 8 tot.

Remarks: DF 15 and DF 25 have General Motors diesels developing 2,190 bhp a providing 25 kts.

♦ **2 Mistral class** Bldr: C.N. de l'Estérel, Cannes (In serv. 1962)

DF 17 Mistral DF 23 Cers

Cers (DF 23) Leo Van Ginderen,

D: 20 tons (fl) **S:** 20 kts **Dim:** 17.7 × 3.80 × 0.95
A: 1/7.5-mm mg **Electron Equipt:** Radar: . . .
M: 2 G.M. diesels; 2 props; 470 bhp **Range:** 550/15 **Crew:** 8 tot.

Remarks: DF 23 is slightly larger: 18.15 × 4.08 × 1.03.

♦ **5 Taravo class** Bldr: Couach, Arcachon (In serv. 1982–84)

DF 50 Taravo DF 54 Matylis DF 57 Touloubre
DF 51 Tramontana DF 56 Agly

D: 13.5 tons (fl) **S:** 27 kts **Dim:** 14.00 × 4.06 × 1.24
A: 1/7.5-mm mg **M:** 2 Baudouin diesels; 2 props; 1,000 bhp
Range: 460/18 **Crew:** 5 tot.

FRANCE *(continued)*
PATROL BOATS AND CRAFT *(continued)*

L'Aunis (DF 1) Bernard Prézelin, 5-90

Note: In addition to the units detailed above, the Customs Service also operates 34 other patrol craft under 14 m in length (ranging from 5 to 13.5 m o.a.) and three training craft: DF 1 *L'Aunis* (ex-yacht), DF 2 *Louisiane,* and DF 101 *Pingouin.*

GABON

Gabonese Republic

Personnel (1991): approx. 480 total

Naval Aviation: One Embraer EMB 111 Bandeirante maritime patrol aircraft is operated by the air force.

PATROL BOATS AND CRAFT

◆ **2 French "Super PATRA" class** Bldr: CMN, Cherbourg

	Laid down	L	In serv.
P 07 Genéral d'Armée ba Oumar	2-7-86	18-12-87	6-8-88
P 08 Colonel Djoué Dbany	. . .	27-3-90	24-10-90

Genéral d'Armée ba Oumar (P 07) CMN, Cherbourg, 1988

Colonel Djoué Dbany (P 08) Bernard Prézelin, 7-90

D: 371.5 tons (446 fl) **S:** 26 kts (24.5 sust.)
Dim: 54.50 (50.0 pp) × 8.0 (7.7 wl) × 2.54 (2.08 hull)
A: P 07: 1/57-mm Bofors SAK 57 Mk 2 DP—1/20-mm Oerlikon AA; P 08: 2/20-mm Oerlikon AA (I × 2)
Electron Equipt: 1/Decca 1226C nav.
M: 2 UNI UD33 V16 M7 diesels; 2 CP props; 8,000 bhp
Electric: 360 kw **Range:** 4,200/15 **Fuel:** 73 tons
Endurance: 15 days
Crew: 4 officers, 28 enlisted + 23 passengers or 20 troops

Remarks: P 07 ordered 11-84; second unit ordered 2-89. Limiting displacement 446 tons. For search-and-rescue use, carry inflatable launch and can accommodate 23 rescued personnel. Have two contraband storerooms. Armament reduced on P 08 to save money; delivery of the unit was delayed by re-engining. P 07 began refit in France, 11-91.

◆ **1 wooden-hulled** Bldr: Ch. de l'Estérel, Cannes (In serv. 12-1-78)

P 10 Genéral Nazaire Boulingui (ex-*Président el Haj Omar Bongo*)

Genéral Nazaire Boulingui (P 10) Bernard Prézelin, 7-90

D: 100 tons (fl) **S:** 32 kts **Dim:** 42.0 × 7.8 × 1.9
A: 4/SS-12M SSM (II × 2)—1/40-mm Bofors AA—1/20-mm AA
Electron Equipt: Radar: Decca RM 1226 nav.
M: 3 SACM AGO 195 12CSHR diesels; 3 props; 5,400 bhp
Fuel: 28.4 tons **Range:** 1,000/18 **Crew:** 3 officers, 20 men

Remarks: Wire-guided, optically aimed antiship missiles with a weight of 75 kg each and a range of up to 4 km. Re-engined at Port-Gentil, completing early 1985; the original 3 MTU 16V538 TB91 diesels produced 40 kts on 10,500 bhp. Hull is of triple-skinned mahogany construction. At one time bore pendant P 06, and name has also been given as "*Genéral Nazaire Boulingui Kounba,*" the "*Kounba*" having been deleted by 1985.

Note: Patrol boats *N'Guene* (P 03) and *Colonel Djoué Dabany* (P 02, ex-*Président Albert Bernard Bongo*) were stricken by the end of 1989.

AMPHIBIOUS WARFARE SHIPS AND CRAFT

◆ **1 French Champlain-class landing ship** Bldr: Atelier Français de l'Ouest, Grand Quevilly, Rouen, France

	Laid down	L	In serv.
L 05 Président el Hadj Omar Bongo	7-3-83	16-4-84	24-10-84

Président el Hadj Omar Bongo (L 05) 6-85

D: 770 tons (1,336 fl) **S:** 16 kts **Dim:** 80.0 × 13.0 × 2.40
A: 1/40-mm AA—2/81-mm mortars (I × 2)—2/12.7-mm mg (I × 2)—1/7.62-mm mg
Electron Equipt: Radar: 1/Decca 1226 nav.
M: 2 SACM 195V12 diesels; 2 CP props; 3,600 bhp
Range: 4,500/13 **Crew:** 47

Remarks: Purchase announced 28-2-84. Capacity: 340 tons stores, plus 138 troops and 7 combat vehicles. Helicopter platform aft. Carries one LCVP and one personnel landing craft. By tradition, the largest ship of the Gabonese Navy bears the name of the nation's "President for Life."

GABON *(continued)*
AMPHIBIOUS WARFARE SHIPS AND CRAFT *(continued)*

♦ **1 utility landing craft** Bldr: DCAN, Dakar (In serv. 11-5-76)

L . . . Manga

D: 152 tons **S:** 9 kts **Dim:** 24.0 × 6.4 × 1.3
A: 2/12.7-mm mg (I × 2)
Electron Equipt: Radar: Decca 101
M: 2 Poyaud V8-520 diesels; 2 props; 480 bhp **Crew:** 10 tot.

Remarks: Equipped with bow doors and ramp.

SERVICE CRAFT

♦ **2 harbor launches** Bldr: Tanguy Marine, Le Havre (In serv. 1985)

D: 2.5 tons (7.5 fl) **S:** . . . **Dim:** 12.00 × 2.95 × 0.30
M: 2 Volvo Penta AQAD-40B diesel outdrives; 165 hp

Remarks: One unit is only 10.00 m o.a., 2.25 tons (6.25 fl). Ordered 10-84. Have bow ramps.

♦ **10 service launches**

Remarks: In 6-85, ten small GRP craft were ordered from Simonneau, Foutenay, France. These included one 11.8-m and two 8.10-m patrol craft, each powered by a Volvo Penta TAMD-608 inboard/outboard diesel of 235 bhp, and seven 6.8-m personnel landing craft powered by a 110-bhp Volvo Penta AQAD-30/DP diesel.

THE GAMBIA

Republic of the Gambia

MARINE UNIT OF THE GAMBIAN NATIONAL ARMY

Personnel (1991): 60 total

Note: The "unification" of the Gambia and Senegal, agreed to on 1-2-82 but never consummated, was canceled on 30-9-89.

PATROL BOATS AND CRAFT

♦ **2 Chinese Shanghai-II class** (In serv. 5-79)

101 Gonjur 102 Brufut

Gonjur (101) Eric Grove, 1-90

D: 121 tons (131 fl) **S:** 28.5 kts (26 sust.)
Dim: 38.78 × 5.41 × 1.49 (hull; 1.554 full load)
A: 6/25-mm 2M-8 AA (II × 3)
Electron Equipt: Radar: 1/Furuno 1505 nav.
M: 2 M50F-4 (Chinese Type L12-180) 1,200-bhp, and 2/12D6 (Chinese Type L12-180Z) 910-bhp diesels; 4 props; 4,200 bhp
Endurance: 7 days **Electric:** 39 kw **Range:** 750/16.5
Crew: 34 tot.

Remarks: Received as a gift of the People's Republic of China Army Navy on 2-2-89 after refits in China; commissioned in Gambian service in 5-89. The standard Shanghai-II armament of two twin 37-mm and two twin 25-mm AA had been altered, a Japanese commercial radar was substituted for the original Pot Head, and the fantail has been left clear to accommodate an inspection dinghy.

♦ **1 British Tracker 2 class** Bldr: Fairey Marine, Cowes, U.K. (In serv. 1978)

P 12 Jato

D: 31.5 tons (fl) **S:** 29 kts **Dim:** 19.25 × 4.98 × 1.45
A: 1/20-mm Oerlikon AA—2/7.62-mm mg (I × 2)
Electron Equipt: Radar: 1/Decca 110 nav., 1/. . . nav.
M: 2 G.M. Detroit Diesel 12V-71 TI diesels; 2 props; 1,290 bhp
Range: 650/20 **Crew:** 11 tot.

Remarks: GRP construction. Air-conditioned. Two sisters listed previously, *Challenge* (P 3) and *Champion* (P 4), were returned to Senegal in 9-89.

Jato (P 12) Eric Grove, 1-90

♦ **1 British Lance class** Bldr: Fairey Marine, Cowes (In serv. 28-10-76)

Sea Dog

Sea Dog Eric Grove, 1-9

D: 17 tons **S:** 24 kts **Dim:** 14.81 × 4.76 × 1.30
A: removed **Electron Equipt:** Radar: 1/Decca 110 nav.
M: 2 General Motors Detroit Diesel 8V-71 TI diesels; 2 props; 850 bhp
Range: 500/15 **Crew:** 6 tot.

Remarks: Now used primarily for training. Formerly carried 1/20-mm AA a 3/7.62-mm mg. Can accommodate up to 10 additional personnel.

GERMANY

Federal Republic of Germany

Note: The ships of the former *Volksmarine* became the property of the Federal Rep lic of Germany on 3 October 1990. A great many had already been stricken and sold scrap or placed in commercial service. Many serviceable units, however, were ta over for service with the *Bundesmarine* and were to be operated for up to two ye other still-serviceable units are being retained as spare parts sources, were transfe to other German government agencies, or are being made available to foreign nati Many of the units taken over for the *Bundesmarine* had already been discarded by cut-off date of this edition. The fates of the various *Volksmarine* units are delineat the appropriate points in the ship data section.

Personnel (1991): Approx. 34,000 (including 6,000 officers). The number is t reduced to about 31,000 by 1994.

Naval Aviation: In 1991, about 6,000 personnel were involved in the *Marinefli* German naval aviation. Aircraft included:

♦ 1 squadron of 19 Bréguet Atlantic-1150 aircraft, of which 5 have been modifie electronic warfare. The ASW aircraft underwent modernization in 1981–83. In 3- was announced that these aircraft would be replaced by 12 U.S. P-7A to be deli 1996–97.

♦ 1 squadron of 22 Mk 43 Sea King helicopters for search-and-rescue opera Twenty Sea Kings are being upgraded to permit carrying 4 Sea Skua antiship mis a Sea Spray Mk 3 search radar, electronic intercept gear, chaff, LINK 11 compute system, and the Bendix AQS-18 dipping sonar. The first two were to have complet 1984 and all by 1988, but delays moved initial redeliveries to 1987, with the l deliver during 1989. Procurement of 32 NH-90 helicopters to replace the SH- anticipated for the 1990s; at least 6 will be in search-and-rescue configuration.

♦ 2 wings of 45 MRCA Tornado fighter-bombers, with 105 total aircraft avai Naval Air Wing 1 is to be transferred to the *Luftwaffe* leaving about 55 in *Bund*

NAVAL AVIATION *(continued)*

rine service. On 7-4-76 the German government decided to begin construction of 112 MRCA Tornado variable-geometry fighter-bombers for the navy. The first four entered service in 7-82. Characteristics are:

Length: 17.2 meters
Wingspan: 13.90 meters max./8.40 meters min.
Maximum takeoff weight: 26,000 kg
Maximum speed: Mach 2.2
Ceiling: 15,200 m
Weapons: 4 Kormoran ASM and/or HARM ARM or 10 Mk 83 or Mk 82 bombs or 8 BL 755 cluster bombs—plus 2 AIM 9 Sidewinder and a 27-mm gun

Tornado Marineamt, Wilhelmshaven, 1990

♦ Fourteen Westland/Bréguet WG-13 Lynx Mk 88 ASW helicopters. The Bendix DAQS-18 dipping sonar is employed. First 4 delivered 1981, 8 in 1982, 4 in 1983, 2 in 1986, five in 7-88 to 1989.
♦ There are also 18 Dornier DO-28D-2 liaison aircraft, 4 IAI Westwind target tugs are operated for the navy by a private company, and a Dornier 228-212 98 + 77 pollution control aircraft delivered 10-4-91.

The Naval Air Division is organized into four wings:

Naval Air Wing 1 at Schleswig: 2 attack squadrons of Tornados (to transfer to the *Luftwaffe*)
Naval Air Wing 2 at Eggebek: 1 attack and 1 reconnaissance squadron of Tornados
Naval Air Wing 3 at Nordholz: 2 squadrons Atlantics, 1 of Lynx helos
Naval Air Wing 5 at Holtenau: 1 squadron Sea Kings, 1 of Dornier 28s, and the Dornier 228-212

rman Atlantic I Marineamt, Wilhelmshaven, 1990

-90 mockup Norman Friedman, 9-90

Sea King in SAR configuration Leo Van Ginderen, 6-90

Lynx Mk 88 Marineamt, Wilhelmshaven, 1990

WEAPONS AND SYSTEMS

Note: Soviet systems aboard former *Volksmarine* units are being retained, as there were sufficient supplies of ammunition and spare parts to keep them operational for the period through which they will be employed. The systems used by the *Bundesmarine* itself are:

MISSILES

Surface-to-air:

♦ Standard SM-1 MR on board the 3 *Charles F. Adams*-class destroyers (see U.S. section for characteristics).
♦ RIM-116A RAM (Rolling Air-frame Missile), developed as a close-in defense weapon in cooperation with General Dynamics in the United States. The system will carry 21 missiles per launcher. The first 350 were ordered from RAMSYS GmbH in 10-89 for delivery in 1991, and by 1995 some 2,000 are to have been acquired, along with 52 Mk 49 launchers, the first 10 of which were to have been received during 1991. The system is about 11 years behind schedule.

Surface-to-surface:

♦ MM 38 Exocet on board *Hamburg*-class destroyers and Types 143A, 143, and 148 guided-missile patrol boats. The U.S. Harpoon (RGM-84A) is carried by the Type 122 frigates and by refitted units of the *Charles F. Adams*-class destroyers. The Anglo-French ANS missile will replace both MM 38 Exocet and the Kormoran air-launched antiship missile beginning in the late 1990s; plan to acquire 280 total.

Air-to-surface:

♦ Kormoran and U.S. HARM missiles, carried by Tornado aircraft. Kormoran II, with a new digital seeker, is in development.

GUNS

♦ Automatic 127-mm U.S. Mk 42 Mod. 10 on *Adams*-class destroyers.
♦ French Model 1953 100-mm dual-purpose on *Hamburg*-class destroyers and *Rhein*-class tenders.
♦ OTO Melara Compact 76-mm guns on board Types 143, 143A, and 148 guided-missile patrol boats and Type 122 frigates.
♦ Bofors 40-mm (70-caliber), in single or twin mounts on many types of ships. Replaced by open Breda mountings in combatants. Bofors "Trinity" elevating masses and 100-round ready-service magazines ordered 1986 to update existing 40-mm mounts.
♦ 20-mm Oerlikon and Rheinmetall in single mountings.

Note: Three 30-mm Goalkeeper close-in weapons systems leased from the Netherlands on 23-1-91 were returned at the conclusion of hostilities in the Mideast.

ANTISUBMARINE WARFARE

Rocket launchers:

- ♦ Quadruple 375-mm Bofors, automatically loaded in a vertical position.
- ♦ The U.S. ASROC system, with a Mk 112 octuple launcher for missiles having a Mk 46 ASW torpedo payload.

Torpedoes:

- ♦ U.S. Mk 37 Mod. 0 on submarines (possibly no longer in use).
- ♦ U.S. Mk 44 and Mk 46 on *Charles F. Adams*-class destroyers, Type 122 frigates, and Bréguet Atlantic-1150 ASW patrol aircraft.
- ♦ Wire-guided DM 1 "Seeschlange" type on submarines: weight 1,370 kg; range: 20,000 m; 18 or 34 knots; 275 kg warhead.
- ♦ Wire-guided DM 2 A1 "Seeal" type (20,000-m range) on Type 143 missile boats.
- ♦ Wire-guided DM 2 A3 "Seehecht" in development. DM 2A4 version will be deeper diving and will have a new propulsion system. 116 ordered 16-12-91, with option for 63 kits to convert earlier torpedoes to Seehecht standard.

MINES

The *Seegrundmine 90* is in development with Denmark by Krupp-Atlas; 3,000 were to be delivered 1990–93. Numerous other mines are available for air, submarine, and surface launch.

ELECTRONICS

In addition to the U.S. radars mounted in the *Charles F. Adams*-class destroyers, the West German Navy uses the following Dutch radars (Hollandse Signaal-Apparaaten):

LW-02 long-range air search (D-Band)
SGR-105 multipurpose search (E/F-Band)
SGR-103 surface search (I-Band)
M45 X-band for 100-mm and 40-mm fire control

Type 148 missile patrol boats have a Thomson-CSF Triton target-designation radar and Vega fire-control system with Pollux radar.

Type 143 missile patrol boats carry the AGIS fire-control system combined with Dutch H.S.A. WM 27 M radar. AGIS has two UNIVAC computers, one for fire control and the other for real-time threat-processing. WM 27 has two antennas within its dome, one for search and one for tracking. An automatic data link permits AGIS to relay information with other units of the Type 143, *Charles F. Adams* class, and with future combatants. The *Adams*-class destroyers have received the Lockheed-built Mk 86 gunfire-control system, with SPQ-9 and SPG-60 radar.

Aside from the SQS-23 on the *Adams* class, sonars are of West German origin.

SUBMARINES

♦ **0 (+12) Type 212** Bldr: Howaldtswerke, Kiel, and Thyssen Nordseewerke, Emden

	Laid down	L	In serv.
S . . . U . . .	. . .	1996	1997
S . . . U . . .	. . .	. . .	. . .
S . . . U . . .	. . .	. . .	. . .
S . . . U . . .	. . .	. . .	. . .
S . . . U . . .	. . .	. . .	. . .
S . . . U . . .	. . .	. . .	. . .
S . . . U . . .	. . .	. . .	. . .
S . . . U . . .	. . .	. . .	. . .
S . . . U . . .	. . .	. . .	. . .
S . . . U . . .	. . .	. . .	. . .
S . . . U . . .	. . .	. . .	. . .
S . . . U . . .	. . .	. . .	. . .

D: 1,200 tons surf./1,800 sub. **S:** . . . **Dim:** 51.0 × 6.9 × 6.4
A: 6/533-mm TT fwd (Seeal 3 wire-guided torpedoes)
Electron Equipt:
Radar: . . . . .—EW: . . . . . .
Sonar: Krupp-Atlas . . . suite, with FAS 3-1 flank array and PRS 3-15 passive ranging, Ferranti FMS 52 HF active, . . . towed array
M: diesel-electric, with fuel cells for air-independent cruising; 1 prop; . . . shp
Range: . . ./. . . **Crew:** 22 tot.

Remarks: Program development began 1988 as a replacement for the larger (and too expensive) Type 211. First seven were originally to have been ordered in 1990, with trials of the first ship in 1994 and delivery in 1995, but none had been funded through the 1992 budget. Ship's design by IKL, Lübeck, is not yet firm, and the final design may be smaller than that delineated above. The air-independent propulsion (AIP) system would employ the HDW fuel-cell system tested in U 1.

♦ **18 Type 206 and 206A*** Bldr: (A)—Howaldtswerke-Deutsche Werft, Kiel; (B)—Rheinstahl Nordseewerke, Emden; Modernized by: (C)—Howaldtswerke; (D)—Thyssen Nordseewerft

	Bldr/Mod.	Laid down	L	In serv.
S 192 U 13	A	24-11-69	28-9-71	19-4-73
S 193 U 14	B	10-9-70	1-2-72	19-4-73
S 194 U 15*	A/D	29-5-70	15-6-72	17-4-74
S 195 U 16*	B/C	22-4-71	29-8-72	9-11-73
S 196 U 17*	A/C	19-10-70	10-10-72	28-11-73
S 197 U 18*	B/C	28-7-71	31-10-72	19-12-73
S 198 U 19	A	14-1-71	15-12-72	9-11-73
S 199 U 20	B	15-2-72	16-1-73	24-5-74
S 170 U 21	A	14-4-71	9-3-73	16-8-74
S 171 U 22*	B/D	3-5-72	27-3-73	26-7-74
S 172 U 23*	B/D	21-8-72	22-5-73	2-5-75
S 173 U 24	B	10-7-72	26-6-73	16-10-74
S 174 U 25*	A/C	6-10-71	23-5-73	14-6-74
S 175 U 26*	B/D	17-11-72	20-11-73	13-3-75
S 176 U 27*	A/D	11-1-72	21-8-73	16-10-74
S 177 U 28*	B/C	26-1-72	22-1-74	18-12-74
S 178 U 29*	A/C	29-2-72	5-11-73	27-11-74
S 179 U 30*	B/D	27-4-73	26-3-74	13-3-75

* In Type 206A modernization program

U 21 (S 170) Leo Van Ginderen, 11-9(

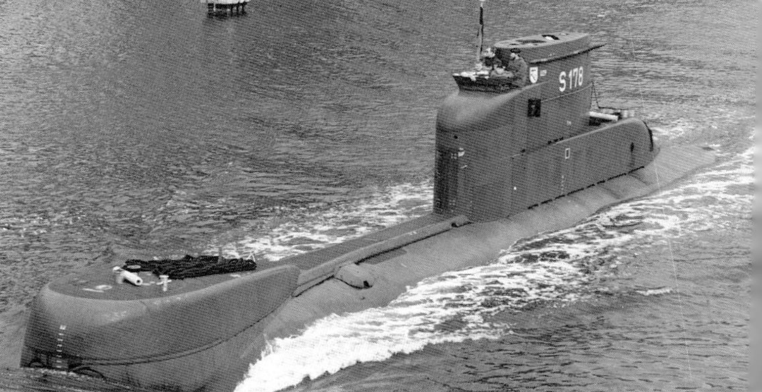

U 29 (S 178) Leo Van Ginderen, 5-9

U 14 (S 193) Leo Van Ginderen,

SUBMARINES *(continued)*

27 (S 176)—with telescoping masts raised Gilbert Gyssels, 5-90

D: 450 tons surf./520 tons sub. **S:** 10 surf./17 kts sub. (5 snorkel)
Dim: 48.60 × 4.70 × 4.30 surfaced
A: 8/533-mm TT—(16 DM-1 and DM-2 A1/A3 torpedoes or 16 mines)—24 mines in external removable container
Electron Equipt:
Radar: 1/Thomson-CSF Calypso II—EW: . . . intercept
Sonar: WSU AN 410A4 (Type 206A: DBQS-21D) active, GHG AN 5039A1 passive, DUUX-2 passive ranging
M: 2 MTU 12V493AZ diesels; 600 bhp each, 2/405-kw generators, 1 electric motor; 2,300 shp
Range: 4,500/5 (snorkel); 200/5 submerged **Fuel:** 23.5 tons
Crew: 4 officers, 18 enlisted

marks: *U 13* to *U 24* authorized in 1969, *U 25* to *U 30* in 2-70. An external inebelt" container has been developed for these submarines to permit them to carry ull complement of torpedoes plus 20 mines. Three batteries, 92 cells each, total ight 98 tons. Pressure hulls are constructed of high-tensile strength austenitic n-magnetic) steel. Unmodified Type 206 have H.S.A. Mk 8 weapons control system. he 12 Type 206A modernized units have the Krupp-Atlas CSU 83 weapons control tem, DBQS-21D active/passive sonars, provision for a towed passive hydrophone ay, new periscopes, extensively overhauled propulsion plants, Global Positioning tem receivers, and accommodations improvements. Work began with *U 29* at HDW)-6-87 and on *U 23* at Thyssen on 18-7-87; the final unit, *U 26*, is to be completed in 2. Modified units can be distinguished by their lengthened sail structures.

5 Type 205 Bldr: Howaldtswerke, Kiel

	Laid down	L	In serv.
81 U 2	1-19-64	15-7-66	11-10-66
88 U 9	10-12-64	20-10-66	11-4-67
89 U 10	15-7-65	5-6-67	28-11-67
90 U 11	1-4-66	9-2-68	21-6-68
91 U 12	1-9-66	10-9-68	14-1-69

: 419 tons surf./455 sub. **S:** 10 surf./17 kts sub.
im: 43.50 × 4.60 × 3.80
: 8/533-mm TT (8 DM 2 A1 Seeal torpedoes)

Electron Equipt:
Radar: 1/Thomson-CSF Calypso II
Sonar: 1/SRS-M1H, 1/GHG AN5039A1
M: 2 MTU 12V493AZ, 600-bhp diesels, 2/405-kw generators, 1 electric motor; 2,300 shp
Range: 228/4 sub.; 3,950/4 snorkel **Crew:** 4 officers, 17 enlisted

U 12 (S 191)—with lengthened sail structure Stefan Terzibaschitsch, 6-91

U 2 (S 181)—standard Type 205 appearance Leo Van Ginderen, 3-90

Remarks: *U 10* is 43.8 m overall; *U 11, 12:* 45.8 m overall. Diving depth: 150 m. The poor quality of the antimagnetic steel used in the first six of this class caused serious pitting, which made it necessary to rebuild the *U 1* and *U 2* (originally launched 21-10-61 and 25-1-62) with regular steel. Beginning with the *U 9*, laid down in 1964, the other submarines were built with an improved antimagnetic steel. Have H.S.A. Mk 8 torpedo f.c.s. *U 11* has been used since 1988 as a "padded" torpedo target, and *U 12* is used in sonar trials. *U 3* was stricken in 1968, *U 4* and *U 8* in 1974, *U 5* in 1975, and *U 6* and *U 7* in 1974. *U 2* to strike 19-3-92, and the others will likely be stricken by the mid-1990s.

U 1 refitted at HDW, Kiel, 19-3-87 to 11-87 for trials with oxygen/hydrogen fuel-cell closed-cycle propulsion system; six cells produced a total of 150 kw for battery charging. The equipment was removed in 5-90, and the submarine was stricken on 29-11-91.

GUIDED-MISSILE DESTROYERS

◆ **3 U.S. Charles F. Adams class (Type 103B)** Bldr: Bath Iron Works, Bath, Maine

	Laid down	L	In serv.
D 185 Lütjens (ex-DDG 28)	1-3-66	11-8-67	22-3-69
D 186 Mölders (ex-DDG 29)	12-4-66	13-4-68	20-9-69
D 187 Rommel (ex-DDG 30)	22-8-67	1-2-69	2-5-70

Lütjens (D 185) Dr. Giorgio Arra, 2-89

Mölders (D 186) Stefan Terzibaschitsch, 6-91

GUIDED-MISSILE DESTROYERS *(continued)*

Rommel (D 187) Leo Van Ginderen, 5-91

D: 3,550 tons (4,720 fl) **S:** 35 kts
Dim: 134.4 (128.1 pp) × 14.38 × 6.4 (max.)
A: 1/Tartar Mk 13 missile launcher (40 Harpoon and Standard SM-1 MR missiles)—2/127-mm Mk 42 DP (I × 2)—1 Mk 112 ASROC ASW RL (VIII × 1)—6/324-mm Mk 32 ASW TT (III × 2, Mk 46 torpedoes)
Electron Equipt:
Radar: 1/Kelvin-Hughes 14/9 nav., 1/SPS-10 surf. search, 1/SPS-40 air search, 1/SPS-52 3-D air search, 2/SPG-51C missile f.c., SPQ-9 gun f.c., 1/SPG-60 missile/gun f.c.
Sonar: 1/KAE DSQS-21B(2) hull-mounted—TACAN: URN-20
EW: FL-1800S intercept, 2/Mk 36 RBOC decoy RL (VI × 2)
M: 2 sets geared steam turbines; 2 props; 70,000 shp
Boilers: 4 Combustion Engineering; 84 kg/cm^2 pressure, 500° C
Electric: 3,000 kw tot. **Range:** 1,600/30; 4,030/18 **Fuel:** 950 tons
Crew: 21 officers, 319 enlisted

Remarks: Authorized 1964. They differ in several ways, especially in profile, from the *Charles F. Adams* design, on which they are based. Installation of the SM-1 MR system and digitalization of some computer equipment was completed 1981–82.

All three were further modernized, with most of the improvements originally planned for the U.S. Navy units of the class: the Mk 13 missile system was revised to permit carrying Harpoon antiship missiles; the Mk 68 gunfire-control system was replaced by the Mk 86 GFCS with SPQ-9 and SPG-60 radars (the latter permitting a third SAM fire-control channel as well); the U.S. SYS-1 computerized data systems, the Mk 36 Super RBOC system, and the substitution of the German FL-1800S EW system for WLR-6, and Raytheon solid-state transmitters for the sonar. D 185 began modernization 5-85, completing 16-12-86. D 186 refitted from 12-83 to 29-3-84, and D 187 from 12-83 to 26-7-85. Subsequently, DSQS-21B(2) sonar has replaced the SQS-23. Have Satir-1 NTDS data link. Will later receive two RAM launchers (XXI × 2) on fantail and before the bridge.

D 186 damaged by fire 12-87; in repair to 11-89. Programmed to be retired 2002–2003. To be replaced by four Type 124; see addenda.

◆ **3 Hamburg class (Type 101B)** Bldr: H. C. Stülcken, Hamburg

	Laid down	L	In serv.
D 181 Hamburg	29-1-59	26-3-60	23-3-64
D 182 Schleswig-Holstein	20-8-59	20-8-60	12-10-64
D 183 Bayern	14-9-60	14-8-62	6-7-65

Schleswig-Holstein (D 182) Leo Van Ginderen, 7-91

D: 3,500 tons (4,700 fl) **S:** 35 kts
Dim: 133.70 (128.0 pp) × 13.40 × 5.20 (max.)
A: 4/MM 38 Exocet SSM—3/100-mm Mod. 1953 DP (I × 3)—8/40-mm Breda AA (II × 4)—4/533-mm ASW TT—2/375-mm Bofors ASW RL (IV × 2)— 2/d.c. racks (12 d.c.)—60–80 mines
Electron Equipt:
Radar: 1/Kelvin-Hughes 14/9, 1/H.S.A. DA-08 air/surf. search, 1/H.S.A. LW-04 early warning, 1/ H.S.A. SGR-103 surf. search, 3/H.S.A. M 45 gun f.c.
Sonar: KAE ELAC 1BV med. freq. hull-mounted
EW: WLR-6 intercept, 2/Breda SCLAR decoy RL (XVIII × 2)
M: 2 sets Wahodag geared steam turbines; 2 props; 68,000 shp
Boilers: 4 Wahodag; 59 kg/cm^2, 465° C **Electric:** 5,400 kw
Range: 920/34; 3,400/18 **Fuel:** 810 tons
Crew: 19 officers, 249 enlisted

Remarks: Between the beginning of 1975 and the end of 1977, refitted with four MM 38 to replace an after superfiring 100-mm gun mount. At the same time, five fixed antiship torpedo tubes (3 in bows, 2 aft) removed, 40-mm replaced by later model, and new air-search radar installed. The d.c. racks are bolted to the mine rails. Further modernizations were planned but have been canceled. Sister *Hessen* (D 184), the newest unit of the class, was laid up 1-7-89 during mid-overhaul and stricken 29-3-90. Due to political pressure, the others are likely to be stricken before the Type 123 frigates intended to replace them are available.

FRIGATES

◆ **0 (+4) Brandenburg class (Type 123)**

	Bldr.	Laid down	L	In serv.
F 215 Brandenburg	Blohm + Voss, Hamburg	20-1-92	7-92	3-9[illegible]
F 216 Schleswig-Holstein	Howaldtswerke, Kiel	1993	1994	9-9[illegible]
F 217 Bayern	Thyssen, Emden	1993	1994	3-9[illegible]
F 218 Mecklenburg Vorpommern	Thyssen, Emden	1994	1995	9-9[illegible]

Hamburg (D 181), Schleswig-Holstein (182), and Bayern (D 183) Marineamt, Wilhelmshaven, [illegible]

FRIGATES *(continued)*

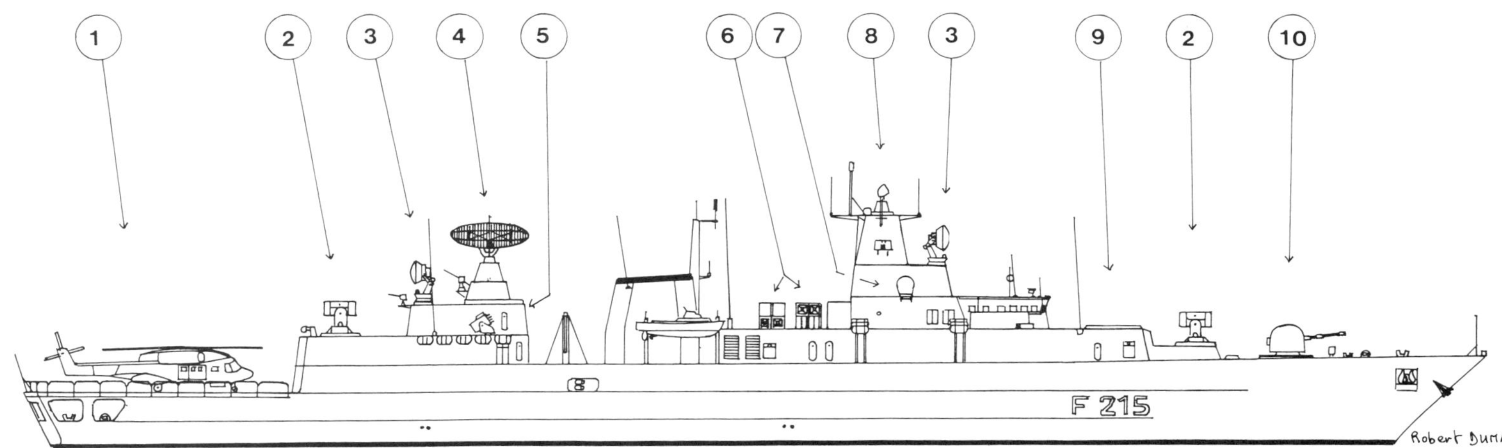

Deutschland (F 215): 1. NH-90 helicopter 2. Mk 49 launcher for RAM missiles 3. STIR fire-control radar 4. LW-08 early-warning radar 5. SCLAR decoy launcher 6. MM 38 Exocet antiship missiles 7. SCOT SATCOMM antenna radome 8. SMART target-designation radar 9. Mk 41 vertical-launch Sea Sparrow launch grouping 10. 76-mm OTO Melara DP gun Robert Dumas

eutschland—Type 123 Jochen Sachse/Blohm + Voss, 2-89

D: 3,600 tons (4,490 fl) **S:** 29 kt on gas turbines, 18 kts on diesels
Dim: 138.85 (126.90 pp) × 16.70 (15.08 wl) × 4.35 (6.30 over sonar)
A: 4/MM 38 Exocet (*see* Remarks)—1/Mk 41 vertical-launch Sea Sparrow SAM complex (16 RIM-7M missiles)—2/Mk 49 RAM point-defense SAM launchers (XX × 2; . . . RIM-116A missiles)—1/76-mm OTO Melara DP—4/324-mm Mk 32 ASW TT (II × 2, fixed)—2/Lynx Mk 88 or NH 90 helicopters
Electron Equipt:
Radar: 2/Raytheon Raypath nav., 1/H.S.A. LW-08 air search, 1/H.S.A. SMART-S air/surf. search and targeting, 2/STIR-18 f.c.
Sonar: KAE DSQS-23BZ hull-mounted, provision for towed array
EW: A.E.G. FL-1800S intercept; 2/Breda SCLAR decoy RL (XVIII × 2)
M: CODOG: 2 G.E. LM-2500 gas turbines (25,840 shp each), 2 MTU 20V956 TB92 diesels (5,700 bhp each); 2 CP props; 51,680 shp max.
Electric: 3,000 kw (4 × 750 kw, MWM TBD-602-V16K diesels driving)
Range: 4,000/18 **Endurance:** 21 days
Crew: 219 total (including 22 air department)

marks: Ordered 28-6-89 from a consortium lead by Blohm + Voss with Thyssen dseewerke and Howaldtswerke, in place of an earlier plan to build a modified Type . Will employ Blohm + Voss MEKO modular outfitting concepts, with hull having double-walled bulkheads and three 1-m-sq. box girders for strength. Steel superstructure. Fin stabilizers. Extensive signature reduction measures.

The MM 38 missiles (to be taken from the *Hamburg* class) are to be replaced later by the Franco-German ANS. The SMART (Signal Multibeam Acquisition Radar for Targeting) radar will surmount the foremast. U.K. SCOT SHF SATCOMM will be fitted; the decoy RL may be the Breda SCLAR system. Unisys/Krupp-Atlas SATIR combat data system with UYK-43 computers. The antisubmarine system is the Krupp-Atlas (KAE) ASO-90. Will be LINK 11 compatible. Will receive towed sonar arrays, beginning in 1997.

◆ 8 Bremen class (Type 122)

	Bldr	Laid down	L	In serv.
F 207 Bremen	Bremer-Vulkan	9-7-79	27-9-79	7-5-82
F 208 Niedersachsen	AG Weser, Bremen	9-11-79	9-6-80	15-10-82
F 209 Rheinland-Pfalz	Blohm + Voss, Hamburg	25-9-79	3-9-80	9-5-83
F 210 Emden	Nordseewerke, Emden	23-6-80	17-12-80	9-10-83
F 211 Köln	Blohm + Voss, Hamburg	16-6-80	29-5-81	19-10-84
F 212 Karlsruhe	Howaldtswerke, Kiel	10-3-81	8-1-82	19-4-84
F 213 Augsburg	Bremer-Vulkan	4-4-87	17-9-87	3-10-89
F 214 Lübeck	Thyssen, Emden	1-6-87	15-10-87	19-3-90

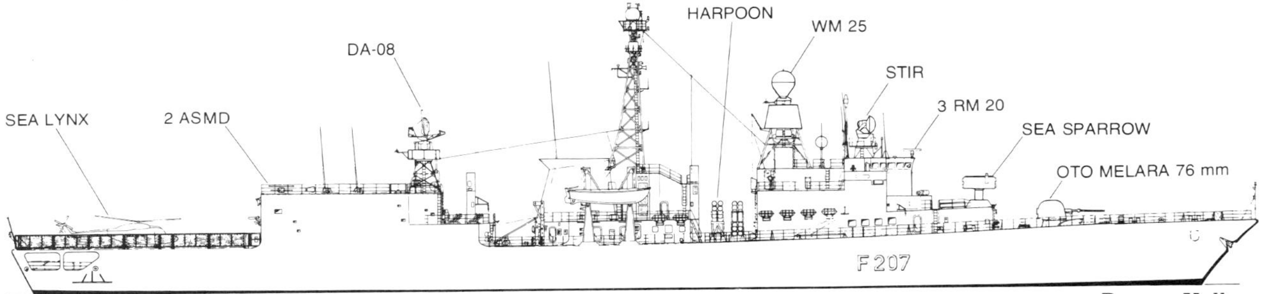

Bremen (F 207)—Type 122 Bremer-Vulkan

FRIGATES *(continued)*

Augsburg (F 213) Maritime Photographic, 10-9

Lübeck (F 214) Ben Sullivan, 4-91

Niedersachsen (F 208)—with Goalkeeper atop hangar Luciano Grazioli, 6-91

Karlsruhe (F 212)—with SCOT SATCOMM Bernard Prézelin, 5-90

D: 2,950 tons (3,800 fl) **S:** 30 kts
Dim: 130.00 (121.80 wl) × 14.40 × 4.26 (6.00 sonar)
A: 8/Harpoon SSM (IV × 2)—1/NATO Sea Sparrow SAM system (VIII × 1, Mk 29 launcher, 24 RIM-7M missiles)—1/76-mm OTO Melara DP— 4/324-mm Mk 32 ASW TT (I × 4)—2/Lynx Mk 88 ASW helicopters
Electron Equipt:
Radar: 1/ S.M.A. 3RM 20 nav., 1/H.S.A. DA-08 air search, 1/H.S.A. WM-25 track-while-scan f.c., 1/H.S.A. STIR-18 missile f.c.
Sonar: 1/DSQS-21BX (BO) bow-mounted
EW: A.E.G. FL 1800S intercept array (7.5–17 gHz), Mk 36 Super RBOC decoy RL (VI × 4), SLQ-25 Nixie torpedo decoy
M: CODOG: 2 G.E.-Fiat LM-2500 GT (50,000 shp); 2 MTU 20V956 TB92 diesels (10,400 bhp); 2/5-bladed Escher-Wyss CP props
Electric: 3,000 kw (4/750-kw diesel sets) **Range:** 5,700/17
Fuel: 610 tons
Crew: 21 officers, 160 enlisted (plus 6-officer/12-enlisted air complement)

Remarks: Germanized version of Dutch *Kortenaer* class. First six ordered 7-77, l two on 6-12-85. Bremer-Vulkan performed the weapons and electronics outfitting a integration. The helicopters are equipped with DAQS-13D dipping sonar and Mk torpedoes. Two RAM point-defense SAM launchers are to be added atop the hangar. F stabilizers fitted. Have SATIR tactical data system (with Unisys UYK-7 compute H.S.A. Vesta helicopter transponder and Beartrap haul-down and deck control syst are installed. Are LINK 11-compatible. Fitted with U.S. Prairie/Masker bubbler s tem to reduce radiated noise, fin stabilizers, a citadel nuclear-biological-gas protect system. F 212 has a revised engine air intake system. Carry 16 torpedoes for helos, 8 tubes. Three sets U.K. SCOT 1A SATCOMM gear acquired for use aboard deplo units of this class; has been on F 209 and F 212.

During 2-91, three H.S.A. Goalkeeper close-in defense systems were installed each on deckhouses emplaced atop the port after corner of the hangar on F 207, 208, 212 for use during a Mediterranean deployment under a 2-year loan agreement sig 23-1-91; they were returned shortly after the cessation of hostilities in the Mideast. 49 RAM launchers are to be installed during refits between 1992 and 1997, du which measures to reduce radar signature will be taken; completed ships will be T 122A. All receiving Racal SADIE EW processors in 1992–93.

Note: Of the three former East German Soviet-built Koni-class small frigates, *Ros* (ex-141) was operated until 18-4-91 as F 224, *Halle* (ex-142), which had had the SA- system removed for exploitation, was operated as F 225 until 3-91, and *Berlin Haupstadt der DDR* (142) was not taken over for operation; all are available for for transfer, with Algeria mentioned as a possible recipient.

CORVETTES

◆ **4 Parchim class (Type 630)** Bldr: Peenewerft, Wolgast

	In serv.		In se
P 6167 Gadebusch (ex-211)	6-85	P 6169 Lübz (ex-221)	19
P 6168 Teterow (ex-234)	1984	P 6169 Wismar (ex-241)	3-9

D: 840 tons (920 fl) **S:** 24 kts **Dim:** 72.5 × 9.4 × 3.0 (hull)
A: 2/57-mm AK-57 DP (II × 1)—2/30-mm AK-230 AA (II × 1)—2/ N-5 SAM systems (IV × 2)—4/400-mm ASW TT (I × 4)—2/RBU
A: 6000 ASW RL (XII × 2)—2/d.c. racks
Electron Equipt:
Radar: 1/TSR-333 nav., 1/Strut Curve air/surf. search, 1/Muff Cob f.c.
Sonar: medium-freq. hull-mounted; high-freq. dipping sonar
EW: 2/Watch Dog intercept, 2/chaff RL (XVI × 2)
M: 3 Type M504 56-cyl. diesels; 3 props; 14,250 bhp **Crew:** 60 to

CORVETTES *(continued)*

Gadebusch (P 6167) Stefan Terzibaschitsch, 6-91

Teterow (P 6168) Leo Van Ginderen, 6-91

Remarks: Survivors of 16 completed 1981–85 as the East German Project 133.1. Manned by former *Volksmarine* personnel and were to be discarded by end-1991 or early 1992. Reportedly suffer from too much topweight. Previously referred to by NATO as the "Bal-Com-4" and by the press as the "Koralle" class. Helicopter dipping sonar deploys through door on starboard side of main deck superstructure. D.C. racks exit through doors in stern. The centerline propeller has controllable pitch; the others are fixed.

Sister *Grevesmühlen* (ex-212) was to have been taken over for operation as P 6164 but was not. The other eleven also survive, and may be available for foreign transfer: *Parchim* (242), *Perleberg* (243), *Bützow* (244), *Bad Doberan* (222), *Pirna* (223), *Prenzlau* (231), *Ludwigslust* (232), *Ribnitz-Damgarten* (233), *Bergen* (213), and *Angermünde* (214), and one other (ex-224).

3 Thetis class (Type 420) Bldr: Roland Werft, Bremen-Hemelingen

	Laid down	L	In serv.
6053 Hermes	8-10-59	9-8-60	16-21-61
6055 Triton	15-8-60	5-8-61	10-11-62
6056 Theseus	1-7-61	20-3-62	15-8-63

D: 575 tons (658 fl) **S:** 23.5 kts
Dim: 69.78 (65.5 pp) × 8.2 × 2.65 (hull)
A: 2/40-mm Bofors AA (II × 1)—1/Bofors 375-mm ASW RL (IV × 1)— 4/533-mm ASW TT (I × 4, U.S. Mk 46 TT)—2 d.c. racks (12/d.c.)—mines
Electron Equipt:
Radar: 1/Kelvin-Hughes 14/9 nav., 1/Thomson-CSF TRS-3001 surf. search
Sonar: Krupp-Atlas ELAC 1BV HF hull-mounted
M: 2 M.A.N. V84V diesels; 2 props; 6,800 bhp **Electric:** 540 kw
Range: 2,760/15 **Fuel:** 78 tons **Crew:** 5 officers, 43 enlisted

Remarks: Former torpedo-recovery boats, well designed for operations in the Baltic. Have H.S.A. Mk 9 torpedo f.c.s. and an optical lead-computing gun f.c.s. Carry 20 ASW projectiles. EW gear removed. Torpedo tubes formerly carried German-made -mm passive homing torpedoes but now launch U.S.-made Mk 46 324-mm torpedoes through the use of liners. Sisters *Thetis* (P 6052) and *Najade* (P 6054) transferred to Greece 6-9-91. Remainder to be transferred to Greece on retirement 7-9-92 (P 6056: -92).

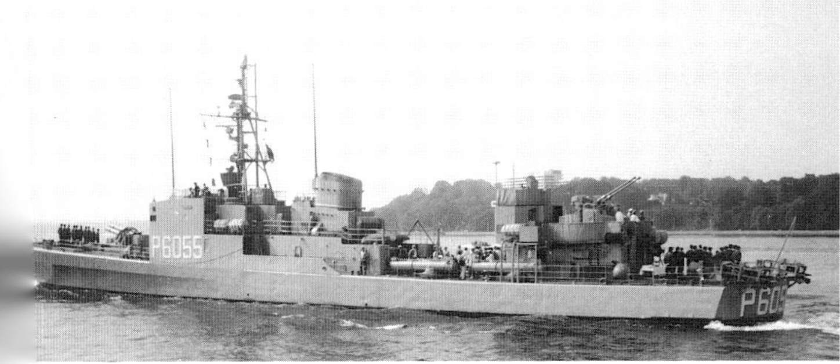

Triton (P 6055) Stefan Terzibaschitsch, 6-90

Hermes (P 6053) Leo Van Ginderen, 6-90

GUIDED-MISSILE PATROL BOATS

◆ **10 Type 143A** Bldrs: A: Lürssen, Vegesack; B: Kröger, Rendsburg

	Bldr	Laid down	L	In serv.
P 6121 Gepard (S 71)	A	11-7-79	25-9-81	7-12-82
P 6122 Puma (S 72)	A	17-12-79	8-2-82	24-2-83
P 6123 Hermelin (S 73)	B	1-2-80	8-12-81	28-4-83
P 6124 Nerz (S 74)	A	24-7-80	18-8-82	14-7-83
P 6125 Zobel (S 75)	B	3-7-80	30-6-82	29-9-83
P 6126 Frettchen (S 76)	A	22-12-80	26-1-83	15-12-83
P 6127 Dachs (S 77)	B	9-3-80	14-12-82	1-3-84
P 6128 Ozelot (S 78)	A	25-6-81	7-6-83	3-5-84
P 6129 Wiesel (S 79)	A	5-10-80	8-8-83	12-7-84
P 6130 Hyäne (S 80)	A	7-12-81	5-10-83	13-11-84

Puma (P 6122)—with Mk 41 RAM launcher aft Marineamt, Wilhelmshaven, 1990

Hyäne (P 6130) Leo Van Ginderen, 6-91

Nerz (P 6124)—showing mine rails Stefan Terzibaschitsch, 6-91

GUIDED-MISSILE PATROL BOATS *(continued)*

D: 300 tons (390.6 fl) **S:** 36 kts (32 fl)
Dim: 57.6 (54.4 pp) × 7.76 × 2.99 (2.56 hull)
A: 4/MM 38 Exocet—P 6122 only: 1/RAM ASMD (XXI × 1, RIM-116A missiles)—1/76-mm OTO Melara DP—mines (2 rails)
Electron Equipt:
Radar: 1/SMA 3RM 20 nav., 1/H.S.A. WM-27 track-while-scan f.c.
EW: AEG FL 1800 intercept, Buck-Wegmann Hot Dog/Silver Dog chaff dispenser
M: 4 MTU 16V956 SB80 diesels; 4 props; 16,000 bhp
Electric: 540 kw **Range:** 600/30; 2,600/16 **Fuel:** 116 tons
Crew: 4 officers, 18 petty officers, 12 ratings

Remarks: Ordered 1978 from AEG-Telefunken, with shipbuilders listed above as subcontractors. A repeat Type 143 intended to have the inordinately delayed RAM point-defense SAM system in place of the Type 143s after 76-mm gun, and mine rails in place of the wire-guided torpedoes. Wood-planked hull on steel frame. Have AGIS integrated data system. Lack after optical GFCS found on Type 143/143B. Chaff is dispensed from a vertical pipe attached to the after side of the tripod mast. Some have Racal Octopus EW suite (Cutlass B-1 intercept, Scorpion jammer).

Constitute the 7th Fast Patrol Boat Squadron. RAM to become operational circa 1992 after a great many delays; P 6122 has prototype operational RAM launcher, which was integrated with the boat's weapons control system during 1991. All in 7th Squadron, Kiel.

◆ 10 Type 143/143B
Bldrs: A: Lürssen, Vegesack; B: Kröger, Rendsburg

	Bldr	Laid down	L	In serv.
P 6111 Albatros (S 61)	A	4-5-72	22-10-73	1-11-76
P 6112 Falke (S 62)	A	25-10-72	21-3-74	13-4-76
P 6113 Geier (S 63)	A	14-2-73	18-9-74	2-6-76
P 6114 Bussard (S 64)	A	4-7-73	14-4-75	14-8-76
P 6115 Sperber (S 65)	B	18-1-73	15-1-74	27-9-76
P 6116 Greif (S 66)	A	12-12-73	4-9-75	25-11-76
P 6117 Kondor (S 67)	B	19-6-73	6-3-75	17-12-76
P 6118 Seeadler (S 68)	A	12-6-74	17-11-75	28-3-77
P 6119 Habicht (S 69)	B	25-1-74	5-6-75	23-12-77
P 6120 Kormoran (S70)	A	26-11-74	14-4-76	29-7-77

Greif (P 6116) Peter Voss, 6-89

Geier (P 6113) Leo Van Ginderen, 6-90

D: 300 tons (393 fl) **S:** 36 kts (32 fl)
Dim: 57.6 (54.4 pp) × 7.76 × 2.82 (2.56 hull)
A: 4/MM 38 Exocet—2/76-mm OTO Melara AA (I × 2)—2/533-mm TT (aft-launching, for Seeal wire-guided torpedoes)
Electron Equipt:
Radar: 1/SMA 3RM 20 nav., 1/HSA WM-27 track-while-scan f.c.
EW: Thoson-CSF DR 2000 intercept, Buck-Wegmann Hot Dog/Silver Dog chaff dispenser
M: 4 MTU 16V956 TB91 diesels; 4 props; 16,000 bhp
Electric: 540 kw **Range:** 600/30; 2,600/16 **Fuel:** 116 tons
Crew: 4 officers, 18 petty officers, 12 ratings

Remarks: Wood-planked hull on steel frame. Were to be refitted to Type 143A standard, becoming Type 143B and receiving FL 1800 EW system, deleting the torpedo tubes, adding the RAM SAM system, and receiving mine rails; the modernization program, however, is on hold, pending the availability of the ANS missile to replace MM 38 Exocet.

There is a secondary OGR-7/3 optical f.c.s. for the aft 76-mm gun. P 6119 carried a *mockup* RAM launcher aft during 1983. Are the 2nd Squadron, based at Olpenitz.

◆ 20 Type 148, steel-hulled
Bldrs: A: CMN, Cherbourg; B: Lürssen, Vegesack

	Bldr	Laid down	L	In serv.
P 6141 Tiger (S 41)	A	11-10-71	27-9-72	30-10-72
P 6142 Iltis (S 42)	A	2-2-72	12-12-72	8-1-73
P 6143 Luchs (S 43)	A	23-3-72	7-3-73	9-4-73
P 6144 Marder (S 44)	A	15-4-72	5-5-73	14-7-73
P 6145 Leopard (S 45)	A	13-9-72	3-7-73	21-8-73
P 6146 Fuchs (S 46)	B	10-3-72	21-5-73	17-10-73
P 6147 Jaguar (S 47)	A	29-11-72	20-9-73	13-11-73
P 6148 Löwe (S 48)	B	10-7-72	10-9-73	9-1-74
P 6149 Wolf (S 49)	A	23-1-73	11-1-74	26-2-74
P 6150 Panther (S 50)	B	30-9-72	10-12-73	27-3-74
P 6151 Häher (S 51)	A	5-4-73	26-4-74	12-6-74
P 6152 Storch (S 52)	B	12-3-73	25-3-74	17-7-74
P 6153 Pelikan (S 53)	A	11-9-73	4-7-74	24-9-74
P 6154 Elster (S 54)	B	29-6-73	8-7-74	14-11-74
P 6155 Alk (S 55)	A	9-4-74	15-11-74	7-1-75
P 6156 Dommel (S 56)	B	13-12-73	30-10-74	12-2-75
P 6157 Weihe (S 57)	A	2-7-74	13-2-75	3-4-75
P 6158 Pinguin (S 58)	B	11-3-74	26-2-75	22-5-75
P 6159 Reiher (S 59)	A	8-11-74	15-5-75	24-6-75
P 6160 Kranich (S 60)	B	9-5-74	26-5-75	6-8-75

Pelikan (P 6153) Peter Voss, 6

Fuchs (P 6146) Leo Van Ginderen,

GUIDED-MISSILE PATROL BOATS *(continued)*

D: 234 tons (264 fl) **S:** 35.8 kts **Dim:** 47.0 (45.9 pp) × 7.1 × 2.66 (fl)
A: 4/MM 38 Exocet—1/76-mm DP OTO Melara (fwd)—1/40-mm Bofors AA (aft)—8 mines in place of the 40-mm AA
Electron Equipt:
Radar: 1/SMA 3RM 20 navigation, 1/Thomson-CSF Triton-G air/surf. search, 1/Thomson-CSF Castor-II f.c.
EW: Racal . . . or Thomson-CSF DR 2000 intercept, Wolke chaff dispenser
M: 4 MTU MD 872 16-cyl. diesels; 4 props; 14,000 bhp (12,000 sust.)
Electric: 270 kw **Range:** 570/30; 1,600/15 **Fuel:** 39 tons
Crew: 4 officers, 13 petty officers, 13 ratings

Remarks: Ordered 18-12-70, as CMN's type *Combattante II* A4L. Design by Friedrich Lürssen Werft, Vegesack. All hulls fitted out at Cherbourg. Steel construction.

Thomson-CSF Vega fire-control system with Pollux radar; Triton is used for target designation. In 1980, P 6152 received Triton II search radar and Castor II fire-control radar, the latter with a Piranha optronic attachment. Another ship conducted trials with the CSEE Naja optronic and CSEE Panda optical directors during 1982–83. Triton-G and Castor-II ordered for rest of class in 1986 to replace the Pollux fire-control radar, for installation in all by 1990, along with new EW equipment. All have the PALIS (Passive-Active-Link) system for data sharing and can use NATO LINK 11. An enclosed Mauser 40-mm gun mounting has replaced the original open mount aft.

P 6141–P 6150 are the 3rd Squadron, at Flensburg. The others are the 5th Squadron at Olpenitz.

Note: Of the five *Volksmarine* Soviet Tarantul-I guided-missile patrol boats, *Rudolf Egelhofer* (572) became the *Hiddensee* (P 6166) in 10-90 but was stricken on 21-5-91 and transferred to the U.S.A. in 12-91. Of the others, *Albin Köbis* (571) and *Fritz Globig* (573), may be transferred to Poland; and Malta will receive *Paul Eisenschneider* (574) and *Hans Beimler* (575), which were stricken 4-6-91 and 3-5-91, respectively. The 12 *Volksmarine* Osa-I (Project 205) guided-missile patrol boats had all been stricken prior to unification, as had the 6 remaining Shershen-class torpedo boats (several of which were scrapped in Denmark in 7-90) and the remaining Libelle-class torpedo boats.

Ex-Paul Eisenschneider (574)—laid up at Kiel with three sisters awaiting their fates Stefan Terzibaschitsch, 6-91

Hiddensee (P 6166)—while active in *Bundesmarine* Hans J. Vanhöfen, 11-90

PATROL BOATS

Ex-East German Project 151A (Type 620) Bldr: Peenewerft, Wolgast

	L	In serv.
P 6165 SASSNITZ (ex-591)	1988	31-7-90

D: 331 tons (369 fl) **S:** 37 kts **Dim:** 48.90 (45.00 pp) × 8.65 × 2.15
A: 1/76-mm AK-72 DP—1/30-mm AK-630 gatling AA
Electron Equipt:
Radar: 1/ TSR-333 nav., 1/Plank Shave surf. search, 1/ Bass Tilt f.c.
EW: 2/ decoy RL (XVI × 2)
M: 3 M 520 diesels; 3 props; 16,200 bhp (14,570 sust.)
Electric: 366 kw (1 × 183-kw, 2 × 128-kw diesel sets)
Range: 2,400/20 **Endurance:** 5 days **Crew:** 7 officers, 26 enlisted

Sassnitz (P 6165) Frank Behling, 11-90

Remarks: The first of nine laid down out of a planned dozen for the *Volksmarine* and up to 38 others for the U.S.S.R. and Poland; as prototype, was given project number 151.0. When first seen by NATO was given temporary code "Bal-Com-10"). Was equipped with eight tubes for the Soviet SS-N-25 antiship missile for trials purposes, but they had been removed by the summer of 1990. Each "star radial" M 520 diesel has eight rows of seven cylinders. Decommissioned 12-7-91 and may be transferred to the Border Guard 10-91 with sisters *Sellin* and *Binz*.

Of the eight series-construction units for which work had been begun, their fate is as follows:

	Laid down	L	In serv.	Disposal
592 SELLIN	20-1-89	16-12-89	2-10-90	To Border Guard 10-91
593 BINZ	3-5-89	26-2-23	12-90	To Border Guard 10-91
594 PIORUN	26-6-89	10-5-90	. . .	To Poland, 3-10-90
595 HURAGAN	18-9-89	7-7-90	. . .	To Poland, 3-10-90
596 ORKAN	10-7-90	9-90	. . .	To Poland, 3-10-90
597	23-4-90	9-90	. . .	Available for sale
598	25-4-90	. . .	. . .	Available for sale
599	27-5-90	. . .	. . .	Available for sale

The three delivered to Poland had no engines or combat equipment.

Note: The nine surviving East German Bremse (GB 23)-class patrol craft have been incorporated in the Sea Border Patrol (*Bundesgrenzschuts-See*), along with two MB 13-class launches.

MINE WARFARE SHIPS

Note: Of the former East German Kondor-II-class patrol minesweepers, the following were operated into 1991 with ex-*Volksmarine* crews: *Sömmerda* (M 2670, ex-311), *Eisleben* (M 2671, ex-312), *Bitterfeld* (M 2672, ex-332), *Bernau* (M 2673, ex-343), and *Eilenburg* (M 2674, ex-344); sister *Tangerhütte* (333) was to have been operated as M 2669 but was not. Of the other Kondor-IIs, nine were earmarked for service with the Sea Border Patrol (*Bundesgrenzschutz-See*), four have been transferred to Uruguay,and the others were scrapped. Of the surviving Kondor-Is (many of which had been stricken prior to unification), one serves as a fisheries protection ship (which see), and others have been offered to Portugal and Tunisia.

Bernau (M 2693)—while active in *Bundesmarine* Leo Van Ginderen, 6-91

◆ **0 (+10) Type 332 coastal minehunters** Bldrs: A: Lürssen, Vegesack; B: Abeking & Rasmussen, Lemwerder; C: Krögerwerft, Rendsburg

	Bldr	Laid down	L	In serv.
M 1060 WEIDEN	B	. . .	. . .	3-93
M 1061 ROTTWEIL	C	. . .	. . .	7-93
M 1062 SULZBACH-ROSENBERG	C	. . .	. . .	12-95
M 1063 BAD RAPPENAU	B	. . .	. . .	4-95
M 1064 GRÖMITZ	C	. . .	. . .	8-95
M 1065 DILLINGEN	B	. . .	. . .	4-95
M 1066 FRANKENTHAL	A	6-12-89	6-2-92	12-92
M 1067 BAD BEVENSEN	A	. . .	. . .	12-93
M 1068 DATTELN	A	. . .	. . .	12-94
M 1069 HOMBURG	A	. . .	. . .	8-95

MINE WARFARE SHIPS *(continued)*

Type 332 minehunter Jochen Sachse, 1986

D: 590 tons (650 fl) **S:** 24.5 kts
Dim: 54.40 (51.00 pp) × 9.20 × 2.60 (3.3 props)
A: 1/40-mm Bofors AA—2/Stinger SAM positions
Electron Equipt:
Radar: 1/Raytheon SPS-64 nav.
Sonar: Krupp-Atlas DSQS-11M minehunting
M: 2 MTU 16V396 TB84 diesels; 2 Voith-Schneider vertical cycloidal props; 6,140 bhp—low-speed drive
Electric: . . . **Range:** . . .
Crew: 5 officers, 6 chief petty officers, 13 petty officers, 6 ratings

Remarks: Ordered 26-2-88 from Messerschmidt-Bölkow-Blohm as prime contractors; to build 4 by Lürssen, 3 by Abeking & Rasmussen, and 3 by Krögerwerft. Minehunter version of Type 343 with slightly different hull form, minehunting sonar and low-speed drive. Intended to carry the Pinguin B3 remote-controlled mine location/destruction submersible and four mine-clearance divers. The Pinguin weighs 1.35 tons, is 3.5 m long, and travels at up to 8 kts. Will have the Krupp-Atlas MWS 80-4 minehunting system with SATAM command system. The 40-mm gun is in a Mauser mounting. To be based at Emden as the 2nd Minesweeper Squadron.

A planned second group, to have been built 1996–99, were to have had "Troika" control systems but will now probably not be built.

Note: The Type 355 pressure minesweeper program has apparently been canceled.

♦ 10 Type 343 minesweepers

Bldrs: (A) Lürssen Werft, Vegesack; (B) Abeking & Rasmussen, Lemwerder; (C) Krögerwerft, Rendsburg

	Bldr	Laid down	L	In serv.
M 1090 Pegnitz	A	6-7-87	14-3-89	8-3-90
M 1091 Kulmbach	B	1988	20-6-89	23-5-90
M 1092 Hameln	A	18-6-86	15-3-88	29-6-89
M 1093 Auerbach	A	15-3-88	23-8-90	7-5-91
M 1094 Ernsdorf	A	2-1-89	14-12-89	14-12-89
M 1095 Überherrn	B	8-10-86	30-8-88	11-11-89
M 1096 Passau	B	1989	13-3-90	18-12-90
M 1097 Laboe	C	2-3-87	19-3-88	7-12-89
M 1098 Siegburg	C	12-10-87	18-4-89	26-7-90
M 1099 Herten	C	30-6-88	14-12-89	5-3-91

D: 620 tons (fl) **S:** 24.5 kts
Dim: 54.40 (51.00 pp) × 9.20 × 2.50 (3.20 props)
A: 2/40-mm Bofors AA (I × 2)—2/Stinger point-defense SAM positions—up to 60 mines

Pegnitz (M 1092) Leo Van Ginderen, 6-90

Überherrn (M 1095) Gilbert Gyssels, 6-90

Electron Equipt:
Radar: 1/Raytheon SPS-64 nav., 1/H.S.A. WM-20/2 track-while-scan f.c.
Sonar: Krupp-Atlas DSQS-11H (M 1091, 1095, 1097: DSQS-11M)
EW: Thomson-CSF DR 2000 intercept, 2/Silver Dog decoy RL
M: 2 MTU 16V396 TB84-DB51L diesels; 2 Escher-Wyss CP props; 6,080 bhp
Electric: 1,050 kw (3 MWM TBD 601 65 diesels, 639 bhp each, driving)
Range: . . ./. . . **Crew:** 4 officers, 20 petty officers, 13 ratings

Remarks: Messerschmidt-Bölkow-Blohm (MBB) was selected as prime contractor 10-1-85. The Type 343s are configured for mechanical, acoustic, and magnetic mine-sweeping to replace Type 340/341 (*Schütze*)-class patrol minesweepers. Have PALIS data link, SARIE signal analyzer for the EW system. Constructed using antimagnetic steel left over from the Type 206 submarine program. The M 20 radar systems come from stricken *Zobel*-class torpedo boats. The sonar has not been a success and is being upgraded to the DSQS-11M version. The 40-mm guns are in Mauser mountings.

The name for M 1093 was originally to have been *Auerbach/Opf,* a contraction fo "Auerbach in Oberpfaltz." M 1095 and M 1097 deployed to the Mediterranean in 8-90 in support of the UN Desert Shield operation but did not go to the Persian Gulf in 1991 The class constitutes the 5th Minesweeper Squadron, based at Olpenitz. All to conver to act as Troika controllers and to carry the Pinguin ROV.

♦ 6 Type 351 drone minesweeper-control ships

Bldr: Burmester, Bremen

	L	In serv.	Conversion completed
M 1073 Schleswig	2-10-57	30-10-58	19-3-81
M 1076 Paderborn	5-12-57	16-12-58	17-9-81
M 1079 Düren	12-6-58	22-4-59	7-11-83
M 1081 Konstanz	30-9-58	23-7-59	24-5-82
M 1082 Wolfsburg	10-12-58	8-10-59	4-3-82
M 1083 Ulm	10-2-59	7-11-59	11-11-81

D: 488 tons (fl) **S:** 16.5 kts **Dim:** 47.50 × 8.50 × 2.75
A: 1/40-mm Bofors AA
Electron Equipt:
Radar: 1/Krupp-Atlas TRS-N nav.—Sonar: DSQS-11A
M: 2 MD 871 UM/1D diesels; 2 CP props; 3,300 bhp
Range: 2,200/16 **Electric:** . . . **Crew:** 4 officers, 40 enlisted

Remarks: Wooden construction, with non-magnetic engines. Former Type 320 mir sweepers, each converted to control three F-1 "Troika" drone magnetic/acoust mechanical minesweepers. Also carry and tow an Oropesa sweep rig and stow num ous channel-marking ("Dan") buoys. The 40-mm gun is controlled by a remote le computing optical director. M 1073 and M 1076 participated in UN coalition mi countermeasures work in the Persian Gulf beginning in 3-91.

Schleswig (M 1073) Bernard Prézelin,

MINE WARFARE SHIPS *(continued)*

Konstanz (M 1081) Piet Sinke, 9-90

♦ 18 Type HL 351 "Troika" drones Bldr: MAK, Kiel

	In serv.		In serv.
Seehund 1	1-8-80	Seehund 10	11-11-81
Seehund 2	1-8-80	Seehund 11	11-11-81
Seehund 3	1-8-80	Seehund 12	11-11-81
Seehund 4	17-7-81	Seehund 13	1-9-82
Seehund 5	17-7-81	Seehund 14	1-9-82
Seehund 6	17-7-81	Seehund 15	1-9-82
Seehund 7	17-9-81	Seehund 16	13-5-82
Seehund 8	17-9-81	Seehund 17	13-5-82
Seehund 9	17-9-81	Seehund 18	13-5-82

eehund 3 Marineamt, Wilhelmshaven, 1991

D: 91 tons (96.5 fl) **S:** 9.4 kts **Dim:** 24.92 × 4.46 × 1.8 **A:** none
M: 1 MWM TRHS 518A diesel; Schottel prop; 445 hp
Electric: 208 kw **Range:** 520/8.8 **Crew:** 3 tot. (for transit)

emarks: Ordered 1977, to operate three-apiece with the Type 351 control ships. ssentially remote-controlled, self-propelled magnetic minesweeping solenoids with l machinery highly shock-protected. Also able to stream two sets Type SDG-21 ropesa mechanical minesweeping gear. Dates given are completions; were originally mmissioned in groups of three on same date as Type 351 control ships were recom-issioned (see above).

11 Type 331A* and 331B minehunters Bldr: Burmester, Bremen

	L	In serv.
1070 Göttingen	1-4-57	31-5-58
1071 Koblenz	6-5-57	8-7-58
1072 Lindau	16-2-57	24-4-58
1074 Tübingen	12-8-57	25-9-58
1075 Wetzlar	24-6-57	20-8-58
1077 Weilheim	4-2-59	28-1-59
1078 Cuxhaven	11-3-58	11-3-59
1080 Marburg	4-8-58	11-6-59
1085 Minden	9-6-59	22-1-60
1086 Fulda*	19-8-59	5-3-60
1087 Völklingen	20-10-59	21-5-60

D: 388 tons (402 fl) **S:** 17 kts
Dim: 47.45 × 8.5 × 3.68 (sonar down)
A: 1/40-mm Bofors AA
lectron Equipt:
Radar: 1/ KAE TRS-N or Kelvin-Hughes 14/9 nav.
Sonar: KAE DSQS-11A (M 1086: DSQS-11H)
1: 2 Maybach diesels; 2 CP props; 3,340 bhp **Electric:** 220 kw
ange: 1,400/16; 3,950/9 **Crew:** 5 officers, 38 enlisted

Minden (M 1085) Hartmut Ehlers, 12-90

Göttingen (M 1070) Bernard Prézelin, 8-90

Remarks: Wooden construction, with non-magnetic engines. All are conversions from the Type 320, *Lindau*-class, wooden-hulled minesweepers. The Type 331A was converted 1968–72 (with Plessey Type 193M Mk 20G sonars), the Type 331Bs in 1975–79. None have mechanical sweep gear. Minehunting speed is 6 kts, on two 50-kw electric motors. Six divers and 2 French PAP-104 remote-controlled minehunting devices are carried. DSQS-11 sonar has not proven as successful as had been hoped; M 1086 conducted trials with improved DSQS-11H. The 40-mm gun is controlled by a lead-computing optical director on the bridge.

M 1070 and M 1080 participated in the UN Coalition mine countermeasures effort in the Persian Gulf, beginning in 3-91. Sister *Flensburg* (M 1084, Type 331A) was stricken 26-6-91. *Fulda* (M 1086) to strike 26-3-92.

♦ 5 Type 340 and 341* patrol minesweepers Bldr: Abeking & Rasmussen, Lemwerder

	L	In serv.	Strike
M 1053 Stier (ex-Y 849, ex-M 1052)	30-10-58	28-6-61	. . .
M 1054 Pollux	15-9-60	28-4-61	26-2-92
M 1058 Mars	1-12-60	18-7-61	27-2-92
M 1059 Spica	25-5-60	10-5-61	30-9-92
M 1062 Schütze*	20-5-58	14-4-59	26-11-92

D: 241 tons (280 fl) **S:** 24.6 kts **Dim:** 47.44 × 7.20 (6.96 wl) × 2.40
A: 1/40-mm AA
Electron Equipt: Radar: 1/ KAE TRS-N nav.—Sonar: none
M: Maybach or Mercedes-Benz diesels; 2 Escher-Wyss cycloidal props; 4,000/4,200 bhp
Electric: 120-kw plus 340-kw sweep generator **Fuel:** 22 tons
Range: 640/22; 1,000/18 **Crew:** 4 officers, 32 enlisted

Remarks: Survivors of a class of 30 wooden-construction multipurpose ships originally intended to be employed as minesweepers, coastal patrol craft (with 2/40-mm AA), and minelayers (2 mine rails), the minesweeping gear to be removed in the latter two instances. Appeared only in the minesweeping configuration for many years. Type 340 had Mercedes-Benz diesels; Type 341 had Maybach diesels.

Pollux (M 1054) Peter Voss, 6-89

MINE WARFARE SHIPS *(continued)*

Stier (M 1053)—Type 341 mine-clearance divers' support ship
Gilbert Gyssels, 5-88

Stier (originally M 1052, then Y 849) was reclassified as a diving tender but in 1987 was redesignated in the mine-warfare category; she has a decompression chamber in a stern deckhouse and was refitted in 1991 for further service. M 1054 is to strike 28-2-92, M 1058 on 29-5-92, M 1059 on 11-12-92, and M 1062 on 1-12-92.

Sisters *Capella* (ex-M 1098), *Krebs* (ex-M 1052), *Orion* (ex-M 1053), *Steinbock* (ex-M 1091), and *Uranus* (ex-M 1099) have been operated by the *Deutscher Marinebund* youth organization since the mid-1970s; *Algol* (ex-M 1068) is used by the naval damage-control school, and *Mira* (ex-M 1050), formerly used by the Naval Technical School, was sold for scrap in 1984. *Pluto* (M 1092) stricken 1-7-87, *Herkules* (M 1095) on 25-8-87. *Deneb* (M 1064) was stricken 8-9-89 (sold to private interests 15-6-90), *Atair* (M 1067) stricken on 30-6-88 (sold to private interests 15-12-89), *Wega* (M 1069) on 20-12-88 (sold private 27-2-89), *Perseus* (M 1090) on 30-9-88 (sold to private interests 15-12-89), *Jupiter* (M 1065) on 29-9-89 (sold private 15-6-90), *Widder* (M 1094) on 14-7-89 (became training hulk at Borkum on 28-11-89), *Fische* (M 1096) on 20-4-89 (transferred to German Navy League 5-6-90), *Gemma* (M 1097) on 18-12-87 (sold private on 27-2-89), *Castor* (M 1051) on 21-6-91, *Sirius* (M 1055) in 1990, *Rigel* (M 1056) on 29-3-90, *Regulus* (M 1057) on 28-9-90, *Skorpion* (M 1060) on 10-5-90, *Waage* (M 1063) on 1-11-90, and *Neptun* (M 1093) on 28-2-90 (transferred to German Navy League 7-8-90). Strike dates for remainder in table above.

◆ **10 Type 394 inshore minesweepers** Bldr: Krögerwerft, Rendsburg

	L	In serv.
M 2658 Frauenlob	26-2-65	27-9-66
M 2659 Nautilus	19-5-65	26-10-66
M 2660 Gefion	19-6-65	17-2-67
M 2661 Medusa	25-1-66	17-2-67
M 2662 Undine	16-5-66	20-3-67
M 2663 Minerva	25-8-66	16-6-67
M 2664 Diana	13-12-66	21-9-67
M 2665 Loreley	14-3-67	29-3-68
M 2666 Atlantis	20-6-67	29-3-68
M 2667 Acheron	11-10-67	10-2-68

Medusa (M 2661) Leo Van Ginderen, 5-90

D: 238 tons (246 fl) **S:** 14.3 kts **Dim:** 38.01 × 8.03 × 2.10
A: 1/40-mm Bofors AA
Electron Equipt: Radar: 1/KAE TRS-N nav.
M: 2 Mercedes-Benz MB 820 Db diesels; 2 props; 2,000 bhp
Electric: 554 kw **Range:** 648/14; 1,770/7 **Fuel:** 30 tons
Crew: 2 officers, 23 enlisted

Remarks: Wooden construction. Differs from Type 393 in having a 260-kw diesel sweep-current generator. Formerly had "Y,"- and earlier "W,"-series pendants. There is a lead-computing optical director on the bridge for the 40-mm gun. Constitute the 7th Minesweeping Squadron.

◆ **6 Type 393 inshore minesweepers** Bldr: Krögerwerft, Rendsburg

	L	In serv.		L	In serv.
M 2651 Freya	25-6-60	6-1-62	M 2655 Nixe	3-12-62	20-6-63
M 2653 Hertha	18-2-61	7-6-62	M 2656 Amazone	27-2-63	4-9-63
M 2654 Nymphe	20-9-62	8-5-63	M 2657 Gazelle	14-8-63	19-2-63

D: 199–205 tons light (252 fl) **S:** 14.3 kts **Dim:** 38.01 × 8.03 × 1.99
A: 1/40-mm Bofors AA
Electron Equipt: Radar: 1/KAE TRS-N nav.
M: 2 Mercedes-Benz MB 820 Db diesels; 2 props; 2,000 bhp
Electric: 554 kw **Range:** 830/12 **Fuel:** 30 tons
Crew: 2 officers, 23 enlisted

Gazelle (M 2657) Stefan Terzibaschitsch, 6-91

Remarks: Similar to Type 394, but have a 260-kw gas-turbine sweep current generator. Constitute the 3rd Minesweeping Squadron. Sisters *Ariadne* (M 2650) and *Vineta* (M 2652) stricken on 11-12-91 and 20-12-91. The others are to strike as follows: M 2651 on 5-5-92, M 2653 on 7-5-92, M 2654 on 18-6-92, M 2655 on 2-4-92, M 2656 on 9-4-92 and M 2657 on 2-7-92.

◆ **1 Type 732 small mine-clearance tender** Bldr: Burmester, Bremen

M 1050 TB 1 (ex-Y 1678) (In serv. 21-6-72)

TB 1 (M 1050) Leo Van Ginderen, 8-

D: 70 tons (fl) **S:** 14 kts **Dim:** 27.75 × 5.77 × 1.90
Electron Equipt: Radar: 1/. . . nav. **Electric:** 36 kw
M: 1 MWM 12-cyl. diesel; 1 prop; 950 bhp

Remarks: Renumbered in the mine warfare pendant series 1987. Also used for search.

AMPHIBIOUS WARFARE CRAFT

Note: The 12 East German Frosch-class landing ships were stricken from service 2-10-90 and are to be scrapped: *Hoyerswerda* (611), *Schwerin* (612), *Frankfurt/O.* (613), *Cottbus* (614), *Eisenhüttenstadt* (615), *Grimmen* (616), *Lübben* (631), *Hagen* (632), *Neubrandenburg* (633), *Eberswalde-Hinow* (634), *Anklam* (635), and *Schw* (636). Also stricken on the same date were the modified Frosch-class support sh *Nordperd* (E 171) and *Südperd* (E 172), which are, however, being maintained possible sale.

◆ **14 Type 520 utility landing craft** Bldr: Howaldtswerke, Hamburg

	L		L
L 760 Flunder	6-1-66	L 767 Tümmler	14-6-66
L 761 Karpfen	5-1-66	L 789 Brasse	28-3-65
L 762 Lachs	17-2-66	L 768 Wels	15-6-66
L 763 Plötze	16-2-66	L 769 Zander	13-7-66
L 764 Rochen	18-3-66	L 788 Butt	28-3-65
L 765 Schlei	17-5-66	L 795 Inger	14-7-66
L 766 Stör	18-5-66	L 797 Muräne	23-8-66

D: 166 tons (403 fl) **S:** 11 kts
Dim: 40.04 (36.7 pp) × 8.8 × 1.6 (2.1 max.)
A: 2/20-mm Rheinmetall Rh 202 AA (II × 1) **Range:** 1,200/11
Electron Equipt: Radar: 1/Kelvin-Hughes 14/9 nav.
M: 2 MWM 12-cyl. diesels; 2 props; 1,200 bhp
Electric: 130 kVA **Crew:** 17 tot.

Remarks: Design based on the American LCU 1646 class. Cargo: 237 tons max.; normal. *Renke* (L 798) and *Salm* (L 799), in reserve for several years, transferr Greece 16-11-89. *Inger* (L 795) used for reserve training. The others are bas Kiel-Stickenhörn. Sisters *Barbe* (L 790), *Delphin* (L 791), *Dorsch* (L 792), *Felch* 793), *Forelle* (L 794), and *Makrele* (L 796) were stricken 1991. Strikes in 1992: L 7 30-1-92, L 764 on 7-2-92, L 767 on 16-9-92, L 768 on 11-12-92, L 788 on 4-12-92, L 7 16-4-92; L 793 and L 794 to transfer to Greece 31-1-92.

AMPHIBIOUS WARFARE CRAFT *(continued)*

Lachs (L 762) Leo Van Ginderen, 7-90

◆ **17 Type 521 landing craft** Bldr: Rheinwerft, Walsum (LCM 1, 2: Blohm + Voss, Hamburg) (In serv. 1964–67)—13 in reserve

LCM 1 SEETAUCHER	LCM 11 HUCHEN
LCM 2 SEENADEL	LCM 12 SPROTTE
LCM 3 SEEDRACHE	LCM 13 SARDINE
LCM 4 SEESPINNE	LCM 14 SARDELLE
LCM 5 SEEOTTER	L 784 MUSCHEL (LCM 25)
LCM 6 SEEZUNGE	L 785 KORALLE (LCM 26)
LCM 7 SEELILIE	L 786 GARNELLE (LCM 27)
LCM 8 SEEFEDER	L 787 LANGUSTE (LCM 28)
LCM 9 SEEROSE	

protte (LCM 12) Stefan Terzibaschitsch, 6-91

D: 116 tons (168 fl) **S:** 10.6 kts **Dim:** 23.56 × 6.40 × 1.46
Electron Equipt: Radar: 1/. . . nav. (active units only)
M: 2 MWM 8-cyl. diesels; 2 props; 684 bhp
Range: 690/10; 1,430/7 **Crew:** 7 tot.

emarks: Design based on U.S. LCM (8). LCM 1 to LCM 11 are in reserve. Cargo: 60 ns or 50 troops. LCM 11 has a 20-kw diesel generator and a 2-ton cargo boom and can used to carry up to 18 torpedoes. During 1981, six were reclassified as auxiliaries: CM 21 as A 1423, and LCM 22–26 as A 1430–A 1434; LCM 15 reclassified A 1408 in 85. All active restored to L-pendants 1987–88, but LCM 1–11, in reserve, have no ndant numbers. LCM 25–26 are used by the Beachmaster Company at Eckenförde training. LCM 27 and 28 are used in training by the Coastal Service School at össenbrode.

Sister *Seenelke* (LCM 10) stricken and transferred to Greece 5-3-91; *Hering* (LCM 15, 74), *Orfe* (LCM 16, L 775), *Maräne* (LCM 17, L 776), *Saibling* (LCM 18, L 777), *Stint* CM 19, L 778), *Äsche* (LCM 20, L 779), *Hummer* (LCM 21, L 780), *Krille* (LCM 22, L 2), *Krabbe* (LCM 23, L 782), and *Auster* (LCM 24, L 783) were stricken 25-4-91 and nsferred to Greece.

UXILIARY SHIPS

YDROGRAPHIC SURVEY SHIP

te: *Planet* is to be replaced by a Type 751 large SWATH (Small Waterplane Twin-ll) vessel to be ordered in the early 1990s.

1 Type 750 Bldr: J. R. Köser Norderwerft, Hamburg

	Laid down	L	In serv.
.452 PLANET (ex-Y 843)	30-4-64	23-9-65	15-4-67

D: 1,513 tons (1,917 fl) **S:** 13.9 kts
Dim: 80.43 (74.0 pp) × 12.60 × 3.97
Electron Equipt: Radar: 2/. . . nav.—Sonar: mapping sonars
M: 4 MWM 12-cyl., 850-hp diesels, electric drive; 1 prop; 1,390 bhp
Electric: 650 kw **Range:** 9,300/13.4
Crew: 39 tot. plus 13 scientists

arks: Operated for the Ministry of Communications by a civilian crew. Hangar ne helicopter. Capable of conducting geophysical, meteorological, biological, chem-, and hydrographic research. Denny-Brown stabilizers, 125-bhp Pleuger active er and bow-thruster fitted. Main engines provide 560 kw of the electrical power. n broadened 1988 for cable handling; also has cable sheaves at bow. Antenna atop nast is a balloon-tracking radar. Painted white, with buff stack and mast.

Planet—pendant number A 1452 not painted on; hull and superstructure white, and masts yellow Leo Van Ginderen, 1989

SUPPORT TENDERS

◆ **0 (+6) Type 404 multipurpose tenders** Bldrs: A: Bremer-Vulkan; B: Lürssen, Vegesack; C: Neue Flensburger Schiffsbau, Flensburg

	Bldr	Laid down	L	In serv.
A ELBE	. . .	. . .	. . .	11-92
A MOSEL	. . .	. . .	. . .	. . .
A RHEIN	. . .	. . .	. . .	. . .
A WERRA	. . .	. . .	. . .	. . .
A MAIN	. . .	. . .	. . .	. . .
A DONAU	. . .	. . .	. . .	1994

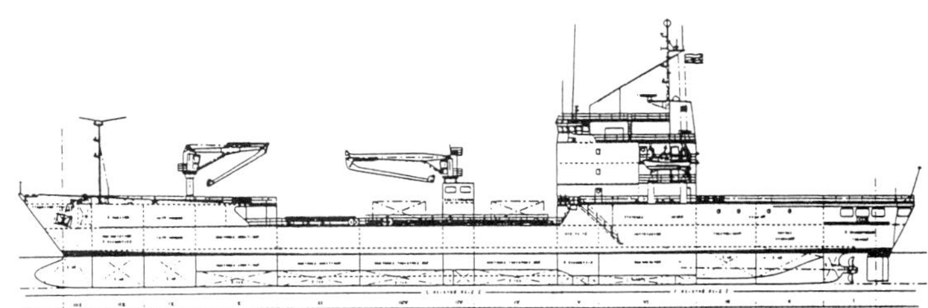

Type 404 multipurpose tender Marineamt, Wilhelmshaven, 1990

D: 3,450 tons (fl) **S:** 15 kts **Dim:** 94.80 (87.00 pp) × 15.80 × 4.05
A: none **Electron Equipt:** Radar: 1/. . . nav.
M: 2 diesels; . . . props; 3,300 bhp **Endurance:** 30 days
Crew: 40 ship's company + 50 technicians or passengers

Remarks: Ordered 10-90 as replacements for the *Rhein* class. Will carry up to 24 standard-sized 20-ft containers for supplies and repair shops, 450 tons of cargo fuel, 11 tons lube oil, 27 tons provisions, and 129 tons ammunition. Built to commercial standards. Helicopter platform aft. Two electrohydraulic cranes.

◆ **4 Rhein-class (Type 401) missile boat tenders**

	Bldr	L	In serv.
A 58 RHEIN	Schlieker, Hamburg	10-12-59	6-11-61
A 61 ELBE	Schlieker, Hamburg	5-5-60	17-4-62
A 63 MAIN	Lindenauwerft, Kiel	23-7-60	29-6-63
A 69 DONAU	Schlichting, Travemünde	26-11-60	23-5-64

D: 2,370 tons (3,000 fl) **S:** 20 kts (trials, 22)
Dim: 98.20 × 11.83 × 5.20
A: 2/100-mm AA (I × 2)—4/40-mm AA (I × 4)—mines
Electron Equipt:
Radar: 1/Kelvin-Hughes 14/9 nav., 1/H.S.A. ZW 01 surf. search, 1/H.S.A. DA 02 air search, 2/H.S.A. M 45 f.c.
EW: WLR-1B intercept, . . . jammer
M: 6 Maybach diesels; 2 CP props; 11,400 bhp
Electric: 2,250 kw **Fuel:** 334 tons **Range:** 2,500/16
Crew: 153 tot. (space for 40 officers, 40 petty officers, 130 ratings)

Elbe (A 61) Leo Van Ginderen, 1990

SUPPORT TENDERS *(continued)*

Donau (A 69) Marineamt, Wilhelmshaven, 1991

Remarks: Survivors of a class of 13 similar ships in three series. Carry 200 tons of cargo fuel oil. Have two M4 radar directors for the guns. A 58 and A 61 are to strike on 26-6-92 and 17-12-92, the other two in 1994.

Of Type 401 sisters, *Weser* (A 62) was transferred to Greece in 1975, *Ruhr* (A 64) was transferred to Turkey in 1976, *Neckar* (A 66) was stricken 30-11-89, and *Werra* (A 68) was stricken 21-3-91. Of the similar Type 402 mine countermeasures ship tenders, *Isar* (A 54) was transferred to Turkey 30-9-82, *Saar* (A 65) was stricken 15-2-91, and *Mosel* (A 67) was stricken 28-6-90. Two generally similar Type 403 submarine tenders have also been stricken, *Lech* (A 56) on 30-6-89 (sold for scrap 31-8-90) and *Lahn* (A 55) on 25-4-91.

REPLENISHMENT SHIPS

♦ 7 Type 701A, Type 701C, and 701E supply ships

	Bldr	Laid down	L	In serv.
(*a*) Type 701A:				
A 1411 Lüneburg	Flensburger Werft	8-7-64	3-5-65	31-1-66
A 1416 Nienburg	Flensburger Werft	16-11-65	28-7-66	1-8-68
A 1417 Offenburg	Blohm + Voss, Hamburg	1966	10-9-66	27-5-68
(*b*) Type 701C:				
A 1414 Glücksburg	Flensburger Werft	18-8-65	3-5-66	9-7-68
A 1415 Saarburg	Blohm + Voss, Hamburg	1-3-66	15-7-66	30-7-68
A 1418 Meersburg	Flensburger Werft	5-8-65	22-3-66	25-6-68
(*c*) Type 701E:				
A 1413 Freiburg	Blohm + Voss, Hamburg	1965	15-4-66	27-5-68

Nienburg (A 1416)—Type 701A, prior to modification Mike Louagie, 6-89

Saarburg (A 1414)— Type 701C, forward gun mount removed Leo Van Ginderen, 10-90

Freiburg (A 1413)—Type 701E, note helo deck Leo Van Ginderen, 6-89

D: Type 701A: 1,896 tons light (3,483 fl); Type 701C: 3,709 tons (fl); Type 701E: 3,900 tons (fl)
S: 17 kts
Dim: 104.15 (98.00 pp) × 13.20 × 4.20 (Type 701C: 114.90 overall; Type 701E: 118.30 overall)
A: 4/40-mm AA (II × 2) in preservation (fwd. mount active in A 1415, A 1413)
Electron Equipt: Radar: 1/Kelvin-Hughes 14/9 nav.
M: 2 Maybach MD 872 diesels; 2 CP props; 5,600 bhp
Electric: 1,935 kw **Range:** 3,000/17; 3,200/14 **Crew:** 71–82 tot.

Remarks: Originally configured to carry more than 1,100 tons of cargo, including 64 tons fuel, 205 tons ammunition, 100 tons spare parts (10,000 separate items), and 13 tons fresh water, plus 267 m³ refrigerated stores. A 1415 lengthened 11.5 meters i 1974–75 to carry spare Exocet missiles and other supplies for Type 143 and Type 14 missile boats; stowage for spare parts increased to 30,000 items, with inventory ma agement by the Nixdorf computer system. A 1412, A 1414, A 1418 also converted Type 702C standard 1975–77. A 1413, converted 1981–84 to support Type 122 frigate is equipped with helicopter facilities to permit vertical replenishment, 9 spare Harpo missiles, repair facilities for Mk 88 Lynx helicopters, and new articulated cranes. A are equipped with fin stabilizers, one 3-ton and two 2-ton cranes. A 1417 refitted 198 has new bridge windows, 2 SCLAR decoy RL. The forward 40-mm gun mount has be removed from several.

A 1418 reconfigured yet again to serve as a submarine tender in 1990 to replace *La* (A 55), and A 1416 reconfigured 1991 to serve as an interim missile-boat tender in pla of *Werra* (A 68) until the new Type 404 class is ready. Sister *Coburg* (A 1412, Ty 701C) was transferred to Greece in 25-9-91.

♦ 2 Type 760 ammunition ships Bldr: Orenstein & Koppel, Lübeck

	Laid down	L	In serv.
A 1435 Westerwald	3-11-65	25-2-66	11-2-67
A 1436 Odenwald	3-11-65	5-5-66	23-3-67

Odenwald (A 1436) Leo Van Ginderen, 6

D: 3,460 tons (4,042 fl) **S:** 17 kts **Dim:** 105.30 × 14.00 × 4.60
A: 4/40-mm AA (II × 2, in preservation on A 1436)
Electron Equipt: Radar: 1/Kelvin-Hughes 14/9 nav.
M: 2 Maybach MD 872 diesels; 2 CP props; 5,600 bhp—bow-thruster
Electric: 1,285 kw **Range:** 3,500/17
Crew: 60 tot. (A 1436: 31 civilians tot.)

Remarks: Similar to Type 701, but carry only ammunition. Cargo: 1,080 tons. T are two optical lead-computing directors for the 40-mm guns. A 1436 is rese crewed.

♦ 1 Type 762 mine-supply ships Bldr: Blohm + Voss, Hamburg

	Laid down	L	In serv.
A 1438 Steigerwald	9-5-66	10-3-67	20-8-69

D: 2,962 tons (3,380 fl) **S:** 17 kts **Dim:** 110.70 × 13.90 × 3.79
A: 4/40-mm AA (II × 2)—mines
Electron Equipt: Radar: 2/. . . nav.
M: 2 Maybach MD 872 diesels; 2 CP props; 5,600 bhp
Electric: 1,300 kw **Range:** 3,500/17 **Crew:** 65 tot.

Remarks: The designation "supply ship" is something of a euphemism, since ships have four mine ports at the stern and are actually minelayers, capable of ca 668 to 1,048 mines, depending on type. Construction of a torpedo-transport versio canceled. There are two optical lead-computing directors for the 40-mm gun m The stack has been modified to a more rectangular profile than on sister *Sachse* (A 1437), which was stricken 26-9-91.

REPLENISHMENT SHIPS *(continued)*

Steigerwald (A 1438) Leo Van Ginderen, 5-90

teigerwald (A 1438) Leo Van Ginderen, 5-90

5 Darss-class small supply ships Bldr: Neptunwerft, Rostock

	In serv.
1430 Wittow (ex-E 661)	1984
1431 Mönchgut (ex-E 111)	1983
1432 Darss (ex-E 441)	27-2-82
1433 Kühlung (ex-P 441)	1983
1434 Werdau (ex-V-815)	1984

rss (A 1432) Leo Van Ginderen, 1-92

): 2,292 tons (fl) **S:** 12 kts **Dim:** 76.52 × 12.37 × 4.15
: provision for 6/25-mm AA (II × 3)
lectron Equipt: Radar: 1/TSR-333 nav.
l: 1 12-cyl. Type 40 DM diesel; 1 CP Kort-nozzle prop; 2,000 bhp
lectric: 520 kw (4 × 130 kw) **Endurance:** 14 days
ange: 1,000/12 **Crew:** 16 tot.

arks: 950 dwt. Total cargo volume: 1,350 m³. Approx. 800 tons missiles, ammun, dry stores, etc., plus about 200 tons cargo fuel. Intended for dead-in-the-water enishment at sea, as indicated by the heavy rubbing strakes on the hull sides and 2 rubber fenders carried. Can refuel two ships simultaneously over stern. Between two holds is an 8-ton crane. A 1432 laid down 14-12-81, launched 27-7-82. A –1432 were typed as "High Seas Supply Ships" (*Hochseeversorger*), A 1433 (which used as cadet training ship during 1984) was a "Workshop Ship" (*Werkstattschiff*), A 1434 typed as a research ship (*Versuchschiff*). Sister *Jasmund* (D 41) was pped as an intelligence collector and is to be scrapped; *Granitz* (V 816) was not n over and is available for foreign transfer. A 1431 and A 1434 were inactive by the ner of 1991; A 1432–1435 were used during the winter of 1990-91 to ferry food to ngrad from Germany. All were to be discarded by end-1991 but may be retained to nue relief efforts.

: U.S. *Aristaeus*-class repair ship *Odin* (Y 847, ex-*Ulysses*, ARB 9, ex-LST 967) en 20-12-91 and sister *Wotan* (Y 848, ex-*Diomedes*, ARB 11, ex-LST 1119) on 91.

Wittow (A 1430) Hartmut Ehlers, 6-91

Werdau (A 1434) Leo Van Ginderen, 7-91

REPLENISHMENT OILERS

◆ **2 Type 704 former merchant tankers** Bldr: Krögerwerft, Rendsburg

Rhön (A 1443) Stefan Terzibaschitsch, 6-90

D: 14,260 tons (fl) **S:** 16 kts **Dim:** 130.2 × 19.3 × 8.20
Electron Equipt: Radar: 1/. . . nav.
M: 1 MAK 12-cyl. diesel; CP prop; 8,000 bhp
Electric: 2,000 kw **Range:** 7,400/16 **Crew:** 42 tot. (civilians)

Remarks: 6,103 grt/10,800 dwt. Purchased from Bulk Acid Carriers, Monrovia, in 1976 and converted as replenishment oilers. Fitted with one underway-replenishment station per side. Cargo: 9,500 m³ distillate fuel, 1,650 m³ fuel oil, 400 m³ water. Pronounced bulbous bow.

◆ **4 Type 703 small oilers** Bldr: Lindenauwerft, Kiel

	Laid down	L	In serv.
A 1424 Walchensee	12-10-64	10-7-65	29-6-66
A 1425 Ammersee	28-3-66	9-7-66	2-3-67
A 1426 Tegernsee	21-4-66	22-10-66	23-3-67
A 1427 Westensee	28-10-66	8-4-67	6-10-67

Westensee (A 1427) Gilbert Gyssels, 6-89

REPLENISHMENT OILERS *(continued)*

D: 2,191 tons (fl) **S:** 12.5 kts **Dim:** 71.9 × 11.2 × 4.28
Electron Equipt: Radar: 2/. . . nav.
M: 2 MWM 12-cyl. diesels; 1 CP prop; 1,200 bhp
Electric: 635 kw **Range:** 3,250/12 **Crew:** 21 tot. (civilians)

Remarks: Cargo capacity: 1,130 m³ fuel/60 m³ water. One alongside refueling station that can work to either beam.

◆ **1 Type 763 former merchant tanker** Bldr: Lindenauwerft, Kiel

	Laid down	L	In serv.
A 1407 Wittensee (ex-*Sioux*)	15-2-58	23-9-58	5-12-58

Wittensee (A 1407) Stefan Terzibaschitsch, 6-90

D: 1,237 tons (1,854 fl) **S:** 12 kts **Dim:** 67.45 × 9.84 × 4.25
Electron Equipt: Radar: 1/. . . nav.
M: 1 MAK 6-cyl. diesel; 1,250 bhp **Electric:** 216 kw
Range: 6,240/12 **Crew:** 21 tot. (civilians)

Remarks: 998 grt. Purchased 26-3-59. Cargo: 1,274 m³ fuel/64 m³ water. One alongside refueling station that can work to either beam. Sister *Bodensee* (A 1406) transferred to Turkey 8-77.

◆ **1 Type 766 former merchant tanker** Bldr: Norderwerft, Hamburg

	Laid down	L	In serv.
A 1429 Eifel (ex-*Friedrich Jung*)	5-11-57	2-4-58	26-7-58

Eifel (A 1429) Leo Van Ginderen, 6-89

D: 6,647 tons (fl) **S:** 13 kts **Dim:** 101.76 × 14.43 × 7.1
Electron Equipt: Radar: 2/. . . nav.
M: 2 M.A.N. 8-cyl. diesels; 1 prop; 3,360 bhp **Electric:** 760 kVA
Range: 7,300/12 **Crew:** 40 tot. (naval reserves)

Remarks: 3,444 grt. Purchased and commissioned 27-5-63. Cargo: 4,700 m³ fuel, 63 m³ fresh water, 75 m³ boiler feed. One fueling station per side, plus over-the-stern capability. To strike 6-3-92.

◆ **1 Type 766 former merchant tanker** Bldr: Norderwerft, Hamburg

	Laid down	L	In serv.
A 1428 Harz (ex-*Claere Jung*)	31-3-53	2-9-53	26-11-53

Harz (A 1428) Hartmut Ehlers, 7-87

D: 5,381 tons (fl) **S:** 12 kts **Dim:** 92.40 × 13.60 × 6.70
Electron Equipt: Radar: 1/. . . nav.
M: 2 OEW 8-cyl. diesels; 1 prop; 2,520 bhp **Electric:** 380 kVA
Range: 7,200/11 **Crew:** 28 tot. (civilians)

Remarks: 2,800 grt. Purchased and commissioned 27-5-63. Cargo: 3,700 m³ fuel, 60 m³ fresh water, 50 m³ boiler feed. Equipped for underway replenishment, one station per side, and also for over-the-stern refueling. To strike 31-3-92.

Note: Former East German *Riems*-class (Project 600) small oilers *Hiddensee* (C 111, ex-C 11), *Poel* (C 12, ex-C 43), and *Riems* (C 61) were not taken over for *Bundesmarine* service; *Hiddensee* had been stricken from the *Volksmarine* on 15-5-90 and sold into commercial service 25-5-90 under the same name.

INTELLIGENCE COLLECTORS

◆ **3 Type 423** Bldr: Flensburger Schiffsbau, Flensburg

	Laid down	L	In serv.
A 50 Alster	14-3-88	10-11-88	5-10-89
A 52 Oste	16-12-86	15-5-87	30-6-88
A 53 Oker	16-12-86	24-9-87	18-11-88

Oste (A 52) Hans J. Vanhöfen, 3-

Alster (A 50) Hartmut Ehlers, 5

D: 2,375 tons (fl) **S:** 18 kts **Dim:** 83.50 (75.70 pp) × 14.60 × 4.18
Electron Equipt:
Radar: 1/Decca. nav., 1/TRC . . . nav.
Sonar: Krupp-Atlas. . . .
EW: Intercept suite 300 MHz—40 GHz
M: 2 Deutz-MWM 8BV16M628 diesels; 2 fixed-pitch, 5-bladed props 8,800 bhp—2/380-shp electric motors for low speeds
Range: . . . **Crew:** 40 ship's company + 40 technicians

Remarks: A 52, A 53 ordered 3-7-85 as replacements for ships of the same name; ordered 15-12-86. Also carry electro-optical surveillance equipment. Built to com cial standards. Ships' operating crews are civilians.

◆ **1 Type 740 converted inshore minesweeper** Bldr: Abeking & Rasmussen, Lemwerder

	Laid down	L	In serv.
A 1400 Holnis	15-8-64	20-5-65	31-3-66

D: 150 tons (180 fl) **S:** 16.5 kts **Dim:** 36.87 × 7.40 × 1.80
Electron Equipt: Radar: 1/Kelvin-Hughes 14/9 nav.
M: 2 Mercedes-Benz MB 820Db diesels; 2 props; 2,000 hp
Electric: 380 kw **Fuel:** 13 tons **Crew:** 21 tot.

INTELLIGENCE COLLECTORS *(continued)*

Holnis (A 1400) Leo Van Ginderen, 1990

Remarks: Wooden construction, prototype of a class of 20 Type 390 inshore minesweepers, the other 19 of which were canceled. Altered circa 1968 as an intelligence collector. Renumbered from Y 836 to A 836 in 1985, and to A 1400 in 1987.

Note: East German *Darss*-class intelligence collector *Jasmund* (D 41) was at Kröslin in 9-90 awaiting scrapping; modified Kondor-I class intelligence collectors *Komet* (D 42) and *Meteor* (D 43) were at Peenemünde in 9-90 awaiting scrapping.

SEAGOING TUGS

◆ **6 Baltrum (Type 722) class** Bldr: Schichau, Bremerhaven

	Laid down	L	In serv.
A 1439 Baltrum (ex-Y 1661, ex-A 1454)	29-6-66	2-6-67	8-10-68
A 1440 Juist (ex-Y 1644, ex-A 1456)	23-9-67	15-8-68	1-10-71
A 1441 Langeoog (ex-Y 1665, ex-A 1453)	12-7-66	2-5-67	14-8-68
A 1451 Wangerooge	1-10-65	4-7-66	9-4-68
A 1452 Spiekeroog	20-11-65	26-9-66	14-8-68
A 1455 Norderney	29-5-67	28-2-68	15-10-70

Spiekeroog (A 1452) Leo Van Ginderen, 6-90

D: 854 tons (1,039 fl) **S:** 13.6 kts **Dim:** 51.78 × 12.11 × 4.20
A: 1/40-mm Bofors AA (in preservation)
Electron Equipt: Radar: 1/Kelvin-Hughes 14/9 nav.
M: 4 MWM 16-cyl. diesels, electric drive; 2 props; 2,400 shp
Electric: 540 kw **Range:** 5,000/10 **Crew:** 24 tot.

Remarks: A 1451 is used at Cuxhaven in support of aircrew survival training. *Baltrum* has been used as a diving-training tender since 1974; *Juist* and *Langeoog* were configured for training duties during 1977–78 and carry up to 33 additional personnel. The ships are employed as salvage tugs and port icebreakers.

◆ **2 Helgoland-class salvage tugs (Type 720)** Bldr: Schichau, Bremerhaven

	Laid down	L	In serv.
A 1457 Helgoland	24-7-64	9-4-65	8-3-66
A 1458 Fehmarn	23-4-65	25-11-65	1-2-67

D: 1,304 tons (1,558 fl) **S:** 16.6 kts **Dim:** 67.90 × 12.74 × 4.20
A: 2/40-mm Bofors AA (II × 2)
Electron Equipt: Radar: 1/Kelvin-Hughes 14/9 nav.
M: 4 MWM 12-cyl. diesels, electric drive; 2 props; 3,300 shp
Electric: 1,065 kw **Range:** 6,400/16 **Crew:** 34 tot.

Remarks: *Fehmarn* (Type 720B) serves as a tender to the submarine training establishment. Equipped to serve as mine planters, if required. Both have high-frequency equipment for salvage work and are equipped for fire fighting. Ice-strengthened to permit use as harbor icebreakers. A 1457 has a naval reserve crew.

Fehmarn (A 1458)—with gun mount forward Leo Van Ginderen, 3-90

◆ **1 Type 660 former East German seagoing salvage tug** Bldr: Peenewerft, Wolgast (In serv. 30-9-63)

A 1459 Thale (ex-A 113, ex-A 14)

Thale (A 1459)—with *Volksmarine* pendant Hartmut Ehlers, 9-90

D: 700 tons (791 fl) **S:** 12 kts **Dim:** 44.70 × 10.70 (10.00 wl) × 3.90
Electron Equipt: Radar: 1/TSR-333 nav.
M: 2 Johannisthal 12KVD 21 diesels, electric drive; 2 props; 1,760 shp
Range: 3,000/12 **Crew:** 6 officers, 33 enlisted

Remarks: Former East German Type 600 salvage tug; not likely to be retained in service. 505 grt. Sister to Bulgarian *Jupiter*. Bollard pull: 16 tons. Provision made to mount 2/25-mm AA (II × 1). Will probably strike soon.

◆ **2 Eisvogel-class icebreaking tugs (Type 721)** Bldr: Hitzler, Lauenburg

	Laid down	L	In serv.
A 1401 Eisvogel	10-3-59	28-4-60	11-3-61
A 1402 Eisbär	12-5-59	9-6-60	1-11-61

Eisbär (A 1402) Leo Van Ginderen, 3-91

SEAGOING TUGS *(continued)*

D: 496 tons (641 fl) **S:** 13 kts **Dim:** 37.8 × 9.7 × 4.2
Electron Equipt: Radar: 1/Kelvin-Hughes 14/9 nav.
M: 2 Maybach 12-cyl. diesels; 2 CP props; 2,400 bhp
Electric: 180 kw **Range:** 2,000/12 **Crew:** 16 tot.

Remarks: Provision for 1/40-mm Bofors AA aft. A 1401 completed refit 10-91 at Warnowwerft, Warnemünde, in former East Germany.

Note: The former East German Polish-built *Piast*-class salvage ship *Otto von Guericke* (A 46) was not taken over for *Bundesmarine* service and has been offered to Uruguay.

EXPERIMENTAL SHIPS

◆ **0 (+1) Type 751 air-cushion experimental ship** Bldr: Blohm + Voss, Hamburg

	Laid down	L	In serv.
A	. . .	. . .	. . .

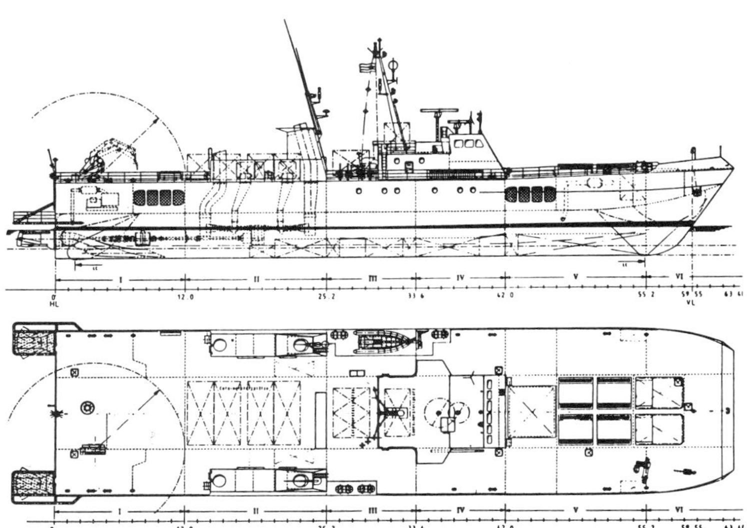

Type 751 Blohm + Voss

D: . . . tons **S:** 60+ kts **Dim:** 63.61 (59.55 pp) × . . . × . . .
A: . . . **Electron Equipt:** Radar: . . .
M: 2 . . . gas turbines; 2 waterjets; 27,000 shp
Range: . . . **Crew:** . . .

Remarks: Proposed for construction during the 1990s. Blohm + Voss "SES 700" design, rigid-sidewall surface-effect ship. Would carry up to four trials instrumentation modules amidships. Typed as an *Erprobungsboot Schnell* (Fast Trials Craft). May not be funded. The company-funded Blohm + Voss technology demonstrator *Corsair* (see under trials craft) is, in effect, a prototype for this ship.

◆ **0 (+2) Type 749 trials ships** Bldr: . . .

	Laid down	L	In serv.
A	. . .	. . .	. . .
A	. . .	. . .	. . .

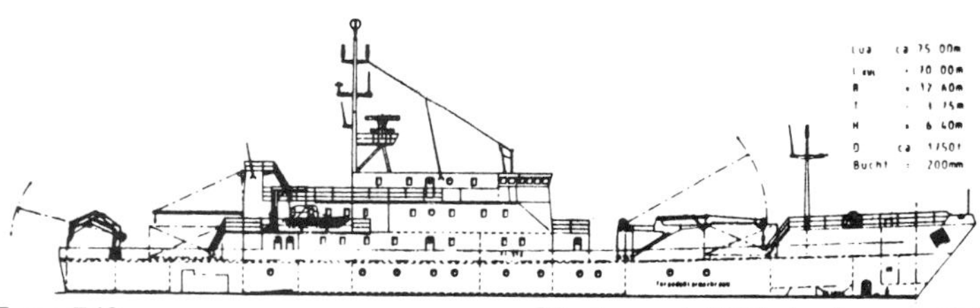

Type 749 Marineamt, Wilhelmshaven, 1987

D: approx. 1,750 tons (fl) **S:** . . .
Dim: 75.00 (70.00 pp) × 12.60 × 3.75
A: 2/533-mm TT (1 trainable, above water, to port: 1 fixed, submerged)
Electron Equipt: Radar: 2/. . . nav.—Sonar: . . .
M: 2 . . . diesels; . . . props; . . . bhp
Range: . . . **Crew:** . . .

Remarks: One to be configured for torpedo and other weapons trials and the other to test sensors; programmed to replace *Hans Bürkner* (A 1449) and *Heinz Roggenkamp* (Y 871). Hydraulic cranes on stern and to starboard, forward, for weapons retrieval. Three portable van positions aft. Construction delayed for lack of funds.

Note: The Type 421 trials ship *Hans Bürkner* (A 1499) was stricken 26-10-90. The former *Volksmarine* trials ship *Rügen* (V 84) had been stricken 29-9-86; the torpedo retrievers of the Kondor-I class, V 661 and V 662, were not taken over for *Bundesmarine* service.

SAIL-TRAINING SHIP

◆ **1 Type 441** Bldr: Blohm + Voss, Hamburg

	Laid down	L	In serv.
A 60 Gorch Fock	24-2-58	23-8-58	17-12-58

Gorch Fock—pendant number A 60 not carried
Marineamt, Wilhelmshaven, 199

D: 1,819 tons (2,005 fl) **S:** 10 kts (15 kts under sail)
Dim: 89.32 (81.44 hull, 70.20 pp) × 12.02 × 5.25
Electron Equipt: Radar: 2/. . . nav.
M: 1 Deutz-MWM S8V6M 628 diesel; 1 CP prop; 890 bhp
Electric: 450 kw
Range: 1,100/10 **Crew:** 10 officers, 56 enlisted, 200 cadets

Remarks: 1,904 m^2 sail area. Carries 350 tons permanent ballast. Has made 2 nautical miles progress in one day. Major refit 1985. Has MARISAT SATCOM extensive navigation aids. Refitted 21-1-91 to 24-5-91.

Note: The training ship *Deutschland* (A 59) was laid up 27-3-90 and stricken 6- cadet cruises are now to be conducted by operational destroyers and frigates. T former East German Society for Sports and Mechanics sail-training ship *Wilhelm Pi* was sold 23-11-90 to a U.K. owner for conversion to a yacht, while her *Volksmar* namesake was not taken over. Other *Bundesmarine* training craft are discussed un the "Training Craft" section.

YARD AND SERVICE CRAFT

HARBOR TUGS

◆ **6 (+ 6) Type 725 large harbor tugs** Bldr: Y 812–Y 815: Husemer Schiffswerft; Y 816–Y 819: Orenstein & Koppel, Lübeck

	Laid down	L	In serv.
Y 812 Lütje Horn	30-8-89	. . .	9-90
Y 814 Knechtsand	22-9-89	. . .	10-90
Y 815 Schärhorn	13-10-89	. . .	16-11-90
Y 816 Vogelsand	1-4-86	30-1-87	14-4-87
Y 817 Nordstrand	1-4-86	24-10-86	20-1-87
Y 819 Langeness	1-4-86	28-11-86	15-5-87

Langeness (Y 819) Stefan Terzibaschitsch,

HARBOR TUGS *(continued)*

D: 445 tons (fl) **S:** 12 kts **Dim:** 30.25 (28.00 pp) × 9.10 × 2.55
Electron Equipt: Radar: 1/. . . nav.
M: 2 Deutz SBV6M628 diesels; 2 Voith-Schneider Model 24 G-11/165 vertical cycloidal props; 2,230 bhp
Range: . . . **Crew:** 10 tot. (civilians)

Remarks: 212 grt. Bollard pull: 25 tons. Class intended to replace *all* present harbor tugs, with eventual total of 15 planned. Launched via crane. Second trio ordered 5-89. Six more planned for construction by 1994, if funds permit.

◆ **3 former East German Project 414 (Type 660)** Bldr: Yachtwert/Volkswerft, Strabund (In serv. 1989–90)

Y 1651 Koos (ex-*Delphin,* A 08)
Y 1656 Wustrow (ex-*Zander,* A 45)
Y 1658 Dranske (ex-*Kormoran,* A 68)

ranske (Y 1658) Hartmut Ehlers, 4-91

D: 320 tons (fl) **S:** 11 kts **Dim:** 29.3 × 8.3 × 3.7
A: 4/23-mm AA (II × 2, provision for)
Electron Equipt: Radar: 1/SRN-402 nav.
M: 2 AKA 501 diesels; 1 Kort-nozzle prop; 1,200 bhp
Range: 1,800/11 **Crew:** 13 tot.

marks: 140 grt. The three completed units of a planned 5-unit class to replace lier *Volksmarine* tugs. The 23-mm gun mounts were placed abreast the stack idships. Fitted with one water monitor for fire fighting.

1 former East German Soviet Prometey-class tug (Type 660) Bldr: Gorokhovets SY, Leningrad (In serv. 8-83)

1650 Ummanz (ex-A 10, ex-A 16)

D: 319 tons (fl) **S:** 11 kts **Dim:** 29.3 (28.2 pp) × 8.3 × 3.2
M: 2 Type 6D30/50-4 diesels; 1 Kort-nozzle CP prop; 1,200 bhp
Range: 1,800/12 **Electric:** 50 kw **Crew:** 3–5 tot.

marks: Has ice-strengthened hull, 14-ton bollard pull at 9 kts. Over 100 sisters lt in U.S.S.R. since 1971 as Type KM U1. To strike 12-92.

manz (Y 1650) Hartmut Ehlers, 3-91

◆ **3 Heppens (Type 724) class** Bldr: Schichau, Bremerhaven

	Laid down	L	In serv.
Y 1680 Neuende	29-12-70	2-6-71	27-10-71
Y 1681 Heppens	19-3-71	15-9-71	17-12-71
Y 1682 Ellerbek	29-12-70	2-6-71	26-11-71

D: 232 tons (319 fl) **S:** 12 kts **Dim:** 26.6 × 7.4 × 2.6
M: 1 MWM 8-cyl. diesel; 800 bhp
Electric: 120 kw **Crew:** 6 tot. (civilians)

Ellerbek (Y 1682) Peter Voss, 6-89

◆ **4 Sylt (Type 724) class** Bldr: Schichau, Bremerhaven

	L	In serv.		L	In serv.
Y 820 Sylt	29-4-61	5-7-62	Y 822 Amrum	6-10-61	25-1-63
Y 821 Föhr	13-5-61	11-10-62	Y 823 Neuwerk	12-10-61	5-4-63

Neuwerk (Y 823) Leo Van Ginderen, 6-90

D: 266 tons (282 fl) **S:** 12 kts **Dim:** 30.2 × 7.9 × 4.0
M: 1 MAK 8-cyl. diesel; 1,000 bhp
Range: 1,775/12 **Crew:** 10 tot. (civilians)

Remarks: All four to be discarded shortly.

◆ **4 former East German Type 270 harbor tugs (Type 660)** Bldr: Peenewerft, Wolgast (In serv. 1957–59)

Y 1654 Havel (ex-A 442) Y 1659 Oder (ex-A 661)
Y 1655 Zingst (ex-A 443) Y 1660 Saale (ex-*Erich Krenkel,* A 662)

D: 261 tons **S:** 10 kts **Dim:** 30.50 × 8.00 (7.50 wl) × 2.50
M: 1 Buckau-Wolf R6DV 148 diesel; 1 prop; 550 bhp
Range: 1,400/10 **Crew:** 12 tot.

Remarks: Provision for 2/25-mm AA (II × 1). Refitted 1983, new auxiliary machinery. Nine-ton bollard pull at 10 kts. Two others, located at Kröslin, were not taken over and were for sale in 9-90: Peene (A 111) and Spee (A 112). Y 1654 to remain in use, others to strike 1-92.

Note: The five remaining *Lütje Horn*-class (Type 723) tugs have been transferred to Greece: *Lütje Horn* (Y 812) stricken 18-12-89 and transferred 5-3-91 , *Mellum* (Y 813) stricken 20-12-90 and transferred 25-4-91, *Knechtsand* (Y 814) stricken 18-10-90 and transferred 5-3-91, *Schärhorn* (Y 815) stricken 2-8-90 and transferred 5-3-91, and *Trischen* (Y 818) stricken 20-12-90 and transferred 25-4-91.

All other former *Volksmarine* tugs were discarded: 8 Warnow class (A 14–18, 80, 81, 91) in 7-90, small harbor tug *Elbe* (A 23), and icebreaking river tugs *Hai* (A 11, sold commercial in the U.K.) and *Hai-II* (A 09).

HARBOR TUGS *(continued)*

Oder (Y 1659) Hartmut Ehlers, 4-91

HARBOR FUEL LIGHTERS

◆ **2 former East German Gustav Koenigs class (Type 670)** Bldr: VEB Rosslau/Elbe (In serv. 1960)

Y 1652 Kölpinsee (ex-C 11) Y 1657 Fleesensee (ex-C 40)

Fleesensee (Y 1657) Hartmut Ehlers, 4-91

D: 1,010 tons (fl) **S:** 8 kts **Dim:** 67.00 × 8.16 × 2.18
M: 1 Type R8DV diesel; 1 prop; 420 bhp

Remarks: Survivors of a class of five, retained to provide fueling services to former *Volksmarine* units operating from eastern German ports. Have low freeboard, minimal superstructure, and folding masts to permit passage beneath low bridges. Not likely to be retained long. Y 1652 to strike 12-92, Y 1657 in 1-92.

WATER TANKERS

◆ **2 Type 705**

	Bldr	Laid down	L	In serv.
A 1403 FW 1	Schichau, Bremerhaven	5-4-63	22-7-63	30-11-63
A 1405 FW 5	Ranke, Hamburg	26-7-63	26-11-63	21-2-64

FW 5 (A 1405) Stefan Terzibaschitsch, 6-91

D: 598 tons (647 fl) **S:** 9.5 kts **Dim:** 44.03 (41.1 pp) × 7.80 × 2.63
M: 1 MWM 12-cyl. diesel; 230 bhp **Electric:** 130 kVA
Fuel: 15 tons **Range:** 2,150/9 **Crew:** 12 tot. (civilians)

Remarks: Cargo: 343 tons. Given "A" pendants 1987; formerly Y 864 and Y 868. Sister FW 2 to Turkey in 1975, FW 3 to Greece in 1976. FW 4 (A 1404) stricken 12-4-91 and sold to a private owner 11-6-91. FW 6 (A 1406) stricken 7-90 and transferred to Greece 5-3-91.

Note: Former *Volksmarine* Type 506/1 water lighter C 41 was not taken over.

TORPEDO-RECOVERY BOATS

◆ **4 Type 430** Bldr: Burmester, Bremen, and Schweers, Bardenfleth

	L
Y 851 TF 1	13-10-65
Y 852 TF 2	22-9-65
Y 853 TF 3	13-10-65
Y 855 TF 5	28-2-66

TF 2 (Y 852) Stefan Terzibaschitsch, 6-

D: 56 tons (63.5 fl) **S:** 17 kts **Dim:** 25.22 × 5.40 × 1.60
M: 1 MWM 12-cyl. diesel; 1 prop; 1,000 bhp **Crew:** 6 tot.

Remarks: Wooden construction. Sisters TF 107 (Y 873) and TF 108 (Y 874) strick 31-8-89 and 16-11-89, respectively, for transfer to Turkey and Greece. TF 101 strick 16-6-89. TF 4 (Y 854) stricken 28-9-90, TF 6 (Y 856) stricken 5-3-91, TF 106 (Y 8 stricken 12-4-90; all three transferred to Greece.

AIR-SEA RESCUE CRAFT

◆ **7 KW 15 class (Type 369)**

	Bldr	L
Y 827 KW 15 (ex-BG 1, ex-KW 15, ex-H 15, ex-U.S.N. 57)	Schweers, Bardenfleth	6-10-
Y 830 KW 16 (ex-BG 2, ex-KW 16, ex-H 16, ex-U.S.N. 54)	Lürssen, Vegesack	1
Y 832 KW 18 (ex-H 18, ex-U.S.N. 55)	Abeking & Rasmussen	17-11
Y 845 KW 17 (ex-BG 3, ex-KW 17, ex-H 17, ex-U.S.N. 58)	Schürenstedt	27-3
Y 846 KW 20 (ex-BG 4, ex-KW 20, ex-H 20, ex-U.S.N. 56)	Lürssen, Vegesack	1
Y 857 H 11 (ex-FL 5, ex-KW 11, ex-H 11, ex-P 1)	Lürssen, Vegesack	1
Y 859 H 13 (ex-FL 7, ex-KW 13, ex-H 13, ex-P 3)	Burmester	1

D: 59.5 tons (69.6 fl) **S:** 25.0 **Dim:** 28.90 × 4.70 × 1.42
Electron Equipt: Radar: 1/Kelvin-Hughes 14/9 nav.
M: 2 MTU 12-cyl. diesels; 2 props; 2,000 hp
Electric: 10 kw **Crew:** 17 tot.

KW 17 (Y 845) Leo Van Ginderen

AIR-SEA RESCUE CRAFT *(continued)*

Remarks: Built as patrol boats for U.S. Navy, taken over 30-11-56. Served in Border Guard 1963–1969/70. Y 857 and Y 859, stricken 17-10-75, reacquired 8-12-85 for use as safety boats at Todendorf Firing Range.

Note: The 488-ton East German air/sea rescue ship *Hugo Eckener* (A 114, ex-A 15, ex-U 33, ex-Havel-class fishing cutter *Usedom 256*) was taken over in 10-91 under pendant number Y 896 but was reported 7-91 to have been donated to a private organization for use as an oceanographic research ship.

EXPERIMENTAL AND TRIALS CRAFT

◆ **1 privately owned air-cushion vehicle trials craft** Bldr: Blohm + Voss, Hamburg

CORSAIR (L: 2-89)

Corsair—with 57-mm gun forward Leo Van Ginderen, 1991

D: approx. 190 tons (fl) **S:** . . . kts
Dim: 36.0 × 13.0 × 4.1 moulded depth
A: 1/57-mm Bofors SAK 57 Mk 2
Electron Equipt:
Radar: 1/. . . nav., 1/H.S.A. Gemini system (*see* Remarks)
M: 2 MTU diesels; 2 CP props; 4,280 bhp

Remarks: *Corsair* is not a unit of the *Bundesmarine.* In 1-91, the craft was outfitted with a Bofors 57-mm gun and the H.S.A. Gemini weapons-control system for trials that concluded in 3-91. Gemini incorporates an I-band search radar and a K-band tracking radar with an auxiliary optronic tracker. The craft has an extensive navigation system including Anschütz 3-axis gyro, Global Positioning System, SATNAV receiver, and autopilot.

◆ **3 (+1) Type 748 multipurpose trials craft**

	Bldr	Laid down	L	In serv.
Y 860 SCHWEDENECK	Nobiskrug, Rendsburg	1-11-86	19-2-87	20-10-87
Y 861 KRONSORT	Elsflether Werft, Elsfleth	6-10-86	9-5-87	2-12-87
Y 862 HELMSAND	Krögerwerft, Rendsburg	1-14-86	15-10-87	4-3-88

Kronsort (Y 861) Leo Van Ginderen, 6-90

D: 999 tons (fl) **S:** 12.6 kts (13.2 kts trials)
Dim: 56.50 (50.00 pp) × 10.80 × 3.65
Electron Equipt: Radar: 2/. . . nav.
M: 3 MTU 6V396 TB93 (700 bhp each) diesels, electric drive, 2/750-kw AEG alternators; 1 prop; 1,490 shp—side-thrusters fore and aft
Range: 2,400/12 **Crew:** 13 civilian crew + 10 technicians

Remarks: 850 grt. Ordered 14-12-85 with Lürssen as prime contractor, subcontracted to yards above, as replacements for *Adolf Bestelmeyer* (Y 881), *Rudolf Diesel* (Y 889), *Hans Christian Oersted* (Y 877), and *Friedrich Voge* (Y 888). Space for four modular trials equipment containers, two on fantail, two amidships. Quadrantial scientific equipment gallows crane at stern. All based at Eckenförde research center. One is to be refitted with a Siemens 3-phase propulsion motor. All three have NAVSTAR global positioning system. A fourth is planned to replace *Walther Von Ledebur* (Y 841) post-1995.

◆ **5 (+2) Type 745 small multipurpose trials tenders**

	Bldr	Laid down	L	In serv.
Y 863 STOLLERGRUND	Kröger, Rendsburg	24-5-88	1-9-88	31-5-89
Y 864 MITTELGRUND	Elsflether Werft	10-6-88	26-4-89	21-6-89
Y 865 KALKGRUND	Kröger, Rendsburg	7-9-88	2-2-89	23-11-89
Y 866 BREITGRUND	Elsflether Werft	10-1-89	10-8-89	19-12-89
Y 867 BANT	Kröger, Rendsburg	. . .	3-7-89	28-5-90

Mittelgrund (Y 864) Leo Van Ginderen, 7-90

Bant (Y 867)—with equipment van aft Leo Van Ginderen, 6-91

D: 400 tons (456 fl) **S:** 12 kts
Dim: 38.55 (34.60 wl; 32.12 pp) × 9.20 × 3.10
Electron Equipt: Radar: 2/. . . nav.
M: 1 KHD-SBV6 M628 diesel; 1 prop; 1,210 bhp **Range:** 900/12
Electric: 310 kVA (2 MWM D234V8 diesels driving) **Fuel:** 18 tons
Endurance: 5 days **Crew:** 7 civilian crew, 6 technicians

Remarks: These five replaced seven earlier units: diving tender TB 1 (Y 1678), radio trials craft KW 3 (Y 829), and five of the Type 430 torpedo retrievers. Two more planned for delivery post-1995 to replace *Wilhelm Pullwer* (Y 838) and two more torpedo retrievers. Nine were originally programmed. Torpedo recovery ramp to starboard through transom stern, divers' stage to port. Space for two trials equipment vans on stern. Becker flap rudder. Built under sub-contract from Lürssen.

EXPERIMENTAL AND TRIALS CRAFT *(continued)*

◆ **1 Type 742 magnetic mine countermeasures research ship**

	Bldr	L	In serv.
A 1410 Walther von Ledebur	Burmester, Bremen	30-6-66	21-12-67

Walther von Ledebur (A 1410) Gilbert Gyssels, 6-90

D: 775 tons (825 fl) **S:** 19 kts **Dim:** 63.20 × 10.60 × 3.00
Electron Equipt: Radar: 1/Kelvin-Hughes 14/9 nav.
M: 2 Maybach 16-cyl. diesels; 2 props; 5,200 bhp
Electric: 1,620 kw **Crew:** 11 civilian crew + 10 technicians

Remarks: One of the largest wooden ships built in modern times. Used in mine-warfare research and can be employed as a minesweeper. Two 600-kw sweep current generators. Renumbered from Y 841 in 1987. To be replaced after 1995 by a projected fourth Type 748 trials ship.

◆ **2 Type 741 net tenders** Bldr: Schürenstedt, Bardenfleth

	Laid down	L	In serv.
A 1408 SP 1	7-9-65	21-6-66	29-6-67
A 1409 Wilhelm Pullwer (ex-SP 2)	4-10-65	16-8-66	22-12-67

SP 1 (A 1408) Stefan Terzibaschitsch, 6-91

D: 132 tons (160 fl) **S:** 12.5 kts **Dim:** 31.54 × 7.50 × 2.20
Electron Equipt: Radar: 1/. . . nav.
M: 2 Mercedes-Benz 8-cyl. diesels; 2 Voith-Schneider cycloidal props; 792 bhp
Electric: 120 kw **Crew:** 17 civilians plus trials personnel

Remarks: Used in experimental trials. Wooden hulls. SP 1 pendant changed 1985 from Y 837 to Y 838; renumbered again 1987, as was A 1409 (from Y 838).

◆ **1 Type 740 torpedo-trials ship** Bldr: AG Weser, Bremerhaven

	Laid down	L	In serv.
Y 871 Heinz Roggenkamp (ex-*Greif*)	23-8-52	8-11-52	30-12-52

Heinz Roggenkamp (Y 871) Hartmut Ehlers, 3-88

D: 935 tons (996 fl) **S:** 12 kts **Dim:** 57.19 (51.50 pp) × 9.04 × 3.10
A: 1/533-mm torpedo tube **Electric:** 192 kw
M: 1 Klöckner-Humboldt-Deutz 8-cyl. diesel; 1 prop; 1,145 bhp (800 sust.)
Crew: 19 civilians + trials personnel

Remarks: Former trawler purchased 1963; commissioned after reconstruction 25-9-64. Civilian crew. To be replaced by a Type 749 trials ship at unspecified date. Has carried 1/533-mm TT and 3/324-mm ASW TT (III × 1) on deck; removed by 3-88.

◆ **1 weapons-trials barge** Bldr: Howaldstwerke, Kiel (In serv. 26-6-64)

Y 844 Barbara

Barbara (Y 844)—with spuds extended Leo Van Ginderen, 19

D: 3,500 tons (fl) **Dim:** 62.1 × 24.2 × 3.0 **Electric:** 1,650 kVA

Remarks: Non-self-propelled. Eight extending legs to anchor ship to bottom. Used test guns. Civilian crew. Helicopter deck, 12-ton crane. Named for the patron saint artillerists.

◆ **1 former Swedish submarine** Bldr: Karlskronavarvet, Karlskrona

	L	In serv.
Jonas (ex-*Valen*)	24-4-55	4-3-57

Jonas Gilbert Gyssels,

D: 785 tons surf. (1,000 sub.) **Dim:** 66.0 × 5.1 × 5.5
A: 4/533-mm TT fwd—deactivated
M: 2 Hedemora-Pielstick 16V-12PA diesels, 830 bhp each; 2 electric motors; 1 prop; 1,500 shp—inoperable

Remarks: Former Swedish Navy *Hajen*-class submarine stricken 1978. Hulk chased 1984 and towed to Kiel for conversion to tethered target and underwater platform for Trials Station 71 at Eckenförde to replace *Wilhelm Bauer.*

LAUNCHES

◆ **1 support launch** Bldr: Motorenwerk, Bremerhaven

Y 1686 AK 2

D: 46 tons **S:** 10 kts **Dim:** 19.80 × 4.40 × 1.20
Electron Equipt: Radar: 1/. . . nav. **M:** 1 M.A.N. diesel; 280 bh

◆ **1 high-speed personnel launch** Bldr: Lürssen, Vegesack

VB 2 (In serv. 1987)

D: 40 tons (fl) **S:** 30 kts **Dim:** 21.0 × 4.0 × . . . **M:** . . . diesels

◆ **5 Type 946 utility trials craft** Bldr: Hans Boost, Trier

	In serv.		In serv.
Y 1671 AK 1	3-85	Y 1677 MA 3	7-85
Y 1672 AK 3	3-85	Y 1687 Borby	9-85
Y 1676 MA 2	5-85		

D: 25 tons (fl) **S:** . . . **Dim:** 12.00 × 3.90 × 1.90 (moulded dept
M: 1 M.A.N. D2540 MTE diesel; 1 prop; 366 bhp **Crew:** . . .

LAUNCHES *(continued)*

AK 2 (Y 1686) Peter Voss, 5-88

B 2 Peter Voss, 4-88

1 (Y 1671) Leo Van Ginderen, 6-90

arks: MA in alphanumeric name means the craft is assigned to the Wil-shaven Arsenal. AK craft are assigned to the Kiel Arsenal, and AM craft are ned to Establishment 71 at Eckenförde.

♦ **Type 740 utility launches** Bldr: . . . (In serv. . . .)

73 AK 5 (ex-AM 4) Y 1675 AM 8
83 AK 6 Y 1684 PETER BACHMANN
74 AM 6

18.5 tons (fl) **S:** 18.5 kts **Dim:** 15.50 (14.40 wl) × 3.14 × 1.37
ectron Equipt: Radar: 1/. . . nav.
2 Klöckner-Humboldt-Deutz 6-cyl. diesels; 2 Schottel vertical cycloidal props; 500 bhp

arks: Sisters ST 1, ST 2, and AM 1 served as navigational training craft until sold -81. Y 1673 is used in radar trials, the others as general-purpose launches. AK are assigned to the Kiel Arsenal, and AM craft are assigned to Establishment 71 kenförde.

AK 5 (Y 1673) Leo Van Ginderen, 6-90

♦ **1 Type 743 support launch** Bldr: Fritz Staack, Lübeck (In serv. 1980)

Y 1679 AM 7

AM 7 (Y 1679) Hartmut Ehlers, 10-87

D: 27 tons (fl) **S:** 10 kts **Dim:** 16.30 × 4.38 × 1.06
Electron Equipt: Radar: 1/. . . nav.
M: 1 MWM diesel; 1 prop; 180 bhp

Remarks: Glass-reinforced plastic construction. Assigned to Establishment 71 at Eckenförde.

♦ **1 Type 945 trials craft/diving tender**

Y 1685 DÜKER (ex-AM 3, ex-MB 8)

Remarks: No characteristics available. Is assigned to Establishment 71 at Eckenförde.

Note: Type 740 trials craft EF 3 (Y 840, ex-UW 10, ex-U.K. FPB 5030, ex-German S 130), a former World War II torpedo boat, was stricken 18-1-91.

♦ **16 or more personnel launches**

V 1–16

Remarks: No data available.

V 14 Leo Van Ginderen, 6-91

TRAINING CRAFT

◆ **1 Type 368 ketch, former patrol/fishing cutter** (In serv. 1942–44?)

Y 834 Nordwind (ex-W 43)

Nordwind (Y 814)—white, with natural wood bulwarks
Leo Van Ginderen, 6-91

D: 100 tons (110 fl) **S:** 11 kts
Dim: 27.00 (24.00 hull, 21.48 pp) × 6.39 × 2.94
Electron Equipt: Radar: 1/Kelvin-Hughes 14/9 nav. **Crew:** 10 tot.
M: 1 Demag 5-cyl. diesel; 1 prop; 137 bhp **Range:** 1,200/7

Remarks: Taken over by U.S. Navy 1945; acquired 1-7-56 by German Navy. Wooden hull; 195 m^2 sail area. Operated for the Mürwik Naval School.

Note: There are also 70 smaller sail-training craft, all bearing names. Included are 26 Type 914 class, 5 m long; 10 Type 913 class, 7.64 m long; 25 Type 910 (most 10.46 m o.a.); 6 Type 911; and 1 Type 912.

ACCOMMODATIONS SHIPS

◆ **1 accommodations barge (Type 130)** Bldr: J.I. Setas, Hamburg

Y 811 Knurrhahn (In serv. 12-89)

D: . . . **Dim:** 48.0 × 14.0 × . . . **Crew:** 230 berths

Knurrhahn (Y 811) Gerhard Koop, 4-91

◆ **5 Vogtland-class self-propelled barracks ships (Type 650)** Bldr: Peenewerft, Wolgast

	In serv.	Based at
Y 890 Vogtland (ex-H 71)	5-9-84	Warnemünde
Y 892 Altmark (ex-H 11)	1984	Wilhelmshaven
Y 893 Uckermark (ex-H 91)	1985	Dranske-Bug
Y 894 Börde (ex-H 72)	1985	Rostock-Gehlsdorf
Y 895 Wische (ex-Harz, H 31)	1984	Dranske-Bug

D: 2,393 tons (fl) **S:** 8 kts **Dim:** 89.41 × 13.22 × 2.36
A: 4/25-mm Type 2M-8 AA (II × 1)—2/SA-N-5 SAM syst. (IV × 2)
Electron Equipt: Radar: 1/TSR-333 nav.
M: 2 Type 6VD 18/5 Al-1 diesels; 2 CP props; 944 bhp—bow-thruster
Crew: 200 accommodations in 2-, 4-, and 6-person staterooms.

Vogtland (Y 890) Hartmut Ehlers, 4-91

Börde (Y 894) Hartmut Ehlers, 4-

Remarks: NATO "Ohre" class. Built as Project 162 to replace East Germany's no self-propelled *Jugend*-class barracks/base ships and officially described as "Wohn-un Kampfschiff." Equipped with bow-thruster, one 8-ton Type 2Hy SWK8 electrohydra lic crane. Are equipped with a cinema, gymnasium, sauna, "club," and bakery. M can seat 84 at one sitting. Y 894 launched 21-2-84. Propulsion engines to be remov Sister *Havilland* (Y 892) stricken 31-12-91.

Note: The old *Jugend*-class (Project 62) barracks barge *Maria* was still at Peenew in 9-90 to support crews of ships and craft under construction; she was not taken o for *Bundesmarine* service. A sister was converted 1990 for service as a floating hotel 143 guests.

MISCELLANEOUS SERVICE CRAFT

◆ **2 pollution-control ships (Type 738)** Bldr: C. Lühring, Brake

	Laid down	L	In serv.
Y 1643 Bottsand	14-11-83	22-9-84	26-10-84
Y 1644 Eversand	. . .	. . .	11-6-88

Bottsand (Y 1643) Leo Van Ginderen,

Eversand (Y 1644)—note ribbed sides to superstructure, lifebo slipway at stern Hartmut Ehler

MISCELLANEOUS SERVICE CRAFT *(continued)*

D: approx. 1,100 tons (fl) **S:** 10 kts **Dim:** 46.30 × 12.00 × 3.10
Electron Equipt: Radar: 1/. . . nav.
M: 1 Deutz BA 12M 816 diesels, 2 rudder-props, 1,600 bhp— 2 omnidirectional bow-thrusters; 400 bhp
Crew: 3 officers, 3 unlicensed (civilians)

Remarks: 500 grt/650 dwt. Twin hulls, hinged near the stern to open scissors-fashion to 65-deg., leaving a 42-m-wide Vee opening to collect oil spills at the rate of approx. 140 m^3/hr, at a speed of 1 knot. When folded can also be used as coastal tankers and bunkerage craft. Six cargo/spill tanks totaling 790 m^3. Concept known as THOR (Twin Hull Oil Recovery), which is also the name of a smaller civil-operated prototype completed in 1983 and operated by the Ministry of Transport. Y 1643 built for the Niedersachsen Ministry for the Environment, but turned over to the *Bundesmarine* on loan, 24-1-85.

◆ **2 Type 710 tank-cleaning craft** Bldr: Deutsche Werft, Hamburg

	Laid down	L	In serv.
Y 1641 Förde	12-1-67	10-3-67	14-12-67
Y 1642 Jade	18-5-67	19-7-67	6-11-67

Jade (Y 1642) Leo Van Ginderen, 9-88

D: 1,830 tons (fl) **S:** 8 kts **Dim:** 58.46 × 10.40 × 4.10 (light)
Electron Equipt: Radar: 1/. . . nav.
M: 1 MWM 16-cyl. diesel; 1 prop; 390 bhp **Range:** 750/8
Crew: 16 tot. (civilian)

Remarks: For steam-cleaning fuel tanks and for sludge removal. To strike 30-10-92 and 27-5-92, respectively.

Note: Former *Volksmarine* sludge/bilgewater disposal tanker *Vilm* (C 112, ex-C 12) was stricken 6-90 at Kröslin.

◆ **1 ex-East German Breitling-class navigational buoy tender (Type 680)** Bldr: Peenewerft, Wolgast (In serv. 1967–68)

Y 1653 Kollicker Ort (ex-D 116)

Kollicker Ort (Y 1653) Hartmut Ehlers, 3-91

D: 151.8 tons (fl) **S:** 11 kts **Dim:** 29.50 × 6.20 × 1.86
Electron Equipt: Radar: 1/TSR-333 nav.
M: 1 Type 8NVD 36.1A diesel; 1 prop; 580 bhp **Crew:** . . . tot.

Remarks: The only one of nine sisters formerly operated by the East German Naval Hydrographic Service (SHD) to be taken over for *Bundesmarine* use.

The larger SHD buoy tender/survey ships *Dornbusch* of the Polish-built Finik (Project 872) class and the Polish-built *Buk II* of the Kamenka class were taken over by the German Hydrographic Institute.

◆ **2 Type 711 self-propelled floating cranes** Bldr: Rheinwerft, Walsum

Y 875 Hiev (In serv. 2-10-62) Y 876 Griep (In serv. 15-5-63)

Hiev (Y 875) Stefan Terzibaschitsch, 6-87

D: 1,830 tons (1,875 fl) **S:** 6 kts **Dim:** 52.9 × 22.0 × 2.1
M: 3 MWM 600-bhp diesels, electric drive; 3 vertical cycloidal props; 1,425 shp
Electric: 358 kVA **Crew:** 12 tot. (civilians)

Remarks: Electric crane capacity: 100 tons.

Note: Former East German floating cranes M 11 and M 34 were not taken over, nor was the pile-driver *Der Bock*.

◆ **12 Type 737 fuel barges** (In serv. 1986–87)

Ölschute 1–12

Ölschute 2 Leo Van Ginderen, 6-91

D: . . . **Dim:** 20.00 × . . . × . . . **Cargo:** 150 tons

◆ **3 Type 718 battery-charging craft** Bldrs: LP 1, 3: Jadewerft, Wilhelmshaven; LP 2: Oelkers, Hamburg

LP 1 (In serv. 18-2-64) LP 2 (In serv. 17-4-64) LP 3 (In serv. 16-9-74)

LP 1 Stefan Terzibaschitsch, 6-90

MISCELLANEOUS SERVICE CRAFT *(continued)*

D: 192 tons (234 fl) **S:** 8 kts **Dim:** 27.6 × 7.0 × 1.6 **Crew:** 6 tot.
M: 1 MTU diesel; 250 bhp **Electric:** 960 kw (LP 3: 1,110 kw)

Remarks: Each has two 405-kw generators and one (LP 3: two) 150-kw generator for charging submarine batteries. LP 3 is 7.5 m in beam, 1.8 m draft, 267 tons (fl).

FLOATING DRY DOCKS

◆ **2 Type 712** Bldr: Krupp, Rheinhausen

HEBEWERK 2 (In serv. 15-3-61) HEBEWERK A (In serv. 13-1-61)

D: 1,000 tons **Dim:** 66.01 × 21.10 × . . .

Remarks: Serviced by 4 Type-713 "Hebeponton": 500 tons, 56 m by 14.8 m.

◆ **1 Type 714 self-propelled** Bldr: Flenderwerft, Lübeck (In serv. circa 1945)

Y 879 SCHWIMMDOCK B

Schwimmdock B (Y 879)—with submarine compression chamber aboard Stefan Terzibaschitsch, 6-91

D: 4,500 tons **S:** . . . **Dim:** 156.00 × 25.00 × 3.50
M: 4 MWM 16-cyl. diesels, electric drive; 2 Schottel props; 500 shp

Remarks: In German naval service 26-10-63 at Kiel. The propellers are at the starboard forward and port aft corners.

◆ **1 Type 715** Bldr: Howaldtswerke, Hamburg (In serv. 1961)

Y 842 SCHWIMMDOCK 3

D: 8,000 tons **Dim:** 164.0 × 30.0 × 3.5

Remarks: Seven-pontoon sectional dock.

◆ **1 Type 715** Bldr: Flenderwerke, Lübeck (In serv. 8-9-67)

DRUCKDOCK *("Dock C")*

D: . . . tons **Dim:** 93.0 × 26.5 × 3.6

ARMY RIVER ENGINEERS

Organized into four companies located at four cities on the Rhine. Each company has 9 landing craft, 3 patrol craft, and a tug. Pendant numbers are organized by location: 80011–80031 at Krefield, 80111–80131 at Koblenz, 85011–85031 at Neuwied, and 85111–85131 at Wiesbaden.

◆ **12 patrol craft** Bldr: Hitzler, Regensburg (In serv. 1953–54)

Army patrol craft S-80102 Leo Van Ginderen, 8-85

D: 27 tons (fl) **S:** 20.5 kts **Dim:** 25.0 × 3.8 × 1.0
A: 4/12.7-mm mg (I × 4) **Electron Equipt:** Radar: 1/. . . nav.
M: 2 MWM RHS 418A diesels; 2 props; 440 bhp **Crew:** 7 tot.

◆ **22 Mannheim 59-class landing craft** Bldr: Schiffs und Motorenwerke AG, Mannheim (In serv. 1959–60)

D: 89 tons (200 fl) **S:** 9 kts **Dim:** 27.4 × 7.2 × 1.2
A: 4/7.62-mm mg (I × 4) **Electron Equipt:** Radar: 1/. . . nav.
M: 2 MWM RHS 518A diesels; 2 props; 432 bhp **Crew:** 9 tot.

Mannheim-class landing craft F-85032 Leo Van Ginderen, 198

Remarks: Cargo: 70 tons normal/90 max. Five served in *Bundesmarine* until 4-6 Bow ramp, shallow tank deck. One was transferred to Tonga during 1989.

◆ **13 Bodan-class landing craft** Bldr: . . .

Bodan-class landing craft F-85023 Leo Van Ginderen, 8-

D: 150 tons (fl) **S:** 6 kts **Dim:** 30.0 × 5.8 × . . .
A: 1/20-m AA **M:** 4 MWM diesels; 4 Schottel props; 596 bhp

Remarks: Each consists of 12 pontoon sections. Cargo capacity: 90 tons.

◆ **4 river tugs** Bldr: . . .

T 80001 T 80101 T 85001 T 85101

D: . . . **S:** 11 kts **Dim:** 28.0 × 5.9 × 1.2
A: 2/7.62-mm mg (I × 2) **Electron Equipt:** Radar: 1/. . . nav.
M: 2 KHD SBF 12M716 diesels; 2 props; 760 bhp **Crew:** 7 tot.

Note: The German Army also operates the following craft:

◆ **144 MB 3 river-crossing craft** Bldr: . . . (In serv. 1988–91)

Army MB 3-class river-crossing craft Leo Van Ginderen,

D: 0.39 tons light (4.7 tons fl) **S:** 8.5 kts loaded/16 kts light
Dim: 7.00 (6.45 pp) × 3.24 × 0.45 loaded
M: 2 diesels; 2 pumpjets; 356 bhp **Crew:** 2 + 10 passengers

SEA BORDER PATROL
(Bundesgrenzschutz-See)

Note: A separate paramilitary force of 1,000 men. Craft have blue hulls with superstructures. Several SA 330 Puma helicopters are used. Three *Sassnitz* 620)-class former East German patrol boats were taken over late in 1991; see pag

PATROL BOATS

◆ **1 seagoing patrol boat** Bldr: Elsflether Werft, Elsfleth

	Laid down	L	In serv.
BG 21 BREDSTEDT	3-3-88	18-12-88	24-5-89

D: 673 tons (fl) **S:** 25 kts (12 cruise)
Dim: 65.40 (57.25 pp) × 9.20 × 2.92
A: 1/40-mm AA **Electron Equipt:** Radar: . . .

PATROL BOATS *(continued)*

:edstedt (BG 21) Leo Van Ginderen, 1991

M: 1 MTU 20V 1163 TB93 diesel; 1 prop; 10,880 bhp (8,323 sust.)—A.E.G. diesel-electric cruise set; 500 shp
Electric: 788 kw (2 × 344 kw, MTU 12V 183 diesels driving; 1 × 100 kw)
Range: 2,450/20; 7,000/10 **Crew:** 13 + 9 spare

marks: Helicopter platform aft. Ordered 21-11-87. Trials began 20-5-89. Has a rn ramp-launched Avon Searider inspection/rescue launch.

3 former East German Kondor-I-class (Project 89.1) patrol minesweepers Bldr: Peenewerft, Wolgast (In serv. 1968-70)

31 Boltenhagen (ex-GS 09, ex-G 443)
32 Kühlungsborn (ex-GS 07, ex- G 445)
33 Ahrenskoop (ex-GS 08, ex-G 415)

): 327 tons (377 fl) **S:** 19 kts **Dim:** 52.00 × 6.70 × 2.40
: 2/25-mm Type 2M-8AA (II × 1)
lectron Equipt:
Radar: 1/TSR-333 nav.—Sonar: Tamir-11 high-freq.
I: 2 Type 40DM diesels; 2 CP Kort-nozzle props; 4,400 bhp (4,000 sust.)
rew: 30 tot.

marks: Typed "High Seas Minesweepers-Short" by the *Volksmarine.* Retained in ice with East German crews. *Boltenhagen* replaced *Templin* (ex-GS 06, ex-G 442) G 31 during mid-1991. Retained as spares sources are sisters *Ückermünde* (GS 01, 411), *Demmin* (GS 02, ex-G 422), *Malchin* (GS 03, ex-. . .), *Altentreptow* (GS 04, 414), and *Pasewalk* (GS 05, ex-G 423). To strike 1992.

Neustadt class Bldrs: Lürssen, Vegesack

	Laid down	L	In serv.
11 Neustadt	25-11-68	27-2-69	25-11-69
2 Bad Bramstedt	10-1-69	2-4-69	1969
4 Duderstadt	21-2-69	3-6-69	1970
5 Eschwege	27-3-69	16-9-69	19-3-70
6 Alsfeld	31-5-69	11-11-69	1970
7 Bayreuth	15-9-69	9-1-70	1970
8 Rosenheim	8-11-69	12-3-70	11-70

adt (BG 11) Hartmut Ehlers, 5-89

D: 191 tons (218 fl) **S:** 30 kts **Dim:** 38.50 (36.00 pp) × 7.00 × 2.15
A: 2/40-mm Bofors AA (I × 2)
Electron Equipt: Radar: 1/Kelvin-Hughes 14/9 nav.
M: 2 Maybach 16-cyl. diesels; 2 props; 7,200 bhp—cruise engine: 1 MWM diesel; 1 prop; 685 bhp
Electric: 156 kw **Range:** 450/27 **Fuel:** 15 tons **Crew:** 23 tot.

Remarks: Two planned additional units canceled. Sister *Uelzen* (BG 13) was transferred to Mauritania in 2-90.

PATROL CRAFT

♦ **2 Schlutup-class river patrol craft** Bldr: . . . (In serv. 1988)

BG . . . Schlutup BG . . . .

Small patrol boat BG 7 Stefan Terzibaschitsch, 6-90

D: . . . **S:** 20 kts **Dim:** 10.0 × . . . × . . . **M:** . . .

Remarks: Used for border patrol at Lübeck. Also in use are former Army River Engineers patrol craft BG 6 and BG 7: 6 kts, 15.0 m o.a.

♦ **9 former East German Bremse (GB 23) class** Bldr: VEB Yachtswerft, Berlin (In serv. 1971–72)

GS 23	GS 30 (ex-G 734)	GS 31	GS 32 (ex-G 732)
GS 40 (ex-G 731)	GS 42	GS 51 (ex-G 767)	GS 52
GS 41			

GS 42 and a sister Hartmut Ehlers, 4-91

D: 25 tons (fl) **S:** 14 kts **Dim:** 23.13 (20.97 pp) × 4.58 × 1.50
A: small arms **Electron Equipt:** Radar: 1/. . . nav.
M: 1 Type 6VD 18/15 diesel; 1 prop; 496 bhp **Crew:** 10 tot.

Remarks: Manned by former East German crews. Formerly used by the East German Border Guard for patrol on rivers and inland waterways. To be discarded 1992.

Note: Also taken over were two East German MB 13 launches, G 646 and G 648.

SERVICE CRAFT

♦ **1 tug** Bldr: Mützelbeldt-Werft, Cuxhaven (L: 29-1-76)

BG 5 Rettin

Rettin (BG 5) Peter Voss, 1989

SERVICE CRAFT *(continued)*

D: 99.9 grt **S:** 9 kts **Dim:** 22.5 (20.0 pp) × 6.6 × 2.9
Electron Equipt: Radar: 1 Kelvin-Hughes 14/9
M: 2 MWM diesels; 1 prop; 590 bhp **Crew:** 4 tot.

Note: Numerous other Federal Republic of Germany government and local agencies operate patrol boats and craft, including city police forces and the Customs Service.

Patrol boat Maithabu of the Gewässerschutz at Kiel Leo Van Ginderen, 6-90

Police patrol and rescue boat Fehmarn—based at Heiligenhafen Hartmut Ehlers, 8-90

Police boat Bremen 2—based at Bremerhaven Leo Van Ginderen, 1987

Customs Service patrol boat Bremerhaven—with rescue/inspection launch on stern slipway Hartmut Ehlers, 5-8

Customs Service patrol boat Kniepsand Hartmut Ehlers, 5

Customs patrol boat Helgoland Leo Van Ginderen, 1

FISHERIES PROTECTION SHIPS

Note: Operated by the Ministry of Food and Agriculture. Have black hulls "*Fischereischutz*" (Fisheries Protection) on sides where appropriate, gray superstructures, buff-colored masts, and orange boats.

◆ **1 fisheries patrol ship** Bldr: Orenstein & Koppel

SEEFALKE (In serv. 4-8-81)

Seefalke—note folding edge to helo deck Peter Voss,

FISHERIES PROTECTION SHIPS *(continued)*

D: 2,386 tons (fl) **S:** 20.5 kts **Dim:** 83.10 (76.20 pp) × 12.80 × 4.70
M: 2 MWM TBD 510 L8 diesels; 2 CP props; 8,000 bhp **Crew:** 29 tot.

Remarks: 1,790 grt. Equipped to operate in East Greenland Sea; fin stabilizers, elaborate navigation equipment, helicopter platform, bow-thruster, 7-bed infirmary.

♦ **1 fisheries patrol ship** Bldr: Lürssen, Vegesack

MEERKATZE (In serv. 1976)

Meerkatze Peter Voss, 3-84

D: 2,386 grt **S:** 15 kts **Dim:** 76.5 × 11.8 × 5.5
M: 3 MWM diesels, electric drive; 2 props; 2,300 shp
Crew: 30 ship's company + 15 passengers/scientists

♦ **1 fisheries patrol ship** Bldr: Schlichting, Travemünde

FRITHJOF (In serv. 1967)

D: 2,140 tons **S:** 15 kts **Dim:** 76.0 × 11.8 × 5.2
M: 3 Maybach diesels, electric drive; 2 props; 2,650 shp
Crew: 35 tot.

1 Kondor-I-class former minesweeper Bldr: Peenewerft, Wolgast (In serv. 1968)

WARNEMÜNDE (ex-. . .)

D: 327 tons (377 fl) **S:** 18 kts **Dim:** 52.00 × 6.70 × 2.40
Electron Equipt: Radar: 1/. . . nav.
M: 2 Type 40 Dm diesels; 2 CP props; 4,000 bhp **Crew:** . . . tot.

Remarks: Former East German Border Guard patrol minesweeper taken over for fisheries protection duties in former East German waters. Reportedly the second or third Kondor-I built.

0 (+1) new construction fisheries research ship Bldr: Kröger, Rendsburg

. . . . (In serv. 1993)

D: 999 grt **S:** 11.5 kts **Dim:** 56.2 × 11.4 × 2.8
M: 2 MTU diesels, electric drive; 1 prop; 1,400 shp
Crew: 16 ship's company + 7 scientists

1 fisheries research ship Bldr: Sieghold, Bremerhaven

SOLEA (In serv. 1974)

Solea Leo Van Ginderen, 10-75

D: 337 grt **S:** 12 kts **Dim:** 33.5 × 9.0 × 3.6
M: 1 Deutz diesel; 640 bhp **Crew:** 11 ship's company + 5 scientists

♦ **1 fisheries research ship** Bldr: Schlichting, Travemünde

WALTHER HERWIG (In serv. 1972)

Walther Herwig Peter Voss, 9-83

D: 2,500 tons **S:** 15.5 kts **Dim:** 77.0 × 14.9 × 5.2
M: 2 M.A.N. diesels; 2 props; 3,380 bhp
Crew: 40 ship's company + 14 scientists

GOVERNMENT CIVIL RESEARCH SHIPS

Note: Operated by the German Hydrographic Institute, which is subordinated to the Ministry of Transport. The Ministry of Transport also has the Water and Navigation Board, which operates three icebreakers (*Hanse, Max Waldeck,* and the former East German *Stephen Jantzen; Hanse* is stationed in Finland) and navigational buoy tenders (*Walter Körte, Kurt Burkowitz, Otto Treplin, Gustav Meyer, Konrad Meisel, Barsmeister Brehme,* and *J.G. Repsold*); also subordinated to the Water and Navigation Board is the Maritime Police (*Schiffahrtspolizei*), which operates the oil-pollution recovery and salvage ships *Mellum, Scharhörn, Oland, Nordsee, Bruno Illing,* and *Kiel.*

Schiffahrtspolizei pollution-control ship Scharhörn Peter Voss, 7-89

Schiffahrtspolizei pollution-control ship Bruno Illing Peter Voss, 11-88

OCEANOGRAPHIC RESEARCH AND HYDROGRAPHIC SURVEY SHIPS

◆ **1 polar research ship and transport**

	Bldr	Laid down	L	In serv.
Polarstern	Howaldtswerke, Kiel	22-9-81	8-1-82	8-12-82

Polarstern Leo Van Ginderen, 12-86

D: 15,000 tons (fl) **S:** 15.5 kts
Dim: 117.55 (102.20 pp) × 25.00 × 10.50
M: 4 Deutz diesels, electric drive; 2 Kort-nozzle CP props; 21,120 shp
Electric: 5,400 kVA × 2,580 kw
Crew: 36 ship's company, 40 scientists, 30 relief staff

Remarks: 3,900 dwt. Built for the Alfred Wegener Institute for Polar Research, Bremerhaven. Capable of carrying 1,500 tons of liquid cargo, plus stores to support Germany's Antarctic research station; 100 tons of provisions are carried in refrigerated vans on the forecastle. Helicopter deck and hangar. Can break 2-m ice; shell plating 43.5 mm at waterline. Has bow and stern side-thrusters. INDAS V system ("Integrated Navigation system with Data Acquisition and automatic ship's Steering"). Received Krupp-Atlas Hydrosweep and Parasound echo-sounders in 1989.

◆ **2 Alkor class**

	Bldr	Laid down	L	In serv.
Alkor	Cassens Werft, Emden	22-5-89	11-9-89	2-5-90
Friedrich Heincke	Detlef Hegemann, Berne	. . .	24-11-89	8-6-90

Alkor Peter Voss, 5-91

D: 1,200 tons **S:** 12.7 kts **Dim:** 30.0 × 8.5 × 2.2
M: 3 diesel alternator sets (600 bhp each), 1 motor; 1,200 shp
Range: 7,500/12 **Electric:** 155 kw
Crew: 11 ship's company + 13 scientists

Remarks: *Alkor* operates for the Institute for Sea Studies, Kiel; *Heincke* operates for the Helgoland Biological Institute and replaces a ship of the same name.

◆ **2 Atair class** Bldr: Krögerwerft, Rendsburg

Atair (In serv. 3-8-87) Wega (In serv. 14-10-90)

D: 1,075 tons (fl) **S:** 11.6 kts **Dim:** 51.50 (49.80 pp) × 11.40 × 3.20
M: diesel-electric: 2 MTU 8V396 TC 53 diesels (740 bhp each), 2/463 kw generator sets (*Wega:* 510 kw); 1 Kort-nozzle CP prop; 800 shp (*Wega:* 1,034 shp)
Range: 2,000/10 **Fuel:** 125 tons **Electric:** 276 kw
Crew: 16 crew + 7 scientists

Remarks: 999 grt. Intended as coastal survey and shipwreck search ships. Keel for *Atair* laid 4-87. *Wega,* with more powerful propulsion plant, was laid down 14-12-88 and launched 2-3-90. Replaced earlier ships of the same name.

Wega Peter Voss, 2-91

◆ **1 multipurpose research vessel** Bldr: Schlichting Werft, Travemünde

Meteor (In serv. 15-3-86)

Meteor Peter Voss, 7-8

D: 3,128 tons (fl) **S:** 14 kts **Dim:** 98.50 × 16.50 × 4.80
M: diesel-electric; 1 prop, 4,760 shp **Range:** 10,000/14
Crew: 38 ship's company, 29 scientific party

Remarks: Has asymmetrical stern form and "Grim Wheel," free-wheeling prop aba regular propeller to improve performance by roughly 10 percent. Launched 3-9-8 Previous *Meteor* sold 12-85 to New Zealand.

◆ **1 small research ship** Bldr: Schlömer, Oldersum

Uthörn (In serv. 1982)

D: 250 grt **S:** 10.4 kts **Dim:** 30.5 × 8.5 × 2.2
M: 2 MWM diesels; 1 prop; 626 bhp **Crew:** . . .

◆ **1 oceanographic and hydrographic research ship** Bldr: Schlichtingwerft, Travemünde

Gauss (In serv. 6-5-80)

Gauss Peter Voss,

OCEANOGRAPHIC RESEARCH AND HYDROGRAPHIC SURVEY SHIPS *(continued)*

D: 1,372 tons (1,813 fl) **S:** 13.5 kts
Dim: 68.7 (61.0 pp) × 13.0 × 4.25
Electron Equipt: Radar: 1 Raytheon 1660/12SR nav., 1 Raytheon RM1650/9 × R nav.
M: 3 MAK 331 AK 800-hp diesels, electric drive; 1 prop; 1,647 shp
Electric: 220 kVA **Range:** 4,000/13.5
Crew: 19 ship's company + 12 scientists

Remarks: Has special free-wheeling prop aft of propulsion propeller. Equipped with Becker flap-rudder, Denny-Brown fin stabilizers, and a 725-hp drop-down bow-thruster. Ship's service power from main engine generators. Grim Wheel propeller substituted, added 9 percent to fuel efficiency. Has SATCOMM capability.

♦ **1 Soviet Finik (Projekt 872) class** Bldr: Stocznia Pólnocna, Gdańsk

Dornbusch (In serv. 12-80)

D: 1,200 tons (fl) **S:** 13 kts **Dim:** 61.30 x11.80 (10.80 wl) × 3.27
Electron Equipt: Radar: 2/Don-2 nav.
M: 2 Cegielski-Sulzer diesels; 2 CP props; 1,920 bhp (plus two 75-kw electric motors for quiet, 6-kt operations)—176 shp bow-thruster
Electric: 675 kVA **Endurance:** 15 days **Range:** 3,000/13
Crew: 5 officers, 23 men

Remarks: Replaced a navigational buoy tender/light cable layer of the same name. Acquired at the unification of Germany and transferred from the former East German Naval Hydrographic Service (SHD). Intended for navigational buoy tending and hydrographic survey, for which 4 echo-sounders are fitted. Will probably not long be retained.

♦ **1 modified Kondor-II class** Bldr: Peenewerft, Wolgast

Carl Fr. Gauss (In serv. 1976)

arl Fr. Gauss 1990

D: 490 tons (fl) **S:** 19 kts **Dim:** 56.52 × 7.76 × 2.35
Electron Equipt: Radar: 1/TSR-33 nav.
M: 2 Type 40DM diesels; 2 CP props; 4,000 bhp **Crew:** 40 tot.

marks: Acquired from the East German Naval Hydrographic Service (SHD) at the fication of Germany. Built on a Kondor-II minesweeper hull; no Kort-nozzle shrouds props. Carries small hydrographic survey launch to starboard and several smaller ts at the extreme stern.

1 oceanographic research ship Bldr: Schichau,Unterweser

seidon (In serv. 1976)

eidon Peter Voss, 1989

D: 1,050 grt **S:** 15 kts **Dim:** 58.0 × 11.4 × . . .
M: MWM diesels; 1,800 bhp

♦ **1 small oceanographic research ship** Bldr: Schichau, Bremerhaven

Victor Hensen (L: 1975)

Victor Hensen Leo Van Ginderen, 5-88

D: 423 grt **S:** 12 kts **Dim:** 37.04 (33.99 pp) × 9.50 × 3.07
M: 2 MTU 6-cyl. diesels; 1 prop; . . . bhp **Crew:** 28 tot.

Remarks: Operated for the Alfred Wegener Institute.

♦ **1 hydrographic survey ship** Bldr: Jadewerft, Wilhelmshaven

Komet (In serv. 1969)

Komet—note the three survey launches each side Peter Voss, 1989

D: 1,253 grt **S:** 15 kts **Dim:** 68.0 × 11.5 × 4.0
M: 2 Maybach diesels; 1 prop; 2,650 bhp **Crew:** 42 tot.

♦ **1 Soviet Kamenka class** Bldr: Stocznia Pólnocna, Gdańsk

Buk II (In serv. 1969)

D: 703 tons (fl) **S:** 12 kts **Dim:** 53.50 × 9.10 × 2.60
Electron Equipt: Radar: 1/TSR-33 nav.
M: 2 Zgoda-Sulzer 6 NVD 48 A2U diesels; 2 CP props; 1,765 bhp
Range: 4,000/10 **Crew:** 40 tot.

Remarks: 480-grt buoy tender and survey ship; one 5-ton crane. Acquired from the former East German Naval Hydrographic Service (SHD) at the unification of Germany.

SERVICE CRAFT

♦ **up to 11 Breitling-class former East German navigational buoy tenders** Bldr: Peenewerft, Wolgast (In serv. 1967–1977)

D: 151.8 tons **S:** 11 kts **Dim:** 29.50 × 6.20 × 1.86
Electron Equipt: Radar: 1/TSR-33 nav.
M: 1 Type 8NVD 36.1A diesel; 1 prop; 580 bhp **Crew:** . . . tot.

Remarks: Acquired at the unification of Germany from the former Naval Hydrographic Service. Names of available units include: *Arkona, Breitling, Darsser Ort,*

GERMANY, FEDERAL REPUBLIC OF GERMANY *(continued)*
SERVICE CRAFT *(continued)*

Esper Ort, Gellen, Golwitz, Grass Ort, Landtieff, Palmer Ort, Ramzow, and *Rosen Ort.* Sister *Kollicker Ort* (Y 1653) serves in the *Bundesmarine.*

Gellen Hartmut Ehlers, 9-90

◆ **1 former East German floating workshop** Bldr: VEB Yachtswerft, Berlin

MERCATOR (In serv. 1989)

D: 138 tons (fl) **Dim:** 37.06 × 5.33 × 0.82
Electric: 66 kVA (1 × 51 kVA, 1 × 15 kVA) **Crew:** 3 tot.

Remarks: Acquired from the East German Naval Hydrographic Service at the unification of Germany. Sister to *Volksmarine* N 88, which was not taken over.

GHANA

Republic of Ghana

Personnel (1991): 800 total

Naval Aviation: Two Fokker F 27 400M maritime patrol aircraft

FISHERIES PATROL AND SEARCH-AND-RESCUE BOATS

◆ **2 Modified FBP 57 class** Bldr: Lürssen, Vegesack, Germany

	Laid down	L	In serv.
P 28 ACHIMOTA	1978	14-3-79	27-3-81
P 29 YOGAGA	1978	14-3-79	27-3-81

Yogaga (P 29) Ben Sullivan, 5-89

D: 380 tons (410 fl) **S:** 30 kts **Dim:** 58.10 × 7.62 × 2.83
A: 1/76-mm OTO Melara DP—1/40-mm Bofors AA
Electron Equipt:
Radar: 1/Decca 1226 nav., 1/Thomson-CSF Canopus-A surf. search
M: 3 MTU 16V538 TB91 diesels; 3 props; 10,800 bhp **Crew:** 40 tot.

Remarks: Have LIOD optronic gun director atop pilothouse. Carry 250 rounds 76-mm, 750 rounds 40-mm. Carry rubber dinghy for air/sea rescue and inspection purposes. P 29 completed refit by Swan Hunter, U.K., 8-5-89; P 28 in refit in France 1991–92. P 29 was hit by mortar fire during the Liberian civil war, 1990.

◆ **2 Modified FPB 45 class** Bldr: Lürssen, Vegesack, Germany

	Laid down	L	In serv.
P 26 DZATA	16-1-78	19-9-79	4-12-79
P 27 SEBO	1-78	19-9-79	2-5-80

Dzata (P 261) Ben Sullivan, 5-89

D: 212 tons (252 fl) **S:** 30 kts
Dim: 44.90 (42.25 wl) × 7.00 × 2.50 (props)
A: 2/40-mm Bofors AA (I × 2)
Electron Equipt: Radar: 1/Decca 1226 nav.
M: 2 MTU 16V538 TB91 diesels; 2 props; 7,200 bhp (6,000 sust.)
Electric: 408 kVA **Range:** 1,100/25; 2,000/15
Crew: 5 officers, 30 enlisted

Remarks: Flare RL on sides of both 40-mm mounts. Planned Thomson-CSF Canopus-A radar not mounted. P 26 completed refit by Swan Hunter, U.K., 8-5-89; P 27 badly in need of refit by 1991.

Note: The two Spear-class patrol craft received in 1978 had been discarded by 1990, as had the two Sea Truck service launches.

GREECE

Hellenic Republic

Personnel (1991): 19,500 total, including 2,600 officers and 12,800 12-month conscripts

Naval Aviation: Four Alouette-III ASW helicopters (No. 1 Squadron) fitted with AS-12 antiship, wire-guided missiles and 16 Agusta-Bell AB-212 helicopters (No. 2 and No. 3 Squadrons) are based at Eleusis. Six to twelve new ASW helicopters are to be acquired.

The Air Force has 14 HU-16B Grumman Albatross amphibians for maritime reconnaissance; they carry mixed Navy/Air Force crews and have been modernized by Grumman with MEL Super Searcher radars, IFF gear, and Marconi LAPADS sonobuoy signal processors. The HU-16Bs are to be replaced by 6 modernized P-3A Orion maritime patrol aircraft to be transferred by the United States.

SUBMARINES

◆ **8 Type 209/1100 and 209/1200*** Bldr: Howaldtswerke, Kiel

	Laid down	L	In serv.
S 110 GLAVKOS	1-9-68	15-9-70	5-11-71
S 111 NEREUS	15-1-69	7-6-71	10-2-72
S 112 TRITON	1-6-69	19-10-71	23-11-72
S 113 PROTEUS	1-10-69	1-2-72	23-11-72
S 116 POSEIDON*	15-4-76	21-3-78	22-3-79
S 117 AMFRITITI*	16-9-76	14-6-78	14-8-79
S 118 OKEANOS*	1-10-76	16-11-78	15-11-79
S 119 PONTOS*	15-1-77	22-3-79	29-4-80

D: 990 tons light/1,100 surf./1,207 sub. (S 116–119: 1,185 surf./1,285 sub.)
S: 22 kts max. sub. for 15 min., 11.5 kts surfaced
Dim: 54.10 (116–118: 56.1) × 6.20 × 5.90
A: 8/533-mm TT fwd (+6 reserve torpedoes)
Electron Equipt:
Radar: Thomson-CSF Calypso-II—EW: . . .
Sonar: Atlas AN 526 passive, CSU AN 406 A9 active, DUUX-2 passive ranging

Amfrititi (S 117) Greek Navy,

SUBMARINES *(continued)*

Okeanos (S 118) Greek Navy, 1990

M: diesel-electric propulsion; 4 MTU 12V493 TY60 diesels (550 bhp each), each linked to an AEG generator of 420 kw; 1 Siemens motor; 1 prop; 5,000 shp
Range: 25/20; 230/8; 400/4 sub.; 8,600/4 snorkel (S 116–119: 28/20; 466/4 sub.; 11,300/4 snorkel
Crew: 6 officers, 25 enlisted **Fuel:** 49 tons (S 116–119: 85 tons)

Remarks: Diving depth 250 m. All have battery arrangement with four groups of 120 cells producing 11,500 amp./hr. The second group have a higher bow and H.S.A. SINBADS M8/42 weapons control with Mk 8 torpedo f.c.s. All have two periscopes.

S 110 through S 113, under a contract placed 5-5-89 in Germany, are being updated, one at Howaldtswerke, Kiel, and the other three at Salamis, to the same standard as the West German Type 206A. Receiving Sub-Harpoon launch capability from new HDW torpedo-tube launch system, new electronics, Krupp-Atlas CSU 83-90-series sonar suite (with DBQS-21 active set), U.S. Unisys fire-control system, etc. The work began in 1991 and is to be completed in 1996.

◆ **1 ex-U.S. Guppy III class** Bldr: Portsmouth Naval SY, New Hampshire

	Laid down	L	In serv.
S 115 Katsonis (ex-*Remora,* SS 487)	5-3-45	12-7-45	3-1-46

atsonis (S 115) D. Dervissis, 9-79

D: 1,660 tons std./1,975 surf./2,540 sub.
S: 17.2 kts surf./14.5 kts sub.
Dim: 99.52 × 8.23 × 5.18
A: 10/533-mm TT (6 fwd, 4 aft; 24 torpedoes)
Electron Equipt:
Radar: 1/SS-2A—EW: WLR-1 intercept
Sonar: BQG-4 (PUFFS) passive ranging, BQR-2B passive, BQA-8 intercept, BQC-1 underwater telephone, BQS-4C active
M: 4 Fairbanks-Morse 38D8Q 10-cyl. diesels (1,600 bhp each), electric drive; 2 props; 6,400 bhp/5,480 shp
Range: 10,000–12,000/10; 95/5 sub. **Crew:** 8 officers, 78 enlisted

marks: Purchased 29-10-73. Guppy III conversion completed 1962 at Pearl Harbor . Employed primarily for training and will soon be discarded.

1 ex-U.S. Guppy IIA class Bldr: Manitowoc SB, Wisconsin

	Laid down	L	In serv.
114 Papanikolis (ex-*Hardhead,* SS 365)	7-7-43	12-12-43	18-4-44

panikolis (S 114) D. Dervissis, 9-79

: 1,517 tons std./1,870 surf./2,440 sub. **S:** 18 kts surf./13.5 kts sub.
im: 93.60 × 8.23 × 5.18
: 10/533-mm TT (6 fwd, 4 aft, 24 torpedoes)
lectron Equipt:
Radar: 1/SS-2A—EW: WLR-1 intercept
Sonar: BQR-2B passive, BQS-4C active, BQC-1 underwater telephone, BQA-8 intercept
M: 3 G.M. 16-278A diesels (1,600 bhp each), 2 electric motors; 2 props; 3,430 bhp/5,480 shp
Range: 10,000/10; 95/5 (sub.) **Fuel:** 330 tons
Crew: 9 officers, 76 enlisted

Remarks: Purchased 26-7-72. The fourth diesel generator set was removed to permit enlargement of the sonar compartment during Guppy II conversion completed 1953. Two 126-cell batteries. Sister *Triana* (S 86), ex-*Scabbardfish* (SS 397), is used for pierside training, and S 114 is employed primarily for seagoing training.

GUIDED-MISSILE DESTROYERS

◆ **1 (+3) ex-U.S. Navy Charles F. Adams class**

	Bldr	Laid down	L	In serv.
DDG 218 Kimon (ex-*Semmes,* DDG 18)	Avondale SY, New Orleans	18-8-60	20-5-61	10-12-62
DDG 220 Formion (ex-*Joseph Strauss,* DDG 16)	New York SB, Camden, NJ	27-12-60	9-12-61	20-4-63
D . . . . (ex-*Berkeley,* DDG 15)	New York SB, Camden, NJ	12-4-61	6-2-62	7-3-64
D . . . . (ex-*Waddell,* DDG 24)	Todd, Seattle	6-2-62	26-2-63	28-8-64

Ex-Semmes (DDG 18)—in U.S. Navy service Dr. Giorgio Arra, 6-90

D: 3,570 tons light (4,825 fl) **S:** 31.5 kts
Dim: 133.19 (128.0 wl) × 14.32 × 6.1 (8.3 over sonar)
A: 1/Mk 13 single launcher (6 Harpoon and 34 Standard SM-1 MR missiles)—2/127-mm Mk 42 DP (I × 2)—1/Mk 112 ASROC RL (VIII × 1; 8 or 12 missiles)—6/324-mm Mk 32 ASW TT (III × 2)
Electron Equipt:
Radar: 1/. . . nav., 1/SPS-10F surf. search, 1/SPS-40B/D air search, 1/SPS-52B 3-D air search, 2/SPG-51C missile f.c., 1/SPG-53A gun f.c.
Sonar: 1/SQS-23A (5–7 kHz hull-mounted in ex-DDG 15, 16, 18; bow-mounted in ex-DDG 24)
EW: SLQ-32(V)2 intercept, SLQ-20 intercept (ex-DDG 24: WLR-1 intercept also), Mk 36 SRBOC (VI × 4), SLQ-25 Nixie torpedo decoy syst.
TACAN: URN-25
M: 2 sets geared steam turbines; 2 props; 70,000 shp **Fuel:** 900 tons
Boilers: 4; 84 kg/cm², 520° C **Range:** 1,600/30; 6,000/14
Electric: 2,200 kw (DDG 19, 20, 22: 3,000 kw)
Crew: 20–24 officers, 319–330 enlisted

Remarks: Ex-DDG 18 transferred on lease to Greece 13-9-91, to arrive in-country in 1-92; the others will be transferred on 1-10-92.

Ex-DDG 23 and DDG 24 have bow-mounted sonars and stem-mounted anchors. SLQ-32(V)2 replaced the earlier WLR-1F and ULQ-6B suite, and Mk 36 SRBOC launchers have been added; URN-25 lightweight TACAN replaced SRN-6; the Mk 68 GFCS received a digital computer system in ex-DDG 18; SPS-39A radars have been replaced by SPS-52B, and other improvements were made to the communications suites during U.S. Navy service. Harpoon missiles were probably not transferred but may be acquired later. Ex-DDG 15 has a twin Mk 11 SAM launcher.

DESTROYERS

◆ **6 ex-U.S. Gearing FRAM I class**

	Bldr	Laid down	L	In serv.
D 212 Kanaris (ex-*Stickell,* DD 888)	Consolidated Steel	5-1-45	16-6-45	26-9-45
D 213 Kontouriotis (ex-*Rupertus,* DD 851)	Bethlehem, Quincy	2-5-45	21-9-45	8-3-46

DESTROYERS *(continued)*

	Bldr	Laid down	L	In serv.
D 214 Sachtouris (ex-*Arnold J. Isbell,* DD 869)	Bethlehem, Quincy	14-3-45	6-8-45	5-1-46
D 215 Toumbazis (ex-*Gurke,* DD 783)	Todd SY, Seattle	1-7-44	15-4-45	5-12-45
D 216 Apostolis (ex-*Charles P. Cecil,* DD 835)	Bath Iron Wks.	2-12-44	22-2-45	29-6-45
D 217 Kriezis (ex-*Myles C. Fox,* DD 829)	Bath Iron Wks.	14-8-44	13-1-45	20-3-45

D: 2,425 tons (3,500 fl) **S:** 30 kts
Dim: 119.03 × 12.52 × 4.45 (6.40 over sonar)
A: D 212–215: 4/Harpoon SSM (II × 2)—4/127-mm 38-cal. DP (II × 2)—1/76-mm OTO Melara DP—1/Mk 112 ASROC launcher (VIII × 1; 14 missiles)—6/324-mm Mk 32 ASW TT (III × 2)—1/Mk 9 d.c. rack (214 also: 1/40-mm AA)
D 216, 217: 4/127-mm 38-cal. DP (II × 2)—1/76-mm OTO Melara DP—1/40-mm Bofors AA—1/Mk 112 ASROC launcher (VIII × 1; 14 missiles)—6/324-mm ASW TT (III × 2)—1/Mk 9 d.c. rack
Electron Equipt:
Radar: 1/. . . nav., 1/SPS-10 surf. search, 1/SPS-40 air search (SPS-29 on 212, 215, 216), 1/Mk 25 f.c., 1/Orion RTN-20X f.c. (not on D 213, 216)
Sonar: Raytheon DE 1191 or SQS-23D (*see* Remarks)
EW: WLR-1 intercept, ULQ-6 active
M: 2 sets geared steam turbines; 2 props; 60,000 shp
Electric: 1,200 kw
Boilers: 4 Babcock & Wilcox; 43.3 kg/cm², 454° C superheat
Range: 2,400/25; 4,800/15 **Fuel:** 650 tons
Crew: 14 officers, 260 enlisted

Kanaris (D 212)—note Harpoons and 76-mm gun on former helo deck; in background is the now-stricken *Velos* (D 16) Greek Navy, 1990

Sachtouris (D 214) Greek Navy, 1990

Kanaris (D 212) Frank Behling, 9-9

Remarks: D 212 transferred 1-7-72; D 213 on 10-7-73 (purchased 11-7-78); D 214 o 4-12-73 (purchased 11-7-78); D 215 purchased 17-3-77; D 216 purchased 2-8-80 origi nally for cannibalization; and D 217 purchased 8-7-81. Also purchased were ex-*Corr* (DD 817) and ex-*Dyess* (DD 880), on 8-7-81 for cannibalization spares.

All six active units have been given an Elsag NA-21 fire-control system aft, 1/76-m OTO Melara Compact on the helicopter deck. D 212–214 carry the Harpoon SS athwartships, just abaft the former Dash drone helicopter hangar. D 216–217, moder ized 1984–87, may receive Harpoon later. In D 215, which was equipped as Fle Flagship 1980–81, two of the boilers are Foster-Wheeler. The 1980–81 purchase shi had LN-66 navigational radars. Three had DE 1191 sonar (digital version of SQS-2 by 1990; sets for the others were ordered 1990.

♦ **1 ex-U.S. Gearing DDR FRAM II class**

	Bldr	Laid down	L	In ser
D 210 Themistocles (ex-*Frank Knox,* DD 742)	Bath Iron Wks.	8-5-44	17-9-44	11-12-

Themistocles (D 210)—with AB 212 helo on deck Greek Navy, 1

D: 2,425 tons (3,500 fl) **S:** 30 kts
Dim: 119.03 × 12.52 × 4.45 (6.40 over sonar)
A: 6/127-mm DP (II × 3)—2/20-mm Rheinmetall AA (I × 2)—2/12.7-mm mg (I × 2)—6/324-mm Mk 32 ASW TT (III × 2)—2 Hedgehog—1/AB 212 ASW helicopter
Electron Equipt:
Radar: 1/. . . nav., 1/SPS-10 surf. search, 1/SPS-29 air search, 1/ 25 f.c.
Sonar: SQS-43C hull-mounted MF—EW: WLR-1 intercept
M: 2 sets geared steam turbines; 2 props; 60,000 shp
Electric: 1,200 kw
Boilers: 2 Babcock & Wilcox; 43.3 kg/cm², 454° C superheat
Range: 2,400/25; 4,800/15 **Fuel:** 650 tons
Crew: 16 officers, 253 enlisted

Remarks: Purchased 30-1-71, having been extensively rebuilt after a groundi 1966. Radar picket features deleted and helicopter hangar added in Greece by 1 place of the after 01 level deckhouse. Received 3-section 19.17-m-long telesc hangar and enlarged flight deck for AB 212 helicopter during 1987, and variable- sonar was removed. Will probably be retired with the arrival of the *Charles F. A* class.

DESTROYERS *(continued)*

◆ **1 ex-U.S. Allen M. Summer class** Bldr: Federal SB & DD, Kearny, NJ

	Laid down	L	In serv.
D 211 Miaoulis (ex-*Ingraham*, DD 694)	4-4-43	16-1-44	10-3-44

Miaoulis (D 211)—prior to modernization Greek Navy

D: 2,200 tons (3,320 fl) **S:** 30 kts
Dim: 114.76 × 12.49 × 4.39 (5.79 over sonar)
A: 6/127-mm, 38-cal. DP (II × 3)—2/40-mm AA (I × 2)—2/20-mm Rheinmetall AA (I × 2)—2/12.7-mm mg (I × 2)—2/Hedgehog ASW mortars (XXIV × 2)—6/324-mm Mk 32 ASW TT (III × 2)—1/AB-212 ASW helicopter
Electron Equipt:
Radar: 1/. . . nav., 1/SPS-10 surf. search , 1/SPS-40 air search, 1/Mk 25 f.c.
Sonar: SQS-29 hull-mounted MF—EW: WLR-1 intercept
M: 2 sets geared steam turbines; 2 props; 60,000 shp
Electric: 1,200 kw
Boilers: 4 Babcock & Wilcox; 43.3 kg/cm², 454° C **Fuel:** 495 tons
Range: 2,400/25; 4,800/15 **Crew:** 14 officers, 260 enlisted

emarks: Transferred 16-7-71. Mk 37 gunfire-control system for 127-mm mounts. odernization commenced 11-86 at Eleusis SY; received helicopter facilities as on *hemistocles* (D 210), and VDS removed. Will probably be retired with the arrival of e *Charles F. Adams* class.

ote: Former U.S. Navy *Fletcher*-class destroyers *Aspis* (D 06, ex-*Conner*, DD 582), *los* (D 16, ex-*Charette*, DD 581), and *Lonchi* (D 56, ex-*Hall*, DD 583) have been icken, the latter on 10-10-90 and the first two in 1990–91. Sister *Sphendoni* (D 85, -*Aulick*, DD 569) is employed as a pierside training platform.

RIGATES

te: Construction of up to a dozen small frigates of around 1,200 tons full load splacement is under consideration. The ships would mount Harpoon missiles and O Melara 76-mm DP gun, a U.S. Mk 15 CIWS, ASW torpedoes, and a suite of air and rface-search radars.

0 (+4) MEKO 200 Mk 3 class

	Bldr	Laid down	L	In serv.
452 Ydra	Blohm + Voss, Hamburg	17-12-90	25-6-91	9-92
453 Spetsai	Hellenic SY, Skaramanga	5-91	. . .	1996
454 Psara	Hellenic SY, Skaramanga	. . .	. . .	. . .
455 Salamis	Hellenic SY, Skaramanga	. . .	. . .	2000

D: 2,800 tons (3,100 fl) **S:** 31.75 kts (21 kts on diesel)
Dim: 117.50 (109.50 pp) × 14.80 (13.80 wl) × 6.00 (4.12 hull)
A: 8/Harpoon SSM (IV × 2)—1/Mk 48 VLS group for NATO Sea Sparrow SAM (16 RIM-7M missiles)—1/127-mm MK 45 DP—2/20-mm Mk 15 gatling CIWS—6/324-mm Mk 32 ASW TT (III × 2)—1/10-ton helicopter
Electron Equipt:
Radar: 1/Decca 2690BT nav., 1/H.S.A. MW-08 3-D air search, 1/H.S.A. DA-08 early warning, 2/H.S.A. STIR-18 f.c.
Sonar: Raytheon SQS-56 (DE 1160)
EW: Argo APECS-II intercept, Mk 36 SRBOC decoy syst, (VI × 4), SLQ-25 Nixie torpedo decoy syst.
M: CODOG: MTU 20V956 TB82 diesels (5,200 bhp each), 2 G.E. LM-2500-30 gas turbines (30,328 shp each); 2 CP props
Electric: 2,480 kw (4 × 620-kw diesel sets) **Fuel:** 300 tons
Range: 900/31.75; 4,100/18 (diesel)
Crew: 173 ship's company + 16 staff

Remarks: Basic order to West Germany 10-2-89, with subcontract for Greek-built trio placed 16-5-89. Construction in Greece is behind schedule. Armament and electronics in large part financed by U.S. arms credits, although most equipment will be European. U.S. equipment will include WQC-2A underwater telephone, UQN-4A echo-sounder, SLQ-25 Nixie torpedo decoy, and SWG-1A Harpoon missile launch system. The H.S.A. STACOS combat data system will be installed. Have fin stabilizers. The design is basically similar to the version of the MEKO 200 built for Portugal, and Turkey has similar ships.

◆ **2 Dutch Kortenaer class** Bldr: de Schelde, Vlissingen

	Laid down	L	In serv.
F 450 Elli (ex-*Pieter Floresz*)	2-7-77	15-12-79	10-10-81
F 451 Limnos (ex-*Witte de With*)	13-6-78	27-10-79	18-9-82

Limnos (F 451)—with Phalanx CIWS French Navy, 1990

Elli (F 450) French Navy, 1990

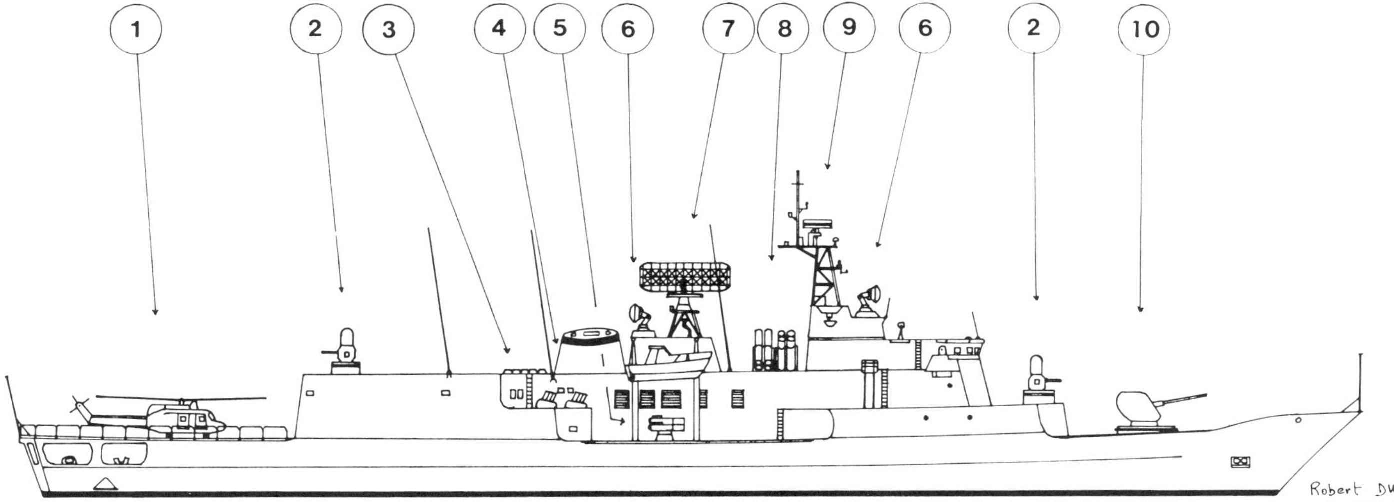

Ydra (F 452) 1. AB-212 helicopter 2. Mk 15 Phalanx CIWS 3. vertical-launch Sea Sparrow SAM cells 4. Mk 36 SRBOC decoy system 5. Mk 32 ASW TT STIR-18 fire control radar 7. DA-08 early warning radar 8. Harpoon missiles 9. MW-08 3-D search radar 10. 127-mm Mk 45 dual-purpose gun

FRIGATES *(continued)*

D: 3,000 tons (3,786 fl) **S:** 30 kts
Dim: 130.2 (121.8 pp) × 14.4 × 4.4 (6.0 props)
A: 8/Harpoon SSM (IV × 2)—1 Mk 29 SAM syst. (VIII × 1; 24 Aspide missiles)—2/76-mm OTO Melara DP (I × 2)—2/20-mm Mk 15 gatling CIWS—4/324-mm Mk 32 ASW TT (II × 2)—1/AB-212 ASW helicopter
Electron Equipt:
Radar: 1/H.S.A. ZW-06 surf. search, 1/H.S.A. LW-08 early warning, 1/H.S.A. WM-25 track-while-scan f.c., 1/H.S.A. STIR-18 f.c.
Sonar: Canadian Westinghouse SQS-505 hull-mounted MF
EW: Elettronica Sphinx intercept syst., Mk 36 SRBOC decoy syst. (VI × 4)
M: COGOG: 2 Rolls-Royce Tyne RM-1C cruise gas turbines, 4,900 shp each, 2 Rolls-Royce Olympus TM-3B gas turbines, 25,800 shp each; 2 LIPS CP props; 51,600 shp max.
Electric: 3,000 kw (4 × 1,500 kw SEMT-Pielstick PA4 diesel generator sets)
Range: 4,700/16 (on one Tyne turbine)
Crew: 17 officers, 182 enlisted

Remarks: *Elli* was officially turned over to Greece on 26-6-81 at the commencement of sea trials, having been ordered 7-81, along with the second unit. Both were taken from production for the Dutch Navy, in order to speed delivery. Plans to build a third ship in Greece were canceled. Have Denny-Brown fin stabilizers. Hangar lengthened 2.2 m to accept Italian-built helicopter vice Lynx used by Dutch Navy. Have H.S.A. SEWACO II combat data system. See also class notes in Netherlands section.

One U.S. Mk 15 CIWS 20-mm gatling AA was to have been added in place of the after 76-mm gun for close-in defense, but instead, in 1991, the 76-mm weapon was retained, *two* Mk 15 CIWS were added port and starboard forward of the hangar (in place of the Corvus decoy rocket launchers), the number of Harpoon missiles was doubled over the original installation, and U.S. Hycor Mk 136 decoy rocket launchers were added on the forward superstructure.

◆ **0 (+2) U.S. Knox class** Bldr: Avondale SY, Westwego, La.

	Laid down	L	In serv.
F . . . Makedonia (ex-*Vreeland*, FF 1068)	20-3-68	14-6-69	13-6-70
F . . . . (ex-*Trippe*, FF 1015)	29-7-68	1-11-69	19-9-70
F . . . . (ex-*Connole*, FF 1056)	23-3-67	20-7-68	30-8-69

D: 3,075 tons light (4,260 fl) **S:** 27+ kts
Dim: 134.0 (126.5 wl) × 14.33 × 4.60 (7.55 over sonar)—*see* Remarks
A: 4/Harpoon SSM (using Mk 112 ASROC launcher system)—1/127-mm Mk 42 DP—1/20-mm Mk 15 CIWS—1/Mk 116 ASROC system (VIII × 1)—4/324-mm Mk 32 fixed ASW TT—1/. . . . . ASW helicopter
Electron Equipt:
Radar: 1/LN-66 or SPS-53 nav., 1/SPS-67surf. search, 1/SPS-40B air search, 1/SPG-53 gun f.c.
Sonar: 1/SQS-26CX hull-mounted LF, SQS-35(V) VDS—*see* Remarks
EW: SLQ-32(V)1 or 32(V)2 intercept, Mk 36 SRBOC RL syst. (VI × 2)
TACAN: SRN-15
M: 1 set Westinghouse geared turbines; 1 prop; 35,000 shp
Boilers: 2 Babcock & Wilcox or Combustion Eng.; 84 kg/cm², 510° C
Electric: 3,000 kw **Range:** 4,300/20 **Fuel:** 750 tons
Crew: 17–20 officers, 255–265 enlisted (in U.S. Navy service)

Remarks: Announced 7-91 that two *Knox*-class frigates decommissioned from the U.S. Navy would be leased to Greece during 1993. Prior to tranfer, are to receive updated data links to make them compatible with the Kortenaer and MEKO-200-class frigates. To transfer 6-92, 7-92, and 8-92.

The ASROC system has an automatic reloading magazine beneath the bridge; it is also used to stow Harpoon missiles, which are launched from the port pair of eight launcher cells. The ASW torpedo tubes are fixed, in the forward end of the hangar superstructure, aimed outboard at an angle of 45°. Beginning with twelve ships under FY 80, the SQS-35 towed VDS transducer body and hoist was modified to permit towing the SQR-18A TACTASS. Non-VDS ships got instead SQR-18A(V)2 TACTASS; whether the ships to be transferred to Greece will retain TACTASS has not been determined. All carry a Mk 68 gunfire-control system with SPG-53A, D, or F radar. Have Mk 114 ASW fire-control system. Anti-rolling fin stabilizers fitted in all. Prairie-Masker bubbler system fitted to hulls and propellers to reduce radiated noise. All received the ASWTDS (ASW Tactical Data System) during the 1980s.

Note: The former West German *Rhein*-class tender *Aegeon* (D 03, ex-*Weser*, A 62), which had been used as a frigate, was stricken 1991.

◆ **4 ex-U.S. Cannon class** Bldrs: D 01, D 31: Tampa SB, Tampa, Florida; D 54, D 67: Federal SB, Port Newark, New Jersey

	Laid down	L	In serv.
D 01 Aetos (ex-*Ebert,* DE 768)	1-4-43	11-5-44	12-7-44
D 31 Hierax (ex-*Slater,* DE 766)	9-3-43	13-2-44	1-5-44
D 54 Leon (ex-*Garfield Thomas,* DE 193)	23-9-43	12-12-43	24-1-44
D 67 Panthir (ex-*Eldridge,* DE 173)	22-2-43	25-6-43	27-8-43

Hierax (D 31) Leo Van Ginderen, 7-80

D: 1,300 tons (1,750 fl) **S:** 19 kts
Dim: 93.0 (91.5 pp) × 11.17 × 3.25
A: 3/76.2-mm DP—6/40-mm AA (II × 3)—14/20-mm AA (II × 7)—6/324-mm Mk 32 ASW TT (III × 2)—1 Hedgehog—8/d.c. projectors—2/d.c. racks
Electron Equipt:
Radar: 1/. . . nav., 1/Mk 26 f.c.
Sonar: QCU-2 HF **M:** 4 G.M. 16-278A diesels, electric drive; 2 props; 6,000 shp
Electric: 680 kw **Range:** 5,500/19; 11,500/11 **Fuel:** 300 tons
Crew: 150 tot.

Remarks: First two transferred 15-3-51, other two on 15-1-51. Have Mk 52 GFCS for 76.2-mm guns (plus separate rangefinder), 3 Mk 51 Mod. 2 lead-computing directors for 40-mm AA. Obsolete SA radar removed by 1980. Thoroughly obsolete but retained in close to original World War II configuration for use as economical patrol ships; will be retired shortly.

CORVETTES

◆ **0 (+ 2 + 1) P 100 class** Bldr: Hellenic SY, Skaramanga

	Laid down	L	In serv.
P 20	1-91	. . .	. . .
P 21	. . .	. . .	. . .

P 100 design—artist's rendering Hellenic SY, 19

D: 550 tons (fl) **S:** 24 kts (at 450 tons)
Dim: 56.50 (51.50 wl) × 10.00 (9.50 wl) × 2.50 max.
A: 4/Harpoon SSM (II × 2)—1/76-mm OTO Melara DP—2/40-mm Breda AA (II × 2)—2/20-mm Rheinmetall AA (I × 2)
Electron Equipt: Radar: 1/. . . nav., 1/. . . surf./air search
M: 2 MTU 1163 TB93 diesels; 2 props; 9,870 bhp
Electric: . . . kw **Range:** 220/15; 800/. . .
Crew: 36 tot. + 25 troops

Remarks: Revised version of the modified Osprey design below. Two units with op for third ordered 19-2-89, and first unit reported laid down in 1-91. Program appe however, to have halted and may have been canceled during 1991.

◆ **2 modified Osprey 55-series guided-missile corvettes** Bldr: Hellenic SY, Skaramanga

	Laid down	L	In serv.
P 18 Armatolos	8-5-89	19-12-89	9-3-90
P 19 Navhamos	9-11-89	16-5-90	15-7-90

D: 515 tons (fl) **S:** 24.7 kts (at 415 tons)
Dim: 54.75 (50.83 pp) × 10.50 (8.08 wl) × 2.55 (hull)
A: 1/76-mm OTO Melara DP—2/20-mm Rheinmetall AA (I × 2)—portable mine rails
Electron Equipt: Radar: 1/. . . nav.
M: 2 MTU 1163 TB93 diesels; 2 props; 9,870 bhp
Electric: 480 kw (2 × 240 kw, 2 MTU 12V183 AA51 diesels drivin
Range: 500/22 **Crew:** 36 ship's company + 25 troops

CORVETTES *(continued)*

Armatolos (P 18)—on trials Danyard, 1990

Remarks: Design licensed from Frederickshavn Vaerft, Denmark. First two (with option for two more) ordered 3-88, with plans to construct up to ten, but further units were canceled in favor of a very similar design of indigenous origin. Similar, but far less heavily armed, ships are operated by Morocco and Senegal, and the original shorter-hulled version is operated by Denmark and Burma. Have a stern ramp and internal stowage for a rigid-inflatable inspection/SAR launch. Were originally planned to carry four Harpoon missiles amidships, a Breda twin 40-mm AA mount aft, Plessey AWS-6 air/surface search radar, and an H.S.A. WM-25 track-while-scan weapons fire-control system, with an associated LIROD director; now plan Selenia NA-21 system with RTN-20X radar director.

♦ **2 (+3) ex-German Thetis class (Type 420)** Bldr: Roland Werft, Bremen

		Laid down	L	In serv.
P . . .	NIKI (ex-*Thetis,* P 6052)	19-6-59	22-3-60	1-7-61
P . . .	DOXA (ex-*Najade,* P 6054)	22-3-60	6-12-60	12-5-62

'iki (P . . .)—in German service Leo Van Ginderen, 6-91

›oxa (P. . .)—in German service Stephen Terzibaschitsch, 6-91

D: 575 tons (658 fl) **S:** 23.5 kts
Dim: 69.78 (65.5 pp) × 8.2 × 2.65 (hull)
A: 2/40-mm Bofors AA (II × 1)—1/Bofors 375-mm ASW RL (IV × 1)—4/533-mm ASW TT (I × 4, U.S. Mk 46 TT)—2 d.c. racks (12/d.c.)—mines
Electron Equipt:
Radar: 1/Kelvin-Hughes 14/9 nav., 1/Thomson-CSF TRS-3001 surf. search
Sonar: Krupp-Atlas ELAC 1BV HF hull-mounted
M: 2 M.A.N. V84V diesels; 2 props; 6,800 bhp **Electric:** 540 kw
Range: 2,760/15 **Fuel:** 78 tons **Crew:** 5 officers, 43 enlisted

Remarks: First two transferred to Greece 6-9-91; the other three units of the class are to be transferred during 1992. Data above are as in German service; may later be re-equipped in Greece with newer weapons and sensors.

Former torpedo-recovery boats, designed for operations in the Baltic. Have H.S.A. Mk 9 torpedo f.c.s. and an optical lead-computing gun f.c.s. Carry 20 ASW RL projectiles. EW gear removed. Torpedo tubes formerly carried German-made 533-mm passive homing torpedoes but now launch U.S.-made Mk 46 324-mm torpedoes through the use of liners. *Doxa* had forward superstructure extended toward bow to accommodate a medical facility.

GUIDED-MISSILE PATROL BOATS

♦ **10 Combattante III N class** Bldr: P 20–23: CMN, Cherbourg; others: Hellenic SY, Skaramanga

	L	In serv.
P 20 ANTIPLIARCHOS LASCOS	6-7-76	2-4-77
P 21 ANTIPLIARCHOS BLESSAS	10-11-76	19-7-77
P 22 ANTIPLIARCHOS TROUPAKIS	6-1-77	8-11-77
P 23 ANTIPLIARCHOS MYKONIOS	5-5-77	10-2-78
P 24 SIMAIFOROS KAVALOUTHIS	10-11-79	14-7-80
P 25 ANTIPLIARCHOS KOSTAKOS	1-3-80	9-9-80
P 26 IPOPLIARCHOS DEYIANNIS	14-7-80	12-80
P 27 SIMAIFOROS XENOS	8-9-80	31-3-81
P 28 SIMAIFOROS SIMITZOPOULOS	12-10-80	6-82
P 29 SIAIFOROS STARAKIS	1981	12-10-81

D: P 20–23: 385 tons (447 fl); P 24–29: 396 tons (fl)
S: 36.5 kts (P 24–29: 32.6 kts)
Dim: 56.65 (53.00 pp) × 8.00 × 2.70 (props), 2.04 (hull)
A: P 20–23: 4/MM 38 Exocet SSM (II × 2)—2/76-mm OTO Melara DP (I × 2)—4/30-mm Emerlec AA (II × 2)—2/533-mm TT (2 SST-4 wire-guided torpedoes)
P 24–29: 6 Penguin SSM (I × 6)—2/76-mm OTO Melara Compact DP (I × 2)—4/30-mm Emerlec AA (II × 2)—2/533-mm TT (2 SST-4 torpedoes)
Electron Equipt:
Radar: 1/Decca 1226 nav., 1/Thomson-CSF Triton surf./air search, 1/Thomson-CSF Castor f.c.
M: P 20–23: 4 MTU 20V538 TB92 diesels; 4 props; 20,800 bhp (18,000 sust.)
P 24–29: 4 MTU 20V538 TB91 diesels; 4 props; 15,000 bhp (13,400 sust.)
Electric: 450 kw **Range:** 800/32.5; 2,000/15
Crew: 7 officers, 36 enlisted

:ipliarchos Kostakos (P 25)—launching Penguin missile Greek Navy, 1990

GUIDED-MISSILE PATROL BOATS *(continued)*

Antipliarchos Blessas (P 21)—Exocet version Greek Navy, 1990

Remarks: First four ordered 22-5-75. Second group, built in Greece, and with less expensive weapon, sensor, and propulsion systems, ordered 22-12-76; displace 396 tons fl. Each 76-mm gun has 350 rounds, with 80 in ready service. The Emerlec 30-mm mounts are furnished with 3,200 rounds and fire at 700 rounds/barrel/minute. Ships have excellent habitability; accommodations and operations spaces are air-conditioned. There are 3 Jeumont-Schneider 150-kw generator sets (440v., 3-ph., 60-Hz.). First group has Thomson-CSF Vega weapon-control system, later ships Vega II. All have 2 CSEE Panda optronic directors for the 30-mm AA.

◆ **4 Combattante II class** Bldr: CMN, Cherbourg

	L	In serv.
P 14 Ipopliarchos Arliotis (ex-*Evniki*)	26-4-71	4-72
P 15 Ipopliarchos Anninos (ex-*Navsithoi*)	8-9-71	6-72
P 16 Ipopliarchos Konidis (ex-*Kimothoi*)	20-12-71	7-72
P 17 Ipopliarchos Batsis (ex-*Kalypso*)	26-1-71	12-71

Ipopliarchos Arliotis (P 14) Peter Voss, 10-86

D: 234 tons (255 fl) **S:** 36.5 kts **Dim:** 47.0 (44.0 pp) × 7.1 × 2.5 (fl)
A: 4/MM 38 Exocet SSM (II × 2)—4/35-mm Oerlikon GDM-A AA (II × 2)—2/533-mm wire-guided TT aft
Electron Equipt:
Radar: 1/Decca 1226 nav., 1/Thomson-CSF Triton air/surf. search, 1/Thomson-CSF Castor f.c.
M: 4 MTU MD 872 diesels; 4 props; 12,000 bhp **Fuel:** 39 tons
Range: 850/25; 2,000/15 **Crew:** 4 officers, 36 enlisted

Remarks: Steel hull, light steel alloy superstructure. Ordered 1969. Thomson-CSF Vega weapon-control system to be updated.

◆ **2 Kelefstis Stamou class** Bldr: CN de l'Estérel, Cannes

P 286 Kelefstis Stamou (In serv. 28-7-75)
P 287 Diopos Antoniou (In serv. 4-12-75)

Kelefstis Stamou (P 286) Leo Van Ginderen, 8-84

D: 80 tons (115 fl) **S:** 30 kts **Dim:** 32.0 × 5.8 × 1.5
A: 4/SS-12 wire-guided SSM—1/20-mm AA—2/12.7-mm mg (I × 2)
Electron Equipt: Radar: 1/Decca . . . nav.
M: 2 MTU 12V331 TC81 diesels; 2 props; 2,700 bhp
Range: 1,500/15 **Crew:** 17 tot.

Remarks: These wooden-hulled ships were ordered by Cyprus, but acquired by Greece. Pendant numbers were P 28 and P 29 until 1980.

PATROL BOATS

◆ **2 U.S. Asheville class** Bldr: Peterson Bldrs., Sturgeon Bay, Wisc.

	In serv.
P 229 Ormi (ex-*Beacon*, PG 99)	21-11-69
P 230 Tolm (ex-*Green Bay*, PG 101)	5-12-69

Ormi (P 229)—as *Beacon* (PG 99) Gilbert Gyssels, 12-7

D: 225 tons (240 fl) **S:** 40 kts (16 on diesels)
Dim: 50.14 (46.94 pp) × 7.28 × 2.90
A: 1/76.2-mm Mk 34 DP—1/40-mm Mk 3 AA—4/12.7-mm mg (II × 2)
Electron Equipt: Radar: 1/SPS-53 nav., 1/SPG-50 f.c.
M: CODAG: 1 G.E. LM-1500 Mk 7 gas turbine (12,500 shp), 2 Cummins 875V12 diesels (1,450 bhp total); 2 props
Range: 325/35; 1,700/16 **Fuel:** 50 tons
Crew: 3 officers, 21 enlisted

Remarks: Transferred 22-11-89, having been in reserve since 4-77. Commission 6-90 after overhauls in Greece. Have Mk 63 GFCS for 76.2-mm gun. Sisters in Turki South Korean, and Colombian navies.

TORPEDO BOATS

◆ **5 ex-German Type 141 class** Bldr: Lürssen, Vegesack (P 55: Krögerwerft, Rendsburg)

	Laid down	L	In serv.
P 50 Esperos (ex-*Seeadler*)	23-9-57	1-2-58	29-8-58
P 53 Kyklon (ex-*Grief*)	5-2-58	28-6-58	3-3-59
P 54 Laiaps (ex-*Kondor*)	2-1-58	17-5-58	24-2-59
P 55 Scorpios (ex-*Kormoran*)	2-2-59	16-7-59	9-11-59
P 56 Tyfon (ex-*Geier*)	27-5-58	1-10-58	3-6-59

Tyfon (P 56) French Navy,

D: 195 tons (221 fl) **S:** 42.5 kts **Dim:** 42.62 × 7.10 × 2.39
A: 2/40-mm AA (I × 2)—4/533-mm TT (I × 4)
Electron Equipt: Radar: 1/Decca . . . nav.
M: 4 Maybach 16-cyl. diesels; 4 props; 14,400 bhp
Electric: 192 kw **Range:** 500/39; 1,000/32 **Crew:** 39 tot.

Remarks: Transferred 1976–77. Three others, ex-*Albatros*, ex-*Bussard*, an *Sperber*, were transferred to be cannibalized for spares. Wooden-planked hull sk metal frame. *Kataigis* (P 51, ex-P 197, ex-*Falke*) stricken late 1981. *Kentauros* ex-*Habicht*) stricken 1985, for cannibalization. The 40-mm guns have been give auto-loading systems. Can carry eight mines in lieu of torpedoes.

◆ **4 Norwegian Nasty class** Bldr: Båtservice, Mandal

	In serv.		In serv.
P 196 Andromeda	11-66	P 199 Pigassos	4-67
P 198 Kykonos	2-67	P 228 Toxotis	5-67

TORPEDO BOATS *(continued)*

D: 69 tons (76 fl) **S:** 40 kts **Dim:** 24.50 (22.86 pp) × 7.50 × 1.95
A: 1/40-mm Bofors AA—1/20-mm Rheinmetall AA—4/533-mm TT (I × 4)
Electron Equipt: Radar: 1/. . . nav.
M: 2 MTU 12V331 TC83 diesels; 2 props; 3,060 bhp
Range: 676/17 **Fuel:** 10 tons **Crew:** 20 tot.

Remarks: Wooden construction. Had been discarded 1983 but were refurbished and re-engined for further service in 1988. Originally had 2 Napier Deltic T1827 K diesels of 3,140 bhp each.

PATROL CRAFT

◆ **3 Dilos class** Bldr: Hellenic SY, Skaramanga (In serv. 1977–79)

P 267 Dilos P 268 Lindos P 269 Knossos

Lindos (P 268) Leo Van Ginderen, 7-78

D: 75 tons (86 fl) **S:** 27 kts **Dim:** 29.00 (27.00 wl) × 5.00 × 1.62
A: 2/20-mm AA (I × 2) **Electron Equipt:** Radar: 1/. . . nav.
M: 2 MTU 12V331 TC81 diesels; 2 props; 2,720 bhp
Range: 1,600/25 **Crew:** 15 tot.

Remarks: Designed by Abeking & Rasmussen, West Germany. Used for air/sea rescue. Three also built for Customs Service and five for Coast Guard. Round-bilge steel-construction hull.

◆ **3 Panagopoulos I class** Bldr: Hellenic SY, Skaramanga

P 61 E. Panagopoulos I (In serv. 23-6-76)
P 70 E. Panagopoulos II (In serv. 1980)
P 96 E. Panagopoulos III (In serv. 1981)

Panagopoulos I (P 61) Leo Van Ginderen, 7-79

D: 35 tons (fl) **S:** 38 kts **Dim:** 23.00 (21.00 wl) × 5.00 × 0.97
A: 1/12.7-mm mg—2/106-mm RL (II × 6)
Electron Equipt: Radar: 1/Decca . . .
M: 2 MTU 12V331 TC92 diesels; 2 props; 3,060 bhp **Crew:** 6 tot.

Remarks: Aluminum alloy hull with hard-chine form. The unguided rocket launchers flank the small pilothouse, which is mounted at the extreme stern. Typed as "Pursuit Craft."

Note: Patrol craft *N.I. Goulandris II* (P 290) was retired during 1990.

MINE WARFARE SHIPS

◆ **2 minelayers** Bldr: Charleston Naval SY, Charleston, South Carolina

	Laid down	L	In serv.
N 04 Aktion (ex-MMC 6, ex-LSM 301)	18-10-44	19-11-44	1-1-45
N 05 Amvrakia (ex-MMC 7, ex-LSM 303)	8-10-44	14-11-44	6-1-45

Amvrakia (N 05)

D: 720 tons (1,100 fl) **S:** 13 kts **Dim:** 62.0 × 10.5 × 2.4
A: 8/40-mm Bofors AA (II × 4)—6/20-mm Oerlikon AA (I × 6)—100 to 300 mines, depending upon type
Electron Equipt: Radar: 1/. . . nav. **Crew:** 65 tot.
M: 2 G.M. 16-278A diesels; 2 props; 2,800 bhp **Range:** 3,500/12

Remarks: Former U.S. LSM 1-class landing ships converted prior to transfer in 1953. Four derricks, two forward and two aft, for handling mines. Two minelaying rails. Four 30-cm searchlights, one of 60 cm. Four Mk 51 Mod. 2 optical GFCS for the 40-mm AA. Twin rudders. Three of the same class ships were transferred to Turkey and two to Norway, which passed them on to Turkey in 1961.

◆ **9 U.S. MSC 294-class coastal minesweepers** Bldr: Peterson Bldrs, Sturgeon Bay, Wisconsin (M 246: Tacoma Boatbldg, Tacoma, Washington)

	In serv.
M 211 Alkyon (ex-MSC 314)	3-12-68
M 213 Klio (ex-*Argo*, ex-MSC 317)	7-8-68
M 214 Avra (ex-MSC 318)	3-10-68
M 240 Pleias (ex-MSC 319)	22-6-67
M 241 Kichli (ex-MSC 308)	14-7-64
M 242 Kissa (ex-MSC 309)	1-9-64
M 246 Aigli (ex-MSC 299)	4-1-65
M 247 Dafni (ex-MSC 307)	23-9-64
M 248 Aedon (ex-MSC 310)	13-10-64

Dafni (M 247) Luciano Grazioli, 5-91

D: 300 tons (394 fl) **S:** 13 kts **Dim:** 44.32 × 8.29 × 2.55
A: 2/20-mm Oerlikon AA (II × 1)
Electron Equipt: Radar: 1/. . . nav.—Sonar: UQS-1D HF
M: 2 Waukesha L-1616 diesels; 2 props; 1,200 bhp
Fuel: 40 tons **Range:** 2,500/10 **Crew:** 4 officers, 27 enlisted

Remarks: Built for Greece under the Military Aid Program; transferred on completion. Sister *Doris* (A 475, ex-M 245, ex-MSC 298) is employed as a hydrographic survey ship. Original Decca 707 radar replaced by 1984. Are being re-engined, and a new sonar is to be procured.

◆ **5 ex-Belgian U.S. Adjutant-class coastal minesweepers** Bldrs: Consolidated SB, Morris Heights, N.Y. (M 205, M 206: Hodgdon Bros., East Boothbay, Maine)

	In serv.
M 202 Atalanti (ex-*St. Truiden*, ex-MSC 169)	2-54
M 205 Antiopi (ex-*Herve*, ex-MSC 153)	3-54
M 206 Phedra (ex-*Malmedy*, ex-MSC 154)	5-54
M 210 Thalia (ex-*Blankenberge*, ex-MSC 170)	5-54
M 254 Niovi (ex-*Laroche*, ex-MSC 171)	8-54

D: 330 tons (402 fl) **S:** 13 kts (8 sweeping)
Dim: 43.0 (41.50 pp) × 7.95 × 2.55
A: 2/20-mm Oerlikon AA (II × 1)
Electron Equipt: Radar: 1/Decca . . . nav.—Sonar: UQS-1D HF
M: 2 G.M. 8-268A diesels; 2 props; 880/1,000 bhp **Fuel:** 40 tons
Range: 2,500/10 **Crew:** 4 officers, 27 enlisted

Antiopi (M 205) Dr. Giorgio Arra, 1973

MINE WARFARE SHIPS *(continued)*

Remarks: Transferred to Belgium on completion; M 202 and 205 retransferred to Greece 29-7-69, others on 26-9-69. M 202 was configured as a hydrographic survey ship from the late 1970s to 1982.

♦ 4 ex-U.S. 50-ft-class minesweeping launches

D: 21 tons (fl) **S:** 8 kts **Dim:** 15.20 × 4.01 × 1.31
M: 1 Navy DB diesel; 60 bhp **Range:** 150/8 **Crew:** 6 tot.

Remarks: Wooden-hulled former personnel launches loaned in 1972 and purchased during 1981. Intended for harbor use.

AMPHIBIOUS WARFARE SHIPS

♦ 1 ex-U.S. Cabildo-class dock landing ship

Bldr: Boston Naval SY, Boston, Massachusetts

	Laid down	L	In serv.
L 153 Nafkratoussa (ex-*Fort Mandan,* LSD 21)	16-12-44	6-4-45	31-10-45

D: 4,790 tons (9,375 fl) **S:** 15 kts **Dim:** 139.5 × 21.9 × 5.49
A: 8/40-mm AA (IV × 2)—4/20-mm Rheinmetall AA (I × 4)
Electron Equipt: Radar: 1/. . . nav., 1/SPS-5 surf. search
M: 2 sets geared steam turbines; 2 props; 7,000 shp **Electric:** 600 kw
Boilers: 62/30.6 kg/cm², 393° C **Fuel:** 1,758 tons
Range: 8,000/15 **Crew:** 254 tot.

Remarks: Modernized under the FRAM program and leased 1-71. Purchased outright 5-2-80. Flagship of the amphibious forces. Helicopter deck. Well deck: 103.0 × 13.3. Two 35-ton cranes. Can carry 18 LCMs. SPS-6 air-search radar deleted.

♦ 0 (+5) Jason-class tank landing ships

Bldr: Eleusis SY

	Laid down	L	In serv.
L 200 Chios	13-4-87	16-12-88	1992
L 201 Samos	9-87	5-4-89	1992
L 202 Lesbos	9-5-88	5-7-90	1992
L 203 Ikaria	4-89	. . .	1993
L 204 Rodos	1991	. . .	1993

Chios (L 200)—artist's rendering — Thomson-CSF, 1991

D: 4,400 tons (fl) **S:** 17 kts
Dim: 115.90 (106.00 pp) × 15.30 × 3.44 mean
A: 1/76-mm OTO Melara DP—2/40-mm Bofors AA (I × 1)— 4/20-mm Rheinmetall AA (II × 2)
Electron Equipt:
Radar: 1/Thomson-CSF Triton V search, Thomson-CSF Castor f.c.
M: 2 . . . . diesels; 2 props; 10,600 bhp
Crew: 108 ship's company + 303 troops

Remarks: Ordered 15-5-86 as replacements for U.S. LST 1/511 class. Have a raised helicopter deck aft capable of supporting two Sea King helicopters; carry two LCVP landing craft and two lifeboats. Bow ramp capable of supporting 55-ton vehicles; there is also a stern loading ramp and a ramp from the upper deck amidships to the tank deck. Program considerably delayed by builder's financial troubles, with last ship originally scheduled to complete 9-90. Radar and fire-control system only ordered 4-91 from Thomson-CSF. Not certain that first unit actually commissioned during 1991. Pendant numbers also reported as L 173 through L 177.

♦ 2 ex-U.S. Terrebonne Parish-class tank landing ships

Bldrs: L 104: Bath Iron Works; L 116: Christy Corp.

	Laid down	L	In serv.
L 104 Oinoussai (ex-*Terrell County,* LST 1157)	3-3-52	6-12-52	19-3-53
L 116 Kos (ex-*Whitfield County,* LST 1169)	. . .	22-8-53	14-9-54

D: 2,590 tons (6,225 fl) **S:** 12 kts **Dim:** 112.35 × 16.7 × 3.7
A: 6/76.2-mm AA (II × 3)—3/20-mm Rheinmetall AA (I × 3)
Electron Equipt:
Radar: 1/. . . nav., 1/SPS-10 surf. search, 2/Mk 34 f.c.
M: 4 G.M. diesels; 2 CP props; 6,000 bhp
Crew: 115 ship's company + 395 troops

Remarks: Purchased 17-3-77. Have Mk 63 GFCS for the 76.2-mm guns. Carry four LCVP in davits.

Kos (L 116) — Leo Van Ginderen, 10-80

♦ 5 ex-U.S. LST 1 and LST 511-class tank landing ships

	Bldr	Laid down	L	In serv.
L 144 Syros (ex-LST 325)	Philadelphia NY	10-8-42	27-10-42	1-2-43
L 154 Ikaria (ex-*Potter County,* LST 1086)	American Bridge	5-12-44	28-1-45	24-2-45
L 157 Rodos (ex-*Bowman County,* LST 391)	Newport News SB	14-7-42	28-10-42	3-12-42
L 171 Kriti (ex-*Page County,* LST 1076)	Bethlehem, Hingham	16-3-45	14-4-45	1-5-45
L 172 Lesbos (ex-*Boone County,* LST 389)	Newport News SB	20-6-42	15-10-42	24-11-42

Lesbos (L 172) — Leo Van Gindere

D: 1,653 tons (4,080 fl) **S:** 11.6 kts **Dim:** 99.98 × 15.24 × 3.4
A: 8/40-mm AA (II × 2, I × 4)—4/20-mm AA (II × 2) *or* 2/20-mm Rheinmetall AA (I × 2)
Electron Equipt: Radar: 1/. . . nav.
M: 2 G.M. 12-567A (L 171: 16-278A) diesels; 1,700 bhp
Electric: 300 kw
Range: 15,000/9 **Fuel:** 569 tons
Crew: 8 officers, 87 enlisted + 300 troops

Remarks: L 144 (with reinforced waterline belt for ice operations!) was transferr 29-5-64 after a complete refit and modernization; L 154, L 157, and L 172 transferr 9-8-60; L 171 transferred 3-71 (purchased 11-7-78). All have tripod masts and carry t or four LCVPs in Welin davits. Cargo: 2,100 tons. Are to be discarded on completion the new Jason class, L 172 first.

♦ 4 ex-U.S. LSM 1-class medium landing ships

Bldrs: L 161, 165: Brown Bros. SB, Houston; L 163: Dravo Corp, Wilmington, Del.; L 164: Charleston NSY

	Laid down	L	In se
L 161 Ipopliarchos Grigoropoulos (ex-LSM 45)	6-6-44	30-6-44	31-7-
L 163 Ipopliarchos Daniolos (ex-LSM 227)	17-7-44	9-9-44	5-10
L 164 Ipopliarchos Rousen (ex-LSM 399)	29-12-44	18-1-45	13-8
L 165 Ipopliarchos Krystallidis (ex-LSM 541)	7-7-45	18-8-45	7-12

D: 1,095 tons (fl) **S:** 12.5 kts **Dim:** 62.03 × 10.52 × 2.54
A: 2/40-mm Bofors AA (II × 1)—4/20-mm Oerlikon AA (I × 4)
Electron Equipt: Radar: 1/Decca . . . nav.
M: 2 Fairbanks-Morse 38D/8-10 (L 164: G.M. 16-278A) diesels; 2 props; 2,800 bhp
Electric: 240 kw **Range:** 4,900/12 **Fuel:** 161 tons **Crew:** 60 t

Remarks: Transferred 3-11-58 (L 165: 30-10-58). Some have four *twin* 20-mm Sister *Ipopliarchos Tornas* (L 162, ex-LSM 102) stricken 1990.

♦ 2 (+2) West German Type 520 utility landing craft

Bldr: Howaldtswerke, Hamburg

	In serv.
L 178 Naxos (ex-*Renke,* L 798)	2-9-66
L 179 Paros (ex-*Salm,* L 799)	23-9-66

AMPHIBIOUS WARFARE SHIPS *(continued)*

D: 166 tons (403 fl) **S:** 11 kts
Dim: 40.04 (36.70 pp) × 8.80 × 1.60 (2.10 max.)
A: 2/20-mm Rheinmetall AA (II × 1)
Electron Equipt: Radar: 1/Kelvin-Hughes 14/9
M: 2 MWM diesels; 2 props; 1,200 bhp **Electric:** 130 kVA
Range: 1,200/11 **Crew:** 17 tot.

Remarks: Transferred 16-11-89. Cargo: 237 tons max.; 141.6 tons normal. Ramps fore and aft. Design based on U.S. LCU 1626 class. Sisters *Felchen* (L 793) and *Forelle* (L 794) to transfer 31-1-92.

◆ **6 ex-U.S. LCU 501-class utility landing craft** Bldrs: L 145, 146, 147: Mare Island NSY, Cal.; L 149: Missouri Valley Bridge & Iron, Leavenworth, Kan.; L 150: Pidgeon-Thomas Iron, Memphis, Tenn.; L 152: Kansas City Steel, Kansas City, Missouri

	In serv.
L 145 Kassos (ex-LCU 1382)	30-11-44
L 146 Karpathos (ex-LCU 1379)	17-11-44
L 147 Kimonos (ex-LCU 971)	1-2-44
L 149 Kythnos (ex-LCU 763)	24-12-43
L 150 Sifnos (ex-LCU 677)	11-3-44
L 152 Skyatos (ex-LCU 827)	10-4-44

ythnos (L 149) — Leo Van Ginderen, 9-87

D: 143 tons (309 fl) **S:** 8 kts **Dim:** 36.30 × 9.96 × 1.14
A: 2/20-mm Oerlikon AA (I × 2)
M: 3 G.M. 6-71 diesels; 675 bhp **Electric:** 20 kw **Crew:** 13 tot.

marks: Transferred 1959–62. Have bow and stern ramps, no radars. Will soon be scarded.

2 ex-British LCT(4)-class utility landing craft Bldrs: . . . , U.K. (In serv. 1945)

185 Kythera (ex-LCT 1198) L 189 Milos (ex-LCT 1300)

D: 280 tons light (640 fl) **S:** 9.5 kts **Dim:** 57.07 × 11.79 × 1.30 (aft)
A: 2/20-mm Oerlikon AA
M: 2 Paxman diesels; 2 props; 1,000 bhp **Range:** 500/9.5; 3,100/7
Crew: 12 tot.

marks: Transferred 1946; survivors of a group of 12. Cargo: 350 tons. Will soon be cken.

11 ex-German Type 521 landing craft Bldr: Rheinwerft, Walsum (In serv. 1965–67)

. . (ex-*Seenelke,* LCM 10)
. . (ex-*Hering,* L 774/LCM 15)
. . (ex-*Orfe,* L 775/LCM 16)
. . (ex-*Maräne,* L 776/LCM 17)
. . (ex-*Saibling,* L 777/LCM 18)
. . (ex-*Stint,* L 778/LCM 19)
L . . . (ex-*Äsche,* L 779/LCM 20)
L . . . (ex-*Hummer,* L 780/LCM 21)
L . . . (ex-*Krille,* L 781/LCM 22)
L . . . (ex-*Krabbe,* L 782/LCM 23)
L . . . (ex-*Auster,* L 783/LCM 24)

Orfe, LCM 16 (L 775)—in German service — Leo Van Ginderen, 6-91

D: 116 tons (168 fl) **S:** 10.6 kts max. **Dim:** 23.56 × 6.40 × 1.46
A: none **Electron Equipt:** Radar: 1/. . . nav.
M: 2 MWM 8-cylinder diesels; 2 props; 684 bhp
Range: 690/10; 1,430/7 **Crew:** 7 tot. + 50–60 troops

Remarks: Ex-*Seenelke* transferred 5-3-91, others on 25-4-91. Design based on U.S. LCM (8). Ex-*Seenelke* has a 2-ton cargo boom and a 20-kw generator and can act as an armament stores tender (can carry up to 18 torpedoes); the others can carry up to 60 tons of cargo.

◆ **11 ex-U.S. LCM(6)-class landing craft**

D: 24 tons light (56 fl) **S:** 10 kts **Dim:** 17.07 × 4.37 × 1.17 (aft)
M: 2 Gray Marine 64HN9 diesels; 2 props; 330 bhp
Range: 130/10

Remarks: Cargo: 30 tons. Transferred: five in 3-56, remainder in 3-58. May be stricken with the arrival of the ex-German units above.

◆ **7 LCVP-type landing craft** Bldr: Viking Marine, Piraeus (In serv. 1-80)

D: 13 tons (fl) **S:** 8 kts **Dim:** 10.90 × 3.21 × 1.04 (aft)
M: 1 G.M. 6-71 diesel; 200 bhp

◆ **34 ex-U.S. LCVP-type landing craft**

D: 13 tons (fl) **S:** 9 kts **Dim:** 10.90 × 3.21 × 1.04 (aft)
M: 1 Gray Marine 64HN9 diesel; 225 bhp **Range:** 110/9

Remarks: Carried by LSTs and the LSD. Cargo 36 troops or 3.5 tons cargo. Transferred: 10 in 11-56, 4 in 7-58, 10 in 1-62, 4 in 6-64, 3 in 10-69, and remainder in 3-71. Are probably being replaced by new-construction units in the Jason-class tank landing ships.

HYDROGRAPHIC SHIPS

◆ **1 inshore survey ship** Bldr: Emanuil-Maliris SY, Perama

	L	In serv.
A 476 Strabon	9-88	27-2-89

D: 252 tons (fl) **S:** 12.5 kts **Dim:** 32.70 × 6.10 × 2.50
M: 1 M.A.N. D2842LE diesel; 1 prop; 1,200 bhp
Crew: 2 officers, 18 enlisted

Remarks: Replaced former German KW 1-class coastal survey ships *Archikelefstis Maliopoulos* (A 476) and *Archikelefstis Stasis* (A 477), stricken 1988 and 1989, respectively.

◆ **1 oceanographic survey ship** Bldr: Anastassiadis Tsortanidis, Perama

	L	In serv.
A 474 Pytheas	19-9-83	12-83

D: 670 tons (840 fl) **S:** 15 kts **Dim:** 50.00 (44.91 pp) × 9.60 × 4.22
M: 2 G.M. diesels; 2 props; 1,800 bhp **Crew:** 8 officers, 50 enlisted

Remarks: Programmed 1979, ordered 5-82. Carries two survey launches. A near-sister, *Aigeo,* was completed 1985 for the National Maritime Research Center.

◆ **1 hydrographic survey ship** Bldr: Anastassiadis Tsortanidis, Perama

	L	In serv.
A 478 Naftilos	19-11-75	3-4-76

Naftilos (A 478) — Greek Navy

D: 1,380 tons (1,480 fl) **S:** 15 kts **Dim:** 63.1 (56.5 pp) × 11.6 × 4.0
M: 2 Burmeister & Wain SS28LH diesels; 2 props; 2,640 bhp
Crew: 8 officers, 66 enlisted

Remarks: Sisters *St. Lykoudis* (A 481) and *I. Theophilopoulos Karavoyiannos* (A 485) are lighthouse tenders. Has helicopter landing platform, two survey launches.

◆ **1 modified U.S. Falcon-class coastal minesweeper**

	Bldr	In serv.
A 475 Doris (ex-M 245, ex-MSC 298)	Tacoma Boatbldg.	9-11-64

Remarks: Transferred on completion; converted late 1970s. Crew: 3 officers, 32 enlisted; other details as for minesweeper sisters.

AUXILIARY SHIPS

◆ **1 training ship** Bldr: Anastassiadis Tsortanidis, Perama

	Laid down	L	In serv.
A 74 Aris	10-76	4-10-78	1-81

AUXILIARY SHIPS *(continued)*

Aris (A 74) Maritime Photographic, 7-91

D: 2,400 tons (2,630 fl) **S:** 17.8 kts
Dim: 100.00 (95.00 pp) × 11.00 × 4.50
A: 2/76.2-mm U.S. Mk 26 DP (I × 2)—2/40-mm U.S. Mk 3 Bofors AA (I × 2)—4/20-mm Rheinmetall AA (I × 4)—1/Alouette-III helicopter
Electron Equipt: Radar: 2/Decca TM 1226C nav.
M: 2 MAK diesels; 2 props; 10,000 bhp
Crew: 21 officers, 94 enlisted + 359 cadets

Remarks: Can serve as a hospital ship or transport in wartime. Completion delayed by payment dispute. Two lead-computing GFCS for the 40-mm AA. During 1986 refit received new command center, and helicopter facility was reactivated. MARISAT SATCOMM equipment aboard in 1988.

◆ **2 personnel ferries** Bldr: Anastassiadis Tsortanidis, Perama

A 419 Pandora (In serv. 26-10-73)
A 420 Pandrosos (In serv. 1-12-73)

Pandrosos (A 420) Leo Van Ginderen, 9-86

D: 350 tons (390 fl) **S:** 11 kts **Dim:** 46.80 × 8.30 × 1.90
M: 2 diesels; 2 props; . . . bhp

Remarks: Can carry up to 500 personnel.

◆ **1 ex-German intelligence-collection ship** Bldr: Unterweser, Bremerhaven

	L	In serv.	Converted
A 373 Hermis (ex-*Oker*, ex-*Hoheweg*)	29-8-60	19-10-60	11-2-72

Hermis (A 373)—as *Oker* (A 53) Bernard Prézelin, 5-86

D: 1,187 tons (1,497 fl) **S:** 15 kts
Dim: 72.83 (68.35 pp) × 10.50 × 5.60
A: none **Electron Equipt:** Radar: 2/. . . nav.—EW: intercept suite
M: 1 Klöckner-Humboldt-Deutz 8-cyl. diesel, electric drive; 1 prop; 1,800 shp—1 KHD 8-cyl. auxiliary propulsion diesel, electric drive; 400 shp (8 kts)
Range: . . ./. . . **Crew:** 10 officers, 50 enlisted

Remarks: Former fishing boat converted for intelligence-collection duties for the West German Navy. Stricken 4-12-87 and transferred to Greece 12-2-88. Sister ex-*Alster* (A 50) transferred to Turkey 2-89.

◆ **1 netlayer and mooring buoy tender** Bldr: Krögerwerft, Rendsburg

A 307 Thetis (ex-U.S. AN 103) (In serv. 4-60)

Thetis (A 307) D. Dervissis, 7-79

D: 560 tons (975 fl) **S:** 12.8 kts
Dim: 48.50 (51.70 over horns) × 10.60 × 3.70
A: 1/40-mm U.S. Mk 3 Bofors AA—3/20-mm Oerlikon AA (I × 3)
Electron Equipt: Radar: 1/Decca 707 nav.
M: 1 M.A.N. G7V 40/60 diesel; 1 prop; 1,470 bhp **Fuel:** 134 tons
Range: 6,500/10.2 **Crew:** 5 officers, 45 enlisted

Remarks: Launched 1959. Transferred 4-60. Has 152 tons water ballast. The 40-mm AA is normally not aboard; can carry 1,600 rds 40-mm, 25,200 rds 20-mm ammunition.

◆ **1 ex-German Type 701C multipurpose replenishment ship** Bldr: Flensburger Schiffswerft, Flensburg

	Laid down	L	In serv.
A . . . Axios (ex-*Coburg*, A 1412)	9-4-65	15-12-65	9-7-68

Axios (A . . .)—in German service Leo Van Ginderen, 6

D: 3,709 tons (fl) **S:** 17 kts **Dim:** 114.90 (108.00 pp) × 13.20 × 4.2
A: 4/40-mm Bofors (II × 2) **Electron Equipt:** Radar: 1/. . . nav.
M: 2 Maybach MD 872 diesels; 2 CP props; 5,600 bhp—bow-thruster
Electric: 1,935 kw **Range:** 3,000/17; 3,200/14 **Crew:** 82 tot.

Remarks: Transferred 25-9-91. Converted to Type 701C configuration 1975–7 carry spare Exocet missiles and other supplies for missile boats; carry over 30,000 sp parts in addition to 640 tons cargo fuel, 205 tons ammunition, 131 tons fresh water, 267m² refrigerated stores. Has fin stabilization system, one 3-ton and two 2-ton elec cranes. There are two lead-computing optical directors for the 40-mm guns.

◆ **2 ex-U.S. Patapsco-class oilers** Bldr: Cargill Inc., Savage, Minn.

	Laid down	L	In serv.
A 377 Arethousa (ex-*Natchaug*, AOG 54)	15-8-44	6-12-44	11-6-45
A 414 Ariadni (ex-*Tombigbee*, AOG 11)	23-10-42	18-11-43	13-7-44

D: 1,850 tons (4,335 fl) **S:** 13 kts
Dim: 94.72 (89.00 pp) × 14.78 × 4.78
A: A 377: 4/76.2-mm U.S. Mk 26 DP (I × 4); A 414: 2/76.2-mm DP (I × 2)— 2/20-mm Rheinmetall AA (I × 2)
Electron Equipt:
Radar: 1/. . . nav., 1/SPS-5 surf. search, 1/Mk 26 f.c.
M: 2 G.M. 16-278A diesels; 2 props; 3,300 bhp **Electric:** 460 kw
Fuel: 295 tons **Crew:** 6 officers, 40 enlisted

AUXILIARY SHIPS *(continued)*

Ariadni (A 414) French Navy, 1988

Remarks: 2,575 dwt. Former gasoline tankers. Cargo: 2,040 tons. One Mk 52 radar GFCS and one Mk 51 lead-computing GFCS. Can rig one liquid refueling station per side, forward.

♦ **2 Orion-class coastal tankers** Bldr: Hellenic SY, Skaramanga

	In serv.		In serv.
A 489 ORION	5-5-89	A 490 ZEUS	21-2-89

Zeus (A 490) Hellenic SY, 1989

D: approx. 2,100 tons (fl) **S:** 10.9 kts
Dim: 67.02 (60.35 pp) × 10.00 × 4.20
A: none **Electron Equipt:** Radar: 1/. . . nav.
M: 1 MWM-B&W 12V 20/27 diesel; 1 prop; 1,600 bhp
Crew: 28 (accommodations)

emarks: 866 grt/1,240 dwt. Ordered 9-86. Cargo: 960 m³ diesel or fuel oil, 102 m³ P-5, 115 m³ fresh water, 146 m³ potable water. Freeboard when loaded is only 0.45 m. nproved version of class below, with hose-handling crane on platform forward. Con- ruction of a planned third unit was not carried out.

• **2 coastal tankers** Bldr: Kynossoura SY, Piraeus

	In serv.		In serv.
416 OURANOS	29-1-77	A 417 HYPERION	27-2-77

D: 2,100 tons (fl) **S:** 12 kts **Dim:** 67.70 (60.40 pp) × 10.00 × 4.70
A: 2/20-mm Oerlikon AA (I × 2)
Electron Equipt: Radar: 1/. . . nav.
M: 1 M.A.N.-Burmeister & Wain 12V20 diesel; 1 prop; 1,750 bhp
Crew: 28 tot.

emarks: Cargo: 1,323 m³. Employed as fuel-oil tankers. One additional unit, a water nker, was begun and launched by Khalkis SY, but was to be completed by Hellenic (or, according to other sources, Nafsi SY); in the event, this does not appear to have ppened.

te: *Kronos* (A 373), built in 1943, still exists as a fuel lighter, unpowered; cargo: 110 is. The small tanker *Vivies* (A 471) was stricken in 1989.

1 ex-German ammunition ship Bldr: Dubigeon, Nantes, France

	Laid down	L	In serv.
415 EVROS (ex-German *Schwarzwald,* ex-French *Amalthée*)	30-6-55	31-1-56	7-6-56

D: 2,395 tons **S:** 15 kts **Dim:** 80.18 × 11.99 × 4.65
A: 4/40-mm AA (II × 2)
M: 1 Sulzer 6-SD-60 diesel; 3,000 bhp **Electric:** 500 kw
ange: 4,500/15 **Crew:** 32 tot.

marks: 1,667 grt. Former cargo ship purchased 2-60 by the German Navy and verted for naval use, commissioning 11-10-61. Transferred to Greece 2-6-76.

2 lighthouse tenders Bldr: Anastassiadis Tsortanidis, Perama

79 I. THEOPHILOPOULOS KARAVOYIANNOS (In serv. 2-1-76)
81 ST. LYKOUDIS (In serv. 17-3-76)

: 1,350 tons (1,450 fl) **S:** 15 kts
im: 63.24 (56.50 pp) × 11.6 × 4.0
lectron Equipt: Radar: 2/Decca . . . nav.
: 1 MWM TBD-500-8UD diesel; 2,400 bhp **Crew:** 40 tot.

arks: Near sisters to hydrographic survey ship *Naftilos* (A 478). Have a helicop- latform aft.

I. Theophilopoulis Karavoyiannos (A 479) Leo Van Ginderen, 12-84

♦ **1 ex-British Bustler-class salvage tug** Bldr: Henry Robb, Leith

	Laid down	L	In serv.
A 428 ATLAS (ex-*Nisos Zakynthos,* ex-HMS *Mediator*)	18-10-43	21-6-44	8-11-44

D: 1,118 tons (1,630 fl) **S:** 16 kts
Dim: 62.48 (59.4 pp) × 12.32 × 5.18
M: 2 Atlas diesels; 2 props; 3,200 bhp **Range:** 3,400/11
Fuel: 340 tons **Crew:** 42 tot.

Remarks: Purchased from Royal Navy 1965 by private owner. Acquired 1-8-79 by Greek Navy and commissioned 12-79.

SERVICE CRAFT

♦ **3 Doirani-class water lighters**

A 434 PRESPA (ex-*Doirani*) (In serv. 10-10-72)
A 467 DOIRANI (In serv. 1972)
A 468 KALIROI (In serv. 26-10-72)

Prespa (A 434) Peter Voss, 10-86

D: 850 tons (fl) **S:** 13 kts **Dim:** 54.77 × 7.95 × 3.87
Electron Equipt: Radar: 1/Decca . . . nav.
M: 1 MWM 6-cyl. diesel; 1,300 bhp

Remarks: A 467 is 58.88 m overall, 4.02 m draft; 765 dwt. A 434 is 600 dwt. A 468 is 671 dwt and has a 1,005-bhp MWM diesel. A 434 taken over from another government agency 1979. Very low freeboard.

♦ **2 ex-German FW 1-class water lighters** Bldr: A 433: Jadewerft, Wilhelmshaven; ex-FW 6: Renke, Hamburg

	Laid down	L	In serv.
A 433 KERKINI (ex-FW 3)	14-6-63	15-10-63	11-5-64
A . . . . (ex-FW 6)	4-11-63	25-2-64	19-6-64

Kerkini (A 433) Leo Van Ginderen, 12-84

SERVICE CRAFT *(continued)*

D: 598 tons (624 fl) **S:** 9.5 kts **Dim:** 44.03 (41.10 pp) × 7.80 × 2.63
Electron Equipt: Radar: 1/Kelvin-Hughes 14/9 nav.
M: 1 MWM 12-cyl. diesel; 1 prop; 230 bhp **Electric:** 83 kw
Range: 2,150/9 **Crew:** 12 tot.

Remarks: A 433 transferred 22-4-76, second ship on 5-3-91. Cargo: 350 m^3.

◆ **2 miscellaneous small water lighters**

A 470 Kastoria (In serv. . . .)—Cargo: 520 tons
A 473 Trichonis (In serv. 1980)—Cargo: 650 tons

◆ **5 liquid-cargo barges** Bldr: Eleusis SY (In serv. 1988)

D: approx. 400 tons (fl) **Dim:** 27.1 × 7.2 × 1.5

Remarks: Cargo: 300 tons. Four for fuel oil, the other for water.

◆ **2 Kekrops-class coastal tugs** Bldr: Hellenic SY, Skaramanga

A 435 Kekrops (In serv. 1989) A 422 Kadmos (In serv. 1989)

D: . . . tons **S:** . . . kts **Dim:** . . . × . . . × . . .
M: . . .

Remarks: Ordered 1-86. No data available.

◆ **3 Heraklis-class coastal tugs** Bldr: Anastassiadis Tsortanidis, Perama

A 423 Heraklis (In serv. 6-4-78) A 425 Odisseus (In serv. 28-6-78)
A 424 Jason (In serv. 6-3-78)

D: 345 tons **S:** 12 kts **Dim:** 30.0 × 7.9 × 3.4
M: 1 MWM diesel; 1,200 bhp

◆ **2 Atromitos-class harbor tugs** (In serv. 20-6-68)

A 410 Atromitos A 411 Adamastos

D: 310 tons **S:** 10 kts **Dim:** 30.0 × 7.9 × 3.0
M: 1 diesel; 1 prop; 1,260 bhp

◆ **5 ex-German Lütje Horn (Type 723)-class harbor tugs**

	L
A . . . . (ex-Lütje Horn, Y 812)	9-5-58
A . . . . (ex- Mellum, Y 813)	23-10-58
A . . . . (ex-Knechtsand, Y 814)	3-12-58
A . . . . (ex-Schärhorn, Y 815)	9-5-58
A . . . . (ex-Trischen, Y 818)	27-2-59

D: 52.2 tons (57.5 fl) **S:** 10 kts **Dim:** 15.2 × 5.06 × 2.2
M: 2 Deutz 8-cyl. diesels; 2 Voith-Schneider cycloidal props; 340 bhp
Range: 550/9 **Crew:** 4 tot.

Remarks: *Lütje Horn* (Y 812) stricken 18-12-89 and transferred 5-3-91 , *Mellum* (Y 813) stricken 20-12-90 and transferred 25-4-91, *Knechtsand* (Y 814) stricken 18-10-90 and transferred 5-3-91, *Schärhorn* (Y 815) stricken 2-8-90 and transferred 5-3-91, and *Trischen* (Y 818) stricken 20-12-90 and transferred 25-4-91. Sisters *Vogelsand* (Y 816) stricken 16-2-87; *Nordstrand* (Y 817) stricken 1-11-86; *Langeness* (Y 819) 15-1-87.

◆ **1 ex-U.S. Army Design 3006-class large harbor tug** (In serv. 1954–55)

A 432 Gigas (ex-LT 1941)

D: 295 tons (390 fl) **S:** 12.75 kts **Dim:** 32.61 × 8.08 × 3.71
M: 1 Fairbanks-Morse 38 D 8 $^1/_8$ diesel; 1 prop; 1,200 bhp
Range: 3,300/12 **Fuel:** 54 tons **Electric:** 80 kw **Crew:** 16 tot.

Remarks: Transferred 26-11-61. Bollard pull: 12 tons.

◆ **1 ex-U.S. YTM 764-class harbor tug** Bldr: Luders Marine Construction, Stamford, Connecticut (In serv. 11-5-45)

A 412 Aias (ex-U.S. *Ankachak,* YTM 767, ex-YTB 501)

D: 260 tons (350 fl) **S:** 11 kts **Dim:** 30.48 × 7.62 × 2.92
M: 2 Enterprise diesels; 1 prop; 1,270 bhp **Crew:** 8 tot.

Remarks: Transferred 1972.

◆ **1 ex-U.S. YTM 518-class harbor tug** Bldr: Gibbs Gas Engine Co., Jacksonville, Florida (In serv. 2-1-45)

A 428 Nestor (ex-U.S. *Wahpeton,* YTM 527)

D: 260 tons (310 fl) **S:** 11 kts **Dim:** 30.8 × 8.5 × 3.3
M: 2 G.M. diesels; 1 prop; 820 bhp **Crew:** 8 tot.

Remarks: Transferred 22-11-89.

◆ **1 ex-U.S. YTM 174-class harbor tug** Bldr: Gulfport Boiler Works, Port Arthur, Texas (In serv. 12-3-42)

A 427 Danaos (ex-U.S. *Dekanisora,* YTM 252, ex-YT 252, ex-BYT 4)

D: 210 tons (320 fl) **S:** 12 kts **Dim:** 31.1 × 7.6 × 3.0
M: 2 G.M. diesels; 1 prop; 820 bhp **Crew:** 8 tot.

Remarks: Transferred 22-11-89.

Note: The harbor tugs *Minotauros* (A 421, ex-U.S. Army ST 539) and *Titan* (A 431) were stricken 1991.

◆ **4 West German Type 430 torpedo retrievers** Bldr: Schweers, Bardenfleth

	L
A 460 Evrotas (ex-TF 106, Y 872)	10-6-66
A 461 Arachthos (ex-TF 108, Y 874)	22-9-65
A 462 . . . . (ex-TF 6, Y 856)	4-5-66
A 463 . . . . (ex-TF 4, Y 854)	21-10-65

D: 56 tons (63.5 fl) **S:** 17 kts **Dim:** 25.22 × 5.40 × 1.60
Electron Equipt: Radar: 1/. . . nav.
M: 1 MWM 12-cyl. diesel; 1 prop; 1,000 bhp **Crew:** 6 tot.

Remarks: First two transferred to Greece 16-11-89. Ex-TF 4 transferred 28-9-90 and ex-TF 6 on 12-4-90.

◆ **5 miscellaneous floating cranes**

◆ **1 floating dry dock** Bldr: Eleusis SY

Naval Drydock No. 7 (L: 2-5-88; in serv. 9-5-88)

Remarks: 6,000-ton capacity, 145.0 m. o.a. Technical assistance from Götaverken, Sweden.

◆ **1 wooden trireme rowing galley** Bldr: . . . . . .

Olympias (In serv. 1987)

Olympias Ships of the World, 198

D: . . . . . . **S:** 9–12 kts **Dim:** 37.0 × 5.2 × 1.5
M: 170 oars in three rows; auxiliary square sail
Crew: 10 officers, 170 galley "slaves"

Remarks: Built for historic research and to commemorate the Greek naval traditi[on]. As rowers are volunteers, whips are unnecessary.

Greek Navy 70-ton floating crane Hellenic SY,

COAST GUARD
(Limenikon Soma)

The Greek Coast Guard has some 4,300 personnel (750 officers), most of w[hom] are shore-based. There are some 159 patrol craft. Two Cessna 172RG Cutlass a[nd] SOCATA TB20 Trinidad light aircraft are used for coastal patrol.

◆ **5 Dilos-class patrol boats** Bldr: Hellenic SY, Skaramanga (In serv. 1977–88)

LS 81–LS 85

COAST GUARD *(continued)*

LS 82 Peter Voss, 11-81

D: 75 tons (86 fl) **S:** 27 kts **Dim:** 29.00 (27.00 wl) × 5.00 × 1.62
A: 2/20-mm AA (I × 2) **Electron Equipt:** Radar: 1/. . . nav.
M: 2 MTU 12V331 TC81 diesels; 2 props; 2,720 bhp
Range: 1,600/25 **Crew:** 15 tot.

Remarks: Designed by Abeking & Rasmussen, West Germany. Used for air/sea rescue. Three each also built for Navy and Customs Service. Round-bilge steel-construction hull.

◆ **. . . LS 51-class inshore patrol boats** Bldr: Olympic Marine, Lavrio

S 52 Hartmut Ehlers, 5-84

D: 13 tons (fl) **S:** 23 kts **Dim:** 13.2 × 3.5 × 1.0
M: 2 diesels; 2 props; 600 bhp **Range:** 400/. . .

emarks: U.K. Keith Nelson GRP hull design.

. . . OL 44 class Bldr: Olympic Marine, Lavrio

88 Hartmut Ehlers, 6-86

: 13.8 tons (fl) **S:** 23 kts **Dim:** 13.50 (12.10 wl) × 4.35 × 0.61
: 2 diesels; 2 props; 600 bhp **Crew:** 4–6 tot.

arks: GRP construction. There are a total of 33 craft in the above two classes.

◆ **38 8.23-m class** Bldr: . . . . . .

LS 72 Hartmut Ehlers, 5-84

Remarks: Outdrive-powered GRP craft. Also in service for patrol/SAR duties are 26 5.7-m U.S. Chris Craft launches and 10 semi-rigid inflatable boats (the latter used by the 35-man Underwater Mission Squad).

◆ **11 miscellaneous anti-pollution craft**

Pollution-collection boat LS 24 Hartmut Ehlers, 5-84

Pollution-control landing craft LS 69 Hartmut Ehlers, 5-86

CUSTOMS SERVICE

◆ **3 Dilos-class patrol craft** Bldr: Hellenic SY, Skaramanga (In serv. 1977–79)

A/L 16 Leo Van Ginderen, 9-87

GREECE *(continued)*
CUSTOMS SERVICE *(continued)*

D: 75 tons (86 fl) **S:** 27 kts **Dim:** 29.00 (27.00 wl) × 5.00 × 1.62
A: 2/20-mm AA (I × 2) **Electron Equipt:** Radar: 1/. . . nav.
M: 2 MTU 12V331 TC81 diesels; 2 props; 2,720 bhp
Range: 1,600/25 **Crew:** 15 tot.

Remarks: Designed by Abeking & Rasmussen, West Germany. Used for air/sea rescue. Three also built for Navy and five for the Coast Guard. Round-bilge steel-construction hull.

♦ **10 OL 76 class** Bldr: Olympic Marine S.A., Lavrio (In serv. 1986–87)

A/L 04 Hartmut Ehlers, 6-86

D: 50 tons (fl) **S:** 28 kts **Dim:** 23.16 (19.50 pp) × 5.03 × 1.00
A: 2/20-mm AA (I × 2)—2/12.7-mm mg (I × 2)
M: 2 MTU diesels; 2 props; 2,600 bhp **Crew:** 11 tot.

GRENADA

COAST GUARD

Personnel (1991): 34 total, under the Commissioner of Police

♦ **1 U.S. 106-ft patrol boat** Bldr: Lantana Boatyard, Lantana, Florida

PB 01 Tyrrel Bay (In serv. 21-11-84)

Tyrrel Bay (PB 01) Lantana Boatyard, 11-84

D: 94 tons (fl) **S:** 24 kts **Dim:** 32.31 × 6.25 × 2.13 (props)
A: 2/12.7-mm mg (I × 2)—2/7.62-mm mg (I × 2)
Electron Equipt: Radar: 1/Furuno . . . nav.
M: 3 G.M. Detroit Diesel 12V71 TI diesels; 3 props; 2,250 bhp
Electric: 100 kw **Fuel:** 21 tons **Crew:** 4 officers, 12 enlisted

Remarks: Laid down 1-84 to U.S. Government order. Aluminum construction. Has a Magnavox MX4102 NAVSAT receiver.

♦ **2 U.S. Boston Whaler-class launches** Bldr: Boston Whaler, Rockland, Massachusetts (In serv. 1988–89)

D: 1.3 tons (fl) **S:** 40 kts **Dim:** 6.81 × 2.26 × 0.40
A: 1/12.7-mm mg **M:** 2 gasoline outboards; 240 bhp
Range: 167/40 **Crew:** 4 tot.

Remarks: Foam-core, "unsinkable" construction.

Note: 12.2-m patrol boat PB 02 stricken 1990; three "Spear"-class patrol craft stricke[n] 1988–90.

GUATEMALA

Republic of Guatemala

Personnel (1991): 1,200 total: 125 officers, 875 enlisted, including 700 Marines

PATROL BOATS AND CRAFT

♦ **1 U.S. Broadsword class** Bldr: Halter Marine, Chalmette, La.

P 1051 Kukulkan (In serv. 4-8-76)

Kukulkan (P 1051)—on trials with *Bitol* (P 655), *Picuda* (P 361), a[nd] *Barracuda* (P 362) Halter Marine, 19[..]

D: 90.5 tons light (110 fl) **S:** 32 kts
Dim: 32.0 (29.4 wl) × 6.3 × 1.9 (props)
A: 1/20-mm Oerlikon GAM B01 AA—1/12.7-mm mg—2/7.62-mm mg (I × 2)—2/75-mm recoilless rifles (I × 2)
Electron Equipt: Radar: 1/Decca 1226 nav.
M: 2 G.M. 16V149 TI diesels; 3,200 bhp **Electric:** 60 kw
Range: 1,150/20 **Fuel:** 16 tons **Crew:** 5 officers, 15 enlisted

Remarks: Aluminum construction. Oerlikon 20-mm AA replaced forw[ard] 12.7-mm mg in 1989.

♦ **2 U.S. 85-foot Commercial Cruiser class** Bldr: Sewart Seacraft, Berwick, La.

P 851 Utatlan (In serv. 5-67)
P 852 Subteniente Osorio Saravia (In serv. 11-72)

Subteniente Osorio Saravia (P 852) PH1 J. Hilton, USN

GUATEMALA *(continued)*
PATROL BOATS AND CRAFT *(continued)*

D: 43.5 tons (54 fl) **S:** 23 kts **Dim:** 25.9 × 5.8 × 2.2 (props)
A: 1/20-mm Oerlikon GAM B01 AA (I × 2)—1/12.7-mm mg—2/7.62-mm mg (I × 2)—1/75-mm recoilless rifle
Electron Equipt: Radar: Decca 1226 nav.
M: 2 G.M. 16V71 TI diesels; 2 props; 2,200 bhp **Range:** 780/15
Fuel: 8 tons **Electric:** 40 kw **Crew:** 7 officers, 10 enlisted

Remarks: Aluminum construction. Oerlikon AA replaced the forward 12.7-mm mg in 1989 on P 851; P 852 was non-operational in 1991 and does not seem to have been rearmed.

◆ **6 U.S. Cutlass class** Bldr: Halter Marine, New Orleans, La.

	In serv.		In serv.
P 651 Tecunuman	26-11-71	P 654 Tzacol	8-76
P 652 Kaibilbalan	8-2-72	P 655 Bitol	8-76
P 653 Azumanche	8-2-72	P 656 Gukamatz	8-81

D: 34 tons (45 fl) **S:** 25 kts **Dim:** 19.7 × 5.2 × 0.9
A: 1/20-mm Oerlikon GAM B01 AA—1/12.7-mm mg—2/7.62-mm mg (I × 2)
Electron Equipt: Radar: 1/Decca . . . nav.
M: 2 G.M. 12V71 diesels; 2 props; 1,020 bhp **Electric:** 20 kw
Range: 400/15 **Crew:** 2 officers, 8 enlisted

◆ **30 river patrol craft** Bldr: Trabejos Baros SY, Guatemala (In serv. 1979)

Alioth Escuintla Dinjebm Kochab Lago de Atitlan
Mazatenango Mero Mirfak Pampano Pollux Procyon
Retalhuleu Sardina Schedar Sirius Spica Stella Maris
Vega—and 12 others

D: . . . tons **S:** 19 or 28 kts **Dim:** 9.14 × 3.66 × 0.61
A: 2/7.62-mm mg (I × 2)
M: 1 diesel; 1 prop; 150 or 300 bhp **Range:** 400–500 n.m.

Remarks: Wooden construction—in two series, with different engines.

AMPHIBIOUS WARFARE CRAFT

◆ **2 U.S. Machete-class personnel landing craft** Bldr: Halter Marine, New Orleans, La. (In serv. 4-8-76)

P 361 Picuda P 362 Barracuda

D: 6 tons **S:** 36 kts **Dim:** 11.0 × 4.0 × 0.76
M: 2 G.M. 6V53 PI diesels; 2 waterjets; 540 bhp
Crew: 2 tot. + 20 troops

Remarks: Square bows, aluminum construction.

Note: Also in service are two small yachts (one named *Mendieta*) and a ferry, *Tical* (691).

GUINEA

Republic of Guinea

Personnel (1991): 600 total

PATROL BOATS AND CRAFT

◆ **2 Soviet Bogomol class** Bldr: Ulis SY, Vladivostok

P-320 . . . . . . (In serv. 4-89) P-321 . . . . . . (In serv. 4-90)

D: 245 tons (fl) **S:** 35 kts **Dim:** 38.60 × 7.60 × 2.00
A: 1/76-mm AK-176 DP—1/30-mm AK-630 gatling AA—1/SA-N-5 SAM syst. (IV × 1)
Electron Equipt:
Radar: 1/Pot Drum surf. search, 1/Bass Tilt f.c.
IFF: 1/Square Head interrogator
M: 3 M504 diesels; 3 props; 14,750 bhp
Range: 500/34; 750/25 **Crew:** 30 tot.

Remarks: Design employs Osa-II hull and propulsion plant and is similar to the class export patrol boat except for the heavier gun armament forward and the lack of provision for torpedo tubes. Two sisters serve in Guinea-Bissau fleet, and two were ...ered to Iraq.

◆ **1 U.S. 77-ft class** Bldr: Swiftships, Morgan City, La. (In serv. 18-12-86)

P-328 Intrépide

D: 39.8 tons (47.6 fl) **S:** 24 kts **Dim:** 23.47 × 6.10 × 1.52
A: 2/12.7-mm mg (I × 2)—2/7.62-mm mg (I × 2)—1/60-mm mortar
Electron Equipt: Radar: 1/. . . nav.
M: 3 G.M. 12V71 TI diesels; 3 props; 2,385 bhp
Range: 1,800/15 **Crew:** 10 tot.

Intrépide (P-328) Linda Turgeon, 12-86

Remarks: Ordered 7-85. Aluminum construction. Made 27 kts on trials. Sisters serve El Salvador.

◆ **1 U.S. 65-ft class** Bldr: Swiftships, Inc., Morgan City, La. (In serv. 6-85)

P-300 Vigilante

Vigilante (P-300) Swiftships, 6-85

D: 31.7 tons (36.3 fl) **S:** 24 kts **Dim:** 19.96 × 5.61 × 1.52
A: 2/12.7-mm mg (I × 2)—2/7.62-mm mg (I × 2)
Electron Equipt: Radar: 1/. . . nav.
M: 2 G.M. 12V71 TI diesels; 2 props; 1,590 bhp
Range: 500/18 **Crew:** 10 tot.

Remarks: Aluminum construction. Resembles El Salvador's GC-11.

◆ **2 Soviet Zhuk-class patrol boats**

P-. . . . . P-. . . . .

D: 48 tons (60 fl) **S:** 34 kts **Dim:** 24.0 × 5.0 × 1.2 (1.8 props)
A: 4/14.5-mm mg (II × 2) **Electron Equipt:** Radar: 1/Spin Trough
M: 2 M50F-4 diesels; 2 props; 2,400 bhp **Fuel:** 10 tons
Range: 700/28; 1,100/15 **Crew:** 12 tot.

Remarks: Delivered 7-87.

◆ **2 U.S. Stinger class** Bldr: MonArk, Monticello, Arkansas (In serv. 3-6-85)

P-30 P-35

P-30 MonArk, 1985

GUINEA *(continued)*
PATROL BOATS AND CRAFT *(continued)*

D: 2.7 tons (fl) **S:** 35 kts **Dim:** 7.92 × 3.25 × 0.91
A: 2/12.7-mm (I × 2)
Electron Equipt: Radar: 1/Raytheon 1200 nav.
M: 2 OMC 55 XL "Commercial" outboard motors; 310 bhp
Crew: 4 tot.

Remarks: Ordered 10-84. Aluminum construction. Camouflaged in three shades of green.

♦ **1 French 28-m class** Bldr: Chantiers Navals de l'Estérel, Cannes

P-400 Almariy Bocar Biro Barry (In serv. 8-79)

D: 56 tons (fl) **S:** 35 kts **Dim:** 28.0 × 5.2 × 1.6 **A:** 1/7.62-mm mg
M: 2 MTU 12V331 TC82 diesels; 2 props; 2,600 bhp
Range: 750/15 **Crew:** 12 tot.

Remarks: Construction of two additional units was abandoned in 1987.

AMPHIBIOUS WARFARE CRAFT

♦ **1 utility landing craft** Bldr: . . ., France (In serv. 1978)

Kinkon

Remarks: 150 tons full load; no other data available. Also in service are three small personnel/vehicle landing craft delivered 1978 from France.

SERVICE CRAFT

♦ **1 1,500-ton-capacity floating dry dock**

GUINEA-BISSAU

Republic of Guinea-Bissau

Personnel (1991): Approximately 400 total

Naval Aviation: One Cessna 337 for coastal surveillance

PATROL BOATS

♦ **2 Soviet Bogomol-class patrol boats** Bldr: Ulis SY, Vladivostok

Guinea-Bissau Navy Bogomol—note derelict Shershen-class torpedo boat in background at left French Navy, 1988

D: 245 tons (fl) **S:** 35 kts **Dim:** 38.60 × 7.60 × 2.00
A: 1/76.2-mm 59-cal. AK-176 DP—1/30-mm AK-630 gatling AA—1/SA-N-5 SAM syst. (IV × 1)
Electron Equipt:
Radar: 1/Pot Drum surf. search, 1/Bass Tilt f.c.
IFF: 1/Square Head interrogator, 1/High Pole B Transponder
M: 3 M504 diesels; 3 props; 14,750 bhp
Range: 500/34; 750/25 **Crew:** 30 tot.

Remarks: First unit delivered 2-88, the second in 2-89. Design employs Osa-II hull and propulsion plant and is similar to the Mol-class export patrol boat except for the heavier gun armament forward and the lack of provision for torpedo tubes.

PATROL CRAFT

♦ **0 (+ 3) new construction** Bldr: Ars. Alfeite, Portugal

D: 50 tons (fl) **S:** 28 kts **Dim:** 20.40 (18.50 wl) × 5.90 × . . .
A: . . . **M:** 3 . . . . . . diesels; 3 waterjets; 1,000 bhp
Crew: . . .

Remarks: Ordered summer 1991 for delivery 1993.

♦ **2 Chinese Shantou class** (In serv. 1955–60)

D: 80 tons (fl) **S:** 28 kts **Dim:** 25.1 × 6.0 × 1.8
A: 4/37-mm AA (II × 2)—2/14.5-mm mg (I × 2)
Electron Equipt: Radar: 1/Skin Head surf. search **Crew:** 30 tot.
M: 2 M50 series, 1,200 bhp and 2 Type 3D12, 300-bhp diesels; 4 props; 3,000 bhp

Remarks: Two transferred late 1983 and since discarded; two more transferred in 3-86. Steel construction. Of little value due to age.

♦ **7 Spanish LVC-1 class** Bldr: Aresa, Barcelona (In serv. 1979–82)

D: 20.8 tons (fl) **S:** 23.3 kts **Dim:** 16.00 × 4.36 × 1.30
A: 1/12.7-mm mg
M: 2 Baudouin DNP-8 M1R diesels; 2 props; 700 bhp
Range: 400/18 **Crew:** 6 tot.

SERVICE CRAFT

♦ **1 1,600-ton-capacity floating dry dock**

Remarks: Delivered 10-90 from the United States.

Note: The Polish-built Soviet Biya-class buoy tender/survey ship listed in previous editions does not, in fact, seem to have been transferred. Discarded by 1991 were two Soviet-supplied Poluchat-I-class torpedo retriever/patrol craft.

CUSTOMS SERVICE

PATROL CRAFT

♦ **1 Dutch PT 1903 Mk III class** Bldr: Le Comte, Vianen, Netherlands

Naga (In serv. 5-81)

D: 30 tons (33 fl) **S:** 30 kts **Dim:** 19.27 × 4.95 × 1.25
A: 2/12.7-mm mg (I × 2) **Range:** 1,650/17; 2,300/12
M: 2 MTU 8V331 TC92 diesels; 2 props; 1,770 bhp **Crew:** 10 tot.

Note: French-built Plascoa-1900 patrol launches *Cabo Roxo* and *Ilha de Poilão* h[ave] been discarded by 1991.

GUYANA

Cooperative Republic of Guyana

Personnel (1991): 100 total

PATROL BOATS AND CRAFT

♦ **1 103-foot British patrol boat** Bldr: Vosper Thornycroft, Portsmouth, U.K.

	L	In serv.
DF 1010 Peccari	26-3-76	26-1-77

D: 96 tons (109 fl) **S:** 27 kts **Dim:** 31.4 × 6.0 × 1.6
A: 2/20-mm Oerlikon AA (I × 2)
Electron Equipt: Radar: 1/Decca . . . nav.
M: 2 Paxman Ventura 12-cyl. diesels; 2 props; 3,500 bhp
Range: 1,400/14 **Crew:** 22 tot.

Remarks: A second unit was ordered in 1977 but was canceled because of la[ck of] funds. *Peccari* is probably in poor condition.

♦ **3 wooden-hulled ex-fishing boats**

DF 1007 Ekereku DF 1008 Waitipu DF 1017 Maipuru

D: . . . tons (fl) **S:** 9.5 kts **Dim:** 21.0 × 5.4 × 2.1 **A:** . . .
M: 1 Caterpillar 343 diesel; 1 prop; . . . bhp **Crew:** 4 tot.

HAITI

Republic of Haiti

Personnel (1991): 325 total

PATROL BOATS AND CRAFT

◆ **1 U.S. Sotoyomo-class former auxiliary ocean tug** Bldr: Levington SB, Orange, Texas

	Laid down	L	In serv.
MH 20 Henri Christophe (ex-*Samoset*, ATA 190)	5-6-44	14-7-44	27-9-44

enri Christophe (MH 20) Leo Van Ginderen, 1988

D: 689 tons (835 fl) **S:** 13 kts **Dim:** 43.6 (40.75 pp) × 10.37 × 3.65
A: 2/40-mm U.S. Bofors Mk 3 AA (I × 2)—2/12.7-mm mg (I × 2)
Electron Equipt: Radar: 1/. . . nav.
M: 2 G.M. 12-278A diesels, electric drive; 1 prop; 1,500 shp
Electric: 120 kw **Fuel:** 154 tons **Range:** 16,500/9 **Crew:** 40 tot.

marks: Transferred 18-9-78. One 40-mm on fantail, one forward.

9 U.S. 3812-VCF-class patrol craft Bldr: MonArk, Monticello, Arkansas (In serv. 1980–81)

H 11 Le Maroon
H 12 Oge
H 13 Chavannes
H 14 Capois La Mort
H 15 Bauckman
MH 16 Makandal
MH 17 Charlemagne Perrault
MH 18 Sonthonax
MH 24 Bois Rond Tonnerre

(MH 12) MonArk, 1980

: 8.5 tons (9.0 fl) **S:** 25 kts **Dim:** 12.34 × 4.11 × 1.10
: 1/12.7-mm Browning mg—2/7.62-mm mg (I × 2)
: 2 G.M. 6V71N diesels; 2 props; 480 bhp
ange: 350/20 **Crew:** 4 tot.

arks: Only six operational by 1990, with the other three used as parts sources.

: Two U.S.-built Halter Marine 78-ft. patrol boats built for Haiti and launched g 1982 were never delivered and were still in the builder's hands as of 1989. U.S. Commercial Cruiser-class patrol craft MH 21, MH 22, and MH 23 were discarded -90.

HONDURAS

Republic of Honduras

Personnel (1991): 1,600 total (150 officers)

Naval Aviation: Four Embraer EMB111 Bandeirante delivered 1983 for coastal surveillance; flown by naval crews. Two Lake Seawolf amphibians delivered 1987.

PATROL BOATS AND CRAFT

◆ **2 U.S. Guardian class** Bldr: Lantana Boatyard, Lantana, Florida

FNH 106 Copan (In serv. 6-86)
FNH 107 Tegucigalpa (ex-FNH 105) (In serv. 1983)

Tegucigalpa (FNH 107) Bender SB & Repair, 6-86

D: 94 tons (fl) **S:** 35 kts **Dim:** 32.31 × 6.25 × 2.13 (props)
A: 1/20-mm Sea Vulcan 20 gatling gun—3/20-mm Hispano-Suiza AA (III × 1)—2/12.7-mm mg (I × 2)
Electron Equipt: Radar: 1/Furuno . . . nav.
M: 3 G.M. Detroit Diesel 16V92 TI diesels; 3 props; 3,900 bhp
Electric: 100 kw **Range:** 1,500/18 **Fuel:** 21 tons
Crew: 4 officers, 12 enlisted

Remarks: Aluminum construction. Have Magnavox MX 4102 NAVSAT receiver and two echo-sounders. HSV-20NCS optronic control system for 20-mm gatling gun. A third unit, to have been named *Comayguela,* was canceled and became Jamaica's *Paul Bogle.*

◆ **3 U.S. 105-foot class** Bldr: Swiftships, Morgan City, Louisiana

FNH 101 Guaymuras (In serv. 4-77)
FNH 102 Honduras (In serv. 3-80)
FNH 103 Hibures (In serv. 3-80)

Honduras (FNH 102)—old number and paint scheme Swiftships, Inc., 3-80

D: 103 tons (111 fl) **S:** 24 kts **Dim:** 32.00 × 7.20 × 3.1 (props)
A: 1/20-mm Sea Vulcan 20 gatling gun—2/12.7-mm mg (I × 2)
Electron Equipt: Radar: 1/. . . nav.
M: 2 MTU diesels; 2 props; 7,000 bhp **Electric:** 80 kw
Range: 1,200/18 **Fuel:** 21 tons **Crew:** 3 officers, 14 enlisted

Remarks: Aluminum construction. Gatling gun and HSV-20NCS f.c.s. added 1987. FNH 103 has 6/20-mm Hispano-Suiza (III × 2) vice listed armament.

◆ **1 U.S. 85-foot Commercial Cruiser class** Bldr: Swiftships, Morgan City, Louisiana

HONDURAS *(continued)*
PATROL BOATS AND CRAFT *(continued)*

FNH 851 Chamelecon (ex-*Rio Kuringwas*) (In serv. 1967)

D: 50 tons (54 fl) **S:** 23 kts **Dim:** 25.9 (23.1 wl) × 5.8 × 1.0 (hull)
A: 1/20-mm Sea Vulcan 20 gatling—2/12.7-mm mg (I × 2)
Electron Equipt: Radar: 1/. . . nav.
M: 2 G.M. 12V71 TI diesels; 2 props; 1,400 bhp **Electric:** 40 kw
Range: 780/15 **Crew:** 2 officers, 10 enlisted

Remarks: Craft defected from Nicaragua in 1979. Aluminum construction. Received gatling gun and HSV-20NCS f.c.s. in 1987.

♦ **5 U.S. 65-foot Commercial Cruiser class** Bldr: Swiftships, Morgan City, Louisiana

	In serv.
FNH 651 Nacaome (ex-*Aguan*, ex-*Gral*)	12-73
FNH 652 Goascoran (ex- *Gral. J.T. Cabanas*)	1-74
FNH 653 Petula	1980
FNH 654 Ulua	1980
FNH 655 Chuluteca	1980

D: 33 tons (36 fl) **S:** 28 or 36 kts
Dim: 19.9 (17.4 wl) × 5.6 × 1.6 (props)
A: 2/12.7-mm mg (I × 2)
Electron Equipt: Radar: 1/Decca . . . nav.
M: 2 G.M. 12V71 TI or MTU diesels; 2 props; 1,300 or 1,590 bhp
Electric: 20 kw **Range:** 2,000/22 **Fuel:** 5 tons
Crew: 2 officers, 7 enlisted

Remarks: First pair were originally ordered for Haiti, were delivered to Honduras for use as customs launches in 1977, and were later transferred to the navy. The others, ordered 1979, have more powerful diesels. Aluminum construction.

♦ **8 river patrol craft** Bldr: Lantana Boatyard, Lantana, Florida (In serv. 3-2-86)

Lantana 11-meter patrol craft Lantana, 1-86

D: 8.16 tons (fl) **S:** 26 kts (22 sust.)
Dim: 11.00 (10.06 wl) × 3.05 × 0.53
A: 2/12.7-mm mg (I × 2)—2/7.62-mm mg (I × 2)
Electron Equipt: Radar: 1/Furuno 3600 nav.—EW: VHF D/F
M: 2 Caterpillar 3208 TA diesels; 2 props; 630 bhp
Endurance: 5 days **Crew:** 5 tot.

Remarks: Aluminum construction, with Kevlar armor. One damaged in fight with Nicaraguan forces, 9-88.

♦ **14 U.S. Outrage-class inshore patrol craft** Bldr: Boston Whaler, Rockland, Massachusetts (In serv. 1982–90)

D: 2.2 tons **S:** 35 kts **Dim:** 7.62 × 2.40 × 0.40
A: 1/12.7-mm mg—1/7.62-mm mg
Electron Equipt: Radar: 1/Furuno 3600 nav.
M: 2 outboard gasoline engines; 2 props; 300 shp
Range: 200/35 **Crew:** 4 tot.

♦ **1 inshore patrol craft** Bldr: Ampela Marine, Honduras (In serv. 1981)

FNH 251 N . . . .

D: 3 tons (fl) **S:** 24 kts **Dim:** 7.62 × 2.74 × 0.38
A: 1/12.7-mm mg—1/7.62-mm mg
M: 1 Chrysler 6M655 TI diesel, waterjet drive; . . . bhp
Range: 250/18 **Crew:** 4 tot.

Remarks: Built of wood and glass-reinforced plastic.

AMPHIBIOUS WARFARE CRAFT

♦ **1 utility landing craft** Bldr: Lantana Boatyard, Lantana, Florida

	Laid down	L	In serv.
FNH 1491 Punta Caxinas	11-86	. . .	5-88

Punta Caxinas (FNH 1491) Bender SB & Repair, 5-88

D: 419 tons light (625 fl) **S:** 14.5 kts
Dim: 45.42 × . . . × . . . (loaded)
A: none **Electron Equipt:** Radar: 1/Furuno 3600 nav.
M: 3 Caterpillar 3416 diesels; 3 props; 2,025 bhp
Range: 3,500/12 **Crew:** 3 officers, 15 enlisted

Remarks: Was originally to have been completed 1-12-88. Cargo can include 100 ton of vehicles or cargo on deck, or four standard 20-ft cargo containers and 50,000 gallon of fuel. Has Magnavox NAVSAT receiver.

♦ **3 U.S. LCM (8)-class landing craft**

FNH 7401 Warunta FNH 7402 Tansin FNH 7403 Caratasca

D: 56 tons (116 fl) **S:** 12 kts **Dim:** 22.43 × 6.40 × 1.40 (aft)
A: 2/12.7-mm mg (I × 2) **Electron Equipt:** Radar: 1/. . . nav.
M: 4 G.M. 6-71 diesels; 2 props; 620 bhp **Range:** 140/9
Crew: 3–4 tot. + 150 troops for brief periods

Remarks: Transferred 1987. Cargo: 54 tons in 13.4 × 4.4-m cargo well.

AUXILIARY AND SERVICE CRAFT

♦ **1 ex-U.S. Coast Guard Hollyhock-class buoy tender**

	Bldr	In serv.
FNH 252 Yojoa (ex-*Walnut*)	Moore Drydock Co., Oakland, Cal.	27-6-39

D: 825 tons (986 fl) **S:** 12 kts **Dim:** 53.4 × 10.4 × 3.7
M: 2 diesels; 2 props; 1,350 bhp **Range:** 6,500/12; 10,000/7.5
Crew: 4 officers, 36 enlisted

Remarks: Transferred 1-7-82 for navigational support duties. One 20-ton buoy cra[ne]. Refitted 1986 at Tracor SY, Ft. Lauderdale, Florida.

♦ **6 miscellaneous ex-fishing boats for logistics support**

FN 7501 Juliana FN 7503 Carmen FN 7505 Yosuro
FN 7502 San Rafael FN 7504 Mairy FN 7506 Jose Gregori

HONG KONG

British Crown Colony of Hong Kong

Note: In addition to the craft listed below, the Royal Navy maintains three *Peac[ock]* class corvettes at Hong Kong, operated by a contingent of 560 Royal Navy person[nel] (including about 315 locally recruited Chinese). Also operated for the Royal Navy three 250-seat personnel ferries (*Susie, Jenny,* and *Ahmoy*), three 75-seat launc[hes] and four 25-seat launches. The British Army Royal Corps of Transport 415 Marit[ime] Troop keeps several landing craft at Hong Kong as well.

The Royal Hong Kong Auxiliary Air Force operates one BN-42B/T Maritime [De]fender and two Beech King Air craft for coastal patrol, and eight Sikorsky [S-76] helicopters for rescue and patrol work.

ROYAL HONG KONG POLICE FORCE MARINE REGION

Personnel (1991): 2,920 total organized into five "Sea Divisions"

♦ **2 command boats** Bldr: Hong Kong SY, Kowloon

	Laid down	L	Delivered	In serv.
PL 3 Sea Panther	17-6-86	17-4-87	27-7-87	1-2-88
PL 4 Sea Horse	17-6-86	14-7-87	28-9-87	1-2-88

D: 420 tons (450 fl) **S:** 14 kts **Dim:** 40.0 × 8.5 × . . . (3.2 mould[ed] depth)
A: 2/12.7-mm mg (I × 2)
Electron Equipt: Radar: 2/Decca . . . nav.
M: 2 Caterpillar 3512 diesels; 2 props; 2,350 bhp **Range:** 1,300/1[...]
Crew: 27–33 tot. + two platoons of police for short periods

ROYAL HONG KONG POLICE FORCE *(continued)*

Remarks: Have Racal CANE 100 data-logging and navigational plot system, along with Racal Hyper-Fix and thermal-imaging cameras for police records functions. Were originally intended to replace *Sea Lion* (PL 1) and *Sea Tiger* (PL 2), but they have been retained in service.

♦ **2 command boats** Bldr: Hong Kong United DY (In serv. 1965)

PL 1 Sea Lion PL 2 Sea Tiger

ea Lion (PL 1) Dr. Giorgio Arra, 11-86

D: 222 tons (fl) **S:** 11.8 kts **Dim:** 33.9 × 7.3 × 3.2
A: 2/12.7-mm mg (I × 2) **Electron Equipt:** Radar: 1/Decca . . . nav.
M: 2 Cummins diesels; 2 props; 674 bhp **Range:** 5,200/11.8
Crew: 29 tot. + 2 platoons police for short periods

emarks: Plans call for replacing these craft with two modified Damen Mk 3 (*King ai*)-class patrol boats.

ATROL BOATS

0 (+6) new construction

emarks: Contract offers were requested 9-90 for construction of six 32-meter patrol ats to replace the seven *Sea Cat* class. Six Australian ASI 315-class patrol boats were dered 8-91; see addenda for details. All to deliver 8-92 to 6-93.

15 Damen Mk 3 design Bldr: Chung Wah SB & Eng, Kowloon

	Laid down	L	In serv.
L 70 King Lai	28-2-84	14-7-84	29-10-84
L 71 King Yee	28-2-84	17-7-84	29-11-84
72 King Lim	28-2-84	29-7-84	17-12-84
73 King Hau	15-3-84	2-11-84	31-1-85
74 King Dai	15-3-84	8-11-84	28-2-85
75 King Chung	15-3-84	12-11-84	1-4-85
76 King Shun	17-8-84	26-1-85	17-5-85
77 King Tak	25-8-84	4-2-85	10-6-85
78 King Chi	17-8-84	1-2-85	2-7-85
79 King Tai	1-12-84	29-4-85	19-8-85
80 King Kwan	1-12-84	4-5-85	18-9-85
81 King Mei	1-12-84	8-5-85	7-10-85
82 King Yan	8-3-85	19-8-85	4-11-85
83 King Yung	8-3-85	30-8-85	25-11-85
84 King Kan	8-3-85	2-9-85	18-12-85

Chung (PL 75) Dr. Giorgio Arra, 7-86

D: 85 tons (97 fl) **S:** 25 kts **Dim:** 26.50 (24.27 pp) × 5.80 × 1.80
A: 1/7.62-mm mg **Electron Equipt:** Radar: 1/Decca RM 1290 nav.
M: 2 MTU 12V396 TC83 diesels (1,483 bhp each); 1/M.A.N. MB OM-424A V-12 cruise diesel (465 bhp); 2 props; 1 waterjet
Range: 600/14; 1,400/8 **Crew:** 17 tot.

Remarks: PL 70–78 ordered 10-83; PL 79–84 ordered 1-12-84. Modified version of the PL 60 class; Damen Stan Patrol 2600/Chung Wah Mk 3 design. Can make up to 7 kts on the centerline waterjet. Carry an Avon SeaRaider semi-rigid inspection boat. Three near sisters built for Hong Kong Customs, and two more may be built to replace the command craft *Sea Lion* and *Sea Tiger*.

♦ **10 Damen Mk 1 and Mk 2-design** Bldr: Chung Wah SB & Eng., Kowloon

	In serv.		In serv.
PL 57 Mercury	26-1-82	PL 62	2-80
PL 58 Vulcan	22-3-82	PL 63	1980
PL 59 Ceres	29-3-82	PL 64	1980
PL 60	29-2-80	PL 65 Cetus	2-9-80
PL 61 Pisces	29-2-80	PL 66 Dorado	8-9-80

PL 60—Mk 1 patrol version Dr. Giorgio Arra, 11-86

Ceres (PL 59)—Mk 2 logistics version Dr. Giorgio Arra, 11-86

D: 86 tons (normal) **S:** 23 kts **Dim:** 26.2 × 5.9 × 1.80
A: 1/12.7-mm mg **Electron Equipt:** Radar: 1 Decca 150 nav.
M: 2 MTU 12V396 TC82 diesels (1,300 bhp each), 1 M.A.N. D2566 cruise diesel (195 bhp); 3 props (Schottel on centerline); 2,600 bhp
Range: 1,400/8
Crew: PL 57–59: 5 tot.; others: 1 officer, 13 constables

Remarks: First Mk 1s, PL 60 and PL 61, laid down 9-79 to a Dutch design and have a cruise engine providing 7–8-kt max. speeds. Mk 2 units, PL 57–59, ordered 3-81 for logistics support duties, with same engines, but waterjet vice Schottel propeller for cruise (2 to 7 kts): have restricted patrol range, but have a cargo hold; also differ in lacking bow bulwarks and in having smaller pilothouse.

♦ **7 78-foot craft** Bldr: Vosper Thornycroft, Singapore (In serv. 5-72 to 5-73)

PL 50 Sea Cat PL 53 Sea Eagle PL 55 Sea Lynx
PL 51 Sea Puma PL 54 Sea Hawk PL 56 Sea Falcon
PL 52 Sea Leopard

D: 82 tons (fl) **S:** 20.7 kts **Dim:** 23.7 × 5.2 × 1.7
A: 1/12.7-mm mg **M:** 2 Cummins diesels; 2 props; 1,500 bhp
Range: 4,000/20 **Crew:** 16 tot.

Remarks: To be replaced by six new-construction patrol boats.

HONG KONG *(continued)*
PATROL BOATS *(continued)*

Sea Eagle (PL 53) Dr. Giorgio Arra, 1980

PATROL CRAFT

Note: Up to 11 8- to 9-m patrol craft are to be ordered during 1992.

♦ **7 Petrel-class harbor patrol craft** Bldr: Chung Wah SB & Eng. Co. (In serv. 1986–87)

PL 11 Petrel PL 14 Tern PL 16 Puffin
PL 12 Auk PL 15 Skua PL 17 Gannet
PL 13 Gull

D: 36 tons **S:** 12 kts **Dim:** 16.0 × 4.6 × 1.5
A: . . . **Electron Equipt:** Radar: 1/. . . nav.
M: 2 Cummins NTA 855M diesels; 2 props; 700 bhp **Crew:** 7 tot.

♦ **2 Interceptor catamaran GRP launches** Bldr: Shark Cat, Queensland, Australia (In serv. 9-88)

PL 20 PL 21

D: 4–5 tons (fl) **S:** 40+ kts **Dim:** 8.30 × 2.80 × 0.50
M: 2 outboard motors; 350 shp **Crew:** 4 tot.

Remarks: Have proven unsatisfactory and are to be replaced.

♦ **3 40-foot patrol launches** Bldr: Cheoy Lee SY

PL 6 Jetstream (In serv. 17-4-86)
PL 7 Swiftstream (In serv. 25-5-86)
PL 8 Tidestream (In serv. 12-6-86)

Swiftstream (PL 7) Dr. Giorgio Arra, 11-86

D: 24 tons (fl) **S:** 18 kts **Dim:** 16.4 × 4.5 × 0.85
M: 2 MTU diesels; 2 Hamilton 421 waterjets; 455 bhp
Range: 300/15 **Crew:** 8 tot.

Remarks: GRP construction. Replaced trio by same builder with same names. Employed for patrol of the Deep Bay area.

♦ **9 30-foot Spear class** Bldr: Fairey Allday Marine, Hamble, U.K.

PL 37 to PL 45 (In serv. 1981)

D: 4.5 tons (fl) **S:** 28 kts **Dim:** 9.10 × 2.89 × 0.84
A: 1/7.62-mm mg **Electron Equipt:** Radar: 1/Decca. . . nav.
M: 2 Perkins T6.3544 diesels; 2 props; 370 bhp
Range: 250/25 **Crew:** 4 tot.

Remarks: Glass-reinforced plastic construction.

MISCELLANEOUS CRAFT

Note: Four 12-m logistics launches are to be ordered in 1992.

♦ **1 support launch** Bldr: Reliance Marine, Salisbury, U.K.

PL . . . . (In serv. 5-82)

D: 3 tons (fl) **S:** 25 kts **Dim:** 8.8 × 2.9 × 0.76
M: 1 Volvo Penta AQAD-40/280 diesel; 155 bhp **Crew:** 4 tot.

♦ **1 personnel launch** Bldr: Hip Hing Cheung SY (In serv. 1975)

PL 7 Dragon

D: 18.5 tons **S:** 23.5 kts **Dim:** 16.0 × . . . × . . .
A: small arms **M:** 2 diesels; 2 props; 700 bhp
Range: 300/20 **Crew:** 6 tot.

♦ **7 Win-class motor launches** Bldr: Cheoy Lee SY (In serv. 1970)

PL 35 PL 36 PL 85 PL 86 PL 87 PL 88 PL 89

D: 4.8 tons **S:** 20 kts **Dim:** . . . × . . . × . . .
M: 1 diesel; 1 prop; . . . bhp **Range:** 160/20 **Crew:** . . .

♦ **8 7-meter Typhoon rigid inflatable craft** Bldr: Task Force Boats, U.K.

PV 30–37

Remarks: Ordered 1987. Powered by two 120-bhp outboard motors for 35 kts.

♦ **8 9.5-meter Typhoon rigid inflatables** Bldr: Task Force Boats, U.K.

PV 10–17

Remarks: Capable of 50 kts; powered by two V-8, 270-shp outboard motors. First tw delivered 1988, third in 7-91, rest in 1991–92.

♦ **4 Tempest rigid inflatable craft** Bldr: Task Force Boats, U.K.

PV 14 PV 15 PV 16 PV 17

♦ **9 Stillinger rigid inflatable craft** Bldr: Stillinger, U.K.

PV 90–98

Note: All of the rigid inflatable boats are organized into the Small Boat Unit and a referred to as "High Speed Interceptors."

CUSTOMS SERVICE

PATROL BOATS

♦ **3 Damen 26-meter class** Bldr: Chung Wah SB & Eng., Hong Kong

6 Sea Glory (In serv. 28-7-86) 8 Sea Leader (In serv. 3-11-86)
7 Sea Guardian (In serv. 28-8-86)

D: 96 tons (fl) **S:** 24 kts **Dim:** 26.50 (24.79 pp) × 5.80 × 1.80
A: . . . **Electron Equipt:** Radar: 1/Decca RM 1290 nav.
M: 2 MTU 12V396 TB93 diesels; 2 props; 3,000 bhp
Range: 600/14 **Electric:** 120 kVA **Crew:** . . .

Remarks: Similar to police Damen Mk 3 design, but lack waterjet cruise system a have a higher pilothouse with open bridge atop it.

HUNGARY

Hungarian Republic

HUNGARIAN ARMY MARITIME FORCE

Personnel (1991): Approx. 500 total

MINE COUNTERMEASURES AND PATROL CRAFT

♦ **6 Yugoslav Nestin-class minesweeper/patrol boats** Bldr: Brodotehnika, Belgrade (In serv. 1981–83)

AM 11 Újpest AM 22 Óbuda
AM 12 Baja AM 31 Dunaúváros
AM 21 Szazhalombatta AM 32 Dunafoldvar

D: 66 tons (78 fl) **S:** 15 kts **Dim:** 27.00 × 6.50 × 1.15 max.
A: 6/20-mm AA (IV × 1, I × 2)—24 small countermine charges
Electron Equipt: Radar: 1/Decca 101 nav.
M: 2 diesels; 2 props; 520 bhp **Range:** 860/11
Crew: 1 officer, 16 enlisted

Remarks: Have 2 flare/chaff RL. Sweep gear includes KRAM magnetic/ac sweep, AEL-1 explosive sweep, and MDL-1 and -2 mechanical wire sweeps. Sist Yugoslav and Iraqi navies.

♦ **45 AN-2-class aluminum river patrol/minesweeping craft** (In serv. early 1960s)

542-001 through 542-0059 (with omissions)

D: 10 tons (11.5 fl) **S:** 9 kts **Dim:** 13.4 × 3.8 × 0.6
A: 1/14.5-mm mg
M: 2 . . . diesels; 2 props; 220 bhp **Crew:** 7 tot.

Remarks: Minesweeping gear consists of simple wire sweeps only. Four are tained in reserve. 542-004 is equipped as a diving tender. These craft are assig "mine-watching" units on the Danube above and below Budapest, each wi command-configured and six regular boats.

HUNGARY *(continued)*

SERVICE CRAFT

♦ **1 400-ton landing craft/transport**
CS-S001 (ex-511-002)

♦ **2 service launches**
583-001 (In serv. 1955) 583-002 (In serv. 1960)

Remarks: One named *Döbrente*; have Volvo diesels.

♦ **1 fire boat**

♦ **1 small tug**

♦ **2 diving pontoons: B-1, D-2**

ransport lighter CS-S001 Siegfried Breyer, 1989

ote: Most of the service craft above are maintained in reserve.

CELAND

epublic of Iceland

COAST GUARD

rsonnel (1991): 130 total

iation: One Fokker F-27 Mk 200 Friendship patrol aircraft, 1 Hughes 500 D licopter, and 1 SA-365N Dauphin II helicopter.

SHERIES-PROTECTION SHIPS

te: In 1990, Icelandic Coast Guard units received red, white, and blue diagonal ipes on either side of the hull, and the word *Landhelgisgæslan* (Coast Guard) painted either side.

2 Ægir class

	Bldr	L	In serv.
IR	Aalborg SY, Denmark	1967	1968
R	Dannebrog Vaerft, Aarhus, Denmark	10-10-74	15-3-78

r B. Olafsson, 1986

–showing new diagonal striping paint scheme
Leo Van Ginderen, 4-90

D: 1,150 tons (1,500 fl) **S:** 20 kts
Dim: 69.84 (62.18 pp) × 10.02 × 5.02
A: 1/57-mm (6-pdr.) low-angle, single-fire
Electron Equipt: Radar: 3/. . . nav.—Sonar: *Týr:* HF, hull-mounted
M: 2 M.A.N. R8V 40/54 diesels; 2 KaMeWa CP props; 8,600 bhp
Electric: 630 kVA **Range:** 10,000/19 **Crew:** 22 tot.

Remarks: Although built ten years apart, these two ships are nearly identical. Helicopter hangar between twin stacks. 20-ton bollard-pull towing winch, passive rolling tanks. *Týr* is 70.90 m o. a.

♦ **1 Odinn class**

	Bldr	Laid down	L	In serv.
Odinn	Aalborg SY, Denmark	1-59	9-59	1-60

D: 1,000 tons (fl) **S:** 18 kts **Dim:** 63.63 (56.61 pp) × 10.0 × 4.8
A: 1/57-mm (6-pdr.), low angle **Electron Equipt:** Radar: 2/. . . nav.
M: 2 Burmeister & Wain diesels; 2 props; 5,050 bhp
Range: 10,000/18 **Crew:** 22 tot.

Remarks: Rebuilt in 1975 by Aarhus Flydedock, Denmark, with hangar, helicopter deck, and passive antirolling tanks. Articulated crane added 1989 to starboard at the forward end of the helicopter deck to handle rigid inflatable inspection and rescue craft.

Note: The small patrol boat *Arvakur* was stricken 1989. A survey/patrol launch, *Baldur*, was acquired 1991; see addenda.

CUSTOMS SERVICE

♦ **1 Nelson 45-foot customs launch** Bldr: W. S. Souter, Cowes, U.K.
Valur (In serv. 1978)
S: 17 kts **M:** 2 Cummins V555M diesels

♦ **1 Type 21-SS Smuggler-class patrol launch** Bldr: Norway, 1975
S: 36 kts **M:** Castoldi waterjets

INDIA

Republic of India

Personnel (1991): Approx. 55,000 total, including 1,000 Marines and 5,000-strong Naval Air Arm.

Naval Aviation: Shipboard aircraft include 31 Magic air-to-air missile-equipped Sea Harrier FRS.51 V/STOL fighters, 38 Sea King helicopters (3 Mk 42A delivered 8-80, 12 Mk 42 and 6 Mk 42C transports delivered from 5-2-87, and 20 Mk 42B, equipped with Sea Eagle antiship missiles and Sintra-Alcatel MS-12 dipping sonars, delivered 1989–91), 13 Ka 27 Helix-A ASW helicopters (3 configured as trainers), 7 Ka 25 Hormone-A ASW helicopters, and 20 Chetak (Alouette-III) light ASW/liaison helicopters.

For land-based maritime surveillance, 5 Soviet Il-38 May and 8 Soviet Tu-142M Bear-F are in use. Four of a planned total of 24 Dornier 228 coastal surveillance aircraft were in service by 7-88; some of the 24 will enter Coast Guard service. Six BN-42B/T Maritime Defender coastal patrol aircraft are also in use. Training and logistics-support aircraft include 5 Mk 60 Harrier V/STOL trainers, 4 Hughes 300 helicopters, and 8 HPT-32 Deepak and 12 HAL Kiran Mk I, IA, and II trainers. The Indian Navy may order 4 to 6 Mk 42D air early-warning Sea King helicopters and 7 additional Sea Harrier FRS.51 V/STOL fighters.

A naval variant of the HAL Advanced Light Helicopter is in development to replace the Chetak for liaison, transport, search-and-rescue, and ASW duties:

Weight: 2,352 kg (5,000 kg max.) **S:** 156 kts
Range: 216 n.m. with 700-kg payload
Engines: 2 Turbomeca TM 333-2B turbines (2,000 shp)
Fuel: 2,850 liters

Indian Navy Sea Harrier Mk 51 British Aerospace

NAVAL AVIATION *(continued)*

Indian Navy Tu-142M Bear-F VF-114, U.S. Navy, 1989

Weapons and Sensors: A mixture of Western (primarily British and Dutch) and Soviet weapons and sensors, with Western designs built in India under license. Hindustan Aeronautics Ltd. is developing an air-to-ground missile for Air Force and Navy use; it will have a range of 100 km at Mach 4 to Mach .85 at 30,000-foot altitude and will have a 35-kg payload.

AIRCRAFT CARRIERS

♦ 0 (+1) new-construction aircraft carrier

Remarks: After discussions had been held with the U.K. (*Invincible* class) and Spain (*Principe de Asturias* class), a contract was placed 21-12-88 with DCN for a design for a gas-turbine-propelled version of the French *Charles de Gaulle* class to be built in India at Cochin. The contract was abrogated in early 1991, and the Indian Navy attempted to continue with a somewhat smaller in-house design, although funding for the program was not included in the 1991–92 budget. By mid-1991, it was reported that an ASW-only carrier of some 13,000–14,000 tons was contemplated but that it would not enter service until around 2015. The Indian Minister of Defense stated in 7-91 that the Indian Navy did not need a new aircraft carrier.

♦ 1 U.K. Hermes class Bldr: Vickers-Armstrong, Barrow-in-Furness

	Laid down	L	In serv.
R 22 VIRAAT (ex-*Hermes*)	21-6-44	16-2-53	18-11-59

D: 23,900 tons (28,706 fl) **S:** 28 kts
Dim: 226.85 (198.12 pp) × 48.78 (27.43 wl) × 8.80
Air Group: 12/Sea Harrier FRS.Mk 51, 9/Sea King Mk 42 helicopters
A: 2/Sea Cat GWS. 22 SAM systems (IV × 2)
Electron Equipt:
Radar: 2/1006 nav., 1/965 early warning, 1/Plessey 994 air/surf. search, 2/Plessey Type 904 missile f.c.
Sonar: Graseby Type 184 hull-mounted (8–9 kHz)
TACAN: FT13-S/M—IFF: Cossor 1010 (Mk 10)
EW: . . . intercept; 2 Corvus RL (VIII × 2)

Viraat (R 22) Joachim Grulms, 10-90

Viraat (R 22) Walter Sartori, 7-87

M: 2 sets Parsons geared steam turbines; 2 props; 76,000 shp
Boilers: 4 Admiralty 3-drum **Electric:** 9,000 kw
Range: 6,500/14 **Fuel:** 4,200 tons, plus 320 tons aviation fuel
Crew: 143 officers, 1,207 enlisted, including air group

Remarks: Purchased 19-4-86, having been paid off 12-4-84 from the Royal Navy and stricken 1-7-85. Turned over to Indian control 14-11-86 during reactivation and minor modernization overhaul, and commissioned 12-5-87 at Devonport. Formally commissioned in India 15-2-89. The name means "Mighty." Will require replacement circa 2005.

Had been converted from a standard carrier to a helicopter commando carrier 1971–73 and converted again 1976–77 as an ASW helicopter carrier; again modified 5-80 to 9-5-81 to operate Sea Harrier V/STOL attack fighters, receiving a 230-ton, 45.7-m-long by 13.7-m-wide by 4.9-m-high 12° "ski-jump" takeoff ramp. Retained commando transport capability for 750 troops and continues to carry four LCVP landing craft aft. Has two elevators. Has 25–50-mm armor over magazines and machinery spaces, and flight deck is approx. 20-mm thick.

During the Falkland War (when she was the last RN warship still using black oil fuel), the ship operated as many as 12 Harriers and a large number of helicopters. The air group in the Indian Navy includes two 6-aircraft Sea Harrier squadrons, plus three Sea King Mk 42C logistics helicopters and six Sea King Mk 42B ASW helicopters which are also equipped to launch Sea Eagle antiship missiles. There are plans to equip the ship with up to 30 Sea Harriers, with helicopters to be flown primarily from *Vikrant.*

During reactivation, NBC warfare protection was improved, and Deck Approach Projector System (DAPS), Horizon Approach Path Indicator (HAPI), the CTL all weather approach system landing aids, new Decca Type 1006 navigational radars, and an Italian TACAN system (replacing the U.K. system removed in 4-82) were added. New EW equipment added in India. Has limited steaming endurance.

♦ 1 Glory class Bldr: Vickers-Armstrong, Barrow-in-Furness

	Laid down	L	In serv.
R 11 VIKRANT (ex-*Hercules*)	14-10-43	22-9-45	4-3-61

D: 15,700 tons (19,500 fl) **S:** 24 kts (max.), 17 kts cruising
Dim: 211.25 (198.0 wl) × 24.29 × 7.1
Air Group: 6/Sea Harrier FRS.51 V/STOL fighters, 3/Sea King Mk 42C and 6/Sea King Mk 42B heavy helicopters, 1 or more Chetak light helicopters
A: 8/40-mm Bofors AA (I × 8)
Electron Equipt:
Radar: 1/H.S.A. ZW-06 surf. search, 1/H.S.A. DA-05 air search, 1/H.S.A. LW-08 early warning
Sonar: Graseby Type 750 medium frequency, hull-mounted
M: 2 sets Parsons geared steam turbines; 2 props; 40,000 shp
Boilers: 4 Admiralty; 28 kg/cm^2
Range: 6,200/23; 12,000/14 **Fuel:** 3,200 tons
Crew: peacetime: 1,075 tot.; wartime: 1,340 tot.

Remarks: Bought in Great Britain in 1-57 while still incomplete. Air-condition[illegible] Flight deck: 210 × 34 m. Modernized 1979 to 3-1-82 with new boilers, engines, n[illegible] CIC, and new Dutch-design radars and Bofors L 70 single 40-mm AA in place [illegible] original British Mk 5 twin and Mk 9 single mountings. A further refit from 12-82 [illegible] 2-83 made the ship ready for its Sea Harrier complement, but did not include a plann[illegible] ski-jump ramp. Catapult and arrester gear were retained to permit continued us[illegible] Alizé ASW aircraft. With the delivery of additional Sea Harriers in 1984 and later, [illegible] Alizés moved ashore and were discarded in 1990. The ship received the IPN-10 com[illegible] data system in 1985, and four LAPADS directors were added for the 40-mm [illegible] Recommissioned 15-2-89 after addition of the long-awaited ski-jump bow, but [illegible] began post-overhaul trials 28-8-89.

Long-range plans call for adapting the elderly vessel for an assault rôle, with up t[illegible] Sea King Mk 42C transport helicopters. Between 1979 and 1989, *Vikrant* spent [illegible] months in various yard periods and still has an unreliable propulsion plant [illegible] restricts operation of Harriers to light loads. The ship is scheduled to be discar[illegible] around 2001.

SUBMARINES

Note: The Soviet Charlie-I-class nuclear-powered cruise-missile submarine *Cha*[illegible] leased (apparently without missiles) on 5-1-88, was returned to the U.S.S.R. without replacement; reports of the loan of a second Charlie I, to have been na[illegible] *Chitra,* were incorrect. Although research has been ongoing in India since 1974 to[illegible] the construction of an indigenously designed and constructed nuclear-powered [illegible]marine, the building of an actual submarine is many years in the future.

Viraat (R 22) at left, Vikrant (R 11) at right—both with ski-jump bows *The Navy,*

SUBMARINES *(continued)*

◆ 0 (+4) new-construction submarines   Bldr: Mazagon DY, Bombay

Remarks: As a follow-on to the SSK-1500 program, it has been proposed to construct four 2,000-ton submarines of West German IKL design in a version of the submarine that was offered to Australia. No contracts had been let by 12-91, and negotiations were also ongoing with Sweden's Kockums. Nonetheless, six ship-fits of the Thomson-Sintra ASM TSM 2272 Eledone active/passive sonar suite have been ordered for delivery 1997–1999, and it appears that continued construction of the Type 209/1500 is contemplated.

◆ 2 (+2+5) West German Type 209/1500

	Bldr	Laid down	L	In serv.
S 44 Shishumar	Howaldtswerke, Kiel	1-5-82	13-12-84	28-9-86
S 45 Shankush	Howaldtswerke, Kiel	1-9-82	11-5-84	20-11-86
S 46 Shalki	Mazagon DY, Bombay	5-6-84	30-9-89	7-2-92
S 47 Shankul	Mazagon DY, Bombay	. . .	5-92	1994

hankush (S 45)   Peter Voss, 7-86

ankush (S 45)   U.S. Navy, 2-87

): 1,450 tons std.; 1,655 tons surf./1,810 sub.
: 13 kts surf./22.5 kts sub.
im: 64.40 × 6.50 × 6.20
: 8/533-mm fwd. (14 AEG SUT wire-guided torpedoes)—mines (*see* Remarks)
lectron Equipt:
Radar: Kelvin-Hughes Type 1007—EW: . . . intercept
Sonar: Krupp Atlas CSU-83 search and attack suite, Thomson-Sintra DUUX-5 passive ranging and intercept
: 4 MTU 16V493 TY60 (or AZ 80) diesels (800 bhp each), 4/430 kw generators, 2 Siemens motors; 1 7-bladed prop; 6,100 shp
ange: surf.: 13,000/10; 18,000/4.5; snorkel: 8,200/8; sub.: 30/20; 400/4.5; 524/4
ıel: 157 tons **Endurance:** 50 days **Crew:** 8 officers, 28 enlisted

arks: Final order, signed 11-12-81, included an option to build two additional in India. Indian-built units are far behind schedule; dock trials on the first began 39. An option to build a third and fourth in India was dropped, although a number ıponents had been delivered from Germany and then abandoned. Nonetheless, up additional units may be built. Diving depth: 250 m.
ve Singer-Librascope SFCS Mk 1 weapons-control system and the Gäbler sphericape chamber to provide emergency exit from within the 2-compartment pressure The four 132-cell Varta batteries weigh 280 tons; the Indian-built units have e-built British Chloride Industrial Batteries, Ltd. batteries. Have two Kolln periscopes. Strap-on minelaying pods were purchased for these ships. The ı-built units have the later AZ 80 diesel variant and are receiving Thomson- ASM DUUX 5 Fenelon sonars, which will also be backfitted to the German-built uring refits commencing in 1995. Also being installed are French Nereides towed nt VLF communications antenna cables.

◆ 8 (+ ?) Soviet Kilo class   Bldr: Admiralty SY, Leningrad

	In serv.		In serv.
S 55 Sindhugosh	30-4-86	S 59 Sindhuratna	22-12-88
S 56 Sindhudhvaj	12-6-87	S 60 Sindhukesari	16-2-89
S 57 Sindhuraj	20-10-87	S 61 Sindhukirti	4-1-90
S 58 Sindhuvir	26-8-88	S 62 Sindhuvijay	8-3-91

Sindhukirti (S 61)   French Navy, 2-90

Sindhuvijay (S 62)—note bow sonar "window" above upper row of two torpedo tube shutters, smaller door between shutters   Leo Van Ginderen, 2-91

Sindhudhvaj (S 56)   Luciano Grazioli, 9-87

D: 2,400 tons (surf.)/3,000 tons (sub.) **S:** 12/20 kts
Dim: 73.00 × 9.91 × 6.50 **A:** 6/533-mm TT fwd (18 torpedoes)
Electron Equipt:
Radar: 1/Snoop Tray—EW: Brick Pulp intercept; Quad Loop D/F
Sonar: Shark Gill passive array; low-freq. active
M: 3 diesels, electric drive; 1/6-bladed prop; 6,800 shp
Range: . . . **Crew:** 12 officers, 41 enlisted

Remarks: S 55 arrived in India 17-9-86. Appear to have a shoulder-launched SA-7/14 SAM position at the aft end of the sail, which could only be used, of course, with the submarine surfaced. Diving depth: 250 m normal, 300 max. All are based at Vishnakapatnam. Reported continued acquisitions past the original eight have not been substantiated.

◆ 8 Soviet Foxtrot class

	In serv.		In serv.
S 20 Kursura	12-70	S 40 Vela	31-8-73
S 21 Karanj	10-70	S 41 Vagir	3-11-73
S 22 Kandheri	1-69	S 42 Vagli	10-8-74
S 23 Kalvari	16-7-68	S 43 Vagsheer	26-12-74

SUBMARINES *(continued)*

Vagli (S 42) Dr. Giorgio Arra, 1982

D: 1,950/2,400 tons **S:** 16/15.5 kts **Dim:** 92.0 × 7.0 × 6.0
A: 10/533-mm TT (6 fwd, 4 aft; 22 torpedoes or 44 mines)
Electron Equipt:
Radar: 1/Snoop Tray—EW: Stop Light intercept; Quad Loop D/F
Sonar: 1/MF active, passive array
M: 3 Type 2D42 diesel generator sets (2,000 bhp each), 3 motors; 3 props; 5,300 shp
Range: 11,000/8 (snorkel); 350/2 (sub.) **Fuel:** 360 tons
Endurance: 70 days **Crew:** 8 officers, 67 enlisted

Remarks: All were new on delivery. Most have had at least one refit in the U.S.S.R. S 40 collided with the destroyer *Rana* during 1990; 17 dead. Have two 124-cell batteries. Two reported to be in reserve as of 1989, but all are apparently to be retained.

DESTROYERS

◆ 0 (+3+ . . .) Delhi class (Project 15) Bldr: Mazagon DY, Bombay

	Laid down	L	In serv.
D . . . Delhi	3-87	1-2-91	1995
D . . . Mysore	2-91	. . .	. . .
D	. . .	. . .	. . .

D: 5,000 tons (6,500 fl) **S:** . . . **Dim:** 160.0 × 17.0 × . . .
A: 4/SS-N-2C SSM(I × 4)—2/Trishul SAM systems—2/76.2-mm Soviet AK-762 DP (II × 1)—4/30-mm AK-630 gatling AA (I × 4)—6/324-mm ASW TT (III × 2; NST-58 torpedoes)—2/Sea King helicopters
Electron Equipt:
Radar: 1/. . . nav., 1/Bharat RALW-02 early warning, 3/. . . f.c.
Sonar: Bharat-Thomson-Sintra APSOH (2633 Spherion) hull-mounted
EW: Bharat INDRA suite
M: CODOG: 2 Soviet AM-50 gas turbines (27,000 shp each), 2 MTU diesels (5,000 bhp each); 2 CP props; 54,000 shp—*see* Remarks
Range: . . ./. . . **Crew:** . . . tot.

Remarks: First unit ordered 3-86 as a follow-on to the *Godavari* class. As of mid-1991, funding for the second and third had not been approved, although the keel for the second had officially been laid. Ultimately, as many as six may be built.

To have fin stabilizers. Soviet weapons and European-designed/Indian-improved-and-manufactured electronics will be employed, including Bharat Electronics APSOH (Advanced Panoramic Sonar), a license-built Thomson-Sintra TSM 2633 Spherion. The RALW-02 radar is a license-built Signaal LW-08. The Trishul surface-to-air missile reportedly has much in common with the British Sea Wolf and employs command to line-of-sight guidance by way of a license-built Contraves Shikari (IPN-10 variant) weapons-control system and three missile/gun control radars. The third and any later units will employ license-built U.S. General Electric LM-2500 gas turbines in lieu of the Soviet turbines in the first two.

◆ 5 Soviet Kashin class Bldr: 61 Kommuna SY, Nikolayev

	In serv.		In serv.
D 51 Rajput	30-9-80	D 54 Ranvir	28-8-86
D 52 Rana	28-6-82	D 55 Ranvijay	15-1-88
D 53 Ranjit	24-11-83		

Rajput (D 51) R.A.N., 10-9

Ranvir (D 54)—with Helix helicopter on deck and hangar doors open
8

Ranjit (D 53) U.S. Navy,

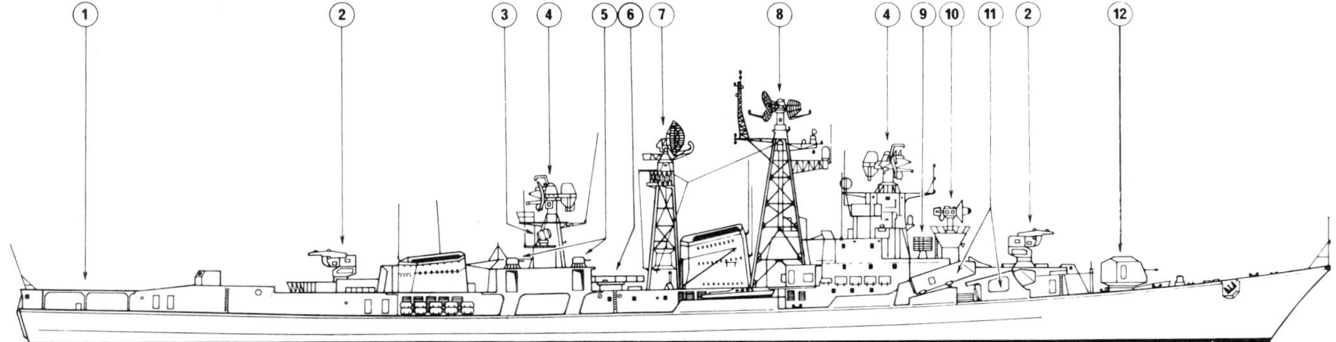

Rajput (D 51) 1. helicopter deck 2. SA-N-1 SAM launchers 3. Drum Tilt radar GFCS (Bass Tilt on D 54, D 55) 4. Peel Group SAM-control radar 5. twin 30-mm AK-230 AA guns (AK-630 gatling AA guns on D 54, D 55) 6. quintuple torpedo tube mount 7. Big Net early-warning radar antenna 8. Head Net-C air/surface search radar antenna 9. RBU-6000 ASW rocket launchers 10. Owl Screech radar GFCS for 76.2-mm gun mount 11. SS-N-2C Styx SSM 12. 76.2-mm twin gun mount
Robert Dumas

DESTROYERS *(continued)*

D: 3,950 tons (4,950 fl) **S:** 35 kts **Dim:** 147.0 × 15.8 × 5.0 (hull)
A: 4/SS-N-2C SSM (I × 4)—2/SA-N-1 SAM syst. (II × 2; 44 Goa missiles)—2/76-mm DP (II × 1)—8/30-mm AK-230 AA (II × 4) (D 54, 55: 4/30-mm AK-630 gatling AA)—5/533-mm TT (V × 1)— 2/RBU-6000 ASW RL (XII × 2)—1/Ka-25 Hormone-A ASW helicopter (D 54, 55: Ka-27 Helix-A)
Electron Equipt:
Radar: 2/Don Kay nav., 1/Big Net early warning, 1/Head Net C surf./air search, 2/Peel Group SAM f.c., 1/Owl Screech 76-mm gun f.c., 2/Drum Tilt 30-mm AA f.c. (D 54, 55: Bass Tilt)
Sonar: hull-mounted med. freq., med.-freq. VDS, high-freq. attack
EW: 2/Watch Dog intercept, 2 Top Hat A intercept, 2 Top Hat B intercept, 4/chaff RL (XVI × 4)
IFF: 2/High Pole B transponders, interrogation by radars
M: 4 M-3 gas turbines; 2 props; 94,000 shp **Range:** 900/35; 5,000/18
Crew: 35 officers, 330 enlisted

Remarks: New-construction units, not conversions from former Soviet Navy units. Program for first three was far behind delivery schedule; two more ordered 20-12-82. Plans to acquire five more were canceled.

In contrast to Soviet Navy "Modified Kashins," the SS-N-2C missiles are mounted forward and fire forward, while the after twin 76-mm gun mount has been omitted in favor of a hangar below the main-deck level in the location occupied by an aft 76-mm magazine in Soviet units; it is accessed by an inclined elevator. D 54 and D 55 carry the barreled 30-mm gatling AA weapon with Bass Tilt radar directors in place of the twin 30-mm/Drum Tilt of the initial trio and were delivered with Helix helicopters aboard.

FRIGATES

0 (+3) Improved Godavari class (Type 16A) Bldr: Garden Reach DY, Calcutta

	Laid down	L	In serv.
. . . .	1989	1992	. . .
. . . .	. . .	. . .	. . .
. . . .	. . .	. . .	. . .

D: 3,700 tons (4,300 fl) **S:** 29 kts
Dim: 126.4 (123.6 pp) × 14.5 × 4.5 (hull)
A: 4/SS-N-2C SSM (I × 4)—1/SA-N-4 SAM syst. (II × 1; 20 Gecko missiles)—2/57-mm AK-257 DP (II × 1)—4/30-mm AK-630 gatling AA (I × 4)—6/324-mm ASW TT (III × 2; NST-58 torpedoes)—1/Sea King ASW helicopter—1/Chetak helicopter
Electron Equipt:
Radar: 1/ZW-06 surf. search, 1/Head Net C (MR.310) surf./air search, 1/RALW-02 early warning, 1/Pop Group SAM f.c., 1/Muff Cob 57-mm gun f.c. , 2/Bass Tilt 30-mm gun f.c.
Sonar: Bharat-Thomson Sintra APSOH (2630 Spherion) hull-mounted MF
EW: Bharat INDRA suite—TACAN: FT13-S/M
M: 2 Soviet AM-50 gas turbines; 2 five-bladed props; 54,000 shp
Electric: 2/750-kw turbogenerators, 3/. . . kw diesel sets
Range: . . ./. . . **Crew:** . . . tot.

Remarks: Construction reported 1990. Characteristics above estimated, based on the previous Type 16 design. May incorporate diesel engines in a CODOG (Combined Diesel or Gas Turbine) arrangement.

◆ **3 Godavari class (Type 16)** Bldr: Mazagon Docks, Bombay

	Laid down	L	In serv.
F 20 Godavari	2-6-78	15-5-80	10-12-83
F 22 Ganga	1980	15-11-81	1-1-86
F 23 Gomati	1981	20-3-84	16-4-88

D: 3,700 tons (4,300 fl) **S:** 27 kts
Dim: 126.4 (123.6 pp) × 14.5 × 4.5 (hull)
A: 4/SS-N-2C SSM (I × 4)—1/SA-N-4 SAM syst. (II × 1; 20 Gecko missiles)—2/57-mm AK-257 DP (II × 1)—8/30-mm AK-230 AA (II × 4)—6/324-mm ASW TT (III × 2; NST-58 torpedoes)— 1/Sea King ASW helicopter—1/Chetak helicopter
Electron Equipt:
Radar: 1/ZW-06 surf. search, 1/Head Net C (MR.310) air/surf. search, 1/RALW-02 early warning, 1/Pop Group SAM f.c., 1/Muff Cob 57-mm gun f.c., 2/Drum Tilt 30-mm gun f.c.

Ganga (F 22)—still without EW antenna suite Mike Louagie, 5-90

Ganga (F 22) Leo Van Ginderen, 5-90

[Goda]vari (F 20) U.S. Navy, 1987

FRIGATES *(continued)*

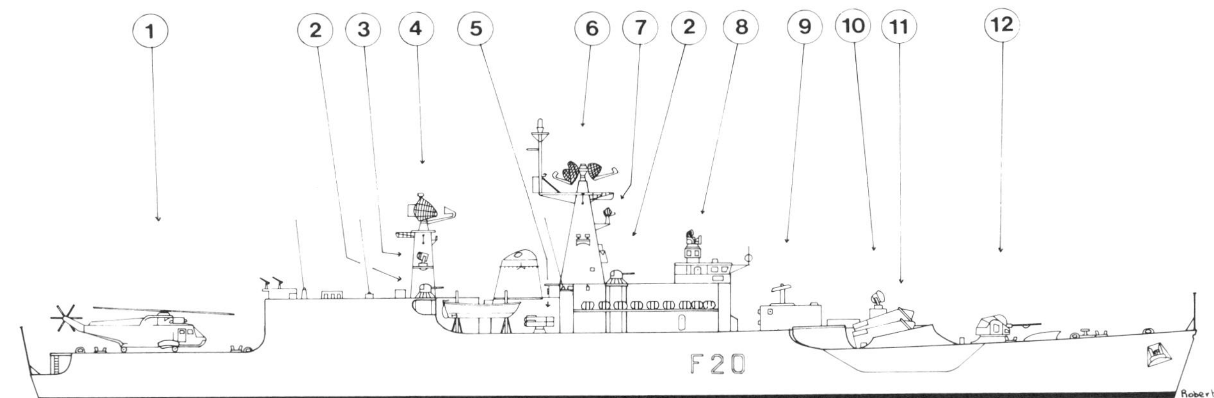

Godavari (F 20) 1. Sea King helicopter 2. twin 30-mm AK-230 AA 3. Drum Tilt radar GFCS 4. Bharat RALW-02 early-warning radar antenna 5. ILAS-3 triple ASW torpedo tubes 6. Head Net-C air/surface search radar antenna 7. H.S.A. ZW-06A navigational/surface search radar antenna 8. Pop Group track-while-scan SAM control radar director 9. SA-N-4 ZIF-122 launcher 10. Muff Cob radar/electro-optical director for 57-mm gun mount 11. SS-N-2C SSM Styx SSM 12. twin 57-mm AK-257 dual-purpose gun mount Robert Dumas

Sonar: Bharat-Thomson Sintra APSOH (2630 Spherion) med.-freq. hull-mounted (F 20: Canadian SQS-505)
EW: Bharat Ajanta intercept—TACAN: FT13-S/M
M: 2 sets geared steam turbines; 2 five-bladed props; 30,000 shp
Boilers: 2 Babcock & Wilcox, 3-drum; 38.7 kg/cm^2, 450° C
Electric: 2/750-kw turbogenerators, 3/. . . kw diesel sets
Range: 4,500/12
Crew: 51 officers, 262 enlisted (362 accommodations)

Remarks: Design derived from the *Leander* class, with the same propulsion plant but larger hull. Electronics and weapons systems a very diverse selection of Western European–designed/Indian-built and Soviet systems.

Steel superstructure. Two pairs Vosper fin stabilizers. Bharat's RALW-02 radar uses the same antenna as the H.S.A. DA-08. There are two backup manual directors for the twin AK-230 30-mm AA guns and two for the AK-57 57-mm mount. The hangar is sized for two Sea Kings, but only one (often with a Chetak light helo aboard also) is normally carried for stability reasons. The Bear Trap helicopter landing and traversing system is fitted. The Selenia IPN-10 combat data system is employed, as is a comprehensive EW sensor suite—but no decoy launchers. The ships carry the Graseby G 738 (Type 182) towed acoustic torpedo decoy. During 1990, F 22 had a crew of 26 officers and 386 enlisted—a very large number of personnel for a ship of this size.

♦ 6 U.K. Leander class Bldr: Mazagon Docks, Bombay

	Laid down	L	In serv.
F 33 Nilgiri	10-66	23-10-68	3-6-72
F 34 Himgiri	1967	6-5-70	23-11-74
F 35 Udaygiri	14-9-70	24-10-72	18-2-76
F 36 Dunagiri	1-73	9-3-74	5-5-77
F 41 Taragiri	1974	25-10-76	16-5-80
F 42 Vindhyagiri	1976	12-11-77	8-7-81

Udaygiri (F 35)—amidships detail U.S. Navy, 5-87

Taragiri (F 41)—composite photo 1983

D: 2,250 tons (2,800 fl); later units: 3,250 tons (fl) **S:** 30 kts
Dim: 113.38 × 13.1 × 4.27 (avg.)
A: 2/114-mm DP (II × 1)—F 33: 1/Sea Cat GWS 22; others: 2/Sea Ca with M-4 directors—1/Limbo Mk 10 ASW mortar (III × 1; not on F 41 and F 42, which have 1/375-mm Bofors ASW RL (II × 1)—2/20-mm AA (I × 2)—1/Chetak ASW helicopter (Sea King on F 4 and F 42)— F 41, 42 also: 6/324-mm ILAS-3 ASW TT (III × 2)
Electron Equipt:
Radar: F 33: 1/978 nav., 1/993 air/surf. search, 1/965 early warnin 2/903 f.c.; F 34 on: 1/Decca 1226 nav., 1/ZW-06 surf. search,1/LW-08 (Bharat RALW-02) early warning, 1/M 44 gun f.c., 2/M 45 SAM f.c.
Sonar: F 33, 35, 36: Can. Westinghouse SQS-505 med.-freq. hull-mounted; F 33–36: Can. Westinghouse SQS-502 targe depth-determining (for Limbo); F 33–36: Can. Westinghous SQS-505 VDS; F 34: APSOH hull-mounted; F 41, 42: Thomson-Sintra Diodon hull-mounted
EW: Bharat Ajanta intercept, Telegon HF D/F—*see* Remarks
M: 2 sets geared steam turbines; 2 five-bladed props; 30,000 shp
Boilers: 2 Babcock & Wilcox, 3-drum; 38.7 kg/cm^2, 450° C
Electric: 2,500 kw tot. **Range:** approx. 4,500/12 **Fuel:** 500 tons
Crew: 40 officers, 370 enlisted

Remarks: The first two are very similar to British versions of the *Leander* class, later units were progressively improved, using H.S.A. radars and an ever-gre proportion of Indian-built components.

F 41 and F 42 have very large telescoping hangars situated much nearer the s and requiring removal of the three-barreled Limbo ASW mortar (replaced by a Bofors ASW RL on the forecastle); their hangars hold a Westland Sea King helicopter, and their flight decks incorporate Canadian Bear Trap haul-down gear. and F 42 also have openings in the hull sides beneath the helicopter deck at the s F 33 and F 34 received Type 199 variable-depth sonar; later units did not. The s Sea Cat quadruple SAM launcher in the F 33 has one MRS-3 director; later ships two Dutch M-4 directors (with M-45 radar).

Later units have Racal Cutlass jamming gear. All have Graseby G 738 towed to decoys. F 33, 35, and 36 have received Canadian Westinghouse sonar equip (including VDS) in place of their original British equipment. F 41 and F 42 hav FT13-S/M TACAN system. F 34 has the prototype APSOH (Advanced Pano Sonar) active-passive system, a license-built version of the Thomson-Sintra TSM Spherion. Very crowded, due to unusually large crews.

Note: Training frigate *Betwa* (F 38) was stricken 31-12-91.

♦ 2 U.K. Whitby class

	Bldr	Laid down	L	In serv.
F 40 Talwar	Cammell Laird, Birkenhead	1957	18-7-58	6-60
F 43 Trishul	Harland & Wolff, Belfast	1957	18-6-58	1-60

D: 2,144 tons (2,560 fl) **S:** 30 kts
Dim: 112.7 × 12.5 × 5.4 (over sonar)
A: 3/SS-N-2 Styx SSM (I × 3)—8/30-mm Ak-230 AA (II × 2)—6/324-mm ILAS- 3 ASW TT (III × 2)—1/Limbo triple ASW mortar—1/Chetak light ASW helicopter
Electron Equipt:
Radar: 1/ZW-06A surf. search, 1/RALW-04 early warning, 1/Sq Tie missile target detection, 2/Drum Tilt gun f.c.
Sonar: Type 177 search (7-9 kHz), Type 170B search (15 kHz), T 162 attack (high-freq.)—all hull-mounted; *see* Remarks
EW: Telegon HF D/F, Racal Cutlass intercept

ʼRIGATES *(continued)*

M: 2 sets geared steam turbines; 2 props; 30,000 shp
Boilers: 2 Babcock & Wilcox; 38.7 kg/cm², 450° C
Electric: 1,140 kw tot. **Range:** 4,500/12 **Fuel:** 370 tons
Crew: 11 officers, 220 enlisted

ishul (F 43)—amidships detail U.S. Navy, 3-87

marks: Three SS-N-2 Styx launchers—removed from Osa-I-class, guided-missile rol boats—replaced the twin 114-mm Mk 6 gun mount in these two ships. Soviet are Tie radar associated with Styx replaced the gun director, atop the pilothouse. 0 further refitted 1982–83 at Mazagon Dockyard, Bombay, with larger hangar and icopter haul-down system (at the expense of one Limbo ASW mortar), new radars, Soviet AA guns. Modernization of F 43 reported delayed by yard problems, 7-85, completed by early 1987. F 40 mistakenly omitted from last edition.

RVETTES

4 (+4+4) Khukri (DP 25) class

		Bldr	Laid down	L	In serv.
9	KHUKRI	Mazagon DY, Bombay	27-9-85	3-12-86	23-8-89
	KHUTAR	Mazagon DY, Bombay	9-86	4-89	7-6-90
	KIRPAN	Garden Reach DY, Calcutta	1987	16-8-88	12-1-91
	KHANJAR	Garden Reach DY, Calcutta	1987	16-8-88	29-10-91
	. . . . . .	Garden Reach DY, Calcutta	1990	. . .	. . .
	. . . . . .	Garden Reach DY, Calcutta	1990	. . .	. . .
	. . . . . .	Garden Reach DY, Calcutta	. . .	. . .	. . .
	. . . . . .	Garden Reach DY, Calcutta	. . .	. . .	. . .

1,350 tons (fl) **S:** 28 kts **Dim:** 91.0 × 11.0 × 2.5 (hull)
4/SS-N-2C (P 21) Styx SSM (II × 2)—1/76.2-mm AK-176 DP—2/30-mm AK-630 gatling AA—2/SA-N-5 SAM positions (I × 2)—1/Chetak helo (no hangar)

ectron Equipt:
Radar: 1/Bharat 1245 nav., 1/Cross Dome (Pozitiv-E) air search, 1/Plank Shave (Harpun) missile target desig., 1/Muff Cob (Vympal) f.c.
Sonar: none
EW: Bharat Ajanta intercept; 2/decoy RL (XVI × 2)

M: 2 Kirloskar-SEMT-Pielstick 18 PA6 V280 diesels; 2 props; 14,400 bhp
Range: 4,000/. . . **Crew:** 8 officers, 74 enlisted

Khangar (P 44) R.A.N., 10-91

Khukri (P 49) Leo Van Ginderen, 5-90

Khukri (P 49) Leo Van Ginderen, 5-90

· (P 49) Mike Louagie, 5-90

CORVETTES *(continued)*

Remarks: Intended to replace the Petya class. First two ordered 12-83, next pair in 1985; units five through eight, ordered 4-90, may incorporate gas turbines in the propulsion system and may have a Soviet-supplied SA-N-4 SAM system. First four have no ASW capability and have diesels made in France. All have Magnavox MX 1102-NV NAVSAT receiver, Krupp-Atlas echo-sounder. "Pozitiv-E" air-search radar, in a radome (NATO "Cross Dome") at the masthead, is a Soviet set with a 70–75 n.m. range and may be derived from the target designation component of the Cross Sword radar control system for the Soviet SA-N-9 system. Four more are planned, funds permitting.

♦ 3 Soviet Nanuchka-II class
Bldr: Petrovskiy SY, Leningrad

K 71 VIJAYDURG (In serv. 12-76)
K 72 SINDHUDURG (In serv. 5-77)
K 73 HOSDURG (In serv. 1-78)

Sindhudurg (K 72) 4-79

D: 675 tons (fl) **S:** 32 kts **Dim:** 59.3 × 12.6 × 2.4 (hull)
A: 4/SS-N-2C (P-21) Styx SSM (II × 2)—1/SA-N-4 SAM system (II × 1, 20 Gecko missiles)—2/57-mm AK-257 DP (II × 1)
Electron Equipt:
Radar: 1/Don-2 nav., 1/Square Tie surface target designation, 1/Pop Group SAM f.c., 1/Muff Cob gun f.c.
IFF: 2/Square Head interrogators, 1/High Pole transponder
EW: . . . passive, 2/82-mm chaff RL (XVI × 2)
M: 3 Type M521-TM5 diesels; 3 props; 25,996 bhp
Range: 900/30; 2,500/12 **Crew:** 60 tot.

Remarks: Arrived in India 3-77, 8-77, and 3-78. Three or more additional units were reportedly ordered 20-12-82, but no deliveries took place. Poor sea boats. The "Band Stand" radome covers a Square Tie antenna in these export units. The diesels each are composed of two tropicalized, end-for-end coupled M504 diesel engines, with the gearboxes between them.

♦ 6 Soviet Petya-II class
Bldr: U.S.S.R.

P 68 ARNALA
P 69 ANDROTH
P 73 ANJADIP
P 75 AMINI
P 77 KAMORTA
P 78 KADMATH

Andaman (P 74)—lost August 1990 Dr. Giorgio Arra, 1982

D: 950 tons (1,150 fl) **S:** 29 kts
Dim: 81.80 (78.00 pp) × 9.20 × 2.90 (hull)
A: 4/76.2-mm AK-276 DP (II × 2)—4/RBU-2500 ASW RL (XVI × 4)—3/533-mm TT (III × 1)—2/d.c. racks—2/mine rails
Electron Equipt:
Radar: 1/Don-2 nav., 1/Slim Net air/surf. search, 1/Hawk Screech f.c.
Sonar: 1 Hercules med.-freq. hull-mounted
EW: Telegon HF D/F
M: CODOG: 1 Type 61-D3 diesel (6,000 bhp), 2 gas turbines (15,000 shp each); 3 props (centerline CP)—2/75-kw auxiliary electric motors: 3 kts
Range: 450/29; 4,800/10 **Crew:** 98 tot.

Remarks: Transferred in 1969, 1972, and 1975. Were new-construction, export-version ships. Sisters *Kavaratti* (P 80) stricken 8-86, *Kiltan* (P 79) in 1987, and *Katchal* (P 81) in 1990; *Andaman* (P 74) foundered 21-8-90 in the Bay of Bengal. To be replaced by *Khukri* class.

PATROL SHIPS

♦ 6 (+1) Sukanya class

	Bldr	Laid down	L	In serv
P 50 SUKANYA	Korea-Tacoma, Masan	. . .	1989	31-8-89
P 51 SUBHADRA	Korea-Tacoma, Masan	. . .	1989	25-1-90
P 52 SUVARNA	Korea-Tacoma, Masan	. . .	22-8-90	7-90
P 53 SAVITRI	Hindustan SY, Vishnakapatnam	6-88	23-5-89	27-11-90
P 54 SARAYU	Hindustan SY, Vishnakapatnam	. . .	16-10-89	10-9
P 55 SHARADA	Hindustan SY, Vishnakapatnam	9-88	22-8-90	27-10-9
P 56 SUJATHA	Hindustan SY, Vishnakapatnam	11-88	25-10-91	199

Sukanya (P 50) Indian Navy, 19

D: 1,650 tons (1,890 fl) **S:** 22 kts
Dim: 101.95 (96.00 pp) × 11.50 × 3.40
A: 2/40-mm Bofors 56-cal. (I × 2)—1/Chetak helicopter
Electron Equipt:
Radar: 1/Bharat 1245 nav., 1/Decca 2459 surf. search
M: 2 Kirloskar-SEMT-Pielstick 16PA 6V280 diesels; 2 props;12,800 bhp
Range: 7,000/15 **Fuel:** . . . **Electric:** . . .
Crew: 12 officers, 92 enlisted (accommodations for 157 tot.)

Remarks: First three ordered from South Korea 3-87; others, built with Ko[rean] assistance, in 8-87. Three more ordered for the Indian Coast Guard in 1990. Inter[nded] for offshore patrol vessel duties for the protection of oil platforms and the In[dian] economic exclusion zone. Have helicopter beacon, fin stabilizers, fire-fighting w[ater] monitor, and towing capability, and INMARSAT satellite communications. Wea[pons] initially installed were simple Mk 3 powered mountings with local control only. C[arry] a rigid inflatable inspection dinghy to starboard. An eighth is planned.

GUIDED-MISSILE PATROL BOATS

♦ 6 (+14+ . . .) Soviet Tarantul-I class (Project 1241 RE)
Bldrs: A: Volodarskiy SY, Rybinsk, U.S.S.R.; B: Mazagon Dockyard, Bombay; C: Mazagon Goa SY; D: Garden Reach Dockyard, Calcutta

	Bldr	In serv.		Bldr	In
K 40 VEER	A	12-5-87	K 50	. . .	
K 41 NIRBHIK	A	2-88	K 51	. . .	
K 42 NIPAT	A	1-89	K 52	. . .	
K 43 NISHAK	A	12-9-89	K 53	. . .	
K 44 NIRGHAT	A	6-90	K 54	. . .	
K 45 VIBHUTI	B	3-6-91	K 55	. . .	
K 46 VIPUL	B	1992	K 56	. . .	
K 47 VINASH	B	. . .	K 57	. . .	
K 48	B	. . .	K 58	. . .	
K 49	B	. . .	K 59	. . .	

Vibhuti (K 45) French Nav

GUIDED-MISSILE PATROL BOATS *(continued)*

irbhik (K 41) French Navy, 2-88

D: 480 tons (550 fl) **S:** 41 kts
Dim: 56.50 (52.30 wl) × 10.20 (9.50 wl) × 2.50 (3.80 props)
A: 4/SS-N-2C (P-21) SSM (II × 2)—1/76-mm AK-176 DP—1/SA-N-5 SAM syst. (IV × 1; 8 Grail missiles)—2/30-mm AK-630 gatling AA (I × 2)
Electron Equipt:
Radar: 1/Kivach nav., 1/Plank Shave missile target desig., 1/Bass Tilt f.c
IFF: 1/Square Head interrogator, 1/High Pole transponder
M: COGAG: 2 NK-12MV gas turbines (12,100 shp each); two cruise gas turbines (3,000 shp each); 3 props—*see* Remarks
Range: 400/36; 2,000/20 **Fuel:** 50 tons
Crew: 6 officers, 32 enlisted

marks: First five ordered 1984 for delivery 1986–89 from the U.S.S.R. Six to be lt by Mazagon Dockyard at Bombay ordered 1-87, followed by orders for a reported e to be built at Mazagon's Goa facility and three or more at Garden Reach Dockyard, cutta. Some sources indicate that as many as 35 are (or were) planned. They are nded to replace Osa-I and Osa-II missile boats, taking their names. K 45 was nched 26-4-90; K 46 was laid down 5-90 and launched 3-1-91; K 47 launched -92.

eginning with the units to be delivered in 1993, it is intended to power the t with one HAL-G.E. LM-2500 gas turbine (approx. 30,000 shp) and one or two oskar-Pielstick diesels, driving two shafts in a CODOG arrangement.

8 Soviet Osa-II class

0 Prachand	K 92 Prabal	K 94 Chamak	K 96 Chapak
1 Pralaya	K 93 Pratap	K 95 Chapal	K 97 Charag

al (K 92) French Navy, 1986

215 tons (240 fl) **S:** 35 kts **Dim:** 38.60 × 7.60 × 2.00
4/SS-N-2B (P-15) Styx SSM (I × 4)—4/30-mm AK-230 AA (II × 2)
ctron Equipt:
adar: 1/Square Tie surf. search/missile target designation, 1/Drum Tilt gun f.c.
3 M504 diesels; 3 props; 15,000 bhp **Range:** 500/34; 750/25
w: 30 tot.

rks: First four in service 17-2-76, second four on 5-11-76. To be replaced shortly Tarantul-I-class missile boats.

The last Osa-I-class unit, *Vinash* (K 85), was stricken 15-1-90.

PATROL BOATS

♦ 4 Soviet Modified Pauk class Bldr: Volodarskiy SY, Rybinsk

	In serv.		In serv.
P 33 Abhay	3-89	P 35 Aksay	1-91
P 34 Ajay	12-89	P 36 Agray	2-91

D: 440 tons (510 fl) **S:** 34 kts
Dim: 58.50 (52.30 wl) × 9.80 (9.50 wl) × 2.50 hull (3.80 props)
A: 1/76.2-mm AK-176 DP—1/SA-N-5 SAM syst. (IV × 1, 8 SA-7 Grail missiles)—1/30-mm AK-630 gatling AA—4/533-mm ASW TT (II × 2)— 2/RBU-1200 ASW RL (V × 2)—2/d.c. racks (12 d.c.)

Ajay (P 34) French Navy, 2-90

Ajay (P 34)—showing dipping sonar cabinet projecting past transom stern Hartmut Ehlers, 2-90

PATROL BOATS *(continued)*

Electron Equipt:
Radar: 1/Pechora nav., 1/Cross Dome (Pozitiv-E) air/surf. search, 1/Bass Tilt f.c.
Sonar: MF hull-mounted, MF dipping sonar at stern
EW: . . .—IFF: 2/Square Head interrogators
M: 2 M 517-series multi-row radial diesels; 2 props; 20,000 bhp
Range: 2,000/20 **Fuel:** 50 tons **Crew:** 2 tot.

Remarks: Delivered via the Black Sea, in parallel with the similar Tarantul-I class. Reportedly, only four ordered from U.S.S.R., although licensed production of later units in India is possible. Housing for dipping sonar projects well beyond the transom stern. The Indian units of the class (and the sole example built for Cuba) differ from the Soviet version in having larger torpedo tubes, the pilothouse set farther forward on the superstructure, and the substitution of the Cross Dome radar for Strut Curve. The torpedo tubes must be trained out to launch. There is a secondary manned backup director for the gatling gun.

◆ **7 SDB Mk 3 class** Bldr: Garden Reach SB & Eng., Calcutta (In serv. 1985–86)

D: 210 tons (fl) **S:** 34 kts **Dim:** 37.80 × 7.50 × 1.30 (hull)
A: 2/40-mm Bofors AA (I × 2) **Electron Equipt:** Radar: 1/. . . nav.
M: 2 MTU 16V538 TB92 diesels; 2 props; 9,200 bhp **Crew:** 34 tot.

Remarks: Intended as an improved version of the SDB Mk 2 with better hull form, less rake to propeller shafts. Probably also have a centerline cruise engine. Speed also reported as 28 kts for Goa-built units. May also carry depth charges.

◆ **5 SDB Mk 2 class** Bldr: Garden Reach SB & Eng., Calcutta

Rajtarang (T-57)—Coast Guard SDB Mk 2 French Navy, 1991

D: 160 tons (203 fl) **S:** 29 kts **Dim:** 37.50 × 7.50 × 1.75
A: 1/40-mm Bofors AA—2/d.c. racks (18 Mk 7 d.c.)
M: 2 Deltic 18-42K diesels; 2 props; 6,240 bhp; 1 Kirloskar-Cummins NH-220 cruise diesel, 165 bhp (for 6-kt cruising)
Electric: 220 kVA **Range:** 1,400/14 **Crew:** 4 officers, 26 enlisted

Remarks: Five sisters operated by Indian Coast Guard.

MINE WARFARE SHIPS

◆ **0 (+10) new-construction minehunters** Bldr: Goa SY (?)

Remarks: Construction of a license-built version of a standard modern Western European GRP-construction, twin-screwed minehunter is planned, if funding permits. The Tripartite, Karlskrona *Landsort,* Vosper Thornycroft *Sandown,* and Intermarine *Lerici* designs are in competition. In 1990, it was reported that pendant numbers M 89 through M 94 would be assigned to six minehunters to be built at Goa.

◆ **12 Soviet Natya-class seagoing minesweepers** Bldr: Ust Izhora SY, Kolpino

	In serv.		In serv.
M 61 Pondicherry	4-78	M 67 Karwar	9-86
M 62 Porbandar	4-78	M 68 Cannanore	11-87
M 63 Bedi	7-79	M 69 Cuddalore	11-87
M 64 Bhavnagar	7-79	M 70 Kakinada	5-87
M 65 Alleppy	8-80	M 71 Kozhikode	12-88
M 66 Ratnagiri	8-80	M 72 Konkan	12-88

Konkan (M 72)—with SA-N-5 SAM launchers abaft lattice mast French Navy, 11-88

Kakinada (M 70) Fouad Sadek, 5-8

D: 750 tons (877 fl) **S:** 18 kts **Dim:** 61.0 × 10.2 × 3.3 (5.3 max.)
A: 4/30-mm AK-230 AA (II × 2)—4/25-mm 2M-8 AA (II × 2)—2/RBU-1200 ASW RL (V × 2)—mines; M 67–M 72 also: 2/SA-N-5 point-defense SAM systems (IV × 2; 16 SA-7 Grail missiles)
Electron Equipt:
Radar: 1/Don-2 nav., 1/Drum Tilt f.c.
Sonar: 1/HF hull-mounted (49 kHz)
IFF: 2/Square Head interrogators, 1/High Pole B transponder
M: 2 diesels; 2 props; 5,000 bhp
Range: 1,800/16; 5,200/10 **Crew:** 10 officers, 89 enlisted

Remarks: Second group of six, ordered 20-17-82, were delivered out of pendant nu ber order. Differ from the units in the Soviet Navy in that they do not have a ramp the stern. Can be used as ASW escorts. Aluminum/steel alloy construction. Ca Soviet PEMT-3 magnetic and MPT mechanical sweep gear. One reportedly has b modified to act as an intelligence collector.

◆ **6 Soviet Yevgenya-class inshore minesweepers** (First 3 in serv. 15-5-83, others: 3-2-84)

M 83 Mahe	M 85 Mangalore	M 87 Mulki
M 84 Malwan	M 86 Malpe	M 88 Magdala

D: 80 tons (90 fl) **S:** 11 kts **Dim:** 26.2 × 6.1 × 1.5
A: 2/25-mm 2M-8 AA (II × 1)—6 to 12 small mines
Electron Equipt: Radar: 1/Spin Trough nav.
M: 2 diesels; 2 props; 600 bhp **Range:** 300/10 **Crew:** 10 tot.

Remarks: Glass-reinforced plastic construction. Equipped for shallow-water m hunting to depths of 30 meters with a towed television and marker-buoy dispenser. also carry two or three mine-clearance divers. Additional units may be built in I under license.

◆ **4 U.K. "Ham"-class inshore minesweepers**

	Bldr	L
M 79 Bimlipatham (ex-*Hildersham*)	Vosper, Portsmouth	5-2-54
M 80 Bassein (ex-*Littleham*)	Brooke Marine, Lowestoft	4-5-54
M 81 Bhatkal	Mazagon DY, Bombay	4-67
M 82 Bulsar	Mazagon DY, Bombay	17-5-6

Bhatkal (M 81)

D: 120 tons (159 fl) **S:** 14 kts (9, sweeping)
Dim: 32.43 (30.48 pp) × 6.45 × 1.70 **A:** 1/20-mm Oerlikon AA
Electron Equipt: Radar: 1/Type 978 nav.
Crew: 2 officers, 13 enlisted
M: 2 Paxman YHAXM diesels; 2 props; 1,000 bhp **Fuel:** 25 ton

Remarks: M 79 and M 80 were transferred in 1955. The Indian-built uni teakwood hulls but are otherwise almost identical.

AMPHIBIOUS WARFARE SHIPS

Note: A larger dock-landing ship is in the design/planning stage.

◆ **1 (+2+5) Magar-class tank landing ships**

	Bldr	L	In serv.
L 20 MAGAR	Garden Reach, Calcutta	7-11-84	15-7-87
L 23 GHARIAL	Hindustan SY, Vishakapatnam	2-4-91	1992-93
L	Hindustan SY, Vishakapatnam	. . .	. . .

Magar (L 20) 92 Wing, RAAF, 10-90

Magar (L 20) *The Navy,* 1989

D: 3,200 tons (5,655 fl) **S:** 15 kts
Dim: 124.90 (120.00 pp) × 17.50 × 3.80
A: 4/40-mm Bofors AA (I × 4)—1/122-mm barrage RL (XVIII × 2)
Electron Equipt: Radar: 1/. . . nav.—EW: Bharat Ajanta intercept
M: 2 SEMT-Pielstick 8P C2 V-400 Mk 3 diesels; 2 props; 8,560 bhp (8,000 sust.)
Range: 3,000/14 **Crew:** 16 officers, 120 enlisted

Remarks: Second unit ordered 1985; third in 4-90; five more planned. Carries four Sea ...ck-type LCVP in separate davits. Helicopter deck and hangar aft for Sea King Mk ... transport. Ramp forward to tank deck. No stern door/ramp. Can beach on 1/40 ...dient. Barrage rocket launchers on bow may have been removed from scrapped ...ocny-A landing ships *Guldar* (L 13) and *Gharial* (L 12).

◆ **8 Soviet Polnocny-C and -D class** Bldr: Stocznia Pólnocna, Gdańsk, Poland

... GHORPAD	L 15 KESARI	L 16 SHARDUL	L 17 SHARABH
... CHEETAH	L 19 MAHISH	L 21 GULDAR	L 22 KUMBHIR

D: 1,350 (fl) **S:** 18 kts **Dim:** 81.1 × 9.3 × 1.2 fwd/2.6 aft (loaded)
A: 4/30-mm AK-230 AA (II × 2)—2/140-mm rocket launchers (VIII × 2)
Electron Equipt:
Radar: 1/Don-2 nav. (Kivach in L 18–L 21), 1 Drum Tilt gun f.c.
M: 2 Type 40D diesels; 2 props; 5,000 bhp
Range: 900/17; 1,500/14 **Crew:** 11 officers, 107 enlisted

Remarks: All constructed for India. L 14 and L 15 transferred in 1975, L 16 and L 17 ...76, L 18 in 12-84, L 19 in 7-85, L 21 in 11-86, and L 22 in 2-86. First four ...ocny-C) do not have a helicopter platform as on Polnocny-Ds. Cargo: 350 tons and ...140 troops. Upper deck is primarily a shelter for the tank deck and cannot support ... vehicles; there is no ramp to the tank deck, the hatch forward being intended for ...ation and loading vehicles aboard by crane.

◆ **7 Vasco da Gama-class utility landing craft** Bldrs: L 34, L35: Hoogly Dockyard, Calcutta; others: Goa Shipyard

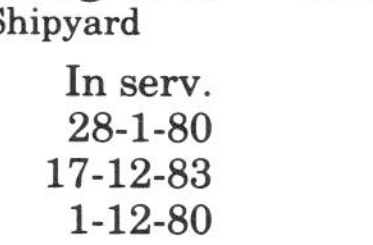

	L	In serv.
L 34 VASCO DA GAMA	29-11-78	28-1-80
L 35	16-3-80	17-12-83
L 36	13-1-79	1-12-80
L 37	22-7-85	1986
L 38 MIDHUR	2-86	1987
L 39 MANGALA	2-86	25-3-87
L 40	. . .	25-3-87

Mangala (L 39) Indian Navy, 1989

D: 500 tons (fl) **S:** 9 kts **Dim:** 55.96 × 7.94 × 1.71 (aft)
A: 2/40-mm Bofors AA (I × 2)—mines
Electron Equipt: Radar: 1/. . . nav.
M: 3 Kirloskar-M.A.N. W8V 17.5/22 AMAL diesels; 3 Kort-nozzle props; 1,245 bhp
Range: 1,000/8 **Crew:** . . . tot.

Remarks: Cargo: 250 tons or 150 troops. Goa SY is a subsidiary of Mazagon Docks, Bombay. Strongly resemble the long-stricken Soviet MP-8 class.

HYDROGRAPHIC SURVEY SHIPS

◆ **4 (+2) Sandhayak class** Bldr: Garden Reach SB & Engineers, Calcutta

	L	In serv.
J . . . SANDHAYAK	6-4-77	26-2-81
J 19 . NIRDESHAK	16-11-78	4-10-83
J . . . NIRUPAK	10-7-81	14-8-85
J . . . INVESTIGATOR	. . .	1-90
J . . . JUMNA	9-89	1992
J	. . .	. . .

Nirupak Gilbert Gyssels, 1987

D: 1,200 tons (1,820 fl) **S:** 16.75 kts
Dim: 85.77 (78.80 pp) × 12.30 × 3.34
A: 1/40-mm Bofors AA—1/Chetak helicopter
Electron Equipt: Radar: 1/Decca TM-1629 nav.
M: 1 GRSE-M.A.N. G8V 30/45 ATL diesel; 1 prop; 3,920 bhp—1 Pleuger 200-bhp active rudder; 5 kts
Fuel: 264 tons **Range:** 6,000/14 **Crew:** 12 officers, 134 enlisted

Remarks: 2,050 grt. Telescoping hangar. Four inshore survey launches with "Hydro-dist" fixing system. Have 3 precision depth-finders, Decca "Navigator," Decca "Hi-Fix," taut-wire measuring gear, and a gravimeter. Carry 169 tons water and 5 tons aviation fuel. Have Telegon IV HF D/F.

Note: The large hydrographic survey ship *Darshak* (J 14) was stricken 12-89.

HYDROGRAPHIC SURVEY SHIPS *(continued)*

◆ **4 inshore survey ships** Bldr: Goa SY (In serv. 1984–85)

J 33 MAKAR J 34 MITHUN J 35 MEEN J 36 MESH

D: 185 tons (210 fl) **S:** 12.5 kts **Dim:** 37.50 × 7.50 × 1.90
A: 1/40-mm Bofors AA **Electron Equipt:** Radar: 1/. . . nav.
M: 2 diesels; 2 props; 1,124 bhp **Range:** 1,500/12.5
Crew: 4 officers, 32 enlisted

Remarks: J 34 launched 28-5-83 and J 35 on 10-8-83. Steel-hulled. Same hulls as SDB Mk 2 patrol-boat class.

Note: The modern and elaborately equipped research ships operated by the National Oceanographic Institute are non-naval. They include: *Sagar Kanya, Sagar Sampada, Samudra Manthan, Samudra Sarveshak, Samudra Nidhi,* and *Samudra Sandhari.* The small inshore research craft *Gaveshani* and a sister launched in 1976 are also civilian.

AUXILIARY SHIPS

◆ **1 Soviet Ugra-class submarine tender**

A 54 AMBA (In serv. 28-12-68)

D: 6,750 tons (9,650 fl) **S:** 20 kts **Dim:** 145.0 × 17.7 × 6.4
A: 4/76.2-mm AK-276 DP (II × 2)
Electron Equipt:
Radar: 1/Don-2 nav., 1/Slim Net surf./air search, 2/Hawk Screech f.c.
IFF: 2 Square Head interrogators, 1 High Pole A transponder
M: 4Type 2D42 diesels; 2 props; 8,000 bhp **Range:** 21,000/10
Crew: approx. 400 tot.

Remarks: Helicopter platform. Quarters for 750 men. Two 6-ton cranes, one 10-ton crane.

◆ **0 (+2) submarine rescue and support ships** Bldr: Rauma Repola, Finland

	Laid down	L	In serv.
A	. . .	. . .	1992
A	. . .	. . .	. . .

D: 7,000 tons (fl) **S:** 13 kts **Dim:** 101.8 (91.0 pp) × . . . × . . .
A: . . . . . . **Electron Equipt:** Radar: . . .
M: 2 . . . . . . diesels (3,285 bhp each), electric drive; 1 prop; . . . shp— 2 bow-thrusters; 4,020 shp—2 rotatable stern thrusters; 4,830 shp
Range: 19,500/12 **Crew:** 28 officers, 56 enlisted + 26 spare

Remarks: Ordered 1990. Modified oilfield rescue ship design. Will have Kongsberg ADP 503 Mk II dynamic positioning system, one 120-ton crane, medical facilities, helicopter platform forward, and two 12-man submersible rescue vehicles capable of rescue to 300 depths. Will be able to undertake a variety of submarine rescue, general salvage, and diving support duties.

◆ **1 chartered salvage and diving support ship** Bldr: Mazagon DY, Bombay

	Laid down	L	In serv.
NIREEKSHAK	8-82	1-84	8-6-89 (Indian Navy)

D: 3,600 tons (fl) **S:** 12 kts **Dim:** 70.5 × 17.5 × 5.0
Electron Equipt: Radar: . . .
M: 2 Bergens Mek. Verk. diesels; 2 CP props; 5,015 bhp— 2 bow-thrusters; 910 shp—2 stern-thrusters; 910 shp
Range: . . . **Crew:** 15 officers, 48 enlisted

Remarks: Chartered 8-6-89 for three years, with option for purchase to replace *Nistar* (A 55) until the two new units above are available. Carries two 12-man submersible rescue vehicles capable of operating to 300 m and has Kongsberg ADP 503 Mk II dynamic positioning system. Had been built as a commercial oilfield support ship and is capable of a variety of salvage and rescue missions.

Note: The Soviet T-58-class submarine rescue ship *Nistar* (A 55) was reported stricken in 1989, as was the repair ship *Dharini* (A 52).

◆ **1 hospital ship** Bldr: Hindustan SY, Calcutta

LAKSHADWEEP (L: 28-8-81)

D: . . . **S:** 12 kts **Dim:** 52.0 (46.8 pp) × 9.5 × 3.0
M: 2 diesels; 2 props; 900 bhp
Crew: 19 ship's company +15 medical staff , 90 hospital berths

Remarks: Laid down 2-81.

◆ **1 (+1) cadet training ships** Bldr: Mazagon DY, Bombay

	L	In serv.
A 86 TIR	15-4-83	21-2-86
A	6-91	. . .

D: 2,000 tons (3,000 fl) **S:** 23 kts **Dim:** 107.0 × . . . × . . .
A: 2/40-mm Bofors AA (II × 1, Mk 5 mount)
Electron Equipt: Radar: 2/Bharat-Decca . . . nav.
M: 2 Kirloskar-SEMT-Pielstick 18 PA6 V280 BTC diesels; 2 props; 16,920 bhp
Range: 6,000/12 **Crew:** 35 officers, 204 enlisted, 120 cadets

Tir (A 86) Vic Jeffery, RAN, 5-90

Remarks: *Tir,* ordered 1981, was to have completed 3-84, delayed by yard problems. Second ship ordered 5-86 from same builder. Helicopter deck, but no hangar. Have Telegon IV HF D/F, Decca collision-avoidance system, satellite navigation facilities, and 4 saluting cannon. Intended to replace the *Leopard*-class frigates used as cadet training ships at Cochin.

◆ **0 (+1+1) Rajaba Gan Palan-class replenishment oilers** Bldr: Garden Reach SB & Eng., Calcutta

	Laid down	L	In serv.
A . . . RAJABA GAN PALAN	. . .	. . .	. . .

D: approx. 22,000 tons (fl) **S:** 20 kts **Dim:** 172.00 × 23.00 × 9.14
A: 3/40-mm AA Bofors (I × 3)—1/. . . helicopter
Electron Equipt: Radar: . . .
M: 2 diesels (?); 1 prop; 24,000 bhp—bow-thruster
Range: 10,000/16 **Crew:** 191 ship's company, 6 air group

Remarks: 16,211 dwt. First unit ordered 7-87. Design is a modified version of the Deepak class, with a repair capability added. Cargo: 14,200 m diesel and aviation fuel 2,250 m fresh water, 2,170 m ammunition, provisions, and spares. A second unit is planned, but no reports of progress on the first have been received.

◆ **2 Deepak class** Bldr: Bremer-Vulkan Schiffbau, Bremen-Vegesack, Germany

A 50 DEEPAK (In serv. 20-11-72) A 57 SHAKTI (In serv. 21-2-76)

Shakti (A 57) French Navy, 19

D: 6,785 tons (22,000 fl) **S:** 20 kts
Dim: 168.43 (157.50 pp) × 23.0 × 9.14
A: A 50: 3/40-mm AA (I × 3)—2/20-mm AA (I × 2); A 57: 4/40-mm AA (I × 4)
Electron Equipt:
Radar: 2/Decca 1226 nav.—EW: Telegon IV HF D/F
M: 1 set Type BV/BBC geared steam turbines; 1 prop; 16,500 shp
Boilers: 2 Babcock & Wilcox **Range:** 5,500/18.5 **Crew:** 169 tot.

Remarks: 12,690 grt/15,800 dwt. Two liquid-replenishment stations per side, w British-style jackstay rigs, plus over-the-stern fueling. Telescoping hangar and fl deck for one Chetak helicopter. Carry 12,624 tons fuel oil, 1,280 tons diesel fuel, 1 tons aviation fuel, 812 tons fresh water, and some dry cargo.

◆ **2 Gaj-class oceangoing tugs** Bldr: Garden Reach SB & Eng., Calcu

A 51 GAJ (In serv. 20-9-73) A . . . MATANGA (L: 29-10-77; in serv. 19

Gaj (A 51)

AUXILIARY SHIPS *(continued)*

D: 1,465 tons (1,600 fl) **S:** 15 kts **Dim:** 66.0 (60.0 pp) × 11.6 × 4.0
A: none **M:** 2 GRSE-M.A.N. G7V diesels; 2 CP props; 3,292 bhp
Range: 8,000/12

Remarks: Fitted for salvage work. 40-ton bollard pull. *Matanga* reported as 62.0 m overall by 12.3 beam, 3,920 bhp.

YARD AND SERVICE CRAFT

◆ **1 coastal tanker** Bldr: Central Inland Water Transport Corp., Rajabagan SY, Calcutta

PALAN (In serv 5-86)

D: approx. 1,200 tons (fl) **S:** . . .
Dim: 57.94 (54.39 pp) × 9.10 × 3.10
M: 2 M.A.N. diesels; 1 prop; 1,440 bhp

Remarks: 624 grt/715 dwt.

◆ **2 Poshak-class fuel lighters** Bldr: Rajabagan SY, Bombay

POSHAK (In serv. 4-82) PURAN (In serv. 1988)

D: 600 tons **S:** 8 kts **Dim:** 36.3 × 7.6 × 2.4
M: 1 M.A.N. diesel; 255 bhp **Cargo:** 200 tons dwt.

◆ **2 Purak-class fuel lighters** Bldr: Rajabagan SY, Bombay

ᴾURAK (In serv. 3-6-77) PRADHAYAK (In serv. 2-78)

D: 960 tons (fl) **S:** 9 kts **Dim:** 49.7 × 8.1 × 3.0
M: 1 diesel; 1 prop; 560 bhp **Cargo:** 376 tons dwt.

3 water lighters Bldr: 1 by Rajabagan SY, Bombay; others: Mazagon DY, Bombay

.MBUDA COCHIN . . . . . .

D: 200 tons **S:** 9 kts **Dim:** 32.0 × . . . × 2.4
M: 1 diesel; 1 prop; . . . bhp

1 torpedo trials and retrieval craft Bldr: P.S. & Co., Bombay

71 ASTRAVAHINI (In serv. 8-9-83)

emarks: No details available.

2 torpedo retrievers Bldr: Goa SY

72 . . . . . . (In serv. 16-9-82) A 73 . . . . . . (L: 5-11-80)

D: 110 tons (fl) **S:** 11 kts **Dim:** 28.5 × 6.1 × 1.4
M: 2 Kirlosker-M.A.N. 12-cyl. diesels; 2 props; 720 bhp **Crew:** 13 tot.

3 diving tenders Bldr: Cleback SY (In serv. 1979, 2-84, 8-84)

D: 36 tons (fl) **S:** 12 kts **Dim:** 14.89 (13.37 pp) × 4.40 × 1.21
M: 2 Premier Auto-Meadows diesels; 2 props; 130 bhp **Fuel:** 2 tons

1 coastal tug Bldr: Garden Reach S.B. & Eng., Calcutta

.JAJI (In serv. 7-82)

): 428 tons **S:** 12.5 kts **Dim:** 30.5 × 9.5 × 3.8
M: 2 Garden Reach-M.A.N. diesels; 2 Kort-nozzle props; 2,120 bhp

:e: Construction of five new tugs was authorized under the 1985 Budget; they were ortedly delivered during 1988.

3 large harbor tugs Bldr: Mazagon Dock, Bombay (In serv. 1973–74)

ARAL ARJUN BALSHIL

narks: No data available.

1 sail-training craft Bldr: Alcock Ashdown, Bhavnagar

.UNA (In serv. 20-4-81)

: 130 tons (fl) **Dim:** 30.5 × . . . × . . .

arks: Two-masted brig for training 26 Sea Cadets. Construction of a second training ship has been proposed; to carry 90 cadets.

: There are undoubtedly a large number of other yard and service craft, for which ames or data are available. A new floating dry dock for Ft. Blair in the Andaman ds was announced 1986.

COAST GUARD

onnel (1991): 460 officers, 2,497 enlisted

e Coast Guard was established 1-2-77 to ensure surveillance of India's 200-cal-mile economic zone. Now commanded by a vice admiral, it consisted initially ps and craft transferred from the Indian Navy. The Indian Customs Service was ed with the Coast Guard in April 1982. The name "Coast Guard" is written in black letters on the sides of ship hulls, which are painted white and have diagonal guard"-style stripes. There are planned to be 72 ships and craft in service by including 24 offshore patrol vessels, 6 deep-sea patrol ships, 6 pollution-control and 36 inshore patrol boats.

t Guard Aviation: Thirty-six Do-228 and 34 helicopters are expected to be in e by 2000.Coast Guard Squadrons in service in 1991 include:
700 at Calcutta: 2 Fokker F 27-200 Maritime surveillance
744 at Daman: 12 Dornier/HAL-Dornier 228 surveillance
800 at Goa: 6 Chetak helicopters

PATROL SHIPS

Note: The Indian National Institute of Oceanography research ship *Sagar Sampada* was chartered by the Indian Coast Guard during the summer of 1991 to check for petroleum pollution in the Arabian sea as a result of the Iraqi oil-spill in the Persian Gulf; none was found. In the future, the Indian Coast Guard plans to play a larger rôle in pollution control and will acquire six specialized pollution-control ships.

◆ **0 (+3+9) Sukanya class** Bldr: Hindustan SY, Vishnakapatnam

	Laid down	L	In serv.
T . . . PRIYADARSHINI	. . .	. . .	1993
T	. . .	. . .	. . .
T	. . .	. . .	. . .

D: 1,650 tons (1,890 fl) **S:** 22 kts
Dim: 101.95 (96.00 pp) × 11.50 × 3.40
A: 2/40-mm Bofors 56-cal. (I × 2)—1/Chetak helicopter
Electron Equipt: Radar: 1/Bharat 1245 nav., 1/Decca 2459 surf. search
M: 2 Kirloskar-SEMT-Pielstick 16PA 6V280 diesels; 2 props; 12,800 bhp
Range: 7,000/15 **Fuel:** . . . **Electric:** . . .
Crew: 12 officers, 92 enlisted (accommodations for 157 tot.)

Remarks: First three ordered 4-90; sisters to seven units in the Indian Navy. A total of twelve is planned. Intended for offshore patrol vessel duties for the protection of oil platforms and the Indian economic exclusion zone. Will have helicopter beacon, fin stabilizers, fire-fighting water monitor, towing capability, and INMARSAT satellite communications. Carry a rigid inflatable inspection dinghy to starboard.

◆ **9 Vikram class** Bldr: Mazagon DY, Bombay

	L	In serv.
T 33 VIKRAM	26-9-81	20-12-83
T 34 VISAYA	. . .	13-4-84
T 35 VEERA	30-6-84	3-5-86
T 36 VARUNA	1-2-86	27-2-88
T 37 VAJIRA	31-1-87	22-12-88
T 38 VIVEK	5-11-87	19-8-89
T 39 VIGRAHA	12-88	12-4-90
T 40 VARAD	2-9-89	19-7-90
T 41 VARAHA	. . .	3-91

Varad (T 40) French Navy, 9-90

D: 940 tons (1,100 fl) **S:** 22 kts
Dim: 74.60 (69.00 pp) × 11.39 × 3.24 (hull)
A: 1/40-mm Bofors L 60 AA—1/Chetak helicopter
Electron Equipt: Radar: 1/Decca 1230 nav., 1/Decca . . . nav.
M: 2 Kirloskar-Pielstick 16 PA6 V80 diesels; 2 CP props; 12,800 bhp
Electric: 880 kw tot. **Range:** 3,500/14 **Fuel:** 108 tons
Crew: 10 officers, 60 enlisted

Remarks: First three ordered 1979; second three ordered 1983. Have fin stabilizers, hangar for Chetak (license-built Alouette-III) helicopter, pollution-control equipment, diving gear, and fire-fighting monitors. *Varuna* has training facilities on the fantail in lieu of the anti-pollution equipment. Design not fully satisfactory; cannot operate helicopter in heavy weather due to rolling.

PATROL BOATS

◆ **6 Tara Bai class** Bldr: T 71, T 72: Singapore SB & Eng., Ltd; others: Garden Reach SB & Eng., Ltd., Calcutta

	L	In serv.		L	In serv.
T 71 TARA BAI	4-87	20-5-87	T 74 AKKA DEVI	. . .	9-89
T 72 AHALYA BAI	5-87	9-9-87	T 75 NAIKI DEVI	. . .	12-89
T 73 LAKSHI BAI	. . .	4-89	T 76 GANGA DEVI	. . .	4-90

Tara Bai (T 71)—on trials Singapore SB & Eng., 5-87

INDIA *(continued)*
PATROL BOATS *(continued)*

D: 173 tons normal (195 fl) **S:** 26 kts
Dim: 44.90 (42.30 wl) × 7.00 × 1.89 (2.59 props)
A: 1/40-mm Bofors AA—2/7.62-mm mg (I × 2)
Electron Equipt: Radar: 1/Decca 1226 nav.
M: 2 MTU 12V538 TB82 diesels; 2 props; 4,400 bhp (4,000 sust.)
Electric: 260 kw (2 × 100 kw; 1 × 60 kw) **Endurance:** 7 days
Range: 2,400/14 **Fuel:** 30 tons
Crew: 5 officers, 27 enlisted + 2 spare

Remarks: T 71 and T 72 ordered 6-86, with license for the four to build in India. Air-conditioned. Five-ton towing hook. Rigid inflatable boat. Ten tons fresh water, with 3 ton/day distiller. HF/DF, echo-sounder, autopilot. Intended for SAR, fisheries patrol, sovereignty patrol, etc. Hull design based on standard Lürssen 45-m hull; steel construction.

◆ **7 Japanese design** Bldr: T 64: Sumidagawa SY, Tokyo; others: Garden Reach SB & Eng., Calcutta

	In serv.		In serv.
T 64 Jija Bai	20-6-83	T 68 Ramadevi	1985
T 65 Chand Bibi	1985	T 69 Habbah Khatun	19-10-85
T 66 Rani Jindan	1985	T 70 Avvaiyar	1986
T 67 Kittur Chinnama	1985		

Jija Bai (T 64) Sumidigawa, 1983

D: 273 tons (fl) **S:** 25 kts (sust.)
Dim: 44.02 (41.10 pp) × 7.40 × 1.50 (hull)
A: 1/40-mm Bofors AA—2/7.62-mm mg (I × 2)
Electron Equipt: Radar: 1/Decca 1226 nav.
M: 2 MTU 12V538 TB82 diesels; 2 props; 4,030 bhp
Range: 2,375/14 **Crew:** 7 officers, 27 enlisted

Remarks: Same basic design as Philippine Coast Guard's *Bessang Pass* class. Plan to build eight more dropped in favor of the *Tara Bai* class.

◆ **5 SDB Mk 2 class** Bldr: Garden Reach SB & Eng., Calcutta (T58, 59: Goa SY)

	In serv.		In serv.
T 56 Rajhans	23-12-80	T 60 Rajshiree	9-84
T 57 Rajtarang	26-11-81	T 61 Rajkamal	9-86
T 59 Rajkiran	3-84		

D: 160 tons (203 fl) **S:** 29 kts **Dim:** 37.50 × 7.50 × 1.75
A: 1/20-mm AA **Electron Equipt:** Radar: 1/. . . nav.
M: 2 Deltic 18-42K diesels; 2 props; 6,240 bhp; 1 Kirloskar-Cummins NH-220 cruise diesel; 165 bhp (6 kts)
Range: 1,400/14 **Crew:** 4 officers, 26 enlisted **Electric:** 220 kVA

Remarks: The Indian Navy also operates five units of this class. T 57 ran aground 12-90, was salved. See photo page 258.

PATROL CRAFT

◆ **0 (+10) P-2000 design** Bldr: Anderson Marine, Pty, Kadras/Goa SY

D: 49 tons (fl) **S:** 25 kts **Dim:** 20.8 × 5.8 × 1.5
A: 1/20-mm Oerlikon AA **Electron Equipt:** Radar: 1/. . . nav.
M: 2 MWM diesels; 2 props; 1,800 bhp
Range: 600/15 **Crew:** 4 officers, 6 enlisted

Remarks: Ordered 9-90. Built in cooperation with Seaking Industries. To begin delivery to Goa Shipyard 1992 for assembly. GRP hull.

◆ **24 U.S.-design** Bldr: American Body Armor & Equipment

D: 7 tons (fl) **S:** 58 kts **Dim:** 12.0 × 3.0 × 0.6
A: 1/7.62-mm mg **M:** 2 diesel outdrives; . . . bhp **Crew:** 4 tot.

Remarks: Ordered 1990. Kevlar hull construction.

◆ **8 (+12) South Korean design** Bldr: Swallow Craft, Pusan (In serv. 1980–82, 1992–. . .)

C01–C08

D: 32 tons (35 fl) **S:** 26 kts **Dim:** 20.0 × 4.8 × 1.3
A: 1/7.62-mm mg **Electron Equipt:** Radar: 1/nav.
M: 2 MTU diesels; 2 props; 1,350 bhp **Range:** 600/20 **Crew:** 12 tot.

Remarks: First six in service 24-7-80; next two taken over from India Oil Corp. 22-5-82. Reported that 12 more were ordered from an Indian yard in 1989, but there has been no indication of any completions.

◆ **5 12.5-meter class** Bldr: Mandovani Marine, . . . (In serv. 198. . .)

D: 10 tons (fl) **S:** 18 kts **Dim:** 12.5 × . . . × . . .
M: 2 Cummins diesels; 2 Hamilton waterjets; 550 bhp

Remarks: GRP construction, deep-vee hull form.

◆ **20 Norwegian SM-43 Smuggler-class launches** Bldr: GRW, India

D: . . . **S:** 36 kts **Dim:** 14.9 × . . . × . . .
M: 2 diesels; 2 Arneson ASD-10 outdrives; . . . hp **Crew:** 4 tot.

Remarks: Acquired when the Coast Guard merged with the Customs Service in 4-82. Glass-reinforced plastic construction. Original design by Båtservice, Mandal, Norway. Were originally 13.4 m overall; being re-engined 1990 onward, lengthened, and outdrives replacing original Castoldi waterjets. Names reported include: *Bhawaji, Burga, Jaya, Joan of Arc, Kali,* and *Shakti.*

INDONESIA

Personnel (1991): 44,000, including 14,000 Marines and 800 Naval Aviation

Naval Aviation: The Indonesian Navy has a coastal-surveillance and logistic-suppo[rt] force consisting of 10 Australian N22B and 6 N22SL Searchmaster maritime survei[l]lance aircraft, 6 C-47 Skytrain transports, 2 Aero Commander Model 100 light tran[s]ports, and 4 CASA-212 Aerocar light transports, plus 2 AS-332 Super Puma 4 NB[O] 105, 1 Alouette-III, and 10 Wasp HAS.1 helicopters. The first of what were to be 2[?] Nuritanio-built AS-332 Puma (NAS 132) helicopters was delivered 29-12-84, with a[ll] to be delivered by end 1986 and fitted with AS.39 Exocet antiship missiles, Ome[ga] ORB-22 radar, Thomson-Sintra HS-12 dipping sonar, and ASW torpedoes; unfo[r]tunately, only four were ever delivered, and of those, two have been lost.

The Air Force has 2 Boeing 737 Surveiller long-range maritime patrol aircraft (fir[st] delivered 6-83) with "Slammer" side-looking radar; also used are 3 C-130H-MP an[d] ITPN-Casa CN-235 maritime surveillance aircraft.

Note: The names of Indonesian ships are preceded by the designation KRI (*Kap[al] perang Republik Indonesia,* or Warship of the Republic of Indonesia).

SUBMARINES

Note: Acquisition of two additional submarines has been a long-time goal, frustra[ted] by lack of funds.

◆ **2 German Type 209/1300** Bldr: Howaldtswerke, Kiel

	Laid down	L	In serv.
401 Cakra	25-11-77	10-9-80	18-3-81
402 Nanggala (ex-*Candrasa*)	14-3-78	10-9-80	6-7-81

Cakra (401) Skyfotos

SUBMARINES *(continued)*

Nanggala (402) Leo Van Ginderen, 8-87

D: 1,100 tons std./1,265 surf./1.395 sub. **S:** 11 kts surf./21.5 kts sub.
Dim: 59.50 × 6.30 × 5.50
A: 8/533-mm TT fwd. (14 AEG SUT wire-guided torpedoes)
Electron Equipt:
Radar: 1/Thompson-CSF Calypso-II—EW: . . . intercept
Sonar: Krupp-Atlas CSU 3-2 suite: AN 526 passive, 407 A9 passive, DUUX-2 intercept
M: 4 MTU 12V493AZ diesels (600 bhp each), 1 Siemens electric motor; 1 prop; 5,000 shp
Range: snorkel: 1,200/4; 8,200/11; submerged: 16/21.5; 25/20; 230/8; 400/4
Fuel: 87 tons (108 emergency) **Endurance:** 50 days
Crew: 6 officers, 28 enlisted

Remarks: Ordered 2-4-77 from Ferrostaal, Essen, consortium. Can dive to 250 m. H.S.A. Sinbads weapons control. Have four 120-cell batteries, producing 11,500 amp/hr and weighing 257 tons. Both completed thorough refits by builder in late 1980s, *Cakra* completing in 1987, and *Nanggala* in 9-89.

Note: The Soviet-built Whiskey-class submarine *Pasopati* (410) was stricken 11-90.

DESTROYERS

Note: The Dutch guided-missile destroyers *De Ruyter* (F 806) and *Tromp* (F 801) will very likely be sold to Indonesia on completion of their programmed replacements in the late 1990s.

FRIGATES

◆ **0 (+23) FSG 90 project** Bldr: P.T. PAL SY, Surabaja

D: 2,300–2,800 tons (fl) **S:** 30 kts **Dim:** . . . × . . . × . . .
A: 8/. . . SSM (IV × 2)—1/ Albatros point-defense SAM syst. (VIII × 1)— 1/76-mm OTO Melara DP—1/. . . CIWS—6/324-mm ASW TT (III × 2)
Electron Equipt: . . .
M: . . . **Range:** . . . **Crew:** . . .

Remarks: An ambitious plan to replace all existing frigates with a uniform, Indonesian-built class. The first unit would be built abroad. Designs under consideration include the Blohm + Voss MEKO-200, a British update of the *Leander*, a French design, and a variant of the Chinese Fl 25. At end-1991, no decision had been announced, and retired foreign ships may be acquired instead.

◆ **1 training frigate** Bldr: Uljanic SY, Split, Yugoslavia

	Laid down	L	In serv.
Hajar Dewantara	11-5-79	11-10-80	20-8-81

Hajar Dewantara (364) 10-81

D: 1,850 tons (fl) **S:** 27 kts **Dim:** 96.70 (92.00 wl) × 11.20 × 3.55
A: 4/MM 38 Exocet SSM (II × 2)—1/57-mm Bofors DP—2/20-mm AA (I × 2)—2/ASW TT (2 AEG SUT wire-guided torpedoes)—mines—1/NBO-105 helicopter
Electron Equipt:
Radar: 1/Decca 1229 nav., 1/H.S.A. WM-28 track-while-scan f.c.
Sonar: PHS-32 (MF)
EW: SUSIE-I intercept—2/128-mm flare RL (II × 2)
M: CODOG: 1 Rolls-Royce Olympus TM-3B gas turbine, 27,250 shp; 2 MTU 16V956 TP91 diesels, 7,000 bhp; 2 CP props
Range: 1,150/27 (gas turbine); 4,000/20 (diesels) **Fuel:** 338 tons
Crew: 11 officers, 80 enlisted + 14 instructors, 100 students

Remarks: Ordered 14-3-78 to same basic design as ship laid down in 1977 for Iraq. SEWACO GM 101-41 computerized data system. Fin stabilizers, 114 tons water ballast, 50 tons potable water, 7 tons helo fuel. Carries two LCVP-type landing craft. 1,000 rounds 57-mm, 3,120 rounds 20-mm ammunition. Gas turbine rated at 22,300 hp in tropics. WM-28 track-while-scan fire-control radar not fitted at time of delivery and may still not be aboard. Second unit, reported ordered 7-83, did not materialize.

◆ **3 Fatahilah class** Bldr: Wilton-Fijenoord, Schiedam, the Netherlands

	Laid down	L	In serv.
361 Fatahilah	31-1-77	22-12-77	16-7-79
362 Malahayati	28-7-77	19-6-78	21-3-80
363 Nala	27-1-78	11-1-79	11-8-80

Malahayati (362) Ross Gillett, 11-84

Nala (363)—with hangar in folded state 1980

D: 1,160 tons (1,450 fl) **S:** 30 kts (21 diesel)
Dim: 83.85 × 11.10 × 3.30
A: 361, 362: 4/MM 38 Exocet SSM (II × 2)—1/120-mm Bofors L-46 DP—1/40-mm Bofors L-70 AA—2/20-mm AA (I × 2)—2/375-mm Bofors SR-375A ASW RL (II × 1)—6/324-mm Mk 32 ASW TT (III × 2); 363: 4/MM 38 Exocet (II × 2)—1/120-mm Bofors L-46 DP—2/40-mm AA (I × 2)—2/20-mm AA (I × 2)—1/NBO-105 helicopter
Electron Equipt:
Radar: 1/Decca AC 1229 nav. , 1/H.S.A. DA-05/2 air/surf. search, 1/WM-28 track-while-scan f.c.
Sonar: PHS-32 (MF)
EW: SUSIE-I intercept—2/Corvus decoy RL (VIII × 2)
M: CODOG: 1 Rolls-Royce Olympus TM-3B gas turbine, 22,360 shp (tropical); 2 MTU 16V956 TB81 diesels; 800 bhp; 2 CP props
Electric: 1,350 kw **Range:** 4,250/16 (diesels)
Crew: 11 officers, 71 enlisted

Remarks: Ordered 8-75. *Nala* has a helicopter deck that folds around the helicopter to form a hangar, two single 40-mm AA instead of one, and *no* ASW torpedo tubes. All have the H.S.A. DAISY computerized combat data system. Have an NBC warfare citadel. Living spaces air-conditioned. Fin stabilizers. Ammunition supply: 400 rounds 120-mm, 3,000 rounds 40-mm, 12 ASW torpedoes, 54 Nelli and Erica ASW rockets, 50 rounds chaff. The GFCS includes a LIROD t.v./laser/infrared backup director.

◆ **6 ex-Dutch Van Speijk class** Bldrs: 351, 352, 356: Nederlandse Dok en Scheepsbouw Mij, Amsterdam; others: Koninklijke Maatschappij de Schelde, Vlissingen

	Laid down	L	In serv.
351 Ahmad Yani (ex-*Tjerk Hiddes*, F 804)	1-6-64	17-12-65	16-8-67
352 Slamet Riyadi (ex-*Van Speijk*, F 802)	1-10-63	5-3-65	14-2-67
353 Yos Sudarso (ex-*Van Galen*, F 803)	25-7-63	19-6-65	1-3-67
354 Oswald Sihaan (ex-*Van Nes*, F 805)	25-7-63	23-6-66	9-8-67
355 Abdul Halim Perdanakasuma (ex-*Evertsen*, F 815)	6-7-65	18-6-66	21-12-67
356 Karel Satsui Tubun (ex-*Isaac Sweers*, F 814)	6-5-65	10-3-67	15-5-68

FRIGATES *(continued)*

Ahmad Yani (351) Ross Gillett, 5-90

Yos Sudarso (353)—Wasp helicopter on deck U.S. Navy, 1990

Abdul Halim Perdanakasuma (355)—note now-empty housing for towed passive sonar array at stern Leo Van Ginderen, 5-90

D: 2,305 tons (2,940 fl) **S:** 28.5 kts
Dim: 113.42 (109.75 pp) × 12.51 × 4.57
A: 4/Harpoon SSM (II × 2—*see* Remarks)—2/Sea Cat SAM systems (IV × 2)—1/76-mm OTO Melara DP—4/12.7-mm mg (I × 4)—6/324-mm ASW TT (III × 2)—1/Wasp HAS.1 helicopter
Electron Equipt:
Radar: 1/Decca TM 1229C nav., 1/ H.S.A. DA-05/2 air/surf. search, 1/H.S.A. LW-03 early warning, 2/H.S.A. M-44f.c. (for Sea Cat), 1/H.S.A. M-45 f.c. (for 76-mm)
Sonar: 1/PHS-32 (MF) hull-mounted
EW: British UA-8 and UA-9 intercept, FH-12 HFD/F, 2/Corvus decoy RL (VIII × 2)
M: 2 sets Werkspoor-English Electric double-reduction geared steam turbines; 2 props; 30,000 shp
Boilers: 2/Babcock & Wilcox; 38.7 kg/cm², 450°C
Range: 4,500/12 **Electric:** 1,900 kw **Crew:** 180 tot.

Remarks: 351 decommissioned 6-1-86 from Dutch Navy, 352 on 13-9-86; both transferred to Indonesia 13-10-86 and 1-11-86, respectively. 353 decommissioned 2-87 for transfer 2-11-87, and 354 decommissioned 2-87 for transfer 11-88. 355 transferred 1-11-89, 356 transferred 1-11-90.

Design based on British *Leander* class, but with broader enclosed bridge and *two* Sea Cat SAM systems, each with a radar director. Major modifications begun 1977, during which the twin, Mk 6, 114-mm DP gun mount was replaced by the OTO Melara Compact 76-mm weapon; the Limbo ASW mortar was deleted and two triple ASW TT were added; the hangar was enlarged, and new sonars, radars, and the SEWACO-II data system were added. Provision was made for carrying up to 8 Harpoon, but only two were normally aboard and the U.S. initially permitted transfer of Harpoon to Indonesia only on 351 and 352, but 353 fired one 11-89, indicating others have been backfitted. U.S. SQR-18A towed passive sonar array removed from 355 and 356 before transfer. Conversions took place: 351: 15-12-78 to 1-6-81; 352: 24-12-76 to 3-1-78; 353: 15-7-77 to 30-11-79; and 354: 31-3-78 to 1-8-80. New infrared suppression stack caps added early 1980s.

◆ **3 ex-U.K. "Tribal" class** Bldrs: 331: Alex Stephen & Sons, Govan; 332: John I. Thornycroft, Ltd., Woolston; 333: HM Dockyard, Devonport

	Laid down	L	In serv.
331 Martha Khristina Tiyahahu (ex-*Zulu,* F 124)	13-12-60	3-7-62	17-4-64
332 Wilhelmus Zakarias Yohannes (ex-*Gurkha,* F 122)	3-11-58	11-7-60	13-2-63
333 Hasanuddin (ex-*Tartar,* F 133)	22-10-59	19-9-60	26-2-62

Wilhelmus Zakarias Yohannes (332) R.A.N., 4-

Hasanuddin (333) Leo Van Ginderen,

FRIGATES *(continued)*

D: 2,300 tons (2,700 fl) **S:** 24 kts
Dim: 109.73 (106.68 pp) × 12.95 × 3.80 (5.30 props)
A: 2/114-mm Mk 5 DP (I × 2)—2/Sea Cat GWS.21 syst. (IV × 2)—2/20-mm Oerlikon AA (I × 2)—2/12.7-mm mg (I × 2)—1/Limbo Mk 10 ASW mortar (III × 2)—1/d.c. rack (3 d.c.)—1/Wasp HAS.1 helicopter (Mk 44/46 torpedoes)
Electron Equipt:
Radar: 1/Type 978 nav., 1/Type 993 air/surf. search, 1/Type 965 early warning, 1/Type 903 gun f.c., 2/ Type 262 missile f.c.
Sonar: Graseby Type 177 hull-mounted search (7–9 kHz), Graseby Type 17OB hull-mounted attack (15 kHz), Kelvin-Hughes Type 162 bottomed target classification (50 kHz)
EW: . . . intercept, 2/Corvus decoy RL (VIII × 2)
M: COSAG: 1 set Metrovik geared steam turbines (15,000 shp) and 1 A.E.I. gas turbine (7,500 shp); 1/5-bladed prop; 22,500 shp
Boilers: 1 Babcock & Wilcox 3-drum; 38.7 kg/cm^2, 450° C
Range: 5,400/12 **Crew:** 26 officers, 242 enlisted

Remarks: Survivors of a class of seven Royal Navy "General-Purpose" frigates, stricken 3-84 after having been recommissioned because of the Falklands War. Purchased by Indonesia 16-4-84 and towed to Vosper Thornycroft, Woolston, for overhaul/modernization during April–June 1984. 331 began post-refit trials 22-3-85 and recommissioned 2-5-85; 332 recommissioned 21-10-85. 333 redelivered 22-1-86 and commissioned 3-4-86.

Twin rudders, one pair fin stabilizers. The helicopter flight deck has a small hangar beneath, into which the aircraft is lowered by elevator; the resultant hole is covered with segmented panels normally stowed beside the Limbo mortar position. MRS.3 director with Type 903 radar for the 114-mm guns, two modified MRS.8 directors with Type 262 radars for the Sea Cat systems. 332 had Type 199 variable-depth sonar removed prior to transfer.

♦ **4 ex-U.S. Claud Jones class** Bldrs: 341, 343: Avondale Marine, Westwego, La.; 342, 344: American SB, Toledo, Ohio—In reserve

	L	In serv.
341 SAMADIKUN (ex-*John R. Perry,* DE 1034)	29-7-58	5-5-59
342 MARTADINATA (ex-*Charles Berry,* DE 1035)	17-3-59	25-11-60
343 MONGISIDI (ex-*Claud Jones,* DE 1033)	27-5-58	10-2-59
344 NGURAH RAI (ex-*McMorris,* DE 1036)	26-5-59	4-3-60

D: 1,720 tons (1,970 fl) **S:** 22 kts
Dim: 95.10 (91.75 wl) × 11.84 × 3.70 (hull)/5.54 (sonar)
A: 1 or 2/76.2-mm DP (I × 1 or 2)—0 or 2/37-mm AA (II × 1)—0 or 2/25-mm AA (II × 1)—6/324-mm ASW Mk 32 TT (III × 2)—341 also: 2/Mk 11 Hedgehog ASW spigot mortars (XXIV × 2)—4/Mk 6 DCT—1/Mk 9 d.c. rack (18 total d.c.)

urah Rai (344) Ross Gillett, 11-84

idikun (341) Airfoto, 5-86

Electron Equipt:
Radar: 1/Decca 1226 nav., 1/SPS-10 surf. search, 1/SPS-6 air search, 1/SPG-52 f.c.
Sonar: 341: EDO 786; 342: SQS-45 (V); 343: SQS-39 (V); 344: SQS-42 (V) hull-mounted, medium-freq.
EW: WLR-1 intercept (not in 341)
M: 4 Fairbanks-Morse 38ND8 $^1/_8$ diesels; 1 prop; 9,240 bhp
Electric: 600 kw **Range:** 3,590/22; 10,300/9 **Fuel:** 296 tons
Crew: 12 officers, 159 enlisted

Remarks: No. 341 was transferred on 20-2-73, No. 342 on 31-1-74, Nos. 343 and 344 on 16-12-74. Nos. 341 and 342 have a twin Soviet 37-mm AA in place of one 76.2-mm on fantail and a twin 25-mm at the forecastle break, abaft the stack. Navigational radar added 1980–81. Have Mk 70 Mod. 2 GFCS, Mk 105 ASW FCS. 341 has no EW equipment but does have additional ASW ordnance. Refitted 1979–82 at Subic Bay Naval Station, the Philippines.

GUIDED-MISSILE PATROL BOATS

♦ **4 PSK Mk 5 class** Bldr: Korea-Tacoma SY, Masan, Korea

	In serv.		In serv.
621 MANDAU	20-7-79	623 BADEK	2-80
622 RENCONG	20-7-79	624 KERIS	2-80

Mandau (621) *Ships of the World,* 1990

Keris (624)—alongside tanker *Sambu* (902) Ross Gillett, 11-84

D: 250 tons (290 fl) **S:** 41 kts **Dim:** 53.58 × 8.00 × 1.63 (hull)
A: 4/MM 38 Exocet (II × 2)—1/57-mm Bofors DP—1/40-mm Bofors AA—2/20-mm Rheinmetall AA (I × 2)
Electron Equipt: Radar: 1/Decca AC 1229 nav. , 1/H.S.A. WM-28 f.c.
M: CODOG: 1 G.E.-Fiat LM-2500 gas turbine, 25,000 shp; 2 MTU 12V331 TC81 diesels, 1,120 bhp each; 2 CP props
Range: 2,500/17 **Electric:** 400 kw
Crew: 7 officers, 36 enlisted

Remarks: First unit laid down 5-77. Modification of U.S. *Asheville*-class design. A second group of four were not ordered as planned. Have Selenia NA-18 optronic backup gun director. 623 and 624 have electronic intercept gear.

PATROL BOATS

♦ **4 Lürssen PB 57 design search-and-rescue boats**
Bldrs: Friedrich Lürssen, Vegesack, and P.T. PAL SY, Surabaja

	In serv.		In serv.
811 KAKAP	29-6-88	813 BERVANG	26-2-89
812 KERAPU	8-88	814 TONGKOL	1-90

D: 356 tons at half load (425 fl) **S:** 30.5 kts (28.1 sust.)
Dim: 58.10 (54.40 wl) × 7.62 × 2.73 (prop)
A: 1/40-mm Bofors SAK 40 AA—2/7.62-mm mg (I × 2)
Electron Equipt: Radar: 1/Decca 2459 nav.
M: 2 MTU 16V956 TB92 diesels; 2 props; 8,260 bhp
Range: 2,200/28; 6,100/15 **Endurance:** 15 days
Electric: 270 kVA (2 × 135 kVA, 450 v, 60 Hz)
Crew: 9 officers, 40 enlisted + 8 spare berths

PATROL BOATS *(continued)*

Kakap (811)—with NBO-105 helo on deck Leo Van Ginderen, 5-90

Kerapu (812) Mike Louagie, 5-90

Remarks: Ordered 1982, with midbody sections for first two shipped from Germany. Manned and operated by the Indonesian Navy for the Customs Service, which paid for them. Intended for search-and-rescue and inspection duties. Helicopter deck 13 × 7.1 m for one NBO-105. Carry 1,000 rds 40-mm ammunition. Two water cannon with 294 m^3/hour capacity, 70-m range. Two rescue launches stowed aft.

◆ **4 (+. . .) Lürssen PB 57 design** Bldr: Lürssen, Vegesack, and P.T. PAL SY, Surabaja

	L	In serv.		L	In serv.
650 Andau	15-4-86	4-88	652 Tongkak	. . .	4-4-89
651 Singa	1-10-86	8-88	653 Ajak	. . .	4-4-89

Singa (651) R.A.N., 5-90

Ajak (653) Leo Van Ginderen, 5-90

D: 423 tons (fl) **S:** 27.25 kts
Dim: 58.10 (54.40 wl) × 7.62 × 2.73 (prop)
A: 1/57-mm Bofors SAK 2 DP—1/Bofors SAK 40 AA—2/20-mm Rheinmetall AA (I × 2)—2/533-mm TT (aft-firing, 2 reloads; AEG SUT wire-guided torpedoes)
Electron Equipt:
Radar: 1/Decca 2459 nav.; 1/H.S.A. WM 22 track-while-scan f.c.
Sonar: H.S.A. PHS-32 (MF) hull-mounted
EW: 650, 651: Thomson-CSF DR 2000 S3 intercept, 1/Dagaie decoy RL (XVIII × 1)
M: 2 MTU 16V956 TB92 diesels; 2 props; 8,260 bhp
Range: 2,200/27; 6,100/15 **Endurance:** 15 days **Fuel:** 110 tons
Electric: 324 kw (3 × 108 kw) **Crew:** 9 officers, 44 enlisted

Remarks: Midbody for 650 shipped from Germany 1-84 for addition of bow, stern, and armament in Indonesia. Second unit shipped 7-84. Other pair built entirely in Indonesia. Planned production of four more in 414-ton full load gunboat version without ASW equipment has not materialized. Have H.S.A. LIOD 73 optronic director for 57-mm gun, Dalia signal analyzer for EW suite.

Note: Of the five Boeing Jetfoil Model 929 hydrofoils listed in previous editions, the prototype is in fact fitted out as a personnel transport, and the four delivered in 1986 by Boeing to P.T. PAL (P.T. Pabrik Kapal) for fitting out have had no work accomplished and can be considered to have been abandoned. The remaining units of the Carpentaria-class patrol craft have been transferred to the marine police.

◆ **2 Indonesian design** Bldr: P.T. PAL, Surabaja (In serv. 1983)

860 . . . . 861 . . . .

Patrol boat 861 George R. Schneider, Jr., 9-8?

D: approx. 150 tons (fl) **S:** 20 kts **Dim:** 32.0 × . . . × . . .
A: 1/40-mm Mk 3 AA—2/12.7-mm mg (I × 2)
Electron Equipt: Radar: 1/Decca . . . nav.
M: 2 . . . . . . diesels; 2 props; . . . bhp **Crew:** 22 tot.

Remarks: Design appears to be based on that of the *Attack* class, but they have lowe[r] freeboard, more massive superstructure, and no bow bulwarks.

◆ **8 Australian Attack class** Bldrs: 847, 848, 859, 862: Walkers Ltd.; others: Evans Deakin, Ltd.

	Laid down	L	In serv.
847 Sibaru (ex-*Bandolier*)	7-68	2-10-68	14-12-68
848 Suliman (ex-*Archer*)	7-67	2-12-67	15-5-68
857 Sigalu (ex-*Barricade*)	12-67	29-6-68	26-10-68
858 Silea (ex-*Acute*)	4-67	29-8-67	26-4-68
859 Siribua (ex-*Bombard*)	4-68	6-7-68	5-11-68
862 Siada (ex-*Barbette*)	11-67	10-4-68	16-8-68
863 Sikuda (ex-*Attack*)	9-66	8-4-67	17-11-67
864 Sigurot (ex-*Assail*)	. . .	18-11-67	12-7-68

D: 146 tons (fl) **S:** 21 kts
Dim: 32.76 (30.48 pp) × 6.2 × 1.9
A: 1/40-mm Bofors AA—1/7.62-mm mg
Electron Equipt: Radar: 1/Decca RM 916 nav.
M: 2 Davey-Paxman Ventura 16 YJCM diesels; 3,460 bhp
Range: 1,220/13 **Fuel:** 20 tons **Crew:** 3 officers, 19 enlisted

Silea (858) George R. Schneider, Jr.,

PATROL BOATS *(continued)*

Remarks: Light-alloys superstructure. Air-conditioned. 847 transferred 16-11-73, 848 in 1974, 857 on 22-4-82, 858 on 6-5-83, 859 later in 1983, 862 on 2-2-85, 863 on 24-5-85, and 864 on 30-1-86.

Note: The last three Yugoslav PBR-500-class submarine chasers, *Kayang* (819), *Dorang* (822), and *Todak* (823), were placed in reserve in 1989 for probable disposal in the near future.

PATROL CRAFT

♦ **18 Kal Kangean class** Bldr: P.T. PAL (In serv. 1987–90)

1101–1118

D: 44.7 tons (fl) **S:** 18 kts **Dim:** 24.5 × 4.3 × 1.0
A: 2/25-mm Soviet 2M-8 AA (II × 1)—2/14.5-mm Soviet 2M-7 AA (II × 1)
Electron Equipt: Radar: 1/. . . nav. **M:** 2 diesels; 2 props; . . . bhp
Range: . . ./. . . **Crew:** . . . tot.

Remarks: Ordered 1984. Make use of surplus Soviet mounts removed from discarded Indonesian Navy ships and craft. Very low freeboard limits seaworthiness.

Note: The Australian-built Carpentaria-class patrol craft have been transferred to the Maritime Police.

MINE COUNTERMEASURES SHIPS

♦ **2 Alkmaar ("Tripartite")-class minehunters** Bldr: Van der Giessen de Noord, Alblasserdam, the Netherlands

	Laid down	L	In serv.
711 Pulau Rengat (ex-*Willemstad*)	29-3-85	23-7-87	26-3-88
712 Pulau Rupat (ex-*Vlardingen*)	22-7-85	27-8-87	26-3-88

Pulau Rengat (711)—portable decompression chamber aft — Mike Louagie, 6-88

D: 510 tons (568 fl) **S:** 15.5 kts
Dim: 51.50 (47.10 pp) × 8.90 × 2.47 (2.62 max.)
A: 2/20-mm Rheinmetall AA (I × 2)
Electron Equipt:
Radar: 1/Decca AC 1229 nav.—Sonar: Thomson-Sintra TSM 2022
M: 2 MTU 12V396 TCDb51 diesels; 2 CP props; 1,900 bhp—2/75-hp bow-thrusters; 2/120-hp Schottel active rudders (7 kts)
Electric: 910 kw (3 × 250 kw, 1 × 160 kw) **Endurance:** 15 days
Range: 3,500/10; 3,000/12 **Crew:** 46 tot.

Remarks: Ordered 29-3-85 and 30-8-85; taken from Royal Netherlands Navy production. Both left for Indonesia 18-8-88. Planned construction of up to ten more in Indonesia has been delayed by lack of funds. Indonesia is obviously lacking in mine countermeasures capability.

Glass-reinforced plastic construction. Carry two PAP-104 MK 5 remote-controlled minehunting/destruction submersibles. Have TSM 2060 plot, TMV628 Trident III radio location system. Sweep equipment includes Fiskars F-82 magnetic sweep tail, SA Marine AS203 acoustic gear, and OD-3 mechanical sweep; there are two sweep-gear cranes. The minehunting system is the Thomson-CSF IBIS V. Guns located on forecastle and abaft superstructure.

AMPHIBIOUS WARFARE SHIPS

Note: Other Indonesian Navy–operated amphibious warfare-capable ships and craft listed later in the Military Sealift Command (KOLINLAMIL) section.

♦ **6 Teluk Semangka-class tank landing ships** Bldr: Korea-Tacoma SY, Masan, South Korea

	In serv.		In serv.
512 Teluk Semangka	20-1-81	515 Teluk Sampit	1981
513 Teluk Penyu	20-1-81	516 Teluk Banten	5-82
514 Teluk Mandar	7-81	517 Teluk Ende	2-9-82

D: 1,800 tons (3,770 fl) **S:** 15 kts
Dim: 100.0 × 15.4 × 4.2 (3.0 mean)

Teluk Banten (516)—command version with helicopter hangar, raised poop/helicopter deck aft, boats forward of superstructure, and engine exhausts at waterline — 1982

Teluk Penyu (513)—boat davits and engine exhaust stack stop after superstructure, helo pads fore and aft — R.A.N., 1985

A: 2/40-mm Bofors AA (I × 2)—2/20-mm Rheinmetall AA (I × 2)
Electron Equipt: Radar: 1/. . . nav.
M: 2 diesels; 2 props; 6,860 bhp (5,600 sust.) **Electric:** 750 kw
Range: 7,500/13 **Crew:** 13 officers, 104 enlisted + 202 troops

Remarks: First four ordered 6-79; two more, modified as command ships and fitted with helicopter hangars, ordered in 6-81.

Beaching load: 690 tons (17 main battle tanks), or up to 1,800 tons max. Helicopter decks amidships and aft (aft only on 516, 517). Carry 4 LCVP landing craft. There is a 50-ton-capacity turntable in the tank deck and an elevator to the upper deck. 516 and 517 have a large hangar incorporated in the superstructure, the helicopter deck raised one level, the forward helicopter positions deleted, the landing craft davits moved forward of the superstructure, and increased command facilities to act as flagships; they can carry three NAS.332 Super Puma helicopters. One from the initial quartet has been equipped to act as a hospital ship.

♦ **5 ex-U.S. LST 542-class tank landing ships** Bldrs: Chicago Bridge & Iron Wks., Seneca, Ill., except 509 and 511: American Bridge, Ambridge, Pa.

	Laid down	L	In serv.
501 Teluk Langsa (ex-LST 1128)	23-11-44	19-2-45	9-3-45
504 Teluk Kau (ex-LST 652)	24-7-44	19-10-44	1-1-45
509 Teluk Sindoro (ex-M/V *Inagua Shipper*, ex-*Presque Isle*, APB 44, ex-LST 678)	29-4-44	16-6-44	30-6-44
510 Teluk Saleh (ex-*Clarke County*, LST 601)	21-10-43	4-3-44	25-3-44
511 Teluk Bone (ex-*Iredell County*, LST 839)	25-9-44	12-11-44	6-12-44

D: 1,650 tons light (4,080 fl) **S:** 11.6 kts
Dim: 99.98 × 15.24 × 4.29
A: 6 or 7/40-mm or 37-mm AA (I × 6 or 7)
M: 2 G.M. 12-567A diesels; 2 props; 1,800 bhp **Electric:** 300 kw
Fuel: 590 tons **Range:** 6,000/9 (loaded)
Crew: 119 ship's company + 264 troops

Remarks: Transferred in 3-60, 1961, and Nos. 510 and 511 in 7-70 under the Military Assistance Program. Can carry 2,100 tons of cargo. Sisters *Teluk Bayer* and *Teluk Tomani* are in the Military Sealift Command, as is the Japanese-built near-sister *Teluk Amboina*. Are not likely to remain effective much longer. Information in previous edition that five sisters had been purchased from Singapore was erroneous.

♦ **20 U.S. LCM (6)-class landing craft** Bldr: . . . SY, Taiwan (In serv. 1988)

D: 24 tons (57.5 fl) **S:** 13 kts light **Dim:** 17.07 × 4.37 × 1.14
M: 2 G.M. Detroit Diesel 6V71 diesels; 2 props; 450 bhp
Range: 130/9 loaded **Crew:** 5 tot. + 80 troops

AMPHIBIOUS WARFARE SHIPS *(continued)*

Remarks: GRP construction. Cargo: 30 tons. Cargo well 11.9 × 3.7 m. Also available are approximately 24 LCVP-type landing craft, 10 wooden-hulled aboard the old U.S.-built LSTs, and 18 GRP-hulled delivered with the Korean-built LSTs.

HYDROGRAPHIC SHIPS

♦ **1 Burudjulasad class** Bldr: Schlichtingwerft, Travemünde

931 Burudjulasad (L: 8-65; In serv. 1967)

Burudjulasad (931) 1981

D: 1,815 tons (2,165 fl) **S:** 19 kts
Dim: 82.00 (78.00 pp) × 11.40 × 3.50
Electron Equipt: Radar: 1/Decca TM 262 nav.
M: 4 M.A.N. V6V 22/30 diesels; 2 CP props; 6,400 bhp
Electric: 1,008 kw **Fuel:** 600 tons **Range:** 14,500/15.7
Crew: 15 officers, 93 enlisted, 28 technicians

Remarks: Can carry one light helicopter and is equipped to perform oceanographic and hydrometeorological research as well as to perform hydrographic surveys. Carries one LCVP landing craft and three hydrographic launches. Refitted in U.K. 3- to 10-86.

♦ **1 U.K. Hecla class** Bldr: Yarrow & Co., Blythswood

	Laid down	L	In serv.
932 Dewa Kembar (ex-*Hydra,* A144)	14-5-64	14-7-65	5-5-66

Dewa Kembar (932) Leo Van Ginderen, 9-86

D: 1,915 tons (2,733 fl) **S:** 14 kts
Dim: 79.25 (71.63 pp) × 14.94 × 4.00
Electron Equipt:
Radar: 2/Decca 1226 nav.—Sonar: Type 2034 sidescan
M: diesel-electric: 3 Paxman Ventura diesels (12 cyl.) 1,280 bhp each; 2 electric motors; 1 prop; 2,000 shp
Range: 12,000/11; 20,000/9 **Fuel:** 450 tons
Crew: 14 officers, 109 enlisted

Remarks: Purchased 18-4-86, refitted by Vosper Thornycroft, Southampton, 24-4-86 to 16-7-86. Recommissioned 10-9-86 and left for Indonesia 1-10-86. Bow-thruster, hangar, and platform for light helicopter. Retains MARISAT satellite communications gear. Carries two survey launches.

♦ **1 hydrometeorological and oceanographic research ship**
Bldr: Sasebo Heavy Industries, Japan

933 Jalanidhi (In serv. 12-1-63)

D: 740 tons (985 fl) **S:** 12.7 kts
Dim: 53.9 (48.5 pp) × 9.5 × 4.3
Electron Equipt: Radar: 1/. . . nav.
M: 1 M.A.N. G6V 30/42 diesel; 1,000 bhp **Electric:** 261 kw
Fuel: 165 tons **Range:** 7,200/10.5
Crew: 13 officers, 74 enlisted + 26 technician/scientists

Remarks: Weather-balloon facility aft.

Jalanidhi (933) French Navy, 1991

AUXILIARY SHIPS

♦ **1 command ship** Bldr: Ishikawajima Harima, Tokyo, Japan

561 Multatuli (L: 13-6-61)

Multatuli (561) John Jedrlinic, 198

D: 3,220 tons (6,741 fl) **S:** 18.5 kts
Dim: 111.35 (103.0 pp) × 16.0 × 6.98
A: 6/37-mm Soviet V-47M AA (II × 2, I × 2)—4/14.5-mm 2M-7 AA (II × 2)
Electron Equipt: Radar: 1/. . . nav.
M: 1 Burmeister & Wain diesel; 5,500 bhp **Fuel:** 1,400 tons
Range: 6,000/16 **Crew:** 134 tot.

Remarks: Built as a submarine-support ship, converted as a fleet command ship i the late 1960s. Has a helicopter platform aft. Equipped with British ICS-3 integrate communications suite. Can supply fuel and stores to ships in company. Construction two similar ships of about 10,000 tons, to carry fuel, troops, and hospital facilities, planned.

Note: The Soviet-built Don-class submarine tender *Ratulangi* (400) was stricke 11-89.

♦ **1 ex-U.S. Achelous-class repair ship** Bldr: Chicago Bridge & Iron, Seneca, Illinois

	Laid down	L	In ser
921 Jaja Widjaja (ex-*Askari,* ARL 30, ex-LST 1131)	8-12-44	2-3-45	15-3-

Jaja Widjaja (921)

D: 2,130 (3,640 fl) **S:** 11 kts **Dim:** 99.98 × 15.24 × 4.25
A: 8/40-mm AA (IV × 2) **Electron Equipt:** Radar: 1/. . . nav.
M: 2 G.M. 12-267A diesels; 2 props; 1,800 bhp
Electric: 520 kw **Fuel:** 590 tons **Crew:** 11 officers, 169 enlisted

Remarks: Leased 31-8-71; purchased 22-2-79. Cargo capacity: 300 tons.

♦ **1 replenishment oiler** Bldr: Trogir SY, Yugoslavia

911 Sorong (In serv. 4-65)

AUXILIARY SHIPS *(continued)*

Sorong (911) 1979

D: 5,100 (dwt) **S:** 15 kts **Dim:** 112.17 × 15.4 × 6.6
A: 4/12.7-mm mg (II × 2) **Electron Equipt:** Radar: 1/. . . nav.
M: 1 diesel; 1 prop; . . . bhp **Crew:** 110 tot.

Remarks: Cargo: 3,000 tons fuel/300 tons water. Can conduct underway replenishments.

♦ **1 ex-Soviet Khobi-class coastal oiler**

909 Pakan Baru (In serv. 1959)

D: 1,525 tons (fl) **S:** 12.7 kts **Dim:** 67.4 (63.7 pp) × 10.0 × 4.4
M: 2 diesels; 2 props; 1,600 bhp **Range:** 2,500/12.5

Remarks: 795 grt/834 dwt. Cargo: 700 tons fuel oil. Two sisters discarded.

♦ **1 sail-training barkentine** Bldr: Stülcken, Hamburg

Dewarugi (L: 21-1-52; in serv. 9-7-53)

ewarugi R.A.N., 5-90

D: 847 tons fl **S:** 9 kts **Dim:** 58.30 (41.50 pp) × 9.5 × 4.23
M: 1 M.A.N. diesel; 575 bhp
Crew: 110 ship's company, 78 cadets

marks: Steel construction. Sail area: 1,091 m². Placed in reserve in 1991 but will bably be retained due to her fame as a worldwide cruising vessel.

1 Jetfoil Model 929 hydrofoil personnel ferry

	Bldr	L	In serv.
. Bima Samudera I	Boeing, Seattle	22-10-81	14-12-81

: 115 tons (fl) **S:** 46 kts
im: 27.4 (foils down) × 9.1 × 1.9 (5.2 foils down, 2.0 max. foiling)
lectron Equipt: Radar: 1/Decca . . . nav.

a Samudera I Boeing, 1981

M: 2 Allison 501-K20A gas turbines; 2 Rocketdyne R-20 waterjet pumps; 7,560 hp—2 G.M. 8V92 TI diesels; 2 props; 900 bhp for hull-borne cruise
Range: 900/40; 1,500/15 **Fuel:** 33.4 tons
Crew: 6 tot. + 260 passengers

Remarks: *Bima Samudera I* was purchased by the Indonesian Agency for the Development and Application of Technology for evaluating such a craft in naval patrol, logistics support, and civil roles. Naval-manned. Delivered in-country 2-82. Has enhanced fuel tankage over standard commercial model. Aluminum construction.

The hydrofoil contract with Boeing Marine Services called for two each of two versions of the basic Jetfoil design, with completion taking place at P.T. Pabrik Kapal (P.T. PAL), Indonesia. Another 6 craft were on option, and a total of 47 was once foreseen. The first production boat was laid down 10-12-83. The first two were delivered 1-85 to P.T. PAL for outfitting and completion by 1986 as troop transports to carry up to 100 troops and be armed with a 20-mm AA and 2/12.7-mm mg (I × 2). Numbers 3 and 4, intended as gunboats, were completed by Boeing 6-3-86 and 23-7-86, but were delivered unoutfitted and, like 1 and 2, remain laid up incomplete. Further craft of this type are no longer programmed.

♦ **1 ex-U.S. Cherokee-class fleet tug** Bldr: United Eng., Alameda, Cal.

	Laid down	L	In serv.
922 Rakata (ex-U.S. *Menominee,* ATF 73)	27-9-41	14-2-42	25-9-42

D: 1,640 tons (fl) **S:** 15 kts **Dim:** 62.5 × 11.7 × 4.7
A: 1/76.2-mm U.S. Mk 26 DP—2/40-mm U.S. Mk 3 AA (I × 2)— 4/25-mm Soviet 2M-8 AA (II × 2)
Electron Equipt: Radar: 1/. . . nav. **Electric:** 260 kw tot.
M: 4 G.M. 12-278A diesels, Allis-Chalmers electric drive; 1 prop; 3,000 shp
Range: 6,500/16; 15,000/8 **Fuel:** 315 tons **Crew:** 67 tot.

Remarks: Transferred 3-61. Placed in reserve 1990 and unlikely to see further active service.

♦ **1 coastal tug** Bldr: Ishikawajima Harima, Tokyo (L: 4-61)

934 Lampo Batang

D: 250 tons **S:** 11 kts **Dim:** 28.1 × 7.6 × 2.6
M: 2 M.A.N. diesels; 2 props; 600 bhp
Range: 1,000/11 **Fuel:** 18 tons **Crew:** 13 tot.

♦ **2 Tambora-class coastal tugs** Bldr: Ishikawajima Harima, Tokyo (both L: 6-61)

935 Tambora 936 Bromo

D: 250 tons (fl) **S:** 10.5 kts **Dim:** 24.1 × 6.6 × 3.0
M: 2 M.A.N. diesels; 2 props; 600 bhp
Range: 690/10.5 **Fuel:** 9 tons **Crew:** 15 tot.

MILITARY SEALIFT COMMAND (KOLINLAMIL)

Formed in 1978 to coordinate the Indonesian Navy's logistic support for its far-flung bases and outposts in the Indonesian Archipelago. Some of the units have been taken over from the Indonesian Army and others from the Navy.

AMPHIBIOUS LOGISTICS TRANSPORTS

♦ **1 tank landing ship** Bldr: Sasebo Heavy Industries, Japan

503 Teluk Amboina (L: 17-3-61)

Teluk Amboina (503) Leo Van Ginderen, 11-88

D: 4,145 tons (fl) **S:** 13 kts **Dim:** 99.9 × 15.2 × 4.6
A: 6/37-mm Soviet V-47M AA (I × 6)
M: 2 M.A.N. V6V 22.30 diesels; 2 props; 3,200 bhp (2,850 sust.)
Electric: 135 kw **Fuel:** 1,200 tons **Range:** 4,000/13
Crew: 88 ship's company + 212 passengers

Remarks: Built as reparations. Near duplicate of U.S. LST 542 design. Cargo: 2,100 tons maximum; can carry 654 tons cargo water. Has a 30-ton crane, davits for four LCVPs.

AMPHIBIOUS LOGISTICS TRANSPORTS *(continued)*

♦ **2 ex-U.S. LST 542-class tank landing ships** Bldr: 502: Chicago Bridge & Iron, Seneca, Ill.; 508: American Bridge, Ambridge, Pennsylvania

	Laid down	L	In serv.
502 TELUK BAJER (ex-LST 616)	12-2-44	12-5-44	29-5-44
508 TELUK RATAI (ex-*Teluk Tomini*, ex-*Inagua Crest*, ex-*Brunei*, ex-*Polk County*, LST 356)	27-11-44	19-1-45	19-2-45

D: 1,650 tons (4,080 fl) **S:** 11 kts **Dim:** 99.98 × 15.24 × 4.29
A: none **M:** 2 G.M. 12-567A diesels; 2 props; 1,800 bhp
Fuel: 590 tons **Range:** 6,000/9 (loaded)
Crew: 119 ship's company + 264 passengers (502)

Remarks: *Teluk Ratai* is used as a cattle-carrier and does not carry passengers (by mutual agreement?). Both acquired around 1961. Cargo: approx. 2,100 tons max.

♦ **3 Kupang-class utility landing craft** Bldr: Surabaja DY

582 KUPANG (In serv. 3-11-78) 584 NUSANTARA (In serv. 1980)
583 DILI (In serv. 27-2-79)

D: 400 tons (fl) **S:** 11 kts **Dim:** 42.9 (36.27 pp) × 9.14 × 1.80
M: 4 diesels; 2 props; 1,200 bhp **Range:** 700/11 **Crew:** 17 tot.

Remarks: Based on U.S. LCU 1610 class. Cargo: 200 tons. 582 is used as a diving and salvage tender.

♦ **2 Amurang-class landing craft** Bldr: Korneuberg SY, Austria (In serv. 1968)

580 DORE 581 AMURANG

D: 182 tons (255 fl) **S:** 8 kts **Dim:** 38.30 (36.00 pp) × 10.00 × 1.30
M: 2 diesels; 2 props; 420 bhp **Range:** 600/8 **Crew:** 12 tot.

Remarks: 200 grt. Sister *Banten* and one other in merchant service.

TANKERS

♦ **1 small tanker** Bldr: . . . . . . , Japan (In serv. 1969)

902 SAMBU (ex-*Taiyo Maru No. 3*)

Sambu (902)—with missile boats *Keris* (624) and *Rencong* (622) alongside Ross Gillett, 11-84

D: 2,800 tons (fl) **S:** 11 kts **Dim:** 70.4 × 11.4 × 5.8
A: 4/14.5-mm mg (II × 2)
Electron Equipt: Radar: 1/. . . nav.
M: 1 diesel; 1 prop; . . . bhp **Crew:** . . . tot.

Remarks: Purchased 1978.

♦ **1 small tanker** Bldr: . . . SY, Japan (In serv. 1965)

BALIKPAPAN (ex-*Komado V*)

D: . . . **S:** 11 kts **Dim:** 69.6 × 9.6 × 4.9
Electron Equipt: Radar: 1/. . . nav.
M: 1 diesel; 1 prop; 1,300 bhp **Crew:** 26 tot.

Remarks: 1,780-dwt commercial tanker purchased 1977.

CARGO SHIPS

♦ **2 Hungarian Tisza-class cargo ships** Bldr: Angyalfold SY, Budapest

959 TELUK MENTAWI 960 KARAMAJA

D: 2,000 tons (fl) **S:** 12 kts **Dim:** 74.5 (67.4 pp) × 11.3 × 4.6
A: some ships: 4/14.5-mm mg (II × 2)
M: 1 Lang 8-cyl. diesel; 1,000 bhp **Electric:** 746 kw
Range: 4,200/10.7 **Fuel:** 98 tons **Crew:** 26 tot.

Remarks: Transferred 1963–64. Taken over from the army in 1978. Had originally been naval. 1,296 grt/1,280 dwt. Cargo: 1,100 tons. Sisters *Telaud* (951), *Nusatelu* (952), *Natuna* (953), and *Karamundsa* (957) stricken by 1991.

♦ **. . . coastal cargo lighters** Bldr: Fasharkan DY, Manokwari, Irian

D: . . . **S:** 8 kts **Dim:** 31.1 × 6.26 × 1.80 **M:** diesels

Remarks: 200 dwt. First unit delivered 7-3-82. Others may have been built.

PERSONNEL TRANSPORTS

♦ **1 former passenger-cargo ship** Bldr: N.V. Scheepswerfen Machinefabrik de Merwede, Hardinxveld, the Netherlands (In serv. 1959)

972 TANJUNG OISINA (ex-*Tjut Njak Dhien*, ex-*Prinses Irene*)

D: . . . **S:** 16.5 kts **Dim:** 139.92 × 18.67 × 8.61
Electron Equipt: Radar: 2/Decca 1226 nav.
M: diesels; 1 prop; 8,600 bhp **Crew:** 94 tot.

Remarks: 8,456 grt/8,618 dwt. Purchased 1978 for use as a transport.

♦ **1 former pilgrim transport** Bldr: Blohm + Voss, Hamburg (In serv. 1936)

971 TANJUNG PANDAN (ex-*Genung Djati*, ex-*Empire Orwell*, ex-*Empire Doon*, ex-*Pretoria*)

D: 16,067 tons (fl) **S:** **Dim:** 175.8 (167.6 pp) × 22.0 × . . .
M: 8 sets geared steam turbines; 4 props; . . . shp **Crew:** 125 tot.

Remarks: 17,362 grt. Former German liner, used as a barracks during W.W. II; t U.K. in 1945, used as a troopship, then transport for religious pilgrims. Sold to Indone sia 1962. Acquired 1981 for Kolinlamil, but has remained immobile at Tanjung Priok

SEA COMMUNICATIONS AGENCY

Established in 1978 to patrol Indonesia's 200-nautical-mile economic zone and maintain navigational aids. Full name: Indonesian Directorate General of Sea Com munication/Department of Transport, Communications and Tourism.

PATROL BOATS

♦ **4 Golok class** Bldr: Schlichtingwerft, Harmsdorf, Germany

	In serv.		In serv.
PAT 206 GOLOK	12-3-82	PAT 208 PEDANG	12-5-82
PAT 207 PANAN	12-3-82	PAT 209 KAPAK	12-5-82

D: 200 tons (fl) **S:** 28 kts **Dim:** 37.50 × 7.00 × 2.00
A: 1/20-mm AA **Range:** 1,500/18 **Crew:** 18 tot.
M: 2 MTU 16V652 TB61 diesels; 2 props; 4,200 bhp

Remarks: Intended for search-and-rescue duties. 120 m^3/hr. fire pump and wa monitor, rescue launch, 8-man sick bay. Hulls built by Deutsche Industrie Wer Berlin.

♦ **5 Kujang class** Bldr: SFCN, Villeneuve-la-Garenne, France

	Laid down	L	In serv.
PAT 201 KUJANG	5-80	17-10-80	19-8-81
PAT 202 PARANG	7-80	18-11-80	19-8-81
PAT 203 CELURIT	9-80	20-3-81	1981
PAT 204 CUNDRIK	7-9-80	10-11-80	1981
PAT 205 BELATI	2-81	21-5-81	10-81

Kujang (PAT 201) SFCN,

D: 126 tons (162 fl) **S:** 28 kts
Dim: 38.32 (35.46 pp) × 6.00 × 1.78 (2.60 props)
A: 1/12.7-mm mg **Electron Equipt:** Radar: 1/ . . . nav.
M: 2 S.A.C.M. AGO V12 195 CZ SHR T5; 2 props; 4,400 bhp
Range: 1,500/18 **Crew:** 18 tot.

Remarks: Equipped for search-and-rescue duties.

PATROL BOATS *(continued)*

◆ **6 PAT-01-class patrol craft** Bldr: Tanjung Priok SY, 1978–79

PAT 01 to PAT 06

D: 12 tons (fl) **S:** 14 kts **Dim:** 12.15 × 4.25 × 1.0
A: 1/7.62-mm mg **M:** 1 Renault diesel; 260 bhp

PERSONNEL TRANSPORTS

◆ **2 (+1) Tatamailau class** Bldr: Joseph L. Meyer GmbH & Co., Papenburg, Germany

Tatamailau (In serv. 30-11-90) Sirimau (In serv. 1991)
Awu (In serv. 1992)

D: . . . **S:** 15 kts **Dim:** 99.80 (90.50 pp) × 18.30 × 4.20
M: 2 MaK 6M453C diesels; 2 CP props; 4,300 bhp **Crew:** . . . tot.

Remarks: 6,041 grt/1,400 dwt. Equipped as troop transports.

◆ **2 Lawit class** Bldr: Joseph L. Meyer GmbH & Co., Papenburg, Germany

Lawit (In serv. 7-86) Kelimutu (In serv. 7-86)

awit George R. Schneider, Jr., 6-90

D: approx. 4,200 tons (fl) **S:** 14 kts (sust.)
Dim: 99.80 × 18.00 × 4.20
Electron Equipt: Radar: 2/. . . nav. (1 X-band, 1 S-band)
M: 2 Mak 6 MU453 diesels; 2 props; 4,352 bhp—653-hp CP bow-thruster
Range: 4,000/14 **Electric:** 2,310 kVA (4 × 525 kVA, 1 × 210 kVA)
Crew: 84 ship's company + 920 passengers

marks: 5,685 grt. Eleven watertight compartments, 8 motor lifeboats, 20 rafts. *vit* named for mountain on Borneo, *Kelimutu* a mountain on Flores. Intended as erisland passenger ships in peacetime and as military transports in time of war.

5 Kerinci class Bldr: Joseph L. Meyer GmbH & Co., Papenburg, Germany

rinci (In serv. 6-83) Rinjani (In serv. 10-84)
mbuna (In serv. 8-83) Umsini (In serv. 1985)
ar (In serv. 9-88)

sini George R. Schneider, Jr., 4-86

: approx. 11,700 tons (fl) **S:** 20 kts
im: 144.0 (130.0 pp) × 23.4 × 5.9
: 2 Mak 6MU601 diesels; 2 props; 17,000 bhp—1,000-hp bow-thruster
ectric: 3,520 kw **Range:** 5,500/20
ew: 119 crew + 1,596 to 1,737 passengers

arks: 13,861 to 13,954 grt/3,400 dwt. Intended for interisland revenue nger-carrying in peacetime and as military transports in time of war. Accommo-ns for approximately 100 first, 200 second, 300 third, and 496 fourth class and us economy passengers.

NAVIGATIONAL AID TENDERS

◆ **0 (+11) lighthouse and buoy tenders** Bldr: Carrington Slipway, Tomago, Australia

Remarks: Ordered 12-84. To fit out in Indonesia. No data available.

◆ **2 coastal service** Bldr: . . . , Japan (In serv. 1976)

Karakata Kumba

D: 569 grt/552 dwt **S:** 13 kts
Dim: 50.50 (47.43 pp) × 10.00 × 3.71
M: 2 Niigata diesels; 1 prop; 850 bhp

◆ **2 seagoing buoy tender/cargo ships** Bldr: . . . (In serv. 1963)

Majang Mizan

D: 2,150 tons (fl) **S:** 14 kts **Dim:** 78.0 (71.0 pp) × 13.7 × 4.0
M: 1 set 4-cyl. compound reciprocating steam; 1 prop; 1,800 hp
Boilers: Two 16 kg/cm^2 **Fuel:** 376 tons **Crew:** 70 tot.

Remarks: 1,705 grt/1,170 dwt. Resemble small cargo ships, with bridge forward, engine aft, and holds amidships.

◆ **1 seagoing buoy tender and cable layer** Bldr: . . . , the Netherlands

Biduk (L: 30-10-51; in serv. 7-52)

D: **S:** 12 kts **Dim:** 65.0 × 12.0 × 4.5
M: 1 set triple-expansion reciprocating steam; 1 prop; 1,600 bhp
Boilers: two 16-kg/cm^2 **Crew:** 66 tot.

Remarks: 1,250 dwt. Cable sheaves over bow. Transferred from navy, 1978 (ex-pendant 1003).

◆ **2 split-hopper dredges** Bldr: Tanjung Priok SY, Jakarta

. . . . (In serv. 1983) . . . . (In serv. 1983)

D: 1,600 tons (fl) **S:** 10.7 kts **Dim:** . . . × . . . × 4.05 m
M: 2 Bolnes 6DNL 150 diesels; 2 CP props; 1,692 bhp—272-hp bow-thruster
Electric: 1,280 kwt **Crew:** 25 tot.

Remarks: 1,000 m^3 capacity, able to dredge to 14 m depths. Built with assistance from IHC Holland. Ordered 1981, laid down 1982.

◆ **1 suction hopper dredge** Bldr: Orenstein & Koppel, Lübeck, Germany

Irian (L: 26-6-81)

D: 9,500 tons (fl) **S:** 12 kts **Dim:** 110.0 × 18.0 × 7.1
M: 2 MWM diesels; 2 props; 7,700 bhp

CUSTOMS SERVICE

PATROL BOATS

Note: In addition to the units listed below, the Customs Service "owns" the Indonesian Navy–manned PB 57-design large patrol and search-and-rescue boats described under patrol boats in the naval section.

◆ **30 Lürssen FPB 28 class**

	Bldr	Laid down
BC 4001–BC 4006	Lürssen, Vegesack	4-81 to . . .-81
BC 5001–BC 5006	Lürssen, Vegesack	. . . to . . .
BC 6001–BC 6005	BSC, Belgium	11-81 to 8-82
BC 7001–BC 7006	BSC, Belgium	8-2-82 to 8-82
BC 8001–BC 8006	P.T. PAL SY, Surabaja	1-85 to -86
BC 9001–BC 9006	P.T. PAL SY, Surabaja	. . .

D: 61 tons (68.5 fl) **S:** 30 kts **Dim:** 28.0 (26.0 wl) × 5.4 × 1.6
A: 1/12.7-mm mg **Crew:** 6 officers, 13 enlisted
M: BC 4001–4003 and BC 6001–6005: 2 Deutz SBA 16M 816LCK-R diesels; 2 props; 2,720 bhp—others: 2MTU diesels; 2 props; 2,620 bhp
Electric: 36 kVA **Fuel:** 10 tons
Range: 700/27.5; 1,050/17

BC 5001 Lürssen, 1985

PATROL BOATS *(continued)*

Remarks: Built to replace a series of very similar craft built by Lürssen in 1962–63. A collaborative effort by Lürssen, Abeking and Rasmussen of Germany, and BSC—Belgium Shipbuilding Corp., a consortium of Fulton Marine, Ruisbrock, and Scheepswerfen Van Langebrugge—delivering prefabricated sections to PAL shipyard, Surabaja, in addition to building complete boats. BC 5001–5003 rated at 30.6 kts. BC 6001 and 7001 series ordered 1980; BC 8001 and 9001 series ordered 1-81; program well behind schedule, with only two launched by 12-84.

♦ **7 BC 2001 class** Bldr: CMN, Cherbourg, France

	L	In serv.		L	In serv.
BC 2001	27-9-79	8-2-80	BC 2005	19-8-80	5-9-80
BC 2002	20-12-79	8-2-80	BC 2006	14-10-80	7-11-80
BC 2003	4-3-80	3-4-80	BC 2007	9-12-80	10-2-81
BC 2004	14-5-80	9-6-80			

BC 2003 Leo Van Ginderen, 1990

D: 58.5 tons (70.3 fl) **S:** 29.7 kts (at 64.4 tons)
Dim: 28.5 (26.5 wl) × 5.4 × 1.3 (1.65 props)
A: 1/12.7-mm mg
M: 2 MTU 12V331 TC92 diesels; 2 props; 2,440 bhp
Crew: . . . tot.

♦ **7 BC 3001 class** Bldr: Chantiers Navals de l'Estérel, Cannes

	In serv.		In serv.		In serv.
BC 3001	9-7-79	BC 3004	12-6-80	BC 3006	22-1-81
BC 3002	24-1-80	BC 3005	22-10-80	BC 3007	3-4-81
BC 3003	24-4-80				

BC 3002 11-83

D: 57 tons (71 fl) **S:** 34 kts **Dim:** 28.2 × 5.2 × 1.6
A: 1/12.7-mm mg
M: 2 MTU 12V331 TC81 diesels; 2 props; 2,700 bhp
Range: 800/15 **Crew:** 2 officers, 16 men

Remarks: Similar design to BC 1001 class; also built of wood.

♦ **3 BC 1001 class** Bldr: Chantiers Navals de l'Estérel, Cannes

BC 1001 (In serv. 4-75) BC 1002 (In serv. 6-75)
BC 1003 (In serv. 11-75)

D: 56 tons (fl) **S:** 34 kts **Dim:** 28.0 (26.6 wl) × 5.3 × 1.6
A: 1/12.7-mm mg
M: 2 MTU 12V331 TC81 diesels; 2 props; 2,700 bhp
Fuel: 10 tons **Range:** 750/15 **Crew:** 15 tot.

♦ **up to 24 BC 401 series** Bldr: Lürssen, Vegesack (In serv. 1960–62)

BC 401–404	BC 501–504	BC 601–604
BC 701–704	BC 801–804	BC 901–904

Remarks: Data and appearance as for BC 4001 series with Deutz engines. BC 401, BC 502, BC 703 and others remain in service pending completion of duplicate replacements.

BC 1002 John Jedrlinic, 5-84

MARITIME POLICE

PATROL BOATS

♦ **9 DKN 908 class** Bldr: Baglietto, Italy; Riva Trigoso, Italy (In serv. 1961–64)

DKN 908–DKN 916

D: 139 tons (159 fl) **S:** 21 kts **Dim:** 42.0 × 6.5 × 1.8
A: 3/20-mm AA (I × 3)
M: 2 Maybach MD655 diesels; 2 props; . . . bhp
Range: 1,500/17 **Crew:** 22 tot.

♦ **10 DKN 504 class** Bldrs: DKN 504–508: Ishikawajima Harima, Tokyo; others: Uraga Dockyard, Yokosuka (In serv. 1963–64)

DKN 504–DKN 513

DKN 507 19

D: 314 tons light (390 std., 444 fl) **S:** 15.3 kts
Dim: 48.1 (44.0 pp) × 7.5 × 2.9
A: 1/20-mm AA, 2/12.7-mm mg (I × 2)
M: 2 M.A.N. W8V 22/30 ALU diesels; 2 props; 1,400 bhp
Electric: 126 kw **Fuel:** 41 tons **Range:** 2,700/14 **Crew:** 35 tot.

Remarks: Have cargo hold with 75-ton capacity.

♦ **6 Carpentaria class** Bldr: De Havilland Marine, Australia (In serv. 1976–77)

DKN– . . .–. . .

D: 27 tons (fl) **S:** 25 kts **Dim:** 15.7 × 5.0 × 1.3
A: 2/12.7-mm mg (I × 2)
Electron Equipt: Radar: 1/Decca 110
M: 2 MTU 8V331 diesels; 2 props; 1,400 bhp
Range: 950/18 **Crew:** 10 tot.

Remarks: Grant-aid from Australia. Aluminum construction. Ex-*Sasila* (852) *Sabola* (853) transferred to Sea Police 1981; ex-*Samadar* (851), *Sawangi* (852), *Sac* (855), and *Salmaneti* (856) transferred late 1980s.

Ex-Samadar—while in Indonesian Navy service

INDONESIA *(continued)*

PATROL CRAFT

♦ **32 "chase boats"** Bldr: P.T. Kodjo, Jakarta (In serv. 1982–86)

D: 3.7 tons (fl) **S:** 28.3 kts **Dim:** 7.6 × 2.7 × . . .
A: small arms **Crew:** 3 tot. **Fuel:** 150 lit.
M: 1 Caterpillar 3208T diesel; 1 Hamilton 1031 waterjet; 260 bhp

Remarks: Trihedral hull form, GRP construction. Converted from original propeller drive.

INDONESIAN ARMY (ADRI)

At one time the Indonesian Army operated a great variety of ships, including up to 29 units in the ADRI-I series, most of which were old passenger-cargo ships acquired for use as troop transports. Most of its serviceable ships were turned over to the new Military Sealift Command in 1977 and 1978, but a new series of logistics landing craft was constructed.

♦ **28 utility landing craft** Bldr: Koja SY, Tanjung Priok (In serv. 1978–1982)

Adri XXXI to Adri LVIII

D: 580 tons (fl) **S:** 10 kts **Dim:** 42.0 (38.0 wl) × 10.7 × 1.8
M: 2 G.M. 6-71 diesels; 2 props; 680 bhp **Electric:** 100 kw
Fuel: 40 tons **Range:** 1,500/10 **Crew:** 15 tot.

Remarks: 300 dwt. Cargo: 122 tons vehicles/stores; 120 tons water. Two 150-dwt landing craft were also completed during 1980, while in 1982 the first of several 30-dwt landing craft and 180-dwt cargo lighters were acquired.

INDONESIAN AIR FORCE (AURI)

The Indonesian Air Force operates six passenger-cargo logistics ships that were completed in the mid-1960s. Of about 600 dwt, they are intended to beach and are equipped with bow doors.

IRAN

Islamic Republic of Iran

Personnel (1991): Approx. 1,100 officers, 11,400 enlisted, plus Revolutionary Guards

Maritime Aviation: Believed still to be in service are 6 ASH-3D Sea King, 7 AB-212, AB-205A, 14 AB-206A, and 2 Sikorsky RH-53D helicopters. Fixed-wing assets remaining include 2 P-3F Orion long-range patrol aircraft; 4 Fokker F-27 Mk 400M Friendship transports; 4 Falcon 20 and 4 Aero Commander utility transports. The Iranian Air Force employs 5 Lockheed C-130H-MP long-range maritime reconnaissance aircraft.

Iranian P-3F Orion 1991

Weapons: Three Iranian destroyers use General Dynamics–developed fixed-train, elevatable box-launchers to fire U.S.-supplied Standard SM-1 MR surface-to-*air* missiles; these have a secondary antiship capability. Target tracking and illumination is supplied by shipboard gunnery radars. Four Vosper Mk 5 frigates carry a quintuple-position, trainable launcher for Italian Sea Killer Mk 2 antiship missiles:

Length: 4.70 m **Range:** 25 km
Diameter: 20.6 cm **Speed:** 300 m/sec.
Span: 99.9 cm (cruciform)
Guidance: beam-rider/command with optical backup **Weight:** . . .
Engine: 100-kg-thrust solid-fuel with 4,400-kg-thrust solid booster

Guns and torpedoes are of U.S., Italian, Swedish, and British origin. Only twelve U.S. Harpoon missiles were supplied, and all are believed to have been expended.

Coast Defense: Chinese-supplied HY-2 Silkworm and C-801 (FL-7) antiship missiles are employed at coastal positions, and there have been attempts to launch them from a naval auxiliary vessel as well.

SUBMARINES

Note: The U.S. *Tang*-class submarine *Kusseh* (ex-*Trout*, SS 566) was abandoned at New London, Connecticut, in 5-79; the ship is nominally Iranian property and still exists. The Iranian Chief of Naval Operations announced in the spring of 1991 that a seagoing submarine had been ordered from abroad; it is believed that two Kilo-class submarines will be delivered from Russia in 1992.

♦ **1 North Korean midget submarine** (In serv. 6-88)

Remarks: No characteristics available; additional units may follow.

♦ **1 Iranian-design midget** Bldr: Bandar Abbas Navy Yard (In serv. 1988)

D: 27/30 tons **S:** 6.5/6 kts **Dim:** 15.6 × 1.7 × 1.7
A: 14 limpet mines or 2 tons stores **Range:** 1,200/6
M: 1 diesel, electric drive; 1 prop; . . . shp **Man:** 5 tot.

Remarks: Initially completed 5-87, but diving trials were evidently not successful, and the craft was altered during 1988. May have been abandoned.

GUIDED-MISSILE DESTROYERS

♦ **1 ex-U.K. Battle class** Bldr: Cammell Laird, Birkenhead

	Laid down	L	In serv.
51 Damavand (ex-*Artemiz*, ex-*Sluys*, D 60)	24-11-43	28-2-45	30-9-46

Damavand (51) U.S. Navy, 1988

D: 2,325 tons (3,360 fl) **S:** 31 kts
Dim: 115.32 (108.2 pp) × 12.95 × 5.2 (fl)
A: 4/Standard SM-1 MR SAM box launchers (8 missiles)—4/114-mm DP (II × 2)—4/40-mm Bofors AA (I × 4)—2/23-mm AA (II × 1)—1/Squid ASW mortar (III × 1)
Electron Equipt:
Radar: 1/Decca 629 nav., 1/Plessey AWS-1 air-search, 1/Contraves Sea Hunter RTN-10X fire-control
Sonar: Plessey PMS-26 hull-mounted (10 kHz)
EW: 1 Decca RDL-1 intercept, FH-12 D/F
M: 2 sets Parsons geared steam turbines; 2 props; 50,000 shp
Boilers: 2 Admiralty 3-drum **Range:** 3,200/20 **Fuel:** 680 tons
Crew: 260 tot.

Remarks: Modernized before transfer on 20-1-67. Antiship missiles added after refit in South Africa, 1975–76. Standard missiles are SAM version, vice SSM, using Sea Hunter for fire control. Renamed 1985. Sea Cat SAM launcher replaced by a twin 23-mm Soviet AA mount, although the optical missile director remains; the second twin 23-mm AA mount was placed forward of the bridge superstructure. 114-mm guns are 45-cal, fire at 15 rpgpm.

♦ **2 ex-U.S. Allen M. Sumner FRAM II class** Bldr: Todd Pacific, Seattle

	Laid down	L	In serv.
61 Babr (ex-*Zellars*, DD 777)	24-12-43	19-7-44	25-10-44
62 Palang (ex-*Stormes*, DD 780)	15-2-44	4-11-44	27-1-45

D: 2,200 tons (3,320 fl) **S:** 30 kts **Dim:** 114.75 × 12.45 × 5.6
A: 4/Standard SM-1 MR SAM box-launchers (8 missiles)—4/127-mm 38-cal. DP (II × 2)—2/23-mm AA (II × 1)—6/324-mm Mk 32 ASW TT (III × 2)—1/AB-204 helicopter
Electron Equipt:
Radar: 1/. . . nav., 1/SPS-10 surf. search, 1/SPS-29 air search, 1/Mk 25 f.c.
Sonar: 61: SQS-42; 62: SQS-44 hull-mounted
EW: WLR-1 intercept, ULQ-6 jamming/deception
M: 2 sets geared steam turbines; 2 props; 60,000 shp
Boilers: 4 Babcock & Wilcox; 43.3 kg/cm^2, 454° C
Fuel: 650 tons **Range:** 1,260/30; 4,600/14
Crew: 14 officers, 276 enlisted

Palang (62) French Navy, 3-88

GUIDED-MISSILE DESTROYERS *(continued)*

Remarks: Purchased in 3-71 and delivered in 10-73 and 1974 after major refits at the Philadelphia Navy Yard that included installation of more powerful air-conditioning and a telescoping helicopter hangar and modifications to the armament. Sisters *Bordelon* (DD 881) and the *Kenneth D. Bailey* (DD 713) were transferred for cannibalization.

The Standard missile launchers are on a platform between the stacks and also on the 01 level forward of the bridge. Mk 37 fire control for the 127-mm guns and the standard SAMs. VDS now removed from the *Babr*. A twin Soviet 23-mm mount is located at the extreme stern. Hedgehog ASW mortars have been removed. Sonars are essentially the same but operate on different frequencies to avoid interference; they are digital versions of the SQS-29. Both operated during 1990.

FRIGATES

♦ 3 Saam (Vosper Mk 5) class

	Bldr	Laid down	L	In serv.
71 Alvand (ex-*Saam*)	Vosper Thornycroft	22-5-67	25-7-68	20-5-71
72 Alborz (ex-*Zaal*)	Vickers, Newcastle	3-3-68	25-7-68	1-3-71
73 Sabalan (ex-*Rastam*)	Vickers, Barrow	10-12-67	4-3-69	28-2-72

Alborz (72) French Navy, 1-91

D: 1,250 tons (1,540 fl) **S:** 39 kts (17.5 diesel)
Dim: 94.5 (88.4 pp) × 11.07 × 3.25
A: 1/Sea Killer SSM system (V × 1)—1/114-mm DP Mk 8—2/35-mm AA (II × 1)—4/20-mm Oerlikon GAM B01 AA (I × 4)—2/12.7-mm mg (I × 2)—1/Limbo Mk 10 ASW mortar (III × 1)
Electron Equipt:
Radar: 1/Decca 1226 nav., 1/Plessey AWS-1 air-search, 2/Contraves Sea Hunter RTN-10X fire control
Sonar: Graseby Type 174 hull-mounted search (7–9 kHz), Type 170 hull-mounted attack (15 kHz)
EW: Decca RDL-2AC intercept, FH-5 HF D/F
M: CODOG: 2 Rolls-Royce Olympus TM3A gas turbines; 2 Paxman 16-cyl. Ventura diesels for cruising; 2 CP props; 46,000 shp (turbines), 3,800 bhp (diesels)
Range: 5,000/15 **Fuel:** 150 tons (250 with overload)
Crew: 135 tot.

Remarks: Air-conditioned. Retractable fin stabilizers. Vickers Mk 8 automatic guns replaced the originally fitted semi-automatic Mk 6 during refits in the 1970s. Twin 23-mm Soviet AA mounts replaced the original Sea Cat SAM launcher and were in turn later replaced by two single 20-mm mounts. Normally, only 3 Seakiller canisters are carried on the trainable launcher.

All renamed 1985. Sister *Sahand* (ex-*Faramarz*) hit by 3 Harpoon and cluster bombs, lost to U.S. forces 19-4-88. *Sabalan*, severely damaged the same date, was reported repaired by the Iranian Navy during 1989 but has not been noted at sea through 1991.

CORVETTES

♦ 2 U.S. PF 103 class Bldr: Levingston SB, Orange, Texas

	Laid down	L	In serv.
81 Bayandor (ex-PF 103)	20-8-62	7-7-63	18-5-64
82 Naghdi (ex-PF 104)	12-9-62	10-10-63	22-7-64

Bayandor (81) 1990

D: 900 tons (1,135 fl) **S:** 20 kts
Dim: 83.82 × 10.06 × 3.05 (4.27 sonar)
A: 2/76.2-mm 50-cal. Mk. 34 DP (I × 2)—2/40-mm AA (II × 1)—2/20-mm Oerlikon GAM B01 AA (II × 1)—2/12.7-mm mg (I × 2)
Electron Equipt:
Radar: 1/Decca 1226 nav., 1/Raytheon 1650 nav., 1/SPS-6 air search
Sonar: SQS-17A hull-mounted high-freq. search (prob. removed)
M: 4 Fairbanks-Morse 38D8$^{1}/_{8}$-10 diesels; 2 props; 5,300 bhp
Electric: 750 kw **Range:** 2,400/18; 3,000/15 **Fuel:** 110 tons
Crew: 133 tot.

Remarks: Transferred under the Military Aid Program. Twin Soviet 23-mm AA were added forward of the bridge in place of the single Hedgehog ASW spigot mortar during the 1980s; the mount has in turn been replaced with a single 20-mm AA. Have Mk 63 GFCS for 76.2-mm guns (radar on fwd gun mount); Mk 51 Mod. 2 GFCS with lead computing optical director for 40-mm mount. Sisters *Milanian* (83, ex-PF 105) and *Kahnamuie* (84, ex-PF 106) reported lost to Iraqi forces by 1982–83. 82 was refitted and re-engined during 1988, and by 1990, the depth-charge equipment had been removed from both and replaced by a single 20-mm at the extreme stern, while the Mk 34 fire control radar associated with the original Mk 63 had been removed from the forward 76.2-mm gun mount.

PATROL BOATS

♦ 10 Combattante-II class Bldr: CMN, Cherbourg

	L	In serv.
P 21 Kaman	8-1-76	6-77
P 22 Zoubin	14-4-76	6-77
P 23 Khadang	15-7-76	15-3-78
P 26 Falakhon	2-6-77	31-3-78
P 27 Shamshir	12-9-77	31-3-78
P 28 Gorz	28-12-77	15-9-78
P 29 Gardouneh	23-2-78	23-10-78
P 30 Khanjar	27-4-78	1-8-81
P 31 Neyzeh	5-7-78	1-8-81
P 32 Tabarzin	15-9-78	1-8-81

D: 249 tons (275 fl) **S:** 36 kts
Dim: 47.0 × 7.1 × 1.9
A: 1/76-mm OTO Melara DP—1/40-mm Bofors AA
Electron Equipt:
Radar: 1/Decca 1226 nav., 1/H.S.A. WM-28 track-while-scan f.c.
EW: TSF TMV-433 suite: (DR-2000 receiver, DALIA analyzer, Alligator 5-A jammer)

Alvand (71) LSPH K. Degener, R.A.N., 1

PATROL BOATS *(continued)*

Zoubin (P 22)—with old number CMN, 1977

M: 4 MTU 16V538 TB91 diesels; 4 props; 14,400 bhp
Electric: 350 kw **Range:** 700/33.7 **Fuel:** 41 tons **Crew:** 31 tot.

Remarks: Contracted 19-2-74 and 14-10-74. The last three were embargoed at Cherbourg 4-79 and released 22-6-81. P 32 captured off Spain 13-8-80 by anti-Khomeini forces but abandoned later at Toulon. P 31 and 32 had no Harpoon tubes on delivery, and all missiles delivered by the U.S. are believed to have been expended. *Peykan* (P 24) was reported lost to Iraqi forces 11-80, and *Joshan* was sunk by U.S. forces on 19-4-88.

◆ **3 North Korean Chaho class** (Transferred 4-87)

D: 80 tons (fl) **S:** 40 kts **Dim:** 27.7 × 6.1 × 1.8
A: 4/23-mm AA (II × 2)—1/122-mm RL (XL × 1; 40 reloads)
Electron Equipt: 1/Decca . . . nav.
M: 4 diesels; 4 props; 4,800 bhp **Crew:** 22–24 tot.

Remarks: Reportedly, the original M50F series diesels were replaced after delivery. Twin 23-mm Soviet AA replaced the original twin 14.5-mm mg mounts. Reload rockets for the trainable launcher are kept in a magazine at the stern.

◆ **3 U.S. PGM 71 class** Bldr: Peterson Builders, Inc., Sturgeon Bay, Wisconsin (In serv. 1967–70)

11 Parvin (ex-PGM 103) 212 Bahram (ex-PGM 112)
Nahid (ex-PGM 122)

D: 102 tons light (142 fl) **S:** 17 kts **Dim:** 30.81 × 6.45 × 2.3
A: 1/40-mm AA—4/20-mm AA (II × 2)—4/12.7-mm mg (II × 2)
Electron Equipt: Radar: 1/Decca 303 nav.
M: 8 General Motors 6-71 diesels; 2 props; 2,120 bhp
Electric: 30 kw **Range:** 1,000/17 **Fuel:** 16 tons
Crew: 30 tot.

Remarks: Thought to have been sunk during the Iran-Iraq War, but have been sighted still in service. ASW equipment originally fitted (SQS-17 hull-mounted sonar, Mousetrap ASW rocket launchers, and depth charges) has probably been removed, and the radar may have been replaced.

◆ **3 U.S. Coast Guard Cape class** Bldr: U.S. Coast Guard, Curtis Bay, Md. (In serv. 1956–59)

201 Keyvan 202 Azadi (ex-*Tiran*) 203 Mehran

D: 85 tons (107 fl) **S:** 20 kts **Dim:** 29.0 × 6.2 × 2.0
A: 1/40-mm Bofors AA (U.S. Mk 3 mount)—2/23-mm Soviet AA (II × 1)—2/12.7-mm mg (I × 2)
M: 4 Cummins VT-12-M700 diesels; 2,200 bhp
Electric: 40 kw **Range:** 1,500/15 **Crew:** 15 tot.

Remarks: Sister *Mahvan* (P 204) lost 1980–83. 202 and 203 had been damaged during the Iran-Iraq War but have been refitted for further service. ASW ordnance (and probably the sonar as well) has been removed.

PATROL CRAFT

◆ **32 special forces craft** Bldr: Boghammar Marin, Stockholm, Sweden (In serv. 1986–. . .)

D: 6.4 tons (fl) **S:** 45 kts **Dim:** 12.80 × 2.66 × 0.90
A: 2/12.7-mm mg (I × 2)—1/106-mm recoilless rifle and/or RPG-7 anti-tank rocket launchers or 107-mm RL (XII × 4)
Electron Equipt: Radar: 1/Decca 170 nav. or none
M: 2 Volvo Penta TAMD-71A diesels; 2 props; 714 bhp
Range: 500/38 **Crew:** 5–6 tot.

Remarks: Ordered 1984; 37 delivered by 7-87 for use by Revolutionary Guards in attacks on undefended merchant ships. U.S. forces destroyed 5 during 1988. Aluminum construction. Resemble small patrol craft, not pleasure boats. Two versions delivered: Model RL-118 and Model RL-130-4A. Have stepped hydroplane hull form. Apparently not under naval control.

◆ **35 or more GRP launches** Bldr: Boston Whaler, Rockland, Mass.

D: 1.3 tons (fl) **S:** 40 kts **Dim:** 6.7 × 2.3 × 0.4 (prop)
A: 1/12.7-mm mg and/or 1/107-mm RL (XII × 1)
M: 2 gasoline outboard motors; 240 shp

Remarks: Some imported, some built locally in Iran. Used for harassing attacks on unarmed merchant vessels during Iran-Iraq War. Also in use by the Revolutionary Guards are 7.5-meter Damen, Gorinchem-built assault boats, several other types of outboard-powered launches, a few wooden dhows of around 23 m o.a. for mine laying, and European-manufactured semi-rigid inflatable craft.

◆ **11 U.S. Mk III class** Bldr: Marinette Marine, Marinette, Wisconsin (In serv. 1975–76)

D: 28 tons (36.7 fl) **S:** 24 kts **Dim:** 19.78 × 5.50 × 1.80 (props)
A: 3/12.7-mm mg (II × 1, I × 1, as delivered)
Electron Equipt: Radar: LN-66 nav.
M: 3 G.M. 8V71 TI diesels; 3 props; 1,800 bhp
Endurance: 3 days
Range: 450/26; 2,000/ . . . **Crew:** 9 tot.

Remarks: Survivors of 20 originally delivered; remainder lost in Iran-Iraq War. Probably have now been more heavily armed. Aluminum construction, with pilothouse offset to starboard side.

◆ **approx. 20 U.S. 50-ft. class** Bldr: Peterson Bldrs., Sturgeon Bay, Wisc. (In serv. 1975–78)

D: 22 tons (fl) **S:** 28 kts **Dim:** 15.24 × 4.80 × 1.9
A: 1/12.7-mm mg **Range:** 500/30
M: 2 G.M. 8V71 TI diesels; 3 props; 850 bhp **Crew:** 6 tot.

Remarks: Sixty-one were ordered in 1976. Nineteen were delivered complete from the U.S., and the others were shipped as kits for assembly in Iran by Arvandan Maritime Corp., Abadan, where they were still being assembled into the 1980s. Aluminum construction. Placed under naval control with the other Revolutionary Guards craft in 1990. Many others were lost during the Iran-Iraq War, and a number of the kits were apparently never completed.

◆ **20 U.S. Swift Mk II class** Bldr: Peterson Bldrs., Sturgeon Bay, Wisc. (In serv.1976–77)

1201 to 1220

D: 22 tons (fl) **S:** 26 kts **Dim:** 15.3 × 4.8 × 1.9
A: 4/12.7-mm mg (II × 2)
Electron Equipt: Radar: 1/Raytheon 1900 nav.
M: 2 G.M. 12V 71 diesels; 2 props; 900 bhp **Crew:** 6 tot.

Remarks: Survivors of 26 ordered 1976–77. Originally equipped to carry extra personnel and given no fixed armament; have subsequently been armed. Aluminum construction. Six were delivered complete from the U.S. and taken overland to the Caspian Sea for use by the Iranian Navy; another twenty, delivered as kits for assembly by Arvandan Maritime Corp., Abadan, were lost during the Iran-Iraq War or were scrapped.

◆ **12 U.S. Enforcer class** Bldr: Bertram Yacht, Miami (In serv. 1972)

D: 4.7 tons (fl) **S:** 28 kts **Dim:** 9.5 × 3.4 × 0.9
A: 1/12.7-mm mg **Electron Equipt:** Radar: 1/Apelco AD7-7 nav.
M: 2 G.M. 6V53 diesels; 2 props; 360 bhp **Range:** 146/16
Crew: 4 tot.

Remarks: Survivors of 36 delivered. GRP hull construction.

◆ **3 U.S. 40-ft. class** Bldr: Sewart Seacraft, Louisiana (In serv. 1963)

Mahmavi-Hamaraz Mahmavi-Vahedi Mahmavi-Taheri

D: 10 tons **S:** 30 kts **Dim:** 12.2 × 3.4 × 1.1
A: 2/12.7-mm mg (I × 2)
M: 2 G.M. diesels; 2 props; 600 bhp

Remarks: Three given to Sudan in 12-75: *Mardjan, Morvarid,* and *Sadaf*; three others stricken.

MINE WARFARE SHIPS

◆ **2 ex-U.S. Falcon-class minesweepers**

	Bldr	In serv.
301 Shahrokh (ex-MSC 276)	Bellingham SY, Bellingham, Wash.	1958
303 Karkas (ex-MSC 292)	Peterson Bldrs., Sturgeon Bay, Wisc.	3-3-61

D: 320 tons (378 fl) **S:** 12.5 kts (8, sweeping)
Dim: 43.0 (41.5 pp) × 7.95 × 2.55 **A:** 2/20-mm AA (II × 1)
Electron Equipt: Radar: 1/Decca 707 nav.— Sonar: UQS-1
M: 2 G.M. 8-268A diesels; 2 props; 890 bhp
Range: 2,500/10 **Fuel:** 27 tons **Crew:** 3 officers, 35 enlisted

Remarks: Sister *Shabaz* lost through fire in 1975, *Simorgh* (302) to Iraqi forces 1980–81. 301 operates in the Caspian Sea, primarily as a training ship. 303 had been thought lost during the Iran-Iraq War but is still in service.

◆ **1 U.S. Cape-class inshore minesweeper**

	Bldr	In serv.
312 Riazi (ex-MSI 14)	Tacoma Boat, Tacoma, Washington	15-10-64

D: 203 tons (239 fl) **S:** 12.5 kts **Dim:** 34.06 × 7.14 × 2.40
A: 1/12.7-mm mg
Electron Equipt: Radar: 1/Decca 303 nav.
M: 4 G.M. Detroit Diesel 6-71 diesels; 2 props; 960 bhp
Electric: 120 kw **Range:** 1,000/9 **Fuel:** 20 tons
Crew: 5 officers, 16 enlisted

MINE WARFARE SHIPS *(continued)*

Remarks: Wooden construction. Built for Iran under the Military Aid Program. Thought lost with sister *Harachi* (311, ex-*Kahnamuie,* ex-MSI 13) during the Iran-Iraq War but is apparently still in service. Appearance as for sisters in Turkish Navy.

AMPHIBIOUS WARFARE SHIPS

◆ **4 Hengam-class LSTs** Bldr: Yarrow & Co., Scotstoun, U.K.

	L	In serv.		L	In serv.
51 Hengam	27-9-73	12-8-74	53 Lavan	12-6-78	16-1-85
52 Larak	7-5-74	12-11-74	54 Tonb	6-12-79	11-7-85

Lavan (53)—with temporary number 2-91

Hengam (51) U.S. Navy, 6-88

D: 2,940 tons (fl) **S:** 14.5 kts
Dim: 92.96 (86.87 wl) × 14.94 × 3.00 max.
A: 8/23-mm AA (II × 4)—1/122-mm RL (40 tubes)—1 or more 12.7-mm mg—2/SA-7 Grail SAM launchers (IV × 2)
Electron Equipt: Radar: 1/Decca TM 1229 nav.—TACAN: URN-25
M: 51, 52: 4 Paxman Ventura 12 YJCM diesels; 2 CP props; 5,600 bhp 53, 54: 4 MTU 12V562 TB61 diesels; 2 CP props; 5,800 bhp
Range: 3,500/12 **Fuel:** 295 tons **Electric:** 1,280 kw
Crew: 75 ship's company + 168 troops

Remarks: Were used to transport small combatants during the Iran-Iraq War. 53, 54, laid up since completion, were released by the British government 5-10-84 on the excuse that they would be used in the unlikely role of hospital ships. Negotiations continued into 1985 for the construction of two more, originally ordered 7-77, for which considerable material had been accumulated.

Flight deck for one Sea King–sized helicopter aft. Cargo capacity of 600 tons on 39.6 × 8.8 × 4.5m (high) vehicle deck, with 15-m-long bow ramp. Can also carry up to 300 tons liquid cargo in lieu of some vehicle stowage. Can stow 12 Soviet T-55 or 6 British Chieftain battle tanks. Upper deck forward has a 10-ton crane to handle two Uniflote cargo lighters (LCVP) and twelve Z-boat rubber personnel landing craft. Intended for logistics support (when ten 20-ton or thirty 10-ton containers would be carried) or for amphibious assault. 53 has an additional Decca 1216 nav. radar. 23-mm AA replaced four single 40-mm AA in the first two.

Note: The three Iran Hormuz 24-class and two Iran 21-class ships listed as naval amphibious warfare units in the previous edition are in fact legitimate merchant vessels, although they could be employed in over-the-beach military logistics support.

◆ **2 tank-landing ships** Bldr: Teraoka SY, Japan (In serv. 1978)

Iran Asr (ex-*Arya Akian*) Iran Ghadr (ex-*Arya Dokht*)

D: 614 tons light (2,274 fl) **S:** 11 kts
Dim: 53.65 (48.01 pp) × 10.81 × . . .
A: 2/12.7-mm mg (I × 2)—mines, small arms
Electron Equipt: Radar: 1/. . . nav.
M: 2 diesels; 2 props; 2,200 bhp **Crew:** 30 tot.

Remarks: 984 grt/1,660 dwt. Blunt-bowed, commercial landing craft taken over by the Iranian Navy at the outset of the Iran-Iraq War. Have bow ramp; single hatch with sliding cover. One 10-ton cargo boom. Mines are deck-stowed atop the hatch cover and launched over the side. Sister *Iran Ajr* (ex-*Arya Rakhsh*) captured 21-9-87 by U.S. forces while laying mines in international waters and scuttled 26-9-87. Sisters *Iran Bahr* (ex-*Arya Sahand*) and *Iran Badr* (ex-*Arya Boum*) lost 1980.

Iran Ajr—just prior to scuttling U.S. Navy, 1987

◆ **1 (+ . . .) Foque-class utility landing craft** Bldr: Construction Jihad, Nuh-e Nabi SY, Bandar Abbas

101 Foque (L: 17-6-88)

D: 250 tons (fl) **S:** 10 kts **Dim:** 36.6 × 8.0 × 1.5
A: . . . **Electron Equipt:** Radar: . . .
M: 2 MWM TBD 234 V8 diesels; 2 props; 880 bhp

Remarks: Additional units appear to have been built, but they are apparently employed in civilian service. Can carry 100 tons deck cargo or up to 79 tons liquid in tanks.

◆ **12 or more Type 412 sea truck landing craft** Bldr: Rotork, U.K.

D: 9 tons (fl) **S:** 28 kts **Dim:** 12.7 × 3.2 × 0.9
A: 2 or 4/7.62-mm mg (I × 2 or 4)
M: 2 Volvo Penta diesels; 2 props; 240 bhp

Remarks: GRP construction. Can carry up to 30 troops or a small vehicle.

HOVERCRAFT

◆ **4 BH.7 Wellington class** Bldr: British Hovercraft, Cowes, U.K. (In serv. 1970–75)

D: 50 to 55 tons (fl) **S:** 65 kts **Dim:** 23.9 × 13.8 × 10.36 (high)
A: 2/12.7-mm mg (I × 2) **Electron Equipt:** Radar: 1/Decca 914 nav.
M: 1 Rolls-Royce Proteus 15M549 gas turbine; 1 6.4-m-diameter prop; 4,250 shp
Electric: 110 kVA **Fuel:** 9 tons **Range:** 400/56

Remarks: Four were of the logistics-support version, with a 14-ton payload. Two were of the Mk 4 version with recess for two SSM, which were not mounted. The Mk 4 uses the Gnome 15M541 engine of 4,750 hp and can carry 60 troops in side compartments as well as assault vehicles on its 56-m cargo deck. Speed in both versions is reduced to 35 kts in a 1.4-meter sea. Overhauled at builders beginning with two in 2-84 and two more in 1985; new engines, skirts, etc. Two others, plus eight SR-N6 Winchester-class hovercraft, are inoperable.

◆ **1 small hovercraft**

Yunus (L: 1-89)

Remarks: Built for Revolutionary Guards service. Iranian design, no characteristics available.

AUXILIARY SHIPS

◆ **1 large replenishment oiler**

	Bldr	Laid down	L	In serv.
431 Kharg	Swan Hunter, Wallsend-on-Tyne	1-76	3-2-77	25-4-80

D: 33,014 tons (fl) **S:** 21.5 kts
Dim: 207.15 (195.00 pp) × 25.50 × 9.14
A: 1/76-mm OTO Melara Compact DP—12/23-mm AA (II × 6)
Electron Equipt: Radar: 2/Decca 1229 nav.—TACAN: URN-20

Kharg (431)

AUXILIARY SHIPS *(continued)*

Kharg (431) U.S. Navy, 1987

M: 1 set Westinghouse geared steam turbines; 1 prop; 26,870 shp
Boilers: 2 Babcock & Wilcox 2-drum
Electric: 7,000 kw **Crew:** 248 tot.

Remarks: Ordered 10-74. 21,100 grt/20,000 dwt. Carries fuel and ammunition. Design is greatly modified version of the Royal Navy's *Olwen* class. Ran initial trials 11-78, but delays in fitting out made delivery before the revolution impossible; remained at builders until released 5-10-84; ran trials again 4-9-84. Delivered without armament; originally had an OTO Melara 76-mm Compact (with local control) forward. One 40-mm AA was installed on the former 76-mm pedestal, the other on the helo deck during 1985, replaced by present armament 1986. Has INMARSAT satellite communications equipment. Can accommodate three Sea King–sized helicopters.

♦ **2 Bandar Abbas-class small replenishment oilers** Bldr: C. Lühring, Brake, Germany

421 Bandar Abbas (L: 14-8-73) 422 Booshehr (L: 22-3-74)

D: 4,673 tons (fl) **S:** 20 kts **Dim:** 108.0 × 16.6 × 4.5
A: 2/23-mm AA (II × 1)—2/20-mm Oerlikon GAM B01 AA (I × 2)
Electron Equipt: Radar: 1/Decca 1226 nav., 1/. . . nav.
M: 2 M.A.N. R6V 52/56 diesels; 2 props; 12,000 bhp
Range: 3,500/16 **Crew:** 60 tot.

Remarks: 3,186 grt/3,250 dwt. Telescoping helicopter hangar. Carry fuel, food, ammunition, and spare parts. Armed after delivery. Used for patrol duties 1984 on, due to lack of operable combatants.

Booshehr (422) French Navy, 1989

♦ **2 water tankers** Bldr: Mazagon Dock, Bombay, India

Kangan (L: 4-78) Taheri (L: 17-9-78)

D: 12,000 tons (fl) **S:** 12 kts
Dim: 147.95 (140.00 pp) × 21.50 × 5.00
A: 2/23-mm AA (II × 1)—2/12.7-mm mg (I × 2)
Electron Equipt: Radar: 1/Decca 1229 nav.
M: 1 M.A.N. 7L52/55A diesel; 7,385 bhp **Crew:** 20 tot.

Kangan 1979

Remarks: 9,430 dwt. Intended to supply Persian Gulf islands. Liquid cargo: 9,000 m³. Also used in patrol duties 1984-on.

♦ **7 Delvar-class support ships** Bldr: Karachi SY & Eng. Wks., Pakistan (In serv. 1978–82)

Delvar Dayer Charak Chiroo Sirjan Dilim Souru

D: approx. 1,300 tons (fl) **S:** 9–11 kts
Dim: 63.45 (58.48 pp) × 11.00 × 3.03
A: 2/23-mm AA (II × 1)
Electron Equipt: Radar: 1/Decca 1226 nav.
M: 2 M.A.N. G6V-23.5/33 ATL diesels; 2 props; 1,560 bhp
Crew: 20 tot.

Remarks: 900 grt. *Delvar* and *Sirjan* configured as ammunition lighters; *Dayer* and *Dilim* (with rounded sterns and one crane vice two) are water tankers; the others are coastal cargo lighters. Designed and built with British assistance.

Delvar-class support ship Piet Sinke, 2-87

Booshehr (422) LSPH K. Degener, R.A.N., 12-90

AUXILIARY SHIPS *(continued)*

◆ **1 ex-U.S. Amphion-class repair ship** Bldr: Tampa SB, Florida

	Laid down	L	In serv.
441 Chah Bahar (ex-*Amphion,* AR 13)	20-9-44	15-5-45	30-1-46

D: 8,670 tons light (14,450 fl) **S:** 16 kts
Dim: 150.0 × 21.4 × 8.4
A: removed **M:** 1 set geared steam turbines; 1 prop; 8,500 shp
Boilers: 2 Foster-Wheeler "D"; 30.6 kg/cm^2, 382° C
Electric: 3,600 kw **Fuel:** 1,850 tons
Crew: quarters for 921 men

Remarks: Transferred on loan in 10-71 and purchased 1-3-77. Employed as stationary repair facility at Bandar Abbas, but can steam.

◆ **1 former imperial yacht for Caspian Sea** Bldr: Boele's Scheepswerf, Bolnes, the Netherlands

155 Hamzeh (ex-*Chah Sevar*)

D: 530 tons **S:** 15 kts **Dim:** 53.0 × 7.65 × 3.2
M: 2 Stork diesels; 2 props; 1,300 bhp

Remarks: Probably employed in training and oceanographic duties. Smaller yacht *Kish,* formerly employed for the Shah in the Persian Gulf, has apparently been discarded.

YARD AND SERVICE CRAFT

◆ **1 inshore survey craft, former yacht** Bldr: Malahide SY, Dublin

Abnegar (ex-*Glimmer*)

D: 85 tons (fl) **S:** . . . kts **Dim:** 20.7 × . . . × . . .
M: 1 Kelvin T8 diesel; 240 bhp

Remarks: Acquired 1974.

◆ **2 Aras-class harbor tugs** Bldr: B.V. Scheepswerf K. Damen, Hardinxveld-Giessendam, Netherlands (In serv. 1985)

Aras Atrak

D: 91 grt **S:** . . . **Dim:** 22.00 × 7.12 × 2.65
M: 2 MTU diesels; . . . bhp

◆ **5 Hamoon-class harbor tugs**

	Bldr	L	In serv.
Hamoon	Deltawerf, Sliedrecht, Neth.	. . .	4-84
Hirmand	Damen, Hardinxveld, Neth.	1-8-84	1984
Menab	. . . . . .	. . .	1985
Hari-Rud	. . . . . .	. . .	1985
Sefid-Rud	. . . . . .	. . .	1985

D: 300 tons (fl) **S:** 12 kts
Dim: 25.63 (23.53 pp) × 6.81 × 3.19
M: 2 MTU GV396 TC62 diesels; 2 props; 1,200 bhp

Remarks: 122 grt.

◆ **2 ex-German tugs**

1 (ex-*Karl*) 2 (ex-*Ise*)

D: 134 tons **S:** . . . kts **Dim:** . . . × . . . × . . . **M:** . . . . . .

Remarks: Built in 1962–63, and acquired on 17-6-74.

◆ **8 (+ 4) Hendijan-class general-purpose tenders**
Bldr: Damen, Gorinchem, the Netherlands (last four: . . . SY, Iran)

	In serv.		In serv.
Bakhtaran	1985	Koramshahr	1985
Hendijan	1987	Kalat	1987
Konarak	11-88	Genavah	9-88
Sirik	4-89	Gaveter	1990
Bamregan	. . .	Hogan	. . .
Nayband	. . .	Rostam	. . . .

D: 650 tons (fl) **S:** 25 kts **Dim:** 50.8 (47.0 pp) × 8.6 × 3.5
A: . . . **Electron Equipt:** Radar: Decca 2070 nav.
M: 2 MTU diesels; 2 props; . . . bhp **Crew:** 15 tot.

Remarks: 439–445 grt. Used to transport cargo and personnel over short distances and probably also as patrol craft. Cargo: 40 tons on deck, 12 below, plus 40 tons potable water. *Bakhtaran* and *Koramshahr* are slightly larger than the others.

Hendijan Leo Van Ginderen, 6-88

Konarak Gilbert Gyssels, 7-8

◆ **2 small fuel lighters** Bldr: Karachi SY & Eng. Wks. (In serv. 1981)

1703 1704

D: . . . **S:** . . . **Dim:** 30.51 × 9.30 × 1.83
M: 2 M.A.N. diesels; 2 props; 326 bhp

Remarks: 195 grt/200 dwt.

◆ **2 water barges** Bldr: Karachi SY & Eng. Wks. (In serv. 1977–78)

1701 1702

D: 1,410 grt **Dim:** 65.0 × 13.0 × 2.6

Note: In addition to the four units immediately above, Karachi Shipyard and Eng neering Works delivered seven other yard and service craft between 1977 and 7-81. were designed in Great Britain. A variety of craft were built, all initially number 1701 through 1718. Types included a self-propelled dredge (1711), a pontoon bar (1710), a diving tender (1705), and garbage lighter (120 m^3 hopper with compacter

◆ **3 coastal tankers** Bldr: Scheepswerf Ravestein, Deest, the Netherlands (In serv. 1983)

Iran Parak Iran Shalak Iran Youshat

D: approx. 800 fl **S:** 6 kts
Dim: 40.01 (38.82 pp) × 10.01 × 2.6
M: 2 G.M. 6-71 diesels; 2 props; 730 bhp
Fuel: 5 tons **Electric:** 12 kw

Remarks: 400 grt/540 dwt. Originally purchased for commercial purposes.

◆ **1 modified U.S. 174-foot-class yard oiler** Bldr: Nav. Mec. Castellammare, Italy (In serv. 2-56)

Hormuz (ex-U.S. YO 247)

Hormuz

D: 1,400 tons (fl) **S:** 9 kts **Dim:** 54.4 × 9.8 × 4.3
A: 2/20-mm AA (I × 2) **Electron Equipt:** Radar: 1/Decca 707 n
M: 1 Ansaldo Q370 diesel; 600 bhp **Fuel:** 25 tons

Remarks: Built under U.S. Military Aid Program. Cargo: 900 tons.

◆ **10 Medina-class motor lifeboats** Bldr: Fairey Marine, Hamble,

1601 to 1610 (In serv. 1978)

D: 15.5 tons (fl) **S:** 16 kts **Dim:** 14.0 × 3.7 × 1.1
M: 2 Ford Sabre Turbo-Plus diesels; 2 props; 500 bhp
Range: 150/12 **Crew:** 4 tot. (plus 12 passengers)

Remarks: Originally assigned to the Iranian Coast Guard but were under control by 1990.

◆ **1 large floating dry dock** Bldr: M.A.N.-G.H.H., Nordenham/Blex Germany

Dolphin (L: 22-11-85)

D: 28,000 tons lift **Dim:** 240.00 × 52.50 × . . .

Remarks: Docking well 230.00 m over keel blocks, 41.00-m free width, 8.50-n able overblocks.

◆ **1 ex-U.S. floating dry dock** Bldr: Pacific Bridge, Alameda, Cal.

400 (ex-ARD 28) (In serv. 7-44)

D: 3,500 tons lift **Dim:** 149.8 × 25.6 × 1.7 (light)

Remarks: Transferred 1-3-77.

IRAQ

Republic of Iraq

Personnel (1991): about 1,600 total, including 200 officers (may be fewer)

Naval Aviation: The Iraqi Air Force still has 6 or 7 French-supplied Super Frélon helicopters armed with AM 39 Exocet antiship missiles. Some of the surviving Mirage F1EQ fighter-bombers can carry one or two AM 39 Exocets. Six AS-332F Super Puma helicopters with Exocet ASM and six SA-365F Dauphin with AS-15TT ASM, which were to deliver fall 1989 to the air force, were not transferred, nor were five Agusta-Bell AB-212 and ten Agusta-Bell A-103A helicopters that were to have been delivered by Italy for the Iraqi Navy.

Note: Lost during the 1991 Gulf War were: 2 Osa-I and 5 Osa-II guided-missile patrol boats (the entire inventory), 4 Zhuk-class patrol craft, numerous smaller patrol craft (the total will probably never be known with accuracy), 1 T-43-class fleet minesweeper (the other having been scrapped prior to hostilities), 3 Nestin-class riverine minesweepers, 1 to 3 Yevgenya-class inshore minesweepers, 2 Polnocny-class landing ships (with a third damaged), the *Spasilac*-class salvage ship *Aka* (which had been in use as a minelayer), and a number of smaller service craft. In addition, the three *Al Zahraa*-class militarized roll-on/roll-off cargo ships have been arrested at various European ports and are unlikely to be returned to Iraqi control.

Of the ships involved in the order from Italy, the four Lupo-class frigates and four non-helicopter-capable *Wadi M'ragh*-class missile corvettes were never delivered and were claimed by the Italian government in the summer of 1991. Their two-helicopter-capable half-sisters were Iraqi property, but remain in Italy and are unlikely to be allowed to leave. The oiler *Agnadeen* and an Iraqi Navy floating dry dock remain in Alexandria.

Iraq captured virtually the entire Kuwaiti Navy during its 8-90 invasion of its neighbor, with the exception of two missile boats and port service craft later incorporated into the Free Kuwaiti fleet. Sunk by UN Coalition force air attacks during the 1991 Gulf War were one FPB 57-class and five TNC-45-class guided-missile boats, as were virtually all of the other craft captured; a detailed list can be found in the Kuwait section.

The ships listed on the following pages are believed to remain in Iraqi hands or under Iraqi ownership, but their condition is likely to be very poor to inoperable.

FRIGATE

1 training frigate Bldr: Uljanic SY, Yugoslavia

	Laid down	L	In serv.
507 Ibn Khaldum	1977	1978	21-3-80

Ibn Khaldum (507) Uljanic SY, 1980

D: 1,500 tons (1,850 fl) **S:** 26 kts
Dim: 96.70 (90.00 pp) × 11.20 × 3.55
A: 1/57-mm Bofors SAK 57 DP—1/40-mm Bofors AA—16/20-mm AA (IV × 4)—1/d.c. rack
Electron Equipt:
Radar: 1/Decca 1226 nav., 1/Decca 1229 nav., 1/ PEAB. . . surface search, 1/PEAB 9LV200 Mk II f.c.
Sonar: Plessey MS 26 hull-mounted
M: CODOG: 1 Rolls-Royce Olympus TM-3B gas turbine, 22,360 shp; 2 MTU 16V956 TB61 diesels, 7,500 bhp; 2 CP props
Range: 1,150/26 (gas turbine); 4,000/20 (diesels)
Electric: 1,976 kw tot. **Crew:** 93 ship's company + 100 students

Remarks: Same basic design as Indonesia's *Hajer Dewantara*, but without a helicopter deck. Originally intended to provide experience in operating larger ships for future expansion of the Iraqi fleet but served as a transport between Europe and the Gulf of ...a during the Iran-Iraq War. Was in Iraqi waters during entire Gulf Crisis/Gulf War period 1990–91 and did not participate, although the ship was apparently damaged by air attacks during 1-91; may no longer be considered operational. Reports that it had been renamed *Ibn Marjid* have not been substantiated.

CORVETTES

2 helicopter-equipped Bldr: Fincantieri, Muggiano

	Laid down	L	In serv.
Mussa Ben Nussair	15-1-82	16-12-82	17-9-86
Tariq Ibn Ziyad	20-5-82	8-7-83	29-10-86

Mussa Ben Nussair (F 210)—outboard *Tariq ibn Ziyad* (F 212) at La Spezia 5-89

Tariq ibn Ziyad (F 212)—and *Mussa Ben Nussair* (F 210) Leo Van Ginderen, 4-90

D: 610 tons (685 fl) **S:** 37.5 kts
Dim: 62.3 (57.8 pp) × 9.3 × 2.9 (hull)
A: 2/Otomat Mk II SSM (I × 2)—1/Albatros SAM syst. (IV × 1, plus 4 reload Aspide missiles)—1/76-mm OTO Melara DP—1/helicopter
Electron Equipt:
Radar: 1/3RM 20 nav., 1/RAN-12L/X air/surf. search, 2/Orion RTN-10X f.c.
Sonar: Thomson-Sintra Diodon hull-mounted (11–13 kHz)
EW: Elettronica Gamma intercept, 1/SCLAR decoy RL (XX × 1)
M: 4 MTU 20V956 TB92 diesels; 4 props; 24,400 bhp (20,400 sust.)
Electric: 650 kw tot. (3 × 200 kw, 1 × 50 kw) **Endurance:** 5 days
Range: 1,200/31; 4,000/18 **Crew:** 51 tot.

Remarks: Ordered 2-81. With the lifting of the Iran-Iraq War embargo on arms deliveries, these ships—technically the property of Iraq, since they were paid for and delivered in 1986—received crews during 1990; they have remained sequestered at La Spezia since the UN embargo was imposed in 8-91 and are unlikely ever to reach Iraqi waters. They may be sold to pay off Iraqi war reparations.

Differ from four sisters built but not delivered in having a helicopter facility (for one Agusta A-109A) with telescoping hangar in place of a twin Dardo 40-mm AA mounting aft. Although intended to receive two triple ILAS-3 ASW torpedo tube mountings, these have not been installed.

PATROL BOATS

♦ **2 Soviet Bogomol class** Bldr: Ulis SY, Vladivostok

D: 245 tons (fl) **S:** 35 kts **Dim:** 38.60 × 7.60 × 2.00
A: 1/76-mm AK-176 DP—1/30-mm AK-630 gatling AA— 1/SA-N-5 SAM syst. (IV × 1)
Electron Equipt:
Radar: 1/Pot Drum surf. search, 1/Bass Tilt f.c.
IFF: 1/Square Head interrogator, High Pole B transponder
M: 3 M504 diesels; 3 props; 14,750 bhp **Range:** 500/34; 750/25
Crew: 30 tot.

Remarks: Delivered 4-90 and, although reportedly damaged during 1991, apparently remain afloat in at least reparable condition. Design employs Osa-II hull and propulsion plant and is similar to the Mol-class export patrol boat except for the heavier gun armament forward and the lack of provision for torpedo tubes. Two sisters serve in Guinea-Bissau fleet and two with the Guinea Navy.

♦ **3 Yugoslav PB 90 class** (In serv. 1990)

D: 80 tons (90 fl) **S:** 32 kts (26 sust.)
Dim: 27.35 × 6.55 × 1.55 (2.20 props)
A: 1/40-mm Bofors AA—4/20-mm Hispano AA (IV × 1)
Electron Equipt: Radar: 1/Decca 1226 nav.
M: 3 MTU diesels; 3 props; 4,350 bhp **Range:** 400/25
Endurance: 5 days **Crew:** 17 tot.

Remarks: A fourth on order was not delivered prior to the 8-90 UN embargo; these three are believed to have survived the hostilities. Have illumination rocket launchers mounted on the sides of the 40-mm gun shield.

Note: The three Soviet-supplied S.O.-1-class patrol boats listed in the previous edition had apparently been stricken by 1990.

PATROL CRAFT

♦ **. . . Swary-series** Bldr: Swary Boatyard, . . ., Iraq (In serv. 1989–91)

D: 7 tons (fl) **S:** 25 kts **Dim:** 11.0 × 2.5 × 0.6
A: 1 or 2/14.5-mm mg—32/57-mm rockets (XXXII × 1)
Electron Equipt: Radar: 1/. . . nav.
M: 2 or 3 diesels; 2 or 3 props; . . . bhp **Crew:** 4–6 tot.

Remarks: GRP-hulled open boats first displayed in 1989 at the Baghdad Arms Show. Armament and propulsion configurations vary, and there may also be variants with different overall lengths. This type of craft accounted for most of the small combatants reported sunk or damaged by UN Coalition forces in 1991. Several hundred were reportedly constructed.

Note: All four of Iraq's Soviet-supplied Zhuk-class patrol craft and the two Poluchat-I-class patrol craft are believed to have been destroyed during the Gulf War.

MINE WARFARE CRAFT

♦ **0 to 2 Yevgenya-class inshore minesweepers**

D: 80 tons (90 fl) **S:** 11 kts **Dim:** 26.2 × 6.1 × 1.5
A: 2/25-mm Type 2M-8 AA (II × 2)—mines
Electron Equipt: Radar: 1/Spin Trough
M: 2 diesels; 2 props; 600 bhp **Range:** 300/10 **Crew:** 10 tot.

Remarks: Three transferred in 1975 as "oceanographic research craft." Have heavier guns than their Soviet Navy sisters. GRP construction. One definitely was sunk during 1-91 by UN Coalition forces, and all three may have been destroyed.

♦ **1 Yugoslav Nestin-class river minesweeper** Bldr: Brodotehnika, Belgrade

D: 68 tons (78 fl) **S:** 15 kts **Dim:** 27.00 × 6.50 × 1.15 max.
A: 5/20-mm AA (III × 1, I × 2)—24 small mines
Electron Equipt: Radar: 1/Decca 101 nav.
M: 2 diesels; 2 props; 520 bhp **Range:** 864/10.8
Crew: 17 tot.

Remarks: Survivor of four transferred 1978–79. Has PEAM acoustic and magnetic sweep, and Types MDL-1 and MDL-2 mechanical sweep gear. Two illumination rocket launchers are fitted. Constructed of light alloy steel. One was named *Salam al Deen*.

AMPHIBIOUS WARFARE SHIPS

♦ **1 Soviet Polnocny-D class** Bldr: Stocznia Pólnocna, Gdańsk, Poland

D: 1,350 tons (fl) **S:** 18 kts **Dim:** 81.1 × 9.3 × 1.6 fwd/2.6 aft
A: 4/30-mm AK-230 AA (II × 2)—2/122-mm rocket launchers (XL × 2)
Electron Equipt: Radar: 1/Don-2 nav., 1/Drum Tilt f.c.
M: 2 Type 40D diesels; 2 props; 5,000 bhp
Range: 900/17; 1,500/14 **Crew:** 30 tot.

Remarks: Has a helicopter platform forward of the superstructure. Barrage rocket launchers differ from others of this class, which use 140-mm rockets. Cargo capacity: 350 tons vehicles and several hundred troops for short distances. Two transferred in 1977, one in 11-78, and one in 9-79. Sister L 78 lost to Iranian Harpoon missiles, 11-80. *Atika* (L 72) was sunk by air attack on 29-1-91, and either *Jawada* (L 74) or *Nouh* (L 76) was also sunk the same day; the survivor was damaged and may have been interned in Iran.

AUXILIARY SHIPS AND CRAFT

♦ **1 Italian Stromboli-class replenishment oiler**

	Bldr	Laid down	L	In serv.
A 102 Agnadeen	Castellamare di Stabia, Naples	29-1-82	22-10-82	29-10-84

D: 8,706 tons (fl) **S:** 19.5 kts (18 sust.)
Dim: 129.0 (118.5 pp) × 18.0 × 6.5
A: 1/76-mm OTO Melara DP
Electron Equipt:
Radar: 1/3RM7-250 nav., 1/Orion RTN-10X f.c.
M: 2 GMT A428SS diesels; 1 CP prop; 11,200 bhp (9,600 sust.)
Electric: 4,200 kw **Range:** 10,000/16 **Crew:** 124 tot.

Remarks: Ordered 2-81. Capable of serving two ships alongside while under way. Delivered 20-12-83 after fitting out at Muggiano, La Spezia. Moored at Alexandria, Egypt, since 1986 and will probably never reach Iraqi waters.

Agnadeen (A 102) Carlo Martinelli, 3-85

Agnadeen (A 102)—sequestered at Alexandria U.S. Navy photo, 6-

♦ **1 transport** Bldr: Wärtsilä, Turku, Finland (In serv. 3-83)

Al Mansur

D: approx. 5,800 tons (fl) **S:** . . .
Dim: 121.01 (96.50 pp) × 17.53 × 5.51
A: none **Electron Equipt:** Radar: . . .
M: 2 Wärtsilä diesels; 2 CP props; 11,994 bhp **Fuel:** 693 tons

Remarks: 7,359-grt/3,795-dwt troop transport with helicopter deck, hangar. Li armor on hull sides, bulletproof portholes. Has bow-thruster. Resembles a small cru liner. Reached Iraqi waters after the Iran-Iraq War and took no part in hostili during 1991. Probably survives in operable condition but is unlikely to deploy.

Note: The seagoing presidential yacht *Al Mansur* was transferred to King Fah Saudi Arabia in 1987 without ever having reached Iraqi waters. The riverine pr dential yacht *Al Qadissiya* does not seem ever to have been delivered. The salvage *Aka* was sunk during the 1991 Gulf War while acting as a minelayer.

♦ **1 floating dry dock** Bldr: Italcantieri, Trieste (In serv. 7-84)

Remarks: Ordered 2-81. 6,000-ton capacity. Moored at Alexandria, Egypt, since 1

Note: The fate of the one Dutch-built diving tender, four Soviet-built Nyryat-2-c diving tenders, Soviet-built Pozharney-I-class fireboat, and Soviet-built Prome class large harbor tug operated by the Iraqi Navy prior to 1-91 is uncertain, but al believed either to have been sunk or rendered inoperable during UN Coalition strikes.

The Iraqi Customs Service operated some 21 small patrol craft and six SRN hovercraft prior to 1-91; all are believed to be out of service, and at least one SRN was sunk on 12-2-91.

IRELAND

Eire

Personnel (1991): 970 total active (The authorized force is 158 officers, 568 officers, 540 enlisted ratings), plus 300 reserves. The Naval Reserve (*Slua Muiri*) recruit women, but the regular naval service will remain all-male.

Naval Aviation: The Irish Air Force operates two SA-365 Dauphin II helicopte the navy and three others for land service. In June 1991, it acquired a second- CASA CN-235 and ordered two new CASA CN-235-100 for delivery 1994, a maritime surveillance duties. A Sikorsky S-61N helicopter was chartered during to provide search-and-rescue services from Shannon Airport.

PATROL SHIPS

♦ **2 ex-U.K. Peacock class** Bldr: Hall Russell, Aberdeen

	Laid down	L	In serv.
P 41 Orla (ex-*Swift*, P 243)	23-9-83	11-9-84	3-5-85
P 42 Ciara (ex-*Swallow*, P 242)	24-4-83	30-3-84	16-11-84

D: 662 tons (712 fl) **S:** 28 kts (25 sust.)
Dim: 62.60 (60.00) × 10.00 × 2.72
A: 1/76-mm OTO Melara DP—4/7.62-mm mg (I × 4)
Electron Equipt: Radar: 1/Kelvin-Hughes Type 1006 nav.
M: 2 APE-Crossley-SEMT-Pielstick 18PA6V280 diesels; 2/3-blade props; 14,188 bhp—1/Schottel S103 drop-down, shrouded prop; 181 shp
Range: 2,500/17 **Fuel:** 44 tons **Electric:** 755 kw tot.
Crew: 6 officers, 33 enlisted including boarding party

PATROL SHIPS *(continued)*

iara (P 42)—as *Swallow* (P 242) Leo Van Ginderen, 9-88

emarks: Former patrol boats at Hong Kong, purchased 8-10-88 and commissioned -11-88 in Irish service. The 76-mm gun is controlled by a GSA 7 Sea Archer optronic rector. Two 50-mm rocket flare launchers fitted. Two rudders. Were bad rollers until eper bilge keels were fitted. Carry two Avon Sea Raider 5.4-m-o.a., 30-kt., 10-man mi-rigid rubber inspection dinghies.

1 P 31 class Bldr: Verolme Dockyard, Cork

	Laid down	L	In serv.
31 Eithne	15-12-82	19-12-83	7-12-84

ne (P 31) Leo Van Ginderen, 7-90

: 1,760 tons (1,915 fl) **S:** 19 kts **Dim:** 81.00 × 12.00 × 4.30
1/57-mm Bofors SAK 57/70 Mk 1 DP—2/20-mm Rheinmetall AA—1/SA-365 Dauphin II helicopter
ectron Equipt:
Radar: 1/Decca TM 1229C nav., 1/Decca AC 1629C nav., 1/H.S.A. DA-05/4 surf./air search
Sonar: Plessey PMS 26L
2 Ruston Paxman 12RKCM diesels; 2 CP props; 7,200 bhp (6,640 sust.)
ectric: 1,625 kVA tot. (3 × 400 kw, 1 × 100 kw)
nge: 7,000/15
el: 290 tons **Crew:** 13 officers, 69 enlisted, plus 4 cadets

rks: P 31 ordered 23-4-82. Construction of a second unit deferred, in part be- yard closed in 1983 for financial reasons, but it is still hoped to acquire a sister. I.S.A. LIOD t.v./laser/IR fire-control system and 2 H.S.A. t.v./optical target ators for the 57-mm gun. Denny-Brown fin stabilizers. Considerable fire-fighting lity and can be replenished under way at sea. Boats include a 7.3-m crew boat, inspection boat, and 2 Avon Sea Raider semi-rigid inflatable boats with 90-hp rd motors. Harpoon landing system for the helicopter. MEL RRB helo transpon- arries 2 Wallop 57-mm flare RL. Has three fire-fighting water monitors. The ter is seldom aboard.

Emer class Bldr: Verolme Dockyard, Cork

	L	In serv.
Emer	1977	18-1-78
Aoife	12-4-79	21-11-79
Aisling	3-10-79	21-5-80

1,003 tons (fl) **S:** 18.5 kts
: 65.20 (58.50 pp) × 10.40 × 4.36
A: 1/40-mm Bofors AA—2/20-mm Oerlikon GAM B01 AA (I × 2)
Electron Equipt:
Radar: 1/Decca TM 1229C nav., 1/Decca AC 1629C nav.
Sonar: Simrad SU side-scan
M: 2 SEMT-Pielstick 6 PA6L-280 diesels; 1 CP prop; 4,800 bhp
Fuel: 170 tons **Range:** 4,500/18; 6,750/12
Crew: 5 officers, 41 enlisted

Aoife (P 22)—with portable van on fantail and MARISAT French Navy, 1990

Remarks: Developed version of the *Deirdre* with raised forecastle instead of bow bulwarks, to improve sea-keeping. Have advanced navigational aids, fin stabilizers. P 22 and P 23 have satellite navigation receivers, a 225-kw bow-thruster, a computerized plotting table, and a new-pattern KaMeWa propeller. Only P 23 has evaporators. All have three Pamou-Markon alternators. New 20-mm AA and MARISAT satellite communications terminal added 1989. P 21 and P 22 were placed in reserve 9-89 and 3-89, respectively, for lack of crews; as of late 1990, however, both were again operational.

◆ **1 Deirdre class** Bldr: Verolme Dockyard, Cork

	L	In serv.
P 20 Deirdre	29-12-71	19-6-72

Deirdre (P 20) Leo Van Ginderen, 6-91

D: 966 tons (fl) **S:** 17.5 kts (15.5 sust.)
Dim: 62.61 (56.20 pp) × 10.40 × 4.35
Electron Equipt:
Radar: 1/Decca TM 1229C nav., 1/Decca AC 1629C nav.
A: 1/40-mm Bofors AA—2/12.7-mm mg (I × 2)
M: 2 British Polar SF 112 VS-F diesels; 1 CP prop; 4,200 bhp
Range: 3,000/15.5; 5,000/12 **Fuel:** 150 tons
Crew: 5 officers, 41 enlisted

Remarks: Vosper fin stabilizers. New KaMeWa CP propeller fitted 1980. Has 2/50-mm rocket flare launchers. The 12.7-mm machine guns were fitted in 1989, and the ship now has MARISAT satellite communications equipment.

◆ **1 naval service launch**

Colleen II (In serv. 1972)

Remarks: Commanding officer's launch, Cork.

◆ **4 Department of Defence service launches**

David F (In serv. 1968) Fainleog
Fiachdubh Seabhac (ex-*Marino*)

Fainleog Bram Risseeuw, 8-89

IRELAND *(continued)*
PATROL SHIPS *(continued)*

David F Bram Risseeuw, 7-89

Remarks: *David F,* on charter since 1968, was taken over in 1988, as was *Fiachdubh. Fainleog* was acquired in 1983, as was *Seabhac,* an 11-meter tug.

♦ **1 sail-training craft** Bldr: Dufour, France

TAILTE

Remarks: 10.7 m o.a. The 120-ton sail-training craft *Asgard II* is the Irish National Youth Training Vessel; she is, on occasion, used by the Irish Defence Forces but does not belong to the Department of Defence.

♦ **2 Naval Reserve (*An Slua Muiri*) training craft**

CREIDNE NANCY BET

Remarks: Bermuda ketches: *Creidne* is 15.8 m o.a. and *Nancy Bet* is 14.6 m o.a. Also in use are five 5.5-m sail/oar boats. The 10.7-m launch *Kathleen Roma* has been retired. The Naval Reserve is hoping to obtain additional craft to serve as "Port and Territorial Waters Patrol Vessels."

Note: The former Royal Navy–chartered salvage vessel *Seaforth Clansman* was acquired 2-88 for use by the Irish government as a lighthouse and navigational aids tender; she is not a unit of the navy.

ISRAEL

State of Israel

Personnel (1991): Active: 6,000, of whom 600 officers and 500 men are specially trained as commandos and frogmen. Reserves: 500 total.

Naval Aviation: 7 IAI Westwind 1124 Sea Scan maritime-reconnaissance aircraft, whose mission is to cooperate with surface forces. Range: 1,350 n.m. at 270 kts. Carry sonobuoys. Two SA-365G (ex-U.S. Coast Guard HH-65A Dolphin prototypes) were delivered 7-85; 12 to 20 more ordered from France, 5-87, but have apparently not yet been delivered.

WEAPONS AND SYSTEMS

The Israeli Navy uses foreign weapons, such as 76-mm OTO Melara Compact, Breda 40-mm, and Oerlikon guns, and it has perfected the Gabriel antiship missile systems:

• Gabriel is a 560-kg, solid-propellant, surface-to-surface missile. After being fired, it climbs about 100 meters, then, at 7,500 meters from the launcher, descends slowly to an altitude of 20 meters. Optical or radar guidance is provided in azimuth, and a radio altimeter determines altitude. At a distance of 1,200 meters from the target, the missile descends to 3 meters, under either radio command or semiactive homing. The explosive charge is a 75-kg conventional warhead.

• The Gabriel II carries a television camera and a transceiver for azimuth and altitude commands. The television is energized when the missile has attained a certain height and sends to the firing ship a picture of the areas that cannot be picked up by shipboard radar. The operator then can send any necessary corrections during the middle and final phases of the missile's flight, and thus find a target that cannot be seen either by the naked eye or on radar. The range of the Gabriel II is about 40,000 meters.

• The Gabriel III system employs a frequency-agile, home-on-jam active radar seeker. An air-launched "Mk 3A/S" version is in development for launch from F-4, Mirage, Kfir, and A-4 Skyhawk aircraft. The sea-launched version has a range of 36,000 m at Mach .73, weighs 560 kg, and is 3.8 m long. Mk 3A/S weighs 600 kg, and has a range of 60,000 m, being launchable at 300- to 30,000-foot altitudes.

• The Gabriel IV, which entered service in 1987, is a further improvement:

Weight: 960 kg	Speed: Mach .85
Length: 4.70 m	Range: 200 km
Diameter: 0.43 m	Propulsion: 368-kg thrust turbojet
Span: 1.60 m	Warhead: 75 to 100 kg

• The Barak surface-to-air point-defense system, originally developed for use with an elevatable/trainable 8-cell box launcher, will now use a 32-cell vertical launch group when it enters service in the mid-1990s:

Weight: 98 kg	Speed: Mach 1.6
Length: 2.175 m	Guidance: semiactive homing
Warhead: 22 kg (tungsten pellets)	Range: 10 km

Barak's system weight with 32 rounds requires 1.3 m deck space plus 2 m below decks volume. The intended fire-control system employs the AMDR (Advanced Missi Detection Radar), an S-band, pulse-doppler set capable of tracking 250 Mach 0.3 to 3. targets. Initial at-sea launchings took place during 8-91.

Also in use are U.S.-supplied Redeye hand-held, IR-homing missiles.

The U.S. Harpoon was acquired beginning in 1978 and is used on guided-missi patrol boats in a mix with Gabriel, in both block 1B and 1C versions. Fourteen U. Vulcan/Phalanx 20-mm close-in weapon systems were delivered for use in vario units of the Sa'ar classes.

Most radar, weapons-control, combat data, communications, and electronics warfa systems are now made in Israel, based primarily on European and U.S. models. development during 1991 were the Rafael ATC-1 towed torpedo decoy and the sar company's "Scutter" expendable torpedo decoy.

SUBMARINES

♦ **0 (+2) Dolphin (Type 209/1500 modified) class**

	Bldr	Laid down	L	In serv.
. . . . . .	HDW, Kiel	. . .	. . .	1997
. . . . . .	Thyssen, Emden	. . .	. . .	1997

D: 1,550 tons (sub.) **S:** 13 kts surf./22.5 kts sub.
Dim: . . . × 6.50 × 6.20
A: 8/533-mm torpedo tubes (14 NT-37 torpedoes & Sub-Harpoon missiles)
Electron Equipt:
Radar: . . .—EW: . . .
Sonar: Krupp-Atlas CSU 90 suite with passive flank arrays
M: diesel-electric: 4 MTU 16V493 AZ80 diesels (800 bhp each), 4/650-k generators, 2 Siemens motor; 1 prop; 6,100 shp
Range: . . . **Endurance:** 50 days **Crew:** 36 tot.

Remarks: Authorized 3-88 to replace the relatively recent Type 206 submari Permission to build two vice the originally planned three was finally given in 8-89, the project was canceled in 11-90. Originally, the ships were to be assembled at Ing Shipyard, Pascagoula, in the United States using sections prefabricated by HD Germany. In 1-91, the project was revived when the German government offere finance fully the construction of two in Germany, using Krupp-Atlas combat equipment vice the originally planned U.S. systems. Will have two Kollmorgen scopes. Probably will have four 132-cell batteries.

♦ **3 German Type 206/500** Bldr: Vickers Ltd., Barrow, U.K.

	Laid down	L	In serv.
72 GAL	1973	2-12-75	12-76
74 TANIN	1974	25-10-76	6-77
76 RAHAV	1975	1977	12-77

Israeli Type 206/500 Israeli Navy,

D: 420 tons surf./600 sub. **S:** 10 kts surf./17 sub.
Dim: 45.00 × 4.60 × 4.30
A: 8/533-mm TT, fwd (10 U.S. NT-37E torpedoes, Sub-Harpoon missiles)
Electron Equipt:
Radar: Plessey . . . nav.
EW: Elbit TIMNEX 4 CH Mk 1 (2–18 gHz)
Sonar: Plessey . . . (active and passive)
M: 2 MTU 12V493 TY60 diesels (600 bhp each), 2 AEG 405 kw generators, 1 Siemens motor; 1 prop; 1,800 shp
Range: 4,500/5 (snorkel); 200/5 sub. **Fuel:** 24 tons
Crew: 22 tot.

Remarks: Ordered in 4-72 and built under license from IKL in Germany Vickers Type 540. Carry two spare torpedoes. These submarines do *not* ca Vickers SLAM submarine-launched antiaircraft missile systems, although p was made for its installation. U.S. Sub-Harpoon missiles provided and fire systems altered, 1983. NT-37E torpedoes ordered 1986. TIOS fire-control syst to be upgraded beginning in 1994 and will thus probably be retained after submarines above enter service.

GUIDED-MISSILE CORVETTES

♦ **0 (+3+1) Sa'ar V class** Bldr: Ingalls SB, Pascagoula, Mississipp

	Laid down	L	In serv.
501 LAHAV	10-2-92	10-92	15-10-93
502	3-8-92	4-93	31-3-94
503	8-2-93	10-93	30-9-94

GUIDED-MISSILE CORVETTES *(continued)*

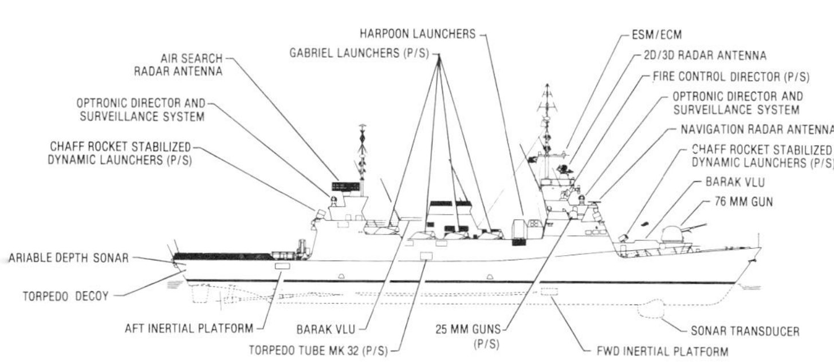

a'ar-V — Ingalls/Litton, 1990

a'ar-V — Ingalls/Litton, 1990

D: 1,162 tons (fl) **S:** 33 kts (20 on diesels)
Dim: 85.64 (76.60 wl) × 11.88 (10.39 wl) × 3.17 (hull)
A: 8/Harpoon SSM (IV × 2)—8/Gabriel IV SSM (I × 8)—2/Barak vertical-launch SAM groups (64 missiles)—1/76-mm U.S. Mk 75 DP—2/25-mm G.E. Sea Vulcan gatling AA—6/324-mm Mk 32 ASW TT (III × 2)— 1/SA-365G Dauphin helicopters (with rockets, etc.)
lectron Equipt:
Radar: 1/Cardion SPS-55 surf. search, 1/Cardion modified TPS-44 3-D air search, 2/Elta EL/M-2221 GM STGR f.c.
Sonar: EDO Type 796 hull-mounted MF, towed passive array
EW: . . . intercept, 4/72-tube decoy RL, 2/24-tube smoke RL, SLQ-25 Nixie torpedo decoy
1: CODOG: 1 G.E. LM-2500 gas turbine (30,000 shp), 2 MTU 12V1163 TB82 diesels (3,000 bhp each); 2 KaMeWa CP props; 30,000 shp max.
lectric: 1,880 kw (4 × 470 Siemens-MTU diesel sets)
ange: 3,500/17 **Endurance:** 20 days
rew: 16 officers, 7 CPO, 41 ratings + air group: 4 officers, 6 CPO

narks: Three (with option for fourth to be exercised by 4-92) ordered 2-89, all to be t in U.S. Were originally to have been eight, then four. Dates given above are der's projections.
esign emphasizes radar, noise, and heat-signature suppression. To cost around) million each. Will have Elta EL/S-9000 computers (based on the Motorola 68020 oprocessor). There will be three Elta optronic weapons directors for the guns. Have atertight compartments, Prairie-Masker bubbler underwater noise radiation supsion system. May carry the Israeli-developed Helstar helicopter reconnaissance e.

IDED-MISSILE PATROL BOATS

Nirit class Bldr: Israel SY, Haifa

	L	In serv.
z	10-90	3-91

: 488 tons (fl) **S:** 32 kts (30 sust.)
im: 61.70 (58.21 wl) × 7.62 (7.09 wl) × 2.76
4/Harpoon RGM-84 SSM (II × 2)—6/Gabriel-III SSM (I × 6)—4/ Barak point-defense SAM vertical-launch groups (VIII × 4; 32 tot. missiles)—1/76-mm OTO Melara Compact DP—1/20-mm Mk 15 Phalanx CIWS—2/20-mm Oerlikon AA (I × 2)—4/12.7-mm mg (I × 4)
Electronics:
Radar: 1/. . . K-band surf./air search, 2/Elta EL/M-2221 GM STGR f.c.
EW: Elta . . . intercept, 1/45-tube-trainable decoy RL, 8/smoke RL, 2/24-tube decoy RL
4 MTU 16V538 TB93 diesels; 4 props; 16,376 bhp (at 1,700 rpm)
ectric: . . . kw tot. (4 × 440V, 60 Hz diesel sets)
nge: 3,000/17 **Fuel:** 116 tons **Crew:** 50 tot.

Hetz — U.S. Navy, 1991

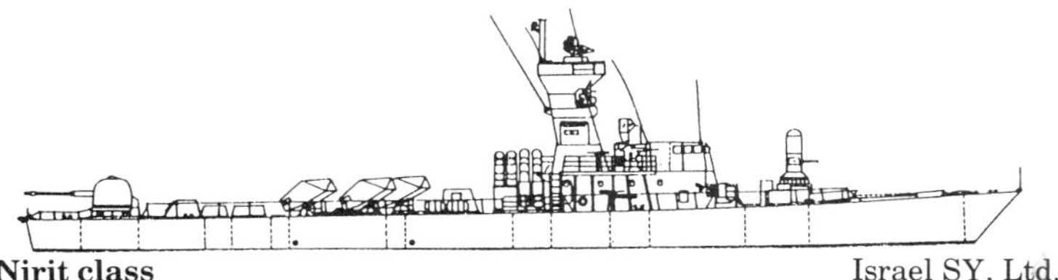
Nirit class — Israel SY, Ltd.

Remarks: Begun as a third unit of the *Romat* class during the early 1980s and completed as the seagoing trials ship for the Barak anti-missile missile system and advanced electronics. The four Barak vertical launch groups are recessed into the after deck. Their directors (essentially an Israeli-made version of the Orion RTN-10X) are mounted on platforms abreast the tower mast; initially, only the starboard-side radar director was installed. There is a standard optronic director for the Gabriel-III antiship missiles and an integrated weapons fire-control system. Has a round-bilge, semi-displacement mild-steel construction hull with more powerful diesel engines than earlier ships of the series.

◆ **2 Romat class** Bldr: Israel SY, Haifa

	L	In serv.		L	In serv.
Romat	1981	10-81	Keshet	10-82	1982

Romat—note elaborate D/F array atop mast — French Navy, 10-89

D: 375 tons (488 fl) **S:** 31 kts
Dim: 61.7 (58.21 wl) × 7.62 (7.09 wl) × 2.78
A: 8/Harpoon RGM-84 SSM (IV × 2)—6/Gabriel III SSM (I ×6) —1/76-mm OTO Melara Compact DP—1/20-mm Mk 15 Phalanx CIWS—2/20-mm Oerlikon AA (I × 2)—4/12.7-mm mg (I × 4)
Electron Equipt:
Radar: 1/TH-D 1040 Neptune surf./air search, 1/Orion RTN-10X f.c.
EW: MN-53 intercept system, NATACS communications intercept, NS 9010 D/F, 1/45-tube trainable chaff RL, 4/24-tube fixed chaff RL, 4/smoke RL
M: 4 MTU 16V956 TB91 diesels; 4 props; 14,000 bhp
Range: 1,500/30; 4,000/17 **Fuel:** 116 tons
Crew: 5 officers, 45 enlisted

Remarks: Employ the lengthened *Aliyah*-class hull, substituting additional armament for the helicopter facility. Third unit completed as *Hetz,* above. Have optronic director for the Gabriel-III missiles, Elbit Automatic Countermeasures Dispensing System (ACDS).

◆ **2 Aliyah (Sa'ar 4.5) class** Bldr: Israel SY, Haifa

	L	In serv.		L	In serv.
Aliyah	10-7-80	8-80	Geoula	10-80	31-12-80

D: 500 tons (fl) **S:** 31 kts (29 sust.)
Dim: 61.70 (58.21 wl) × 7.62 (7.09 wl) × 2.78
A: 4/Harpoon RGM-84 SSM (II × 2)—4/Gabriel-III SSM (I × 4)—1/20 mm Mk 15 Phalanx CIWS—2/20-mm Oerlikon AA (I × 2)—4/12.7-mm mg (I × 4)—1/helicopter
Electron Equipt:
Radar: 1/TH-D 1040 Neptune air/surf. search, 1/Orion RTN-10X f.c.

GUIDED-MISSILE PATROAL BOATS *(continued)*

Aliyah or Geoula—with SA-365G helo Israeli Navy, 1989

Aliyah—note D/F array atop mast, trainable decoy rocket launcher atop hangar French Navy, 10-89

EW: MN-53 intercept system, NATACS communications intercept, NS 9010 D/F, 1/45-tube trainable decoy RL, 4/24-tube chaff RL, 4/single smoke RL
M: 4/MTU 16V956 TB91 diesels; 4 props; 14,000 bhp
Range: 1,500/30; 4,000/17 **Fuel:** 116 tons **Crew:** 53 tot.

Remarks: The helicopter was intended to provide an over-the-horizon targeting capability to utilize fully the range capabilities of the Harpoon missiles, which are mounted athwartships in the gap between the fixed hangar and the bridge superstructure. Each *Aliyah* was to lead a group of missile boats. U.S. Mk 15 CIWS replaced original 40-mm mount forward. Have Elbit Automatic Countermeasures Dispensing System (ACDS).

♦ 8 Reshev (Sa'ar IV) class Bldr: Israel SY, Haifa

	L	In serv.		L	In serv.
Reshev	19-2-73	4-73	Nitzahon	10-7-78	9-78
Kidon	7-74	9-74	Atzmaut	3-12-78	2-79
Tarshish	1-75	3-75	Moledet	22-3-79	5-79
Yafo	2-75	4-75	Komemiyut	19-7-79	8-80

Reshev class 11-83

Reshev class French Navy, 1989

D: 415 tons (450 fl) **S:** 32 kts **Dim:** 58.10 × 7.62 × 2.40
A: 4/Harpoon RGM-84 SSM (II × 2)—6–8 Gabriel SSM (I × 6–8)—1/76-mm OTO Melara Compact DP—1/20-mm Mk 15 Phalanx CIWS—2/20-mm Oerlikon AA (I × 2)—4/12.7-mm mg (I × 4)
Electron Equipt:
Radar: 1/Thomson-CSF Neptune TH-D 1040 air/surf. search, 1 Selenia Orion RTN-10X f.c.
EW: Elta MN-53 intercept, NATACS communications intercept, NS 9010 D/F, 0 or 1/45-tube trainable decoy RL, 4 or 6/24-tube fixed decoy RL, 4/single smoke RL
M: 4 MTU 16V956 TB91 diesels; 4 props; 14,000 bhp (10,680 sust.)
Range: 1,650/30; 4,000/17.5 **Crew:** 45 tot.

Remarks: Quarters are air-conditioned. The *Tarshish* had a temporary helicopter deck in place of the after 76-mm gun for experiments with over-the-horizon targeting for Harpoon in 1979. Original missile armament was seven Gabriel. The Gabriel launchers are fixed. The 76-mm guns have been specially adapted for shore bombardment. The forward 76-mm mount was replaced by a 40-mm AA in *Nitzahon* and *Komemiyut*, pending availability of the U.S. Vulcan/Phalanx CIWS, the first of which was fitted to a *Reshev* in 2-83; all had it by 1985. Sisters *Keshet* and *Romach* were transferred to Chile 1979–80, with planned transfer of *Reshev* and one other in 198 canceled. Three were built in Israel for South Africa, six others were built in South Africa under license at Durban. The elaborate ECM/ESM system was designed by the Italian firm Elettronica and manufactured by Israel's Elta. Have Elbit Automati Countermeasures Dispensing System (ACDS). Some are likely to receive the Barak vertical-launch antimissile SAM system during major refits in the 1990s. One has bee used for trials with the Helstar drone reconnaissance helicopter.

♦ 1 Sa'ar III class Bldr: CMN, Cherbourg

Soufa (L: 4-2-69)

Sa'ar III class—with 2 Harpoon, 3 Gabriel, 1/76-mm gun French Navy, 19

♦ 6 Sa'ar II class Bldr: CMN, Cherbourg

	L		L		L
Mivtach	11-4-67	Misgav	1967	Haifa	14-6-68
Miznag	1967	Eilath	14-6-68	Akko	1968

Sa'ar II—with EDO 780 VDS aft and triple Mk 32 ASW TT to port

D: 220 tons (250 fl) **S:** 40 kts **Dim:** 45.0 × 7.0 × 1.8 (2.5 fl)
A: *Sa'ar II:* 5/Gabriel SSM (III × 1, I × 2)—1/40-mm AA Breda (I 2)—2/12.7-mm mg—3/324-mm Mk 32 ASW TT (III ×
Sa'ar III: 2/Harpoon SSM (I × 2)—3/Gabriel SSM (III × 1)—1/76 mm OTO Melara Compact DP—4/12.7-mm mg (I ×
Electron Equipt:
Radar: 1/Thomson-CSF Neptune TH-D 1040 air/surf. search, 1/Selenia Orion RTN-10X f.c.
Sonar: Sa'ar-II only: EDO 780 VDS
EW: VHFD/F and Elta MN-53 or NS 9000 intercept gear—6/24-tube fixed decoy RL, 4/single-tube smoke RL
M: 4 MTU MD871 diesels; 4 props; 14,000 bhp **Fuel:** 30 tons
Range: 1,000/30; 1,600/20; 2,500/15 **Crew:** 5 officers, 30–35 me

GUIDED-MISSILE PATROAL BOATS *(continued)*

Remarks: Excellent sea qualities and endurance. *Sa'ar I* is the name that was used for these ships in an all-gun configuration. Units of the *Sa'ar II* variant now carry an EDO 780 variable-depth sonar aft and triple 324-mm Mk 32 ASW TT (Mk 46 torpedoes) to port amidships and have no after gun mount. *Sa'ar III* has no ASW capability. Armaments now fairly standardized, but triple Gabriel launchers can be interchanged with the after 40-mm mountings. All have Elbit Automatic Countermeasures Dispensing System (ACDS). Sa'ar III units *Hanit* and *Hetz* sold to Chile early 1989, and sisters *Sa'ar, Gaasch,* and *Herev* were stricken 1990.

GUIDED-MISSILE HYDROFOILS

◆ **2 Grumman Mk II/M 161 class**

	Bldr	L	In serv.
M 161 Shimrit	Lantana BY, Lantana, Fla.	26-5-81	7-82
M 162 Livnit	Israel SY, Haifa	1983	1983

Shimrit Grumman, 1981

Livnit Israeli Navy, 1989

D: 71 tons light (103.5 fl) **S:** 45 kts (47 trials)
Dim: 31.79 foils retracted (25.62 hull; 23.40 wl) × 12.95 (7.32 hull) × 4.75 at rest (1.93 foiling; 1.52 foils retracted)
A: 4/Harpoon SSM (II × 2)—2/Gabriel SSM (I × 2)—2/30-mm BMARC GCM A-02 AA (II × 1)—2/12.7-mm mg (I × 2)
Electron Equipt: Radar: 1/. . . nav.—EW: . . .
M: 1 Allison 501-KF gas turbine; 1 CP, 4-bladed prop; 5,400 shp—2 G.M. 6V53 diesels driving retractable 80-bhp hydraulic motors for hull-borne maneuvering
Electric: 400 kw (2 × 200 kw; 2 Pratt & Whitney ST-6 gas turbines)
Range: 750/42 foiling; 2,600/8 hullborne **Fuel:** 21 tons
Endurance: 3 to 5 days **Crew:** 15 tot.

Remarks: First unit ordered 1978 from Grumman, with prototype construction subcontracted to Lantana. Numerous delays in program. *Livnit* built simultaneously at . Aluminum construction. Pineapple-shaped radome conceals intercept array. Maximum speed on auxiliary system: 10 kts. Turning radius at 45 kts: 200 m. Design on U.S. Navy's *Flagstaff* (PGH 2). *Livnit* has navigational radar atop radome, ent engine air intakes. Original plans for 15 cut to 3 in 1982: did not make 52-kt. ed speed. Reported third unit purportedly named *Snapirit* apparently never d.

PATROL CRAFT

◆ **1 non-naval Shaldag-class prototype** Bldr: Israel SY Ltd., Haifa (In serv. 1-90)

Shaldag prototype Israel SY, 1-90

D: 50 tons (56 fl) **S:** 50+ kts **Dim:** 24.80 × 6.00 × 1.15
A: 2/20-mm Oerlikon AA (I × 2)—2/12.7-mm mg (I × 2)
Electron Equipt: 1/. . . nav.
M: 2 Deutz-MWM TBD 604 B V16 diesels; 2 waterjets; 5,000 bhp
Electric: 50 kw tot. (2 × 25 kw, 440 V AC diesel sets)
Range: 890/45, 990/33 **Endurance:** 2–3 days
Crew: 8 tot.

Remarks: Builder-funded design not purchased on completion by the Israeli Navy. Aluminum-construction, deep-vee hull. Five watertight compartments. Air-conditioned. Can be equipped with night-vision devices and heavier armament. At the direction of Congress, has been tested by the U.S. Navy, which was apparently also not interested. Painted olive-green by builder. Has also been reported to have a range of 640 n.m. at 45 knots and 850 n.m. at 16 knots.

◆ **9 Super Dvora class** Bldr: RAMTA-Israeli Aircraft Industries, Be'er Sheva (In serv. 1-89 to . . .-91)

Super Dvora class RAMTA-I.A.I., 1990

D: 48 tons (fl) **S:** 36 kts **Dim:** 22.40 × 5.49 × 1.00
A: 2/20-mm AA (I × 2)—2/12.7-mm mg (I × 2)—provision for SSM and/or 1/84-mm Carl Gustav mortar
Electron Equipt: Radar: 1/Raytheon . . . nav.
M: 2 MTU 12V396 TB93 diesels; 2 props; . . . bhp **Electric:** 30 kw
Range: 700/14 **Crew:** 1 officer, 8 enlisted

Remarks: Improved version of basic Dvora design. Ordered by Israeli Navy and Sri Lanka during 1987. Depending on engine selected, can make 25 to 40 kts maximum speed. Maximum displacement of 54 tons would be as a missile boat. Aluminum construction. Can also be equipped with depth charges, ASW torpedoes, or 130-mm barrage rocket launchers. Three more to order 1990. Of six ordered 3-87, first was delivered 1-89, rest in 1989–90. This design is offered for foreign sale in a Mk II version with two—and Mk II version with three—700 bhp G.M. diesels driving Arneson surface-piercing articulating outdrives; the three-engine version would theoretically be capable of 50 knots.

◆ **1 Dvora class** Bldr: Israeli Aircraft Industries, Be'er Sheva (In serv. 1978)

D: 47 tons (fl) **S:** 36 kts **Dim:** 21.62 × 5.49 × 0.94 (1.82 props)
A: 2/20-mm AA (I × 2)—2/12.7-mm mg (I × 2)
Electron Equipt: Radar: 1/Decca 926 nav.
M: 2 MTU 12V331 TC81 diesels; 2 props; 2,720 bhp
Electric: 30 kw **Range:** 700/32 **Crew:** 8–10 tot.

Remarks: Privately funded prototype, acquired in 1979. The design has been offered with two Gabriel SSM and has been exported to Nicaragua, Argentina, and Chile without missiles. Fifty have also been built in Taiwan in slightly modified form as the "Hai Ou" class.

◆ **31 Dabur class** Bldrs: 12 by Sewart Seacraft, U.S.A.; others by Israeli Aircraft Industries, Be'er Sheva (In serv. 1973–77)

D: 25 tons (35 fl) **S:** 25 kts (22 cruise)
Dim: 19.8 × 5.8 × 0.8
A: 2/20-mm (I × 2)—2/12.7-mm mg (I × 2)
Electron Equipt: Radar: 1/Decca 101 or 926 nav.
M: 2 G.M. 12V71 TI diesels; 2 props; 960 bhp
Electric: 20 kw **Range:** 1,200/17
Crew: 1 officer, 5 men

ISRAEL *(continued)*
PATROL CRAFT *(continued)*

Dabur class Israeli Navy, 1989

Remarks: Aluminum construction design based on U.S. 65-ft Commercial Cruiser class. Quarters air-conditioned. Small enough for land transport by truck. Some may be equipped with depth charges or 324-mm Mk 32 antisubmarine torpedo tubes. Five given to Christian forces in Lebanon in 1976, six sold to Chile in 1991. Also built for export in Israel, with four sold to Argentina and four to Nicaragua in 1978 and, possibly, two to Sri Lanka in 1984.

◆ **16 Yatush class (U.S. PBR type)**

D: 6.5 tons (8.9 fl) **S:** 25 kts **Dim:** 9.73 × 3.53 × 0.81
A: 2/7.62-mm mg (I × 2)
Electron Equipt: Radar: 1/Raytheon 1900 nav.
M: 2 G.M. 6V53N diesels; Jacuzzi waterjets; 430 bhp
Range: 150/23 **Crew:** 5 tot.

Remarks: Early units built by Uniflite, Bellingham, Washington, bought in the United States in 1968; later ones built in Israel. Several may be stationed in the Red Sea. Two given to Lebanese Christians, 1975–76. Some are used by the National Police. Nine discarded 1990.

AMPHIBIOUS WARFARE SHIPS

Note: Construction of two new landing ships was planned: approx. 117.0 × 17.0 × 2.2, helicopter platform, facilities for several hundred troops, but funding has not materialized.

◆ **1 former commercial landing craft** Bldr: . . . , Germany

Bat Sheva (In serv. 1967)

Bat Sheva Israeli Navy, 1989

D: 900 tons (1,150 fl) **S:** 10 kts **Dim:** 95.1 × 11.2 × . . .
A: 4/20-mm Oerlikon AA (I × 4)—4/12.7-mm mg (I × 4)
Electron Equipt: Radar: 1/. . . nav.
M: 2 diesels; 2 props: . . . bhp **Crew:** 26 tot.

Remarks: Bought in South Africa in 1968.

◆ **3 Ashdod-class tank landing craft** Bldr: Israel SY, Haifa (In serv. 1966–67)

61 Ashdod 63 Ashkelon 65 Ahziv

Ashdod class 1971

D: 400 tons (730 fl) **S:** 10.5 kts **Dim:** 62.7 × 10.0 × 1.8
A: 2/20-mm Oerlikon AA (I × 2)
Electron Equipt: Radar: 1/. . . nav.
M: 3 MWM diesels; 3 props; 1,900 bhp
Fuel: 37 tons **Crew:** 20 tot.

Remarks: Ashdod has been employed in Barak antimissile SAM system development trials. One was used during the 1970s for helicopter trials.

Note: The three *Etziongueber*-class landing craft, *Etziongueber, Shikmona,* and *Kessaraya,* are believed to have been stricken 1990–91.

◆ **1 U.S. LCSR swimmer-delivery boat** (In serv. 1964)

D: 16.5 tons (24.3 fl) **S:** 35 kts **Dim:** 16.00 × 4.35 × 1.68 (loaded)
A: 2/12.7-mm mg (I × 2)
M: 2 Saturn T-1000 gas turbines; 2 props; 2,000 shp
Range: 200/35 **Crew:** 3 crew, 22 troops

Remarks: Transferred from U.S. Navy late 1960s. Can also transport about 1 ton of supplies. Three sisters discarded by 1991.

Note: The Israeli Army also employs several 54-ton (light) river-crossing craft capable of transporting 130-ton loads.

AUXILIARIES

◆ **1 training ship** Bldr: Kasado DY, Japan (In serv. 1979)

Qeshet (ex-. . .)

D: . . . **S:** . . . **Dim:** 115.0 × . . . × . . .
M: . . . diesels; . . . props; . . . bhp

Remarks: Former 2,800-grt/4,634-dwt passenger-cargo vessel equipped as a trainin ship for the navy and merchant marine; replaced the *Nogah* in 1991.

◆ **1 small missile-boat tender**

Naharya

Remarks: Base craft for the missile craft stationed at Eilath. No data available.

◆ **1 missile-boat tender** Bldr: Todd SY, Seattle (In serv. 1976)

Nir (ex-*Ma'oz*)

Remarks: 4,000-ton oilfield-supply vessel used as a missile-boat tender in the Mec terranean.

◆ **1 tug**

Sufa

Remarks: No data available.

NATIONAL POLICE

◆ **1 (+ . . .) Snaparit class**

D: 7.8 tons (8.3 fl) **S:** 30 kts (26 sust.)
Dim: 11.8 (10.0 wl) × 3.6 × 0.6
A: . . .
M: 2 Volvo Penta TAMD 70 diesels; 2 Castoldi waterjets; 372 bhp
Range: 216/26 **Fuel:** 800 liters **Crew:** 3–4 tot.

Remarks: GRP construction; truck-transportable. Intended for service on the Se Galilee.

Note: The National Police also employ several of the Yatush-class patrol craft scribed above.

ITALY

Italian Republic

Personnel (1991): 49,100 (including 5,000 officers and 18,600 petty officers); 1,000-man San Marco Battalion is also part of the Italian Navy.

Naval Aviation: About 1,900 personnel are involved in Italian naval aviation. *Marinavia* operates 93 helicopters: 36 SH-3D Sea King heavy ASW (shore-based aboard *Giuseppe Garibaldi*) and 57 AB-212 light ASW helicopters for service ab frigates and destroyers and for training. Italy is a partner in the development o EH-101 heavy ASW helicopter, and the navy hopes to acquire 30 to replace the Kings. To replace the AB-212s, it is planned to acquire 64 NH-90 helicopters. Th SH-3D squadrons are based at Luni (1st Squadron) and Catania (3rd Squadron) 2nd, 4th, and 5th AB-212 squadrons are based at Luni, Taranto, and Catania, re tively.

With permission secured from the Italian parliament, 15 AV-8B+ Harrier V/S shipboard fighters equipped with APG-65 radars and two 2-seat TAV-8B trainers ordered from McDonnell Douglas in the United States in 1990. The two TA trainers were delivered on 23-8-91 at Norfolk, Virginia, and the single-seat ai will be delivered late 1992–early 1993 for service aboard *Giuseppe Garibaldi* an be based ashore at Taranto. The navy would like to acquire Grumman E-2C Hav radar aircraft for land-based operations in support of the Harriers.

The air force conducts fixed-wing maritime ASW patrol, using 18 Bréguet At Mk 1 ordered in 1968 and delivered by 1973. The Atlantics are based at Catania (Squadron) and Cagliari/Elmas (No. 88 Squadron). The Atlantics have been mode to Atlantique Mk 2 standard with Iguane radar, Litton inertial navigation syst new acoustic processor, and sonobuoy dispensers. Italian Air Force Tornado fighters carry the Kormoran I missile for antiship missions. Fifteen Agusta variants of the U.S. Coast Guard Sikorsky HH-3F Pelican helicopter were ordere for the *Protezione Civile* for search-and-rescue service.

The Bell AB-212 was built under license from Bell Helicopter by Agusta in Ita EH-101 is a cooperative venture between Westland in the U.K. and Agusta in

NAVAL AVIATION *(continued)*

♦ **EH-101:**

Length: 22.90 m
Rotor diameter: 18.59 m
Max. weight: 13,000 kg
Engines: 3 CT7-6A turboshaft, 1,723 shp each
Crew: 4 total
Max. speed: 170 kts
Cruise speed: 160 kts
Endurance: 5 hours
Armament: 4 ASW torpedoes
Sensors: APS-748 radar, Helras dipping sonar

♦ **SH-3D:**

Length: 22.16 m
Rotor diameter: 18.90 m
Max. weight: 9,300 kg
Engines: 2 1,400-shp turboshaft
Crew: 3 tot.
Max. speed: 144 kts
Cruise speed: 118 kts
Endurance: 4 hr 50 min
Armament: 2 Mk 46 torpedoes or depth charges, or 2 Marte Mk 2 ASM

♦ **AB-212:**

Length: 17.40 m
Rotor diameter: 14.60 m
Height: 4.40 m
Max. weight: 5,086 kg
Engine: 1 1,290-shp turboshaft
Max speed: 130 kts
Cruise speed: 100 kts
Max. altitude: 5,000 ft.
Endurance: 4 hr 15 min
Crew: 3 tot.
Armament: 2 Mk 46 torpedoes, depth charges, or 2 AS-12 missiles
Sensors: AQS-13B dipping sonar

alian Navy AB-212 — Italian Navy, 1990

lian Navy SH-3D Sea King — Italian Navy, 1990

ian Navy TAV-8B Harrier — McDonnell Douglas, 1991

WEAPONS AND SYSTEMS

MISSILES

♦ Surface-to-air

e: Italy has joined with France in the development of the FSAF/FAMS surface-to-issile program as a replacement for the systems currently employed. Development e Idra vertically launched Aspide replacement has apparently been terminated.

ndard SM-1 ER and SM-1 MR (see under U.S.A.)

ide Bldr: Selenia

Ceiling: 15 m (min); 5,000 m (max.)
Length: 3.673 m
Wingspan: 0.644 m
Range: 10,000 m
Diameter: 0.204 m
Weight: 217 kg at launch
Guidance: semiactive homing

Aspide is, in effect, the Italian version of the U.S. Sea Sparrow. The system employs an octuple, 7-ton Albatros launcher built by OTO Melara; elevation: 5 to +65°. Controlled by NA-30 radar fire control system. A quadruple launcher has been produced for use on export corvettes.

♦ **Surface-to-surface**

Otomat Mk 2 ("Teseo")

Length: 4.820 m
Diameter: 0.460 m (1.060 m with boosters)
Wingspan: 1.19 m
Weight: 750 kg
Range: 150 km
Guidance: autopilot, active radar homing
Warhead weight: 200 kg
Speed: 300 m/sec

This model differs from the original Otomat Mk 1 in having an Italian (SMA) active radar homing head, instead of a French one. It is also a "sea-skimmer"; that is, it flies close to the water after firing. Its ramjet propulsion system allows it to be used at ranges limited only by its guidance system and its target designation. The system is to be upgraded through the provision of "stealth" signature-reduction techniques. The original Otomat Mk 1 is also still in use by the Italian Navy.

Two additional projects are in development: "Briaero," a Mach 1.0 weapon with a 200–400-km range, and "Otomach," a Mach 2, turbojet-powered weapon being developed by OTO Melara and Alfa-Romeo that will incorporate "low-observable" signature reduction.

♦ **Air-to-surface**

Marte Mk 2:

Length: 4.84 m (with 1.09-m booster)
Diameter: 31.6 cm
Span: 98.7 cm (cruciform)
Weight: 340 kg
Speed: Mach 0.8
Range: over 20 km
Warhead: 70 kg

For use by Sea King helicopters. Guidance is by gyro autopilot and radar altimeter over mid-course, with active pseudo-monopulse radar homing, using the same seeker as the Otomat. Fuzing is influence and impact. The airframe is basically that of the obsolescent Sistel Sea Killer surface-launched antiship missile.

Note: The French S.N.I.A.S. AS-12 wire-guided antishipping missile has been adopted for use by AB-212 helicopters.

B. GUNS

127-mm OTO Melara Compact:

Single-barreled automatic, remote control

Length: 54 calibers
Muzzle velocity: 807 m/sec
Max. effective range, surface fire: 15,000 m
Max. effective range, antiaircraft fire: 7,000 m
Rate of fire: 45 rounds/min, automatic setting

Weight of the mount: 32 tons because of the use of light alloys and a fiberglass shield. The gun has a muzzle brake; it can automatically fire 66 rounds, thanks to 3 loading drums, each with 22 rounds. Two hoists serve two loading trays with rounds coming from the magazine, and a drum may be loaded even while the gun is firing. An automatic selection system allows a choice of ammunition (antiaircraft, surface target, pyrotechnics, chaff for cluttering radar).

This equipment has also been purchased by the Canadian Navy, Argentina, Peru, Venezuela, Japan, and Nigeria.

76-mm OTO Melara Compact:

Single-barreled light antiaircraft automatic fire; entirely remote control with muzzle brake and cooling system. Development is continuing on a course-corrected shell for this weapon, using a shipboard data link to the projectile.

Length: 62 calibers
Rate of fire: 85 rounds/min
Muzzle velocity: 925 m/sec
Weight of mount: 7.35 tons
Max. effective range, surface fire: 8,000 m
Max. effective range, antiaircraft fire: 4,000–5,000 m

Has 80 ready-service rounds in the drum. The current "Super Rapid" version of the weapon weighs 7.5 tons and fires at 1, 10, or 120 rds/min, with 85 rds on mount.

76-mm OTO Melara:

Single-barreled automatic for air, surface, and land targets; obsolescent

Length: 62 calibers
Muzzle velocity: 850 m/sec
Max. effective range, surface fire: 8,000 m
Max. effective range, antiaircraft fire: 4,000–5,000 m
Rate of fire: 60 rds/min/barrel

40-mm Breda/Bofors Compact twin:

Length: 70 calibers
Rate of fire: 300 rds/min/barrel
Muzzle velocity: 1,000 m/sec
Projectile weight: 0.96 kg
Max. effective range, antiaircraft fire: 3,500–4,000 m
Number of ready-service rounds: 444 or 736 (depending on installation)
Fire control: Dardo system (Selenia RTN-20X radar)
Impact or proximity fuzing

30-mm Breda/Mauser:

Employed by the *Guardia di Finanza* and available for export.

GUNS *(continued)*

Muzzle velocity: 1,040 m/sec Rate of fire: 800 rds/min
Max. effective range: 1,500 m Elevation: −13° to +85°

Note: The Myriad CIWS, employing two GAU-8 30-mm gatling AA guns, is under development by a consortium of Breda, Selenia, Elsag, and Contraves.

C. ANTISUBMARINE WEAPONS

Milas (*Missile de Lutte Anti-Sousmarine*):

Under development by OTO Melara and France's Engins Matra using the Otomat propulsion section. It will weigh 800 kg (1,800 kg with launcher), carry an A-290 torpedo payload in the Italian Navy version, and have a range of 40 km. Initial trials were conducted during 1989, and initial service is possible by 1993.

Length: 6.0 m Speed: 1,080 km/hr
Diameter: 0.46 m Range: 40 km
Wingspan: 1.06 m Weight: 800 kg (Italian version)

K113 Menon mortar

The system, now used only on the frigate *Alpino* (F 580), has a single 305-mm barrel some 4.6 m long, with automatic loading. The mortar is fired at a 45° angle; 160-kg depth charge rounds employ gas relief valves from three powder chambers with adjustable vents to produce ranges varying from 400 to 900 m. The weapon is automatically reloaded from the magazine by hoist.

ASW Torpedoes

American Mk 46 and Italian Whitehead Motofides A-244 small ASW torpedoes are used on ships (using the triple ILAS-3 tube mount, similar to the U.S. Mk 32 ASW torpedo tube set) and helicopters.

The Whitehead Motofides A-184 (6.0 m long; 1,245 kg) wire-guided torpedo is a 533-mm weapon with a range of over 15,000 m.

A-290, a 50-knot, 324-mm by 2.75-m weapon using the A-244's seeker has been in development since 1981 and was to begin trials in 1984; it will use a lithium battery and was expected to enter service in 1992. Instead, the Italian program is to be merged with the French Murène ASW program as the Mu-90.

D. MINES

The following mines are in production in Italy for domestic and export use:

—MR 80: Mod. A: 1,035 kg (with 856-kg explosive); Mod. B: 790 kg (with 611-kg explosive); Mod. C: 630 kg (with 451-kg explosive). All versions can be used to 300-m depths.
—Manta: 240-kg (170-kg explosive) bottom influence mine; up to 100-m depths.
—Seppia: 870 kg (200-kg explosive), usable in waters up to 300-m depth.

E. RADARS

The Italian Navy has used a number of American search and missile-control radars (SPS-12, SPS-52, SPG-51, SPG-55, etc.), but now primarily uses a number of systems developed in Italy by Gem Elettronica, SMA, and the Selenia-Elsag division of Alenia. The designation system employed by the Italian armed forces is like that used in the United States, except that the prefix letters before the slash (omitted in the ship listings that follow) are "MM"(*Marina-Militaire*) vice "AN."

Type	*Band*	*Remarks*
MM/BPS-704	I/S(X)	SMA 3 RM 20 adapted for submarines
BX-732	I	Gem navigational set widely employed on smaller ships
MM/SPN-703	I	SMA navigational radar; also known as 3 RM 28B
MM/SPN-704	I	SMA navigational radar, 3 RM 20 for submarines
MM/SPN-720	I	Landing-aid radar, a variant of SPS-702
MM/SPN-728	X	SMA navigational/helo-control; dual antenna
MM/SPN-748	X	Gem Elettronica navigational
MM/SPN-749(V)	I(X)	Gem Elettronica navigational set on *Garibaldi;* 2 antennas (9345–9405 MHz)
MM/SPN-751	I(X)	Commercial navigational set, used in auxiliaries
MM/SPN-753(V)	I	Gem Elettronica navigational set; introduced 1989
MM/SPQ-2A/D	I/J (X)	SMA navigational/surface/air search set; obsolescent
MM/SPQ-701	I	SMA frequency-agile, sea-skimmer detector; upgraded variant of SPQ-2, for *Sparviero*-class hydrofoils
MM/SPS-702	I	SMA frequency-agile, sea-skimmer detector; modern version of SPQ-2
MM/SPS-768	D(S)	Selenia 3-D air search, also known as RAN-3L
MM/SPS-774	E/J (S/X)	Selenia air/surf. surveillance, also known as RAN-10S; entered service 1980
MM/SPY-790	G	Selenia EMPAR 3-D frequency-agile phased array surf./air search (in development)
MM/SPG-70	I/J(X)	Selenia gun and missile fire control (RTN-10X Orion for Argo system)
MM/SPG-74	I/J (X)	Selenia 40-mm gun f.c. (RTN-20X Dardo)
MM/SPG-75	I/J (X)	Selenia missile f.c. (RTN-30X for Albatros syst.)

F. SONARS

Most of the newest equipment is American or Dutch.

Type		*Frequency*
CWE 610	Hull	LF (Dutch)
DE 1160B	Hull	MF (U.S.)
DE 1164	Hull or VDS	MF (U.S.)
SQQ-14	Minehunting	HF (U.S.)
SQQ-14IT	Minehunting	HF (It.)
SQS-23	Hull	MF (U.S.)
SQS-29	Hull	MF (U.S.)
SQS-11A	Hull	MF (U.S.)
SQS-39	Hull	MF (U.S.)
SQS-10	Hull	MF (U.S.)
SQA-10	VDS	MF (U.S.)
SQS-36	VDS	HF (U.S.)

Note: An experimental tactical towed array sonar (TASS) was in trials aboard the frigate *Maestrale* during 1989.

G. TACTICAL INFORMATION SYSTEM

The Italian Navy has developed the SADOC system, which is compatible wit American NTDS and French SENIT systems through NATO Link-11.

H. COUNTERMEASURES

A wide variety of intercept arrays, many with stabilized cylindrical radome an tennas, are in use. The Lambda intercept system employs the SLQ-D and SLR- intercept arrays combined with a superheterodyne receiver; the similar Newton has simpler receiver. Elettronica's Nettuno integrated ECM/ESM system employs fou stabilized radome-mounted antennas.

The Breda SCLAR chaff rocket-launching system is used on frigates and large ships; it has 20 tubes for 105-mm rockets in a trainable, elevatable launcher. A numbe of Wallops Barricade chaff rocket launchers were ordered 1984, and the French Saga is being used on the new *Animoso*-class guided-missile destroyers.

The Whitehead C303 Effector decoy system for submarines employs two 21-tu launch arrays mounted in the sail.

HELICOPTER CARRIER

◆ **1 (+1) Garibaldi class** Bldr: Italcantieri, Monfalcone

	Laid down	L	In serv.
C 551 Giuseppe Garibaldi	26-3-81	4-6-83	30-9-85

D: 9,369 tons (13,240 fl) **S:** 29.5 kts
Dim: 180.2 (173.8 wl, 162.8 pp) × 30.4 (23.8 wl) × 6.7
A: 8/Otomat-Teseo Mk 2 SSM (II × 4)—2/Albatros SAM syst. (VIII × 2; 48 Aspide missiles)—6/40-mm AA Breda Dardo (II × 3)—6/324 mm ILAS-3 ASW TT (III × 2)—16/SH-3D Sea King helicopters (*se* Remarks)
Electron Equipt:
Radar: 1/MM/SPN-749(V) nav. (2 antennas), 1/SPN-702 surf. search, 1/SPS-768 air early warning, 1/SPS-774 air search, 1/ U.S. SPS-52C 3-D air search, 3/SPG-74 (RTN-20 gun f.c., 2/SPG-75 (RTN-30X) missile f.c.
Sonar: Raytheon DE 1160 LF bow-mounted
EW: Elettronica Nettuno SLQ-732 integrated receiver/jammer system, 2/SCLAR 105-mm decoy RL (XX × 2), SLQ-25 Nixie towed torpedo decoy
TACAN: SRN-15A
M: 4 G.E./Fiat LM-2500 gas turbines; 2 5-bladed props; 80,000 shp
Electric: 9,360 kw (6 GMT B230-12M diesel alternator sets)
Range: 7,000/20
Crew: 550 ship's company + 230 air group, 45 flag staff

Remarks: Ordered 20-2-78. Began sea trials 3-12-84; delivered 31-7-85. A se ship, possibly some 1,000 tons greater in displacement, is planned and would be na *Giuseppe Mazzini* or *Conte de Cavour* if built. Ship type: *Incrociatore Porto-Aeromo* Serves as fleet flagship, replacing *Vittorio Veneto* in that capacity.

The *Garibaldi* was completed as an ASW ship for helicopters, although the de permits the handling of V/STOL aircraft as well. The flight deck is 173.8 meters There are two elevators, one forward of and one abaft the island. There are six fl deck spaces for flight operations. The hangar (110 × 15 × 6 meters) can accommo 12 Sea King, or 10 Sea Harriers and 1 Sea King. Trials with 6 Royal Navy Sea Har successfully conducted 5-88. Permission to begin acquisition of Sea Harrier/Ha aircraft was given 29-1-89, and 16 McDonnell Douglas AV-8B+ Harrier with AP radar will begin deliveries late 1992 to perform interceptor and maritime attack d

Steel superstructure. To permit helicopter operations in heavy weather, much a tion was given to stability, and the ship has two pairs of fin stabilizers; the bow small "ski-jump" sheer, which will be of assistance in Harrier launchings. Ther five decks: the flight deck; the hangar deck, which is also the main deck; and two and a platform deck below the hangar deck. Thirteen watertight bulkheads divid ship into 14 sections, and the interior can be sealed against NBC warfare. Has II (SADOC 2) computerized data system with 13 consoles and is capable of handlin threat tracks simultaneously. Has MARISAT SATCOMM gear and can employ N Link-11, -14, and -16.

The propulsion train employs Tosi reverse/reduction gearing rather controllable-pitch propellers.

The number of antiship missiles was doubled when Otomat Mk 2 launchers, st one atop the other, were substituted for the original Mk 1 version late in the 19

Carries two personnel transport launches, MEN 215 and MEN 216, each cap carrying up to 250 persons in SAR, commando, and disaster relief duties; s description of these craft on later page.

HELICOPTER CARRIER *(continued)*

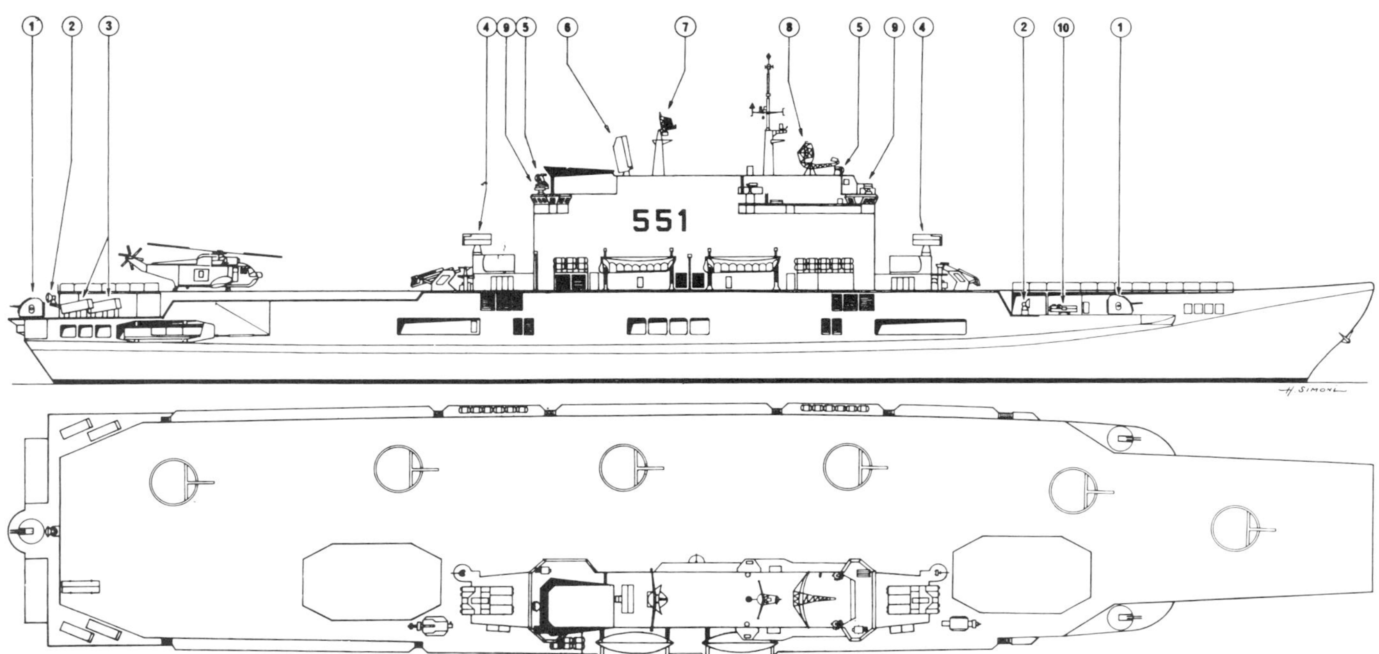

Giuseppe Garibaldi 1. twin Breda 40-mm AA 2. Dardo f.c. system radar (RTN-20X/SPG-74) 3. Otomat-Teseo Mk 2 SSM launchers 4. Albatros SAM system launchers 5. RTN-30X/SPG-75 f.c. radar for Albatros system's Aspide missiles 6. SPS-768 radar 7. SPS-774 radar 8. SPS-52C radar 9. Breda SCLAR decoy launcher 10. ILAS-3 triple ASW TT Robert Dumas

eppe Garibaldi (C 551) Pradignac & Léo, 5-89

HELICOPTER CARRIER *(continued)*

Giuseppe Garibaldi (C 551) Giorgio Arra, 8-91

Giuseppe Garibaldi (C 551) Giorgio Arra, 8-91

SUBMARINES

♦ **0 (+4) S 90 class—projected** Bldr: Fincantiere, Monfalcone

	Laid down	L	In serv.
S.	. . .	. . .	1997
S.	. . .	. . .	. . .

D: 2,500 tons surf./2,780 sub. **S:** 11 kts surf./22 sub.
Dim: 69.7 × 8.2 × 6.3
A: 6/533-mm TT (24 Harpoon missiles and torpedoes)
Electron Equipt:
Radar: . . .
Sonar: . . .
EW: . . .
M: 3 GMT A210 16 NM diesels (1,200 bhp each), 3 895-kw generator sets, 1 twin Marelli 4,500-kw motor, 2,400 kw sust.; 1/7-bladed prop
Range: 6,000/6 snorkel **Fuel:** . . . **Endurance:** . . .
Crew: 8 officers, 42 enlisted

Remarks: Follow-on design to *Primo Longobardo* class, with same propulsion plant but greater endurance and diving depth (400-m test depth). Design not frozen, and above data are provisional. First two would be ordered in 1993 for delivery beginning in 1997; second pair would begin replacement of the *Sauro* class.

♦ **0 (+2) Primo Longobardo class** Bldr: Italcantieri, Monfalcone

	Laid down	L	In serv.
S 524 Primo Longobardo	28-7-88	10-91	2-93
S 525 Gazzana Priaroggia	1989	5-92	9-93

D: 1,653 tons surf./1,862 sub. **S:** 11 kts surf./19 sub.
Dim: 66.35 (65.70 pp) × 6.83 × 6.00
A: 6/533-mm TT fwd (12 A-184 torpedoes or Sub-Harpoon SSM)
Electron Equipt:
Radar: 1/BPS-704 nav.—EW: Elettronica BLD-727 Thetis intercept
Sonar: IPD-705 active/passive, MD 100S passive flank array
M: diesel-electric: 3 GMT A 210 16NM diesel alternator sets (895 kw each), 1 electric motor; 1 7-bladed prop; . . . shp
Range: 5,100/5 snorkel, 240/4 submerged **Crew:** . . . tot.

Remarks: Ordered 28-7-88. Further development of the two preceding classes employing improved hydrodynamic form and HY-80 steel for the construction of the pressure hull. Will dive to 300 m. Will have SACTIS BSN-716 combat system, Litton PL-41 inertial navigation system.

♦ **2 Salvatore Pelosi class** Bldr: Fincantiere, Monfalcone

	Laid down	L	In serv.
S 522 Salvatore Pelosi	23-7-86	29-11-86	14-7-88
S 523 Giuliano Prini	30-7-87	12-12-87	11-11-89

D: 1,476 tons surf./1,662 sub.
S: 11 kts surf./12 kts snorkel/19 sub.
Dim: 64.36 × 6.83 × 5.66
A: 6/533-mm TT fwd (12 Type A-184 torpedoes)

Giuliano Prini (S 523) Leo Van Ginderen, 1991

Giuliano Prini (S 523) Dr. Maurizio del Prete, 199

Electron Equipt:
Radar: 1/BPS-704 nav.—EW: Elettronica BLD-727 intercept
Sonar: USEA/Selenia IPD-70/3 passive linear flank array, Elsag MI 100S passive ranging, Velox M5 sonar intercept
M: 3 GMT A210 16NM, 895-kw diesel generator sets, 1 twin Marelli 3,140-kw motor (2,400 kw sust.); 1/7-bladed prop; 4,270 shp max. at 233 rpm
Range: 3,000/11 surf.; 2,500/12 snorkel; 250/4 sub. **Fuel:** 144 tons
Endurance: 45 days **Crew:** 7 officers, 43 enlisted

Remarks: Improved version of *Sauro* class, with .5 m added amidships, one wat tight bulkhead. Ordered 7-3-83. Have capability to launch U.S. Sub-Harpoon SSM, b missiles have not yet been acquired. Two Kollmorgen S76 models 322 and 323 pe scopes (one with laser range finder, one with ranging radar), Litton PL-41 inert navigation system, improved SMA BSN-716(V)2 SACTIS combat data-weapons c trol system with NATO Link-11 receive-only capability. Do not have "crash-di ballast tank as in *Sauro* class. Pressure hull of U.S. HY-80 steel. Test depth 300 collapse depth 600 m. Two 148-cell batteries, 6,500 amp/hr. Have 15-kHz act ranging/underwater telephone transducers at the bow.

♦ **4 Nazario Sauro class** Bldr: C.R.D.A., Monfalcone (last two: Italcantiere, Monfalcone)

	Laid down	L	In serv.
S 518 Nazario Sauro	26-6-74	9-10-76	1-3-80
S 519 Carlo Fecia Di Cossato	15-7-76	16-11-77	1-3-80
S 520 Leonardo da Vinci	1-7-76	20-10-79	6-11-82
S 521 Guglielmo Marconi	23-10-79	20-9-80	16-10-82

Nazario Sauro (S 518) Italian Navy,

Guglielmo Marconi (S 521) Leo Van Ginderen

SUBMARINES *(continued)*

D: 1,450 tons surf./1,637 sub.
S: 11 kts surf./12 kts snorkel/19.3 kts sub.
Dim: 63.85 × 6.83 × 5.70 (12.38 keel to top of sail)
A: 6/533-mm B.512 TT fwd (12 Type A-184 torpedoes)
Electron Equipt:
Radar: 1/BPS-704 nav.—EW: BLD-727 intercept
Sonar: USEA/Selenia IPD-70/S passive system, Velox M5 intercept
M: diesel-electric: 3 GMT A210 16NM, 895-kw generator sets, 1 twin 3,140-kw (2,400-kw cont.) motor; 1 7-bladed prop; 4,270 shp
Range: 6,150/11 surf.; 2,500/12 snorkel, 250/4 sub.
Fuel: 144 tons **Endurance:** 45 days
Crew: 6 officers, 43 enlisted

Remarks: First two authorized 1972; second pair ordered 12-2-76. Maximum diving depth is 300 meters. Completion of first pair delayed by need to replace original batteries. Batteries: 2 148-cell, 6,000 amp/hr, one hour rate. Have SISU-1 fire-control system, which can track 4 targets simultaneously. Sonar system operates 200 Hz–kHz passive, 8–15 kHz active, and has active, passive, passive-ranging, and surveillance modes. S 521 has a smaller "crash-dive" ballast tank than the others. S 519 began mid-life refit 1990 to improve habitability and replace batteries; other three will complete refit by 1995.

2 Enrico Toti class Bldr: C.R.D.A., Monfalcone

	Laid down	L	In serv.
513 Enrico Dandolo	10-3-67	16-12-67	29-9-68
514 Lazzaro Mocenigo	12-6-67	20-4-68	11-1-69

...rico Dandolo (S 513) French Navy, 1990

...zaro Macenigo (S 514) Leo Van Ginderen, 9-91

D: 460 std., 536 tons surf./593 sub. **S:** 9.7 kts surf./14 sub.
Dim: 46.20 × 4.75 × 3.99 **A:** 4/533-mm TT (6 A-184 torpedoes)
Electron Equipt:
Radar: 1/BPS-704 nav.—EW: . . . intercept
Sonar: Selenia-Elsag MD-64 active/passive/passive-ranging, Velox passive intercept
M: diesel-electric: 2 Fiat/MB 820 diesels; 1 electric motor; 1 prop; 2,200 shp
Range: 7,500/4.5 snorkel **Crew:** 4 officers, 22 men

Remarks: Can make 15 kts for one hour submerged. Diving depth: 180 m. Have IPD-60/64 combat data/fire-control system. Sister *Attilio Bagnolini* (S 505) to reserve 31-7-90 and will not see further service. Sister *Attilio Bagnolini* (S 505) to reserve 31-7-90 and stricken 4-2-91; *Enrico Toti* (S 506) stricken 31-12-91.

CRUISERS

♦ **1 Vittorio Veneto class**

	Bldr	Laid down	L	In serv.
C 550 Vittorio Veneto	Cant. Riuniti Castellammare	10-6-65	5-2-67	12-7-69

D: 8,130 tons (9,500 fl) **S:** 30.5 kts
Dim: 179.60 (170.61 pp) × 19.42 (hull) × 5.50 (7.9 max.)
A: 1/Mk 20 Mod. 7 Aster launch system (20 ASROC ASW and 40 Standard SM-1 ER SAM)—4/Otomat-Teseo Mk II SSM (I × 4)—8/76-mm OTO Melara DP (I × 8)—6/40-mm Breda Dardo AA (II × 3)—6/324-mm ILAS-3 ASW TT (III × 2)—6/AB-212 ASW helicopters
Electron Equipt:
Radar: 1/SPN-748 nav., 1/SPS-702 surf. search, 1/SPS-768 early warning, 1/Hughes SPS-52C 3-D air search, 2/U.S. SPG-55C missile f.c., 4/SPG-70 (RTN-10X) gun f.c., 2/SPG-74 (RTN-20X) f.c.
Sonar: SQS-23G hull-mounted LF—TACAN: SRN-15A
EW: U.K. UAA-1 Abbeyhill intercept, . . . intercept, VHF D/F, MF D/F, SLQ-B/C jammers, 2/Breda SCLAR decoy RL (XX × 2), SLQ-25 Nixie towed torpedo decoy
M: 2 sets Tosi geared steam turbines; 2 props; 73,000 shp
Boilers: 4 Foster-Wheeler; 43 kg/cm², 450° C
Electric: 6,800 kw tot. **Range:** 3,000/28; 6,000/20
Fuel: 1,200 tons **Crew:** 53 officers, 504 enlisted

Vittorio Veneto (C 550)—launching Otomat Mk II missile
Italian Navy, 1990

...io Veneto (C 550)—with Stromboli-class oiler Italian Navy, 1990

CRUISERS *(continued)*

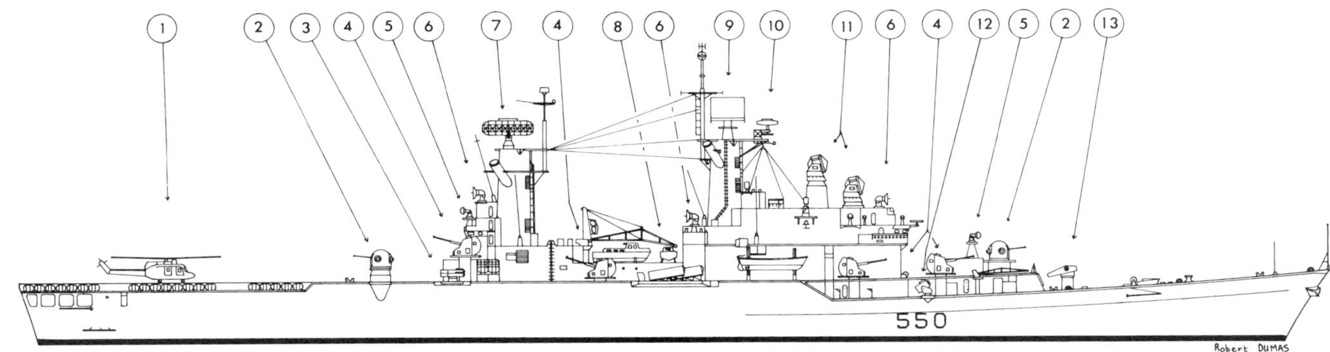

Vittorio Veneto 1. AB-212 helicopter 2. 40-mm Breda twin AA 3. ILAS-3 triple ASW TT 4. 76-mm 62-cal. DP 5. RTN-20X f.c. radar director for 40-mm AA 6. RTN-10X radar director for Argo g.f.c.s. (76-mm guns) 7. SPS-768 (RAN-20X) early-warning radar 8. Otomat-Tesio Mk 2 SSM 9. AN/SPS-52C 3-D radar 10. MM/SPS-702 air/surf. search radar 11. SPG-55B radar tracker for Standard SM-1 SAM 12. Breda SCLAR decoy rocket launcher 13. Mk 20 Aster launcher for Standard SM-1 ER and ASROC missiles Robert Dumas

Remarks: Underwent modernization 1981–83 with 4 Otomat Mk 2 (Teseo) missiles and 3 Dardo 40-mm AA gun systems added. The radar suite was updated, the SPS-40 being replaced by the Italian SPS-768. The flight deck (40 × 18.5) is served from a hangar immediately below by two elevators (18 × 5.3). The hangar (27.5 × 15.3) is two decks in depth. Very extensive, stabilized electronic intercept arrays. Has SADOC-1 combat data system, U.S. Mk 76 SAM control system, 4 Argo fire control systems for the 76-mm guns, and 2 Dardo control systems for the 40-mm guns. Two sets anti-rolling fin stabilizers. The Aster missile launch system can launch either ASROC ASW or Standard SM-1 ER SAM and has a total capacity of 60 missiles on three horizontal magazine drums. Beam listed does not include projections around SCLAR launchers forward or flight deck aft. Will be retired around 2000.

♦ **1 Andrea Doria class** Bldr: C. N. Tirreno, Riva Trigoso

	Laid down	L	In serv.
C 553 Andrea Doria	11-5-58	27-2-63	23-2-64

D: 6,500 tons (7,300 fl) **S:** 30 kts

Dim: 149.3 (144.0 pp) × 17.25 × 4.96 (7.5 fl)

A: 1/Mk 10 launcher (40 Standard SM-1 ER)—8/76-mm OTO Melara DP (I × 8)—6/324-mm ILAS-3 ASW TT (III × 2)—3/AB-212 helicopters

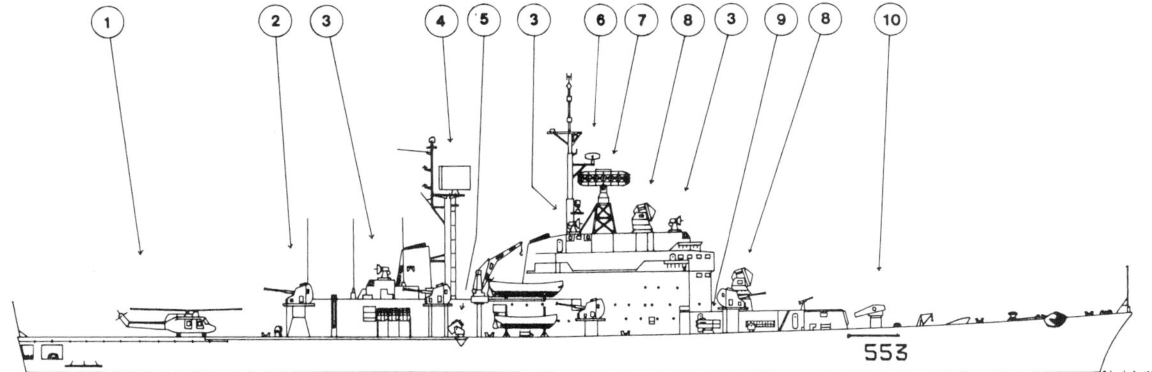

Andrea Doria 1. AB-212 helicopter 2. 76-mm 62-cal. DP 3. RTN-10X radar director for Argo g.f.c.s. 4. AN/SPS-39 3-D air search radar 5. Breda SCLAR decoy rocket launcher 6. SPQ-2D air/surf. search radar 7. MM/SPS-768 early-warning radar 8. SPG-55C radar tracker for Standard SM-1 SAM 9. triple ASW TT 10. Mk 10 launcher for Standard SM-1 ER SAM Robert Dumas

Andrea Doria (C 553) Italian Navy

CRUISERS *(continued)*

Electron Equipt:
Radar: 1/SPN-748 nav., 1/SPS-768 early warning, 1/SPS-39 3-D air search, 2/SPG-55C missile f.c., 4/SPG-70 (RTN-10X) f.c.
Sonar: SQS-23 hull-mounted LF— TACAN: SRN-15A
EW: passive arrays, 2/Breda SCLAR decoy RL (XX × 2)
M: 2 sets geared steam turbines; 2 props; 60,000 shp
Electric: 4,700 kw tot. (4 × 1,000 turbo-alternators, 2 × 350-kw diesel sets)
Boilers: 4 Foster-Wheeler; 43 kg/cm^2, 450° C **Fuel:** 1,100 tons
Range: 6,000/15 **Crew:** 47 officers, 437 enlisted

Remarks: The flight deck is 30 × 16 meters. Hangar on main deck. Fin anti-rolling stabilizers fitted. The engineering spaces are divided into two groups, forward and aft: each has a boiler room with two boilers and a turbine compartment separated by living spaces. The engineering groups are automatic and remote-controlled. Listed beam does not include platforms extending from sides aft.

Received Standard SM-1 ER missiles and associated electronics during refits in the latter 1970s. Has SADOC-1 combat data system, U.S. Mk 76 SAM control system, four Argo NA-9 GFCS.

Sister *Ciao Duilio* (C 554), converted 1979–80 as cadet training ship, was decommissioned to reserve 15-11-89 and stricken 19-7-91. *Andrea Doria* will reduce to reserve in 1992 for later disposal.

GUIDED-MISSILE DESTROYERS

◆ **0 (+2+2) Animoso class** Bldr: Fincantieri, Riva Trigoso (fit-out at Muggiano)

	Laid down	L	In serv.
D 560 Animoso	26-7-86	29-10-89	6-92
D 561 Ardimentoso	3-12-89	13-4-91	12-93

D: 4,500 tons (5,250 fl) **S:** 31.5 kts
Dim: 135.60 × 16.10 (15.00 wl) × 5.00 (hull)

Animoso (D 560)—at launch, 29-10-89 Luciano Grazioli

Ardimentoso (D 561)—at launch, 13-4-91 Maurizio Brescia

A: 8/Otomat-Teseo Mk 2 SSM (II × 4)—1/U.S. Mk 13 launch syst. (40 SM-1 Standard MR missiles)—1/Albatros point-defense SAM syst. (VIII × 1; . . . Aspide missiles)—1/127-mm OTO Melara DP—3/76-mm OTO Melara Super Rapid DP (I × 3)—6/324-mm ILAS-3 ASW TT (III x 2)—2/SH-3D helicopters (with Marte Mk 2 SSM)
Electron Equipt:
Radar: 1/SPN-748 nav., 1/SPS-702 surf. search, 1/SPS-774 air/surf. search, 1/SPS-768 early warning, 1/ SPS-52C 3-D air search, 2/SPG-51D SAM f.c., 4/SPG-76 (RTN-30X) f.c.
Sonar: Raytheon DE 1164 hull-mounted LF—TACAN: SRN-15A
EW: SLQ-732 Nettuno integrated intercept, 2 Sagaie decoy RL, SLQ-25 Nixie towed torpedo decoy
M: CODOG: 2 Fiat/G.E. LM-2500 gas turbines (27,500 shp each), 2 GMT BL230-20DVM diesels (6,300 bhp each); 2 CP props
Range: 7,000/18 (diesel) **Electric:** . . . **Fuel:** . . .
Crew: 35 officers, 365 enlisted

Remarks: Ordered 9-3-86 as replacements for *Impavido* class. Steel superstructure, with Mirex (Kevlar-derivative) armor. Two pair fin stabilizers. Twin helicopter hangar, 18.5 m long; flight deck 24.0 × 13.0, with Italian Navy's first haul-down system. SADOC-1 (IPN20) combat data/weapons-control system. Four NA-30 weapons-control systems handle the Albatros SAM and the four guns; U.S. Mk 74 control system for the Standard missiles. Have U.S. Prairie/Masker air-blowing, noise-masking system and flexibly mounted auxiliary engineering systems to reduce emitted noise below the waterline. The 127-mm guns come from the "B" positions of the modernized *Audace* and *Ardito*. The "Super-Rapid" guns are expected to perform as close-in defense against sea-skimming missiles.

Two additional units of this class are programmed for construction as replacements for the *Ardito* class; they will have the Franco-Italian FSAF/FAMS surface-to-air missile system with Aster vertically launched missiles in place of the U.S. Standard SM-1 MR system.

◆ **2 Audace class**

	Bldr	Laid down	L	In serv.
D 550 Ardito	Nav. Mec. Castellammare	19-7-68	27-11-71	5-12-73
D 551 Audace	C. N. del Tirreno, Riva Trigoso	27-4-68	2-10-71	16-11-72

D: 3,600 light/3,950 tons (4,554 fl) **S:** 33 kts
Dim: 140.7 × 14.65 × 4.60 (hull)
A: 8/Otomat-Teseo Mk 2 SSM (II × 4)—1/Mk 13 Mod. 4 missile launcher (40 Standard SM-1 MR)—1/Albatros SAM syst. (VIII × 1, . . . missiles)—1/127-mm OTO Melara Compact DP—4/76-mm OTO Melara Super-Rapid DP (I × 4)—6/324-mm ILAS-3 ASW TT (III × 2)—2/AB-212 helicopters
Electron Equipt:
Radar: 1/SPN-748 nav., 1/SPQ-2D air/surf. search, 1/SPS-774 air/surf. search, 1/ SPS-768(V)3 early warning, 1/SPS-52C 3-D air search, 2/SPG-51C missile f.c., 3/SPG-76 (RTN-3OX Dardo-E) f.c.

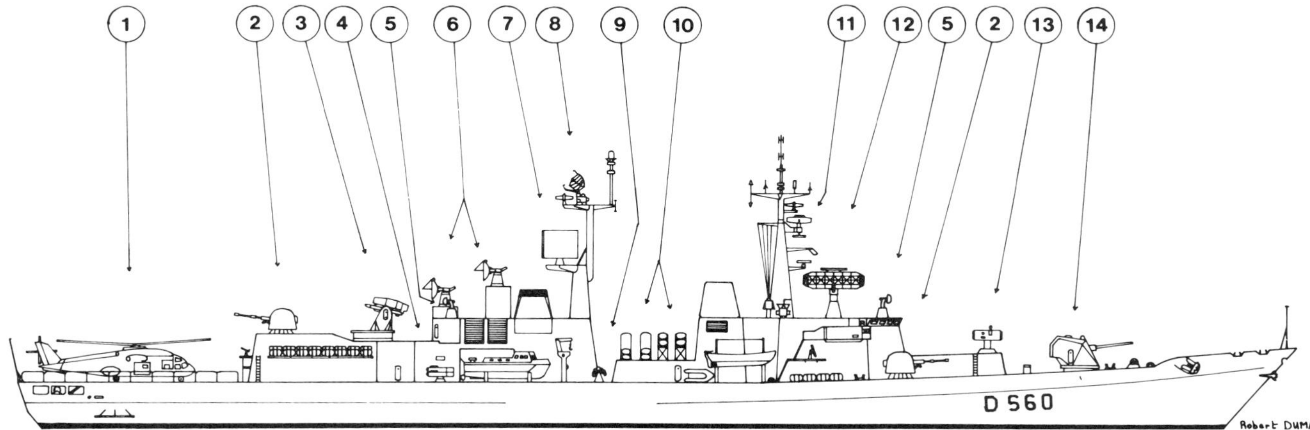

Animoso 1. EH-101 helicopter 2. 76-mm OTO Melara Super-Rapid DP 3. Mk 13 launcher for Standard SM-1 MR SAM 4. ILAS-3 triple ASW TT 5. RTN-30X radar directors for 127-mm and 76-mm guns 6. SPG-51D radar tracker-illuminator for Standard SM-1 MR SAM 7. AN/SPS-52C 3-D air search radar 8. MM/SPS-774 air/surf. search radar 9. Sagaie decoy rocket launcher 10. Otomat-Teseo Mk 2 SSM 11. MM/SPS-702 navigation/surface search radar 12. MM/SPS-768 early-warning radar 13. Albatros octuple launcher for Aspide SAM 14. 127-mm OTO Melara DP Robert Dumas

GUIDED-MISSILE DESTROYERS *(continued)*

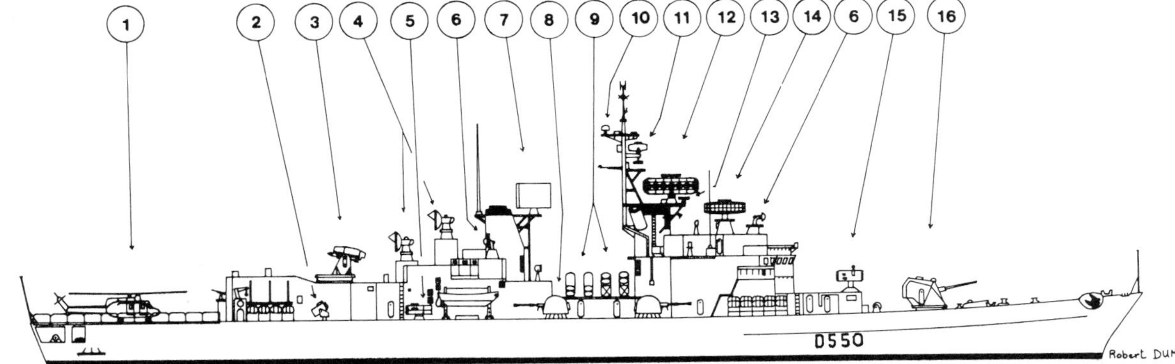

Ardito 1. AB-212 helicopter 2. Breda SCLAR decoy rocket launcher 3. Mk 13 launcher for Standard SM-1 MR SAM 4. AN/SPG-51C radar illuminator-directors for Standard SM-1 MR SAM 5. ILAS-3 triple ASW TT 6. RTN-3OX radar directors for Dardo 40-mm AA system 7. AN/SPS-52C 3-D air search radar 8. 76-mm OTO Melara Compact Super-Rapid DP 9. Otomat-Teseo Mk 2 SSM 10. AN/SRN-15A TACAN 11. MM/SPS-774 air/surf. search radar 12. MM/SPS-768 early-warning radar 13. MM/SPN-748 navigational radar 14. MM/SPS-774 air/surface search radar 15. Albatros launcher for Aspide SAM 16. 127-mm OTO Melara DP Robert Dumas

Ardito (D 550) Leo Van Ginderen, 9-91

Ardito (D 550) Carlo Martinelli, 10-89

Audace (D 551) Italian Navy, 1990

Sonar: CWE-610A hull-mounted MF—TACAN: SRN-15A
EW: passive intercept arrays, SLQ-B/C jammers, 2/SCLAR chaff RL (XX × 2), SLQ-25 Nixie towed torpedo decoys

M: 2 sets geared steam turbines; 2 props; 73,000 shp
Boilers: 4 Foster-Wheeler; 43 kg/cm^2, 450° C
Electric: 5,200 kw
Range: 4,000/25 **Crew:** 30 officers, 350 enlisted

Remarks: Habitability has been given much attention in the design of these very fine ships. Both now have SPS-768 (RAN-20S) air-search radar, replacing SPS-12 (D 550) or RAN-3 (D 551). D 550 completed modernization refit 3-88 with Albatros SAM launcher in place of "B" 127-mm gun, upgraded Super-Rapid 76-mm guns, and the Dardo-E f.c.s. replacing the original Argo system, and four aft-launching wire-guided 533-mm torpedo tubes deleted at the stern; an SPS-774 (RAN-10S) radar was added for target acquisition for the Albatros system's Aspide missiles, and other radars and the EW system were upgraded. Otomat-Teseo launch positions were added amidships, between the funnels. The overall combat data system is now SADOC-2 (IPN-20); for the Standard SM-1 MR SAM system, the U.S. AN/SYS-1 data system was added, with the Mk 13 Mod. 5 weapons direction system and Mk 74 Mod. 13 missile fire-control system. D 551 completed a similar upgrading in early 1991. After modernization, have capabilities very similar to the later *Animoso* class. Both to be retired around 2000.

◆ 1 Impavido class

	Bldr	Laid down	L	In serv.
D 570 Impavido	C.N. del Tirreno, Riva Trigoso	10-6-57	25-5-62	16-11-63

D: 3,201 tons (3,851 fl) **S:** 33.5 kts
Dim: 131.3 × 13.65 × 4.43 (hull)
A: 1/Mk 13 launcher (40 Standard SM-1 MR missiles)—2/127-mm 38-cal. Mk 30 DP (II × 1)—4/76-mm OTO Melara DP (I × 4)—6/324-mm ASW TT (III × 2)
Electron Equipt:
Radar: 1/SPN-748 nav., 1SPQ-2A2 surf./air search, 1/SPS-12 early warning, 1/SPS-39A 3-D air search, 2/SPG-51C SAM f.c., 3/SPG-70 (RTN-10X Argo) gun f.c.
Sonar: SQS-39 hull-mounted MF
EW: passive intercept arrays, 2/SCLAR chaff RL (XX × 2)
M: 2 sets Tosi GT; 2 props; 70,000 shp
Boilers: 4 Foster-Wheeler; 43 kg/cm^2, 450° C **Fuel:** 650 tons
Range: 3,300/20; 2,900/25; 1,500/30 **Crew:** 22 officers, 313 enliste

Remarks: Refitted in 1976–77 with new fire-control systems for the guns and missiles. Has fin stabilizers. Sister *Intrepido* (D 571) reduced to reserve 31-8-90 stricken 31-8-91; D 570 to reserve 31-8-91, for striking.

Impavido (D 570) Pradignac & Léo,

FRIGATES

Note: As a replacement for the abortive NATO frigate program, the Italian Navy hopes to order eight new multipurpose frigates during the late 1990s. The presence in Italy of the four undelivered *Lupo*-class frigates completed for Iraq complicates matters, as the Italian Navy (which does not want the ships due to their non-standard equipment and now-obsolescent design) may be forced to take the vessels for political and economic reasons.

♦ 8 Maestrale class

Bldr: CNR, Riva Trigoso (F 571: CNR, Muggiano)

	Laid down	L	In serv.
F 570 Maestrale	8-3-78	2-2-81	7-3-82
F 571 Grecale	21-3-79	12-9-81	5-2-83
F 572 Libeccio	1-8-79	7-9-81	5-2-83
F 573 Scirocco	26-2-80	17-4-82	20-9-83
F 574 Aliseo	26-2-80	29-10-82	20-9-83
F 575 Euro	15-4-81	25-3-83	7-4-84
F 576 Espero	1-8-82	19-11-83	4-5-85
F 577 Zeffiro	15-3-83	19-5-84	4-5-85

D: 2,700 tons light (3,060 normal; 3,200 fl)
S: 33 kts (21 max. diesel)
Dim: 122.73 (116.4 pp) × 12.88 × 4.10 hull (5.95 max.)
A: 4/Otomat-Teseo Mk 2 SSM (I × 4)—1/Albatros SAM system (VIII × 1, 24 Aspide missiles)—1/127-mm DP OTO Melara—4/40-mm Breda Dardo AA (II × 2)—2/533-mm TT (A-184 torpedoes)—6/324-mm ILAS-3 ASW TT (III × 2)—2/AB-212 helicopters

Scirocco (F 573) — Carlo Martinelli, 9-90

Grecale (F 571)—with AB-212 on deck — Carlo Martinelli, 7-90

Maestrale (F 570) — Leo Van Ginderen, 5-90

Euro (F 575)—note SATCOMM radome aft — Carlo Martinelli, 11-89

Electron Equipt:
Radar: 1/SPN-703 nav., 1/SPS-702 surf. search, 1/SPS-774 air/surf. search, 1/SPG-75 (RTN-30X for NA-30A system), 2/SPG-74 (RTN-20X for Dardo system)
Sonar: 1/Raytheon DE 1164 hull-mounted MF, 1/Raytheon DE 1164 VDS
EW: Elettronica Newton active-passive suite with CO-NEWS communications intercept, 2/SCLAR or Dagaie chaff launchers (XX × 2), SLQ-25 Nixie towed torpedo decoys
M: CODOG: 2 G.E./Fiat LM-2500 gas turbines (25,000 shp each); 2 GMT B 230-20 DVM diesels (5,073 bhp each); 2 CP props
Electric: 3,120 kw **Endurance:** 90 days
Range: 1,500/30; 3,800/22; 6,000/15 **Crew:** 24 officers, 208 enlisted

Remarks: FF 576 and FF 577 ordered 10-80, 572–575 in 12-76, 576 and 577 in 10-80. An enlarged version of *Lupo* with better seaworthiness and hangar space for two helicopters at the expense of four antiship missiles and about 2.5 knots maximum speed. Have U.S. Prairie/Masker bubbler noise-suppression system. F 577 collided with *Orsa* (F 567) on 6-7-90; minor damage.

Have SADOC-2 (IPN-20) computerized data system. There is a Galileo OG-30 optronic backup director to the NA-30A GFCS and two MM 59 optical backup directors for the 40-mm guns. Helo deck is 12 × 27 m. D 1164 is a VDS version of DE 1160 and operates on the same frequencies; the two sonar systems employ identical transducers. There are plans to lengthen the VDS tow cable from 600 m to 900 m and to attach a towed passive linear hydrophone array to the VDS fish; trials to take place with F 570. F 574 fitted with Oerlikon-Breda experimental 25-mm gun mount for trials, 1991. Units deployed to the Mideast during the 1991 Gulf War received Magnavox MX 2400 satellite communications equipment.

Plan to modify all to carry the MILAS antisubmarine missile beginning in 1994—to replace some or all Teseo SSM. All are to receive two French CSEE Dagaie decoy launching systems, beginning in 1991.

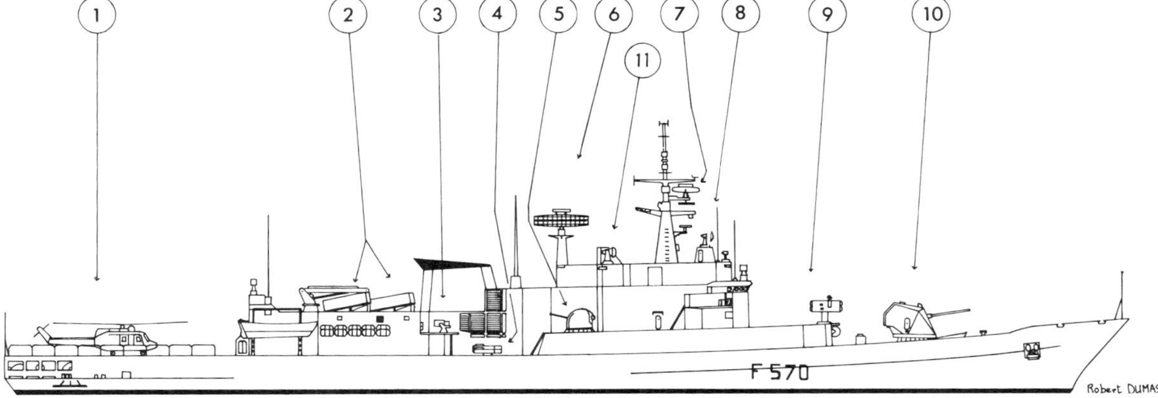

Maestrale 1. AB-212 helicopter 2. Otomat-Teseo Mk 2 SSM (only two usually carried) 3. Breda SCLAR decoy rocket launcher 4. ILAS-3 triple ASW TT 5. 40-mm Breda Dardo twin AA 6. MM/SPS-774 radar 7. MM/SPS-702 air/surf. search 8. RTN-30X gun/missile-control radar 9. Albatros octuple launcher for Aspide SAM 10. 127-mm OTO Melara DP 11. RTN-20X f.c. radar for 40-mm AA (port and starboard) — Robert Dumas

FRIGATES *(continued)*

◆ **4 Lupo class** Bldr: C.N. Riuniti, Riva Trigoso (F 567; CNR Muggiano)

	Laid down	L	In serv.
F 564 Lupo	8-10-74	29-7-76	20-9-77
F 565 Sagittario	4-2-76	22-6-77	18-11-78
F 566 Perseo	28-2-77	8-7-78	1-3-80
F 567 Orsa	1-8-77	1-3-79	1-3-80

D: 2,208 tons (2,340 trials; 2,525 fl)
S: 35.23 kts (trials, *Lupo*); 32 kts at 80% power; 20.3 kts on 2 diesels
Dim: 113.55 (106.00 pp) × 12.00 × 3.54 (hull)
A: up to 8/Otomat Mk 1 and Otomat-Teseo Mk 2 SSM (I × 8)—1/NATO Sea Sparrow system (VIII × 1, RIM-7H missiles)—1/127-mm OTO Melara DP—4/40-mm Breda AA (II × 2)—6/324-mm Mk 32 ASW TT (III x 2)—1/AB-212 helicopter
Electron Equipt:
Radar: 1/SPN-748 nav., 1/SPQ-2F surf. search, 1/SPS-774 air/surf. search, 1/SPG-70 (Orion RTN-10X for NA-10 Mod. 2 Argo f.c. system), 1/Mk 91 Mod. 1 missile f.c., 2/SPG-74 (Orion RTN-20X for Dardo system)
Sonar: Raytheon 1160B hull-mounted MF
EW: SLR-4 intercept suite, SLQ-D jammer, 2/SCLAR chaff RL (XX × 2)
M: CODOG: 2 G.E./Fiat LM-2500 gas turbines, 50,000 shp; 2 GMT A 230-20M diesels, 7,900 bhp; 2 CP props
Electric: 3,120 kw (4 Fiat 236 SS diesel alternator sets)
Range: 900/35; 3,450/20; 4,350/16 (diesels)
Crew: 17 officers, 177 enlisted

Remarks: Fin stabilizers. Telescopic hangar. The Otomat-Teseo Mk-II launchers are mounted two per side abreast the hangar and two per side on the forward superstructure. The *Lupo* had her radar antennae redistributed 1978–79 and a new mast added at the after end of the stack; the others were completed to the new configuration. The SAM system uses the U.S. Mk 29 launcher and a U.S. director, rather than the later Albatros system with the similar Aspide missiles of the *Maestrale* class; the system is to be modified to accept the later RIM-7M version of Sea Sparrow.The highly automated machinery plant is mounted in four compartments: auxiliaries, gas turbines, reduction gearing, and diesel alternator sets. Six ships of the same class were ordered for Venezuela, four for Peru, and four for Iraq (see below). All four to be retained in service until 2000 or later. In F 565 and F 566, the control station for the forward NA-10 f.c.s. has been replaced by a radome. F 564 carried a mix of two Otomat Mk 1 and two Otomat-Teseo Mk 2 missiles, and a SATCOMM radome was mounted atop the pilothouse during her early 1991 tour in support of UN Coalition forces in the Mideast. F 567 collided with *Zeffiro* (F 577) on 6-7-90, experiencing major damage.

Lupo (F 564) Peter Westdyk, 5-90

Sagittario (F 566)—with radome atop pilothouse Italian Navy, 1990

Lupo (F 564) Leo Van Ginderen, 1991

◆ **0(+4) ex-Iraqi modified Lupo class**

	Bldr	Laid down	L	Completed
F . . . . (ex-*Hittin*)	Fincantieri, Ancona	31-3-82	27-7-83	3-85
F . . . . (ex-*Tmi Qar*)	Fincantieri, Ancona	9-82	19-12-84	1985
F . . . . (ex-*Al Qadissiya*)	Fincantieri, Ancona	15-4-83	31-3-84	1986
F . . . . (ex-*Al Yarmouk*)	Fincantieri, Riva Trigoso	12-3-84	20-6-85	4-87

Al Yarmouk (F 17)—on trials Luciano Grazioli, 4-8

D: 2,213 tons (2,525 fl) **S:** 35 kts (20.5 diesel)
Dim: 112.8 (106.0 pp) × 11.98 × 3.84
A: 8/Otomat Mk II SSM (I × 8)—1/Albatros SAM syst. (VIII × 1; no reloads)—1/127-mm DP OTO Melara—4/40-mm AA Breda Dardo (II x 2)—6/324-mm ASW TT (III × 2)—2/ASW helicopters
Electron Equipt:
Radar: 1/3RM20 navigational, 1/RAN-11X surf./air search, 1/RAN-10S air search, 2/Orion RTN-10XRCT f.c., 2/Orion RTN-20X f.c.
Sonar: Raytheon 1160B
EW: Lambda F intercept—2/SCLAR chaff RL
M: CODOG: 2 Fiat/G.E. LM-2500 gas turbines (25,000 shp each); 2 GMT A230-20M diesels (3,900 bhp each); 2 CP props
Electric: 4,000 kVA **Range:** 900/35; 3,450/20.5
Crew: 185 tot.

Remarks: Ordered by Iraq 2-81. 127-mm gun and SAM fire control by two Elsag 10 Mod. 0 systems with NA-10 radar directors; 40-mm f.c. by two Dardo syste Selenia IPN-10 combat data system. SAM system uses Aspide missiles rather t NATO Sea Sparrow. Fin stabilizers fitted. Fixed hangar, as on Venezuelan and P vian units of the class, to which this version is in other ways similar. The Italian N reportedly did not want the ships because of their non-standard equipment and gen obsolescence, but in 1-92 the government decided to add them to the Italian Navy. T will be refitted and commissioned 1993–94.

◆ **2 Alpino class** Bldr: C.N. del Tirreno, Riva Trigoso

	Laid down	L	In serv.
F 580 Alpino (ex-*Circe*)	27-2-63	10-6-67	14-1-68
F 581 Carabiniere (ex-*Climene*)	9-1-65	30-9-67	28-4-68

Alpino (F 580) Pradignac & Léo

FRIGATES *(continued)*

Carabiniere (F 581)—after conversion as trials ship
Carlo Martinelli, 7-91

D: 2,000 tons (2,689 fl) **S:** 28 kts
Dim: 113.3 (106.4 pp) × 13.3 × 3.80 (hull)
A: F 580: 6/76-mm 62-cal. OTO Melara DP (I × 6)—1/305-mm K113 Menon ASW mortar (I × 1)—6/324-mm ASW TT (III × 2)—1/AB-212 helicopter; F 581: 3/76-mm 62-cal. OTO Melara DP (I × 3)—6/324-mm ASW TT (III × 2)—1/AB-212 helicopter (*see* Remarks)
Electron Equipt:
Radar: 1/SPN-748 nav., 1/SPS-702 surf. search, 1/ R.C.A. SPS-12 air search, 2/SPG-70 (RTN-10X Argo systems)
Sonar: 2/Raytheon DE 1164 (1 hull-mounted, 1 VDS) MF
EW: SPR-A intercept, 2/SCLAR chaff RL (XX × 2)
M: CODAG: 4 Tosi OTV-320 diesels, 4,200 bhp each; 2 Tosi-Metrovik G6 gas turbines, 7,700 shp each; 2 props
Electric: 2,400 kw
Range: 4,200/17
Fuel: 275 tons
Crew: 19 officers, 228 enlisted

Remarks: Fin stabilizers. Cruising, 22 knots on diesels. F 580 fitted with experimen-al "MAD" gunfire-control radar in 1975. F 581 received bow-mounted sonar, improved ombat data system, and EW equipment during refit ended 7-85. To be discarded circa 997. Sonars upgraded from original SQS-43 hull-mounted/SQA-10 VDS fit.

F 581 has been refitted to act as weapons trials ship in place of *Quarto* (A 5314). The acated Menon ASW mortar and "B" 76-mm gun mount positions will be replaced by unchers for the MILAS antisubmarine missile. Later, the vacated two aftermost 6-mm gun positions abreast the hangar will be replaced by vertical launchers for the ranco-Italian ASTER-15 surface-to-air missile.

ORVETTES

ote: A new corvette class, to comprise six to eight units, is in the preliminary anning stages.

8 (+4) Minerva class Bldr: Fincantieri, Muggiano and Riva Trigoso, La Spezia

	Yard	Laid down	L	In serv.
551 Minerva	Riva Trigoso	11-3-85	25-3-86	10-6-87
552 Urania	Riva Trigoso	11-3-85	21-6-86	10-6-87
553 Daniade	Muggiano	26-5-85	18-10-86	13-2-88
554 Sfinge	Muggiano	26-5-85	16-5-87	30-9-89
555 Driade	Riva Trigoso	18-3-88	12-3-89	4-12-90
556 Chimera	Riva Trigoso	21-12-88	4-7-90	4-12-90
557 Fenice	Riva Trigoso	6-9-88	4-12-90	11-91
558 Sibilla	Riva Trigoso	16-10-89	15-2-90	11-91

D: 1,029 tons (1,285 fl) **S:** 24 kts
Dim: 86.60 (80.00 pp) × 10.50 × 3.16 (hull)
A: 1/Albatros SAM system (VIII × 1, 8 Aspide missiles)—1/76-mm OTO Melara Super-Rapid DP—6/324-mm ILAS-3 ASW TT (III × 2)

erva (F 551) Stefan Terzibaschitsch, 6-91

Fenice (F 557)—on trials Carlo Martinelli, 10-90

Urania (F 552) Luciano Grazioli, 4-90

Daniade (F 553) Leo Van Ginderen, 9-91

Electron Equipt:
Radar: 1/SPN-728 nav., 1/SPS-774 air/surf. search, 1/SPG-74 (RTN-20X for Dardo-E f.c.s.)
Sonar: 1/Raytheon DE 1167 hull-mounted MF
EW: SLQ-747 suite, 2 Type 207/E (Wallop Barricade) decoy RL, SLQ-25 Nixie towed torpedo decoy
M: 2 GMT BM 230.20 DVM diesels; 2 CP props; 11,000 bhp
Electric: 2,080 kw (4 Isotta Fraschini ID36.55 S12V diesel sets driving)
Range: 3,500/18 **Crew:** 9–10 officers, 112–114 enlisted

Remarks: First four authorized 1983 to begin replacement of earlier corvettes; names for second planned group released 1985; ships ordered 1-87. A third group of four may yet be ordered. Intended for surveillance, coastal escort, fisheries protection, training, and search-and-rescue duties. Weight and space reserved for addition of Aspide reload facility, four Otomat-Teseo Mk 2 SSM, and variable-depth sonar.

Have Selenia SADOC-2 combat data system, with two computers and three displays. Elsag NA-18L Pegaso optronic GFCS for the 76-mm gun, with the Dardo-E radar f.c.s. controlling the SAM system or the gun. Sonars will be the first to be built (although under license) in Italy. Fin stabilizers, satellite nagivation systems fitted. Spherical radomes for Elmer Omega Transit SP 1090 satellite navigation system added during 1988. All now have solid-dish OA-7104 antennna for the SPS-774 radar, while F 554 had a lighter-weight mesh antenna during 1988. The stacks have been raised and deflectors added since completion to reduce turbulence.

F 556 delivered 15-1-91, F 557 on 11-9-90, and F 558 in 4-91; a year of trials and work-up ensues before commissioning. The first four are based at Augusta, Sicily.

Note: The three surviving *Albatros*-class corvettes, *Aquila* (F 542, ex-Dutch *Lynx*), *Alcione* (F 544), and *Airone* (F 545) were due for disposal by end-1991. Four of the six guided-missile corvettes built to Iraqi order were never paid for remain the builder Fincantieri's property, and are for sale; two others were delivered and commissioned but never left Italian waters and are described in the Iraqi section. The undelivered quartet are described as follows:

♦ **0 (+4) modified Wadi M'ragh class** Bldr: Fincantieri, Marghera

	Laid down	L	Completed
F 214 Abdullah ibn abi Serh	22-3-82	5-7-83	1-87
F 216 Kalid ibn al Walid	3-6-82	5-7-83	1-87
F 218 Saad ibn abi Wakkad	17-8-82	30-12-83	1987
F 220 Salah Aldin Ayoobi	17-9-82	30-3-84	1987

CORVETTES *(continued)*

Abdullah ibn abi Serh (F 214)—on trials Aldo Fraccaroli, 10-86

D: 600 tons (675 fl) **S:** 37.5 kts
Dim: 62.3 (57.8 pp) × 9.3 × 2.8 (hull)
A: 6/Otomat Mk II SSM (III × 2)—1/Albatros SAM system (IV × 1, plus 8 reload Aspide missiles)—1/76-mm OTO Melara Compact DP—2/40-mm Breda Dardo AA (II × 1)—6/324-mm ILAS-3 ASW TT (III × 2)
Electron Equipt:
Radar: 1/3RM 20 nav., 1/RAN-12 L/X air/surf. search, 1/Orion RTN-10X f.c.
Sonar: Thomson-CSF Diodon hull-mounted MF
EW: Elettronica Gamma syst., 2/SCLAR chaff RL (XX × 2)
M: 4 MTU 20V956 TB92 diesels; 4 props; 24,400 bhp (20,400 sust.)
Electric: 650 kw **Range:** 1,200/31; 4,000/18
Fuel: 126 tons **Crew:** 51 tot.

Remarks: Ordered 2-81. Attack variant of leader version listed in the Iraqi section. Aspide reload via manual crane. Selenia IPN-10 data system with 2 radar directors and 2 CO3 optical directors for guns. Probably exceed 700 tons displacement on completion. Trials began 4-84 with first ship. Were offered to Algeria by the builder in April 1991.

PATROL SHIPS

◆ **4 (+2) Cassiopea class** Bldr: Fincantieri, Muggiano

	Laid down	L	In serv.
P 401 Cassiopea	16-3-87	19-7-88	21-10-89
P 402 Libra	16-3-87	27-7-88	28-11-89
P 403 Spica	5-9-88	27-5-89	23-3-91
P 404 Vega	30-6-89	24-2-90	23-3-91
P 405 Orione	...	...	23-3-91
P 406	...	...	...

D: 1,052 tons (1,470 fl) **S:** 21 kts (20 continuous)
Dim: 80.70 (71.50 pp) × 11.80 (11.40 wl) × 4.30 (8.50 moulded depth)
A: 1/76-mm 62-cal. OTO Melara DP—2/20-mm Oerlikon AA (I × 2)—1/AB-212 helicopter
Electron Equipt:
Radar: 1/SPN-748 nav., 1/SPS-702 surf. search, 1/SPG-70 f.c.
EW: intercept and D/F gear
M: 2 GMT BL 230.16 diesels; 2 CP props; 8,800 bhp max. (7,490 sust.)

Cassiopea (P 401) Italian Navy, 1990

Libra (P 402) Carlo Martinelli, 3-90

Vega (P 404) Carlo Martinelli, 12-90

Electric: 1,620 kw (3 × 500-kw Isotta-Fraschini 1D 3655 SSV6 gen. sets; 1 × 120-kw emergency set)
Range: 4,100/17 **Fuel:** 165 tons **Endurance:** 35 days
Crew: 8 officers, 70 enlisted

Remarks: Operated for the Coast Guard (formerly Port Captain Corps) by the navy for fisheries patrol, anti-pollution, and search-and-rescue duties. Construction authorized 31-12-82; first four funded by the Ministry of the Merchant Marine and ordered 12-86; P 405 and P 406 expected to order during 1991–92. Were originally to have been eight. Have pollution analysis, oil disposal, cargo transport, light repair, fire-fighting, and towing capabilities and can accommodate rescued personnel. Passive tank and fin stabilizers fitted. Helicopter deck 22.0 × 8.0 and telescoping hangar. The 76-mm guns and fire-control systems were taken from scrapped *Carlo Bergamini*-class frigates.

◆ **4 Pietro de Cristofaro-class former corvettes**

	Bldr	Laid down	L	In serv.
F 540 Pietro de Cristofaro	C.N. del Tirreno	20-4-63	29-5-65	19-12-65
F 541 Umberto Grosso	Ansaldo, Livorno	21-10-62	12-12-64	25-4-66
F 546 Licio Visintini	C.R.D.A., Monfalcone	30-9-63	30-5-65	10-8-66
F 550 Salvatore Todaro	Ansaldo, Livorno	21-10-62	24-10-64	25-4-66

Umberto Grosso (F 541)—in patrol configuration Luciano Grazioli, 4-

Licio Visintini (F 546) Leo Van Ginderen, 9

D: 850 tons (1,020 fl) **S:** 22 kts
Dim: 80.37 (75.0 pp) × 10.28 × 2.80 (hull)
A: 2/76-mm 62-cal. OTO Melara DP (I × 2)
Electron Equipt:
Radar: 1/BX-732 nav., SPQ-2B air/surf. search, 1/Orion RTN-7A
Sonar: removed—EW: SPR-A intercept
M: 2 diesels (*see* Remarks); 2 props; 8,400 bhp **Fuel:** 100 tons
Electric: 600 kw **Range:** 4,600/18
Crew: 7 officers, 122 enlisted

Remarks: High-speed diesels: Fiat 3012 RSS on F 540, F 541, and F 550; To F 546, with reduction gears and Tosi-Vulcan hydraulic linkage. OG-3 gun dir forward, U.S. Mk 51 director aft. SQS-36 hull-mounted and variable-depth so Menon ASW mortars, and ASW torpedo tubes removed from all beginning in when they were reclassified as patrol ships and assigned to fisheries protection d

GUIDED-MISSILE PATROL BOATS

◆ **1 non-naval private-venture DA-360T design** Bldr: Fincantieri, Muggiano

	Laid down	L	In serv.
"920" Saettia	6-84	12-84	12-85

Saettia (920) Fincantieri

D: 330 tons (370 normal, 400 fl) **S:** 40 kts (37.5 sust.)
Dim: 51.70 (47.20 pp) × 8.10 × 2.50 (5.40 moulded depth)
A: 4/Otomat Mk 2 SSM (II × 2)—1/76-mm OTO Melara Compact DP—2/40-mm Breda Dardo AA (II × 1)
Electron Equipt:
Radar: 1/. . . nav., 1/RAN-11 L/X, 1/Orion RTN-10X f.c.
EW: Elettronica Farad A1 intercept; 2 Breda 6105, 105-mm chaff RL
M: 4 MTU 16V538 TB93 diesels; 4 props; 17,600 bhp (16,560 hp sust.)
Electric: 450 kw (3 × 150 kw; 3 Isotta Fraschini ID38 SS6V diesels driving)
Range: 2,200/16 **Endurance:** 12 days
Crew: 3 officers, 30 ratings

Remarks: *Not* a unit of the Italian Navy, which has no plans to acquire the ship. Built in hopes of sales and to test concept. Has fin stabilizers. Elsag NA 21 weapons control system with RTN-10X radar has NA 12 optronic backup director. Selenia's IPN-10 combat data system. EW system includes ELT/521 jammer, ELT/261 signal analyzer. Hull number is unofficial. This unit is very much for sale and was offered to Iraq during 1990.

◆ **6 Sparviero-class hydrofoils** Bldr: CNR, Muggiano (P 420: Alinavi, La Spezia)

	Laid down	L	Delivered	In serv.
P 421 Nibbio	1-8-77	29-2-80	10-11-80	7-3-82
P 422 Falcone	1-10-77	27-10-80	1-3-82	7-3-82
P 423 Astore	1-7-78	20-7-81	6-8-82	5-2-83
P 424 Griffone	15-11-78	1-12-81	16-9-82	5-2-83
P 425 Gheppio	16-5-79	24-6-82	11-5-83	20-9-83
P 426 Condore	21-3-80	25-1-83	19-1-84	7-4-84

D: 63.0 tons (fl) **S:** 50 kts (calm sea), 43 kts (heavy sea)
Dim: 22.95 (24.56, foils retracted) × 7.01 (12.06 max. over foils) × 1.87 (1.45 over foils at speed, 4.37 over foils at rest)
A: 2 Otomat-Teseo Mk II SSM (I × 2)—1/76-mm OTO Melara Compact
Electron Equipt:
Radar: 1/SPQ-701 nav., 1/SPG-70 (Orion RTN-10X) f.c.
M: CODOG: 1 Rolls-Royce Proteus 15 M560 gas turbine; 1 waterjet; 5,044 shp; 1 G.M. 6V-53N diesel; 1 prop; 180 bhp
Range: 1,050/8 (diesels); 400/45 **Fuel:** 11 tons
Crew: 2 officers, 8 enlisted

Nibbio (P 421)—on foil Italian Navy, 1990

Falcone (P 422)—aft foils retracted Luciano Grazioli, 5-90

Remarks: Prototype *Sparviero* (P 420) developed by the Alinavi Society, which was formed in 1964 by Boeing, U.S.A., the Italian government's I.R.I., and Carlo Rodriguez of Messina, builder of commercial hydrofoils. Design based on U.S. *Tucumcari.* Six more (of eight planned) were ordered 1977. A license has been granted for construction of up to 12 in Japan. P 420 stricken 31-8-91.

The three hydrofoils are raised when cruising, and the diesel engine is engaged. All-aluminum construction. Used for short-duration operations, have no berths. P 421 onward have a later navigational/surface-search radar, incorporating an IFF interrogator. All have water injection to increase gas-turbine power output, but they are basically underpowered. Plans to replace the Proteus with a G.M. Allison 570 KF turbine producing 6,394 bhp have been postponed indefinitely. All have NA-10 Mod. 3 gun fire-control system.

PATROL BOATS

◆ **4 converted U.S. Adjutant-class minesweepers** Bldr: CRDA, Monfalcone

	In serv.
P 495 Bambù (ex-M 5521, ex-MSC 214)	8-9-56
P 496 Mango (ex-M 5523, ex-MSC 216)	5-12-56
P 497 Mogano (ex-M 5524, ex-MSC 217)	9-1-57
P 498 Palma (ex-M 5525, ex-MSC 238)	28-2-57

Mango (P 496)—with service craft MOC 1203 in foreground Leo Van Ginderen, 9-91

D: 375 tons (405 fl) **S:** 12 kts
Dim: 43.92 (42.10 pp) × 8.23 × 2.68
A: 2/20-mm AA (II × 1)
Electron Equipt: Radar: 1/BX-732 nav.—Sonar: UQS-1 HF
M: 2 Fiat-G.M. 8-268A diesels; 2 props; 1,200 bhp
Fuel: 40 tons **Range:** 2,500/10
Crew: 2 officers, 29 enlisted

Remarks: Wooden-hulled former minesweepers assigned to the United Nations patrol force in the Red Sea. Retain minesweeping capability.

◆ **1 range patrol boat** Bldr: C.N. Castracani, Ancona

P 492 Barbara (ex-A 3315)

D: 185 tons (195 fl) **S:** 12 kts **Dim:** 30.50 × 6.30 × 1.50
A: small arms **Electron Equipt:** Radar: 1/BX-732 nav.
M: 2 diesels; 2 props; 600 bhp **Crew:** 7 total

PATROL BOATS *(continued)*

Remarks: Purchased 1975 for use in oceanographic research and in support of missile tests, but given a P-series pendant in 1986 and additionally employed on patrol duties. Has a 7.5-ton electrohydraulic crane at the stern. Operated by the Ministry of Defense Technical and Scientific Council at the Perdosdefogu range, Sardinia.

MINE WARFARE SHIPS

Note: Eight units of a new seagoing mine-countermeasures vessel class equipped for mine hunting and deep sweeping are planned to order in the mid-1990s to replace the U.S. *Agile* class. A version of the U.K. Plessey 2095 (improved 2093) sonar is to be employed, and the ships will be able to sweep in depths of up to 400 meters. The design may be patterned on the U.S. *Osprey* (MSH 51) class.

◆ 0 (+6+2) Lerici-II class   Bldr: Intermarine, Sarzana

	Laid down	L	In serv.
M 5554 Gaeta	5-8-88	28-7-90	3-92
M 5555 Termoli	5-12-88	15-12-90	7-92
M 5556 Alghero	5-4-89	4-5-91	10-92
M 5557 Numana	5-8-89	11-91	2-93
M 5558 Crotone	5-12-89	. . .	7-93
M 5560 Viareggio	. . .	. . .	12-93
M 5561 Chioggia	. . .	. . .	. . .
M 5562 Rimini	. . .	. . .	. . . .

Gaeta (M 5554)—fitting out   Leo Van Ginderen, 9-91

D: 665 tons (697 fl) **S:** 14.3 kts
Dim: 52.45 (46.50 pp) × 9.87 × 2.95
A: 1/20-mm Oerlikon AA
Electron Equipt:
Radar: 1/SPN-703 nav.
Sonar: SSN-7M (FIAR SQQ-14/IT) with U.K. Type 2048 (Plessey Speedscan)
M: 1 GMT BL230-BN diesel; 1 prop; 1,985 bhp (3 retractable 120-hp Riva Calzoni thrusters, 360 hp, for 6-kt hunting speed)
Electric: 900 kw (3/430-kw sets, ID 36SS diesels; 1/150-kw set, ID 36N diesel)
Range: 1,500/14; 2,500/12 **Fuel:** 49 tons **Crew:** 50 tot.

Remarks: Names announced 1980, but first six ships not ordered until 30-4-88. Two additional ordered 11-91 to ensure continuity of work at the builder's until a follow-on design is ready. Lengthened version of *Lerici* design, with new minehunting auxiliary thruster system and new sonar (an Italian-built version of the SQQ-14 with digital processor), Plessey Speedscan sidescan route-mapping sonar, Motorola MHS-1C satellite navigation receiver, and an additional generator set. Carry one MIN-77 and one Gaymarine Pluto remote-controlled mine disposal submersibles and Oropesa Mk 4 mechanical sweep gear. Have the MM/SSN-714 command and control system. Carry 2-man decompression chamber and are fitted with passive tank stabilization (using tanks for fuel, range can be extended by 1,500 n.m. at 12 kts).

◆ 4 Lerici-class minehunter/minesweepers   Bldr: Intermarine, Sarzana

	L	In serv.
M 5550 Lerici	3-9-82	4-5-85
M 5551 Sapri	5-4-84	14-12-85
M 5552 Milazzo	4-1-85	14-12-85
M 5553 Vieste	18-4-85	14-12-85

D: 488 tons (520 fl) **S:** 15 kts
Dim: 49.98 (45.50 pp) × 9.56 × 2.70
A: 1/20-mm Oerlikon AA (2 more added during Persian Gulf deployment)
Electron Equipt:
Radar: 1/SPN-703 nav.—Sonar: SQQ-14A (*see* Remarks)
M: 1 GMT B230-8M diesel; 1 prop; 1,840 bhp (2 retractable auxiliary thrusters; 470 hp for 7 kts)
Electric: 650 kw (2/250-kw sets, ID 36SS diesels; 1/150-kw set)
Range: 1,500/14; 2,500/12 **Fuel:** 49 tons
Crew: 4 officers, 43 enlisted (including 7 mine-clearance divers)

Milazzo (M 5552)—with extra mounts for 20-mm AA just forward of the stack   Carlo Martinelli, 5-89

Lerici (M 5550)   Italian Navy, 1990

Remarks: Ordered 4-78. Sisters built for Nigeria and Malaysia, and the U.S. Nav MHC 51 class is based on this design. Glass-reinforced, shock-resistant plastic con struction throughout. Hull material 140-mm thick. SQQ-14 is a high-frequency mine hunting sonar with a retractable transducer; it is being replaced by the digital Italian made, repackaged SQQ-14/IT, which incorporates the Plessey Speedscan (Type 2048 side-scan sonar for route survey work at up to 12 kts. While minehunting, speed is knots, using the two drop-down, shrouded thrusters. Carry 6–7 divers, who use CA mine-destructor charges. One Pluto remote-controlled submersible disposal and on MIN-77 locating submersible carried by each ship, along with Oropesa Mk 4 mechan cal sweep gear. Have Motorola MHS-1A navigation system and MM/SSN-714 com mand and control system. Range at 12 knots can be extended to 4,000 nautical miles using the passive roll stabilization tanks to carry fuel. Delivery of the first two shi delayed by the presence of a bridge blocking the seaward exit from the yard. deployment to the Persian Gulf in 1987, M 5552 carried two extra 20-mm AA.

◆ 2 ex-U.S. Agile-class fleet minesweepers

	Bldr	L	In serv.
M 5431 Storione (ex-MSO 506)	Martinolich, San Diego	13-11-54	23-2-56
M 5433 Squalo (ex-MSO 518)	Tampa Marine	1955	20-6-57

Storione (M 5431)   Leo Van Ginderen, 1

D: 665 tons (750 fl) **S:** 14 kts **Dim:** 52.27 × 10.71 × 4.00 (fl)
A: 1/40-mm Bofors AA in U.S. Mk 3 mounting
Electron Equipt:
Radar: 1/SPN-703 nav., 1/BX-732 nav.—Sonar: UQS-1 HF
M: 2 G.M. 8-278ANW diesels; 2 CP props; 1,600 bhp
Range: 3,000/10 **Fuel:** 46 tons
Crew: 4 officers, 58 enlisted

Remarks: Wooden construction. Sisters *Sgombro* (M 5432, ex-MSO 517), pl in reserve 10-9-90 and *Salmone* (M 5430, ex-MSO 507), which had been used for eries protection duties since 1989, were stricken 31-8-91. All had originally scheduled for disposal 1982–83, and the two remaining units will be retired d 1992.

MINE WARFARE SHIPS *(continued)*

◆ **6 U.S. Adjutant-class mineunters**

	Bldr	In serv.
M 5504 CASTAGNO (ex-MSC 74)	Henry Grebe, New York	7-8-55
M 5505 CEDRO (ex-MSC 88)	Berg SY, Washington	9-11-53
M 5509 GELSO (ex-MSC 75)	Henry Grebe, New York	8-3-54
M 5516 PLATANO (ex-MSC 136)	Bellingham BY, Washington	6-10-54
M 5519 MANDORLO (ex-MSC 280)	Tacoma BY, Washington	16-12-60
M 5538 LOTO	C.N. Celli, Venice	21-1-56

Cedro (M 5505)—standard minehunter configuration
Hartmut Ehlers, 9-90

Mandorlo (M 5519)—minehunter with unique bridge, tall stack
Leo Van Ginderen, 9-91

Platano (M 5516)—smaller bridge, lattice mast (M 5538 is similar)
Luciano Grazioli, 11-87

D: 354.5 tons (405 fl) **S:** 11.4 kts
Dim: 43.92 (42.1 pp) × 8.23 × 2.68
A: 2/20-mm Oerlikon AA (II × 1)
Electron Equipt:
Radar: 1/SPN-703 nav.—Sonar: SQQ-14 hull-deployed HF
M: 2 G.M. 8-268A diesels; 2 props; 810 bhp—1 Voith-Schneider vertical cycloidal propulsor for minehunting: 310 shp
Fuel: 40 tons **Range:** 2,500/10
Crew: 2 officers, 29 men (minehunters: 3 officers, 38 men)

Remarks: All converted from minesweepers by substituting the SQQ-14 sonar for the original UQS-1 and providing facilities for mine clearance divers and remote-controlled minehunting submersibles. M 5538 built with "Offshore" procurement funds and did not receive U.S. Navy MSC-series hull number; the others were built under the U.S. Military Aid Program. M 5519 is of a later design than the others, with a lower bridge and larger stack; she was converted as a minehunter in 1975 and displaces 370 tons; her dimensions are 44.12 × 8.50 × 2.30, and her two 900-bhp diesels provide a 12-kt max. speed. Employ the Pluto remote-controlled submersible, capable of 4.5-kt speeds; the divers aboard use CAM-T destruction charges. All have wooden hulls and nonmagnetic fittings.

Sisters *Mirto* (ex-M 5539) and *Pioppo* (ex-M 5515) have been converted to survey ships, and *Alloro* (M 5532) became a training ship during 1986. Four others, still capable of serving as minesweepers, have been redesignated as patrol boats (see earlier page).

Fourteen other minesweeper-configured sisters were stricken 1974–1983, while *Edera* (M 5533) was stricken during 1987, *Larice* (M 5510) on 30-6-88, *Sandorlo* (M 5527) on 30-10-88, *Agave* (M 5531) on 28-2-89, *Ebano* (M 5522, ex-MSC 215) on 31-12-90, *Gelsomino* (M 5535) on 30-9-90, *Giaggiolo* (M 5536) on 30-11-90, and *Timo* (M 5540) and *Vischio* (M 5542) on 31-8-91. Minehunter *Frassino* (M 5508) retired 30-9-91.

AMPHIBIOUS WARFARE SHIPS

◆ **2 (+1) San Giorgio-class amphibious warfare ships** Bldr: Fincantieri, Riva Trigoso

	Laid down	L	In serv.
L 9892 SAN GIORGIO	26-5-85	25-2-87	13-2-88
L 9893 SAN MARCO	26-3-85	10-10-87	6-5-89
L 9894	9-91	1993	1994

San Marco (L 9893) Leo Van Ginderen, 9-91

San Marco (L 9893) Luciano Grazioli, 6-88

San Giorgio (L 9892) Italian Navy, 1990

San Giorgio (L 9892) Barbensi, 10-90

AMPHIBIOUS WARFARE SHIPS *(continued)*

D: 5,000 tons (7,665 fl) **S:** 21 kts (sust.)
Dim: 133.30 (118.00 pp) × 20.50 × 5.25
A: 1/76-mm 62-cal. OTO Melara DP—2/20-mm Oerlikon AA (I × 2)—2/12.7-mm mg (I × 2)—5/CH-47 or SH-3D helicopters
Electron Equipt:
Radar: 1/SPN-748 nav., 1/SPS-702 air/surf. search, 1/SPG-70 f.c.
M: 2 GMT A420.12, 12-cyl., 4-stroke diesels; 2 CP props; 16,800 bhp—1,000-bhp bow-thruster
Electric: 3,330 kw (4 × 770 kw, 1 × 250 kw)
Range: 4,500/20; 7,500/16
Crew: 170 ship's company, plus 400 troops

Remarks: L 9892, initially requested in 1980, was approved in 1983 and ordered 5-3-84. L 9893, ordered 26-3-85 with funds from the Ministry of Civil Protection, is configured for disaster-relief service and has more extensive medical facilities. Both fitted out at Muggiano and are based at Brindisi. L 9892 is temporarily replacing the cruiser *Caio Duilio* (C 554) as training ship and made a South American cruise during 1991. The third unit, to be configured especially to act as cadet training ship for the Naval Academy at Livorno in peacetime, was authorized during 11-90 and ordered during 3-91; the ship will displace about 300 tons more than the first two and will have a larger island superstructure and different upper-deck boat stowage. L 9893 performed as a hospital facility and supply ship for Italian forces committed to the UN Coalition during the 1990–91 Mid-East crisis.

Carry three 18.5-m LCM (see below), launched via a 20.5 × 7.0 m stern docking well equipped with a 40-ton traveling bridge crane. Three 13.0-m LCVP can be stowed on deck. The helicopters are stowed on deck, not in the 100 × 20.5-m vehicle hangar below, which can hold up to 30 or more personnel carriers; the ships can beach and offload vehicles via a bow ramp. The flight deck is served by a 13.5 × 3.5-m, 30-ton elevator and a 16-ton crane. There is stowage for 99 m^3 of refrigerated and 300 m^3 dry stores and 60 tons aviation fuel. Evaporators producing 90 tons water per day are fitted. Have passive tank stabilization. The old-model 76-mm gun is served by an NA-21 f.c.s.

AMPHIBIOUS WARFARE CRAFT

♦ **2 assault swimmer support craft** Bldr: Crestitalia, Ameglia, La Spezia

	Laid down	L	In serv.
Y 498 Mario Marino (ex-MEN 213)	8-9-83	. . .	23-10-84
Y 499 Alcide Pedretti (ex-MEN 214)	8-9-83	. . .	21-12-84

Alcide Pedretti (Y 499) Carlo Martinelli, 6-90

D: 69.5 tons light (96.6 fl) **S:** 28 kts
Dim: 22.85 × 6.90 × 1.06 (1.50 max.)
Electron Equipt: Radar: 2/. . . nav.
M: 2 Isotta Fraschini ID 36 SS 12V diesels; 2 props; 3,040 bhp
Range: MEN 213: 236/28; 264/23—MEN 214: 450/23.5
Crew: 1 officer, 7 enlisted, . . . swimmers

Remarks: Typed MAS—*Motoscafi Appoggio Subacquei.* Built for San Marco Battalion assault swimmers (COMSUBIN), based at La Spezia. GRP construction. Y 499 has recessed stern for diver recovery, divers' stage, decompression chamber fitted. One near-sister built for the U.A.E.

♦ **2 personnel transports** Bldr: Crestitalia, Ameglia, La Spezia (In serv. 1986)

MEN 215 MEN 216

D: 82 tons (fl) **S:** 28 kts (23 sust.) **Dim:** 27.28 × 6.98 × 1.10
Electron Equipt: Radar: 1/. . . nav.
M: 2 Isotta Fraschini diesels; 2 props; 3,200 bhp
Range: 250/14
Electric: 50 kVA (2 × 25 kVA gen.)
Crew: 4 tot., plus 250 passengers

Remarks: Built to be carried by the carrier *Giuseppe Garibaldi* as commando transports, for search-and-rescue, disaster relief, and other transport duties. GRP construction.

MEN 216 Carlo Martinelli, 6-86

♦ **8 (+3) MTM 217-class vehicle landing craft** Bldr: Fincantieri, Muggiano, La Spezia

	In serv.
MTM 9923–9925, MTM 217–219	9-10-87
MTM 9926–9928, MTM 220–222	8-3-88
MTM 9929–9930, MTM 223–224	1989
MTM 9931–9934, MTM 225–228	1992

D: 62 tons (64.6 tons fl) **S:** 9 kts **Dim:** 18.50 × 5.10 × 0.90
M: 2 Fiat-AIFO 8280 diesels; 2 props; 560 bhp
Range: 300/9 **Crew:** 3 crew + . . . troops

Remarks: GRP construction. First three for *San Giorgio,* next three for *San Marc* plus two spare. Three more ordered 3-91 for the third ship of the *San Giorgio* cla Cargo capacity: 30 tons. MTM: *Mototrasporti Medi.*

♦ **15 U.S. LCM(6)-class vehicle landing craft**

MTM 542–MTM 556

D: 24 tons (56 fl) **S:** 10 kts **Dim:** 17.07 × 4.37 × 1.17 (aft)
M: 2 diesels; 2 props; 330 bhp **Range:** 130/10

Remarks: Transferred 1953. Cargo: 30 tons. Until 1986 were numbered as M 9908–9922.

♦ **8 (+3) MTP 96-class personnel landing craft** Bldr: Crestitalia, Ameglia, La Spezia (MTP 105–107: C.N. Tecnomatic, Ancona)

	In serv.
MTP 9755–9757, MTP 96–98	9-10-87
MTP 9758–9762, MTP 99–103	8-3-88
MTP 9763–9765, MTP 104–106	1992

D: 14.3 tons (fl) **S:** 26 kts **Dim:** 13.70 × 3.80 × 0.70
M: 2 Fiat-AIOF 836J-SRM diesels; 2 props; 700 bhp
Range: 180/24 **Crew:** 3 tot. + 45 troops

Remarks: GRP personnel launches, without bow ramps, for use with the *San Gio* class. Three more ordered 3-91 for use with the third unit of the *San Giorgio* class. = *Mototrasporti Personale.*

Note: For use by seaborne assault troops, there are 24 LVTP-7 armored perso carriers and 1 LVTC-7 armored command post, all tracked amphibious craft t ferred from the United States.

HYDROGRAPHIC SURVEY SHIPS

♦ **1 Ammiraglio Magnaghi class** Bldr: C. N. del Tirreno, Riva Trigo

	Laid down	L	In se
A 5303 Ammiraglio Magnaghi	13-6-73	11-9-74	2-5

Ammiraglio Magnaghi (A 5303) Carlo Martinell

HYDROGRAPHIC SURVEY SHIPS *(continued)*

D: 1,550 tons (1,700 fl) **S:** 17 kts
Dim: 82.70 (76.80 pp) × 13.70 × 3.60
A: 1/40-mm Breda AA (not normally aboard)
Electron Equipt: Radar: 1/SPN-703 nav.
M: 2 GMT B306 SS diesels; 1 CP prop; 3,000 bhp; 1 electric auxiliary engine; 240 shp (4 kts)
Range: 5,500/12; 4,200/16
Crew: 14 officers, 120 enlisted, 15 scientists

Remarks: Equipped for survey and oceanographic studies and for search-and-rescue duties. Passive tank stabilization. Bow-thruster. Part of 1972 program. Has chemistry, physical, oceanography, photo, and hydrology labs, computerized data loggers, underwater TV. Has a helicopter pad aft. Received Qubit TRAC V/CHART 100 integrated hydrographic data acquisition system during major overhaul in 1991 that also saw modifications to the stack.

◆ **0 (+2) new-construction coastal survey ships** Bldr: Intermarine, Sarzana

	Laid down	L	In serv.
A	. . .	. . .	. . .
A	. . .	. . .	. . .

D: 300 tons (fl) **S:** . . . kts **Dim:** 38.0 × . . . × . . .
Electron Equipt: Radar: 1/. . . nav.
M: 2 . . . . . . diesels; 2 props; . . . bhp
Range: . . ./. . . **Crew:** . . . tot.

Remarks: Ordered 2-90 as replacements for *Mirto* (A 5306) and *Pioppo* (A 5307). GRP construction.

◆ **2 U.S. Adjutant-class former minesweepers**

	Bldr	L	In serv.
A 5306 Mirto (ex-M 5539)	C.N. Breda, Marghera	2-11-54	4-8-56
A 5307 Pioppo (ex-M 5515, ex-MSC 135)	Bellingham SY, Wash.	8-53	30-7-54

Mirto (A 5306) Carlo Martinelli, 3-89

D: 322 tons (375 fl) **S:** 12 kts
Dim: 43.92 (42.10 pp) × 8.23 × 2.68
Electron Equipt: Radar: 1/BX-732 nav.
M: 2 G.M. 8-268A diesels; 2 props; 1,200 bhp
Range: 2,500/10 **Fuel:** 40 tons
Crew: 3 officers, 31–35 enlisted

Remarks: Superstructure enlarged, stack raised when converted to survey duties. . . can carry two 20-mm AA (II × 1). Special survey equipment includes Elac Deneb . . .ial scanning sonar, Krupp-Atlas scanning sonar, TORAN F, Raydist, Mini Ranger and LORAN-C. To be replaced by two new 300-ton ships.

REPLENISHMENT OILERS

◆ **0 (+1) Etna-class replenishment oiler** Bldr: . . .

	Laid down	L	In serv.
. Etna	. . .	. . .	. . .

D: 11,810 tons (fl) **S:** 22 kts **Dim:** 132.0 × 21.0 × . . .
A: 1/76-mm OTO Melara Compact DP—2/40-mm Breda AA (II × 1)—1/EH-101 or Sea King helicopter
Electron Equipt: 1/. . . nav., 1/. . . surf. search, 2/SPG-75 f.c.
M: 2 G.M.T. 420.16 diesels; 2 props; 22,400 bhp
Range: 6,300/22 **Crew:** 230 tot.

Remarks: Proposed addition to fleet, to accompany *Giuseppe Garibaldi*. Would carry . . . tons gas turbine/diesel fuel, 500 tons aviation fuel, and 2,000 m^3 ammunition, . . .ions, and spares. Two replenishment stations on each beam. The program was . . .n" in 2-90 due to lack of funds but may be revived later unless the Italian Navy . . . absorb the third unit of the *Stromboli* class (see below).

◆ **2 Stromboli-class oilers** Bldr: C.N. del Tirreno, Riva Trigoso

	Laid down	L	In serv.
A 5327 Stromboli	1-10-73	20-2-75	31-10-75
A 5329 Vesuvio	1-7-74	4-6-77	18-11-78

Stromboli (A 5327) Italian Navy, 1990

Vesuvio (A 5329) Leo Van Ginderen, 9-91

D: 4,200 tons (8,706 fl) **S:** 19.5 kts
Dim: 129.00 (118.5 pp) × 18.00 × 6.50 (3.17 light)
A: 1/76-mm 62-cal. OTO Melara DP—2/20-mm Oerlikon AA (I × 2)
Electron Equipt:
Radar: 1/SPN-703 nav., 1/SPG-70 f.c.
M: 2 GMT C428 SS diesels: 1 LIPS 4-bladed CP prop; 11,200 bhp (9,600 sust.)
Electric: 2,350 kw **Range:** 10,000/16
Crew: 10 officers, 114 enlisted

Remarks: Cargo: 1,370 tons fuel oil, 2,830 tons diesel, 480 tons aviation fuel, and 200 tons miscellaneous (torpedoes, missiles, projectiles, spare parts). Capable of serving one unit on each beam using constant-tension fueling rigs, each capable of delivering 650 m^3/hr of fuel oil and 480 m^3/hr of diesel fuel or aviation fuel. Can also refuel over the stern at the rate of 430 m^3/hr. There are also constant-tension cargo transfer rigs on either side, each capable of transferring 1.8-ton loads, as well as two stations for lighter loads. The ships can also replenish via helicopters, although they do not have hangars. Twenty repair-party personnel can also be accommodated, and the ships can carry up to 250 passengers. NA-10 Argo GFCS for the 76-mm gun.

Sister *Agnadeen,* completed and handed over to Iraq, has been sequestered at Alexandria, Egypt, since 1986 and may be seized and turned over to the Italian Navy to satisfy its need for a third replenishment ship; the Italian Navy, however, does not want the ship whose ownership is well entangled.

EXPERIMENTAL SHIPS

◆ **1 underwater systems trials craft** Bldr: C.N. Picchiotti, Viareggio

	L	Delivered	In serv.
A 5320 Vincenzo Martellotta	28-5-88	2-3-89	22-12-90

D: 340 tons (fl) **S:** 17.5 kts **Dim:** 44.50 × 7.90 × 2.30
A: 1/533-mm TT—3/324-mm ILAS-3 ASW TT (III × 1)
Electron Equipt: Radar: 1/. . . nav.—Sonar: . . .

Vincenzo Martellota (A 5320) Carlo Martinelli, 7-90

EXPERIMENTAL SHIPS *(continued)*

M: 2 Isotta-Fraschini; ID36 N12V diesels; 2 CP props; 3,500 bhp—1/. . . drop-down outdrive aft for low-speed operations—bow-thruster
Range: 700/15 **Crew:** 1 officer, 8 enlisted, 8 technicians

Remarks: Revised version of *Raffaele Rossetti* (A 5315) below, intended for ASW torpedo trials, the laying and recovery of acoustic buoys, and trials with remotely controlled underwater vehicles. Has a bulbous bow, unlike A 5315, and can lay a 3-dimensional torpedo-tracking hydrophone array. Operated from La Spezia with A 5315 by the Commission for War Materials Experiments.

◆ **1 underwater systems trials craft** Bldr: C.N. Picchiotti, Viareggio

	L	In serv.
A 5315 Raffaele Rossetti	21-7-86	20-12-86

Raffaele Rossetti (A 5315) Carlo Martinelli, 7-88

D: 282 tons (320 fl) **S:** 14.5 kts
Dim: 44.60 (40.00 pp) × 7.90 × 2.10
A: 2/533-mm TT (1 submerged, *Sauro*-type; 1 surface, *Maestrale*-type, for A-184-series wire-guided torpedoes)—3/324-mm ILAS-3 ASW TT (III × 1)
Electron Equipt: Radar: 1/. . . nav.—Sonar: . . .
M: 2 Isotta Fraschini ID36 N12V diesels; 2 CP props; 3,500 bhp
Electric: . . . kw (2 gen.) **Range:** 12,000/12
Crew: 1 officer, 8 enlisted, 8 technicians

Remarks: Ordered 3-84. For torpedo, sonar, and electronic-warfare equipment trials. Has 96-cell battery for electric, low-speed silent propulsion.

◆ **1 Aragosta-class former inshore minesweeper** Bldr: C.N. Apuana, Marina di Currara (In serv. 1957)

A 5305 Murena (ex-*Scampo,* M 5466)

Murena (A 5305)—with ILAS-3 ASW TT to port amidships
Carlo Martinelli, 10-90

D: 130 tons (188 fl) **S:** 13.5 kts **Dim:** 32.35 × 6.47 × 2.14
A: 3/324-m ILAS-3 ASW TT (III × 1)
Electron Equipt: Radar: 1/BX-732 nav.
M: 2 Fiat-MTU MB 820D diesels; 2 props; 1,000 bhp
Range: 2,000/9
Fuel: 15 tons **Electric:** 340 kw **Crew:** 4 officers, 12 enlisted

Remarks: New superstructure, with enclosed bridge. Formerly carried a fixed 533-mm torpedo tube at the stern.

Note: The surface weapons trials ship *Quarto* (A 5314), originally built as a medium landing ship, was stricken 30-4-91; she is being replaced by the modified frigate *Carabiniere* (F 581).

SUPPORT TENDER

◆ **1 U.S. Barnegat-class special forces tender** Bldr: Lake Washington SY, Houghton, Washington

	Laid down	L	In serv.
A 5301 Pietro Cavezzale (ex-*Oyster Bay,* AGP 6, ex-AVP 28)	17-4-42	23-5-43	17-11-43

Pietro Cavezzale (A 5301) Leo Van Ginderen, 9-91

D: 1,766 tons (2,800 fl) **S:** 16 kts **Dim:** 94.6 × 12.58 × 3.7
A: 2/40-mm Bofors AA (II × 1)
Electron Equipt: Radar: 1/SPN-748 nav.
M: 2 Fairbanks-Morse 38D8Q × 10 diesels; 2 props; 6,000 bhp
Electric: 600 kw **Fuel:** 400 tons **Range:** 10,000/11
Crew: 7 officers, 105 enlisted

Remarks: Transferred 23-10-57. Serves as tender to assault swimmers and amphibious support craft. Had last U.S. SPS-6 radar and 76.2-mm gun remaining in Italian Navy; removed by 4-90. Was to have been retired during 1991 but has been retained for lack of a suitable replacement.

SALVAGE SHIPS

◆ **1 salvage ship/submersible tender**

	Bldr	Laid down	L	In serv.
A 5309 Anteo	C.N. Breda, Mestre	1977	11-11-78	31-7-80

Anteo (A 5309) Italian Navy, 19

D: 2,178 tons (3,070 fl) **S:** 18.3 kts
Dim: 98.4 (93.0 pp) × 15.8 × 5.18
A: 2/20-mm AA (II × 1)—1/AB-212 helicopter
Electron Equipt: Radar: 1/SPN-748 nav.
M: 3 GMT A-230-12V diesels (4,050 bhp each), electric drive (2 motors); 1 prop; 6,000 shp (5,360 sust.)—bow-thruster
Range: 4,000/14 **Fuel:** 270 tons
Crew: 9 officers, 104 enlisted

Remarks: Ordered 1977. Carries U.S. Navy–style submarine rescue equipment cluding a McCann rescue bell capable to 150 meters, and two decompression chamb A Type MSM-1/S, 22-ton salvage submersible named *Usel* is also carried; 9.0 × 2 2.7 meters, it can submerge to 600 meters and has a 120-hour autonomous endur with a 4-kt max. speed. Also carried is a Gaymarine Pluto remote-controlled un water vehicle. The ship supports saturation diving to 350 meters and has a 27 bollard pull towing capacity at 10 kts.

◆ **1 former submarine rescue ship** Bldr: CNR, Ancona

	Laid down	L	In serv.
A 5310 Proteo (ex-*Perseo*)	1943	1944	24-8-51

Proteo (A 5310) Luciano Grazioli

SALVAGE SHIPS *(continued)*

D: 1,865 tons (2,147 fl) **S:** 16 kts
Dim: 75.70 × 11.70 × 6.10
A: 2/20-mm AA (I × 2)
Electron Equipt: Radar: 1/SPN-748 nav.
M: 2 Fiat diesels; 1 prop; 4,800 bhp
Range: 7,500/13 **Crew:** 8 officers, 106 enlisted

Remarks: Seized by German forces after launch, towed to Trieste; returned to Ancona, and fitting out resumed 1949. Relieved by *Anteo* (A 5309) as submarine rescue ship, but is retained as an ocean tug and salvage ship. Has submersible decompression chamber, extensive divers' support equipment, and 4-point mooring capability. Refitted 1984–85 with new stack and an electrohydraulic crane.

Note: The salvage ship *Alicudi* (A 5304, ex-U.S. AN 99), built as a net tender, was reduced to reserve on 30-4-91 for eventual disposal.

WATER TANKERS

♦ 1 Simeto class Bldr: CINET, Molfetta

	Laid down	L	In serv.
A 5375 Simeto	14-3-86	4-2-88	9-7-88

D: 1,914 tons (fl) **S:** 13 kts **Dim:** 68.35 (63.60 pp) × 10.06 × 3.90
A: . . . **Electron Equipt:** Radar: 1/SPN-748 nav.
M: 2 GMT B 230.6 diesels; 1 prop; 2,400 bhp—125-shp bow-thruster
Electric: 420 kw (3 × 140 kw) **Crew:** 2 officers, 25 enlisted

Remarks: Cargo: 1,200 tons. Replaced the canceled second *Tevere* (A 5355), which was scrapped incomplete in 1985 when her builder, Ferbex, went bankrupt. *Simeto* design based on *Basento* class. Has 3 Isotta-Fraschini ID30SS6L diesels driving the generators. A second new water tanker was authorized in 1982 but was not ordered.

♦ 1 Piave class

	Bldr	L	In serv.
A 5354 Piave	C.N. Orlando, Livorno	18-12-71	23-5-73

iave (A 5354) Leo Van Ginderen, 8-86

D: 5,003 tons (fl) **S:** 13.6 kts
Dim: 97.8 (86.7 pp) × 13.4 × 5.9 **A:** removed
Electron Equipt: Radar: 1/3RM-7 nav.
M: 2 diesels; 2,560 bhp
Range: 1,500/12 **Crew:** 5 officers, 42 enlisted

marks: Cargo: 3,500 tons. Sister *Tevere* (A 5355) sold commercially 1976. Forrly carried 4/40-mm AA (II × 2).

3 Basento class Bldr: INMA, La Spezia

5356 Basento (In serv. 19-7-71)
5357 Bradano (In serv. 29-12-71)
5358 Brenta (In serv. 18-4-72)

D: 1,930 tons (fl) **S:** 12.5 kts **Dim:** 68.65 × 10.07 × 3.90
A: removed **Electron Equipt:** Radar: 1/SPN-703 nav.
M: 2 Fiat LA-230 diesels; 1 prop; 1,730 bhp
Range: 1,650/12.5 **Crew:** 2 officers, 25 enlisted

marks: Cargo capacity: 1,200 tons. Can carry 2/20-mm AA (I × 2). Can make 13.1 in light condition.

ento (A 5356) Carlo Martinelli, 6-90

♦ 1 small water tanker Bldr: C.N. di Venezia

A 5374 Mincio (In serv. 1930)

D: 645 tons **S:** 6 kts **Dim:** 43.1 × 8.00 × 3.00
M: 1 diesel; 350 bhp **Crew:** 1 officer, 19 enlisted

Note: Ex-U.S. Army 327E-class water tanker *Adige* (A 5369, ex-YW 92), the last of three sisters in Italian Navy service, was stricken 31-8-91. Small water tanker *Bormida* (A 5359, ex-GGS 1011) was to be stricken during 1991.

TRAINING SHIPS

Note: The landing ship *San Giorgio* (L 9892) is serving as temporary Naval Academy training ship pending completion of a sister especially configured for the rôle in 1994.

♦ 5 Aragosta-class former inshore minesweepers

	Bldr	L	In serv.
A 5378 Aragosta (ex-M 5450)	CRDA, Monfalcone	8-56	19-7-57
A 5379 Astice (ex-M 5452)	CRDA, Monfalcone	16-1-57	19-7-57
A 5380 Mitilo (ex-M 5459)	Picchiotti, Viareggio	1-6-57	11-7-57
A 5381 Polipo (ex-M 5463)	Costaguta, Voltri	15-6-57	10-7-57
A 5382 Porpora (ex-M 5464)	Costaguta, Voltri	1-6-57	10-7-57

Aragosta (A 5378)—with deckhouse aft Luciano Grazioli, 10-90

D: 120 tons (178 fl) **S:** 13.5 kts **Dim:** 32.35 × 6.47 × 2.14
A: none **Electron Equipt:** Radar: 1/BX-732 nav.
M: 2 Fiat/MTU MB 820D diesels; 2 props; 1,000 bhp
Electric: 340 kw **Range:** 2,000/9 **Fuel:** 15 tons
Crew: 2 officers, 13 enlisted

Remarks: Based on British "Ham"-class design. Originally 20 in class. Built with U.S. Military Assistance Program funds. Wooden construction. Single 20-mm AA fwd removed. A 5381 and A 5382 reclassified 1984–85 for use as administrative tenders and navigational training craft at the Naval Academy. A 5378 is equipped as a combat swimmer training craft and has a decompression chamber in a deckhouse aft. Two sisters serve as ferries (GLS 501, GLS 502), and *Murena* (A 5305) serves as a torpedo trials and retriever craft.

♦ 1 U.S. Adjutant-class former minesweeper Bldr: CRDA, Monfalcone

	Bldr	In serv.
A 5308 Alloro (ex-M 5532)	CRDA, Monfalcone	1-2-56

D: 322 tons (375 fl) **S:** 12 kts
Dim: 43.92 (42.10 pp) × 8.23 × 2.68
Electron Equipt: Radar: 1/BX-732 nav.
M: 2 G.M. 8-268A diesels; 2 props; 1,200 bhp
Range: 2,500/10 **Fuel:** 40 tons
Crew: 4 officers, 36 enlisted

Remarks: Converted to serve as training tender for the Petty Officer's School at La Maddalena. Four sisters serve as patrol boats and seven as minehunters. Wooden construction.

♦ 1 sail-training full-rigged ship Bldr: Nav. Mec. Castellammare

	Laid down	L	In serv.
A 5312 Amerigo Vespucci	12-5-30	22-2-31	15-5-31

D: 3,545 tons (4,146 fl) **S:** 10 kts (under power)
Dim: 101.00 over bowsprit/82.38 hull (70.72 pp) × 15.56 × 6.7
A: 4/40-mm Bofors AA (I × 4)—1/20-mm Oerlikon AA
Electron Equipt: Radar: 2/SPN-748 nav.
M: 2 Tosi E6 diesels, electric drive: 2 Marelli motors; 1 prop; 1,900 shp
Range: 5,450/6.5 **Crew:** 13 officers, 228 enlisted, 150 cadets

Remarks: Sail area: 2,100 m^2. Steel construction, including masts. Refitted 1984.

♦ 1 sail-training barkentine Bldr: Dubigeon, France (In serv. 1920)

A 5311 Palinuro (ex-*Cdt Louis Richard*)

D: 1,042 tons (1,341 fl) **S:** 10 kts (7.5 sail)
Dim: 68.9 (59.0 pp) × 10.1 × 4.8
A: 2/76-mm (saluting battery)

TRAINING SHIPS *(continued)*

Amerigo Vespucci (A 5312) Maritime Photographic, 8-91

Palinuro (A 5311) Italian Navy, 1990

Electron Equipt: Radar: 1/SPN-748 nav.
M: 1 M.A.N. G8V23.5/33 diesel; 450 bhp
Range: 5,385/7.5 under power **Crew:** 4 officers, 44 enlisted

Remarks: Former French cod-fishing craft bought in 1951, refitted and recommissioned 16-7-55. Steel hull.

♦ **1 new-construction sail-training ketch** Bldr: S.A.I. Ambrosini, Passignano (In serv. 10-91)

A . . . CRISTOFORO COLOMBO II

D: 82 tons (fl) **S:** . . . kts **Dim:** 31.50 × . . . × . . .
M: 1 diesel; 1 prop; . . . bhp—919.7 m² sail area
Crew: 24 tot.

Remarks: Ordered 9-90. Kevlar-reinforced plastic hull. Built for participation in a 1992 regatta to commemorate the 500th anniversary of the first discovery voyage of her namesake.

♦ **1 sail-training yawl** Bldr: Costaguta, Genoa (In serv. 5-1-61)

A 5316 CORSARO II

D: 41 tons **Dim:** 20.9 × 4.7
M: 1 auxiliary engine; 96 bhp
Electron Equipt: Radar: 1/Decca 060
Crew: 2 officers, 14 cadets

Remarks: Based at Naval Academy, Livorno. Very similar to *Stella Polare* (A 5313). Sail area: 205 m².

♦ **1 RORC-class cruising yacht** Bldr: Sangermani, Chiavari (In serv. 7-10-65)

A 5313 STELLA POLARE

D: 41 tons (47 fl) **S:** . . . **Dim:** 20.9 × 4.7 × 2.9
M: 1 Mercedes-Benz diesel; 1 prop; 96 bhp
Crew: 2 officers, 14 cadets

Remarks: Sail area: 197 m². Based at Naval Academy, Livorno.

♦ **1 sail-training yawl** Bldr: Baglietto, Varazze (In serv. 1948)

A 5302 CAROLY

D: 60 tons (fl) **S:** 9 kts (6.5 power)
Dim: 26.60 (23.75 pp) × 4.80 × 3.10
M: 1 G.M. diesel; 100 bhp **Crew:** 13 officers, 3 enlisted

Remarks: Donated to navy 25-4-83. There are also a number of smaller sail-training craft in use.

SEAGOING TUGS

♦ **6 Ciclope-class** Bldr: Ferrari, La Spezia

	L	In serv.		L	In serv.
A 5319 CICLOPE	20-2-85	11-9-85	A 5328 GIGANTE	. . .	18-7-86
A 5324 TITANO	2-3-85	7-12-85	A 5330 SATURNO	29-7-87	5-4-88
A 5325 POLIFEMO	15-6-85	21-4-86	A 5365 TENACE	31-8-87	9-7-88

Tenace (A 5365) Leo Van Ginderen, 9-9

D: 600 tons (658 fl) **S:** 14.5 kts
Dim: 38.95 (32.30 pp) × 9.85 × 3.32
Electron Equipt: Radar: 1/SPN-748 nav.
M: 2 GMT BL230.6L diesels; 1 CP prop; 3,264 bhp
Electric: 500 kw (2 × 200 kw, 1 × 100 kw)
Range: 3,000/14.5 **Crew:** 12 tot.

Remarks: Bollard pull: 45 tons (36 tons sustained at 8.3 kts). Two 130-m³/hr wa cannon, 23-ton-capacity foam tank. Enlarged and improved version of *Atlante* cla Last two ordered 29-5-86.

♦ **2 Atlante class** Bldr: C.N. Visitini, Donada (Both in serv. 14-8-75)

A 5317 ATLANTE A 5318 PROMETEO

Prometeo (A 5318) Leo Van Ginderen,

D: 478 tons light (750 fl) **S:** 13.5 kts **Dim:** 38.9 × 9.6 × 3.70
M: 1 Tosi QT 320/8SS diesel; 1 CP prop; 2,670 bhp (3,000 max.)
Range: 4,000/12 **Crew:** 25 tot.

SERVICE CRAFT

♦ **2 Aragosta-class former inshore minesweepers**

GLS 501 (ex- . . .) GLS 502 (ex-*Riccio*, M 5465)

Remarks: Retyped as personnel transports 1979–80. Characteristics under administrative tender/navigational training craft sisters.

♦ **1 yacht/ambulance craft** Bldr: Picchiotti, Viareggio (In serv. 12-9-70)

R. Paolucci

R. Paolucci Luciano Grazioli, 2-90

D: 70 tons (fl) **S:** 21.3 kts **Dim:** 27.72 × 7.40 × . . .
M: 2 diesels; 2 props; . . . bhp **Crew:** 1 officer, 7 enlisted

♦ **1 torpedo transport** (In serv. circa 1939–41)

GIS 61

IS 61 Carlo Martinelli, 1983

D: 230 tons **S:** 7 kts **Dim:** . . . × . . . × . . .
A: 1/533-mm TT
M: 1 diesel; 1 prop; . . . bhp **Crew:** . . . tot.

emarks: Supports submarines. Former harbor net tender. Sister GS 59 discarded 90.

1 torpedo-recovery craft Bldr: Crestitalia, Ameglia, La Spezia

EN 212 (In serv. 10-83)

D: 32 tons (fl) **S:** 23 kts **Dim:** 17.65 × 5.10 × 1.00
M: 2 diesels; 2 props; 1,380 bhp **Range:** 250/20
Crew: 4 tot.

marks: Can stow 3 torpedoes. Glass-reinforced plastic construction. Three others ted in previous editions were evidently not built, but there are a number of other all torpedo retrievers.

N 212—with smaller MCN 1595 in background Leo Van Ginderen, 9-92

♦ **5 MTF-series lighthouse and navigational buoy tenders** Bldr: C.N. Mario Morini, Ancona

	Laid down	L	In serv.
A 5365 Ponza (MTF 1304)	25-3-87	24-9-88	20-12-88
A 5366 Levanzo (MTF 1305)	25-3-87	24-11-88	28-2-89
A 5367 Tavolara (MTF 1306)	25-3-87	12-2-89	19-5-89
A 5368 Palmaria (MTF 1307)	25-3-87	28-2-89	6-9-89
A 5369 Procida (MTF 1308)	15-9-89	23-6-90	14-11-90

Palmaria (A 5368) Carlo Martinelli, 8-90

D: 402 tons light (608 fl) **S:** 14.8 kts
Dim: 56.72 (50.00 pp) × 10.00 × 2.50
A: provision for 2/7.62-mm mg (I × 2)
Electron Equipt: Radar: 1/BX-732 nav.
M: 2 Isotta-Fraschini ID36 SS 8V diesels; 2 CP Kort-nozzle props; 1,690 bhp—1/120-shp bow-thruster
Electric: 464 kw tot. (2 × 232 kw) **Range:** 1,500/14; 2,800/10
Crew: 2 officers, 32 enlisted

Remarks: MTF = *Mototrasporti Fari.* First four ordered 23-9-86. Variation of the design used for the MTC 1011-class coastal transports. One 15-ton-capacity electrohydraulic crane aft; one 1.5-ton crane forward.

♦ **6 MTC 1011-class coastal transports** Bldr: C.N. Mario Morini, Ancona

	L	In serv.
A 5347 Gorgona (MTC 1011)	12-7-86	23-12-86
A 5348 Tremiti (MTC 1012)	13-9-86	2-3-87
A 5349 Caprera (MTC 1013)	8-11-86	10-4-87
A 5351 Pantellaria (MTC 1014)	31-1-87	26-5-87
A 5352 Lipari (MTC 1015)	7-5-87	10-7-87
A 5353 Capri (MTC 1016)	18-6-87	16-9-87

Lipari (A 5352) Luciano Grazioli, 1991

D: 631 (fl) **S:** 14+ kts **Dim:** 56.72 × 10.00 × 2.50
A: provision for 1/20-mm AA—2/7.62-mm mg (I × 2)—mine rails
Electron Equipt: Radar: 1/BX-732 nav.
M: 2 CRM 12D/SS diesels; 2 props; 1,520 bhp
Electric: 484 kw (2 × 192 kw, 1 × 100 kw) **Range:** 1,500/14
Crew: 4 officers, 28 enlisted

Remarks: MTC 1011 laid down 12-7-86, MTC 1014 on 31-1-87. MTC = *Mototrasporti Costieri.* Two electrohydraulic cranes. Intended to carry palletized cargo on their open decks and fuel and water below decks. Replaced World War II–era MTCs of the MZ class. A 5347 based at La Spezia, A 5348 at Ancona, A 5349 and A 5351 at La Maddalena, the last two at the Naval Academy, Livorno.

♦ **5 ex-British LCT(3)-class coastal transports** (In serv. 1943–44)

A 5331 MOC 1201 A 5333 MOC 1203 A 5335 MOC 1205
A 5332 MOC 1202 A 5334 MOC 1204

SERVICE CRAFT *(continued)*

MOC 1201 (A 5331)—torpedo retriever/workshop Dr. Giorgio Arra, 1981

D: 711–752 tons (fl) **Dim:** 58.25 × 9.22 × 2.0–2.2
A: 2/20-mm AA (I × 2; not in all)
Electron Equipt: Radar: 1/BX-732 nav.
M: 2 diesels; 2 props; 1,000 bhp
Crew: 1–2 officers, 20–26 enlisted

Remarks: MOC 1201 is used for torpedo recovery; the remainder serve as repair craft for minesweepers and small combatants. The bow door/ramp has been welded closed. MOC 1207 (A 5337), used as an ammunition transport, stricken 31-12-90. Similar MTF 1302 (A 5362) and MTF 1303 (A 5363) stricken 1986–87; MTF 1301 (A 5301) stricken 30-4-91.

♦ **1 ex-German MFP-D cargo lighter, former landing craft**

A 5341 MTC 1001 (In serv. 1942)

MTC 1001 (A 5341) Leo Van Ginderen, 9-91

D: 218 tons (fl) **S:** 10 kts **Dim:** 49.8 × 6.6 × 1.12
A: 2/20-mm AA **Electron Equipt:** Radar: 1/BX-732 nav.
M: 3 Deutz diesels; 3 props; 450 bhp
Range: 540/9 **Crew:** 1 officer, 17 enlisted

Remarks: Can carry 150 tons cargo; beaching capability retained. To be stricken soon.

Note: Of the two MZ-class lighters listed in the last edition, MTC 1010 (A 5350) was stricken in 1989 and MTC 1006 (A 5346) in 1991.

♦ **4 seagoing fuel lighters** Bldr: Cantieri Ferrari, La Spezia

	L	In serv.
A 5370 MCC 1101	26-10-85	26-8-86
A 5371 MCC 1102	16-11-85	6-12-86
A 5372 MCC 1103	3-2-86	18-5-87
A 5373 MCC 1104	14-11-87	20-5-88

MCC 1101 (A 5370) Leo Van Ginderen, 9-91

D: 863 tons (fl) **S:** 13 kts **Dim:** 47.30 × 10.00 × 3.30
Electron Equipt: Radar: 1/BX-732 nav.
M: 2 Isotta-Fraschini ID 36 SSV6 diesels; 2 props; 1,320 bhp
Range: 2,000/13 **Crew:** 11 tot.

Remarks: Cargo: 550 tons. MMC = *Motocisterne Combustibili* (fuel lighter).

♦ **6 harbor fuel lighters** Bldr: C.N. De Poli, Pellestrina, Venezia

GGS 1010 GGS 1013
GGS 1011 GGS 1014
GGS 1012 GGS 1015

D: . . . tons **S:** . . . kts
Dim: 37.50 (pp) × 8.50 × . . . (4.00 moulded depth)
M: 2 AIFO 8281 SRM 08 diesels; 2 props; 544 bhp

Remarks: 508 dwt. Five ordered 30-6-88, sixth on 15-9-89.

♦ **5 harbor fuel lighters**

GRS 172 GRS 173 GRS 175 GRS 178 XI

Remarks: All of about 500 tons capacity. Also in use are five water barges in the GGS 502–507 series.

♦ **1 degaussing tender** Bldr: Crestitalia, Ameglia

JDG 10 (In serv. 1989)

D: 135 tons (fl) **S:** 2–4 kts **Dim:** 25.20 × 8.00 × 0.95
M: 2 outboard engines; 110 bhp **Crew:** . . .

Remarks: Barge-like hull with tapered ends. Outboard engines mounted within vertical wells through hull.

LARGE HARBOR TUGS

♦ **9 Porto class** Bldr: first six: C.N. De Poli, Pellestrina; others: C.N. Giacalone, Mazzara del Vallo, Trapani

	L	In serv.
Y 421 PORTO EMPEDOCLE	4-12-85	19-3-86
Y 422 PORTO PISANO	22-10-85	20-8-85
Y 423 PORTO CONTE	21-11-85	28-9-85
Y 425 PORTO FERRAIO	21-7-85	3-4-85
Y 426 PORTO VENERE	13-5-85	12-2-85
Y 428 PORTO SALVO	13-9-85	4-7-85
Y 413 PORTO FOSSONE	. . .	24-9-90
Y 416 PORTO TORRES	3-9-90	16-1-91
Y 417 PORTO CORSINI	2-11-90	4-3-91

D: 412 tons (fl) **S:** 11.5 kts **Dim:** 32.36 (28.00 pp) × 8.50 × 3.32
Electron Equipt: Radar: 1/BX-732 nav.
M: 1 GMT B230-8M diesel; 1 CP prop; 1,600 bhp
Range: 1,800/11.5
Fuel: 46 tons **Electric:** 200 kw (2 × 100 kw) **Crew:** 13 tot.

Porto Corsini (Y 417) Luciano Grazioli,

Remarks: Bollard pull: 25 tons (15 tons at 5 kts). Two water cannons, two 130- pumps. First six ordered 2-6-83; other three originally ordered from Ferbex, Naple 29-10-87; reordered 18-5-88 from Giacalone after Ferbex closed and laid down 18- The final three have two 200-kw generator sets. All have an ELAC LAZ-50 sounder.

♦ **2 Porto d'Ischia class** Bldr: CNR, Riva Trigoso (In serv. 1969–70)

Y 436 PORTO D'ISCHIA Y 443 RIVA TRIGOSO

D: 250 tons (296 fl) **S:** 12 kts **Dim:** 25.5 × 7.1 × 3.3
M: 1 diesel; 1 CP prop; 850 bhp

Note: The *Ercole*-class tugs *Vigoroso* (Y 451) was stricken 31-50-90; single-uni *Ustica* (Y 448) and *Panaria* (Y 431) were stricken 30-4-91.

LARGE HARBOR TUGS *(continued)*

Riva Trigoso (Y 443) Leo Van Ginderen, 9-91

SMALL HARBOR TUGS

◆ **10 RP 125 class** Bldr: (A) C.N. Vittoria, Adria; (B) C.N. Ferrari, La Spezia; (C) CINET, Molfetta

	Bldr	In serv.		Bldr	In serv.
Y 478 RP 125	A	1983	Y 483 RP 130	B	10-8-84
Y 479 RP 126	A	24-9-83	Y 484 RP 131	B	28-8-84
Y 480 RP 127	B	29-3-84	Y 485 RP 132	C	7-7-84
Y 481 RP 128	B	4-84	Y 486 RP 133	C	3-11-84
Y 482 RP 129	B	5-6-84	Y 487 RP 134	B	1985

RP 126 (Y 479) Luciano Grazioli, 3-91

D: 78 tons (120 fl) **S:** 9.5 kts
Dim: 19.85 (17.00) × 5.20 × 2.10
M: 1 Fiat AIFO 828-SM diesel; 1 prop; 368 bhp
Electric: 28 kw **Range:** 400/9.5 **Crew:** 3 tot.

Remarks: 76 grt. First six ordered 18-8-83. One 120-m³/hr water cannon.

◆ **10 RP 113 class** Bldr: C.N. Visitini, Donada (In serv. 1978–1981)

	In serv.		In serv.
Y 463 RP 113	1978	Y 471 RP 120	1980
Y 464 RP 114	1980	Y 472 RP 121	1980
Y 465 RP 115	1980	Y 473 RP 122	1980
Y 466 RP 116	1980	Y 474 RP 123	1980
Y 470 RP 119	1980	Y 475 RP 124	1981

RP 122 (Y 473) Leo Van Ginderen, 9-91

Remarks: Characteristics similar to RP 101 class below, but have a larger superstructure. Details differ. RP 117 (Y 467) and RP 118 (Y 468) deleted, date not available.

◆ **12 RP 101 class** Bldr: C.N. Visitini-Loreo, Donado (In serv. 1972–75)

Y 403 RP 101	Y 408 RP 105	Y 456 RP 109
Y 404 RP 102	Y 410 RP 106	Y 458 RP 110
Y 406 RP 103	Y 413 RP 107	Y 460 RP 111
Y 407 RP 104	Y 452 RP 108	Y 462 RP 112

RP 107 (Y 413) Leo Van Ginderen, 9-91

D: 36 tons (75 fl) **S:** 12 kts **Dim:** 18.8 × 4.5 × 1.9
M: 1 diesel; 500 bhp

Note: The three miscellaneous small harbor tugs *Albenga* (Y 412), *Linaro* (Y 430), and San *Benedeto* (Y 446) had been stricken by 1991.

FLOATING DRY DOCKS

◆ **14 miscellaneous**

	In serv.	Capacity (tons)		In serv.	Capacity (tons)
GO 53	10-2-90	6,000	GO 18A	1920	800
GO 52	1979	6,000	GO 17	1917	500
GO 51	1971	2,000	GO 11	1911	2,700
GO 23	1935	1,000	GO 10	1900	2,000
GO 22	1935	1,000	GO 8	1904	3,800
GO 20	1935	1,600	GO 5	1893	100
GO 18B	1920	600	GO 1	1942	1,000

Remarks: GO 52 is 150.5 m long by 29.6 m (21.6-m internal width). GO 53 was laid down 30-1-89 and launched 10-2-90 by Cantieri Ferrari, La Spezia, for use at Augusta, Sicily: D: 152.40 × 29.60 × 16.45 high (14.95 m maximum submersion).

Note: There are a large number of harbor service craft, launches, etc., with hull numbers in the GAS, GAA, GD, GTM, GGS, MDN, VS, GT, MCN, and MEN (personnel launch) series. Fireboats VF 681 and VF 682 delivered 7-89 and 18-11-89 by CN De Poli, Pellestrina, for service at Venice. GD 325–328, 18.0 × 5.97, laid down 1989 by C.N. Vernaglione, Taranto (GD 328 by C.N. Balsamo, Brindisi). GHIF 261, 20.00 × 5.00, laid down 10-8-89 by Vernaglione, Taranto. G 14, a sullage barge, was delivered 5-90 by C.N. Solimano, Savona.

MCN 1644—personnel launch Luciano Grazioli, 11-88

MEN 225—personnel launch at Venice A. Molinari, 4-89

FLOATING DRY DOCKS *(continued)*

GE/25—an open barge Luciano Grazioli, 11-87

MEN 210—personnel launch A. Molinari, 8-89

GZ 330—target barge Luciano Grazioli, 4-88

MCN 1514—service launch Luciano Grazioli, 5-91

MEN 220—former LCM(6)-class landing craft Leo Van Ginderen, 9-9

Mooring service barge Leo Van Ginderen, 9-

COAST GUARD
(Guardia Costa)

Renamed from the Port Captain Corps (*Corpo delle Capitanerie di Porto*) of Italian Navy in 1989, the *Guardia Costa* comes under the control of the Ministry of Merchant Marine in peacetime and the Navy in wartime and has police, fisher protection, oil spill recovery, and SAR duties. There are 80 detachments at vari Italian ports, operating some 140 large and 60 smaller patrol craft. Boats be displaying "*Guardia Costiera*" vice "*Capitanerie*" on their sides during late 1989. personnel complement is to grow to 10,000 by the year 2000.

Aviation: The Coast Guard has 12 Piaggio P166 DL3/SEM aircraft for surveilla duties and 4 AB-212 helicopters. It is planned to have seven helicopter flight secti each with 3 Agusta-Bell AB-412 helicopters, the first of which was delivered du 9-91. Ultimately, there are to be 25 helicopters, with an additional dozen include long-range planning.

Piaggio P 166 DL3/SEM of the former Port Captain Corps Luciano Grazioli

Note: The Italian Navy operates the seagoing large patrol boats of the *Cassiopea* for the Coast Guard. Ten new patrol boats, class and type unspecified, were auth for acquisition during 1990.

SEAGOING PATROL AND RESCUE BOATS

◆ **0 (+1) CP 409 class** Bldr: C.N.R., Ancona (In serv. 1992)

CP 409 . . . .

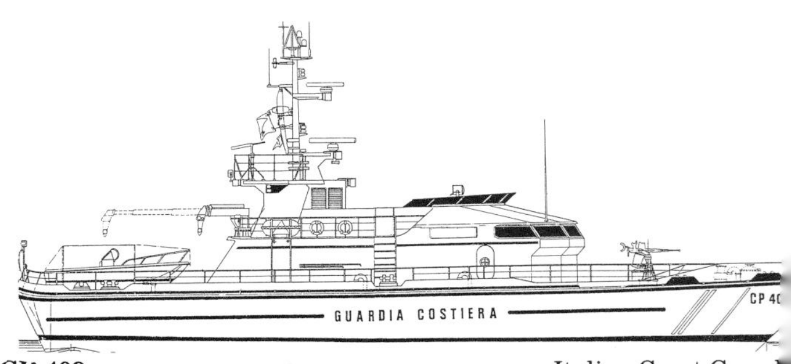

CP 409 Italian Coast Guard

SEAGOING PATROL AND RESCUE BOATS *(continued)*

D: . . . tons **S:** 22 kts **Dim:** 34.60 × 7.10 × 2.10
A: 1/20-mm AA **Electron Equipt:** Radar: 2/. . . nav.
M: . . . diesels; . . . props; . . . bhp **Crew:** . . tot.

Remarks: Ordered 1991. Has daughter rescue boat stowed on ramp at stern, electro-hydraulic telescoping crane to assist in recovery, fire-fighting water monitor on mast platform, stern wedge to improve speed and fuel economy.

◆ **4 CP 405 class** Bldr: Bacino di Carenaggio S.p.A., Trapani (In serv. 1990–91)

CP 405 Francesco Mazzinghi — CP 406 Antonio Scialoia
CP 407 Michele Lolini — CP 408 Mario Grabar

Mario Grabar (CP 408) — Luciano Grazioli, 5-91

D: 136 tons (fl) **S:** 22 kts **Dim:** 29.50 × 6.70 × 1.83
Electron Equipt: Radar: 1/. . . nav.
M: 4 CRM 12D/SS diesels; 2 props; 5,500 bhp (4,340 sust.)
Range: 1,000/. . . **Crew:** 11 tot. + 50 rescuees

Remarks: No daughter boat. Two water cannon for fire fighting. Named as for the CP 401 class below, except that CP 406 is named for Italy's greatest maritime law scholar. CP 408 launched 31-3-90, CP 406 the following month.

◆ **4 CP 401 class** Bldr: CNR, Ancona (In serv. 1987–91)

CP 401 Oreste Cavallari — CP 402 Renato Pennetti
CP 403 Walter Fachin — CP 404 Gaetano Magliano

Walter Fachin (CP 403) — Giuseppe Valentini, 12-90

D: 130 tons (fl) **S:** 22 kts **Dim:** 28.60 × 6.20 × 2.00
Electron Equipt: Radar: 1/. . . nav.
M: 4 Isotta-Fraschini ID36 SS 8V diesels; 2 props; 3,520 bhp
Range: 1,000/. . . **Crew:** 11 tot. + 50 rescuees

Remarks: Carry a 3.8-ton daughter boat for rescue work on ramp aft: Dim: 8.00 × 2.40 × 0.?0. Can be equipped to carry 1/20-mm AA, 2/7.62-mm mg (I × 2). CP 403 delivered ... All named for former members of the Port Captain Corps of the Italian Navy who died or were wounded during World War II or were lost at sea. CP 403 delivered ...

◆ **2 (+13) CP 314-class rescue boats** Bldr: C.N. Baglietto, Varezze

CP 314 Gemma (L: 20-2-88)–CP 318 . . . . . . (L: 30-6-88–1991)

D: 43.1 tons (fl) **S:** 20 kts
Dim: 18.05 (17.96 wl) × 5.75 × 1.20
Electron Equipt: Radar: 1/Decca . . .
M: 2 CRM 12DS diesels; 2 props; 1,700 bhp
Range: 400/16 **Crew:** 7 tot. + 20 rescuees

Remarks: GRP construction with low amidships freeboard to facilitate rescues. Fin stabilizers. Sixteen more planned but have not yet been ordered.

CP 316 — Leo Van Ginderen, 9-91

◆ **1 Vosper-Thornycroft design** Bldr: Nelson, Viareggio

CP 313 Dante Novaro (In serv. 1977)

Dante Navarro (CP 313) — Luciano Grazioli, 2-90

D: 57 tons (fl) **S:** 24 kts **Dim:** 22.85 × 6.10 × 1.75
A: small arms **Electron Equipt:** Radar: 1/. . . nav.
M: 2 Isotta-Fraschini ID 36 SS diesels; 2 props; 2,760 bhp
Range: 1,000/. . . **Crew:** 11 tot.

◆ **1 seagoing rescue lifeboat** Bldr: Scheerswerft, Bardenfleth, Germany

CP 312 Bruno Gregoretti (In serv. 1972)

D: 65 tons (fl) **S:** 19 kts **Dim:** 23.20 × 5.30 × 1.50
Electron Equipt: Radar: 1/. . . nav.
M: 1 Mercedes-Benz 12V493 diesel (1,310 bhp), 2 Mercedes-Benz diesels (480 bph each); 3 props; 2,270 bhp
Range: 1,000/19 **Crew:** 11 tot.

Bruno Gregoretti (CP 312) — Carlo Martinelli, 5-88

SEAGOING PATROL AND RESCUE BOATS *(continued)*

Remarks: Typical West German lifeboat design with Maierform hull and stern ramp for 6.5-m rescue boat CVP 312/5: 6.75 × 2.20 × 0.52, 1.8 tons, 54 bhp, range 200/8.

♦ **1 seagoing rescue lifeboat** Bldr: Pellegrino, Naples

CP 307 Michele Fiorillo (In serv. 1968)

Michele Fiorillo (CP 307) Giuseppe Valentini, 1989

D: 84 tons (97 fl) **S:** 15 kts **Dim:** 26.60 × 5.60 × 1.62
A: 2/12.7-mm mg (I × 2) **Electron Equipt:** Radar: 1/. . . nav.
M: 2 Mercedes-Benz MB820 diesels (1,320 bhp), 2 MB836 diesels (800 bhp each) diesels; 3 props; 2,920 bhp
Range: 1,000/17 **Crew:** 11 tot.

Remarks: Another German-style rescue boat with Maierform hull and stern ramp for 3-ton rescue boat CP 307/S: 8.50 × 2.0 × 0.63; 1 Mercedes-Benz diesel; 100 bhp; 11 kts.

Note: Also in service are five "Seppietta"-series motor lifeboats, the most recent being a class of three delivered 1988.

♦ **3 CP 603 class** Bldr: Italcraft, Gaeta (all L: 6-5-88)

CP 603–CP 605

D: 3.5 tons **S:** 16 kts **Dim:** 8.50 × 2.78 × 0.80
M: 2 VM HR 694 diesels; 1 prop; 248 bhp
Range: 200/16 **Crew:** 2 tot.

CP 605 Antonio Scrimali, 4-89

FAST PATROL BOATS

♦ **2 CP 256 class** Bldr: Italcraft, Gaeta

CP 256 (In serv. 9-7-85) CP 257 (In serv. . . .)

CP 257 Giuseppe Valentini, 3-89

D: 20.75 tons (23.7 fl) **S:** 33 kts **Dim:** 16.00 × 5.25 × 0.98
A: . . . **Electron Equipt:** Radar: 1/. . . nav.
M: 2 CRM 12D/S-2 diesels; 2 Riva-Calzoni waterjets; 1,700 bhp
Range: 350/24 **Fuel:** 3,500 l. **Crew:** 7 tot.

♦ **2 CP 254 class** Bldr: Tecnomarine, Viareggio (In serv. 1984)

CP 254 CP 255

D: 21 tons (22.5 fl) **S:** 31 kts **Dim:** 15.10 × 5.25 × 0.98
A: 2/12.7-mm mg (I × 2) **Electron Equipt:** Radar: 1/. . . nav.
M: 2 Isotta-Fraschini ID 36-SS-6V diesels; 2 Riva-Calzoni IRC-43-DL waterjets; 1,520 hp
Range: 350/24 **Crew:** 7 tot.

CP 254 Luciano Grazioli, 6-

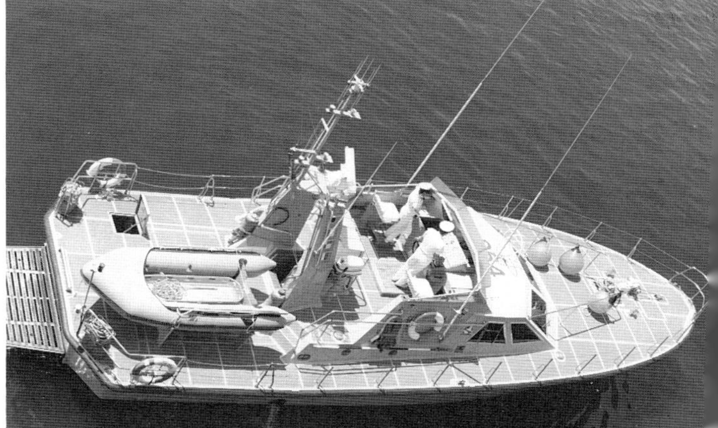

CP 254 Luciano Grazioli,

♦ **8 CP 246 class** Bldr: CP 246: Navaltecnica, Anzio; others: Canados Navale, Ostia Lido

CP 246 (In serv. 1977) CP 247–253 (In serv. 1980–81)

D: 22 tons (fl) **S:** 28–29 kts **Dim:** 15.00 × 4.85 × 1.60
A: 1/20-mm AA **Electron Equipt:** Radar: 1/. . . nav.
M: 2 Isotta-Fraschini ID 36 SS 6V diesels; 2 props; 1,380 bhp
Range: 450/. . . **Crew:** 7 tot.

♦ **6 CP 239 class** Bldr: Rodriguez, Messina

CP 239, 240, 242, 243 (In serv. 1971) CP 244, CP 245 (In serv. 197

CP 239 Luciano Graziol

FAST PATROL BOATS *(continued)*

D: 25 tons (fl) **S:** 30 kts **Dim:** 16.8 × 5.0 × 1.7
A: 1/12.7-mm mg **Electron Equipt:** Radar: 1/. . . nav.
M: 2 Isotta-Fraschini ID36 SS 6V diesels; 2 props; 1,380 bhp
Range: 450/. . . **Crew:** 7 tot.

Remarks: Sister CP 241 sank summer 1991.

◆ **8 CP 231 (Super Speranza) class** Bldr: Rodriguez, Messina

CP 231–238 (In serv. 1966–70)

P 236 Mauricio Brescia, 6-91

D: 14 tons (16 fl) **S:** 26 kts **Dim:** 13.4 × 4.8 × 1.3
A: 2/12.7-mm mg **Electron Equipt:** Radar: 1/. . . nav.
M: 2 diesels; 2 props; 754–850 bhp **Range:** 400/. . .
Crew: 7 tot.

marks: CP 231 has AIFO 828 diesels, CP 233 has AIFO 8281; the rest have AIFO diesels.

3 CP 228 class Bldr: Navaltecnica, Anzio (In serv. 1967)

228 CP 229 CP 230

D: 12.1 tons **S:** 20–24 kts **Dim:** 13.40 × 4.75 × 1.20
M: 2 AIFO 828 SRM diesels; 2 props; 900 bhp
Range: 400/20 **Crew:** 7 tot.

2 CP 226 class Bldr: Navaltecnica, Anzio (In serv. 1964)

226 CP 227

D: 15.1 tons (fl) **S:** 22–26 kts **Dim:** 13.12 × 4.73 × 1.20
A: 2 12.7-mm mg (I × 2) **Electron Equipt:** Radar: 1/. . . nav.
M: 2 AIFO diesels; 2 props; 400 bhp **Range:** 400/22 **Crew:** 7 tot.

marks: Levi Hunt "Super Speranza" design.

SHORE PATROL CRAFT

36 Keith Nelson–design GRP launches

	Bldr	In serv.
2001–2005	Vosper Thornycroft, Woolston	1971
2006–2009	Bianchi & Cecchi, Genoa	1973–74
2010–2017	Motomar, Lavagna, Genoa	1972–75
2018–2023	Bianchi & Cecchi, Genoa	1973–74
2024	Navaltecnica, Messina	1973
2025–2031	Keith Nelson, Viareggio	1975–76
2032–2035	Motomar, Lavagna	1975–76
2036–2045	Keith Nelson, Viareggio	1976–78
2046–2048	Motomar, Palermo	1978
2049–2065	Balsamo, Brindisi	1978–79
2066–2068	C.N. La Spezia	1980
2069–2077	Balsamo, Brindisi	1980–83
2078–2081	Mericraft, Baia, Naples	1985
2201–2205	Motomar, Palermo	1986

11–15 tons **S:** 14–22 kts **Dim** (typical): 12.57 × 3.64 × 1.10
2 AIFO V85, V85M, or 828M, Cummins V504M or VT8-370M, Isotta-Fraschini ID32 SS 6L, ID32 SS 6LM, or 6/L diesels; 2 props; 420–800 bhp
nge: 400/. . . **Crew:** 4 tot.

rks: A relatively homogeneous group of craft based on a British pilot-boat , with numerous variations in superstructure and propulsion plants. CP 2024, ed with two D/F loops for aircraft rescue duties, is larger: 15 tons; 13.70 × 3.76 × 4 kts.

CP 2004—CP 2001 series Circomare, Milazzo, 10-89

CP 2041—CP 2036 series Giuseppe Valentini, 12-90

CP 2202—CP 2201 series Luciano Grazioli, 3-90

◆ **22 CP 6001 class** Bldr: Crestitalia, Ameglia (6013-on: Benetti/Azimut, Viareggio)

CP 6001–6010 (In serv. 25-3-86)
CP 6011, CP 6012 (In serv. 21-11-86)
CP 6013, CP 6014 (In serv. 14-11-88)
CP 6015–6022 (In serv. 1988)

D: 3.72 tons **S:** 22–24 kts **Dim:** 8.00 × 2.50 × 0.50
M: 2 VM 4R692-H9 diesels, 2 Castoldi waterjets; 180 bhp
Range: 180/22 **Crew:** 3 crew + 4 passengers

Remarks: GRP construction.

◆ **5 CP 506 class** Bldr: C.N. del Golfo, Gaeta (In serv. 1987–88)

CP 506–CP 510

D: 6.5 tons (fl) **S:** 34 kts **Dim:** 9.73 × 3.50 × 0.70
M: 2 Isotta-Fraschini ID32 SS 62M diesels; 2 props; 600 bhp
Range: 250/34 **Crew:** 3 tot.

INSHORE PATROL CRAFT *(continued)*

CP 6005 Luciano Grazioli, 7-89

♦ **4 waterjet-propelled GRP-hulled** Bldr: Crestitalia, Ameglia, La Spezia

CP 502–505 (In serv. 1983)

D: 6.6 tons (fl) **S:** 28 kts **Dim:** 8.34 × 2.76 × 0.45
A: small arms **M:** 2 AIFO 8061 SM diesels; 2 waterjets; 364 bhp
Range: 200/28 **Crew:** 2 tot.

♦ **5 CP 601 series** Bldrs: Crestitalia, Ameglia, and Italcraft, Gaeta

CP 601–605 (In serv. 1977–87)

D: 3 tons (fl) **S:** 10 kts **Dim:** 8.65 × 2.60 × 0.67
A: small arms
M: 2 AIFO 806 AM diesels; 220 bhp
Range: 250/10 **Crew:** 2 tot.

Remarks: Minor differences in characteristics: 603–605 are 8.50 × 2.78 × 0.80, 2 VM HR 694 diesels; 248 bhp = 16 kts; range: 200/16.

♦ **1 CP 501 class** Bldr: Crestitalia, Ameglia, La Spezia

CP 501 (In serv. 1978)

CP 501 Antonio Scrimali, 4-89

D: 3.6 tons (fl) **S:** 32 kts **Dim:** 8.32 × 2.76 × 0.45
A: small arms
M: 2 AIFO 8061 diesels; 2 Castoldi waterjets; 260 bhp
Range: 200/32 **Crew:** 3 tot.

♦ **6 CP 1001 class** Bldr: Crestitalia, Ameglia, La Spezia

CP 1001–1006 (In serv. 1974–76)

D: 5.2 tons (fl) **S:** 23 kts **Dim:** 9.00 × 3.16 × 0.80
M: 2 AIFO CP3M diesels; 2 props; 320 bhp **Range:** 240/18
Crew: 4 tot.

Remarks: Builder's "Azteca" design; GRP monohedron hull.

♦ **51 CP 5001-series fast launches**

	Bldr	In serv.
CP 5001	Marine Union, Milan	1971
CP 5002–5009, 5011–5012	Vasnautica, Milan	1969–71
CP 5013–5032, 5038–5043, 5052–5054	Marine Union, Milan	1973–79
CP 5034–5037, 5045–5050	Motomar, Milan	1973–7
CP 5051	Motomar, Milan	1975

CP 5013 Giuseppe Valentini, 12-9

	Speed	Dim.	Horsepower
CP 5001	24 kts	5.05 × 1.87 × 0.30	80 bhp
CP 5002 group	24 kts	5.30 × 2.13 × 0.30	80–100 bhp
CP 5013 group	28–30 kts	6.50 × 2.20 × 0.30	130–140 bhp
CP 5034 group	22 kts	5.20 × 2.18 × 0.30	75–85 + 20 bhp aux.
CP 5051	24 kts	5.20 × 2.13 × 0.30	150 bhp

Remarks: All GRP construction. Powered by two Johnson or Volvo Penta Acquamat outboards. Normal crew is 2.

♦ **4 miscellaneous launches**

CP 115 (1969): 9.00 × 2.20 × 0.70; 25 kts/145 bhp
CP 117–118 (1974): 7.17 × 2.28; 20 kts/95 bhp
CP 121 (1985): 9.20 × 2.34; 20 kts/132 bhp

CP 118 Luciano Grazioli, 10

CUSTOMS SERVICE
(Guardia di Finanza)

The Ministry of Finance is organized into 15 administrative areas and 48 squadr Most of the large units have 7.62- or 12.7-mm AA armament. The *Guardia di Fin* also operates 3 Agusta A 109 and several Breda Nardi NH 500 helicopters.

♦ **2 Zara-class seagoing patrol boats** Bldr: Fincantieri, Muggiano

	Laid down	L	In serv.
P. 01 Antonio Zara	. . .	22-4-89	23-2-90
P. 02 Vizzari	31-5-88	25-11-89	4-90

Antonio Zara (P. 01) Carlo Martinelli

D: 316.5 tons (fl) **S:** 27 kts
Dim: 51.00 (47.25 pp) × 7.50 × 1.90
A: 2/30-mm Breda AA—2/7.62-mm mg (I × 2)
Electron Equipt: Radar: 1/SPN-748 nav., 1/SPN-751 nav.
M: 2 Fincantieri-GMT BL 230-12 diesels; 2 props; 7,270 bhp (6,610 sust.)
Range: 2,700/15 **Crew:** 1 officer, 11 petty officers, 20 "Finanzie

Remarks: Design based on builder's *Ratcharit* class for Thailand, but with less ful propulsion plant and lighter armament. Selenia Pegaso-F optronic f.c.s wi CSDA-10 directors. Plans to build two or four more have been suspended; if bu third will be named *Madaglio D'Oro* (P. 03).

;USTOMS SERVICE *(continued)*

◆ **2 (+18) Corrubia class** Bldr: Italcraft, Gaeta

;. 90 CORRUBIA (In serv. 2-90) G. 91 GIUDICE (In serv. 1990)

orrubia (G. 90) Carlo Martinelli, 1990

D: 75 tons (81 fl) **S:** 40 kts **Dim:** 26.17 × 7.40 × 1.06
A: 1/30-mm Breda-Mauser AA—2/7.62-mm mg (I × 2)
Electron Equipt:
Radar: 1/Gem ARPA BX-3072A nav., 1/Gem SC-1400
M: 2 Isotta-Fraschini ID 36SS 16V diesels; 2 props; 6,400 bhp
Range: 700/35 **Crew:** 1 officer, 4 petty officers, 8 "Finanzieri"

:marks: Essentially a competing design to the class following. Have LORAN-C :eiver, Magnavox MX 1402 NAVSAT receiver, Furuno FE 881 echo-sounder, Elsag :dusa optronic director for the 30-mm gun. Up to 18 additional units are planned.

2 (+6) CNL 39 class Bldr: Crestitalia, La Spezia (In serv. 10-10-87)

80 BIGLIANI G. 81 CAVAGLIA

vaglia (G. 81) Antonio Scrimali, 1989

: 73 tons (85 fl) **S:** 45 kts **Dim:** 26.40 × 6.45 × 1.06
: 1/30-mm Breda-Mauser AA—2/7.62-mm mg (I × 2)
lectron Equipt: Radar: G.E.M. ARPA BX-3072A nav.
: 2 MTU 16V396 TB94 diesels; 2 props; 7,680 bhp (6,980 sust.)
ange: 1,200/18.5 **Crew:** 1 officer, 4 petty officers, 8 "Finanzieri"

arks: The original pair of units to have these names and numbers was ordered CN Liguri, Riva Trigoso, and was to displace 210 tons; the completed craft were ted for service and the first two of a new design were ordered in 1984 from titalia. Six additional units were on order as of 1991. The gunhouses differ, that for)-mm mount on G.81 being rounder; there is an Elsag Medusa optronic director for)-mm gun.

U.S. 105-ft Commercial-Cruiser class Bldr: Swiftships, Morgan ity, La.

; GENNA (In serv. 1980)

a (G. 96) Luciano Grazioli, 4-88

D: 120 tons (fl) **S:** 30 kts
Dim: 32.26 × 7.24 × 3.10 (moulded depth)
A: 1/20-mm Oerlikon AA—2/7.62-mm mg
Electron Equipt: Radar: 2/Furuno FR-711 nav.
M: 3 MTU 12V331 TC92 diesels; 3 props; 2,940 bhp
Range: 1,380/30 **Fuel:** 24.4 tons **Crew:** 11 tot.
Electric: 80 kw (2 × 40 kw)

Remarks: Acquired 1984. Aluminum construction. Has LORAN-C receiver, Magnavox MX-1402 NAVSAT receiver, and Raytheon F720-D echo-sounder.

◆ **56 Meattini class** Bldr: Baglietto, Varazze; Picchiotti, Viareggio; Italcraft, Gaeta; Navaltecnica, Messina; Cantiere di Pisa; Cantiere di Lavagna; Cantiere di Chiavari (In serv. 1970–85)

G. 10 MEATTINI	G. 11 AMICI	G. 12 DI BARTOLO
G. 13 R.D.36	G. 14 GORI	G. 15 RAMACI
G. 16 DENARO	G. 17 BAMBACI	G. 18 ARCIONI
G. 19 STERI	G. 20 COTUGNO	G. 21 MANONI
G. 22 GIANNOTTI	G. 23 CARRUBBA	G. 24 UGLIELMI
G. 25 SALONE	G. 26 ESPOSITO	G. 27 RUSSO
G. 28 ZARA	G. 29 RANDO	G. 30 CICALESE
G. 31 DI SESSA	G. 32 COPPOLA	G. 33 RIZZI
G. 34 D'ALEO	G. 35 BACCILE	G. 36 CAVATORTO
G. 37 FUSCO	G. 38 DE TURRIS	G. 39 CHIARAMIDA
G. 40 CAV. D'ORO	G. 41 BIANCA	G. 42 NUVOLETTA
G. 43 PREITE	G. 44 MAZZEO	G. 46 SILANOS
G. 47 IGNESTI	G. 48 BARRECA	G. 49 CIRAULO
G. 50 D'AGOSTINO	G. 51 FIORE	G. 52 NUZIALE
G. 53 TAVANO	G. 54 DE ALEXANDRIS	G. 55 STEFANNINI
G. 56 TRIDENTI	G. 57 FAZIO	G. 58 ATZEI
G. 59 CICALE	G. 60 FIDONE	G. 61 SGUAZZIN
G. 62 TAVORMINA	G. 63 COLOMBINA	G. 64 DARIDA
G. 65 PIZZIGHELLA	G. 66 SCIUTO	

Darida (G. 64) Carlo Martinelli, 11-89

D: 40 tons (fl) **S:** 34 kts **Dim:** 20.10 × 5.20 × 0.90 (hull)
A: 1/20-mm Oerlikon AA—2/7.62-mm mg (I × 2)
Electron Equipt: Radar: 1/3RM 20 nav.
M: 2 CRM 18D-S2 DS-2 diesels; 2 props; 2,500 bhp
Range: 560/21 **Fuel:** 5.8 tons **Electric:** 48 kw (2 × 24 kw)
Crew: 4 officers, 7 "Finanzieri"

Remarks: GRP construction. Made 36 kts on trials. Have LORAN-C receivers.

◆ **2 Gabriele class** Bldr: Picchiotti, Viareggio

G. 70 GABRIELE (In serv. 1966) G. 71 GRASSO (In serv. 1967)

D: 54 tons (fl) **S:** 34 kts **Dim:** 23.20 × 6.60 × 2.00
A: 1/20-mm Oerlikon AA—2/7.62-mm mg (I × 2)
Electron Equipt: Radar: 1/3RM 20 nav.
M: 3 CRM 18D-S2 DS2 diesels; 3 props; 3,150 bhp
Fuel: 9 tons **Range:** 730/20
Crew: 4 officers, 7 "Finanzieri"

Gabriele (G. 70) Giuseppe Valentini, 10-89

PATROL CRAFT

◆ **2 GL. 432 class** Bldr: Picchiotti, Viareggio (In serv. 1968)

GL. 432 GL. 434

D: 13.3 tons (fl) **S:** 34.2 kts **Dim:** 16.50 × 5.15 × 0.90
A: 1/7.62-mm mg
Electron Equipt: Radar: 1/. . . nav.
M: 2 CRM 12-D52 diesels; 2 props; 1,800 bhp
Range: 390/25 **Fuel:** 3.4 tons **Crew:** 7 tot.

◆ **4 GL. 103 class** Bldr: Navaltecnica, Anzio (In serv. 1964)

GL. 103–106

D: 7.1 tons (fl) **S:** 34 kts **Dim:** 10.90 × 3.80 × 1.10
Crew: 7 tot.
A: 1/7.62-mm mg
Electron Equipt: Radar: 1/Sperry Mk 7 AL nav.
M: 2 diesels; 2 props; 872 bhp **Range:** 380/18 **Fuel:** 1.2 tons

Remarks: Wooden construction.

◆ **12 GL. 313 class** Bldr: Baglietto, Varazze; Picchiotti, Viareggio; Fincantieri, Monfalcone (In serv. 1957–59)

GL. 313–321, GL. 324–326

D: 16.5 tons (fl) **S:** 27 kts **Dim:** 15.50 × 4.90 × 1.10
A: 1/7.62-mm mg
Electron Equipt: Radar: 1/Raytheon 2502 nav.
M: 2 AIFO SRM-828 diesels; 2 props; 880 bhp **Range:** 485/20
Fuel: 2 tons **Electric:** 2.5 kw **Crew:** 7 tot.

INSHORE PATROL CRAFT

◆ **2 (+6) V. 5100 class** Bldr: Intermarine, Sarzana (In serv. 1989–1992)

V. 5100 V. 5102 V. 5104 V. 5106
V. 5101 V. 5103 V. 5005 V. 5007

External view

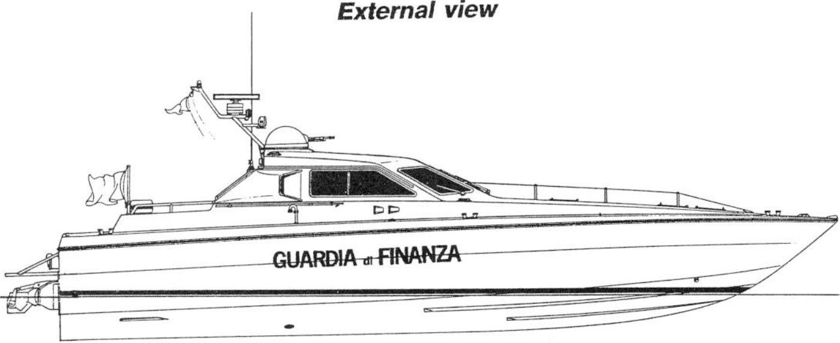

V. 5100 class Intermarine, 1991

D: 20.04 tons (fl) **S:** 48 kts (45 sust.)
Dim: 16.20 × 4.50 × . . .
A: 1/7.62-mm mg
Electron Equipt: Radar: 1/BX-732 nav.
M: 2 Isotta-Fraschini ID 36SS 8V diesels; 2 waterjets; 2,200 bhp (1,950 sust.)
Range: 150/35 **Electric:** 3.5 kw
Crew: 2 petty officers, 3 "Finanzieri"

Remarks: GRP construction. Builder's "Super-Drago" design. First unit laid down 3-10-88, second on 2-3-89; initially rejected after trials failed to produce the required 50 kts and the craft were overweight. Six more ordered fall 1990.

◆ **75 V.A.I. 200 class** Bldr: First unit: Mericraft, Baia, Naples; others: Cantieri Fiat de Napoli (In serv. 1986–. . .)

V.A.I. 200–274

V.A.I. 274 Leo Van Ginderen, 9-91

D: 4 tons (fl) **S:** 35 kts **Dim:** 8.10 (6.58 pp) × 2.48 × 0.65
M: 2 G.M. 692HT-9 diesels; 2 Castoldi Model 06 waterjets; 296 bhp
Range: . . ./. . . **Crew:** 3 tot.

Remarks: GRP construction. For harbor, river, and lake service.

◆ **81 V. 5500 class** Bldr: Crestitalia, Ameglia, La Spezia (In serv. 1979–81)

V. 5500–5581 series

V. 5563 Leo Van Ginderen, 9-

D: 7.8 tons (fl) **S:** 32 kts **Dim:** 12.0 × 3.8 × 0.5
A: small arms **Electron Equipt:** Radar: 1/BX-732 nav.
M: 2 AIFO 8361/SR diesels; 2 Castoldi 06 waterjets; 580 bhp
Range: 224/28 **Fuel:** 0.6 tons **Crew:** 5 tot.

Remarks: GRP construction. One lost.

◆ **15 V. 4000 class** Bldr: Italcraft, Venezia (In serv. 1980–83)

V. 4000–4014

V. 4000 class Giuseppe Valentini, 1

D: 6.9 tons (fl) **S:** 47.7 kts **Dim:** 13.1 × 3.0 × 0.7
A: small arms **Electron Equipt:** Radar: 1/BX-732 nav.
M: 2 Isotta-Fraschini ID 32-SS-61 diesels; 2 props; 720 bhp
Range: 290/37 **Fuel:** 0.7 ton **Crew:** 4 tot.

Remarks: Wooden construction.

◆ **34 V. 5800 class** Bldr: Mericraft, Motomar, Balsamo, and S. Prosperc

V. 5800–5833 (In serv. 1979–84)

V. 5826 Luciano Grazioli

INSHORE PATROL CRAFT *(continued)*

D: 15 tons (fl) **S:** 26 kts **Dim:** 12.6 × 3.6 × 1.2
A: 1/7.62-mm mg
Electron Equipt: Radar: 1/BX-732 nav.
M: 2 Fiat AIFO 8281 SRM diesels; 2 props; 1,000 bhp (880 sust.)
Range: 537/25 **Fuel:** 0.4 ton **Crew:** 5 tot.

Remarks: GRP construction. Keith Nelson-designed. Near sisters in the Coast Guard and the Marine Police.

◆ **3 V. 5300 class** Bldr: Motomar, Lavagna (In serv. 1979–82)

V. 5300–5302

D: 5.1 tons (fl) **S:** 36 kts **Dim:** 8.3 × 2.8 × 0.5
M: 1 AIFO 8361-SM diesels; 1 prop; 480 bhp
Range: 154/36 **Fuel:** 0.5 ton **Crew:** 3 tot.

◆ **1 V. 3000 class** Bldr: SAL Ambrosini, Oristano (In serv. 1978)

V. 3000

D: 2.9 tons (fl) **S:** 40 kts **Dim:** 7.5 × 2.5 × 0.6
M: 1 BPM-Vulcano gasoline engine; Castoldi 06 waterjet; 450 shp
Range: 330/22 **Fuel:** 0.6 ton **Crew:** 3 tot.

◆ **1 V. 1640 class** Bldr: Abbate, Como (In serv. 1979)

V. 1640

D: 6.5 tons (fl) **S:** 42 kts **Dim:** 9.5 × 3.1 × 0.5
Crew: 3 tot.
M: 1 BPM-Vulcano gasoline engine; 760 shp
Range: 189/40 **Fuel:** 0.8 ton

Remarks: For Lake Como service.

1 V. 1630 class Bldr: Italcraft, Gaeta (In serv. 1974)

. 1630

D: 6.8 tons (fl) **S:** 50 kts **Dim:** 13.0 × 2.6 × 0.9
M: 1 Cummins VT-8 gasoline engine; 740 shp
Range: 360/40 **Fuel:** 0.6 ton **Crew:** 3 tot.

2 V. 5901 class Bldr: Motomar, Lavagna (In serv. 1977)

5901–5902

D: 10.5 tons (fl) **S:** 23 kts **Dim:** 12.3 × 3.3 × 1.0
M: 1 Fiat-AIFO CP3-SM diesel; 380 bhp
Range: 630/20 **Fuel:** 1.6 tons **Crew:** 3 tot.

3 V. 2911 class Bldr: Cantieri Fiat de Napoli (In serv. 1973–74)

2911–2913

D: 4.9 tons (fl) **S:** 26 kts **Dim:** 9.5 × 3.3 × 1.6
Crew: 3 tot.
M: 1 OM-CP3-SM gasoline engine; 380 shp
Range: 200/24 **Fuel:** 0.6 ton

te: Also in service as of 11-90 were 135 smaller craft for port, river, and lake service; inflatable lifeboats; and 19 small sailboats for recreation and training.

AINING SHIPS

1 former yacht Bldr: C.N. Lucchese, Venezia (In serv. 1971)

ORGIO CINI

rgio Cini Carlo Martinelli, 4-91

: 800 tons (fl) **S:** 14 kts **Dim:** 54.0 × 10.0 × 2.9
lectron Equipt: Radar: 2/BX-732 nav.
: 1 Fiat B306-SS diesel; 1 prop; 1,500 bhp
el: 65 tons **Range:** 800/14 **Crew:** . . .

arks: Acquired 1981 and refitted for training; operational 1982.

former fishing boat Bldr: Benetti, Viareggio (In serv. 1967)

GIAN MARIA PAOLINI

348 tons **S:** 11 kts **Dim:** 36.8 × 7.7 × 2.3
1/20-mm Oerlikon AA **Electron Equipt:** Radar: . . .
M: 1 Ansaldo 326-R diesel; 1 prop; 530 bhp
Fuel: 33 tons **Range:** 350/10 **Crew:** . . .

Remarks: Acquired 1977 for student training.

MARINE POLICE
(Comando Generale dell'Arma dei Carabinieri Servizio Navale)

Established 1969 for patrol out to the 3-nautical-mile limit, search-and-rescue, research, and police duties.

PATROL CRAFT

◆ **6 700-class launches** Bldr: . . .

D: 22 tons (fl) **S:** 21 kts **Dim:** 15.07 × 4.91 × . . .
A: 1/7.62-mm mg **Electron Equipt:** Radar: 1/. . . nav.
M: 2 AIFO 8280 diesels; 2 props; 808 bhp **Crew:** 5 tot.

◆ **21 600-series Keith Nelson launches** Bldrs: Posillipo; Sabandia (In serv. 1984–85)

CC 622 Giuseppe Valentini, 1989

D: 11–12 tons (fl) **S:** 20–21 kts **Dim:** 12.54 × 3.61 × . . .
A: small arms **Electron Equipt:** Radar: 1/. . . nav.
M: 2 AIFO CP3-SRM or 8361-SRM diesels; 2 props; 380 or 480 bhp
Range: 350/18 **Crew:** 5 tot.

◆ **30 N500-class launches** Bldr: Italcraft, Gaeta (In serv. 23-5-85 to 20-9-85)

N 525 Leo Van Ginderen, 5-86

D: 5.8 tons (fl) **S:** 22 kts **Dim:** 9.10 × 2.95 × . . .
A: small arms **Electron Equipt:** Radar: 1/. . . nav.
M: 2 AIFO 8061-SM diesels; 2 props; 280 bhp
Range: 200/18 **Crew:** 3 tot.

◆ **3 S 500 class** Bldr: . . .

D: 7 tons (fl) **S:** 22 kts **Dim:** 10.00 × 3.40 × . . .
A: small arms **Electron Equipt:** Radar: 1/. . . nav.
M: 2 AIFO 8361-SRM diesels; 2 props; 430 bhp
Range: 200/18 **Crew:** 3 tot.

Remarks: Equipped to support frogmen.

◆ **23 500 class** Bldr: . . .

D: 2.6 tons (fl) **S:** 20 kts **Dim:** 6.46 × 2.37 × . . .
M: 1 AIFO 806-M diesel; . . . bhp
Range: 100/20 **Crew:** 2 tot.

◆ **54 400 class** Bldr: . . .

D: 1.4 tons (fl) **S:** 25 kts **Dim:** 5.50 × 2.10 × . . .
M: 1 AIFO 804-M diesel; . . . bhp **Crew:** 2 tot.

ITALY *(continued)*
PATROL CRAFT *(continued)*

S 501 Leo Van Ginderen, 4-91

Note: A large number of smaller patrol craft are operated by the *Carabinieri*, and local police organizations also have patrol craft. Several examples of Italian small patrol craft are shown below.

S 356 Luciano Grazioli, 10-88

S 120 Luciano Grazioli, 10-88

S 204 Luciano Grazioli, 10-88

One class of Police craft for which data are available is Intermarine's glass-reinforced, plastic-hulled 12 MT design, of which five have been delivered since 1981:

D: 9.0 tons (fl) **S:** 35 kts (32 sust.) **Dim:** 12.00 × 3.33 × 0.60
A: 1/7.75-mm mg **Electron Equipt:** Radar: 1/. . . nav.
M: 2 diesels; 2 Castoldi waterjets; 680 bhp **Electric:** 3 kVA
Range: 200/35; 300/32 **Crew:** 4 tot.

STATE POLICE
(Polizia di Stato)

Note: The Polizia di Stato is yet another national organization that operates a large number of patrol craft. A listing of these craft and their data was not available.

PS 467—La Spezia Police Intermarine

PS 489—La Spezia Police Luciano Grazioli, 7-8

PS 400—La Spezia Police Mike Louagie, 7

ITALIAN ARMY

The Italian Army has a number of small river-crossing craft. The most rec acquisitions have been:

◆ **70 C 200 class GRP-hulled river-crossing boats** Bldrs: 6 by Posillipo, Sabandia; 13 by S.A.I Ambrosini, Passignano sul Trasimeno; others Nautica Rio, Sarnico (In serv. 1990–91)

D: 2 tons (fl) **S:** 27 kts **Dim:** 6.28 (5.00 pp) × 2.48 × 0.80
M: 1 Volvo Penta AQAD-31A diesel; 1 prop; 130 bhp
Range: 240/18 **Crew:** 2 crew + 5 passengers

IVORY COAST

Côte d'Ivoire—Republic of the Ivory Coast

Personnel (1991): 700 total (70 officers, 630 enlisted)

PATROL BOATS

Note: Negotiations were under way during 1991 for the purchase of 12 riverine craft in 4.9- and 12.5-m lengths from a Danish yard.

IVORY COAST *(continued)*
PATROL BOATS *(continued)*

◆ **2 French Patra class** Bldr: Auroux, Arcachon

	Laid down	L	In serv.
L'Ardent	15-4-77	21-7-78	6-10-78
L'Intrepide	7-7-77	21-7-78	6-10-78

'Ardent Auroux, 1978

D: 125 tons (148 fl) **S:** 26.3 kts
Dim: 40.70 (38.50 pp) × 5.90 × 1.55
A: 1/40-mm Bofors AA—1/20-mm Oerlikon AA—2/7.62-mm mg (I × 2)
Electron Equipt: Radar: 1/Decca 1226 nav. **Endurance:** 5 days
M: 2 AGO 195 V12CZ SHR diesels; 2 CP props; 5,000 bhp (4,400 sust.)
Electric: 120 kw **Range:** 750/20; 1,750/10
Crew: 2 officers, 17 enlisted

emarks: Ordered 1-77 and 4-77, respectively. Planned addition of Exocet missiles d not occur.

2 PR-48 class Bldr: SFCN, Villeneuve-la-Garenne

	Laid down	L	In serv.
igilant	2-67	23-5-67	1968
Valeureux	28-10-75	8-3-76	25-9-76

D: 250 tons (fl) **S:** 23 kts **Dim:** 47.5 (45.5 pp) × 7.0 × 2.25
A: 2/40-mm Bofors AA (I × 2)—2/12.7-mm mg (I × 2)
Electron Equipt: Radar: 1/Decca 1226 nav. **Range:** 2,000/16
M: 2 MGO diesels; 2 props; 4,200 bhp **Crew:** 4 officers, 30 enlisted

marks: *Vigilant* refitted at Brest, France, 1981. *Le Valeureux* received new engines 1987. *Vigilant* can make only 18.5 kts on her less-powerful, 2,400-bhp MGO diesel nt.

MPHIBIOUS WARFARE SHIPS

1 French BATRAL-E-class medium landing ship Bldr: Dubigeon, Normandy

éphant (In serv. 2-2-77)

phant Pradignac & Leo, 7-81

: 750 tons (1,330 fl) **S:** 16 kts
im: 80.0 (68.0 pp) × 13.0 × 3.0 (max.)
: 2/40-mm AA (I × 2)—2/81-mm mortars (I × 2)
ectron Equipt: Radar: 1/Decca 1226 nav.
: 2 SACM diesels; 2 CP props; 1,800 bhp
ange: 4,500/13 **Crew:** 4 officers, 35 enlisted

arks: Ordered 2-8-74. Similar to the French Navy's *Champlain*. Helicopter plat- aft. Refitted at Brest, 1981. Cargo capacity is 350 tons (180 tons beaching), ding a landing team of 5 officers and 123 enlisted and up to 12 vehicles. This ship soon be sold.

Type 412 fast assault boats Bldr: Rotork, U.K. (In serv. 1979–80)

5.2 tons (8.9 fl) **S:** 21 kts **Dim:** 12.65 × 3.20 × . . .
2 Volvo AQAD-40A outdrive diesels; 2 props; 240 bhp

LCVP Bldr: Abidjan, 1970

7 tons (9 fl) **S:** 9 kts **Dim:** 10.9 × 3.2 × 1.0
1 Mercedes-Benz diesel

Sea Truck utility craft Bldr: Tanguy, Le Havre (In serv. 11-87)

rks: No details available, other than 12.0 m o.a.

◆ **7 Arcor 24 launches** Bldr: Arcor, La Teste (In serv. 1982)

D: 2 tons (fl) **Dim:** 7.92 × 3.04 × 0.80
M: 2 Renault diesels; 2 props; 320 bhp

GENDARMERIE

◆ **1 small patrol craft** Bldr: DCAN Cherbourg

Le Barracuda (In serv. 1974)

D: 15 tons **S:** 18 kts **Dim:** 9.0 × 3.0 × . . .
A: 1/12.7-mm mg **Crew:** 2 crew, 18 troops **M:** diesels; . . . bhp

◆ **1 Arcor-30 launch** Bldr: Arcor, La Teste, France (In serv. 1985)

D: 5 tons **S:** 20 kts **Dim:** 9.25 (8.30 pp) × 3.50 × 0.82
M: 2 Renault RC-160-D3 diesels; 2 props; 320 bhp
Crew: 2 tot.

◆ **4 Arcor-31 launches** Bldr: Arcor, La Teste, France (In serv. 1982)

Dim: 9.45 × 3.50 × 0.82 **M:** 2 Renault diesels; 2 props; 240 bhp

JAMAICA

DEFENCE FORCE COAST GUARD

Personnel (1991): 18 officers, 163 enlisted (plus reserves: 12 officers, 35 enlisted)

PATROL BOATS

◆ **1 Guardian class** Bldr: Lantana Boatyard, Lantana, Fla. (In serv. 26-9-85)

P 8 Paul Bogle (ex-*Comayguela*)

Paul Bogle (P 8) LT(SG) G.S. Reynolds, JDFCG, 11-90

D: 93 tons (fl) **S:** 33 kts **Dim:** 32.31 × 6.25 × 1.24 (2.13 props)
A: 1/20-mm AA—2/12.7-mm mg (I × 2)
Electron Equipt: Radar: 1/Furuno 2400 nav.
M: 3 MTU 8V396 TB92 diesels; 3 props; 3,600 bhp
Endurance: 7 days **Electric:** 100 kw (2 G.M. 4-71 diesels)
Crew: 4 officers, 16 enlisted

Remarks: Begun and launched for Honduras, then purchased by Jamaica. Was originally to have been renamed *Cape George*. Aluminum construction. Sisters in Grenadan and Honduran service. The 20-mm AA was added by 7-86.

◆ **1 Fort Charles class** Bldr: Teledyne Sewart, Berwick, La. (In serv. 1974)

P 7 Fort Charles

D: 103 tons (fl) **S:** 32 kts **Dim:** 31.5 × 5.7 × 2.1
A: 1/20-mm AA—2/12.7 mm mg (I × 2)
Electron Equipt: Radar: 1/Sperry 4016
M: 2 MTU MB 16V538 TB90 diesels; 2 props; 6,000 bhp
Range: 1,200/18 **Crew:** 3 officers, 14 enlisted

Remarks: Can carry 24 soldiers and serve as an 18-bed floating dispensary. Refitted 1979–81 at Jacksonville, Florida, and again 1985–86 at Atlantic Marine, Florida.

Note: The three U.S.-built 85-ft. patrol boats *Discovery Bay* (P 4), *Holland Bay* (P 5), and *Manatee Bay* (B 6) were retired during 1991.

JAMAICA *(continued)*
PATROL BOATS *(continued)*

Fort Charles (P 7) LT(SG) G.S. Reynolds, JDFCG, 11-90

PATROL CRAFT

Note: In addition to the craft below, the Jamaican government is seeking several additional small patrol craft from the United States.

◆ **1 (+1) "Protector" class** Bldr: SeaArk, Monticello, Arkansas

P 9 . . . . . . (In serv. 1991) P 10 . . . . . . (In serv. 1992)

D: 15 tons (fl) **S:** 28 kts
Dim: 12.19 (11.13 wl) × 3.86 × 0.69 (hull)
A: 2/12.7-mm mg (I × 2)—2/7.62-mm mg (I × 2)
Electron Equipt: Radar: 1/Furuno 2400 nav.
Crew: 5 tot.
M: 2 Caterpillar 3208 TA diesels; 2 props; 690 bhp
Range: 350/20

Remarks: Aluminum construction. First unit acquired under U.S. Fiscal Year 1991 foreign aid program; second unit authorized 10-91 under FY 91 program.

◆ **6 U.S. GRP-hulled launches** Bldr: Boston Whaler, Rockland, Massachusetts (In serv. 1990)

Jamaican Boston Whaler LT(SG) G.S. Reynolds, JDFCG, 11-90

D: 1.5 tons light (2 fl) **S:** 40 kts **Dim:** 6.81 × 2.26 × . . .
A: small arms **M:** 2 gasoline outboard engines; 360 shp
Range: 167/40; 750/. . . **Crew:** 3 tot.

Note: Also used by the Coast Guard is a 12-meter sail-training craft. The Kingston Constabulary operates CG-121, a 12-meter Bertram patrol craft acquired in 1984 and a 19.8-m search-and-rescue boat purchased from Swiftships, U.S.A., in 1986.

JAPAN

MARITIME SELF-DEFENSE FORCE

Personnel (9-91): 43,055 total active (including 8,694 officers, 1,082 warrant officers, 21,461 noncommissioned officers, and 11,818 nonrated enlisted), plus 1,087 reservists (224 officers, 90 warrant officers, 496 noncommissioned officers, and 277 nonrated enlisted) and about 3,900 civilian employees

The Maritime Self-Defense Force (MSDF), or *Kaiso Jeitai,* was created in 1954. In Article 9 of its constitution, Japan waived the right of belligerence and declared peaceful intentions. Consequently, the armed forces are designed to carry out purely defensive tasks.

In addition to the MSDF, Japan has a large Maritime Safety Agency (*Kaijo Hoan-cho*), which is roughly comparable to the U.S. Coast Guard in function and which in time of war would come under the control of the MSDF. Its ships are listed at the end of this section.

Construction Programs:

1987 Budget:
2 1,900-ton DE (231, 232), 1 2,400-ton SS (584), 2 490-ton MHC (668, 669), 2 8,300-ton AOE (423, 424), 7 service craft

1988 Budget:
1 7,200-ton DDG (173), 1 2,400-ton SS (585), 2 490-ton MHC, 4 service craft

1989 Budget:
2 1,900-ton DE (233, 234), 1 2,400-ton SS (586), 2 1,000-ton MSO, 1 2,800-ton AOS, 5 service craft

1990 Budget:
1 7,200-ton DDG (174), 1 2,400-ton SS (587), 1 1,000-ton MSO, 1 490-ton MSC, 2 50-ton PTG, 1 2,800-ton AOS, 1 420-ton LCU, 5 service craft

1991 Budget:
1 7,200-ton DDG (175), 1 4,400-ton DD, 1 2,400-ton SS (588), 2 1,000-ton MSO, 2 50-ton PGH (1 deferred), 1 4,000-ton TV (training vessel, deferred), 8 service craf

1992 Budget:
1 4,400-ton DD, 1 2,500-ton SS (589), 1 50-ton PGH , 3 490-ton MSC, 1 4,000-to TV (training vessel), 1 4,200-ton ASE (trials vessel), 6 service craft (2 50-ton YT, 490-ton YO, 1 50-ton YL, 1 25-ton YF, 1 5-ton YF)

1991–1995 Ship Acquisition Plan: 2 7,200-ton Aegis DDG, 8 4,400-ton DDG, 2,400-ton SS, 3 1,000-ton MSO, 7 490-ton MSC, 2 3,000-ton MCS (mine countermea sures support ships), 4 50-ton PG (2 deferred from 1991 Budget), 1 8,500-ton LST, 4,000-ton TV (training vessel; originally approved in FY 1991 Budget but deferred 1992), 1 5,000-ton ARC (cable vessel), and 1 4,200-ton ASE (trials ship).

Naval Aviation: Naval air is an integral part of the navy and has about 8,000 me assigned. Its headquarters are in Atsugi, and it has twelve bases along the coasts Japan. The Air Training Command has several centers at Shimofusa. As of 1-9-91, t JMSDF had 279 operational aircraft, including 169 fixed-wing aircraft and 110 he copters. Fixed-wing aircraft included 75 P-3C Orion and 9 P-2J Neptune patrol, US-1A SAR seaplanes, 4 YS-11M-A and 6 YS-11T-A transports, 1 UP-2J and 1 EP- EW aircraft, 4 U-36A target service aircraft, 1 UC-90 and 3 LC-90 EW/utility aircra 2 B-65 and 22 TC-90 light transports, and 25 KM-2 and 8 T-5 trainers. Helicopte included 2 HSS-2A and 74 HSS-2B Sea King and 4 SH-60J Seahawk ASW, 6 MH- mine countermeasures, 15 S-61A SAR, and 2 OH-6J and 6 OH-6D, and 1 Bell 47G utility/trainers. Several Japanese Self-Defense Air Force C-130H transports a equipped to perform aerial sea minelaying.

During the 1991–95 Acquisition Plan period, the following aircraft are to be p cured: 36 SH-60J ASW helicopters (20 for shore-based service), 1 MH-53E mi countermeasures helicopter, 3 US-1A SAR amphibians, 4 V-22 Osprey SAR tilt-roto EP-3E EW aircraft, 3 UP-3C/D trials and training aircraft, 20 T-5 trainers, 6 TC trainers, 8 UH-60J SAR helicopters, 1 NH-60J trials helicopter, and 4 OH-6D traini helicopters. Several AV-8B+ Harrier V/STOL fighters may be ordered before the of the period. Planned force levels by 1996 are 100 P-3C, 32 HSS-2B, 48 SH-60J shore-based), 11 MH-53E, 7 US-1A, 4 YS-11M, 2 EP-3E, 1 UP-3C, 2 UP-3D, 5 LC-9 U-36A, 1 UC-90, 9 S-61A, 6 UH-60J, 6 YS-11T, 30 TC-90, 18 KM-2, 22 T-5, OH-6D/J, and 1 Bell-47G2A. Ultimately, it is planned to procure 100 SH-60J heli ters to complete replacement of the SH-3 Sea Kings, while a total of 18 UH-60J replace the S-61A for search-and-rescue duties. Eleven MH-53E altogether are be acquired to replace the now-stricken V-107 mine countermeasures helicopters.

Authorized under Fiscal Year 1992 were 1 P-3C, 1 US-1A, 1 U-36A, 1 EP-3, 5 T- TC-90, 7 SH-60J, 2 UH-60J, 1 USH-60J, and 1 OH-6D.

JMSDF P-3C Orion *Ships of the World,*

US-1A SAR amphibian Wilhelm Donko

SH-60J ASW helicopter JMSDF

MARITIME SELF-DEFENSE FORCE *(continued)*

MH-53E mine countermeasures helicopter JMSDF, 10-90

HSS-2B ASW helicopter Leo Van Ginderen, 9-91

WEAPONS AND SYSTEMS

Until the 1970s, most weapons and detection gear were of American design, built nder license in Japan. Subsequently, ships have been equipped with Japanese-esigned, long-range, pulse-compression air-search radars and with the 76-mm OTO lelara gun. The latter is built under license. U.S. Vulcan/Phalanx 20-mm CIWS Close-In Weapon System) and Harpoon antiship missiles are being procured in quan-ty, with the latter to be replaced by the superior, Japanese-developed SSM-1B. Iitsubishi has a license to build the U.S. Mk 46 Mod. 5 "Neartips" ASW torpedo, while e indigenously designed Type 89 (formerly GRX-2, a U.S. Mk 48 ADCAP-equivalent) gh-speed homing torpedo for submarine service and the Type 73 (formerly GRX-4) ort-range ASW torpedo for aircraft have been developed for use from P-3 aircraft, licopters, and surface ships. The U.S. Standard SM-1 MR and SM-2 and Sea Sparrow IM-7F surface-to-air missiles are in use, with the latter to be replaced by the RIM-7M. 1990, some 100 Harpoon and 145 Standard SM-1 and SM-2 missiles were ordered om the United States.

For shore defense, 48 6-tubed trucks were delivered beginning in 1989 to launch the itsubishi SSM-1 (known as the Type 88 in service) missile, powered by a TSM-2 rbojet.

ngth: 5.08 m Weight: 660 kg Speed: Mach 0.9
ameter: 35 cm Warhead: 120 kg
an: 1.2 m Range: 100 km

SSM-1B is to replace the Harpoon, with first trials in 1988. An air-launched version, M-1C, for use by P-3C Orions, entered service in 1991.

Mitsubishi and Kawasaki are cooperating on a Sparrow AAM replacement that will o replace Sea Sparrow, and antiship radiation-homing (ARM) and beach-defense ssiles are also in development.

AVAL RADARS

me	Band	Remarks
S-1	X (I/J)	Mitsubishi Electric; also known as Type 72
S-2-12E	. . .	Mitsubishi Electric; radome-enclosed for guns and Sea Sparrow SAM; also known as Type 79 (Type 72 in earlier analog version)
S-2-21A	. . .	Mitsubishi Electric; open radar mount for gun control
S-3	. . .	Phased-array, 360° scanning "Mini-Aegis" weapons control system now in development
S-1	X (G)	Furuno air search, version of U.S. SPS-12 with SPS-6 antenna
S-2	L	Japanese version of U.S. SPS-12 air search; now only on *Katori* (TV 3501)
S-9	X(I/J)	Furuno navigational set, slotted-waveguide antenna
S-11	X(G/H)	Furuno air/surf. search, Japanese design, bedspring antenna
S-12	D	Furuno 3-D phased-array with planar antenna
S-14	L	Furuno air search; OPS-14B has MTI (Moving-Target Indication); OPS-14C has further improvements
-15	D	Furuno surface search, based on U.S. SPS-10
-16	X	Furuno surface search
-17	X	Furuno surface search
-18	C	Nihon Musen surface search/navigational
-19	I	Furuno navigation, slotted-waveguide antenna
-24	. . .	Furuno planar-array successor to OPS-14-series
-28	X (G/H)	Furuno navigational; slotted-waveguide antenna
-34	X	U.S. radar for Mk 63 gun fire-control system
35	X	U.S. radar for Mk 56 gun fire-control system
51C	X	U.S. Raytheon radar for Standard SAM
SPG-62	X	U.S. Raytheon Mk 99 illuminator for Aegis system
SPS-40	B	U.S. Lockheed air search, used only on target service ship *Azuma* (ATS 4201)
SPY-1A	S	U.S. G.E. phased planar array 3-D radar for Aegis system
ZPS-4	X (I)	Furuno nav./surf. search for submarines; antenna in radome
ZPS-6	X (I)	Furuno nav./surf. search for submarines; slotted waveguide antenna

SONARS

Name	Freq.	Remarks
OQS-1/2	MF	License-built versions of U.S. SQS-29-series rotating directional transmisson; the SQS-35J variable-depth version is also employed
OQS-3	LF	License-built version of U.S. SQS-23; bow- or hull-mounted
OQS-4	LF	Japanese-developed improvement on SQS-23/OQS-3
OQS-101	LF	Japanese equivalent to U.S. SQS-53; bow-mounted dome
OQS-102	LF	Japanese equivalent to U.S. SQS-53C
ZQQ-2	. . .	Cylindrical bow array for submarines; also for acoustic intercept
ZQQ-3	. . .	Cylindrical bow array for *Takashio* class
ZQQ-4	. . .	Bow array for *Yushio* class
ZQQ-5	. . .	Bow array for Harushio class; system also incorporates clip-on towed linear passive intercept array
ZQS-2	HF	License-built version of Plessey Type 193M mine-hunting sonar; ZQS-2B is a version of the later Type 2093
RQS-1	HF	Hand-held mine detection sonar for divers

AIRCRAFT CARRIERS

A politically sensitive ship type in Japan, the aircraft carrier would nonetheless be of considerable help to the JMSDF in defending Japan's waters. In 2-88, it was announced that a 20,000-ton carrier had been proposed for inclusion in the 1990–94 Budget, to complete between 1996–1998. There was considerable outcry, and the proposal was shelved for the time being.

SUBMARINES (SS)

♦ 2 (+5+3) Harushio class

	Program	Bldr	Laid down	L	In serv.
583 Harushio	1986	Mitsubishi, Kobe	21-4-87	26-7-89	30-1-90
584 Natsushio	1987	Kawasaki, Kobe	8-4-88	20-3-90	20-3-91
585 Hayashio	1988	Mitsubishi, Kobe	9-12-88	17-1-91	25-3-92
586	1989	Kawasaki, Kobe	8-1-90	18-3-92	3-93
587	1990	Mitsubishi, Kobe	12-12-90	1-93	3-94
588	1991	Kawasaki, Kobe	. . .	. . .	3-95
589	1992	Mitsubishi, Kobe	. . .	. . .	3-96
590	1993	Kawasaki, Kobe	. . .	. . .	3-97
591	1994	Mitsubishi, Kobe	. . .	. . .	3-98
592	1995	Kawasaki, Kobe	. . .	. . .	3-99

D: 2,400 tons std. (2,750 sub.) **S:** 12/20 kts
Dim: 80.0 × 10.0 × 7.7
A: 6/533-mm Type HU-603B TT amidships (20 Type 89 torpedoes and Sub-Harpoon missiles)
Electron Equipt:
Radar: 1/ZPS-6 nav./surf. search—EW: ZLA-7 intercept suite
Sonar: ZQQ-5B suite, with S-TASS towed array

Harushio (SS 583) *Ships of the World,* 11-90

SUBMARINES *(continued)*

Natsushio (SS 584) *Ships of the World,* 3-91

M: 2 Kawasaki 12V-25/25S or Mitsubishi M.A.N. V8/V24-30 MATL, 1,700-bhp generator sets (2,840-kw output), 2 1,850-kw alternators, 2 Fuji or Toshiba electric motors; 1 prop; 7,220 shp
Crew: 10 officers, 65 enlisted

Remarks: An enlarged *Yushio,* incorporating provision for Sub-Harpoon missiles, a towed passive sonar array and passive flank arrays, new EW suite, additional d.c. power, additional noise-reduction features including anechoic coating, and a VLF radio receiver with towed wire antenna. Pressure hull built of NS 110 steel (110 kg/mm^2 yield). Two 480-cell batteries of new design. One per year to be ordered, at least through 1995. SS 589 and later will be of 2,500-ton standard displacement, with greater automation, smaller crews, and other improvements. SS 583 and 584 are attached to the 1st Submarine Flotilla at Kure.

◆ 10 Yushio (Type S 122) class

	Bldr	Laid down	L	In serv.
573 Yushio	Mitsubishi, Kobe	3-12-76	29-3-79	26-2-80
574 Mochishio	Kawasaki, Kobe	28-4-78	12-3-80	5-3-81
575 Setoshio	Kawasaki, Kobe	28-4-79	12-2-81	17-3-82
576 Okishio	Kawasaki, Kobe	17-4-80	5-3-82	1-3-83
577 Nadashio	Mitsubishi, Kobe	16-4-81	27-1-83	6-3-84
578 Hamashio	Kawasaki, Kobe	8-4-82	1-2-84	5-3-85
579 Akishio	Mitsubishi, Kobe	15-4-83	21-1-85	5-3-86
580 Takeshio	Kawasaki, Kobe	3-4-84	19-2-86	3-3-87
581 Yukishio	Mitsubishi, Kobe	11-4-85	23-1-87	11-3-88
582 Sachishio	Kawasaki, Kobe	11-4-86	17-2-88	24-3-89

Takeshio (SS 580) *Ships of the World,* 1990

Akishio (SS 580) *Ships of the World,* 1990

D: SS 573–576: 2,200 tons surf./2,450 sub.; SS 577–582: 2,250 tons surf./2,500 sub.
S: 12/20 kts (13 kts max. snorkel) **Dim:** 76.20 × 9.90 × 7.40
A: 6/533-mm Type HU-603 TT amidships (20 Type 72 and Type 80 torpedoes and Sub-Harpoon SSM)
Electron Equipt:
Radar: ZPS-6 nav./surf. search—EW: ZLA-6 intercept suite
Sonar: SQS-36J active, ZQQ-4 passive suite (SS 576–on: U.S. BQR-15 TASS towed passive array
M: 2 Mitsubishi/M.A.N. V8/V24-30 MATL, 1,700-bhp Kawasaki diesel generator sets (2,840 kw tot.), 2 tandem Fuji electric motors; 1 prop; 7,220 shp
Crew: 10 officers, 65 enlisted

Remarks: Deeper-diving than the *Uzushio* class and have more modern electronic equipment, lower rpm propeller, and towed VLF communications antenna. SS 577 and later were equipped with U.S. Sub-Harpoon missiles as built; the others have all now been backfitted with Sub-Harpoon capability. Double-hull design. Use two 480-cell Nihon-Denchi batteries. Have ZYQ-1 computer/sonar data display system.

All but SS 573 have the U.S. "Masker" bubbler acoustic noise reduction system. SS 573 and 574 have 350-meter working depth, 400-meter maximum depth; later units, with pressure hulls of NS 80 (80 kg/mm^2 yield), have 450-meter maximum depth. SS 579 and later incorporate greater automation.

SS 576 in trials 1988–89 with U.S. BQR-15 towed array, to integrate with ZQQ-5 sonar suite or the ZQQ-5B. SS 577 in collision 23-7-88, repaired. SS 573, 574, and 579 attached to 1st Submarine Flotilla, others to 2nd Submarine Flotilla, Yokosuka.

◆ 5 Uzushio (Type S 119 and 119A) class (3 for training)

	Bldr	Laid down	L	In serv.
ATSS 8001 Isoshio (ex-SS 568)	Kawasaki, Kobe	9-7-70	18-3-72	25-11-72
ATSS 8002 Narushio (ex-SS 569)	Mitsubishi, Kobe	8-5-71	22-11-72	28-9-73
ATSS 8003 Kuroshio (ex-SS 570)	Kawasaki, Kobe	5-7-72	22-2-74	27-11-74
571 Takashio	Kawasaki, Kobe	6-7-73	30-6-75	30-1-76
572 Yaeshio	Kawasaki, Kobe	14-4-75	19-5-77	7-3-78

Takashio (SS 571) *Ships of the World,* 19

Isoshio (ATSS 8001) *Ships of the World,* 1

Narushio (ATSS 8002) *Ships of the World,*

D: 1,850 tons surf./2,430 sub. **S:** 12/20 kts
Dim: 72.00 × 9.90 × 7.50
A: 6/533-mm Type HU-602 TT amidships (SS: 20 Type 72 and Type torpedoes; ATSS: 4 torpedoes only)
Electron Equipt:
Radar: 1/ZPS-4 nav./surf. search—EW: ZLA-5 intercept suite
Sonar: SS: ZQQ-3 passive suite, SQS-36(J) active; ATSS: ZQQ-2 passive suite only
M: diesel-electric propulsion: 2 Kawasaki-M.A.N. V8/V24-30 MAT 1,700-bhp, 850 rpm diesel generator sets, 2 Fuji tandem motors 234 max. rpm prop; 7,200 shp
Crew: SS: 10 officers, 70 enlisted; ATSS: 10 officers, 50 enlisted, 2(trainees

Remarks: Tear-drop hull. Double-hull construction, bow sonar array, torpedo angled out 10-degrees amidships, as in modern U.S. Navy submarines. Tor reloaded via main access hatch on ATSS 8002 and later; earlier units loaded via a in the sail. Operating depth: 200 m, with pressure hull constructed of NS 6 (63 kg/mm^2 yield). Maximum snorkel speed is 13 kts. Have fixed VLF communi antenna in sail. SS 571 and 572 have digital torpedo fire-control systems; the have TDC analog systems. Active sonar is in sail on SS 571, 572.

SUBMARINES *(continued)*

Sister *Uzushio* (566) stricken 24-3-87 after only 16 years of service; *Makishio* (567) struck 11-3-88. SS 568 was redesignated ATSS 8001 on 24-3-89 as a training submarine; SS 569 redesignated ATSS on 8-6-90 and SS 570 on 20-3-91. ATSS have torpedo reload space outfitted as accommodations for trainees and carry only the torpedoes in the tubes. All are attached to the 1st Submarine Flotilla, Kure.

HELICOPTER-CARRYING DESTROYERS (DDH)

♦ 2 Shirane class

	Bldr	Laid down	L	In serv.
143 Shirane	Ishikawajima Harima, Tokyo	25-2-77	18-9-78	17-3-80
144 Kurama	Ishikawajima Harima, Tokyo	17-2-78	20-9-79	27-3-81

Shirane (DDH 143) JMSDF, 10-90

Shirane (DDH 143)—amidships, showing electronics installations *Ships of the World*, 7-90

D: 5,200 tons (6,800 fl) **S:** 32 kts
Dim: 158.8 × 17.5 × 5.3 (hull)
A: 2/127-mm Mk 42 DP (I × 2)—1/Mk 29 launcher (VIII × 24 Sea Sparrow)— 2/20-mm Mk 15 CIWS AA (I × 2)—1/ASROC ASW RL (VIII × 1, 16 missiles)—6/324-mm Type 68 ASW TT (III × 2)—3/ HSS-2B or SH-60J ASW helicopters

Kurama (DDH 144) John Bouvia, 1991

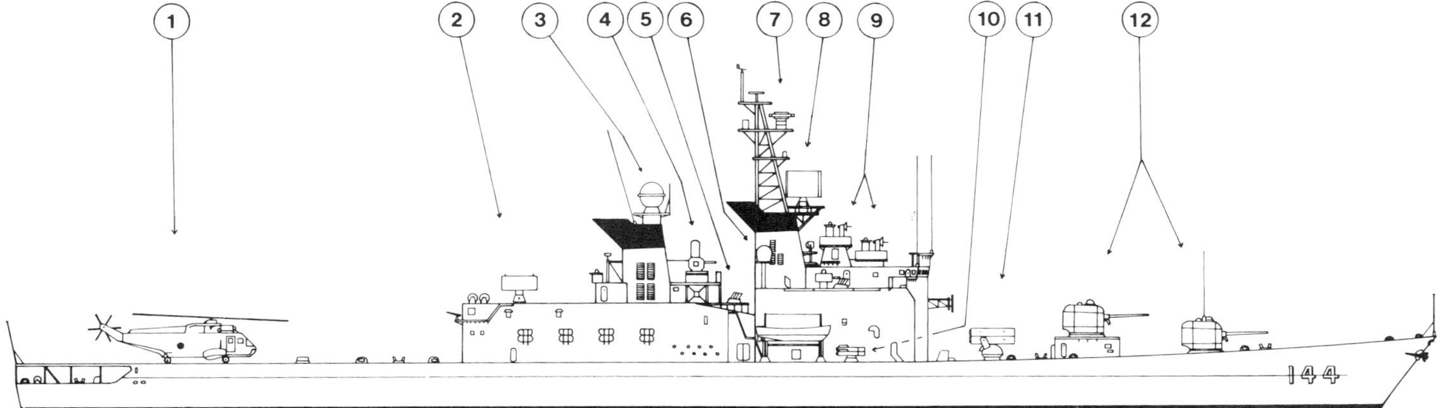

Kurama (DDH 144) 1. HSS-2B helicopter 2. Mk 29 launcher for Sea Sparrow SAM 3. WM-25 track-while-scan fire control radar 4. Mk 15 Phalanx CIWS 5. Mk 36 SRBOC decoy rocket launcher system (Mk 137 launchers) 6. SATCOMM antenna radomes 7. OPS-28 surface-search radar 8. OPS-12 3-D air search radar 9. FCS-1A radar directors 10. Mk 68 triple ASW TT 11. Mk 112 ASROC ASW rocket launcher (VIII × 1) 12. 127-mm Mk 42 DP guns Drawing by Robert Dumas

HELICOPTER-CARRYING DESTROYERS *(continued)*

Electron Equipt:
Radar: 1/OPS-22 nav., 1/OPS-12 3-D air search, 1/OPS-28 air/surf. search, 1/WM-25 Sea Sparrow f.c., 2/GFCS-1A gun f.c., 1/CCA helo control
Sonar: OQS-101 bow-mounted LF, U.S. SQS-35 VDS, U.S. SQR-18A towed array
EW: NOLQ-1 passive-active, OLR-9B intercept—TACAN: U.S. URN-25

M: 2 sets G.E.-Ishikawajima geared steam turbines; 2 props; 70,000 shp
Boilers: 2; 60 kg/cm^2, 480° C **Crew:** 370 tot.

Remarks: Modified *Haruna* class. Both received U.S. SQR-18A TACTASS passive towed hydrophone arrays during 1981. Have U.S. "Prairie" and "Masker" bubble-generating systems to reduce radiated noise. Will eventually receive Harpoon missiles. Have *two* stacks, slightly staggered, compared to one on the *Haruna* class. Both have TDPS-Target Data Processing System, with a U.S. UYK-20 computer and OYQ-5 display. Have LINK 11 and LINK 14 data transmission systems. A landing-control radar is mounted to port of the after stack. Two pair Vosper Thornycroft fin stabilizers fitted, and the Canadian "Bear-trap" helicopter haul-down and deck traversing system is installed for the helicopters. Each ship can carry a rear admiral and 20 staff; 143 is flagship of the 1st Escort Squadron, 144 of the 2nd.

♦ 2 Haruna class

	Bldr	Laid down	L	In serv.
141 Haruna	Mitsubishi, Nagasaki	19-3-70	1-2-72	22-3-73
142 Hiei	Ishikawajima-Harima, Tokyo	8-3-72	13-8-73	27-12-74

Haruna (DDH 141) *Ships of the World,* 1990

Hiei (DDH 142) *Ships of the World,* 1990

D: 4,950 tons (6,550 fl) **S:** 32 kts
Dim: 153.0 × 17.5 × 5.3 (hull)
A: 2/127-mm Mk 42 DP (I × 2)—1/Mk 29 launcher for Sea Sparrow (VIII × 1; . . . reloads)—2/20-mm Mk 15 CIWS (I × 2)—6/324-mm Mk 68 ASW TT (III × 2)—1/Mk 112 ASROC launcher (VIII × 1; . . . reloads)—3/HSS-2B or SH-60J ASW helicopters

Electron Equipt:
Radar: 1/ NOPN-1 nav.,1/OPS-28 air/surf. search, 1/OPS-11C air search, 1/FCS-2-12 Sea Sparrow f.c., 2/FCS-1A gun f.c.
Sonar: OQS-3 bow-mounted MF—TACAN: ORN-6
EW: NOLQ-1-3 intercept/jammer, OPN-7B D/F, OPN-11B D/F, 4/Mk 36 SRBOC decoy RL (VI × 4)

M: 2 sets G.E.-Ishikawajima geared steam turbines; 2 props; 70,000 shp
Boilers: 2; 60 kg/cm^2, 480° C **Crew:** 36 officers, 304 enlisted

Remarks: Modernization of DDH 141, provided in FY 83 Budget, began 1986 for completion by early 1988. Modernization of DDH 42 funded FY 84, took place from 31-8-87 to 16-11-88. Superstructure enlarged to accommodate additional electronics, Sea Sparrow launcher added atop hangar, with FCS-2-12 director abaft "mack," 2 Mk 15 Phalanx CIWS flank superstructure, aft GFCS-1A moved to atop bridge, new EW gear added (including Mk 36 decoy RL). The OYQ-6 Combat Direction System (using the U.S. UYK-20A computer) was installed, replacing the OYQ-3. Planned addition of VDS was not accomplished, and Harpoon missile launchers were not added. The single combined mast/stack is off centerline, to port. Have two pair Vosper Thornycroft fin stabilizers. A Canadian "Beartrap" helicopter haul-down and traversal system is installed in the flight deck. DDH 141 is flagship for 3rd Escort Squadron, DDH 142 for 4th.

GUIDED-MISSILE DESTROYERS (DDG)

♦ 0 (+3 + 1 + 4) Kongo-class Aegis destroyers

	Bldr	Laid down	L	In serv.
173 Kongo	Mitsubishi, Nagasaki	8-5-90	26-9-91	3-93
174	Mitsubishi, Nagasaki	-92	-93	3-94
175	Mitsubishi, Nagasaki	. . .	. . .	3-96
175	. . . . . .	. . .	. . .	. . .

D: 7,200 tons (8,900 fl) **S:** 30 kts
Dim: 161.00 (150.50 pp) × 21.00 (20.00 wl) × 6.10 (hull)
A: 8/Harpoon SSM (IV × 2)—2/Mk 41 VLS groups (90 Standard SM-2 MR block 2 SAM and vertical-launch ASROC ASW missiles)—1/127-mm OTO Melara DP—2/20-mm Mk 15 Block 1 CIWS (I × 2)—6/324-mm ASW TT Mk 68 (III x 2)—platform for 1/HSS-2B or SH-60J ASW helicopter

Electron Equipt:
Radar: 1/OPS-19C nav.,1/OPS-28D air/surf. search, 1/SPY-1D Aegis, 3/SPG-62 illuminator, 1/FCS-2-21 gun f.c.
Sonar: OQS-102 bow-mounted LF, OQR-1 (SQR-19A(V)) TASS
EW: NOLQ-1 intercept, NOLQ-2 intercept, OLT-3 jammer, 4/Mk 36 SRBOC decoy RL (VI × 4), SLQ-25 Nixie acoustic torpedo dec[illegible]
TACAN: ORN-. . .

M: 4 IHI-G.E. LM 2500 gas turbines; 2 CP props; approx. 100,000 shp
Electric: 6,000 kw tot. **Range:** 4,500/20
Fuel: 1,000 tons **Crew:** 310 tot.

Remarks: First ship of four approved under FY 88 Budget, second under FY 1990, third under FY 1991. Fourth planned under FY 1993. First unit ordered 24-6-88. G[illegible] expense caused considerable resistance to program, delaying start by two years. [illegible] ships are intended to assist in the aerial defense of Japan, as well as acting as A[illegible] escorts for task forces. A second increment of four is now envisioned. The first ship initially reported to be named *Yukikaze.*

The design is an enlarged and improved version of the U.S. *Arleigh Burke* c[illegible] adding a back-up surface/air search radar, using a faster-firing 127-mm gun wi[illegible] dedicated fire control system, and incorporating a more elaborate EW system [illegible] active jamming. The VLS ASROC ASW missile is on order despite its check[illegible]

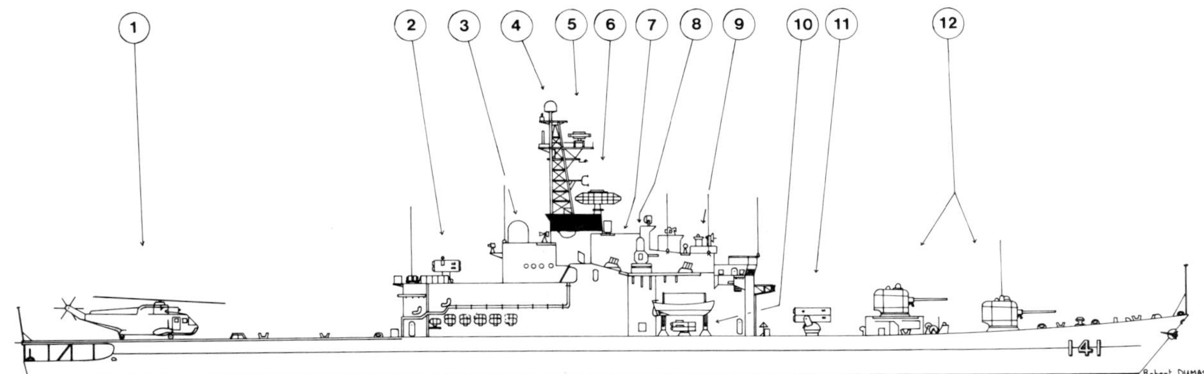

Haruna (DDH 141) 1. HSS-2B ASW helicopter 2. Mk 29 launcher for Sea Sparrow SAM 3. FCS-2-21 radar director for Sea Sparrow 4. ORN-6 TACAN 5. OPS-28 surface-search radar 6. OPS-11C air/surface-search radar 7. Mk 36 SRBOC decoy rocket launcher system (Mk 137 launchers) 8. Mk 15 Phalanx CIWS 9. FCS-1A radar director for 127-m guns 10. Type 68 triple ASW TT 11. Mk 112 ASROC ASW rocket launcher (VIII × 1) 12. 127-mm DP guns
Drawing by Robert Dumas

GUIDED-MISSILE DESTROYERS *(continued)*

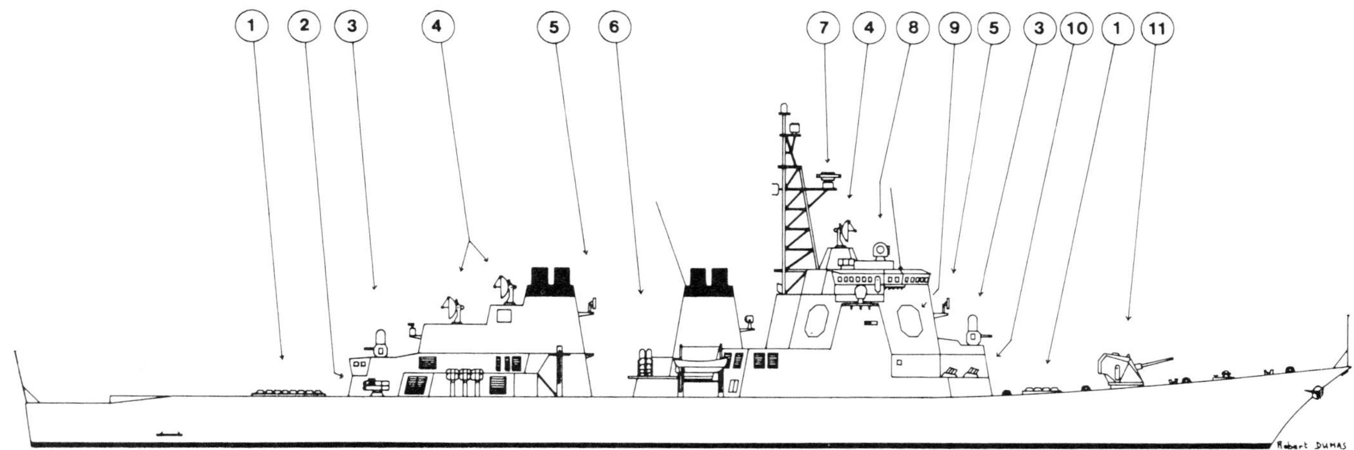

Kongo (DDG 173) 1. Mk 41 vertical launch missile cells 2. Mk 68 triple ASW TT 3. Mk 15 Phalanx CIWS 4. SPG-62 radar illuminator for Aegis system 5. OE-82 antenna for U.S. WSC-3 FLEETSATCOM 6. Harpoon SSM (IV × 2) 7. OPS-28C air/surface-search radar 8. FCS-2-21 radar director for 127-mm gun 9. SPY-1D Aegis radar 10. Mk 36 SRBOC decoy system (Mk 137 rocket launchers) 11. OTO Melara 127-mm DP gun Drawing by Robert Dumas

ongo (DDG 173) *Ships of the World,* 1988

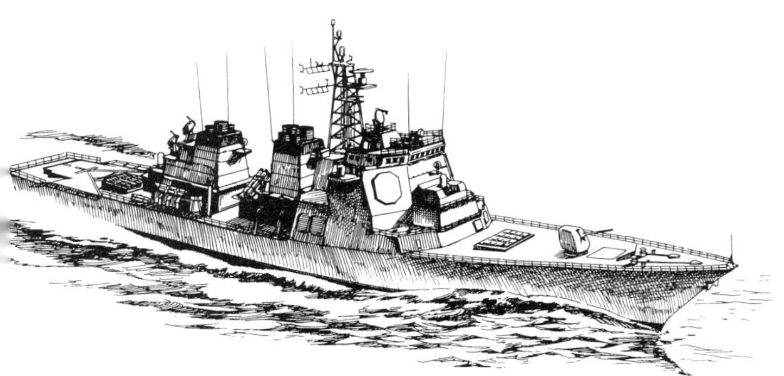

ngo (DDG 173) *Ships of the World,* 1991

development career in the United States. VLS magazines hold 61 missiles aft, 29 forward. The SPG-62 radar illuminators support three Mk 99 Mod. 1 missile fire-control direction systems, and the underwater battery fire-control system is the U.S. Mk 116 Mod. 7. Will have U.S. NATO LINK 11 and LINK 14 capability and will later receive LINK 16. Are equipped with the U.S. "Prairie" and "Masker" bubbler noise-radiation suppression systems and have infrared exhaust signature provisions. The OQS-102 sonar is equivalent to the U.S. SQS-53C. The first U.S.–built Aegis set was delivered 8-91.

♦ 2 Hatakaze class

	Bldr	Laid down	L	In serv.
171 Hatakaze	Mitsubishi, Nagasaki	20-5-83	9-11-84	27-3-86
172 Shimakaze	Mitsubishi, Nagasaki	30-1-85	30-1-87	23-3-88

D: 4,650 tons (5,600 fl) **S:** 32 kts (30 sust.)
Dim: 150.0 × 16.4 × 4.80 (hull)
A: 1/Mk 13 Mod. 4 missile launcher (I × 1, 40 Standard SM-1 MR missiles)—8/Harpoon SSM (IV × 2)—2/127-mm Mk 42 DP (I × 2)—2/20-mm Mk 15 CIWS (I × 2)—1/ASROC Mk 116 ASW RL (VIII × 1)—6/324-mm Type 68 ASW TT (III × 2)—platform for 1/HSS-2B or SH-60J ASW helicopter
Electron Equipt:
Radar: 1/OPS-28B air/surf. search, 1/OPS-11C air search, 1/SPS-52C 3-D air search, 2/SPG-51C SAM f.c., 2/FCS-2-21C gun f.c.
Sonar: OQS-4 Mod. 1 bow-mounted MF—TACAN: U.S. URN-25
EW: NOLQ-1-3 intercept/jammer, OLR-9B intercept, Mk 36 SRBOC chaff RL (VI × 4), U.S. SLQ-25 Nixie torpedo decoy
M: COGAG: 2 Rolls-Royce Spey SM-1A and 2 Olympus TM-3D gas turbines; 2 CP props; 72,000 shp
Range: . . . **Crew:** 260 tot.

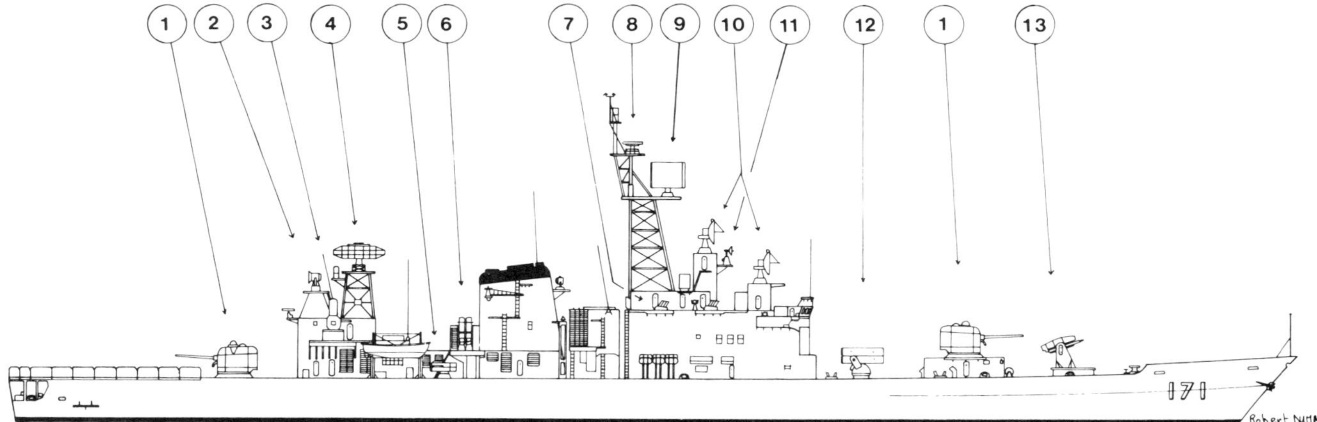

Hatakaze (DDG 171) 1. 127-mm Mk 42 DP gun 2. FCS-2-21C radar director for 127-mm gun 3. Mk 15 Phalanx CIWS 4. OPS-11C air-search radar 5. Type 68 triple ASW TT 6. Harpoon SSM (IV × 2) 7. Mk 36 SRBOC decoy system (Mk 137 RL) 8. OPS-28B air/surface-search radar 9. U.S. SPS-52C 3-D air-search radar 10. SPG-51C radar directors for Standard SM-1 MR SAM 11. telemetry antenna (now removed) 12. Mk 112 ASROC ASW rocket launcher (VIII × 1) 13. Mk 13 Mod. 4 launcher for Standard SM-1 MR SAM Drawing by Robert Dumas

GUIDED-MISSILE DESTROYERS *(continued)*

Shimakaze (DDG 172) John Bouvia, 199

Hatakaze (DDG 171) *Ships of the World,* 12-90

Remarks: No hangar for helicopter. U.S. Mk 74 Mod. 13 missile fire-control syste (2/SPG-51C radar directors) for the Standard missile system. DDG 171 in 1981 Budge 172 in 1983; third unit requested 1985 but denied. DDG 172 ordered 29-3-84. Ha LINK 11 and LINK 14 data links, OYQ-4 Mod. 1 combat data system, NYPX-2 IF system.

◆ **3 Tachikaze class**

	Bldr	Laid down	L	In ser
168 TACHIKAZE	Mitsubishi, Nagasaki	19-6-73	12-12-74	26-3-7
169 ASAKAZE	Mitsubishi, Nagasaki	27-5-76	15-10-77	27-3-7
170 SAWAKAZE	Mitsubishi, Nagasaki	14-9-79	4-6-81	30-3-8

D: 3,850 tons (4,800 fl) **S:** 32 kts **Dim:** 143.0 × 14.3 × 4.6

A: 1/Mk 13 Mod. 4 missile launcher (40 Standard SM-1 MR SAM/ Harpoon SSM)—2/127-mm Mk 42 Mod. 10 DP (I × 2)—2/20-mm Mk 15 CIWS gatling AA (I × 2)—1 Mk 112 ASROC ASW RL (VIII × 1)—6/324-mm Type 68 ASW TT (III × 2)

Electron Equipt:

Radar: OPS-17 (170: OPS-28) air/surf. search, 1/OPS-11B air searc 1/SPS-52B 3-D air search, 2/SPG-51C SAM f.c., 1/GFCS-1A (170: GFCS-2) gun f.c.

Sonar: OQS-3 (170: OQS-4) bow-mounted MF

EW: NOLQ-1 (168: NOLR-6) intercept, OLT-3 jammer, 4/Mk 36 Mod. 2 Super RBOC chaff RL

M: 2 sets Mitsubishi geared steam turbines; 2 props; 70,000 shp

Boilers: 2; 60 kg/cm², 480° C **Crew:** 277 tot.

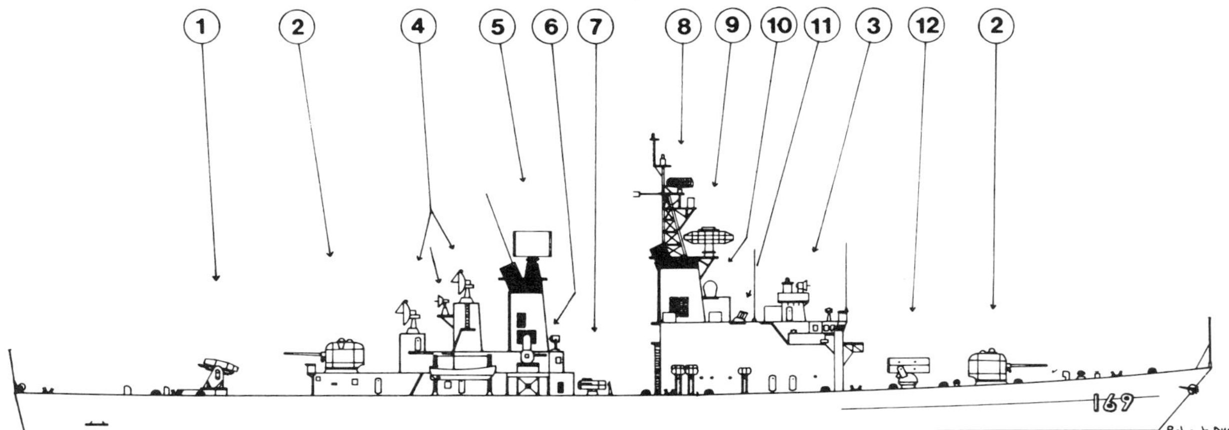

Asakaze (DDG 169) 1. Mk 13 Mod. 4 launcher for Standard SM-1 MR SAM 2. 127-mm Mk 42 DP gun 3. FCS-1A radar director for 127-mm guns 4. SPG-51C radar director for Standard SM-1 MR SAM 5. SPS-52B 3-D air-search radar 6. Mk 15 Phalanx CIWS 7. Mk 68 triple ASW TT 8. OPS-17 surface-search radar 9. OPS-11B air-search radar 10. OLT-3 EW jammer radomes 11. Mk 36 SRBOC decoy system (Mk 137 launchers) 12. Mk 112 ASROC ASW rocket launcher

Drawing by Robert Dumas

GUIDED-MISSILE DESTROYERS *(continued)*

Tachikaze (DDG 168)—with SHF SATCOMM radome antennas abreast base of forward "mack" John Bouvia, 1991

sakaze (DDG 169) *Ships of the World,* 1990

emarks: U.S. Mk 15 Phalanx gatling gun close-in weapons systems (CIWS) and arpoon SSM were added to 168 under 1981 Budget, as well as improvements to SAM stem. Same improvement made to DDG 169 in 1984–85 and to DDG 170 under 1985 dget. The missile-control system is Mk 74 Mod. 13 and uses the two SPG-51C radars. ve the U.S. Mk 114 ASW weapons control system. The propulsion plant is identical that of the *Haruna* class. Have a LINK 14 data-transmission system. The ASROC ıncher has a reload magazine below the bridge. Super-high frequency (SHF) satellite nmunications equipment has been added.

1 Amatsukaze class

	Bldr	Laid down	L	In serv.
3 Amatsukaze	Mitsubishi, Nagasaki	29-11-62	5-10-63	15-2-65

D: 3,050 tons (4,000 fl) **S:** 33 kts
Dim: 131.0 × 13.4 × 4.2 (mean hull)
A: 1/Mk 13 launcher (40 Standard SM-1 MR SAM)—4/76.2-mm 50-cal. Mk 33 DP (II × 1)—1 Mk 112 ASROC ASW RL (VIII × 1)—6/324-mm Type 68 ASW TT (III × 2)—2/Mk 15 trainable Hedgehog ASW spigot mortars (XXIV × 2)

ıtsukaze (DDG 163) *Ships of the World,* 1990

Electron Equipt:
Radar: 1/OPS-17 air/surf. search, 1/U.S. SPS-29A air search, 1/SPS-52C 3-D air search, 2/SPG-51B SAM f.c., 1/GFCS-2-21 gun f.c.
Sonar: U.S. SQS-23 hull-mounted MF—EW: NORL-6 intercept, OLT-1 jammer
M: 2 sets Ishikawajima-G.E. geared steam turbines; 2 props; 60,000 shp
Boilers: 2 Ishikawajima-Foster-Wheeler; 38 kg/cm^2, 438° C
Electric: 2,700 kw tot. **Range:** 7,000/18
Fuel: 900 tons **Crew:** 290 tot.

Remarks: Refitted in 1967 with ASW TT and SPS-52C radar. Crane at stern handles boats stowed in a below-decks hangar. One GFCS-2-21 radar director replaced the original two U.S. Mk 63 GFCS in 1982–83, but planned replacement of the guns by two 76-mm OTO Melara mounts and EW updates were not carried out. There are no reloads for the ASROC launcher. The Mk 15 trainable Hedgehog spigot mortars have a range of 350-m maximum and fire a 26-kg projectile. To be replaced by *Kongo* in 3-93.

DESTROYERS (DD)

◆ **0 (+2+6) 4,400-ton class**

. . . .	. . . . . .	4-93	. . .	3-97
. . . .	. . . . . .	. . .	. . .	. . .
. . . .	. . . . . .	. . .	. . .	. . .
. . . .	. . . . . .	. . .	. . .	. . .
. . . .	. . . . . .	. . .	. . .	. . .
. . . .	. . . . . .	. . .	. . .	. . .
. . . .	. . . . . .	. . .	. . .	. . .
. . . .	. . . . . .	. . .	. . .	. . .

D: 4,400 tons (approx. 5,100 fl) **S:** 30+ kts
Dim: 145.0 × 15.0 × . . .
A: 8/Harpoon or SSM-1B SSM (IV × 2)—1/Mk 49 VLS launch group (29 RIM-7M SAM *and* vertical-launch ASROC ASW missiles)—1/76-mm OTO Melara Compact DP—2/20-mm Mk 15 Block 1 CIWS (I × 2)—6/324-mm Mk 32 ASW TT (III × 2, Type 89 torpedoes)—1/SH-60J ASW helicopter

4,400-ton DD *Ships of the World,* 1991

DESTROYERS *(continued)*

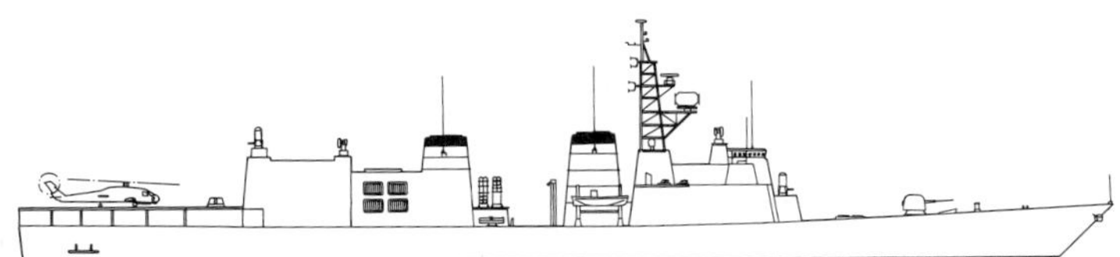

4,400-ton DD *Ships of the World,* 1991

4,400-ton DD *Ships of the World,* 1991

Electron Equipt:
Radar: 1/OPS-28C air/surf. search, 1/OPS-24 air search, 2/FCS-3 gun/SAM f.c.
Sonar: OQS-4A bow-mounted MF, OQR-1 TASS towed passive array
EW: . . .

M: COGAG: 2 Kawasaki-Rolls-Royce SM-1C Spey cruise gas turbines (26,150 shp each), 2 G.E.-IHI LM 2500 boost gas turbines (27,100 shp each); 2 CP props; 106,500 shp

Electric: . . . kw tot. **Range:** . . ./. . . **Crew:** 160 tot.

Remarks: First unit authorized under FY 1991 Budget and two requested under FY 1992. A total of eight are now planned, reduced from the 12–15 originally foreseen. Class is intended to replace the *Hatsuyuki* class in the Escort Flotillas. The propulsion plant is something of a political compromise and would appear to be wasting power on a hull of this size. Design is, in effect, an enlarged *Asagiri* incorporating a vertical-launch cell group forward in place of the Mk 112 ASROC. Berthing for the crew will be 2-high, and there will be a gymnasium.

◆ **8 Asagiri class**

	Bldr	Laid down	L	In serv.
151 Asagiri	Ishikawajima-Harima, Tokyo	13-2-85	19-9-86	17-3-88
152 Yamagiri	Sumitomo, Uraga	5-2-86	8-10-87	25-1-89
153 Yugiri	Mitsui, Tamano	25-2-86	21-9-87	28-2-89
154 Amagiri	Ishikawajima-Harima, Tokyo	3-3-86	9-9-87	17-3-89
155 Hamagiri	Hitachi, Maizuru	20-1-87	4-6-88	31-1-90
156 Setogiri	Sumitomo, Uraga	9-3-87	12-9-88	14-2-90
157 Sawagiri	Mitsubishi, Nagasaki	14-1-87	25-11-88	6-3-90
158 Umigiri	Ishikawajima-Harima, Tokyo	31-10-88	9-11-89	12-3-91

Sawagiri (DD 157) at left, with new OPS-24 air-search radar, an Yamagiri (DD 152) at right, with OPS-14C air-search radar; both hav the new helicopter-associated radome on the platform above the ai search radar antennas *Ships of the World,* 19

Setogiri (DD 156) JMSDF,

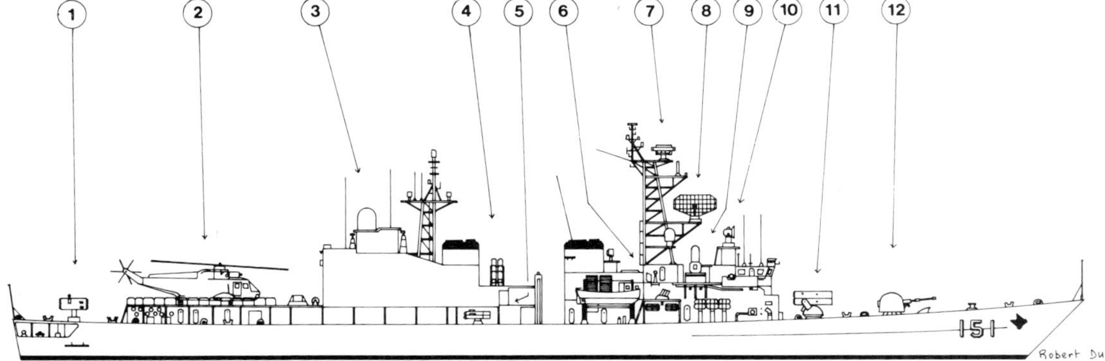

Asagiri (DD 151) 1. Mk 29 launcher for Sea Sparrow SAM (VIII × 1) 2. HSS-2B helicopter 3. FCS-2-12E missile fire-control radar for Sea Sparrow 4. Harpoon SSM (IV × 2) 5. K 68 triple ASW TT 6. Mk 36 SRBOC decoy system (Mk 137 launchers) 7. OPS-28C surface/air-search radar 8. OPS-14C air-search radar 9. Mk 15 Phalanx CIWS 10. FCS-2-21A radar gun director for 76-mm DP 11. Mk 112 ASROC ASW rocket launcher (VIII × 1) 12. 76-mm OTO Melara Compact DP Drawing by Robert Dumas

DESTROYERS *(continued)*

Hamagiri (DD 155) JMSDF, 1990

Yugiri (DD 153) *Ships of the World,* 1990

D: 3,500 tons (4,300 fl) **S:** 30 kts
Dim: 136.5 × 14.6 × 4.50 (mean hull)
A: 8/Harpoon SSM (IV × 2)—1/Mk 29 missile launcher (VIII × 1; 18 Sea Sparrow missiles)—1/76-mm OTO Melara Compact—2/20-mm Mk 15 CIWS AA (I × 2)—1/Mk 112 ASROC ASW RL (VIII × 1; . . . rockets)—6/324-mm Type 68 ASW TT (III × 2 H.O.S. 301 for Mk 46 Mod. 5 torpedoes)—1/HSS-2B or SH-60J ASW helicopter
Electron Equipt:
Radar: 1/OPS-28C air/surf. search, 1/OPS-14C (DD 155–158: OPS-24) air search, 1/FCS-2-21A gun f.c., 1/FCS-2-12E SAM f.c.
Sonar: OQS-4A bow-mounted MF, U.S. SQR-18A(V) TASS
TACAN: U.S. URN-25 (ORN-6)
EW: NOLR-6C intercept, NOLR-9C jammer, OLT-3 D/F, 2 Mk 36 SRBOC decoy RL (VI × 2), U.S. SLQ-25 Nixie acoustic torpedo decoys
M: COGAG: 4 Kawasaki-Rolls-Royce Spey SM-1A gas turbines; 2 CP props; 54,000 shp
Range: . . . **Electric:** . . . **Fuel:** . . . **Crew:** 220 tot.

emarks: Authorized: 1 in FY 83, 3 in FY 84, 3 in FY 85, 1 in FY 86. An improved *atsuyuki* design. DD 151 ordered 29-3-84; 152–154 ordered 23-3-85, DD 155–157 dered 3-86. DD 158, ordered 3-87, was the only ship authorized of two requested der FY 86. Have the OYQ-6 Combat Direction System, employing the U.S.-built YK-20A computer and the Japanese OJ-194B Digital Display Indicator. U.S. airie/Masker bubble underwater noise-suppression system fitted. Have fin sta-izers and a Beartrap/RAST-type helicopter landing and deck-traversing system. The after mast on DD 151 was moved to port and raised after initial trials (to avoid stack heat damage); in the other ships, the mast is raised and retained on the centerline, while the after stacks are offset slightly to port. The OPS-24 D-Band air search radar mounted in the last four employs hundreds of miniature transmitters arrayed on its planar face. A new radome being added on a foremast platform houses the antenna for the U.S. SQQ-28 data link system for the SH-60J ASW helicopter.

♦ 12 Hatsuyuki class

	Bldr	Laid down	L	In serv.
122 Hatsuyuki	Sumitomo, Uraga	14-3-79	7-11-80	23-3-82
123 Shirayuki	Hitachi, Maizuru	3-12-79	4-8-81	8-2-83
124 Mineyuki	Mitsubishi, Nagasaki	7-5-81	17-10-82	26-1-84
125 Sawayuki	Ishikawajima-Harima, Tokyo	22-4-81	21-6-82	15-2-84
126 Hamayuki	Mitsui, Tamano	4-2-81	27-5-82	18-11-83
127 Isoyuki	Ishikawajima-Harima, Tokyo	20-4-82	19-9-83	23-1-85
128 Haruyuki	Sumitomo, Uraga	11-3-82	6-9-83	14-3-85
129 Yamayuki	Hitachi, Maizuru	25-2-83	10-7-84	3-12-85
130 Matsuyuki	Ishikawajima-Harima, Tokyo	7-4-83	25-10-84	19-3-86
131 Setoyuki	Mitsui, Tamano	26-1-84	3-7-85	31-1-87
132 Asayuki	Sumitomo, Uraga	22-12-83	16-10-85	20-2-87
133 Shimayuki	Mitsubishi, Nagasaki	8-5-84	29-1-86	31-3-87

D: DD 122–128: 2,950 tons (3,700 fl); DD 129–133: 3,050 tons (3,800 fl)
S: 30 kts
Dim: 131.7 (126.0 wl) × 13.7 × 4.1 (129 and later: 4.3)(hull)
A: 8/Harpoon SSM (IV × 2)—1/Mk 29 missile launcher (VIII × 1, 18 Sea Sparrow missiles)—1/76-mm OTO Melara Compact DP—124–133: 2/20-mm Mk 15 CIWS AA (I × 2)—1/ASROC ASW RL (VIII × 1, 16 missiles)—6/324-mm Type 68 ASW TT (III × 2)—1/HSS-2B or SH-60J ASW helicopter

Hatsuyuki (DD 122)—still without Mk 15 CIWS, but with SHF SATCOMM antenna radomes added aft, flanking the hangar
Leo Van Ginderen, 8-91

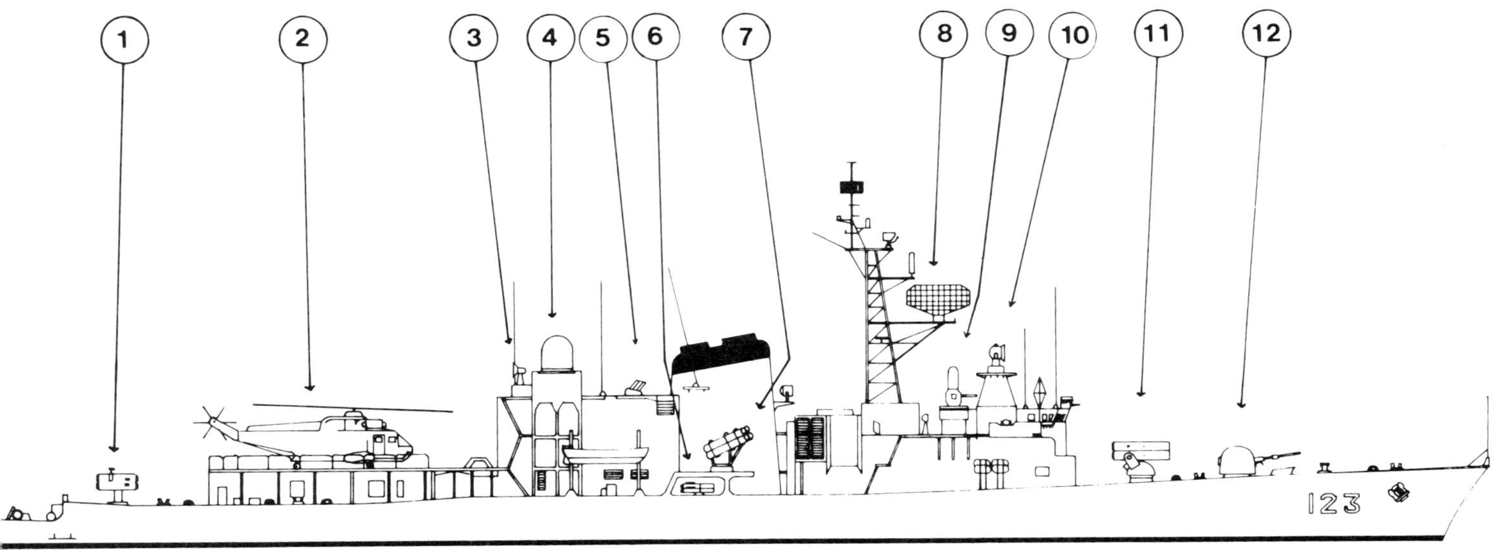

rayuki (DD 123) 1. Mk 29 launcher for Sea Sparrow SAM (VIII × 1) 2. HSS-2B ASW helicopter 3. helicopter landing-control equip-t 4. FCS-2-12A control radar for Sea Sparrow 5. Mk 36 SRBOC decoy rocket launcher system (Mk 137 launchers) 6. Mk 68 triple ASW 7. Harpoon SSM (IV × 2) 8. OPS-14B air-search radar 9. Mk 15 Phalanx CIWS 10. FCS-2-21 fire-control radar for 76-mm gun 11. Mk ASROC ASW rocket launcher (VIII × 1) 12. 76-mm OTO Melara Compact DP

Drawing by Robert Dumas

DESTROYERS *(continued)*

Mineyuki (DD 124) John Bouvia, 199?

Haruyuki (DD 128)—with HSS-2B helicopter on deck and hangar door open *Ships of the World,* 3-90

Yamayuki (DD 129)—on world cadet-training cruise Leo Van Ginderen, 9-91

Electron Equipt:
Radar: 1/OPS-18-1 surf. search, 1/OPS-14B air search, 1/GFCS-2-21 gun f.c., 1/GFCS-2-12 SAM f.c.
Sonar: OQS-4 hull-mounted MF—TACAN: U.S. URN-25
EW: NOLQ-6C intercept, DD 131–133: OLR-9B jammer, OLT-3 D/F, 2 Mk 36 SRBOC chaff RL (VI × 2)
M: COGOG: 2 Kawasaki-Rolls-Royce Olympus TM-3B gas turbines, 28,390 shp each; 2 Tyne RM-1C gas turbines, 5,340 shp each; 2 CP props; 45,000 shp (50,000 max.)
Range: . . ./. . . **Fuel:** . . .
Crew: 17–19 officers, 144–153 enlisted

Remarks: DD 122 in 1977 Budget, 123 in 1978, 124–126 in 1979, 129 and 130 in 198? and 131–133 in 1982. The Olympus engines are rated at 22,500 shp for cruise, 25,00? shp limit, while the Tyne cruise engines are rated at 4,620-shp cruise/5,000-shp ma? and provide speeds up to 19.5 kts. Helicopter deck has the Canadian Beartrap tr? versing/landing system. Have fin stabilizers. All are programmed to receive U.? SQR-18 or 19 TACTASS towed passive linear arrays. Have OYQ-5 TDPS (Tactic? Data Processing System) with a U.S. UYK-20 computer. Have LINK 14 data rel? receiver only. Stack incorporates passive infrared cooling features and a water-spr? system. DD 129 and later have steel vice aluminum superstructures. DD 122 lacks M? 15 CIWS and Mk 36 SRBOC chaff RL; DD 123 lacks CIWS. DD 131–133 have later E? equipment. All have NYPX-2 IFF systems. Most easily made 32 kts on trials.

◆ **2 Takatsuki class**

	Bldr	Laid down	L	In ser
164 TAKATSUKI	Ishikawajima, Tokyo	8-10-65	7-1-66	15-3-6
165 KIKIZUKI	Mitsubishi, Nagasaki	15-3-66	25-3-67	27-3-6

D: 3,250 tons (4,550 fl) **S:** 32 kts
Dim: 136.0 (131.0 pp) × 13.4 × 4.4 (mean)
A: 8/Harpoon SSM (IV × 2)—1/Mk 29 SAM launcher (VIII × 1, 16 Sea Sparrow missiles)—1/127-mm Mk 42 DP—1/20-mm Mk 15 CIWS—1/Mk 112 ASROC ASW RL (VIII × 1, no reloads)—1/375-mm Bofors ASW RL (IV × 1)—6/324-mm Type 68 ASW TT (IV × 2)
Electron Equipt:
Radar: 1/OPS-17 surf. search, 1/OPS-11B-Y air search, 1/Mk 35 gun f.c., 1/FCS-2-12B SAM f.c.
Sonar: OQS-3 hull-mounted MF, SQS-35(J) MF VDS
EW: NOLR-6C intercept, OLT-3 jammer, Mk 36 SRBOC decoy RL (VI × 2)
M: 2 sets Mitsubishi geared steam turbines; 2 props; 60,000 shp
Boilers: 2 Mitsubishi-Combustion Eng.; 43 kg/cm^2, 454° C
Range: 7,000/20 **Fuel:** 900 tons **Crew:** 270 tot.

Takatsuki (DD 164) *Ships of the World,*

DESTROYERS *(continued)*

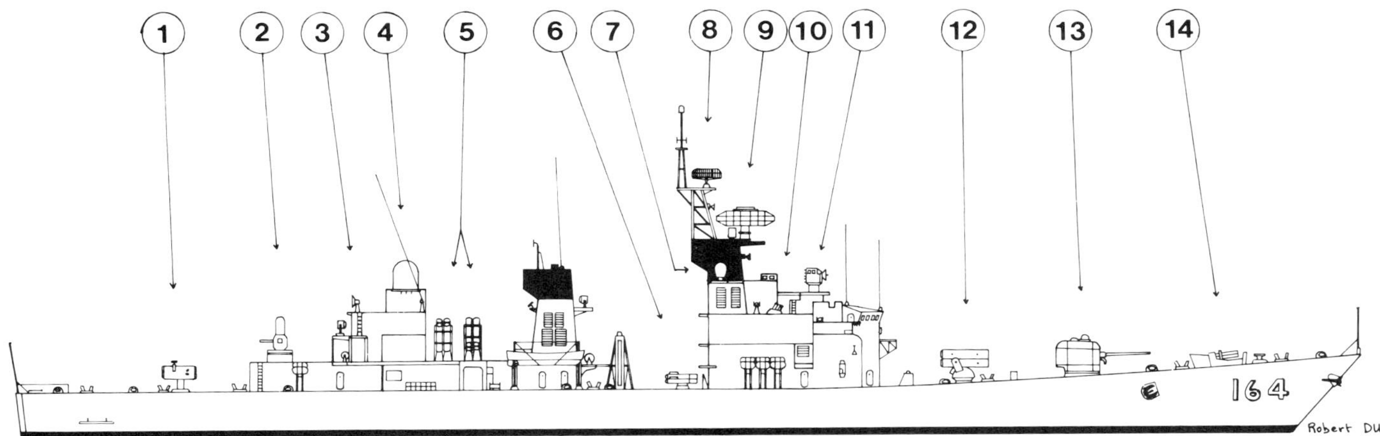

Takatsuki (DD 164) 1. Mk 29 launcher for Sea Sparrow SAM (VIII × 1) 2. Mk 15 Phalanx CIWS 3. unidentified device 4. FCS-2-12B radar director for Sea Sparrow SAM 5. Harpoon SSM (IV × 2) 6. Mk 68 triple ASW TT 7. OLT-3 jammer radomes 8. OPS-17 surface-search radar 9. OPS-11B air-search radar 10. Mk 36 SRBOC decoy rocket system (Mk 137 launchers) 11. Mk 56 fire-control system for 127-mm gun (with Mk 35 radar) 12. Mk 112 ASROC ASW rocket launcher (VIII × 1) 13. 127-mm Mk 42 DP gun 14. Bofors 375-mm ASW rocket launcher (IV × 1)
Drawing by Robert Dumas

ikizuki (DD 165) *Ships of the World,* 1988

emarks: Originally carried three U.S. DASH drone ASW helicopters, removed in 977 and hangar not used. DD 165 has fin stabilizers. DD 164 authorized under 981–82 Budget to receive extensive modernization, completing in 10-85, DD 165 efitted under 1983–84 Budget, completing 26-12-87. The DASH drone helicopter angar and after 127-mm gun were removed during the modernization. Gained were a 1k 29 launcher aft for Sea Sparrow, 8 Harpoon missiles (IV × 2), 1/Mk 15 Phalanx IWS gatling AA gun, upgrading of the OQS-3 sonar, provision for U.S. SQR-18A ACTASS towed passive hydrophone array, replacement of the after Mk 56 GFCS with FCS-2-12, substitution of the NOLR-6C EW system, addition of LINK 14 digital ata-link equipment, installation of the U.S. Mk 36 Super RBOC chaff launching stem.

Unmodernized sisters *Mochizuki* (DD 166) and *Nagatsuki* (DD 167) were reclassified s auxiliaries late in 1991. DD 164 and 165 will be retired by 1995.

SCORT DESTROYERS (DDK)

4 Yamagumo class

	Bldr	Laid down	L	In serv.
5 Asagumo	Maizuru Heavy Industries	24-6-65	25-11-66	29-8-67
9 Aokumo	Sumitomo, Uraga	2-10-70	30-3-72	25-11-72
0 Akigumo	Sumitomo, Uraga	7-7-72	23-10-73	24-7-74
1 Yugumo	Sumitomo, Uraga	4-2-76	31-5-77	24-3-78

D: 2,100 tons (2,700 fl) **S:** 27 kts **Dim:** 114.9 × 11.8 × 4.0 (hull)
A: 4/76.2-mm 50-cal. Mk 33 DP (II × 2)—1/ASROC ASW RL (VIII × 1)— 1/375-mm Bofors ASW RL (IV × 1)—6/324-mm Type 68 ASW TT (III × 2)

igumo (DDK 120)—late version *Ships of the World,* 1990

Asagumo (DDK 115)—early version, without VDS *Ships of the World,* 1991

Electron Equipt:
Radar: 1/OPS-17 surf. search, 1/OPS-11 air search, DDK 115, 119: 1/ U.S. Mk 35 gun f.c., 1/U.S. Mk 34 gun f.c., DDK 120, 121: 2/GFCS 1 gun f.c.
Sonar: OQS-3 (DDK 115: U.S. SQS-23) hull-mounted MF; U.S. SQS-35(J) VDS (not in DDK 115)
EW: NOLR-5 (DDK 115: NOLR-1B) intercept
M: 6 Mitsubishi 12UEV 30/40N diesels; 2 props; 26,500 bhp
Range: 7,000/20 **Crew:** 210–220 tot.

Remarks: Version of the *Minegumo* class completed with ASROC instead of DASH. DDK 115 and 119 were given U.S. Mk 56 gun directors forward (Mk 35 radar) and Mk 63 GFCS aft (Mk 34 radar on after gun mount); DDK 120 and 121 got two Japanese GFCS-1 systems instead. In DDK 119–121 the VDS was installed during construction, and, therefore, the stern was not raised as in two earlier ships of the class (DDK 113, 114) that were backfitted with the system; DDK 115 was never backfitted with VDS. Final three have lattice mainmasts and a bulwark above the pilothouse.

Sisters *Yamagumo* (DDK 113) and *Makigumo* (DDK 114) were reclassified as training ships during 8-91. The others will be retired or redesignated as auxiliaries by 1995.

♦ 3 Minegumo class

	Bldr	Laid down	L	In serv.
116 Minegumo	Mitsui, Tamano	14-3-67	16-12-67	21-8-68
117 Natsugumo	Uraga, Yokosuka	26-6-67	25-7-68	25-4-69
118 Murakumo	Maizuru, Heavy Industries	19-10-68	15-11-69	21-8-70

Natsugumo (DDK 117) *Ships of the World,* 6-88

ESCORT DESTROYERS *(continued)*

Murakumo (DDK 118)—with OTO Melara 76-mm Compact gun and ASROC launcher aft *Ships of the World,* 1990

D: 2,100 tons (2,750 fl) **S:** 27 kts **Dim:** 114.9 × 11.8 × 4.0 (hull)
A: DDK 116, 117: 4/76.2-mm 50-cal. Mk 33 DP (II × 2); DDK 118: 1/76-mm OTO Melara Compact, 2/76.2-mm Mk 33 DP (II × 1)—1/Mk 112 ASROC ASW RL (VIII × 1, with reloads)—1/375-mm Bofors ASW RL (IV × 1)—6/324-mm Type 68 ASW TT (III ×2)
Electron Equipt:
Radar: 1/OPS-17 surf. search, 1/OPS-11 air search; DDK 116; 1/Mk 35 gun f.c., 1/SPG-34 gun f.c.; DDK 118: 1/GFCS-2-12 gun f.c., 1/GFCS-1 gun f.c.; DDK 117: 1/GFCS-1 gun f.c., 1/SPG-34 gun f.c.
Sonar: OQS-4 hull-mounted MF, DDK 118 also : SQS-35(J) MF VDS
EW: NOLR-5 intercept
M: 6 Mitsubishi 12UEV 30/40 diesels; 2 props; 26,500 bhp
Range: 7,000/20
Crew: 19 officers, 196 enlisted

Remarks: Originally differed from the *Yamagumo* class in having a DASH drone-helicopter facility instead of ASROC, but DASH is no longer carried. In 1976, DDK 118 had an OTO Melara 76-mm gun and the prototype GFCS-2-12 radar director substituted for her after 76.2-mm twin mount and U.S. Mk 63 control system; in 1979, she received an ASROC launcher on what had been her DASH flight deck. DDK 116 and 117 received ASROC in 1982–83. DDK 116 has a U.S. Mk 56 GFCS (with Mk 35 radar) forward; the other two have a Japanese GFCS-1, and DDK 116 and 117 have a Mk 63 GFCS aft. DDK 118, with VDS, is 1.0 m longer and displaces 50 tons more.

FRIGATES (DE)

♦ **4 (+2) Abukuma class**

	Bldr	Laid down	L	In serv.
229 Abukuma	Mitsui, Tamano	17-3-88	21-12-88	12-12-89
230 Jintsu	Hitachi, Kanegawa	14-4-88	31-1-89	2-2-90
231 Oyodo	Mitsui, Tamano	8-3-89	19-12-89	23-1-91
232 Sendai	Sumitomo, Uraga	14-4-89	26-1-90	15-3-91
233 Chikuma	Hitachi, Maizuro	14-2-91	22-1-92	2-93
234 Tone	Sumitomo, Uraga	8-2-91	6-12-91	3-93

D: 2,050 tons (approx. 2,550 fl) **S:** 27 kts
Dim: 109.0 × 13.4 × 3.8 (hull)
A: 8/Harpoon SSM (IV × 2)—1/76-mm OTO Melara Compact DP—1/20-mm Mk 15 Phalanx CIWS—1/Mk 112 ASROC ASW RL (VIII ×1)—6/324-mm Mk 68 ASW TT (III × 2)
Electron Equipt:
Radar: 1/OPS-28 air/surf. search, 1/OPS-14C air search, 1/FCS-2-21A gun f.c.

Oyodo (DE 231) *Ships of the World,* 19

Abukuma (DE 229) JMSDF,

FRIGATES *(continued)*

Abukuma (DE 229) *Ships of the World,* 1991

Sonar: OQS-4A bow-mounted MF
EW: NOLQ-6C intercept, OLT-3 jammer, 2/Mk 36 SRBOC decoy RL (VI × 2)

M: CODOG: 2 Kawasaki-Rolls-Royce Spey SM-1C gas turbine, 2 Mitsubishi S12U S200 diesels; 2 CP props; 27,000 shp/10,000 bhp (6,000 sust.)

Range: . . . **Crew:** 120 tot.

Remarks: First pair authorized under FY 1986 Budget; second pair under FY 1987; third pair authorized under FY 1989. One more requested for FY 90 but was rejected, and no more are now planned. The RAM (RIM-116A) point-defense SAM is planned to be added, although Japan has yet to order the system from the U.S. or West Germany. Also to be added later is the U.S. SQR-19A towed tactical sonar system (TASS). The design has considerable improvements in sensors and firepower over the austere *Yubari* and *Ishikari* designs. First two ordered 26-3-87; second two on 26-2-88; third pair on 24-1-89. Hull moulded depth is 7.80 m. *Abukuma* began trials 27-7-89.

♦ 2 Yubari class

	Bldr	Laid down	L	In serv.
227 Yubari	Sumitomo, Uraga	9-2-81	22-2-82	18-3-83
228 Yubetsu	Hitachi, Maizuru	14-1-82	25-1-83	14-2-84

Yubetsu (DE 228) *Ships of the World*

D: 1,470 tons (1,760 fl) **S:** 25 kts **Dim:** 91.0 × 10.8 × 3.6 (hull)

A: 8/Harpoon SSM (IV × 2)—1/76-mm OTO Melara DP—1/375-mm Bofors ASW RL (IV × 1)—6/324-mm Type 68 ASW TT (III × 2)

Electron Equipt:
Radar: 1/OPS-19 nav., 1/OPS-28 surf./air search, 1/GFCS-2-21 gun f.c.
Sonar: OQS-4 hull-mounted MF
EW: NOLQ-6C intercept, OLT-3 jammer, 2/Mk 36 SRBOC decoy RL (VI × 2)

M: CODOG: 1 Kawasaki-Rolls-Royce Olympus TM-3B gas turbine, 28,390 shp; 1 Mitsubishi 6DRV 35/44 diesel, 5,000 bhp; 2 CP props

Range: . . . **Crew:** 98 tot.

Remarks: An enlarged version of the *Ishikari* class, presumably because the earlier ship is too cramped for the mission requirements. DE 227 ordered under 1979 Budget, DE 228 under the 1980 Budget. A third was requested for the 1982 Budget but was not authorized. Planned installation of a U.S. Mk 15 Phalanx CIWS aft has not occurred. Have the OYQ combat data system.

♦ 1 Ishikari class

	Bldr	Laid down	L	In serv.
226 Ishikari	Mitsui, Tamano	17-5-79	18-3-80	30-3-81

D: 1,200 tons (1,450 fl) **S:** 25 kts
Dim: 84.5 × 10.0 × 3.5 (mean hull)

A: 8/Harpoon SSM (IV × 2)—1/76-mm OTO Melara DP—1/375-mm Bofors ASW RL (IV × 1)—6/324-mm Type 68 ASW TT

Electron Equipt:
Radar: 1/OPS-19 nav., 1/OPS-28 surf./air search, 1/GFCS-2-21 gun f.c.
Sonar: OQS-4 hull-mounted MF
EW: NOLQ-6C intercept, OLT-3 jammer, 2/Mk 36 SRBOC decoy RL (VI × 2)

M: CODOG: 1 Kawasaki-Rolls-Royce Olympus TM-3B gas turbine, 28,390 shp; 1 Mitsubishi 6DRV 35/44 diesel, 5,000 bhp; 2 CP props

Crew: 90 tot.

Ishikari (DE 226) *Ships of the World,* 1981

Remarks: Smaller, more lightly armed, faster, and with fewer sensors than the preceding *Chikugo* class. Aluminum superstructure. Either the gas turbine *or* the single diesel will drive both propellers. Ordered under 1977 program. 19 kts max. on diesel. The Combat Information Center (CIC) is below the waterline and is equipped with the OYQ combat data system. Highly automated ship with very small crew for size.

♦ 11 Chikugo class

	Bldr	Laid down	L	In serv.
215 Chikugo	Mitsui, Tamano	9-12-68	13-1-70	31-7-70
216 Ayase	Ishikawajima, Tokyo	5-12-69	16-9-70	20-7-71
217 Mikumo	Mitsui, Tamano	17-3-70	16-2-71	26-8-71
218 Tokachi	Mitsui, Tamano	11-12-70	25-11-71	17-5-72
219 Iwase	Mitsui, Tamano	6-8-71	29-6-72	12-12-72
220 Chitose	Hitachi, Maizuru	7-10-71	25-1-73	21-8-73
221 Niyodo	Mitsui, Tamano	20-9-72	28-8-73	8-2-74
222 Teshio	Hitachi, Maizuru	11-7-73	29-5-74	10-1-75
223 Yoshino	Mitsui, Tamano	28-9-73	22-8-74	6-2-75
224 Kumano	Hitachi, Maizuru	29-5-74	24-2-75	19-11-75
225 Noshiro	Mitsui, Tamano	27-1-76	23-12-76	31-8-77

Ayase (DE 216)—no VDS *Ships of the World,* 1988

Teshio (DE 222)—no VDS *Ships of the World*

Yoshino (DE 223)—with VDS *Ships of the World,* 1988

FRIGATES *(continued)*

D: 1,470–1,530 tons (1,700–1,800 fl) **S:** 25 kts
Dim: 93.0 × 10.8 × 3.5 (hull)
A: 2/76.2-mm 50-cal. Mk 33 DP (II × 1)—2/40-mm AA (II × 1)—1/Mk 112 ASROC ASW RL (VIII × 1)—6/324-mm Type 68 ASW TT (III × 2)
Electron Equipt:
Radar: 1/OPS-16 surf. search, 1/OPS-14 air search, 1/GFCS-1B gun f.c.
EW: NOLR-5 intercept
Sonar: OQS-3 hull-mounted MF, U.S. SQS-35(J) VDS (*see* Remarks)
M: 4 Mitsubishi-Burmeister & Wain UEV 30/40 or Mitshi 28VBC-38 diesels; 2 props; 16,000 bhp
Range: 10,700/12; 12,000/9
Crew: 12 officers, 152 enlisted

Remarks: To date, SQS-35(J) towed, variable-depth sonar has been mounted in only five units; it is stowed in an open well at the stern, offset to starboard. These are the smallest ships in any navy to carry ASROC. A Mk 51 lead-computing director (no radar) controls the twin 40-mm mount. DE 215 and 220 are 1,480 tons std., DE 216–219 and 221 are 1,470 tons std.; later units, 1,500 tons std. DE 215, 217–219, 221, 223, 225 have the Mitsubishi diesels.

Note: The two remaining Isuzu-class frigates, *Kitikami* (DE 213) and *Ohi* (DE 214), were reclassified as auxiliaries on 31-1-90 and renumbered ASU 7016 and ASU 7017, respectively.

GUIDED-MISSILE PATROL BOATS (PG)

♦ **0 (+2 + . . .) modified Italian Sparviero-class hydrofoils**

	Bldr	Laid down	L	In serv.
. . . .	Sumitomo, Uraga	25-3-91	7-92	3-93
. . . .	Sumitomo, Uraga	25-3-91	7-92	3-93

50-ton hydrofoil missile boat *Ships of the World,* 1991

D: 50 tons (63 fl) **S:** 50 kts in calm sea
Dim: 22.95 (24.56 foils retracted) × 7.01 (12.06 max. over foils) × 1.87 (1.45 over foils at speed, 4.37 at rest)
A: 4/SSM-1B SSM (II × 2)—1/20-mm JM-61-MB gatling AA
Electron Equipt: Radar: . . . nav.—EW: . . . intercept, 2 decoy RL
M: 1 gas turbine **Range:** 400/45
Crew: 10 tot.

Remarks: First unit of a 250-ton planing hull design was to have been in 1983 Budget, but was continually postponed to permit further design definition. First two finally approved under FY 1990, but third unit, approved under FY 1991, was deferred to help pay cost of Japanese participation in Mideast conflict and was requested again under the FY 1992 Budget. The license to construct this modified version of the Italian Navy's *Sparveiro*-class (itself a modified version of the U.S. Navy's *Tucumcari,* PGH 1), was not granted until 3-91. Class of six planned to replace the PT 11 class, with a possible additional six to follow. The gatling gun employs a simple pintle mounting and is of the same type as is employed on JMSDF mine countermeasures ships and JMSA patrol ships and craft.

TORPEDO BOATS (PT)

♦ **2 PT 11 class** Bldr: Mitsubishi, Shimonoseki

	Laid down	L	In serv.
814 PT 14	23-3-72	. . .	10-7-73
815 PT 15	23-4-74	. . .	8-1-75

D: 100 tons (125 fl) **S:** 40 kts **Dim:** 35.0 × 9.2 × 1.2
A: 2/40-mm AA (I × 2)—4/533-mm TT (I × 4)
Electron Equipt: Radar: 1/OPS-13 nav/surf. search
M: CODAG: 2 Ishikawajima IM-300 gas turbines, 2 Mitsubishi 24 WZ31MC diesels; 3 props; 11,000 hp
Range: 300/40; 1,000/18 **Crew:** 26 tot.

Remarks: Ships were planned for disposal commencing 3-89, but were extended due to delays in the follow-on hydrofoil missile boat program. Class prototype PT 11 (PT 811) was stricken 28-11-90, PT 12 (PT 812) and PT 13 (PT 813) on 4-10-91. The survivors form the 1st Torpedo Boat Division, based at Yoichi Naval Station, Hokkaido.

PT 12 (PT 812) *Ships of the World,* 7-90

PATROL CRAFT (PB)

♦ **9 PB 19 class** Bldr: Ishikawajima, Yokohama

PB 19 to PB 27 (PB 19–24 in serv. 31-3-72; others, 29-3-73)

PB 19 (PB 919) *Ships of the World,* 19

D: 18 tons **S:** 20 kts **Dim:** 17.0 × 4.3 × 0.8
A: 1/12.7-mm mg **Electron Equipt:** Radar: 1/ Furuno OPS-29 nav
M: 2 Isuzu 17T-MF RCOR diesels; 2 props; 760 bhp
Range: 400/20 **Crew:** 5 tot.

Remarks: GRP hulls. Hull numbers run 919 through 927. Originally had a 20-r AA, replaced by a 12.7-mm mg aft. Two additional units delivered 3-79 and 28-3-80 use as radio-controlled surface gunnery target-towing craft; 850 bhp, 25 kts.

MINE WARFARE SHIPS

Note: Two 3,000-ton standard displacement mine countermeasures support ships included in the 1991–95 ship acquisition plan as replacements for *Souya* (MMC and *Hayase* (MST 462), below. No other details yet released. Will presumably h helicopter facilities to support MH-53E mine countermeasures helicopters.

♦ **1 minelayer (MMC)**

	Bldr	Laid down	L	In serv.
951 Souya	Hitachi, Maizuru	9-7-70	31-3-71	30-9-71

Souya (MMC 951) *Ships of the World,*

D: 2,150 tons (3,250 fl) **S:** 18 kts **Dim:** 99.0 × 15.0 × 4.2 (hull)
A: 2/76.2-mm Mk 33 DP (II × 1)—2/20-mm JM-61-MB gatling AA × 2)—6/324-mm Type 68 ASW TT (III × 2)—200 mines
Electron Equipt:
Radar: 1/OPS-16C nav./surf. search, 1/OPS-air search, 1/GFCS- gun f.c.
Sonar: SQS-11A hull-mounted MF, 1/ZQS-1B hull-mounted HF
M: 4 Kawasaki-M.A.N. V6V 22/30 ATL diesels; 2 props; 6,400 bhp
Range: 7,500/14 **Crew:** 185 tot.

MINE WARFARE SHIPS *(continued)*

Remarks: Platform for MH-53E mine-countermeasures helicopters; six mine rails, two external, four through the transom stern. Can also act as an ASW escort. Often acts as flagship for mine-countermeasures forces. Two hull-mounted sonar domes, with that for the ZQS-1B, which is used for mine avoidance, located forward.

♦ 1 mine-countermeasures support ship/minelayer (MST)

	Bldr	Laid down	L	In serv.
462 Hayase	Ishikawajima-Harima, Tokyo	16-9-70	21-6-71	6-11-71

Hayase (MST 462) *Ships of the World, 4-90*

D: 2,000 tons (3,050 fl) **S:** 18 kts **Dim:** 99.0 × 13.0 × 3.8
A: 2/76.2-mm 50-cal. DP (II × 1)—2/20-mm JM-61-MB gatling AA (I × 2)—6/324-mm Type 68 ASW TT (III × 2)—116 mines
Electron Equipt:
Radar: 1/OPS-16C nav./surf. search, 1/OPS-14 air search, 1/Mk 34 gun f.c.
Sonar: SQS-11A hull-mounted MF, 1/ZQS-1B hull-mounted HF
M: 4 Kawasaki-M.A.N. V6V 22/30 ATL diesels; 2 props; 6,400 bhp
Range: 7,500/14 **Crew:** 180 tot.

emarks: The *Hayase* is similar to the *Souya* but has no forecastle and has five mine ils exiting through the transom stern. She has a U.S. Mk 63 gun-control system. antail cleared as a platform for mine-countermeasures helicopters. Deployed as flag-ip of the Japanese mine countermeasures force in the Persian Gulf 4-91 through -91, equipped with U.S. Global Positioning System satellite navigation equipment d U.S. Fleet SATCOMM equipment.

1 Takami-class mine-countermeasures support ship (MST)

	Bldr	L	In serv.
5 Utone	Hitachi, Kanagawa	6-4-70	3-9-70

one (MST 475) *Ships of the World, 1987*

): 380 tons (approx. 530 fl) **S:** 14 kts **Dim:** 52.0 × 8.8 × 2.4
: 1/20-mm JM-61-MB gatling AA
lectron Equipt: Radar: OPS-9 nav.—Sonar: ZQS-2 hull-mounted
I: 2 Mitsubishi YV12ZC-15/20 diesels; 2 CP props; 1,440 bhp
lectric: 360 kw tot. (2 × 100 kw a.c., 2 × 80 kw a.c.) **Crew:** 38 tot.

narks: Reclassified as tender to MSB 707-class inshore minesweepers on 16-12-86, acing *Kasado*-class unit *Otsu* (MST 474, ex-MSC 621), stricken the same date. er than removal of most portable sweep gear, retains MSC appearance. Will proba-be replaced by a later *Takami*-class minehunter/sweeper.

(+3+3) Yaeyama-class deep-sea mine countermeasures ships

	Bldr	Laid down	L	In serv.
Yaeyama	Hitachi, Kanagawa	30-8-90	29-8-91	3-93
Tsushima	Nippon Kokan, Tsurumi	20-7-90	11-9-91	3-93
. . . . . .	Nippon Kokan, Tsurumi	17-5-91	7-92	3-94
. . . . . .	. . . . . .	. . .	. . .	. . .
. . . . . .	. . . . . .	. . .	. . .	. . .
. . . . . .	. . . . . .	. . .	. . .	. . .

1,000 tons (1,150 fl) **S:** 14 kts **Dim:** 67.0 × 11.8 × 3.1
1/20-mm JM-61-MB gatling AA **Range:** . . ./. . . **Crew:** 60 tot.

Electron Equipt:
Radar: 1/OPS-19 nav.
Sonar: U.S. SQQ-32, U.S. Klein AQS-14 sidescan
M: 2 Mitsubishi 6NMU-series diesels; 2 CP props; 2,400 bhp—bow-thruster

Yaeyama (MSO 301)—artist's rendering *Ships of the World, 1991*

Yaeyama (MSO 301)—at launch *Ships of the World, 9-91*

Remarks: First two units authorized by 1989 Budget, with two per year thereafter planned to a total of six, but only one authorized under FY 90. Three more are planned during FY 1992–95 period. Intended to deploy Type S-7 autonomous minehunting vehicle (with ZQS-3) and Type S-8 deep-sea mine disposal system, the latter a version of the U.S. Honeywell SLQ-48 remote-controlled submersible vehicle. Wooden-hulled construction.

♦ 4 (+7) Awashima-class minehunter/minesweepers (MSC)

	Bldr	Laid down	L	In serv.
670 Awashima	Hitachi, Kanagawa	12-5-88	6-6-89	13-12-89
671 Sakushima	Nippon Kokan, Tsurumi	17-5-88	6-6-89	13-12-89
672 Uwashima	Nippon Kokan, Tsurumi	18-5-89	23-5-90	19-12-90
673 Ieshima	Hitachi, Kanagawa	12-5-89	12-6-90	19-12-90
674	Hitachi, Kanagawa	27-5-91	7-92	2-93
675	. . . . . .	. . .	. . .	. . .
676	. . . . . .	. . .	. . .	. . .
677	. . . . . .	. . .	. . .	. . .
678	. . . . . .	. . .	. . .	. . .
679	. . . . . .	. . .	. . .	. . .
680	. . . . . .	. . .	. . .	. . .
681	. . . . . .	. . .	. . .	. . .

Sakushima (MSC 671) *Ships of the World, 1990*

MINE WARFARE SHIPS *(continued)*

Ieshima (MSC 673) JMSDF, 1990

D: 490 tons (590 fl) **S:** 14 kts **Dim:** 57.7 × 9.40 × 2.90
A: 1/20-mm JM-61-MB gatling AA
Electron Equipt:
Radar: 1/OPS-18B nav.—Sonar: ZQS-2B (MSC 672 on: ZQS-3)
M: 2 6NMU-TAI diesels; 2 CP props; 1,440 bhp **Crew:** 45 tot.
Range: 2,400/10 **Electric:** 1 × 1,450-kw d.c.; 2 × 160-kw a.c.

Remarks: A revised version of the *Hatsushima* class, lengthened primarily to permit 2-high vice 3-high bunking for enlisted personnel. Were to have been of GRP construction but are built of wood. MSC 670 and 671 in 1988 Budget; a request for one under the 1989 Budget was rejected, but the ship was approved under the 1990 Budget, and further construction is now planned for a total of 12 to be requested through FY 1995 in lieu of a class of 600-ton minehunters. Three were requested under the FY 1992 Budget.

Carry S-2 towed noisemakers and S-4 (with ZQS-2B sonar) and S-7 Mod. 1 (with ZQS-3 sonar) autonomous minehunting vehicles. MSC 670 and 671 participated in the Japanese deployment to the Persian Gulf 4-91 through 10-91.

♦ 21 Hatsushima-class minehunter/minesweepers (MSC)

	Bldr	Laid down	L	In serv.
649 Hatsushima	Nippon Kokan, Tsurumi	6-12-77	30-10-78	30-3-79
650 Ninoshima	Hitachi, Kanagawa	8-5-78	9-8-79	19-12-79
651 Miyajima	Nippon Kokan, Tsurumi	8-11-78	18-9-79	29-1-80
652 Nenoshima	Nippon Kokan, Tsurumi	4-10-79	25-7-80	25-12-80
653 Ukishima	Hitachi, Kanagawa	15-5-79	11-7-80	27-11-80
654 Oshima	Hitachi, Kanagawa	2-6-80	17-6-81	26-11-81
655 Miijima	Nippon Kokan, Tsurumi	4-8-80	2-6-81	26-11-81
656 Yakushima	Nippon Kokan, Tsurumi	15-6-81	22-6-82	17-12-82
657 Narushima	Hitachi, Kanagawa	29-5-81	7-6-82	17-12-82
658 Chichijima	Hitachi, Kanagawa	2-6-82	13-7-83	16-12-83
659 Toroshima	Nippon Kokan, Tsurumi	30-6-82	23-6-83	16-12-83
660 Hahajima	Nippon Kokan, Tsurumi	20-5-83	27-6-84	18-12-84
661 Takashima	Hitachi, Kanagawa	7-6-83	18-6-84	18-12-84
662 Newajima	Hitachi, Kanagawa	21-5-84	5-6-85	12-12-85
663 Etajima	Nippon Kokan, Tsurumi	22-5-84	17-6-85	12-12-85
664 Kamishima	Nippon Kokan, Tsurumi	10-5-85	20-6-86	16-12-86
665 Himeshima	Hitachi, Kanagawa	16-5-85	10-6-86	16-12-86
666 Ogishima	Hitachi, Kanagawa	16-5-86	10-6-87	19-12-87
667 Moroshima	Nippon Kokan, Tsurumi	22-5-86	11-6-87	19-12-87
668 Yurishima	Nippon Kokan, Tsurumi	14-5-87	13-5-88	15-12-88
669 Hikoshima	Hitachi, Kanagawa	12-5-87	2-6-88	15-12-88

D: 440 tons (536 fl) **S:** 14 kts **Dim:** 55.00 (52.00 pp) × 9.40 × 2.40
A: 1/20-mm JM-61-MB gatling AA **Range:** 2,400/10 **Crew:** 45 tot.
Electron Equipt:
Radar: OPS-9 or OPS-18B nav. —Sonar: ZQS-2B hull-mounted HF
M: 2 Mitsubishi YV12ZC-18/20 diesels; 2 CP props; 1,440 bhp
Electric: MSC 649–665: 1,690 kw tot. (2 × 725-kw diesel sweep gen., 3 × 80-kw ship's service diesel sets); MSC 666–669: 1,770 kw tot. (1 × 1,450 gas turbine sweep gen., 2 × 160-kw ship's service diesel set)

Remarks: Expansion of the *Takami* design. Wooden construction. MSC 653 and later had the 20-mm Type JM-61-MB gatling gun AA as completed; in the earlier ships a 20-mm AA has been replaced by the gatling gun. MSC 666 and 667 have Mitsubishi 6NMU-TAI diesels. MSC 664 and 665 have Mitsubishi 122C-15/22 diesels. The sweep tail generates 4,300 amps. Carry Type S-2 towed noisemakers and Type S-4 autonomous minehunting vehicles with ZQS-2B sonars; these carry and lay their own disposal charges. MSC 668 and 669 participated in the JMSDF deployment to the Persian Gulf 4-91 through 10-91.

Yakushima (MSC 656) JMSDF, 1990

Hikoshima (MSC 669)—en route Persian Gulf *Ships of the World, 4-9*

♦ 7 Takami-class minehunter/minesweepers

	Bldr	L	In serv.
642 Yokose	Nippon Kokan, Tsurumi	21-7-75	15-12-75
643 Sakate	Hitachi, Kanagawa	5-8-75	17-12-75
644 Oumi	Nippon Kokan, Tsurumi	28-5-76	18-11-76
645 Fukue	Hitachi, Kanagawa	12-7-76	18-11-76
646 Okitsu	Nippon Kokan, Tsurumi	4-3-77	20-9-77
647 Hashira	Hitachi, Kanagawa	8-11-77	28-3-78
648 Iwai	Nippon Kokan, Tsurumi	8-11-77	28-3-78

Iwai (MSC 648) *Ships of the World,*

D: 380 tons (approx. 465 fl) **S:** 14 kts **Dim:** 52.00 × 8.80 × 2.36
A: 1/20-mm JM-61-MB gatling AA **Crew:** 45–47 tot.
Electron Equipt:
Radar: OPS-9 nav.—Sonar: ZQS-2 hull-mounted HF
M: 2 Mitsubishi YV12ZC-15/20 diesels; 2 CP props; 1,440 bhp
Electric: 1,810 kw tot. (2 × 725-kw d.c. sweep gen.; 2 × 100-kw a.c. and 2 × 80-kw a.c. ship's service sets)

MINE WARFARE SHIPS *(continued)*

Remarks: Wooden construction. ZQS-2 sonar is a license-built version of the British Plessey Type 193-M minehunting sonar. OPS-9 radar, used in conjunction with a Mk 20 plotter, is a Japanese version of the British Type 978. These ships are of wooden construction, and they carry four divers for mine clearance. Carry U.S. Mk 4 acoustic noisemaker gear and S2 wire sweep. Have 4,300-amp magnetic sweep. Early units did not have CP props.

Twelve sisters have been reclassified to other functions: *Takami* (MSC 630) and *Iou* MSC 631) to YAS 82 and YAS 83 on 27-3-86; *Miyake* (MSC 632) to YAS 84 on 16-12-86; *Utone* (MSC 633) to MST 475 on 16-12-86; and *Awaji* (MSC 634) and *Toushi* (MSC 635) to YAS 85 and YAS 86 on 24-3-87. *Teuri* (MSC 636) and *Muratsu* (MSC 637) were reclassified YAS 87 and YAS 88 on 23-3-88; *Tashiro* (MSC 638) and *Miyato* (MSC 639) to YAS 89 and YAS 90 on 29-11-89; and *Takane* (MSC 640) and *Muzuki* (MSC 641) to YAS 91 and YAS 92 on 28-11-90. The MSC 642 and 643 to YAS in 3-92. The craft redesignated as YAS are employed as mine-clearance diver support ships.

◆ **6 inshore minesweepers (MSB)** Bldrs: Odd-numbered craft: Hitachi, Kanagawa; even-numbered craft: Nippon Kokan, Tsurumi

	In serv.		In serv.
MSB 707 MSB 7	30-3-73	MSB 710 MSB 10	29-3-74
MSB 708 MSB 8	27-3-73	MSB 711 MSB 11	10-5-75
MSB 709 MSB 9	28-3-74	MSB 712 MSB 12	24-4-75

MSB 8 (MSB 708) — *Ships of the World*, 1990

D: 50 tons (58 fl) **S:** 10 kts **Dim:** 22.5 × 5.4 × 1.1 **A:** none
M: 2 Mitsubishi 4ZV20M diesels; 2 props; 480 bhp **Crew:** 10 tot.

Remarks: Wooden construction. Supported by *Utone* (MST 475). No radar or sonar.

AMPHIBIOUS WARFARE SHIPS

Note: Construction of a 3,500-ton standard displacement LSD was projected in the FY 90 acquisition plan. Funds had not been requested through FY 87. Originally, *two* these ships had been sought. A request for a 5,500-ton LST was rejected under the 9 Budget, but an 8,500-ton LST is now planned that will also carry helicopters and apparently also have a docking well aft.

◆ **3 Miura-class landing ships (LST)** Bldr: Ishikawajima-Harima, Tokyo

	Laid down	L	In serv.
4151 Miura	26-11-73	13-8-74	29-1-75
4152 Ojika	10-6-74	2-9-75	27-3-76
4153 Satsuma	26-5-75	12-5-76	17-2-77

Miura (LST 4151) — *Ships of the World*, 1991

D: 2,000 tons (3,200 fl) **S:** 14 kts **Dim:** 98.0 (94.0 pp) × 14.0 × 3.0
A: 2/76.2-mm 50-cal. U.S. Mk 33 DP (II × 1)—2/40-mm Bofors AA (II × 1)
Electron Equipt:
Radars: 1/OPS-16 surf. search, 1/OPS-16 nav., 1/GFCS-1 gun f.c.
M: 2 Kawasaki-M.A.N. V8V 22/30 AMTL diesels; 2 props; 4,400 bhp
Crew: 118 tot. ship's company + 200 troops

Remarks: Carry 1,800 tons cargo. Tank deck can hold 10 Type 74 battle tanks. LST 4153 carried OTO Melara Compact gun at bow for trials during late 1970s. All have two LCVP in davits and two LCM(6) on deck, the latter served by a traveling gantry with folding rails that can be extended over the sides. GFCS-1 fwd controls 76.2-mm guns; U.S. Mk 51 Mod. 2 lead-computing GFCS aft controls 40-mm mount.

◆ **3 Atsumi class (LSTs)** Bldr: Sasebo Heavy Industries

	Laid down	L	In serv.
4101 Atsumi	7-12-71	13-6-72	27-11-72
4102 Motobu	23-4-73	3-8-73	21-12-73
4103 Nemuro	18-11-76	16-6-77	27-10-77

Nemuro (LST 4103) — *Ships of the World*, 1988

D: 1,480 tons (2,400 fl) **S:** 14 kts **Dim:** 89.0 × 13.0 × 2.7
A: 4/40-mm AA (II × 2) **Electron Equipt:** Radar: 1/OPS-9 nav.
M: 2 Kawasaki-M.A.N. V8V 22/30 AMTL diesels; 2 props; 4,400 bhp
Range: 4,300/12 **Crew:** 100 tot. ship's company + 130 troops

Remarks: Can carry 20 vehicles or 400 tons cargo. LST 4102 and 4103 are 1,550 tons standard and have a max. speed of 13 kts. Have two U.S. Mk 51 Mod. 2 lead-computing GFCS, two LCVP in davits, and can carry one LCVP on deck, amidships. LST 4103 has an electric crane forward of the bridge; the other two have a simple king post and boom.

◆ **2 Yura-class utility landing ships (LSU)** Bldr: Sasebo Heavy Industries

	Laid down	L	In serv.
4171 Yura	23-4-80	10-8-80	27-3-81
4172 Noto	23-4-80	1-11-80	27-3-81

Noto (LSU 4172) — *Ships of the World*, 1988

D: 500 tons (590 fl) **S:** 12 kts **Dim:** 58.0 × 9.5 × 1.7 (aft)
A: 1/20-mm JM 61-MB gatling AA
Electron Equipt: Radar: 1/OPS-. . . nav.
M: 2 Fuji 6L 27.5X diesels; 2 CP props; 3,000 bhp
Crew: 32 tot. ship's company + 70 troops

Remarks: Both in 1979–80 Budget; request for a third in 1981 Budget denied. Have bow doors and ramp, open cargo deck.

◆ **1 (+1) 420-ton utility landing craft (LCU)** Bldr: Sasebo Dockyard

	Laid down	L	In serv.
2001 LC 01	11-5-87	1-10-87	17-3-88
2002 LC 02	15-5-91	1-10-91	3-92

D: 420 tons **S:** 12 kts **Dim:** 52.0 × 8.7 × 1.6
A: 1/20-mm JM-61-MB gatling AA
Electron Equipt: Radar: 1/OPS-. . . nav.
M: 2 Mitsubishi 6SU-MTK diesels; 2 props; 3,000 bhp **Crew:** 28 tot.

Remarks: First unit approved under FY 86 Budget and ordered 24-3-87. Two more projected under FY 86–90 Budgets, with the second approved under the 1990 Budget; the third is no longer planned. Have bluff bow/ramp, open cargo deck.

AMPHIBIOUS WARFARE SHIPS *(continued)*

LC 01 (LCU 2001) *Ships of the World,* 6-88

♦ **15 U.S.-design LCM(6)-class landing craft**

LCM(6) based aboard Motobu (LST 4102) *Ships of the World,* 1991

D: 24 tons (56 fl) **S:** 10 kts **Dim:** 17.07 × 4.37 × 1.17 (aft)
M: 2 Yanmar diesels; 2 props; 450 bhp **Range:** 130/9
Crew: 3 tot. + 80 troops for short distances

Remarks: Total includes 6 units carried aboard the *Miura*-class LSTs. Built in Japan. Able to carry about 34 tons vehicles or cargo. Several others have been built as service craft with YF-series hull numbers.

♦ **22 U.S.-design LCVP-class landing craft**

LCVP based aboard Nemuro (LST 4103) *Ships of the World,* 1991

D: 13 tons (fl) **S:** 8 kts **Dim:** 10.90 × 3.21 × 1.04 (aft)
M: 1 Yanmar diesel; 1 prop; 180 bhp **Crew:** 3 tot.

Remarks: Japanese-built, most with GRP hulls. Total includes the 12–15 carried by the 6 LSTs.

AUXILIARIES

ICEBREAKER (AGB)

♦ **1 Shirase class (AGB)**

	Bldr	Laid down	L	In serv.
5002 Shirase	Nippon Kokan, Tsurumi	5-3-81	11-12-81	12-12-83

D: 11,660 tons (18,900 fl) **S:** 19 kts **Dim:** 134.0 × 28.0 × 9.2
Electron Equipt:
Radar: OPS-22 nav., OPS-18 surf. search—TACAN: U.S. URN-25
M: 6 M.A.N.-Mitsui 12V42M diesels, electric drive; 3 props; 30,000 shp
Crew: 37 officers, 137 enlisted, + 60 passengers **Range:** 25,000/15

Remarks: Built under 1979–80 Budget to replace *Fuji* (AGB 5001). Cargo capacity: 1,000 tons. Hangar and flight deck for 2 S-61A and 1 OH-6J helicopters. Has a large radome-covered weather radar atop the hangar. Is also equipped to conduct oceanographic research.

Shirase (AGB 5002) Leo Van Ginderen, 3-91

Shirase (AGB 5002) Leo Van Ginderen, 3-9

OCEAN SURVEILLANCE SHIPS

♦ **1 (+1+3) ocean surveillance ships (AOS)**

	Bldr	Laid down	L	In serv.
5201 Hibiki	Mitsui, Tamano	28-11-89	27-7-90	30-1-91
5202 Harima	Mitsui, Tamano	26-12-90	11-9-91	3-92
5203	. . . . . .	. . .	. . .	. . .
5204	. . . . . .	. . .	. . .	. . .
5205	. . . . . .	. . .	. . .	. . .

D: 3,715 tons **S:** 11 **Dim:** 71.50 (67.00 pp) × 29.90 × 7.50
Electron Equipt:
Radar: 1/OPS-18 nav., 1/OPS-19 nav.
Sonar: NQQ-2 SURTASS
M: diesel-electric: 4 Mitsubishi S6U MPTK 1,200-bhp diesels, 4 800-kw alternators, 2 motors; 2 props; 3,200 shp
Range: 3,800/10 **Fuel:** 640 tons **Crew:** 40 tot.

Remarks: Japanese equivalent to the U.S. T-AGOS 19 class, employing U.S.-supp towed linear surveillance passive hydrophone array and WSC-6 satellite data r Have SWATH (Small Waterplane, Twin Hull) configuration. First unit approved u 1989 Budget, second under 1990. A total of five are planned. AOS 5201 will be fully operational around 3-92 at the completion of installation of the SURTASS satellite communications gear in the U.S. and trials and check-out. The towed li passive acoustic array employs a 2,600-m-long array with an 1,800-m-long to cable. Crew includes five U.S. technicians.

Hibiki (AOS 5201) *Ships of the World,*

OCEAN SURVEILLANCE SHIPS *(continued)*

Hibiki (AOS 5201)—showing opening for towed array and catamaran hull form *Ships of the World,* 11-90

HYDROGRAPHIC SURVEY SHIPS

◆ **2 Futami class (AGS)**

	Bldr	Laid down	L	In serv.
102 Futami	Mitsubishi, Shimonoseki	20-1-78	9-8-78	27-2-79
104 Wakasa	Hitachi, Maizuru	21-8-84	25-5-85	25-2-86

Futami (AGS 5102) *Ships of the World,* 1988

Wakasa (AGS 5104)—tall stack *Ships of the World,* 1986

D: 2,050 tons (3,175 fl) **S:** 16 kts
Dim: 96.80 (90.00 pp) × 15.00 × 4.50
A: none **Electron Equipt:** Radar: 1/OPS-18 nav.
M: AGS 5102: 2 Kawasaki-M.A.N. V8V 22/30 ATL diesels; 2 CP props; 4,400 bhp; AGS 5104: 2 Fuji 6LS 27-5XF diesels; 2 CP props; 4,580 bhp
Fuel: 556 tons **Electric:** 1,800 kw **Crew:** 105 tot.

Remarks: Configured for both hydrographic surveying and cable-laying. Bow-thruster. Have three diesel and one gas-turbine generator sets. Carry one RCV-225 remote-controlled unmanned submersible. AGS 5104, ordered 29-3-84 under FY 1983 Budget, has a taller stack and differs somewhat in equipage.

◆ **1 Suma class (AGS)** Bldr: Hitachi Heavy Industries, Maizuru

	Laid down	L	In serv.
5103 Suma	24-9-80	1-9-81	30-3-82

Suma (AGS 5103) *Ships of the World,* 1986

D: 1,180 tons **S:** 15 kts **Dim:** 72.0 × 12.8 × 3.4
A: none **Electron Equipt:** Radar: 1/OPS-. . . nav.
M: 2 Fuji 6 LS 27.5X diesels; 2 CP props; 3,000 bhp
Crew: 65 tot.

Remarks: Built under 1979–80 Budget to begin replacement of the *Kusado*-class former minesweepers used as coastal survey ships. Carries one 7.9-m boat and one 11-m inshore survey launch. Passive tank stabilization, bow-thruster fitted. Operated by the "Ocean Management Group."

◆ **1 Akashi class (AGS)**

	Bldr	Laid down	L	In serv.
5101 Akashi	Nippon Kokan, Tsurumi	21-9-68	30-5-69	25-10-69

Akashi (AGS 5101) *Ships of the World,* 1988

D: 1,420 tons **S:** 16 kts **Dim:** 74.0 × 12.9 × 4.3
A: none
Electron Equipt: Radar: OPS-9—EW: NOLR-5 intercept
M: 2 Kawasaki-M.A.N. V8V 22/30 ATL diesels; 2 CP props; 3,800 bhp
Range: 16,500/14 **Crew:** 70 crew, 10 scientists

Remarks: Bow-thruster. Two cranes: one 5-ton and one 1-ton. Has extensive electronics intercept arrays.

EXPERIMENTAL SHIPS

◆ **0 (+1) experimental trials ship (ASE)** Bldr: . . . . . .

	Bldr	Laid down	L	In serv.
. . . .	. . . . . .	. . .	. . .	. . .

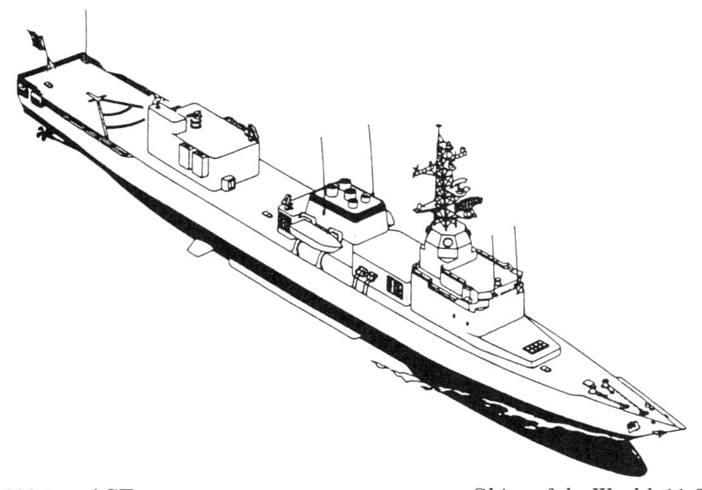

4,200-ton ASE *Ships of the World,* 11-91

EXPERIMENTAL SHIPS *(continued)*

D: 4,200 tons (. . . fl) **S:** 27 kts **Dim:** . . . × . . . × . . .
A: 1/8-cell vertical-launch group (. . . missiles)—1/SH-60J-sized helicopter
Electron Equipt:
Radar: 1/OPS-19 nav., 1/OPS-14B air search, 1/FCS-3 SAM f.c.
Sonar: flank-mounted active/passive array, towed array
EW: . . . intercept
M: COGOG: 2 . . . . . . cruise turbines, 2 . . . . . boost turbines; 2 CP props; . . . shp
Range: . . ./. . .
Crew: 70 ship's company + 100 technicians

Remarks: Approved under the Fiscal Year 1992 Budget to conduct trials with surface warfare systems including the FCS-3 radar weapons control system, which will employ four planar arrays to cover 360 degrees simultaneously. The hull-mounted sonar array will occupy a long sonar dome extending beneath the ship's keel as far aft as the tower mainmast. Will have fin stabilizers and a helicopter haul-down and traversing system. Destroyer-type hull and propulsion plant. The vertical-launch missile cell group will be located forward of the superstructure.

♦ 1 Kurihama-class underwater weapons trials ship (AGE)

	Bldr	Laid down	L	In serv.
6101 Kurihama	Sasebo Heavy Industries	23-3-79	20-9-79	8-4-80

Kurihama (AGE 6101) *Ships of the World,* 1988

D: 959 tons (approx. 1,400 fl) **S:** 15 kts **Dim:** 68.0 × 11.6 × 3.3
A: various **Electron Equipt:** Radar: 1/OPS-9B nav.
M: 2 Fuji 6S 30B diesels; 2 CP props; 2,600 bhp (plus 2 electric auxiliary propulsors; 400 shp)
Crew: 42 ship's company + 13 technicians

Remarks: For testing mines, torpedoes, and sonars. In 1979 Budget. Has Flume-type passive stabilization tanks and gas-turbine generators in superstructure. Retractable bow-thruster. Can be rigged for silent operation. Has extra accommodations for trials personnel. Operated for the Technical Research and Development Institute.

CABLE-LAYER

Note: Funds for a new 5,000-ton standard displacement cable layer are to be requested during the FY 1991–95 period. No details yet available. The former cable-layer *Tsugaru* (ARC 481) was redesignated ASU 7001 in 1979 and was stricken on 15-3-90.

♦ 1 Muroto class (ARC)

	Bldr	Laid down	L	In serv.
482 Muroto	Mitsubishi, Shimonoseki	28-11-78	25-7-79	27-3-80

Muroto (ARC 482) *Ships of the World,* 1988

D: 4,544 tons **S:** 17 kts **Dim:** 131.0 × 17.4 × 5.7
A: none **Electron Equipt:** Radar: 1/OPS-9 nav.
M: 2 Mitsubishi MTU V8V 22/30 diesels; 2 CP props; 4,400 bhp
Crew: 122 tot.

Remarks: Built to replace *Tsugaru* as naval cable layer. Able to lay cable over bow or stern at 2–6 knots. Bow-thruster-equipped. Similar to commercial *Kuroshio Maru.* Also has extensive facilities for oceanographic research.

SUBMARINE RESCUE SHIPS

♦ 1 Chiyoda class (ASR)

	Bldr	Laid down	L	In serv.
405 Chiyoda	Mitsui, Tamano	19-1-83	7-12-83	27-3-85

Chiyoda (ASR 405) Wilhelm Donko, 11-8

D: 3,690 tons (4,450 fl) **S:** 17 kts (16 sust.)
Dim: 112.5 (106.0 pp) × 17.6 (18.0 max.) × 4.8
A: none **Electron Equipt:** Radar: 1/OPS-16 surf. search.
M: 2 Mitsui 8LV42M diesels; 2 CP props; 11,500 bhp—bow and stern-thrusters
Crew: 120 tot.

Remarks: In 1981 Budget as a replacement for *Chihaya* (ASR 401, later ASU 701 and stricken 24-3-89. Carries a deep-submergence rescue vehicle (DSRV) launch 15-10-84 by Kawasaki, Kobe:

D: 40 tons **S:** 4 kts **Dim:** 12.4 × 3.2 × 4.3 (high)
M: electric motors; 40 hp **Crew:** 12 passengers

The DSRV is deployed over the sides, using hoist equipment similar to that of the U Navy's *Pigeon* (ASR 21) class. There is also a deep-diving rescue bell. The helicop platform can accommodate an HSS-2 Sea King. A diver from ASR 405 reached 320 m 11-8-87. Is attached to Submarine Flotilla 2 at Yokosuka.

♦ 1 Fushimi class (ASR)

	Bldr	Laid down	L	In serv.
402 Fushimi	Sumitomo, Uraga	5-11-68	10-9-69	10-2-70

Fushimi (ASR 402) *Ships of the World,*

D: 1,430 tons (approx. 2,000 fl) **S:** 16 kts
Dim: 76.0 × 12.5 × 3.8
Electron Equipt: Radar: OPS-9 nav.—Sonar: SQS-11A
M: 1 Kawasaki-M.A.N. V6V 22/30 ATL diesel; 1 prop; 3,000 bhp
Crew: 102 tot.

Remarks: Has one rescue bell, two decompression chambers, one 12-ton crane ployed as support ship for the First Submarine Flotilla at Kure.

REPLENISHMENT OILERS

♦ 3 Towada class (AOE)

	Bldr	Laid down	L	In serv.
422 Towada	Hitachi, Maizuru	17-4-85	25-3-86	24-3-87
423 Tokiwa	Ishikawajima-Harima, Tokyo	12-5-88	23-3-89	12-3-90
424 Hamana	Mitsui, Tamano	8-7-88	18-5-89	29-3-90

D: 8,300 tons (15,850 fl) **S:** 22 kts
Dim: 167.00 (160.00 pp) × 22.0 × 8.40 (15.90 moulded depth)
A: none
Electron Equipt: Radar: 1/OPS-18-1 surface search
M: 2 Mitsui 16V42M-A diesels; 2 props; 26,400 bhp
Electric: 3,200 kw (4 × 800-kw diesel sets)
Range: 10,500/20
Fuel: 1,659 tons **Crew:** 140 tot.

REPLENISHMENT OILERS *(continued)*

Hamana (AOE 424) JMSDF, 10-90

Towada (AOE 422) Wilhelm Donko, 11-89

emarks: AOE 422 authorized under FY 84 Budget, to replace *Hamana* (AO 411). OE 423 and 424 authorized under FY 87 Budget. Cargo: 5,700 tons total. Are all-urpose liquid, solid stores, and ammunition ships, with two liquid and one solid ansfer stations per side. Helicopter deck aft for vertical replenishment. No provision r armament. AOE 423 supported the JMSDF mine countermeasures squadron in the ersian Gulf, 4-91 through 10-91.

1 Sagami class (AOE)

	Bldr	Laid down	L	In serv.
21 SAGAMI	Hitachi, Maizuru	28-9-77	4-9-78	30-3-79

gami (AOE 421) Wilhelm Donko, 11-89

D: 5,000 tons (11,600 fl) **S:** 22 kts
Dim: 146.0 (140.0 pp) × 19.0 × 7.3
A: none **Electron Equipt:** Radar: 1/OPS-16 surf. search
M: 2 Type 12 DRV diesels; 2 props; 18,600 bhp
Range: 9,500/20 **Crew:** 130 tot.

narks: Has three stations per side, two for liquid transfers, one for solid. Large copter deck but no hangar. In addition to fuel oil, diesel fuel, and JP-5 aviation fuel, ies food and ammunition. 1975 Budget.

AINING SHIPS (TV)

) (+1) new-construction cadet training ship (TV)

	Bldr	Laid down	L	In serv.
2	. . . . . .	. . .	. . .	. . .

-ton cadet training ship *Ships of the World,* 1991

D: 4,000 tons **S:** . . . kts **Dim:** . . . × . . . × . . .
A: 1/76-mm OTO Melara Compact DP—6/324-mm Type 68 ASW TT (III × 2)—4/saluting cannon
Electron Equipt:
Radar: 1/OPS-19 nav., 1/OPS-. . . surf. search, 1/FCS-2-22 f.c.
Sonar: . . . . . .—EW: probable NORL-6 intercept
M: . . . . . . gas turbines; 2 CP props; . . . shp
Range: . . ./. . . **Crew:** 370 (including cadets)

Remarks: Originally authorized under FY 1991 as a replacement for *Katori* to complete around 1995. Construction deferred as part-payment for Japan's contribution to the Middle East conflict. Approved under FY 1992. Will have accommodations for both male and female cadets, all to be berthed in 2-person staterooms. Large open deck aft, as in *Katori,* intended primarily as a ceremonial, assembly, and exercise area but should be able to accept helicopters. Will have modest wartime capability as a command ship and escort.

♦ 1 Katori-class cadet-training ship (TV)

	Bldr	Laid down	L	In serv.
3501 KATORI	Ishikawajima Harima, Tokyo	8-12-67	19-11-68	10-9-69

Katori (TV 3501) James W. Goss/NAVPIC, 8-91

D: 3,372 tons (4,100 fl) **S:** 25 kts
Dim: 127.5 (122.0 pp) × 15.0 × 4.35
A: 4/76.2-mm U.S. Mk 33 DP (II × 2)—1/375-mm Bofors Type 71 ASW RL (IV × 1)—6/324-mm Type 68 ASW TT (III × 2)
Electron Equipt:
Radar: 1/OPS-15 surf. search, 1/OPS-2 (U.S. SPS-12) air search, 1/Mk 34 f.c.
Sonar: OQS-3 hull-mounted MF—EW: NOLR-1B intercept
M: 2 sets Ishikawajima geared steam turbines; 2 props; 20,000 shp
Boilers: 2 **Range:** 7,000/18
Crew: 295 ship's company + 165 cadets

Remarks: U.S. Mk 63 GFCS system for 76.2-mm guns. After superstructure contains an auditorium. Helicopter deck is also used for ceremonial functions and calisthenics. An Intelsat satellite communication sytem was added in mid-1979. To be replaced by new unit described above circa 1995.

♦ 2 Yamagumo-class former escort destroyers (TV)

	Bldr	Laid down	L	In serv.
3506 YAMAGUMO (ex-DDK 113)	Mitsui, Tamano	23-3-64	27-2-65	29-1-66
3507 MAKIGUMO (ex-DDK 114)	Uraga DY, Yokosuka	10-6-64	26-7-65	19-3-66

Yamagumo (TV 3506)—with old number *Ships of the World,* 1991

D: 2,100 tons (2,700 fl) **S:** 27 kts
Dim: 114.9 × 11.8 × 4.0 (hull)
A: 4/76.2-mm 50-cal. Mk 33 DP (II × 2)—1/375-mm Bofors Type 71 ASW RL (IV × 1)—6/324-mm Type 68 ASW TT (III × 2)
Electron Equipt:
Radar: 1/OPS-17 surf. search, 1/OPS-11 air search, 1/ U.S. Mk 35 gun f.c., 1/ U.S. Mk 34 gun f.c.

TRAINING SHIPS *(continued)*

Sonar: U.S. SQS-23 hull-mounted MF; U.S. SQS-35(J) VDS
EW: NOLR-1B intercept
M: 6 Mitsubishi 12UEV 30/40N (Ex-DDK 113; Mitsui) diesels; 2 props; 26,500 bhp
Range: 7,000/20 **Crew:** 210–220 tot.

Remarks: Version of the *Minegumo* class completed with ASROC instead of DASH. Have U.S. Mk 56 gun director forward (Mk 35 radar) and Mk 63 GFCS aft (Mk 34 radar on after gun mount). Were backfitted with the VDS system, requiring the stern to be raised. Were reclassified as training ships during 6-91. Variable-depth sonar removed, ASROC ASW RL replaced by 36-person lecture hall and charthouse. Accommodations for 2 officer and 12 enlisted females added. Are in training squadron 1 at Kure.

Note: *Isuzu*-class former frigate *Mogami* (TV 3505, ex-DE 212) stricken 31-7-91. *Akizuki*-class former destroyer *Teruzuki* (ex-ASU 7012, ex-DD 162) was redesignated ASU in 1991. There are a large number of smaller craft used for training at the Naval Academy at Etajima, where the former destroyer *Harukaze* (DD 101) is moored as a training hulk. The *Uzushio*-class submarine *Isoshio* (SS 568) was redesignated ATSS 8001 on 24-3-89 to serve as a training ship; she was joined by *Narushio* (ATSS 8002, ex-SS 569) on 8-6-90 and *Kuroshio* (ATSS 8003, ex-SS 570) on 20-3-91; see description on submarine pages.

TARGET SERVICE SHIPS (ATS)

◆ 1 Kurobe-class target service ship (ATS)

	Bldr	Laid down	L	In serv.
4202 Kurobe	Nippon Kokan, Tsurumi	31-7-87	23-5-88	23-3-89

Kurobe (ATS 4202) JMSDF, 3-89

D: 2,270 tons (approx. 3,200 fl) **S:** 20 kts **Dim:** 101.0 × 16.5 × 4.0
A: 1/76-mm OTO Melara Compact DP
Electron Equipt:
Radar: 1/OPS-16 surf. search, 1/OPS-14B air search, 1/ TMCATS (*see* Remarks), 1/FCS-2-21A
M: 4 Fuji 8L 27.5SX diesels; 2 props; 9,160 bhp
Range: . . ./. . . **Crew:** 17 officers, 126 enlisted

Remarks: Approved under FY 1986 Budget as a supplement to *Azuma* (ATS 4201). Carries, launches, controls, recovers, and services U.S. Ryan BQM-34J Firebee high-speed and Northrop MQM-74C Chukar supersonic target drones. Also used for air-controlling U-36A manned target-tow aircraft. Has the TMCATS (Target Multi-Control and Tracking System) phased-array radar, with four planar arrays mounted on the faces of the tower mast; the system tracks targets and weapons and records the track data for analysis, employing TELES (Telemetry Measuring System). Large open deck and hangar aft are primarily for drone operations, but helicopters can be accommodated.

◆ 1 Azuma-class target service ship (ATS)

	Bldr	Laid down	L	In serv.
4201 Azuma	Hitachi, Maizuru	15-7-68	14-4-69	26-11-69

D: 1,950 tons (2,400 fl) **S:** 18 kts **Dim:** 98.0 (94.0 pp) × 13.0 × 3.8
A: 1/76.2-mm U.S. Mk 34 DP
Electron Equipt:
Radar: 1/OPS-15 surf. search, 1/U.S. SPS-40 air search, 1/TCATS (*see* Remarks)
Sonar: SQS-11A hull-mounted HF (possibly removed)
M: 2 Kawasaki-M.A.N. V8V 23/30 ATL diesels; 2 props; 4,000 bhp
Electric: 700 kw **Crew:** 185 tot.

Azuma (ATS 4201) *Ships of the World,* 1988

Remarks: Designed to carry, launch, control, recover, and service ten KD2R-5 and four BQM-34-AJ drones. Portable catapult on helicopter deck for launching. Hangar is used for drone check-out and storage. Has the only SPS-40 radar in Japanese service. TCATS (Target Control and Tracking System) radar in large radome atop bridge replaced earlier radar, 1983. Mk 51 Mod. 2 lead-computing director for gun (no radar). Two U.S. Mk 4 flip-launchers for obsolescent U.S. Mk 32 ASW torpedoes have been removed. Was originally to have been replaced by the more-sophisticated *Kurobe* (ATS 4202) but has been retained.

SPECIAL USE AUXILIARIES (ASU)

◆ 5 ASU 81-class target-support craft (ASU) Bldr: ASU 81–83: Sasebo Heavy Industries; Others: . . .

	Laid down	L	In serv.
ASU 81 (ex-YAS 101)	10-10-67	18-1-68	30-3-68
ASU 82 (ex-YAS 102)	25-9-68	20-12-68	31-3-69
ASU 83 (ex-YAS 103)	2-4-71	24-5-71	30-9-71
ASU 84 (ex-YAS 104)	4-2-72	15-6-73	19-9-73
ASU 85 (ex-YAS 105)	20-2-73	16-7-73	19-9-73

ASU 83 *Ships of the World,* 1[illegible]

D: 490 tons (543 fl) **S:** 14.5 kts **Dim:** 51.5 × 10.0 × 2.6
Electron Equipt:
Radar: OPS-10 (ASU 84: OPS-29; ASU 85: OPS-19) nav.
M: 2 Akasaka UH-527-42 diesels; 2 props; 1,600 bhp
Range: 2,500/12
Crew: 26 ship's company + 14 technicians

Remarks: ASU 82 is configured as a rescue ship. The others are intended to ca[rry,] control, recover, and service up to six KD2R-5 drone target aircraft. ASU 81: 480 t[ons] std.; ASU 85: 500 tons std. Crane and mast configurations aft differ; early units h[ave] pole and derrick, later ones have a crane, with a tripod mast stepped on the stack.

◆ 2 Takatsuki-class former destroyers (ASU) Bldr: Ishikawajima Harima Heavy Industries, Tokyo

	Laid down	L	In serv.
7018 Mochizuki (ex-DD 166)	25-11-66	15-3-69	25-3-69
7019 Nagatsuki (ex-DD 167)	2-3-68	19-3-69	12-2-70

Mochizuki (ASU 7018)—prior to reclassification
Ships of the World

D: 3,200 tons (4,500 fl) **S:** 32 kts
Dim: 136.0 (131.0 pp) × 13.4 × 4.4 (mean)
A: 2/127-mm Mk 42 DP (I × 2)—1/Mk 112 ASROC ASW RL (VIII × 1)— 1/375-mm Bofors Type 71 ASW RL (IV × 1)—6/324-mm T[ype] 68 ASW TT (III × 2)
Electron Equipt:
Radar: 1/OPS-17 surf. search, 1/OPS-11B-Y air search, 1/Mk 35 (ASU 7019: 2/GFCS-1) f.c.
Sonar: OQS-3 hull-mounted LF—TACAN: ASU 7019 only: OR[N]
EW: NOLR-6C (167: NOLR-9C) intercept, OLT-3 jammer, Mk 3[6] SRBOC decoy RL (VI × 2, not in 167)
M: 2 sets Mitsubishi geared steam turbines; 2 props; 60,000 shp
Boilers: 2 Mitsubishi-Combustion Eng.; 43 kg/cm², 454° C
Fuel: 900 tons **Range:** 7,000/20 **Crew:** 270 tot.

Remarks: Reclassified as auxiliaries late 1991. Former DASH drone ASW he[licopter] hangar retained, but is too small to accommodate any of the JMSDF's manned [helicop]ters. DD 167 formerly served as a naval cadet training ship in support of *Ka[tori]* (TV 3501). Used as district patrol units and on range safety and other miscellaneou[s duties] as administrative escorts to the two submarine flotillas.

SPECIAL USE AUXILIARIES *(continued)*

◆ **3 Isuzu-class former frigates (ASU)**

	Bldr	Laid down	L	In serv.
7015 ISUZU (ex-DE 211)	Mitsui, Tamano	16-4-60	17-1-61	29-7-61
7016 KITAKAMI (ex-DE 213)	Ishikawajima, Tokyo	7-6-62	21-6-63	27-2-64
7017 OHI (ex-DE 214)	Maizuru, Heavy Ind.	10-6-62	15-6-63	22-1-64

uzu (ASU 7015) *Ships of the World*, 1-90

D: 1,490 tons (1,790 fl) **S:** 25 kts **Dim:** 94.0 × 10.4 × 3.5 (hull)
A: 4/76.2-mm 50-cal. Mk 33 DP (II × 2)—1/375-mm Bofors Type 71 ASW RL (IV × 1)—6/324-mm Type 68 ASW TT (III × 2)
Electron Equipt:
Radar: 1/OPS-16 surf. search, 1/OPS-1 air search, 2/Mk 34 f.c.
Sonar: OQS-12 hull-mounted MF—EW: NOLR-1 intercept
M: *see* Remarks; 2 props; 16,000 bhp **Crew:** 180 tot.

marks: ASU 7015 redesignated from DE 211 on 8-4-88; quadruple 533-mm TT and th-charge rack deleted. ASU 7016 and ASU 7017 reclassified on 31-1-90. Each has a erent diesel propulsion plant: ASU 7015: 4 Mitsui 35VBU 45V diesels; ASU 7016: 4 subishi diesels; and ASU 7017: 4 Mitsui 28 VBU 38 diesels. Have two U.S. Mk 63 CS (Mk 34 radar on gun mounts) for the guns. Sister *Mogami* (ex-DE 212) redesig- ed a training ship, TV 3505, on 7-1-87 and stricken 31-7-91.

2 Akizuki-class former destroyers (ASU) Bldr: Mitsubishi, Nagasaki

	Laid down	L	In serv.
0 AKIZUKI (ex-DD 161)	31-7-58	26-6-59	13-2-60
2 TERUZUKI (ex-TV 3504, x-ASU 7012, ex-DD 162)	15-8-58	24-6-59	29-2-60

ızuki (ASU 7012)—after reclassification *Ships of the World*, 6-91

. 2,300 tons (3,100 fl) **S:** 32 kts
m: 118.0 (115.0 pp) × 12.0 × 4.02
2/127-mm 54-cal. DP Mk 39 (I × 2)—4/76.2-mm 50-cal. DP Mk 33 (II × 2)—1/375-mm Bofors ASW RL (IV × 1)—6/324-mm Type 68 ASW TT (III × 2)
ectron Equipt:
Radar: 1/OPS-15 surf. search, 1/OPS-1 air search, 3/Mk 34 f.c.
Sonar: U.S. SQS-23 hull-mounted LF—EW: NOLR-1 intercept
2 sets Mitsubishi-Escher-Wyss geared steam turbines; 2 props; 45,000 shp
ilers: 4/43 kg/cm², 454° C **Crew:** 170 tot.

rks: Weapons and ASW sensors modernized in 1976–77, the Bofors ASW RL ing a U.S. Mk 108 "Weapon Alfa" ASW rocket launcher, VDS being added, and 3 replacing SQS-29. The 127-mm guns were removed from U.S. *Midway*-class rs. Two U.S. Mk 57 and one Mk 63 gunfire-control systems are carried. *Akizuki* as Fleet Flagship until 27-3-85 when reclassified as an auxiliary (ASU); le-depth sonar and 4/533-mm TT (IV × 1) removed; aft 127-mm mount removed nd replaced with cable reel and winch for towed sonar array trials. *Teruzuki* sified as an ASU on 20-6-91, having served as training ship TV 3504 since 1-7-87; s reclassified from DD 162 on 27-3-86. Both will probably be stricken soon.

Former destroyers *Onami* (ASU 7013, ex-DD 111) and *Makinami* (ASU 7014, 112) both stricken 23-3-90; former cable-layer *Tsugaru* (ASU 7001, ex-ARC 481) n 15-3-90 and subsequently prepared for explosive resistance trials.

YACHT (ASY)

◆ **1 former Mizutori-class submarine chaser (ASY)**

	Bldr	Laid down	L	In serv.
92 HIYODORI (ex-PC 320)	Sasebo Dockyard	26-2-65	26-9-65	28-2-66

Hiyodori (ASY 92) Wilhelm Donko, 1-89

D: 420 tons (450 fl) **S:** 20 kts **Dim:** 60.00 × 7.10 × 2.35
Electron Equipt: Radar: 1/OPS-. . . nav.
M: 2 Kawasaki-M.A.N. V8V diesels; 2 props; 3,800 bhp
Range: 3,000/12 **Crew:** 35 ship's company + 90 passengers

Remarks: Retired as a patrol unit on 19-3-86 and converted by Yokohama Yacht as a replacement for the similar *Hayabusa* (ASY 91). Recommissioned as ASY 92 27-4-87 with stern broadened at main-deck level, a large deckhouse added, and an awning-covered ceremonial area atop it abaft the stack, which was raised.

SERVICE SHIPS AND CRAFT

Note: All Japanese Navy service ships and craft are listed below in the alphabetical order of the two- or three-letter designator system employed to define their functions. Self-propelled units have 2-digit hull numbers following the letter designator (as in "YO 01"). Non-self-propelled craft with the same functions have 3-digit numbers starting with "1" (as in "YO 102"). Self-propelled units that have returned to an original type designation *after* an initial type change receive 3-digit numbers beginning with "2" (as in "YG 202," ex-YO 20, ex-YG 08).

MINE TRIALS AND SERVICE CRAFT (YAL)

◆ **1 YAL 01 class** (In serv. 22-3-76)

YAL 01

D: 240 tons (265 fl) **S:** 12 kts **Dim:** 37.00 × 8.00 × 1.90
A: mine rails **M:** 2 Type 64 H 19-E-4A diesels; 2 props; 800 bhp
Crew: 16 tot.

◆ **1 former U.S. LCU 1466-class landing craft** (L: 5-1-55)

YAL 03

YAL 03 *Ships of the World*, 1988

D: 180 tons (347 fl) **S:** 9 kts **Dim:** 35.08 × 10.36 × 1.60 (aft)
A: 2/20-mm AA (I × 2)—mines
Electron Equipt: Radar: 1/. . . nav.
M: 3 Gray Marine 64YTL diesels; 3 props; 675 bhp
Range: 1,200/6 **Fuel:** 11 tons **Crew:** . . .

Remarks: The survivor of the six-unit LCU 2001 class (ex-U.S. LCU 1602–1607), built in Japan under the Offshore Procurement Program and reconfigured to serve as exercise mine planters. YAL 02 was stricken 24-3-89 and YAL 04 on 31-3-88.

SPECIAL SERVICE CRAFT (YAS)

◆ **11 (+2) Takami-class former minesweeper/minehunters**

	Bldr	L	In serv.
YAS 82 TAKAMI (ex-MSC 630)	Nippon Kokan, Tsurumi	15-7-69	15-12-69
YAS 83 IOU (ex-MSC 631)	Hitachi, Kanagawa	12-8-69	22-1-70

SPECIAL SERVICE CRAFT *(continued)*

	Bldr	L	In serv.
YAS 84 Miyake (ex-MSC 632)	Nippon Kokan, Tsurumi	3-6-70	19-11-70
YAS 85 Awaji (ex-MSC 634)	Nippon Kokan, Tsurumi	11-12-70	29-3-71
YAS 86 Toushi (ex-MSC 635)	Hitachi, Kanagawa	13-12-70	18-3-71
YAS 87 Teuri (ex-MSC 636)	Nippon Kokan, Tsurumi	10-71	10-3-72
YAS 88 Murotsu (ex-MSC 637)	Hitachi, Kanagawa	10-71	3-3-72
YAS 89 Tashiro (ex-MSC 638)	Nippon Kokan, Tsurumi	2-4-73	30-7-73
YAS 90 Miyato (ex-MSC 639)	Hitachi, Kanegawa	3-4-73	24-8-73
YAS 91 Takane (ex-MSC 640)	Nippon Kokan, Tsurumi	8-3-74	28-8-74
YAS 92 Muzuki (ex-MSC 641)	Hitachi, Kanegawa	5-4-74	28-8-74

Miyake (YAS 84) Wilhelm Donko, 11-89

D: 380 tons (510 fl) **S:** 14 kts **Dim:** 52.0 × 8.8 × 2.4 (mean)
A: 1/20-mm AA
Electron Equipt:
Radar: OPS-9 nav.
Sonar: ZQS-2 hull-mounted HF
M: 2 Mitsubishi YV122C-15/20 diesels; 2 CP props; 1,440 bhp
Electric: 1500-kw d.c./360-kw a.c. **Range:** . . . **Crew:** . . .

Remarks: Reclassified and now used as mine-disposal divers' tenders. Wooden construction. Reclassified YAS 82 and YAS 83 on 27-3-86; YAS 84 on 16-12-86; YAS 85 and YAS 86 on 24-3-87; YAS 87 and YAS 88 on 23-3-88; YAS 89 and YAS 90 on 29-11-90; and YAS 91 and YAS 92 on 28-11-90. Seven sisters remain as minesweeper/hunters, and one, *Utone* (MST 475, ex-MSC 633) acts as inshore minesweeper tender. Sisters *Yukose* (MSC 642) and *Sakate* (MSC 643) redesignated as YAS 93 and YAS 94 in 3-92.

Note: The last four former *Kasado*-class coastal minesweepers in the YAS-classification were stricken as follows: *Urume* (YAS 78, ex-MSC 626) on 17-11-89; *Minase* (YAS 79, ex-MSC 627) on 15-6-90; *Ibuki* (YAS 80, ex-MSC 628) on 29-11-89; and *Katsura* (YAS 81, ex-MSC 629) on 14-5-90.

OIL SLUDGE REMOVAL CRAFT (YB)

◆ **1 YB 01-class lighter** (L: 31-3-75)

YB 01

YB 01 *Ships of the World,* 1988

D: 177 tons **S:** 9 kts **Dim:** 27.5 × 5.2 × 1.9
M: 1 diesel; 230 bhp **Cargo:** 100 tons

◆ **4 YB 101-class barges** (In serv. 1975–76)

YB 101–104

D: 100 dwt **Dim:** 17.0 × 5.2 × 2.0 **M:** non-self-propelled

SELF-PROPELLED FLOATING CRANES (YC)

◆ **1 YC 09 class** (In serv. 25-2-74)

YC 09

YC 09 *Ships of the World,* 4-8

D: 260 tons **S:** 6 kts **Dim:** 26.0 × 14.0 × 0.9
M: 2 diesels; 2 props; 280 bhp

◆ **3 YC 06 class** (In serv. 1969–72)

YC 06 (In serv. 31-3-69) YC 07 (In serv. 28-2-70)
YC 08 (In serv. 29-3-72)

D: 150 tons **S:** 5 kts **Dim:** 24.0 × 10.0 × 0.8
M: 2 diesels; 2 props; 240 bhp

◆ **1 YC 05 class** (In serv. 27-3-67)

YC 05

YC 05—pontoon hull, crawler crane *Ships of the World,*

D: 110 tons **S:** 5 kts **Dim:** 22.0 × 10.0 × 0.9
M: 2 diesels; 180 bhp

DOCKYARD SERVICE CRAFT (YD)

YD 01, 02 (In serv. 25-3-75): 0.8 tons, 7.60 × 1.90 m, GRP constru outboard motor
YD 03 (In serv. 1978): 1.7 tons, 7.60 × 1.90 m
YD 04 (In serv. 25-12-79): 0.5 tons

Note: The fireboat/rescue craft *Shobo* 1 (YE 01) was stricken 23-3-90.

COMMUNICATIONS BOATS (YF)

Note: One 25-ton and one 5-ton YF were requested under the Fiscal Year Budget; no data available.

◆ **1 (+ . . .) YF 2126-class GRP personnel launch** Bldr. . .

YF 2126 (In serv. 28-3-91)

D: 12 tons **S:** 10 kts **Dim:** 15.0 × 4.2 × 1.6
M: 2 Type UM 6BD1 diesels; 2 props; 460 bhp
Crew: 3 tot. + 40 passengers

COMMUNICATIONS BOATS *(continued)*

YF 2126—personnel launch *Ships of the World,* 3-91

◆ **3 (+3+ . . .) YF 2121-class landing craft** Bldr: Ishihara Dockyard

	In serv.		In serv.
⁷F 2121	1989	YF 2127	. . .
⁷F 2124	26-2-90	YF 2128	. . .
⁷F 2125	20-3-90	YF 2129	. . .

D: 33 tons (56 fl) **S:** 10 kts **Dim:** 17.00 × 4.30 × 0.70
M: 2 Isuzu E120-MF6R diesels; 2 props; 480 bhp
Crew: 4 tot.

.emarks: YF 2127 through 2129 in the FY 1991 Budget. Replacements for the YF ᴐ97 series; see below. Design again based on the U.S. LCM(6) landing craft. Employed ᵴ local transports for stores and personnel.

2 YF 2123-class personnel launches

F 2123 (In serv. 30-1-87) YF 2130 (In serv. 1991)

D: 14.3 tons **S:** 10 kts **Dim:** 15.0 × 4.2 × 1.6
M: 2 Type UM 6-BDI diesels; 2 props; 480 bhp

emarks: YF 2130 in FY 1991 Budget.

3 YF 1029-class personnel launches Bldr: Ishihara Dockyard

F 1029 YF 1030 (Both in serv. 1982) YF 1031 (In serv. 25-3-88)

D: 11 tons (13.5 fl) **S:** 18 kts **Dim:** 13.5 (12.3 pp) × 3.8 × 0.7
M: 2 Isuzu 6BDITC-MRD diesels; 2 props; 360 bhp

7 YF 1022-class personnel launches (In serv. 1980)

ᶠ 1022 through YF 1028

D: 9 tons (11 fl) **S:** 14 kts **Dim:** 13.00 × 3.80 × 0.60
M: 2 Type E 120 T-MF6RE diesels; 2 props; 280 bhp
Cargo: 73 passengers

43 miscellaneous service launches (YF)

	Tons (light)	Dim	S (kts)	bhp
' 2097, 2098	11	17.0 × 4.2 × 0.8	10	450
' 2066–2074, 2078–2081, :083–2087, 2091, 2110, 2116	8	10.5 × 3.2 × 0.6	9	180
2075	22	17.0 × 3.7 × 0.7	10	400
2076, 2077	0.8	7.0 × 2.2 × 0.3	8	22
2082	5	11.0 × 3.2 × 0.6	9	90
2088–2090, 2092, 2095, 111–2115, 2117–2119, 2122	5.9	11.0 × 3.2 × 0.6	10	135
2120	12.6	15.0 × 3.6 × 0.7	10	230
2124 (In serv. 28-2-90)	11	. . .	. . .	. . .

2124—U.S. LCM(6)-type *Ships of the World,* 2-90

arks: YF 2097 series and YF 2075 are essentially U.S. LCM(6) landing craft ted as utility craft. YF 2066 series are of the U.S. LCVP design. Smaller units are ›oden or glass-reinforced plastic construction. YF 2124 authorized under FY 87. 131, another LCVP-type landing craft, was authorized under FY 1991.
icken since the last edition have been: YF 2097 series: YF 2100 on 5-2-90, YF 2103 -3-90, and YF 2104 on 29-1-90; YF 2060 series: YF 2060 on 28-3-91 and YF 2062 -12-90; and YF 2066 series: YF 2096 on 13-12-89.

JET ENGINE FUEL CRAFT (YG)

◆ **6 YG 07-class lighters** Bldr: Ishikawajima-Harima, Tokyo

	In serv.		In serv.
YG 201 (ex-YG 07)	30-3-73	YG 204	2-7-89
YG 202 (ex-YO 20, ex-YG 08)	29-3-77	YG 205	16-7-90
YG 203	20-9-88	YG 206	1991

YG 204 *Ships of the World,* 7-89

D: 270 dwt **S:** 9 kts **Dim:** 36.0 × 6.80 × 2.80 **Crew:** 5 tot.
M: 1 Shinko Zaki Ogaki S617-S1CM diesel; 1 prop; 360 bhp

Remarks: YG 08 reclassified YO 20 in 1979, then again reclassified YG 202 in 1981. YG 09 authorized under FY 87. YG 203 and 204 are 37.7 m o.a. YG 205 ordered 13-12-89 under FY 1990 Budget and launched 21-5-90; YG 206 ordered under FY 1991 Budget.

CARGO CRAFT (YL)

◆ **3 (+1) YL 09-class lighters** Bldr: Ishihara DY

	Laid down	L	In serv.
YL 09	24-11-79	3-3-80	28-3-80
YL 10	. . .	17-12-82	28-2-83
YL 11	21-12-87	14-3-88	25-3-88
YL 12	. . .	. . .	. . .

YL 09 *Ships of the World,* 1988

D: 120.5 tons (fl) **S:** 9–10 kts **Dim:** 27.00 × 7.00 × 1.04
M: 2 Isuzu E 120 T-MF6 RE diesels; 2 props; 560 bhp **Crew:** 5 tot.

Remarks: 50 dwt. Resemble a U.S. LCM(8) and have a bow ramp, two 2-ton stores cranes. YL 12 approved under FY 1992 Budget.

◆ **1 (+1) YL 08-class lighter**

YL 08 (In serv. 10-3-67) YL 12 (In serv. . . .)

YL 08 *Ships of the World,* 1988

CARGO CRAFT *(continued)*

D: 50 dwt **S:** 8 kts **Dim:** 22.40 × 5.10 × 1.20
M: 1 diesel; 1 prop; 180 bhp

Remarks: The second craft of this class was requested under the Fiscal Year 1992 Budget.

♦ **4 YL 02-class lighters**

YL 03 (In serv. 31-5-54) YL 06 (In serv. 30-11-54)
YL 04 (In serv. 31-5-54) YL 07 (In serv. 30-11-54)

D: 50 dwt **S:** 8 kts **Dim:** 20.00 × 5.10 × 1.20
M: 1 diesel; 1 prop; 100 bhp

♦ **1 YL 119-class barge (non-self-propelled)**

YL 119 (In serv. 20-3-71)

D: 200 dwt **Dim:** 34.00 × 13.00 × 1.00

♦ **3 YL 116-class barges (non-self-propelled)**

YL 116 (In serv. 21-12-63) YL 117 (In serv. 25-2-64)
YL 118 (In serv. 31-3-66)

D: 100 dwt **Dim:** 21.50 × 8.40 × 1.00

♦ **2 YL 114-class barges (non-self-propelled)**

YL 114 (In serv. 20-2-63) YL 115 (In serv. 12-3-63)

D: 80 dwt **Dim:** 18.40 × 7.40 × 0.90

FUEL LIGHTERS (YO)

Note: YO is now applied to all fuel carriers except jet-fuel carriers, which are typed YG.

♦ **7 (+ 4) YO 21 class lighters**

	Bldr	Laid down	L	In serv.
YO 21	Yoshiura SB	. . .	15-3-80	31-3-80
YO 22	Yoshiura SB	11-11-80	26-2-81	28-2-81
YO 23	Yoshiura SB	26-11-82	12-3-83	31-3-83
YO 24	Yoshiura SB	4-11-83	20-1-84	29-2-84
YO 25	Naikai, Innoshima	14-11-88	15-7-88	20-9-88
YO 26	Sagami, Yakosuka	18-4-88	28-7-88	26-9-88
YO 27	Sumidigawa	. . .	2-6-89	18-7-89
YO 29	Sumidigawa	7-91	9-92	11-92
YO 30	Sumidigawa	9-91	11-92	1-93
YO 31	Sumidigawa	11-91	1-93	3-93
YO 32	. . . . . .	. . .	. . .	. . .

YO 27 *Ships of the World,* 7-89

D: 490 tons (694 fl) **S:** 9–10 kts **Dim:** 45.5 × 7.8 × 2.9
M: 2 Yanmar 6 MA diesels; 2 props; 460 bhp

Remarks: YO 25 and 26, with 520 m^3 cargo capacity, authorized under 1987 Budget; YO 27, under 1988, was ordered 6-12-88 and may be larger, with 630 m^3 cargo. One additional requested under 1989 Budget and rejected, but three (YO 29–31) were authorized under FY 1991, and YO 32 was requested under Fiscal Year 1992.

♦ **2 YO 19-class lighters**

YO 19 (ex-YG 06) (In serv. 20-6-63) YO 28 (In serv. 27-7-90)

YO 28 *Ships of the World,* 5-90

D: 270 dwt **S:** 9 kts **Dim:** 34.4 × 6.8 × 2.8
M: 2 diesels; 2 props; 330 bhp

Remarks: YO 19, reclassified under FY 1980, had formerly been typed as a diesel-fuel lighter. Of two additional requested under 1989 Budget, only YO 28 was approved; design probably differs somewhat from the older YO 19.

♦ **1 YO 15-class former diesel fuel lighter** (In serv. 10-1-55)

YO 18 (ex-YG 04)

D: 100 dwt **S:** 8 kts **Dim:** 23.0 × 5.0 × 2.0
M: 1 diesel; 1 prop; 90 bhp

Remarks: Reclassified 1980. Sisters YO 17 (ex-YG 03) stricken 30-3-84, YO 15 (ex-YG 01) on 22-1-88, and YO 16 (ex-YG 02) on 23-3-90.

♦ **1 YO 14-class lighter** (In serv. 31-3-76)

YO 14

D: 490 dwt **S:** 9 kts **Dim:** 45.0 × 7.8 × 2.9
M: 2 diesels; 2 props; 460 bhp

Remarks: Very similar to YO 21; officially considered same class.

♦ **4 YO 10-class lighters**

YO 10 (In serv. 31-3-65) YO 12 (In serv. 21-3-67)
YO 11 (In serv. 14-3-66) YO 13 (In serv. 31-3-67)

D: 290 dwt **S:** 9 kts **Dim:** 36.5 × 6.8 × 2.6
M: 2 diesels; 2 props; 360 bhp

♦ **3 YO 07-class lighters**

YO 07 (In serv. 28-2-63) YO 08 (In serv. 29-2-64)
YO 09 (In serv. 15-3-65)

D: 490 dwt **S:** 9 kts **Dim:** 43.9 × 7.8 × 3.1
M: 2 diesels; 2 props; 400 bhp

♦ **2 YO 03-class lighters**

YO 03 (In serv. 15-4-55) YO 05 (In serv. 15-3-56)

D: 300 dwt **S:** 7 kts **Dim:** 33.0 × 7.0 × 2.6
M: 2 diesels; 150 bhp

Remarks: Sisters YO 03 and YO 04 stricken 24-3-89 and 31-3-88, respectively.

♦ **1 YO 106-class barge** (non-self-propelled)

YO 106 (In serv. 20-5-53)

D: 250 dwt **Dim:** 23.00 × 7.00 × 2.50

Note: Non-self-propelled fuel barge YO 108 stricken 28-3-91.

DEBRIS CLEARANCE CRAFT (YS)

♦ **1 catamaran "sweeper boat"**

YS 01 (In serv. 30-3-79)

YS 01 *Ships of the World,*

D: 80 tons **S:** 9 kts **Dim:** 22.0 × 7.80 × 1.40
M: 2 diesels; 2 props; 460 bhp **Crew:** 6 tot.

Remarks: Stationed at Iwakuni Air Station seaplane base; used to clear fl[illegible] debris in seaplane landing lanes and as a marker-buoy tender.

TUGS (YT)

♦ **13 YT 58-class large harbor tugs** Bldr: Yokohama Yacht

	L	In serv.		L	In serv.
YT 58	. . .	31-10-78	YT 69	15-6-87	16-9-87
YT 63	. . .	27-9-82	YT 70	14-6-88	2-9-88
YT 64	. . .	30-9-83	YT 71	19-5-89	28-7-89
YT 65	. . .	20-9-84	YT 72	25-4-90	27-7-90
YT 66	. . .	20-9-85	YT 73	13-5-91	31-7-91
YT 67	7-6-86	4-9-86	YT 74	7-91	30-9-91
YT 68	9-6-87	9-9-87			

TUGS *(continued)*

T 73 *Ships of the World*, 7-91

D: 262 tons **S:** 11 kts **Dim:** 28.40 × 8.60 × 2.50
Electron Equipt: Radar: 1/. . . nav. **Crew:** . . .
M: 2 Niigata 6L25BX diesels; 2 pivoting Kort-nozzle props; 1,800 bhp

emarks: Have two firefighting water cannon. YT 71 ordered 13-12-88. YT 70 was .ted at 1,600 bhp. YT 72 authorized in 1989 Budget. YT 73 and YT 74, authorized ıder FY 1991 Budget, were both laid down 14-2-91.

4 YT 53-class large harbor tugs

T 53 (In serv. 1974) YT 56 (In serv. 13-7-76)
Γ 55 (In serv. 22-8-75) YT 57 (In serv. 22-8-77)

55 Leo Van Ginderen, 1986

: 195 tons (200 fl) **S:** 11 kts **Dim:** 25.70 × 7.00 × 2.30
: 2 Kubota M6D20BUCS diesels; 1 prop; 1,500 bhp
'rew: 10 tot.

8 YT 35-class harbor tugs

	In serv.		In serv.		In serv.
35	28-2-63	YT 41	31-3-66	YT 46	29-3-67
37	31-3-65	YT 44	29-3-67	YT 48	31-3-68
40	31-3-66	YT 45	30-3-67		

: 100 tons **S:** 10 kts **Dim:** 23.80 × 5.40 × 1.80
: 2 diesels; 2 props; 400 bhp

) Leo Van Ginderen, 1-86

◆ **1 (+2) YT 75-class harbor pusher tugs** Bldr: . . .

YT 75 (In serv. 1991)

D: . . . tons **S:** . . . kts **Dim:** . . . × . . . × . . .
M: . . .

Remarks: First unit authorized under FY 1991 Budget; two more requested under Fiscal Year 1992.

◆ **3 YT 60-class harbor pusher tugs** Bldr: Yokohama Yacht

YT 60 (In serv. 31-3-80) YT 61 (In serv. 26-3-80)
YT 62 (In serv. 16-3-81)

YT 61 *Ships of the World*, 1980

D: 30 tons (37 fl) **S:** 8.6 kts
Dim: 15.50 × 4.20 × 1.50 (0.97 hull)
M: 2 Isuzu E 120-MF64A diesels; 2 cycloidal props; 380 bhp

◆ **11 YT 34-class harbor pusher tugs**

	In serv.		In serv.		In serv.
YT 34	20-3-63	YT 42	31-3-65	YT 51	28-2-72
YT 36	14-3-64	YT 43	29-3-66	YT 54	24-3-75
YT 38	31-3-65	YT 47	20-1-67	YT 59	16-1-79
YT 39	31-3-65	YT 49	5-3-68		

YT 34 Leo Van Ginderen, 10-86

D: 28 tons (30 fl) **S:** 9 kts **Dim:** 14.50 × 4.00 × 1.00
M: 2 diesels; 2 props; 320 bhp **Crew:** 3 tot.

Remarks: Sisters YT 27 and YT 33 stricken 1979, and YT 32 during 1981. YT 59 displaces 30 tons std.

Note: YT 25-class pusher tug YT 29 stricken 23-3-90.

TRAINING TENDERS (YTE)

◆ **1 minesweeper construction experimental craft** Bldr: Hitachi, Kanagawa

	Laid down	L	In serv.
YTE 12 Tokiwa	1980	12-1-82	12-1-83

Tokiwa (YTE 12) *Ships of the World*, 1988

TRAINING TENDERS *(continued)*

D: 110 tons light, 142 std. (180 fl) **S:** 14 kts **Dim:** 35.0 × 7.5 × 1.5
M: 2 diesels; 2 props; 1,100 bhp **Crew:** 18 tot.

Remarks: Built to test glass-reinforced plastic construction techniques for building future mine countermeasures ships and for testing shock resistance and sound transmission properties. Lines based on former inshore minesweeper *Atada;* flush deck, no minesweeping gear as completed. Now employed on training duties.

◆ **1 navigational training tender** Bldr: Ando Iron Works

YTE 11 (In serv. 31-3-73)

YTE 11 *Ships of the World,* 1979

D: 120 tons (170 fl) **S:** 13 kts **Dim:** 33.0 × 7.0 × 1.5
M: 2 Shinko-Zoki SG175/CM diesels; 2 props; 1,400 bhp

Remarks: Based at Etajima Naval Academy to teach officer cadets ship handling and navigation. Can carry 25 cadets.

SEAPLANE BUOY TENDERS (YV)

◆ **3 YV 01 class**

YV 01 (In serv. 30-3-68) YV 02 (In serv. 28-3-69)
YV 03 (In serv. 20-3-70)

YV 02 *Ships of the World, 1988*

D: 45 tons **S:** 10 kts **Dim:** 20.0 × 4.40 × 1.00
M: 2 diesels; 2 props; 240 bhp

Remarks: Maintain seaplane fairway marker buoys. YV 02 and YV 03 have a single hydraulic crane; YV 01 has two smaller davits.

WATER LIGHTERS (YW)

◆ **5 YW 12 class**

YW 12 (In serv. 14-3-64) YW 15 (In serv. 20-3-67)
YW 13 (In serv. 28-3-66) YW 16 (In serv. 20-3-67)
YW 14 (In serv. 30-3-66)

YW 14 *Ships of the World,* 1988

D: 160 dwt **S:** 8 kts **Dim:** 30.5 × 5.7 × 2.2
M: 1 diesel; 180 bhp

◆ **3 (+ 1) YW 11 class**

	Bldr	L	In serv.
YW 11	. . .	. . .	25-6-64
YW 17	Skikoku DY	19-7-88	27-9-88
YW 18	Maehata SY	9-5-89	28-7-89
YW 19	. . .	. . .	. . .

YW 18 *Ships of the World, 7-8*

D: 310 dwt **S:** 10 kts **Dim:** 36.7 × 6.8 × 2.8
M: 2 diesels; 2 props; 360 bhp

Remarks: YW 17 authorized under FY 87 as replacement for YW 02; YW 18 order 2-12-88 under 1988 Budget; YW 19 authorized under FY 1991 Budget.

◆ **1 YW 10 class**

YW 10 (In serv. 20-3-63)

D: 100 dwt **S:** 8 kts **Dim:** 23.5 × 5.1 × 1.0
M: 1 diesel; 160 bhp

◆ **2 YW 03 class**

YW 08 (In serv. 20-12-54) YW 09 (In serv. 20-12-54)

D: 150 dwt **S:** 8 kts **Dim:** 27.0 × 5.5 × 2.1
M: 1 diesel; 75 bhp

Remarks: Sisters YW 03 and YW 04 stricken 31-3-88, YW 05 and YW 06 on 24-3- and YW 07 on 28-3-91.

◆ **1 YW 02 class**

YW 02 (In serv. 20-5-53)

D: 150 dwt **S:** 9 kts **Dim:** 27.0 × 5.5 × 2.1
M: 1 diesel; 90 bhp

MOTOR BOATS (B)

◆ **12 miscellaneous:**

B 4006: 8 tons—13.00 × 3.20 × 0.50—14 kts (In serv. 16-3-76)
B 4007–4013: 1 ton—5.00 × 2.10 × 0.40—22 kts (All in serv. 26-1-76)
B 4014–4016: 8 tons—13.00 × 3.20 × 0.50—14 kts (In serv. 1978–80)
B 4017: 16 tons—17.4 × 3.9 × 1.5—10 kts (In serv. 28-3-85)

B 4015 *Ships of the World,*

Remarks: Glass-reinforced plastic hulled. B 4016 capable of 18 kts. B 4006 bas the same as B 4014–4016. B 4017 has a glass-reinforced plastic hull with pilot offset to port; 180 bhp.

ROWING CRAFT AND SAILBOATS

◆ **55 "C" group rowing boats**

C 5110–5161 series

D: 1.5 tons **Dim:** 9.0 × 2.5 × . . .

Remarks: C 5094–5097 stricken 21-12-87; C 5908–5101 on 10-2-89; and C 5106 stricken 15-2-91. New C 5158–5165 delivered 10-2-89.

ROWING CRAFT AND SAILBOATS *(continued)*

♦ 39 "T" group rowing punts

T 6063–6102

D: 0.5 tons **Dim:** 6.0 × 1.6 × . . .

Remarks: T 6058–6062 stricken 1985, but T 6098–6102 added 26-2-85.

♦ 13 "Y" group sailboats

Y 7010–7022 (Y 7021 and 7022 delivered 26-2-85)

Note: The "C," "T," and "Y"-series craft are all stationed at the Etajima Naval Academy or at other training facilities.

MARITIME SAFETY AGENCY
(Kaijo Hoancho)

Personnel (1991): 12,123 total (2,600 officers)

The Maritime Safety Agency, which was organized in 1948, underwent a massive xpansion in the 1970s, which by 1982 made it one of the world's largest and best-quipped coast guards. In peacetime, it is directed by the Department of Transporta-ion. Although most of its ships are armed, they are not considered part of the navy; hey fly only the national colors (a red disk on a white background), not the flag flown by aval ships. A stylized blue stripe has been added to the hull sides of larger units. In artime, the ships would be under naval control.

The Maritime Safety Agency is organized into 11 districts, 65 offices, 25 detach-ments, 52 stations, 14 air stations, 11 district communications centers, and a traffic dvisory service; there are also 4 hydrographic observatories and 132 aids-to-avigation offices.

Aviation: In 1991, the MSA operated 25 fixed-wing aircraft (2 Falcon 900 jet trans-orts, 5 YS-11A transports, and 2 SC-7 Skyvan 3 and 16 Beech 200T Super King Air ght transports) and 39 helicopters (36 Kawasaki-Bell 212 and 3 Bell 206B Jet-anger).

IGH-ENDURANCE HELICOPTER-CARRYING CUTTERS (PLH)

0 (+1) Shikishima class Bldr: Ishikawajima-Harima, Tokyo

	Laid down	L	In serv.
LH 31 Shikishima	4-28-90	27-6-91	4-92

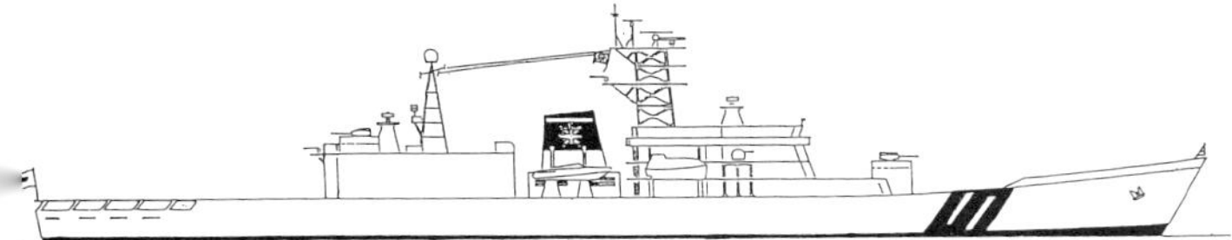

ikishima (PLH 31) MSA, 1990

kishima (PLH 31)—at launch *Ships of the World,* 6-91

: 6,500 tons **S:** 25 kts **Dim:** 150.0 × 17.0 × . . .
: 2/35-mm Oerlikon AA (I × 2)—2/20-mm JM-61-MB gatling AA—2/Kawasaki-Bell 212 helicopters
lectron Equipt: Radar: . . .
: . . . . . . diesels; 2 props; . . . bhp
ange: 20,000/. . . **Crew:** 80 tot.

arks: Intended to act as escort for a ship to carry plutonium from Europe to Japan se in nuclear electric-power generation stations.

Mizuho class

	Bldr	Laid down	L	In serv.
21 Mizuho	Mitsubishi, Shimonoseki	27-8-84	5-6-85	19-3-86
22 Yashima	Nippon Kokan, Tsurumi	3-8-87	20-1-88	1-12-88

4,960 tons (5,204 fl) **S:** 23.3 kts
m: 130.00 (123.00 wl) × 15.50 × 5.25
1/35-mm Oerlikon AA—1/20-mm JM-61-MB gatling AA— 2/Kawasaki-Bell 212 helicopters

Mizuho (PLH 21)—with MARISAT and SHF SATCOMM antena radomes atop helicopter hangar *Ships of the World,* 1991

Mizuho (PLH 21) *Ships of the World,* 1990

Electron Equipt: Radar: 3 navigational sets
M: 2 IHI SEMT-Pielstick 14 PC 2.5V 400 (PLH 22: 12 PC 2V) diesels; 2 CP props; 18,200 bhp—bow-thruster
Range: . . ./. . . **Electric:** 1,875 kVA (3 diesel sets)
Crew: 130 tot.

Remarks: Design is a reduced version of a 5,900-std.-ton patrol and rescue ship. Are the first MSA class to carry two helicopters. Have a flight deck traversing system and two pairs of fin stabilizers. Have MARISAT SATCOMM; an SHF SATCOMM system was added to PLH 21 in 1989. Second unit approved under 1985 Budget. A third was requested under the 1988 Budget but was not approved.

♦ 7 Tsugaru class

	Bldr	Laid down	L	In serv.
PLH 02 Tsugaru	Ishikawajima-Harima, Tokyo	18-4-78	6-12-78	17-4-79
PLH 03 Oosumi	Mitsui, Tamano	1-9-78	1-6-79	18-10-79
PLH 04 Uraga	Hitachi, Maizuru	14-3-79	12-10-79	5-3-80
PLH 05 Zao	Mitsubishi, Nagasaki	23-10-80	29-10-81	19-3-82
PLH 06 Chikuzen	Kawasaki, Kobe	20-4-82	18-3-83	28-9-83
PLH 07 Settsu	Sumitomo, Uraga	5-4-83	21-4-84	27-9-84
PLH 08 Echigo	Mitsui, Tamano	29-3-88	4-7-89	28-2-90

Echigo (PLH 08) *Ships of the World,* 1990

Uraga (PLH 04) *Ships of the World,* 1990

D: 3,730 tons (4,037 fl) **S:** 21.5 kts
Dim: 105.40 (100.00 wl) × 14.60 × 4.85
A: 1/40-mm AA—1/20-mm AA (not in PL 03, 04)—PL 04, 05, 06: 1/35-mm Oerlikon AA—all: 1/Kawasaki-Bell 212 helicopter

HIGH-ENDURANCE HELICOPTER-CARRYING CUTTERS
(continued)

Electron Equipt: Radar: 3/ nav.
M: 2 Pielstick 12PC2-5V400 diesels; 2 CP props; 15,600 bhp (13,260 bhp sust.)
Electric: 1,450 kVA **Range:** 5,700/18 **Fuel:** 864 tons
Crew: 21 officers, 7 warrant officers, 28 enlisted, 15 spare

Remarks: Have bow-thruster, two pair fin stabilizers, normal ship bow for operations in ice-free waters. Also have flume-type passive stabilization tanks in superstructure. Engines manufactured by different builders. PLH 03, 04 built under 1978 program, PLH 05 under 1979 program, PLH 06 under 1981 program, and PLH 07 under the 1983 program. Redesignated from PL on 12-2-86, 4-9-85, 22-11-85, 8-3-86, 17-7-85, and 18-10-85, respectively. PLH 02 has a MARISAT SATCOMM installation. PLH 08 was authorized under the 1987 Budget. Have two 520-kw diesel generator sets and one 120-kw emergency set.

♦ 1 Soya class

	Bldr	Laid down	L	In serv.
PLH 01 Soya	Nippon Kokan, Tsurumi	12-9-77	3-7-78	22-11-78

Soya (PLH 01) *Ships of the World,* 1988

D: 3,562 tons (4,089 fl) **S:** 21 kts
Dim: 98.6 × 15.6 × 5.2
A: 1/40-mm AA—1/20-mm AA—1/Kawasaki-Bell 212 helicopter
Electron Equipt: Radar: 4/. . . nav. (1 aft for helo control)
M: 2 Nippon Kokan-Pielstick 12PC2-5V400 diesels; 2 CP props; 16,000 bhp (13,260 hp sust.)
Electric: 1,450 kVA **Range:** 5,700/18
Fuel: 650 tons **Crew:** 71 tot.

Remarks: Built under the 1977 program, has an icebreaking bow, and operates in the north. Passive tank stabilization only, no bow-thruster. Rounded stern, vice squared on *Tsugaru* class. Redesignated PLH from PL on 13-12-85.

HIGH-ENDURANCE CUTTERS (PL)

♦ 0 (+2) 2,950-ton class

	Bldr	Laid down	L	In serv.
PLH	Ishikawajima-Harima, Tokyo	. . .	. . .	. . .
PLH		. . .	. . .	. . .

D: 2,950 tons **S:** 18 kts
Dim: 115.00 × 14.00 × 5.00 (7.30 moulded depth)
A: 1/35-mm Oerlikon AA—1/20-mm JM-61-MB gatling AA—1/12.7-mm mg
Electron Equipt: Radar: . . .
M: 2 . . . . . . diesels; 2 CP props; 8,000 bhp
Range: 7,000/15 **Crew:** 118 tot.

Remarks: First unit authorized under the FY 1991 Budget and ordered 3-90; second authorized under FY 1991 Budget.

♦ 1 (+1) Ojika class

	Bldr	Laid down	L	In serv.
PL 12 Ojika	Mitsui, Tamano	28-9-90	23-4-91	30-10-91
PL		. . .	. . .	. . .

Ojika (PL 02) at launch—note stern ramp, twin stacks *Ships of the World,* 10-91

D: 1,200 tons (. . . fl) **S:** 20 kts
Dim: 91.4 × 11.0 × . . .
A: 1/20-mm JM-61-MB gatling AA—1/Kawasaki-Bell 212 helicopter
Electron Equipt: Radar: . . .
M: 2 Fuji S540B diesels; 2 CP props; 7,000 bhp—2 bow-thrusters
Range: . . ./. . . **Crew:** . . . tot.

Remarks: PL 12 ordered 11-89; second unit in FY 1991 Budget. Have computerized rescue data system, special display room, helicopter hangar, and fin stabilization. There is a stern-dock for an "unsinkable" rescue craft. Have 30-ton bollard pull towing capacity.

♦ 1 Nojima class

	Bldr	Laid down	L	In serv.
PL 01 Nojima	Ishikawajima-Harima, Tokyo	16-8-88	30-5-89	21-9-89

Nojima (PL 01) *Ships of the World,* 9-8

D: 950 tons light (1,500 fl) **S:** 20 kts (19 sust.)
Dim: 85.00 × 10.50 × 3.50
A: 1/20-mm JM-61-MB gatling AA—helicopter platform
Electron Equipt:
Radar: 2/. . . nav.—Sonar: side-looking wreck-location HF
M: 2 Fuji S8540B diesels; 2 CP props; 7,000 bhp
Electric: 450 kVA tot. (3 × 150 kVA) **Range:** . . ./. . .
Crew: . . .

Remarks: 850 grt. First of a new series intended to replace PL 11–16. Authori under 1986 Budget. Sharp sheer to bow to improve seakeeping while keep amidships freeboard low. Unusual raised helicopter deck over fantail. Fin stabiliz fitted. No more planned, as the design has been supplanted by the larger *Ojima* cla

♦ 28 Shiretoko class

	Bldr	L	In serv.
PL 101 Shiretoko*	Mitsui, Tamano	13-7-78	8-11-78
PL 102 Esan	Sumitomo, Oshima	8-78	16-11-78
PL 103 Wakasa*	Kawasaki, Kobe	8-78	29-11-78
PL 104 Yahiko	Mitsubishi, Shimonoseki	8-78	16-11-78
PL 105 Motobu	Sasebo Dockyard	8-78	29-11-78
PL 106 Rishiri	Shikoku DY	27-3-79	12-9-79
PL 107 Matsushima*	Tohoku DY	11-4-79	14-9-79
PL 108 Iwaki*	Naikai, Innoshima	28-3-79	10-8-79
PL 109 Shikine	Usuki SY, Usuki	27-4-79	20-9-79
PL 110 Suruga*	Kurushima DY, Onishi	20-4-79	28-9-79
PL 111 Rebun*	Narasaki SY, Muroran	6-79	21-11-79
PL 112 Chokai*	Nipponkai Heavy Ind., Toyama	6-79	30-11-79
PL 113 Ashizuri*	Sanoyasu DY, Oshima	6-79	31-10-79
PL 114 Oki	Tsuneishi SY, Numakuma	6-79	16-11-79
PL 115 Noto	Miho SY, Shimuzu	7-79	30-11-79
PL 116 Yonakuni	Hiyashigane SY, Nagasaki	6-79	31-10-79
PL 117 Kudaka (ex-*Daisetsu*)*	Hakodate DY	22-8-79	31-1-80
PL 118 Shimokita	Ishikawajima, Tokyo	9-79	12-3-80
PL 119 Suzuka	Kanasashi SY, Toyohashi	4-10-79	7-3-80
PL 120 Kunasaki	Koyo DY, Mihara	8-10-79	29-2-80
PL 121 Genkai*	Oshima SY, Oshima	9-79	31-1-80
PL 122 Goto*	Onomichi SY, Onomichi	10-79	29-2-8(
PL 123 Koshiki	Kasado DY, Kasado	9-79	25-1-8(
PL 124 Hateruma*	Osaka DY	11-79	12-3-8(
PL 125 Katori	Tohoku DY, Shiogama	5-80	17-10-8(
PL 126 Kunigami	Kanda SY, Kawashiri	28-3-80	21-10-8(
PL 127 Etomo*	Naikai, Innoshima	30-9-81	17-3-8
PL 128 Mashiyu	Shikoku DY, Kochi, Takamatsu	14-10-81	12-3-8

HIGH-ENDURANCE CUTTERS *(continued)*

Iotobu (PL 105) *Ships of the World,* 10-90

akasa (PL 103) Leo Van Ginderen, 1989

D: 974 tons (1,350–1,360 fl) **S:** 20 kts
Dim: 77.8 (73.6 pp) × 9.6 × 3.42
A: 1/40-mm AA—1/20-mm AA—*see* Remarks
Electron Equipt: Radar: 1/JMA 1576 nav., 1/JMA 1596 nav.
M: 2 Niigata 8MA 40 or Fuji 8 S40B diesels; 2 CP props; 7,000 bhp
Electric: 625 kVA **Range:** 4,406/17 **Fuel:** 191 tons
Crew: 41 tot.

marks: Program helped small shipyards to stay in business. Intended to patrol the -nautical-mile economic zone. Starred units have Fuji 8S40B diesels. PL 106 and r have no 20-mm AA, while PL 118, 122, 124–128 have an Oerlikon 35-mm in place he 40-mm AA. Carry 153 tons water. Fuel capacities and endurances vary. Use sive tank stabilization, with tanks in superstructure. Range greater for some: PL : 5,200/17. PL 120 had a serious fire 15-2-82. Name of PL 117 changed 1-4-88.

2 Izu class

	Bldr	L	In serv.
31 Izu	Hitachi, Mukaishima	1-67	31-7-67
32 Miura	Maizuru DY	11-68	15-3-69

ra (PL 32) Leo Van Ginderen, 5-86

2,081 tons (2,200 fl) **S:** 24.6 kts
m: 95.5 (86.45 pp) × 11.6 × 3.8
1/40-mm 60-cal. Mk 3 AA
ectron Equipt: Radar: 2/. . . nav.
2 SEMT-Pielstick 12PC2V diesels; 2 CP props; 10,400 bhp
ectric: 800 kVA tot. **Range:** 5,000/20.5; 14,500/12.7
ew: 72 tot.

rks: Large weather radar in dome aft removed in 1978 and gun added forward. ve stabilization, with Flume-type tanks in superstructure. Based at Yokohama.

Daio class

	Bldr	L	In serv.
5 Daio	Hitachi, Maizuru	19-6-73	28-9-73
6 Muroto	Naikai, Taguma	5-8-74	30-11-74

Muroto (PL 16) *Ships of the World,* 1990

D: 1,206 tons **S:** 20.4 kts **Dim:** 76.6 (73.0 pp) × 9.6 × 3.18
A: 1/40-mm 60-cal. Mk 3 AA—1/20-mm Oerlikon AA
Electron Equipt: Radar: 1/JMA 1576 nav., 1/JMA 1596 nav.
M: 2 . . . diesels; 2 props; 7,000 bhp
Electric: 500 kVA **Range:** 6,600/18 **Crew:** 50 tot.

Remarks: Similar to *Erimo* class but slightly more beam and have more powerful engines. Based at Kushiro and Aburatsu, respectively.

◆ **2 Erimo class**

	Bldr	L	In serv.
PL 13 Erimo	Hitachi, Mukaishima	14-8-65	30-11-65
PL 14 Satsuma	Hitachi, Mukaishima	4-66	30-7-66

Satsuma (PL 14) *Ships of the World,* 1988

D: 980 tons (1,009 fl) **S:** 19.5 kts **Dim:** 76.6 (73.0 pp) × 9.2 × 3.0
A: 1/40-mm 60-cal. Mk 3 AA—1/20-mm AA
Electron Equipt: Radar: 1/JMA 1576 nav., 1/JMA 1596 nav.
M: 2 Burmeister & Wain 635V2 BU45 diesels; 2 props; 4,800 bhp
Electric: 320 kVA **Range:** 5,000/18 **Crew:** 72 tot.

Remarks: The hull of PL 13 is reinforced against ice. Based at Kamaishi and Kagoshima, respectively.

◆ **1 Kojima-class training cutter**

	Bldr	In serv.
PL 21 Kojima	Kure DY	21-5-64

Kojima (PL 21) *Ships of the World,* 1990

D: 1,066 tons (1,206 fl) **S:** 17.3 kts **Dim:** 69.6 × 10.3 × 3.53
A: 1/40-mm 60-cal. Mk 3 AA—1/20-mm Oerlikon AA—1/12.7-mm mg
Electron Equipt: Radar: 2/MM-5A nav., 1/. . . nav.
M: 1 Uraga-Sulzer 7MD51 diesel; 1 prop; 2,600 bhp
Electric: 550 kVA **Range:** 6,120/13
Crew: 17 officers, 42 crew, 47 cadets

Remarks: Used as a training ship at Kure Academy. 76.2-mm DP replaced by relocated 40-mm AA, and second 20-mm AA added between 1982 and 1985.

Note: The last *Nojima*-class cutter, *Ojika* (PL 12), was stricken 21-9-91.

MEDIUM-ENDURANCE CUTTERS (PM)

Note: One new ship in the PM-series was authorized under the FY 1991 Budget; no data available, except that it is to be of 230-tons standard displacement. The ship is to be named *Amami* and was laid down 22-10-91 by Hitachi at Kanagawa.

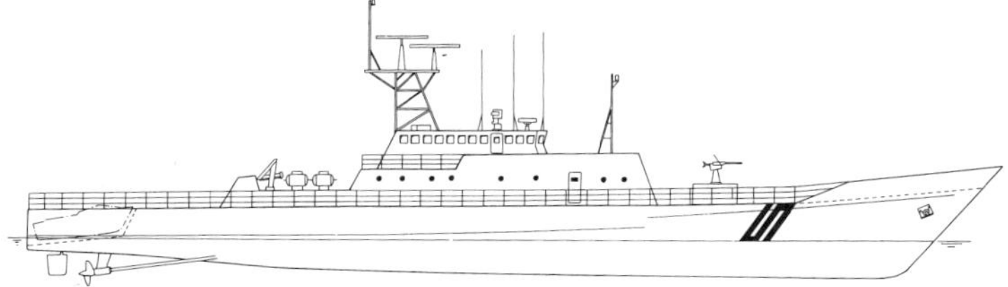

230-ton PM design MSA, 1991

♦ 14 Teshio (500-ton) class

	Bldr	L	In serv.
PM 01 Teshio	Shikoku DY, Kochi	30-5-80	30-9-80
PM 02 Oirase	Naikai, Taguma, Innoshima	15-5-80	29-8-80
PM 03 Echizen	Usuki Iron Wks., Usuki	2-6-80	30-9-80
PM 04 Tokachi	Narazaki, Muroran	21-11-80	24-3-81
PM 05 Hitachi	Tohoku SY, Shiogoma	15-11-80	19-3-81
PM 06 Okitsu	Usuki Iron Wks.	5-12-80	17-3-81
PM 07 Isazu	Naikai, Taguma, Innoshima	29-10-81	18-2-82
PM 08 Chitose	Shikoku DY, Kochi	7-7-81	17-11-82
PM 09 Kumano	Naikai, Taguma, Innoshima	8-81	10-3-83
PM 10 Sorachi	Tohoku SY, Shiogama	27-4-84	27-9-84
PM 11 Yubari	Usuki Iron Wks., Usuki	20-8-85	28-11-85
PM 12 Motoura	Shikoku DY, Takamatsu	7-8-86	21-11-86
PM 13 Kano	Naikai, Taguma, Innoshima	7-8-86	13-11-86
PM 14 Sendai	Shikoku DY, Takamatsu	21-1-88	1-6-88

Sendai (PM 14) *Ships of the World,* 1990

D: 630 tons (670–692 fl) **S:** 18 to 18.6 kts
Dim: 67.80 (63.00 pp) × 7.90 × 2.65
A: 1/20-mm JN-61B gatling AA
Electron Equipt: Radar: 2/JMA-159B nav.
M: 2 Fuji 6S 32F diesels; 2 props; 3,000 bhp **Electric:** 240 kVA tot.
Endurance: 15 days **Range:** 3,200/16 **Crew:** 33 tot.

Remarks: 540 grt. Three built under 1979–80 program, three under 1980–81 program, one under 1981, 1983, and 1984 programs. PM 12 and 13 approved in 1985 Budget and PM 14 in the 1986 Budget. Some have Arakata 6M31EX diesels. PM 07 also used for training and has a lengthened after deckhouse. PM 12 has Niigata 6M31 diesels, a range of 3,900 n.m. at 16 kts, and a full-load displacement of 692 tons.

♦ 2 Takatori (350-ton) class

	Bldr	L	In serv.
PM 89 Takatori	Naikai, Taguma, Innoshima	8-12-77	24-3-78
PM 94 Kumano	Naikai, Taguma, Innoshima	2-11-78	23-2-79

D: 634 tons normal **S:** 15.7 kts **Dim:** 45.70 (44.25 pp) × 9.20 × 3.88
A: none **Electron Equipt:** Radar: 2/. . . nav.
M: 2 Niigata 6M31EX diesels; 1 CP prop; 3,000 bhp
Electric: 200 kVA **Range:** 750/15 **Crew:** 34 tot.

Remarks: 469 grt. Rescue-tug types. Equipped for fire-fighting and salvage duties. Two water cannon (3,000 lit./min. each). Carry an 8-m rescue boat and a 4.6-m speedboat.

Kumano (PM 94) *Ships of the World,* 19

♦ 20 Bihoro (350-ton) class

	Bldr	In serv.
PM 73 Bihoro	Tojoku SY, Shiogama	28-2-74
PM 74 Kuma	Usuki Iron Wks., Usuki	28-2-74
PM 75 Fuji	Usuki Iron Wks., Usuki	7-2-75
PM 76 Kabashima	Usuki Iron Wks., Usuki	25-3-75
PM 77 Sado	Tohoku SY, Shiogama	1-2-75
PM 78 Ishikari	Tohoku SY, Shiogama	13-3-76
PM 79 Abakuma	Tohoku SY, Shiogama	30-1-76
PM 80 Isuzu	Nakai SY, Taguma	10-3-76
PM 81 Kikuchi	Usuki Iron Wks., Usuki	6-2-76
PM 82 Kuzuryu	Usuki Iron Wks., Usuki	18-3-76
PM 83 Horobetsu	Tohoku SY, Shiogama	21-1-77
PM 84 Shirakami	Tohoku SY, Shiogama	3-3-77
PM 85 Sagami	Naikai SY, Taguma	30-11-76
PM 86 Tone	Usuki Iron Wks., Usuki	30-11-76
PM 87 Yoshino	Usuki Iron Wks., Usuki	28-1-77
PM 88 Kurobe	Shikoku DY, Kochi	15-2-77
PM 90 Chikugo	Naikai, Taguma	27-1-78
PM 91 Yamakuni	Usuki Iron Wks., Usuki	26-1-78
PM 92 Katsura	Shikoku DY, Kochi	15-2-77
PM 93 Shinano	Tohoku SY, Shiogama	23-2-78

D: 636 tons (657 fl) **S:** 18 kts **Dim:** 63.35 × 7.80 × 2.53
A: 1/20-mm AA
Electron Equipt:
Radar: 2/JMA-159B or 1/JMA 1576 nav. , 1/JMA 1596 nav.
M: 2 Niigata 6M31EX diesels; 2 CP props; 3,000 bhp
Electric: 200 kVA **Range:** 3,260/16 **Crew:** 34 tot.

Chikugo (PM 90) *Ships of the World*

♦ 7 Kunashiri (350-ton) class

	Bldr	In serv.
PM 65 Kunashiri	Maizuru DY	28-3-69
PM 66 Minabe	Maizuru DY	28-3-70
PM 67 Sarobetsu	Maizuru DY	30-3-71
PM 68 Kamishima	Usuki Iron Wks., Usuki	31-1-72
PM 70 Miyake	Tohoku SY, Shiogama	25-1-73
PM 71 Awaji	Usuki Iron Wks., Usuki	25-1-73
PM 72 Yaeyama	Usuki Iron Wks., Usuki	20-12-72

D: 498 tons (574 fl) **S:** 17.5 kts **Dim:** 58.04 × 7.38 × 2.40
A: 1/20-mm AA **Electron Equipt:** Radar: 2/JMA 1576 or 159
M: 2 Niigata 6MF32H diesels; 2 props; 2,600 bhp
Electric: 120 kVA **Range:** 3,040/16 **Crew:** 40 tot.

Remarks: PM 70 to PM 72 have 6M31EX diesels, 3,000 hp. PM 72 has cont pitch propellers. PM 70–72 have the JMA 1596 radars.

MEDIUM-ENDURANCE CUTTERS *(continued)*

Miyake (PM 70) *Ships of the World,* 1990

♦ 3 Matsuura (350-ton) class
Bldr: Hitachi SY, Mukaishima

PM 62 Amami (In serv. 29-3-65)
PM 63 Natori (In serv. 20-1-66)
PM 64 Karatsu (In serv. 29-7-67)

‹aratsu (PM 64) *Ships of the World,* 1986

D: 425 tons **S:** 16.5 kts (PM 63: 16.8 kts; PM 64: 18 kts)
Dim: 55.33 × 7.00 × 2.30 **A:** 1/20-mm AA
Electron Equipt: Radar: 1/. . . nav.
M: 2 Ikegai 6MSB31S diesels; 2 props; 1,400 bhp (PM 63: 2 Type 6MSB31HS diesels; 1,800 bhp; PM 64: 2 Type 6MA31X diesels; 2,600 bhp)
Electric: 140 kVA **Range:** 3,500/12–13 **Crew:** 37–40 tot.

›marks: Sisters *Matsuura* (PM 60) stricken 1986, *Sendai* (PM 61) stricken 6-5-88.

›ATROL BOATS (PS)

4 Mihashi (180-ton) class

	Bldr	Laid down	L	In serv.
› 01 Mihashi	Mitsubishi, Shimonoseki	16-12-87	18-6-88	9-9-88
› 02 Saroma	Hitachi, Kanagawa	12-12-88	28-6-89	28-11-89
› 03 Inasa	Mitsubishi, Shimonoseki	18-5-89	20-10-89	31-1-90
› 04 Kirishima	Hitachi, Kanagawa	10-5-90	18-1-90	22-3-91

›sa (PS 03) *Ships of the World,* 1-90

›: 180 tons normal (195 fl) **S:** 35 kts **Dim:** 43.0 × 7.5 × 1.7
› 1/12.7-mm mg **Electron Equipt:** Radar: 1/Furuno . . . nav.
›: 2 Mitsubishi S12U-MTK diesels (3,200 bhp each), 1 Mitsubishi S8U-MTK diesel (2,500 bhp); 2 props, 1 waterjet
›nge: 650/34 **Crew:** 13 tot.

›arks: Expansion of the preceding *Shizuki* class, incorporating a centerline water-›opulsor. PS 01 in 1987 Budget, PS 02, 03 in 1988 Budget, PS 04 in 1989.

› The first unit of a new 130-ton class, PS 108, was laid down 20-8-91 by Mit-›ni at Shimonoseki.

Shizuki (130-ton) class
Bldr: Sumidigawa, Tokyo

	Laid down	L	In serv.
›6 Shizuki	26-10-87	21-12-87	24-3-88
›7 Takashio	28-10-87	23-12-87	24-3-88

Shizuki (PS 106) Sumidigawa, 3-88

D: 106 tons (130 fl) **S:** 27 kts **Dim:** 35.0 × 6.3 × 2.0
A: 1/12.7-mm mg **Electron Equipt:** Radar: 1/. . . nav.
M: 2 Ikegai-MTU 16V652 TB 81 diesels; 4,400 bhp
Electric: 120 kVA (2 × 60 kVA) **Crew:** 13 tot.

Remarks: Ordered 31-8-87 under 1987 Budget. Intended for inshore patrol and rescue duties. Have 4.0-m moulded depth aluminum-alloy hull of deep-Vee form.

♦ 5 Akagi (130-ton) class

	Bldr	Laid down	L	In serv.
PS 101 Akagi	Sumidigawa, Tokyo	31-7-79	5-12-79	26-3-80
PS 102 Tsukuba	Sumidigawa, Tokyo	7-7-81	29-10-81	24-2-82
PS 103 Kongo	Ishihara DY, Takasago	1-8-86	17-12-86	16-3-87
PS 104 Katsuragai	Yokohama Yacht	14-10-87	21-1-88	24-3-88
PS 105 Hiromine	Ishihara DY, Takasago	. . .	8-1-88	24-3-88

Hiromine (PS 105) MSA, 3-88

D: 105 tons light (134 fl) **S:** 26.5 kts
Dim: 35.0 (33.0 wl) × 6.3 × 1.3
A: 1/12.7-mm mg **Electron Equipt:** Radar: 1/. . . nav.
M: 2 Pielstick 16PA4 V-185 VG diesels; 2 props; 4,400 bhp
Electric: 40 kVA **Range:** 570/20 **Crew:** 12 tot.

Remarks: PS 101 in 1979 Budget, PS 102 in 1981. Glass-reinforced plastic hull; 4-day endurance. Carry a 25-man rubber rescue dinghy. PS 103 authorized under 1986 Budget and made 28 kts on trails; PS 104 and 105 authorized under 1987 Budget. The machine gun can be interchanged with a fire-fighting water cannon. The last two are optimized for service on Japan's Inland Sea and have longer superstructures.

♦ 4 Hidaka (130-ton) class

	Bldr	In serv.
PS 41 Kamui	Hayashigane SY, Shimonoseki	15-2-66
PS 43 Ashitaka	Usuki Iron Wks., Usuki	10-2-67
PS 44 Kurama	Usuki Iron Wks., Usuki	28-2-67
PS 46 Toumi	Usuki Iron Wks., Usuki	20-2-68

D: 169 tons normal **S:** 13.7 kts **Dim:** 31.72 (30.5 wl) × 6.29 × 1.80
A: 1/12.7-mm mg (usually not mounted)
Electron Equipt: Radar: 1/. . . nav.
M: 1 6MSB 31S diesel; 1 prop; 700 bhp **Electric:** 60 kVA
Range: 1,100/12 **Crew:** 17 tot.

PATROL BOATS *(continued)*

Kurama (PS 44) *Ships of the World,* 1988

Remarks: PS 44 replaced in training role by *Isazu* (PM 07) on 20-4-82. Sisters *Hiyama* (PS 33), *Tsurugi* (PS 34), *Takatsuki* (PS 39), and *Nobaru* (PS 45) stricken 5-3-88: *Hidaka* (PS 32) stricken 8-8-88; *Akiyoshi* (PS 37) stricken 14-10-89; *Ibuki* (PS 45) stricken 18-10-89; *Kunimi* (PS 38) stricken 14-10-89; *Takanawa* (PS 36) stricken 4-1-90; and *Rokko* (PS 35) stricken 14-2-91.

COASTAL PATROL BOATS (PC)

Note: The first seven units of a new 115-ton PC class were authorized under Fiscal Year 1991; they will be waterjet-propelled. No other data yet available.

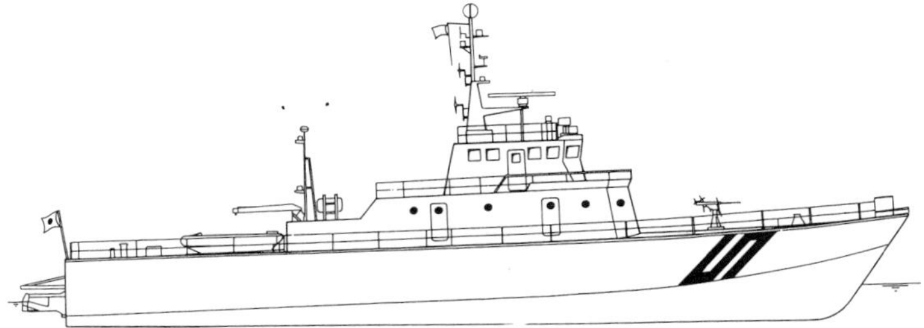
New 115-ton PC design MSA, 4-91

◆ 23 Murakomo (30-meter) class

	Bldr	In serv.
PC 201 Murakomo	Mitsubishi, Shimonoseki	24-3-78
PC 202 Kitagumo	Hitachi, Kanagawa	17-3-78
PC 203 Yukigumo	Hitachi, Kanagawa	27-9-78
PC 204 Asagumo	Mitsubishi, Shimonoseki	21-9-78
PC 205 Hayagumo	Mitsubishi, Shimonoseki	30-1-79
PC 206 Akigumo	Hitachi, Kanagawa	28-2-79
PC 207 Yaegumo	Mitsubishi, Shimonoseki	16-3-79
PC 208 Natsugumo	Hitachi, Kanagawa	22-3-79
PC 209 Yamagiri	Hitachi, Kanagawa	29-6-79
PC 210 Kawagiri	Hitachi, Kanagawa	27-7-79
PC 211 Teruzuki	Maizuru Heavy Ind.	26-6-79
PC 212 Natsuzuki	Maizuru Heavy Ind.	26-7-79
PC 213 Miyazuki	Hitachi, Kanagawa	13-3-80
PC 214 Nijigumo	Mitsubishi, Shimonoseki	29-1-81
PC 215 Tatsugumo	Mitsubishi, Shimonoseki	19-3-81
PC 216 Hamayuki	Hitachi, Kanagawa	27-2-81
PC 217 Isonami	Mitsubishi, Shimonoseki	19-3-81
PC 218 Nagozuki	Hitachi, Kanagawa	29-1-81
PC 219 Yaezuki	Hitachi, Kanagawa	19-3-81
PC 220 Yamayuki	Hitachi, Kanagawa	16-2-82
PC 221 Komayuki	Mitsubishi, Shimonoseki	10-2-82
PC 222 Asagiri	Mitsubishi, Shimonoseki	17-2-82
PC 223 Umigiri	Hitachi, Kanagawa	23-2-83

Isonami (PC 217) *Ships of the World,* 1990

D: 88 tons (125 fl) **S:** 31 kts **Dim:** 31.0 (28.5 pp) × 6.3 × 1.17
A: 1/12.7-mm mg **Electron Equipt:** Radar: 1/. . . nav.
M: 2 Ikegai MTU 16V652 TB81 diesels; 2 props; 4,800 bhp
Electric: 40 kVA **Range:** 350/28 **Crew:** 11 tot.

Remarks: PC 201 to PC 204 built under 1977–78 program. PC 205–208 under 1978–79, PC 209–212 under 1978–79 supplementary program, PC 213 under 1979–80 program, PC 214–219 under 1980–81 program, PC 220–221 under 1981–82.

◆ 4 Natsugiri (23-meter) class Bldr: Ishihara Dockyard

	In serv.		In serv.
PC 86 Natsugiri	29-1-90	PC 88	1991
PC 87 Suganami	29-1-90	PC 89	1991

Natsugiri (PC 86) *Ships of the World,* 1-

D: 54 tons (. . . fl) **S:** 27.5 kts **Dim:** 27.0 × 5.6 × 1.2
A: none **Electron Equipt:** Radar: 1/. . . nav.
M: 2 . . . . . . diesels; 2 props; 3,000 bhp
Electric: 40 kVA tot. (2 × 20 kVA) **Range:** . . ./. . .
Crew: . . . tot.

Remarks: First two in FY 1988 Budget for service in the Yokosuka area as a resu the poor performance of earlier 23-meter-series patrol craft during the rescue ef after the collision of the submarine *Nadashio* (SS 577) with a fishing boat; have lo hulls and greater propeller tip clearance to reduce pitching. PC 88 and 89 laid d 4-10-90.

◆ 15 Akizuki (23-meter) class Bldr: Mitsubishi, Shimonoseki

	In serv.		In serv.
PC 64 Akizuki	28-2-74	PC 79 Shimanami	23-12-77
PC 65 Shinonome	25-2-74	PC 80 Yuzuki	22-3-79
PC 72 Urayuki	31-5-75	PC 81 Hanayuki	27-3-81
PC 73 Iseyuki	31-7-75	PC 82 Awagiri	27-12-82
PC 75 Hatayuki	19-3-75	PC 83 Shimagiri	7-2-84
PC 76 Hatagumo	21-2-76	PC 84 Setogiri	22-3-85
PC 77 Hamazuki	29-11-76	PC 85 Hayagiri	22-2-85
PC 78 Isozuki	18-3-77		

Setogiri (PC 84)—low bridge *Ships of the Worl*

COASTAL PATROL BOATS *(continued)*

sozuki (PC 78)—high bridge Wilhelm Donko, 6-89

D: 77 tons normal **S:** 22.1 kts **Dim:** 26.00 (23.00 pp) × 6.30 × 1.12
A: PC 85 only: 1/20-mm AA
Electron Equipt: Radar: 1/FRA 10 Mk 2
M: 3 Mitsubishi 12 DM 20 MTK diesels; 3 props; 3,000 bhp
Electric: 40 kVA **Range:** 290/21.5 **Crew:** 10 tot.

emarks: Superstructure on PC 83 and later differs (see photos); they also use the 'itsubishi 12V175RTC diesel of 1,000 bhp each. All have a folding rescue platform at ɪe waterline on the starboard side.

1 Matsunami (23-meter) class Bldr: Hitachi, Kanagawa

C 53 Matsunami (In serv. 30-3-71)

D: 59 tons normal **S:** 20.7 kts **Dim:** 24.96 × 6.0 × 1.33
A: none **Electron Equipt:** Radar: 1/. . . nav.
M: 2 Mercedes-Benz MB820Db diesels; 2 props; 2,200 bhp; 2 DA640 cruise diesels: 180 bhp
Electric: 3 kw **Range:** 270/18 **Crew:** 30 tot.

ɪmarks: Especially configured for the late Emperor Hirohito for oceanographic ɪearch. Two cruise diesels can be geared to the props.

17 Shikinami (23-meter) class

	Bldr	In serv.
54 Shikinami	Ishihara, Takasago	24-2-71
55 Tomonami	Ishihara, Takasago	20-3-71
56 Wakanami	Ishihara, Takasago	30-10-71
57 Isenami	Sumidigawa, Tokyo	29-2-72
58 Takanami	Ishihara, Takasago	30-11-71
59 Mutsuki	Sumidigawa, Tokyo	18-12-72
60 Mochizuki	Sumidigawa, Tokyo	18-12-72
61 Haruzuki	Ishihara, Takasago	30-11-72
62 Kiyozuki	Ishihara, Takasago	18-12-72
63 Urazuki	Ishihara, Takasago	30-1-73
66 Uranami	Sumidigawa, Tokyo	22-12-73
67 Tamanami	Ishihara, Takasago	25-12-73
68 Minegumo	Ishihara, Takasago	30-11-73
69 Kiyonami	Ishihara, Takasago	30-10-73
70 Okinami	Sumidigawa, Tokyo	8-2-74
71 Wakagumo	Sumidigawa, Tokyo	25-3-74
74 Asoyuki	Sumidigawa, Tokyo	16-6-75

ɪzuki (PC 61) *Ships of the World,* 1984

46 tons normal **S:** 25.8 kts **Dim:** 21.0 × 5.3 × 1.22
1/12.7-mm mg (usually not mounted)
ɪctron Equipt: Radar: 1/MD 806 nav.
12 Mercedes-Benz MB820Db diesels; 2 props; 2,200 bhp
ɪctric: 2 kw **Range:** 240/23.8 **Crew:** 10 tot.

rks: *Asoyuki* (PC 74) mistakenly deleted from previous edition.

♦ **1 Hamanami (23-meter) class** Bldr: Sumidagawa, Tokyo

PC 52 Hamanami (In serv. 22-3-71)

D: 60 tons (fl) **S:** 20.9 kts **Dim:** 21.0 × 5.1 × 1.22
A: none **Electron Equipt:** Radar: 1/MD 808 nav.
M: 2 Mercedes-Benz MB820Db diesels; 2 props; 2,200 bhp
Electric: 2 kw **Range:** 290/20.9 **Crew:** 10 tot.

♦ **1 Hamagiri (23-meter) class** Bldr: Sumidagawa, Tokyo

PC 48 Hamagiri (In serv. 19-3-70)

D: 51 tons (fl) **S:** 14.6 kts **Dim:** 21.0 × 5.1 × 1.11
A: none **Electron Equipt:** Radar: 1/MD 808 nav.
M: 2 Mitsubishi 12DH 20TK diesels; 2 props; 1,140 bhp
Electric: 2 kw **Range:** 270/12.9 **Crew:** 10 tot.

PATROL CRAFT (CL)

Note: 20-meter patrol craft CL 05–11 were laid down during 1991 to a new design to replace old CL 50–59. Details in addenda.

♦ **4 Isokaze (15-meter) class** Bldr: Yokohama Yacht

CL 01 Isokaze (In serv. 23-3-89)
CL 02 Hayakaze (In serv. 23-3-89)
CL 03 Nadokaze (In serv. 15-3-91)
CL 04 Kotokaze (In serv. 15-3-91)

Isokaze (CL 01) Yokohama Yacht, 3-89

D: 19 tons (21 fl) **S:** 20 (CL 03, 04: 29) kts
Dim: 18.00 × 4.30 × . . .
M: CL 01, 02: 2 Nissan RD10-TA06 diesels; 2 props; 900 bhp; CL 03, 04: 2 . . . . . . diesels; 2 props; 1,400 bhp
Range: 180/19 **Crew:** 6 tot.

Remarks: Revised *Yamayuri* design, with higher superstructure and finer hull lines. CL 01 and 02 laid down 20-9-88 and launched 7-2-89; CL 03 and 04, laid down 17-9-90 and launched 8-2-91, may be one meter shorter.

♦ **64 Yamayuri (15-meter) class**

	Bldr	In serv.
CL 201 Yamayuri	Ishihara, Takasago	27-1-78
CL 202 Tachibana	Ishihara, Takasago	24-2-78
CL 203 Komakusa	Ishihara, Takasago	30-1-79
CL 204 Shiragiku	Ishihara, Takasago	22-2-79
CL 205 Yaguruma	Sumidigawa, Tokyo	31-7-79
CL 206 Hamanasu	Sumidigawa, Tokyo	29-9-79
CL 207 Suzuran	Sumidigawa, Tokyo	31-7-79
CL 208 Isogiku	Sumidigawa, Tokyo	12-9-79
CL 209 Isegiko	Sumidigawa, Tokyo	31-8-79
CL 210 Ayame	Yokohama Yacht	29-10-79
CL 211 Ajisai	Yokohama Yacht	26-9-79
CL 212 Himawari	Yokohama Yacht	29-10-79
CL 213 Hazakura	Yokohama Yacht	29-8-79
CL 214 Hinagiku	Ishihara, Takasago	9-7-79
CL 215 Hamagiku	Yokohama Yacht	19-9-79
CL 216 Fuyume	Ishihara, Takasago	30-7-79
CL 217 Tsubaki	Ishihara, Takasago	10-8-79
CL 218 Sazanka	Ishihara, Takasago	30-8-79
CL 219 Aoi	Sumidigawa, Tokyo	31-10-79
CL 220 Suisen	Yokohama Yacht	29-10-79
CL 221 Yaezakura	Ishihara, Takasago	25-9-79
CL 222 Akebi	Ishihara, Takasago	29-10-79
CL 223 Shirahagi	Sumidigawa, Tokyo	25-1-80
CL 224 Benibana	Sumidigawa, Tokyo	25-1-80
CL 225 Muratsubaki	Ishihara, Takasago	20-12-79
CL 226 Tsutsuji	Sumidigawa, Tokyo	22-2-80
CL 227 Ashibi	Ishihara, Takasago	20-12-79
CL 228 Satozakura	Ishihara, Takasago	26-2-80
CL 229 Yukitsubaki	Ishihara, Takasago	28-2-80
CL 230 Satsuki	Shinki SY, Osaka	22-2-80
CL 231 Ezogiku	Yokohama Yacht	18-11-80
CL 232 Akashio	Sumidigawa, Tokyo	18-11-80
CL 233 Kozakura	Yokohama Yacht	18-11-80
CL 234 Shirame	Ishihara, Takasago	28-11-80

PATROL CRAFT *(continued)*

	Bldr	In serv.
CL 235 Sarubia	Ishihara, Takasago	28-11-80
CL 236 Suiren	Shinki SY, Osaka	19-12-80
CL 237 Hatsugiku	Ishihara, Takasago	29-1-81
CL 238 Hamayura	Ishihara, Takasago	29-1-80
CL 239 Airisu	Yokohama Yacht	18-2-82
CL 240 Yamabuki	Sumidigawa, Tokyo	17-12-81
CL 241 Shirayuri	Nobutaka SY	1-2-82
CL 242 Karatachi	Ishihara, Takasago	17-12-81
CL 243 Kobai	Ishihara, Takasago	18-2-82
CL 244 Hamayuu	Ishihara, Takasago	29-1-82
CL 245 Sasayuri	Sumidigawa, Tokyo	25-1-83
CL 246 Kosumosu	Ishihara, Takasago	17-2-83
CL 247 Shiogiku	Sumidigawa, Tokyo	29-11-82
CL 248 Yamahagi	Yokohama Yacht	29-11-82
CL 249 Mokuren	Shinki SY, Osaka	25-1-83
CL 250 Isobuji	Ishihara, Takasago	7-3-83
CL 251 Tamatsubaki	Sumidigawa, Tokyo	26-1-84
CL 252 Yodoki	Shinki SY, Osaka	22-11-83
CL 253 Iozakura	Ishihara, Takasago	25-11-83
CL 254 Himetsubaki	Ishihara, Takasago	18-1-84
CL 255 Tokikusa	Sumidigawa, Tokyo	24-2-84
CL 256 Mutsugiku	Sumidigawa, Tokyo	15-11-84
CL 257 Terugiko	Shigi SY, Sakai	19-12-84
CL 258 Mayazakura	Ishihara, Takasago	20-12-84
CL 259 Yamagiko	Yokohama Yacht	22-1-85
CL 260 Tobiume	Ishihara, Takasago	24-1-85
CL 261 Kotozakura	Sumidigawa, Tokyo	28-2-85
CL 262 Minogiku	Ishihara, Takasago	14-2-85
CL 263 Kuroyuri	Yokohama Yacht	15-11-84
CL 264 Chiyogiku	Shigi SY, Sakai	8-3-88

Tokikusa (CL 255) *Ships of the World,* 1990

D: 27 tons normal (35.7 fl) **S:** 20.7 kts
Dim: 18.00 (16.60 wl) × 4.30 × 0.82 (1.10 props)
M: 2 RD10T AO6 diesels; 2 props; 900 bhp
Range: 180/19 **Crew:** 6 tot.

Remarks: Three water cannon for fire fighting. CL 251–263 have waterjets, vice propellers, and can make 21.9 kts; their engines are type S6A-MTK (450 bhp each). The final unit, CL 264, reverted to the original propulsion plant.

♦ 4 Nogekaze class Bldr: Sumidagawa, Tokyo

	In serv.		In serv.
CL 99 Nogekaze	10-72	CL 107 Itokaze	11-72
CL 105 Kusukaze	10-72	CL 128 Kawakaze	10-73

Itokaze (CL 107) *Ships of the World,* 1984

D: 22.5 tons normal **S:** 16.6 kts
Dim: 16.00 × 4.10 × 0.80 (hull)
M: 2 Type UDV816 diesels; 2 props; 500 bhp
Electric: 5 kVA
Range: 160/14.7 **Crew:** 6 tot.

♦ 91 Chiyokaze class Bldrs: Ishihara, Nobotuka, Yokohama Yacht, Sumidagawa (In serv. 1968–76)

CL 50 Suzukaze
CL 51 Urakaze
CL 53 Sugikaze
CL 54 Fujikaze
CL 55 Miyakaze
CL 65 Tomakaze
CL 66 Hibakaze
CL 67 Yurikaze
CL 68 Sumikaze
CL 69 Kashima
CL 70 Takekaze
CL 71 Kinukaze
CL 72 Shigikaze
CL 73 Uzukaze
CL 74 Akikaze
CL 75 Setokaze
CL 76 Kurekaze
CL 77 Mojikaze
CL 78 Satakaze
CL 79 Kirikaze
CL 80 Kamikaze
CL 81 Umikaze
CL 82 Yumekaze
CL 83 Makikaze
CL 84 Hakaze
CL 85 Shachikaze
CL 86 Himekaze
CL 87 Isekaze
CL 88 Komakaze
CL 89 Kishikaze
CL 90 Mayakaze
CL 91 Kikukaze
CL 92 Hirokaze
CL 93 Kibikaze
CL 94 Ashikaze
CL 95 Otokaze
CL 96 Kurikaze
CL 97 Imakaze
CL 98 Terukaze
CL 100 Tokitsukaze
CL 101 Tsukikaze
CL 102 Awakaze
CL 104 Miokaze
CL 106 Kiikaze
CL 108 Tamatsukaze
CL 109 Miyokaze
CL 110 Ayakaze
CL 111 Mitsukaze
CL 112 Hatakaze
CL 113 Numakaze
CL 114 Soyokaze
CL 115 Minekaze
CL 116 Okitsukaze
CL 117 Deigo
CL 118 Yuuna
CL 119 Adan
CL 120 Horokaze
CL 121 Somakaze
CL 122 Hatsukaze
CL 123 Sasakaze
CL 124 Hagikaze
CL 125 Tonekaze
CL 126 Shizukaze
CL 127 Murokaze
CL 129 Yamakaze
CL 130 Hikokaze
CL 131 Takakaze
CL 132 Murakaze
CL 133 Nomokaze
CL 134 Kumokaze
CL 135 Yanakaze
CL 136 Yurakaze
CL 137 Washikaze
CL 138 Kushikaze
CL 139 Hoshikaze
CL 140 Getto
CL 141 Iwakaze
CL 142 Matsukaze
CL 143 Oitsukaze
CL 144 Arakaze
CL 145 Tanikaze
CL 146 Kochikaze
CL 147 Okikaze
CL 149 Sachikaze
CL 150 Natsukaze
CL 151 Harukaze
CL 152 Rindo
CL 153 Sawakaze
CL 154 Kaido
CL 155 Nadeshiko
CL 156 Yamazakura

Miokaze (CL 104) *Ships of the World,* 1

D: 19.5 tons normal **S:** 18.4 kts **Dim:** 15.00 × 4.10 × 0.76 (hull)
M: 2 Mitsubishi DH24MK diesels; 2 props; 500 bhp
Range: 180/16.1 **Crew:** 6 tot.

Remarks: *Nomakaze* (CL 103) was lost in 1978. CL 69 is named for her home por 117 to CL 119 are home-ported in Okinawa. Class name-ship *Chiyokaze* (CI stricken 22-2-88; *Suwakaze* (CL 148) stricken 12-8-88; *Chinukaze* (CL 57) and *N kaze* (CL 58) stricken 22-2-91. CL 50–55 to strike early 1992.

GUARD BOATS (GS)

♦ 2 Hayate (12-meter) class Bldr: Yokohama Yacht

GS 01 Hayate (In serv. 21-12-87)
GS 02 Inazuma (In serv. 21-12-87)

D: 7.9 tons **S:** 30 kts **Dim:** 12.20 (11.90 pp) × 3.20 × 1.5
M: 2 . . . diesels; 2 props; 580 bhp **Range:** 150/128
Crew: 3 tot.

Remarks: Ordered 9-6-87. Hull moulded depth 1.5 m. Officially typed "Guard Small" and used at Kansai International Harbor. Aluminum hulls.

HYDROGRAPHIC SHIPS

Note: One HL-series survey ship was authorized under the Fiscal Year 1991 Buc replace *Kaiyo* (HM 06) and will probably take the same name; no data availabl

HYDROGRAPHIC SHIPS *(continued)*

Inazuma (GS 02) *Ships of the World,* 12-87

◆ **1 Meiyo class** Bldr: Kawasaki, Kobe

	Laid down	L	In serv.
HL 03 Meiyo	24-7-89	29-6-90	24-10-90

Meiyo (HL 03) Kawasaki, 10-90

D: 550 tons (. . . fl) **S:** 15 kts **Dim:** 60.00 × 10.5 × . . .
Electron Equipt: Radar: 2/. . . nav.
M: 2 Daihatsu 6 DLM-24S(L) diesels; 2 CP props; 2,200 bhp—bow-thruster
Electric: 480 kw tot. (2 × 160-kw shaft gen., 2 × 80-kw diesel sets)
Range: 5,000/14.5 **Crew:** 25 tot.

Remarks: 1,096 grt. Built as a replacement for the previous *Meiyo* (HL 03), which was stricken 28-9-90. Carries the same survey equipment as the larger *Takuyo* (HL 02), including the 11,000-m depth, 12-kHz "Sea Beam" mapping sonar. Navigation equipment includes Loran-C, GPS, and doppler log. Carries a 16-meter survey launch. Has both passive roll-damping and pitch-damping tanks. The engines are on sound-damping mountings.

◆ **1 Tenyo class**

	Bldr	Laid down	L	In serv.
HL 04 Tenyo	Sumitomo, Uraga	11-4-86	5-8-86	27-11-86

Tenyo (HL 04) *Ships of the World,* 1989

D: 770 tons (. . . fl) **S:** 13.5 kts **Dim:** 56.0 × 9.8 × 2.9
Electron Equipt: Radar: 2/SMA 1596 nav.
M: 2 Akasaka MH23 diesels; 2 CP props; 1,300 bhp
Electric: 320 kVA (2 × 160-kVA diesel sets)
Range: 5,400/12
Crew: 18 officers, 25 enlisted

Remarks: 430 grt. Carries one 10-m survey boat. Has superstructure-mounted passive tank stabilization. Survey equipment includes the 11,000-m depth-capable, 12-kHz "Sea Beam" mapping sonar. Home-ported at Tokyo.

◆ **1 Takuyo (2,600-ton) class** Bldr: Nippon Kokan, Tsurumi

	Laid down	L	In serv.
HL 02 Takuyo	14-4-82	24-3-83	31-8-83

Takuyo (HL 03) *Ships of the World,* 1990

D: 2,979 tons (3,370 fl) **S:** 18.2 kts
Dim: 96.00 (90.00 wl) × 14.20 × 4.51 mean (4.91 max. over sonar)
Electron Equipt: Radar: 2/. . . nav.
M: 2 Fuji 6S40B diesels; 2 CP props; 5,200 bhp—bow-thruster
Electric: 965 kVA tot. **Range:** 12,800/16.9
Endurance: 50 days
Crew: 39 crew + 22 survey party

Remarks: 2,481 grt. In 1981 program to replace earlier unit with same name. Has side-looking, contour-mapping sonars, precision echo-sounders, etc. Carries two survey launches. Has superstructure-mounted passive tank stabilization, and navigational equipment includes Magnavox MX 702 SATNAV receiver and Loran-C. Home-ported at Tokyo.

◆ **1 Shoyo (1,900-ton) class**

	Bldr	L	In serv.
HL 01 Shoyo	Hitachi, Maizuru	18-9-71	26-2-72

Shoyo (HL 01) *Ships of the World,* 1987

D: 2,200 tons normal **S:** 17.4 kts
Dim: 81.70 (78.60 wl) × 12.60 × 4.20
Electron Equipt: Radar: 2/. . . nav.
M: 2 Fuji 12VM32 H2F diesels; 1 prop; 4,800 bhp—bow-thruster
Electric: 1,250 kVA tot. **Range:** 12,000/14
Crew: 23 officers, 35 enlisted

Remarks: 1,900 grt. Carries two survey launches. Navigation equipment includes Magnavox MX 702 SATNAV receiver and Loran-C. Home-ported at Tokyo.

COASTAL HYDROGRAPHIC SHIP

◆ **1 Kaiyo class** Bldr: Ishikawajima Harima, Nagoya

HM 06 Kaiyo (In serv. 14-5-64)

Kaiyo (HM 06) *Ships of the World,* 1990

COASTAL HYDROGRAPHIC SHIP *(continued)*

D: 380 tons normal **S:** 12 kts **Dim:** 44.53 × 8.05 × 2.39
M: 1 Sumiyoshi Tekko S 6 NBS diesel; 1 prop; 450 bhp
Electric: 90 kVA **Range:** 3,160/10
Crew: 13 officers, 22 enlisted

Remarks: Replacement authorized under FY 1991 Budget.

INSHORE HYDROGRAPHIC CRAFT

♦ **1 (+ . . .) Hamashio (20-meter) class**

	Bldr	Laid down	L	In serv.
HS 21 Hamashio	Yokohama Yacht	2-11-90	3-3-91	25-3-91

D: 27 tons (. . . fl) **S:** 15 kts
Dim: 21.0 × 4.5 × . . .
M: 3 diesels; . . . props; 1,015 bhp
Crew: 3 tot.

♦ **1 Kerama (15-meter) class** Bldr: Ito Tekko SY, Sasebo

HS 32 Kerama (In serv. 28-11-73)

D: 23.2 tons normal **S:** 11 kts **Dim:** 15.0 × 4.0 × 0.86
M: 1 UDV 816 diesel; 250 bhp **Range:** 450/10 **Crew:** 7 tot.

Remarks: Glass-reinforced plastic construction.

♦ **4 Akashi (15-meter) class** Bldrs: Various (In serv. 1973–77)

HS 31 Akashi HS 33 Hayatomo HS 34 Kurihama
HS 35 Kurushima

D: 21 tons normal **S:** 10.2 kts **Dim:** 15.0 × 4.0 × 0.84
M: 1 Nissan-MTU UD626 diesel; 180 bhp
Range: 630/9.7 **Crew:** 7 tot.

Remarks: Glass-reinforced plastic hulls. Resemble CL 44-class patrol craft, but have bulwarks surrounding upper deck of the hull.

♦ **10 Hamashio class** Bldr: Nippon Hikaki, Yokosuka (In serv. 1969–72)

HS 02 Iseshio HS 06 Isoshio HS 10 Oyashio
HS 03 Setoshio HS 07 Takashio HS 11 Kuroshio
HS 04 Uzushio HS 08 Wakashio
HS 05 Hayashio HS 09 Yukishio

D: 6 tons normal **S:** 8.9–9.3 kts **Dim:** 10.15 × 2.65 × 0.81
M: 1 Nissan-MTU UD326 diesel; 90 bhp
Range: 343/8.5 **Crew:** 7 tot.

Remarks: Glass-reinforced plastic construction. Sister *Hamashio* (HS 01) stricken 19-2-91.

SEAGOING NAVIGATIONAL AID TENDERS (HL)

♦ **1 Tsushima class** Bldr: Mitsui, Tamano

	Laid down	L	In serv.
LL 01 Tsushima	10-6-76	7-4-77	9-9-77

Tsushima (LL 01) *Ships of the World,* 1990

D: 1,865 tons normal **S:** 16 kts (17.6 trials)
Dim: 75.00 (70.00 wl) × 12.50 × 4.15
M: 1 Fuji-Sulzer 8S 40C diesel; 1 CP prop; 4,200 bhp
Electric: 900 kVA tot. **Fuel:** 477 tons
Range: 10,000/15 **Crew:** 54 tot.

Remarks: Intended for use as a lighthouse supply ship. Has Flume-type passive stabilization tanks in superstructure, bow-thruster. Intelsat SATCOMM added 1988.

♦ **3 Hokuto-class navigational buoy tenders**

	Bldr	Laid down	L	In serv.
LL 11 Hokuto	Sasebo DY	19-10-78	20-3-79	29-6-79
LL 12 Kaio	Sasebo DY	17-7-79	20-10-79	11-3-80
LL 13 Ginga	Kawasaki, Kobe	13-6-79	16-11-79	18-3-80

D: 620 tons light (839 fl) **S:** 13.8 kts
Dim: 55.00 (51.00 wl) × 10.60 × 2.65

Hokuto (LL 11) *Ships of the World*

M: 2 Asakasa MH23 (LL 11: Hanshin 6L 24SH) diesels; 2 props; 1,400 bhp
Electric: 300 kVA **Fuel:** 62 tons **Range:** 3,460/13
Crew: 9 officers, 20 enlisted, 2 technicians

COASTAL NAVIGATIONAL AIDS TENDERS (LM)

♦ **2 (+1) Sekiun (24-meter) class** Bldr: Ishihara DY, Takasago

	Laid down	L	In serv.
LM 203 Sekiun	4-10-90	14-3-91	12-3-91
LM 204 Houn	4-10-90	24-1-91	22-3-91
LM 205 Reiun	. . .	. . .	. . .

Houn (LM 204) *Ships of the World,* 2-

D: 50 tons (62.5 fl) **S:** 14.5 kts
Dim: 24.00 (23.00 pp) × 6.00 × 1.32
M: 2 G.M. 12V71 TI diesels; 2 props; 1,080 bhp (980 sust.)
Range: 240/10 **Fuel:** 2 tons **Crew:** 9 tot.

Remarks: Replace earlier 23-meter group craft with the same names.

♦ **1 Zuiun (270-ton) class**

	Bldr	Laid down	L	In serv.
LM 101 Zuiun	Usuki Iron Wks., Usuki	19-1-83	27-4-83	27-7-83

D: 370 tons normal (398 fl) **S:** 15.1 kts
Dim: 46.00 (41.40 pp) × 7.50 × 2.23
M: 2 Mitsubishi-Akasaka MH 23-series diesels; 2 CP props; 1,300 bh
Range: 1,440/14.5 **Electric:** 120 kw tot.
Fuel: 34 m³ **Crew:** 20 tot.

Remarks: Lighthouse service vessel. Cargo: 85 tons. One diesel is model MH other is MH23. Second unit requested under FY 85 Budget but not approved.

Zuiun (LM 101) *Ships of the World,*

COASTAL NAVIGATIONAL AIDS TENDERS *(continued)*

◆ **1 Miyojo-class navigational buoy tender** Bldr: Ishikawajima, Tokyo

LM 11 Miyojo (In serv. 25-3-74)

Miyojo (LM 11) F. Lauga, 1976

D: 248 tons (303 normal) **S:** 11 kts
Dim: 27.0 × 12.0 × 2.58
M: 2 Niigata 6MG 16HS diesels; 2 CP props; 600 bhp
Electric: 135 kVA **Fuel:** 15 tons
Range: 1,360/10 **Crew:** 18 tot.

Remarks: Has catamaran hull. Replaced a very similar ship with same name and number lost in 4-72.

◆ **5 Hakuun-class navigational aids tenders** Bldr: Sumidagawa, Tokyo (LM 107, 114; Yokohama Yacht)

LM 106 Hakuun (In serv. 28-2-78)
LM 107 Toun (In serv. 3-79)
LM 114 Tokuun (In serv. 23-3-82)
LM 201 Shoun (In serv. 26-3-86)
LM 202 Seiun (In serv. 6-9-88)

iun (LM 202) *Ships of the World,* 9-88

D: 57.6 tons (92.7 fl) **S:** 15 kts
Dim: 24.00 (23.00 pp) × 6.00 × 1.00
Electron Equipt: Radar: 1/FRA-10 Mk III nav.
M: 2 G.M. 12V71 TI diesels; 2 props; 1,080 bhp
Electric: 30 kVA **Range:** 420/13 **Crew:** 10 tot.

marks: LM 201, 202 replaced 23-meter craft of the same name. LM 202, built under 8 Budget, was laid down 6-9-88 and launched 7-12-88.

1 Ayabane class Bldr: Shimoda DY, Shimoda

112 Ayabane (In serv. 25-12-72)

: 187 tons normal **S:** 12.3 kts **Dim:** 32.70 × 6.5 × 1.8
I: 1 Hanshin 6 L24SH diesel; 1 prop; 500 bhp
lectric: 70 kVA **Range:** 2,330/11.9 **Crew:** 18 tot.

2 23-meter group Bldr: Various

102 Reiun (In serv. 11-71) LM 113 Genun (In serv. 3-73)

: 67–74 tons (normal) **S:** 9.7–10.5 kts
im: 22.1 × 4.65 × 1.4
: 1 Yanman or G.M. diesel; 120–200 bhp
ange: 760–1,060/9.5
rew: 11–12 tot.

Genun (LM 113) *Ships of the World,* 1987

Remarks: *Shoun* (LM 109) stricken 10-3-86, *Seiun* (LM 110) stricken 8-2-89, *Sekiun* (LM 105) on 27-2-91, and *Houn* (LM 111) on 9-2-91. LM 102 to strike 15-2-92.

INSHORE NAVIGATIONAL AIDS TENDERS (LS)

◆ **18 17-meter class** Bldr: Yokohama Yacht (LS 216: Sumidagawa, Tokyo; LS 217–221: Ishihara DY, Takasago)

	In serv.		In serv.
LS 204 Hatsuhikari	3-79	LS 213 Miohikari	18-3-83
LS 205 Nahahikari	2-79	LS 214 Urahikari	27-1-84
LS 206 Matsuhikari	3-79	LS 215 Tamahikari	24-2-84
LS 207 Michihikari	14-7-79	LS 216 Fusahikari	18-2-88
LS 208 Nishihikari	14-7-79	LS 217 Haruhikari	6-1-89
LS 209 Kamihikari	17-12-79	LS 218 Setohikari	31-1-89
LS 210 Shimahikari	17-12-79	LS 219 Tohikari	28-2-90
LS 211 Akihikari	27-2-81	LS 220 Takahikari	31-1-90
LS 212 Wakahikari	5-3-82	LS 221 Sekihikari	1990

Sekihikari (LS 221) *Ships of the World,* 1990

D: 20 tons (25 fl) **S:** 16.3 kts (15 sust.) **Dim:** 17.50 × 4.30 × 0.80
M: (LS 216–218: Isuzu E-120-MFGR) diesels; 2 props; 560 bhp
Endurance: 2 days **Range:** 230/14.5 **Crew:** 8 tot.

Remarks: LS 216 approved under 1987 Budget, LS 217–218 under 1988.

Note: The three remaining *Urahikari*-class 17-meter tenders were stricken: *Sekihikari* (LS 156) and *Takahikari* (LS 202) on 18-1-90, and *Tomohikari* (LS 184) on 15-2-90.

◆ **12 12-meter class** Bldr: Nippon Hikoki, Yokosuka (LS 186–193: Ishikawajima, Tokyo; LS 194–195: Ishihara DY, Takasago)

	In serv.		In serv.
LS 181 Keiko	29-6-79	LS 190 Miyoko	24-12-85
LS 185 Shoko	26-2-79	LS 191 Kyoko	21-1-86
LS 186 Toko	30-6-79	LS 192 Suiko	30-1-87
LS 187 Getsuko	30-6-79	LS 193 Saiko	2-2-87
LS 188 Taiko	24-1-85	LS 194 Aiko	24-11-87
LS 189 Choko	20-12-85	LS 195 Hakuko	24-11-87

D: 9.4 tons (10 fl) **S:** 15 kts **Dim:** 12.00 × 3.20 × 0.60
M: 1 diesel; 1 prop; 210 bhp **Range:** 120/13.5 **Crew:** 6 tot.

Remarks: LS 194, 195 in 1987 Budget; both launched 20-10-87. GRP construction.

◆ **3 No. 1 Reiko (10-meter) class** Bldr: . . .

LS 168 No. 1 Reiko (In serv. 2-12-86)
LS 169 No. 2 Reiko (In serv. 30-11-87)
LS 170 No. 3 Reiko (In serv. 30-11-87)

INSHORE NAVIGATIONAL AIDS TENDERS *(continued)*

Hakuko (LS 195) *Ships of the World,* 11-87

No. 1 Reiko (LS 168) *Ships of the World,* 1987

D: 4.9 tons **S:** 15 kts **Dim:** 9.9 × 2.5 × 1.1
M: 1 diesel; 1 prop; 115 bhp **Range:** 140/13

Remarks: GRP construction. LS 168 laid down 1-10-86, launched 21-11-86; LS 169, 170 launched 18-11-87.

◆ 5 No. 1 Zuiko (10-meter) class Bldr: . . .

	Laid down	L	In serv.
LS 161 No. 1 Zuiko	20-9-85	20-11-85	5-12-85
LS 164 No. 2 Zuiko	29-9-85	26-11-85	12-12-85
LS 165 No. 3 Zuiko	8-10-85	2-12-85	18-12-85
LS 166 No. 4 Zuiko	16-10-85	19-12-85	17-1-86
LS 167 No. 5 Zuiko	24-10-85	9-1-86	24-1-86

No. 3 Zuiko (LS 165) *Ships of the World,* 1988

D: 4–5 tons **S:** 14 kts **Dim:** 9.9 × 2.8 × 1.6
M: 1 diesel; 1 prop; 115 bhp
Range: 130/13 **Crew:** 8 tot.

Remarks: GRP construction.

◆ 10 No. 1 Kaiko (10-meter) class Bldr: Nippon Hikoki, Yokosuka

	In serv.		In serv.
LS 144 No. 1 Kaiko	5-3-81	LS 154 No. 6 Kaiko	1982
LS 145 No. 2 Kaiko	12-3-81	LS 155 No. 7 Kaiko	12-1-84
LS 146 No. 3 Kaiko	19-3-81	LS 157 No. 8 Kaiko	17-1-84
LS 148 No. 4 Kaiko	10-12-81	LS 158 No. 9 Kaiko	13-2-84
LS 149 No. 5 Kaiko	1982	LS 160 No. 10 Kaiko	21-2-84

No. 9 Kaiko (LS 158) *Ships of the World,* 198

D: 5.2 tons **S:** 13 kts **Dim:** 9.00 × 2.25 × . . .
M: 2 Nissan FD606 diesels; 1 prop; 230 bhp
Range: 130/12.5 **Crew:** 6 tot.

Remarks: Glass-reinforced plastic construction.

◆ 6 No. 1 Yoko (10-meter) class Bldr: IHI Craft, Yokohama (In serv. 1975–79)

LS 114 No. 3 Yoko	LS 182 No. 2 Yoko	LS 142 No. 5 Yoko
LS 180 No. 1 Yoko	LS 141 No. 4 Yoko	LS 143 No. 6 Yoko

D: 3 tons (5 fl) **S:** 16.2 kts **Dim:** 7.3 × 2.45 × 0.5
M: 1 G.M. 3-53N diesel; 112 bhp **Range:** 100/12
Crew: 8 tot.

◆ 4 Wako No. 4 class Bldr: Yanmar Diesel, Arai

LS 123 Wako No. 4 (In serv. 31-1-74)
LS 117 Wako No. 2 (In serv. 11-10-78)
LS 116 Wako No. 1 (In serv. 11-10-78)
LS 118 Wako No. 3 (In serv. 24-3-79)

Wako No. 2 (LS 117) *Ships of the Wo*

D: 2 tons **S:** 17 kts **Dim:** 5.99 × 2.41 × . . .
M: 1 Yanmar diesel; 115 bhp **Range:** 70/17

Remarks: Same basic design as the *Orion*-class oil-spill surveillance craft.

◆ 4 Tenko No. 1 class Bldr: Yanmar Diesel, Arai

LS 102 Tenko No. 2 (In serv. 30-9-71)
LS 103 Tenko No. 3 (In serv. 30-9-71)
LS 137 Tenko No. 4 (In serv. 30-9-72)
LS 105 Tenko No. 5 (In serv. 4-12-73)

Tenko No. 5 (LS 105) *Ships of the*

INSHORE NAVIGATIONAL AIDS TENDERS *(continued)*

D: 0.6 tons **S:** 9 kts **Dim:** 5.6 × 1.6 × . . .
M: 1 Yanmar outboard; 12 bhp **Range:** 20/9

Remarks: Wooden outboard motor boats. Sister *Tenko No. 1* (LS 125) stricken 31-3-91, and the others will soon follow.

LARGE FIREBOATS (FL)

Note: Most JMSA patrol ships, boats, and craft are also fitted for fire fighting.

♦ **5 Hiryu class** Bldr: Nippon Kokan, Yokohama (FL 05: Yokohama Yacht)

	In serv.		In serv.
FL 01 Hiryu	4-3-69	FL 04 Kairyu	18-3-77
FL 02 Shoryu	4-3-70	FL 05 Suiryu	24-3-78
FL 03 Nanryu	4-3-71		

Iiryu (FL 01) Leo Van Ginderen, 1985

D: 199 tons (251 normal) **S:** 13.7 kts **Dim:** 27.5 × 10.4 × 2.1
M: 2 Ikegai-MTU MB820Db diesels; 2 props; 2,200 bhp
Electric: 70 kVA **Range:** 400/13 **Crew:** 14 tot.

emarks: Catamaran hulls. For fighting fires on board supertankers. 14.5 m^3 tank r fire-fighting chemicals. One 45-meter-range chemical sprayer; seven 60-meter-nge water cannon.

EDIUM FIREBOATS (FM)

10 Ninobiki class Bldrs: FM 02, FM 06, FM 08, FM 10: Sumidagawa, Tokyo; others: Yokohama Yacht

	In serv.		In serv.
1 01 Ninobiki	25-2-74	FM 06 Nachi	14-2-76
1 02 Yodo	30-3-75	FM 07 Kegon	29-1-77
1 03 Otowa	25-12-74	FM 08 Minoo	27-1-78
1 04 Shiraito	25-2-75	FM 09 Ryusei	24-3-80
1 05 Kotobiki	31-1-76	FM 10 Kyotaki	25-3-81

gon (FM 07) *Ships of the World,* 1987

: 89 tons (99 normal) **S:** 13.4 kts **Dim:** 23.00 × 6.00 × 1.55
: 1 Ikegai MTU MB820Db and 2 Nissan UDV 816 diesels; 3 props; 1,600 bhp
lectric: 40 kVA **Range:** 234/13.4 **Crew:** 12 tot.

iarks: Four fire pumps: one of 6,000 lit./min., two of 3,000 lit./min., and one of) lit./min. Have two 750-liter and one 5,000-liter foam tanks.

ENVIRONMENTAL MONITORING CRAFT

Note: A new 15-meter MS 01 was to be delivered 2-92 by Ishihara Dockyard, Takasago.

♦ **1 Katsuren-class radiation monitoring craft** Bldr: Ishihara, Takasago

MS 03 Katsuren (In serv. 13-12-75)

Katsuren (MS 03) *Ships of the World,* 1987

D: 30 tons (46 fl) **S:** 12.3 kts **Dim:** 16.50 × 5.50 × 1.10
M: 2 UDV 816 diesels; 2 props; 500 bhp
Range: 190/10.8 **Crew:** 9 tot.

♦ **2 Kinagusa-class radiation monitoring craft** Bldr: Sumidagawa, Tokyo

MS 01 Kinagusa (In serv. 25-9-70) MS 02 Saikai (In serv. 1-10-70)

Kinagusa (MS 01) *Ships of the World,* 1987

D: 16 tons (23 fl) **S:** 8.1 kts **Dim:** 10.50 × 5.00 × 0.63
M: 2 UD 326 diesels; 2 props; 180 bhp
Range: 170/7.6 **Crew:** 8 tot.

Remarks: MS 01 to strike 13-1-92.

SPILL SURVEILLANCE CRAFT (SS)

♦ **1 Sazankurosu-class oil-spill surveillance craft**

SS 35 Sazankurosu (In serv. 20-9-84)

D: 4.7 tons **S:** 25 kts **Dim:** 7.0 × 2.3 × . . . **Crew:** . . . tot.
M: 1 AQ 260A inboard/outboard motor; 130 bhp **Range:** 70/25

Remarks: GRP-construction unsinkable lifeboat design.

♦ **32 Orion-class oil-spill surveillance craft** Bldr: Yokohama Yacht and Yanmar Diesel, Arai (In serv. 1972–1979)

SS 01 Orion	SS 13 Shiriusu	SS 25 Andoroomeda
SS 02 Pegasusu	SS 14 Bega	SS 26 Altairu
SS 04 Nebuchun	SS 16 Puroshion	SS 27 Herukuresu
SS 05 Jupitaa	SS 17 Reo	SS 28 Jiemini
SS 06 Binaou	SS 18 Porarisu	SS 29 Eriizu
SS 07 Kashiopia	SS 19 Rigeru	SS 30 Kometto
SS 08 Fuenikkisou	SS 20 Shigunasu	SS 31 Regurusu
SS 09 Saapensu	SS 21 Denebu	SS 32 Betelgeuse
SS 10 Kariina	SS 22 Maakyurii	SS 33 Arudebaran
SS 11 Kapera	SS 23 Peruseusu	SS 34 Pureadesu
SS 12 Supika	SS 24 Kentaurusu	

SPILL SURVEILLANCE CRAFT *(continued)*

Kapera (SS 11) Leo Van Ginderen, 5-85

D: 2.1 tons (5 fl) **S:** 28.0 kts **Dim:** 5.99 × 2.44 × . . .
M: 1 AQ 200 inboard/outboard motor; 130 bhp
Range: 85/25 **Crew:** 6 tot.

Remarks: Propulsion and speeds vary: 16–28 kts from 130–210 hp. Four sisters serve as navigational aids tenders (LS 116–118, 123). Names are European astronomical terms, rendered phonetically.

♦ **1 Antaresu-class oil-spill surveillance craft** Bldr: Sajima Marina, Aburappo

SS 15 Antaresu (In serv. 1-7-75)

D: 1.6 tons **S:** 25 kts **Dim:** 5.49 × 2.41 × . . .
M: 1 Yanmar YA-19J2 diesel; waterjet; 220 bhp
Range: 170/24 **Crew:** 6 tot.

OIL-SPILL RECOVERY CRAFT (OR)

♦ **5 Shirasagi-class** Bldr: Various (In serv. 1977–79)

OR 01 Shirasagi OR 03 Mizunagi OR 05 Isoshigi
OR 02 Shiratori OR 04 Chidori

Shiratori (OR 02) *Ships of the World,* 1984

D: 78.5 tons (153 fl) **S:** 6.8 kts **Dim:** 22.0 × 6.4 × 0.9
M: 2 UD 626 diesels; waterjet drive; 390 bhp
Range: 160/6 **Crew:** 7 tot.

OIL-SPILL SKIMMER CRAFT (OS)

♦ **3 Uraga-class** Bldr: Lockheed, U.S.A. (In serv. 1975–76)

OS 01 Tsurumi (ex-*Uraga*) OS 02 Bisan OS 03 Naruto

D: 11 tons (fl) **S:** 6 kts **Dim:** 8.26 × 5.00 × 0.70
M: 1 HR-6 diesel; 2 props; 90 bhp
Range: 90/4.5 **Crew:** 4 tot.

Remarks: Can be broken down into sections for truck transport.

Naruto (OS 03) *Ships of the World,* 1991

OIL-BOOM EXTENDER BARGES (OX)

♦ **18 M 101-class** Bldrs: Various (In serv. 1974–76)

OX 01 to OX 06, OX 08 to OX 19 (M 101 to M 119)

D: 48 tons **Dim:** 22.00 × 7.20 × 0.45

M 101 (OX 01) 197

♦ **2 miscellaneous wooden oil-spill craft** Bldr: Eidai Sangyo (In serv 1967)

M 603 No. 02 M 804 No. 34

D: 1.1 tons **S:** 23.4 kts **Dim:** 6.0 × 2.1 × . . .
M: 1 outboard motor; 80 bhp **Range:** 80/23

TRAINING CRAFT

♦ **1 A-class**

Aoba (In serv. 12-75)

Aoba *Ships of the World,* 1

D: 15 tons **S:** 15.5 kts **Dim:** 14.0 × 3.6 × . . .
M: 1 diesel; 325 bhp **Range:** 243/15.5

♦ **2 C-I class** Bldr: Yanmar Diesel, Arai (In serv. 9-75)

C-I C-II

D: 1 ton **S:** 28 kts **Dim:** 4.9 × 2.1 × . . .
M: 1 gasoline engine; 380 bhp **Range:** 80/28

Remarks: Small GRP open, runabout launches of commercial design.

JORDAN

Hashemite Kingdom of Jordan

Personnel (1991): 290 total, including headquarters personnel and combat swimmers

Note: Jordan's "Coastal Guard" was redesignated the Royal Jordanian Navy in 1991.

PATROL BOATS AND CRAFT

◆ **3 Hawk-class patrol boats** Bldr: Vosper Thornycroft, Portchester (In serv. 10-91)

101 AL HUSSEIN 102 AL HUSSAN 103 ABDULLAH

Abdullah (103) Maritime Photographic, 10-90

.l Hussein (101) U.S. Navy, 2-92

D: 95 tons light (124 fl) **S:** 32.5 kts
Dim: 30.45 (26.55 pp) × 6.87 × 1.50 (hull)
A: 2/30-mm Oerlikon GCM-A03-2 AA (II × 2)—1/20-mm Oerlikon GAM-B01—2/7.62-mm mg (I × 2)
Electron Equipt:
Radar: 1/Kelvin-Hughes Type 1007—EW: 2 Wallop Stockade decoy RL
M: 2 MTU 16V396 TB94 diesels; 2 props; . . . bhp—2 Volvo TAMD 71A cruise diesels; . . . bhp
Range: 750/15 **Fuel:** 18 tons **Crew:** 3 officers, 13 enlisted

:marks: Ordered 3-88. First unit launched 12-88 and ran trials 17-5-89. Second npleted 12-89 and third during 6-90. GRP construction. Up to seven were desired. .ve a Rademac 2000 optronic director for the 30-mm mount. Delivery delayed by yment problems; did not leave United Kingdom until 16-9-91, as deck cargo on heavy ship *Happy Buccaneer*.

4 U.S.-supplied GRP small craft Bldr: Bertram, Miami

YSAL HAN HASAYU MUHAMMED

D: 8 tons **S:** 25 kts **Dim:** 11.6 × 4.0 × 0.5 **Crew:** 8 tot.
A: 1/12.7-mm mg—2/7.62-mm mg **M:** 2 diesels; 2 props; 600 bhp

te: The 15-meter pilot boat/patrol craft *Husni* at Aqaba, delivered 1988 by Trinity rine's Equitable Shipyard, New Orleans, is not under Coastal Guard control.

KENYA

Republic of Kenya

Personnel (1991): approx. 1,000 total

GUIDED-MISSILE PATROL BOATS

◆ **2 "Province" class** Bldr: Vosper Thornycroft, Portchester, U.K.

	Laid down	L	In serv.
P 3126 NYAYO	11-84	20-8-86	23-7-87
P 3127 UMOJA	11-84	5-3-87	7-9-87

Umoja (P 3127) Maritime Photographic, 3-88

D: 311 tons light (363 fl) **S:** 40 kts **Dim:** 56.7 (52.0 pp) × 8.2 × 2.1
A: 4/Otomat Mk II SSM (II × 2)—1/76-mm OTO Melara Compact DP—2/30-mm BMARC/Oerlikon GCM A02 AA (II × 1)—2/20-mm GAM-B01 AA (I × 2)
Electron Equipt:
Radar: 1/Decca AC 1226 nav., 1/Plessey AWS-4 air/surf. search, 1/H.S.A. Lirod 423 radar/optronic f.c.
EW: Racal Cutlass-E intercept, Racal Cygnus jammer, 2/Wallops Barricade decoy RL (XVIII × 2)
M: 4 Paxman Valenta 18 RP 200 CM diesels; 4 props; 17,900 bhp (15,000 sust.)—2 electric outdrives; 160 bhp
Electric: 420 kw **Range:** 2,000/15 **Fuel:** 45.5 tons **Crew:** 40 tot.

Remarks: Ordered 9-84. Generally similar to craft built for Oman and Egypt. Use Ferranti WSA.423 combat data/fire-control system. Carry a semi-rigid inspection boat on the stern. Both departed U.K. for Kenya on 29-3-88.

◆ **3 32-meter class** Bldr: Brooke Marine, Lowestoft, U.K.

	L	In serv.
P 3121 MADARAKA	28-1-75	16-6-75
P 3122 JAMHURI	14-3-75	16-6-75
P 3123 HARAMBEE	2-5-75	28-8-75

Harambee (P 3123)—with Gabriel missiles French Navy, 1989

Madaraka (P 3121)—at completion of refit in U.K. Leo Van Ginderen, 8-90

KENYA *(continued)*
GUIDED-MISSILE PATROL BOATS *(continued)*

D: 120 tons (145 fl) **S:** 25.5 kts **Dim:** 32.60 × 6.10 × 1.70
A: 4/Gabriel SSM (I × 4)—2/30-mm BMARC GCM-A02 AA (II × 1)
Electron Equipt:
Radar: 1/Decca AC 1226 nav., 1/Orion RTN-10X f.c.
M: 2 Paxman Valenta 16-cyl. diesels; 2 props; 5,400 bhp
Range: 2,300/12 **Crew:** 3 officers, 18 enlisted

Remarks: Ordered 10-5-73. P 3121 and 3123 received Gabriel missiles during 1982; P 3122 in 1983, with 2/40-mm AA removed. Have radar/optronic director. P 3121 arrived Vosper Thornycroft, Portchester, for refit on 4-5-89, departing on 30-7-90.

♦ **1 37.5-meter class** Bldr: Brooke Marine, Lowestoft, U.K.

	Laid down	L	In serv.
P 3100 Mamba	17-2-72	6-11-73	7-2-74

Mamba (P 3100)—at completion of refit in U.K. Leo Van Ginderen, 9-90

D: 130 tons (160 fl) **S:** 25 kts **Dim:** 37.5 × 6.86 × 1.78
A: 4/Gabriel SSM (I × 4)—2/30-mm BMARC GCM-A02 AA (II × 1)
Electron Equipt:
Radar: 1/Decca AC 1226 nav., 1/Orion RTN-10X f.c.
M: 2 Paxman Valenta 16-cyl. diesels; 2 props; 4,000 bhp
Range: 3,500/13 **Crew:** 3 officers, 22 enlisted

Remarks: Rearmed 1982, with 2/40-mm AA removed. Has radar/optronic director. Arrived Vosper Thornycroft, Portchester, for refit on 4-5-89, departing 7-11-90.

AUXILIARIES

♦ **1 large harbor tug** Bldr: James Lamont, Port Glasgow, U.K.

Ngamia (In serv. 1969)

D: . . . **S:** 14 kts **Dim:** 35.3 × 9.3 × 3.9
M: diesels; 1 prop; 1,200 bhp

Remarks: 298 grt. Transferred to Navy from Mombasa Port Authority, 1-83.

CUSTOMS POLICE SERVICE

PATROL CRAFT

♦ **12 12-meter patrol craft** Bldr: Friedrich Fassmer Werft, Mutzen/Weser (In serv. 1989–90)

D: 10 tons (fl) **S:** 28 kts **Dim:** 12.0 (10.5 pp) × 3.6 × 0.7
M: 2 Perkins 4M240Ti diesels; 2 props; 440 bhp
Crew: . . . tot.

Note: First six were ordered in 1988 and delivered by 5-89; second group of six ordered 12-89. Originally intended for use by police at Mombasa, but some are also based on Lake Victoria.

♦ **1 Dutch-built patrol craft** Bldr: Akerboom, Leyden (In serv. 1983)

Kiongozi

D: 55 tons (fl) **S:** 12 kts **Dim:** 22.5 × 5.3 × 1.8
M: 2 Kelvin TAS-6 diesels; 2 props; 560 bhp **Crew:** 8 tot.

Remarks: Used primarily as a pilot boat, carrying four pilots. A planned second unit was not acquired.

♦ **2 17-meter workboats** Bldr: Cheverton, Cowes, U.K. (In serv. 10-82)

M'Chunguzi M'Linzi

D: 25 tons (fl) **S:** 24 kts **Dim:** 17.0 × 4.4 × 1.5
M: 2 diesels; 2 props; 688 bhp **Crew:** 8 tot.

♦ **1 14-m launch** Bldr: Tremlett Powerboats, Topsham, U.K. (In serv. 1986)

D: . . . **S:** 20 kts **Dim:** 14.0 × . . . × . . .
M: 2 Perkins diesels; 2 props; . . . bhp

Remarks: Ordered 20-6-86, for use at Mombasa.

♦ **2 12-m launches** Bldr: Tremlett Powerboats, Topsham, U.K. (In serv. 1986)

D: 10 tons **S:** 20 kts **Dim:** 12.0 × . . . × . . .
M: 2 Perkins diesels; 2 props; . . . bhp

Remarks: Ordered 20-6-86 for use on Lake Victoria.

KOREA, NORTH

Democratic People's Republic of Korea

Personnel (1991): Approximately 9,000 total, plus reserves (*Note:* Some sources give as many as 60,000 active, plus 40,000 reserves, which seems unlikely, given the size of the fleet)

Naval Aviation: There is no naval aviation *per se,* but the air force has three regiments of obsolescent Il-28 Beagle bombers (82 total aircraft) that can perform maritime strike, plus one regiment of 20 obsolescent Su-7 Fitters and two regiments of even older MiG-19 Farmers (100 aircraft) that are configured for ground attack. There are also a small number of recently acquired Su-25 Frogfoot ground-attack aircraft.

Note: Data for North Korea are only marginally reliable, due to the secrecy of the North Korean government and the reluctance of South Korea and other governments to release information. The fleet is divided between the Yellow Sea and Sea of Japan and units do not transfer between. The East Coast Fleet is headquartered at Toej Dong, with major bases also at Najin and Wonsan. The West Coast Fleet is headquartered at Nampo, with major bases at Pip Got and Sagon Ni. There are numerous smaller bases along both coasts.

In November of 1991, the U.S. Department of Defense stated that North Korea ha 24 submarines, one frigate (the Soho catamaran, below), two corvettes (the Naji class), 39 missile boats (apparently still including the Komar class), 150 torpedo boat 238 coastal patrol craft of all types and sizes, 23 mine warfare craft, and 194 amphibious craft. Some sources, however, report that a number of the units below, possibly including some of the submarines, are in fact dummies without propulsion plants functioning equipment. In any case, the ships and craft of the North Korean Navy a of extremely primitive design and are equipped with equipment in general designed later than the mid-1950s. Most weapons and sensors are of Soviet or Chinese origi except for the use of imported Japanese Furuno commercial navigational radars.

There is also reported to be a "Maritime Coastal Security Police" with several patr boats and up to 100 small patrol craft.

SUBMARINES

♦ **20 (+ . . .) Soviet (Chinese version) Romeo class** (In serv. 1973–. . .)

D: 1,319/1,712 tons **S:** 15.2/13 kts **Dim:** 76.60 × 6.70 × 4.95
A: 8/533-mm TT (6 fwd/2 aft; 14 torpedoes or 28 mines)
Electron Equipt:
Radar: 1/Snoop Plate nav./surf. search—EW: Stop Light intercept
Sonar: Tamir-5L active, Feniks passive
M: diesel-electric: 2 Type 1Z38 diesels, 2,400 bhp each; 2 props; 2,700 shp—2 electric creep motors: 100 shp
Endurance: 60 days **Range:** 14,000/9 surf.; 350/9 sub.
Crew: 8 officers, 43 enlisted

Remarks: Four are of Chinese construction, transferred in 1973 (two) and 1974 (tw The others have been built at Mayang Do in North Korea. One additional unit lost east coast 20-2-85. Also called Project 33. Generally similar to the Soviet version b in the late 1950s, but with numerous changes in equipment and detail. Diving de 300 meters (270 normal). 224-cell battery: 6,600 amp/hr.

♦ **4 Soviet Whiskey class**

D: 1,049/1,349 tons **S:** 16/17 kts **Dim:** 76.00 × 6.3 × 4.8
A: 6/533-mm TT (4 fwd, 2 aft; 12 torpedoes or 24 mines)
Electron Equipt:
Radar: 1/Snoop Plate nav./surf. search—EW: Stop Light intercep
Sonar: Tamir-5 active MF, Herkules, passive array
M: 2 Type 37D diesels of 2,000 bhp, diesel-electric drive; 2 props; 2,5 shp—2 electric creep motors, 100 shp
Endurance: 60 days **Range:** 4,000/5 (snorkel) **Crew:** 50 tot.

Remarks: Transferred 1974 to replace four transferred from the U.S.S.R. du 1960s. Probably at—or near—the end of their useful lives. All based on the west on the Yellow Sea.

♦ **45 (+ . . .) North Korean-design midget submarines** Bldr: Yukdaeso-ri Shipyard (In serv. 1965–. . .)

D: 17 tons surf./25 submerged **S:** 10 kts surf./4 sub.
Dim: 20.0 × 2.0 × 1.6
A: 2/533-mm TT (fwd, not in all; 2 torpedoes)
M: 1 MTU diesel, electric drive; 1 prop; 160 shp
Range: 550/10 surf.; 50/4 sub. **Crew:** 2 + 6–7 swimmers

SUBMARINES *(continued)*

Remarks: One may have been captured by South Korean forces in 1965–66. Some may have been imported from Yugoslavia or designed with Yugoslav assistance. Primarily intended for the insertion of saboteurs and other special forces personnel.

◆ **1 41-meter midget submarine** Bldr: . . .

Remarks: No data available other than length and possibility that two 533-mm torpedo tubes are fitted; reported first in the late 1970s.

◆ **8 "semi-submersibles"** Bldr: . . . SY, Wonsan (In serv. 1985–. . .)

D: 5 tons **S:** 50 kts (surf.) **Dim:** 8.60 × 2.50 × . . .
M: . . . **Crew:** 6 tot.

Remarks: Intended for saboteur delivery to South Korea, traveling surfaced until near insertion point and then ballasting down to run in awash. Sighted at Pusan 20-10-85.

FRIGATES

◆ **1 Soho class** Bldr: Najin SY (In serv. 1983)

D: 1,600 tons (1,845 fl) **S:** 27 kts **Dim:** 75.0 × 15.0 × 3.8 (hull)
A: 4/SS-N-2A Styx SSM (I × 4?)—1/100-mm 56-cal. DP—2/37-mm AA (II × 1)— 4/25-mm AA (II × 2)—2/RBU-1200 ASW RL (V × 2)
Electron Equipt:
Radar: 1/. . . nav., 1/Square Tie f.c., . . .
Sonar: . . .
M: 2 or 4 diesels; 2 props; . . . bhp **Crew:** 190 tot.

Remarks: Reported launched 1980. Catamaran hull. Reportedly has a helicopter platform aft. Design evidently not a success.

◆ **2 Najin class** Bldr: Najin SY

531 (In serv. 1973) . . . (In serv. 1975)

Najin-class frigate 531—Nampo-class patrol craft conversion in foreground Siegfried Breyer Collection

D: 1,200 tons (1,500 fl) **S:** 25 kts **Dim:** 100.0 × 10.0 × 2.7
A: 2/SS-N-2 Styx SSM (II × 1)—2/100-mm DP (I × 2)—4/57-mm AA (II × 2)— 8/25-mm AA (II × 4)—8/14.5-mm mg (II × 4)—4/RBU-1200 ASW RL (V × 4)—2/d.c. mortars—30 mines
Electron Equipt:
Radar: 1/Skin Head surf. search, 1/Pot Head surf. search, 1/Slim Net air search, 1/Square Tie surf. search/missile target acquisition, 1 Drum Tilt gun f.c.
Sonar: probable hull-mounted HF search (Soviet Tamir-11 equivalent)
M: 2 diesels; 2 props; 15,000 bhp **Range:** 4,000/14
Crew: 180 tot.

Remarks: Very primitive design, crude in finish and appearance. Trainable missile launcher mount (Chinese?) replaced 3/533-mm TT (III × 1) in early 1980s and was again replaced by fixed Styx launchers evidently removed from an Osa-class missile boat during the later 1980s. Reports of two others apparently incorrect.

CORVETTES

◆ **3 Sariwon class** Bldr: North Korea (In serv. 1965)

D: 475 tons (600 fl) **S:** 21 kts **Dim:** 62.1 × 7.3 × 2.4
A: 1/76-mm DP—2/57-mm AA (II × 2)—4/25-mm AA (II × 2)—4/d.c. projectors
Electron Equipt:
Radar: 1/Don-2 nav., 1/Skin Head surf. search
M: 2 diesels; 2 props; 3,000 bhp **Range:** 2,700/18 **Crew:** 65–70 tot.

Remarks: Data approximate only. Design based on Soviet Tral-class minesweeper. Possible pendant numbers: 725, 726, 727, 728. One reportedly serves as flagship of the Maritime Coastal Security Police fleet.

GUIDED-MISSILE PATROL BOATS

◆ **3 (+ . . .) Soju class** Bldr: North Korea (In serv. 1981–. . .)

D: approx. 220 tons (fl) **S:** 34 kts **Dim:** 43.0 × 7.5 × 1.8
A: 4/SS-N-2 Styx SSM (I × 4)—4/30-mm AK-230 AA (II × 2)
Electron Equipt:
Radar: 1/Square Tie surf. search/missile target acquisition
M: 3 Type M503A diesels; 3 props; 12,000 bhp
Range: . . . **Crew:** 30–40 tot.

Remarks: North Korean version of Osa-I. May also have a Drum Tilt gun fire-control radar.

◆ **6 Sohung class** Bldr: North Korea (In serv. 1980–81)

D: 80 tons (fl) **S:** 40 kts **Dim:** 26.8 × 6.2 × 1.5
A: 2/SS-N-2 Styx SSM—2/25-mm AA (II × 1)
Electron Equipt:
Radar: probably 1/Square Tie surf. search/missile target acquisition
M: 4 M50F-4 diesels; 4 props; 4,800 bhp **Crew:** 19–20 tot.

Remarks: Steel-hulled version of Soviet Komar class. Considering the small number built, may not have been successful.

◆ **12 Soviet Osa-I/Chinese Huangfeng class**

D: 170 tons (209 fl) **S:** 35 kts **Dim:** 38.75 × 7.60 × 1.70 mean
A: 4/SS-N-2A Styx SSM (I × 4)—4/30-mm AK-230 AA (II × 2)
Electron Equipt:
Radar: 1/Square Tie surf. search/missile target acquisition, 1/Drum Tilt gun f.c.
M: 3 M503A diesels; 3 props; 12,000 bhp
Range: 500/34; 750/25 **Crew:** 30 tot.

Remarks: Twelve transferred 1968 from U.S.S.R. and four more in 1972–83, but of those, eight have been discarded to date. Four Chinese-built versions transferred 1982.

Note: The eight Soviet-built Komar-class wooden-hulled missile boats listed in the previous edition are believed to have been stricken by 1990.

TORPEDO BOATS

◆ **58 Soviet P 6/North Korean Sinpo class**

D: 55 tons (66.5 fl) **S:** 43 kts **Dim:** 25.3 × 6.1 × 1.7
A: 4/25-mm AA (I × 2)—2/533-mm TT—8/d.c. in tilt racks
Electron Equipt:
Radar: 1/Skin Head or Pot Head surf. search
M: 4 M50F-4 diesels; 4 props; 4,800 bhp
Range: 450/30 **Crew:** 15–20 tot.

Remarks: Forty-five transferred by U.S.S.R. during early 1960s; wooden construction. Eighteen similar Sinpo-class units were built in Korea during the early 1970s with steel hulls. Some lack torpedo tubes but have additional AA guns. The wooden-hulled P 6-class units are gradually being stricken.

◆ **12 Iwon class** Bldr: North Korea (In serv. 1970s)

D: 25 tons (fl) **S:** 45 kts **Dim:** 19.2 × 3.7 × 1.5
A: 2/25-mm AA (II × 2)—2/533-mm TT
Electron Equipt: Radar: 1/Skin Head surf. search
M: 3 diesels; 3 props; 3,600 bhp **Crew:** 15–20 tot.

◆ **6 An Ju class** Bldr: North Korea (In serv. 1970s)

D: 35 tons (fl) **S:** 50 kts **Dim:** 19.8 × 3.7 × 1.8
A: 2/25-mm AA (II × 2)—2/533-mm TT
M: 4 M50 diesels; 4 props; 4,800 bhp **Crew:** 20 tot.

◆ **74 Sin Hung class** Bldr: North Korea (In serv. 1970s)

D: 25 tons (fl) **S:** 40 kts **Dim:** 18.3 × 3.4 × 1.7
A: 4/14.5-mm (II × 2)—2/450-mm TT
M: 2 diesels; 2 props; 2,400 bhp

Remarks: A number have been transferred to foreign clients, including Nicaragua. Some reported to have had hydrofoils fitted forward as in the Chinese Huchuan class.

Note: Three Soviet Shershen-class torpedo boats transferred in 1968 are believed to have been discarded by 1990.

PATROL BOATS

◆ **10 (+ . . .) Taechong class** Bldr: North Korea (In serv. 1975–. . .)

D: 385 tons (410 fl) **S:** 30 kts **Dim:** 59.8 × 7.2 × 2.0
A: 1/100-mm 56-cal. DP—2/57-mm AA (II × 1)—2/25-mm AA (II × 1)— 4/14.5-mm mg (II × 2)—2/RBU-1200 ASW RL—2/d.c. racks—mines
Electron Equipt:
Radar: 1/Pot Head surf. search—Sonar: Tamir-11 (HF)
M: 4 Soviet Type 40D diesels; 4 props; 8,800 bhp **Range:** 2,00/12
Crew: 75–80 tot.

Remarks: Design strongly resembles the Chinese Hainan class but has a lower superstructure and slightly more freeboard to the hull. The first eight have characteristics as above; later units are 60.8 meters overall and displace about 420 tons full load. Some may have a Soviet Drum Tilt gun fire-control radar.

◆ **6 Chinese Hainan class**

D: 375 tons (400 fl) **S:** 30.5 kts **Dim:** 58.77 × 7.20 × 2.20 (hull)
A: 4/57-mm AA (II × 2)—4/25-mm AA (II × 2)—4/RBU-1200 ASW RL (V × 4)—2/d.c. projectors—2/d.c. racks—mines
Electron Equipt:
Radar: 1/Pot Head surf. search—Sonar: Tamir-11 (HF)

KOREA, NORTH *(continued)*
PATROL BOATS *(continued)*

M: 4 Type 9D diesels; 4 props; 8,800 bhp
Range: 2,000/14 **Crew:** 70 tot.

Remarks: Two transferred in 1975, two in 1976, and two in 1978.

♦ **66 Chaho class** Bldr: North Korea

D: 82 tons (fl) **S:** 40 kts **Dim:** 27.7 × 6.1 × 1.8
A: 4/14.5-mm AA (II × 2)—1/120-mm artillery RL (40 tubes; 40 reloads)
Electron Equipt: Radar: 1/. . . navigational
M: 4 Soviet M50-series diesels; 4 props; 4,800 bhp
Range: 325/19 **Crew:** 24 tot.

Remarks: Based on P 6 torpedo boat design, but have steel hull. Three transferred to Iran in 4-87 had a twin 23-mm AA mount aft and no gun mount forward; some or all of the North Korean examples may now be similarly armed.

♦ **52 Chong Jin class** Bldr: North Korea (In serv. 1975–. . .)

Remarks: Data as for Chaho class, except armaments include one 85-mm tank gun and four 14.5-mm antiaircraft guns (II × 2).

♦ **14 Chinese Shanghai-II class**

D: 122.5 tons (134.8 fl) **S:** 28.5 kts **Dim:** 38.78 × 5.41 × 1.49 (hull)
A: 4/37-mm AA (II × 2)—4/25-mm AA (II × 2)—d.c.—mines
Electron Equipt: Radar: 1/Pot Head navigational
M: 2 M50F-4, 1,200-bhp and 2/12D6, 910-bhp diesels; 4 props; 4,220 bhp
Range: 750/16.5 **Electric:** 39 kw **Endurance:** 7 days
Crew: 36 tot.

Remarks: Transferred circa 1967–69. One was stricken circa 1988.

♦ **18 Soviet S.O.-1 class**

D: 190 tons (215 fl) **S:** 28 kts **Dim:** 42.0 × 6.1 × 1.9
A: Soviet version: 4/25-mm AA (II × 2)—4 RBU-1200 ASW RL (V × 4)— 2/d.c. racks—mines
North Korean version: 1/85-mm DP—2/37-mm AA (I × 2)—4/14.5-mm mg (II × 2)
Electron Equipt:
Radar: 1/Pot Head or Don-2 nav.—Sonar: 1/Tamir-11 (HF)
M: 3 Type 40D diesels; 3 props; 7,500 bhp
Range: 1,100/13 **Crew:** 30–40 tot.

Remarks: Six transferred from U.S.S.R. in antisubmarine configuration 1957–61; remainder built in Korea for patrol purposes and in service by 1968. Design considered cramped by Soviets, and the craft are bad rollers and very noisy.

♦ **3 Chodo class** Bldr: North Korea (In serv. late 1950s)

D: 130 tons **S:** 24 kts **Dim:** 42.7 × 5.8 × 2.6
A: 1/76-mm DP—2/37-mm AA (I × 2)—4/25-mm AA (II × 2)
Electron Equipt: Radar: 1/Skin Head surf. search
M: 2 diesels; 2 props; 6,000 bhp **Range:** 2,000/10 **Crew:** 24 tot.

Remarks: Some have 3/37-mm AA, no 76-mm DP.

♦ **1 Soman class**

D: 190 tons (fl) **S:** 10 kts **Dim:** 27.9 × 5.8 × 1.9
A: 4/25-mm AA (II × 2)—4/14.5-mm mg (II × 2)—mines
Electron Equipt: Radar: 1/Skin Head surf. search
M: 1 Soviet 3D12 diesel; 1 prop; 300 bhp
Range: 1,200/9 **Crew:** 60 tot.

Remarks: Apparently only one built and may serve in a flagship role due to low power. All data estimated. The Skin Head radar is a thoroughly obsolescent design derived in the U.S.S.R. from the World War II U.S. SO-8 around 1950.

PATROL CRAFT

♦ **. . . TB-11PA class** Bldr: . . ., North Korea

D: 8 tons (fl) **S:** 35 kts **Dim:** 11.2 × 2.7 × 1.0
A: 1/14.5-mm mg **Electron Equipt:** Radar: 1/Type 24 nav.
M: 2 DOHC diesels; 2 props; 520 bhp **Range:** 200/15
Crew: 4 tot.

Remarks: GRP hull construction. Used for harbor patrol by the Maritime Coastal Security Police. There is also a larger version known as the "TB 40A."

♦ **. . . infiltration craft** Bldr: . . ., North Korea

D: 5 tons (fl) **S:** 35 kts **Dim:** 9.3 × 2.5 × 1.0
A: 1/14.5-mm mg **Electron Equipt:** Radar: 1/Furuno 701 nav.
M: 1 8-cyl. OHC diesel; 260 bhp **Crew:** 2 + 4–6 infiltrators

Remarks: Above characteristics are typical of the large number of craft built over the last 30 years to infiltrate saboteurs into South Korea. Most have had wooden hulls and are distinguished by a very low freeboard to avoid being discovered.

MINE COUNTERMEASURES CRAFT

♦ **23 Yukto-I and -II class** Bldr: . . ., North Korea

D: 60 tons (fl) **S:** 12 kts **Dim:** 24.0 × 4.0 × . . .
A: 2/14.5-mm AA (II × 1)—4 mines
M: 2 diesels; 2 props; . . . bhp **Crew:** 16–20 tot.

Remarks: Characteristics estimated. Built during the 1980s as replacements for the 1950s-supplied Soviet KM-4 class. The Yukto-II class is reportedly 21.0 meters overall. All are of wooden construction.

AMPHIBIOUS CRAFT

♦ **8 Hantae-class medium landing ships** (In serv. 1980s)

Remarks: Reportedly 50 m overall and capable of carrying three tanks.

♦ **9 Hanchon-class medium landing craft** Bldr: North Korea

D: 145 tons (fl) **S:** 10 kts **Dim:** 35.7 × 7.9 × 1.2
A: 2/14.5-mm AA (II × 1)
Electron Equipt: Radar: 1/Skin Head surf. search
M: 2 Soviet 3D12 diesels; 600 bhp **Range:** 600/6 **Crew:** 16 tot.

Remarks: Data estimated. Believed capable of carrying two tanks or 200 troops fo short distances.

♦ **100 Nampo-class assault landing craft** Bldr: North Korea

D: 82 tons (fl) **S:** 40 kts **Dim:** 27.7 × 6.1 × 1.8
A: 4/14.5-mm AA (II × 2)
Electron Equipt: Radar: 1 Skin Head or Pot Head surf. search
M: 4 M50F-4 diesels; 4 props; 4,800 bhp
Range: 325/19 **Crew:** 19 tot.

Remarks: Some exported as patrol craft with bow door welded up, and some may be a similar status in North Korea. Hull is essentially that of the Chaho/Chong Jin serie using forward compartment to accommodate about 30 troops but no vehicles.

Note: There are evidently also about 80 smaller landing craft if the U.S. Departme of Defense total of 194 is correct.

SERVICE CRAFT

Remarks: There are undoubtedly a large number of small service craft for use stores carriers, personnel ferries, etc., but no data are available. One "Kowan"-cl submarine rescue ship was reportedly built during the late 1980s.

KOREA, SOUTH

Republic of Korea

Personnel (1991): Approximately 23,000 men, plus 25,000 Marines

Naval Aviation: About a dozen land-based U.S. S-2E Tracker aircraft remain ployed for surveillance and ASW; they may be upgraded with turboprop engines, South Korea has ordered 8 new U.S. P-3C Orion maritime patrol aircraft. Ten or n Alouette-III helicopters are available for use on destroyers. Twelve Westland Lynx 99 (with option for 3 more) ordered 1988; first delivered 1-90.

South Korean S-2E Tracker French Navy,

Note: Pendant numbers are subject to change at unspecified intervals. The num "0" and "4" are considered unlucky and are not used. Three "batteries" of shore- Harpoon antiship missiles were ordered early 1987. South Korean destroyer patrol craft employ a locally built gatling AA mount using the G.E. 20-mm Vulcar

SUBMARINES

♦ **0 (+6+6) West German IKL Type 1400**

	Bldr	Laid down	L	In se
. . . .	Howaldtswerke, Kiel	. . .	. . .	19
. . . .	Daewoo SY, Okpo	1991	. . .	.
. . . .	Daewoo SY, Okpo	1991	. . .	.
. . . .	Daewoo SY, Okpo	. . .	. . .	.
. . . .	Daewoo SY, Okpo	. . .	. . .	.
. . . .	Daewoo SY, Okpo	. . .	. . .	.

D: 1,325 tons surf./1,475 sub. **S:** 11/21.5 sub.
Dim: 61.20 × 6.25 × 5.50 (surf.)
A: 8/533-mm TT fwd (14 . . . . . . torpedoes or 28 mines)

SUBMARINES *(continued)*

Electron Equipt:
Radar: . . .—Sonar: Krupp-Atlas CSU-83 suite
EW: G.T.E. Ferret intercept (1–40 gHz)
M: 4 MTU 12V493 AZ80 diesels (600 bhp each), 4 Siemens 405-kw generator sets, 1 electric motor; 1 prop; 5,000 shp
Range: 8,200/8 surf.; 400/4; 230/8 sub. **Fuel:** 106 tons
Crew: 30 tot.

Remarks: The Republic of Korea Navy hopes to acquire 12 seagoing submarines, in four "phases" of three each, although there have been problems with the initial trio, the first of which is building in West Germany while the other two are being assembled in South Korea using components shipped from Germany. Phase II units will all be built in Korea, with a steadily increasing proportion of all-Korean technology. Phases III and IV will be entirely Korean-built, with Phase IV possibly being a new design, although these six submarines may now not be built. First three ordered 2-88, to standard IKL design; a second group of three ordered during 1991.

Maximum diving depth is 320 meters. Have two 240-cell, 11,500 Amp/hr batteries weighing a total of 257 tons. Equipped with the ISUS (Integrated Sensor Underwater System) for combat control. Will have the Ferranti FMS-15 acoustic processor for a towed passive linear hydrophone system. Later units of the class, if built, may incorporate an air-independent auxiliary propulsion system.

MIDGET SUBMARINES

◆ **7 Italian-designed SX 756 class** Bldrs: First unit: COS.M.O.S., Livorno; others: Korea Tacoma SY, Masan (In serv. 1988–. . .)

D: 78 tons surf./83 sub. **S:** 9 kts surf./6 sub.
Dim: 25.2 × 2.02 × . . .
A: 2/533-mm torpedoes in drop gear or 8 mines
M: diesel-electric: 1 diesel generator set; 1 prop; . . . shp
Range: 1,600/7 surf.; 60/4.5 sub. **Crew:** 6 tot. + 8 swimmers

4 KSS-1 (Tolgorae) class Bldr: Hyundai SY, Ulsan (In serv. 1983–88)

D: 150 tons surf./175 sub. **S:** . . . **Dim:** . . . × . . . × . . .
A: 2/533-mm TT **M:** 1 or 2 diesel generator sets **Crew:** . . .

Remarks: Reported first delivered 1983, other three in 1988. Employ Krupp-Atlas passive sonar suites. Photos show a broad hull, a bulbous bow sonar installation, and a small sail incorporating a folding snorkel mast.

DESTROYERS

0 (+1+11) KDX (DW-4000) class Bldrs: Daewoo SY, Okpo (including first unit), Hyundai SY, Ulsan

	Bldr	Laid down	L	In serv.
. . . .	Daewoo SY, Okpo	1992	. . .	6-96

D: 4,000 tons (3,800 fl) **S:** 30 kts **Dim:** 124.0 × 13.4 × 3.9 (hull)
A: 8/Harpoon SSM (IV × 2)—1/Sea Sparrow vertical-launch SAM group (XVI × 1)—1/127-mm 54-cal. DP—2/30-mm Goalkeeper CIWS (I × 2)—6/324-mm ASW TT (III × 2)—1/Sea Lynx helicopter
Electron Equipt:
Radar: 1/. . . nav., 1/ H.S.A. DA-08 or Raytheon SPS-49 air search, 2/Marconi S-1802 f.c.
Sonar: Thomson-Sintra Spherion-B or Krupp-Atlas DSQS-21 hull-mounted
EW: Argo . . . or SLQ-32 (V) 2 intercept; 2 decoy RL (VI × 2)
M: CODOG: 2 G.E. LM-2500 gas turbines, 2 MTU or Pielstick diesels; 2 props
Range: 4,000/18 **Crew:** . . .

Remarks: Components for a replacement class for the aging U.S.-supplied destroyers began to be ordered in late 1986. The ships were originally to have employed license-built British radars and weapons-control systems, including the Ferranti WSA-423 combat data–weapon-control system and Rademac optronic backup gun directors, but subsequently a number of other candidate systems have been mentioned. The combat direction system will reportedly be either the Krupp-Atlas/Oerlikon-Contraves/Siemens-Plessey COSYS 200 or Dowty-Siemens/H.S.A. SSCS, either with eight display consoles. The first ship may be completed as a prototype before the others are constructed; 16 more are planned, half to be built by Hyundai.

◆ **5 ex-U.S. Gearing class, FRAM I** Bldr: Consolidated Steel, Orange, Texas (except 922: Federal SB, Newark, N.J.)

	Laid down	L	In serv.
919 Taejon (ex-*New,* DD 818)	14-4-45	18-8-45	5-4-46
921 Kuang Ju (ex-*Richard E. Kraus,* DD 849)	31-7-45	2-3-46	23-5-46
922 Kang Won (ex-*William R. Rush,* DD 714)	19-10-44	8-7-45	21-9-45
923 Kyong Ki (ex-*Newman K. Perry,* DD 883)	10-10-44	17-3-45	26-7-45
925 Jeong Ju (ex-*Rogers,* DD 876)	3-6-44	20-11-44	26-3-45

D: 2,425 tons (3,500 fl) **S:** 30 kts
Dim: 119.03 (116.74 wl) × 12.52 × 4.45 (6.4 sonar)
A: 919, 921, 922: 8 Harpoon SSM (IV × 2)—4/127-mm DP (II × 2)—2/40-mm AA (II × 1)—2/20-mm gatling AA (I × 2)—6/324-mm Mk 32 ASW TT (III × 2)—1/Mk 9 d.c. rack (12 d.c.)—1/Alouette-III ASW helo
923, 925: 4/127-mm DP (IV × 2)—2/40-mm AA (II × 1)—2/20-mm gatling AA (I × 2)—1/Mk 112 ASROC ASW RL (VIII × 1)—6/324-mm Mk 32 ASW TT— 1/Mk 9 d.c. rack (12 d.c.)
Electron Equipt:
Radar: 1/SPS-10 surf. search, 1/SPS-29 air search (919, 921: SPS-40), 1/Mk 25 f.c.
Sonar: SQS-23 hull-mounted LF
EW: WLR-1 intercept, 2 chaff RL
TACAN: 919, 921, 922: SRN-15
M: 2 sets geared steam turbines; 2 props; 60,000 shp
Electric: 1,200 kw
Boilers: 4 Babcock & Wilcox; 39.8 kg/cm^2, 454° C **Fuel:** 640 tons
Range: 4,800/15; 2,400/25 **Crew:** 274 tot.

Remarks: 919, 921 were transferred 25-2-77; 922 on 1-7-79; 923 on 25-7-81; 925 on 11-8-81. Have one Mk 37 director and one Mk 51 Mod. 2 for 40-mm; 40-mm AA added forward between the ASW torpedo tubes. Korean-designed mountings for G.E. Vulcan gatling gun amidships on Harpoon ships, on former helicopter deck on ASROC ships. Harpoon added 1979 on ships without ASROC. ULQ-6 ECM equipment removed. At least one ship has been upgraded with a Raytheon 1191 solid-state transmitter for the sonar. Harpoon, where carried, is mounted in lieu of the SROC ASW rocket launcher amidships, firing athwartships.

Jeong Ju (925)—ASROC-equipped Leo Van Ginderen, 11-86

[Kua]ng Ju (921)—Harpoon missiles vice ASROC French Navy, 1991

DESTROYERS *(continued)*

◆ **2 ex-U.S. Gearing class, FRAM II** Bldr: Bath Iron Works, Bath, Maine

	Laid down	L	In serv.
915 Chung Buk (ex-*Chevalier,* DD 805)	12-6-44	29-10-44	8-9-44
916 Jeong Buk (ex-*Everett F. Larson,* DD 830)	4-9-44	28-1-45	6-4-45

Chung Buk (915) 1988

Jeong Buk (916) Leo Van Ginderen, 11-81

D: 2,400 tons (3,500 fl) **S:** 30 kts **Dim:** 119.17 × 12.45 × 5.80
A: 8/Harpoon (IV × 2)—6/127-mm DP (II × 3)—2/20-mm gatling AA (I × 2)— 2/12.7-mm mg (I × 2)—6/324-mm Mk 32 ASW TT (III × 2)— 2/Mk 11 Hedgehog ASW spigot mortars (XXIV × 2)—1/Mk 9 d.c. rack (12 d.c.)—1/Alouette-III helicopter
Electron Equipt:
Radar: 1/SPS-10 surf. search, 1/SPS-40 air search, 1/Mk 25 f.c.
Sonar: SQS-29 series hull-mounted MF—TACAN: SRN-15
EW: WLR-1 intercept, 2 chaff RL
M: 2 sets geared steam turbines; 2 props; 60,000 shp
Electric: 1,200 kw
Boilers: 4 Babcock & Wilcox; 39.8 kg/cm², 454° C **Fuel:** 640 tons
Range: 4,800/15; 2,400/25 **Crew:** 14 officers, 260 enlisted

Remarks: Transferred on loan 5-7-72 and 30-10-72; sold outright 31-1-77. One Mk 37 director for 127-mm guns. Harpoon added 1979, flight deck widened and strengthened. ULQ-6 ECM equipment removed.

◆ **2 ex-U.S. Allen M. Sumner class, FRAM II** Bldrs: 917: Federal SB, Kearny, N.J.; 918: Bath Iron Works, Bath, Maine

	Laid down	L	In serv.
917 Dae Gu (ex-*Wallace L. Lind,* DD 703)	19-9-43	14-6-44	8-9-44
918 Inchon (ex-*De Haven,* DD 727)	9-8-43	9-1-44	31-3-44

D: 2,350 tons (3,320 fl) **S:** 34 kts **Dim:** 114.8 × 12.4 × 5.2
A: 8/Harpoon SSM (IV × 2)—6/127-mm DP (II × 3)—4/40-mm AA (II × 2)— 2/20-mm gatling AA (I × 2)—6/324-mm Mk 32 ASW TT (III × 2)— 2/Mk 11 Hedgehog ASW spigot mortars (XXIV × 2)—1/Mk 9 d.c. rack (12 d.c.)—1/Alouette-III helicopter
Electron Equipt:
Radar: 1/SPS-10 surf. search, 1/SPS-40 (918: SPS-29) air search, 1/Mk 25 f.c.
Sonar: 1/SQS-29 series hull-mounted MF, 1/SQA-10 VDS (917 only)
EW: WLR-1 intercept, 2 chaff RL—TACAN: SRN-15
M: 2 sets G.E. geared steam turbines; 2 props; 60,000 shp
Electric: 1,200 kw
Boilers: 4 Babcock & Wilcox; 39.8 kg/cm², 454° C **Crew:** 235 tot

Remarks: Transferred 12-73. Harpoon added 1978–79; helicopter deck and hangar enlarged to accommodate Alouette-III, 1978. VDS may have been removed from 917.

Note: The U.S. *Fletcher*-class destroyer *Chung Mu* (911, ex-*Erben,* DD 631) has been relegated to pierside training service; her sister *Pusan* (913, ex-*Hickox,* DD 673) was stricken 4-89.

FRIGATES

◆ **7 Ulsan (HDF-2000) class**

	Bldr	L	In serv.
951 Ulsan	Hyundai SY, Ulsan	8-4-80	1-1-81
952 Seoul	Korea SB, Pusan	24-4-84	18-12-84
953 Chung Nam	Korea Tacoma SY, Masan	26-10-84	20-7-85
955 Masan	Daewoo SY, Okpo	1985	1988
956 Keong Buk	Korea SB, Pusan	1985	10-89
957 Jeong Nam	Hyundai SY, Ulsan	19-4-88	6-89
958 Che Ju	Daewoo SY, Okpo	1988	1-1-90

D: 1,600 tons (1,940 normal, 2,180 fl) **S:** 35 kts
Dim: 105.00 (98.00 pp) × 12.00 × 3.50
A: 8/Harpoon SSM (IV × 2)—2/76-mm OTO Melara Compact DP (I × 2)—8/30-mm Emerlec AA (II × 4)—6/324-mm Mk 32 ASW TT (III × 2)—2/d.c. racks (6 d.c. each) (955 and later: 6/40-mm Dardo AA (II × 3) vice 30-mm)
Electron Equipt:
Radar: 951–956: H.S.A. ZW-06 surf. search, 1/H.S.A. DA-05 air

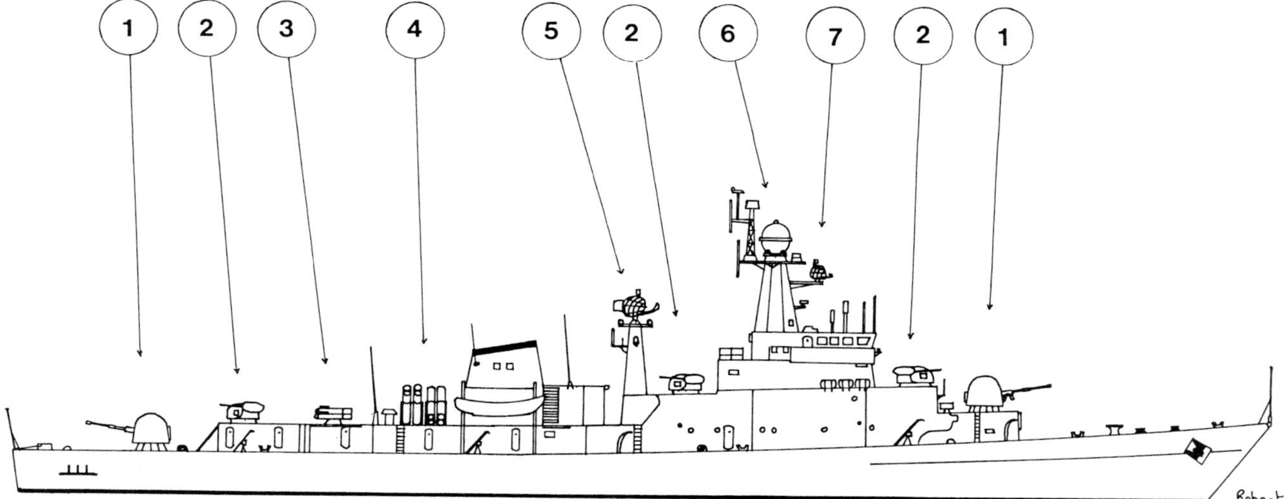

Ulsan (951) 1. 76-mm OTO Melara Compact DP 2. Emerlec twin 30-mm AA 3. Mk 32 Mod. 5 triple ASW torpedo tubes 4. quadruple Harpoon SSM 5. DA-05 air/surface-search radar 6. WM-25 track-while-scan fire-control radar 7. ZW-06 surface-search radar

FRIGATES *(continued)*

search, 1/H.S.A. WM-25 track-while-scan f.c
957–958: 1/SPS-10 surf. search—1/Samsung-Marconi 1810 surf./air search, 1/H.S.A. DA-05 air search, 1/Samsung-Marconi ST-1802 f.c.
Sonar: H.S.A. PHS-32 (957–958: Raytheon DE 1167) hull-mounted MF
EW: Goldster ULQ-11K intercept, Mk 36 SRBOC decoy syst. (2 Mk 137 launchers, VI × 2), SLQ-25 Nixie towed torpedo decoy system
TACAN: SRN-15
M: CODOG: 2 G.E. LM-2500 gas turbines, 54,400 shp; 2 MTU 12V956 TB82 diesels, 7,200 bhp; 2 CP props
Range: 900/35; 4,000/18 **Electric:** 1,600 kw tot.
Crew: 25 officers, 120 men

Chung Nam (953)—early unit with Dutch electronics, four twin 30-mm AA   Maritime Photographic, 11-91

asan (955)—with Breda 40-mm AA and Dutch electronics   French Navy, 1990

e Ju (958)—with Korean-made British electronics, after 40-mm mounts ed one deck   Hartmut Ehlers, 11-91

arks: Dutch electronic equipment, including 2 H.S.A. LIOD optronic standby directors in the first five units. 955–958 employ three twin Breda 40-mm AA in of the four 30-mm mounts; 957–958 in addition have a radar fire-control system for after two 40-mm mounts, which are mounted a deck higher than in the other ships. e stern-wedge hull form to improve fuel efficiency and maximum speed. 957 and ave the Ferranti WSA-423 combat data/control system and Rademac HK-409-029 ro-optical directors. All are to receive a Litton Data Systems computerized combat control system beginning in 1992.

2 (+4) Po Hang (KCX) class

	Bldr	In serv.
Po Hang	Korea SB & Eng., Pusan	18-12-84
Kun San	Korea Tacoma SY, Masan	18-12-84
Kyong Ju	Hyundai SY, Ulsan	1986
759 Mok Po	Daewoo SY, Okpo	1988
761 Chung Ju	Korea Tacoma, Masan	5-85
762 Kim Chon	Korea SB & Eng., Pusan	5-85
763 Jin Ju	Hyundai SY, Ulsan	1986
765 Yo Su	Daewoo SY, Okpo	1986
766 An Dong	Korea SB & Eng., Pusan	2-89
767 Sun Chon	Korea Tacoma SY, Masan	6-89
768 Won Ju	Daewoo SY, Okpo	8-89
769 Yee Ree	Hyundai SY, Ulsan	1989
771 Je Chon	Korea Tacoma SY, Masan	1989
772 Chon An	Korea SB & Eng., Pusan	1989
773 Song Nam	Daewoo SY, Okpo	1989
775 Bu Cheon	Hyundai SY, Ulsan	1989
776 Dae Chon	Korea Tacoma SY, Masan	1990
777 Jin Hae	Korea SB & Eng., Pusan	1990
778	Daewoo SY, Okpo	1991
779	Hyundai SY, Ulsan	1991
781	Korea Tacoma SY, Masan	1991
782	Korea SB & Eng., Pusan	1991
783	. . . . . .	1992
785	. . . . . .	1992
786	. . . . . .	1992
787	. . . . . .	1992

Kun San (757)—with 2 MM 38 Exocet, only one 76-mm gun   9/90

Chung Ju (762)—with Dutch electronics, two 76-mm guns   ROKN

Sun Chon (767)—with Korean-made electronics   French Navy, 1991

Bu Cheon (775)—with Korean-made electronics   9-90

D: 950 tons (1,300 fl) **S:** 31 kts
Dim: 88.00 (83.47 wl) × 10.00 (9.80 wl) × 2.90 (hull)
A: 756–759 : 2/MM 38 Exocet SSM—1/76-mm OTO Melara Compact DP—4/30-mm Emerlec AA (II × 2)—6/324-mm Mk 32 ASW TT (III × 2)— 2/d.c. racks (6 d.c. each)
Later units: 2/76-mm OTO Melara Compact DP—4/40-mm Breda AA (II × 2)— 6/324-mm Mk 32 ASW TT (III × 2)—2/d.c. racks (6 d.c. each)

FRIGATES *(continued)*

Electron Equipt:
Radar: 756–766: 1/Raytheon SPS-64(V) nav., 1 H.S.A. WM-28 track-while-scan f.c.
Later units: 1/Raytheon SPS-64(V) nav., 1/Marconi ST 1802 surf./air search, 1/Marconi S 1810 f.c.
Sonar: 756–759: Edo 768 (SQS-58); later units: H.S.A. PHS-32 hull-mounted MF
EW: Goldster ULQ-12K intercept/jammer, 756–759: Mk 36 SRBOC decoy syst. (2 Mk 137 launchers, VI × 2), later units: 4 MEL Proteus decoy RL (IX × 4)
M: CODOG: 1 LM-2500 gas turbine, 27,200 shp; 2 MTU 12V956 TB82 diesels, 6,260 bhp; 2 CP props
Range: 800/31 (turbine), 4,000/15 (diesel) **Electric:** 1,200 kw tot.
Crew: 10 officers, 85 enlisted

Remarks: Only the first four have antiship missiles; they have a twin 30-mm AA mount on the fantail in place of the after 76-mm mount. Units through 765 are equipped with one H.S.A. LIROD optronic director for the 76-mm guns, with the 30-mm weapons being essentially locally controlled. 766 and later have two twin Breda 40-mm AA, no SSM, mount the Marconi 1810 radar at the masthead, and have two Rademac 2400 optronic directors for the 40-mm guns. The first four have the H.S.A. SEWACO ZK combat data system; the others have the Ferranti WSA 423 combat system. All carry the Motorola MX 1105 satellite navigation system receiver.

First four had gas turbine rated at 27,200 shp, later units at 27,800 shp. Later units (1988–on) may substitute 4 MTU 12V493 A280 diesels for the 2 MTU 12V956 TB82 diesels.

♦ 4 Dong Hae (HDC 800) class

	Bldr	In serv.
751 Dong Hae	Korea SB & Eng, Pusan	1982
752 Su Won	Korea Tacoma SY, Masan	1983
753 Kang Reung	Hyundai SY, Ulsan	30-11-83
754 An Yang	Daewoo SY, Okpo	12-83

Dong Hae (751) 9-90

Su Won (752) Korea Tacoma, 1983

D: 800 tons (1,076 fl) **S:** 31 kts
Dim: 78.50 × 10,00 (9.60 wl) × 2.60 (mean hull)
A: 1/76-mm OTO Melara Compact DP—2/40-mm Bofors AA (II × 1, U.S. Mk 1 mount)—4/30-mm Emerlec DP (II × 2)—6/324-mm Mk 32 ASW TT (III × 2)—2/d.c. racks (6 d.c. each)
Electron Equipt:
Radar: 1/SPS-64(V) nav., 1/H.S.A. WM-28 track-while-scan f.c.
Sonar: Edo 768 hull-mounted MF
EW: . . . intercept, RBOC decoy syst. (2 Mk 136 launchers, VI × 2)
M: CODOG: 1 LM-2500 gas turbine, 27,800 shp; 2 MTU 12V956 TB82 diesels, 6,260 bhp; 2 CP props
Range: 800/31; 4,000/15 **Endurance:** 21 days
Crew: 10 officers, 85 enlisted

Remarks: A reduced version of a similar class built for the Korean Coast Guard. The 40-mm twin AA is of World War II design; the mount is controlled by an electro-optical director or U.S. Mk 51 GFCS. Distinguished by narrower superstructure, lattice mast, and less distance between mast and stack than the *Po Hang* class.

GUIDED-MISSILE PATROL BOATS

♦ 8 Paek Ku (PSMM-5) class
Bldrs: PGM 352 to 355: Tacoma Boatbuilding Co.; others: Korea Tacoma, Chinhae

	In serv.		In serv.
PGM 352 Paek Ku 52	14-3-75	PGM 357 Paek Ku 57	1977
PGM 353 Paek Ku 53	14-3-75	PGM 358 Paek Ku 58	1977
PGM 355 Paek Ku 55	1-2-76	PGM 359 Paek Ku 59	1977
PGM 356 Paek Ku 56	1-2-76	PGM 361 Paek Ku 61	1978

Paek Ku 56 (PGM 356) French Navy, 1990

Paek Ku 61 (PGM 361) *Ships of the World,* 19[illegible]

D: 240 tons (268 fl) **S:** 40 kts **Dim:** 53.68 (50.30 pp) × 8.00 × 1.63
A: PGM 352–356: 2 Standard-ARM SSM box launchers (4 missiles)—1/76.2-mm 50-cal. U.S. Mk 34 DP—2/12.7-mm mg (I × 2)
PGM 357–361: 4/Harpoon SSM (II × 2)—1/76-mm OTO Melara Compact DP— 2/30-mm Emerlec AA (II × 1)—2/12.7-mm mg (I × 2)
Electron Equipt:
Radar: PGM 352–356: 1/LN-66 HP nav., 1/SPG-50 f.c.
PGM 357–361: 1/LN-66 HP nav., 1/HC 75 surf. search, 1/SPS-58 air search, 1/Westinghouse W-120 f.c.
EW: 2 Mk 33 RBOC decoy syst. (Mk 136 launchers, VI × 2)
M: 6 AVCO TF-35 gas turbines; 2 CP props; 16,800 shp
Range: 2,400/18 **Crew:** 5 officers, 27 enlisted

Remarks: Korean-built units have Westinghouse M-1200 fire-control systems, us[illegible] inputs from the LN-66 HP radar and a Kollmorgen optical director. PGM 352–355 h[illegible] the U.S. Mk 63 GFCS with SPG-50 radar, 2 Standard ARM SSM launchers (each w[illegible] one reload). Hull form derived from the U.S. Navy *Asheville* (PG 84) class. Three turbines per shaft, geared in as necessary to produce desired speed range. Paek means "sea gull."

♦ 1 ex-U.S. Asheville class
Bldr: Tacoma Boat, Tacoma, Wash.

	L	In serv.
PGM 351 Paek Ku 51 (ex-*Benicia*, PG 96)	20-12-69	25-4-70

D: 225 tons (249 fl) **S:** 40 kts **Dim:** 50.14 × 7.28 × 2.9
A: 2/Standard ARM SSM box launchers (2 reloads)—1/76.2-mm 50-cal. U.S. Mk 34 DP—1/40-mm 60-cal. U.S. Mk 3 AA—4/12.7-mm mg (II × 2)
Electron Equipt: Radar: 1/Raytheon 1645 nav., 1/SPG-50 f.c.
M: CODOG: 1 G.E. LM-1500-PE102 gas turbine, 12,500 shp; 2 Cummins VT12-875M diesels, 1,450 bhp; 2 CP props
Range: 1,700/16; 390/35 **Crew:** 5 officers, 37 enlisted

Remarks: Transferred on loan 15-10-71. One reload missile carried for each launcher. Mk 63 Mod. 29 radar gun fire-control system for 76.2-mm Mk 34 gun.

GUIDED-MISSILE PATROL BOATS *(continued)*

◆ **2 "Wildcat" type** Bldr: Korea Tacoma SY, Chinhae (In serv. 1971–72)

PKM 271 KILURKI 71 PKM 272 KILURKI 72

Kilurki 71 or 72 Korea Tacoma

D: 120 tons (140 fl) **S:** 34–35 kts **Dim:** 32.90 × 8.00 × 1.10
A: 2/MM 38 Exocet SSM (I × 2)—1/40-mm U.S. Mk 3 AA—2/12.7-mm mg (I × 2)—2/127-mm barrage RL (IV × 2)
Electron Equipt: 1/Raytheon 1645 nav.
M: PKM 271: 2 MTU MB518D diesels; 3 props; 9,960 bhp
PKM 272: 3 MTU 16V538 TB90 diesels; 3 props; 10,800 bhp
Range: 1,000/20 **Crew:** 5 officers, 24 enlisted

PATROL BOATS

◆ **32 "Sea Dolphin" type** Bldr: Korea Tacoma SY, Chinhae, and Korea SB & Eng., Masan (In serv. 1970s)

PKM 211-series KILURKI 11– . . . . . .

"Sea Dolphin" 312 Leo Van Ginderen, 11-88

ea Dolphin" 299—with davit to handle an inspection boat in place of er gatling gun 9-90

D: 113 tons (144 fl) **S:** 34 kts
Dim: 33.10 (31.25 wl) × 6.92 × 1.75 (2.45 props)
A: 1/40-mm AA—2/30-mm Emerlec AA (II × 1)—2/20-mm AA (I × 2)—2/12.7-mm mg (I × 2)—*or:* 2/30-mm Emerlec AA (II × 1)—2/20-mm Vulcan gatling AA
Electron Equipt: Radar: 1/Raytheon 1645 nav.
M: 2 MTU 16V538 TB90 diesels; 2 props; 10,800 bhp (9,000 sust.)
Range: 500/32; 1,000/20 **Fuel:** 15 tons
Crew: 5 officers, 24 enlisted

Remarks: Designed for 38 kts; can make 32 kts continuous. Also known commercially the "Wildcat" class. Most units now probably carry the second armament suite ed.

◆ **39 PK "Schoolboy" or "Sea Hawk" class** Bldr: Korea SB & Eng., Masan, and Korea Tacom SY, Chinhae (In serv. 1974–79)

PK 151 to PK 189 CHEBI 51 to CHEBI 89

"Schoolboy/Sea Hawk" class

PK 153—20-mm AA aft, 40-mm AA forward 1983

D: 70–72 tons (78–80 fl) **S:** 40 kts **Dim:** 25.7 × 5.4 × 1.2
A: 1/40-mm AA—1/20-mm AA—4/12.7-mm mg (II × 2)—2/7.62-mm mg (I × 2)
Electron Equipt: Radar: 1/Raytheon 1645 nav.
M: 2 MTU 16V538 TD90 diesels; 2 props; 5,200 bhp
Range: 500/20; 600/17 **Crew:** 6 officers, 19 enlisted

Remarks: Armament varies: recent units (and those refitted) have a Korean-designed 40-mm power-operated mount and three twin Korean-design 12.7-mm mg mounts (see photo of PK 153); early ships had a U.S. Mk 3 40-mm mount forward.

MINE WARFARE SHIPS

◆ **3 (+13) SK 5000-class minehunters** Bldr: Swallowcraft, Kangnam SB, Pusan

. . . KANG KEONG (In serv. 1988) . . . . (In serv. 1993)
. . . . (In serv. 1991) . . . . (In serv. 1993)
. . . . (In serv. 11-91) . . . . (In serv. 1994)

Kang Keong Kangnam SB, 1988

D: 470 tons (520 fl) **S:** 15 kts **Dim:** 50.0 × 9.6 × 2.6
A: 1/20-mm Oerlikon AA
Electron Equipt:
Radar: 1/. . . nav.—Sonar: Plessey 193M Mod. 1 hull-mounted
M: 2 diesels; 2 Voith-Schneider vertical cycloidal props; 1,600 bhp—bow-thruster
Range: 2,500/12 **Crew:** 40 tot.

MINE WARFARE SHIPS *(continued)*

Remarks: Design based on Italian Intermarine *Lerici* design, but not built under license from the *Lerici* builder, Intermarine. First unit scheduled to deliver 12-86, two more ordered 1987, three in 1989. Glass-reinforced plastic construction, with bow-thruster. Carry two Gaymarine Pluto mine-disposal vehicles and are equipped with Racal-Decca MAINS plotting gear. As many as 16 may ultimately be built. Sonar includes Type 2048 Speedscan forward-looking component.

♦ 5 U.S. MSC-289-class coastal minesweepers
Bldr: Peterson Bldrs., Sturgeon Bay, Wisconsin

	In serv.
MSC 555 Nam Yang (ex-MSC 295)	8-63
MSC 556 Ha Dong (ex-MSC 296)	11-63
MSC 557 Sam Kok (ex-MSC 316)	7-68
MSC 558 Yong Dong (ex-MSC 320)	2-10-75
MSC 559 Ok Cheon (ex-MSC 321)	2-10-75

Yong Dong (MSC 558)—with an old pendant number U.S. Navy, 5-75

D: 315 tons (380 fl) **S:** 14 kts **Dim:** 44.32 × 8.29 × 2.7
A: 2/20-mm AA (II × 1)—3/12.7-mm mg (I × 3)
Electron Equipt:
Radar: 1/Decca. . . nav.—Sonar: UQS-1 hull-mounted HF
M: 4 G.M. 6-71 diesels; 2 props; 1,020 bhp **Electric:** 1,260 kw
Range: 2,500/14 **Fuel:** 33 tons **Crew:** 40 tot.

Remarks: Wooden construction. Built under Military Aid Program. Gas-turbine sweep generator. Lower superstructure than on the MSC 268 class, below. MSC 556–559 may be re-equipped with Thomson-Sintra 2022 minehunting sonar.

♦ 3 U.S. MSC 268-class coastal minesweepers
Bldr: Harbor Boat Building, Terminal Island, California

	In serv.
MSC 551 Kum San (ex-MSC 284)	6-59
MSC 552 Ko Hung (ex-MSC 285)	8-59
MSC 553 Kum Kok (ex-MSC 286)	10-59

Kum San (MSC 551)

D: 320 tons (370 fl) **S:** 14 kts **Dim:** 43.0 (41.5 pp) × 7.95 × 2.55
A: 2/20-mm AA (II × 2)—3/12.7-mm mg (I × 3)
Electron Equipt:
Radar: Decca 45 nav.—Sonar: UQS-1 hull-mounted HF
M: 2 G.M. 8-268A diesels; 2 props; 1,200 bhp
Range: 2,500/16 **Fuel:** 40 tons **Crew:** 40 tot.

Remarks: Built under Military Aid Program. Wooden hulls.

AMPHIBIOUS WARFARE SHIPS

Note: In addition to the new LST class listed below, the Republic of Korea Navy plans to order two larger amphibious warfare ships for delivery around the turn of the century.

♦ 0 (+2) new-construction landing ships
Bldr: Korea Tacoma SY, Masan

	Laid down	L	In serv.
. . . .	. . .	. . .	. . .
. . . .	. . .	. . .	. . .

D: 4,200 tons (fl) **S:** 15 kts **Dim:** 106.90 × 15.30 × 3.00
A: 4/40-mm Breda AA (II × 2)—2/20-mm AA (I × 2)
Electron Equipt: Radar: . . .
M: 2 SEMT-Pielstick 16PA6V diesels; 2 props; 6,400 bhp
Electric: 750 kw tot. **Range:** 7,500/13 **Crew:** . . .

Remarks: First two of a class intended to replace the obsolescent ex-U.S. units liste below; ordered 6-90. Will have a helicopter deck aft and will probably resemble unit built in South Korea for Venezuela and Indonesia. Will be able to carry up to 1,800-ton cargo (690 maximum beaching load) and about 200 troops.

♦ 7 ex-U.S. LST 1- and U.S. LST 542-class landing ships

	Bldr	L	In serv
LST 671 Un Bong (ex-LST 1010)	Bethlehem, Fore River	29-3-44	25-4-4
LST 673 Bi Bong (ex-*Berkshire County,* LST 218)	Chicago Bridge, Seneca, Ill.	20-7-43	12-8-4
LST 675 Kae Bong (ex-LST 288)	American Bridge, Pa.	7-11-43	20-12-4
LST 676 Wee Bong (ex-*Johnson County,* LST 849)	American Bridge, Pa.	30-12-43	16-1-4
LST 677 Su Yong (ex-*Kane County,* LST 853)	Chicago Bridge, Seneca, Ill.	17-11-44	11-12-
LST 678 Buk Han (ex-*Lynn County,* LST 900)	Dravo, Pittsburgh	9-12-44	28-12-
LST 679 Hwa San (ex-*Pender County,* LST 1080)	Bethlehem, Hingham, Mass.	2-5-45	29-5-

Su Yong (LST 677) French Navy,

D: 1,653 tons (4,080 fl) **S:** 10 kts
Dim: 100.04 × 15.24 × 4.30
A: 8/40-mm AA (II × 2, I × 4)—2/20-mm AA (I × 2)
Electron Equipt: Radar: 2/. . . nav.
M: 2 G.M. 12-567A or 12-278A diesels; 2 props; 1,800 bhp
Electric: 300 kw **Range:** 15,000/9 **Fuel:** 569 tons **Crew:** 70 t

Remarks: Transferred 1955–58; all purchased outright 15-11-74. LST 1 class elevators from upper deck to tank deck; later ships had a ramp. Can carry 1,230 cargo maximum/815-tons beaching plus up to 350 troops. Sister *Tuk Bong* (LST ex-LST 227) stricken 1989 after grounding.

♦ 7 ex-U.S. LSM 1-class medium landing ships
Bldr: Brown SB, Houston, Tex. (except: LSM 652: Federal SB, Newark, N.J.; LSM 661: Pullm Standard Car Co., Chicago, Ill.)

	Laid down	L	In serv.
LSM 655 Ko Mun (ex-LSM 30)	7-5-44	28-5-44	1-7-44
LSM 656 Pi An (ex-LSM 96)	15-9-44	7-10-44	28-10-44
LSM 657 Wol Mi (ex-LSM 57)	30-6-44	21-7-44	17-8-44

AMPHIBIOUS WARFARE SHIPS *(continued)*

	Laid down	L	In serv.
LSM 658 Ki Rin (ex-LSM 19)	24-4-44	14-5-44	14-6-44
LSM 659 Nung Ra (ex-LSM 84)	22-8-44	15-9-44	7-10-44
LSM 661 Sin Mi (ex-LSM 316)	6-4-44	18-6-44	21-7-44
LSM 662 Ul Rung (ex-LSM 17)	10-4-44	7-5-44	12-6-44

.a Tok (LSM 653)—since stricken PH1 D. Brockschmidt, USN, 3-82

D: 520 tons (1,095 fl) **S:** 13 kts **Dim:** 62.0 × 10.52 × 2.53
A: 2/40-mm AA (II × 1)—4/20-mm AA (I × 4)
Electron Equipt: Radar: 1/. . . nav.
M: 2 Fairbanks-Morse 38D8Q × 10 diesels; 2 props; 2,880 bhp
Electric: 240 kw **Range:** 5,000/7 **Fuel:** 160 tons **Crew:** 75 tot.

:marks: All transferred 1956. Cargo: 350 tons (165 beaching) plus 48 troops. Sisters *:e Cho* (LSM 651, ex-U.S. LSM 546), *Tyo To* (LSM 652, ex-U.S. LSM 268), and *Ka Tok* SM 653, ex-U.S. LSM 462) stricken 1982. *Pung To* (ex-LSM 54), with minelaying pability, stricken 1984.

6 Mulkae-class utility landing craft Bldr: Korea Tacoma SY, Masan

ULKAE 72–77 (In serv. 1979–81)

D: 220 tons (415 fl) **S:** 12 kts **Dim:** 41.07 × 9.07 × 2.08
A: 2/20-mm AA (I × 2) **Electron Equipt:** Radar: 1/. . . nav.
M: 4 G.M. 6-71 diesels; 2 Kort-nozzle props; 1,200 bhp
Range: 560/11 **Crew:** 14 tot.

marks: Cargo capacity: 143 tons; cargo deck 30.5 × 5.5. Copies of U.S. LCU 1610 ign with higher pilothouse; built with imported equipment. *Mulkae* means "fur ."

10 ex-U.S. Army LCM(8)-class landing craft

D: 58.8 tons (116 fl) **S:** 9.2 kts loaded
Dim: 22.40 × 6.42 × 1.40 (mean)
M: 4 G.M. 6-71 diesels; 2 props; 600 bhp
Range: 150/9.2 (loaded) **Fuel:** 2.4 tons **Crew:** 4 tot.

narks: Transferred 9-78. Cargo: 57.4 tons; can also carry troops for short distances.

e: South Korea also builds glass-reinforced plastic-hulled versions of the U.S. 'P landing craft. For use by the ROK Marines, there are 24 LVTP-7A and 53 'P-7 troop-carrying, 1 LVTC-7A1 and 5 LVTC-7 command, and 3 LVTR-7 recovery ored tracked amphibious landing vehicles.

XILIARIES

) (+1+2) Chun Ji-class replenishment oilers Bldr: Hyundai SY, Jlsan

	Laid down	L	In serv.
R 57 Chun Ji	. . .	. . .	. . .

: 8,000 tons (fl) **S:** 20 kts **Dim:** 130.0 × 17.8 × 6.5
: 4/40-mm AA Breda (II × 2)—2/20-mm gatling AA
lectron Equipt: Radar: 2/ . . . nav.
: 2 SEMT-Pielstick 12 PC 2-5 V 400 diesels; 2 CP props; 15,600 bhp
ange: 4,500/15 **Electric:** 725 kw tot. **Crew:** . . . tot.

. Ji (AOR 57)—model Hyundai, 1990

Remarks: Ordered 6-90. Builder's HDA 8000 design, a reduced version of the *Endeavour* built for New Zealand. Cargo: 4,20 tons fuels, 450 tons stores. Two replenishment stations on each beam, one for liquids and one for solid cargo transfer; also able to refuel over the stern. Helicopter platform and hangar aft. Replaces the stricken Norwegian-built oiler *Chun Ji* (AO 2), which was stricken during the late 1980s; two more planned to replace the U.S.-built ships below.

◆ 2 ex-U.S. Tonti-class gasoline tankers Bldr: Todd SB, Houston, Tex.

	L	In serv.
AO 55 So Yang (ex-*Rincon,* T-AOG 77, ex-*Tarland*)	5-1-45	10-45
AO 56 Chin Yang (ex-*Petaluma,* T-AOG 79, ex-*Raccoon Bend*)	9-8-45	11-45

D: 2,100 tons (6,047 fl) **S:** 10 kts **Dim:** 99.1 × 14.7 × 5.8
A: . . . . . . **Electron Equipt:** Radar: . . .
M: 2 Nordberg diesels; 1 prop; 1,400 bhp **Electric:** 515 kw
Range: 6,000/10 **Fuel:** 154 tons **Crew:** 41 tot.

Remarks: 3,160 grt/3,933 dwt. Cargo 31,284 bbl. light fuels (diesel, JP-5 gasoline). Acquired from Maritime Commission by U.S. Navy 1-7-50 and 7-9-50, respectively. Leased 21-2-82. Are probably armed.

◆ 0 (+1) coastal oiler Bldr: Daewoo SY, Okpo

	Laid down	L	In serv.
YO	. . .	. . .	. . .

D: 3,00 tons (fl) **S:** . . . kts **Dim:** . . . × . . . × . . .
A: . . . . . . **Electron Equipt:** Radar: . . . .
M: . . . . . .

Remarks: Reported ordered 1991. May be a replacement for one of the three units listed below or may be the second of the three planned *Chun Ji*-class replenishment oilers (with the 3,000-tons referring to light-ship weight).

◆ 2 ex-U.S. 174-foot-class harbor tankers

	Bldr	L	In serv.
YO 1 Ku Kyong (ex-YO 118)	R.T.C. SB, Camden, N.J.	6-5-44	8-8-44
YO 6 . . . . (ex-YO 179)	Smith SY, Pensacola, Fla.	24-11-44	26-5-45

D: 1,400 tons (fl) **S:** 7 kts **Dim:** 53.0 × 10.0 × 4.0
A: 2/20-mm AA (I × 2)
M: 1 Union diesel; 1 prop; 560 bhp **Fuel:** 25 tons **Crew:** 36 tot.

Remarks: YO 1 transferred 1946, YO 6 in 9-71. Cargo: 900 tons.

◆ 1 ex-U.S. YO 55-class harbor tanker Bldr: R.T.C. SB, Camden, N.J.

	Laid down	L	In serv.
YO . . . Hwa Chon (ex-*Derrick,* YO 59)	15-6-42	21-11-42	2-2-43

D: 800 tons (2,700 fl) **S:** 10 kts **Dim:** 71.65 × 11.3 × 4.8
A: . . . . . . **Electron Equipt:** Radar: . . .
M: 2 Fairbanks-Morse 37E14-5 diesels; 2 props; 1,150 bhp
Electric: 160 kw **Fuel:** 105 tons **Range:** 4,600/8 **Crew:** 46 tot.

Remarks: Transferred 4-55. Cargo: 1,600 tons. Probably armed with 20-mm AA.

◆ 2 ex-U.S. Diver-class salvage ships Bldr: Basalt Rock Co., Napa, California

	Laid down	L	In serv.
ARS 26 Chang Won (ex-*Grasp,* ARS 24)	27-4-43	31-7-43	22-8-44
ARS 27 Gum I (ex-*Deliver,* ARS 23)	2-4-43	25-9-43	18-7-44

D: 1,530 tons (1,970 fl) **S:** 14.8 kts **Dim:** 65.1 × 12.5 × 4.0
A: 2/20-mm AA **Electron Equipt:** Radar: 1/SPS-53 nav.
M: 4 Cooper-Bessemer GSB 8 diesels; electric drive; 2 props; 2,440 shp
Electric: 460 kw **Fuel:** 300 tons **Range:** 9,000/14; 20,000/7
Crew: 83 tot.

Remarks: ARS 5 transferred 31-3-78; ARS 6 on 15-8-79, both by sale. Equipped for salvage, diver support, and towing.

◆ 2 U.S. Sotoyomo-class auxiliary tugs

	Bldr	Laid down	L	In serv.
ATA 3 Do Bang (ex-*Pinola,* ATA 206)	Gulfport Boiler Wks, Port Arthur, Tex.	26-10-44	14-12-44	10-2-45
ATA 2 Yong Mun (ex-*Keosangua,* ATA 198)	Levingston SB, Orange, Tex.	14-12-44	17-1-45	19-3-45

D: 835 tons (fl) **S:** 13 kts **D:** 43.6 (40.7 pp) × 10.3 × 4.0
A: 1/76.2-mm Mk 22 DP—4/20-mm AA (II × 2)
Electron Equipt: Radar: 1/. . . nav.
M: 2 G.M. 12-278A diesels, electric drive; 1 prop; 1,500 shp
Electric: 120 kw **Fuel:** 158 tons **Crew:** 45 tot.

Remarks: Transferred 2-62. ATA 3 is used in salvage work. Sister *Tan Yang* (ex-*Tillamook,* ATA 192) was acquired 7-1-71 to operate in the Hydrographic Service but never left U.S. waters and was derelict at Long Beach by 1983.

Note: There are also nine harbor tugs, including YTL 13 (ex-U.S.N. YTL 550), YTL 22 (ex-Army ST 2097), YTL 23 (ex-Army ST 2099), YTL 25 (ex-Army YT 2106), YTL 26 (ex-Army ST 2065), and YTL 30 (ex-Army ST 2101). All transferred 1968–72. About 25 other yard and service craft are also in use.

COAST GUARD

The Republic of Korea Coast Guard operates about 60 seagoing patrol boats and 85 small patrol craft. There are about 4,000 personnel, most in shore billets. Although painted the same basic gray as ROKN units, where there is a stack, Coast Guard ships have a horizontal green band on it.

◆ **6 HDC 1150-class patrol ships** Bldr: Korea SB & Eng., Pusan

	In serv.		In serv.
1002	1983	1006	. . .
1003	1983	1007	. . .
1005 Han Kang	1983	1008	1988

Han Kang (1005) *Ships of the World,* 1988

D: 980 tons (1,800 fl) **S:** 31 kts **Dim:** 87.8 × 10.0 × 2.88
A: 1/76-mm OTO Melara DP—1/40-mm Mk 3 AA—2/20-mm gatling AA (I × 2)
Electron Equipt:
Radar: 1/Raytheon SPS-64(V) nav. , 1/H.S.A. WM-28 f.c.
M: CODOG: 1 G.E. LM-2500 gas turbine, 27,800 shp; 2 MTU 12V956 TB 82 diesels, 6,260 bhp; 2 CP props
Range: 4,000/15 **Endurance:** 21 days
Crew: 11 officers, 61 enlisted

Remarks: Lengthened version of HDC 800 design (*Dong Hae* class) built for the ROKN, but without ASW equipment. Have H.S.A. LIOD optronic and a visual backup director to supplement the H.S.A. WM-28 detection/tracking radar.

◆ **1 HDP 1000-class patrol ship** Bldr: Korea SB & Eng., Pusan

1001 Mazinga (In serv. 29-11-81)

Mazinga (1001) Korea SB & Eng.

D: 1,200 tons (1,450 fl) **S:** 21.5 kts **Dim:** 80.50 × 8.90 × 3.15
A: 1/40-mm Mk 3 AA—4/20-mm AA (II × 2)
Electron Equipt: Radar: 2/. . . navigational
M: 2 Niigata SEMT-Pielstick 12 PA6-280 diesels; 2 props; 9,600 bhp
Electric: . . . **Range:** 7,000/18 **Crew:** 11 officers, 58 enlisted

Remarks: A lower-powered and more lightly armed version of the *Po Hang*-class frigates built for the navy. Passive-tank stabilization system. Engines built in Japan under license. Acts as Coast Guard flagship. Ordered 7-11-80.

◆ **6 "Sea Whale"-class patrol boats**

	Bldr	In serv.
501	. . . . . .	1980
502	. . . . . .	. . .
503	. . . . . .	. . .
505	Korea SB & Eng., Pusan	3-80
506	Korea Tacoma SY, Chinhae	5-79
507	Korea Tacoma SY, Chinhae	7-82

D: 410 tons (580 fl) **S:** 24 kts **Dim:** 60.8 × 8.0 × 2.29
A: 1/40-mm Mk 3 AA—2/20-mm AA (I × 2)—2/7.62-mm mg (I × 2)
Electron Equipt: Radar: 1/. . . nav.
M: 2 MTU diesels; 2 props; 9,600 bhp **Range:** 1,500/25; 2,400/20
Crew: 11 officers, 28 enlisted

Remarks: Intended for rescue and inspection duties. Flume-type passive tank roll stabilization on one unit; AA gun in same position on others. The same two builders constructed 501–503.

"Sea Whale" 501 199

◆ **4 Bukhansan class** Bldr: Hyundai SY, Ulsan (In serv. 1989–90)

278 279 281 282

D: 371 tons (fl) **S:** 25 kts **Dim:** 50.0 × 7.3 × 2.2
A: 2/40-mm Breda AA (II × 1)—1/20-mm Oerlikon AA—2/12.7-mm mg
M: 2 MTU diesels; 2 props; 9,000 bhp **Range:** 2,500/15
Crew: 3 officers, 32 enlisted

Remarks: Development of the Sea Wolf/Sea Shark series. Have an optronic direct for the 40-mm mount.

◆ **23 "Sea Shark/Wolf"-class patrol boats** Bldr: Hyundai SY, Ulsar and Korea Tacoma SY, Masan

200 through 277-series

"Sea Shark/Sea Wolf" 251 Leo Van Ginderen, 1

D: 250 tons (280 fl) **S:** 28 kts
Dim: 48.2 × 7.1 × 2.1 (2.5 over props)
A: 4/20-mm AA (II × 2 or II × 1, I × 2)—2/12.7-mm mg (I × 2)
Electron Equipt: Radar: 1/. . . nav.
M: 2 diesels; 2 props; 7,320 bhp **Range:** 3,300/15
Crew: 5 officers, 24 enlisted

Remarks: Some have a raised platform aft. Units from Hyundai known as Shark" class, those from Korea Tacoma as the "Sea Wolf" design. Range also giv 2,000 n.m. at 17 kts.

◆ **18 "Sea Gull" class** Bldr: Korea SB & Eng., Pusan (In serv. early 1970s)

"Sea Gull" class Korea SB &

D: 80 tons **S:** 30 kts **Dim:** 24.0 × 5.5 × . . .
A: 1 or 2/20-mm AA (I) **M:** 2 MTU diesels; 2 props; 3,920 bhp
Range: 950/20 **Crew:** 18 tot.

◆ **. . . "Swallow" class, glass-reinforced plastic construction** Bldr: Korea SB & Eng., Pusan

D: 32 tons (fl) **S:** 25 kts **Dim:** 20.0 × 4.7 × 1.3
A: 1/12.7-mm mg—1/7.62-mm mg **Range:** 500/20
M: 2 G.M. 12V71 TI diesels; 2 props; 1,060 bhp **Crew:** 8 tot.

KOREA, SOUTH *(continued)*
COAST GUARD *(continued)*

'Swallow"-class P-52 Leo Van Ginderen, 11-87

KUWAIT

tate of Kuwait

rsonnel (1991–post-war): Approximately 600 tot.

te: Lost to Iraqi forces by the navy during the war were six guided-missile patrol ats (see below), four Loadmaster Mk II-class landing craft, and two tugs. The Coast ard lost 16 patrol craft, six landing craft, a fireboat, and six utility launches. The stoms service lost all six of its patrol craft. Of the other units listed in the previous tion, the eight 36-foot Vosper Thornycroft–built patrol craft had been discarded by 89, as had the patrol craft *Mahroos;* six SR.N6-class air-cushion vehicles do not pear ever to have been acquired.

IDED-MISSILE PATROL BOATS

1 FPB 57 class Bldr: Lürssen, Bremen-Vegesack, Germany

5702 ISTIQLAL (In serv. 9-8-83)

qlal (P 5702) U.S. Navy, 11-90

lal (P 5702)—with yacht *Shaikhan* used as patrol craft alongside C.V. Gheerbrant, 3-91

353 tons (398 fl) **S:** 36 kts
: 58.10 (54.40 wl) × 7.62 × 2.83
4/MM 40 Exocet (II × 2)—1/76-mm OTO Melara DP—2/40-mm Breda AA (II × 1)—2/7.62-mm mg (I × 2)—mines

Electron Equipt:
Radar: 1/Decca 1226C nav., 1/PEAB 9LV200 surf./air search, 1/9LV228 f.c.
EW: Racal RDL-2 intercept, Racal Cygnus jammer, 1/Dagaie decoy RL
M: 4 MTU 16V956 TB91 diesels; 4 props; 18,000 bhp
Electric: 405 kw (3 × 135 kw) **Range:** 1,300/30 **Fuel:** 90 tons
Crew: 4 officers, 35 enlisted

Remarks: Two ordered 1980 to function as leaders for the six TNC-45 class. Name means "Freedom." Sister *Sabhan* (P 5704) captured by Iraqi forces 8-90 and sunk by UN Coalition forces 29-1-91.

◆ **1 TNC-45 class** Bldr: Lürssen, Bremen-Vegesack, Germany

	L	In serv.
P 4505 AL SANBOUK (ex-*Jalboot*)	5-82	26-4-84

Al Sanbouk (P 4505) U.S. Navy, 11-90

D: 231 tons (259 fl) **S:** 41.5 kts **Dim:** 44.90 (42.30 wl) × 7.00 × 2.40
A: 4/MM 40 Exocet—1/76-mm OTO Melara DP—2/40-mm Breda AA (II × 1)—2/7.62-mm mg (I × 2)
Electron Equipt:
Radar: 1/Decca 1226 nav., 1/PEAB 9LV200 surf./air search, 1/PEAB 9LV200 f.c.
EW: Racal RDL-2 intercept
M: 4 MTU 16V538 TB92 diesels; 4 props; 15,600 bhp (15,000 sust.)
Electric: 369 kw tot. (3 × 123 kw) **Range:** 500/38.5; 1,500/16
Crew: 5 officers, 27 enlisted

Remarks: Six ordered 1980. Carries 250 rounds 76-mm, 1,800 rounds 40-mm ammunition. Has CSEE Lynx optronic gun director for the 40-mm mount. Philips 9LV200 system for the 76-mm gun and missiles, and a flare rocket launcher amidships. First three, accepted 26-4-84 after extensive training period, had been delivered 8-82, 9-82, and 10-82, respectively. Five were captured by invading Iraqi forces, 8-90, and were subsequently sunk by UN Coalition forces (one on 18-1-91, one on 30-1-91, and the others uncertain): *Al Boom* (P 4501, ex-*Werjiya*), *Al Betteen* (P 4503, ex-*Mashuwah*), *Al Saadi* (P 4507, ex-*Istiqlal*), *Al Ahmadi* (P 4509), and *Al Abdali* (P 4511, ex-*Al Mubareki*).

PATROL BOATS

◆ **0 (+ 2) ASI 315 class** Bldr: Australian SB Ind. (WA), Pty, Ltd., South Coogie (In serv. 11-92)

D: 165 tons (fl) **S:** 26 kts (20 sust.)
Dim: 32.60 (28.60 wl) × 8.10 × 2.12 (1.80 hull)
A: . . . **Electron Equipt:** Radar: 1/Furuno 1011 (I/J-band)
M: 2 Caterpillar 3516 diesels; 2 props; 2,820 bhp (2,400 sust.); 1 Caterpillar 3412 TA cruise diesel; 1 Hamilton 521 waterjet; 775 bhp
Range: 2,500/12 **Fuel:** 27.9 tons **Endurance:** 8–10 days
Electric: 116 kw (2 × 50 kw; Caterpillar 3304 diesels; 1 × 16 kw)
Crew: 3 officers, 14 enlisted

Remarks: Originally ordered 7-90, just prior to the Iraqi invasion; order reinstated post-war. Australian foreign aid program "Pacific Patrol Boat" design. Carry a 5-m aluminum boarding boat. Extensive navigational suite, including Furuno FSN-70 NAVSAT receiver, 525 HF/DF, 120 MH/HF/DF, FE-881 echo-sounder, and DS-70 doppler log. Are of the version building for Hong Kong, with a cruise/loiter engine added.

PATROL CRAFT

Note: In addition to the units listed below, about a dozen other small ex-Iraqi or former private craft have been pressed into service for patrol or utility duties.

◆ **2 ex-Iraqi Soviet Zhuk class**

D: 48 tons (60 fl) **S:** 24 kts **Dim:** 24.0 × 5.0 × 1.2 (1.8 props)
A: 4/14.5-mm mg (IV × 1)
Electron Equipt: Radar: 1/Spin Trough nav.
M: 2 M50F-4 diesels; 2 props; 2,400 bhp
Range: 700/28; 1,100/15 **Fuel:** 10 tons **Crew:** 12 tot.

Remarks: Left behind by fleeing Iraqi forces and pressed into service. Will probably not be retained long.

KUWAIT *(continued)*

AUXILIARIES

◆ **2 Sawahil 35-class self-propelled barracks ships** Bldr: Inchon SB & Eng., South Korea (In serv. 1986)

Sawahil 35 Sawahil 50

Sawahil 35 C.V. Gheerbrant, 3-91

D: approx. 1,800 tons (fl) **S:** 8 kts **Dim:** 55.00 × 20.0 × 2.0
A: 2/12.7-mm mg (I × 2)
Electron Equipt: Radar: 1/. . . nav.
M: 2 diesels; 2 props; 2,400 bhp **Crew:** . . . tot.

Remarks: 545 dwt. Built for the Kuwait Shipbuilding and Repair Ministry for use as oilfield barracks. *Sawahil 35* escaped capture by Iraqi forces and operated in support of Free Kuwaiti forces as a supply tender, carrying fuel and ammunition. *Sawahil 50* was recaptured post-war and was armed at the time with two quadruple 23-mm AA; she may belong to the Coast Guard rather than the navy. Both have a 20 × 20-meter helicopter deck. Sisters *Sawahil 40* and *Sawahil 43* were lost during the war.

COAST GUARD

Note: The Kuwaiti Coast Guard has been reconstituted post-war and was reported to have acquired some 37 small patrol craft by 9-91. Some of the craft are probably captured Iraqi Swary-class patrol craft or former private yachts and launches. The craft built by Cougar Marine listed below were all ordered 1-91 by the then-government in exile and delivered post-hostilities.

◆ **4 UFPB 1300 class** Bldr: Cougar Marine, Washington, U.K. (In serv. 6-91)

D: . . . tons (fl) **S:** . . . kts **Dim:** 13.0 × . . . × . . . **A:** . . .
M: 2 Ford Sabre 380C diesels; 2 Arneson surface-piercing props; 760 bhp

◆ **4 UFPB 1200 class** Bldr: Cougar Marine, Washington, U.K. (In serv. 6-91)

D: . . . tons (fl) **S:** . . . kts **Dim:** 12.0 × . . . × . . . **A:** . . .
M: 2 Ford Sabre 380C diesels; 2 Arneson surface-piercing props; 760 bhp

◆ **3 UFPB 1100 Predator-class GRP-hulled** Bldr: Cougar Marine, Washington, U.K. (In serv. 6-91)

D: . . . tons (fl) **S:** . . . kts **Dim:** 11.0 × . . . × . . .
A: . . . **M:** 2 Yamaha 200B gasoline outboards; 400 bhp

◆ **3 UFPB 1000-class GRP-hulled** Bldr: Cougar Marine, Washington, U.K. (In serv. 4-91)

D: . . . tons (fl) **S:** . . . kts **Dim:** 10.00 × . . . × . . .
A: . . . . **M:** 2 Yamaha 200B gasoline outboards; 400 bhp

◆ **3 Cat 900-class catamarans** Bldr: Cougar Marine, Washington, U.K. (In serv. 5-91)

D: 2 tons (fl) **S:** 35 kts **Dim:** 9.0 × . . . × . . .
A: . . . **M:** 2 Yamaha 200B gasoline outboards; 400 bhp

◆ **1 or more "Sea Gull" class** Bldr: Korea SB & Eng., Pusan (In serv. 1985–89)

D: 80 tons **S:** 30 kts **Dim:** 24.0 × 5.5 × . . . **A:** . . .
M: 2 diesels; 2 props; 3,920 bhp **Range:** 950/20 **Crew:** 18 tot.

Remarks: First five ordered 1985; second group in 1988. Aluminum construction. Most lost to Iraqi invaders or later UN Coalition action, but one or two are believed to have survived.

LAOS

ARMY MARINE SECTION

Personnel (1991): Approximately 600 total

◆ **40 river patrol craft**

Remarks: Reported by press to have been a gift of the U.S.S.R. in 1985. No other data available. Also possibly in service are four landing craft. There are probably other locally built craft in service.

LEBANON

Republic of Lebanon

Personnel (1991): Approximately 200 total

PATROL CRAFT

Note: Semi-independent Christian forces have operated five Dabur-class patrol craft, transferred by Israel in 1976; for characteristics, see Israel section. As many as 20 additional patrol craft are operated by Christian and other Lebanese factions, but details are unavailable. Six Azteca-class patrol craft acquired in 1980 are believed to be out of service.

◆ **1 Tracker Mk II class** Fairey Allday Marine, Hamble, U.K. (In serv. 1980)

D: 31.5 tons (fl) **S:** 29 kts **Dim:** 19.25 × 4.98 × 1.45 **A:** . . .
M: 2 G.M. 12V71 TI diesels; 2 props; 990 bhp
Range: 650/20 **Crew:** 11 tot.

Remarks: Intended primarily for customs service. One other, under Christian Militi control since 1983, may no longer be in service.

AMPHIBIOUS WARFARE SHIPS

◆ **2 French EDIC-III-class landing craft** Bldr: SFCN, Villeneuve-la-Garenne

Sour (In serv. 1-85) Damour (L: 11-12-84)

D: 375 tons (712 fl) **S:** 10 kts
Dim: 59.00 (57.00 pp) × 11.90 × 1.67 (1.10 light)
A: 2/20-mm AA (I × 2)—1/81-mm mortar
Electron Equipt: Radar: 1/. . . nav.
M: 2 SACM MGO 175-V12-A diesels; 2 props; 1,040 bhp
Range: 1,800/10 **Fuel:** 35 tons **Crew:** 18 tot. + 33 troops

Remarks: Ordered 30-7-83 as aid from the French government. *Sour* replaced earlier EDIC (L 9096) of the same name that had been loaned on 7-11-83. Can carry trucks or 5 armored personnel carriers.

LIBERIA

Republic of Liberia

Personnel (1991): Approximately 50 total

Note: The Liberian National Coast Guard was restyled the Liberian Navy in 1 Plans to acquire one 33.5-m and two 19.8-m patrol boats from the U.S. fell throug 1987. The U.S. Swiftships 33.5-m patrol boat, *Farandugu,* described in the last edi was in fact delivered to Sierra Leone. Rebel forces under Charles Taylor have acce several fishing boats and have used them to capture foreign fishing craft operati Liberian waters and hold them for ransom. No details of the craft are available.

PATROL CRAFT

◆ **1 CG 27 class** Bldr: Karlskrona Varvet, Sweden

8802 Albert Porte (In serv. 27-9-80)

Master Sergeant Samuel K. Doe (8801)—since lost

D: 50 tons **S:** 25 kts **Dim:** 26.72 × 5.23 × 1.13
A: 1/12.7-mm mg—2/7.62-mm mg (I × 2)
Electron Equipt: Radar: 1/Decca 1226C nav.
M: 2 MTU 8V331 TC82 diesels; 2 props; 1,866 bhp
Fuel: 11 tons **Range:** 1,000/18 **Crew:** 8 tot.

Remarks: Aluminum alloy construction. Names changed due to revolution; al nally named for rivers. Same design as Swedish Coast Guard TV 102. Sisters *Sergeant Samuel K. Doe* (8801, ex-*Nuah River*) and *General Thomas Quiwoukpa* were sunk 20-7-90 in bombardment by rebel forces.

LIBYA

Socialist People's Libyan Arab Jamahiriya

Personnel (1991): Approximately 3,000 total

Naval Aviation: About 18 Soviet-supplied Mi-14 Haze-A land-based ASW helicopters, 6 French-supplied Super Frélon (with AM 39 Exocet antiship missiles, L5 ASW torpedoes, and Sintra-Alcatel HS 73 dipping sonar), and 12 French Alouette-III helicopters are in service for naval use.

SUBMARINES

Note: Press reports in 1-87 indicated that two more Soviet-built submarines may be "leased," but the economic condition of both nations makes the delivery of further submarines unlikely for the foreseeable future.

◆ **6 Soviet Foxtrot class** Bldr: United Admiralty SY, Sudomekh Division, St. Petersburg

	In serv.		In serv.
311 Al Badr	12-76	314 Al Mitraqah	30-3-81
312 Al Fateh	2-78	315 Al Khyber	4-82
313 Al Ahad	3-78	316 Al Hunayn	2-83

Libyan Foxtrot 23rd Flot., French Navy, 2-83

D: 1,954 tons surf./2,400 tons sub.
S: 15.5 kts surf./18 kts sub. **Dim:** 91.1 × 7.0 × 6.0
A: 10/533-mm TT (6 fwd, 4 aft)—22 torpedoes or 44 mines
Electron Equipt:
Radar: Snoop Tray surf./air search—EW: Stop Light intercept
Sonar: Herkules active MF, passive arrays
M: 3 Type 42D diesels (2,000 bhp each), electric motors; 3 props; 5,300 shp
Endurance: 70 days **Range:** 11,000/8 (snorkel); 350/2 (sub.)
Fuel: 360 tons **Crew:** 12 officers, 70 enlisted

Remarks: Were new construction and lack the HF folding radio mast found on Soviet Navy units. One has been in a Soviet Baltic port for several years undergoing overhaul, and the rest are said to operate very seldom.

◆ **6 Type R2, Mala-class swimmer-delivery vehicles** Bldr: Brodosplit, Split

D: 1.4 tons **S:** 4.4 kts **Dim:** 4.90 × 1.22 × 1.32 (1.70 fins)
A: 2/50-kg mines **Range:** 18/4.4; 23/3.7
M: 1 electric motor; 1 prop; 6 hp **Crew:** 2 tot.

Remarks: Delivered two in 1987 and four in 1981–82. Diving depth: 60 m. Free-flooding craft with plexiglas bow fairing over crew compartment. Have echo-sounder, compass, and bow and stern hydroplanes.

GUIDED-MISSILE FRIGATES

◆ **2 Soviet Koni class** Bldr: Zelenodolsk SY

212 Al Hani (In serv. 28-6-86) 213 Al Ghardabia (In serv. 23-10-87)

Al Hani (212)—with dark gray camouflage striping Leo Van Ginderen, 7-91

Al Hani (212) Leo Van Ginderen, 7-91

D: 1,440 tons (1,600 fl) **S:** 30 kts **Dim:** 96.40 × 12.55 × 3.48 (hull)
A: 4/SS-N-2C SSM (II × 2)—1/SA-N-4 SAM system (II × 1; 20 Gecko missiles)— 4/76-mm AK276 DP (II × 2)—4/30-mm AK-230 AA (II × 2)—1/RBU-6000 ASW RL (XII × 1)—4/400-mm ASW TT (I × 4, fixed)—2/mine rails
Electron Equipt:
Radar: 1/Don-2 nav., 1/Plank Shave missile target designation/surf. search, 1/Strut Curve surf./air search,1/Hawk Screech f.c., 1/Pop Group missile f.c., 1/Drum Tilt f.c.
Sonar: hull-mounted MF
EW: 2/Watch Dog intercept, 2 decoy RL (XVI × 2)
IFF: 2/Square Head interrogator, 1/Salt Pot transponder
M: CODAG: 1 19,000-shp gas turbine; 2 Type 68B, 8,000-bhp diesels; 3 props
Range: 1,800/14 **Crew:** approx. 130 total

Remarks: Were the 11th and 12th-built of this export class. First version of Koni (NATO "Koni-III") to have SSM and ASW torpedoes, at the expense of one ASW rocket launcher. Plank Shave radar acts as surface search and acquisition for SS-N-2C missiles; Pop Group track-while-scan radar controls the SA-N-4 SAMs, Hawk Screech (with two pedestal target designators) handles the 76-mm guns, and Drum Tilt (again with two visual backup directors) serves the 30-mm guns. The deckhouse amidships is continuous in order to accommodate additional air-conditioning equipment. Although two depth-charge racks can be bolted onto the after end of the mine rails, they have not been carried by the Libyan pair.

◆ **1 Vosper Mk 7** Bldr: Vosper Thornycroft, Woolston, U.K.

	Laid down	L	In serv.
211 Dat Assawari	27-9-68	9-69	1-2-73

Dat Assawari (211) Carlo Martinelli, 5-84

D: 1,325 tons (1,650 fl) **S:** 37/17 kts
Dim: 101.6 (94.5 pp) × 11.08 × 3.36
A: 4/Otomat Mk 2 SSM (I × 4)—1/114-mm Mk 8 DP—1/Albatros Mk 2 SAM syst. (IV × 1; Aspide missiles)—2/40-mm AA (I × 2)—2/35-mm Oerlikon AA (II × 1)—6/324-mm ILAS-3 ASW TT (III × 2)
Electron Equipt:
Radar: 1/Decca TM 1226 nav., 1/RAN-10S surf. search, 1/RAN-12 air search, 2/Orion RTN-10X f.c.
Sonar: 1/Thomson-Sintra Diodon (TSM 2310) hull-mounted MF

GUIDED-MISSILE FRIGATES *(continued)*

EW: Decca RDS-1 intercept, Selenia INS-1 intercept, Marconi FH-12 HFD/F
M: CODOG: 2 Rolls-Royce TM 2A Olympus gas turbines, 24,000 shp each; 2 Paxman Ventura diesels, 1,900 bhp each; 2 CP props
Range: 1,000/36; 5,700/17 **Fuel:** 390 tons **Crew:** 132 tot.

Remarks: Began refitting at CNR, Genoa, Italy, 1979; damaged by bomb 29-10-80. Ran trials in 3-83 and recommissioned 1-10-83, but did not return to Libya until 6-85. Sea Cat SAM and Limbo ASW mortar replaced by 4-cell Albatros launcher and ASW TT for Whitehead Motofides A244 torpedoes. Received Selenia IPN-10 combat data system and Otomat missiles, and new radars and sonar were added. The Selenia RTN-10X fire-control radars operate with the two NA-10 Mod. 2 gun/missile f.c.s. By 1989 was only semi-operational and returned to Genoa partially disarmed for repairs, which continued into 1991.

CORVETTES

♦ 3 Soviet Nanuchka II class Bldr: Petrovskiy SY, St. Petersburg

	In serv.
416 Tariq-ibn Ziyad (ex-*Ain Mara*)	10-81
417 Ain al Gazala	7-2-83
418 Ain Zaara	10-83

Tariq ibn Ziyad (416)—with dark gray camouflage striping
Leo Van Ginderen, 7-91

D: 675 tons (fl) **S:** 32 kts **Dim:** 59.3 × 12.6 × 2.4
A: 4/SS-N-2C Styx SSM (II × 2)—1/SA-N-4 system (II × 1, 20 Gecko missiles)— 2/57-mm AK-257 DP (II × 2)
Electron Equipt:
Radar: 1/Don-2 nav., 1/Square Tie (in Band Stand radome) surf. search/missile target designation, 1/Pop Group missile f.c., 1/ Muff Cob gun f.c. (with E/O backup)
EW: 1/Bell Tap intercept, 2/decoy RL (XVI × 1)
M: 3 Type M521 diesels; 3 props; 25,996 bhp
Range: 900/30; 2,500/12 (1 engine) **Crew:** 60 tot.

Remarks: Considered to be poor sea boats by some customers, with unreliable propulsion plants (M521 is a tropicalized version of the M507, which is a paired M504 42-cylinder radial diesel sharing a common gearbox). Sister *Ain Zaquit* (419) sunk 24-3-86 by U.S. aircraft. 416, damaged the next day by U.S. aircraft, returned to the Baltic for an extensive repair/overhaul in 1990, returning to Libya in 2-91.

♦ 4 Wadi M'ragh class Bldr: CNR, Riva Trigoso, Italy

	L	In serv.
412 Assad Al Bihar (ex-*Wadi M'ragh*)	29-4-77	14-9-77
413 Assad Al Tadjier (ex-*Wadi Majer*)	20-4-78	12-2-80
414 Assad Al Kalij (ex-*Wadi Mercit*)	15-12-78	28-3-81
415 Assad Al Hudud (ex-*Wadi Megrawa*)	21-6-79	28-3-81

Assad al Tadjier (413) U.S. Navy, 1983

Assad al Hudud (415)—without Otomat missiles
Leo Van Ginderen, 198

D: 547 tons (630 fl) **S:** 34 kts **Dim:** 61.7 (57.8 pp) × 9.3 × 2.7
A: 4/Otomat Mk I SSM—1/76-mm OTO Melara DP—2/35-mm Oerlikon AA (II × 1)—6/324-mm ILAS-3 ASW TT (III × 2)—16 mines
Electron Equipt:
Radar: 1/Decca TM 1226 nav., 1/RAN 11 L/X surf./air search, 1/RTN-10X f.c.
Sonar: Thomson-CSF Diodon hull-mounted MF
EW: Selenia INS-1 intercept
M: 4 MTU 16V956 TB91 diesels; 4 CP props; 16,400 bhp
Electric: 650 kw **Range:** 1,400/33; 4,150/18
Fuel: 126 tons **Crew:** 58 tot.

Remarks: Ordered in 1974. Completion delayed by prolonged trials. Have fin s bilizers, automatic degaussing system, Selenia IPN-10 combat data system, 1/NA Mod. 3 GFCS, with 2C03 optical backup director. Could maintain 31.5 kts sea sp when new. Names changed 1983. Missiles not usually mounted. By 1990, only one w operational, with the others being used to provide spares.

Note: The Vosper Mk 1B corvette *Tobruk* (C 411) was relegated to pierside train duties in 1989.

GUIDED-MISSILE PATROL BOATS

Note: Four Yugoslav Type 400 guided-missile patrol boats reported ordered in 6 were not delivered, the contract having been canceled.

♦ 9 French Combattante-II class Bldr: CMN, Cherbourg

	Laid down	L	In s
518 Sharara (ex-*Beir Grassa*)	13-3-78	28-6-79	9-2
522 Shehab (ex-*Beir Gzir*)	10-6-78	22-1-80	4-3
524 Wahg (ex-*Beir Gtifa*)	30-1-79	20-5-80	29-5
528 Shouaiai (ex-*Beir Algandula*)	12-9-79	14-1-81	2-11
532 Shoula (ex-*Beir Alkitat*)	17-12-79	3-81	29-1
534 Shafak (ex-*Beir Alkirim*)	11-3-80	23-6-81	17-1
536 Bark (ex-*Beir Alkardmen*)	9-6-80	6-10-81	11-
538 Rad (ex-*Beir Alkur*)	20-10-80	30-11-81	19-
542 Laheeb (ex-*Beir Alkuesat*)	20-1-81	9-1-82	29-

D: 258 tons (311 fl) **S:** 39 kts
Dim: 49.0 (46.2 pp) × 7.1 × 2.4 (2.0 hull)
A: 4/Otomat SSM (II × 2)—1/76-mm OTO Melara DP—2/40-mm Breda AA (II × 1)
Electron Equipt:
Radar: 1/Triton search, 1/Castor tracking, 1/Vega II fire-control
M: 4 MTU 20V538 TB91 diesels; 4 props; 18,000 bhp
Range: 1,600/15 **Crew:** 8 officers, 19 enlisted

Remarks: Ordered 5-77. Delivery of first three embargoed 2-81 to 12-81. N changed 1983. Delivery of final unit embargoed until 2-1-84. All electroni Thomson-CSF. Sister *Waheed* (526, ex-*Beir Glulud*) sunk 24-3-86 by U.S. Nav craft; another may have been damaged on 25-3-86.

Waheed (526)—lost 24-3-86 CECLANT PREMA

GUIDED-MISSILE PATROL BOATS *(continued)*

◆ 12 Soviet Osa-II class

511 Al Katum	519 Al Nabha	527 Al Mosha
513 Al Zuara	521 Al Safra	529 Al Mathur
515 Al Ruha	523 Al Fikah	531 Al Bitar
517 Al Baida	525 Al Sakab	533 Al Sadad

uara (513)—in drydock at Malta — Leo Van Ginderen, 1986

210 tons (240 fl) **S:** 34 kts **Dim:** 38.60 × 7.60 × 2.00
4/SS-N-2 Styx SSM (I × 4)—4/30-mm AK-230 AA (II × 2)
ectron Equipt:
Radar: 1/Square Tie surf. search/target designation, 1/Drum Tilt f.c.
IFF: 2/Square Head interrogators, 1/High Pole transponder
3 M504 diesels; 3 props; 15,000 bhp **Range:** 500/34; 750/25
ew: 30 tot.

rks: One transferred in 1976, four in 1977, one in 1978, three in 1979, one in one in 5-80, and the twelfth in 7-80. Reportedly, the original order was reduced 24 to 12. Names and numbers above represent the latest available listing; num- re changed from time to time.

Sölöven class Bldr: Vosper, Ltd, Portsmouth

	L	In serv.
usa	31-8-67	8-68
irte	10-1-68	4-68
ebha (ex-*Sokna*)	29-2-68	1-69

95 tons (115 fl) **S:** 50 kts **Dim:** 30.38 (27.44 pp) × 7.3 × 2.15
8/SS 12 SSM (II × 4)—2/40-mm Bofors AA (I × 2)
ctron Equipt: Radar: 1/Decca 626 nav.
CODOG: 3 Bristol-Siddeley Proteus gas turbines; 3 props; 12,750 shp; 2 G.M. 6-71 cruising diesels; 190 bhp
ge: 450/45 **Crew:** 20 tot.

Susa (512)—firing an SS-12 missile — Vosper, 1968

Remarks: Modeled on the builder's *Sölöven* class for Denmark. All-wood construction, nylon-sheathed hull. Missiles are wire-guided and are not very accurate, particularly at high speeds. Cruise diesels are on outboard propeller shafts. Refitted in Italy 1984–85, with new engines and new electronics. Retained despite marginal combat utility.

Note: Upwards of 125 radio-controlled suicide boats of Libyan, Swedish, and Cypriot construction are said to be in service for coast defense. No details available, except that speeds of 30 knots are attainable.

MINE WARFARE SHIPS

Note: Libya has laid several minefields, apparently employing the naval roll-on/roll-off cargo ship *El Timsah* (burned out and lost, 1986) and her merchant sister *Ghat,* with mine rails on the vehicle deck, for minelaying. Characteristics for *Ghat:*

D: approx. 3,200 tons (fl) **S:** 18 kts **Dim:** 118.6 × 16.1 × 4.9
M: 2 Wärtsilä 8-cyl. diesels; 2 props; 8,000 bhp

Remarks: Completed 1-75 by Nystads Varv A/B, Nystad, Finland. 2,412 grt. Stern door only. Operated by General National Maritime Transport Co., Benghazi. Can carry several hundred mines on temporary rails in the vehicle deck and several hundred troops.

◆ 8 Soviet Natya-class fleet minesweepers

111 Al I'sar (ex-*Ras el Gelais*)	119 Ras al Oula
113 Al Tayyar (ex-*Ras Hadad*)	121 Ras al Dawar
115 Ras al Hamman	123 Ras Massad
117 Ras al Falluga	125 Ras al Hani

Ras al Hani (125)—with SA-N-5 launchers — Peter Voss, 10-86

Al I'sar (111) — Leo Van Ginderen, 1986

D: 777 tons (877 fl) **S:** 18 kts **Dim:** 61.0 × 10.2 × 3.3 (5.3 props)
A: 4/30-mm AK-230 AA (II × 2)—4/25-mm 2M-8 AA (II × 2)—2/RBU-1200 ASW RL (V × 2)—mines—123 on: 2/SA-N-5 Grail SAM syst. (IV × 2)
Electron Equipt:
Radar: 1/Don-2 nav., 1/Drum Tilt f.c.—Sonar: hull-mounted HF
IFF: 2/Square Head interrogators, 1/High Pole B transponder
M: 2 diesels; 2 props; 5,000 bhp **Range:** 1,600/16; 5,200/10
Crew: 50 tot.

Remarks: First pair delivered 3-81, second pair in 2-83, fifth on 3-9-83, the sixth during 2-84, the seventh on 20-1-85, and the last in 10-86. Like the six built for India, they lack the ramp at the stern found on Soviet units. Names on first two changed after delivery but not, apparently, on the remainder. Equipped for mechanical, acoustic, and magnetic minesweeping.

AMPHIBIOUS WARFARE SHIPS

◆ **3 Soviet Polnocny-C-class landing ships** Bldr: Stocznia Północna, Gdansk, Poland

112 Ibn al Hadrami (In serv. 12-77) 116 Ibn Omayar (In serv. 6-79)
118 Ibn el Farat (In serv. 6-79)

Ibn Omayar (116) Leo Van Ginderen, 1990

Ibn al Hadrami (112) U.S. Navy, 1988

D: 980 tons (1,207 fl) **S:** 18 kts **Dim:** 81.3 × 9.3 × 2.6 (aft)
A: 4/30-mm AK-230 AA (II × 2)—2/122-mm artillery RL (XV × 2)
Electron Equipt: Radar: 1/Spin Trough nav., 1/Drum Tilt f.c.
M: 2 Type 40DM diesels; 2 props; 4,400 bhp
Range: 1,000/18 **Crew:** 30 crew + 150 troops

Remarks: Like the Iraqi examples of this Polish-built class of medium landing ships, these export versions have a raised helicopter deck forward of the superstructure. A fourth Libyan unit, the *Ibn al Qyis* (113), was lost on 14 or 15 September 1978 through fire at sea. Can carry five medium tanks.

◆ **2 Ibn Ouf-class landing ships** Bldr: C.N.I.M., La Seyne

	Laid down	L	In serv.
132 Ibn Ouf	1-4-76	22-10-76	11-3-77
134 Ibn Harissa	18-4-77	18-10-77	10-3-78

Ibn Ouf (132) Bernard Prézelin, 5-84

D: 2,800 tons (fl) **S:** 15 kts **Dim:** 100.0 × 15.65 × 2.6
A: 6/40-mm Breda AA (II × 3)—1/81-mm mortar
Electron Equipt: Radar: 1/Decca 1226 nav.
M: 2 SEMT-Pielstick 16 PA4 V185 diesels; 2 CP props; 5,340 bhp
Range: 4,000/14 **Crew:** 35 crew + 240 troops

Remarks: Cargo: 570 tons, including up to eleven tanks. Helicopter platform aft.

◆ **4 Turkish Ç 107-class large landing craft** Bldr: Taskizak SY, Istanbul, and Gölçük Naval SY

130 Ibn al Idrissi (ex-Ç 130) 132 Ras el Hillel (ex-Ç 132)
131 Ibn Marwhan (ex-Ç 131) 133 El Kobayat (ex-Ç 133)

D: 280 tons (600 fl) **S:** 10 kts (8.5 loaded)
Dim: 56.56 × 11.58 × 1.25
A: 2/20-mm AA (I × 2) **M:** 3 G.M. 6-71 TI diesels; 3 props; 900 bhp
Range: 600/10; 1,100/8 **Crew:** 15 tot.

Remarks: Cargo: five heavy tanks, up to 100 troops; up to 350 tons. Design follows World War II–era British LCT(4). Cargo deck 28.5 × 7.9 m. Ordered 7-12-79, with first four taken from among ships built for Turkish Navy and delivered 7-12-79. As many as 50 were to be acquired, with each Turkish yard building 25, but it now appears that only the initial four were received.

AUXILIARY SHIPS

◆ **1 training ship/vehicle transport** Bldr: Naikai SB & Eng., Setoda, Japan

Garyounis (ex-*Mashu*) (In serv. 1973)

D: . . . **S:** 20.5 kts **Dim:** 166.53 (155.00 pp) × 24.36 × 6.47
Electron Equipt: Radar: . . .
M: 2 Nippon Kokan-Pielstick diesels; 2 props; 20,800 bhp—bow-thruster
Electric: 1,860 kw (3 × 620 kw)

Remarks: 6,561 grt/2,593 dwt. Employed as naval cadet training ship during 1989 although ostensibly owned and operated by General National Maritime Transportation Co., Benghazi. Former Ro-Ro/passenger ferry with accommodations for up to 67[illegible] passengers. Stern ramp.

◆ **1 support ship for small combatants**

	Bldr	Laid down	L	In serv.
711 Zeltin	Vosper Thornycroft, Woolston	1967	29-2-68	23-1-69

Zeltin (711) 19[illegible]

D: 2,200 tons (2,470 fl) **S:** 15 kts
Dim: 98.72 (91.44 wl) × 14.64 × 3.05
A: 2/40-mm U.K. Mk 7 AA (I × 2)
M: 2 Paxman Ventura 16 YSCM diesels; 2 props; 3,500 bhp
Electric: 800 kw **Range:** 3,000/14 **Crew:** 15 officers, 86 enlisted

Remarks: The well deck, 41 × 12 m, can receive small craft that draw up to 2.3 [illegible] Hydraulically controlled stern gate. A movable crane (3-ton loading capacity) is ava[illegible] able for the well deck, and a 9-ton crane on the port side supports the workshops.

◆ **1 Yugoslav Spasilac-class submarine rescue ship** Bldr: Tito S[illegible] Belgrad (In serv. 1982)

722 Al Munjed (ex-*Zlatica*)

D: 1,590 tons (fl) **S:** 13.4 kts
Dim: 55.50 × 12.00 × 3.84 (4.34 props)
A: 4/14.5-mm mg (II × 2) **Electron Equipt:** Radar: 1/. . . nav.
M: 2 diesels; 2 Kort-nozzle props; 4,340 bhp **Electric:** 540 kVA
Range: 4,000/13.4 **Crew:** 53 tot.

Remarks: Intended to support the six Foxtrot-class submarines. Has decompres[illegible] chamber and extensive diving equipment, can lay a 4-point moor, and can tow. Ca[illegible] 490 tons cargo fuel and up to 250 tons deck cargo. Can support divers to 300 m. H[illegible] bow-thruster. Equipped with three fire-fighting water cannon.

◆ **1 small transport** Bldr: De Groost & Van Vliet, Slikkerveer (In serv. 11-48)

El Fateh (ex-Panamanian *Mebo II*, ex-*Silvretta*)

D: 640 grt **S:** 10.5 kts **Dim:** 44.00 × 8.90 × 3.20
M: 1 Sulzer 5-cyl. diesel; 500 bhp.

Remarks: Acquired 1977. Engine built in 1945!

◆ **3 harbor tugs** Bldr: Jonker & Stans SY, the Netherlands (In serv. 19[illegible]

A 33 A 34 A 35

D: 150 grt **S:** . . . **Dim:** 26.60 × 7.90 × 2.48
M: 2 diesels; 2 Voith-Schneider vertical-cycloidal props; . . . bhp

Remarks: Two 17.00 × 6.25 × 2.75 harbor tugs were delivered at the same ti[illegible]

◆ **4 Ras El Helal-class tugs** Bldr: Mondego, Foz, Portugal

	In serv.		In serv.
Ras El Helal	22-10-77	Al Keriat	17-2-78
Al Shweiref	17-2-78	Al Tabkah	29-7-78

D: 200 grt **S:** 14 kts **Dim:** 34.8 × 9.0 × 4.0 (moulded depth)
M: 2 diesels; 2 props; 2,300 bhp

◆ **1 Soviet Yelva-class diving tender**

Al Manoud (ex-VM 917)

D: 295 tons (fl) **S:** 12.4 kts **Dim:** 40.90 (37.00 pp) × 8.00 × 2.1[illegible]
Electron Equipt: Radar: 1/Spin Trough nav.
M: 2 Type 3D12 A diesels; 2 props; 600 bhp
Electric: 200 kw **Crew:** 30 tot.

Remarks: Transferred 19-12-77. Can support seven hard-hat divers working [illegible] and has a submersible decompression chamber.

LIBYA *(continued)*
AUXILIARY SHIPS *(continued)*

◆ **1 Soviet Poluchat-I-class torpedo retriever**

D: 90 tons (fl) **S:** 18 kts **Dim:** 29.6 × 6.1 × 1.9 **A:** . . .
Electron Equipt: Radar: 1/Spin Trough nav.
M: 2 M50F diesels; 2 props; 2,400 bhp **Range:** 450/17; 900/10
Crew: 20 tot.

Remarks: Delivered 20-5-85 under tow by Bulgarian tug *Neptun*.

◆ **1 floating dry dock** Bldr: Blohm & Voss, Hamburg (In serv. 1984)

Capacity: 3,200 tons **Dim:** 105.20 × 26.00 × 6.40

Remarks: Ordered 20-2-84, laid down 17-4-84.

CUSTOMS SERVICE

PATROL BOATS AND CRAFT

Note: The 14 Turkish-built SAR-33-class patrol boats listed in previous editons were in fact never delivered, the contract having been canceled.

◆ **4 Swedish-built** Bldr: Boghammar Marin, Stockholm (In serv. 1991)

D: 5.5 tons (fl) **S:** 45 kts **Dim:** 12.80 × 2.66 × 0.90
A: . . . **Electron Equipt:** Radar: 1/. . . nav.
M: 2 Volvo Penta TAMD-E diesels; 2 outdrive props; 610 bhp
Range: 500/38 **Crew:** 5–6 tot.

Remarks: Aluminum construction, with stepped hydroplane hullform.

6 Yugoslav PB 90 class Bldr: Tito Brodotekhnika SY, Belgrade (In serv. 1985–86)

D: 90 tons (fl) **S:** 32 kts **Dim:** 27.35 × 6.55 × 1.15 (2.20 props)
A: 1/40-mm Bofors AA—4/20-mm AA (IV × 1)
Electron Equipt: Radar: 1/Decca 1226 nav.
M: 3 MTU diesels; 3 props; 4,350 bhp **Range:** 400/25 **Crew:** 17 tot.

Remarks: Ordered 1984. May have a small, high-frequency sonar.

4 37-meter Bldr: Brooke Marine, Lowestoft, U.K. (In serv. 1968–70)

PC 1 Zleitan (ex-*Garian*) PC 3 Merawa
PC 2 Khawlan PC 4 Sabratha

D: 100 tons (125 fl) **S:** 23.5 kts **Dim:** 36.58 × 7.16 × 1.75
A: 1/40-mm—1/20-mm AA
M: 2 Paxman Ventura 10 YJCM diesels; 2 props; 3,600 bhp
Range: 1,800/13 **Crew:** 22 tot.

Remarks: Have the same engines as the repair ship *Zeltin*. At least one has carried a Soviet BM-21 multiple 122-mm rocket launcher (XX × 1) in place of the 20-mm AA . PC 1 renamed to commemorate former repair craft, 1982. Refitted at Taskizak Naval SY, Turkey, in 1983–84.

3 security craft Bldr: Vosper Thornycroft, Portsmouth (In serv. 1967–69)

Ina Farwa (ex-*Homs*) Misurata

D: 100 tons **S:** 18–20 kts **Dim:** 30.5 × 6.4 × 1.7 **A:** 1/20-mm AA
M: 3 Rolls-Royce diesels; 1,740 bhp **Range:** 1,800/14 **Crew:** 15 tot.

Remarks: Used for customs and fishery protection. Sisters *Al Rakib, Farwa*, and *ma* ceded to Malta, 1978. Probably in very poor condition.

MADAGASCAR

Democratic Republic of Madagascar/Malagasy Republic

MALAGASY AERONAVAL FORCE

Personnel (1991): 530 total, including a 120-man marine infantry company. The r navy and air force were united in 1991 as the Malagasy Aeronaval Force.

PATROL BOATS

French PR 48-type patrol boat Bldr: SFCN, Villeneuve-la-Garenne

	Laid down	L	In serv.
...ika	11-66	22-3-67	12-67

D: 235 tons (250 fl) **S:** 18.5 kts
Dim: 47.50 (45.50 pp) × 7.10 × 2.25
A: 2/40-mm AA (I × 2)
Electron Equipt: Radar: 1/Decca 1226 nav.
M: 2 MGO diesels; 2 props; 2,400 bhp **Range:** 2,000/15
Crew: 3 officers, 22 enlisted

Remarks: Sisters with more powerful propulsion plants in the Senegalese and Tunisian navies.

◆ **1 North Korean Nampo class** (In serv. 1979)

D: 82 tons (fl) **S:** 40 kts **Dim:** 27.7 × 6.1 × 1.8
A: 4/14.5-mm AA (II × 2)
Electron Equipt: Radar: 1/Pot Head surf. search
M: 4 M50F-4 diesels; 4 props; 4,800 bhp **Range:** 325/19
Crew: 19 tot.

Remarks: Patrol boat version of North Korean fast landing assault craft design. Has no bow ramp or troop accommodations, being intended for use strictly as patrol craft. Metal construction. Three sisters destroyed by typhoon during 4-84, and this unit is probably marginally operational at best.

AMPHIBIOUS WARFARE SHIPS

◆ **1 medium landing ship** Bldr: Diego Suarez Dockyard

Toky (In serv. 10-74)

Toky 1-86

D: 810 tons (avg.) **S:** 13 kts **Dim:** 66.37 (56.00 pp) × 12.50 × 1.90
A: 1/40-mm AA—2/20-mm AA (I × 2)—1/81-mm mortar
Electron Equipt: Radar: 1/Decca 1226 nav.
M: 2 MGO diesels; 2 props; 2,400 bhp
Electric: 240 kw **Range:** 3,000/12 **Crew:** 27 tot.

Remarks: Used as a transport and support ship. Cargo capacity: 250 tons. Quarters for 30 passengers; 120 soldiers can be carried for short distances. Financed by the French government under the Military Cooperation Pact.

◆ **1 French EDIC-class tank landing craft** Bldr: CN Franco Belges (In serv. 1964)

Aina Vao Vao (ex-EDIC L9082)

D: 250 tons (670 fl) **S:** 8 kts **Dim:** 59.00 × 11.95 × 1.30 (1.62 max.)
A: 2/20-mm AA (I × 2)—1/81-mm mortar
Electron Equipt: Radar: 1/Decca 1226 nav.
M: 2 MGO diesels; 2 props; 1,000 bhp **Range:** 1,800/8
Crew: 17 tot.

Remarks: Transferred 27-9-85, having been laid up at Tahiti since stricken from French Navy in 1981. Can carry 11 trucks.

TRAINING SHIP

◆ **1 former trawler** Bldr: A.G. Weser, Bremen (In serv. 1959)

Fanantenana (ex-*Richelieu*)

D: 1,040 tons (1,200 fl) **S:** 12 kts **Dim:** 62.0 (56 pp) × 9.15 × 4.52
A: 2/40-mm AA (I × 2) **Electron Equipt:** Radar: 1/Decca 1226 nav.
M: 2 Deutz diesels ("father-son" system): 1 prop; 1,060 + 500 bhp
Crew: . . .

Remarks: 691 grt. Bought and modified, 1966–67. Can carry 300 tons of freight and up to 120 military passengers. Is in poor condition.

SERVICE CRAFT

◆ **3 launches** Bldr: Deggerdorfer, West Germany (In serv. 1988)

Fiherenga Marola Sambathra

Remarks: No data available, except 14.30 m overall, diesel-powered.

MALAWI

Republic of Malawi

MALAWI POLICE

Personnel (1991): Approximately 120 total

PATROL CRAFT

◆ **1 for Lake Nyasa service** Bldr: SFCN, Villeneuve-la-Garenne, France

P 703 Kasunga (ex-*Chikala*) (In serv. 17-12-84)

MALAWI *(continued)*
PATROL CRAFT *(continued)*

D: 33 tons (36 fl) **S:** 22 kts **Dim:** 21.0 (18.5 wl) × 4.8 × 1.5
A: 1/20-mm GIAT F-2 AA
Electron Equipt: Radar: 1/Decca . . . nav.
M: 2 Poyaud 520-V12-M2 diesels; 2 props; 1,400 bhp
Range: 650/15 **Crew:** 10 tot.

Kasunga (P 703) Leo Van Ginderen, 1984

Remarks: Ordered 8-11-83. Delivered in sections 10-84 and assembled in Malawi.

◆ **1 South African Namicurra class**

. . . . (In serv. 29-10-88)

D: 5 tons (fl) **S:** 30 kts **Dim:** 9.0 × 2.7 × 0.8
A: 1/12.7-mm mg—2/7.62-mm mg (I × 2)
M: 2 diesels; 2 props; . . . bhp **Crew:** 4 tot.

Remarks: Transferred as a gift. GRP construction. Can be road-transported.

◆ **1 Spear-class launch** Bldr: Fairey Marine, Hamble

P 702 (In serv. 1976)

D: 4 tons (fl) **S:** 25 kts **Dim:** 9.1 × 2.8 × 0.8
A: 2/7.62-mm mg (I × 2)
M: 2 Perkins diesels; 2 props; 290 bhp **Crew:** 3 tot.

SERVICE CRAFT

◆ **1 Survey craft** Bldr: SFCN, Villeneuve-la-Garenne

. . . . (In serv. 12-88)

D: 70 tons (fl) **S:** 10.5 kts **Dim:** 21.0 × . . . × . . .
M: 2 Baudouin 6 F11SR diesels; 2 props; . . . bhp **Crew:** . . .

MALAYSIA

Personnel (1991): Approximately 12,500 total (including 2,000 officers) plus 900 reserves (with reserves planned to expand to about 7,000)

Naval Aviation: Established 5-86, the Naval Air Wing 499 Squadron, based at Lumat, operates six Westland Wasp helicopters. Six more helicopters are sought, with the Westland Sea Lynx and Aérospatiale Cougar (Super Puma) established as the leading candidates during 1991.

The air force operates 3 Lockheed C-130H-MP maritime patrol aircraft and during 1991 ordered 4 Beech B200T light maritime patrol aircraft. Also on order for delivery during 1993 are 18 single and 9 two-seat Hawk light fighters that will be equipped with Sea Eagle missiles for ship attack.

SUBMARINES

Navy plans to acquire a submarine force, initially through the lease or purchase of an older, existing boat, have been deferred to 1995 or later for lack of funds. Plans to acquire a British *Oberon*-class submarine fell afoul of an economic dispute between the two nations during 1988, and a widely announced plan to acquire two retired Swedish *Draken*-class submarines (one as an inoperative pierside trainer) and to order two or four tropicalized versions of the Swedish A-19 design fell through in May 1991.

FRIGATES

◆ **0 (+2) Yarrow 1,500-ton corvettes** Bldr: G.E.C. -Yarrow SB, Scotstoun, Glasgow

	Laid down	L	In serv.
27	. . .	. . .	. . .
28	. . .	. . .	. . .

Yarrow 1,500-ton corvette design Yarrow, 1991

D: 1,500 tons (2,270 fl) **S:** 27 kts
Dim: 106.00 × 12.75 × 3.08
A: 8/Harpoon SSM (IV × 2)—1/16-cell Seawolf SAM launch group or 2/Sadral launchers (VI × 2)—1/57-mm Bofors SAK 57 Mk 2 DP—4/30-mm Oerlikon AA (II × 2)—6/324-mm ASW TT (III × 2, Stingray or Mk 46 torpedoes)—1/Lynx or Wasp helicopter
Electron Equipt:
Radar: 1/Kelvin-Hughes Type 1007 nav., 1 H.S.A. DA-08 Ericsson Sea Giraffe surf. air search, 2/Marconi 1802 SW
Sonar: Atlas DSQS-21C hull-mounted MF
EW: Marconi Mentor-A suite, 2/CSEE Dagaie decoy RL (X × 2)
M: 4 MTU 20V163 TB93 diesels; 2 CP props; 16,000 hp; possible slow-speed electric drive
Range: 4,000/18 diesel
Crew: 18 officers, 120 enlisted

Remarks: Contract still awaited as of 12-91. Electronics suite and certain component of the armament suite not yet firm. Has Marconi NAUTIS-F weapons-control system. Rademac Type 2400 electro-optical director will be fitted for the gun, with the rada director fitted aft. Integrated HF/VHF/UHF communications suite. Ordered 31-3-92

◆ **2 Type FS-1500** Bldr: Howaldtswerke, Kiel

	Laid down	L	In serv.
25 Kasturi	31-1-83	14-5-83	15-8-84
26 Lekir	31-1-83	14-5-83	15-8-84

D: 1,690 tons (1,900 fl) **S:** 28 kts
Dim: 97.30 (91.80 pp) × 11.30 × 3.50 (hull)
A: 4/MM 38 Exocet SSM—1/100-mm 55-cal. Creusot-Loire Compact DP—1/57-mm 70-cal. Bofors SAK-57 Mk 1 DP—4/30-mm Emerle AA (II × 2)—1/375-mm Bofors ASW RL (II × 1)—1/Wasp HAS 1 helicopter

Lekir (26) Malcolm Dippy, 1

Kasturi (25) Leo Van Gindere

FRIGATES *(continued)*

Electron Equipt:
Radar: 1/Decca TM1226C nav., 1/H.S.A. DA-08 air search, 1/H.S.A. WM-22 f.c.
Sonar: Krupp-Atlas DSQS-21 hull-mounted MF
EW: Rapids intercept, Scimitar jammer; 2 Dagaie decoy RL (XVIII × 2)
M: 4 MTU 20V1163 TB92 diesels; 2 CP props; 21,460 bhp
Range: 3,600/18; 7,000/14 **Fuel:** 200 tons **Electric:** 1,392 kVA
Crew: 13 officers, 111 enlisted

Remarks: Ordered 10-6-81. There is no hangar, although a telescoping one can be installed later. Have the H.S.A. SEWACO MA combat data system and are equipped for LINK 5 datalink. Two H.S.A. LIOD optronic directors for the 100-mm and 57-mm guns. Both arrived in Malaysia 23-11-84. Can make 23 kts on 2 diesels. There are flare rocket launchers on the sides of the 57-mm mount. Four similar, but shorter and differently equipped, near-sisters were built for Colombia.

♦ **1 "Yarrow frigate" class** Bldr: Yarrow Shipbuilders, Scotstoun, Glasgow, U.K.

	Laid down	L	In serv.
24 Rahmat (ex-*Hang Jebat*)	2-66	18-12-67	31-8-71

ahmat (24) French Navy, 1990

hmat (24) 92 Wing R.A.A.F., 5-90

D: 1,290 tons (1,600 fl) **S:** 27 kts (16.5 on diesel)
Dim: 93.97 (pl. 44 pp) × 10.36 × 3.05
A: 1/114-mm 45-cal. Vickers Mk 6 DP—3/40-mm 70-cal. Bofors AA (I × 3)—1/Mk 10 Limbo ASW mortar (III × 1)
Electron Equipt:
Radar: 1/Decca 626 nav., 1/H.S.A. LW-02 air search, 1/H.S.A. M-22 f.c.
Sonar: Graseby Type 170B hull-mounted MF search, Graseby Type 174 hull-mounted attack (15 kHz)
EW: UA-3 intercept, FH-4D/F
M: CODOG: 1 Rolls-Royce Olympus TM-1B gas turbine, 19,500 shp; 1 Crossley-Pielstick SPC2V diesel; 3,850 bhp; 2 CP props
Electric: 2,000 kw **Range:** 1,000/27; 5,200/16.5
Crew: 12 officers, 128 enlisted

Remarks: Ordered 11-2-66. M-22 fire-control radar atop the mast for the 114-mm gun. ASW mortar is covered by a MacGregor hatch that serves as a platform for a light opter. Sea Cat SAM system and radar director replaced by a third 40-mm AA gun g 1981–82 refit. Plans to replace the 114-mm mount with a French 100-mm act were canceled. Both the 114-mm mount and the after 40-mm mount have 103-mm flare rocket launch rails on either side. The Limbo mortar has a range of n and fires a 92-kg projectile.

British built Bldr: Yarrow Shipbuilders, Scotstoun

	Laid down	L	In serv.
ang Tuah (ex-*Mermaid*)	1965	29-12-66	16-5-73

Hang Tuah (76) 1985

D: 2,300 tons (2,520 fl) **S:** 24/23 kts **Dim:** 103.40 × 12.20 × 4.80
A: 2/102-mm 45-cal. Vickers Mk 19 DP (II × 1)—2/40-mm Bofors AA (I × 2)—4/30-mm Emerlec AA (II × 2)—1/Mk 10 Limbo ASW mortar (III × 1)
Electron Equipt:
Radar: 1/Type 978 nav.—1/Plessey AWS-1 air search—EW: none
Sonar: Graseby Type 174 hull-mounted MF search, Graseby Type 170B hull-mounted attack (15 kHz)
M: 8 16-cyl. Admiralty Standard Range-I diesels; 2 props; 14,400 bhp
Range: 4,800/15 **Fuel:** 230 tons **Crew:** 200–210 tot.

Remarks: Ordered for Ghana in 1964 as a frigate-cum-yacht. Because of the political situation, the ship was not delivered and at the end of 1971 was purchased by the British government. Transferred to Malaysia in 5-77 and delivered 8-77 after refit. Has lead-computing STD Mk 1 optical-only director for the Mk 19 twin 102-mm mount and no fire-control radar. Helicopter pad; no hangar.

OFFSHORE PATROL VESSELS

♦ **2 Musytari class**

	Bldr	L	In serv.
160 Musytari	Korea SB & Eng., Pusan	19-7-84	19-12-85
161 Marikh	Malaysian SY & Eng., Pasir Gudang	21-1-85	8-12-87

Musytari (160) Leo Van Ginderen, 5-90

Marikh (161) 92 Wing R.A.A.F., 5-90

D: 1,000 tons (1,300 fl) **S:** 22 kts **Dim:** 75.00 × 10.80 × 3.70
A: 1/100-mm 55-cal. Creusot-Loire Compact DP—2/30-mm Emerlec AA (II × 1)
Electron Equipt:
Radar: 1/Decca TM 1226 nav., 1/H.S.A. DA-05 air search, 1/PEAB 9GA-600 f.c.
EW: Racal Cutlass intercept
M: 2 Pielstick diesels; 2 props; 12,720 bhp **Range:** 6,000/20
Crew: 9 officers, 57 enlisted

OFFSHORE PATROL VESSELS *(continued)*

Remarks: First two ordered 6-83. Intended to patrol the 200-n.m. economic zone. PEAB 9LV230 radar/electro-optical control system for the 100-mm gun. Large helicopter deck aft, no hangar. Names mean "Jupiter" and "Mars." A planned third unit has been deferred.

GUIDED-MISSILE PATROL BOATS

◆ **4 Spica-M class** Bldr: Karlskrona Varvet, Karlskrona, Sweden

	Laid down	L	In serv.
3511 Handalan	24-5-77	11-11-78	26-10-79
3512 Perkasa	27-6-77	11-11-78	26-10-79
3513 Pendikar	15-7-77	11-11-78	26-10-79
3514 Gempita	21-10-77	11-11-78	26-10-79

Handalan (3511) Leo Van Ginderen, 5-90

D: 240 tons (268 fl) **S:** 37.5 kts (34.5 sust.)
Dim: 43.62 (41.00 pp) × 7.00 × 2.40 (aft)
A: 4/MM 38 Exocet SSM (II × 2)—1/57-mm 70-cal. Bofors SAK 57 Mk 1 DP—1/40-mm 70-cal. Bofors AA
Electron Equipt:
Radar: 1/Decca 1226 nav., 1/PEAB 9LV200 Mk 2 system (1/9LV212 tracker, 1/9GR600 search radar)
Sonar: Simrad SU hull-mounted HF—EW: MEL SUSIE-1 intercept
M: 3 MTU 16V538 TB91 diesels; 3 props; 10,800 bhp
Electric: 400 kVA
Range: 1,850/14 **Fuel:** 80 tons **Crew:** 5 officers, 34 enlisted

Remarks: Ordered 13-8-76, arriving together in Malaysia 26-10-79. Given the names of the four *Perkasa*-class torpedo/patrol boats that were stricken in 1977. Have 103-mm rocket flare launchers on the 57-mm mount and 57-mm RL on the 40-mm mount. Can be equipped with ASW TT if required. The tracking radar at the masthead has a stabilized antenna. P 3511 is squadron flagship.

◆ **4 French Combattante-II 4AL class** Bldr: CMN, Cherbourg

	L	In serv.		L	In serv.
3501 Perdana	31-5-72	21-12-72	3503 Ganas	26-10-72	28-2-73
3502 Serang	22-12-71	31-2-73	3504 Ganyang	16-3-72	20-3-73

Ganyang (3504) 92 Wing R.A.A.F., 5-90

D: 234 tons (265 fl) **S:** 36.5 kts **Dim:** 47.00 × 7.10 × 2.50 (fl)
A: 2/MM 38 Exocet SSM (I × 2)—1/57-mm 70-cal. Bofors SAK-57 Mk 1 DP—1/40-mm 70-cal. Bofors AA
Electron Equipt:
Radar: 1 Decca 1226 nav., 1/ Thomson-CSF Triton THD1040 air/surf. search, 1/Thomson-CSF Pollux f.c.
EW: . . . intercept
M: 4 MTU MB 870 diesels; 4 props; 14,000 bhp
Range: 800/25; 1,800/15 **Fuel:** 39 tons
Crew: 4 officers, 26 enlisted

Remarks: Steel hulls, aluminum-alloy superstructure. Six 103-mm rocket flare launchers on the 57-mm mount, four 57-mm on the 40-mm mount. Thomson-CSF Vega fire-control system with Triton search radar, Pollux f.c. radar. All left France for Malaysia 2-5-73.

PATROL BOATS

◆ **6 Jerong class** Bldr: Hong Leong-Lürssen, Butterworth, Malaysia

	L	In serv.		L	In serv.
3505 Jerong	28-7-75	23-3-76	3508 Yu	17-7-76	15-11-76
3506 Todak	16-3-76	16-6-76	3509 Baung	5-10-76	11-7-77
3507 Paus	2-6-76	18-8-76	3510 Pari	1-77	23-3-77

Yu (3508) Leo Van Ginderen, 5-9

Todak (3506) Mike Louagie, 5

D: 210 tons (255 fl) **S:** 32 kts **Dim:** 44.90 × 7.00 × 2.48 (props)
A: 1/57-mm 70-cal. Bofors SAK Mk 1 DP—1/40-mm 70-cal. Bofors A
Electron Equipt: Radar: 1/Decca 1226 nav.
M: 3 MTU MB 870 diesels; 3 props; 10,800 bhp **Electric:** 384 kVA
Range: 700/31.5; 2,000/15 **Crew:** 5 officers, 31 enlisted

Remarks: Lürssen FPB 45 design. Rocket flare launchers are fitted on both mounts. C.S.E.E. Naja electro-optical director for the 57-mm gun. Fin stabilizers fi

◆ **21 103-foot Vosper type** Bldr: Vosper Ltd., Portsmouth

First group, ordered in September 1961:

	L		L
3139 Sri Selangor	17-7-62	3142 Sri Kelantan	8-1-6
3143 Sri Trengganu	12-12-62		

Second group, ordered in March 1963:

	L		L
3144 Sri Sabah	30-12-63	3145 Sri Sarawak	20-1-6
3146 Sri Negri Sembilan	17-9-64	3147 Sri Melaka	2-11-6

Third group, ordered in 1965:

	L		L
34 Kris	11-3-66	36 Sundang	22-5-66
37 Badek	8-5-66	38 Renchong	22-6-66
39 Tombak	20-6-66	40 Lembing	22-8-66
41 Serampang	15-9-66	42 Panah	10-10-66
43 Kerambit	20-11-66	44 Baladau	11-1-67
45 Kelewang	31-1-67	46 Rentaka	15-3-67
47 Sri Perlis	26-5-67	48 Sri Johore	21-8-67

D: 96 tons (109 fl) **S:** 27/23 kts
Dim: 31.39 (28.95 pp) × 5.95 × 1.65
A: 0, 1, or 2/40-mm 70-cal. Bofors AA (I × . . .)—2/7.62-mm mg (I × 2)
Electron Equipt: Radar: 1/Decca 616 nav.
M: 2 Bristol-Siddeley or Maybach MD 655/18 diesels; 2 props; 3,550 bhp
Range: 1,400/14 **Crew:** 3 officers, 19–20 enlisted

Remarks: Welded hulls. Vosper anti-roll stabilizers. The prototype was deliv February 1963. The middle group have greater range: 1,660/14. The class pro the *Sri Kegah* (P 3138), and the *Sri Pahang* (P 3141) were stricken 1976; *Sr* (P 3140) foundered 1-84. Bulwark configurations vary, while early units h portholes. Aft 40-mm gun removed in at least three, and in 5-90, 3139 and 31 disarmed entirely. The survivors have been modernized. *Sri Melaka* (P 31 group) is detached to Sabah. Five are assigned to training duties: 40, 43, 44, 47,

PATROL BOATS *(continued)*

Sri Sarawak (3145)—second group Mike Louagie, 5-90

elewang (45)—third group 92 Wing R.A.A.F., 5-90

INE WARFARE SHIPS

♦ **4 Italian Lerici-class minehunters** Bldr: Intermarine, Sarzana

	L	In serv.		L	In serv.
MAHAMIRU	24-2-83	11-12-85	13 LEDANG	14-7-83	11-12-85
JERAI	8-12-83	11-12-85	14 KINABULU	19-3-83	11-12-85

ai (12) Leo Van Ginderen, 5-90

ang (13) 92 Wing R.A.A.F., 5-90

D: 578 tons (610 fl) **S:** 16 kts **Dim:** 51.00 (46.50 pp) × 9.56 × 2.85
A: 1/40-mm 70-cal. Bofors AA
Electron Equipt:
Radar: Decca 1226—Sonar: Thomson-CSF TSM 2022
M: 2 MTU 12V396 TC82 (DB512) diesels; 2 CP props; 2,630 bhp (2,394 sust.)—2 electric retractable auxiliary props; 240 shp (for 7 kts sweep speed)
Electric: 1,000 kw (4 MTU V396 TC52 gen. sets)
Endurance: 14 days **Range:** 1,400/14; 2,000/12 **Fuel:** 46 tons
Crew: 5 officers, 37 enlisted

Remarks: Ordered 2-81. Also intended for patrol duties. Arrived in Malaysia 28-3-86. Glass-reinforced plastic construction. Have different main engine, armament, and sonar than Italian Navy sisters. Range at 12 kts can be extended to 4,000 n.m. by using the passive anti-rolling tanks to carry fuel. Thomson-CSF IBIS II minehunting system. Have two PAP-104 remote-controlled minehunting devices, good in depths up to 300 m, and U.K. Oropesa Mk 4 mechanical sweep gear. Active tank stabilization, TSM 2060 autopilot, decompression chamber fitted. Four more are planned, finances permitting. Are based two each at Labuan and Lumut to provide mine countermeasures services on both of Malaysia's coasts.

AMPHIBIOUS WARFARE CRAFT

Note: In addition to these small craft, the multipurpose ships of the *Sri Indera Sakti* class and the miscellaneous utility landing craft listed under auxiliaries can be used for amphibious warfare purposes.

♦ **5 U.S. LCM(6)-class vehicle landing craft** Bldr: De Havilland Marine, Australia (In serv. 1965–70)

LCM 1–5

D: 24 tons (56 fl) **S:** 10 kts **Dim:** 17.07 × 4.37 × 1.17
M: 2 diesels; 2 props; 330 bhp **Range:** 130/10 **Cargo:** 30 tons

♦ **9 RCP-class personnel/vehicle landing craft** Bldr: Hong Leong-Lürssen SY, Butterworth, Malaysia (All in serv. 1974)

RCP 3 Leo Van Ginderen, 5-90

D: 15 tons (30 fl) **S:** 17 kts **Dim:** 15.0 × 4.4 × . . .
A: 1/20-mm AA **M:** 2 diesels; 2 waterjets: . . . bhp

Remarks: Cargo: 35 troops or one small vehicle.

♦ **15 LCP-class personnel landing craft** Bldr: De Havilland Marine, Australia

LCP 1–15

D: 19 tons (fl) **S:** 16 kts **Dim:** 14.6 × 4.3 × 1.0
M: 2 Cummins diesels; 2 props; 400 bhp

Remarks: Transferred 1965–66. Essentially personnel launches, with pointed bows; have light armor over pilothouse amidships. There are also several De Havilland "Titan" Mk 3 12-meter landing craft in service.

Note: The Malaysian Army also operates small landing craft, including:

♦ **165 Damen 540 class** Bldr: 65 by Damen, Gorinchem, Netherlands; 100 by Limbougan Timor, Kuala Trengganu (In serv. 1986–87)

D: . . . **S:** 25–30 kts **Dim:** 5.4 × 1.83 × . . .
M: 1/40-bhp outboard **Crew:** 2 crew, 10 troops

Remarks: Ordered 10-85. About 250–300 other small river-crossing assault boats are available.

HYDROGRAPHIC SHIP

♦ **1 seagoing oceanographic research and hydrographic survey ship**

	Bldr	In serv.
152 MUTIARA	Hong Leong-Lürssen, Butterworth, Malaysia	12-1-78

D: 1,905 tons (fl) **S:** 16 kts **Dim:** 70.0 (64.0 pp) × 13.0 × 4.0
A: 4/20-mm Oerlikon AA (II × 2)
Electron Equipt: Radar: 1/Decca 1226 nav., 1/Decca 1229 nav.
M: 1 Deutz SBA-12M-528 diesel; 1 CP prop; 2,000 bhp
Range: 4,500/16 **Crew:** 14 officers, 141 enlisted

HYDROGRAPHIC SHIP *(continued)*

Mutiara (152) Leo Van Ginderen, 5-90

Remarks: Ordered 1975. Carries six small survey launches and has a small helicopter platform aft. White hull, buff stack.

AUXILIARIES

◆ **2 multipurpose support ships**

	Bldr	Laid down	L	In serv.
1503 SRI INDERA SAKTI	Bremer-Vulcan	15-2-80	1-7-80	24-10-80
1504 MAHAWANGSA	Korea Tacoma, Masan	. . .	. . .	16-5-83

Sri Indera Sakti (1503)—exhaust stack aft Mike Louagie, 5-90

Mahawangsa (1504)—higher helo deck, exhaust discharged through hull sides Malcolm Dippy, 10-91

D: 2,000 tons light (4,300 fl) **S:** 16.8 kts
Dim: 100.00 (91.20 pp) × 15.00 × 4.75
A: 1 (1504: 2)/57-mm 70-cal. Bofors SAK-57 Mk 1 DP (I × 1 or 2)—2/20-mm AA (I × 2)
M: 2 Deutz-KHD SBV 6M540 diesels; 2 CP props; 5,986 bhp—bow-thruster
Electric: 1,200 kw tot. **Endurance:** 60 days
Fuel: 1,350 tons (max.) **Range:** 14,000/15
Crew: 14 officers, 122 enlisted + 75 passengers

Remarks: 1,800 dwt. 1503 ordered 10-79, 1504 in 2-81. Intended to perform a variety of tasks, including providing support (including up to 1,300 tons of fuel and 200 tons water) to deployed small combatants or mine-countermeasures ships, acting as a flagship, performing as vehicle and troop transports in amphibious operations, and acting as cadet training ships. There are 1,000 m^3 of cargo space for spare parts, and ten 20-ft standard cargo containers can be carried on deck amidships. Vehicle holds aft are reached by ramps on either side of the stern, which supports a helicopter deck. They can carry 600 troops on the 680-m^2 vehicle deck. Extensive repair facilities and divers' support equipment are provided. Provisions spaces total 300 m^3, including 100 m^3 of refrigerated stores. A 16-ton crane is installed amidships. Have one or two CSEE Naja optical directors for the 57-mm guns.

1504 lacks a funnel, thus effectively doubling the size of the helicopter deck, which is positioned also higher than on 1503; she is configured to carry 410 tons of ammunition and mounts a second 57-mm DP aft. 1504 is 103.00 o.a., draws 5.00 m, displaces 5,000 tons (fl), and can reach 15.5 kts. Both can carry 17 tanks, while 1504 can stow 11 3-ton trucks on deck beneath the helicopter platform.

◆ **2 U.S. LST 512-class former tank landing ships** Bldr: 1501: Missouri Valley Bridge and Iron Co., Evansville, Indiana; 1502: Chicago Bridge & Iron, Seneca, Illinois

	Laid down	L	In serv.
1501 SRI BANGGI (ex-*Henry County,* LST 824)	28-9-44	8-11-44	30-11-44
1502 RAJAH JAROM (ex-*Sedgewick County,* LST 1123)	1-11-44	29-1-45	19-2-45

Sri Banggi (1501) John Jedrlinic, 198

D: 1,653 tons (4,080 fl) **S:** 11 kts (9 fl)
Dim: 99.98 (96.32 wl) × 15.24 × 4.29
A: 3/40-mm 70-cal. Bofors AA
Electron Equipt: Radar: 1/Decca 1226 nav.
M: 2 G.M. 12-567 diesels; 2 props; 1,700 bhp **Electric:** 300 kw tot.
Range: 15,000/9 **Fuel:** 570 tons **Crew:** 11 officers, 117 enlisted

Remarks: Mistakenly deleted from last three editions. Transferred 1-8-74 on lea and purchased outright 7-10-76. Replaced as seagoing logistics support ships by S *Indera Sakti* (1503) and *Mahawangsa* (1504) and are now largely confined to po acting as tenders to missile and patrol boats. Retain bow doors and ramps and ha ramp leading from load-bearing upper deck to the tank deck. Both had twin king po and two 3-ton cargo booms added just forward of the bridge while in U.S. Navy servi Cargo: 2,100 tons maximum/500 beaching.

SERVICE CRAFT

◆ **2 Lang Siput-class utility landing craft/transports** Bldr: Pena SY, Pulau Jerejah

	L	In serv.		L	In ser
LANG SIPUT	1980	1980	LANG TIRAM	25-9-80	21-10-8

D: 630 grt **S:** 9 kts **Dim:** 48.4 (45.0 pp) × 10.5 × . . .
M: 2 Caterpillar D3408 diesels; 2 props; 700 bhp

◆ **2 Jernih-class utility landing craft/transports** Bldr: Brooke DY Malaysia

JERNIH (In serv. 1977) TERIJAH (In serv. 1978)

D: 290 (fl) **S:** 8 kts **Dim:** 38.0 (35.2 pp) × . . . × 1.4
M: 2 Caterpillar D343T diesels; 2 props; 730 bhp

Remarks: Capacity: 170 tons of dry cargo or 240 tons of fresh water. Intende supply craft for Sarawak.

◆ **1 Meleban-class utility landing craft** Bldr: Brooke DY, Malaysia

MELEBAN (L: 15-10-77)

D: . . . **S:** 8 kts **Dim:** 50.0 (43.5 pp) × . . . × 1.37
M: 2 Caterpillar D343T diesels; 2 props; 730 bhp

◆ **1 diving tender**

	Bldr	L	In serv.
1109 DUYONG	Kall Teck SY, Singapore	18-8-70	5-1-71

Duyong (1109) Leo Van Ginderen

SERVICE CRAFT *(continued)*

D: 140 tons (fl) **S:** 12 kts **Dim:** 33.60 × 6.40 × 1.7
A: removed **Electron Equipt:** 1/Kelvin-Hughes 14/9 nav.
M: 2 Cummins diesels; 2 props; 500 bhp
Range: 1,000/10 **Crew:** 23 tot.

Remarks: Used as training ship for navy and navy special forces (PASKAL) divers; carries a decompression chamber and two inflatable boats. Name means "mermaid." Originally configured as a torpedo retriever. One 20-mm Oerlikon AA can be mounted forward.

♦ **1 sail-training brigantine** Bldr: Brooke Marine, Lowestoft, U.K.

	Laid down	L	In serv.
A 13 TUNAS SAMUDERA	1-12-88	4-8-89	16-10-89

...as Samudera (A 13) 92 Wing R.A.A.F., 5-90

...: 239 tons (fl) **S:** 10 kts power/14 kts sail
...im: 44.00 (35 pp) × 7.8 × 4.0 **M:** 2 diesels; 2 props; . . . bhp
...rew: 12 tot. + 24 trainees

...arks: Operated by navy but trains all Malaysian sea services. Foremast 30 ...rs high, mainmast 32.6. Steel construction hull.

... coastal tugs Bldr: Penang SY, Pulau Jerejah (In serv. 1981–82)

...G TIRAM LANG HINDEK LANG KANGOK LANG SIPUT

... . . . **S:** 12.5 kts **Dim:** 29.0 × 7.0 × 2.0
...: 2 Ruston-Paxman diesels; 2 props; 1,800 bhp

... Tunda Satu-class harbor tugs Bldr: Ironwood SY, Malaysia (In ...rv. 1978–79)

...UNDA SATU 1 A2 TUNDA SATU 2 A3 TUNDA SATU 3

... 150 tons **S:** . . . **Dim:** 26.0 × . . . × . . .
... 1 Cummins diesel; 1 prop: . . . bhp

... 400-grt salvage and fire-fighting tugs

...BADANG I A 21 BADANG II

Tunda Satu 1 (A 1) Leo Van Ginderen, 5-90

♦ **8 miscellaneous tugs**

A 4 PENYU (ex-*Salvigilant*)—398-grt salvage tug, built 1976, purchased 1980
A 5 KETAM
A 6 SOTONG (ex-*Asiatic Charm*)—233 grt, blt. 1976; purchased 1980
A 7 KUPANG—salvage and fire-fighting tug
A 8 KEPAH (ex-*Arctic Supplier*)—432 grt, built 1974, purchased 1980
A 9 SIPUT A 10 TERITUP A 11 BELANKAS

Kepah (A 8) Leo Van Ginderen, 5-90

Sotong (A 6) Leo Van Ginderen, 5-90

♦ **5 miscellaneous launches and service craft**

KEMPONG MANGKASA SELAR PATAK TEPURUK

ROYAL MALAYSIAN MARINE POLICE

Note: Planned acquisitions include three 40-m patrol boats equipped with helicopter platforms and four 32-m patrol boats.

ROYAL MALAYSIAN MARINE POLICE *(continued)*

Selar—wooden-hulled personel launch Leo Van Ginderen, 5-90

PATROL BOATS

◆ **9 Brooke Marine 29-m design** Bldr: Penang SY, Pulau Jerejah (In serv. 1982–83)

PX 28 Sangitan 8 others (PX 29–36)

Sangitan (PX 28) Brooke Marine

D: 114 tons **S:** 36 kts **Dim:** 29.0 (26.5 pp) × 6.0 × 1.7
A: 1/20-mm AA—2/7.62-mm mg (I × 2)
Electron Equipt: Radar: 1/. . . nav.
M: 2 Paxman Valenta 16 RP 200M diesels; 2 props; 8,000 bhp
Range: 1,200/24 **Crew:** 4 officers, 14 constables

Remarks: Ordered 1980. Design evolved from that of the PX 26 class. Carry 2,000 rds 20-mm ammunition.

◆ **15 PZ class** Bldr: Hong Leong Lürssen, Butterworth, Malaysia (In serv. 1981–1983)

PZ 1 . . . . . . PZ 2 . . . . . . PZ 3 . . . . . . PZ 4 Lang Kuik
PZ 5 Balong PZ 6 . . . . . . PZ 7 . . . . . . PZ 8 . . . . . .
PZ 9 . . . . . . PZ 10 Lang Hitan PZ 11 . . . . . .
PZ 12 . . . . . .
PZ 13 . . . . . . PZ 14 . . . . PZ 15 . . . . . .

D: 188 tons (205 fl) **S:** 34 kts **Dim:** 38.50 (36.00 wl) × 7.00 × 2.20
A: 1/40-mm 70-cal. Bofors AA—1/20-mm AA—2/7.62-mm mg (I × 2)
Electron Equipt: Radar: 1/Kelvin-Hughes 14/9 nav.
M: 2 MTU 20V538 TB92 diesels; 2 props; 9,000 bhp
Electric: 130 kVA
Range: 550/31.5; 1,100/16 **Crew:** 3 officers, 24 constables

Balong (PZ 5) Hartmut Ehlers, 12-88

Remarks: Lürssen FPB 38 design. Have 2 rocket flare launchers, carry 1,000 rounds 40-mm and 2,000 rounds 20-mm. Ordered 1979; first delivered 8-81.

◆ **3 PX 26 class** Bldr: Hong Leong-Lürssen, Butterworth, Malaysia (In serv. 1973–74)

PX 25 . . . . . . PX 26 Sri Kudat PX 27 Sri Tawau

D: 62.5 tons **S:** 25 kts **Dim:** 28.0 × 5.4 × 1.6
A: 1/20-mm AA (I × 2)—2/7.62-mm mg (I × 2)
M: 2 MTU MB820Db diesels; 2 props; 2,460 bhp
Range: 1,050/15 **Crew:** 19 tot.

◆ **6 improved PX class** Bldr: Vosper Thornycroft Pty, Singapore (In serv. 1973–74)

PX 19 Alor Star PX 21 Kuala Trengganu PX 23 Sri Menanti
PX 20 Kota Bahru PX 22 Johore Bahru PX 24 Kuching

Sri Menanti (PX 23) Vosper, 19

D: 92 tons (fl) **S:** 25 kts **Dim:** 27.3 × 5.8 × 1.5
A: 2/20-mm AA (I × 2) **Electron Equipt:** Radar: 1/. . . nav.
M: 2 MTU MB820Db diesels; 2 props; 2,460 bhp
Range: 750/15 **Crew:** 18 tot.

◆ **18 PX 1 class** Bldr: Vosper Thornycroft Pty, Singapore, 1963–69

PX 1 Mahkota PX 7 Bentara PX 13 Pekan
PX 2 Temenggong PX 8 Perwira PX 14 Kelang
PX 3 Hulubalang PX 9 Pertanda PX 15 Kuala Kangsa
PX 4 Maharajesetia PX 10 Shahbandar PX 16 Arau
PX 5 Maharajelela PX 11 Sangsetia PX 17 Sri Gumanton
PX 6 Pahlawan PX 12 Laksamana PX 18 Sri Labuan

Shahbandar (PX 10) and Sangsetia (PX 11)

D: 85 tons (fl) **S:** 25 kts **Dim:** 26.29 × 5.7 × 1.45
A: 2/20-mm AA (I × 2)—1/7.62-mm mg
Electron Equipt: Radar: 1/Kelvin-Hughes 14/9 nav.
M: 2 Mercedes-Benz MB820Db diesels; 2 props; 2,460 bhp
Range: 550/20; 700/15 **Crew:** 15 tot.

Remarks: PX 17 and PX 18 are operated by the Sabah government.

PATROL CRAFT

◆ **12 7.5-meter class** Bldr: Destination Marine, Johore, Malaysia (In s 1990–91)

D: . . . tons (fl) **S:** 45 kts **Dim:** 7.5 × 2.5 × 1.0
A: 2/7.62-mm mg (I × 2) **M:** 2 gasoline outboards; 550 bhp
Crew: . . .

Remarks: Ordered 6-89 for anti-piracy duties. Six intended for service at Saba

Note: The Royal Malaysian Marine Police also operate a large number of s patrol and support craft.

MALAYSIAN CUSTOMS AND EXCISE SERVICE

PATROL BOATS

◆ **6 Vosper 103-ft design** Bldr: Malaysian SY & Eng. Co., Pasir Gud

K 1 Bahtera Perak K 2 Bahtera Bayu K 3 Bahtera H
K 4 Bahtera Pulai K 5 Bahtera Jerai K 6 Bahtera J

MALAYASIA *(continued)*
PATROL BOATS *(continued)*

D: 100 tons (143 fl) **S:** 27 kts **Dim:** 32.40 (29.50 pp) × 7.20 × 1.80
A: 1/20-mm Oerlikon AA—2/7.62-mm mg (I × 2)
M: 2 Paxman Valenta 16RP200 diesels; 2 props; 4,000 bhp; 1 Cummins KTA-1550M cruise diesel; 1 prop; 575 bhp
Range: 1,200/10; 2,000/8 **Fuel:** 36 tons **Crew:** 26 tot.

Remarks: Ordered built under license from Vosper Pty, Singapore. First two in service 1982; last delivered 30-3-84. Generally resemble Malaysian Navy units of this design.

Note: The Customs and Excise Service also operates a number of small craft, including 23 13.7-meter craft, 10 11.0-meter craft, and the 18.3-m *Kuala Bengkoka,* completed 3-12-76 by Mengsina, Singapore.

Kuala Bengkoka (KA 34) Leo Van Ginderen, 9-88

.7-meter Customs craft Landok (P 25) Hartmut Ehlers, 12-88

MALDIVE ISLANDS

Republic of the Maldives

COAST GUARD

Personnel (1991): Approximately 250 total

PATROL CRAFT

♦ **1 21-m Tracker** Bldr: Fairey Marine, Cowes, U.K. (In serv. 4-87)

D: 35 tons (38 fl) **S:** 25 kts **Dim:** 21.00 × 5.18 × 1.45
A: 2/7.62-mm mg (I × 2)
Electron Equipt: Radar: 1/Decca 150 nav.
M: 2 G.M. 12V71 TI diesels; 2 props; 1,300 bhp
Range: 450/20 **Endurance:** 7 days **Crew:** 11 tot.

Remarks: Ordered 6-85. Used for fisheries protection. GRP construction.

♦ **3 ex-U.K. Tracker II class** Bldr: Fairey Marine, Hamble (In serv. 1978–79)

. . . . (ex-*Active*) . . . . (ex-*Challenge*)
. . . . (ex-*Champion*)

ex-Champion Maritime Photographic, 4-89

D: 31 tons (34.5 fl) **S:** 21 kts **Dim:** 20.00 (19.30 pp) × 5.18 × 1.45
A: 2/7.62-mm mg (I × 2)
Electron Equipt: Radar: 1/Decca 150 nav.
M: 2 G.M. 12V71 TI diesels; 2 props; 1,300 bhp
Electric: 30 kw **Range:** 650/20 **Crew:** 9 tot.

Remarks: Transferred by U.K. 7-89 and left for Indian Ocean via heavy-lift ship. Formerly operated by H.M. Customs and Excise. GRP hull construction. Designed to mount a 20-mm AA gun.

♦ **1 17-m class** Bldr: Cheverton, Cowes (In serv. 1984)

D: 22 tons (24 fl) **S:** 23.6 kts **Dim:** 17.00 × 4.50 × 1.20
A: 1/7.62-mm mg **Electron Equipt:** Radar: 1/Decca 150 nav.
M: 2 G.M. 8V71 TI diesels; 2 props; 850 bhp
Range: 790/18; 1,000/12 **Crew:** 9 tot.

Remarks: Originally completed 1980 for Kiribati, but not delivered. Purchased 1984 for the Maldives. GRP hull; aluminum superstructure.

SERVICE CRAFT

♦ **1 utility landing craft/transport** Bldr: North SY, Singapore

Ufuli (In serv. 8-91)

D: 108 grt **S:** 8 kts **Dim:** . . . (26.00 pp) × 8.00 × 1.00
M: 2 Cummins NT-855M diesels; 2 props; 480 bhp **Crew:** 6 tot.

Remarks: Has bow ramp.

♦ **1 12.2-meter airfield crash tender** Bldr: Task Force Boats, London (In serv. 4-87)

♦ **3 9-meter launches** Bldr: Fairey Marine, Hamble (In serv. 1986)

Note: The ex-British Royal Air Force RTTL Mk 2 and Type 1300 launches and the ex-Taiwanese trawlers *Gaafaru, Isdu Muli,* and *Maggudu* listed in the previous edition have been discarded, as has the customs craft received in 1975.

MALI

Personnel (1991): About 60 total

♦ **2 Yugoslav-built patrol craft for the Niger River**

Remarks: Transferred 1974 via Libya. Based, as are the craft below, at Bamako, Segou, Mopti, and Timbuktu.

♦ **3 smaller river patrol craft**

MALTA

Republic of Malta

Personnel (1991): About 150 total

Aviation: Helicopter Flight. First Regiment, Armed Forces of Malta: 1 AB-206A and 4 AB-47 helicopters in service; 3 Alouette-III in storage. Two Italian Air Force AB-212 on detachment for SAR duties.

ARMED FORCES OF MALTA MARITIME SQUADRON

PATROL BOATS

Note: On 16-9-88, the government gave authorization to seek bids for three or four new patrol boats of 35-m o.a., a speed of 35 kts, and a range of 1,500 n.m. at 20 kts; none have been ordered to date.

◆ **0 (+ 2) ex-East German Navy Tarantul-I-class (Soviet Project 1241) former guided-missile patrol boats** Bldr: Petrovskiy SY, St. Petersburg

	In serv.
C . . . (ex-*Rudolf Egelhofer*, 572)	2-4-85
C . . . (ex-*Fritz Globig*, 573)	6-7-85

D: 470 tons (530 fl) **S:** 41 kts
Dim: 56.5 (52.3 wl) × 10.2 (9.5 wl) × 3.7 (2.4 hull)
A: . . . **Electron Equipt:** Radar: 1/TRR-333 nav.
M: COGAG: 2 cruise gas turbines (3,500 shp each) ; 2 NK-12MV boost gas turbines (12,000 shp each); 3 props; 31,200 shp tot.
Range: 400/36; 2,000/20 **Fuel:** 50 tons **Crew:** approx 25 tot.

Remarks: Offered to Malta by Germany in the fall of 1991; would be transferred without missiles, 76-mm and 30-mm guns, SA-N-5 point-defense SAM system, and Plank Shave and Bass Tilt radars. With light armament, might be able to exceed the maximum speed listed above.

◆ **1 ex-Libyan customs patrol boat** Bldr: J.I. Thornycroft, Woolston, U. K.

C 28 (ex-*Ar Rakib*)

C 28 Leo Van Ginderen, 9-91

D: 100 tons (fl) **S:** 18 kts **Dim:** 30.5 × 6.4 × 1.7
A: 1/20-mm Oerlikon AA
Electron Equipt: Radar: 1/Decca . . . nav.
M: 3 Rolls-Royce diesels; 3 props; 1,740 bhp
Range: 1,800/14 **Crew:** 15 tot.

Remarks: Transferred in 1978. Sister C 30 (ex-*Farwa*) sank 1981, and C 29 (ex-*Akrama*) was stricken 1989 to provide parts to keep this unit running; will probably be stricken soon if not retired already.

Note: The ex-Yugoslav Type 131 patrol boats *President Tito* (ex-*Durmitor*, 138) and *Ganni Bonnici* (ex-*Dom Mintoff*, ex-*President Mintoff*, ex-Yugoslav *Cer*, 139) were inoperable by 6-90 but were still afloat at Valleta in 1991.

PATROL CRAFT

◆ **2 ex-U.S. National Oceanographic and Atmospheric Administration launches** Bldr: Equitable Equipment Corp., New Orleans, Louisiana (In serv. . . .)

C 25 (ex-NOAA 1255) C 26 (ex-NOAA 1257)

C 26 Leo Van Ginderen, 6-91

D: . . . tons (fl) **S:** 18–20 kts **Dim:** 17.98 × . . . × 1.07
A: none **Electron Equipt:** 1/Furuno . . . nav.
M: 2 G.M. Detroit Diesel 12V71 diesels; 2 props; 960 bhp
Range: . . ./. . . **Crew:** 5 tot.

Remarks: Donated by the U.S. at the order of President Bush after his meeting at Malta with President Gorbachev of the U.S.S.R. Both arrived 11-2-91. Former oilfield crewboats.

◆ **2 ex-U.S. Swift Mk II-class PCF** Bldr: Sewart Seacraft, Berwick, Louisiana (In serv. 1968)

C 23 (ex-U.S. C 6823) C 24 (ex-U.S. C 6824)

C 23 and C 24 Leo Van Ginderen, 6-9(

D: 22.5 tons (fl) **S:** 25 kts **Dim:** 15.6 × 4.12 × 1.5
A: 3/12.7-mm mg (II × 1 and 1 combined with 1/81-mm mortar)
Electron Equipt: Radar: 1/ LN-66 nav.
M: 2 G.M. 12V71T diesels; 2 props; 960 bhp **Electric:** 6 kw tot.
Endurance: 24–36 hours **Range:** 400/22 **Crew:** 6–8 tot.

Remarks: Donated 1-71. In poor condition by 1991 but are still marginally operabl[e]

Note: Ex-German customs launch C 27 (ex-*Brunsbuttel*) stricken 1989. Former Li[b]yan customs launch C 25 (ex-*Arraid*) stricken 1989 and sister C 26 stricken 1990; bo[th] remain afloat as hulks at Valleta.

◆ **1 ex-British RAF 1300-series wooden-hulled launch**

C 20

C 20 Leo Van Ginderen, 9

D: 28.3 tons (fl) **S:** 13 kts **Dim:** 19.2 × 4.7 × 1.5
A: none **Electron Equipt:** 1/Decca . . . nav.
M: 2 Rolls-Royce C65 FLM diesels; 2 props; 190 bhp **Crew:** 4 tot.

◆ **3 small search-and-rescue launches**

C 22 Pepo C 27 C 29

Pepo (C 22)—with C 20 in background Leo Van Ginderen,

MALTA *(continued)*
PATROL CRAFT *(continued)*

Remarks: C 22 is a small cabin cruiser confiscated 1981 after capture while smuggling. The other two are locally built Barberis 9.5-meter cabin cruisers acquired in 1989.

SERVICE CRAFT

♦ **1 U.S. LCVP Mk 7 personnel landing craft** Bldr: Gulfstream Corp. (In serv. . . .)

D: 13 tons (fl) **S:** 9 kts **Dim:** 10.90 × 3.21 × 1.04 (aft)
M: 1 G.M. Gray Marine 64HN9 diesel; 1 prop; 225 bhp
Range: 110/9 **Crew:** 2 tot.

Remarks: Donated by the U.S. in 1-87. Can carry 36 personnel or 3.5 tons cargo in 5.24 × 2.29-meter cargo well with bow ramp. Used for local transportation at Valleta.

MARSHALL ISLANDS

ersonnel (1991): 55 total

GOVERNMENT OF THE MARSHALL ISLANDS MARITIME AUTHORITY

ATROL BOATS

1 ASI 315 design Bldr: Australian SB Ind. (WA), Pty., Ltd., South Coogie, Western Australia

NMETO 3 (In serv. 29-6-91)

D: 165 tons (fl) **S:** 21 kts **Dim:** 31.50 (28.60 wl) × 8.10 × 2.12
A: 3/12.7-mm mg (I × 3)
Electron Equipt: Radar: 1/Furuno 1011 nav.
M: 2 Caterpillar 3516 diesels; 2 props; 2,820 bhp **Electric:** 116 kw
Endurance: 10 days **Range:** 2,500/12 **Fuel:** 27.9 tons
Crew: 3 officers, 14 enlisted

marks: "Pacific Patrol Boat" design winner for Australian foreign aid program. dered 1989. Sisters in Papua New Guinea, Vanuatu, Fiji, Western Samoa, and omon Islands service. Guns not normally mounted. To be sold during 1992.

1 former oilfield supply boat Bldr: Halter Marine, New Orleans

NMETO 1 (ex-*Southern Light*)

meto 1 W.D. Souter, 2-89

: approx. 110 tons (fl) **S:** 14 kts
im: 30.98 × . . . × . . .
: 2/12.7-mm mg (I × 2) **Electron Equipt:** Radar: 1/. . . nav.
: 2 . . . diesels; 2 props; . . . bhp **Crew:** 12 tot.

arks: Purchased in Gulf of Mexico area, 1987, refitted by builder; traveled to shall Islands under own power. Fuel tankage increased by 200 percent; new radars, nine-gun mountings provided (guns not normally mounted). Based at Majuro with *eto 2* and *3*.

ex-U.S. Coast Guard Cape class Bldr: U.S.C.G. Yard, Curtis Bay, Id. (In serv. 1953)

IETO 2 (ex-*Cape Small*, WPB 95300)

Ionmeto 2 W.D. Souter, 2-89

D: 87 tons (106 fl) **S:** 20 kts **Dim:** 28.96 × 6.10 × 1.55
A: 2/12.7-mm mg (I × 2)
Electron Equipt: Radar: 1/SPS-64(v)1 nav.
M: 4 Cummins VT-12-M700 diesels; 2 props; 2,324 bhp
Range: 460/20; 2,600/9 **Electric:** 40 kw **Crew:** 15 tot.

Remarks: First "95-footer," stricken from U.S. Coast Guard 13-4-87 and transferred to the Marshall Islands. Had not been modernized with new engines and probably will not survive much longer in service. Guns not normally mounted.

Note: Former U.S. Navy landing craft–type ferries YFU 76 and YFU 77 were acquired from the U.S. Department of the Interior (which received them from the U.S. Navy on 1-12-84) on 1-12-87 for use by a Marshall Islands government civil agency for interisland public transportation. Also in use by the civil agency are former LCU 1552 and LCMs 6057 and 15967.

MAURITANIA

Islamic Republic of Mauritania

Personnel (1991): 35 officers, 445 enlisted

Naval Aviation: Two Piper Cheyenne II, twin-turboprop aircraft were delivered 1981 for coastal surveillance duties. Capable of 7-hour patrols (1,525 n.m.), they have a belly-mounted Bendix RDR 1400 radar.

OFFSHORE PATROL VESSEL

♦ **1 Jura class** Bldr: Hall Russell & Co., Aberdeen, Scotland (In serv. 1975)

N'MADI (ex-*Criscella*, ex-*Jura*)

N'Madi—as *Jura* Leo Van Ginderen, 10-81

D: 778 tons (1,285 fl) **S:** 16.5 kts **Dim:** 59.6 × 10.7 × 4.4
A: probably none **Electron Equipt:** 2/. . . nav.
M: 2 British Polar SP112VS-F diesels; 1 CP prop; 4,200 bhp
Endurance: 18 days **Crew:** 28 tot.

Remarks: 885 grt. Former Department of Agriculture and Fisheries for Scotland fisheries protection ship sold commercial to J. Marr, Ltd., in 1-88 and chartered to Mauritania in 7-89 for fisheries protection and offshore patrol vessel duties. Design (with different engines) employed for Royal Navy's "Isles"-class offshore patrol vessels. Has passive tank stabilization system.

PATROL BOATS

♦ **1 French PATRA class** Bldr: C.N. Auroux, Arcachon

	Laid down	L	In serv.
P 411 El Nasr (ex-*Dix Juillet*, ex-*Rapiere*, P 674)	15-2-81	3-6-81	1-11-81

MAURITANIA *(continued)*
PATROL BOATS *(continued)*

El Nasr (P 411) C.N. Auroux, 1981

D: 115 tons (148 fl) **S:** 28 kts **Dim:** 40.70 (35.40 wl) × 5.90 × 1.55
A: 1/40-mm Bofors AA—1/20-mm Oerlikon AA—2/12.7-mm mg (I × 2)
Electron Equipt: Radar: 1/Decca 1226 nav.
M: 2 AGO 195 V12 CZSHR diesels; 2 CP props; 5,000 bhp (4,400 sust.)
Electric: 120 kw **Range:** 750/20; 1,500/15
Crew: 2 officers, 25 enlisted

Remarks: Built on speculation, acquired by French Navy 1-11-81, and then sold to Mauritania, commissioning 14-5-82. Reported to be in need of overhaul, 1987; renamed 1988.

♦ **3 Spanish Barcelo class** Bldr: E.N. Bazán, San Fernando

	In serv.		In serv.
P 362 El Viaz	12-79	P 363 El Beg	5-79
P 364 El Kenz	8-82		

D: 134 tons (fl) **S:** 36.5 kts **Dim:** 36.2 × 5.8 × 1.75
A: 1/40-mm Bofors AA—1/20-mm Oerlikon GAM-B01 AA—2/12.7-mm mg (I × 2)
Electron Equipt: Radar: 1/Raytheon 1620 nav.
M: 2 MTU MD 16V538 TB90 diesels; 6,000 bhp **Electric:** 330 kVA
Range: 1,200/17 **Fuel:** 18 tons **Crew:** 3 officers, 16 enlisted

Remarks: Delivery of the first two was greatly delayed when they collided on trials, 12-78. The third unit was ordered in 1979, with delivery delayed over financial problems. Have had engineering difficulties; P 362 could achieve only 14 kts during 1988.

♦ **1 ex-German Neustadt class** Bldr: Lürssen, Vegesack

	Laid down	L	In serv.
Z'Bar (ex-*Uelzen,* BG 13)	17-5-69	25-7-69	24-2-70

D: 191 tons (218 fl) **S:** 30 kts **Dim:** 38.50 (36.00 pp) × 7.00 × 2.15
A: 2/40-mm Bofors AA (I × 2)
Electron Equipt: Radar: 1/Kelvin-Hughes 14/9 nav.
M: 2 Maybach 16-cyl. diesels; 2 props; 7,200 bhp—cruise engine: 1 MWM diesel; 1 prop; 685 bhp
Electric: 156 kw (3 × 52-kw diesel sets) **Range:** 450/27
Fuel: 15 tons **Crew:** 5 officers, 18 enlisted

Remarks: Former German Sea Border Guard (*Bundesgrenzschutz-See)* patrol boat donated 19-3-90 and commissioned 29-4-90.

PATROL CRAFT

♦ **4 Indian Mandovi class** Bldr: Garden Reach DY, Calcutta (In serv. 1990)

D: 15 tons (fl) **S:** 24 kts **Dim:** 15.0 × 3.6 × 0.8
A: 1/7.62-mm mg **Electron Equipt:** Radar: 1/Furuno FR 8030 nav.
M: 2 MWM TD-232 VI 2 diesels; 2 Hamilton waterjets; 750 bhp
Range: 240/12 **Crew:** 8 tot.

Remarks: Same basic design also built for Mauritius by designer, Mandovi Marine.

♦ **1 customs launch** Bldr: . . . . . ., France (In serv. 1984)

Lieutenant Sid'Amar

Remarks: No data available.

Note: French-built 32-meter patrol craft *Tichitt* (P 321) and *Dar el Barka* (P 322) and 18-meter patrol craft *Imag'ni* were stricken 1988–89.

MAURITIUS

NATIONAL COAST GUARD ORGANIZATION

Personnel (1991): Approximately 500 total, including personnel manning 12 shore stations

Aviation: One Indian Hindustan Aeronautic-built Dornier 228 with MEL surveillance radar delivered 1990.

PATROL BOAT

Note: It is hoped to order a seagoing offshore patrol vessel in 1993.

♦ **1 ex-Indian Ajay class** Bldr: Garden Reach DY, Calcutta

P 1 Amar (In serv. 1961; transferred 4-74)

Amar (P 1) French Navy, 9-86

D: 120 tons (160 fl) **S:** 18 kts **Dim:** 35.7 (33.52 pp) × 6.1 × 1.5
A: 1/40-mm 60-cal. Mk 7 Bofors AA
Electron Equipt: Radar: 1/Kelvin-Hughes 14/9
M: 2 Paxman YHAXM diesels; 2 props; 1,000 bhp; 1 Foden FD 6 cruise diesel; 100 bhp
Range: 1,000/8; 500/12 **Fuel:** 23 tons **Crew:** 4 officers, 15 enlisted

Remarks: Retained former Indian Navy name. Antisubmarine equipment removed

PATROL CRAFT

♦ **2 Soviet Zhuk-class** (In serv. 3-12-89)

Rescuer Retriever

D: 48 tons (60 fl) **S:** 34 kts **Dim:** 24.0 × 5.0 × 1.2 (1.8 props)
A: 4/14.5-mm mg (II × 2)
Electron Equipt: Radar: 1/Spin Trough nav.
M: 2 M50F-4 diesels; 2 props; 2,400 bhp **Range:** 700/28; 1,100/15
Fuel: 10 tons **Crew:** 4 officers, 13 enlisted

Remarks: Were a gift of the Soviet Union originally offered in the early 1980s.

♦ **9 Mandowi-class** Bldr: Garden Reach SY, Calcutta

Barracuda	Canopus	Capella	Castor	Marlin
Polaris	Pollux	Rigel	Sirius	

D: 15 tons (fl) **S:** 24 kts **Dim:** 15.0 × 3.6 × 0.8
A: 1/7.62-mm mg **Electron Equipt:** Radar: 1/Furuno FR 8030 na
M: 2 MWM TD-232 VI 2 diesels; 2 Hamilton waterjets; 750 bhp
Range: 240/12 **Crew:** 8 tot.

Remarks: Ordered 24-7-87. Two delivered 1989, rest in 1990. Designed by Mand Marine Private, Ltd. Resemble oilfield crewboats and have "Coast Guard" painted sides.

Note: Also in service are 34 smaller craft, including two 12-meter U.S. Ma launches donated in 1990, two Rover 663 launches donated by Australia, and outboard-powered, rigid inflatable rescue craft.

MEXICO

United Mexican States

Personnel (1991): 38,000 total, including 9,000 marines. The number of marines be reduced to 6,000.

Naval Aviation: The Mexican Navy operates 5 Grumman HU-16 Albatross phibians, 10 Casa 212 coastal surveillance aircraft, 1 DNC Buffalo, 1 Fokker F-27, 40 light fixed-wing aircraft, including: 1 Learjet 24D, 12 Beach B-55, 1 Cessna 4 Beech King Air 90, 4 Rockwell Turbo-Commander, 1 Piper Aztec, 1 Cessna 337 Beech D590, 1 Cessna 206A, 1 Cessna 441, 8 Cessna 152, 3 Beech T-34 Mentor, a Beech F-33 Bonanza trainers. Helicopters include 11 MBB BO-105CB, 3 Alouette- McDonnell Douglas MD 500E and 1 MD 500, 3 Hughes 269 A, and 2 Bell HU-1H, 10 SA-315 Lama helicopters for search-and-rescue duties. Two locally designed T tiah trainers were completed in 1984 at Veracruz.

DESTROYERS

♦ **2 ex-U.S. Gearing FRAM I class** Bldr: Bethlehem Steel, Staten Island

	Laid down	L	In serv.
E-03 Quetzalcoatl (ex-*Vogelgesang,* DD 862)	3-8-44	15-1-45	28-4-45
E-04 Netzahualcoyotl (ex-*Steinaker,* DD 863)	1-9-44	13-2-45	26-5-45

DESTROYERS *(continued)*

D: 2,448 tons light (3,528 fl) **S:** 30 kts
Dim: 119.03 × 12.52 × 4.45 (6.4 sonar)
A: 4/127-mm 38-cal. DP (II × 2)—1/Mk 112 ASROC ASW RL (VIII × 1)—6/324-mm Mk 32 ASW TT (III × 2)—1/BO-105CB helicopter
Electron Equipt:
Radar: 1/LN-66 nav., 1/SPS-10 surf. search, 1/SPS-40B (E-04: SPS-29) air search, 1/Mk 25 f.c.
Sonar: SQS-23 hull-mounted LF—EW: WLR-1 intercept
M: 2 sets General Electric geared steam turbines; 2 props; 60,000 shp
Boilers: 4 Babcock & Wilcox; 43.3 kg/cm², 454° C
Electric: 1,200 kw **Range:** 1,500/31; 5,800/12 **Fuel:** 650 tons
Crew: approx. 275 total

Remarks: Transferred to Mexico 24-2-82 by sale, as intended replacements for the then-two *Fletcher*-class destroyers. Retained ASROC launcher. Have unusual heat-signature-suppressant stack caps. Have Mk 37 gun fire-control system with one radar director to control the 127-mm guns, and Mk 112 control system for the ASW ordnance.

◆ **1 ex-U.S. Fletcher class** Bldr: Consolidated Steel, Orange, Texas

	Laid down	L	In serv.
E-02 CUITLAHUAC (ex-*John Rodgers*, DD 574)	25-7-41	7-5-42	25-1-43

uitlahuac (E-02) 1983

D: 2,050 tons (2,850 fl) **S:** 30 kts
Dim: 114.73 × 12.06 × 5.50 (max.)
A: 5/127-mm 38-cal. Mk 30 DP (I × 5)—14/40-mm AA (IV × 2, II × 3)— 5/533-mm antiship TT (V × 1)
Electron Equipt:
Radar: 1/Kelvin-Hughes 14/9 nav., 1/Kelvin-Hughes 17/9 nav., 1/Mk 12/22 f.c.
M: 2 sets General Electric geared steam turbines; 2 props; 60,000 shp
Boilers: 4 Babcock & Wilcox; 39.8 kg/cm², 454° C
Electric: 590 kw **Range:** 4,400/15; 1,260/30
Fuel: 650 tons **Crew:** 197 tot.

marks: Transferred 8-70. All ASW capability and obsolete U.S. electronics systems w deleted. Has one Mk 37 director for 127-mm guns and five Mk 51 Mod. 2 directors 40-mm guns; the fire-control radar is obsolete World War II equipment and probably no longer functional. Could make 35 kts when new. Sister *Cuauhtemoc* E-01 (ex-*rrison*, DD 573) discarded 1982. In need of replacement.

IGATES

te: Former U.S. Navy frigates *Bronstein* (FF 1037) and *McCloy* (FF 1038) were red to Mexico in 1-92; see addenda for details.

1 ex-U.S. Charles Lawrence* and 2 Crosley class

	Bldr	Laid down	L	In serv.
6 USUMACINTA x-*Don O. Voods*, APD 18, ex-DE 721)	Consolidated Steel, Orange, Tex.	1-12-43	19-2-44	28-5-45
7 COAHUILA x-*Barber*, APD 7, ex-DE 161)*	Norfolk Navy Yd, Norfolk, Va.	27-4-43	20-5-43	10-10-43
8 CHIHUAHUA x-*Rednour*, PD 102, ex-DE 29)	Bethlehem SB, Hingham, Mass.	30-12-43	12-2-44	30-12-44

: 1,450 tons (2,130 fl) **S:** 23 kts **Dim:** 93.26 × 11.28 × 3.83
: 1/127-mm 38-cal. Mk 30 DP—6/40-mm 60-cal. AA (II × 3)—B-07 also: 2/20-mm Oerlikon AA (I × 2)
lectron Equipt: Radar: 1/Kelvin-Hughes 14/9 nav.
: 2 sets General Electric geared steam turbines, turbo-electric drive; 2 props; 12,000 shp
oilers: 2 "D"-Express; 30.6 kg/cm², 399° C **Electric:** 680 kw
ange: 5,000/15 **Fuel:** 350 tons **Crew:** 204 tot.

Coahuila (B-07) Leo Van Ginderen, 6-74

Remarks: Former high-speed transports. B-06 transferred 12-63; B-07 and B-08, 17-2-69. Used primarily as patrol ships; no longer carry the four landing craft that were once stowed amidships. Converted to APD while being built. B-07, with a high bridge and lattice mast aft, is a member of the *Charles Lawrence* class; the others each have a low bridge and a tripod aft to support the 10-ton-capacity cargo boom. The 127-mm gun has no director, while there are three Mk 51 Mod. 2 directors for the 40-mm antiaircraft gun mounts. Two others have been lost: *California* (B-3, ex-*Belet*, APD 109) went aground 16-1-72, and *Papaloapan* (B-4, ex-*Earhart*, APD 113) in 1976. Sister *Zacatacas* (B-05, ex-*Tehuantepec*, ex-*Joseph M. Auman*, APD 117, ex-DE 674) stricken 1989. In need of replacement.

CORVETTES

◆ **2 (+4+3) Aguila class** Bldrs: GA-01, 03: Salina Cruz NSY No. 8; others: Tampico NSY No. 1

	Laid down	L	In serv.
GA-01 SEBASTIAN JOSE HOLTZINGER	6-86	. . .	1-6-91
GA-02 BLAS GODINEZ	7-86	. . .	23-11-91
GA-03	. . .	. . .	1993
GA-04	. . .	. . .	1993

D: 907 tons (1,175 fl) **S:** 22 kts
Dim: 74.4 (70.0 pp) × 10.35 × 2.5 (hull)
A: 1/57-mm 70-cal. Bofors SAK-57 Mk 2 DP—1/BO-105CB helicopter
Electron Equipt: Radar: 2/Raytheon SPS-64(V)6A
M: 2 MTU 20V956 TB92 diesels; 2 props; 13,320 bhp (10, 140 sust.)
Endurance: 20 days **Range:** 3,830/18 **Fuel:** 227.4 tons
Crew: 11 officers, 64 enlisted—plus 16 passengers

Remarks: A smaller variant of the Spanish-built Halcón design, with higher speed and heavier armament. Announced 23-6-83, plans called for construction of nine units at four naval shipyards. Reduced to four units in 10-84, with three possibly to be ordered later. Have smaller helicopter deck than Halcón class, less topweight, two (vice one) engine rooms. Originally planned as replacements for *Auk* and *Admirable* classes, and were originally to have been named *Uxmal, Mitla, Peten,* and *Anahuac*, respectively. Have a Selenia Elsag NA-18 optronic fire-control system for the 57-mm gun.

◆ **6 "Halcón" class** Bldr: E.N. Bazán, San Fernando, Cadiz, Spain

	Laid down	L	In serv.
GH-01 CADETE VIRGILIO URIBE	1-7-81	13-12-81	10-9-82
GH-02 TENIENTE JOSÉ AZUETA	7-9-81	29-1-82	15-10-82
GH-03 CAPITAN DE FRAGATA PEDRO SAINZ DE BARBRANDA	22-10-81	26-2-82	3-83
GH-04 COMODORO CARLOS CASTILIO BRETÓN	11-11-81	26-2-82	9-6-82
GH-05 VICE ALMIRANTE OTHÓN P. BLANCO	18-12-81	26-3-82	24-2-83
GH-06 CONTRA ALMIRANTE ANGEL ORTIZ MONASTERIO	30-12-81	23-4-82	24-3-83

Contra Almirante Angel Ortiz Monasterio (GH-06) Bázan, 1983

CORVETTES *(continued)*

D: 767 tons (910 fl) **S:** 21 kts **Dim:** 67.00 (63.00 pp) × 10.50 × 3.08
A: 1/40-mm 70-cal. Bofors AA—1/BO-105CB helicopter
Electron Equipt: Radar: 1/Decca AC 1226 nav.—TACAN: SRN-15
M: 2 MTU 20V956 TB91 diesels; 2 props; 13,320 bhp
Electric: 710 kw **Range:** 5,000/18 **Crew:** 10 officers, 42 enlisted

Remarks: Ordered late 1980 for use in patrolling the 200-nautical-mile economic zone. Have been referred to as the "Puma" class. Generally identical to ships built for Argentina, but with more powerful engines and longer helicopter deck. Commissioning of GH-04 delayed by accident; originally completed 4-11-82.

♦ 17 ex-U.S. Auk-class former fleet minesweepers

Bldrs: A: Pennsylvania Shipyard, Beaumont, Tex.; B: Savannah Machine & Foundry Co., Savannah, Ga.; C: General Engineering and Drydock Co., Alameda, Cal.; D: Associated Shipbuilders; E: Gulf Shipbuilding; F: J. H. Mathis, Camden, N.J.; G: Winslow Marine Railway and Shipbuilding, Seattle, Wash.

	Bldr	L
G-01 Leandro Valle (ex-*Pioneer,* MSF 105)(1)	A	26-7-42
G-02 Guillermo Prieto (ex-*Symbol,* MSF 123)(2)	B	2-7-42
G-03 Mariano Escobedo (ex-*Champion,* MSF 314)(3)	C	12-12-42
G-05 Manuel Doblado (ex-*Defense,* MSF 317)(3)	C	18-2-43
G-06 Sebastian Lerdo De Tejada (ex-*Devastator,* MSF 318)(3)	C	19-4-43
G-07 Santos Degollado (ex-*Gladiator,* MSF 319)(3)	C	7-5-43
G-08 Ignacio De La Llave (ex-*Spear,* MSF 322)(2)	D	25-2-43
G-09 Juan N. Alvarez (ex-*Ardent,* MSF 340)(3)	C	22-6-43
G-10 Melchior Ocampo (ex-*Roselle,* MSF 379)(4)	E	29-8-45
G-11 Valentin G. Farias (ex-*Starling,* MSF 64)(5)	C	15-2-42
G-12 Ignacio Altamirano (ex-*Sway,* MSF 120)(2)	F	29-9-42
G-13 Francisco Zarco (ex-*Threat,* MSF 124)(2)	B	15-8-42
G-14 Ignacio L. Vallarta (ex-*Velocity,* MSF 128)(2)	E	19-4-42
G-15 Jésus G. Ortega (ex-*Chief,* MSF 315)(3)	C	5-1-43
G-16 Gutierriez Zamora (ex-*Scoter,* MSF 381)(4)	E	26-9-45
G-18 Juan Aldarma (ex-*Pilot,* MSF 104)(1)	A	5-7-42
G-19 Hermenegildo Galeana (ex-*Sage,* MSF 111)(1)	G	21-11-42

Ignacio L. Vallarta (G-14) and sisters George R. Schneider, Jr., 1-89

D: 890 tons (1,250 fl) **S:** 17/18 kts
Dim: 67.4 (65.5 wl) × 9.8 × 3.28
A: 1/76.2-mm 50-cal. U.S. Mk 22 DP—4/40-mm 60-cal. U.S. Mk 2 AA (II × 2)
Electron Equipt: Radar: 1/SPS-5 or 1/Kelvin-Hughes 14/9 nav.
M: 2 diesels, electric drive (*see* Remarks); 2 props; 2,976, 3,118, or 3,532 bhp
Electric: 300–360 kw **Range:** 4,300/10 **Fuel:** 216 tons
Crew: 9 officers, 96 enlisted

Remarks: The numbers in parentheses after the ships' names refer to five different diesels used in propulsion plants: (1) Busch-Sulzer 539; (2) G.M. 12-278; (3) Baldwin VO-8; (4) G.M. 12-278A; (5) Alco 539. Diesels (1) and (5) produce 3,118 bhp total, (2) and (4) produce 3,532 bhp, and (3) produces 2,976 bhp.

All transferred in 1973. All minesweeping and ASW equipment removed. One other unit, *Mariano Matamoros* (ex-*Herald,* MSF 101), was converted for use as a surveying ship. Some have a small deckhouse between the stacks; some have no main deck bulwarks. New radars have been added to ships transferred without SPS-5. Sister *Ponciano Arriaga* (G-04, ex-*Competent,* MSF 316) stricken 1988; the others are in need of replacement.

♦ 12 ex-U.S. Admirable-class former fleet minesweepers

	Bldr	L
D-01 DM 01 (ex-*Jubilant,* MSF 255)	American SB, Lorain, Oh.	20-2-43
D-03 DM 03 (ex-*Execute,* MSF 232)	Puget Sound SY, Seattle, Wash.	22-1-44
D-04 DM 04 (ex-*Specter,* MSF 306)	Associated Shipbldrs.	15-2-44
D-05 DM 05 (ex-*Scuffle,* MSF 298)	Winslow, Seattle, Wash.	8-8-43
D-11 DM 11 (ex-*Device,* MSF 220)	Tampa SB, Fla.	21-5-44
D-12 DM 12 (ex-*Ransom,* MSF 283)	General Eng. & DD	18-9-43
D-13 DM 13 (ex-*Knave,* MSF 256)	American SB, Lorain, Oh.	13-3-43
D-14 DM 14 (ex-*Rebel,* MSF 284)	General Eng. & DD	28-10-43
D-15 DM 15 (ex-*Crag,* MSF 214)	Tampa SB, Fla.	21-3-43
D-17 DM 17 (ex-*Diploma,* MSF 221)	Tampa SB, Fla.	21-5-44
D-18 DM 18 (ex-*Invade,* MSF 254)	Savannah Mach., Ga.	6-2-44
D-19 DM 19 (ex-*Intrigue,* MSF 253)	Savannah Mach., Ga.	8-4-44

D: 650 tons (945 fl) **S:** 15 kts **Dim:** 56.24 (54.86 wl) × 10.06 × 2.97
A: 1/76.2-mm 50-cal. U.S. Mk 22 DP—2/40-mm 60-cal. U.S. Mk 3 AA (I × 2)—6/20-mm AA (I × 6)
Electron Equipt: Radar: 1/Kelvin-Hughes 14/9 nav.
M: 2 Cooper-Bessemer GSB-8 diesels; 2 props; 1,710 bhp
Electric: 240 or 280 kw **Range:** 4,300/10 **Fuel:** 138 tons
Crew: 9 officers, 86 enlisted

Remarks: All minesweeping and ASW equipment deleted. Three more units were scrapped, and DM 20 was converted into a hydrographic survey ship. DM 04 was transferred 2-73; all others, 1-10-62. Stricken in 1986 were DM 02 (D-02, ex-*Hilarity,* MSF 241), DM 06 (D-06, ex-*Eager,* MSF 224), DM 10 (D-10, ex-*Instill,* MSF 252) and DM 16 (D-16, ex-*Dour,* MSF 223). In need of replacement; not all operable in 1991.

DM 19 (D-19)—and two sisters Dr. Yves Alloucherie, 7-8

PATROL BOATS

Note: The ordering of six Cormoran-class patrol boats from E.N. Bazán, San Fe nando, Spain, in 8-89, as reported in the previous edition, did not in fact occur.

♦ 31 Azteca class

	Bldr	In ser
P-01 Andres Quintana Roo	Ailsa SB Co., Troon	1-11-7
P-02 Matias De Cordova	Scott & Sons, Bowling	22-10-7
P-03 Miguel Ramos Arizpe	Ailsa SB Co., Troon	23-12-7
P-04 José Maria Izazago	Ailsa SB Co., Troon	19-12-7
P-05 Juan Bautista Morales	Scott & Sons, Bowling	19-12-7
P-06 Ignacio Lopez Rayon	Ailsa SB Co., Troon	19-12-
P-07 Manuel Crescencio Rejon	Ailsa SB Co., Troon	4-7-
P-08 Antonio De La Fuente	Ailsa SB Co., Troon	4-7-
P-09 Leon Guzman	Scott & Sons, Bowling	7-4-
P-10 Ignacio Ramirez	Ailsa SB Co., Troon	17-7-
P-11 Ignacio Mariscal	Ailsa SB Co., Troon	23-9-
P-12 Heriberto Jara Corona	Ailsa SB Co., Troon	7-11-
P-13 José Maria Mata	J. Lamont	13-10-
P-14 Felix Romero	Scott & Sons, Bowling	23-6-
P-15 Fernando Lizardi	Ailsa SB Co., Troon	24-12-
P-16 Francisco J. Mujica	Ailsa SB Co., Troon	21-11-
P-17 Pastor Rouaix José Maria	Scott & Sons, Bowling	7-11-
P-18 José Maria Del Castillo Velasco	J. Lamont	14-1-
P-19 Luis Manuel Rojas	J. Lamont	3-4
P-20 José Natividad Macias	J. Lamont	2-9
P-21 Esteban Baca Calderon	J. Lamont	18-6
P-22 General Ignacio Zaragoza	Vera Cruz NSY	1-6
P-23 Tamaulipas	Vera Cruz NSY	18-5
P-24 Yucatan	Vera Cruz NSY	3-7
P-25 Tabasco	Vera Cruz NSY	1-1
P-26 Veracruz	Vera Cruz NSY	1-1
P-27 Campeche	Vera Cruz NSY	1-3
P-28 Puebla	Vera Cruz NSY	1-6
P-29 Margarita Maza De Juarez	Salina Cruz NSY	29-1
P-30 Leona Vicario	Salina Cruz NSY	1-
P-31 Josefa Ortiz De Dominguez	Salina Cruz NSY	1-

D: 115 tons (165 fl) **S:** 23 kts **Dim:** 36.50 (30.94 pp) × 8.6 × 2.0
A: 1/7.62-mm mg (some: 1/40-mm 60-cal. Bofors AA—1/20-mm Oerlikon AA)
Electron Equipt: Radar: 1/. . . nav.
M: 2 Ruston-Paxman Ventura 12-cyl. diesels; 7,200 bhp
Electric: 80 kw **Range:** 2,500/12 **Crew:** 2 officers, 22 enlisted

Remarks: Original order for 21 placed 27-3-73 with Associated British Machin Makers, Ltd., which subcontracted the actual construction in the United Kingdo later assisted with the construction of another 11 in Mexico. The 21 built in th were being rehabilitated in Mexico with British assistance for 10 more years' s beginning in 1987. The original armament, where fitted, consisted of 1/40-mm A 1/20-mm AA; most now have the single light machine gun. Very lightly constru

PATROL BOATS *(continued)*

Heriberto Jara Corona (P-12)—with 40-mm gun U.S. Navy, 7-76

♦ **2 ex-U.S. Coast Guard Cape class** Bldr: Coast Guard Yard, Curtis Bay, Md.

	In serv.
P 44 Cozumel (ex-*Point Verde*, WPB 82311)	15-3-61
P 46 Punta Nastun (ex-*Point Herron*, WPB 82318)	14-6-61

D: 64 tons (67 fl) **S:** 23.7 kts **Dim:** 25.30 × 5.23 × 1.95
A: 2/12.7-mm mg (I × 2)
Electron Equipt: Radar: 1/SPS-64(V)1 nav.
M: 2 Cummins VT-12-M diesels; 2 props; 1,600 bhp
Range: 490/23.7; 1,500/8 **Fuel:** 5.7 tons **Crew:** 1 officer, 7 enlisted

Remarks: Donated by the U.S. Government for anti-drug patrol duties, P 44 on 19-7-91 and P 46 on 26-7-91. The engines are controlled from the bridge. Are equipped for towing.

♦ **2 ex-U.S. Coast Guard Cape-class** Bldr: Coast Guard Yard, Curtis Bay, Md.

	In serv.	Recommissioned
P 43 Cabo Catoche (ex-*Nayarit*, ex-*Vanguard*, ex-*Cape Hedge*, WPB 95311)	21-12-53	21-4-90
P 45 Jalisco (ex-*Cape Carter*, WPB 95309)	7-12-53	1-4-90

D: 87 tons (106 fl) **S:** 20 kts **Dim:** 28.96 × 6.10 × 1.55
A: 2/12.7-mm mg (I × 2)
Electron Equipt: Radar: 1/SPS-64(V)1 nav.
M: 2 G.M. 16V 149TI diesels; 2 props; 2,470 bhp **Electric:** 60 kw
Endurance: 5 days **Range:** 550/20; 1,900/11.5
Crew: 1 officer, 14 enlisted

Remarks: Both re-engined during the 1980s; the original four Cummins VT-12-M-00 diesels produced 18 kts from 2,324 bhp. Can make 24 kts, but are restricted due to hull damage at speeds over 20 kts. P 43 had been transferred to the U.S. Navy as a pilot boat after being stricken from the U.S. Coast Guard 7-1-87 and transferred 1-90. P 45 stricken 19-1-90 from U.S. Coast Guard and transferred 2-90. P 43 was renamed again during 8-91.

PATROL CRAFT

♦ **20 (+ . . .) Taipei class** Bldr: Acapulco NSY (In serv. 1990–. . .)

D: 1.5 tons **S:** 37 kts **Dim:** 6.40 × . . . × . . .
A: 1/7.62-mm mg **M:** 2 Johnson gasoline outboards; 240 bhp
Range: 144/28 **Crew:** 4–6 tot.

Remarks: GRP construction riverine patrol craft.

♦ **13 Olmeca class** Bldr: Acapulco NSY (In serv. 1979–84)

F-21 AM 11 F-25 AM 15 F-29 AM 19 F-33 AM 23
F-22 AM 12 F-26 AM 16 F-30 AM 20
F-23 AM 13 F-27 AM 17 F-31 AM 21
F-24 AM 14 F-28 AM 18 F-32 AM 22

D: 18 tons (fl) **S:** 20 or 25 kts **Dim:** 16.7 × 4.4 × 2.4
A: 1/12.7-mm mg **Electron Equipt:** Radar: 1/Raytheon 1900 nav.
M: 2 G.M. 8V92 TI diesels; 2 props; 1,140 bhp *or* 2 Cummins UT-series diesels; 800 bhp
Range: 460/15 **Crew:** 2 officers, 13 enlisted

Remarks: GRP construction. Last unit of initial six with Cummins diesels was delivered 22-2-83. Five additional with G.M. diesels ordered 23-6-83 and delivered by end 84. Have a fire-fighting water monitor forward.

♦ **4 Polimar class** Bldrs: Astilleros de Tampico (F-01, F-04); Iscacas SY, Guerrero (F-02, F-03)

	L		L
F-01 Polimar 1	1962	F-03 Polimar 3	1966
F-02 Polimar 2	1966	F-04 Polimar 4	1968

D: 57 tons (fl) **S:** 16 kts **Dim:** 20.5 × 4.5 × 1.3
A: 2/12.7-mm mg (II × 1) **M:** 2 diesels; 2 props; 450 bhp

Polimar 1 (F-01) 1962

♦ **2 Azueta class** Bldr: Astilleros de Tampico

F-06 Villalpando (In serv. 1959) F-07 Azueta (In serv. 1960)

D: 80 tons (fl) **S:** 12 kts **Dim:** 26.0 × 5.0 × 2.1
A: 2/12.7-mm mg **M:** 2 Superior diesels; 2 props; 600 bhp

Remarks: Were to have been retired in 1988 but remain in service. River patrol craft.

♦ **5 AM-1 class** Bldr: Ast. de Tampico and Vera Cruz NSY (L: 1959–61)

F-14 AM 4 F-15 AM 5 F-16 AM 6 F-17 AM 7 F-18 AM 8

D: 37 tons (fl) **S:** 6 kts **Dim:** 17.7 × 5.0 × . . .
A: . . . **M:** 1 diesel; 1 prop; . . . bhp

Remarks: Riverine patrol craft with low freeboard, bulwarks surrounding hull. Sisters AM 1–3 and AM 9 stricken by 1986, AM 10 in 1988.

AUXILIARIES

HYDROGRAPHIC SURVEY AND OCEANOGRAPHIC RESEARCH SHIPS

♦ **1 former stern-haul trawler** Bldr: . . . Japan (In serv. 1977)

H-04 Onjuku (ex-. . .)

D: 494 tons (fl) **S:** 12 kts **Dim:** 36.9 × 8.0 × 3.5
Electron Equipt: Radar: 1/Furuno . . . nav.
M: 1 Yanmar 6UA-UT diesel; 1 prop; 700 bhp
Range: 5,645/10.5 **Crew:** 4 officers, 16 enlisted

Remarks: Acquired 1987. Equipped with Furuno fish-finding sonar. Appears intended primarily for fisheries research and retains fishing gear.

♦ **1 ex-U.S. Robert D. Conrad-class oceanographic research ship**

	Bldr	L	In serv.
H-05 Altair (ex-*James M. Gillis*, AGOR 4)	Christy Corp., Wisconsin	19-5-62	5-11-62

Altair (H-05) George R. Schneider, Jr., 10-85

D: 1,200 tons (1,380 fl) **S:** 13.5 kts
Dim: 63.7 (58.30 pp) × 11.37 × 4.66
Electron Equipt: Radar: 1/Raytheon TM 1600/6X; 1/TM 1660/123
M: 2 Caterpillar D-378 diesels; electric drive; 1 prop; 2,000 shp—bow-thruster
Electric: 850 kw **Fuel:** 211 tons **Range:** 10,000/12
Crew: 12 officers, 14 enlisted + 18 scientists

Remarks: Returned to U.S. Navy by University of Miami in 1980 and laid up until leased to Mexico on 15-6-83; Mexico bore the expense of subsequent reactivation. The large stack contains a 620-shp gas-turbine generator to drive the main shaft at speeds up to 6.5 kts for experiments requiring "quiet" sea conditions. Also has a retractable electric bow-thruster/propulsor, which can drive the ship to 4.5 kts. Refitted and recommissioned 27-11-84. 965 grt.

HYDROGRAPHIC SURVEY AND OCEANOGRAPHIC RESEARCH SHIPS *(continued)*

◆ **1 ex-U.S. Admirable-class former minesweeper** Bldr: Willamette Iron & Steel, Oregon

	Laid down	L	In serv.
H-2 DM 20 (ex-*Oceanografico,* ex-DM 20, ex-*Harlequin,* MSF 365)	3-8-43	3-6-44	28-9-45

D: 615 tons (910 fl) **S:** 15 kts **Dim:** 56.24 (54.86 wl) × 10.06 × 2.80
Electron Equipt: Radar: 1/Decca . . . nav.
M: 2 Cooper-Bessemer GSB-8 diesels; 2 props; 1,710 bhp
Electric: 240 or 280 kw **Range:** 4,300/10 **Fuel:** 138 tons
Crew: 12 officers, 50 enlisted

Remarks: Converted 1976–78; armament deleted, oceanographic winches and davits installed, space at aft end of forecastle employed for portable research containers.

Note: U.S. *Auk*-class former fleet minesweeper *Mariano Matamoros* (H-01, ex-*Herald,* MSF 101) was stricken in 1988.

REPAIR SHIP

◆ **1 ex-U.S. Fabius-class former aircraft repair ship** Bldr: American Bridge Co., Ambridge, Pennsylvania

	Laid down	L	In serv.
A-05 General Vicente Guerrero (ex-*Megara,* ARVA 6, ex-LST 1095)	22-1-45	25-3-45	27-6-45

General Vicente Guerrero (A-05) Leo Van Ginderen, 7-84

D: 4,100 tons (fl) **S:** 11.6 kts **Dim:** 100.0 (96.3 wl) × 15.24 × 3.4
A: 8/40-mm 60-cal. U.S. Mk 2 AA (IV × 2)
M: 2 G.M. 12-567A diesels; 2 props; 1,700 bhp **Electric:** 520 kw
Range: 10,000/10 **Fuel:** 474 tons **Crew:** 28 officers, 85 enlisted

Remarks: Transferred 1-10-73. Originally one of two U.S. Navy tank landing ships converted while under construction to act as repairing aircraft airframes. One 10-ton boom. Two Mk 51 Mod. 2 GFCS for the 40-mm AA. Normally carries two U.S. LCVP personnel landing craft.

TRANSPORTS

◆ **2 Huasteco class** Bldr: Ast. de la Secretaud de Marina, Guaymas

A-21 Huasteco (In serv. 21-5-86) A-22 Zapoteco (In serv. 1-6-86)

Huasteco (A-21) Leo Van Ginderen, 1988

D: 2,650 tons (fl) **S:** 14 kts **Dim:** 72.3 × 12.8 × 5.5
A: 1/40-mm 60-cal. Mk 3 AA—1/BO-105CB helicopter (platform only)
Electron Equipt: Radar: 2/. . . nav.
M: 1 . . . . . . diesel; 1 prop; 3,600 bhp
Range: 5,500/14 **Crew:** 57 ship's company + up to 300 troops

Remarks: Ordered 1984 as troop transports, vehicle carriers, transports for construction materials, food, and hospital equipment and to act as floating infirmaries and civil disaster relief ships.

◆ **1 vehicle and passenger transport** Bldr: Kure Zosenko, Kure, Japan (In serv. 1964)

A-08 Iguala (ex-*La Paz*)

Iguala (A-08) U.S. Navy, 4-91

D: 4,205 tons (fl) **S:** 17.5 kts **Dim:** 109.02 (99.04 pp) × 17.53 × 4.31
A: none **Electron Equipt:** Radar: . . .
M: 2 Hitachi 10-35VBF62, 10-cyl. diesels; 2 props; 5,676 bhp
Electric: 960 kw (3 × 320-kw 450v 60Hz)
Crew: 23 officers, 40 enlisted

Remarks: 2,350 grt/794 dwt. Acquired from government Secretariat of Communications and Transportation in 1989 after the ship had suffered a fire. Has bow and stern vehicle cargo ramps.

◆ **1 small naval transport** Bldr: Ast. Ulua, Veracruz (In serv. 1960)

B-02 Zacatacas

D: 780 tons **S:** 10 kts **Dim:** 47.5 × 8.2 × 2.7
A: 1/40-mm 60-cal. Mk 3 AA—2/20-mm AA (I × 2)
M: 1 M.A.N. diesel; 1 prop; 560 bhp **Crew:** 13 officers, 37 enlisted

Remarks: 400 dwt. Mistakenly deleted from last two editions; was originally to have been retired in 1985. Armament may have been removed.

CARGO SHIPS

◆ **1 former commercial dry-cargo vessel** Bldr: . . . , Sweden

A-25 Tarasco (ex-. . . . . .)

D: . . . tons (fl) **S:** . . . kts **Dim:** . . . × . . . × . . .
M: . . . diesels; 1 prop; . . . bhp

Remarks: Acquired 1990 and commissioned 1-3-90 without significant modificatio[n]. Three-hold dry-cargo ship with two electric cranes, superstructure aft.

◆ **1 former lighthouse supply vessel** Bldr: . . . (In serv. 1962)

A-23 Maya

D: 924 tons (fl) **S:** 12 kts **Dim:** 48.8 × 11.8 × 4.9
M: 1 M.A.N. diesel; 1 prop; . . . bhp **Crew:** 8 officers, 7 enlisted

Remarks: Taken over in 1988 and commissioned 1-6-88.

TRAINING SHIPS

◆ **1 sail-training ship** Bldr: Ast. y Talleres Celaya, Bilbao, Spain

	Laid down	L	In serv.
A-07 Cuauhtemoc	27-4-81	1-82	11-12-82

Cuauhtemoc (A-07) Leo Van Ginderen,

D: 1,200 tons (1,800 fl) **S:** 15 kts **Dim:** 90.0 (67.0 pp) × 10.6 ×
M: 1 G.M. 12V149 diesel; 1 prop; 750 bhp
Crew: 20 officers, 165 enlisted + 90 cadets

Remarks: Ordered 1980.

MEXICO *(continued)*
TRAINING SHIPS *(continued)*

♦ **1 ex-U.S. Edsall-class training frigate** Bldr: Brown SB, Houston, Texas

	Laid down	L	In serv.
A-06 Manuel Azueta (ex-*Hurst*, DE 250)	27-1-43	14-4-43	30-8-43

Manuel Azueta (A-06) Leo Van Ginderen, 7-81

D: 1,200 tons (1,590 fl) **S:** 21 kts **Dim:** 93.26 × 11.15 × 3.73
A: 3/76.2-mm 50-cal. Mk 22 DP (I × 3)—8/40-mm AA (IV × 1, II × 2)
Electron Equipt:
Radar: 1/Kelvin-Hughes 14/9 nav. , 1/Kelvin-Hughes 17/9 nav. , 1/Mk 26 f.c.
M: 4 Fairbanks-Morse 38DQ, 10-cyl. diesels; 2 props; 6,000 bhp
Electric: 680 kw **Range:** 13,000/12 **Fuel:** 258 tons
Crew: 15 officers, 201 enlisted

Remarks: Transferred 1-10-73. Former destroyer escort. Used as training ship for the Gulf Fleet. Has one Mk 52 radar fire-control director and one Mk 51 range-finder for the 76.2-mm guns, and three Mk 51 Mod. 2 directors for the 40-mm AA. All antisubmarine equipment removed.

♦ **1 former frigate** Bldr: Union Naval de Levante, Valencia, Spain

	Laid down	L	In serv.
-01 Durango	1934	28-6-35	1936

D: 1,600 tons (2,000 fl) **S:** 18 kts **Dim:** 78.2 × 11.2 × 3.1
A: 1/102-mm—2/57-mm (I × 2)—4/20-mm AA (II × 2)
M: 2 Enterprise DMR 38 diesels; electric drive; 2 props; 5,000 shp
Fuel: 140 tons **Range:** 3,000/12 **Crew:** 24 officers, 125 enlisted

Remarks: Originally built as an armed transport with accommodations for 20 officers, 450 troops, and a number of horses. Steam-turbine propulsion plant replaced 1967. Immobile as a training hulk for new recruits, but in 1982 it was announced that she was to be rehabilitated for seagoing training and VIP cruising duties.

TUGS

♦ **4 ex-U.S. Abnaki-class fleet tugs** Bldrs: A-17: United Engineering, Alameda, California; others: Charleston SB & DD, Charleston, South Carolina

	Laid down	L	In serv.
A-17 Otomi (ex-*Molala*, ATF 106)	26-7-42	23-12-42	29-9-43
A-18 Yaqui (ex-*Abnaki*, ATF 96)	28-11-42	22-4-43	15-11-43
A-19 Seri (ex-*Cocopa*, ATF 101)	23-5-43	5-10-43	25-3-44
A-20 Cora (ex-*Hitchiti*, ATF 103)	24-8-43	29-1-44	27-5-44

D: 1,325 tons (1,675 fl) **S:** 16.5 kts **Dim:** 62.48 × 11.73 × 4.67
A: 1/76.2-mm 50-cal. Mk 22 DP
Electron Equipt: Radar: 1/LN-66 nav.
M: 4 Busch-Sulzer BS539 diesels, electric drive; 1 prop; 3,000 shp
Electric: 400 kw **Fuel:** 304 tons **Range:** 7,000/15; 15,000/8
Crew: 75 tot.

Remarks: A-17 purchased 1-8-78, the others on 30-9-78. Unarmed on delivery. Used for patrol duties and as rescue tugs.

♦ **2 ex-U.S. Maritime Administration V-4 class** Bldr: Pendleton SY, New Orleans (In serv. 1943–44)

A-12 R-2 (ex-*Montauk*) A-13 R-3 (ex-*Point Vicente*)

D: 1,825 tons (fl) **S:** 14 kts **Dim:** 59.23 × 11.43 × 5.72
Electron Equipt: Radar: 1/Kelvin-Hughes 14/9 nav.
M: 2 Enterprise diesels; 2 Kort-nozzle props; 2,250 bhp
Range: 19,000/14 **Fuel:** 566 tons **Crew:** 90 tot.

Remarks: Purchased 6-69. Unarmed at time of transfer, but later received one ...mm DP and two 20-mm AA; by 1982 the weapons had been removed. Sister R-4 ...n 1973; R-6 discarded in 1970; R-1 in 1978; and R-5 in 1979. This design was ...ally considered not to have been a success in U.S. service.

SERVICE CRAFT

♦ **2 ex-U.S. 174-foot-class fuel lighters**

	Bldr	L	In serv.
A-03 Aguascalientes (ex-YOG 6)	J. H. Mathis, Camden, N.J.	3-4-43	15-11-43
A-04 Tlaxcala (ex-YO 107)	George Lawley, Neponset, Mass.	3-11-43	27-11-43

D: 440 tons (1,480 fl) **S:** 8 kts **Dim:** 53.0 × 9.75 × 2.5
A: 1/20-mm AA **M:** 1 or 2 diesels; 1 prop; 500–600 bhp
Crew: 5 officers, 21 enlisted

Remarks: Purchased 8-64 and commissioned 11-64. Cargo capacity: 980 tons (6,570 bbl).

♦ **1 harbor tug** Bldr: Ast. Angulo Ciudad del Carmen (In serv. 1989)

A-24 Progreso

D: 152 grt **S:** 12 kts **Dim:** 22.4 × 6.5 × . . . **M:** diesel; . . . bhp

♦ **2 yard tugs**

Pragmar Patron

Remarks: Bought in 1973.

♦ **1 ex-U.S. ARD-12-class floating dry dock**

	Bldr	In serv.
. . . .(ex-ARD 15)	Pacific Bridge, Alameda, Cal.	1-44

Lift capacity: 3,500 tons **Dim:** 149.87 × 24.69 × 1.73 (light)

Remarks: Transferred 4-71 on loan; purchased 1981.

♦ **2 ex-U.S. ARD-2-class floating dry docks** Bldr: Pacific Bridge, Alameda, Cal.

. . . . .(ex-ARD 2) (In serv. 4-42) . . . . .(ex-ARD 11) (In serv. 10-43)

Lift capacity: 3,500 tons **Dim:** 148.0 × 21.64 × 1.6 (light)

Remarks: Transferred 8-63 and 6-74.

♦ **1 ex-U.S. small auxiliary floating dry dock** Bldr: Doullut & Ewin, Mobile, Alabama (Transferred 1-73)

. . . .(ex-AFDL 28) (In serv. 8-44)

Lift capacity: 1,000 tons **Dim:** 60.96 × 19.51 × 1.04 (light)

♦ **7 ex-U.S. floating cranes**

(ex-YD 156) (ex-YD 179) (ex-YD 183) (ex-YD 203)
(ex-YD 157) (ex-YD 180) (ex-YD 194)

Remarks: Transferred 1964–71; purchased 7-78 (except YD 179, 194).

♦ **1 ex-U.S. pile driver** (Leased 8-68)

. . . .(ex-YPD 43)

MICRONESIA

Federated States of Micronesia

DIVISION OF SURVEILLANCE
ATTORNEY GENERAL'S OFFICE

Personnel (1991): Approx. 75 tot.

Note: Micronesia became independent on 10-5-89 and consists of the Caroline Islands archipelago of Kosrai, Pohnpei, Truk, and Yap. The United States retains the responsibility to provide defense against external threat.

PATROL BOATS

♦ **2 ASI-315 "Pacific Forum" class** Bldr: Australian SB Industries (WA), Pty, Ltd., South Coogie

	Laid down	L	In serv.
FSM 01 Palakir	19-6-89	. . .	28-4-90
FSM 02 Micronesia	22-1-90	. . .	3-1-90

D: 165 tons (fl) **S:** 21 kts
Dim: 31.50 (28.60 wl) × 8.10 × 2.12 (1.80 hull)
A: 2/12.7-mm mg (I × 2)
Electron Equipt: Radar: 1/Furuno 1011 nav.
M: 2 Caterpillar 3516 diesels; 2 props; 2,820 bhp (2,400 sust.)
Range: 2,500/12 **Fuel:** 27.9 tons **Endurance:** 8–10 days
Electric: 116 kw (2 × 50 kw, Caterpillar 3304 diesel sets; 1 × 16 kw)
Crew: 4 officers, 14 enlisted

MICRONESIA *(continued)*
PATROL BOATS *(continued)*

Palakir (FSM 01) R.A.N., 5-90

Micronesia (FSM 02) R.A.N., 11-90

Remarks: Arrived at Port Kolonia on 7-6-90 and 25-1-91, respectively. FSM 02 was originally to have been named *Paluepap.* Standard Australian foreign aid patrol boat design. Carry a 5-m rigid inflatable boarding boat. Extensive navigational suite, including Furuno FSN-70 NAVSAT receiver, Furuno 525 HFD/F, Furuno 120 MH-HFD/F, FE-881 echo-sounder, Furuno 500 autopilot, DS-70 doppler log, and a "Weatherfax" receiver. Differ from earlier units of the class in having a spray strake forward on the hull sides. Agreement for establishment of a Micronesian maritime patrol capability was reached during discussions held 15- to 19-8-88.

♦ **2 ex-U.S. Coast Guard Cape class** Bldr: Coast Guard Yard, Curtis Bay, Md.

	In serv.	Transferred
FSM 03 . . . . . . (ex-*Cape Cross,* WPB 95321)	20-8-58	30-3-91
FSM 04 . . . . . . (ex-*Cape Corwin,* WPB 95326)	14-11-58	30-9-91

D: 87 tons (106 fl) **S:** 20 kts **Dim:** 28.96 × 6.10 × 1.55
A: 2/12.7-mm mg (I × 2)
Electron Equipt: Radar: 1/SPS-64(V)1 nav.
M: 2 G.M. 16V 149TI diesels; 2 props; 2,470 bhp
Electric: 60 kw **Endurance:** 5 days
Range: 550/20; 1,900/11.5 **Crew:** 1 officer, 14 enlisted

Remarks: Transferred by the U.S. Government as Grant Aid. Both re-engined and otherwise modernized, completing 16-4-82 and 15-10-82, respectively; the original four Cummins VT-12-M-700 diesels produced 18 kts from 2,324 bhp. Can make 24 kts, but are restricted due to hull damage at speeds over 20 kts.

MONTSERRAT

Colony of Montserrat

MONTSERRAT POLICE FORCE

PATROL CRAFT

♦ **1 M 160 class** Bldr: Halmatic, Havant, U.K. (In serv. 16-1-90)

SHAMROCK

D: 17.3 tons (light) **S:** 27 kts **Dim:** 15.40 (12.20 pp) × 3.86 × 1.15
A: 1/7.62-mm mg
Electron Equipt: Radar: 1/Racal-Decca 370 BT nav.
M: 2 G.M. 6V92 TA diesels: 2 props; 1,100 bhp (770 sust.)
Range: 300/20; 500/17 **Fuel:** 2,700 gallons **Crew:** 6 tot.

Remarks: GRP construction, provided by U.K. as a replacement for patrol craft *Emerald Star,* lost by grounding 6-1-87. Has semi-rigid inflatable rescue dinghy at stern. Sister to Anguilla's *Dolphin,* British Virgin Islands' *Ursula,* and Turks and Caicos's *Sea Quest.*

MOROCCO

Kingdom of Morocco

Personnel (1989): 6,500 men, including 150 officers, 1,000 senior petty officers, and 500 marines

FRIGATE

Note: Negotiations with E.N. Bazán began in 1985 toward the ordering of two modified versions of the *Descubierta* design with a helicopter facility, the H.S.A. STACOS Mod. 4 combat data and command system, MW-08 search radar, and STING radar tracker; no order had been placed by 12-91, and during the fall of 1991, Denmark offered the decommissioned frigates *Peder Skram* and *Herlof Trolle* as an alternative to new construction.

♦ **1 Spanish Descubierta class** Bldr: E.N. Bazán, El Ferrol

	Laid down	L	In serv.
501 LIEUTENANT COLONEL ERRHAMANI	20-3-79	26-2-82	28-3-8.

Lieutenant Colonel Errhamani (501) Gilbert Gyssels, 8-

D: 1,270 tons (1,479 fl) **S:** 26 kts
Dim: 88.88 (85.8 pp) × 10.4 × 3.25 (3.7 fl)
A: 1/Albatros SAM syst. (24 Aspide missiles)—1/76-mm 62-cal. OTO Melara DP—2/40-mm 70-cal. Bofors AA (I × 2)—1/375-mm Bofors ASW RL (II × 1, 24 rockets)—6/324-mm U.S. Mk 32 Mod. 5 ASW TT (III × 2, Mk 46 torpedoes)
Electron Equipt:
Radar: 1/ZW-06 surf. search, 1/DA-05 surf./air search, 1/WM-25 Mod. 41 f.c. (all H.S.A.)
Sonar: Raytheon DE 1160B hull-mounted MF
EW: Elettronica ELT 715 intercept/jammer, 2/CSEE Dagaie decoy RL
M: 4 Bazán-MTU 16MA956 TB91 diesels; 2 CP props; 18,000 bhp
Electric: 1,810 kw **Range:** 4,000/18 (one engine) **Fuel:** 150 tons
Crew: 100 tot.

Remarks: Ordered 14-6-77. Carries 600 rds 76-mm. Has fin stabilizers. Planned provision for four MM 38 Exocet missiles not made, although space remains available amidships.

GUIDED-MISSILE PATROL BOATS

♦ **4 Spanish Lazaga class** Bldr: E.N. Bazán, Cadiz

	In serv.
304 COMMANDANT AL KHATTABI	3-6-81
305 COMMANDANT BOUTOUBA	11-12-81
306 COMMANDANT EL HARTI	25-2-82
307 COMMANDANT AZOUGGARH	2-8-82

D: 303 tons (420 fl) **S:** 29.6 kts **Dim:** 57.40 (54.4 pp) × 7.60 × 2
A: 4/MM 38 Exocet SSM (II × 2)—1/76-mm 62-cal. OTO Melara D—1/40-mm 70-cal. Bofors-Breda AA—2/20-mm Oerlikon GAM-BO AA (I × 2)
Electron Equipt:
Radar: 1/H.S.A. ZW-06 surf. search, 1/H.S.A. WM-25 track-while-scan f.c.

GUIDED-MISSILE PATROL BOATS *(continued)*

Commandant al Khattabi (304) and a sister Leo Van Ginderen, 1986

M: 2 Bazán-MTU MA16V956 TB91 diesels; 2 props; 7,780 bhp
Electric: 405 kVA **Range:** 700/27; 3,000/15 **Crew:** 41 tot.

Remarks: Ordered 14-6-77. First unit launched 21-7-80. Carry 300 rds 76-mm, 1,472 rds 40-mm, 3,000 rds 20-mm ammunition. Have added fuel capacity over Spanish Navy version. CSEE Naja optical director aft for the 40-mm gun. Normally carry only two MM 38 Exocet.

PATROL BOATS

♦ **4 (+2) Osprey 55 class** Bldr: Danyard A/S, Frederikshavn

	L	In serv.
308 El Lahiq	7-87	11-87
309 El Tawfiq	10-87	2-88
316 El Hamiss	4-90	8-90
317 El Karib	7-90	12-90
. . . .	. . .	. . .
. . . .	. . .	. . .

Tawfiq (309) Leo Van Ginderen, 1990

Lahiq (308) Danyard, 11-87

: 420 tons (500 fl) **S:** 18 kts **Dim:** 55.00 (51.80 pp) × 8.08 × 2.75
: 1/40-mm 70-cal. Bofors AA—2/20-mm Oerlikon AA (I × 2)
lectron Equipt: Radar: 2/Decca . . . nav.
: 2 M.A.N.-Burmeister & Wain Alpha 12V.23/30 DVO diesels; 2 props; 4,960 bhp
ange: 4,500/16 **Fuel:** 125 tons **Electric:** 268 kw
rew: 15 tot. + 16 passengers

arks: First two ordered early 1986 for fisheries protection and search-and-rescue es. Second pair ordered 30-1-89. Third pair reported ordered 6-90, although not in if order was actually consummated. Similar ships in Danish, Burmese, and galese service. Armament not mounted at time of delivery. 317 carries the vard Oil Containment System with "Desmi" skimmer capable of accumulating 0 m³/hr. of oil contaminent. All have a stern ramp and door for launching a rigid able rescue/inspection craft.

♦ **6 Vigilance class** Bldr: E.N. Bazán, Cadiz

	In serv.		In serv.
310 Lieutenant de Vaisseau Rabhi	16-9-88	313 El Maher	20-6-89
311 Errachiq	16-12-88	314 El Majid	26-9-89
312 El Akid	4-4-89	315 El Bachir	19-12-89

Lieutenant de Vaisseau Rabhi (310) Bernard Prézelin, 6-90

D: 307 tons (425 fl) **S:** 22 kts **Dim:** 58.1 (54.4 pp) × 7.60 × 2.70
A: 1/40-mm 70-cal. Bofors AA—2/20-mm Oerlikon AA (I × 2)
Electron Equipt: Radar: 2/Decca . . . **Endurance:** 10 days
M: 2 MTU 16V956 TB82 diesels; 2 props; 7,600 bhp (sust.)
Range: 3,800/12 **Crew:** 4 officers, 32 enlisted + 15 passengers

Remarks: Three ordered 2-10-85, with option for three more taken up shortly thereafter. "Series P200/D" design, a reduced-power version of the *Lazaga* for 200-n.m. economic zone patrol. Have a CSEE Naja optronic director for the 40-mm gun.

♦ **2 French Type PR-72** Bldr: SFCN, Villeneuve-la-Garenne

	L	In serv.		L	In serv.
302 Okba	10-10-75	16-12-76	303 Triki	2-2-76	12-7-77

Triki (303) Gilbert Gyssels, 10-82

D: 370 tons (440 fl) **S:** 28 kts (at 413 tons)
Dim: 57.0 (54.0 pp) × 7.6 × 2.5
A: 1/76-mm 62-cal. OTO Melara DP—1/40-mm 70-cal. Bofors AA
Electron Equipt: Radar: 1/Decca 1226 nav.
M: 4 SACM AGO 195V16 SZSHR diesels; 2 props; 11,040 bhp
Electric: 360 kw **Range:** 2,500/16 **Crew:** 5 officers, 48 enlisted

Remarks: Ordered in 6-73. Have 2 CSEE optronic gun directors. 302 refitted 1985.

Note: French-built patrol boat *Al Bachir* (202) and *Fougueux*-class patrol boat *Lieutenant Riffi* (301) were stricken 1990–91.

PATROL CRAFT

♦ **6 French Type P 32** Bldr: CMN, Cherbourg

	L	In serv.		L	In serv.
203 El Wacil	12-6-75	9-10-75	206 El Khafir	21-1-76	16-4-76
204 El Jail	10-10-75	3-12-75	207 El Haris	31-3-76	30-6-76
205 El Mikdam	1-12-75	30-1-76	208 Essahir	2-6-76	16-7-76

D: 89 tons **S:** 28 kts **Dim:** 32.0 × 5.35 × 1.7 (1.42 hull)
A: 2/20-mm AA (I × 2) **Electron Equipt:** Radar: 1/Decca . . . nav.
M: 2 MGO 12V BZSHR diesels; 2 props; 2,700 hp **Range:** 1,200/1
Crew: 12 tot.

Remarks: Ordered 2-74. Plastic-sheathed, laminated-wood hull. Four additional sisters were ordered 6-85 for the customs service.

PATROL CRAFT *(continued)*

El Wacil (203) CMN, 1975

AMPHIBIOUS WARFARE SHIPS

♦ **3 French Champlain-class medium landing ships** Bldr: Dubigeon, Normandy

	In serv.
402 Daoud Ben Aicha	28-5-77
403 Ahmed Es Sakali	9-77
404 Abou Abdallah El Ayachi	12-78

Abou Abdallah El Ayachi (404) Bernard Prézelin, 4-90

D: 750 tons (1,305 fl) **S:** 16 kts **Dim:** 80.0 (68.0 pp) × 13.0 × 2.4 mean
A: 2/40-mm 70-cal. Bofors AA (I × 2)—2/12.7-mm mg (I × 2)—2/81-mm mortars (I × 2)
Electron Equipt: Radar: 1/Decca 1226 nav.
M: 2 SACM V-12 diesels; 2 CP props; 3,600 bhp
Range: 4,500/13 **Crew:** 30 officers, 54 enlisted

Remarks: First two ordered 12-3-75, third on 19-8-75. Can carry 133 troops and about 12 vehicles. Helicopter platform aft. Cargo capacity: 330 tons beaching. Can also carry 208 tons potable water.

♦ **1 French EDIC-class utility landing craft** Bldr: C.N. Franco-Belges

401 Lieutenant Malghagh (In serv. 1965)

Lieutenant Malghagh (401)—wearing old number 1977

D: 292 tons (642 fl) **S:** 8 kts **Dim:** 59.0 × 11.95 × 1.3 (1.62 fl)
A: 2/20-mm Oerlikon AA (I × 2)—1/120-mm mortar (fwd)
Electron Equipt: Radar: 1/Decca 1226 nav.
M: 2 MGO diesels; 2 props; 1,000 bhp **Range:** 1,800/8
Crew: 16 tot.

Remarks: Ordered 1963. Can carry 11 trucks in open vehicle well; has a bow ramp.

AUXILIARIES

♦ **1 vehicle and personnel transport** Bldr: . . . . . . (In serv. 1964)

407 Arrafiq (ex-M/V *Arrafiq,* ex-Swedish *Thjelvar,* ex-Swedish *Götland*)

D: approx. 3,500 tons (fl) **S:** 18.5 kts
Dim: 93.20 (84.00 pp) × 16.41 × 4.17
A: . . . **Electron Equipt:** Radar: 1/. . . nav.
M: 4 Werkspoor 16-cyl. diesels; 2 props; 8,000 bhp **Crew:** . . .

Remarks: Acquired 1987 from Moroccan commercial service. Typical 1960s-era passenger/vehicle ferry with bow, stern, and side doors. Can carry several hundred troops and their vehicles but requires a pier for unloading.

♦ **2 former Danish cargo ships** Bldr: Frederikshavn Vaerft & Tjrdok, Frederikshavn

	In serv.
405 El Aigh (ex-*Merc Caribe*)	1972
406 El Dakhla (ex-*Anglian Merchant,* ex-*Merc Nordia*)	1973

El Dakhla (406) Leo Van Ginderen, 8-8

D: approx. 2,000 tons (fl) **S:** 12 kts **Dim:** 76.61 × 12.30 × 3.47
A: 2/20-mm AA (I × 2) **Electron Equipt:** Radar: 2/. . . nav.
M: Burmeister & Wain Alpha, 10-cyl. diesel; 1 prop; 1,250 bhp
Range: . . . **Crew:** . . .

Remarks: 499 grt/326 nrt/1,327 dwt. Ice-strengthened hulls with pronounced b bous bow. Two holds. Four 5-ton cranes. Acquired to provide logistic support operations along Saharan coast. Originally built for Per R. Henriksen P/R, Cope hagen. 405 bought 1981 by Moroccan Ministry of Travel and Commerce, then tra ferred to navy. 406, sold to British interests 1978, acquired directly by Moroccan Na in 1981.

SERVICE CRAFT

♦ **1 training craft**

Essaouira

Remarks: Presented by Italy in 1967. Former 60-ton yacht used for training wat standers.

♦ **1 yacht**

Oued Eddahab (ex-*Akhir*) (In serv. 1981)

♦ **1 harbor launch** Bldr: ARCOR, La Teste, France

Al Makbas

D: 11 tons (fl) **S:** 17 kts **Dim:** 13.00 (11.30 pp) × 3.80 × 1.10
M: 1 Baudouin 12-F11-Sm diesel; 1 prop; 426 bhp
Range: 400/. . . **Crew:** 4 tot.

Remarks: Ordered 1-85. Glass-reinforced plastic construction.

♦ **1 floating dry dock** (acquired from France 1990)

Capacity: 4,500 tons **Dim:** 126.00 × 28.75 × . . .

CUSTOMS SERVICE

♦ **4 French Type P32 patrol boats** Bldr: CMN, Cherbourg

	Laid down	L	In serv.
209 Erraid	4-86	26-12-87	18-3-88
210 Erracel	30-6-86	21-1-88	15-4-88
211 El Kaced	1-12-86	10-3-88	16-6-88
212 Essaid	. . .	19-5-88	4-7-88

D: 24 tons light (88.7 fl) **S:** 29 kts
Dim: 32.00 (30.09 pp) × 5.35 (4.92 wl) × 1.42 (hull)
A: 2/20-mm Oerlikon AA (I × 2)
Electron Equipt: Radar: 1/. . . nav.
M: 2 UNI UD 30V16 M7 diesels; 2 props; 2,540 bhp
Range: 1,200/12 **Crew:** 12 tot.

Remarks: Ordered 6-85. Wooden construction. Six near-sisters in navy.

MOROCCO *(continued)*
CUSTOMS SERVICES *(continued)*

◆ **18 Arcor-46 patrol craft** Bldr: Arcor, CN d'Aquitaine, La Teste, France (In serv. 1987–88)

D 01 through D 18

D: 12.3 tons (15.1 fl) **S:** 33 kts **Dim:** 14.50 × 4.00 × 1.20
A: 2/12.7-mm mg (I × 2)
Electron Equipt: Radar: 1/Furuno 701 nav.
M: 2 UNI UDV 8M5 diesels; 2 props; 1,120 bhp
Range: 300/20 **Crew:** 6 tot.

Remarks: Ordered 6-85. Glass-reinforced plastic construction.

◆ **5 Arcor-17 launches** Bldr: Arcor, CN d'Aquitaine, La Teste, France (In serv. 1989–90)

D: . . . **S:** 50 kts **Dim:** 5.5 × 2.2 × 0.8
A: 1/7.62-mm mg **M:** . . .

MOZAMBIQUE

eople's Republic of Mozambique

ersonnel (1991): Approx. 800 total

ATROL BOATS

2 ex-Soviet S.O.-1 class Bldr: . . .

31 462

D: 190 tons (215 fl) **S:** 28 kts (new) **Dim:** 42.0 × 6.1 × 1.9 (hull)
A: 4/25-mm 80-cal. 2M-8 AA (II × 2)—4/RBU-1200 ASW RL (V × 4)— 2/d.c. racks (24 d.c.)—minerails
Electron Equipt:
Radar: 1/Pot Head surf. search—Sonar: Tamir-11 hull-mounted HF
M: 3 Type 40D diesels; 3 props; 7,500 bhp **Range:** 340/28; 1,900/7
Crew: 30 tot.

marks: Delivered 21-6-85. Built 1958–64 and hard-used, they are not likely to be of ch combat value. Considered to be poorly built, very noisy, and bad rollers. IFF gear noved.

TROL CRAFT

3 Soviet Zhuk class Bldr: . . .

1 312 313

): 48 tons (60 fl) **S:** 34 kts **Dim:** 24.0 × 5.0 × 1.2 (1.8 props)
: 4/14.5-mm mg (II × 2)
lectron Equipt: Radar: 1/Spin Trough nav.
I: 2 M50F-4 diesels; 2 props; 2,400 bhp
ange: 700/28; 1,100/15 **Fuel:** 10 tons **Crew:** 12 tot.

narks: Standard Soviet export-model Zhuks, with twin, side-by-side, enclosed ntings for the machine guns. A total of seven delivered new (one in 7-79, two in 30, two in 2-81, two in 1982), but by 1989 only three were operable.

10 Indian-built Bldr: Mazagon Dock, Goa (In serv. 1984–85)

: . . . tons **S:** 20 kts **Dim:** 18.0 × 5.0 × 1.1
: 1/. . . mg **M:** 2 diesels; 2 props; 1,100 bhp **Crew:** . . .

narks: First four launched together 4-84; last delivered 12-85. Can be employed owing and are intended for inshore patrol and search-and-rescue duties.

NE COUNTERMEASURES CRAFT

Soviet Yevgenya class Bldr: Sredniy Neva SY, Kolpino

525 GRACIOSA PM . . . .

: 80 tons (90 fl) **S:** 11 kts **Dim:** 26.2 × 6.1 × 1.5
: 2/25-mm 80-cal. 2M-8 AA (II × 1)—2 minerails
lectron Equipt: Radar: 1/Spin Trough nav.
: 2 diesels; 2 props; 600 bhp **Range:** 300/10 **Crew:** 10 tot.

arks: Both arrived 6-9-85 as deck cargo. GRP construction. Employ television hunting system to locate mines in waters up to 30 m deep.

VICE CRAFT

small self-propelled cargo lighters

arks: No details available. Two 200-ton ordered 1983 from Mazagon Dock, Goa, four 30-ton ordered from A.C.N. Chalons-sur-Saône in 1984. May not be subordi- to the navy.

MYANMAR

The Socialist Republic of the Union of Myanmar (formerly Burma)

Personnel: Approx. 7,000, including reserves and 800 naval infantry

Note: Three Fokker F-27 Maritime surveillance aircraft were on order in 1990 but have not been delivered due to the government's position on human rights. One or more frigates may be ordered from China to replace the obsolescent corvettes listed below.

CORVETTES

◆ **1 U.S. PCER 848 class** Bldr: Williamette Iron & Steel, Portland, Ore.

	Laid down	L	In serv.
41 YAN TAING AUNG (ex-*Farmington*, PCER 894)	7-12-42	15-5-43	10-8-44

D: 640 tons (903 fl) **S:** 15 kts
Dim: 56.24 (54.86 wl) × 10.08 × 2.87 (hull)
A: 1/76.2-mm 50-cal. Mk 26 DP—6/40-mm AA (II × 3)—8/20-mm AA (II × 4)—1/Mk 10 Hedgehog ASW spigot mortar (XXIV × 1)—2/Mk 6 d.c. mortars—2/d.c. racks
Electron Equipt:
Radar: 1/. . . nav., 1/SPS-5 surf. search
Sonar: 1/QCU-2 hull-mounted HF searchlight
M: 2 G.M. 12-567A diesels; 2 props; 1,800 bhp **Electric:** 240 kw
Range: 9,000/10 **Fuel:** 125 tons **Crew:** 100 tot.

Remarks: Transferred 18-6-55. Present condition uncertain.

◆ **1 U.S. Admirable-class former fleet minesweeper** Bldr: Williamette Iron & Steel, Portland, Ore.

	Laid down	L	In serv.
42 YAN GYI AUNG (ex-*Creddock*, MSF 356)	10-11-43	22-7-44	18-12-45

D: 650 tons (905 fl) **S:** 14 kts
Dim: 56.24 (54.86) × 10.08 × 2.87 (hull)
A: 1/76.2-mm 50-cal. Mk 26 DP—2/40-mm AA (II × 1)—4/20-mm AA (II × 2)—1/Mk 10 Hedgehog ASW spigot mortar (XXIV × 1)—2/Mk 6 d.c. mortars—2/d.c. racks
Electron Equipt:
Radar: 1/. . . nav., 1/SPS-5 surf. search
Sonar: QCU-2 hull-mounted HF searchlight
M: 2 Busch-Sulzer Type 539 diesels; 2 props; 1,710 bhp
Electric: 280 kw **Range:** 9,300/10 **Fuel:** 140 tons **Crew:** 100 tot.

Remarks: Minesweeping gear removed prior to transfer 21-3-67. Present condition uncertain.

PATROL BOATS

◆ **6 Chinese Hainan class (Project 037)** (In serv. 1964–. . .)

43 YAN SIT AUNG
44 YAN MYAT AUNG
45 YAN NYEIN AUNG
46 YAN KINN AUNG
47 YAN MIN AUNG
48 YAN YE AUNG

D: 375 tons (400 fl) **S:** 30.5 kts
Dim: 58.77 × 7.20 × 2.20 (hull)
A: 4/57-mm AA (II × 2)—4/25-mm 2M-8AA (II × 2)—4/RBU-1200 (V × 4)—2/BMB-2 d.c. mortars—2/d.c. racks—mines
Electron Equipt:
Radar: 1/Pot Head surf. search
Sonar: Tamir-11 hull-mounted HF—IFF: 1/High Pole A transponder
M: 4 Type 12VEZ3025/Z diesels; 4 props; 8,800 bhp
Range: 2,000/14 **Crew:** 70 tot.

Remarks: Delivered 1-91; were probably refurbished PLAN units rather than new construction.

◆ **3 PGM 412 class** Bldr: Burma Naval Dockyard, Rangoon (In serv. 1983–84)

412 413 414

D: 128 tons (fl) **S:** 16 kts **Dim:** 33.5 × 6.7 × 2.0
A: 2/40-mm AA (I × 2) **Range:** 1,400/14 **Crew:** 17 tot.
M: 2 Deutz SBA 16MB216 LLKR diesels; 2 props; 2,720 bhp

Remarks: A planned fourth unit evidently was not built.

◆ **6 U.S. PGM 43 class** Bldrs: 401–404: Marinette Marine, Marinette, Wisc.; 405, 406: Peterson Bldrs, Sturgeon Bay, Wisc.

	In serv.		In serv.
401 (ex-PGM 43)	8-59	404 (ex-PGM 46)	9-59
402 (ex-PGM 44)	8-59	405 (ex-PGM 51)	6-61
403 (ex-PGM 45)	9-59	406 (ex-PGM 52)	6-61

D: 100 tons (141 fl) **S:** 17 kts
Dim: 30.81 × 6.45 × 2.30
A: 1/40-mm AA—4/20-mm AA (II × 2)—2 mg (I × 2)

PATROL BOATS *(continued)*

Electron Equipt:
Radar: EDO 320 nav. (405, 406: Raytheon 1500)
M: 8 G.M. 6-71 diesels; 2 props; 2,040 bhp **Fuel:** 16 tons
Range: 1,000/16 **Crew:** 17 tot.

RIVERINE PATROL VESSELS

◆ **4 18.3-meter class**
Bldr: Engineering Dept., Rangoon DY (In serv. 11-4-90)

Remarks: No data available, except that they are armed with 3 12.7-mm mg.

◆ **3 Yugoslav PB-90 class** Bldr: Brodotehnika, Belgrade (In serv. 1990)

Y 336 Y 337 Y338

D: 90 tons **S:** 32 kts (26 sust.)
Dim: 27.35 × 6.55 × 1.15 (2.20 props)
A: 1/40-mm AA—4/20-mm AA (IV × 1)
Electron Equipt: Radar: 1/Decca 1226 nav. **Crew:** 17 tot.
M: 3 diesels; 3 props; 4,350 bhp
Range: 400/25 **Endurance:** 5 days

Remarks: Have four illumination/chaff RL on foredeck.

◆ **2 improved 301 class** Bldr: Similak, Burma (In serv. 1967)

Y 311 Y 312

D: 250 tons **S:** 14 kts **Dim:** 37.0 × 7.3 × 1.1
A: 2/40-mm AA (I × 2)—2/20-mm AA (I × 2)
M: 2 Mercedes-Benz diesels; 2 props; 1,000 bhp

◆ **2 Nawarat class** Bldr: Dawbon DY, Rangoon (In serv. 1961)

NAWARAT NAGAKYAY

Nawarat

D: 400 tons (450 fl) **S:** 12 kts **Dim:** 49.7 × 8.23 × . . .
A: 2/25-pounder guns (army ordnance)—2/40-mm AA (I × 2)
M: 2 Paxman-Ricardo diesels; 2 props; 1,160 bhp **Crew:** 43 tot.

◆ **10 Y 301 class** Bldr: Uljanik SY, Pula, Yugoslavia (In serv. 1957–60)

Y 301–Y 310

Y 301 class

D: 120 tons **S:** 13 kts **Dim:** 32.0 × 7.25 × 0.8
A: 2/40-mm AA (I × 2)—2/20-mm AA (I × 2)
M: 2 Mercedes-Benz diesels; 2 props; 1,100 bhp
Crew: 29 tot.

◆ **6 U.S. PBR Mk II-class patrol craft** Bldr: Uniflite, Bellingham, Washington (In serv. 1978)

PBR 211–216

D: 8.9 tons (fl) **S:** 24 kts **Dim:** 9.73 × 3.53 × 0.81
A: 3/12.7-mm mg (II × 1, I × 1)—1/60-mm mortar
Electron Equipt: Radar: 1/Raytheon 1900 nav.
M: 2 G.M. GV53N diesels; 2 waterjets; 430 bhp
Range: 150/23 **Crew:** 4–5 tot.

Remarks: GRP construction.

AUXILIARIES

◆ **10 30- to 40-ton river launches** Bldr: Burma (In serv. 1951–52)

◆ **25 30- to 40-ton river launches** Bldr: Yugoslavia (In serv. 1965)

◆ **1 hydrographic survey ship** Bldr: Tito SY, Belgrade, Yugoslavia

THU TAY THI (In serv. 1965)

Thu Tay Thi

D: 1,100 tons (1,271 fl) **S:** 15 kts
Dim: 62.21 (56.80 pp) × 11.00 × 3.60
M: 2 MB820Db diesels; 2 props; 1,710 bhp **Crew:** 99 tot.

Remarks: Helicopter platform. Carries 2 inshore survey craft. Can be armed wit[h] 1/40-mm AA, 2/20-mm AA (I × 2).

◆ **1 inshore survey boat** Bldr: Netherlands (In serv. 1957)

807 YAY BO

D: 108 tons **Crew:** 25 tot.

◆ **1 coastal cargo ship**
Bldr: A/S Nordsøvaerftet, Ringkobing, Denmark (In serv. 1975)

AYIDAWAYA (ex- . . . . . .)

D: . . . tons (fl) **S:** 11 kts
Dim: 49.71 (44.46 pp) × 8.34 × 3.46
M: 1 diesel; 1 prop; 600 bhp **Crew:** . . . tot.

Remarks: 300 grt/699 dwt. Taken over 1990–91 for logistic support duties.

◆ **4 logistics landing craft** Bldr: Yokohama Yacht, Japan (L: 3-69)

604 AIYAR MAI 606 AIYAR MIN THA MEE
605 AIYAR MAUNG 607 AIYAR MIN THAR

Aiyar Maung (605) Yokohama Yacht, 1

D: 250 tons (fl) **S:** 10 kts **Dim:** 38.25 × 9.14 × 1.4
M: 2 Kubota diesels; 2 props; 560 bhp
Cargo: 100 tons **Crew:** 10 tot.

◆ **2 logistics landing craft** Bldr: Yokohama Yacht, Japan (In serv. 19

601 SINDE 602 HTONBO

D: 220 tons (fl) **S:** 10 kts **Dim:** 29.5 × 6.72 × 1.4
M: 2 Kubota diesels; 2 props; 300 bhp
Cargo: 50 tons, 30 passengers

◆ **1 U.S. LCU 1610-class logistics landing craft** Bldr: Southern S

603 AIYAR LULIN (ex-U.S. LCU 1626)

D: 190 tons (390 fl) **S:** 11 kts **Dim:** 41.0 × 9.0 × 2.0
A: 2/20-mm AA (I × 2)
M: 4 G.M. 6-71 diesels; 2 props; 1,200 bhp

Remarks: Used as a transport. Transferred on completion, 10-67.

◆ **1 520-ton diving and repair tender** Bldr: . . . , Japan (In serv.

YAN LONG AUNG

Remarks: Formerly a torpedo retriever and torpedo-boat tender.

PEOPLE'S PEARL AND FISHERIES MINISTRY

◆ **3 Danish "Osprey"-class fisheries protection ships** Bldr: Danyard AS, Frederikshavn

MYANMAR *(continued)*
PEOPLE'S PEARL AND FISHERIES MINISTRY *(continued)*

In Daw In Ma In Ya

D: 385 tons (505 fl) **S:** 20 kts
Dim: 49.95 (45.80 pp) × 10.5 (8.8 wl) × 2.75
A: 2/40-mm AA (II × 1)—1/20-mm AA **Electric:** 359 kVA
M: 2 Burmeister & Wain "Alpha" 16V23L-VO diesels; 2 CP props; 4,640 bhp
Range: 4,500/16 **Crew:** 15 or more tot.

Remarks: First unit completed 5-80, other two on 25-3-82. Sisters to Danish *Havørn-en.* Armed in Burma. Helicopter hangar and flight deck aft. Rescue launch recessed into inclined ramp at stern. Second pair arrived in Burma 24-5-82.

◆ **6 "Carpentaria"-class fisheries patrol boats** Bldr: De Havilland Marine, Homebush Bay, Australia (1979–80)

urmese "Carpentaria" class — Leo Van Ginderen, 1980

D: 27 tons (fl) **S:** 27 kts **Dim:** 16.0 × 5.0 × 1.2
A: 2/7.62-mm mg (I × 2)
Electron Equipt: Radar: 1/Decca 110
M: 2 G.M. 12V71 TI diesels; 2 props; 1,120 bhp
Range: 700/22 **Crew:** 8 tot.

marks: Ordered 12-78. Sisters in Indonesian and Solomon Islands forces. Alumi-n construction.

3 U.S. 105-ft. Commercial Cruiser aluminum patrol craft Bldr: Swiftships, Morgan City, La.

1 (In serv. 31-3-79) 422 (In serv. 31-3-79) 423 (In serv. 28-9-79)

D: 103 tons (111 fl) **S:** 24 kts **Dim:** 31.5 × 7.2 × 2.1
A: . . . **Electron Equipt:** Radar: 1/. . . navigational
M: 2 diesels; 2 props; . . . bhp **Range:** 1,200/18 **Fuel:** 21.6 tons
Crew: 16 tot.

NAMIBIA

e: Namibia achieved independence on 20-3-90. Two small patrol boats are in ation; no characteristics data available.

NATO

h Atlantic Treaty Organization

: The oceanographic research ships described below are the only vessels "owned" y by the NATO nations. There is, however, a NATO Standing Force of frigates and oyers, which would be augmented in time of war by warships from the major tory nations. The NATO Frigate Program (NFR-90) collapsed in 1989–90 when y one the partners withdrew from the effort, unable to agree on the final charac-ics for what was to have been a "uniform" class of ships to be built by the U.K., e, Italy, Germany, Canada, and Spain; the United States was a partner but had ention of building one of the ships.

◆ **1 oceanographic research ship**

	Bldr	L	In serv.
A 1956 Alliance	Fincantieri, Muggiano	9-7-86	1988

Alliance — Leo Van Ginderen, 7-89

D: 2,466 tons (3,019 fl) **S:** 17 kts (16.3 sust.)
Dim: 93.00 (82.00 pp) × 15.20 × 5.10
Electron Equipt: Radar: 2/. . . nav.—Sonar: . . .
M: 2 GMT B.230-series diesels, AEG CC 3127 generators, electric drive: 2 AEG 1,470-kw motors; 2 props; 4,000 shp—side-thrusters fore and aft
Electric: 1,850 kw (including 1/1,605-kw Kongsberg gas-turbine set)
Range: 8,000/12 **Crew:** 10 officers, 20 unlicensed, 20 scientists

Remarks: 3,200 grt/533 dwt. Based at Naples and operated for the NATO ASW Research Center, La Spezia. Operated by U.K. Denholm Ship Management, Glasgow, with German Naval Auxiliary Service officers and multinational nonrated personnel. Flies German flag. Has 6,100 m² total working deck space, 400 m² lab space. Towing winch, 20-ton bollard pull, with 6,000 m of 50-mm cable. Also has 1,000-kg oceanographic crane with telescopic arm. Special attention paid to quieting. Has Flume-type passive tank stabilization. The pendant number (not borne) is from a block assigned to the German Navy. During 1991, began trials with a 64-hydrophone vertical-array towed passive sonar system.

◆ **1 ex-U.S. Army T-boat, oceanographic tender** Bldr: Missouri Valley Steel (In serv. 1953)

Manning (ex-T-514)

D: 96 tons (fl) **S:** 75 kts **Dim:** 20.0 × 5.4 × 2.1
M: Caterpillar D375 diesel; 325 bhp
Crew: 3 crew, 9 scientists **Range:** 400/7

Remarks: Acquired 1955 by Columbia University, Crumb School of Mines; acquired by NATO 1964 and operated for NATO ASW Research Center, La Spezia. Used for studies of the effect of the sea floor on acoustic energy, propagation studies, and demonstration projects.

NETHERLANDS

Kingdom of the Netherlands

Personnel (1991): 16,944 including 2,430 Marines, 1,700 Naval Air Service, and 850 female personnel; 6,500 civilian employees

Naval Aviation: The Navy's aircraft are divided into four administrative groups: three maritime patrol squadrons at Valkenburg (2 Sq. for training, and 320 and 321 Sq. operational) and one helicopter squadron (860 Sq.) at Dekoog. Principal types include (as of 1-92): 13 Lockheed P-3C Update II Orion, 2 F-27 Maritime (stationed in the Netherlands Antilles), and 22 Westland WG-13 Sea Lynx helicopters.

The WG-13 Lynx are of the following subtypes: 6 UH-14A search-and-rescue, delivered in 1976; 9 SH-14B with dipping sonar; and 8 SH-14C. The SH-14B Lynx were to be upgraded to SH-14C standard with Rolls-Royce Gem 42 engines and French DUAV-4 dipping sonar, but funds are not available; no ASQ-81 MAD gear for the SH-14Cs was ever acquired. Up to 24 NH-90 helicopters may be ordered during the 1990s to replace the Sea Lynx.

Note: The shipyard listed below as Koninklijke Maatschappij de Schelde was reorganized 1-1-92 as Koninklijke Schelde Groep and is known as "Royal Schelde" in English.

NAVAL AVIATION *(continued)*

P-3C Orion of the Royal Netherlands Navy R. Neth. N., 1990

SH-14B Sea Lynx Bernard Prézelin, 5-90

WEAPONS AND SYSTEMS

A. MISSILES

◆ *surface-to-air*

U.S./SM-1 MR Standard on the *Tromp*-class destroyers and on the two *Jacob Van Heemskerck*-class frigates. U.S. RIM-7M Sea Sparrow on the *Tromp*-class destroyers and the *Karel Doorman, Jacob Van Heemskerck,* and the *Kortenaer*-class frigates.

◆ *surface-to-surface*

U.S. Harpoon on the *Tromp, Van Heemskerck, Kortenaer,* and *Karel Doorman* classes. Sub-Harpoon has not been acquired for the submarines.

B. GUNS

◆ 120-mm Bofors twin-barreled automatic in the *Tromp*-class destroyers:

Weight: 65 tons Arc of elevation: 10° to +85°
Muzzle velocity: 850 m/sec.
Direction rate: 25° in train, 40° in elevation
Rate of fire: 45 rounds/min./barrel
Maximum effective range in surface fire: 13,000 m
Maximum effective range in antiaircraft fire: 7,000 m

◆ 76-mm OTO Melara Compact on the *Kortenaer*- and *Karel Doorman* class frigates; being upgraded to fire at 100 rpm

◆ 40-mm 70-cal. Bofors in single Bofors L70 mountings

◆ 30-mm SGE-30 "Goalkeeper," using the U.S. General Electric GAU-8A 30-mm gatling gun and EX-30 mounting co-mounted with an H.S.A. track-while-scan radar fire-control system. The latter uses independent I-band search/acquisition and I/K-band tracking radars. The 7-barreled gatling gun has a 4,200-rd/min. maximum rate of fire; 1,190 rds are carried on-mount. Muzzle velocity is 1,021 m/sec. Total weight, with ammunition, is 6,372 kg.

◆ 20-mm Oerlikon AA in single World War II–era 70-cal. and modern GIAT 90-cal. 20 F-2 mountings

C. ANTISUBMARINE WEAPONS

◆ U.S. Mk 44 and Mk 46 torpedoes on ships and aircraft

◆ U.S. NT-37C/D/E (Reworked Mk 37) and Mk 48 torpedoes on submarines

D. RADARS

All designed and manufactured by Hollandse Signaal Apparaaten (H.S.A.), a division of Thomson-CSF:

Name	Type	Band
ZW-06	Navigation/surface search	I
ZW-07	Submarine, nav./surf. search	I
LW-02/03	Long-range air search	D
LW-04	Long-range air search	D
LW-08*	Long-range air search	D
DA-05, 05A	Combined surveillance	F
DA-08	Medium-range air search	E/F
SPS-01	3-D air search	F
WM-20/25	Missile- and gunfire-control	K
MR-05	Medium-range air search	D (12,000–14,000 MHz)
MW-08	Air search, multi track	G
SCOUT	Low-observable search	X
SMART†	3-D air-search	
STING	Lightweight automatic f.c.	I/K dual-freq.
STIR‡	Missile- and gunfire-control	I/K (X + Ka)
LIROD-8	Radar, optronic weapon control	. . .

* An extended-range version of LW-08 is under development.

†SMART—"Signaal Multi-beam Acquisition Radar for Targeting," L-band. Plan to deliver 20 successor SMART-L sets at the rate of 2/yr. beginning in 1995 with the two *Tromp*-class destroyers. Range against an air target is 400 km. MW-08 is essentially a G-band variant and can detect and track up to 20 air and 10 surface contacts simultaneously.

‡STIR—"Separate Tracking and Illumination Radar"; has 1.8- or 2.9-m-dia. parabolic dish antennas and co-mounted t.v. camera.

E. SONARS

DUBM-21: French Thomson-Sintra HF minehunting array
DUUX-5: French Thomson-Sintra "Fenelon" passive-ranging
Octopus: Active/passive submarine array on *Walrus* class, derived from French Thomson-CSF TSM-2272 "Eledone"
PHS-32, MF: Export sonar, hull-mounted or VDS (9.3, 10.5, or 11.7 kHz)
PHS-36, MF: License-built Canadian SQS-509; on the *Tromp*-class destroyers and *Jacob Van Heemskerck*- and *Karel Doorman*-class frigates (5.5, 6.5, 7.5 kHz)
SQR-18A: U.S. towed passive linear array on *Jan Van Brakel* (F 825)
SQR-19A: U.S. towed array, to be fitted on *Witte de With* and *Karel Doorman* classes
SQS-505, MF: license-built Canadian: On the *Kortenaer*-class frigates
SQS-509, MF: license-built Canadian: on some *Kortenaer*-class frigates (PHS-36)
Type 2026: British passive linear hydrophone array for submarines

F. ELECTRONIC WARFARE

In use are the "Scimitar" J-Band deception and jamming system, "Rapids" I 18-gH passive intercept array, and "RAMSES" I/J-Band passive and deceptive repeat equipment. U.S. Argo Systems APECS-2/AR-700 intercept equipment has been or dered for the *Karel Doorman*-class frigates. Chaff rocket launchers in use are th British-designed Knebworth/Corvus, 8-tubed, 76.2-mm launcher and the U.S. Mk 3 Super RBOC system with two Hycor 6-tubed Mk 136 launchers.

G. DATA-PROCESSING

SEWACO (Sensoren Wapens Commando): built by Hollandse Signaal Apparaat and centrally directed by a DAISY 1, 2, 3, 4, or 5 digital computer system. It exists four versions (SEWACO I, II, III, and IV) tailored to the sensors and weapon systems the ships that carry it.

SINBADS: Submarine tracking system. Can track five targets and engage thr simultaneously.

The *Tromp* class, the *Jacob Van Heemskerck* class, and the *Karel Doorman* class ha the NATO LINK 11 data link.

SUBMARINES

Note: Plans to order the first of a new-class, smaller submarine in 1990–91 a substitute for the abandoned fifth and sixth planned units of the *Walrus* class also ha been frustrated by a lack of funds. Data for the Moray-class design are given in previous edition.

Dutch submarines operate primarily under NATO control in an ASW mission m Patrols are commenced at Faslane, in Scotland, where the "clip-on" towed pass linear hydrophone arrays are maintained.

◆ **1 (+3) Walrus class** Bldr: Rotterdamse Droogdok Maatschappij, Rotterdam

	Laid down	L	Trials	In serv.
S 802 WALRUS	11-10-79	28-10-85*	12-9-90	6-92
S 803 ZEELEEUW	24-9-81	20-6-87*	28-10-88	25-4-90
S 808 DOLFIJN	12-6-86	25-4-90	1991	1993
S 810 BRUINVIS	18-4-88	. . .	1992	1994

* Relaunched 13-4-89

Walrus (S 802) Leo Van Ginderen

D: 1,900 tons light/2,450 surf./2,800 sub.
S: 12 kts surf./21 kts sub. **Dim:** 67.73 × 8.40 × 7.0
A: 4/533-mm TT fwd. (20 Mk 48 Mod. 4 or NT.37C/E torpedoes/m

SUBMARINES *(continued)*

Zeeleeuw (S 803) Ben Sullivan, 6-89

Electron Equipt:
Radar: 1/ZW-07 (U.K. Decca Type 1001) nav./surf. search
Sonar: Octopus (TSM 2272) active/passive, U.K. Type 2026 linear passive array; DUUX-5 Fenelon passive-ranging
EW: . . . intercept
M: diesel-electric: 3 SEMT-Pielstick 12 PA4V 200VG, 2 Type 304 980-kw diesel generator groups; 1 Holec motor; 1 5-bladed prop; 3,950 surf./5,430 sub. shp (*see* Remarks)
Range: 10,000/9 (snorkel) **Fuel:** 310 tons
Endurance: 60 days **Crew:** 7 officers, 43 enlisted

Remarks: First two ordered 19-6-78 and 17-12-79. Second pair authorized 5-1-84. S 808 ordered 16-10-84, S 810 ordered 16-8-85. Construction of first pair delayed by need to lengthen hull after keels laid in order to accommodate larger diesel generator sets. *Walrus* severely damaged by fire 14-8-86, returned to land 2-5-87 for repairs, and was relaunched 13-9-89. *Zeeleeuw* began trials 28-10-88 scheduled to run to 10-89, then followed by a three-month yard period and one-year "shakedown," with full operational capability early in 1991. Plans to construct two more canceled 7-88 by Dutch Parliament.

Second pair refitted with Brons-Werkspoor 0-RUB 215X12 diesels. Propulsion plant on resilient mountings to reduce noise emissions. Each Holec a.c./d.c. generator has built-in rectifiers and produces 980 kw. There are three 140-cell batteries. Endurance 60 days. Diving depth: 300 m; periscope depth: 18 m. "X" stern configuration controls surfaces; sail-mounted bow planes. Torpedo tubes are of the "water-slug" type, capable of launching at any operational depth. Hull construction is of MAREL steel, with single-hull mid-body and double-hull ends; reserve buoyancy is 12%. Have GIPSY (*Integreed In Formatie en Presentatie Systeem*) data system, Sperry Mk 29 Mod. 2A inertial navigation system, NAVSAT receiver, and passive EW equipment. Second pair will have SEWACO VII data system with Signaal SMR-MV data processor. Fitted to launch Sub-Harpoon antiship missiles, but none procured.

2 Zwaardvis class Bldr: Rotterdamse Droogdok Maatschappij, Rotterdam

	Laid down	L	In serv.
S 806 Zwaardvis	7-67	2-7-70	18-2-72
S 807 Tijgerhaai	7-67	25-5-71	20-10-72

D: 2,350 tons surf./2,408 surf. full load/2,640 tons sub.
S: 13 kts surf./20 kts sub. **Dim:** 66.92 × 8.40 × 7.10
A: 6/533-mm TT fwd. (20 U.S. Mk 48 Mod. 4 and NT-37C/E torpedoes)
Electron Equipt:
Radar: 1/ZW-06 nav./surf. search—EW: . . . .
Sonar: Octopus (TSM-2272) active/passive hull; U.K. type 2026 towed array, DUUX-5 Fenelon passive-ranging
M: diesel-electric: 3 sets Werkspoor RUB 215X12, 1,400-bhp diesel generators, 920 kw each; 1 3,800-kw motor; 1 5-bladed prop; 5,100 shp
Range: 10,000/9 (snorkel) **Endurance:** 60 days
Crew: 8 officers, 57 enlisted

Remarks: Ordered 24-12-65 and 14-7-66. Based on the U.S. Navy's *Barbel* class. Use of Dutch equipment necessitated modifications to the original design. For silent running, all noise-producing machinery is mounted on a spring-suspension "raft." Three 196-cell batteries. Mid-life refits in 1987–88 (S 806) and 1988–90 (S 807); received U.K. Type 2026 towed passive sonar arrays, new hull sonar (version of Thomson-CSF Eledone), new H.S.A. GIPSY weapons control, etc. The pair collided during 7-91 with minor damage. They are to be retired in 2000.

Tijgerhaai (S 807) Leo Van Ginderen, 9-91

Zwaardvis (S 806) R. Neth. N., 1990

◆ **1 Potvis class** Bldr: Wilton-Fijenoord, Schiedam

	Laid down	L	In serv.
S 804 Potvis	17-9-62	12-1-65	2-11-65

Potvis (S 804) James W. Goss/NAVPIC, 10-90

D: 1,140 tons light/1,510 tons surf./1,830 tons sub.
S: 14.5 kts surf./17 kts sub. **Dim:** 79.50 × 7.84 × 4.95
A: 8/533-mm TT (4 fwd, 4 aft; 16 tot. U.S. Mk 37/NT-37 torpedoes)
Electron Equipt:
Radar: 1/ZW-06 nav./surf. search—EW: . . .
Sonar: Sintra Alcatel DUUX-2A passive-ranging
M: diesel-electric: 2 SEMT-Pielstick 12 PA4V185 diesels, 1,550 bhp each; 2/920-kw electric motors; 2 props; 4,400 shp—*see* Remarks
Endurance: 45 days **Crew:** 8 officers, 59 men

Remarks: Authorized in 1962. The hull incorporates three parallel interior pressure cylinders; the upper hull contains the weapons and living spaces, the lower pair the engines and batteries. Diving depth 300 m. Has two 168-cell batteries. *Potvis* was given new engines in 1979. Sister *Dolfijn* (S 808) placed in reserve without refit or batteries during 1983 and was stricken 1-2-85 and sold for scrap 22-7-85. *Zeehond* (S 809) was to strike in 1986–87 but was extended in service to 11-1-90 and sold to RDM on 29-6-90 for conversion as DTV (Dive Test Vessel) *Zeehond* for trials in 1993 with the RDM/Cosworth SPECTRE (Submarine Power for Extended Continuous Tail and Range Enhancement) air-independent power plant consisting of four 500-kw diesel generator sets. *Tonijn* (S 805) was stricken 10-1-91. S 804 will be retired in 1992.

GUIDED-MISSILE DESTROYERS

Note: The present intention is to replace the *Tromp* class around 2000 with two new air-defense frigates; the German Type 124 design is under consideration. The Netherlands ships would have the SMART-L surveillance radar and carry the ESSM (Evolved Sea Sparrow Missile) and a longer-ranged area air-defense missile.

◆ **2 Tromp class** Bldr: Koninklijke Maatschappij de Schelde, Vlissingen

	Laid down	L	In serv.
F 801 Tromp	4-8-71	4-6-73	3-10-75
F 806 De Ruyter (ex-*Van Heemskerck*)	22-12-71	9-3-74	3-6-76

D: 3,665 tons (4,308 fl) **S:** 28 kts (30 on trials)
Dim: 138.2 (131.0 pp) × 14.8 × 4.6 (6.6 max.)
A: 4/Harpoon SSM (II × 2)—1 Mk 13 missile launcher (I × 1, 40 SM-1 MR SAM)—1/NATO Sea Sparrow SAM system (VII × 1, Mk 29, 16 missiles)—2/120-mm 50-cal. Bofors DP (II × 1)—1/30-mm Goalkeeper gatling CIWS—6/324-mm Mk 32 ASW TT (III × 2)—1/SH-14B Sea Lynx ASW helicopter
Electron Equipt:
Radar: 2/Decca 1226 nav., 1/SPS-01 3-D early warning, 1/WM-25 f.c. (for 120-mm DP and Sparrow), 2/SPG-51C f.c. (for Standard SAM), 1/Goalkeeper f.c.

GUIDED-MISSILE DESTROYERS *(continued)*

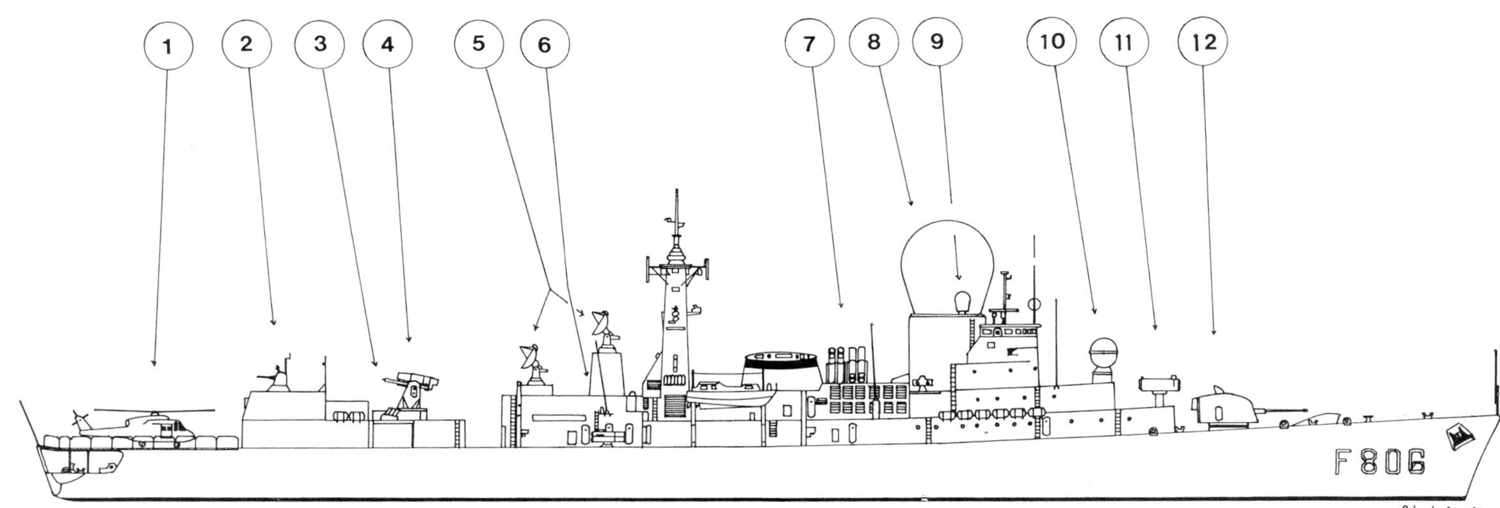

De Ruyter (F 806) 1. SH-14B Sea Lynx helicopter 2. Goalkeeper SGE-30 CIWS 3. Mk 36 Super RBOC decoy RL syst. 4. Mk 13 missile launcher 5. SPG-51C SAM direction radars 6. triple MK 32 ASW TT 7. Harpoon SSM 8. SPS-01 3-D radar 9. SCOT SHF SATCOMM antennas 10. WM-25 radar for Sea Sparrow and 120-mm guns 11. Mk 29 octuple Sea Sparrow SAM launcher 12. twin 120-mm 50-cal. Bofors DP gun mount

De Ruyter (F 806) R. Neth. N.,

De Ruyter (F 806)—showing Goalkeeper CIWS to starboard of hangar Ben Sullivan, 5-91

Tromp (F 801)—still without Goalkeeper Leo Van Ginderen,

GUIDED-MISSILE DESTROYERS *(continued)*

Sonar: 1/PHS-36 (SQS-509) hull-mounted MF
EW: Ramses active/passive array, Mk 36 SRBOC decoy RL syst. (VI × 4), SLQ-25 Nixie towed torpedo decoy syst.
M: COGOG: 2 Rolls-Royce Olympus TM-3B gas turbines, 27,000 shp each; 2 Tyne RM-1C gas turbines, 4,100 shp each, for cruising (18 kts); 2 CP 4-bladed props; 54,000 shp max.
Electric: 4,000 kw **Range:** 5,000/18 **Fuel:** 600 tons
Crew: 34 officers, 271 enlisted

Remarks: Construction authorized 1967. Although the Netherlands Navy designates hem as frigates, these ships, by virtue of their armament and size, are more closely elated to guided-missile destroyers.

They have fin stabilizers and are excellent sea boats. The 120-mm gun mounts, iodernized, come from the stricken destroyer *Gelderland*. Equipped with an admiral's abin and command facilities, they can act as flagships. The propulsion machinery is rranged in three compartments, forward to aft: 2 Olympus gas turbines, 2 generator ets, and the auxiliary boilers; 2 Tyne gas turbines; 2 generator sets. The 450-V, -phase, 60-Hz current is produced by four groups of 1,000-kw generators, each driven y a SMIT/Paxman Valenta RP 200, 12-cylinder diesel; two sets are sufficient for full mbat power. There are three auxiliary boilers for heating.

Fitted with Harpoon 1977/78; normally carry only 2 (I × 2), but can carry 8 (IV × 2). EWACO-I data system. New plastic radomes for SPS-01 radar, 1980, called "Kojack." W system updated 1984 on *Tromp* and LINK 11 data-exchange system added; F 806 llowed in 1985. U.K. SCOT VHF SATCOMM added to *Tromp* 1988–89 and to *De uyter* in 1990–91. Goalkeeper close-in weapon system added to starboard of helicopter angar in both 1989–91.

UIDED-MISSILE FRIGATES

2 Jacob Van Heemskerck class Bldr: Koninklijke Maatschappij de Schelde, Vlissingen

	Laid down	L	In serv.
812 Jacob Van Heemskerck (ex-*Pieter Florisz*)	21-1-81	5-11-83	15-1-86
813 Witte De With	15-12-81	25-8-84	17-9-86

D: 3,000 tons (3,750 fl) **S:** 30 kts (20 kts on cruise engines)
Dim: 130.20 (121.8 pp) × 14.40 × 4.23 (6.0 props)

te De With (F 813) Hartmut Ehlers, 10-91

Jacob Van Heemskerck (F 812) Hartmut Ehlers, 11-91

Jacob Van Heemskerck (F 812) Leo Van Ginderen, 5-90

A: 8 Harpoon SSM (IV × 2)—1/Mk 13 Mod. 4 launcher (I × 1, 40 SM-1 MR SAM)—1/Mk 29 launcher (VIII × 1, 24 Sea Sparrow missiles)—1/30-mm Goalkeeper gatling CIWS—4/324-mm ASW TT (II × 2, fixed)
Electron Equipt:
Radar: 1/Decca 1226 nav., 1/ZW-06 surf. search, 1/DA-08 air/surf. search, 1/LW-08 early-warning, 1/STIR-18 f.c., 2/STIR-24 f.c., 1/Goalkeeper f.c. array
Sonar: PHS-36 (SQS-509) hull-mounted MF
EW: Sphinx intercept, Ramses active (with SRR03/100 jammer); Mk 36 Super RBOC decoy RL syst. (VI × 2), SLQ-25 Nixie torpedo decoy syst.
M: COGOG: 2 Rolls-Royce Olympus TM-3B gas turbines, 25,800 shp each; 2 Rolls-Royce Tyne RM-1C cruise gas turbines, 4,900 shp each; 2 LIPS CP props; 51,600 shp max.
Electric: 3,000 kw **Range:** 4,700/16 (on 1 Tyne turbine)
Crew: 23 officers, 174 enlisted plus 20 flag staff

Remarks: Built as replacement hulls for a pair with the same pendant numbers (and original names) sold to Greece. Have the basic *Kortenaer* design modified to replace the helicopter facility with the U.S. Standard missile system. Equipped to act as flagships, permitting the Dutch Navy to operate four escort flotillas in wartime and obviating the need for the originally planned "13th *Kortenaer*" but are now intended to provide air-defense escort to one of two escort flotillas. Have the SEWACO II data system and LINK 11 data-link capability. The DA-08 radar atop the foremast is to be replaced by H.S.A.'s new SMART-L 3-D radar after 1995, and the ships have provision for a towed passive hydrophone array. May also receive the Franco-Italian MILAS antisubmarine missile system. Have the U.S. SLQ-25 Nixie torpedo decoy system. During service in the Mideast in 1990–91, both carried MARISAT commercial SATCOMM equipment in addition to SCOT and an additional 2/20-mm AA and 2/12.7-mm mg in single mountings. Unlike the *Kortenaer* class, these ships normally carry all eight Harpoons.

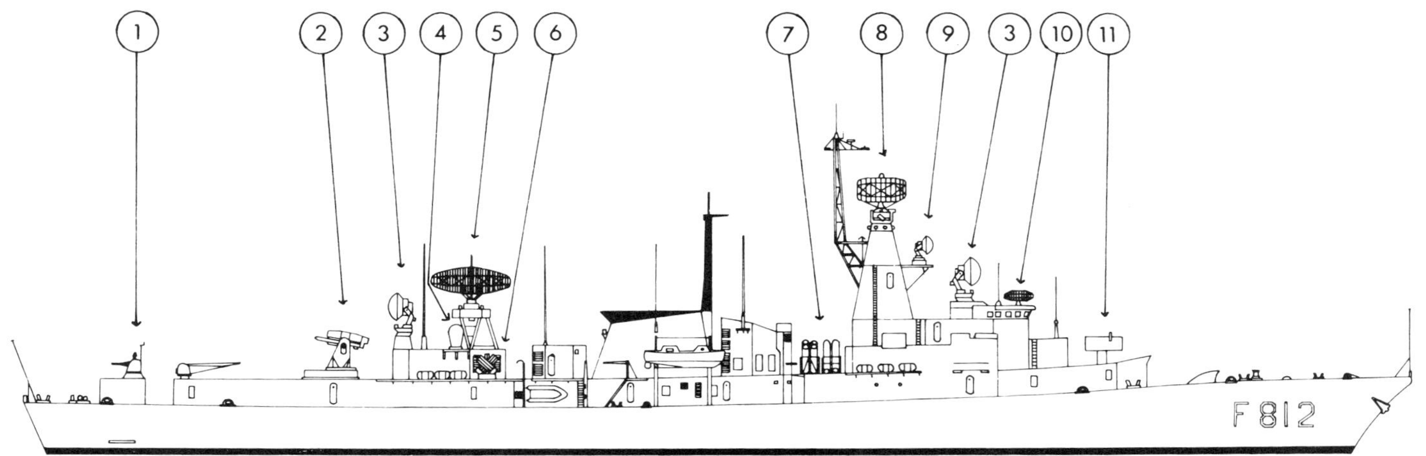

Jacob Van Heemskerck 1. Goalkeeper SGE-30 CIWS 2. Mk 13 Mod. 4 launcher for Standard SM-1 MR missiles 3. modified STIR-24 radar directors for Standard SM-1 MR 4. SCOT SHF SATCOMM antennas 5. LW-08 early-warning radar 6. Mk 36 Super RBOC syst. (Mk 136 sextuple launchers) 7. Harpoon SSM 8. DA-08 air/surface-search radar 9. STIR-18 radar director for Sea Sparrow 10. ZW-06 navigational/surf.-search radar 11. Mk 29 octuple Sea Sparrow SAM launcher Robert Dumas

FRIGATES

◆ **2 (+6) Karel Doorman class** Bldr: Koninklijke Maatschappij de Schelde, Vlissingen

	Laid down	L	In serv.
F 827 Karel Doorman	26-2-85	20-4-88	31-5-91
F 829 Willem Van Der Zaan	6-11-85	21-1-89	28-11-91
F 830 Tjerk Hiddes	28-10-86	9-12-89	1992
F 831 Van Amstel	3-5-88	19-5-90	1993
F 832 Abraham Van Der Hulst	8-2-89	7-4-91	2-94
F 833 Van Nes	10-1-90	10-91	1994
F 834 Van Galen	7-6-90	9-92	1995
F 828 Van Speijk	1-10-91	1-94	1995

Karel Doorman (F 827)—with SMART radar mounted
Nicolaus Sippel, 7-91

Willem Van Der Zaan (F 829)—on trials Leo Van Ginderen, 6-91

D: 2,800 tons light (3,320 fl) **S:** 29 kts (21 kts on diesels)
Dim: 122.25 (114.40 pp) × 14.37 (13.10 wl) × 4.30 (6.05 sonar)
A: 4/Harpoon SSM (II × 2)—VLS Sea Sparrow SAM syst. (16 missiles)—1/76-mm OTO Melara DP—1/30-mm Goalkeeper gatling CIWS—2/20-mm 70-cal. Oerlikon AA (I × 2)—4/324-mm ASW TT (II × 2, fixed)—1/SH-14B Sea Lynx ASW helicopter
Electron Equipt:
Radar: 1/Decca 1690/9 nav., 1/SMART 3-D air-search, 1/LW-08 early-warning, 2/STIR-18 gun f.c., 1/Goalkeeper f.c. array
Sonar: PHS-36 (SQS-509) hull-mounted MF; last four: Thomson-Sintra Anaconda (DSBV-61A) towed array
EW: last four: Argo APECS-II/AR-700 active/passive, Mk 36 SRBOC decoy RL syst. (VI × 2), SLQ-25 Nixie towed torpedo decoy syst.
M: CODOG: 2 Stork-Werkspoor 12 SWD 280 V-12 cruise diesels, 4,225 bhp each; 2 Rolls-Royce SM-1A or C Spey gas turbines; 2 CP props; 37,540 shp (F 829 and later: 48,972 shp)
Electric: 2,720 kw (4 × 650-kw diesel sets; 1 × 120-kw diesel set)
Range: 5,000+/18 **Endurance:** 30 days
Crew: 16 officers, 138 enlisted (163 max. accommodations)

Tjerk Hiddes (F 830)—fitting out Leo Van Ginderen, 3-

Karel Doorman (F 827)—on trials Leo Van Ginderen, 1

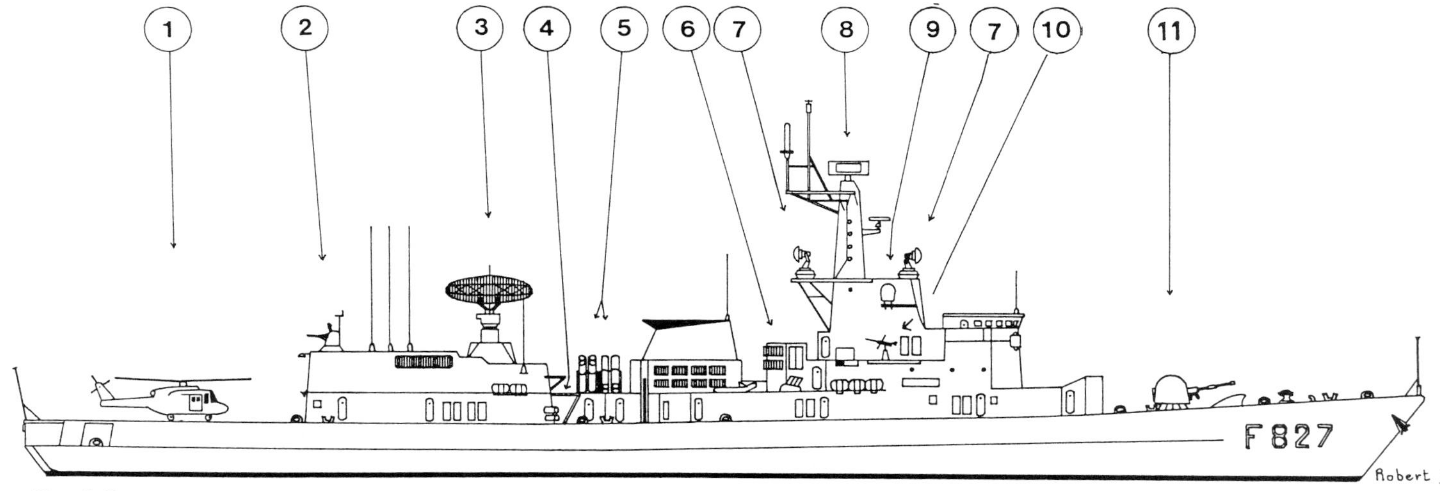

Karel Doorman 1. SH-14B Sea Lynx helicopter 2. Goalkeeper SGE-30 CIWS 3. LW-08 early-warning radar 4. ASW TT 5. Harpoo SSM 6. Mk 36 Super RBOC decoy syst. (sextuple Mk 136 launchers 7. STIR-18 missile/gun radar directors 8. SMART 3-D search radar 9. SCOT SHF SATCOMM 10. 20-mm AA 11. 76-mm 62-cal. OTO Melara Compact DP

FRIGATES *(continued)*

ırel Doorman (F 827)—showing vertical-launch Sea Sparrow cells to port of hangar R. Neth. N., 1991

marks: Originally known as the "M" class. First four ordered 29-2-84, three years lier than planned, to help shipbuilding industry; second group of four ordered 4-86. Will nominally replace the scrapped *Roofdier* class, but are far more capable ps; indeed, they are little inferior to the larger *Kortenaers*. Intended for fisheries rol and 200-nautical-mile economic zone patrol in peacetime. Accommodations for ıale crew members incorporated, plus bunks for 30 marines. Four more were origi-ly projected.

ave computer-controlled rudder roll-stabilization system vice fins. Three rubber ıi-rigid boats. DAISY VII/SEWACO VII data system with full LINK 10, 11, and 16 ability, but delays in developing the combat system will keep first ship from being y operational until 1992; the SEWACO system on the first four is designated "VIIA" ndicate that the ships are not yet fitted with towed arrays or EW suites. F 827 has y SM-1A gas turbines operating at 14 MW each; the remainder have the 18-MW -1C, to be back-fitted in F 827. The 76-mm gun fires at up to 100 rpm. Are later to e British SCOT SHF SATCOMM System, and the SMART-L 3-D L-band air-search ır will be substituted for the original SMART beginning in 1996.

ıe ships were originally to have been named *Groningen, Friesland, Utrecht, Noord bant, Limburg, Overijssel, Drenthe,* and *Gelderland.* Again changed 18-3-87 to e *Van Speijk* from second to last.

◆ **10 Kortenaer class** Bldrs: F 823 and F 824: Wilton-Fijenoord, Schiedam; others: Koninklijke Maatschappij de Schelde, Vlissingen

	Laid down	L	In serv.
F 807 Kortenaer	8-4-75	18-12-76	26-10-78
F 808 Callenburgh	30-6-75	12-3-77	26-7-79
F 809 Van Kinsbergen	2-9-76	16-4-77	24-4-80
F 810 Banckert	25-2-76	13-7-78	29-10-80
F 811 Piet Heyn	28-4-77	3-6-78	14-4-81
F 816 Abraham Crijnssen	25-10-78	16-5-81	26-1-83
F 823 Philips Van Almonde	1-10-77	11-8-79	2-12-81
F 824 Bloys Van Treslong	1-5-78	15-11-80	25-11-82
F 825 Jan Van Brakel	16-11-79	16-5-81	14-4-83
F 826 Pieter Florisz (ex-*Willem Van Der Zaan*)	15-1-80	8-5-82	1-10-83

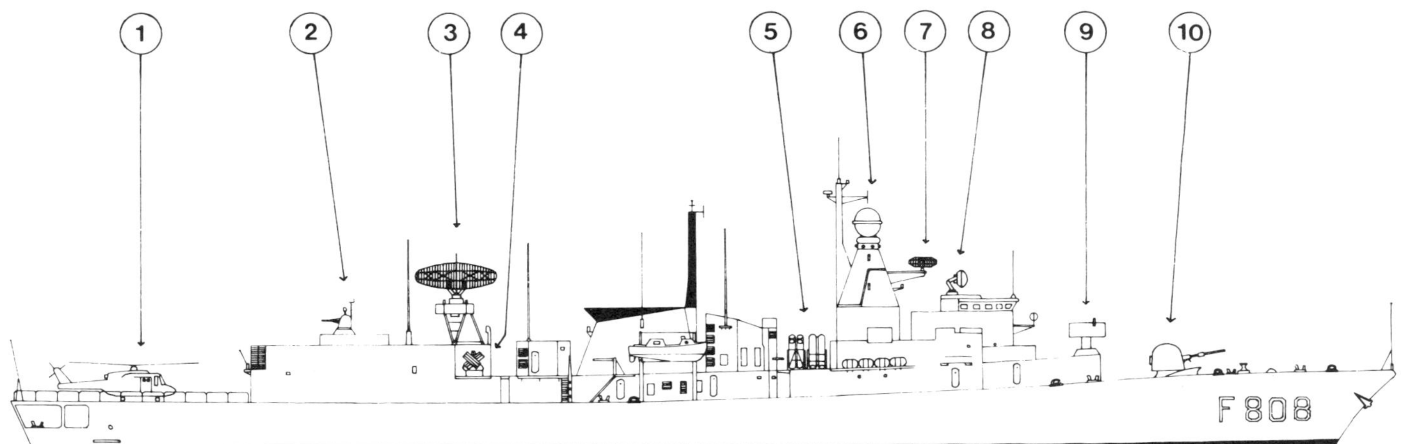

Callenburgh 1. SH-14B/C Sea Lynx helicopter 2. 30-mm Goalkeeper SGE-30 CIWS 3. LW-08 early-warning radar 4. MK 36 Super RBOC decoy syst. (4 Mk 137 launchers) 5. Harpoon SSM 6. WM-25 track-while-scan fire-control radar 7. ZW-06 navigational/surf.-search radar 8. STIR-18 Sea Sparrow illumination radar 9. Mk 29 octuple Sea Sparrow launcher 10. 76-mm 62-cal. OTO Melara Compact DP Robert Dumas

FRIGATES *(continued)*

Jan Van Brakel (F 825) Maritime Photographic, 9-91

Jan Van Brakel (F 825)—showing AN/SQR-18(A) TASS installation in lieu of helicopters, Goalkeeper and MARISAT SATCOMM antenna atop hangar Leo Van Ginderen, 11-91

Van Kinsbergen (F 809) Gilbert Gyssels, 12-9

Banckert (F 810) PH1 Michael D.P. Flynn, USN, 2-

Philips Van Almonde (F 823) James W. Goss/NAVPIC,

Pieter Florisz (F 826) and Witte De With (F 813)—en route to the Mideast, showing the variations in layout between the two versions of the same design R. Neth. N.,

FRIGATES *(continued)*

braham Crijnssen (F 816) R. Neth. N., 1990

D: 3,000 tons (3,786 fl) **S:** 30 kts (20 on 2 Tyne turbines)
Dim: 130.2 (121.8 pp) × 14.4 × 4.4 (6.0 props)
A: 4/Harpoon SSM (II × 2)—1/Mk 29 SAM launcher (VIII × 1, 24 Sea Sparrow missiles)—1/76-mm OTO Melara DP (I × 2)—1/30-mm Goalkeeper gatling CIWS—4/324-mm Mk 32 ASW TT (II × 2)- 1/ SH-14B/C Sea Lynx ASW helicopter (not in F 825, 826)
Electron Equipt:
Radar: 1/ZW-06 nav./surf. search, 1/LW-08 air search, 1/WM-25 f.c., 1/STIR-1.8 f.c.
Sonar: 1/SQS-505 (F 823–826: SQS-509) hull-mounted MF, F 825, 826 also: SQR-18A towed passive array
EW: Sphinx intercept, Ramses active system, 2/Mk 36 SRBOC (VI × 2), SLQ-25 Nixie towed torpedo decoy syst.
M: COGOG: 2 Rolls-Royce Olympus TM-3B gas turbines, 25,800 shp each; 2 Rolls-Royce Tyne RM-1C cruise gas turbines, 4,900 shp each; 2 LIPS CP props; 51,600 shp max.
lectric: 3,000 kw **Range:** 4,700/16 (on 1 Tyne turbine)
rew: 18 officers, 182 enlisted

narks: F 807 to F 810 ordered 31-8-74; F 811 to F 816 ordered 28-11-74; F 823–F ordered 29-12-76. The original *Pieter Florisz* (F 812) and *Witte De With* (F 813) of class were sold to Greece in 1981. Current plans call for retiring F 807 through F during 1994–96 and offering them for sale, placing two others in reserve, and ating only the four newest, which are to be further modernized.
itially, F 807 and F 808 had two 76-mm guns, replaced by a 40-mm mount by 1982. have now had the 40-mm AA replaced by a 30-mm Goalkeeper gatling AA gun em; F 808 received the prototype system in 9-84. In peacetime, only one Lynx opter is carried, but a second can be accommodated in the hangar. Normally, only or four Harpoon SSM (II × 2) are carried, but up to eight can be accommodated. All s have the Sperry Mk 29 Mod. 1 inertial navigation system.
e engineering plant is distributed in four compartments, forward to aft: auxi- es; Olympus gas turbines; Tyne gas turbines plus reduction gears; auxiliaries. The volt, 3-phase, 60-Hertz electric current is supplied by four generators driven by SEMT-Pielstick PA4, 750-kw diesels. There are two auxiliary boilers and two orators.
e hull is divided by 15 watertight bulkheads. One pair of Denny-Brown nonre- ing fin stabilizers is fitted. Particular attention has been paid to habitability. F ltered to provide berthing for 25 female crew 1985–86.
e Mk 36 Super RBOC chaff system (2, 6-tubed Hycor Mk 136 launchers) replaced riginal Knebworth/Corvus RL. All have the SEWACO II data system. F 826 first ckfit with Ramses (Reprogrammable Advanced Multimode Shipboard ECM Sys- in 1-86, now fitted to all. All can be equipped with modular British SCOT SHF ite communications systems, with the antenna radomes mounted atop the hangar st the LW-08 radar.
25 was fitted with the prototype SMART radar for trials 4-90 to 6-90, subse- ly removed. F 825 and F 826 carry SQR-18A towed arrays removed from Van -class frigates sold to Indonesia: the equipment is in the hangar and the winch on licopter flight deck. F 826 was fitted with 2/20-mm AA and 2/12.7-mm mg during st service in 1990–91.

: The six *Van Speijk*-class frigates have been decommissioned and sold to Indone- *an Speijk* (F 802) stricken 13-9-86, transferred 1-11-86; *Van Galen* (F 803) en 1-11-86 for transfer 2-11-87; *Tjerk Hiddes* (F 804) stricken 6-1-86 and trans- 13-10-86; *Van Nes* (F 805) decommissioned 11-86 for transfer in 2-88; *Evertsen*) stricken and transferred 1-11-89; and *Isaac Sweers* (F 814) in 11-90.

E WARFARE SHIPS

(+6) new-construction deep-sea minesweeper/hunters Bldr: n der Giessen de Noord, Alblasserdam

	Laid down	L	In serv.
. . . .	. . . .	. . .	1999
. . . .	. . . .	. . .	. . .
. . . .	. . . .	. . .	. . .
. . . .	. . . .	. . .	. . .
. . . .	. . . .	. . .	. . .
. . . .	. . . .	. . .	2001

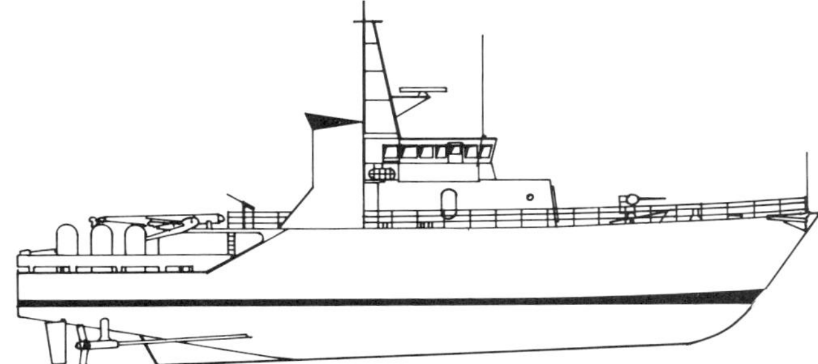

New deep-sea mine countermeasures ship A. D. Baker III, 1990

D: 610 tons (fl) **S:** 15 kts (10 kts sweeping)
Dim: 47.0 (43.0 pp) × 9.6 × 3.6
A: 1/20-mm 90-cal. GIAT AA—2/12.7-mm mg (I × 2, for mine disposal)
Electron Equipt:
Radar: 1/. . . . . .nav.—Sonar: . . . . . .
M: 2 . . . . . . diesels; 2 props; 2,200 bhp **Range:** 3,000/12
Crew: 25 tot. + 5 mine-disposal divers

Remarks: Lineal replacements for the *Dokkum* class, intended to work out to the 100-meter curve. Fifteen originally planned, then ten, with six larger deep-sea mine- sweepers to deliver during late 1990s. This has been further reduced to six of the smaller class. First of new class was initially expected to commence trials 1992, with seven operational by 1996, but the program has been further delayed, and deliveries are now expected to take place 1999–2001. Being designed in cooperation with Bel- gium and Portugal. Design contract to Van der Giessen de Noord in cooperation with Belgium's Beliard Polyship placed 11-90; to be ordered 1993. Trials with the Thomson- Sintra "Sterne" minesweeping system intended for this class began in 10-91; the ships may also carry the French AP-4 acoustic sweep array.

◆ 15 Alkmaar ("Tripartite")-class minehunters
Bldr: Van der Giessen de Noord, Alblasserdam

	Ordered	Laid down	L	In serv.
M 850 ALKMAAR	26-7-77	30-1-79	18-5-82	28-5-83
M 851 DELFZIJL	26-7-77	29-5-80	29-10-82	17-8-83
M 852 DORDRECHT	23-1-79	5-1-81	26-2-83	16-11-83
M 853 HAARLEM	23-1-79	16-6-81	9-7-83	12-1-84
M 854 HARLINGEN	31-3-81	30-11-81	9-7-83	12-4-84
M 855 SCHEVENINGEN (ex-*Hellevoetsluis*)	31-3-81	24-5-82	2-12-83	18-7-84
M 856 MAASSLUIS	16-12-81	7-11-82	5-5-84	12-12-84
M 857 MAKKUM	16-12-81	25-2-83	27-9-84	13-5-85
M 858 MIDDELBURG	21-7-82	11-7-83	23-2-85	10-12-86
M 859 HELLEVOETSLUIS (ex-*Scheveningen*)	21-7-82	12-12-83	18-7-85	20-2-87
M 860 SCHIEDAM	10-12-83	6-5-84	26-4-86	9-7-86
M 861 URK	10-12-83	30-9-84	2-5-86	10-12-86
M 862 ZIERIKZEE (ex-*Veere*)	3-7-84	28-2-85	4-10-86	7-5-87
M 863 VLAARDINGEN	3-7-84	6-5-86	6-8-88	15-3-89
M 864 WILLEMSTAD	3-7-84	3-10-86	27-1-89	20-9-89

D: 510 tons (540 fl) **S:** 15 kts (7 kts hunting)
Dim: 51.6 (47.1 pp) × 8.96 × 2.45 (2.6 max.)
A: 1/20-mm 90-cal. GIAT 20F-2 AA
Electron Equipt:
Radar: 1/Decca TM 1229C nav.—Sonar: 1/DUBM-21B
M: 1 Brons-Werkspoor A-RUB 215 × 12 diesel; 1 CP prop; 1,900 bhp; 2/75-shp bow-thrusters; 2/120-shp ACEC active rudders
Electric: 880 kw **Range:** 3,500/10 **Crew:** 34–42 tot.

Vlardingen (M 863) Leo Van Ginderen, 3-90

MINE WARFARE SHIPS *(continued)*

Willemstad (M 864) Leo Van Ginderen, 1-92

Willemstad (M 864) Leo Van Ginderen, 3-90

Willemstad (M 864) Leo Van Ginderen, 1-92

Remarks: Same design as "Tripartite" minehunters for France and Belgium. The original *Vlaardingen* (M 863) and *Willemstad* (M 864) were sold to Indonesia while under construction in 1985 and were replaced with later units. M 858 and M 859 were to have been transferred to Egypt as *Mecca* and *Medina,* but the transaction was never completed. Five, including M 851 and M 852, are in reserve; two more are to be reduced to reserve during 1992, leaving only eight operational. Two are to be converted to serve as coastal survey ships in 1999.

Hull made of a compound of glass fiber and polyester resin. The 20-mm AA gun is not always aboard. Mine countermeasures equipment includes 2 PAP 104 Mk 4 remote-controlled submersibles, the EVEC 20 plot table, autopilot, Toran and Syledis radio navaids, and the Decca HiFix-6 precision navigation system. Can also tow a mechanical drag sweep and carry OD-3 mechanical sweep gear. The DUBM-21B sonar can detect mines in waters up to 80-m depth, at slant ranges up to 500 m.

Have 3 × 270-kw gas-turbine generator sets and one 160-kw diesel set. Active tank stabilization. The 5-ton modular van abaft the superstructure can contain a decompression station, communications equipment, drone control gear, etc. M 852, 854, and 862 deployed to the Mideast during 3-91 and were equipped with MARISAT satellite communications equipment, 2/12.7-mm mg, and Stinger shoulder-launched surface-to-air missiles.

♦ 11 Dokkum class (5 in reserve*)

	Bldr	Laid down	L	In serv.
M 802 Hoogezand* (ex-MSC 173)	Gusto/F.A. Smulders, Schiedam	18-7-53	22-3-55	7-11-55
M 809 Naaldwijk* (ex-MSC 175)	De Noord, Alblasserdam	2-11-53	1-2-55	8-12-55
M 810 Abcoude (ex-MSC 176)	Gusto/F.A. Smulders, Schiedam	10-11-53	2-9-55	18-5-56
M 812 Drachten (ex-MSC 177)	Niestern SB, Hellevoetsluis	9-12-53	24-3-55	27-1-56
M 813 Ommen (ex-MSC 178)	J. & K. Smits, Kinderdijk	22-12-53	5-4-55	19-4-56
M 815 Giethoorn* (ex-MSC 179)	L. Smit & Son, Kinderdijk	22-12-53	30-3-55	29-3-56
M 817 Venlo* (ex-MSC 180)	Arnhemse SB, Arnhem	10-2-54	21-5-55	26-4-56
M 823 Naarden (ex-MSC 183)	Wilton-Fijenoord, Schiedam	28-10-54	27-1-56	18-5-56
M 827 Hoogeveen (ex-MSC 184)	De Noord, Alblasserdam	1-2-55	8-5-56	6-11-5
M 830 Sittard (ex-MSC 186)	Niestern SB, Hellevoetsluis	10-3-55	26-4-56	19-12-5
M 841 Gemert* (ex-MSC 187)	J. & K. Smits, Kinderdijk	5-4-55	13-3-56	7-9-5

Drachten (M 812) Leo Van Ginderen, 6

Abcoude (M 810) Leo Van Ginderen,

D: 373 tons (453 fl) **S:** 15 kts **Dim:** 46.62 × 8.75 × 2.28
A: 1/20-mm 70-cal. AA
Electron Equipt: Radar: 1/Decca TM 1229C nav.
M: 2 Fijenoord-M.A.N. V 64 diesels; 2 props; 2,500 bhp
Range: 2,500/10 **Crew:** 27–36 tot.

Remarks: Wooden construction units of same basic design as British "Ton French *Sirius* classes. Funded by the United States. All units of the similar *Wild* class were disposed of by 1976. M 827, placed in reserve 5-11-82, was reactivated The surviving active units are expected to serve until the late 1990s. By 1989, 809, 815, 817, and 841 were in reserve. The original 2/40-mm "Boffin" AA began to be replaced by a single 20-mm Oerlikon AA forward in all from 1982

Four *Dokkums* converted to function as minehunters (with Plessey Type 193M during 1968–73 have been disposed of: *Dokkum* (M 801), placed in unmain reserve 4-83, was retrieved for use in oil-fuel trials in 1984; *Drunen* (M 81 stricken 19-4-84; *Staphorst* (M 828) was stricken 20-1-84; and *Veere* (M 84 stricken 19-10-84. Of three reconfigured as mine-disposal divers' tenders, (M 844, ex-MSC 189) was stricken 1-1-84 and sold for scrap 12-3-86; *Roermond* ex-MSC 174) was stricken 16-4-87; and *Woerden* (M 820, ex-MSC 182) was nated as a general-purpose auxiliary (A 882) for service in the Netherlands Ant 25-4-86 and stricken 26-6-91. *Sittard* (M 830) stricken 12-6-87.

AMPHIBIOUS WARFARE SHIPS AND CRAFT

Note: Planned construction of a 90.0 o.a. by 15.6-m beam landing ship d canceled by the Dutch Parliament in 2-89. The ship would have transported u Dutch marines, who now travel in other NATO navies' (principally Britis during exercises. The ship was to have been delivered in 1996. In 1991, the

AMPHIBIOUS WARFARE SHIPS AND CRAFT *(continued)*

was resurrected, with the projected 9,000-ton, 140-m by 21-m ship to carry 6 helicopters and a 600-man battalion of marines; it may be designed in cooperation with Spain, whose navy desires a similar ship, and it is hoped to order the ship in 1992 for completion in 1996.

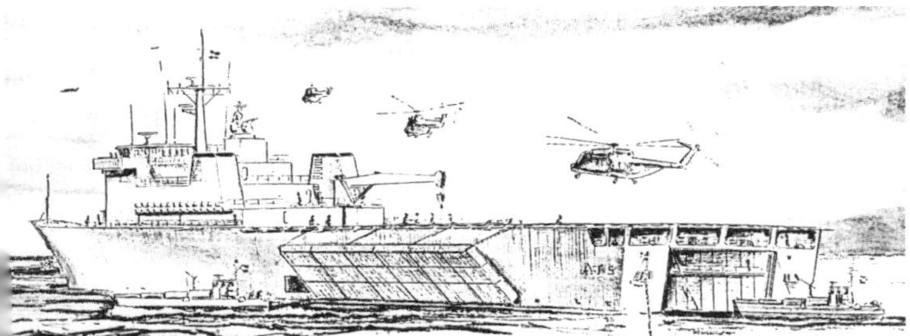

'ossible appearance of new landing ship Alle Hens, 2-89

5 (+1) LCA Mk 3 landing craft Bldr: Van der Giessen de Noord, Alblasserdam

	In serv.		In serv.		In serv.
. 9536	19-2-90	L 9538	29-10-90	L 9540	9-91
9537	6-8-90	L 9539	22-4-91	L 9541	2-92

9536 and L 9537 Leo Van Ginderen, 11-91

D: 23 tons (28.5 fl) **S:** 18 kts light/13 full load
Dim: 16.90 × 4.77 × 1.10 **A:** 1/12.7-mm mg
Electron Equipt: Radar: 1/. . . nav.
M: 2 DAF-Turbo DKS-1160M diesels; 2 Schottel swiveling props; 520 bhp
Range: 220/13 **Crew:** 3 tot. + 35 troops

marks: GRP construction. Ordered 10-12-88. First laid down 10-8-89. L 9540 laid vn 16-5-91 and L 9541 on 4-9-91.

6 LCA Mk 2 landing craft Bldr: Naval Shipyard, Den Helder

	In serv.		In serv.		In serv.
530	10-10-84	L 9532	4-7-85	L 9534	13-12-85
531	20-12-84	L 9533	13-12-85	L 9535	5-1-87

532 Peter Voss, 6-90

: 8.5 tons (13.6 fl) **S:** 11 kts **Dim:** 16.0 × 4.4 × 1.3
: 1/7.62-mm mg **Electron Equipt:** Radar: 1/Decca 110
: 1 DAF-Turbo diesel; 1 Schottel swiveling prop; 260 bhp
ange: 220/11 **Crew:** 3 tot. + 25 troops

arks: Glass-reinforced plastic construction, intended to replace the 10 LCA Mk 1 leted 1962–64. Were to have been 12, but only 6 were ordered. Can carry a Land truck or BV 202 tracked snow vehicle in place of the 25 troops. The machine gun unted to port of the ramp at the bow.

LCA Mk 1 landing craft Bldrs: L 9512, 9513: Naval SY, Den Helder; 9514, 9515: A. La Comte, Jutphaas; others: Verolme, Heusden (In serv. 962–64)

.2 L 9513 L 9514 L 9515 L 9518 L 9520

L 9513 Leo Van Ginderen, 8-87

D: 8.5 tons (13.6 fl) **S:** 11.6 kts **Dim:** 14.45 × 3.82 × 1.3
A: 1/7.62-mm mg **Crew:** 3 tot., plus 25 troops
M: 1 Rolls-Royce diesel; 1 Schottel propeller; 200 bhp

Remarks: GRP construction. Sisters L 9510, L 9511, L 9517, and L 9522 stricken 1987.

◆ **23 (+ 2) rigid inflatable assault craft** Bldr: Mulder & Rijke, Ijmuiden (In serv. 2-89 through 1992)

WM8-8701, WM8-8801–WM8-8804, WM8-8901–8909, WM8-9001–9009, WM8-9109, WM8-9102

D: . . . tons **S:** 26 kts **Dim:** 7.00 × 2.6 × 0.80
M: 1 Volvo Penta TAMD 32A diesel outboard; 110 bhp

Remarks: For transport aboard frigates, etc., and used by Dutch marines. At least six similar craft were in use by 1987.

HYDROGRAPHIC SHIPS

◆ **1 Tydeman class** Bldr: B.V. De Merwede, Hardinxveld-Giessendam

	Laid down	L	In serv.
A 906 Tydeman	29-4-75	18-12-75	10-11-76

Tydeman (A 906) Pieter Westdijk, 5-90

Tydeman (A 906) Leo Van Ginderen, 6-90

D: 3,000 tons (fl) **S:** 15 kts **Dim:** 90.15 × 14.43 × 4.75
Electron Equipt:
Radar: 1/Decca 1226, 1/Decca 1229 nav.
Sonar: Kelvin-Hughes hull-mounted side-scan, Klein towed sidescan, Elac bow-mounted HF wreck-location
M: 3 Stork-Werkspoor 8-FCHD-240 diesels, electric drive; 1 prop; 2,730 shp—2 bow-thrusters; 1 active rudder
Electric: 1,400 kw **Range:** 10,300/13.5; 15,700/10.3
Crew: 8 officers, 54 enlisted + 15 scientists/technicians

Remarks: Assigned to civilian and military research. Hangar and flight deck for one small helicopter. Has passive tank stabilization system, eight laboratories, two in portable 20-ft containers. Any two of the three main diesels power the propulsion motors, the other then provides ship's service power. Conducted trials 1991 with British Aerospace Systems & Equipment version of the French DUBM-41 high-definition minehunting sonar. Atlas DESO-25 echo-sounders added 1991; also has COMPLOT charting system, Decca HiFix-6 radio precision navigation system. Carries one 10-ton and one 4-ton crane plus several A-frame oceanographic cranes. To be stricken 1999 without replacement.

HYDROGRAPHIC SHIPS *(continued)*

◆ **2 Blommendal class** Bldr: Boele's Scheepswerven en Machinefabriek BV, Bolnes

	Laid down	L	In serv.
A 904 BUYSKES	31-1-72	11-7-72	9-3-73
A 905 BLOMMENDAL	1-8-72	21-11-72	22-5-73

Buyskes (A 904) Leo Van Ginderen, 3-90

Blommendal (A 905) Leo Van Ginderen, 2-91

D: 867 tons (1,025 fl) **S:** 14 kts **Dim:** 58.80 × 11.13 × 3.70
Electron Equipt:
Radar: 1/Decca TM 1226 nav., 1/Decca 1229 nav.
Sonar: hull-mounted HF sidescanning, various echo-sounders
M: 2 Paxman 742-hp 12 RPHCZ7 diesels, Smit electric drive; 1 prop; 1,100 shp
Electric: 745 kw **Range:** 7,000/10 **Crew:** 6 officers, 37 enlisted

Remarks: Carry two survey launches and two chain-clearance drag boats. Automated data-logging system. Used in wreck surveys; have sidescan sonar and wire-drag equipment. Atlas DESO-25 echo-sounders added 1991. Operate mainly in the North Sea. To be replaced around 1999 by two converted Tripartite-class minehunters.

REPLENISHMENT SHIPS

◆ **0 (+2) joint Dutch-Spanish project** Bldr: Koninklijke Maatschappij de Schelde, Vlissingen (hull to build at Merwede)

	Laid down	L	In serv.
A . . . JAN VAN GHENT	1992	. . .	1994
A	. . .	. . .	. . .

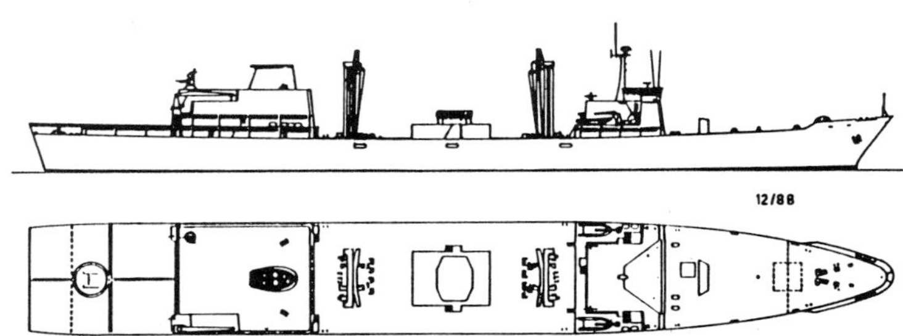

New replenishment oiler R. Neth. N., 12-88

D: 17,050 tons (fl) **S:** 21 kts **Dim:** 175.00 × 23.7 × 8.00
A: 1/30-mm Goalkeeper CIWS—2/20-mm AA (I × 2)—2/. . . helicopters
Electron Equipt:
Radar: . . .
EW: . . . intercept, 2 Mk 36 RBOC RL (VI × 2)
M: diesel-electric: 2 M.A.N. diesels, 2 motors; 2 props; . . . shp
Range: 13,000/22
Crew: 136 crew + 25 air complement, 70 spare berths

Remarks: First unit ordered 9-91 to replace *Poolster*; a second planned ship would replace *Zuiderkruis*. Joint design between Netherlands' Nevesbu and Spain's Bazán design bureaus. Will have two alongside replenishment stations, VERTREP position forward. Cargo deadweight: 10,300 tons, including around 9,000 tons fuel, plus repair capability. Some reports give crew as 150 plus 20 air group and 100 passengers. Twent percent of the crew will be females.

◆ **1 improved Poolster class** Bldr: Verolme, Alblasserdam

	Laid down	L	In serv.
A 832 ZUIDERKRUIS	16-7-73	15-10-74	27-6-75

Zuiderkruis (A 832)—with Goalkeeper atop hangar Leo Van Ginderen, 3-

D: 17,357 tons **S:** 21 kts
Dim: 169.59 (157.00 pp) × 20.3 × 8.4 (max.)
A: 1/30-mm Goalkeeper gatling CIWS—5/20-mm AA (I × 5)—1/d.c. rack (8 d.c.)—3/UH-14A Sea Lynx helicopters
Electron Equipt:
Radar: 2/Decca TM 1226C nav.
EW: passive intercept syst., Mk 36 Super RBOC decoy RL (VI × 4)
M: 2 Werkspoor TM 410 16-cyl. diesels; 2 props; 21,000 bhp
Electric: 3,000 kw
Crew: 17 officers, 26 petty officers, 130 non-rated

Remarks: Cargo capacity: 9,000 tons fuel, 400 tons JP-5 aviation fuel, 200 tons fr water, spare parts, ammunition. Hangar for three Lynx helicopters. Can carry A torpedoes and other stores to support up to five ASW helicopters. Two fueling stati per side, amidships, and one sliding-stay, constant-tension, solid transfer station e side, forward. Accommodations for 266 total. Goalkeeper SGE-30 CIWS added Mideast service 1990.

◆ **1 Poolster class** Bldr: Rotterdamse Droogdok Maatschappij, Rotterda

	Laid down	L	In serv.
A 835 POOLSTER	18-9-62	16-10-63	10-9-64

Poolster (A 835) David Smith,

D: 16,836 tons (fl) **S:** 21 kts
Dim: 168.41 (157.00 pp) × 20.33 × 8.24
A: 2/40-mm AA (I × 2)—1/d.c. rack (8 d.c.)
Electron Equipt:
Radar: 1/Decca TM1229 nav., 1/Decca 2459 surf. search
Sonar: 1/CWE-610 hull-mounted MF
EW: passive intercept syst., Mk 36 Super RBOC decoy RL (VI ×
M: 2 sets geared steam turbines; 1 prop; 22,500 shp **Boilers:** 2
Electric: 2,100 kw **Crew:** 17 officers, 183 enlisted

Remarks: Cargo capacity: 10,300 tons, including 8,000 tons of fuel. Hangar fo Lynx helicopters. Also a combat supply ship capable of participating effectiv antisubmarine warfare with a hunter/killer group, thanks to her ability to three Lynx ASW helicopters if required. For short distances, she can carry 300 m as well as her own crew. Decca 2459 dual F/I-band radar replaced DA-01 rada A 835 will operate until 1995.

TENDERS

◆ **1 torpedo-trials ship** Koninklijke Maatschappij de Schelde, Vlissingen

	Laid down	L	In serv.
A 900 Mercuur	6-11-85	25-10-86	21-8-87

Mercuur (A 900) Ben Sullivan, 2-88

D: 1,200 tons (1,500 fl) **S:** 14 kts **Dim:** 64.85 × 12.00 × 4.30
A: 2/12.7-m mg (I × 2)—2/533-mm TT (underwater)—3/324-mm ASW TT (III × 1)—mines
Electron Equipt:
Radar: 1/Decca TM 1229 nav.
Sonar: hull-mounted active and passive
M: 2 Brons-M.A.N. diesel generator sets (650 kw each); electric drive; 2 props; 1,100 shp—bow-thruster
Crew: 6 officers, 30 enlisted + 3 trials personnel

Remarks: Ordered 13-6-84 to replace U.S. *Agile*-class former minesweeper of the same name as torpedo-trials ship. An ASW escort version of the design is offered commercially. Has a helicopter vertical-replenishment deck above the torpedo workshop.

◆ **1 support ship for the Netherlands Antilles** Bldr: Vindholmen Offshore A/B, Arendal, Norway (In serv. 1984)

A 801 Pelikaan (ex-*Kilindoni*)

Pelikaan (A 801) Hartmut Ehlers, 11-90

D: approx. 710 tons (fl) **S:** 12 kts (10 sust.)
Dim: 46.23 (41.61 pp) × 10.61 × 2.48 **A:** 2/12.7-mm mg (I × 2)
Electron Equipt: Radar: 2/. . . nav.
M: 2 Caterpillar 3412 diesels; 2 props; 1,040 bhp
Crew: 15 tot. + 40 marines

Remarks: Former 505-grt oilfield supply tug acquired 28-5-90 from the Tanzania ...l Shipping Line, Arendal, Norway, and refitted at Curaçao as a replacement for ...kkum-class former minesweeper *Woerden* (A 882). Commissioned 5-7-90 for use ...eral-purpose tender/supply ship in the Netherlands Antilles and for transport...rines as required.

The Netherlands Antilles support tender *Woerden* (A 882, ex-M 806, ex-MSC ...) was stricken 26-6-91.

...OING TUGS

◆ **... Linge-class coastal tugs** Bldr: Delta SY, Sliedrecht (hulls for A 874, ...875 by Scheepswerf Bijlsma B.V., Wartena)

	Laid down	L	In serv.
Linge	12-6-86	15-11-86	20-2-87
Regge	23-6-86	10-1-87	6-5-87
Hunze	17-12-86	21-8-87	20-10-87
Rotte	17-12-86	21-8-87	20-10-87

Regge (A 875) Pieter Sinke, 4-90

D: approx. 500 tons (fl) **S:** 12.5 kts
Dim: 27.45 (26.30 pp) × 8.30 × 3.80
Electron Equipt: Radar: 1/Decca TM 1229 nav.
M: 2 Stork Werkspoor Type DRO 218 K diesels; 2 Kort-nozzle props; 1,632 bhp
Fuel: 55 tons **Electric:** 192 kw **Crew:** 7 tot.

Remarks: Other sources report hulls for first pair by Gruensscheepwerf, Leeuwarden. The first two were ordered 16-4-86. All based at Den Helder.

◆ **1 Westgat-class coastal tug** Bldr: Rijkswerf Willemsoord, Den Helder

	Laid down	L	In serv.
A 872 Westgat	3-4-67	22-8-67	10-1-68

D: 206 tons (fl) **S:** 12 kts **Dim:** 27.18 × 6.97 × 2.34
A: none **Electron Equipt:** 1/Kelvin-Hughes 14/9
M: 1 Bolnes diesel; 1 prop; 720 bhp **Crew:** 9 tot.

Remarks: Based at Den Helder. Can be fitted with 2/20-mm AA. Sister *Wielingen* (A 873) stricken 15-11-91.

TRAINING SHIPS

◆ **1 Balder-class former patrol boat** Bldr: Rijkswerf Willemsoord, Den Helder

	Laid down	L	In serv.
A 880 Bulgia (ex-P 803, ex-SC 1628)	10-53	24-4-54	9-8-54

Bulgia (A 880) Leo Van Ginderen, 1-91

D: 150 tons (163 fl) **S:** 15.5 kts
Dim: 36.35 (35.00 pp) × 6.21 × 1.80
A: none **Electron Equipt:** Radar: 1/Kelvin-Hughes 14/9 nav.
M: 2 Werkspoor RUB 1612 diesels; 2 props; 1,050 bhp
Range: 1,000/13 **Electric:** 60 kw **Crew:** 29 tot.

Remarks: Redesignated as navigational training craft for midshipmen at the Naval College 30-9-86. Sister *Hadda* (P 805) retained as source of spare parts until sold for scrap 21-11-90. Built with U.S. "Offshore Construction" funds. Carried 4/20-mm AA (I × 4) and 2 d.c. in drop racks when last used in patrol duties.

◆ **1 former pilot ship** Bldr: J.&K. Smit, Kinderijk

	Laid down	L	In serv.
A 903 Zeefakkel	28-11-49	21-7-50	16-3-51

D: 303 tons (384 fl) **S:** 12 kts **Dim:** 45.38 × 7.5 × 2.2
Electron Equipt: Radar: 1/Decca . . . nav.
M: 2 M.A.N. diesels; 2 props; 640 bhp **Crew:** 26 tot.

Remarks: Used for seamanship training at Den Helder. Re-engined 1980.

TRAINING SHIPS *(continued)*

Zeefakkel (A 903) Leo Van Ginderen, 10-87

♦ **1 sail-training ketch** Bldr: Haarlemse Scheepsbouw Mij., Haarlem

	L	In serv.
Y 8050 Urania (ex-*Tromp*)	1929	23-4-38

Urania (Y 8050) Leo Van Ginderen, 1991

D: 76.4 tons (fl) **S:** 5 kts (10 under sail) **Dim:** 23.94 × 5.29 × 3.15
M: 1 Kromhout diesel; 1 prop; 65 bhp (625 m² sail area)
Crew: 17 tot.

Note: There are also 24 small sport and training sail yachts under naval control. Former *Dokkum*-class minesweeper *Grypskerk* (ex-M 826) was donated to Sea Cadets in 1985, and the hulked former destroyer *Gelderland* (D 811) was stricken 17-12-90 and donated to the Sea Cadets.

ACCOMMODATIONS SHIPS

♦ **1 non-self-propelled** Bldr: Koninklijke Maatschappij de Schelde, Vlissingen

A 887 Thetis (In serv. 27-6-85)

Thetis (A 887) Leo Van Ginderen, 4-85

Tax (Y 8500) Gilbert Gyssels, 7-8

D: 1,000 tons (fl) **Dim:** 68.47 (62.85 pp) × 12.82 × 1.60

Remarks: Launched 1-83. Replaced former gunboat *Soemba* (A 891) as accommodations barge at Den Oever for use by diver and frogman trainees. Three floatin fenders, delivered 1986, serve with A 887: Y 8611, Y 8612, Y 8613. The former carg lighter *Tax* (Y 8500) is moored with *Thetis* to provide additional accommodations.

♦ **1 non-self-propelled** Bldr: Voorwarts SY, Hoogezand

	Laid down	L	In serv.
A 886 Cornelius Drebbel	18-5-70	19-11-70	30-11-71

D: 775 tons (fl) **Dim:** 63.22 × 11.82 × 1.1 **Crew:** 201 tot.

Remarks: Stationed at Rotterdam to serve ships in overhaul.

SERVICE CRAFT (SELF-PROPELLED)

♦ **1 Dokkum-class fuel-trials craft, former minehunter**

	Bldr	Laid down	L	In serv
Y 8001 Van Speijk (ex-*Dokkum,* M 801, ex-MSC 172)	Wilton Fijenoord, Schiedam	15-6-53	12-10-54	26-7-5

Van Speijk (Y 8001) Hartmut Ehlers,

Remarks: Details generally as for minesweeper sisters; no armament. After h been placed in unmaintained reserve in 4-83, was reclaimed and adapted for te fuels. Renamed 1-11-86 to keep tradition of a *Van Speijk* in R. Neth. N. service.

♦ **1 fuel lighter** Bldr: H.H. Bodewes, Millingen (In serv. 1963)

Y 8536 Patria

Patria (Y 8536) Leo Van Ginderer

D: 827 dwt **S:** . . . **Dim:** 61.6 × 8.1 × . . .
M: 1 Bolnes diesel; 1 prop; . . . bhp **Crew:** . . . tot.

Remarks: Purchased 1978. Based at Den Helder.

♦ **2 Breezand-class harbor tugs** Bldr: Deltawerf, Sliedrecht

Y 8018 Breezand (In serv. 12-89) Y 8019 Balgzand (In serv. 15-1

D: . . . **S:** . . . **Dim:** 16.50 × 5.00 × 1.80
M: 2 Volvo Penta diesels; . . . props; 760 bhp

SERVICE CRAFT (SELF-PROPELLED) *(continued)*

algzand (Y 8019) Peter Voss, 6-90

emarks: Ordered 5-12-88 to replace the stricken *Bambi* (Y 8016) and *Dombo* (Y 17). First launched 22-11-89, second 27-12-89.

1 small harbor tug Bldr: Foxhol (In serv. 1938)

8028 (ex-A 868, ex-RS 28, ex-KM 15, ex-*Eems*)

028 Gilbert Gyssels, 7-88

: 70 tons (fl) **S:** . . . kts **Dim:** 19.5 × 5.1 × 2.3
: 1 Bolnes diesel; 1 prop; 200 bhp **Crew:** 7 tot.

DT-2750-class steel tug/workboats Bldr: Deltawerf, Sliedrecht

55 Schelde (In serv. 18-2-87)
56 Wierbalg (In serv. 18-2-87)
57 Malzwin (In serv. 24-12-86)
Y 8058 Zuidwal (In serv. 16-2-87)
Y 8059 Westwal (In serv. 16-2-87)

alg (Y 8056) Leo Van Ginderen, 6-89

. . **S:** . . . **Dim:** 10.80 × 3.76 × 1.60
AF diesel; 1 prop; 115 bhp

◆ **0 (+4) Cerburus-class diving tenders** Bldr: Visser, den Helder

	Laid down	L	In serv.
A 851 Cerburus	5-91	18-12-91	1-92
A 852 Argus	16-9-91	. . .	3-92
A 853	12-91	. . .	6-92
A 854	3-92	. . .	9-92

D: 200 tons (fl) **S:** 9 kts
Dim: 28.50 (27.35 pp) × 8.50 × 1.50
M: 2 Volvo Penta TAMD diesels; 2 props; 380 bhp
Crew: . . .

Remarks: First three ordered 29-11-90, fourth later. Intended to replace the *Triton* class.

◆ **3 Triton-class diving tenders** Bldr: Rijkswerf Willemsoord, Den Helder

	Laid down	L	In serv.
A 848 Triton (ex-Y 8125)	3-2-64	27-2-64	5-8-64
A 849 Nautilus (ex-Y 8126)	17-3-64	1-5-64	20-4-65
A 850 Hydra (ex-Y 8127)	21-5-64	1-7-64	20-4-65

D: 69.3 tons (fl) **S:** 9 kts **Dim:** 23.28 × 5.15 × 1.35
M: 1 Volvo Penta diesel; 1 prop; 105 bhp **Crew:** 8 tot.

Remarks: To be stricken 1992 on completion of the *Cerburus* class.

◆ **6 harbor launches** Bldr: Mulder & Rijke, IJmuiden

Y 8200 (In serv. 11-89)
Y 8201 (In serv. 8-12-89)
Y 8202 (In serv. 16-2-90)
Y 8203 (In serv. 16-3-90)
WM1-9001(In serv. 27-4-90)
WM1-9002 (In serv. 8-12-90)

Personnel launch Y 8202 Leo Van Ginderen, 10-90

D: 4.75 tons (fl) **S:** 14.5 kts **Dim:** 9.50 × 3.70 × 1.45
M: 1 Volvo-Penta TAMD 41 diesel; waterjet; 170 bhp
Crew: 4–6 tot.

Remarks: First four ordered 12-1-89; fifth and sixth later. Damen "Polycat" glass-reinforced plastic hulls. Y 8200 used for inshore survey work.

◆ **2 harbor launches**

Y 8011 (In serv. 1974) Y 8012 (In serv. 1973)

D: 8 tons (fl) **Dim:** 11.38 × 3.54 × . . . **M:** 1 diesel; 60 bhp

Remarks: GRP construction; resemble LCA Mk 1 landing craft.

◆ **6 fast self-propelled target craft** (In serv. 1982–83)

Y 8694 Y8699–8703

SERVICE CRAFT (NON-SELF-PROPELLED)

◆ **2 sludge barges** Bldr: Scheepswerf DeHoop B.V., Lobith

Y 8351 Y 8352 (Both in serv. 3-9-86)

D: . . . **Dim:** 25.25 × 6.24 × 3.30

Remarks: Ordered 14-2-86 and laid down 4-4-86.

◆ **6 miscellaneous fuel barges**

Y 8335 (In serv. 1952)
Y 8538 (In serv. 1955)
Y 8347 (In serv. 2-3-83)
Y 8349 (In serv. 5-11-83)
Y 8348 (In serv. 20-7-83)
Y 8350 (In serv. 5-11-83)

◆ **2 steam supply craft:** Y 8122 (In serv. 1937), Y 8260 (In serv. 1940)

◆ **1 tank-cleaning boat:** Y 8262 (In serv. 1918)

◆ **1 hull-cleaning boat:** Y 8263 (In serv. 1967)

◆ **1 floating crane:** Y 8514 (In serv. 1974)

◆ **4 target barges**

Y 8692 Y 8700 Y 8704 (acquired 5-86) Y 8019 (In serv. 1-12-88)

SERVICE CRAFT (NON-SELF-PROPELLED) *(continued)*

◆ **13 miscellaneous dry-cargo barges** (In serv. 1900–1965)

Y 8321, Y 8322, Y 8324, Y 8327, Y 8331, Y 8332, Y 8334, Y 8337, Y 8338, Y 8339, Y 8340, Y 8341, Y 8377

Cargo barge Y 8334—rigged with staging — Leo Van Ginderen, 1990

Remarks: Y 8377 is ex-Army RV 141, transferred 10-89 for use by marines in ship-to-shore transits. Barge Y 8333 stricken 15-11-91.

◆ **26 mooring pontoons**

Y 8578 (In serv. 20-10-87); Y 8579 (In serv. 30-4-86); Y 8581 (In serv. 2-4-86); Y 8582 (In serv. 28-5-86); Y 8594, Y 8595 (In serv. 1956); Y 8597, Y 8598 (In serv. 1971); Y 8599 (In serv. 1977); Y 8604–07 (In serv. 3-2-81); Y 8604, Y 8605 (In serv. 14-10-83); Y 8611–13 (In serv. 23-6-86); Y 8614–Y 8617 (acquired 25-9-86), Y 8711–14 (In serv. 1940)

Remarks: Y 8597, Y 8598, and Y 8599 are used with submarines. Y8611–13 are used with the berthing barge *Thetis* (A 887).

◆ **12 diving pontoons**

Y 8551 (In serv. 2-4-86), Y 8552 (In serv. 28-5-86), Y 8579 (In serv. 30-5-86), Y 8580 (In serv. 18-12-85), Y 8583–86 (In serv. 1951), Y 8588–90 (In serv. 1952), Y 8591 (In serv. 1953)

◆ **6 miscellaneous barges**

Het Beultje (Y 8342) (In serv. 1982), Y 8592 (In serv. 1953), Y 8600–03

◆ **2 floating dry docks**

Y 8678 Dok IV (In serv. 1949) Y 8679 Dok V (In serv. 1960)

Dok IV (Y 8678) — Leo Van Ginderen, 7-91

Remarks: *Dok IV* is 40.0 × 9.0 × 3.8, with a 420-ton capacity. *Dok V* is 40.0 × 10.6 × 4.0, with a 450-ton capacity. Both based at Willemsoord.

COAST GUARD

The Netherlands Coast Guard, established 26-2-87, has no vessels of its own but employs ships, boats, and craft supplied by other services: the Royal Netherlands Navy (which provides two lifeboat commanding officers), the National Constabulary, Customs, the Ministry of Transport, the Corps of Military Police, the Fisheries Inspection Service, and Scheveningen Radio. Units in Coast Guard use continue to carry their original markings while adding diagonal red, white, and blue stripes, the Coast Guard shield, and the work "Kustwacht" on their hull sides.

ROYAL NETHERLANDS ARMY

◆ **1 RV 40-class tank landing craft**

	Bldr	In serv.
RV 40	Grave B.V.	22-11-79

D: 815 tons **S:** 9.4 kts **Dim:** 45.8 × 9.5 × 2.20
M: 2 Mercedes-Benz OM404 diesels; 2 props; 654 bhp
Crew: 4 tot.

◆ **58 Type ASA-540 aluminum river assault boats** Bldr: Damen, Gorinchem (In serv. 1980s)

River assault boat — Damen, 9-

D: 1.8 tons (fl) **S:** 25–30 kts **Dim:** 5.40 × 1.83 × 0.1
M: 1 25–40-bhp diesel outboard **Crew:** 4–8 tot.

◆ **. . . Type 700 Bridge Support Boats** Bldr: Damen, Gorinchem

D: 6 tons (fl) **S:** 8.6 kts **Dim:** 7.00 × 2.90 × 0.75
M: 1 Deutz BF 8L 513 diesel; 2 props; 250 bhp

Type 700 Bridge Support Boat — Damen,

Remarks: Steel construction, intended to be carried by DAF YGZ 2300 truck used in assembling and positioning pontoon bridges. Have 2.6-ton bollard poll. are full-swiveling and ducted.

◆ **1 diving tender** Bldr: Werf Vervaco, Heusden

RV 50 (L: 8-9-89; in serv. 3-11-89)

Remarks: No data available.

◆ **1 diving tender** Bldr: . . . (In serv. 1954)

RV 29 Torpedisten

Torpedisten (RV 29) — Leo Van Gindere

ROYAL NETHERLANDS ARMY *(continued)*

D: . . . **S:** 8.6 kts **Dim:** 25.00 × 5.75 × 1.90
M: 1 G.M. 6071 diesel; 1 prop; 150 bhp **Crew:** . . .

◆ **2 tenders** (In serv. 1952)

RV 154 RV 157

D: . . . **S:** 8.6 kts **Dim:** 9.49 × 2.50 × 1.50
M: 1 Volvo MD50A diesel; 1 prop; 75 bhp

ROYAL CORPS OF MILITARY POLICE (Koninkliike Marechausée)

◆ **3 RV 165-class patrol boats** Bldr: Damen, Gorinchem

RV 165 (In serv. 1975) RV 166 (In serv. 1984) RV 169 (In serv. 1975)

RV 165—in Coast Guard colors Mike Louagie, 8-89

D: . . . **S:** 17.5 kts **Dim:** 17.30 (15.30 pp) × 5.00 × 1.30
M: 2 G.M. diesels; 2 props; 700 bhp

Remarks: Also in service are four smaller patrol boats, including RV 176.

NETHERLANDS NATIONAL POLICE CONSTABULARY (MINISTRY OF JUSTICE)

Note: This organization operates about 70 patrol craft. A number of other jurisdictions, including the Customs Service of the Ministry of Finance, the Rotterdam City Police, and the Department of Communications, also operate patrol craft. Ships and craft carry the word "*Rijkspolitie*" (National Police) on both sides, and some also appear simultaneously in *Kustwacht* (Coast Guard) colors.

◆ **1 (+ . . .) RP 9 class** Bldr: Damen, Gorinchem

RP 9 (In serv. 1991)

D: 85 tons (96 fl) **S:** 13.5 kts **Dim:** 21.75 × 5.60 × 1.65
Electron Equipt: Radar: 1/Decca . . . nav.
M: 2 MTU 12V183 TE61 diesels; 2 props; . . . bhp

Remarks: Pilot-boat design.

RP 9—dark blue hull, white upperworks, orange trim Damen, 1991

◆ **5 RP 16 class** Bldr: Schottel, Warmond

RP 16 Carel Polak (In serv. 21-2-84)
RP 20 (In serv. 19-7-84)
RP 21 (In serv. 1985)
RP 25 . . . . (In serv. 1986)
RP 56 (In serv. 10-84)

RP 25—in Coast Guard colors M. Voss, 5-88

D: 49 tons (fl) **S:** 18.5 kts **Dim:** 23.50 × 5.30 (5.08 wl) × 1.60
Electron Equipt: 1/Racal Decca . . . nav. **Crew:** 6 tot.
M: 3 M.A.N. D2842 ME diesels; 3 Schottel SRP 132 Azimuth props; 1,266 bhp

◆ **5 15-meter class** Bldr: Schottel, Warmond

RP 63 (In serv. 17-10-84) RP 71 (In serv. 13-3-85)
RP 69 (In serv. 4-2-83) RP 72 (In serv. . . .)
RP 70 (In serv. 12-12-84)

RP 72 Leo Van Ginderen, 7-89

D: 17.5 tons **S:** 17 kts **Dim:** 15.36 × 3.78 × 1.25
M: RP 69: 2 DAF DKA-1160M diesels; 2 props; 440 bhp; others: 1 M.A.N. D2842-ME diesel; 1 prop; 422 bhp
Crew: 3 or 4 tot.

◆ **7 RP 41 class** Bldr: Schottel, Warmond (In serv. 1977–78)

RP 41 RP 49 RP 59 RP 63 RP 69 RP 70 RP 71

RP 41 M. Voss, 5-88

D: 18 tons (fl) **S:** 17 kts **Dim:** 15.36 × 3.78 × 1.25
M: 2 DAF DKA-1160M diesels; 2 props; 440 bhp
Crew: 3 tot.

◆ **6 RP 43 class** Bldr: Schottel, Warmond (In serv. 1982–83)

RP 24 RP 40 RP 43 RP 45 RP 57 RP 69

NETHERLANDS NATIONAL POLICE CONSTABULARY *(continued)*

RP 40 Leo Van Ginderen, 10-87

D: . . . **S:** 16.7 kts **Dim:** 15.36 × 3.70 × 1.25
M: 2 DAF diesels; 2 Schottel props; 440 bhp **Crew:** . . .

Remarks: Intended for use on the river and canal system.

◆ **1 De Ruiter class** Bldr: Schottel, Warmond

RP 15 De Ruiter (In serv. 5-79)

De Ruiter (RP 15) Mike Louagie, 4-88

D: 27 tons (fl) **S:** 18.5 kts **Dim:** 19.13 × 4.27 × 1.3
M: 2 Mercedes-Benz OM904 12-cyl. diesels; 2 Schottel vertical cycloidal props; 680 bhp
Crew: 3–4 tot.

◆ **4 RP 17 class** Bldr: Schottel, Warmond (In serv. 1974–. . .)

RP 16 RP 17 RP 26 RP 28

RP 17 Leo Van Ginderen, 6-84

D: 29 tons **S:** 15 kts **Dim:** 15.75 × 3.83 × 1.05
M: 1 MTU OM403 diesel; 1 Schottel vertical cycloidal prop; 250 bhp

◆ **9 10.8-meter class** Bldr: Le Comte, Vianen, 1970–. . .

RP 38 RP 42 RP 48 RP 51 RP 53 RP 54 RP 60 RP 61 RP 62

D: 8.5 tons **S:** 14.5 kts **Dim:** 10.8 × 3.22 × 1.2
M: 1 MTU OM346 diesel; 1 Schottel prop; 165 bhp

RP 54 Leo Van Ginderen, 7-89

◆ **RP 10** Bldr: Schouten, Muiden, 1968

D: 70 tons (104 fl) **S:** 14 kts **Dim:** 27.8 × 5.46 × . . .
M: 1 Bolnes GDNL diesel; 600 bhp

RP 10 Mike Louagie, 8-9

◆ **RP 3** Bldr: Koopman, Dordrecht, 1967

D: 63 tons (fl) **S:** 12.7 kts **Dim:** 22.00 × 5.24 × 1.50
M: 2 G.M. 12V71 diesels; 2 props; 670 bhp

MINISTRY OF FINANCE (CUSTOMS)

PATROL BOATS AND CRAFT

◆ **1 Stan Patrol 2600 class** Bldr: Damen SY, Gorinchem

Zeevalk (In serv. 1981)

Zeevalk—in Coast Guard colors Pieter Sinke, 1

D: 85 tons (96 fl) **S:** 25 kts
Dim: 26.50 (24.27 pp) × 5.80 × 1.80
Electron Equipt: Radar: 1/. . . nav.
M: 2 Deutz SBA 16M816 diesels (1,350 bhp each), 1 Deutz SA GM8 diesel (208 bhp); 3 props; 2,908 bhp
Range: 600/14 **Crew:** 6 tot.

Remarks: Sisters in Hong Kong service. Based at Hook of Holland. Other Minis Finance Customs craft include, in alphabetical order:

	Year	Dimensions	Kts	Base
Aalscholver	1978	14.55 × 4.82 × 1.10	18.6	Delfzijl
Alexander Gogel	1964	25.60 × 5.34 × 1.34	9.7	Harlin
Dinkel	1971	10.80 × 3.22 × 1.20	13.0	Rotterd
Dolfijn	. . .	. . .	. . .	. . .
Donge	1971	10.80 × 3.22 × 1.20	13.0	Lalysta
Kokmeeuw*	1974	12.62 × 3.82 × 1.10	16.6	Rotterc
Lek*	1976	12.62 × 3.82 × 1.10	16.6	Lobith
Maas	1985	15.36 × 3.78 × 1.25	16.5	Lobith
Mantelmeeuw	1967	14.40 × 3.85 × 1.40	16.5	Rotter
Recherche I*	1976	12.62 × 3.82 × 1.10	16.6	Amste
Recherche III	1971	10.80 × 3.22 × 1.25	15.4	Amste
Rijn	1983	15.36 × 3.78 × 1.84	16.5	Lobith
Stormeeuw*	1974	12.62 × 3.82 × 1.10	16.6	Rotter
Waal*	1974	12.62 × 3.82 × 1.10	16.6	Lobith
IJssel*	1974	12.62 × 3.82 × 1.10	16.6	Lobith
Zeearend	1973	23.44 × 5.30 × 1.50	16.0	Den H
Zilvermeeuw	1968	14.40 × 3.85 × 1.25	16.3	Rotter

Craft marked * built, as were most of the above, by Schottel, Warmond, and ha G.M. 8V53 diesels: 244 bhp total. Also in use by the Ministry of Finance are fo under the Domeinen branch, which takes care of government property: *Donge* 10.80 m o.a.), *Lemmar* (1975, 12.65 m o.a.), *Osiris* (1964, 20.75 m o.a.), and *Ur* 11.0 m o.a.).

DIRECTOR GENERAL OF PUBLIC WORKS

In service are 5 seagoing survey ships, 5 coastal survey craft, 1 large pollution-control ship, 3 fireboats, 48 survey and inspection launches, and nearly 200 riverine craft. Typical units are:

◆ **1 survey ship** Bldr: Damen SY, Vianen

MITRA (In serv. 2-7-82)

D: 1,223 grt **S:** 12 kts **Dim:** 56.3 × 11.6 × . . .
M: 2 500-bhp diesels, 1 297-bhp diesel **Crew:** 10 tot.

Mitra Leo Van Ginderen, 1984

1 pollution-control ship Bldr: Boelwerf, Temse

SMAL AGT (In serv. 1961)

D: 1,132 grt **S:** 10 kts **Dim:** 54.0 × 9.2 × 3.5
M: 2 diesels; . . . props; 600 bhp **Crew:** 10 tot.

Remarks: Former dump barge rebuilt 1976 by De Groot & Van Vliet for pollution-control duties.

Smal Agt Leo Van Ginderen, 4-84

MINISTRY OF TRANSPORT DIRECTORATE GENERAL OF MARITIME AFFAIRS

In 1989, the Pilot Service of the Directorate General of Maritime Affairs (DGSM), which had been transferred from the Navy in 1981, was again transferred to private management; the large pilot vessels described in the previous edition have been deleted. The DGSM continues to operate a number of Port Authority patrol boats (Verkeerdienst-DGSM) and navigational buoy tenders, which are listed below. The DGSM is organized into four regions: Rotterdam, Northern, Flushing (Vlissingen), and IJmuiden-Amsterdam.

PORT AUTHORITY PATROL BOATS

◆ **1 V-27 class** Bldr: . . . (In serv. 1968)

V-27 (RHD 7) Based at Hook of Holland

Leo Van Ginderen, 4-88

D: . . . **S:** 13 kts **Dim:** 33.20 × 7.20 × 2.95
M: 1 Bolnes 8 DL diesel (600 bhp), 1 Bolnes 5 L diesel (260 bhp); 1 prop

◆ **1 V-85 class** Bldr: . . . (In serv. 1970)

V-85 STUVESANT (RHD 85) Based at Vlissingen

D: . . . **S:** 11.6 kts **Dim:** 26.95 × 6.39 × 2.55
M: 1 Caterpillar D 379 diesel; 1 prop; 566 bhp

Stuvesant (V-85)—note fire-fighting gear Leo Van Ginderen, 1989

◆ **4 V-23 class** Bldr: . . .

	In serv.		In serv.
V-23 (RHD 3)	1972	V-29 (RHD 9)	1976
V-28 (RHD 8)	1973	V-87 AVESANT (RHD 87)	1976

D: . . . **S:** 11 kts **Dim:** 24.15 × 5.50 × 1.85
M: 1 Bolnes 6 KNL diesel; 1 prop; 420 bhp

Remarks: Based at Rotterdam, Rotterdam, Hook of Holland, and Hansweert, respectively.

Avesant (V-87) Leo Van Ginderen, 7-87

◆ **1 V-24 class** Bldr: . . . (In serv. 1968)

V-24 NIEUWE WATERWEG Based at Maassluis

D: . . . **S:** 9.2 **Dim:** 18.43 × 4.43 × 1.55
M: 2 G.M. 6V92 diesels; 2 props; 400 bhp

◆ **1 V-64 class** Bldr: . . . (In serv. 1978)

V-64 (RHD 64) Based at IJmuiden

D: . . . **S:** 9.9 kts **Dim:** 17.05 × 4.25 × 1.65
M: 1 Mercedes-Benz OM403 diesel; 1 prop; 250 bhp

◆ **2 V-62 class** Bldr: . . . (In serv. 1971)

V-62 WORTMAN (RHD 62) V-86 OTHENE (RHD 86)

D: . . . **S:** 9 kts **Dim:** 16.96 × 4.25 × 1.50
M: 1 DAF DK 1160M diesel; 1 prop; 169 bhp

Remarks: Based at IJmuiden and Terneuzen, respectively.

Othene (V-86) Leo Van Ginderen, 3-91

NETHERLANDS *(continued)*
PORT AUTHORITY PATROL BOATS *(continued)*

◆ **1 V-63 class** Bldr: . . . (In serv. 1981)

V-63 (RHD 63) Based at IJmuiden

D: . . . **S:** 10 kts **Dim:** 16.64 × 5.02 × 1.65
M: 1 Mercedes-Benz OM404 diesel; 1 prop; 341 bhp

◆ **3 V-21 class** Bldr: . . . (In serv. 1982)

V-21 (RHD 21) V-22 (RHD 22) V-25 (RHD 25)

V-25 (RHD 25) Gilbert Gyssels, 6-85

D: . . . **S:** 17.8 kts **Dim:** 14.95 × 4.08 × 1.36
M: 2 Mercedes-Benz OM404 diesels; 2 props; 680 bhp

Remarks: GRP construction. V-21, V-22 based at Rotterdam, V-25 at Dordrecht.

◆ **1 V-89 class** Bldr: . . . (In serv. 1977)

V-89 Grutto Based at Vlissingen

Grutto (V-89) Leo Van Ginderen, 12-86

D: . . . **S:** 17.3 kts **Dim:** 14.75 × 4.65 × 0.90
M: 2 G.M. diesels; 2 props; 922 bhp

◆ **1 V-41 class** Bldr: . . . (In serv. 1977)

V-41 Zeekoet

D: . . . **S:** 18.6 kts **Dim:** 14.55 × 4.82 × 1.10
M: 2 Mercedes-Benz OM404 diesels; 2 props; 672 bhp

Remarks: Based at Harlingen. Also in service is *Kluut* (V-40); no data available.

NAVIGATIONAL BUOY TENDERS

	Year	Dimensions	Bhp	Kts
Breeveertien	1973	61.25 × 11.30 × 3.40	1,230	13.0
Terschelling	1988	. . . × . . . × . . .	. . .	. . .
Rotterdam	1987	. . . × . . . × . . .	. . .	. . .
Frans Naerebout	1989	. . . × . . . × . . .	. . .	. . .
Delfshaven	1959	40.60 × 7.96 × 2.83	400	11.3
Eems	1961	28.80 × 5.86 × 1.63	200	9.2
Grevelingen	1950	30.63 × 6.43 × 1.95	200	9.2
Haringvliet	1961	28.80 × 5.86 × 1.58	200	9.3
Honte	1961	28.80 × 5.86 × 1.70	200	9.2
Krammer	1950	30.63 × 6.43 × 1.85	200	9.2
Texelstroom	1959	24.10 × 5.56 × 1.58	140	8.0
Vliestroom	1961	28.80 × 5.86 × 1.55	200	9.3
Vlissingen	1969	40.50 × 7.96 × 2.80	480	11.1
Waddenzee	1959	28.80 × 5.96 × 1.60	200	9.5
Zaandam	1953	41.10 × 7.53 × 2.89	430	11.4

Breeveertien—at 1,000 grt, the largest Netherlands navigational buoy tender, in Coast Guard colors Leo Van Ginderen, 3-91

Frans Naerebout—delivered 1989 and the newest of the Ministry of Transport navaids tenders Leo Van Ginderen, 8-9

Note: Also in service are three shallow-draft workboats for service on the Waddenze *Breehorn, Garnal,* and *Krab* (1982–84; 8.00 × 2.60 × 0.30; 86 bhp = 8 kts).

MINISTRY OF AGRICULTURE AND FISHERIES

◆ **6 fisheries inspection boats**

	Year	Dimensions	Bhp	Kts
Zwaluw	1954	18.35 × 4.45 × 1.50	100	8.5
Valk	1959	23.00 × 5.20 × 1.40	212	9.5
Stormvogel	1964	25.60 × 5.32 × 1.38	340	9.7
Cornelis Bos	1965	21.05 × 5.23 × 1.58	330	9.2
Slenk	1976	24.10 × 5.49 × 1.40	169	8.9
Kokhaan	1979	15.90 × 4.80 × 1.50	338	9.2

◆ **1 fisheries and hydrographic research ship** Bldr: De Merwede, Hardinxveld

Tridens (In serv. 1990)

D: 2,600 tons (fl) **S:** . . . kts
Dim: 73.54 (64.02 pp) × 14.08 × 4.60
M: 2 Deutz SBV 8M628 diesels; 2 CP props; 5,800 bhp

Remarks: 2,199 grt/600 dwt sternhaul and beam-trawler/seiner fisheries resea ship with refrigerated hold; can also perform hydrographic surveys. Also in service the research ship and craft:

	Year	Dimensions	Bhp
Dr. P. P. C. Hoek	1955	12.00 × 3.50 × 1.15	97
Schollevaar	1963	20.25 × 4.90 × 1.45	240
Stern	1963	21.00 × 5.65 × 1.70	200
Stavast	1982	9.45 × 3.00 × 0.30	97
Isis	1983	28.00 × 7.60 × 2.52	800

Note: Other Dutch Government vessels include the patrol boat *Aeolus* of the Min of Social Affairs, oceanographic research vessel *Tyro* of the Ministry of Education fireboats *Gelderland, Zuid-Holland,* and *Batouwe* of the Ministry of Internal A (which are operated, however, by local fire-fighting organizations). The city of Rc dam has a patrol-boat force, with craft numbered in the "P" series.

NEW ZEALAND

Dominion of New Zealand

Personnel (1991): 2,500 total (plus 450 reserves)

Naval Aviation: Seven Wasp helicopters are available for the *Leander*-class fr and the survey ship *Monowai;* the helicopters are flown by R.N.Z.N. crews but tained by six-man R.N.Z.A.F. detachments. Five Lockheed P-3B Orion patrol belong to No. 5 Squadron, Royal New Zealand Air Force; a sixth P-3B, ex-R.A.A. not yet been updated. A second round of modernizations for all six, called "Rigel planned to bring the aircraft up to P-3C standard, was canceled 8-90. Three F F-27-100 Maritime, primarily for transport, also perform search-and-rescue The R.N.Z.A.F.'s 22 A-4 Skyhawks have a maritime attack role. Plan to acquir helicopters to replace the Wasps but not until the late 1990s.

FRIGATES

◆ **0 (+2+2) ANZAC frigate (MEKO 200 variant) class** Bldr: Australian Marine Engineering Consolidated, Ltd. (AMECON), Williamstown and Newcastle

	Laid down	L	In serv.
F	. . .	. . .	2-97
F	. . .	. . .	11-98

ANZAC frigate—artist's impression Jeff Isaacs/R.A.N., 1990

D: 3,195 tons (3,495 fl) **S:** 27 kts (20 kts on diesel)
Dim: 117.50 (109.50 pp) × 14.80 (13.80 wl) × 5.99 (4.12 hull)
A: 1/Mk 41 VLS module (VIII × 1; 8 Sea Sparrow missiles)—1/127-mm 54-cal. U.S. Mk 45 Mod. 2 DP—1/Sea Lynx helicopter
Electron Equipt:
Radar: 1/Krupp-Atlas ARPA 8600 nav., 1/ Ericsson 150 HC Sea Giraffe search, 1/Raytheon SPS-49(v)8 air search, 1/ BEAB 9LV200 f.c.
Sonar: Thomson-Sintra Spherion-B hull-mounted; towed array (*see* Remarks)
EW: MEL Sceptre XL intercept; Mk 36 SRBOC decoy syst. (4 Mk 136 RL), SLQ-25 Nixie towed acoustic torpedo decoy syst.
M: CODOG: 2 MTU 12V1163 TB83 diesels (4,420 bhp each), 1 G.E. LM-2500-30 gas turbine (30,000 shp each); 2 CP props
Electric: 2,600 kw (4 × 650 kw MTU TB 396 series diesel sets)
Fuel: 300 tons **Range:** 900/31.75; 4,100/18 (2 diesels); 6,000/ . . .
Crew: 22 officers, 41 petty officers, 100 other enlisted

Remarks: Contract awarded 14-8-89 for eight for the Royal Australian Navy, with options for two or four more for New Zealand, which decided in 9-89 to order only two. A decision on whether or not to order two more is to be made in 1996. All to be launched at Williamstown, in part using modules built at Newcastle and in New Zealand. Construction, however, may be delayed by the failure of Carrington Slipways at Newcastle, which was to have built hull modules. Only lightly equipped, they will be more offshore patrol vessels than combatants.

Will have BEAB 9LV453 Mk 3 combat data/fire-control system, with only one Sea Viking (9LV 200-derivative) director (although space for a second is present). ASSTASS (Australian Surface Ship Towed Array Surveillance System), a variant of the Karriwara submarine TASS, or the Ferranti FMS 15/2 towed array may be carried. Will not have ASW torpedo tubes as on Australian units; there is space for a second vertical-launch Sea Sparrow module and for the U.S. Mk 15 CIWS. Will not have a helicopter haul-down and deck-traversing system.

◆ **2 U.K. Broad-Beam Leander class**

	Bldr	Laid down	L	In serv.
F 69 WELLINGTON (ex-*Bacchante*)	Vickers-Armstrong, Newcastle	27-10-66	29-2-68	17-10-69
F 421 CANTERBURY	Yarrow, Scotstoun	12-4-69	6-5-70	22-10-71

D: F 69: 2,500 tons std. (3,184 fl); F 421: 2,470 tons light (3,638 fl)
S: 28 kts (30 on trials)
Dim: 113.38 (109.73 pp) × 13.12 × 5.49 (F 69)
A: 2/114-mm 45 cal. Mk 6 DP (II × 1)—1 Sea Cat GWS.22 syst. (IV × 1)—4/12.7-mm mg (I × 4)—6/324-mm ASW TT (III × 2, for U.S. Mk 46 Mod. 2 torpedoes)—1/Wasp HAS.1 helicopter
Electron Equipt:
Radar: 1/Kelvin-Hughes Type 1006 nav., 1/Marconi Type 965 early-warning (F 421: H.S.A. LW-08), 1/Plessey Type 994 air/surf. search, 1/RCA R76C5 f.c. for 114-mm guns, 1/Plessey Type 904 f.c. for Sea Cat GWS.22
Sonar: 1/Type 184M (F 69: Graseby G750) hull-mounted MF, 1/162M hull-mounted HF bottomed-target classification
EW: Argo Phoenix PST 1288 intercept, Type 668/669 jammers, FH-12 D/F, Mk 36 SRBOC decoy syst. (Mk 136 RL, VI × 2)
M: 2 sets White–English Electric geared steam turbines; 2/5-bladed props; 30,000 shp
Boilers: 2 Babcock & Wilcox 3-drum; 38.7 kg/cm^2, 450° C Superheat
Electric: 2,500 kw **Fuel:** 500 tons (F 69: 720)
Range: 4,500/12 (F 69: 6,500/12) **Crew:** 15 officers, 230 men

Remarks: F 69 was purchased and commissioned in the New Zealand Navy on 4-10-82, proceeding to Auckland for a refit scheduled to end in 1-85, but delayed to 25-8-86. The ship's 20-mm AA and chaff RL were removed prior to transfer. The Type 199 VDS was removed and stored as a spare for *Southland*. The MRS.3 gunfire-control system was replaced by the RCA R76C5 system in F 69. F 69 also received a Marconi NTC-1 communications suite, Mk 32 ASW TT removed from *Taranaki* (F 148), and U.S. Mk 36

:erbury (F 421)—LW-08 radar aft R.N.Z.N., 1991

FRIGATES *(continued)*

Super RBOC decoy RL. The Limbo ASW mortar was removed. F 69 was transferred with a Wasp helicopter aboard.

F 421 refitted 11-87 to 1990 with the new electronics, plus Signaal LW-08 radar in place of Type 965, but did not receive additional fuel tankage. Contract let 10-87 to study life extension until 2004 and 2006, respectively; were also to receive the Plessey NAUTIS combat data system during 1991–92. Both may also get Ferranti FMS 15/2 towed passive sonar arrays.

Wellington (F 69)—Type 965 radar aft — Ross Gillett, 10-91

◆ **1 U.K. Leander class**

	Bldr	Laid down	L	In serv.
F 55 Waikato	Harland & Wolff, Belfast	10-1-65	18-2-65	16-9-66

Waikato (F 55) — Percy Hunt, 1-92

D: 2,533 tons (2,950 fl) **S:** 28 kts
Dim: 113.38 (109.73 pp) × 12.50 × 5.50 hull
A: 2/114-mm 45-cal. Mk 6 DP (II × 1)—1/Sea Cat GWS.22 SAM syst. (IV × 1)—4/12.7-mm mg (I × 4)—6/324-mm ASW TT (III × 2, U.S. Mk 46 Mod. 2 torpedoes)—1/HAS.1 Wasp helicopter
Electron Equipt:
Radar: 1/Kelvin-Hughes Type 1006 nav., 1/ Marconi Type 965 early-warning, 1/Plessey Type 993 air/surf. search, 1/Plessey Type 903 gun f.c., 1/Plessey Type 904 f.c. for Sea Cat GWS.22
Sonar: 1/Graseby Type 184 hull-mounted MF, 1/Kelvin-Hughes Type 162M HF bottomed-target classification
EW: Argo Phoenix PST 1288 intercept, Type 668/669 jammers, FH-12 D/F, Mk 36 SRBOC decoy syst. (Mk 136 RL, VI × 2)
M: 2 sets White–English Electric geared steam turbines; 2 5-bladed props; 30,000 shp
Boilers: 2 Babcock & Wilcox; 38.7 kg/cm², 450°C
Electric: 1,900 kw **Range:** 4,100/12
Fuel: 460 tons **Crew:** 15 officers, 228 enlisted

Remarks: Built specifically for New Zealand. Originally had a Mk 10 Limbo triple ASW mortar and no ASW TT; refitted in 1977, when the Type 170B depth-determining sonar was also removed. Refitted again summer 1986 to 11-87, and another refit was completed 5-9-91, during which the EW suite was updated. Planned to strike 1996–97.

◆ **1 ex-U.K. "Ikara Leander" class** Bldr: Yarrow & Co., Scotstoun

	Laid down	L	In serv.
F 104 Southland (ex-*Dido*, ex-*Hastings*)	2-12-59	22-12-61	18-9-63

Southland (F 104) — Leo Van Ginderen, 10-91

D: 2,625 tons (3,035 fl) **S:** 28 kts
Dim: 113.38 (109.73 pp) × 12.50 × 5.52
A: 2/40-mm 60-cal. Bofors Mk 9 AA (I × 2)—2/Sea Cat GWS.22 syst. (IV × 2)—6/12.7-mm mg (I × 6)—1/Ikara GWS.46 ASW syst. (16 missiles)—6/324-mm ASW TT (III × 2, U.S. Mk 46 Mod. 2 torpedoes)—1/HAS.1 Wasp helicopter
Electron Equipt:
Radar: 1/Kelvin-Hughes Type 1006 nav., 1/Plessey Type 994 surf./air search, 1/Plessey Type 904 f.c for Sea Cat GWS.22, 1/Ikara GWS.46 control
Sonar: 1/Graseby Type 184 hull-mounted MF, 1/Graseby Type 170B hull-mounted HF depth-determining, 1/Type 199 MF VDS
EW: Argo Phoenix PST 1288 intercept; Type 668/669 jammers
M: 2 sets White–English Electric geared steam turbines; 2/5-bladed props; 30,000 shp
Boilers: 2 Babcock & Wilcox 3-drum; 38.7 kg/cm², 450° C Superheat
Electric: 1,600 kw **Fuel:** 460 tons **Range:** approx. 4,100/12
Crew: 19 officers, 238 enlisted

Remarks: Purchased and transferred to New Zealand in 18-7-83, with Wasp helico[pter] aboard. Commissioned 21-12-83 after refit in U.K., with Limbo ASW mortar delet[ed] and ASW TT added, Argo EW gear installed, and Type 993 radar updated to Type 99[4]. The two Sea Cat short-range SAM launchers share a single radar director. Lit[tle] capability for AAW or surface warfare. Planned to strike 1996–97. Australia ceased [to] support the Ikara ASW missile system by the end of 1991; the boost-glide missile ha[s a] range of 24 km and carries a Mk 46 Mod. 2 ASW torpedo payload; in emergencies, it c[an] be directed at a surface target. Received a 35-week refit during 1989.

PATROL CRAFT

◆ **4 Moa-class naval reserve training/patrol craft** Bldr: Whangar[ei] Engineering Co., Auckland

	L	In serv.		L	In se[rv.]
P 3553 Moa	16-7-83	19-2-84	P 3555 Wakakura	29-10-84	26-3-[...]
P 3554 Kiwi	7-5-84	2-9-84	P 3556 Hinau	8-5-85	4-10-[...]

Moa (P 3553) — Leo Van Ginderen, [...]

D: 90 tons light (110.7 fl) **S:** 12 kts
Dim: 26.82 (24.38 wl) × 6.10 × 2.18
A: none **Electron Equipt:** Radar: 1/Decca . . . nav.
M: 2 Cummins KT-1150M diesels; 2 props; 730 bhp
Fuel: 11 tons **Range:** 1,000/12
Crew: 1 officer, 4 officer trainees, 10 enlisted (18 accom.)

PATROL CRAFT *(continued)*

Remarks: Ordered 11-2-82. Design derived from Australian 88-ft torpedo retriever; survey craft *Takapu* and *Tarapunga* and training craft *Kahu* are to same basic design. Can be fitted with 1/12.7-mm mg. Based as follows for naval reserve training: *Moa* at Dunedin, *Kiwi* at Lyttleton, *Wakakura* at Wellington, and *Hinau* at Auckland. In 1991, received sidescan sonars and enhanced navigation equipment to permit use as "Q-route" (cleared passage) mine survey boats and are planned to receive influence mine countermeasures gear at a later date. The similar *Kahu* (A 04) is also used for training.

Note: The four "Lake-"class patrol boats laid up in 1988–89 were put up for sale in 1990: *Pukaki* (P 3568), *Rotoiti* (P 3569), *Taupo* (P 3570), and *Hawea* (P 3571).

MINE COUNTERMEASURES SHIPS

Remarks: The R.N.Z.N. has long-range plans to acquire mine countermeasures ships during the 1990s. As an interim solution, the six *Moa/Takapu*-class craft and the survey ship *Monowai* have been outfitted with a mine location capability.

AMPHIBIOUS WARFARE SHIPS

Note: The program to construct a 160-meter vehicle and troop transport also capable of underway replenishment and disaster-relief work was halted in 8-90 but may be revived later; characteristics are given in the previous edition.

HYDROGRAPHIC SURVEY SHIPS

◆ **1 converted passenger-cargo ship**
Bldr: Grangemouth Dockyard (L: 4-60)

A 06 Monowai (ex-*Moana Roa*)

Ionowai (A 06) R.N.Z.N., 5-89

D: 4,027 tons (fl) **S:** 13.5 kts **Dim:** 90.33 (82.30 pp) × 14.02 × 5.21
A: 2/20-mm AA (I × 2)—1/HAS.1 Wasp helicopter
Electron Equipt:
Radar: 1/Decca 1290A nav., 1/Decca ARPA 1690S nav.
M: 2 Clark-Sulzer 7-cyl. diesels; 2 CP props; 3,640 bhp (3,080 sust.)—bow-thruster
Fuel: 300 tons **Range:** 12,000/13
Crew: 11 officers, 115 enlisted (12 female)

marks: Taken over from a government-run commercial service in 1974 and con-rted at Scott-Lithgow, Greenock, Scotland, 9-77 to 4-10-77. Telescoping helicopter hangar fitted. Two 10.36-meter and one 8.84-meter survey ft carried, as well as one Rotork "Sea Truck" workboat. Decca HiFix positioning tem and Omega radio navigational aids installed, as well as a navigational satellite eiver. One 4-ton crane. Side-scanning mapping sonar and other sophisticated survey ipment carried. Guns added 1980. Two "Phantom HDX" remote-operated submersi-s purchased in the U.S. in 2-87 to permit the ship to operate in a mine-clearance role; rance diver support gear also added by 4-87. Racal HADLAPS (Hydrographic tomatic Logging & Processing System) added 1988 to ship and her three survey nches. Predecessor *Lachlan*, a former U.K. "River"-class frigate, is used as a bar-ks hulk.

2 inshore survey craft Bldr: Whangarei Eng. Ltd., Auckland

	L	In serv.		L	In serv.
7 Takapu	5-6-80	8-7-80	A 08 Tarapunga	5-11-79	9-4-80

apu (A 07) Ross Gillett, 10-91

D: 90 tons (112.6 fl) **S:** 12 kts **Dim:** 26.82 (24.38 wl) × 6.10 × 2.18
Electron Equipt: Radar: 1/Decca . . . nav.
M: 2 Cummins KT-1150M diesels; 2 props; 730 bhp **Fuel:** 11 tons
Range: 1,000/12 **Crew:** 2 officers, 10 men

Remarks: Ordered 30-11-77. Similar to *Moa*-class patrol craft and training craft *Kahu*. Have Magnavox MX 1102 NAVSAT receiver, E.G. and G. Mk 1B sidescan sonar, Decca Trisponder position fixing, and Atlas Deso 10 echo-sounder. Used in "Q-route" mine survey work: planned to receive influence mine countermeasures equipment. Racal HADLAPS (see above entry) added during refits completed 7-91 (A 07) and 6-91 (A 08).

OCEANOGRAPHIC RESEARCH SHIP

◆ **1 ex.-U.S. Robert D. Conrad class** Bldr: Christy Corp., Sturgeon Bay, Wisconsin

	Laid down	L	In serv.
A 02 Tui (ex-*Charles H. Davis*, T-AGOR 5)	15-6-61	30-6-62	25-1-63

Tui (A 02) P. C. Hunt, 1-91

D: 1,219 tons (1,402 fl) **S:** 12 kts
Dim: 70.0 (63.7 pp) × 11.4 × 4.7 (6.3 max.)
Electron Equipt: Radar: 1/. . . nav.
M: 2 Caterpillar D-378 diesels, electric drive; 1 prop; 1,000 shp—175-shp bow-thruster
Electric: 850 kw **Fuel:** 211 tons **Range:** 12,000/12
Crew: 8 officers, 16 enlisted, 15 scientists

Remarks: Transferred on lease 28-7-70 and commissioned 11-9-70. Lease expires 7-95, at which time a replacement will be sought from the United States. Has been used in acoustics research for the New Zealand Defense Scientific Establishment, which modified the ship so that it could be used to lay and tow hydrophone arrays. Fitted with Ferranti FMS 15/2 towed passive linear hydrophone array 1989–91 for trials and has provision for laying lightweight cable. Has a 620-kw gas-turbine generator to drive the prop for quiet running.

SEAGOING DIVING TENDER

◆ **1 former oilfield diving ship** Bldr: Alexander Cochrane SB, Selby, Yorkshire, U.K. (In serv. 5-79)

A 09 Manawanui (ex-*Star Perseus*)

D: 911 tons (fl) **S:** 10.7 kts **Dim:** 43.97 (38.25 pp) × 9.86 × 3.31
A: none **Electron Equipt:** Radar: 2/Decca . . . nav.
M: 2 Caterpillar D379TA diesels; 2 CP props; 1,130 bhp 1/55-ton-thrust bow-thruster
Range: 5,000/10.7; 8,000/10 **Endurance:** 130 days
Crew: 2 officers, 22 enlisted

Manawanui (A 09) R.N.Z.N., 11-90

SEAGOING DIVING TENDER *(continued)*

Remarks: 480 grt/396 dwt oilfield service and diving tender purchased 3-88 from Star Offshore Service Marine, Ltd., and commissioned in R.N.Z.N. 5-4-88. Relieved the smaller *Manawanui* (now *Kahu*) as fleet diving tender on completion of six-week refit in New Zealand, late 1988. Capable of four-point mooring. Can support three divers working at 76 m and has a triple-lock decompression chamber. Electrohydraulic 13-ton crane on after deck and can carry 150 tons of deck cargo. Divers' stage to starboard.

REPLENISHMENT SHIP

◆ **1 small replenishment oiler** Bldr: Hyundai SY, Ulsan, S. Korea

	Laid down	L	In serv.
A 11 ENDEAVOUR	10-4-87	8-87	8-4-88

Endeavour (A 11) Percy Hunt, 1-92

D: 7,300 tons (12,300 fl) **S:** 14 kts
Dim: 138.05 (128.00) × 18.40 × 7.20 (4.50 light)
A: provision for 2/20-mm AA (I × 2)—1/HAS.1 Wasp helicopter
Electron Equipt:
Radar: 1/Decca-Racal RM-1290A/9 nav., 1 Decca-Racal ARPA-1690S nav.
EW: . . . intercept, 2 decoy RL
M: 1 Hyundai-Burmeister & Wain 12V-32/36 diesel; 1 CP prop; 5,300 bhp—LIPS 600-shp bow-thruster
Electric: 1,920 kw (3/600-kw alternators; 3 Daihatsu 6DL-20 890-bhp diesels); 1/120-kw Cummins emergency set
Range: 8,000/14 **Fuel:** 400 tons
Crew: 6 officers, 24 enlisted (35 accom.)

Remarks: 8,400 dwt/6,990 grt. Ordered 28-7-86. Cargo: 7,500 tons fuel, 120 tons aviation fuel in five tanks. Deck storage for four 20-ft refrigerated cargo containers. Fueling stations to port and starboard, plus over-the-stern fueling rig. Has Magnavox 2290 NAVSAT receiver. Helicopter hangar incorporated within starboard side of the superstructure. Launch and completion dates delayed by shipyard labor and machinery problems; was to have delivered 20-1-88. Left Ulsan 14-4-88 and arrived in New Zealand 25-5-88.

SERVICE CRAFT

◆ **1 leased large harbor tug** Bldr: . . .

WAITANGI

Waitangi Leo Van Ginderen, 10-91

D: 410 tons **S:** 12 kts **Dim:** 32.0 × 8.5 × 4.5
M: 2/10-cyl. diesels; 2 props; 1,720 bhp **Crew:** 4 tot.

Remarks: Lease through mid-1991 with option to buy or extend lease from Northland Harbour Board. Bollard pull: 21 tons.

◆ **1 harbor tug** Bldr: Price SY, Auckland (L: 1969)

A 10 ARATAKI (ex-*Aorangi*)

Arataki (A 10) Leo Van Ginderen, 10-91

D: 170 tons (264 fl) **S:** 12 kts **Dim:** 25.30 × 7.62 × 3.0
M: 1 Ruston 6ARM diesel; 1 prop; 1,100 bhp—bow-thruster
Crew: 4 tot.

Remarks: Purchased 26-10-84 from Timaru Harbour Board to replace earlier tu *Arataki* and commissioned 16-11-84. Has 16-ton bollard pull.

◆ **1 basic-training boat** Bldr: Whangarei Eng. Ltd.

	L	In serv.
A 04 KAHU (ex-*Manawanui*)	8-12-78	28-5-79

Kahu (A 04) Leo Van Ginderen, 10

D: 91.5 tons (110 fl) **S:** 12 kts **Dim:** 26.82 (24.38 wl) × 6.10 × 2.2
Electron Equipt: Radar: 1/Decca. . . nav.
M: 2 Cummins KT 1150M diesels; 2 props; 730 bhp
Range: 1,000/12 **Crew:** 16 max.

Remarks: Built as a diving tender; renamed and reassigned as a basic navigat and maneuvering training craft at HMNZS *Taranaki* training center on acquisiti the "new" *Manawanui* in 1988. Same basic design as the *Moa*-class patrol/trai craft and the survey craft *Takapu* and *Tarapunga* but has a light tripod mast derrick aft.

◆ **4 Chico-40-class sail-training sloops** (all L: 21-5-90)

6911 PAEA II 6912 MAKO II 6913 MANGA II 6914 HAKU II

D: 7.3 tons (fl) **S:** 7 kts (under power)
Dim: 12.00 (9.80 wl) × 3.90 × 2.00
M: 1 diesel; 1 prop; . . . bhp—80 m^2 sail area **Crew:** 10 max.

Remarks: Kept at R.N.Z.N. *Devonport*, Auckland, for proficiency training and ation.

◆ **1 workboat** Bldr: Miller & Tunnage, Port Chalmers (In serv. 1976)

MEOLA

D: 6 tons **S:** 9 kts **Dim:** 13.1 × . . . × . . .
M: 1/4-cyl. Gardner diesel; . . . bhp

NEW ZEALAND *(continued)*
SERVICE CRAFT *(continued)*

Meola Ross Gillett, 10-91

Remarks: Transferred from Ministry of Public Works 1976. Used as diving tender and general tender to naval headquarters.

♦ **2 personnel launches** (In serv. 1966–67)

MATAMUA MAHANGA

D: . . . tons **S:** 9 kts **Dim:** 15.9 × 4.8 × . . .
M: 1 diesel; . . . bhp

♦ **1 100-ton capacity self-propelled floating crane** (In serv. 1988)

HIKINUI

ikinui Leo Van Ginderen, 10-91

1 air-support training craft Bldr: Naval DY, HMNZS *Philomel* (In serv. 4-84)

ATUA

D: 8 tons **S:** 14 kts **Dim:** 12.0 × . . . × . . . **Crew:** 2–4 tot.
M: 2 Perkins diesels; 2 props; . . . bhp **Range:** 200/14

marks: Used for parachute recovery, helo winch training, diver support, patrol, d rescue duties at Naval Air Support Unit, Hobsonville. Plywood hull. The same ;anization also operates two 12.2-m, 16-kt. crash boats and one 10-m, 8-kt. personnel nch.

DEPARTMENT OF SCIENTIFIC AND INDUSTRIAL RESEARCH

on-naval New Zealand government agency headquartered at Wellington.

1 oceanographic research ship Bldr: Seebeckwerft A.G.Weser, Bremerhaven

PUHIA (ex-*Meteor*) (In serv. 1963)

): 2,800 tons **S:** 14 kts **Dim:** 82.1 (77.3 pp) × 13.5 × 5.2
I: diesel-electric; 3,765 shp **Crew:** 52 crew + 24 scientists

narks: Elaborately equipped for oceanographic and hydrometeorological re- ·ch. Acquired 12-85 and sailed for New Zealand 14-6-87, having traveled over 000 n.m. in West German service. Red hull, white upperworks.

NICARAGUA

ublic of Nicaragua

onnel (1991): Approximately 3,500 total (including 2,000 naval infantry)

: With the discontinuation of support from the former U.S.S.R. and North Korea, ondition of most of the craft listed below is deteriorating.

PATROL CRAFT

♦ **9 North Korean Sin Hung-class former torpedo boats**

GC-400–406, GC-408, GC-410

D: 25 tons **S:** 40 kts **Dim:** 18.3 × 3.4 × 1.7
A: 4/14.5-mm mg (II × 2)
M: 2 M50-series diesels, 2 props; 2,400 bhp **Crew:** 10 tot.

Remarks: Torpedo boats, with tubes deleted. First two delivered 10-83, two in 1984, six more in 3-89. One had been deleted by 1991, and the others are likely to follow shortly. Have a stepped hydroplane hull.

♦ **2 North Korean Kimjin class**

GC-306 GC-308

D: 25 tons (fl) **S:** 42 kts
Dim: 20.3 × 3.4 × 1.7 **A:** 4/14.5-mm mg (II × 2)
M: 2 M50-series diesels; 2 props; 2,400 bhp
Range: 220/20 **Crew:** 10 tot.

Remarks: Transferred in the early 1980s. Two others have been discarded. Stepped hydroplane hull. Previously misidentified as ex-Bulgarian P-4-class torpedo boats.

♦ **1 French 28.2-meter class** Bldr: C.N. de l'Estérel (In serv. 2-9-83)

D: 57 tons (fl) **S:** 24 kts **Dim:** 28.2 × 5.2 × 1.6
A: 4/14.5-mm mg (II × 2) **Range:** 800/15 **Crew:** 12 tot.
M: 2 SACM AGO diesels; 2 props; 1,500 bhp

Remarks: Two ordered 12-81 for customs duties. Launched 6-9-83 and 26-5-83; delivered 24-6-83. Wooden construction. Sister *El Tayacan* lost 25-2-84 to a mine at El Bluff. Hull number is in 300 series. Original armament of two single 20-mm AA replaced by Soviet-supplied weapons.

♦ **8 Soviet Zhuk class**

GC-304 GC-307 GC-311 GC-315
GC-305 GC-309 GC-313 GC-317

D: 48 tons (60 fl) **S:** 34 kts **Dim:** 24.0 × 5.0 × 1.2 (1.8 props)
A: 4/14.5-mm mg (II × 2)
Electron Equipt: Radar: 1/Spin Trough nav.
M: 2 M50 diesels; 2 props; 2,400 bhp
Range: 700/28; 1,100/15 **Fuel:** 10 tons **Crew:** 12 tot.

Remarks: First unit transferred 4-82 via Algeria; second unit delivered 24-7-83, third in 1984, fourth and fifth early in 1986, sixth through eighth late 1986, early 1987, and three delivered 9-89 from Cuba. Have side-by-side, enclosed machine-gun mountings. Three have been retired to date.

♦ **2 Israeli Dabur class** Bldr: Israeli Aircraft Industries (In serv. 5-78)

GC-231 GC-235

D: 25 tons (35 fl) **S:** 19.6 kts **Dim:** 19.79 × 5.40 × 1.75
A: 2/20-mm AA (I × 2)—2/12.7-mm mg (I × 2)
M: 2 G.M. 12V72 diesels; 2 props; 960 bhp
Electric: 20 kw **Range:** 700/16 **Crew:** 6 tot.

Remarks: One sister lost 4-85 to gunfire from Honduran units. Two larger *Dvora*-class patrol craft were also ordered from Israel, but their delivery was embargoed in 1979 at the request of the U.S. government. May have been rearmed with Soviet-supplied weapons.

MINE WARFARE CRAFT

♦ **4 Yevgenya-class inshore minesweepers** Bldr: Sudostroitel'noye Obyedineniye "Almaz" (Sredniy Neva), Kolpino (In serv. 1984–. . .)

BM-501 BM-503 BM-504 BM-506

D: 80 tons (90 fl) **S:** 11 kts **Dim:** 26.2 × 6.1 × 1.5
A: 2/25-mm AA2M-8 Type (II × 1)
Electron Equipt:
Radar: 1/Spin Trough nav.—IFF: High Pole B transponder
M: 2 diesels; 2 props; 600 bhp **Range:** 300/10
Crew: 1 officer, 9 enlisted (+ 2–3 clearance divers)

Remarks: Two delivered via Cuba in 10-84, two later. Glass-reinforced plastic hull. Employ a television minehunting system useful to 30-m depths that dispenses marker buoys to permit later disposal of mines. Two based on each coast.

♦ **4 Polish K-8-class minesweeping boats** Bldr: Stocznia Pólnocna, Gdańsk (In serv. 1954–59)

BM-500 BM-502 BM-581 BM-583

D: 19.4 tons (26 fl) **S:** 12 kts **Dim:** 16.9 × 3.2 × 0.8
A: 2/14.5-mm mg (II × 1) **Range:** 300/9
M: 2 3D6 diesels; 2 props; 300 bhp **Crew:** 6 tot.

Remarks: Transferred 11-84. Wooden construction. Tow, but do not carry, wire sweeps.

AMPHIBIOUS WARFARE CRAFT

♦ **2 tank-landing lighters** Bldr: Damen, Gorinchem, Netherlands (In serv. 1985)

D: . . . **S:** 9 kts **Dim:** 45.8 × 9.5 × 2.5
M: 2 diesels; 2 props; 714 bhp

NIGERIA

Republic of Nigeria

Personnel (1991): 550 officers, 4,500 men

Naval Aviation: Three Lynx Mk 89 ASW helicopters with Gem 3, 1,128-hp turbines for use aboard N.N.S. *Aradu* and two Bo-105 light helicopters for shore-based liaison. The air force has four Fokker F 27 Maritime patrol aircraft, delivered 1983–84 for coastal surveillance, six Dornier DO128-6MPA twin-engine aircraft that are used for coastal patrol and smuggling interdiction, and 20 MBB BO-105C light helicopters that can be used for search-and-rescue work.

FRIGATES

♦ 1 MEKO 360-H class   Bldr: Blohm + Voss, Hamburg, Germany

	Laid down	L	In serv.
F 89 ARADU (ex-*Republic*)	2-5-79	25-1-80	22-2-82

Aradu (F 89) Hartmut Ehlers, 9-87

D: 3,680 tons (fl) **S:** 30.5 kts
Dim: 125.9 (119.0 pp) × 15.0 (14.0 wl) × 4.32 (5.8 props)
A: 8/Otomat Mk 1 SSM (I × 8)—1/127-mm 54-cal. OTO Melara DP—1/Albatros Mk 2 Mod. 9 SAM syst. (VIII × 1, 24 Aspide missiles)—8/40-mm Breda AA (II × 4)—6/324-mm Plessey STWS-1BASW TT (III × 2, 18 A244S torpedoes)—1/d.c. rack—1/Lynx Mk 89 ASW helicopter
Electron Equipt:
Radar: 1/Decca 1226 nav., 1/Plessey AWS-5D air search, 1/H.S.A. WM-25 gun f.c., 1/H.S.A. STIR-18 missile illumination for Aspide
Sonar: 1/Krupp-Atlas DSQS-21 hull-mounted MF
EW: Decca RDL-2 intercept, RCM-2 jammer—2/Breda SCLAR 105-mm decoy RL (XX × 2)
M: CODOG: 2 Rolls-Royce Olympus TM-3B gas turbines, 50,000 shp; 2 MTU 20V956 TB92 diesels, 11,070 bhp; 2/5-bladed CP props
Electric: 4,120 kVA **Fuel:** 440 tons **Range:** 4,500/18
Crew: 26 officers, 169 enlisted, 35 cadets

Remarks: Ordered 3-11-77. Renamed 1-11-80; name means "Thunder." Arrived at Lagos 21-12-81. Ran aground in Congo River 7-87, collided with pier 8-87 at Lagos, and also suffered a collision at sea the same year. Began refit at Victoria Island Naval Dockyard, Lagos, in 10-90 for completion late in 1991.

Similar ships (but with COGOG propulsion, two helicopters, and different electronics) built for Argentina. Makes use of modular containers for electronics and weapon systems. Carries 460 rounds of 127-mm ammunition, 10,752 rounds of 40-mm ammunition, and 120 chaff rounds for the Elsag/Breda chaff rocket launchers. Has H.S.A. SEWACO-BV combat data system and H.S.A. Vesta ASW torpedo f.c.s. Current sonar replaced the original H.S.A. PHS-32 set.

♦ 1 training frigate

	Bldr	Laid down	L	In serv.
F 87 OBUMA (ex-*Nigeria*)	Wilton-Fijenoord, Schiedam, Netherlands	9-4-64	12-4-65	16-9-66

Obuma (F 87) Hartmut Ehlers, 6-83

D: 1,724 tons (2,000 fl) **S:** 25 kts
Dim: 109.85 (104.0 pp) × 11.3 × 3.35
A: 2/102-mm 45-cal Mk 19 DP (II × 1)—4/40-mm AA (I × 4)
Electron Equipt:
Radar: 1/Decca . . . nav., 1/Plessey AWS-4 air-search
M: 4 M.A.N. VV24/30B diesels; 2 props; 16,000 bhp
Range: 3,500/15 **Crew:** 216 tot.

Remarks: Renamed 1981. Refit by Cammell Laird, 1970–71, and again by builder in 1977. By late 1980s was little more than a hulk and has not been refitted since. Only a simple lead-computing director is fitted for the 102-mm gun mount. Acts as pierside training ship. Helicopter platform serves primarily as a ceremonial deck. Modernization, delayed since 1983, was to include replacing the 102-mm mount with an OTO Melara 76-mm Compact and adding an optronic f.c.s. and decoy rocket launchers. Former Squid ASW mortar and sonar sets deleted.

CORVETTES

♦ 2 Erin'mi class (Vosper Mk 9)   Bldr: Vosper Thornycroft, Portsmouth, U.K.

	Laid down	L	In serv.
F 83 ERIN'MI	14-10-75	20-1-77	29-1-80
F 84 ENYMIRI	11-2-77	9-2-78	2-5-80

Enymiri (F 84) Hartmut Ehlers, 7-

D: 850 tons (fl) **S:** 27 kts
Dim: 69.0 (64.0 pp) × 9.6 × 3.0 (3.6 max.)
A: 1/76-mm 62-cal. OTO Melara DP—1/Sea Cat SAM system (III × 1 15 missiles)—1/40-mm Bofors AA—2/20-mm Oerlikon AA (I × 2)—1/375-mm Bofors ASW RL (II × 1)
Electron Equipt:
Radar: 1/Decca TM 1226 nav., 1/Plessey AWS-2 air search, 1/H.S.A WM-24 f.c.
Sonar: 1/Plessey PMS-26 hull-mounted MF (10 kHz)
EW: Decca Cutlass intercept, 2/Protean decoy RL (CXLIV × 2)
M: 4 MTU 20V956 TB92 diesels; 2 CP props; 20,512 bhp
Electric: 889 kw (3 × 260 kw MTU 6V51 sets, 1 × 109-kw emergency set)
Range: 2,200/14 **Endurance:** 10 days **Crew:** 90 tot.

Remarks: Can sustain 20 kts on two diesels. Carry 750 rounds 76-mm ammunit 24 rounds ASW rockets. Have 2/50-mm flare launchers. Funnel heightened on F after initial trials. Both names are local words for "hippopotamus." Both in margi condition with many systems inoperative by 1989.

♦ 1 Dorina (Vosper Mk 3) class   Bldr: Vosper Thornycroft, Portsmouth, U.K.

	Laid down	L	In serv.
F 82 OTOBO	28-9-70	25-5-71	11-72

Otobo (F 82)—in refit at Genoa Antonio Srimali,

CORVETTES *(continued)*

D: 650 tons (fl) **S:** 22 kts **Dim:** 61.57 (55.40 pp) × 7.45 × 3.35 max.
A: 1/40-mm Bofors AA (*see* Remarks)
Electron Equipt: Radar: 2/. . . navigational
M: 2 diesels; 2 props; approx. 4,400 bhp **Electric:** 600 kw
Range: 3,500/14 **Fuel:** 68 tons **Crew:** approx. 60 tot.

Remarks: Had been stricken 4-87 after fumigation had caused excessive corrosion; sister *Dorina* (F 81) sank at moorings 16-4-87, was raised 18-5-87, and now is damage-control training hulk at Sapele. Decision was reached to refit and modernize *Otobo*, and she arrived in Italy 21-4-88 via deckship for what was intended to be a two-year overhaul at OARN, Genoa, during which the ship was to be reconfigured as an offshore patrol vessel. The original twin 102-mm Mk 19 DP mount forward was to be replaced by a 40-mm mount (although an OTO Melara 76-mm mount may be installed instead), and the original Decca TM 1226, Plessey AWS-1, and H.S.A. M22 radars were to be replaced by two navigational/surface-search sets; the two M.A.N. V8V 24/30-B diesels were to be replaced with new engines. No ASW ordnance was ever carried, and the Plessey MS-22 sonar has been removed. As of 2-92, however, the work was far from complete, largely because payments had not been received from Nigeria.

GUIDED-MISSILE PATROL BOATS

◆ **3 Combattante-IIIB class** Bldr: CMN, Cherbourg, France

	Laid down	L	In serv.
181 Siri	15-5-79	3-6-80	19-2-81
182 Ayam	7-9-79	10-11-80	11-6-81
183 Ekun	14-11-79	11-2-81	18-9-81

ri (P 181)—when operational CMN, 1981

(P 181) and Ekun (P 183)—ashore in France Bernard Prézelin, 7-91

: 376 tons light (430 fl) **S:** 37 kts
im: 56.0 (53.0 pp) × 8.16 (7.61 wl) × 2.15 (hull)
: 4/MM 38 Exocet SSM (II × 2)—1/76-mm 62-cal. OTO Melara DP—2/40-mm Breda AA (II × 1)—4/30-mm Emerlec AA (II × 2)
lectron Equipt:
Radar: 1/Decca 1226 nav., 1/Thomson-CSF Triton air/surf. search, 1/Thomson-CSF Castor II gun f.c.
EW: Decca RDL intercept
: 4 MTU 16V956 TB92 diesels; 4 props; 20,840 bhp (17,320 sust.)
ange: 2,000/15 **Crew:** 42 tot.

arks: Ordered 11-77. Remained at Cherbourg until 9-5-82 because of payment te. Official commissioning date was 6-2-82 for all. Refitted 1986–88 by builder, e ships remained in France through 4-92 because of non-payment for the work. Thomson-CSF Vega gun and missile f.c.s., with 2 CSEE Panda optical irectors also fitted. The U.S.-made 30-mm guns have a range of 6 km and fire at rds/min per mount.

FPB 57 class Bldr: Friedrich Lürssen Werft, Vegesack, Germany

	Laid down	L	In serv.
3 Ekpe	17-2-79	17-12-79	8-80
Damisa	17-2-79	27-3-79	4-81
Agu	17-2-79	7-11-80	4-81

Damisa (P 179) Lürssen, 4-81

Agu (P 180) and a sister Gerhard Koop, 11-83

D: 373 tons (436 fl) **S:** 35 kts
Dim: 58.1 (54.4 wl) × 7.62 × 2.83 (props)
A: 4/Otomat Mk 1 (I × 4)—1/76-mm 62-cal. OTO Melara DP—2/40-mm Breda-Bofors AA (II × 1)—4/30-mm Emerlec AA (II × 2)
Electron Equipt:
Radar: 1/Decca TM 1226C nav., 1/H.S.A. WM-28 track-while-scan f.c.
EW: Decca RDL intercept
M: 4 MTU 16V956 TB92 diesels; 4 props; 20,840 bhp (17,320 sust.)
Electric: 405 kVA **Range:** 1,600/32; 3,000/16 **Crew:** 40 tot.

Remarks: Ordered late 1977. Sailed for Nigeria 21-8-81. Navigation systems include Decca Mk 21 "Navigator" NAVSAT receiver, Omega receiver, and Marconi "Lodestone" D/F. Made 42 kts on trials. Refitted by builders, 1983–84; P 180 badly damaged during 1984, losing 76-mm mount. Last refitted 1984. All in marginal operating condition by 1987.

PATROL BOATS

Note: See also Coast Guard section.

◆ **4 Makurdi class** Bldr: Brooke Marine Ltd., Lowestoft, U.K.

	L	In serv.
P 167 Makurdi	21-3-74	14-8-74
P 168 Hadejia	25-5-74	14-8-74
P 171 Jebba	1-12-76	29-4-77
P 172 Oguta	17-1-77	29-4-77

Hadejia (P 168) Brooke Marine, 1982

D: 115 tons (143 fl) **S:** 20.5 kts **Dim:** 32.6 × 6.1 × 3.5
A: 4/30-mm Emerlec AA (II × 2)
Electron Equipt: Radar: 1/Decca 1226 nav.
M: 2 Ruston-Paxman YJCM diesels; 2 props; 3,000 bhp
Fuel: 18 tons **Range:** 2,300/12 **Crew:** 4 officers, 20 enlisted

Remarks: First two refitted by builders, 1981–82, others refitted in Nigeria; rearmed, engines overhauled. Originally had 2/40-mm AA (I × 2).

◆ **4 Argundu class** Bldr: Abeking & Rasmussen, Lemwerder, Germany

	L	In serv.
P 165 Argundu	4-7-73	10-74
P 166 Yola	12-6-73	10-74
P 169 Bras	12-1-76	3-76
P 170 Epe	9-2-76	3-76

PATROL BOATS *(continued)*

Yola (P 166) and Bras (P 169) Peter Voss, 3-82

D: 90 tons **S:** 20 kts **Dim:** 32.0 (29.0 pp) × 6.0 × 1.7
A: 4/30-mm Emerlec AA (II × 2)
Electron Equipt: Radar: 1/Decca 1229 nav.
M: 2 MTU diesels; 2 props; 2,070 bhp **Range:** . . . **Crew:** 25 tot.

Remarks: Refitted 1981–82 by builders; originally had 1/40-mm AA, 1/20-mm AA.

MINE COUNTERMEASURES SHIPS

♦ **2 Italian Lerici class** Bldr: Intermarine, Sarzana

	Laid down	L	Delivered	In serv.
M 371 OHUE	23-7-84	22-11-85	28-5-87	4-88
M 372 MARABA	11-3-85	6-6-86	25-2-88	4-88

Maraba (M 372) Carlo Martinelli, 6-87

D: 470 tons (550 fl) **S:** 15.5 kts
Dim: 51.00 (46.50 pp) × 9.56 × 2.80
A: 2/30-mm Emerlec AA (II × 1)—2/20-mm Oerlikon GAM-B01 AA (I × 2)
Electron Equipt:
Radar: 1/3 ST7/DG nav.
Sonar: Thomson-Sintra TSM 1022 hull-mounted HF
M: 2 MTU 12V396 TC83 diesels; 2 Turbomeccanica PG2000 waterjets; 2,840 bhp
Electric: 600 kw (2 × 300 kw, MTU 6V396 TC diesels driving)
Range: 2,500/12 **Endurance:** 14 days
Crew: 5 officers, 145 enlisted

Remarks: First ship ordered 9-4-83, second in 5-84, with option for two more (not taken up); difficulties in obtaining an export license delayed delivery. Glass-reinforced plastic construction throughout. For free running, the swiveling waterjets are locked centerline, and twin rudders are used for steering; when minehunting, the waterjets are swiveled for steering. Range at 12 kts can be extended to 4,000 n.m. by using the passive roll stabilization tanks as fuel tanks. Can support 6–7 mine-disposal divers. Carry two Gaymarine Pluto remote-controlled minehunting submersibles, Oropesa Mk 4 mechanical sweep gear, Thomson-CSF IBIS-V minehunting control system. Have Galeazzi two-man decompression chambers for mine-disposal divers.

AMPHIBIOUS WARFARE SHIPS

♦ **2 German Type-502 landing ships** Bldr: Howaldtswerke, Hamburg

	Laid down	L	In serv.
L 1312 AMBE	3-3-78	7-7-78	11-5-79
L 1313 OFIOM	15-9-78	7-12-78	7-79

D: 1,190 tons light (1,470 normal, 1,750 fl) **S:** 17 kts
Dim: 86.9 (74.5 pp) × 14.0 × 2.30
A: 1/40-mm 70-cal. Breda AA—2/20-mm Oerlikon GAM-B01 AA (I × 2)
Electron Equipt: Radar: 1/Decca 1226 nav. **Electric:** 900 kw
M: 2 MTU 16V956 TB92 diesels; 4 props; 7,000 bhp
Range: 5,000/12
Crew: 6 officers, 53 enlisted, plus 540 troops (1,000 for short distances)

Ambe (L 1312) Leo Van Ginderen, 197[illegible]

Remarks: Cargo: 400 tons vehicles plus troops (typically: 5/40-ton tanks or 7/18-ton tanks plus 4/45-ton trucks). Articulated bow ramp, short stern ramp for loading from a pier. Can fit an 81-mm mortar forward. Each engine drives two props. Bow ramp on L 1312 now welded shut.

HYDROGRAPHIC SHIPS

♦ **1 British Bulldog class** Bldr: Brooke Marine Ltd., Lowestoft, U.K.

	Laid down	L	In serv.
A 498 LANA	5-4-74	4-3-76	15-7-76

Lana (A 498) Hartmut Ehlers, 12

D: 800 tons (1,100 fl) **S:** 15 kts
Dim: 60.95 (57.80 pp) × 11.43 × 3.70
A: 2/20-mm Oerlikon AA (I × 2)
Electron Equipt: Radar: 1/Decca 1226 nav.
M: 4 Lister-Blackstone ERS-8-M diesels; 2 KaMeWa CP props; 2,640 bhp
Electric: 880 kw **Range:** 4,000/12 **Crew:** 5 officers, 34 enlisted

Remarks: Can carry one 8.7-meter survey launch. Has passive tank stabiliza[tion] system.

♦ **1 coastal survey craft** Bldr: Akerboom, Leiden, the Netherlands

	L	In serv.
MURTULA MUHAMED	14-8-76	28-9-76

Murtula Muhammed Hartmut Ehlers,

D: 13 tons **S:** 9 kts **Dim:** 11.75 × 3.5 × 1.0
M: 1 Perkins 6-354M diesel; 1 prop; 75 bhp

TRAINING SHIP

♦ **1 training ship** Bldr: Van Lent, Kaag, the Netherlands (In serv. 10

A 497 RUWAN YARO (ex-*Ogina Bereton*)

TRAINING SHIP *(continued)*

Ruwan Yaro (A 497) Hartmut Ehlers, 12-83

D: 400 tons (fl) **S:** 17 kts **Dim:** 50.0 (44.2 pp) × 8.0 × 2.0
A: none **Electron Equipt:** Radar: 1/Decca TM 1626 nav.
M: 2 Deutz SBA 12M528 diesels; 1 CP prop; 3,000 bhp—bow-thruster
Range: 3,000/15 **Fuel:** 64 tons
Crew: 31 tot. + 11 in officers' training

Remarks: Purchased 1976. Originally a private yacht; has a glass-reinforced plastic hull.

SERVICE CRAFT

◆ **1 large harbor tug** Bldr: Scheepswerf de Wiel BV, Asperen, the Netherlands

A 499 Commander Apayi Joe (In serv. 9-83)

Commander Apayi Joe (A 499) Leo Van Ginderen, 7-87

D: 310 tons (fl) **S:** 11 kts **Dim:** 23.17 × 7.19 × 2.91
M: 2 M.A.N. diesels; 2 props; 1,510 bhp

Remarks: 130 grt. Sister *Commander Rudolf* (A 500) was completed but not paid for was retained by the builder for commercial use.

◆ **3 Dutch Sea Truck tenders** Bldr: Damen, Gorinchem (In serv. 10-85)

P 239 P 240 P 242

D: . . . tons **S:** 20 kts
Dim: 14.50 × 4.40 × 0.8 **A:** 1/7.62-mm mg
M: 2 MTU diesels; 2 props, 1,200 bhp **Crew:** 8 tot.

Remarks: Aluminum construction, bow ramp for beaching. P 242 used for inshore survey.

P 242—used for inshore survey Hartmut Ehlers, 12-85

◆ **1 water lighter**

Water Barge One

Note: There are also 44 service launches built by Fairey Marine, Hamble: 2 × 10 m, 22 × 7 m, 15 × 6.7 m, and 5 × 5.5 m. Four Cheverton 8.2-m launches are also in use. Eight flight refueling "Sea Flash" 8.5-m, radio-controlled target boats were delivered in 1987. Two 11.75-m torpedo retrievers were delivered by Crestitalia, Ameglia, in 1986. Damen SY, Gorinchem, delivered two 27-m fuel lighters and two small "Pushy-Cat 46" tugs early in 1986 for naval use.

NIGERIAN COAST GUARD

Note: The Coast Guard is under the operational control of the Nigerian Navy, and naval personnel man its craft. One patrol craft was lost 24-7-90, class unknown.

PATROL CRAFT

◆ **2 P2000-class** Bldr: Steelship, Truro, Scotland (In serv. 1988)

P 225 Okrika P 226 Abonnema

D: 45 tons (49 fl) **S:** 30 kts **Dim:** 21.80 (19.00 wl) × 5.80 × 1.50
A: 1/20-mm Rheinmetall AA—2/7.62-mm mg (I × 2)
Electron Equipt: Radar: 1/Decca . . .
M: 2 MTU 8V396 TB93 diesels; 2 props; 2,600 bhp (2,176 sust.)
Range: 660/22 **Crew:** . . .

Remarks: Watercraft design; GRP construction. Ordered 25-1-85, but completion delayed by Watercraft's bankruptcy.

◆ **6 Type SM-5115** Bldr: Simonneau, Fontenay-le-Comte, France (In serv. 1986–87)

P 233 P 234 P 235 P 236 P 237 P 238

P 234 Simonneau, 1986

D: 22 tons (25 fl) **S:** 33 kts **Dim:** 15.80 × 4.60 × 0.90
A: 2/7.62-mm mg (I × 2)
Electron Equipt: Radar: 1/Decca 976 nav.
M: 2 MTU 6V396 TC82DE diesels; 2 props; 2,400 bhp
Range: 375/25 **Crew:** 6 tot.

Remarks: Aluminum construction. First delivered 5-86, second in 6-86.

◆ **6 Stan Pat-1500 patrol craft** Bldr: Damen, Gorinchem, the Netherlands

P 227–229 (In serv. 4-86) P 230–232 (In serv. 6-86)

P 230 Leo Van Ginderen, 8-87

PATROL CRAFT *(continued)*

D: 16 tons (fl) **S:** 32 kts
Dim: 15.11 (13.57 wl) × 4.45 × 1.40 (0.75 mean hull)
A: 1/7.62-mm mg **Electron Equipt:** Radar: 1/Decca . . . nav.
M: 2 MTU 6V331 TC82 diesels; 2 props; 2,250 bhp
Fuel: 2 m^3 **Crew:** 6 tot.

Remarks: At least one (P 230) remained in the Netherlands as late as 8-87.

◆ **4 65-ft Commercial Cruiser class** Bldr: Swiftships, Inc., Morgan City, La. (In serv. 24-2-86)

P 221 Iseyin P 222 Eruwa P 223 Afikto P 224 Aba

Aba (P 224) Skeets Photo/Swiftships, 12-85

D: 36 tons (fl) **S:** 32 kts **Dim:** 19.96 × 5.59 × 1.52
A: . . . **Electron Equipt:** Radar: 1/Raytheon 1210 nav.
M: 2 MTU 8V396 TB93 diesels; 2 props; 2,176 bhp (sust.)
Range: 500/18 **Electric:** 20 kw **Crew:** 6 tot.

Remarks: Aluminum construction.

◆ **5 Millspeed P/20 class** Bldr: Van Mill Marine Service, Hardinxveld-Giessendam

P 215 (In serv. 11-9-85)
P 216 (In serv. 11-9-85)
P 217 (In serv. 14-12-85)
P 218 (In serv. 14-12-85)
P 219 (In serv. 17-1-86)

P 215 Van Mill, 1985

D: 45 tons (fl) **S:** 35+ kts **Dim:** 20.20 (18.00 wl) × 5.30 × 1.75
A: 1/20-mm Rheinmetall AA—2/7.62-mm mg (I × 2)
Electron Equipt: Radar: 1/Decca . . . nav.
M: P 215, 216: 3 G.M. 12V71 TI diesels; 3 props; 2,100 bhp; P 217–219: 2 MTU 6V331 TC82 diesels; 2 props; 2,250 bhp
Range: 950/25; 1,200/11 **Crew:** 2 officers, 10 enlisted

Remarks: GRP construction. Sister P 220 presented to Equatorial Guinea, 27-6-86.

◆ **7 Type Mk 2 AM class** Bldr: Intermarine, La Spezia, Italy

	In serv.		In serv.
P 200 Abeokuta	7-81	P 206 Iloren	11-81
P 202 Bauchi	7-81	P 207 Jos	11-81
P 203 Benin City	7-81	P 208 Kaduna	11-81
P 205 Ikeja	9-81		

Maidugiri (P 210)—outboard *Ikeja* (P 205) Hartmut Ehlers, 11-8

D: 22 tons (fl) **S:** 32 kts (28 sust.) **Dim:** 16.80 × 4.50 × 1.00 max.
A: 1/20-mm AA—2/7.62-mm mg (I × 2)
Electron Equipt: Radar: 1/Decca . . . nav.
M: 2 MTU 8V331 TB91 diesels; 2 Castoldi waterjets; 2,700 bhp
Electric: 6 kw **Range:** 400/28 **Crew:** 6 tot.

Remarks: Ordered 10-78. Glass-reinforced plastic construction. Sister *Port Harcou* (P 213) lost 1984. Survivors refitted by builder, 1986. By 1988 sisters *Enugu* (P 204 *Kano* (P 209), *Maidugiri* (P 210), *Minno* (P 211), *Ourerri* (P 212), and *Sokoto* (P 21 were inoperable, stored ashore, and apparently beyond repair; sister *Akure* (P 201) employed as a display.

MARINE POLICE

Note: Used for operations on the Niger River and Lake Chad. All craft built glass-reinforced plastic. Present operability of all craft uncertain.

PATROL AND SERVICE CRAFT

◆ **6 14-m patrol craft** Bldr: Schottel, Warmond, the Netherlands (In serv 1982)

◆ **4 8-m patrol craft** Bldr: Copeland, U.K. (In serv. 1982)

◆ **12 9.8-m patrol craft** Bldr: Halmatic, Havant, U.K. (In serv. 1982–83)

D: 5.5 tons (6.5 fl) **S:** 25 kts **Dim:** 9.8 (8.8 wl) × 3.4 × 0.9
M: 2 Mermaid diesels; 2 props; 360 bhp **Crew:** 4–6 tot.

◆ **13 Skua Q33-class patrol craft** Bldr: Horne Bros., Fishbourne, U.K (In serv. 1981–82)

D: 5 tons (fl) **S:** 30 kts **Dim:** 7.9 × 2.8 × 0.4 **Crew:** 2–4 tot.
M: 2 Volvo Penta AQAD-40/280 diesels; 2 outdrive props; 310 bhp

◆ **1 P 1200-class patrol craft** Bldr: Watercraft, Ltd., Shoreham, U.K. (serv. 2-81)

D: 9.7 tons (fl) **S:** 27 kts **Dim:** 11.9 × 4.1 × 1.1
M: 2 G.M. 8V71 TI diesels; 2 props; 480 bhp **Range:** 240/25

◆ **5 P 800-class patrol craft** Bldr: Watercraft, Shoreham, U.K. (In serv 12-80)

D: 3.2 tons (fl) **S:** 26 kts **Dim:** 8.0 × 2.6 × 0.8
M: 1 Volvo AQAD-40 outdrive diesel; 1 prop; 150 bhp
Range: 104/26

◆ **10 Tiger-class air-cushion vehicles** Bldr: Air Vehicles, Cowes, U. (In serv.: 5 in 8-82; 5 in 1984–85)

D: 1 ton (fl) **S:** 34 kts **Dim:** 8.45 × 4.57 × 2.81 (high)
A: 1 diesel engine; 1 lift fan/1 prop; 200 bhp **Crew:** 12 tot.

◆ **2 Skima-12 hovercraft** Bldr: Pindair, U.K. (In serv. 1982)

◆ **3 Q26-class landing craft** Bldr: Horne Bros., Fishbourne, U.K. (In serv. 1982)

D: 17 tons (fl) **S:** 35 kts **Dim:** 10.0 × 3.5 × 0.75
A: 2/7.62-mm mg (I × 2) **Crew:** 2 crew, plus 24 police troops
M: 2 Sabre diesels; 2 props; 500 bhp

◆ **8 7-meter work boats** Bldr: Fairey Marine, Hamble, U.K. (In serv. 1982)

CUSTOMS SERVICE

◆ **1 patrol boat** Bldr: Chung Mu SY, Hong Kong (In serv. 14-9-83)

Yan-Yan

D: 100 tons (fl) **S:** 27.5 kts **Dim:** 34.0 (32.0 wl) × 6.0 × 1.34
A: . . . **M:** 2 MTU 12V396 TB93 diesels; 2 props; 3,560 bhp
Fuel: 13 tons **Crew:** 12 tot.

◆ **6 Watercraft 18-ton, 13-meter, 18-kt patrol craft** (In serv. 1982

NORWAY

Kingdom of Norway

Personnel (1991): 2,500 officers, 400 officer candidates, 5,000 enlisted ratings, and 2,000 civilians. About 860 personnel were serving on board ships and craft. The total number of naval personnel is to be cut by about 20 percent by 1995.

Naval Aviation: The Royal Norwegian Navy itself operates no aircraft. Six WG-13 Lynx helicopters are used by the Coast Guard. The Royal Norwegian Air Force can use its F-16 fighters in a maritime strike rôle, using Penguin Mk 3 missiles. In addition, it operates 8 Westland Sea King Mk 43, 1 Mk 43A, and 20 Bell UH-1D helicopters in search-and-rescue duties; an additional Sea King Mk 43B was ordered 8-89, and the others are being modernized (Mk 43B) by Westland. Of the former seven P-3B Orions used for maritime patrol, five have been sold to Spain, and the other two now support the Coast Guard. Four P-3C Orion ordered 9-6-87 were to deliver during 1989.

Coastal Defenses: Norway's coastline near important ports and harbors is heavily fortified. Existing facilities employ 103-mm, 127-mm, and 150-mm guns of German World War II–era manufacture, 75-mm 60-cal. Bofors guns acquired during the 1960s, shore-mounted torpedo tubes, Penguin antiship missiles, and Swedish RBS-70 surface-to-air missiles. The Bofors 120-mm automatic ERSTA coastal-defense gun was ordered in 1981, and first firings took place at Trondheim in 1991; the weapon has a 27-km range and fires 24.5 or 24.6-kg shells at 25 rpm.

WEAPONS AND SYSTEMS

The Norwegian Navy uses mostly British, American, and Swedish weapons and ystems, but it has built two systems of its own, the Terne automatic ASW rocket ystem and the Penguin surface-to-surface missile, which are described below. Subnarines are equipped with Swedish T-61 (45 kts, 20,000 m) or American NT37C 20,000 m) and Mk 37 Mod. 2 wire-guided torpedoes. On 16-12-91, 146 DM2A3 wireuided torpedoes were ordered for the *Ula*-class submarines. Some 190 British Stingay ASW torpedoes were delivered 1990–92 for use on P-3C Orion aircraft. The French 1istral point-defense missile system was selected 1991 for use on small combatants nd mine countermeasures ships. Norway has also developed its own radar and elecrooptical gun and missile fire-control systems. Sonars are manufactured by the imrad Co.

'erne Mk III (ASW)

Maximum range: 900 m. The entire system incorporates: search sonar, attack sonar Terne Mk 3" for range/depth determination), computer, and a sextuple launcher ıount with a rapid-reloading system.

The sextuple launcher mount weighs a little less than 3 tons. Fires at 45° to 75° evation, the latter for minimum range. Six rounds are ripple-fired at a time. Reloads tomatically in 40 seconds. The rocket is 1.97 m in length, 0.2 m in diameter, 120 kg in eight (warhead: 48 kg) and has a combination timed and proximity fuse. Employed on e *Oslo* and *Sleipner* classes. Receiving "Mk 10" upgrade 1991–93.

enguin Mk 1—Norsk Forsvarsteknologie (NFT, formerly Kongsberg)

ngth: 2.95 m	Maximium range: 20,000 m
ingspan: 1.42 m	Speed: Mach 0.7
ameter: 0.28	Guidance: Infrared homing
eight: 330 kg	

e missile is protected by a fiberglass container that also serves as a launcher. No ger in production.

enguin Mk 2 —Norsk Forsvarsteknologie (NFT, formerly Kongsberg)

ngth: 3.00 m	Maximum range: 26,000 m
ngspan: 1.42 m	Speed: Mach 0.8
ameter: 0.28 m	Guidance: Infrared homing
ight: 340 kg	Warhead: 120-kg Bullpup Mk 19 (50-kg explosive)

Mk 2 Mod. 7 helicopter-launched version has been developed for the U.S. Navy.

enguin Mk 3 (air-launched)—Norsk Forsvarsteknologie (NFT, merly Kongsberg)

ngth: 3.20 m	Maximum range: 40,000+ m
ngspan: 1.00 m	Speed: Mach 0.8
meter: 0.28 m	Guidance: Infrared homing
ight: 360 kg (400 vith launcher)	Warhead: 120 kg (50-kg explosive)

guin Mk 3 can be launched at altitudes of 150 to 30,000 ft.

mm Bofors gun

ingle-barrel Swedish automatic gun mounted on the *Storm*-class patrol boats. Not nded for AA. Also used by the Singapore Navy.

ret weight (no ammunition): 6.5 tons	Cartridge weight: 11.3 kg
gth: 50 calibers	Shell weight: 5.9 kg
zzle velocity: 825 m/sec	Warhead weight: 0.54 kg
e of train: 25/sec	Maximum range, surface mode: 8,000 m
e of elevation: 25/sec	Arc of elevation: -10° to +30°
e of fire: 30 rounds/min	

3MARINES

: Four additional submarines of a new design are planned.

(+1) Project 6071 (German Type 210) Bldr: Thyssen Nordseewerke, Emden

	Laid down	L	Delivered by builder
S 300 Ula	29-1-87	1-7-88	10-91 (accepted)
S 301 Utsira	15-6-90	. . .	5-92
S 302 Utstein	6-12-89	4-91	14-11-91 (completed)
S 303 Utvær	8-12-88	19-4-90	1-11-90 (completed)
S 304 Uthaug	5-6-89	18-10-90	6-91 (completed)
S 305 Uredd	23-6-88	22-9-89	3-5-90 (accepted 10-91)

Uthaug (S 304) Stefan Terzibaschitsch, 6-91

Ula (S 300) Leo Van Ginderen, 1991

D: 940 tons standard, 1,040 tons (surf.) (fl); 1,150 tons (sub.)
S: 11 kts surf./23 kts sub. **Dim:** 59.00 × 5.40 × 4.50
A: 8/533-mm TT (14 German DM2A3 wire-guided torpedoes)
Electron Equipt:
Radar: 1/U.K. 1007 nav./surf. search—EW: Racal Sealion intercept
Sonar: Krupp Atlas DBQS-21F (CSU-83); Thomson-CSF passive conformal arrays
M: 2 MTU 16V652 MB 1,260-bhp diesels, 2/870-kw, 3-phase NEBB generator sets, electric drive; 1 prop; 6,000 shp
Range: 5,000/8 (snorkel) **Endurance:** 40 days **Fuel:** 100 tons
Crew: 3 officers, 15–17 enlisted

Remarks: Six ordered 30-9-82, with option to order two more later dropped. Have X-form stern control surfaces. Norsk Forsvarsteknologie MSI-90U torpedo f.c.s. Diving depth: 250 m. Anker batteries, Zeiss periscopes. All but first have pressure hulls built by Kværner Brug, Oslo. Rockwell-Collins NAVSTAR global positioning navigation system. Use Riva Calzoni Trident non-pressure hull-penetrating masts. S 300 was to commission 4-90 after one year of trials, which began 27-4-89; was hit by practice torpedo 11-11-89, minor damage. S 305 damaged in docking accident, 3-1-91. S 300 placed in reserve 15-11-91 pending delivery of torpedoes beginning in 1994, and the others are also likely to be placed in maintained reserve until they can be made fully operational. Reportedly, the ships have also been plagued with noisy machinery and are the source of considerable dissatisfaction.

◆ **6 Modernized German Type 207** Bldr: Rheinstahl-Nordseewerke, Emden

	Laid down	L	In serv.	Mod. completed
S 306 Skolpen	1-11-65	24-3-66	17-8-66	10-89
S 308 Stord	1-4-66	2-9-66	9-2-67	26-10-90
S 314 Sklinna (ex-S 305)	17-8-65	21-1-66	17-8-66	9-1-89
S 315 Kaura	19-5-64	16-10-64	5-2-65	4-92
S 318 Kobben	9-12-63	25-4-64	17-8-64	5-91
S 319 Kunna	3-3-64	16-7-64	1-10-64	12-91

D: 469 tons surf./524 tons sub. **S:** 12 kts surf./17 kts sub.
Dim: 47.41 × 4.6 × 3.80
A: 8/533-mm TT, fwd (8 Swedish Type 61 and U.S. NT 37C torpedoes)
Electron Equipt:
Radar: 1/Thomson-CSF Calypso-II nav.—EW: . . . intercept
Sonar: Krupp Atlas DBQS-21F active, passive arrays
M: 2 MTU 12V493 AZ, 600-bhp diesels, 2 405-kw generators, 1 1,100-kw motor; 1 prop (2.3-m diameter); 1,700 shp
Range: 14/17 sub.; 141/6 sub.; 5,000/8 (snorkel)
Crew: 5 officers, 13 enlisted

Remarks: Originally a class of fifteen, financed by the United States. S 316 renamed and renumbered 12-3-87; S 314 in 1988. Original sister *Kinn* (S 316) stricken 1982. *Stadt* (S 307), which was to have gone to Denmark, damaged in grounding spring 1987 and stricken; replaced by *Kya* (S 317). Also transferred to Denmark were *Utvær* (S 303) and *Uthaug* (S 304). *Kinn* (S 316, ex-*Ula*, S 300) was returned to U.S. custody 23-5-91 and then transferred to Denmark for spares to repair the sunken *Sælen* (ex-*Uthaug*, S 304). The unmodernized *Utsira* (S 301), *Utstein* (S 302), and *Svenner* (S 309) were stricken at the end of 1991.

SUBMARINES *(continued)*

Sklinna (S 314) Defence Command Norway, 1-89

Design based on the West German Type 205, but deeper diving. Units modernized by Mjellum and Karlsen, near Bergen, received MSI-90U torpedo f.c.s. in place of MSI-70U, new sonar and communications suites, Thorn-EMI D-3 data-distribution systems, and a propulsion-system overhaul. Lengthened 2 meters during modernization. Diving depth: 190 m.

◆ **1 German Type 207 training submarine** Bldr: Rheinstahl-Nordseewerke, Emden

	Laid down	L	In serv.
S 309 Svenner	8-9-66	27-1-67	1-7-67

D: 435 tons surf./485 tons sub. **S:** 10 kts surf./17 kts sub.
Dim: 46.41 × 4.60 × 3.80
A: 8/533-mm TT, fwd (8 Swedish Type 61 and U.S. NT-37C torpedoes)
Electron Equipt:
Radar: 1/Thomson-CSF Calypso-II nav./surf. search
Sonar: Krupp-Atlas DBQS-21F active/passive set
M: 2 Mercedes-Benz MB 820Db, 600-bhp diesels, 2 405-kw generator sets, 1 electric motor; 1 prop (2.3 m diameter); 1,700 shp
Range: 14/17 sub.; 141/6 sub.; 5,000/8 snorkel
Crew: 5 officers, 12 enlisted

Remarks: The only surviving unmodernized Kobeen-class (Type 207) submarine. Was built 1 meter longer than sisters and equipped with a second periscope for training. Likely to be discarded shortly.

FRIGATES

Note: Up to seven new frigates are planned to be ordered beginning as early as 1995, with the last to deliver in 2012; the design may incorporate rigid-sidewall air-cushion vehicle technology.

◆ **5 Oslo class** Bldr: Marinens Hovedverft (Naval Dockyard), Horten

	Laid down	L	In serv.	Mod. completed
F 300 Oslo	1963	17-1-64	29-1-66	1-2-91
F 301 Bergen	1963	23-8-65	15-5-67	4-4-90
F 302 Trondheim	1963	4-9-64	2-6-66	30-11-87
F 303 Stavanger	1964	4-2-66	1-12-67	5-6-89
F 304 Narvik	1964	8-1-65	30-11-66	21-10-88

Bergen (F 301) Hartmut Ehlers, 11-91

Narvik (F 304) Maritime Photographic, 10-9

D: 1,450 tons (1,850 fl) **S:** 25 kts
Dim: 96.62 (93.87 pp) × 11.17 × 4.4
A: 4/Penguin SSM (I × 4)—1/Mk 29 SAM launcher (VIII × 1, 24 RIM-7M Sea Sparrow missiles)—2/76.2-mm 50-cal. U.S. Mk 33 DP (II × 1)—1/40-mm 70-cal. Bofors AA—2/20-mm Rheinmetall AA (I × 2)—1/Terne-III ASW RL (VI × 1)—6/324-mm Mk 32 ASW TT (III × 2; 6 Marconi Stingray or U.S. Mk 46 torpedoes)—1/d.c. rack (6 d.c.)
Electron Equipt:
Radar: 1/Decca TM 1226 nav., 1/Thomson-CSF DRBV-22 air search 1/Nobeltech 9LV 200 Mk 2 gun f.c., 1/Raytheon Mk 91 Mod. 0 SAM f.c.
Sonar: Thomson-Sintra TSM 2633 (Spherion) hull-mounted and VD MF, Terne Mk 3 hull-mounted HF attack
EW: Argo . . . intercept, Nera SR-1A intercept, . . . decoy RL
M: 1 set Laval-Ljungstrom PN 20 geared steam turbines; 1 prop; 20,000 shp
Boilers: 2 Babcock & Wilcox; 42.18 kg/cm², 454°C
Electric: 1,100 kw **Range:** 4,500/15
Crew: 11 officers, 19 petty officers, 120 enlisted

Remarks: Based on the U.S. *Dealey*-class destroyer escorts, but with higher freebo forward and many European subsystems. Rebuilt during the late 1970s with Penguin antiship missile, NATO Sea Sparrow point-defense SAM, and ASW torp tubes. In the Sea Sparrow system, the Mk 91 radar director is on a pylon atop missile-reload magazine.

All modernized again in the late-1980s/early 1990s with Thomson-CSF TSM 2 (Spherion) hull and VDS sonars in place of the U.S. AN/SQS-36 (requiring replacem of the aft 76.2-mm gun mount with a 40-mm AA mount and the removal of two Peng positions and the depth-charge rack in order to accommodate the VDS installati MSI 3100 digital (*vice* analog) weapons-control systems, rocket decoy system ad and habitability improvements. The original H.S.A. M24 f.c. system was replace the Philips 9LV 200 Mk 2 radar/t.v. f.c. system (the associated TVT-300 optr director is mounted atop the pilothouse), and 2/20-mm AA are resited above and a the bridge. Have NATO Link 14 datalink capability.

Stavanger (F 303) Leo Van Ginderen

CORVETTES

◆ **2 Sleipner class (In reserve)** Bldr: Nylands Verksted, Oslo

	L	In serv.		L	In serv.
F 310 Sleipner	9-11-63	29-4-65	F 311 Aeger	24-9-65	31-3-67

Aeger (F 311) James W. Goss/NAVPIC, 9-91

leipner (F 310) Leo Van Ginderen, 1991

D: 600 tons (790 fl) **S:** 20+ kts
Dim: 69.33 × 7.90 × 2.50 (hull)
A: 1/76.2-mm 50-cal. Mk 34 DP—1/40-mm 70-cal. Bofors AA—1/ Terne-III ASW RL (VI × 1)—6/324-mm Mk 32 ASW TT (III × 2)—1/d.c. rack (6 d.c.)
Electron Equipt:
Radar: 1/Decca TM 1226 nav., 1/Decca 202 nav.
Sonar: Thomson-Simrad TSM 2633 (Spherion) hull-mounted MF, Terne Mk 3 hull-mounted HF attack
M: 4 Maybach diesels; 2 props; 9,000 bhp **Crew:** 63 tot.

marks: In recent years, employed primarily for training; both placed in reserve ring 1991. U.S. Mk 63 GFCS replaced by 2 Philips TVT 300 optronic systems. tallation of Spherion hull-mounted sonar in place of original SQS-36 completed 8-88 in F 310, 2-5-89 in F 311.

IDED-MISSILE PATROL BOATS

0 (+12) new construction Bldr: . . .

): 125 tons (fl) **S: 52 kts **Dim:** . . . × . . . × . . .
: . . . **M:** . . . gas turbines

narks: Originally to have been a class of 24 to replace the *Storm* and *Snøgg* sses. The *Storm*-class missile boat *Storm* was fitted during 1987 with a prototype erjet propulsion system for the new boat, the first of which was originally to have n completed in 1992. No orders, however, had been announced as of 2-92. The visional data above is for one of the proposed designs, a Kevlar or GRP-hulled d-sidewall air-cushion vehicle.

14 Hauk class Bldrs: Bergens Mekaniske Verksteder (1st 10); Westamarin A/S, Alta (last 4)

(P 999) Gerhard Koop, 5-84

Ørn (P 987) Leo Van Ginderen, 6-86

	L	In serv.		L	In serv.
P 986 Hauk	2-77	17-8-78	P 993 Lom	. . .	15-1-80
P 987 Ørn	2-78	19-1-79	P 994 Stegg	. . .	18-3-80
P 988 Terne	5-78	13-3-79	P 995 Falk	. . .	30-4-80
P 989 Tjeld	8-78	25-5-79	P 996 Ravn	. . .	20-5-80
P 990 Skarv	10-78	17-7-79	P 997 Gribb	. . .	10-7-80
P 991 Teist	6-12-78	11-9-79	P 998 Geir	. . .	16-9-80
P 992 Jo	. . .	1-11-79	P 999 Erle	. . .	10-12-80

D: 130 tons (155 fl) **S:** 35 kts **Dim:** 36.53 × 6.3 × 1.65
A: 6/Penguin Mk II SSM (I × 6)—1/40-mm 70-cal. Bofors AA—1/20-mm 90-cal. Rheinmetall AA—2/533-mm TT for T-61 wire-guided torpedoes
Electron Equipt:
Radar: 2/Decca TM 1226 nav.
Sonar: Simrad SQ3D/SF hull-mounted HF
M: 2 MTU 16V538 TB92 diesels; 2 props; 7,340 bhp
Range: 440/34 **Crew:** 22 tot.

Remarks: The MSI-80S fire-control system, developed by Kongsberg, uses two Decca radars plus a Philips TVT-300 electro-optical tracker and an Ericssen laser rangefinder. Have 2/50-mm flare RL. Normally carry only four Penguin missiles. Are to receive one Simbad twin-launcher for Mistral surface-to-air missiles during 1992–93 refits. P 994 aground 14-9-90 but salvaged and repaired.

◆ **6 Snøgg class** Bldr: Båtservice Verft, Mandal (In serv. 1970–71)

P 980 Snøgg (ex-*Lyr*) P 982 Snarr P 984 Kvik
P 981 Rapp P 983 Rask P 985 Kjapp

Rask (P 983) Lt. Arild Engelsen, R. Nor. N, 2-88

Snarr (P 982)—with two Penguins aft Leo Van Ginderen, 1990

D: 115 tons (140 fl) **S:** 36 kts **Dim:** 36.53 × 6.3 × 1.65
A: 4/Penguin Mk I SSM (I × 4)—1/40-mm AA—4/533-mm TT for T-61 wire-guided torpedoes—2/d.c. racks (6 d.c. each, usually not mounted)

GUIDED-MISSLE PATROL BOATS *(continued)*

Electron Equipt:
Radar: 1/Decca TM 1626, 1/PEAB TORC-1 f.c.
M: 2 MTU 16V538 TB92 diesels; 2 props; 7,200 bhp
Range: 550/36 **Crew:** 3 officers, 17 enlisted

Remarks: To receive new electronics and one twin Simbad launcher for French Mistral surface-to-air missiles during early 1990s refits. Normally carry no Penguin missiles, and the depth-charge racks are rarely fitted.

◆ **18 Storm class** Bldrs: P 963, P 966, P 969, P 972, P 975, and P 978: Westermoen, Mandal; others: Bergens Mekaniske Verksted, Bergen

	L		L
P 961 Blink	28-6-65	P 970 Brann	3-7-66
P 962 Glimt	27-9-65	P 971 Tross	29-9-66
P 963 Skjold	17-2-66	P 972 Hvass	20-12-66
P 964 Trygg	25-11-65	P 973 Traust	18-11-66
P 965 Kjekk	27-1-66	P 974 Brott	27-1-67
P 966 Djerv	28-4-66	P 975 Odd	7-4-67
P 967 Skudd	25-3-66	P 977 Brask	27-5-67
P 968 Arg	24-5-66	P 978 Rokk	1-6-67
P 969 Steil	20-9-66	P 979 Gnist	15-8-67

Hvass (P 972)—with six Penguin missiles Gerhard Koop, 5-84

D: 100 tons (125 fl) **S:** 37 kts **Dim:** 36.53 × 6.3 × 1.55
A: 4–6/Penguin Mk I SSM (I × 4-6)—1/76-mm 50-cal. Bofors—1/40-mm 70-cal. Bofors AA
Electron Equipt:
Radar: 1/Decca TM 1226 nav., 1/H.S.A. WM-26 fire-control
M: 2 Maybach MB 872A diesels; 2 props; 7,200 bhp
Range: 550/36 **Crew:** 4 officers, 9 petty officers, 13 enlisted

Remarks: Back-fitted with TVT-300 electro-optical tracker and laser range-finder, in a tub abaft the radar mast. Diesels are essentially the same as those in the *Hauk* and *Snøgg* classes above. Two d.c. racks can be carried in lieu of the after two Penguin containers. All to be fitted with one Simbad twin launcher for French Mistral point-defense surface-to-air missiles.

Pil (P 976), stricken 1982 and placed on land, has been used since for fire-fighting training. The original *Storm,* launched 19-3-63, was stricken 1965 and replaced by a new unit, *Storm* (P 960), launched 28-11-68; that ship was stricken 1986 for use in waterjet propulsion trials, using two Hedemora 2,600-bhp diesels; she has been renumbered VSD 11.

Note: The eight remaining *Tjeld*-class torpedo boats, *Sel* (P 343), *Hval* (P 348), *Laks* (P 349), *Knurr* (P 357), *Skrei* (P 380), *Hai* (P 381), *Lyr* (P 387), and *Delfin* (P 388), were stricken1990–91.

MINE WARFARE SHIPS

◆ **2 Vidar-class minelayers** Bldr: Mjellem & Karlsen, Bergen

	Laid down	L	In serv.
N 52 Vidar	1-3-76	18-3-77	21-10-77
N 53 Vale	1-2-76	5-8-77	10-2-78

Vidar (N 52) Leo Van Ginderen, 1991

D: 1,500 tons (1,722 fl) **S:** 15 kts
Dim: 64.8 (60.0 pp) × 12.0 × 4.0 (hull)
A: 2/40-mm 70-cal. Bofors AA (I × 2)—6/324-mm Mk 32 ASW TT (II × 2)— 2/d.c. racks—320 mines
Electron Equipt:
Radar: 2/Decca TM 1226 nav.
Sonar: Simrad SQ3D hull-mounted HF
M: 2 Wichmann 7AX diesels; 2 props; 4,200 bhp; 425-shp bow-thruster
Fuel: 247 tons **Electric:** 1,000 kw **Crew:** 50 tot.

Remarks: Ordered 11-6-75. Capable of serving as minelayers (mines carried on three decks, with electric elevators to first platform deck and upper deck and three minelaying rails), torpedo-recovery ships, personnel and cargo transports, fisheries-protection ships, and ASW escorts.

◆ **1 inshore mine-planter** Bldr: Marinens Hovedverft, Horten (L: 29-4-60)

N 51 Borgen

Borgen (N 51) French Navy, 5-9

D: 282 tons (fl) **S:** 9 kts **Dim:** 31.28 × 8.00 × 3.35
A: 1/20-mm 90-cal. Rheinmetall AA—2 mine rails
Electron Equipt: Radar: 1/Decca 707 nav. **Crew:** . . . tot.
M: 2 G.M. 3-71 diesels; 2 Voith-Schneider cycloidal props; 330 bhp

Remarks: Patterned on the Swedish MUL-12 class. Designed to "plant" sho controlled mines by crane.

Note: The Norwegian Navy also intends to employ civilian passenger/vehicle ferr as minelayers in wartime; the 1,435 grt/841 dwt ferry *Stavanger,* delivered 31-3-90 Myklebust Mekaniske Verksted, is intended for wartime use in such a rôle.

◆ **0 (+9) new construction minehunter/minesweepers**
Bldr: Kværner Mandal A/S, Mandal

4 Minehunters:

	Laid down	L	In se
M 340 Oksøy	1-12-90	1-9-92	8-
M 341 Karmøy	. . .	. . .	3-
M 342 Måløy	. . .	. . .	9
M 343 Hinnøy	. . .	. . .	6

5 Minesweepers:

M 350 Alta	. . .	. . .	19
M 351 Otra	. . .	. . .	6
M 352 Rauma	. . .	. . .	3
M 353 Orkla	. . .	. . .	9
M 354 Glomma	. . .	. . .	3

D: 275 tons light (335 tons standard, 367 fl) **S:** 30 kts (22 cruising
Dim: 54.20 (52.00 pp) × 13.55 × 2.35 (0.87 on cushion)
A: 1/Sadral SAM system (VI × 1, . . . Mistral missiles)—1/20-mm 90-cal. Rheinmetall AA—2/12.7-mm mg (I × 2)

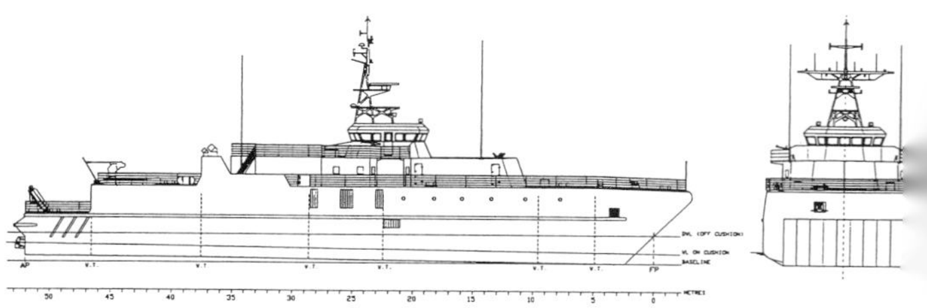

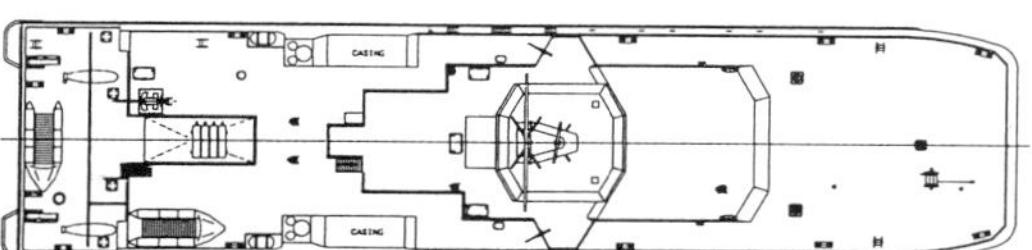

Oksøy-class minehunter Kværner,

MINE WARFARE SHIPS *(continued)*

ksøy (M 350)—artist's rendering Kværner, 1991

Electron Equipt:
Radar: 2/Decca . . . nav.
Sonar: minesweepers: Simrad SA 950 hull-mounted mine-avoidance (95 kHz); minehunters: Thomson-Sintra TSM-2023N variable-depth HF
M: 2 MTU 12V396 TE84 propulsion diesels (1,920 bhp each), 2 MTU 8V396 TE54 diesels for lift fans (940 bhp each); 2 KaMeWa waterjets; 3,840 bhp—jet-vane bow-thruster
Electric: 500 kw tot. (2 MTU 12V182 TE51 diesels driving)
Range: 1,200/20 **Fuel:** 50,000 liters
Crew: 14 officers, 23 enlisted

marks: Approved 3-8-87 by Ministry of Defense and ordered 9-11-89. Rigid-ewall air-cushion vehicle design like abortive U.S. *Cardinal* class. The minehunters l carry two PAP 104 Mk 5 submersibles and will be equipped with the MICOS nehunting system. All will have U.S. Global Positioning System receivers. The hion area will be 48.50 × 10.00 × 2.35 m high. Will have hydraulic drive for -speed operations.

5 U.S. Falcon-class minesweeper/minehunters

	Bldr	In serv.
313 Tana (ex-*Roeselare*, x-MSC 103)	Hodgdon Bros., Gowdy & Stevens, Boothbay Harbor, Maine	9-53
314 Alta (ex-*Arlon*, ex-ISC 104)	Hodgdon Bros., Gowdy & Stevens, Boothbay Harbor, Maine	10-53
31 Tista	Forenede Båtbyggeri, Risør	27-4-55
32 Kvina	Båtservice Verft, Mandal	12-7-55
34 Utla	Båtservice Verft, Mandal	15-1-55

: 300 tons (372 fl) **S:** 13 kts (8, sweeping)
im: 43.0 × 7.95 × 2.55
: 2/20-mm 90-cal. Rheinmetall AA (I × 2)
lectron Equipt:
Radar: 1/Decca 1226 nav.
Sonar: 1/UQS-1 hull-mounted HF (M 313: Thomson-Sintra TSM 2023N; M 332: Simrad SA-950)
: 2 G.M. 8-268A diesels; 2 props; 1,200 bhp
ange: 2,500/10 **Fuel:** 40 tons **Crew:** 38 tot. (M 313: 39)

a (M 332) Peter Voss, 11-90

Tana (M 313)—minehunter, deckhouse aft Gerhard Koop, 1988

Remarks: *Tana* and *Alta* (and the stricken *Glomma*) were transferred by Belgium in 1966 in exchange for two ocean minesweepers, *Lagen* and *Namsen*. In 1977, *Tana* was converted to a prototype minehunter, with British Type 193M sonar, two PAP-104 remote-controlled minehunting devices, and divers' facilities in a large deckhouse aft. She was rearmed with 2/20-mm Rheinmetall AA guns (I × 2), now back-fitted into the others. At the waterline, across the stern, she has a platform for diver recovery; this extends her overall length by more than one meter. *Tana* now has the Thomson-Sintra TSM-2023N minehunting sonar installed for trials, *Kvina* has the Simrad Subsea SA-950 mine-avoidance sonar, and *Utla* is employed in testing other equipment for the new minehunter/minesweepers listed above. Sisters *Sauda* (M 311, ex-MSC 102) and *Ogna* (M 315) stricken 1986 and sold 1991; *Sira* (M 312), *Vosso* (M 316), and *Glomma* (M 317, ex-*Bastogne*, ex-MSC 151) stricken 1991. M 332 damaged in collision with German supply ship *Coburg* 14-3-91 in the Mediterranean; minor damage repaired.

AMPHIBIOUS WARFARE SHIPS

◆ **5 Reinøysund-class utility landing craft** Bldr: Mjellem & Karlsen, Bergen (In serv. 1972–73)

L 4502 Reinøysund — L 4503 Sørøysund — L 4504 Maursund — L 4505 Rotsund — L 4506 Borgsund

Rotsund (L 4505) and Reinøysund (L 4502) French Navy, 6-90

D: 596 tons (fl) **S:** 11 kts **Dim:** 51.4 × 10.3 × 1.85
A: 2/20-mm 90-cal. Rheinmetall AA (I × 2)—4/12.7-mm mg (II × 2) rails for 120 mines
M: 2 MTU diesels; 2 props; 1,350 bhp **Crew:** 2 officers, 7 enlisted

Remarks: Double-folding bow-ramp door. Cargo capacity: 5 Leopard tanks, 80–180 men. Similar to class below.

◆ **2 Kvalsund-class utility landing craft** Bldr: P. Høivolds Mek. Verksted, Kristiansand

L 4500 Kvalsund (In serv. 6-68) — L 4501 Raftsund (In serv. 3-69)

D: 590 tons (fl) **S:** 11 kts **Dim:** 50.0 × 10.2 × 1.8
A: 2/20-mm 90-cal. Rheinmetall AA—rails for 120 mines
M: 2 MTU diesels; 2 props; 1,350 bhp **Crew:** 2 officers, 8 enlisted

Kvalsund (L 4500) R.Nor.N.

AMPHIBIOUS WARFARE SHIPS *(continued)*

Remarks: Cargo capacity: 5 Leopard tanks, 80–180 men. Both subordinate to Home Guard rather than the navy.

Note: The Norwegian Army has six M.A.N. GHH MLC 60 bridging ferries of 26-m span, propelled by Schottel pumpjets; they are named *Håling-I* through *Håling-VI*.

AUXILIARY SHIPS

Note: The 14,989-grt auto/passenger ferry *Peter Wessel* was acquired by the government in 9-85 for conversion to a casualty-evacuation ship with a medical staff of 450 and facilities for 800 seriously wounded and 1,200 lightly wounded troops; she is not under naval control and normally operates in commercial service. A new acoustic research ship, to be named *Minerva,* is due for completion in 1994.

◆ **1 intelligence-collection ship** Bldr: Mjellem & Karlsen, Bergen (In serv. 1976)

MARJATA

Marjata French Navy, 6-90

D: approx. 1,800 fl **S:** . . . kts **Dim:** 58.36 (55.35 pp) × 11.00 × 4.65
Electron Equipt: Radar: 2/. . . nav.—EW: various intercept arrays
M: 2 MaK diesels; 2 props; 2,600 bhp **Electric:** 240 kw
Crew: . . . tot.

Remarks: 1,385 grt. Is equipped with a plethora of intercept antennas on the masts and has a large radome running over the top of the superstructure for about half the length of the ship. Painted with gray hull, white superstructure, and yellow masts.

◆ **1 logistics-support ship** Bldr: Horten Verft, Horten

	Laid down	L	In serv.
A 530 HORTEN	28-1-77	12-8-77	9-6-78

D: 2,500 tons (fl) **S:** 16.5 kts **Dim:** 87.0 (82.0 pp) × 13.7 × . . .
A: 2/40-mm 70-cal. Bofors AA (I × 2)—mines
Electron Equipt: Radar: 3/Decca . . . nav.
M: 2 Wichmann 7AX diesels; 2 props; 4,200 bhp **Crew:** 86 tot.

Horten (A 530) Leo Van Ginderen, 1990

Remarks: Used to support submarines and small combatants. Can accommodate up to 190 additional personnel. Helicopter deck. Bow-thruster. Acted as Royal Yacht, 1985–86.

◆ **1 royal yacht** Bldr: Camper & Nicholson's, Gosport, U.K. (L: 17-2-37)

A 533 NORGE (ex-*Philante*)

Norge (A 533)—white hull, yellow stack Mike Louagie, 7-9

D: 1,686 tons **S:** 17 kts **Dim:** 76.27 × 8.53 × 4.65
M: 2 8-cyl. diesels; 2 props; 3,000 bhp **Electric:** 300 kw
Fuel: 175 tons **Range:** 9,900/17

Remarks: Built as a yacht, then used by the Royal Navy as an ASW escort from 19 to 1943, then as a training ship. Purchased by Norway in 1948. Displacement listed in Thames Yacht Measurement. Can carry 50-passenger royal party. Severe f 8-3-85, repaired by summer 1986.

SERVICE CRAFT

Note: For service craft, the first letter of the pendant number indicates the na district subordination, i.e., R = Rogaland, Ø = Østlandet, etc.

◆ **1 coastal transport, former trials craft** Bldr: Eikefjord Marine

HSD 12 GARSØY (In serv. 19-8-88)

D: 195 tons **S:** 27 kts **Dim:** 34.0 × 7.0 × 1.8
Electron Equipt: Radar: 1/Decca 1226 nav.
M: 2 MWM TBD64 BV8 diesels; 2 props; 2,300 bhp
Crew: 4 + 80 passengers

Remarks: Built to test glass-reinforced plastic sandwich-core hull structure for Oksøy-class mine countermeasures ships. Since completion of trials, employec coastal transport and local patrol craft.

◆ **1 torpedo-recovery and oil-spill cleanup ship** Bldr: Fjellstrand Hardinger (In serv. 10-78)

VSD 1 VERNØY

D: 150 grt **S:** 12 kts **Dim:** 31.3 × 6.67 × 2.0
M: 2 MWM diesels; 2 Schottel props; . . . hp

Vernøy (VSD 1) Lt. Arild Engelsen, R.Nor.N

◆ **8 Torpen-class support tenders**

		Bldr	In se
VSD 4	TORPEN	Båtservice Verft, Mandal	15-12
ØSD 2	WISTING	Voldnes Skipsverft, Fosnavåg	30-1
ØSD 5	OSKARSBORG	. . . . . .	
TSD 5	TAUTRA	Båtservice Verft, Mandal	15-
NSD 35	ROTVÆR	Båtservice Verft, Mandal	
VSD 5	VIKEN (ex-*Fjøløy,* RSD 23)	Voldnes Skipsverft, Fosnavåg	
HSD 15	KRØTTØY	Voldnes Skipsverft, Fosnavåg	
TRSD 4	KARLSØY	P. Høivolds, Kristianstad	

SERVICE CRAFT *(continued)*

'isting (ØSD 2) Leo Van Ginderen, 6-91

karsborg (ØSD 5) Leo Van Ginderen, 10-90

D: 215 tons (300 fl) **S:** 11 kts **Dim:** 29.0 × 6.4 × 2.57
A: 1/12.7-mm mg
Electron Equipt: Radar: 1/Decca 1226 nav.
M: 1 MWM TBD 601-6K diesel; 1 CP prop; 530 bhp
Range: 1,200/11 **Fuel:** 11 tons
Crew: 6 enlisted + 100 passengers

marks: Basically similar craft tailored to a variety of duties, including logistics port, ammunition transport, personnel transport, and divers' support. Cargo: 100 . ØSD 5 is probably one of the other units renamed and renumbered, as there were rtedly only seven units of this class built.

◆ **2 navigational training craft** Bldr: Fjellstrand, Omastrand (In serv. -78)

58 Hessa (ex-*Hitra*, ex-*Kvarven*, VSD 6)
59 Vigra (ex-*Marsteinen*, VSD 2)

a (P 359) R.Nor.N, 1982

D: 40 tons **S:** 22 kts **Dim:** 23.2 × 5.0 × 1.1 **A:** 1/12.7-mm mg
M: 2 G.M. 12V71 diesels; 2 props; 1,800 bhp
Crew: 5 men + 8 cadets

Remarks: Aluminum construction. For use at the Naval Academy. Renamed and renumbered 1981. P 358 renamed 5-87 to free name for craft below.

◆ **2 personnel transport/district patrol craft** Bldr: Fjellstrand, Omastrand

RSD 23 Brimse (ex-TSD 1)(In serv. 1-12-74)
ØSD 1 Welding (In serv. 1-11-74)

D: 27.5 tons **S:** 15 kts
Dim: 16.3 × 5.3 × 1.2 **A:** 1/12.7-mm mg
Electron Equipt: Radar: 1/Decca . . . nav.
M: 2 G.M. 6V71 diesels; 2 props; 800 bhp **Crew:** 4 tot.

◆ **2 tenders for combat divers** Bldr: Nielsen, Harstad (In serv. 1972)

A 531 Sarpen (ex-VDS 11, ex-SKV 11) A 532 Draug (ex-SKV 10)

Sarpen (A 351)—old number R.Nor.N., 1981

D: 250 tons **S:** 12 kts **Dim:** 29.0 × 6.7 × 2.5
M: 1 diesel; 1 prop; 530 bhp

Remarks: Renumbered 1982. Support frogmen and mine-clearance divers.

◆ **1 logistics support tender**

Kjøey (In serv. 1969)

D: 190 tons **S:** . . . kts **Dim:** 20.90 × . . . × . . .
M: 1 diesel; . . . bhp

Remarks: Generally similar to the craft of the *Torpen* class listed above.

◆ **1 coastal tanker** Bldr: . . . . . ., Sweden (In serv. 1969)

VSD 14 Marina

Marina (VSD 14)—coastal tanker acquired 1985
Lt. Arild Engelsen, R.Nor.N., 6-87

D: 250 tons (fl) **S:** 8 kts **Dim:** 27.83 × 5.24 × 2.43
M: 1 diesel; 1 prop; 200 bhp

Remarks: 93 grt/166 dwt.

◆ **1 former Storm-class guided-missile patrol boat** Bldr: Båtservice, Mandal (L: 28-11-68)

VSD 11 Storm (ex-P 960)

D: 100 tons (125 fl) **S:** 30+ kts **Dim:** 36.53 × 6.3 × 1.55
A: none **Electron Equipt:** Radar: 1/Decca TM 1226 nav.
M: 2 Hedemora diesels; 2 waterjets; 5,200 bhp **Crew:** . . .

Remarks: Retired 1986 as a missile boat and converted for use in waterjet propulsion trials; re-engined.

SERVICE CRAFT *(continued)*

♦ **1 relic/training tender** Bldr: Fisher Boat Works, Detroit

	Laid down	L	In serv.
P . . . Hitra (ex-U.S. SC 718)	22-9-42	31-3-43	25-5-43

Hitra Lt. Arild Engelsen, R.Nor.N., 6-87

D: 95 tons light (148 fl) **S:** 21 kts (new)
Dim: 33.80 (32.77 wl) × 5.18 × 1.98
A: 1/40-mm Mk 3 AA—3/20-mm Oerlikon AA (I × 3)—2/Mk 20 Mousetrap ASW RL (IV × 2)—2/Mk 6 DCT—2/d.c. racks (12 d.c. tot.)—when operational
M: 2 G.M. Electromotive Div. 16-184A diesels; 2 props; 1,540 bhp
Fuel: 16 tons **Crew:** . . .

Remarks: Survivor of the ships and craft that served Free Norwegian naval forces during World War II. Reacquired 8-5-87 for restoration to operational service as cadet-training craft and museum ship. Wooden construction. Original armament restored and original engines located and reinstalled.

♦ **1 harbor tug** Bldr: Haugesund Slip, Haugesund (In serv. 1979)

VSD 2 Kvarven (ex-*Oscar Tybring*)

Kvarven (VSD 2) Lt. Arild Engelsen, R.Nor.N., 1989

D: 97 grt **S:** 11 kts **Dim:** 22.50 × 6.30 × . . .
M: 1 G.M. Detroit 16V-149 diesel; 1 prop; 900 bhp

Remarks: Acquired 1988 to replace *Ramnes* (VSD 13). Built originally as a rescue ship.

♦ **1 harbor tug** Bldr: Norderwerft Köser & Meyer, Hamburg, Germany (In serv. 1939)

VSD 7 Samson (ex-German *Nathurn*)

D: 147 grt **S:** 11 kts **Dim:** 28.75 × 7.10 × 2.86
M: 1 MWM diesel; 1 prop; 450 bhp

Note: Other service craft, for which no data are available, include: *Gleodden* (SKV 20); *Varodden* (VSD 8); VSD 20; VSD 63; VSD 10, *Foracs II* (RSD 20); *Petra;* SKØ 121; *Fjordbåt;* SKS 55; SSD 8; *Akerøy; Sigurd A.* (RSD 21); VSD 3; *Torpedofisken; Arnøy; Folden* (ØSD 14, ex- SKØ 122; 60 tons, built 1974); NSD 33; NSD 81, NSD 84, ØESD 66; *Nordkep* (ØSD 15); *Fjoly* (RSD 22); ØSD 11 (ex-SKØ 121; 23 tons, built 1968); and *Rogin* (RSD 28). SKN 407 is a torpedo retriever.

Samson (VSD 7) Lt. Arild Engelsen, R.Nor.N., 3-88

COAST GUARD (KYSTVAKT)

The Norwegian Coast Guard was established in 1976 to perform fisheries-protection duties, patrol the waters in the vicinity of offshore oil rigs, and maintain surveillance over the 200-nautical-mile economic zone. The Coast Guard operates six WG-13 Lynx Mk 86 helicopters.

PATROL SHIPS

♦ **3 Norkapp (Type 320) class**

	Bldr	L	In serv.
W 320 Nordkapp	Bergens Mek. Verksted, Bergen	2-4-80	25-4-8
W 321 Senja	Horten Verft, Horten	16-3-80	8-3-8
W 322 Andenes	Haugesund Verksted, Haugesund	21-3-81	30-1-8

Andenes (W 322) Ben Sullivan, 7

Andenes (W 322) Leo Van Ginderen,

D: 2,165 tons light (3,240 fl) **S:** 23 kts
Dim: 105.00 (97.50 pp) × 13.85 × 4.55
A: 1/57-mm 70-cal. Bofors DP—4/20-mm 90-cal. Rheinmetall AA (I × 4)—6/324-mm Mk 32 ASW TT (III × 2)—1/d.c. rack (6 d.c.)—1/WG-13 Sea Lynx helicopter
Electron Equipt:
Radar: 2/Decca TM 1226 nav., 1/Decca RM914 nav., 1/Plessey AWS-4 air search, 1/PEAB GLF 218 (9LV 200 Mk 2) f.c.
Sonar: 1/Simrad SS105 hull-mounted MF (14 kHz)
M: 4 Wichmann 9-AXAG diesels; 2 CP props; 14,400 bhp
Electric: 1,600 kw **Range:** 7,500/15 **Fuel:** 350 tons
Crew: 42 ship's company + 6 helo crew (109 accomm.)

Remarks: Program delayed by design changes and lack of funding; four add units deferred. In time of conflict, six Penguin II antiship missiles and chaff lau are to be added. Fin stabilized. Carry three 300-m/hr. water cannon for fire fighti have meteorological reporting gear. The Kongsberg MSI-805 NAVKIS data sy fitted. W 322 acted as support ship for the Danish corvette *Nils Juel* in the M during Operation Desert Shield/Desert Storm, 1990–91.

PATROL SHIPS *(continued)*

◆ **1 former stern-haul trawler** Bldr: Båtservice Verft, Mandel (In serv. 5-78)

V 319 GRIMSHOLM

rimsholm (W 319) Lt. Arild Engelsen, R.Nor.N., 5-87

D: 1,189 grt **S:** . . . **Dim:** 62.71 (54.60 pp) × 11.63 × 6.43
A: 1/40-mm Mk 3 AA **Electron Equipt:** Radar: 2/. . . nav.
M: 1 MaK 9-cyl. diesel; 1 prop; 3,400 bhp—bow- and stern-thrusters
Electric: 524 kw **Crew:** 13 tot.

:marks: Fitted out by Ulstein-Hatlø A/S, Ulsteinvik. Chartered 1980 for Coast ıard; returned to owners 11-85; rechartered 1987.

1 former purse-seiner Bldr: Fredrikstad Mek. Verksted, Fredrikstad (In serv. 1956)

318 GARPESKJÆR (ex-*Sun Tuna*, ex-*Star I*)

rpeskjær (W 318) Lt. Arild Engelsen, R.Nor.N., 8-86

: 1,122 grt **S:** . . . **Dim:** 66.54 × 10.09 × 5.54
: 1/40-mm Mk 3 AA **Electron Equipt:** Radar: 2/. . . nav.
: 1 Burmeister & Wain Alpha diesel; 1 prop; 4,240 bhp
rew: . . .

arks: Leased 1986 to replace *Grimsholm* (W 319). Built as a whaler, converted as ·se-seiner in 1971. Hull built by Pusnaes Mekaniske Verksted, Arendal.

. former stern-haul purse-seiner Bldr: Brødrene Lothes, Haugesund ·n serv. 7-78)

.7 LAFJORD

814 grt **S:** 14.6 kts **Dim:** 55.40 × 9.81 × 6.18
1/40-mm Mk 3 AA
1 Wichmann 7-cyl. diesel; 1 prop; 2,100 bhp
ectric: 419 kw **Fuel:** 220 tons **Range:** 7,700/14.6

ırks: Chartered 1980. Side-thrusters fore and aft.

rd (W 317) Lt. Arild Engelsen, R.Nor.N., 2-88

◆ **1 former stern-haul purse-seiner** Bldr: Smedvik, Tjørvåg (In serv. 4-78)

W 315 NORDSJØBAS

Nordsjøbas (W 315) Lt. Arild Engelsen, R.Nor.N., 3-86

D: 814 grt **S:** 13.5 kts **Dim:** 52.04 (44.75 pp) × 10.01 × 6.55
A: 1/40-mm Mk 3 AA **Electric:** 1,088 kw **Range:** 8,300/13.5
M: 1 MaK 6-cyl. diesel; 1 prop; 2,400 bhp **Fuel:** 180 tons

Remarks: Chartered 1980. Side-thrusters fore and aft.

◆ **1 former purse-seiner** Bldr: Beliard, Crighton & Cie., France (In serv. 1955)

W 314 STÅLBAS (ex-*Trålbas*, ex-*Cdt. Charcot*, ex-*Jean Charcot*)

Stålbas (W 314) Lt. Arild Engelsen, R.Nor.N., 2-88

D: 498 grt **S:** . . . **Dim:** 58.76 × 9.41 × 4.51
A: 1/40-mm Mk 3 AA **Crew:** . . .
M: 1 Klöckner-Humboldt-Deutz 8-cyl. diesel; 1 prop; 1,500 bhp

Remarks: Side-thrusters fitted, fore and aft. Originally built as a trawler.

◆ **1 former standby ship** Bldr. Haarlemsche Scheepsbouw Mij., Harlem (L: 8-57)

W 313 KIM (ex-*Rescue Kim*, ex-*Andennes*)

Kim (W 313)—as *Rescue Kim* Per Alsaker, 8-82

PATROL SHIPS *(continued)*

D: 700 tons (1,000 fl) **S:** 15 kts **Dim:** 60.0 × 9.0 × 4.7
A: 1/40-mm Bofors Mk 3 AA **Electron Equipt:** Radar: 2/. . . nav.
M: 2 M.A.N. 10-cyl. diesels; 1 prop; 2,300 bhp
Range: 6,720/10 **Crew:** 27 tot.

Remarks: 568 grt. Built as a whaler for Cia. de Nav. Rosina SA, Panama, and is a sister to the Argentine Prefecture naval patrol ship *Delfin.* In 1964 was bought by the Norwegian Navy and renamed *Andennes* (W 303), along with two sisters renamed *Nordkapp* (W 305), and *Senja,* (W 304), serving on coast guard/fisheries-patrol duties until sold 11-81, converted as an oilfield standby vessel and renamed *Rescue Kim.* Chartered 1991 to replace the former W 313, *Malene Østervold* (ex-*Ross Intrepid,* ex-*Ross Kennedy,* ex-*Cape Kennedy*).

♦ **1 former whale catcher** Bldr: Fredrikstad Mekaniske Verksted (In serv. 1950)

W 316 Volstad Jr. (ex-*Pol XIV*)

Volstad Jr. (W 316) Lt. Arild Engelsen, R.Nor.N., 3-86

D: 617 grt **S:** . . . **Dim:** 51.39 (45.32 pp) × 9.05 × 5.67
A: 1/40-mm Mk 3 AA **Electric:** 224 kw **Crew:** . . .
M: 2 Klöckner-Humboldt-Deutz NE-66 8-cyl. diesels; 1 CP prop; 1,200 bhp

Remarks: Chartered from Einar Volstad Partrederi in 1977. Built as a whaler, converted to a side-haul trawler 1966, and well deck filled in.

♦ **1 former naval fisheries-protection ship**

	Bldr	L
W 300 Nornen	Mjellem & Karlsen, Bergen	20-8-62

Nornen (W 300) Lt. Arild Engelsen, R.Nor.N., 5-87

D: 1,060 tons (fl) **S:** 17 kts **Dim:** 61.5 × 10.0 × 3.8
A: 1/40-mm Mk 3 AA **M:** 4 diesels; 1 prop; 3,700 bhp
Crew: 32 tot.

Remarks: Considerably altered, 1976–77: bridge enlarged, stack heightened, mast moved aft, hull side openings plated up, two new radars added.

♦ **2 former naval fisheries-protection ships**

	Bldr	L
W 301 Farm (ex-A 532)	Ankerløkken Verft, Florø	22-2-62
W 302 Heimdal (ex-A 534)	Bolsones Verft, Molde	7-3-62

Farm (W 301) Leo Van Ginderen, 6-9

D: 600 grt **S:** 16.5 kts **Dim:** 54.28 (49.0 pp) × 8.2 × 3.2
A: 1/40-mm Mk 3 AA **Electric:** 150 kVa **Crew:** 29 tot.
M: 2 Wichmann 9ACAT diesels; 2 CP props; 2,400 bhp

Remarks: Modernized 1979 (W 301) and 1980 (W 302) by Bergens Mekanisk Verksted with completely revised superstructure, new bridge resembling *Nornen,* new armament, and revised hull sides along the forecastle.

OCEAN SURVEILLANCE AND RESEARCH SHIP

♦ **1 H.U. Sverdrup II class** Bldr: Kaldnes Industrier A/S, Tønsberg (completed by Sigbj. Iversen A/S, Flekkefjord, 6-90)

H.U. Sverdrup II

H.U. Sverdrup II Arne Tandberg, 1

D: 1,387 grt **S:** . . . kts **Dim:** 55.00 × 13.00 × 5.38
M: 1 8-cyl. Bergens diesel; 1 prop; 2,000 bhp

Remarks: Operated for the Forsvarets Forskingsinstitut (Military Research Institute) by the Coast Guard. White hull, red pilothouse and masts, red-blue-red diagonal hull stripe. Equipped with MARISAT satellite communications equipment, stern-trawl equipment, large oceanographic crane aft.

FISHING EQUIPMENT PATROL (BRUKSVAKT)

Note: The *Bruksvakt* employs unarmed, chartered civilian craft painted a un naval gray and is employed in fisheries-regulation duties. It is subordinated t Coast Guard.

♦ **1 former oilfield standby ship, ex-purse seiner** Bldr: Brattvå Skipsinnredning, Brattvåg (In serv. 1957)

Borgundfjord

D: 318 grt **S:** 12 kts **Dim:** 44.60 × 7.10 × 3.66
M: 1 Wichmann diesel; 1 prop; 1,375 bhp

Remarks: Re-engined 1975.

♦ **1 former long-lines fishing boat** Bldr: Løland Motorverksted, Leirvik i Sogn

Harljet Helen (ex-*Brimøy,* ex-*Henning*) (In serv. 1958)

D: 120 grt **S:** 10.5 kts **Dim:** 29.53 × 6.21 × . . .
M: 1 Burmeister & Wain Alpha diesel; 1 prop; 400 bhp

Remarks: Lengthened 1969; re-engined 1970.

♦ **1 former stern trawler** Bldr: Trondhjems Mekaniske Verksted, Trondheim

Havkyst (ex-*Håen,* ex-*Br. Småvik*) (In serv. 1965)

D: 320 grt **S:** . . . kts **Dim:** 38.10 × 8.01 × 4.87
M: 1 Wichmann diesel; 1 prop; 900 bhp

Remarks: Ice-strengthened to Ice Class C.

NORWAY *(continued)*
FISHING EQUIPMENT PATROL (BRUKSVAKT) *(continued)*

◆ **1 former coastal passenger ship** Bldr: A/S Stord Vaerft, Leirvik

LOFOTHAV (ex-*Helgeland*) (In serv. 1954)

D: 286 grt **S:** . . . kts **Dim:** 38.77 × 7.19 × . . .
M: 1 M.A.N. diesel; 1 prop; 505 bhp

◆ **1 former coastal passenger ship** Bldr: Kaarbøs MV, Harstad

POLARGIRL (ex-*Tanahorn*) (In serv. 1962)

D: 286 grt **S:** 11 kts **Dim:** 38.30 × 7.62 × 3.81
M: 1 Wichmann diesel; 1 prop; 600 bhp

◆ **1 former passenger vessel** Bldr: P. Høivold, Kristiansand (In serv. 1954)

LANGØYSUND (ex-*Skjervøy*, ex-*Flakstad*)

D: 149 grt **S:** . . . kts **Dim:** 27.85 × 6.15 × . . .
M: 1 Caterpillar diesel; 1 prop; 425 bhp

1 former passenger vessel Bldr: Kaarbe Mek. Verksted, Harstad (In serv. 1959)

ORVAKT (ex-*Mårøy*)

D: 197 grt **S:** . . . kts **Dim:** 32.37 × . . . × . . .
M: 1 Caterpillar diesel; 1 prop; 565 bhp

1 former passenger vessel Bldr: E.M. Moen, Risør (In serv. 1949)

INE

D: 149 grt **S:** . . . kts **Dim:** 28.46 × 6.85 × 3.96
M: 1 Cummins diesel; 1 prop; 470 bhp

marks: Wooden hull; re-engined 1976.

1 former oilfield standby ship Bldr: Rickmers Reismühlen, Rhederei & Schiffbau, AG, Bremerhaven

JAN (ex-*Veavåg*, ex-*Willelm*, ex-*Herzogin Ingeborg*) (In serv. 1911)

D: 261 grt **S:** . . . kts **Dim:** 36.05 × 7.04 × . . .
M: 1 Callesen diesel; 1 prop; 450 bhp

marks: Built as a herring lugger, then converted to a purse-seiner, and later to a ndby ship. Lengthened 1956. 131 nrt.

1 former coastal passenger ship Bldr: Lindstøl Skips- & Båtbyggeri, Risør

NDRINGEN (ex-*Tamsøy*) (In serv. 1956)

D: 142 grt **S:** 10 kts **Dim:** 27.49 × 6.15 × . . .
M: 1 Caterpillar diesel; 1 prop; 425 bhp

marks: Re-engined 1967. 29 nrt.

1 former oceanographic research ship Bldr: Orens MV, Trondheim

ORSTEINSON (ex-*H.U. Sverdrup*, ex-U.S. AGOR 2) (In serv. 1960)

D: 400 tons (fl) **S:** 11.5 kts **Dim:** 38.89 × 7.62 × 3.30
M: 1 Wichmann diesel; 1 prop; 600 bhp **Electric:** 104 kw
Range: 5,000/10 **Fuel:** 65 tons.

marks: Transferred from the Norwegian Navy 1986. 295-grt trawler hull.

e — Mike Louagie, 10-88

Note: The Ministry of the Environment also operates eight ships with its own personnel: *Lance* (960 tons, in serv. 1978); *Sjøvern* (215 tons, in serv. 1948); *Sjørokk* (75 tons, in serv. 1964); *Sjødrev* (80 tons, in serv. 1973); *Sjøtroll* (80 tons, in serv. 1976), *Oljevern 01–04* (200 tons, in serv. 1978), *Johan Hjort* (2,000 tons, delivered 12-90), and the tug-supply vessel *Aldona* (1,615 grt, acquired 11-91 as an oil-spill recovery ship). The survey ship *Hydrograf* was sold commercial 8-89 and renamed *Stril Guard* as a standby vessel. Data for *Lance:*

Bldr: Sterkoder Mek. Verksted, Kristiansund (In serv. 1978)

D: 1,334 grt **S:** 14 kts **Dim:** 60.70 × 12.63 × 4.19
M: 1 MaK 9-cylinder diesel; 1 prop; 3,200 bhp

Remarks: Built as a fishing vessel and acquired 6-80 by the Ministry of the Environment. Has ice-strengthened hull.

OMAN

Sultanate of Oman

Personnel (1991): 3,445 total (including civilian employees); all personnel are volunteers.

Naval Aviation: Two Dornier 228-100 light maritime surveillance aircraft for coastal patrol. Omani Air Force Super Puma or Sea King helicopters can land aboard platforms on several of the larger ships.

CORVETTES

◆ **0 (+2) Vigilance class** Bldr: Vosper Thornycroft, Woolston

	Laid down	L	In serv.
. . . .	. . .	. . .	. . .
. . . .	. . .	. . .	. . .

Vosper "Vigilance" design — Vosper Thornycroft, 1991

D: 1,135 tons (1,400 fl) **S:** 31 kts
Dim: 83.70 (78.50 pp) × 11.50 × 3.30 (hull)
A: 8/MM 40 Exocet SSM (IV × 2)—1/76-mm OTO Melara Compact DP—1/30-mm Goalkeeper CIWS—2/20-mm Oerlikon GAM-B01 AA (I × 2)—2/7.62-mm mg (I × 2)
Electron Equipt:
Radar: . . .
Sonar: none—EW: . . .
M: 4 Crossley-SEMT-Pielstick 16PA6 V280 STC diesels; 2 CP props; 32,000 bhp
Electric: 1,200 kw tot. (3 × 400 kw diesels sets) **Range:** 5,500/12
Crew: 55 tot. + 30 spare

Remarks: Although an order was announced as imminent in 9-91, it was not placed until 17-3-92, while discussions continued over details of the equipment. The pair would have either the Ferranti System 500 or Signaal STACOS Mod. 4 combat system, the latter combined with the MW-08 search radar and either a STIR fire-control radar or a NobelTech 9LV Mk 2 fire-control system. The ships would be fitted for later installation of a vertical-launch surface-to-air missile system and are to have a helicopter deck but no hangar. Will have no provision for ASW, despite the new threat of Iranian submarines.

GUIDED-MISSILE PATROL BOATS

◆ **4 "Province" class** Bldr: Vosper Thornycroft, Portchester, U.K.

	Laid down	L	In serv.
B 10 DHOFAR	30-9-80	14-10-81	7-8-82
B 11 AL SHARQUIYAH	10-81	2-12-82	5-12-83
B 12 AL BAT'NAH	9-12-81	11-82	18-1-84
B 14 MUSSANDAM	8-10-87	19-3-88	31-3-89

D: 311 tons light (363 fl) **S:** 40 kts
Dim: 56.7 (52.0 pp) × 8.2 × 2.1 (hull)
A: 6–8/MM 40 Exocet SSM (III or IV × 2)—1/76-mm 62-cal. OTO Melara Compact DP—2/40-mm 70-cal. Breda AA (II × 1)—2/12.7-mm mg (I × 2)

GUIDED-MISSILE PATROL BOATS *(continued)*

Al Sharquiyah (B 11) Royal Omani Navy, 1990

Dhofar (B 10)—with AWS-4 radar, 6 Exocet J. St. J. Wilkes, 1988

Electron Equipt:
Radar: B 11: 1/Decca 1226 nav., 1/Plessey AWS-4; others: 1/Decca TM 1226 nav., 1/PEAB 9LV 300 syst.
EW: Racal 242 suite (Cutlass intercept, Scorpion jammer, Sadie processor), 2 Wallops Barricade decoy RL (IX × 2)
M: 4 Paxman Valenta 18RP200 diesels; 4 props; 17,900 bhp (15,000 sust.)— 2/80-hp electric outdrives
Electric: 420 kw **Fuel:** 45.5 tons **Range:** 2,000/15
Crew: 5 officers, 40 enlisted, plus 19 trainees

Remarks: B 10 ordered 1980; B 11, 12 in 1-81; B 14 ordered 3-1-86. B 10 sailed for Oman 21-10-82. B 10 has the Sperry Sea Archer Mk 2 fire-control system, with two optical trackers. Complement includes trainees. B 11–14 have 8/MM 40 Exocet (IV × 2), PEAB 9LV 300 f.c.s. with I-band search radar and J-band radar/electro-optical fire-control director forward and a separate t.v./IR director aft for the 40-mm AA. The Exocet launchers have now been "boxed-in" with metal heat shielding. Similar ships are operated by Egypt and Kenya, and the U.S. Navy is building 13 variants of the design with greatly reduced armament.

PATROL BOATS

Note: Planned are two 45-meter patrol boats; no details available.

♦ **4 37.5-meter class** Bldr: Brooke Marine Ltd., Lowestoft, U.K.

	In serv.		In serv.
B 4 AL WAFI	24-3-77	B 6 AL AUL	20-7-77
B 5 AL FULK	24-3-77	B 7 AL JABBAR	6-10-77

D: 153 tons (166 fl) **S:** 25 kts **Dim:** 37.50 × 6.86 × 1.78
A: 1/76-mm 62-cal. OTO Melara Compact DP—1/20-mm Oerlikon GAM-B01 AA—2/7.62-mm mg (I × 2)
Electron Equipt: Radar: 1/Decca 1226 or 1229 nav.
M: 2 Paxman Ventura 16 RP200 diesels; 2 props; 4,800 bhp
Range: 3,250/12 **Crew:** 3 officers, 24 enlisted

Al Wafi (B 4) Royal Omani Navy, 1990

Remarks: Ordered 26-4-74. Carry 130 rounds 76-mm ammunition. Sperry "Sea Archer" fire-control system, with Lawrence Scott optical director. The similar, missile-equipped *Al Mansur* (B 2) was stricken in 1986.

PATROL CRAFT

♦ **4 25-meter class** Bldr: Vosper Pty, Singapore (In serv. 15-3-81)

B 20 AL SEEB B 21 AL SHINAS B 22 AL SADAH B 23 AL KHASAB

Al Shinas (B 21) Royal Omani Navy, 19

D: 60.7 tons (75 fl) **S:** 26 kts
Dim: 25.00 (23.00 pp) × 5.80 × 1.50
A: 1/20-mm Oerlikon GAM-B01 AA—2/7.62-mm mg (I × 2)
Electron Equipt: Radar: 1/Decca 1226 nav.
M: 2 MTU 12V331 TC92 diesels, plus 1 Cummins N855M cruise diese (197 bhp); 3 props; 3,072 bhp
Range: 750/14; 2,300/8 **Crew:** 13 tot.

Remarks: Ordered 24-4-81. Craft had been completed 1980 on speculation by buil Glass-reinforced plastic hulls. Have five spare berths. Max. speed on cruise die 8 kts.

♦ **2 Tyler Vortex class** Bldr: Cheverton, Cowes (In serv. 1981)

QRB 1 QRB 2

D: 12 tons **S:** 30 kts **Dim:** 12.1 (11.5 pp) × 4.6 × . . .
A: . . . **M:** 2 Sabre 500 diesels; 2 props; 1,000 bhp

Remarks: Officially typed as "Quick-reaction Boats."

AMPHIBIOUS WARFARE SHIPS AND CRAFT

♦ **1 troop and vehicle transport** Bldr: Bremer-Vulkan, Bremen-Vegesack, Germany

	Laid down	L	In s
L3 FULK AL SALAMAH (ex-*Ghubat al Salamah,* ex-*Tulip*)	17-1-86	29-8-86	3-

Fulk al Salamah (L 3) French Navy,

Fulk al Salamah (L 3) Maritime Photographi

AMPHIBIOUS WARFARE SHIPS AND CRAFT *(continued)*

D: approx. 10,000 tons (fl) **S:** 19.5 kts **Dim:** 136.4 × 21.0 × 6.0
A: none **Electron Equipt:** Radar: 2/Decca . . . nav.
M: 4 G.M.T. A420.6 diesels; 2 props; 16,800 bhp
Range: . . . . **Crew:** . . .

Remarks: 10,864 grt/5,186 nrt combination attack transport/logistic support vessel. Has VHF SATCOMM equipment, hangar and flight deck for two AS-332C Super Puma :ransport helicopters, two Sea Truck landing craft in davits below the helicopter deck, arge cargo hold forward, accommodations for at least 240 troops, and a large vehicle oading door to starboard (plus four personnel/stores doors through the hull sides). *'ulip* was cover name while building. Delivered without armament. Was attached to he United Nations UNESCO organization during 1991 as an "investigation ship."

◆ **1 Nasr Al Bahr-class landing ship** Bldr: Brooke Marine, Lowestoft, U.K.

	Laid down	L	In serv.
2 Nasr al Bahr	. . .	16-5-84	13-2-85

asr al Bahr (L 2) Mike Louagie, 5-90

D: 2,500 tons (fl) **S:** 15.5 kts
Dim: 93.00 (80.00 pp) × 15.50 × 2.3 (mean)
A: 4/40-mm 70-cal. Breda AA (II × 2)—2/20-mm Oerlikon GAM-B01 AA (I × 2)
Electron Equipt:
Radar: 1/Decca 1226 nav., 1/Decca 1290 nav.
EW: . . . intercept; 2 Barricade RL (IX × 2)
M: 2 Paxman Valenta 18RP200CM diesels; 2 CP props; 7,800 bhp
Range: 4,000/13 **Endurance:** 28 days (10 days with troops)
Crew: 13 officers, 16 chief petty officers, 52 enlisted + troops: 13 officers, 16 noncommissioned officers, 211 enlisted

narks: Ordered 18-3-82. A refined version of the *Al Munassir* design. Two also t for Algeria. Vehicle deck 75 m × 7.4 m, with 30-m × 7-m cargo hatch; bow ramp n long by 4.5 m wide; stern ramp: 5 m by 4 m. Intended to land 450 tons cargo or en main battle tanks on a gradient of up to 1:40. Two Sea Truck LCVP carried. icopter deck for one Sea King/Commando or Super Puma helicopter. Traveling on crane spans cargo deck forward. Max. cargo: 650 tons. PEAB 9LV 200 weapons rol system with one CSEE Lynx electro-optical gunsight; 2,000 rds 40 mm, 0 rds 20 mm, 244 chaff rounds.

1 logistic support landing ship (in reserve)

	Bldr	Laid down	L	In serv.
Al Munassir	Brooke Marine, Lowestoft	4-7-77	25-7-78	3-4-79

lunassir (L 1) French Navy, 5-81

2,169 tons (fl) **S:** 12 kts
n: 84.0 (81.25 pp) × 15.03 × 2.15 (max.)
1/76-mm 62-cal. OTO Melara DP—2/20-mm Oerlikon GAM-B01 AA (I × 2)
ctron Equipt: Radar: 1/Decca TM 1229 nav.
2 Mirrlees-Blackstone ESL8MGR diesels; 2 CP props; 2,400 bhp
nge: 2,500/12 **Crew:** 9 officers, 38 enlisted + 188 troops

Remarks: Greatly modified version of British *Ardennes* class built by the same builder. Cargo: 550 tons of stores or 8 heavy tanks. Has bow doors and ramp for beaching. Large helicopter deck aft can accommodate Sea King/Commando or Super Puma helicopter and is spanned by a 16-ton-capacity traveling crane. Unusually bluff-bowed hull form. Sperry "Sea Archer" weapons-control system with Lawrence Scott optical fire-control director. Maintained in reserve and used for harbor training.

◆ **3 utility landing craft** Bldr: Vosper Pty, Singapore

	Laid down	L	In serv.
C 8 Saba al Bahr	. . .	30-6-81	17-9-81
C 9 Al Doghas	9-7-82	12-11-82	10-1-83
C 10 Al Temsah	8-9-82	15-12-82	12-2-83

Al Doghas (C 9) Royal Omani Navy, 1990

D: 230 tons (fl) **S:** 8 kts **Dim:** 30.0 (25.6 pp) × 8.0 × 1.2
M: 2 Caterpillar 3408 TA diesels; 2 props; 1,840 bhp
Range: 1,800/8 **Crew:** 11 tot.

Remarks: C 8 ordered 24-4-81, C 9 and C 10 in 7-82. Cargo: 100 tons vehicles or stores, or 45 tons deck cargo plus 50 tons fresh water (plus 35 tons water ballast). C 9 and C 10 are 33 m overall.

◆ **1 utility landing craft** Bldr: Lewis Offshore, Stornaway, Scotland

C 7 Al Neemran (In serv. 1979)

D: 85 dwt **S:** 8 kts **Dim:** 25.5 × 7.4 × 1.8 **M:** 2 diesels; 300 bhp

◆ **1 75-foot Loadmaster-class landing craft** Bldr: Cheverton, Cowes, U.K.

C 4 Al Sansoor (In serv. 1-75)

D: 64 tons (130 fl) **S:** 8.75 kts **Dim:** 22.86 × 6.1 × 1.07 (max.)
M: 2 diesels; 2 props; 300 bhp

Remarks: Sister *Al Doghas* (C 5) stricken 1981. Employed since 1967 as a fuel-tank-cleaning craft.

AUXILIARY SHIPS

◆ **1 training ship** Bldr: Brooke Marine, Lowestoft, U.K.

	L	In serv.
A 1 Al Mabrukah (ex-*Al Said*)	7-4-70	1971

Al Mabrukah (A 1) Leo Van Ginderen, 1991

D: 785 tons (930 fl) **S:** 17 kts **Dim:** 54.70 × 10.70 × 3.05
A: 1/40-mm 70-cal. Bofors AA—2/20-mm Oerlikon GAM-B01 AA (I × 2)
Electron Equipt:
Radar: 1/Decca TM 1226 nav.
EW: . . . intercept, 2 Barricade RL (IX × 2)
M: 2 Paxman Ventura 12YJCM diesels; 2 props; 3,350 bhp
Crew: 11 officers, 23 enlisted + 37 passengers/trainees

AUXILIARY SHIPS *(continued)*

Remarks: Renamed and converted from royal yacht to fleet training ship at builders 1-83 to 4-84. Received new accommodations arrangements, communications suit, and armament; the helicopter deck was enlarged. Occasionally used on patrol duties.

◆ **1 supply ship** Bldr: Conoship, Groningen, the Netherlands

	L	In serv.
A 2 AL SULTANA	18-5-75	4-6-75

Al Sultana (A 2) Royal Omani Navy, 1990

D: 900 tons (1,380 dwt) **S:** 11 kts **Dim:** 65.4 × 10.7 × 4.2
A: none **Electron Equipt:** Radar: 1/Decca TM1226 nav.
M: 1 Mirrlees-Blackstone diesel; 1,150 bhp **Crew:** 20 tot.

Remarks: Traveling crane straddles one continuous hold. Replaced in training role by *Al Mabrukah.*

◆ **1 inshore survey craft** Bldr: Watercraft, U.K. (In serv. 4-81)

H 1 AL RAHMANYAI

Al Rahmanyai (H 1) Royal Omani Navy, 1990

D: 23.6 tons (fl) **S:** 13.5 kts **Dim:** 15.5 (14.0 pp) × 4.0 × 12.5
Electron Equipt: Radar: 1/Decca 101 nav.
M: 2 Volvo TMD 120A diesels; 2 props; 520 bhp
Electric: 25 kVA **Range:** 500/12 **Crew:** . . . tot.

Remarks: Glass-reinforced plastic construction. Raytheon DE 719B and Kelvin-Hughes MS 48 echo-sounders, Decca DMU transponder and Sea Fix receiver, and Hewlett-Packard 9815A data-storage computer fitted.

◆ **1 sail-training craft** Bldr: Hard & MacKenzie, Buckie, Scotland (In serv. . . .)

S 1 SHABAB OMAN (Ex-*Youth of Oman*, ex-*Captain Scott*)

D: 386 tons **S:** . . . **Dim:** 44.0 × 8.5 × 4.6
M: 2 diesels; 1 prop; . . . bhp
Crew: 5 officers, 15 enlisted + 3 officer/instructors, 24 trainees

Remarks: Three-masted barkentine, purchased 1977 in U.K. for training Omani youth in seamanship and commissioned 1979.

◆ **10 miscellaneous workboats** Bldr: Cheverton, Cowes, U.K.

W 4, 5, 7–11 WF 41–43 (In serv. 4-75)

D: 3.5 tons **S:** 25 kts **Dim:** 8.28 × 2.7 × 0.8 **M:** 2 diesels

◆ **1 or more Sea Flash radio-controlled target boats** Bldr: Flight Refuelling, U.K. (In serv. 1987)

Shabab Oman (S 1) Leo Van Ginderen, 8-9

ROYAL YACHT SQUADRON

◆ **1 royal yacht** Bldr: Picchiotti, Viareggio, Italy (In serv. 1982)

AL SAID

Al Said Ben Sullivan, 7-

D: 3,250 tons (fl) **S:** 18 kts **Dim:** 106.0 × 17.0 × 5.0
Electron Equipt: 1/Decca TM 1226C nav., 1/Decca ACS 1230C nav.
M: 2 GMT A420-6 diesels; 2 CP props; 8,400 bhp
Crew: 16 officers, 140 enlisted

Remarks: Replaced former *Al Said* (now training ship *Al Mabrukah*). Not conside to be a naval vessel, unlike her predecessor. Helicopter pad, bow-thruster, V SATCOMM, fin-stabilizers. Carries one Rotork LCVP and three launches. Refittec Devonport DY, U.K., for 8 weeks in mid-1988.

ROYAL OMAN POLICE

Aviation: Two Pilatus Porter light transports for search-and-rescue duties, delive 4-84.

PATROL BOATS AND CRAFT

Note: Tenders out for six new patrol craft 2-88, but no order announced as of 2-9

◆ **1 P 2000 class** Bldr: Watercraft Ltd., Shoreham, U.K.

DHEEB AL BAHAR 1 (In serv. 12-84)

D: 80 tons **S:** 38 kts **Dim:** 20.80 (18.00 pp) × 5.80 × 1.50
A: 1/20-mm Oerlikon GAM-B01 AA—2/7.62-mm mg (I × 2)
Electron Equipt: Radar: 1/Furuno FR-701 nav.
M: 2 MTU 12V396 TB93 diesels; 2 props; 3,920 bhp (3,260 sust.)
Range: 423/35; 660/22 **Crew:** 8 tot.

Remarks: Glass-reinforced plastic construction, with aluminum superstructure

◆ **2 P 1200 class** Bldr: Watercraft Ltd., Shoreham, U.K. (In serv.9-84)

D: 10 tons **S:** 35 kts **Dim:** 11.90 (10.16 pp) × 4.08 × 1.06
A: 1/12.7-mm mg—6/7.62-mm mg (I × 6)
Electron Equipt: Radar: 1/. . . nav.
M: 2 M.A.N. diesels; 2 props; 1,100 bhp
Range: 300/. . . **Crew:** 8 tot.

Remarks: Ordered 7-82. Glass-reinforced plastic construction.

◆ **1 Type PT 1903 Mk III patrol craft** Bldr: Le Comte, Vianen, th Netherlands

HARAS 8 (In serv. 8-81)

D: 30 tons (33 fl) **S:** 30 kts **Dim:** 19.27 × 4.95 × 1.25
A: 2/12.7-mm mg (I × 2) **Range:** 1,650/17; 2,300/12
M: 2 MTU 8V331 TC92 diesels; 2 props; 1,770 bhp
Crew: 10 tot.

OMAN *(continued)*
PATROL BOATS AND CRAFT *(continued)*

heeb al Bahar John Bouvia, 1991

3 CG 29 class Bldr: Karlskrona Varvet, Karlskrona, Sweden

ARAS 7 (In serv. 6-81) HARAS 9 (In serv. 1982)
ARAS 10 (In serv. 14-4-82)

ras 10 John Bouvia, 1991

): 82 tons (fl) S: 25 kts Dim: 28.9 × 5.4 × 1.3
**\: 2/20-mm Oerlikon GAM-B01 AA (I × 2)
lectron Equipt: Radar: 1/Decca 1226C
1: 2 MTU 8V331 IC82 diesels; 2 props; 1,866 bhp **Range:** 600/15
rew: 13 tot.

narks: Aluminum construction, enlarged version of design built for Liberia. *as 9* also reported to have MTU 12V396 diesels.

1 CG 27 class Bldr: Karlskrona, Sweden (In serv. 1980)

RAS 6

): 53 tons (fl) S: 27 kts **Dim:** 24.0 × 5.5 × 1.0
.: 1/20-mm Oerlikon GAM-B01 AA **Crew:** 11 tot.
I: 2 MTU 12V331 diesels; 2 props; 2,800 bhp

narks: Glass-reinforced plastic construction.

Haras 1-class fiberglass-hulled Bldr: Vosper Pty., Singapore

AS 1–4 (In serv. 22-12-75) HARAS 5 (In serv. 11-78)

s 1 1980

D: 45 tons (fl) **S:** 24.5 kts **Dim:** 22.9 × 6.0 × 1.5
A: 1/20-mm Oerlikon GAM-B01 AA
Electron Equipt: Radar: 1/Decca 101
M: 2 Caterpillar D348 diesels; 2 props; 1,840 bhp
Range: 600/20; 1,000/11 **Crew:** 11 tot.

◆ **5 small patrol craft** Bldr: *Zahra 14–17:* Watercraft, Shoreham (In serv. 1981); *Zahra 18, 21:* Emsworth SY, UK (In serv. 1987)

ZAHRA 14 ZAHRA 15 ZAHRA 17 ZAHRA 18 ZAHRA 21

Zahra 15 and a sister John Bouvia, 1991

D: 17.25 tons (fl) **S:** 22 kts **Dim:** 13.9 (12.6 wl) × 4.3 × 1.1
M: 2 Cummins VTA-903M diesels; 2 props; 700 bhp
A: 1/7.62-mm mg **Range:** 700/20 **Crew:** 6 tot.

Remarks: Last two begun (hulls moulded) in 1981, finished by Emsworth. Hulls are to standard Keith Nelson design. Have a navigational radar.

◆ **3 landing craft** Bldr: Le Comte, Vianen, the Netherlands (In serv. 1981–82)

ZAHRA 16 ZAHRA 20 ZAHRA 22

D: 11 tons (23 fl) **S:** 20 kts **Dim:** 18.0 × 3.0 × 0.5
A: 2/7.62-mm mg (I × 2) **Range:** . . . **Crew:** 4 tot.
M: 2 Volvo Penta AQD 70/750 diesel outdrives; 540 bhp

Remarks: *Zahra 20* used as a fueling tender. *Zahra 22* is 16.0 m o.a. Have Decca navigational radars.

Note: Also in service are *Zahra* 4–11 (3.5-ton, 8.2-m, 25-kt Cheverton workboats acquired 1975); one 19-m and one 18-m tender delivered by Le Comte, Vianen, the Netherlands, in 1983; a 16-m craft and an 8.2-m workboat delivered by Cheverton, Cowes, U.K., in 1983; and two 8.5-m patrol craft powered by 2/140-hp Evinrude outboards for 40 kts, delivered in 1985 by Gulf Craft, Ajman, United Arab Emirates.

PAKISTAN

Islamic Republic of Pakistan

Note: Fleet goals include the eventual acquisition of nuclear submarines, six destroyers, six (three already ordered) long-range maritime patrol aircraft, four conventional submarines, and coast-defense missiles. Recent rapid expansion has placed strains on personnel and logistics resources, and the embargo placed on the delivery of military equipment and spares by the United States has hurt readiness.

Personnel (1991): 1,325 officers, 15,000 enlisted—plus 5,000 reservists. A Marine Corps was formally established on 25-11-90; it is intended to grow to brigade size.

Naval Aviation: The naval arm consists of: five Westland Sea King Mk 45 and one Mk 45C helicopters (111 Squadron) armed with AM-39 Exocet antiship missiles, four Alouette-III helicopters (333 Squadron: two are equipped with radar, MAD, and torpedoes for shipboard use), two Cessna liaison aircraft, and two Fokker F-27-200 maritime patrol aircraft (27 Squadron). The four Bréguet Atlantic Mk 1 maritime patrol aircraft of 29 Squadron have been retired.

On 1-1-88, three Lockheed P-3C Update II.5 Orion were ordered, and in 5-89, six SH-2F LAMPS I helicopters (with option for three more) with T58-6E turbines were ordered from Kaman; delivery of the completed P-3Cs and the helicopters has been embargoed by the U.S.A.

Pakistani P-3C Orion—now in storage in U.S.A.
Naval Aviation News, 1991

NAVAL AVIATION *(continued)*

All six of Pakistan's Sea King helicopters Pakistani Navy, 1990

SUBMARINES

Note: Discussions with China over the possible purchase or lease of a Han-class nuclear-powered attack submarine appear to have halted with the return of India's leased Charlie-I-class submarine to the U.S.S.R. In the mid-1980s, China and Pakistan also discussed the possible purchase of Romeo or Ming-class diesel submarines.

◆ 2 French Agosta class Bldr: Dubigeon, Nantes

	Laid down	L	In serv.
S 135 HASHMAT (ex-*Astrant*)	15-9-76	14-12-77	17-2-79
S 136 HURMAT (ex-*Adventurous*)	. . .	1-12-78	18-2-80

Hashmat (S 135) Pakistani Navy, 1990

D: 1,230 tons std./1,480 tons max. surf./1,725 tons sub.
S: 12.5 kts surf./20.5 kts sub. **Dim:** 67.90 × 6.80 × 5.40
A: 4/550-mm TT fwd (20 F-17P torpedoes and Sub-Harpoon SSM)
Electron Equipt:
Radar: 1/Thomson-CSF DRUA-33 nav./surf. search
Sonar: all Thomson-Sintra: DUUA-1D active HF, DUUA-2A/B active/passive search/attack (8 kHz), DSUV-2H passive, DUUX-2A passive-ranging
EW: ARUR intercept, ARUD intercept
M: 2 SEMT-Pielstick A16 PA4 185 diesels, electric drive; 1 prop; 4,600 shp—1 23-hp cruise motor
Range: 7,900/10 (snorkel); 178/3.5 (submerged) **Fuel:** 200 tons
Crew: 7 officers, 47 enlisted

Remarks: Originally ordered for South Africa, but sale canceled in 1977 by arms embargo and completion slowed. Sold to Pakistan in 11-78. Very quiet, highly automated submarines. Diving depth: 300 m. Battery capacity twice that of the *Daphné* class. Fitted for U.S. Sub-Harpoon antiship missiles in 1984–85.

◆ 4 French Daphné class

	Bldr	Laid down	L	In serv.
S 131 HANGOR	Naval Arsenal, Brest	1-12-67	30-6-69	12-1-70
S 132 SHUSHUK	C.N. Ciotat, Le Trait	1-12-67	30-7-69	12-1-70
S 133 MANGRO	C.N. Ciotat, Le Trait	8-7-68	7-2-70	8-8-70
S 134 GHAZI (ex-*Cachalote*)	Dubigeon, Nantes	27-10-66	16-2-68	25-1-69

Ghazi (S 134) U.S. Navy, 1991

D: 700 tons std./869 tons surf./1,043 tons sub.
S: 13.5 kts surf./16 kts sub. **Dim:** 57.75 × 6.75 × 4.56
A: 12/550-mm TT (8 fwd, 4 aft, no reloads; L5 Mod. 3 torpedoes, Sub-Harpoon SSM)
Electron Equipt:
Radar: 1/ Thomson-CSF DRUA 31 nav./surf. search
Sonar: all Thomson-Sintra: DUUA-1 active/passive search/attack, DSUV-1 passive search
EW: ARUR intercept, ARUD intercept
M: 2 SEMT-Pielstick 12PA4-135 450-kw diesel generator sets; 2 1,300-shp (1,000 sust.) electric motors; 2 props
Range: 4,300/7.5 (snorkel) **Crew:** 5 officers, 45 enlisted

Remarks: S 134 purchased in 12-75 from Portugal. S 131 sank the Indian frigat *Khukri* in 1971. Diving depth: 300 m. U.S. Sub-Harpoon capability added 1985–86.

◆ 4 (+ . . .) SX-756-class midget submarines Bldr: COS.M.O.S., Livorno, Italy

D: 78 tons surf./83 tons sub.
S: 9 kts surf. (7 kts cruise)/6 kts sub.
Dim: 25.20 × 2.02 × 5.40 (high)
A: 2/533-mm torpedoes in drop gear or 8/300-kg mines
M: 1 diesel generator set, 1 electric motor; 1/3-bladed prop; . . . shp
Range: 1,600/7 surf.; 60/4.5 sub.
Crew: 6 crew + 8 combat swimmers

Remarks: Began delivery 1988 to replace the earlier SX-404-class midget subs, whi have all been retired; at least two more are expected to be completed. Diving dep 100 m maximum. A number of two-man Chariots from the same builder are also service.

DESTROYERS

Note: Pakistan has expressed interest in obtaining four U.S. *Charles F. Adams*-cl guided-missile destroyers, should the arms embargo be lifted.

◆ 1 ex-U.K. County class Bldr: Swan Hunter & Wigham Richardson, Wallsend-on-Tyne, U.K.

	Laid down	L	In serv.
C 84 BABUR (ex-*London*, D 16)	26-2-60	7-12-61	4-11-63

Babur (C 84) *Ships of the World,*

D: 5,440 tons (6,200 fl) **S:** 32.5 kts (30 sust.)
Dim: 158.55 (153.90 pp) × 16.46 × 6.30 (max.)
A: 4/114-mm 45-cal. Mk 6 DP (II × 2)—6/37-mm Soviet V-47M AA × 3)—4/23-mm Soviet ZSU-23 AA (IV × 2)—1/20-mm U.S. Mk CIWS gatling AA—1/Alouette-III helicopter
Electron Equipt:
Radar: 1/ Decca Type 978 nav., 1/Marconi Type 965M early warning, 1/Marconi Type 992Q air/surf. search, 1/Type 27 height-finder, 1/Plessey Type 903 gun f.c.
Sonar: Graseby Type 177 hull-mounted (MF), Type 177 passive torpedo-warning, Type 162 hull-mountd bottomed-target classification (HF)
EW: Argo APECS-II intercept/jammer suite, 2/Knebworth/Corv chaff RL (VIII × 2)
M: COSAG: 2 sets A.E.I. geared steam turbines (15,000 shp each) a 4 G6 gas turbines (7,500 shp each); 2 props; 60,000 shp
Boilers: 2 Babcock & Wilcox; 43.3 kg/cm², 510° C superheat
Fuel: 600 tons **Electric:** 3,750 kw **Range:** 3,500/28
Crew: 36 officers, 434 enlisted

Remarks: Purchased from U.K. on 22-3-82 and commissioned 22-4-82. Conside be a cruiser by Pakistan and employed primarily as a training ship.
The obsolete Sea Slug Mk 1 missile launcher, with its attendant Type 901 radar, initially remained aboard but was inactivated and removed in 1984 (alt

DESTROYERS *(continued)*

ts associated Type 277 height-finding radar has been retained); the magazine space is ısed for accommodations for trainees. Although the two Sea Cat point-defense missile aunchers have been retained, their radar directors have been replaced by two twin 37-mm AA, and the missile system is no longer operational. The 114-mm guns are controlled by a single MRS.3 director with Type 903 radar.

Extension of the helicopter flight deck was completed 7-88, but the original small angar, opening to port, was retained. U.S. Vulcan/Phalanx CIWS is atop the leckhouse abaft the hangar, and ZSU-23 AA mounts are located abreast the foremast nd on the fantail. The EW suite incorporates the AR-700 receiver (0.5-18 gHz coverge) and two stabilized jammer antennas; the same system is mounted on Pakistani Gearing-class destroyers.

◆ **4 ex-U.S. Gearing, FRAM-I class**

	Bldr	Laid down	L	In serv.
D 160 ALAMGIR (ex-*Cone,* DD 866)	Bethlehem SY, Staten Island	30-11-44	10-5-45	18-8-45
D 164 SHAHJAHAN (ex-*Harold J. Ellison,* DD 864)	Bethlehem SY, Staten Island	3-10-44	14-3-45	18-12-46
D 166 TAIMUR (ex-*Epperson,* DD 719)	Todd Pacific SY, Seattle, Wash.	20-6-45	29-12-45	19-3-49
D 167 TUGHRIL (ex-*Henderson,* DD 785)	Todd Pacific SY, Seattle, Wash.	27-10-44	28-5-44	4-8-45

Tughril (D 167) Mike Louagie, 10-88

D: 2,425 tons (3,460 fl) **S:** 30 kts
Dim: 119.00 × 12.45 × 5.80 (max.)
A: 6/Harpoon SSM (III × 2)—2/127-mm 38-cal. Mk 30 DP (II × 1)—8/23-mm ZSU-23 AA (IV × 2)—1/20-mm Mk 15 CIWS (not in D 164)— 1/Mk 116 ASROC ASW RL (VIII, 17 missiles)—6/324-mm Mk 32 ASW TT (III × 2)—1/Alouette-III helicopter
Electron Equipt:
Radar: 1/Decca nav., 1/SPS-10B surf. search, 1/Lockheed SPS-40 air search, 1/Western Electric Mk 25 gun f.c.
Sonar: SQS-23D hull-mounted MF (with Raytheon DE 1191 solid-state transmitter)
EW: Argo APECS II intercept/jammer suite, 2/Plessey Shield decoy RL (VI × 2)
M: 2 sets G.E. geared steam turbines; 2 props; 60,000 shp
Boilers: 4 Babcock & Wilcox; 43.3 kg/cm², 454° C **Fuel:** 600 tons
Range: 2,400/25; 4,800/15 **Electric:** 1,300 kw
Crew: 27 officers, 247 enlisted

Remarks: D 166 bought 29-4-77 and overhauled at Puget Sound NSY to 16-2-78. ? bought 30-9-80, D 160 on 1-10-82, and D 164 on 1-10-83. Sister *Tariq* (D 165, *iltsie,* DD 716, purchased 29-4-77) was placed in unmaintained reserve 1988, and *Sultan* (D 168, ex-*Damato,* DD 871) has been transferred to the Maritime ity Agency. The survivors received new sonar transmitters in 1984–85, and three been equipped with the Vulcan/Phalanx CIWS in place of the former aft twin ım mount. The 23-mm mounts flank the forward stack. The helicopter facility is tional, but it is seldom used.

GUIDED-MISSILE FRIGATES

◆ **ex-U.S. Brooke class** Bldr: Bath Iron Works (D 162: Lockheed SB, Seattle)

	Laid down	L	In serv.
D 161 BADR (ex-*Julius A. Furer,* FFG 6)	12-7-65	22-7-66	11-11-67
D 162 KHAIBAR (ex-*Brooke,* FFG 1)	10-12-62	19-7-63	12-3-66
D 163 TABUK (ex-*Richard L. Page,* FFG 5)	9-1-65	4-4-66	5-8-67
D 169 HUNAIN (ex-*Talbot,* FFG 4)	4-5-64	6-1-66	2-4-67

D: 2,643 tons (3,600 fl) **S:** 29 kts (27.2 sust)
Dim: 123.33 (121.90 wl) × 13.47 × 7.90 (over sonar)
A: 1/Mk 22 SAM launcher (I × 1, 16 Standard SM-1MR missiles)—1/127-mm 38-cal. DP—1/MK 116 ASROC ASW RL (VIII × 1, 8 reloads in all but D 162)—6/324-mm Mk 32 ASW TT (III × 2)—1/Alouette-III helicopter

Hunain (D 169)—with *Badr* (D 161) in background
Pakistani Navy, 1990

Hunain (D 169) Alexandre Sheldon-Duplaix, 7-89

Electron Equipt:
Radar: 1/LN-66 nav., 1/SPS-I0F surf. search, 1/SPS-52B air search/height-finder, 1/SPG-51C SAM illuminator, 1/Mk 35 gun f.c.
Sonar: SQS-26AX or BX hull-mounted LF—TACAN: SRN-15
EW: SLQ-32 (V)2 intercept, Mk 36 SRBOC decoy RL syst. (VI × 2)
M: 1 set G.E. (D 162: Westinghouse) geared steam turbines; 1 prop; 35,000 shp
Boilers: 2 Foster-Wheeler; 84 kg/cm², 510° C turbopressurized
Range: 4,000/20 **Fuel:** 600 tons **Electric:** 2,000 kw
Crew: 17 officers, 260 enlisted

Remarks: All acquired on 5-year lease. D 161 decommissioned from U.S. Navy 10-11-88 and recommissioned by Pakistan 31-1-89; D 162 decommissioned 17-9-88 and recommissioned 8-2-89; D 163 decommissioned 30-9-88 and recommissioned 31-3-89; D 169 decommissioned 30-9-88 and recommissioned 31-5-89. All considered to be "destroyers" because of their surface-to-air missile systems.

The SH-2G LAMPS I ASW helicopters ordered for operation from all four have not been delivered; the hangar is telescoping. Have obsolescent Mk 56 Mod. 43 director for 127-mm gun; missile *system* is Mk 74 Mod. 6 with Mk 4 Mod. 2 weapons-control system. Have Mk 114 ASW fire-control system. Did not receive Harpoon SSM capability. D 161 has SQS-26AXR sonar, the others SQS-26BX. Do not have SLQ-25 Nixie torpedo decoy system. Equipped with fin stabilizers. Complex engineering system may make it difficult to keep them operational.

FRIGATES

◆ **2 ex-U.K. "Broad-beamed Leander" class** Bldr: Yarrow, Scotstoun, Glasgow, Scotland

	Laid down	L	In serv.
F 262 ZULFIQUAR (ex-*Apollo,* F 70)	1-5-69	15-10-70	28-5-72
F 263 SHAMSHER (ex-*Diomede,* F 16)	30-1-68	15-4-69	2-4-71

Zulfiquar (F 262) Alexandre Sheldon-Duplaix, 11-88

FRIGATES *(continued)*

Shamsher (F 263) Leo Van Ginderen, 7-88

D: 2,660 tons (3,120 fl) **S:** 27 kts
Dim: 113.38 (109.73 pp) × 13.12 × 4.50 (5.49 props)
A: 2/114-mm 45-cal. Mk 6 DP (II × 1)—1/Sea Cat GWS.22 SAM system (IV × 1)—2 (F 262: 4)/20-mm Oerlikon AA (I × 2; F 262 also: II × 1)—1/Limbo ASW mortar (III × 1)—1/SA-319B Alouette-III helicopter
Electron Equipt:
Radar: 1/Kelvin-Hughes Type 1006 nav., 1/Plessey Type 994 surf./air search, 1/Marconi Type 965 early warning, 1/Plessey Type 903 gun f.c., 1/Plessey Type 904 missile f.c.
Sonar: Graseby Type 184P hull-mounted MF, Graseby Type 170B hull-mounted HF attack , Kelvin-Hughes Type 162M bottomed-target classification
EW: UA-8/9 intercept, Type 668 jammer, F 262: UA-13, F 263: FH-12 HFD/F, 2/DLC decoy RL (VIII × 2), Type 182 towed torpedo decoy
M: 2 sets White-English Electric geared steam turbines; 2 5-bladed props; 30,000 shp
Boilers: 2 Babcock & Wilcox 3-drum; 38.7 kg/cm^2, 450° C
Range: 4,500/12 **Fuel:** 500 tons **Electric:** 2,500 kw
Crew: 15 officers, 220 enlisted

Remarks: F 262 decommissioned and sold to Pakistan 14-10-88 and F 263 decommissioned 7-7-88 and sold 15-7-88. F 262 left for Pakistan 2-12-88, F 263 in 8-88. Although among the newest Royal Navy *Leanders*, they had not been modernized. Two more may be purchased on disposal by U.K. F 262 had the modern single Oerlikon 20-mm GAM-B01 AA gun removed from its stern location prior to transfer; F 263 retained a World War II–era twin 20-mm mount in the same location.

◆ **4 ex-U.S. Garcia class**

	Bldr	Laid down	L	In serv.
F 264 SAIF (ex-*Garcia*, FF 1040)	Bethlehem SY, San Francisco	16-10-62	31-10-63	21-12-64
F 265 ASLAT (ex-*O'Callahan*, FF 1051)	Defoe SB, Michigan	19-2-64	20-10-65	13-7-68
F 266 HARBAH (ex-*Brumby*, FF 1044)	Avondale SY, Westwego, La.	1-8-63	6-6-64	5-8-65
F 267 SIQQAT (ex-*Koelsch*, FF 1049)	Defoe SB, Michigan	19-2-64	8-6-65	10-6-67

D: 2,624 tons (3,400–3,560 fl) **S:** 29 kts (27 sust.)
Dim: 126.33 (121.90 wl) × 13.47 × 7.90 (over sonar)
A: 2/127-mm 38-cal. DP (I × 2)—1/Mk 116 ASROC ASW RL (VIII × 1; 8 reloads in F 265, 267)—6/324-mm Mk 32 ASW TT (III × 2)—all except F 264: 1/helicopter—*see* Remarks

Aslat (F 265) John Bouvia, 2-89

Siqqat (F 267) Alexandre Sheldon-Duplaix, 7-8

Electron Equipt:
Radar: 1/LN-66 nav., 1/SPS-10 surf. search, 1/SPS-40 air search, 1/Mk 35 f.c.
Sonar: SQS-26 BX (F 265, 267: AXR) hull-mounted LF
EW: WLR-1, WLR-3 intercept, Mk 33 RBOC decoy RL syst. (VI × 2)
TACAN: SRN-15 (not in F 264)
M: 1 set G.E. geared steam turbines; 1 prop; 35,000 shp
Electric: 2,000 kw
Boilers: 2 Foster-Wheeler; 83.4 kg/cm^2, 510° C turbopressurized
Range: 4,000/20 **Fuel:** 600 tons **Crew:** 18 officers, 252 enlisted

Remarks: Acquired on 5-year lease. F 264 decommissioned from U.S. Navy 10-11-8 and recommissioned 30-1-89 in Pakistani Navy; F 265 decommissioned 20-12-88 ar recommissioned 8-2-89; F 266 decommissioned 31-3-89 and recommissioned same dat F 267 decommissioned 31-5-89 and recommissioned same date.

All but F 264 had had original DASH ASW drone helicopter hangar replaced by 14 × 5.4-m telescoping hangar for LAMPS I manned helicopters. Have obsolescent Mk radar director for 127-mm guns, Mk 114 ASW fire-control system. ASROC relo magazine below bridge in F 265, F 267. Primarily ASW ships, with little surface AAW capability. Engineering plants difficult to maintain.

GUIDED-MISSILE PATROL BOATS

◆ **4 ex-Chinese Huangfen (Soviet Osa-I/Type 205) class**

P 1025 SABQAT P 1026 RAHAT P 1027 RAFAQAT P 1028 SADAQAT

Sadaqat (P 1028) Pakistani Navy,

D: 186.5 tons normal (205 fl) **S:** 35 kts
Dim: 38.75 × 7.60 × 1.70 (mean hull)
A: 4/HY-2 (CCS-N-1 Styx) SSM—4/25-mm Soviet 2M-8 AA (II × 2)
Electron Equipt:
Radar: 1/Square Tie surf. search/target acquisition
M: 3 M503A diesels; 3 props; 12,000 bhp **Range:** 800/30
Electric: 65 kw **Crew:** 28 tot.

Remarks: Arrived at Karachi 27-4-84 as deck cargo; probably ex-PLAN units r than new-construction.

◆ **4 ex-Chinese Hoku class**

P 1021 HAIBAT P 1022 JALALAT P 1023 JURA P 1024 SHUJAAT

D: 68 tons (79 fl) **S:** 38 kts
Dim: 27.0 × 6.3 × 1.30 mean (1.8 props)
A: 2/HY-2 (CSS-N-1 Styx) SSM (I × 2)—2/25-mm Soviet 2M-8 AA (II × 1)
Electron Equipt: Radar: 1/Pot Head surf. search
M: 4 M50F-4 diesels; 4 props; 4,800 bhp **Electric:** 65 kw
Range: 520/26 **Endurance:** 5 days **Crew:** 20 tot.

Remarks: Transferred: 2 in 10-81 and 2 in 5-82.

GUIDED-MISSILE PATROL BOATS *(continued)*

hujaat (P 1024) French Navy, 12-82

ATROL BOATS

◆ 4 Chinese Hainan class

155 BALUCHISTAN P 159 SIND P 161 SARHAD P 197 PUNJAB

aluchistan (P 155) 1978

D: 360 tons (400 fl) **S:** 30.5 kts
Dim: 58.77 × 7.20 × 2.20 (mean hull)
A: 4/57-mm/70 cal. DP (II × 2)—4/25-mm Type 2m-8 AA (II × 2)—4/ RBU-1200 ASW RL (V × 4)—2/d.c. throwers—2/d.c. racks—mines
Electron Equipt:
Radar: 1/Pot Head surf. search—Sonar: hull-mounted HF searchlight
M: 4 Type 9D diesels; 4 props; 8,800 bhp
Range: 1,000/10 **Crew:** 60 tot.

marks: First pair transferred in 1976, *Punjab* and *Sarhad* in 4-80. Were probably v-construction rather than ex-PLAN units.

8 Chinese Shanghai-II class

40 LAHORE	P 145 PISHIN	P 154 BANNU
43 MARDAN	P 147 SUKKUR	P 156 KALAT
44 GILGIT	P 149 BAHAWALPUR	

kur (P 147) French Navy, 1980

: 122.5 tons normal (134.8 fl) **S:** 28.5 kts
m: 38.78 × 5.41 × 1.55 (hull)
4/37-mm 62-cal. Type V-47M AA (II × 2)—4/25-mm 80-cal. Type 2M-8 AA (II × 2)—mines
ectron Equipt: Radar: 1/Pot Head surf. search
: 2 M50F-4, 1,200-bhp diesels, 2 12D6, 910-bhp diesels; 4 props; 4,220 bhp
ectric: 39 kw **Endurance:** 7 days
nge: 750/16.5 **Crew:** 36 tot.

Remarks: Eight transferred in 1972, four in 1973. Very primitive ships. Sisters *Quetta* (P 141), *Bannu* (P 154), *Kalat* (P 156), and *Sahival* (P 160), officially in reserve since 1982, were renovated and transferred to the Maritime Security Agency on 1-1-87 but stricken in 1990. The naval-subordinated units are in poor condition, and most are little better than hulks, stripped of armament and fittings.

◆ **1 32-meter class** Bldr: Brooke Marine, Lowestoft, U.K. (In serv. 1965)

P 140 RAJSHAHI

D: 115 tons (143 fl) **S:** 24 kts **Dim:** 32.62 (30.48 pp) × 6.10 × 1.55
A: 2/40-mm 70-cal. Bofors Mk 9 AA (I × 2)—2/14.5-mm AA (I × 2)
Electron Equipt: Radar: 1/ Decca . . . nav.
M: 2 MTU 12V538 diesels; 2 props; 3,400 bhp **Crew:** 19 tot.

Remarks: Last survivor of a class of four; one also in Bangladesh Navy. Machine guns have been added on platforms forward of the pilothouse.

TORPEDO BOATS

◆ **4 Chinese Huchuan-class semi-hydrofoils**

HDF 01 HDF 02 HDF 03 HDF 04

HDF 03 1973

D: 39 tons (45 fl) **S:** 50 kts
Dim: 22.50 × 3.80 (6.26 over foils) × 1.15 (1.12 foilborne)
A: 4/14.5-mm AA (II × 2)—2/533-mm TT
Electron Equipt: Radar: 1/Skin Head surf. search
M: 3 M50F diesels; 3 props; 3,600 bhp **Range:** 500/30
Electric: 5.6 kw **Crew:** 11 tot.

Remarks: Maintained in land storage to prevent corrosion. Cruising speed: 32 kts. Foils forward only; stern planes on surface.

MINE WARFARE SHIPS

◆ **0 (+3+3) Tripartite class** Bldr: First two: Lorient Arsenal; others: Karachi Naval Dockyard

	Laid down	L	In serv.
M . . . . (ex-*Sagittaire*, M 650)	13-11-85	9-11-88	27-7-89
M	. . .	. . .	. . .
M	. . .	. . .	. . .

Sagittaire (M 650)—prior to transfer Leo Van Ginderen, 6-91

D: 535 tons (605 fl) **S:** 15 kts on main engine, 7 kts while hunting
Dim: 51.6 (47.1 pp) × 8.96 × 2.49 hull (3.50 max.)
A: 1/20-mm 90-cal. GIAT AA—2/12.7-mm mg (I × 2)
Electron Equipt:
Radar: 1/Decca 1229 nav.—Sonar: DUBM 21B
M: 1 Brons-Werkspoor A RUB 215V12 diesel; 1 CP prop, 1,900 bhp—2 ACEC electric maneuvering props, 120 shp each; bow-thruster
Electric: 750 kw **Range:** 3,000/12
Crew: 5 officers, 23 petty officers, 21 ratings

Remarks: First three ordered 17-1-92, with option for three additional, in the culmination of a decision process begun in 8-84. The first ship will be transferred from the French Navy in 8-92, the second built at Lorient, and the third built at Karachi with French assistance. France, Belgium, and the Netherlands cooperated in building these ships for the requirements of the three countries.

Hull built of glass-reinforced polyester plastic. Have one mechanical drag sweep, and French Navy units also have the AP-4 acoustic sweep. Have the EVEC 20 automatic plotting table and Decca HiFix and Syledis radio precision navigation equipment, and two PAP-104 remote-controlled minehunting submersibles. Have a six-man portable decompression chamber module at the aft end of the forecastle deck.

MINE WARFARE SHIPS *(continued)*

◆ **2 ex-U.S. Falcon-class coastal minesweepers**

	Bldr	In serv.
M 160 Mahmood (ex-MSC 267)	Quincy Adams Yacht, Quincy, Mass.	4-57
M 165 Mukhtar (ex-MSC 274)	Bellingham SY, Bellingham, Wash.	7-59

Mukhtar (M 165) 1974

D: 320 tons (372 fl) **S:** 13 kts (8, sweeping)
Dim: 43.0 × 7.95 × 2.55
A: 4/23-mm Soviet ZSU-23 AA (IV × 1)
Electron Equipt:
Radar: 1/Decca 45 nav.—Sonar: UQS-1D HF mine-avoidance
M: 2 G.M. 8-268A diesels; 2 props; 1,200 bhp
Range: 2,500/10 **Crew:** 39 tot.

Remarks: Wooden hulls. Built under the Military Assistance Program. *Munsif* (M 166, ex-MSC 273) stricken 1979; *Murabak* (ex-MSC 262) and similar MSC 289-class units *Momin* (ex-MSC 293) and *Moshal* (ex-MSC 294) stricken 1983; *Falcon*-class *Mujahid* (M 164, ex-MSC 261) stricken 1990. Are in poor condition.

◆ **8 Chinese Futi-class (Type 312) drone minesweepers** (In serv. 1991)

MSI-01 through MSI-08

D: 46.95 tons (fl) **S:** 12 kts **Dim:** 20.94 × 4.20 × 1.30
M: 1 Type 3D12 diesel; 1 CP prop; 300 hp **Crew:** 3 tot. (for ferrying)

Remarks: Normally operated by radio control to a range of 3 n.m., but can be manned. Electric propulsion for sweeping at 1 to 5 kts. Diesel generator amidships powers integral electromagnet for magnetic sweeping and a noisemaker for actuating acoustic mines. All equipment shock-mounted. Laser precision navigation system. Officially stated not to be good sea boats.

AUXILIARY SHIPS

Note: The cargo vessel Columbialand was chartered in 12-90 to support the Pakistani Antarctic Station "Jinnah." The ship operated under joint Pakistani Navy/Military Science Agency control and carried two chartered Bell JetRanger helicopters.

◆ **1 oceanographic research ship**

	Bldr	Laid down	L	In serv.
Behr Paima	Ishikawajima Harima, Tokyo	16-2-82	. . .	17-12-82

D: . . . **S:** 13.75 kts **Dim:** 61.0 × 11.8 × 3.7
M: 2 Daihatsu diesels; 2 props; 2,000 bhp
Crew: 16 officers, 68 enlisted

Remarks: Ordered 15-4-81. 1,183 grt. Carries two hydrographic-survey launches.

◆ **1 ex-U.S. Vulcan-class repair ship** Bldr: Los Angeles SB

	Laid down	L	In serv.
A 20 Moawin (ex-*Hector*, AR 7)	28-7-41	11-11-42	7-2-44

Moawin (A 20)—prior to transfer Leo Van Ginderen, 4-83

D: 9,325 tons light (16,245 fl) **S:** 19.2 kts
Dim: 161.37 (158.5 pp) × 22.35 × 7.11
A: 4/20-mm Mk 67 AA (I × 4)
Electron Equipt: Radar: 1/CRP-1500 nav., 1/SPS-10 surf. search
M: 2 sets Allis-Chalmers geared steam turbines; 2 props; 11,535 shp
Boilers: 4 Babcock & Wilcox; 28.2 kg/cm², 382° C
Range: 15,000/14 **Fuel:** 3,800 tons **Electric:** 4,500 kw
Crew: 29 officers; 812 enlisted

Remarks: Transferred on lease 20-4-89 and towed to Subic Bay, Philippines, for reactivation, completed 4-90; had been placed in reserve 31-3-87. Very elaborately equipped repair facilities. Two 10-ton cranes. May be more or less permanently moored and carries smaller crew than when in U.S. Navy service.

◆ **1 Chinese Fuqing-class replenishment oiler**

	Bldr	L	In serv.
A 47 Nasr	Dalian SY	. . .	31-7-87

Nasr (A 47) *Ships of the World,* 199

D: 14,600 tons (21,740 fl) **S:** 18.6 kts
Dim: 160.82 × 21.80 × 9.40
A: 4/37-mm 62-cal. V-47M AA (II × 2)
Electron Equipt: Radar: 2/Decca 1226 nav.
M: 1 Dalian-Sulzer 8 RLB 66 diesel; 1 prop; 17,400 bhp
Range: 18,000/14.6 **Crew:** 26 officers, 120 enlisted

Remarks: Two liquid and one solid transfer stations per side. Helicopter deck ca accommodate a Sea King or Alouette-III, but there is no hangar. Four electric cran and two derricks for cargo handling. Can carry 11,000 tons fuel oil, 1,000 tons dies fuel, 200 tons feedwater, 200 tons potable water, and 50 tons of lube oil.

◆ **1 ex-U.S. T-2-SE-A2-class replenishment oiler** Bldr: Marinship Corp., Sausalito, California (In serv. 21-6-44)

A 41 Dacca (ex-*Mission Santa Clara,* TAO 132)

Dacca (A 41)—with *Hangor* (S 131) alongside 1

D: 5,730 tons light (22,380 fl) **S:** 15 kts
Dim: 159.57 (153.32 pp) × 20.73 × 9.45
A: 6/40-mm Mk 3 AA (I × 6)
Electron Equipt: Radar: 1/. . . nav.
M: 2 sets G.E. geared steam turbines, electric drive; 1 prop; 10,000 s
Boilers: 2 Combustion Engineering "D"; 42.2 kg/cm², 441° C
Electric: 1,150 kw **Fuel:** 1,375 tons **Crew:** 15 officers, 145 men

Remarks: Acquired by U.S. Navy 11-5-47. Loaned 17-1-63, after conversion to pe underway replenishment alongside, one station each side. Bought outright 31- Cargo: 15,300 tons. Refit completed 8-91 by Karachi Shipyard and Engineering W

◆ **1 ex-U.S. Cherokee-class ocean tug** Bldr: Commercial Iron Wks. Portland, Ore.

	Laid down	L	In serv.
A 42 Madadgar (ex-*Yuma,* ATF 94)	13-2-43	17-7-43	31-8-43

D: 1,325 tons (1,675 fl) **S:** 16.5 kts
Dim: 62.48 (59.44 pp) × 11.73 × 4.67
A: 2/40-mm 60-cal. Bofors Mk 3 AA (I × 2)—1/20-mm AA
Electron Equipt: Radar: 1/. . . nav.
M: 4 G.M. 12-278 diesels, electric drive; 1 prop; 3,000 shp
Electric: 260 kw **Range:** 6,500/16; 15,000/8
Fuel: 295 tons **Crew:** 85 tot.

Remarks: Transferred 25-3-59. Employed as a salvage and rescue tug and in s of mine countermeasures and submarines.

AUXILIARY SHIPS *(continued)*

ladadgar (A 42) Jean-Claude Bellonne, 1977

ERVICE CRAFT

2 Bholu-class harbor tugs Bldr: Damen, Hardinxveld, the Netherlands

HOLU GAMA (Both in serv. 2-91)

D: 265 tons (fl) **S:** 12 kts **Dim:** 26.00 (24.36 pp) × 6.81 × 2.15
Electron Equipt: Radar: 1/. . . nav. **Crew:** 6 tot.
M: 2 Cummins KTA-38M diesels; 2 props; 1,900 bhp **Fuel:** 36 tons

marks: Replace two former U.S. small harbor tugs with the same names.

1 large harbor tug Bldr: Karachi SY & Eng. Wks. (In serv. 1990)

NBAZ

D: 282 grt **S:** . . . kts **Dim:** 35.01 (32.62 pp) × 9.30 × 3.90
M: 1 Niigata diesel; 1 prop; . . . bhp

1 small pusher tug Bldr: Karachi SY & Eng. Wks. (In serv. 11-1-83)

GA

marks: No data available. Also in service is the small tug *Jhara*.

1 Kalmat-class water lighter Bldr: Karachi SY & Eng. Wks.

	Laid down	L	In serv.
LMAT	23-2-90	11-6-91	1991

: 885 grt **S:** . . . kts **Dim:** 63.00 × 11.00 × . . .
I: 1 diesel; 1 prop; . . . bhp

iarks: Cargo: 350 m^3 liquid. Can also carry deck cargo. Replaces *Zum Zum*.

1 Gwadar-class fuel lighter Bldr: Karachi SY & Eng. Wks.

ADAR (In serv. 1984)

: 831 grt **S:** . . . **Dim:** 62.84 (57.92 pp) × 11.31 × 3.03
: 1 Sulzer diesel; 1 prop; 550 bhp

utility launches Bldr: Karachi SY & Eng. Wks. (In serv. 1991)

428

57 grt **S:** . . . kts **Dim:** 19.96 (17.63 pp) × 5.04 (4.88 wl) × 1.50
: 2 G.M. 8V71 TI diesels; 2 props; 680 bhp **Electric:** 44 kw

logistics craft Bldr: Le Comte, Vianen, the Netherlands (In serv. 3-2-82)

13 tons (fl) **S:** 21 kts **Dim:** 18.1 × 3.8 × 0.9
2 Volvo Penta AQAD 40 diesels; 2 outdrives; 520 bhp

rks: Glass-reinforced plastic landing craft.

degaussing tender Bldr: Karachi SY & Eng. Wks. (In serv. 1979)

260 tons (fl) **S:** 10 kts **Dim:** 35.22 (34.0 wl) × 7.00 × 2.4
1 diesel; 1 prop; 375 bhp **Crew:** 5 tot.

rks: Built with French technical assistance and very similar in design to French Y 732. Wooden hull.

floating dry dock Bldr: Karachi SY & Eng. Wks. (In serv. 1981)

. . . . **Lift capacity:** 2,000 tons

U.S. ARD-2-class floating dry dock Bldr: Pacific Bridge, Alameda serv. 4-43)

AWAR (ex-ARD 6)

148.03 × 21.64 × 1.6 (light) **Lift capacity:** 3,500 tons

ks: Transferred 6-61.

◆ **1 small floating dry dock** (In serv. 1974)

FC II **Lift capacity:** 1,200 tons

MARITIME SECURITY AGENCY

Established 1-1-87 to patrol the maritime exclusion zone. Aircraft are to be acquired. Personnel transferred from the navy, to which the M.S.A. is subordinated. Ships and boats are painted white, with red and blue diagonal stripes and "MSA" on the side.

DESTROYER

◆ **1 ex-U.S. Gearing FRAM-I class** Bldr: Federal SB & DD, Newark, N.J.

	Laid down	L	In serv.
D 156 NAZIM (ex-*Tariq*, D 165, ex-*Wiltsie*, DD 716)	13-3-45	31-8-45	12-1-46

D: 2,425 tons (3,460 fl) **S:** 30 kts
Dim: 119.00 × 12.45 × 5.80 (max.)
A: 4/127-mm 38-cal. Mk 30 DP (II × 1)—8/14.5-mm AA (IV × 2)
Electron Equipt:
Radar: 1/Decca nav., 1/SPS-10B surf. search, 1/Lockheed SPS-40 air search, 1/Western Electric Mk 25 gun f.c.
EW: WLR-1 intercept
M: 2 sets G.E. geared steam turbines; 2 props; 60,000 shp
Boilers: 4 Babcock & Wilcox; 43.3 kg/cm², 454° C
Fuel: 600 tons **Range:** 2,400/25; 4,800/15
Electric: 1,300 kw **Crew:** 27 officers, 247 enlisted

Remarks: Transferred from the Pakistani Navy 25-1-90 and renamed. Serves as flagship of the Maritime Security Agency. Had originally been purchased from the United States on 29-4-77. The quadruple machine gun mounts are not always installed. The helicopter facility aft remains usable. ASW equipment has been removed

PATROL BOATS AND CRAFT

◆ **4 Barkat class** Bldr: Huangpu SY, China (In serv.: P 60, 61: 1-90; P 62, P 63: 8-90)

P 60 BARKAT P 61 REHMAT P 62 NUSRAT P 63 VEHAT

D: 390 tons (435 fl) **S:** 27 kts
Dim: 58.77 × 7.20 × 2.40 (mean hull)
A: 2/37-mm/62 cal. V-47M AA (II × 2)—4/25-mm Type 2m-8 AA (II × 2)
Electron Equipt: Radar: 1/Chinese Type 756 nav.
M: 4 MTU diesels; 4 props; 8,700 bhp **Range:** 1,800/18
Crew: 60 tot.

Remarks: First two delivered 29-12-89 for commissioning 2-90 in Pakistan. Are built on Hainan-class naval patrol boat hulls.

Note: The Shanghai-II-class patrol boats *Quetta* (P 141), *Sehwan* (P 148), *Larkana* (P 159), and *Sahival* (P 160) were stricken 1990.

◆ **4 MV 55 class** Bldr: Crestitalia, Ameglia, Italy

P . . . . P . . . .
P . . . . P . . . .

D: 22.8 tons (fl) **S:** 35 kts **Dim:** 16.5 × 5.2 × 0.88
A: 1/20-mm AA **Electron Equipt:** Radar: 1/. . .
M: 2 MTU diesels; 2 props; 2,200 bhp
Range: 425/25 **Crew:** 5 tot.

Remarks: Ordered 1986. More powerful version of Customs Service craft.

COAST GUARD

Note: Organized 1985, manned by Pakistani Army personnel, and subordinated to the Ministry of the Interior. All of the craft listed below have glass-reinforced plastic hulls.

PATROL CRAFT

◆ **1 Italian MV 70 class** Bldr: Crestitalia, Ameglia (In serv. 1987)

SAIF

D: . . . tons **S:** . . . kts **Dim:** 20.0 × . . . × . . . **M:** . . .

◆ **2 Italian MV 62 class** Bldr: Crestitalia, Ameglia (In serv. 1987)

SHABAZ WAQIR

Shabaz French Navy, 1983

PAKISTAN *(continued)*
PATROL CRAFT *(continued)*

D: . . . tons **S:** . . . kts **Dim:** 19.0 × . . . × . . . **M:** . . .

♦ **2 Italian MV 55 class** Bldr: Crestitalia, Ameglia (In serv. 1987)

Burq Sadd

D: 22.8 tons (fl) **S:** 35 kts **Dim:** 16.50 × 5.20 × 0.88
A: 1/20-mm AA **Electron Equipt:** Radar: 1/. . . nav.
M: 2 MTU diesels; 2 props; 2,200 bhp
Range: 425/25 **Crew:** 5 tot.

CUSTOMS SERVICE

Note: Pakistani Customs Service craft are naval-manned and would come under naval control in wartime.

PATROL CRAFT

♦ **18 MV55 class** Bldr: Crestitalia, Ameglia, Italy (In serv. 1979–80)

P 551–568

D: 22.8 tons (fl) **S:** 30 kts **Dim:** 16.5 × 5.2 × 0.88
A: 1/14.5-mm mg **M:** 2 V6 diesels; 2 props; 1,600 bhp
Range: 425/25 **Crew:** 5 tot.

Remarks: Glass-reinforced plastic construction. P 552 named *Shabaz,* P 553 named *Vaqar;* others presumably also named. Four near-sisters serve in the Maritime Security Agency.

♦ **1 (+ . . .) "Swallow" class** Bldr: Swallowcraft/Kangnam SB, Pusan, South Korea

P . . . (In serv. 3-86)

D: 32 tons (fl) **S:** 25 kts **Dim:** 20.0 × 4.7 × 1.3 **A:** . . .
Range: 500/20 **Crew:** 8 tot.
M: 2 G.M. 12V71 TI diesels; 2 props; 1,060 bhp

Remarks: GRP construction. First unit of a planned 12 delivered 3-86; further program developments uncertain; only the prototype may have been delivered.

♦ **2 U.S.-built** Bldr: Uniflite, Bellingham, Wash. (In serv. 1983)

D: 10.0 tons (fl) **S:** 16 kts **Dim:** 12.19 × . . . × . . .
A: . . . **M:** 2 G.M. 6-71N diesels; 2 waterjets; 512 bhp

♦ **2 U.S. PBR Mk III class** Bldr: Uniflite, Bellingham, Wash. (In serv. 1983)

D: 8.9 tons (fl) **S:** 30 kts **Dim:** 9.73 × 3.53 × 0.81
A: 3/12.7-mm mg (II × 1, I × 1)—1/60-mm mortar
Electron Equipt: Radar: 1/Raytheon 1900 nav.
M: 2 G.M. 6V53T diesels; 2 Jacuzzi waterjets; 550 bhp
Range: 150/23 **Crew:** 4 tot.

Remarks: The above four glass-reinforced plastic construction craft were ordered 6-82, apparently for trials and comparison purposes.

PANAMA

Republic of Panama

NATIONAL MARITIME SERVICE

Personnel (1991): Approx. 3,000 tot.

Naval Aviation: There are no "naval" aircraft. The air force operates a number of aircraft with a secondary maritime patrol role, including two DHC Twin Otter, six CASA C-212, two Britten-Norman Islander, two Cessna U-17, and a Cessna 172. Helicopters include eight Bell UH-1B, nine UH-1H, and four UH-1N. Larger transports include an L-188 Electra, four C-47s, one Skyvan, and a Falcon 20 for VIP transport.

Note: Lost during the U.S. invasion in 12-89 were: 65-ft. patrol boats *Commandante Torrijos* (P 201) and *Presidente Porras* (P 202); 103-ft. patrol boat *Ligia Elena* (P 302); 63-ft. patrol boat *Marti* (PR 101); two LCM(8) landing craft; and a number of other small support craft. Subsequently, the remaining 103-ft. patrol boat, *Panquiaco* (P 301), was retired. The U.S. Coast Guard is assisting in the reconstruction of the Panamanian maritime patrol force, providing training and small patrol craft.

PATROL BOATS AND CRAFT

♦ **1 (+3) U.S. Coast Guard 82-ft. "Point" class** Bldr: J. Martinac SB, Tacoma, Washington (In serv. 4-10-66)

3 De Noviembre (ex-*Point Barrow,* WPB 82348)

D: 64 tons (69 fl) **S:** 23.7 kts **Dim:** 25.30 × 5.23 × 1.95
A: 2/12.7-mm mg (I × 2)
Electron Equipt: Radar: 1/Raytheon SPS-64(V)1 nav.
M: 2 Cummins VT-12-M diesels; 2 props; 1,600 bhp
Range: 490/23; 1,500/8 **Fuel:** 5.7 tons **Crew:** 8 tot.

Remarks: Transferred 7-6-91; up to three more may be transferred later. Well-equipped with navigational and salvage equipment; can tow small craft.

♦ **1 or more Whaler patrol craft** Bldr: Boston Whaler, Rockland, Mass.

D: 1.5 tons (2 fl) **S:** 40 kts **Dim:** 6.81 × 2.26 × . . .
A: 2/12.7-mm mg (I × 2) **M:** 2 outboard motors; 360 bhp
Range: 167/40 **Crew:** 3 tot.

Remarks: Glass-reinforced plastic, foam-core construction.

Note: Also in use in 1991 were three leased shrimp boats and a former pleasure boat no data available.

SERVICE CRAFT

♦ **2 ex-U.S. Army LCM (8)-class landing craft**

Coiba Cebaco

D: 115 tons (fl) **S:** 9 kts **Dim:** 22.7 × 6.4 × 1.4
A: none **M:** 4 G.M. 6-71 diesels; 2 props; 600 bhp **Crew:** 6 tot.

Remarks: Transferred prior to 1989; several others discarded or lost. Employed i logistics support duties. Only one may be operational.

PAPUA NEW GUINEA

Personnel (1991): 420 total

Naval Aviation: The Papua New Guinea Defense Force operates six Nomad N.2 light transports, one Super King Air 200, and one Gulfstream II transport for coas patrol and logistics duties.

PATROL BOATS

♦ **4 ASI 315 class** Bldr: Australian SB Ind. (WA), Pty, Ltd., South Coogie, W.A.

	Laid down	L	In serv.
P 01 Tarangau	. . .	. . .	16-5-87
P 02 Dreger	12-1-87	7-9-87	29-10-87
P 03 Seeadler	21-3-88	21-9-88	28-10-88
P 04 Basilisk	19-10-88	. . .	1-7-89

D: 165 tons (fl) **S:** 21 kts (20 sust.)
Dim: 31.50 (28.60 wl) × 8.10 × 2.12 (1.80 hull)
A: 1/20-mm Oerlikon GAM-B01 AA—2/12.7-mm mg (I × 2)
Electron Equipt: Radar: 1/Furuno 1011 (I/J-band) nav.
M: 2 Caterpillar 3516 diesels; 2 props; 2,820 bhp (2,400 sust.)
Range: 2,500/12 **Fuel:** 27.9 tons **Endurance:** 8–10 days
Electric: 116 kw (2 × 50 kw; Caterpillar 3304 diesels; 1 × 16 kw)
Crew: 3 officers, 14 enlisted

Remarks: First two ordered 19-3-85, other pair 3-10-85. Australian foreign ai gram "Pacific Patrol Boat," with sisters in a number of Southwest Pacific–area i nation forces. Carry a 5-m aluminum boarding boat. Extensive navigational including Furuno FSN-70 NAVSAT receiver, 525 HF/DF, 120 MH/HF/DF, F echo-sounder, and DS-70 doppler log.

Tarangau (P 01)—with armament installed Leo Van Gindere

PAPUA NEW GUINEA *(continued)*
PATROL BOATS *(continued)*

3asilisk (P 04) Leo Van Ginderen, 5-90

♦ **1 Australian Attack class** Bldr: Evans Deakin & Co., Queensland (In serv. 28-11-66)

*94 Madang

D: 149 tons (fl) **S:** 24 kts **Dim:** 32.76 (30.48 pp) × 6.2 × 1.9
A: 1/40-mm Bofors Mk 7 AA—2/7.62-mm mg (I × 2)
Electron Equipt: Radar: 1/Decca RM 916 nav.
M: 2 Davey-Paxman Ventura 16 YJCM diesels; 2 props; 3,500 bhp (2,460 sust.)
Range: 1,220/13 **Crew:** 3 officers, 15 enlisted

emarks: Survivor of a group of five transferred in 1975; put back into service in 1990 ing materials cannibalized from sisters, of which *Aitape* (P 84) is still afloat as a hulk. eel hull; light-alloy superstructure; air-conditioned.

MPHIBIOUS WARFARE SHIPS

2 ex-Australian Balikpapan-class utility landing craft Bldr: Walkers, Maryborough

Salamaua (In serv. 19-10-73) 32 Buna (In serv. 7-12-73)

amaua (31) Gilbert Gyssels, 1980

: 310 tons (503 fl) **S:** 8 kts **Dim:** 44.5 × 12.2 × 1.9
: 2/12.7-mm mg (I × 2)
lectronic Equipt: Radar: 1/Decca RM 916 nav.
: 3 G.M. 12V71 diesels; 3 props; 675 bhp
ange: 1,300–2,280/10 depending on load
rew: 2 officers, 11 enlisted

arks: In service in 1972 and transferred 1975. Cargo: 140–180 tons. Refitted –86.

Kokuba-class personnel landing craft Bldr: Australia (In serv. 975)

02

12 tons (fl) **S:** 9 kts **Dim:** 12.0 × 4.0 × 1.0
: 2 Gardner diesels; 2 props; 150 bhp

arks: Survivors of a class of seven. Have a bow-ramp.

ex-Australian tug Bldr: Perrin, Brisbane (In serv. 1972)

503

47.5 tons **S:** 9 kts **Dim:** 15.4 × 4.6 × . . .
2 G.M. diesels; 2 props; 340 bhp **Range:** 710/9 **Crew:** 3 tot.

rks: Transferred in 1974. Retained R.A.N. number.

GOVERNMENT-OWNED SHIPS

Burfoam-class utility landing craft Bldr: Sing Koon Seng SY, ngapore

	In serv.		In serv.
Burfoam	21-7-81	Bursea	6-4-82
Burcrest	8-9-81	Burwave	18-5-82

D: 200 tons light (725 fl) **S:** 9 kts
Dim: 37.25 (33.50 pp) × 9.00 × . . .
M: 2 Deutz SBA-6M-816-1 LKR diesels; 2 props; 626 bhp
Range: 1,870/9 **Fuel:** 160 tons **Crew:** 18 tot.

Remarks: 260 grt/350 dwt. Owned by government; employed primarily in commercial and logistics service, but occasionally used for military transport.

♦ **1 navigational buoy tender** Bldr: Sing Koon Seng Yard, Singapore

Sepura (In serv. 14-12-82)

Sepura Leo Van Ginderen, 1990

D: 944 grt **S:** 12 kts **Dim:** . . . × . . . × . . .

Note: The government also operates two pilot boats delivered 3-89 by FBM Marine, Cowes, U.K.: *Davara* (12.0 m) and *Nancy Daniel* (8.2 m).

PARAGUAY

Republic of Paraguay

Personnel (1991): 5,265 total, including 500 Marines and Coast Guard

Naval Aviation: 2 Helibras AS-350B helicopters; 3 Cessna U-206 and 1 Cessna 150M light utility aircraft.

RIVER GUNBOATS

♦ **1 Brazilian Roraima class** Bldr: Ars. de Rio de Janeiro, Brazil

	Laid down	L	In serv.
P. 05 Itaipu	3-3-83	16-3-84	2-4-85

D: 220 tons light (384 fl) **S:** 14.5 kts
Dim: 46.3 (45.0 pp) × 8.45 × 1.42 (max.)
A: 1/40-mm—4/12.7-mm mg (II × 2)—2/81-mm mortar/12.7-mm mg (I × 2)
Electron Equipt: Radar: 3/navigational **Range:** 4,500/11
M: 2 M.A.N. V6V 16/18 TL diesels; 2 props; 1,824 bhp (1,732 sust.)
Endurance: 30 days **Crew:** 40 tot. ship's company + 30 marines

Remarks: Order announced 11-4-83. Has small helicopter deck and can accommodate one of the AS-350 helicopters. Carries medical personnel for civic action duties.

♦ **2 ex-Argentinian Bouchard-class former ocean minesweepers**

	Bldr	L	In serv.
P. 02 Nanawa (ex-*Bouchard*)	Rio Santiago NY	20-3-36	16-5-37
P. 04 Teniente Farina (ex-*Py*)	Rio Santiago NY	31-3-38	1-7-38

D: 450 tons (650 fl) **S:** 16 kts **Dim:** 59.5 × 7.3 × 2.6
A: 4/40-mm Bofors AA (II × 2)—2/12.7-mm mg (I × 2)—mines
M: 2 M.A.N. diesels; 2 props; 2,000 bhp
Range: 3,000/12 **Crew:** 70 tot.

Remarks: Transferred: P.02 donated 1-64, P.04 purchased on 6-3-68. Sister *Capitána Meza* (P.03, ex-M.2, ex-*Seaver*) is now employed as an immobile barracks hulk.

Note: Large river gunboats *Paraguay* (C.1) and *Humaita* (C.2) have been stricken.

PARAGUAY *(continued)*
RIVER GUNBOATS *(continued)*

◆ **1 old former tug** Bldr: Werf Conrad, Haarlem (In serv. 1908)

P. 01 Cabral (ex-*Adolfo Riquelme*)

D: 190 tons (fl) **S:** 8 kts **Dim:** 34.50 (30.00 pp) × 7.10 × 1.71
A: 1/40-mm Bofors Mk 3 AA—2/20-mm Oerlikon AA (I × 2)—2/12.7-mm mg (I × 2)
M: 1 Caterpillar diesel; 1 prop; 336 bhp **Crew:** 40 tot.

Remarks: Wooden hull, used for riverine patrol on the Upper Paraña River. Originally reciprocating steam-powered; re-engined and rearmed late 1980s.

PATROL CRAFT

◆ **5 (+7) P.07 class** Bldr: Asunción Naval Yard

	L		L		L
P. 07	9-89	P. 11	12-9-91	P. 15	9-93
P. 08	10-9-90	P. 12	9-92	P. 16	9-94
P. 09	10-9-90	P. 13	9-92	P. 17	9-94
P. 10	12-9-91	P. 14	9-93	P. 18	9-95

D: 18 tons (fl) **S:** 12 kts **Dim:** 14.70 × 3.06 × 0.85
A: 2/12.7-mm mg (I × 2)
M: 2 G.M. 6-71 diesels; 2 props; 340 bhp
Range: 240/12 **Crew:** 4 tot.

Remarks: Steel construction units designed by the Paraguayan Navy and built at its own facilities to save funds. Replace six small patrol craft delivered by the U.S. in 1967–71.

AUXILIARY SHIPS

◆ **1 repair/headquarters ship** Bldr: Brown SB, Houston

	Laid down	L	In serv.
BC. 1 Boqueron (ex-*Teniente Pratt Gil,* 1, ex-*Corrientes,* ex-LSM 86)	22-8-44	15-9-44	13-10-44

D: 743 tons (1,095 fl) **S:** 12.6 kts **Dim:** 61.88 × 10.51 × 2.54
A: 2/40-mm AA (II × 1)
M: 2 Fairbanks-Morse 38D8Q × 10 diesels; 2 props; 2,800 bhp
Electric: 240 kw **Crew:** . . .

Remarks: An ex-U.S. LSM-1-class landing ship donated by Argentina on 13-1-72 after conversion to a command and repair ship. Well deck plated over to create a helicopter deck aft; superstructure enlarged and moved to the centerline. Renamed 1980. May no longer be mobile.

◆ **1 cargo and training ship** Bldr: Tomás Ruiz de Velasco, Bilbao, Spain

Guarani (In serv. 2-68)

Guarani Leo Van Ginderen, 3-88

D: approx. 1,800 tons (fl) **S:** 12.2 kts **Dim:** 73.6 × 11.9 × 3.7
M: 1 MWM diesel; 1 prop; 1,300 bhp **Crew:** 21 total

Remarks: 714 grt/1,047 dwt. Purchased to provide seagoing experience for naval cadets and to engage in commercial voyages to raise revenue for running the navy. Cargo: approximately 900 tons. Home-ported at Asunción.

SERVICE CRAFT

◆ **1 riverine survey craft** Bldr: . . . (In serv. 1957)

Draga

Remarks: 110 tons full load; crew of 2 officers, 17 enlisted.

◆ **2 riverine survey launches** Bldr: . . . (In serv. 1957)

Lancha Ecografa Grua Flotante

Remarks: Displace 50 tons each and have crews of 1 officer and 9 enlisted.

◆ **2 ex-U.S. LCU-501-class landing craft** (In serv. circa 1944–45)

BT 1 (ex-YFB 82, ex-LCU . . .) BT 2 (ex-YFB 86, ex-LCU . . .)

D: 143 tons (309 fl) **S:** 10 kts **Dim:** 36.3 × 9.8 × 1.2 (aft)
M: 3 Gray Marine 64YTL diesels; 3 props; 675 bhp

Remarks: Transferred in 6-70. Used for logistics duties and as ferries. Cargo: 125 tons.

◆ **2 ex-U.S. 64-foot YTL-422-class tugs**

	Bldr	Laid down	L	In serv.
R 5 (ex-YTL 211)	Robert Jacob, Inc.	26-12-41	20-6-42	21-8-42
R 11 (ex-YTL 567)	Gunderson Bros.	5-3-45	17-8-45	30-10-45

D: 84 tons **S:** 9 kts **Dim:** 20.2 × 5.5 × 2.4
M: 1 diesel; 300 bhp **Crew:** 5 tot.

Remarks: Transferred in 3-67 and 4-74.

◆ **1 ex-U.S. floating dry dock** Bldr: Doullut & Ewin, Mobile, Ala.

DF 1 (ex-AFDL 26) (In serv. 6-44)

Dim: 60.96 × 19.5 × 1.04 (light) **Lifting capacity:** 1,000 tons

Remarks: Transferred in 3-65.

◆ **1 ex-U.S. floating workshop**

	Bldr	Laid down	L	In serv.
. . . (ex-YR 37)	Mare Island Naval SY	14-12-41	12-1-42	15-5-42

D: 600 tons (fl) **Dim:** 45.72 × 10.36 × 1.8
Electric: 210 kw **Crew:** 47 tot.

Remarks: Transferred 3-65.

◆ **3 dredges**

D. 1 Progreso (In serv. 1907)—140 tons, 30 crew
D. 2 Teniente O. Carreras Saguier (In serv. 1957)—110 tons, 19 crew
D. 3 . . . . (In serv. 1988)—550 bhp

Note: Also believed in service are river transport *Presidente Stroessner* (T. 1, 150 tons, 10 kts, in serv. 1901), buoy tender B. 1 (30 tons), and several small stores carriers.

PERU

Republic of Peru

Personnel (1991): 2,500 officers, 22,500 men + 2,500 officers and men of the Nav Infantry

Naval Aviation: The air arm consists of the following helicopters and fixed-wi aircraft: nine AM 39 Exocet SSM-equipped SH-3D Sea King, six Agusta-Bell AB 21 six Bell 206 JetRanger, one Bell 205A, and two Alouette-III helicopters; two C-13 Maritime patrol/transports, nine Grumman S-2 Tracker ASW aircraft, two C-47 tra ports, and five Beech T-34C trainers.

Note: Ship names are preceded by BAP—*Buque Armada Peruana* ("Peruvian Na Ship").

SUBMARINES

◆ **6 German Type 209/1200** Bldr: Howaldtswerke, Kiel

	L	In serv.
SS 31 Casma	31-8-79	19-12-80
SS 32 Antofagasta	19-12-79	14-3-80
SS 33 Pisagua (ex-*Blume*)	19-5-81	8-4-82
SS 34 Chipana (ex-*Pisagua*)	7-8-81	12-7-83
SS 35 Islay	11-10-73	23-1-75
SS 36 Arica	5-4-74	4-4-75

Pisagua (SS 33) Peruvian Navy,

SUBMARINES *(continued)*

Arica (SS 36) Peruvian Navy, 1991

D: 1,000 tons surf. std. (1,180 tons surf. fl)/1,285 tons sub.
S: 21 kts for 5 minutes, sub./12 kts snorkel/11 kts surf.
Dim: 55.90 × 6.30 × 5.50
A: 8/533-mm TT—(14 total Whitehead A-184 wire-guided torpedoes)
Electron Equipt:
Radar: 1/Thomson-CSF Calypso nav./surf. search
Sonar: S 31, 32: Krupp-Atlas CSU 3-Z active, PRS 3-4 passive; others: Krupp-Atlas CSU-83 active/passive suite; Thomson-Sintra DUUX-2C intercept
EW: . . . . . . intercept
M: 4 MTU Type 12V493 TY60 diesels, each linked to a 450-kw AEG generator, 1 Siemens electric motor; 1 prop; 5,000 shp
Range: 28/20 sub.; 460/ 4 sub.; 11,300/4 surf.
Endurance: 40 days
Fuel: 63 tons **Crew:** 5 officers, 26 enlisted

Remarks: SS 31 and SS 32 were ordered 12-8-76, and two more in 3-77. SS 33 and later are 56.1 m overall, 1,185 tons surfaced/1,290 tons submerged. SS 31, 32 use H.S.A. Mk 8 Mod. 24 combat data sytem; others use H.S.A. SINBADS. SS 33 delivery delayed by collision 2-4-82. SS 35 and SS 36 have DUUX-2CN sonar intercept equipment. Italian SEPA Mk 3 torpedo fire-control equipment and Whitehead A-184 wire-guided torpedoes ordered 6-86. Diving depth: 250 m. The battery has four groups of 120 cells, weighs 257 tons, and produces 11,500 amp/hr.

♦ **3 Dos de Mayo class** Bldr: General Dynamics, Groton, Conn.

	Laid down	L	In serv.
S 41 Dos de Mayo (ex-*Lobo*)	12-5-52	6-2-54	14-6-54
S 42 Abtao (ex-*Tiburon*)	12-5-52	27-10-53	20-2-54
S 44 Iquique (ex-*Merlin*)	27-10-55	5-2-57	1-10-57

Iquique (SS 44)—without bow dome Peruvian Navy, 1991

D: 825 tons std. surf./1,400 tons sub. **S:** 16 kts surf./10 kts sub.
Dim: 74.1 × 6.7 × 4.2
A: S 41, S 42: 1/127-mm 25-cal. WET DP—all: 6/533-mm TT (4 fwd, 2 aft 14 tot. U.S. NT-37C torpedoes)
Electron Equipt:
Radar: 1/SS-2A nav./surf. search—EW: . . . . . . intercept
Sonar: SS 41, 42: EDO 1102/1105 suite; SS 44: BQA-1A, BQR-3 passive
M: 2 G.M. 12-278A diesels, 2 electric motors; 2 props; 2,400 shp
Fuel: 45 tons **Range:** 5,000/10 (snorkel) **Crew:** 40 tot.

Remarks: Patterned after the U.S. *Marlin* class of 1941. These were the last U.S. submarines to be built for a foreign customer. SS 41 and SS 42 were refitted in 1965, SS and SS 44 in 1968. SS 41 and SS 42 are the last submarines in any navy to mount guns. New installed batteries 1981. EDO 1102/1105 sonar suite (with large bow dome) installed on first two in Peru during 1980s is a solid-state electronics update to original BQA-1A/BQR-3 suite. Sister *Angamos* (SS 43, ex-*Atun*) stricken early).

Note: U.S. GUPPY-IA-class submarine *La Pedrera* (SS 49, ex-*Sea Poacher*, SS 406) been relegated to pierside training service, along with the hulk of her sister *cha* (SS 50, ex-*Atule*, SS 403), which was sunk in collision 26-8-88 and salvaged in .

CRUISERS

♦ **ex-Dutch former guided-missile cruiser** Bldr: Rotterdamse Droogdok Maatschappij, Rotterdam

	Laid down	L	In serv.
CH 84 Aguirre (ex-*Almirante Grau*, ex-*De Zeven Provincien*, ex-*Eendracht*, ex-*Kijkduin*)	19-5-39	22-8-50	17-12-53

Aguirre (CH 84)—with Sea King landing Peruvian Navy, 1991

D: 9,850 tons (12,250 fl) **S:** 32 kts
Dim: 185.7 (182.4 pp) × 17.25 × 6.7
A: 4/152-mm 53-cal. Bofors DP (II × 2)—6/57-mm 80-cal. Bofors DP (II × 3)—4/40-mm 70-cal. Bofors AA (I × 4)—2/d.c. racks (8 d.c.)—3 SH-3D Sea King helicopters with AM 39 Exocet
Electron Equipt:
Radar: 2/Decca 1226 nav., 1/H.S.A. ZW-03 surf. search, 1/H.S.A. LW-02 early warning, 1/H.S.A. DA-02 target designation, 1/H.S.A. M25 f.c., f.c. for 152-mm guns, 2/H.S.A. M45 f.c.
Sonar: H.S.A. CWE-10N hull-mounted MF searchlight (10.5–11.0 kHz)
M: 2 sets Parsons geared steam turbines; 2 props; 79,000 shp
Boilers: 4 Yarrow-Werkspoor, three-drum
Electric: 4,000 kw **Range:** 6,000/17 **Crew:** 856 tot.

Remarks: Purchased in 8-76. The U.S. Terrier SAM missile system installed while in Dutch service was replaced by a hangar (20.4 × 16.5) and a helicopter platform (35.0 × 17.0) at Rotterdam. Recommissioned on 31-10-77. The hangar roof is also a helicopter platform. Carries 1,620 rounds 152-mm, 6,400 rds 57-mm, 8,000 rds 40-mm ammunition. The armor consists of a 76- to 102-mm belt and 20–25-mm on two decks; the 152-mm gun houses are lightly armored. Took name of half-sister during latter's 1985–89 refit period, as by law there must always be an *Almirante Grau* in service. Boilers retubed 1986.

♦ **1 ex-Dutch light cruiser** Bldr: Wilton-Fijenoord, Schiedam

	Laid down	L	In serv.
CH 81 Almirante Grau, (ex-*de Ruyter*, ex-*de Zeven Provincien*)	5-9-39	24-12-44	18-11-53

Almirante Grau (CH 81) Peruvian Navy, 1991

Almirante Grau (CH 81) Leo Van Ginderen, 7-88

D: 9,529 tons (11,850 fl) **S:** 32 kts
Dim: 187.32 (182.4 pp) × 17.25 × 6.70
A: 8/152-mm 53-cal. Bofors DP (II × 4)—2/d.c. racks (8 d.c.)—*see* Remarks
Electron Equipt:
Radar: 1/Decca 1226 nav., 1/H.S.A. DA-08 surf. search, 1/H.S.A. LW-08 early warning, 1/H.S.A. WM-25 track-while-scan gun/missile f.c., 1/H.S.A. STIR-24 SAM illuminator, 2/LIROD gun f.c.
Sonar: CWE-610 (EDO 610) hull-mounted (6, 7, 8-kHz)
EW: H.S.A. . . . intercept, H.S.A. Ramses (SLQ-503) jammer, 1/Sagaie decoy RL, 2/Dagaie decoy RL
M: 2 sets Parsons geared steam turbines; 2 props; 85,000 shp
Boilers: 4 Yarrow-Werkspoor, three-drum
Electric: 4,000 kw **Range:** 2,100/32; 6,900/12
Crew: 49 officers, 904 enlisted

CRUISERS *(continued)*

Remarks: Purchased 7-3-73, commissioning 23-5-73. Planned refitting at Amsterdamse Droogdok Maatschappij 26-3-85 to 1987; delayed by shipyard bankruptcy and Peruvian payment difficulties. During refit was known as *Proyecto 01*. Left the Netherlands 22-1-88 and was officially recommissioned 7-89 in Peru, but without many of the weapons and systems planned for her modernization. Most of the new electronics systems are incomplete. It had been hoped to complete the modernization at SIMA, Callao, but finances have not permitted, and the ship is effectively non-operational. *Almirante Grau* is now the world's oldest commissioned cruiser.

Eight Otomat missiles removed from Peruvian frigates were intended to be mounted amidships, but this does not seem to have been accomplished. Four twin 57-mm Bofors DP removed prior to departure for Europe, and eight single 40-mm AA were removed during her period in the Netherlands and sent to Sweden for rehabilitation; they have not been remounted. Was to have received two octuple Albatros SAM launchers for Selenia Aspide missiles during the refit; although the foundations were added, the launchers were not. The EW suite does not seem to have been completed, and the Sagaie and Dagaie launchers may not be aboard. Can carry 3,250 rounds 152-mm and 16,000 rounds 40-mm. Originally had a CWE-10N sonar, but it may have been removed during modernization. The armor arrangements dupicate those of her half-sister *Aguirre.*

DESTROYERS

♦ 4 ex-Dutch Friesland class

	Bldr	Laid down	L	In serv.
DD 76 Capitán Quiñones (ex-*Limburg,* D 814)	Kon. Mij. de Schelde, Vlissingen	28-11-53	5-9-55	31-10-56
DD 77 Villar (ex-*Amsterdam,* D 819)	Nederlandse Dok, Amsterdam	26-3-55	25-8-56	10-8-58
DD 78 Galvez (ex-*Groningen,* D 813)	Nederlandse Dok, Amsterdam	4-2-52	9-1-54	19-9-56
DD 79 Diez Canseco (ex-*Rotterdam,* D 818)	Rotterdamse DDM, Rotterdam	7-4-54	26-1-56	28-2-57

D: 2,496 tons (3,100 fl) **S:** 36 kts
Dim: 116.0 (112.8 pp) × 11.77 × 5.2
A: 4/120-mm 50-cal. Bofors DP (II × 2)—4/40-mm 70-cal. Bofors AA (I × 4)—2/375-mm Bofors ASW RL (IV × 2)—1/d.c. rack (8 d.c.)
Electron Equipt:
Radar: 1/Decca TM1229 nav., 1/H.S.A. ZW-06 surf. search, 1/H.S.A. DA-05 surf./air search/target designation, 1/H.S.A. LW-02 early warning, 1/H.S.A. M45 f.c.
Sonar: 1/CWE-10N hull-mounted searchlight (10.5–11.0 kHz), 1/PAE-1N hull-mounted attack (24 kHz)

Diez Canseco (DD 79) Peruvian Navy, 1991

Capitán Quiñones (DD 76) French Navy, 1986

M: 2 sets G.E. geared steam turbines; 2 props; 60,000 shp
Boilers: 4 Babcock & Wilcox; 39.8 kg/cm^2, 454° C
Electric: 1,350 kw **Range:** 920/36; 3,300/22; 4,000/15
Crew: 284 tot.

Remarks: DD 77 transferred 19-5-80; DD 76 transferred 27-6-80; DD 78 purchased 27-8-80 and transferred 2-2-81; DD 79 transferred 11-7-81. DD 76 and DD 78, in reserve for several years, were recommissioned during 1989. Sister *Guise* (DD 72, ex-*Drenthe,* D 816) stricken 8-85; sisters *Colonel Bolognesi* (DD 70, ex-*Overijssel,* D 815) and *Castilla* (DD 71, ex-*Utrecht,* D 817) stricken 1990 but are retained for spare parts. Plans for further modernization of the survivors have been canceled.

Two forward 40-mm AA removed 1965; fire-control directors for remaining 40-mm AA removed 1977–78. Same propulsion plant as U.S. *Gearing* class. Have one 103-mm rocket flare launcher with 100 rds. Carry 1,300 rds 120-mm and 4,300 rds 40-mm ammunition and 98 rds 375-mm ASW rockets.

♦ 2 ex-U.K. Daring class Bldr: Yarrow, Scotstoun, Glasgow

	Laid down	L	In serv.
DM 73 Palacios (ex-*Diana*)	3-4-47	8-5-52	29-3-54
DM 74 Ferré (ex-*Decoy*)	22-9-46	29-3-49	28-3-53

Ferré (DM 74)—with 3 114-mm gun mounts Peruvian Navy, 19

Palacios (DM 73)—with no 114-mm gun mount aft French Navy,

D: 2,800 tons (3,700 fl) **S:** 30 kts
Dim: 118.87 (111.55 pp) × 13.10 × 5.50
A: 4/MM 38 Exocet SSM (I × 4)—4 (DM 74: 6)/114-mm 45-cal. Mk DP (II × 2 or 3)—4/40-mm 70-cal. Breda Dardo AA (II × 2)
Electron Equipt:
Radar: 1/Decca TM1226 nav., 1/Thomson-CSF TMD-1040 Triton surf. search, 1/Plessey AWS-1 air search, 1/Selenia RTN-10X f.c.
Sonar: none—EW: . . . intercept
M: 2 sets English Electric geared steam turbines; 2 props; 54,000 s
Boilers: 2 Foster-Wheeler; 45.7 kg/cm^2, 454° C
Range: 3,000/20 **Fuel:** 584 tons **Crew:** 297 total

Remarks: Purchased 1969 and refitted by Cammell Laird in the U.K., comp 1973. Modernized again 1977–78 with Selenia NA-10 gun fire-control system a DM 73, a telescoping hangar in place of the after 114-mm mount; both received 40-mm mounts abreast the foremast. The hangar was later removed from D leaving a blast shield to protect the helicopter deck, which is larger than on D Both reported for sale in 1984 but were still operational in 1990. Very lightly with troublesome propulsion plants. Have no ASW capability and only one w director.

GUIDED-MISSILE FRIGATES

♦ 4 Italian Lupo class Bldrs: FM 51, 52: Fincantieri, Riva Trigoso; FM 53, 54: SIMA, Callao

GUIDED-MISSILE FRIGATES *(continued)*

	Laid down	L	In serv.
FM 51 Meliton Carvajal	8-10-74	17-11-76	5-2-79
FM 52 Manuel Villavicencio	6-10-76	7-2-78	25-6-79
FM 53 Montero	10-78	8-10-82	25-7-84
FM 54 Mariategui	1979	8-10-84	10-10-87

D: 2,208 tons (2,500 fl) **S:** 32 kts
Dim: 108.4 (106.0 pp) × 11.28 × 3.66
A: 8/Otomat Mk 2 SSM (I × 8)—1/127-mm 54-cal. OTO Melara DP—1/Albatros SAM system (VIII × 1; 8 Aspide missiles)—4/40-mm 70-cal. Breda Dardo AA (II × 2)—6/324-mm Mk 32 ASW TT (III × 2)—1/AB-212 ASW helicopter
Electron Equipt:
Radar: 1/S.M.A. 3RM20 nav., 1/Selenia RAN-11LX surface search, 1/Selenia RAN-10S air search, , 1/Selenia RTN-10X f.c., 2/RTN-20X f.c., 1/RTN-30X f.c.
Sonar: Edo 610E hull-mounted (6, 7, 8-kHz)
EW: . . . . . . intercept, 2/SCLAR decoy RL (XX × 2)
M: CODOG: 2 Fiat-G.E. LM-2500 gas turbines, 25,000 shp each; 2 GMT A230-20M diesels, 3,900 bhp each; 2 CP props

[M]eliton Carvajal (FM 51)—with AB-212 helo aboard — Peruvian Navy, 1991

[Mo]ntero (FM 53) — U.S. Navy, 1984

Electric: 3,120 kw
Range: 900/35 (on gas turbines); 3,450/20.5 (on diesels)
Crew: 20 officers, 165 men

Remarks: Italian technicians assisted in the building of Nos. 53 and 54 at Callao. Differ from the Italian Navy's version in having a fixed (vice telescoping) hangar and a step down to the hull at the stern; the Dardo 40-mm mounts are one deck higher, and the SAM fire-control system also differs. Selenia IPN-IC data system fitted. There are no reloads for the Albatros SAM system. The helicopter provides over-the-horizon targeting and mid-course guidance for the Otomat missiles. In 1989, fitted with equipment to permit refueling hovering Sea King helicopters. These are by far the most capable surface combatants in the Peruvian Navy.

GUIDED-MISSILE CORVETTES

◆ **6 French PR-72-560 class** Bldr: SFCN, Villeneuve-la-Garenne (hulls of CM 21, 23, 25 by Arsenal de Lorient)

	L	In serv.
CM 21 Velarde	16-9-78	25-7-80
CM 22 Santillana	11-9-79	25-7-80
CM 23 De los Heroes	20-5-79	17-11-80
CM 24 Herrera	16-2-79	26-2-81
CM 25 Larrea	20-5-79	16-6-81
CM 26 Sanchez Carrion	28-6-79	14-9-81

De los Heroes (CM 23) — Peruvian Navy, 1991

D: 470 tons light (560 normal, 610 fl) **S:** 37 kts (34 sust.)
Dim: 64.0 (59.0 pp) × 8.35 × 2.60 (max.)
A: 4/MM 38 Exocet SSM (II × 2)—1/76-mm 62-cal. OTO Melara Compact DP—2/40-mm 70-cal. Breda-Bofors AA (II × 1)
Electron Equipt:
Radar: 1/Decca TM1226 nav., 1/Thomson-CSF THD 1040 Triton air/surf. search, 1/Thomson-CSF Castor-II fire control
EW: Thomson-CSF DR2000 intercept
M: 4 SACM AGO 240, V-16 diesels; 4 props; 22,000 bhp
Electric: 560 kw **Range:** 1,200/30; 2,500/16
Crew: 36 tot. (accommodations for 46)

Remarks: Were given the names of the Vosper patrol boats that had been transferred to the Peruvian Coast Guard. Originally were numbered P 101–106. Vega weapons-control system, with CSEE Panda backup optical gun director.

RIVER GUNBOATS

◆ **2 Marañon class** Bldr: John I. Thornycroft, Woolston, U.K.

	Laid down	L	In serv.
CF 401 Ucayali	4-50	7-3-51	7-51
CF 402 Marañon	4-50	23-4-51	7-51

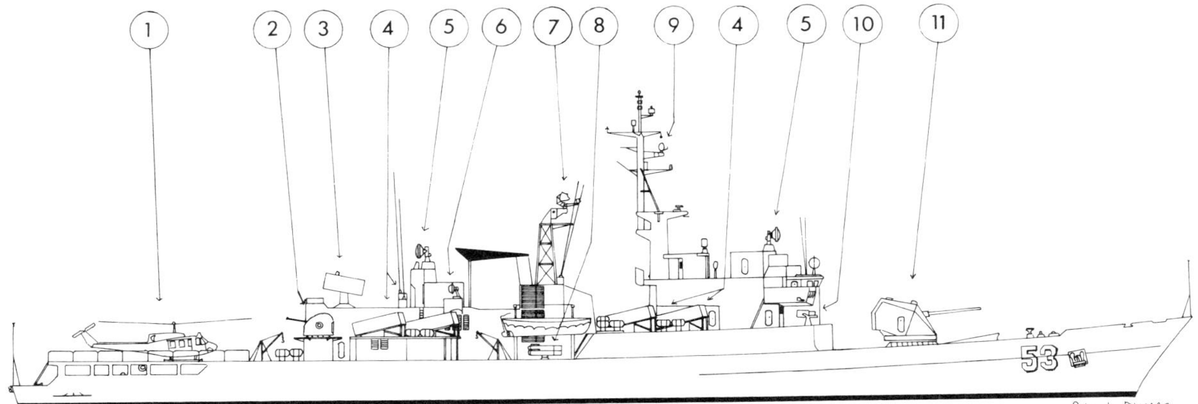

Montero 1. AB-212 helicopter 2. 40-mm twin Dardo AA mount 3. Albatros octuple SAM launcher 4. Otomat antiship missiles 5. RTN-30X (aft) and RTN-10X (fwd) fire-control radar directors 6. RTN-20X fire-control radar directors 7. RAN-10S air-search radar 8. ILAS-3 triple ASW torpedo tubes 9. RAN-11LX surface-search radar 10. SCLAR rocket launchers 11. OTO Melara 127-mm gun

RIVER GUNBOATS *(continued)*

Ucayali (CF 401) Peruvian Navy, 1991

D: 350 tons (365 fl) **S:** 12 kts **Dim:** 47.22 × 9.75 × 1.22
A: 2/76.2-mm 50-cal. U.S. Mk 26 DP (I × 2)—1/40-mm 60-cal. Mk 3 AA—4/20-mm (II × 2)
M: 2 British Polar 441 diesels; 2 props; 800 bhp
Range: 5,000/10 **Crew:** 4 officers, 36 enlisted

Remarks: Based at Iquitos for service on the Upper Amazon. Steel-hulled with aluminum-alloy superstructures.

♦ **2 Amazonas class** Bldr: Electric Boat Co., Groton, Conn. (In serv. 1934)

CF 403 Amazonas CF 404 Loreto

Amazonas (CF 403) Peruvian Navy, 1991

D: 250 tons **S:** 15 kts **Dim:** 46.7 × 6.7 × 1.2
A: 2/76.2-mm 50-cal. U.S. Mk 26 DP (I × 2)—2/40-mm 60-cal. Mk 3 AA (I × 2)—2/20-mm AA (I × 2)
M: 2 diesels; 2 props; 750 bhp **Range:** 4,000/10
Crew: 5 officers, 20 enlisted

Remarks: Based at Iquitos on the Upper Amazon.

Note: Old river gunboat *America* (15), reported non-operational 1981, may be retained as a hulk or relic. The former U.S. *Cannon*-class frigate *Castilla* (ex-*Bangust,* DE 739) is hulked at Iquitos on the upper Amazon as headquarters and training ship for the Amazon Flotilla.

AMPHIBIOUS WARFARE SHIPS

♦ **4 ex-U.S. Terrebonne Parish-class tank landing ships** Bldr: Ingalls SB, Pascagoula, Mississippi (ADT 144: Bath Iron Works, Bath, Maine)

	L	In serv.
ADT 141 Paita (ex-*Walworth County,* LST 1164)	18-5-53	26-10-53
ADT 142 Pisco (ex-*Waldo County,* LST 1163)	17-3-53	17-9-53
ADT 143 Callao (ex-*Washoe County,* LST 1165)	14-7-53	30-11-53
ADT 144 Eten (ex-*Traverse County,* LST 1160)	3-10-53	19-12-53

Paita (ADT 141) Dr. Giorgio Arra, 9-91

D: 2,590 tons (6,225 fl) **S:** 13 kts
Dim: 117.35 × 16.76 × 3.7 mean (5.18 max.)
A: 5/40-mm 60-cal. AA (II U.K. Mk 5 × 2, I U.S. Mk 3 × 1)
Electron Equipt: Radar: 1/. . . nav.
M: 4 G.M. 15-278A diesels; 2 CP props; 6,000 hp
Electric: 600 kw **Range:** 6,000/9 **Fuel:** 1,060 tons
Crew: 116 tot.

Remarks: Leased from U.S. for five years on 7-8-84, extended another five years on 8-8-89. Reactivated from Maritime Administration reserve by Todd SY, San Francisco, Cal., and delivered mid-10-84. Having been in Military Sealift Command Service from 1972 until deactivated, they were unarmed at time of transfer; formerly carried six 76.2-mm DP (II × 3), with two Mk 63 GFCS; received 40-mm AA after arrival in Peru. Have accommodations for 395 troops, bow ramp. Cargo: approx. 2,200 tons. All officially recommissioned 4-3-85.

HYDROGRAPHIC SURVEY SHIPS

♦ **1 oceanographic research and survey ship** Bldr: SIMA, Callao

	Laid down	L	In serv.
Humboldt	3-1-77	13-10-78	1980

Humboldt Peruvian Navy, 19[illegible]

D: 1,200 tons (1,980 fl) **S:** 14 kts **Dim:** 76.0 × 12.0 × 4.4
A: none **Electron Equipt:** Radar: 2/. . . nav.
M: 2 diesels; 2 props; 3,000 bhp **Crew:** 53 tot.

Remarks: Aground 26-2-89 at King George Isl., South Shetlands; salvaged and paired at Punta Arenas, Chile. Modified stern-haul factory trawler design, w[illegible] equipped for oceanographic and fisheries research.

♦ **1 ex-U.S. Sotoyomo-class former tug** Bldr: Levingston SB, Orange, Tex.

	Laid down	L	In se[illegible]
AH 170 Unanue (ex-*Wateree,* ATA 174)	5-10-43	18-11-43	20-7-[illegible]

D: 534 tons (835 fl) **S:** 13 kts **Dim:** 43.59 × 10.31 × 4.01
A: none **Electron Equipt:** Radar: . . .
M: 2 G.M. 12-278A diesels, electric drive; 1 prop; 1,500 bhp
Electric: 120 kw **Range:** 16,500/9 **Fuel:** 154 tons
Crew: 3 officers, 28 enlisted

Remarks: Sold to Peru in 11-61. Refitted 1985 with reinforced bow, improved heat for Antarctic expedition 1985–86.

♦ **2 Dutch Van Straelen-class inshore survey ships, former inshore minesweepers** Bldr: De Vries-Leutsch, Amsterdam

	Laid down	L	In s[illegible]
AH 175 Carillo (ex-*Icaro,* ex-*Van Hamel,* M 871)	27-4-59	28-5-60	14-1[illegible]
AH 176 Melo (ex-*Van der Wel,* M 878)	30-5-60	3-5-61	6-1[illegible]

D: 151 tons (171 fl) **S:** 13 kts
Dim: 33.08 (30.30 wl) × 6.88 × 1.80
Electron Equipt: Radar: 1/. . . nav.
M: GM 16V92N diesels; 2 props; 1,400 bhp
Crew: 2 officers, 15 enlisted

Remarks: Purchased 23-2-85 for conversion in Peru to inshore survey dutie[illegible] ceived Interplot 200 survey system and new engines. Wooden construction.

♦ **1 inshore survey craft** Bldr: SIMA, Chimbote

AH 174 (In serv. 1982)

D: 49 tons **S:** 13 kts **Dim:** 19.8 × 5.2 × 0.9
M: diesels **Crew:** 2 officers, 6 enlisted

Remarks: Has side-looking sonar for bottom mapping to 1,200-m depths.

HYDROGRAPHIC SURVEY SHIPS *(continued)*

arillo (AH 175) Peruvian Navy, 1991

◆ 1 river survey ship Bldr: MacLaren, Niteroi, Brazil (In serv. 1981)

H 172 Stiglich

iglich (AH 172) Peruvian Navy, 1991

D: 250 tons (fl) **S:** 15 kts **Dim:** 34.0 × 8.0 × . . .
M: 2 G.M. 12V71 TI diesels; 2 props; 1,800 bhp
rew: 2 officers, 28 enlisted

marks: Incorrectly described in previous editions as a former "Anchova"-class rol boat. Operates on the Amazon from Iquitos.

1 river survey craft

173 (In serv. 5-76)

im: 23.5 × . . . × . . . **Crew:** 1 officer, 3 enlisted

narks: Operated on the Amazon by the navy for the Oceanographic Institute.

ERS

1 former commercial tanker Bldr: C.N. de la Ciotat (In serv. 1976)

P 150 Bayovar (ex-*Loreto II*, ex-*St. Vincent*)

: 15,175 tons light (107,320 fl) **S:** 16 kts **Crew:** . . . tot.
im: 250.53 (239.55 pp) × 35.56 × 14.57
: 1 Sulzer 7RND90 diesel; 1 prop; 20,300 bhp **Range:** . . .

arks: 44,489 grt/92,145 dwt. Acquired by navy 1986 for commercial revenue ice.

Talara class Bldr: SIMA, Callao

	Laid down	L	In serv.
152 Talara	1975	9-7-76	3-77

: 30,000 tons (fl) **S:** 16.25 kts
im: 171.18 (161.55 pp) × 25.38 × 9.53
: 1 Burmeister & Wain 6K 47EF diesel; 1 prop; 11,600 bhp
ectric: 1,890 kw **Crew:** . . . tot.

arks: 16,633 grt, 25,648 dwt. Cargo: 35,642 m. Sisters *Trompeteros* and *Bayovar* sferred 1979) are operated by Petroperu, the state fuel monopoly, which trans- l this ship to the navy upon completion. One underway fueling station per side.

Talara (ATP 152) A. de Kruijf/Piet Sinke, 5-91

◆ **2 Sechura class** Bldr: SIMA, Callao

	Laid down	L	In serv.
ATP 158 Zorritos	8-10-55	8-10-58	1959
ATP 159 Lobitos	1964	5-65	1966

Zorritos (ATP 158) Hartmut Ehlers, 9-85

D: 8,700 tons (fl) **S:** 12 kts
Dim: 116.82 (109.73 pp) × 15.91 × 6.63
M: 1 Burmeister & Wain 562-VTF-115 diesel; 1 prop; 2,400 bhp
Electric: 750 kw **Fuel:** 549 tons **Crew:** . . . tot.

Remarks: 4,297 grt, 5,732 dwt. Cargo: 7,488 m. Sister *Sechura*, built in England 1952–55 and fully equipped for underway replenishment, was stricken in 1968. Nos. 158 and 159 are used for commercial cargoes for Petroperu, but have one fueling station on either beam. Navy crews.

Note: The tanker *Parinas* (ATP 156, ex-*Pimental*) was stricken 1991.

CARGO SHIP

◆ **1 Ilo-class** Bldr: SIMA, Callao (In serv. 15-12-71)

ATA 131 Ilo

Ilo (ATA 131) Hartmut Ehlers, 12-90

D: 18,400 tons (fl) **S:** 15.6 kts
Dim: 153.85 (144.53 pp) × 20.4 × 9.2
M: 1 Burmeister & Wain 6K 47EF diesel; 1 prop; 11,600 bhp
Electric: 1,140 kw **Crew:** 60 tot.

Remarks: Cargo: 13,000 tons. Sister *Rimac* is in commercial service for the state shipping company. *Ilo* is also used to carry commercial cargo. Navy crew. Flooded engine room 1-91 off Spanish coast while carrying 11,000 tons sugar.

Note: The ex-U.S. *Bellatrix*-class attack cargo ship *Independencia* (ATA 130, ex-*Bellatrix*, AKA 3) was sold for scrap 10-91; the ship had been used for cadet training and in revenue cargo service.

TUGS

◆ **1 ex-U.S. Cherokee-class ocean tug** Bldr: Cramp SB, Philadelphia, Pa.

	Laid down	L	In serv.
ARB 123 Guardian Rios (ex-*Pinto*, ATF 90)	10-8-42	5-1-43	1-4-43

D: 1,235 tons (1,675 fl) **S:** 16.5 kts **Dim:** 62.48 × 11.73 × 4.67
A: none **Electron Equipt:** Radar: 1/. . . nav.
M: 4 G.M. 12-278 diesels, electric drive; 1 prop; 3,000 shp
Electric: 260 kw **Crew:** 85 tot.

Remarks: Transferred in 12-60. Used for salvage and rescue.

TUGS *(continued)*

Guardian Rios (ARB 123) Peruvian Navy, 1991

SERVICE CRAFT

◆ **1 hospital craft for Amazon service** Bldr: SIMA, Iquitos (In serv. 1977)

ABH 302 Morona

Morona (ABH 302) Peruvian Navy, 1991

D: 150 tons (fl) **S:** 12 kts **Dim:** 30.0 × 6.0 × 0.6
M: diesels; . . . bhp **Crew:** . . . tot.

Remarks: Based at Iquitos on the upper Amazon River. Plans to construct two sisters canceled. There are also several smaller hospital launches on the Amazon.

◆ **1 hospital craft for Lake Titicaca service** Bldr: Cammell Laird, Birkenhead, U.K. (In serv. 1879)

ABH 300 Puno (ex-*Yapura*)

Puno (ABH 300) Peruvian Navy, 1991

D: 500 grt **S:** . . . kts **Dim:** . . . × . . . × . . .
M: 1 gasoline engine

Remarks: Sister *Chuquito* (ARB 19, ex-*Yavari*) stricken 1990 after 119 years' service. Formerly used as a tug.

◆ **2 Selendon-class harbor tugs** Bldr: Ruhrorter, Duisburg, Germany (In serv. 1967)

ARB 128 Olaya ARB 129 Selendon

D: 80 grt **S:** 10 kts **Dim:** 61.3 × 20.3 × 2.3
M: 1 diesel; 1 prop; 600 bhp

◆ **1 ex-U.S. harbor tug** Bldr: Ira S. Bushey, Brooklyn, N.Y. (In serv. 1939)

ARB 124 Franco (ex-*Tigre*, ex-*Menewa*, YTM 2, ex-YN 34, ex-*Consultor*)

D: 192 tons (fl) **S:** 9 kts **Dim:** 27.73 × 7.01 × 3.35
M: 1 diesel; 1 prop; 805 bhp

Remarks: Purchased 1940 by U.S. Navy for use as a net tender. Transferred 14-3-47. Has push-bar built across bows for handling barges. Operates in the Upper Amazon Flotilla.

◆ **3 small harbor tugs**

ARB 120 Mejia ARB 121 Huerta ARB 126 Duenas

Remarks: No data available.

◆ **5 river push tugs** Bldr: SIMA, Iquitos (In serv. . . .)

ARB 184 Contramestre Navarro—50 tons
ARB 180 ARB 181 ARB 185 ARB 186

Remarks: Serve on the upper Amazon. ARB 180, 181, 185, and 186 are smaller than ARB 184.

◆ **2 ex-U.S. 174-foot-class yard oilers**

	Bldr	Laid down	L	In serv.
ACP 118 Noguera (ex-YO 221)	Jeffersonville Boat & Mach., Ind.	15-1-45	22-5-45	31-8-45
ACP 111 Gauden (ex-YO 171)	RTC Shbldg., Camden, N.J.	18-3-44	20-7-44	15-11-44

D: 1,400 tons (fl) **S:** 10 kts **Dim:** 53.04 × 9.75 × 4.0
M: 2 diesels; 2 props; 540 bhp **Range:** 2,000/8 **Crew:** 20 tot.

Remarks: Ex-YO 221 transferred in 2-75; ex-YO 171 purchased 26-1-81. Cargo: approximately 900 tons (6,570 barrels).

◆ **2 ex-U.S. 174-foot water tankers**

	Bldr	Laid down	L	In serv.
ACA 110 Mantilla (ex-YW 122)	Henry C. Grebe, Chicago, Ill.	29-6-45	22-9-45	17-11-45
ACA 119 Colayeras (ex-YW 128)	Leatham D. Smith, Wisc.	9-4-45	22-5-45	28-7-45

D: 440 tons (1,390 fl) **S:** 7 kts **Dim:** 53.04 × 9.75 × 4.0
M: 1 G.M. diesel; 1 prop; 640 bhp **Fuel:** 25 tons
Crew: 23 tot.

Remarks: ACA 110 transferred in 3-63; ACA 119 purchased 26-1-81. Cargo: 930 tons

◆ **2 Amazon river water barges** Bldr: SIMA, Iquitos (In serv. 1972)

ABA 330 ABA 332

Remarks: May not be sisters; ABA 330 reported as having 800-ton capacity, ABA 33[illegible] as being 330 tons full load.

◆ **1 torpedo retriever** Bldr: Friedrich Lürssen Werft, Vegesack, Germany

ART 322 San Lorenzo (In serv. 1-12-81)

San Lorenzo (ART 322) Peter Voss, 9[illegible]

D: 51.5 tons (65.5 fl) **S:** 19 kts
Dim: 25.35 (23.47 pp) × 5.62 × 1.68
M: 2 MTU 8V396 TC82 diesels; 2 props; 1,590 bhp
Range: 500/15 **Fuel:** 14 tons **Crew:** 9 tot.

Remarks: Can stow four long or eight short torpedoes on ramp aft.

◆ **1 new-construction floating dry dock** Bldr: SIMA, Callao (In se[illegible] 2-91)

ADF 104

Lift capacity: 4,500 tons **Dim:** 115.8 × 30.1 × . . .

Remarks: Launched 12-12-90. Designed by Senermar, Spain. Intended for u[illegible] Callao. Internal dimensions: 99.8 × 23.8 m. Replaced the U.S. ARD 2-class ADI (ex-WY 20, ex-ARD 8), which was stricken in 1991.

◆ **1 floating dry dock** Bldr: . . . . . ., Germany (In serv. 1979)

ADF 109

Lift capacity: 15,000 tons **Dim:** 195.0 × 42.0 × . . .

Remarks: Ordered 13-2-78; first unit lost en route Peru, 1978, and replaced w[illegible] duplicate. Lift capacity can be increased to 18,000 tons by use of extension sec[illegible] bringing total length to 225 meters.

SERVICE CRAFT *(continued)*

◆ **1 ex-U.S. AFDL 7-class floating dry dock** Bldr: Foundation Co., Kearny, N.J. (In serv. 10-44)

ADF 111 (ex-WY 19, ex-AFDL 33)

Lift capacity: 1,900 tons **Dim:** 87.78 × 19.51 × 0.99 (light)

Remarks: Transferred in 7-59.

◆ **1 small floating dry dock** Bldr: John I. Thornycroft, Southampton (In serv. 1951)

ADF 108

Lift capacity: 600 tons **Dim:** 59.13 × 18.7 × . . .

Remarks: Serves the Amazon Flotilla at Iquitos.

◆ **1 ex-U.S. YR 24-class floating workshop** Bldr: DeKom SB, Brooklyn, NY

	Laid down	L	In serv.
ART 105 (ex-YR 59)	3-11-43	22-4-44	24-8-44

D: 520 tons (770 fl) **Dim:** 45.72 × 10.36 × 1.8
Electric: 220 kw **Fuel:** 75 tons **Crew:** 47 tot.

Remarks: Transferred 8-8-61.

◆ **1 120-ton-capacity floating crane** (Serves at Callao)

AGF 101

Note: There are a number of other service craft available, including the sail-training craft *Marte* and craft named *Andrade, Jupiter, Neptuno, Pucalipa, Robles, Sandoval, Tapuina,* and *Zambrano.*

arte Peruvian Navy, 1991

COAST GUARD

The Peruvian Coast Guard was established in 1975 and is intended to patrol to the ent of the 200-nautical-mile economic zone.

TROL BOATS

5 Rio Cañete class Bldr: SIMA, Chimbote

	In serv.		In serv.
243 Rio Nepeña	1-12-81	PC 246 Rio Huarmey	1982
244 Rio Tambo	1982	PC 247 Rio Zaña	12-2-85
245 Rio Ocoña	1982		

D: 296 tons (fl) **S:** 22 kts **Dim:** 50.98 (49.1 pp) × 7.4 × 1.7
A: 1/40-mm 60-cal. Mk 3 AA—1/20-mm AA
Electron Equipt: Radar: 1/Decca TM 1226 nav.
M: 4 Bazán/MTU V8V 16/18 TLS diesels; 2 props; 5,640 bhp
Electric: 170 kw **Endurance:** 20 days **Range:** 3,000/17
Crew: 4 officers, 26 enlisted

Ocoña (PC 245) Peruvian Navy, 1991

Remarks: Have steel hulls, aluminum superstructure. Class prototype *Rio Cañete* (PC 248) was stricken 1990.

◆ **2 ex-U.S. PGM 71 class**

	Bldr	In serv.
PC 222 Rio Sama (ex-PGM 78)	Peterson, Sturgeon Bay, Wis.	9-66
PC 223 Rio Chira (ex-PGM 11)	SIMA, Callao	6-72

D: 130 tons (145 fl) **S:** 17 kts
Dim: 30.8 (30.2 wl) × 6.4 × 1.85
A: 1/40-mm 60-cal. Mk 3 AA—4/20-mm AA (II × 2)—2/12.7-mm mg (I × 2)
Electron Equipt: Radar: 1/Raytheon 1500 Pathfinder nav.
M: 8 G.M. 6-71 diesels; 2 props; 2,200 bhp
Range: 1,000/12 **Crew:** 15 tot.

Remarks: Transferred to the Coast Guard in 1975. *Rio Chira* was built with U.S. aid and equipment.

◆ **2 110-foot class** Bldr: Vosper, Portsmouth, U.K.

	L
PC 225 Rio Pativilca (ex-*Herrera*)	26-10-64
PC 227 Rio Locumba (ex-*Sanchez Carrion*)	18-2-65

D: 100 tons (130 fl) **S:** 30 kts
Dim: 33.4 (31.46 wl) × 6.4 × 1.7
A: 2/20-mm AA (I × 2)
Electron Equipt: Radar: 1/Decca TM 707 nav.
M: 2 Napier Deltic T38-37 diesels; 2 props; 6,280 bhp
Range: 1,100/15 **Crew:** 4 officers, 27 men

Remarks: Delivered under own power. Never fully equipped with armament, although fittings for four 533-mm torpedo tubes were installed in the decks. Air-conditioned. Steel hull, aluminum-alloy superstructure. Transferred to the Coast Guard in 1975 and renamed, their old names going to a new class of naval guided-missile corvettes. Sisters *Rio Ica* (PC 228, ex-*Sautillana*) stricken 1982, *Rio Huaora* (PC 226, ex-*Larrea*) in 1983; *Rio Chicama* (PC 224, ex-*De los Heroes*) in 1986; and *Rio Vitor* (PC 229, ex-*Velarde*) in 1990.

PATROL CRAFT

Note: Funds for six 12.2-m patrol craft for drug patrol duties on Peruvian rivers were provided in the U.S. FY 90 budget, but none had been ordered as of 12-91.

◆ **6 "Anchova" class** Bldr: MacLaren, Niteroi, Brazil (In serv. 1981–82)

PP 230 La Punta	PP 232 Rio Santa	PP 235 Rio Viru
PP 231 Rio Chillon	PP 233 Rio Majes	PP 236 Rio Lurin

D: 31 tons (43 fl) **S:** 25 kts **Dim:** 18.60 × 5.25 × 1.62
A: 2/20-mm AA (I × 2) **Electron Equipt:** Radar: 1/Decca 101 nav.
M: 2 G.M. 12V71 TI diesels; 2 props; 1,800 bhp
Range: 700/15 **Electric:** 10 kw **Crew:** 1–2 officers, 5–6 enlisted

Remarks: Wooden construction. Chile also operates units of this class. Sister *Rio Reque* (PP 234) wrecked 1990.

◆ **3 P 33 class** Bldr: American Shipbldg. & Designs, Miami, Fla.

PL 290 Rio Ramis (In serv. 15-9-82)
PL 291 Rio Ilave (In serv. 20-11-82)
PL 292 Rio Azangaro (In serv. 4-2-83)

Rio Ramis (PL 290)—old number Am. Shipbldg., 1982

D: 4.8 tons (fl) **S:** 27 kts
Dim: 10.06 (9.19 pp) × 3.35 × 0.76
A: 1 or 2/12.7-mm mg (I × 1 or 2)
Electron Equipt: Radar: 1/Raytheon 2800 nav. **Range:** 450/27
M: 2 Perkins ST-6-354-4M diesels; 2 props; 480 bhp **Crew:** 4 tot.

Remarks: Glass-reinforced plastic construction with Kevlar armor. Employed on Lake Titicaca.

◆ **2 Rio Zarumilla class** Bldr: Korody Marine, Viareggio, Italy (In serv. 5-9-60)

PC 241 Rio Tumbes PC 242 Rio Piura

PERU *(continued)*

PATROL CRAFT *(continued)*

D: 37 tons (fl) **S:** 18 kts **Dim:** 20.0 × 5.2 × 1.1
A: 2/40-mm 60-cal. Mk 3 AA (I × 2)
M: 2 G.M. 8V71 diesels; 2 props; 1,200 bhp **Range:** 1,000/14

Remarks: Sister RIO *Zarumilla* (PC 240) stricken 1990.

◆ **3 river patrol craft** (In serv. 1975)

PF 272 RIO MANU PF 273 RIO INAMBARI PF 274 RIO TAMBOPATA

Remarks: Based at Madre de Dios on the Bolivian border. Carry 1/12.7-mm mg and can make 18 kts. Also used for river patrol service is the *Rio Lagato* (MP 147).

PHILIPPINES

REPUBLIC OF THE PHILIPPINES

Personnel (1991): 11,500 Navy, plus 9,500 Marines and 2,000 Coast Guard

Naval Aviation: Ten Philippine-built Britten-Norman BN-2 Defender light maritime patrol aircraft and 10 MBB BO-105 helicopters; not all are operational. The air force has two Fokker F-27 Maritime patrol aircraft.

FRIGATE

◆ **1 ex-U.S. Cannon class** Bldr: Federal SB & DD Co., Newark, N.J.

	Laid down	L	In serv.
PF 6 RAJAH HUMABON (ex-*Hatsuhi*, ex-*Atherton*, DE 169)	14-1-43	27-5-43	29-8-43

D: 1,240 tons (1,620 fl) **S:** 20 kts
Dim: 93.27 (91.44 wl) × 11.15 × 3.56 (hull)
A: 3/76-mm 50-cal. Mk 26 DP (I × 3)—6/40-mm 60-cal. Mk 2 AA (II × 3)—12/20-mm AA (II × 6)—2/12.7-mm mg (I × 2)—1/Mk 10 Hedgehog ASW spigot mortar (XXIV × 1)—6/Mk 6 d.c.mortars—1/d.c. rack (9 d.c.)
Electron Equipt:
Radar: 1/. . . navigational, 1/Mk 26 f.c.
Sonar: EDO SQS-17B hull-mounted (12–14 kHz)
M: 4 G.M. 16-278A diesels, electric drive; 2 props; 6,000 bhp
Electric: 680 kw **Fuel:** 260 tons **Range:** 11,600/11
Crew: 165 tot.

Remarks: Transferred to Japan on 14-6-55 and stricken 6-75, reverting to U.S. ownership; sold to the Philippines 23-12-78 but remained laid up in Japan until towed to South Korea for overhaul in 1979. Recommissioned 27-2-80. Has one Mk 52 radar GFCS and one Mk 41 rangefinder for 76.2-mm gun control, plus three Mk 51 Mod. 2 lead-computing optical GFCS for the 40-mm guns. Sister *Datu Kalantiaw* (PS 76, ex-*Booth*, DE 170) was grounded in a typhoon 21-9-81 and capsized; *Datu Sikatuna* (ex-*Asahi*, ex-*Amick*, DE 168) was stricken 1989.

CORVETTES

◆ **2 ex-U.S. Auk-class former minesweepers**

	Bldr	Laid down	L	In serv.
PS 69 RIZAL (ex-*Murrelet*, MSF 372)	Savannah Mach. & Foundry, Ga.	24-8-44	29-12-44	21-8-45
PS 70 QUEZON (ex-*Vigilance*, MSF 324)	Associated SB, Seattle, Wash.	28-11-42	5-4-43	28-2-44

Rizal (PS 69)—prior to addition of helicopter deck
Leo Van Ginderen, 5-65

D: 890 tons (1,250 fl) **S:** 18 kts
Dim: 67.39 (65.53 wl) × 9.8 × 3.28
A: 1/76.2-mm 50-cal. Mk 26 DP—4/40-mm 60-cal. Mk 2 AA (II × 2)—4/20-mm AA (II × 2)—3/324-mm Mk 32 ASW TT (III × 2)—1/Mk 10 Hedgehog ASW spigot mortar (XXIV × 1)—2/Mk 6 d.c. mortars—2/d.c. racks (6 d.c. each)
Electron Equipt:
Radar: 1/SPS-5C surf. search
Sonar: EDO SQS-17B hull-mounted (14 kHz)
M: 2 G.M. 12-278 (PS 70: 12-278A) diesels, electric drive; 2 props; 3,532 bhp
Electric: 360 kw **Fuel:** 216 tons **Crew:** 100 tot.

Remarks: PS 69 transferred 18-6-65, PS 70 on 19-8-67. A small raised helicopter deck has replaced the former after 76.2-mm gun. PS 70 has bulwarks amidships, PS 69 does not.

◆ **7 ex-U.S. PCE 827 and PCER 848 classes** Bldrs: A: Pullman Standard Car Co., Chicago; B: Willamette Iron & Steel Corp., Portland, Ore.; C: Albina Eng. & Machine Works, Portland, Ore.

	Bldr	Laid down	L	In serv
PS 19 MIGUEL MALVAR (ex-*Ngoc Hoi*, ex-*Brattleboro*, EPCER 852)	A	28-10-43	1-3-44	26-5-44
PS 22 SULTAN KUDARAT (ex-*Dong Da II*, ex-*Crestview*, PCE 895)	B	2-12-42	18-5-43	30-10-4
PS 23 DATU MARIKUDO (ex-*Van Kiep II*, ex-*Amherst*, PCER 853)	A	16-11-43	18-3-44	16-6-4
PS 28 CEBU (ex-PCE 881)	C	11-8-43	10-11-43	31-7-4
PS 29 NEGROS OCCIDENTAL (ex-PCE 885)	C	25-2-44	20-6-44	30-4-4
PS 31 PANGASINAN (ex-PCE 891)	B	28-10-42	24-4-43	15-6-4
PS 32 ILOILO (ex-PCE 897)	B	16-12-42	3-8-43	6-1-4

D: 903 tons (fl) **S:** 15 kts **Dim:** 56.24 (54.86 wl) × 10.08 × 2.87
A: 1/76.2-mm 50-cal. Mk 26 DP—3/40-mm 60-cal. Mk 3 AA (I × 3)—4/12.7-mm mg (I × 4)—3/7.62-mm mg (I × 3)
Electron Equipt: Radar: 1/. . . nav.
M: 2 G.M. 12-278A diesels; 2 props; 2,000 bhp (PS 19, 28, 31: 2 G.M. 12-567A diesels; 2 props; 1,800 bhp)
Electric: 240–280 kw **Fuel:** 125 tons **Range:** 9,000/10
Crew: 8 officers, 77 enlisted

Remarks: PS 28 through PS 32 were transferred 7-48; a fifth transferred at the sa time, *Leyte* (PS 30, ex-PCE 885), was lost by grounding in 1979. PS 19 through 23 we transferred to South Vietnam on 11-7-66, 29-11-61, and 6-70, respectively, and escap Vietnam in 5-75; they were sold to the Philippines 11-75 (PS 23: 5-4-76). All AS equipment is now deleted from all units. Ex-PCER and EPCER units were built w longer forecastles as rescue ships. All generally resemble *Magat Salamat*, below.

PS 19, 22, 31, and 32 completed two-year rehabilitations 1990–91 with armam listed above and new radar; PS 28 and PS 29 may retain three twin 40-mm AA, f single 20-mm AA; PS 23 may retain secondary armament of two single 40-mm AA, f single 20-mm AA, and an 81-mm mortar. Six of this class are to be retained in serv through the end of the century.

◆ **1 ex-U.S. Admirable-class former minesweeper** Bldr: Winslow Marine Railway, Seattle, Wash.

	Laid down	L	In se
PS 20 MAGAT SALAMAT (ex-*Chi Lang II*, ex-*Gayety*, MSF 239)	14-11-43	19-3-44	23-9-

Magat Salamat (PS 20)

D: 650 tons light (905 fl) **S:** 14 kts
Dim: 56.24 (54.86 wl) × 10.06 × 2.75
A: 1/76.2-mm 50-cal. Mk 26 DP—2/40-mm 60-cal. Mk 3 AA (I × 2)—8/20-mm AA (II × 4)
Electron Equipt: Radar: 1/. . . nav.
M: 2 Cooper-Bessemer GSB-8 diesels; 2 props; 1,710 bhp
Electric: 280 kw **Range:** 9,300/10 **Fuel:** 140 tons
Crew: 5 officers, 77 enlisted

CORVETTES *(continued)*

Remarks: Transferred to Vietnam and escaped to the Philippines 4-75. Acquired by the latter in 11-75.

GUIDED-MISSILE PATROL BOATS

♦ **0 (+ 3) Spanish Cormoran class** Bldr: first unit: E.N. Bazán, San Fernando; others: Cavite Navy Yard

	Laid down	L	In serv.
. . . .	. . .	. . .	12-93
. . . .	. . .	. . .	. . .
. . . .	. . .	. . .	. . .

D: 300 tons (374 fl) **S:** 33 kts **Dim:** 56.60 × 7.59 × 1.97 (hull)
A: 4/MM 40 Exocet SSM (II × 2)—1/76-mm 62-cal. OTO Melara Compact DP—2/40-mm 70-cal. Breda-Bofors AA (II × 1)—2/12.7-mm mg (I × 2)
Electron Equipt:
Radar: 1/Raytheon SPS-64(V)11 nav., 1/. . . surf./air search, 1/Selenia RTN-10X f.c.
EW: . . . . . . intercept
M: 3 Bazán-MTU MA 16V956 TB91 diesels; 3 props; 13,500 bhp (11,250 sust.)
Range: 2,000/15 **Crew:** . . .

Remarks: Letter of intent to order signed 30-9-91. Second pair would be built with panish assistance. Will have Selenia NA-21 gun-fire-control system. First unit may be ne begun some years ago on speculation by the builder. Lack of funds may halt program.

ATROL BOATS

0 (+3+3) Australian-design Bldr: first unit: Australian Submarine Company (ASC), Carrington Slipway, Newcastle; others: . . . . . ., Philippines

	Laid down	L	In serv.
. . . .	. . .	. . .	2-94
. . . .	. . .	. . .	. . .
. . . .	. . .	. . .	. . .

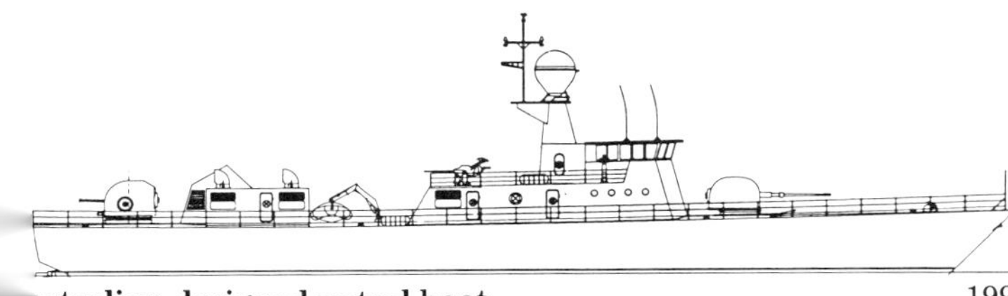

ıstralian-designed patrol boat 1990

D: 396 tons (fl) **S:** 30 kts **Dim:** 57.0 × . . . × . . .
A: 1/76-mm 62-cal. OTO Melara Compact DP—2/40-mm 70-cal. Breda-Bofors AA (II × 1)—2/25-mm Breda-Oerlikon KBA chain-gun AA
Electron Equipt:
Radar: 1/. . . nav., 1/H.S.A. WM-22 track-while-scan f.c.
M: 3 MTU 16V956 TB 91 diesels; 3 props; 13,500 bhp (11,250 sust.)
Range: . . ./. . . **Crew:** . . . tot.

marks: Letter of intent to order signed 22-10-91. Design by Rikard-Bell, Australia, inally for Launceton Marine, Hobart, Tasmania, but rights sold to Australian marine Corp. in 1991. Were originally to have had waterjet propulsion, with a G.E. 500 gas turbine on the centerline. The centerline propeller will have controllable ı. Three more may be ordered later, but lack of funds may halt entire program.

5 (+3+27) U.S. 77-ft. class Bldr: PCF 370–377: Trinity-Equitable SY, New Orleans; others: . . . . . .

370 (In serv. 8-90)	PCF 374 (In serv. 24-6-91)
371 (In serv. 24-6-91)	PCF 375 (In serv. 1-92)
372 (In serv. 24-6-91)	PCF 376 (In serv. 1-92)
373 (In serv. 24-6-91)	PCF 377 (In serv. 1-92)

370 Trinity Marine, 8-90

D: 56.4 tons (fl) **S:** 28 kts
Dim: 23.66 × 6.06 × 1.01 hull (1.76 props)
A: 4/12.7-mm M3 mg (I × 4)—2/7.62-mm mg (I × 2)
Electron Equipt: Radar: 1/Raytheon SPS-64(V)11
M: 2 G.M. 16V92 TAB diesels; 2 props; 2,800 bhp
Range: 600/24, 1,200/. . . **Crew:** 1 officer, 7 enlisted
Endurance: 5 days **Electric:** 70 kw (2 × 35 kw)
Fuel: 18,950 liters

Remarks: First four ordered 9-89 for $9.4m; fifth ordered 4-90; three more in 8-90. Others to build in the Philippines with U.S. aid, with funds for ten more provided under the FY 1992 U.S. Foreign Military Sales program. Aluminum construction. Were originally intended to operate in flotillas of seven, each attached to a larger patrol boat acting as leader. Provision made to install a 40-mm Mk 3 gun on the foredeck and an 80-mm mortar aft. Carry 4,000 rounds 12.7-mm, 2,000 rounds 7.62-mm ammunition. A 4-m rigid inflatable boat powered by a 40-bhp outboard motor is stowed amidships.

♦ **0 (+1) "Guided-Missile Boat"** Bldr: Cavite Naval Shipyard

	L	In serv.
PM 140 GENERAL AMILIO AGUINALDO	23-6-84	21-11-90

D: 215 tons (fl) **S:** 18 kts **Dim:** 44.0 × . . . × . . .
A: 2/40-mm 60-cal. Mk 3 AA (I × 2)—2/20-mm AA (I × 2)—4/12.7-mm mg (II × 2)
M: 4 G.M. 12V92 TA diesels; 4 props; . . . bhp

Remarks: Was originally to have carried four SSM.

♦ **3 Katapangan class**

	Bldr	In serv.
P 101 KAGITINGAN	W. Müller, Hameln, West Germ.	9-2-79
P 102 BAGONG LAKAS	W. Müller, Hameln, West Germ.	9-2-79
P 104 BAGONG SILANG	Cavite NSY	1982

D: 132 tons (150 fl) **S:** 16 kts **Dim:** 37.0 × 6.2 × 1.7
A: 2/30-mm AA Emerlec (II × 1)—2/12.7-mm mg (I × 2)
M: 2 MTU MB 820 Db1 diesels; 2 props; 2,050 bhp

Remarks: Designed in West Germany. Prototype delivered for trials 11-10-78. Program to build more at BOSECO, Bekan, abandoned due to poor performance; intended to reach 28 kts, but obviously underpowered. First Philippine-built unit, *Katapangan* (P 103), stricken 1989 for spares, and P 101 and P 102 are currently inoperable.

♦ **4 ex-U.S. PGM 39 class** Bldr: Tacoma Boat, Tacoma, Wash.

	In serv.
PG 61 AGUSAN (ex-PGM 39)	3-60
PG 62 CATANDUANES (ex-PGM 40)	3-60
PG 63 ROMBLON (ex-PGM 41)	3-60
PG 64 PALAWAN (ex-PGM 42)	6-60

D: 122 tons **S:** 17 kts **Dim:** 30.6 × 6.4 × 2.1 (props)
A: 2/20-mm AA (I × 2)
Electron Equipt: Radar: 1/Raytheon 1500 nav.
M: 2 MTU MB 820 diesels; 2 props; 1,900 bhp **Crew:** 15 tot.

Note: U.S. PGM 71-class patrol boat *Basilan* (PG 60, ex-*Hon Troc*, ex-PGM 83) was stricken 1989. U.S. PC 461-class patrol boat *Nueva Viscaya* (ex-U.S. Air Force *Altus*, ex-PC 568) was lost 13-11-89 in a typhoon, and her sister *Negros Oriental* (PS 29, ex-French *L'Inconstant*, ex-PC 1171) was stricken 1991.

MINE COUNTERMEASURES SHIPS

Note: During the 1990s, it is hoped to order four coastal minehunter/minesweepers, funds permitting.

AMPHIBIOUS WARFARE SHIPS

♦ **0 (+2) U.S. Army Gen. Frank S. Besson-class vehicle landing ships** Bldr: Halter–Moss Point Marine, Escatawpa, Mississippi

D: 1,612 tons light (4,199 fl) **S:** 12 kts (11.6 sust.)
Dim: 83.14 (78.03 pp) × 18.28 (18.16 wl) × 3.66 (max.) **A:** . . .
Electron Equipt: 1/Raytheon SPS-64(V)2 nav., 1/SPS-64 (V) . . . nav.
M: 2 G.M. EMD 16-645-E2 diesels; 2 props; 3,900 bhp
Electric: 500 kw (2 × 250-kw diesel sets) **Range:** 8,358/11
Endurance: 38 days **Fuel:** 524 tons **Crew:** 6 officers, 24 enlisted

Remarks: Ordered 4-92, to deliver 6-93, 9-93. Design based on Australian roll-on/roll-off beachable cargo ship *Frances Bay*. Will be built to commercial specifications. Intended to transport up to 1,815 metric tons of vehicles or cargo containers on 975 m^2 cargo deck. Can also carry up to 122 tons of potable water. Bow ramp 8.23-m wide. Version for the Philippines will have a helicopter deck and increased accommodations for 150 troops in place of stern cargo area and ramp.

♦ **0 (+2) Chinese Yudao (Type 073)-class medium landing ships** Bldr: China State SB Corp., Guangzhou SY (In serv. . . .)

LP . . . . LP . . . .

D: 1,460 tons (fl) **S:** . . . kts **Dim:** 82.07 (78.00 pp) × 12.60 × 3.10
A: . . . . . .
Electron Equipt: Radar: 1/Chinese Type 756 nav.
M: . . . diesels; 2 props; . . . bhp **Crew:** 5 officers, 40 enlisted

Remarks: To be ordered during 1992. Chinese Navy version is armed with 8/25-mm AA (II × 4).

AMPHIBIOUS WARFARE SHIPS *(continued)*

◆ **9 ex-U.S. LST 1 and LST 542-class landing ships** Bldrs: A: Bethlehem Steel, Hingham, Mass.; B: Jeffersonville Boat and Machinery Co., Jeffersonville, Ind.; C: Dravo Corp., Pittsburgh, Pa.; D: Chicago Bridge & Iron Co.; E: American Bridge, Ambridge, Pa.; F: Missouri Valley Bridge & Iron Co., Evansville, Ind.

	Bldr	In serv.
LT 86 ZAMBOANGA DEL SUR (ex-*Marion County,* LST 935)	A	29-8-44
LT 87 COTABATO DEL SUR (ex-*Thi Nai,* ex-*Cayuga County,* LST 529)	B	29-2-44
LT 98 ILOCOS NORTE (ex-*Madera County,* LST 905)	C	20-1-45
LT 501 LAGUNA (ex-T-LST 230)	D	3-11-43
LT 502 SAMAR ORIENTAL (ex-T-LST 287)	E	15-12-43
LT 504 LANAO DEL NORTE (ex-T-LST 566)	F	29-5-44
LT 507 BENGUET (ex-*Davies Cty.,* T-LST 692)	B	10-5-44
LT 510 SAMAR DEL NORTE (ex-*Shiretoko,* ex-*Nansemond County,* LST 1064)	A	12-3-45
LT 512 TAWI-TAWI (ex-T-LST 1072)	A	12-4-45

D: 1,620 tons (4,080 fl) **S:** 11 kts
Dim: 99.98 (96.32 wl) × 15.24 × 4.29
A: 7–8/40-mm AA (II × 1 or 2, I × 4–6)—2–4/20-mm AA (ex-T-LST: 6/20-mm AA)
M: 2 G.M. 12-567A diesels (LT 510, 512: 2 G.M. 12-278A); 2 props; 1,700 bhp
Electric: 300 kw **Fuel:** 570 tons **Crew:** 60–100 tot.

Remarks: LT 86 was transferred 15-10-76; later deactivated, she was recommissioned 21-11-90. LT 87 escaped from Vietnam (to which she had been transferred in 12-63) in 4-75; she was officially transferred to the Philippines on 17-11-75. LT 501, LT 502, LT 504, LT 507, and LT 512 were purchased in 1976, having previously been stricken by the U.S.N. and laid up in Japan. LT 510 had been transferred to Japan 4-61 and stricken in 1975; she was purchased in 1978. All the LT 500 series were refitted and thoroughly overhauled in Japan, recommissioning in 1978–79. Armament: Some ex-T-LSTs carry only four 20-mm AA (I × 4), while others received a single 40-mm forward after transfer, plus several 20-mm AA. LT 87 has four sets of Welin davits for LCVP landing craft, the others only two; some ex-T-LSTs do not carry LCVPs.

None of the survivors other than LT 96 are in good condition. Stricken since the last edition have been: *Agusan del Sur* (LT 54, ex-*Nha Trang,* ex-*Jerome County,* LST 848), *Mindoro Occidental* (LT 93, ex-T-LST 222), *Suragao del Norte* (LT 94, ex-T-LST 488), *Suragao del Sur* (LT 95, ex-T-LST 546), *Maquindanao* (LT 96, ex-*Caddo Parrish,* LST 515), *Cagayan* (LT 97, ex-*Hickman County,* LST 825), *Tarlac* (LT 500, ex-T-LST-47), *Lanao del Sur* (LT 503, ex-T-LST 491), *Leyte del Sur* (LT 505, ex-T-LST 491), *Davao Oriental* (ex-*Oosumi,* ex-*Daggett County,* LST 689), *Aurora* (LT 508, ex-*Harris County,* T-LST 822), and *Cotabato del Norte* (LT 511, ex-*Orleans Parrish,* T-LST 1069, ex-MCS 6, ex-LST 1069).

Note: The four U.S. LSM 1-class medium landing ships *Isabela* (LP 41, ex-LSM 463), *Batanes* (LP 65, ex-*Huong Giang,* ex-*Oceanside,* ex-LSM 175), *Western Samar* (LP 66, ex-*Hat Giang,* ex-LSM 335), and *Mindoro Oriental* (LP 68, ex-LSM 320) have been stricken since the last edition, as have U.S. LSSL 1-class gunfire-support landing ships *Camarines Sur* (LF 48, ex-*Nguyen Duc Bong,* ex-LSSL 129), *Sulu* (LF 49, ex-*Nguyen Ngoc Long,* ex-LSSL 96), and *La Union* (LF 50, ex-*Doan Ngoc Tang,* ex-*Hallebarde,* ex-LSSL 9) and three former U.S. LCU 1466-class utility landing craft.

◆ **9 U.S. LCM(8)-class landing craft**

LCM 257 LCM 258 LCM 260–LCM 266

D: 118 tons (fl) **S:** 9 kts **Dim:** 22.43 × 6.42 × 1.4 (aft)
M: 4 G.M. 6-71 diesels; 2 props; 600 bhp
Range: 140/9 **Crew:** 3 tot.

Remarks: Transferred 19-3-75. Cargo capacity: 54 tons or 120 troops. The similar *Bagong Filipino* (TK 81) and *Dakila* (TK 82), built in the Philippines, have been stricken. LCM 260 sank during a typhoon 13-11-90 but has been salvaged.

◆ **50 ex-U.S. LCM(6)-class landing craft**

D: 24 tons (56fl) **S:** 10 kts
Dim: 17.07 × 4.37 × 1.17 (aft) **Crew:** 3 tot.
M: 2 G.M. Gray Marine 64HN9 diesels; 2 props; 330 bhp
Range: 130/9

Remarks: Transferred 1955—75. Cargo capacity: 30 tons or 80 troops. Twenty-five others have been discarded.

◆ **7 U.S. "Mini-ATC" class** Bldr: Tacoma BY, Tacoma, Washington (In serv. 1978)

D: 9.3 tons light (13 fl) **S:** 28.5 kts **Dim:** 10.97 × 3.89 × 0.30
A: up to 4/12.7-mm mg (I × 4)—1/40-mm Mk 19 grenade launcher—1/160-mm M60 mortar
M: 2 G.M. 8V53N diesels; 2 Jacuzzi 14Y waterjets; 566 bhp
Range: 37/28 **Crew:** 2 crew + 15 troops

Remarks: Aluminum construction. Rectangular planform. Can carry small radar. Very quiet in operation. Three others have been discarded.

AUXILIARY SHIPS

FLEET FLAGSHIP

◆ **1 ex-U.S. Barnegat-class former seaplane tender** Bldr: Lake Washington SY, Houghton, Washington

	Laid down	L	In serv.
PS 7 ANDRES BONIFACIO (ex-*Ly Thuong Kiet,* ex-*Chincoteague,* WHEC 375, ex-AVP 24)	23-7-41	15-4-42	12-4-43

Andres Bonifacio (PS 7)—prior to alterations 197

D: 1,766 tons (2,800 fl) **S:** 17 kts (*see* Remarks)
Dim: 95.72 (91.44 wl) × 12.55 × 4.27
A: 1/127-mm 38-cal. Mk 30 DP—4/40-mm 60-cal. AA (II × 2)—2/20-mm AA (I × 2)—2/12.7-mm mg (I × 2)
Electron Equipt:
Radar: 1/. . . nav., 1/SPS-29 air search, 1/Mk 26 f.c.
M: 4 Fairbanks-Morse 38D 8⅛ × 10 diesels; 2 props; 6,080 bhp
Electric: 600 kw **Range:** 18,000/15
Fuel: 400 tons **Crew:** 160 tot.

Remarks: Transferred from U.S. Navy to U.S. Coast Guard 1946 and to Vietnam 1971 after an extensive overhaul. Escaped 4-75 from Vietnam to the Phillippines, which she was formally sold on 5-4-76. Placed in reserve due to poor mechani condition in 6-85, but has been reactivated and is employed as fleet flagship. Rar gets under way, and during a 3-92 exercise could make only 8 knots. A helicopter de was fitted aft in 1978–79, at which time a twin 40-mm AA mount was added projecting past the stern and adding 1 m to the original overall length. Has a Mk 52 g fire-control system with Mk 26 ranging radar for the 127-mm gun, but it is proba inoperable.

Sisters *Gregorio de Pilar* (PS 8, ex-*Ngo Kuyen,* ex-*McCulloch,* WHEC 386, *Wachapreague,* AGP 8, ex-AVP 56), *Diego Silang* (PS 9, ex-*Tran Quang Khai, Bering Strait,* WHEC 382, ex-AVP 34), and *Francisco Dagahoy* (PS 10, ex-*Tran B Trong,* ex-*Castle Rock,* WHEC 383, ex-AVP 35) were also deactivated in 6-85 but r still exist as hulks.

YACHT

◆ **1 presidential yacht** Bldr: Vosper Pty., Singapore (In serv. 12-77)

TP 77 ANG PINUNO

Ang Pinuno (TP 77) Philippine

D: 150 tons **S:** 28.5 kts **Dim:** 37.9 × 7.2 × 3.8 **Range:** . . .
A: none **Electron Equipt:** Radar: 1/. . . nav. **Crew:** . . .
M: 3 MTU 12V538 TB91 diesels; 3 props; 7,500 bhp

Remarks: Used as a "command ship" for the president. White-painted. Sister is used as a search-and-rescue ship by the Coast Guard.

REPAIR SHIPS

◆ **2 ex-U.S. Achelous-class repair ships** Bldr: Chicago Bridge & Co., Seneca, Ill.

REPAIR SHIPS *(continued)*

	L	In serv.
AR 517 YAKAL (ex-*Satyr,* ARL 23, ex-LST 852)	13-11-44	24-11-44
AR 88 NARRA (ex-*Krishna,* ARL 38, ex-LST 1149)	25-5-45	3-12-45

D: 3,960 tons (fl) **S:** 11.6 kts
Dim: 99.98 (96.32 wl) × 15.24 × 3.71
A: 8/40-mm 60-cal. AA (IV × 2)
M: 2 G.M. 12-567A diesels; 2 props; 1,800 bhp
Electric: 420 kw **Fuel:** 620 tons **Crew:** 250 tot.

Remarks: AR 517 transferred 24-1-77, AR 88 on 31-10-71. Have a 60-ton capacity -frame lift boom to port, one 10-ton derrick, and one 20-ton derrick. Sister *Kamagong* AR 67, ex-*Aklan,* ex-*Romulus,* ARL 22, ex-LST 926) discarded 1989.

CARGO TRANSPORTS

◆ **1 ex-U.S. LST 542-class former small-craft tender** Bldr: Dravo Corp., Neville Island, Pennsylvania

	Laid down	L	In serv.
E 516 APAYAO (ex-*Can Tho,* ex-*Garrett County,* AGP 786, ex-LST 786)	21-5-44	22-7-44	28-8-44

D: 1,620 tons (4,080 fl) **S:** 11.6 kts
Dim: 99.98 (96.32 wl) × 15.24 × 4.29 (max.)
A: 8/40-mm AA (II × 2, I × 4)—4/20-mm AA (II × 2)
M: 2 G.M. 12-567A diesels; 2 props; 1,700 bhp **Electric:** 500 kw
Fuel: 370 tons **Range:** 19,000/10 **Crew:** 160 tot.

Remarks: Converted in the mid-1960s to act as tender to riverine-warfare craft; now parently employed as a cargo or ammunition transport. Retains bow doors, but much the tank deck was filled with repair shops and bins for spare parts. Helicopter deck midships, tripod masts, 10-ton derrick, and enlarged hatch. Transferred to South etnam 4-71; escaped 4-75 and purchased outright on 13-9-77. Sister *Sierra Madre* L 57, ex-*Dumagat,* ex-*My Tho,* ex-*Harnett County,* AGP 821, ex-LST 821) discarded 89.

◆ **1 ex-U.S. Alamosa class** Bldr: Froemming Bros. Inc., Milwaukee, Wis. (In serv. 22-9-45)

90 MACTAN (ex-*Kukui,* WAK 186, ex-*Colquitt,* AK 174)

Mactan (TK 90) R.A.N., 6-82

D: 4,900 tons (7,450 fl) **S:** 12 kts
Dim: 103.18 (97.54 wl) × 15.24 × 6.43
A: 2/20-mm AA (I × 2) **Electron Equipt:** Radar: 1/. . . nav.
M: 1 Nordberg TSM6 diesel; 1 prop; 1,750 bhp
Electric: 500 kw **Fuel:** 350 tons **Crew:** 85 tot.

Remarks: 6,071 dwt. Built for U.S. Maritime Commission, taken over by the U.S. upon completion, then transferred to the U.S. Coast Guard 24-9-45. First plat-deck in cargo-hold area converted to personnel accommodations. Transferred to Philippines 1-3-72 and used as a military transport, supply ship, and lighthouse r. Purchased outright 1-8-80.

◆ **ex-U.S. Army FS 381 class** Bldr: Ingalls, Pascagoula, Miss. (In serv. 43–44)

9 LIMASAWA (ex-*Nettle,* WAK 129, ex-FS 169)
) BADJAO (ex-*Miho,* ex-FS 524)
MANGYAN (ex-*Nasami,* ex-FS 408)

D: 473 tons light (950 fl) **S:** 13 kts
Dim: 53.8 (50.27 pp) × 9.75 × 3.05
A: 2/20-mm AA (I × 2) **Electron Equipt:** Radar: 1/. . . nav.
M: 2 G.M. 6-278A diesels; 2 props; 1,000 bhp **Electric:** 225 kw
Fuel: 67 tons **Range:** 4,150/10; 3,700/11 **Crew:** . . .

Remarks: *Limasawa* was loaned in 1-68 and purchased outright 31-8-78. The other two were purchased 24-9-76 after having served in the Japanese Navy, one as an inshore minesweeper depot ship and one as a mine countermeasures support ship; they were refitted and recommissioned during 1979. All were to serve as buoy tenders and lighthouse supply ships. Cargo capacity: 345 tons.

◆ **1 ex-U.S. Army FS 330 class** Bldr: Higgins, Inc., New Orleans, La. (In serv. 1944)

AE 46 CAPE BOJEADOR (ex-TK 46, ex-FS 203)

D: 420 tons (742 fl) **S:** 10 kts
Dim: 51.77 (48.77 pp) × 9.75 × 2.43
A: 2/20-mm AA (I × 2) **Electron Equipt:** Radar: 1/. . . nav.
M: 4 Buda-Lanova 6 DHMR-1879 diesels; 2 props; 680 bhp
Electric: 225 kw **Range:** 3,830/10 **Fuel:** 50 tons **Crew:** . . . tot.

Remarks: Decommissioned 1988 but refitted for further service and recommissioned 21-11-90; may have been re-engined as well, as obtaining parts for the engines listed above would be extremely difficult. Had been transferred from U.S.A. in 2-50. Cargo capacity: 150 tons. Sister *Lauis Ledge* (TK 45, ex-FS 185) was also stricken in 1988.

◆ **1 ex-Australian motor stores lighter** Bldr: Australia (In serv. 1944)

TK . . . PEARL BANK (ex-U.S. Army LO 4, ex-. . .)

D: 140 tons light (345 fl) **S:** 8 kts **Dim:** 37.26 × 7.47 × 2.07
A: 2/20-mm AA (I × 2) **Electron Equipt:** Radar: 1/. . . nav.
M: 2 Fairbanks-Morse 35F8D diesels; 2 props; 240 bhp
Fuel: 20 tons **Range:** 2,000/6 **Crew:** 35 tot.

Remarks: Transferred 1947. Used as a navigational buoy tender and lighthouse supply ship. Cargo capacity: 170 tons

◆ **1 ex-U.S. Admirable-class former minesweeper** Bldr: Gulf SB Corp., Madisonville, Louisiana

	Laid down	L	In serv.
TK 21 MOUNT SAMAT (ex-*Pagasa,* ex-*Santa Maria,* ex-*Quest,* MSF 281)	24-11-43	16-3-44	25-10-44

Mount Samat (TK 21) Dr. Giorgio Arra, 1977

D: 650 tons (945 fl) **S:** 14.8 kts
Dim: 58.0 (54.86 wl) × 10.06 × 2.97
A: 2/20-mm AA (I × 2) **Electron Equipt:** Radar: 2/. . . nav.
M: 2 Cooper-Bessemer GSB-8 diesels; 2 props; 1,710 bhp
Electric: 280 kw **Fuel:** 138 tons **Crew:** 60 tot.

Remarks: Transferred 2-7-48 and then converted to presidential yacht with considerable additions to superstructure and increased rake to bow. Now primarily used as a lighthouse supply ship.

◆ **1 ex-U.S. Coast Guard Balsam-class buoy tender** Bldr: Marine Iron & SB Corp., Duluth, Minn. (In serv. 2-5-44)

TK 89 KALINGA (ex-*Redbud,* WAGL 398, ex-T-AKL 398, ex-AG 398)

D: 935 tons (1,020 fl) **S:** 13 kts **Dim:** 54.86 × 11.28 × 3.96
A: 1/20-mm AA **Electron Equipt:** Radar: 1/. . . nav.
M: 2 Cooper-Bessemer GSD-8 diesels; electric drive; 1 prop; 1,200 shp
Range: 3,500/7.5 **Crew:** 50 tot.

Kalinga (TK 89) 1977

CARGO TRANSPORTS *(continued)*

Remarks: Built for U.S. Coast Guard, transferred to the U.S. Navy on 25-3-49 as AG 398, to Military Sealift Command on 10-49 as T-AKL 398, and returned 20-11-70 to the U.S. Coast Guard. Transferred to the Philippines 1-3-72. Has helicopter platform and ice-breaking bow—the latter a useful feature in Philippine waters.

SERVICE CRAFT

◆ **1 ex-U.S. 174-foot YOG-class small tanker** Bldr: Puget Sound Naval SY, Bremerton, Washington

	Laid down	L	In serv.
AF 78 Lake Buhi (ex-YO 78, ex-YOG 73)	15-12-43	23-2-44	28-11-44

D: 445 tons light (1,420 fl) **S:** 8 kts **Dim:** 53.04 × 10.01 × 4.27
A: 1/20-mm **Electron Equipt:** Radar: 1/. . . nav.
M: 2 G.M. 8-278A diesels; 2 props; 640 bhp
Fuel: 25 tons **Crew:** 23 tot.

Remarks: Transferred 7-67; had been used as a gasoline tanker by the U.S. Navy. Ex-U.S. YOG 33 and YOG 80, which escaped from Vietnam, were used for cannibalization spares. Cargo capacity: 985 tons. Sister *Lake Mainit* (YO 35) stricken 1979 and *Lake Naujan* (YO 43, ex-YO 173) was stricken in 1989. Redesignated as "AF" in 1990.

◆ **2 ex-U.S. 174-foot YW-class water tankers** Bldrs: AW 33: Marine Iron & SB Co., Duluth, Minn.; AW 34: Leatham D. Smith SB, Sturgeon Bay, Wis.

	Laid down	L	In serv.
AW 33 Lake Buluan (ex-YW 111)	30-9-44	16-12-44	1-8-45
AW 34 Lake Paoay (ex-YW 130)	14-5-45	24-6-45	28-8-45

D: 440 tons light (1,390 fl) **S:** 8 kts **Dim:** 53.04 × 10.01 × 4.0
A: 2/20-mm AA (I × 2) **Electron Equipt:** Radar: 1/. . . nav.
M: 2 G.M. 8-278A diesels; 2 props; 640 bhp **Electric:** 80 kw
Fuel: 25 tons **Crew:** 23 tot.

Remarks: Transferred on 16-7-75. Cargo capacity: 930 tons. Sister *Lake Lanao* (YW 42, ex-U.S. YW 125) stricken 1989.

◆ **1 ex-U.S. YTM 764-class harbor tug** (In serv. 1945)

YQ . . . . (ex-*Hiamonee,* YTM 776)

D: 260 tons (350 fl) **S:** 11 kts **Dim:** 30.8 × 8.5 × 3.7
M: 2 Enterprise diesels; 1 prop; 1,270 bhp **Crew:** 8 tot.

Remarks: Purchased 30-6-90; had been stricken from U.S. Navy 30-11-86.

◆ **5 ex-U.S. YTL 442 class** Bldr: Everett-Pacific Co., Everett, Wash. (YQ 222: Winslow Marine Railway & SB, Winslow, Wash.)

YQ 222 Igorot (ex-YTL 572)
YQ 223 Tagbanua (ex-YTL 429)
YQ 225 Ilongot (ex-YTL 427)
YQ 226 Tasaday (ex-YTL 425)
YQ 271 Afno River (ex-YAS 3, ex-YTL 750)

D: 70 tons (80 fl) **S:** 9 kts **Dim:** 20.17 × 5.18 × 1.5
M: 1 Hamilton 685A diesel; 300 bhp

Remarks: Built 1944–45. Transferred 7-48, 5-63, 12-69, 8-71, and 11-75—the last from Japan, which had received her from the U.S. in 1-55. The ex-Japanese craft was overhauled and arrived in the Philippines during 1979, sister ex-YAS 4 (ex-YTL 748) having been lost overboard en route.

Note: The former U.S. Army tug *Tiboli* (YQ 58, ex-LT 1976) was stricken 1989.

◆ **2 ex-U.S. AFDL floating dry docks** Bldr: V.P. Loftis, Wilmington, N.C. (In serv. 1944–45)

YD 205 (ex-AFDL 44, ex-ARDC 11)
YD . . . (ex-AFDL 40)

Lift Capacity: 2,800 tons **Dim:** 118.6 × 25.6 × 3.1 (light)

Remarks: YD 205 transferred 9-69 and purchased outright 1-8-80; ex-AFDL 40 purchased 30-6-90.

◆ **2 ex-U.S. AFDL 1-class floating dry docks**

	Bldr	In serv.
YD 200 (ex-AFDL 24)	Doullet & Ewin, Mobile, Ala.	1-44
YD 204 (ex-AFDL 20)	G.D. Auchter, Jacksonville, Fla.	6-44

Lift Capacity: 1,000 tons **Dim:** 60.96 × 19.51 × 1.04 (light)

Remarks: YD 200 transferred 7-48, YD 204 loaned 10-61, purchased 1-8-80; ex-AFDL 10, loaned 12-78, returned to U.S. 15-7-87 for disposal as a target.

Note: Ex-U.S. Army floating dry docks YD 201 (ex-AFDL 3681) and YD 203 (ex-AFDL 3682) were stricken in 1989.

◆ **1 ex-U.S. 30-ton-capacity floating crane**

	In serv.	Transferred
YU 206 (ex-YD 163)	12-5-46	1-71

D: 650 tons (fl) **Dim:** 36.58 × 13.72 × 2.13

◆ **1 ex-U.S. 60-ton-capacity floating crane**

	In serv.	Transferred
YU 207 (ex-YD 191)	3-52	8-71

D: 920 tons (fl) **Dim:** 36.58 × 18.24 × 2.13

◆ **1 ex-U.S. Army 230-class 100-ton-capacity floating crane**

	L	Transferred
YD 202 (ex-BCL 1791)	1943	7-49

D: 2,100 tons (fl) **Dim:** 64.0 × 12.5 × 3.4 **A:** 2/20-mm AA (I × 2)

◆ **1 ex-U.S. YCV 3-class former aircraft transport lighter** Bldr: Pearl Harbor Naval SY (In serv. 25-11-43)

YB 206 (ex-YCV 7)

Dim: 33.53 × 9.14 × . . . **Cargo Capacity:** 250 tons

Remarks: Transferred 5-63. Used as a barge.

◆ **2 ex-U.S. Navy barges**

	Transferred		Transferre
YC 227 (ex-YC 1402)	8-59	YC 301 (ex-YC 1403)	8-7

Dim: 24.38 × 8.73 × 1.22

COAST GUARD

Personnel (1991): 300 officers, 1,700 enlisted

The size of the Philippine Coast Guard has fluctuated widely since its establishme in the early 1970s. At one time it had responsibility for maintaining navigational ai and included many of the tenders now returned to the navy. The majority of the patr craft operated by the Coast Guard have been back under naval control since 197 leaving only a few small craft and the larger ships described below still under Coa Guard control. In 1982, most small patrol craft in Philippine military service appear to be under Coast Guard subordination. Up to 60 new patrol craft are planned, b funds are lacking, and in 1990 it was stated that only 88 craft were operational. T Coast Guard is currently subordinated to the Philippine Navy, but it may be tra ferred to the Department of Transportation.

PATROL BOATS

Note: A letter of intent to order two 55-m search-and-rescue patrol boats for Philippine Coast Guard was signed 26-2-91 with Australian Shipbuilding Industr Pty. The two units, if the contract is finalized, would be delivered within 18 month ordering.

◆ **1 Bessang Pass-class search-and-rescue boat** Bldr: Sumidagaw Tokyo, Japan (In serv. 1976–77)

SAR 100 Tirad Pass

D: 275 tons (fl) **S:** 30 kts **Dim:** 44.0 × 7.4 × 1.5
A: none **M:** 2 MTU 12V538 TB82 diesels; 2 props; 4,030 bhp
Range: 2,300/14 **Crew:** 32 tot.

Remarks: Sister *Bessang Pass* (SAR 99) ran aground and was lost 9-83. Similar constructed for Indian Coast Guard. May be out of service.

◆ **1 search-and-rescue boat** Bldr: Vosper Pty., Singapore (In serv.12-

SAR 77 Bataan

Bataan (SAR 77) Leo Van Ginderen,

D: 150 tons **S:** 28 kts **Dim:** 37.9 × 7.2 × 3.8
M: 3 MTU 12V538 TB91 diesels; 3 props; 7,500 bhp

Remarks: Externally identical to presidential yacht *Ang Pinuno* (TP 77) and ently intended more for pleasure than rescue duties.

PATROL CRAFT

◆ **1 Mk II design** Bldr: Cavite Navy Yd. (In serv. 7-85)

D: 24.6 tons (fl) **S:** 36 kts **Dim:** 16.7 × 5.0 × 1.3
A: . . . **Electric Equipt:** Radar: 1/. . . nav.
M: 2 MTU 8V396 TB93 diesels; 2 props; 2,400 bhp

Remarks: Improved version of following class; glass-reinforced-plastic hull. have been 55 built under 18-6-82 order, but by 1986 only 4 hulls were ready, more were built.

PHILIPPINES *(continued)*
PATROL CRAFT *(continued)*

◆ **up to 10 fiberglass-hulled** Bldr: Marcelo Fiberglass Corp., Manila

PSB 411 through PSB 435 (In serv. 1975–76)

'SB 431 R.A.N., 6-82

D: 15 tons (21.75 fl) **S:** 20 kts
Dim: 14.07 × 4.32 × 1.04 (1.48 props)
A: 3/12.7-mm mg (II × 1, I × 1)
Electron Equipt: Radar: 1/LN-66 nav.
M: 2 MTU 8V-331 TC80 diesels; 2 props; 1,800 bhp
Electric: 7.5 kVA **Range:** 200/36 **Crew:** 6 tot.

emarks: Eighty were ordered 8-75, but of 25 hulls completed during 1975, 15 were stroyed by fire, and the program was terminated. Twin machine-gun mount is cessed into the forecastle. Later examples employ Cummins diesels; craft originally tended to achieve 46 kts(!).

6 Australian fiberglass-hulled Bldr: De Havilland Marine, Sydney

: 326–331 (In serv. 20-11-74 to 8-2-75)

D: 16.5 tons (fl) **S:** 25 kts
Dim: 14.0 × 4.6 × 1.0 **A:** 2/12.7-mm mg
M: 2 Caterpillar D348 diesels; 2 props; 740 bhp
Range: 500/12 **Crew:** 8 tot.

17 U.S. Swift Mk III class Bldr: Sewart Seacraft, Morgan City, La., and Peterson Bldrs, Sturgeon Bay, Wis. (In serv. 1975–76)

F 333 through PCF 352 series

' 352 Leo Van Ginderen, 1986

: 28 tons (36.7 fl) **S:** 30 kts **Dim:** 19.78 × 5.5 × 1.8
2/12.7-mm mg (I × 2)—2/7.6-mm mg (I × 2)
ectron Equipt: Radar: 1/LN-66 **Crew:** 8 tot.
: 3 G.M. 8V71 TI diesels; 3 props; 1,950 bhp **Range:** 500/30

arks: Aluminum construction. Pilothouse offset to starboard. Three others have discarded. Last four were built by Peterson Builders.

The remaining *Abra* and U.S. Swift Mk I- and Swift Mk II-class patrol craft have discarded.

COAST AND GEODETIC SURVEY

ships listed below are subordinate to the Ministry of Defense and are used for graphic survey.

survey ship Bldr: Ishikawajima Harima, Tokyo (In serv. 9-2-84)

ORER

500 grt **S:** 12 kts **Dim:** 54.40 × 9.40 × 3.80
2 diesels; 2 props; 1,200 bhp

urvey ship Bldr: Walkers Ltd., Maryborough, Australia (In serv. 9)

IBA

Atyimba Leo Van Ginderen, 1981

D: 611 tons (686 fl) **S:** 11 kts **Dim:** 49.08 (44.3 pp) × 10.14 × 2.74
M: Mirrlees-Blackstone 6-cyl. diesels; 1,620 bhp
Electric: 175 kw **Range:** 5,000/8 **Crew:** 54 tot.

◆ **2 Arinya-class coastal survey ships** Bldr: Walkers, Maryborough, Australia

Arinya (L: 1962) Alunya (L: 1964)

D: 245 tons (fl) **S:** 10 kts **Dim:** 30.64 (27.44 pp) × 6.76 × 2.43
M: 2 G.M. 6-71 diesels; 2 props; 336 bhp
Crew: 6 officers, 27 enlisted

POLAND

Polish Republic

Personnel (1992): 17,260 total, including about 4,000 coast defense and 2,500 naval aviation personnel. In 11-90, the Polish Navy had 19,364 personnel, of whom 5,823 were officers and petty officers; about 6,000 of the remainder were conscripts.

Naval Aviation: 11 Mi- 14PL Haze-A ASW, 3 Mi-14PS Haze SAR, 10 Mi-2 Hoplite, 2 Sokol helicopters, and 10 An-2 Colt transports used for maritime surveillance. The 34th Fighter Regiment, with 32 single-seat MiG-21 and 6 2-seat MiG-21UM jet fighters, was transferred to the Polish Navy in 6-91 to replace a stricken regiment of MiG-17s. Also in use are 14 TS-11 jet trainers. The Polish Navy ordered eight PZL Swidnik W-3RM Anakonda helicopters in 12-91 to begin replacing the Mi-14PS Haze and Mi-2 Hoplite helicopters for SAR duties. Consideration is being given to ordering six TS-11 Iskra jet trainers in a maritime surveillance variant.

Note: It has been officially stated that the Polish Navy is to be reduced to 40 combatant ships and craft; as of 12-90, the fleet was said to have had 206 ships, of which 105 were combatants. The fleet was reorganized 11-91 with two Coastal Defense Flotillas, one Warship Flotilla, and the Naval Air Brigade as its major subdivisions.

WEAPONS AND SENSOR SYSTEMS

While most weapon and sensor systems are of Soviet origin, Poland manufactures some under license and has introduced its own navigational radars as a result of its extensive merchant ship and fishing boat construction industry. A naval gun mounting of Polish design is the twin 23-mm Wrobel-2MR, a variant of the Soviet ZU-23-2 mount that also carries two 9K32M Strela heat-seeking missiles:

Caliber: 23 mm Rate of fire: 1,600-2,000 rds/mount/min.
Effective range: 2,000 m Mount weight: 2,500 kg
Effective altitude: 1,500 m Muzzle velocity: 970 m/sec.

SUBMARINES

◆ **1 Soviet Kilo class (Project 877E)** Bldr: United Admiralty SY, St. Petersburg

291 Orzeł (In serv. 21-6-86)

Orzeł (291) Antoni Kaczorowski, 1991

SUBMARINES *(continued)*

D: 2,325 tons surf./3,076 tons sub. **S:** 10 kts surf./17 kts sub.
Dim: 74.3 (70.0 wl) × 10.0 × 6.6
A: 6/533-mm TT (18 torpedoes, or up to 24 mines)—1/9K32M Strela shoulder-launch SAM position
Electron Equipt:
Radar: 1/Snoop Tray-2 search
Sonar: Shark Gill LF active/passive suite, passive hull array
EW: Brick Pulp or Squid Head intercept; Quad Loop D/F
M: 3 Type 2D-42, 1,825-bhp diesel generator sets, electric drive: 1 motor; 1/6-bladed prop; 5,900 shp
Range: 6,000/7 (surf.); 400/3 (sub.) **Crew:** 12 officers, 41 enlisted

Remarks: *Orzel* was the first Kilo to be exported from the then-U.S.S.R. Additional units were planned to complete replacement of the quartet of Whiskey-class submarines then in service, but lack of funds forced the leasing of the two Foxtrots below instead. Has anechoic hull coating. Diving depth: 300 m. Probably has some means of auxiliary propulsion, such as a low-power (100–150 kw) electric creep motor on the main shaft for low-speed, quiet operations. The shoulder-launched SAM position is at the aft end of the sail.

♦ **2 Soviet Foxtrot class (Project 641)** Bldr: Sudomekh SY or Severodvinsk SY (In serv. 1957–68)

292 Wilk 293 Dzik

Wilk (292) Antoni Kaczorowski, 1991

D: 1,952 tons (surf.)/2,475 tons (sub.) **S:** 15.5 kts (surf.)/18 kts (sub.)
Dim: 91.30 × 7.50 × 6.00
A: 10/533-mm TT (6 fwd, 4 aft—22 torpedoes or 44 mines)
Electron Equipt:
Radar: 1/Snoop Tray-1 search—Sonar: 1/MF active; passive arrays
EW: 1/Stop Light intercept; Quad Loop D/F
M: 3 Type 37D or Type 42 diesels of 2,000/1,825 bhp, 3 electric motors; 3/5 or 6-bladed props; 5,400 shp (sub.)
Range: 20,000/8 (surf.); 11,000/8 (snorkel); 36/18 (sub.); 380/2 (sub.)
Endurance: 70 days **Fuel:** 360 tons
Crew: 9 officers, 50 enlisted

Remarks: *Wilk* leased and commissioned 11-87, *Dzik* on 5-2-89. Will probably soon be returned to Russia.

GUIDED-MISSILE DESTROYER

♦ **1 ex-Soviet Modified Kashin class (Project 61MR)**

	Bldr	L	In serv.
271 Warszawa (ex-*Smel'yy*)	61 Kommuna, Nikolayev	1970	1974

Warszawa (271) Ben Sullivan, 5-8

D: 3,950 tons (4,950 fl) **S:** 35 kts **Dim:** 146.0 × 15.8 × 4.8 (hull)
A: 4/SS-N-26 Styx SSM (I × 4)—2/SA-N-1 SAM launchers (II × 2; 32 RZ-61 Goa missiles)—4/76.2-mm 59-cal. AK-276 DP (II × 2)—4/30-mm AK-630 gatling AA (I × 4)—5/533-mm TT (V × 1, no reloads)—2/RBU-6000 ASW RL (XII × 2)—helicopter deck
Electron Equipt:
Radar: 2/SRN-7453 nav., 1/Don-Kay nav., 1/Head Net-C air search 1/Big Net early warning, 2/Peel Group ("Yakuta") SAM f.c., 2/Owl Screech 76-mm f.c., 2/Bass Tilt 30-mm f.c.
Sonar: M/F hull-mounted, M/F VDS
EW: 2/Bell Squat, 2/Bell Shroud, 4 RK-16 decoy RL (XVI × 4)
IFF: 1/Salt Pot transponder (interrogation on radar)
EO: 2/Tee Plinth trainable t.v., 4/Tilt Pot fixed t.v., 2 bridge periscopes
M: 4 Type M-3 gas turbines; 2 props; 94,000 shp
Range: 1,000/34; 2,600/30; 4,500/18; 7,000/12
Crew: 25 officers, 255 enlisted

Remarks: Transferred on nine-year lease during 12-87 and commissioned 9-1-8 Attached to the 3rd Flotilla and based at Gdańsk. Polish navigational radars replac one Don Kay. Press reports indicate that Poland would like to return her early.

Rebuilt in the U.S.S.R. in the 1970s with variable-depth sonar in new stern th extended hull length by 2 m, helicopter platform atop VDS housing, four Styx missi replacing two RBU-1000 ASW RL, and forward superstructure enlarged to increa officer accommodations. Four six-barreled gatling AA were added amidships. The sh took the name and number of a SAM Kotlin stricken 31-1-86 and scrapped 6-4-91.

CORVETTE

Note: Funds permitting, it is hoped to build four corvettes of about 1,000-tons placement during the mid-to-late 1990s.

♦ **1 Kaszub class (Project 620)** Bldr: Stocznia Północna, Gdańsk

	Laid down	L	In serv.
240 Kaszub	11-5-85	10-10-86	15-3-87

D: 1,051 tons (1,183 fl) **S:** 26.2 kts
Dim: 82.34 × 10.00 × 2.80 (hull)
A: 1/76.2-mm 59-cal. AK-176 DP—6/23-mm AA/twin SAM-combination Wrobel-2MR (II × 3; 2 × 9K32M Fasta-II missiles pe mount)—2/RBU-6000 ASW RL (XII × 2)—4/533-mm DTA 53-62 TT (II × 2)—2/d.c mortars—2/d.c. racks—mines

Warszawa (271) Antoni Kaczorowsk

CORVETTE *(continued)*

Kaszub (240)—prior to addition of 76.2-mm gun M.O.D. Bonn, 12-90

Electron Equipt:
Radar: 1/SRN-744 nav., 1 Strut Curve surf./air search
Sonar: . . . hull-mounted MF, HF dipping
EW: . . . . intercept; 2/82-mm RK-16 decoy RL
IFF: 1/ Square Head interrogator; 1/High Pole B transponder
M: 4 Cegielski-Sulzer AS 16V 25/30 diesels; 2 props; 16,890 bhp
Range: 2,000/18 **Crew:** 80 tot.

Remarks: First seagoing combatant built in Poland since prior to World War II. Work began 9-6-84. Not a success; was found to have warped hull and shafts at launch and had to be repaired at the Gdynia naval yard. Was loaned to the Border Guard from the fall of 1990 for use as a flagship and returned to naval service 1-91. Is attached to the 1th Patrol Boat Squadron.
The helicopter-type dipping sonar is located in the cabinet at the extreme stern. Main gun forward was mounted 9-91. It is hoped to add two 30-mm AK-630 gatling AA mounts at a later date.

GUIDED-MISSILE PATROL BOATS

4 Soviet Tarantul I class (Project 1241) Bldr: Volodarskiy SY, Rybinsk

434 Górnik (In serv. 30-12-83) 436 Metalowiec (In serv. 13-2-88)
435 Hutnik (In serv. 31-3-84) 437 Rolnik (In serv. 5-2-89)

Metalowiec (436) Antoni Kaczorowski, 1991

Rolnik (437) M.O.D. Bonn, 5-89

Górnik (434) M.O.D. Bonn, 7-91

D: 385 tons light (455 fl) **S:** 43 kts
Dim: 56.10 (49.50 pp) × 10.20 (9.40 wl) × 2.14 hull (3.59 props)
A: 4/SS-N-2C SSM (II × 2, 2-each P-21 radar-homing and P-22 infrared-homing missiles)—1/76.2-mm 59-cal. AK-176 DP—1/SA-N-8 (MTU-40S) SAM syst. (IV × 1, 12 Strela missiles)—2/30-mm AK-630 gatling AA (I × 2)
Electron Equipt:
Radar: 1/Kivach-2 nav., 1/Plank Shave (Harpun-E) targeting, 1/ Bass Tilt (Koral-E/MR123) f.c.
EW: 2/RK-16 decoy RL (XVI × 2)
IFF: 1/High Pole transponder, 1/Square Head interrogator
M: M-15E COGAG plant: 2 DMR-76 cruise gas turbines (4,000 shp each), 2 PR-77 boost gas turbines (12,000 shp each); 2 props; 32,000 shp
Range: 400/43; 2,400/14 **Endurance:** 10 days **Fuel:** 50 tons
Crew: 7 officers, 32 enlisted

Remarks: Unlike Soviet Navy version, have no EW gear. Said to be difficult to maneuver at low speeds. Names mean "Miner," "Steelworker," " Metalworker," and "Farmer," respectively. Poland has expressed interest in acquiring at least two of the four remaining former *Volksmarine* units of this class from Germany.

◆ **8 Soviet Osa-I class (Project 205)**

424 Kołobrzeg 430 Darłowo
427 Puck 431 Swinoujście
428 Ustka 432 Dziwnów
429 Oksywie 433 Władysłlawowo

D: 171 tons (209.5 fl) **S:** 40 kts (36 sust.)
Dim: 38.6 × 7.6 × 1.8 (2.9 props)
A: 4/SS-N-2A Styx SSM (I × 4, P-15 missiles)—1/FASTA HN-4 (SA-N-5) SAM syst. (IV × 1, 8 Strela missiles)—4/30-mm AK-230 AA (II × 2)
Electron Equipt:
Radar: 1/Square Tie surf. search/target designation, 1/Drum Tilt gun f.c.
IFF: 2 Square Head interrogators, 1/High Pole B transponder
M: 3 M503A2 diesels; 3 props, 12,000 bhp **Range:** 500/34; 750/25
Crew: 4 officers, 18 enlisted

Remarks: Built in the U.S.S.R. during the early 1960s, transferred 1966–1967. Sisters *Hel* (421) and *Gdańsk* (422) have been discarded; *Gdynia* (423), *Szczecin* (425), and *Elblag* (426) were converted as patrol boats for the Border Guard in 1989. The remaining eight are to be stricken or converted to other functions shortly. All named for coastal cities.

PATROL BOATS

◆ **0 (+3+3) ex-East German Project 151A (Type 620)** Bldr: Peenewerft, Wolgast

	Laid down	L	In serv.
. . . Piorun	26-6-89	10-5-90	. . .
. . . Huragan	18-9-89	7-7-90	. . .
. . . Orkan	10-7-90	9-90	. . .

Orkan Hartmut Ehlers, 9-90

D: 331 tons (369 fl) **S:** 37 kts
Dim: 48.90 (45.00 pp) × 8.65 × 2.15
A: 1/76.2-mm AK-176 DP—1/30-mm AK-630 gatling AA
Electron Equipt:
Radar: 1/SRN-744 nav., 1/Plank Shave surf. search, 1/Bass Tilt f.c.
EW: 2/RK-16 decoy RL (XVI × 2)
M: 3 M 520 diesels; 3 props; 16,200 bhp (14,570 sust.)
Electric: 366 kw (1 × 183 kw, 2 × 128-kw diesel sets)
Range: 2,400/20 **Endurance:** 5 days **Crew:** 7 officers, 26 enlisted

Remarks: Purchased incomplete just prior to the unification of Germany and transferred 3-10-90; little work has been accomplished on completing them, and they are without engines, sensors, or weapons. Poland reportedly would like to buy three further units from Germany that had been launched on 23-4-90, 25-4-90, and 27-5-90, respectively.
The first of nine laid down out of a planned dozen for the *Volksmarine* and up to 38 others for the U.S.S.R. and Poland; as prototype was given project number 151.0. When first seen by NATO was given temporary code "Bal-Com-10"). Prototype *Sassnitz* was equipped with eight tubes for the Soviet SS-N-25 antiship missile for trials purposes, but they had been removed by the summer of 1990. Each "star radial" M 520 diesel has eight rows of seven cylinders.

PATROL BOATS *(continued)*

◆ **8 Modified Obluze class (Project 912M)** Bldr: Stocznia Marynarki Wojennej, Gdynia (In serv. 1970–72)

351 Grożny	354 Zwinny	357 Nieugięty
352 Wytrwały	355 Zwrotny	358 Czujny
353 Zreczny	356 Zawzięty	

Zawzięty (356) M.O.D. Bonn, 8-89

D: 214 tons (237 fl) **S:** 24 kts
Dim: 41.4 (39.5 pp) × 6.3 × 2.0 (hull)
A: 4/30-mm AK-230 AA (II × 2)—4/d.c. racks (2 topside; 2 through stern)
Electron Equipt:
Radar: 1/RN-231 nav., 1/Drum Tilt f.c.
Sonar: 1/Tamir-11 hull-mounted HF searchlight
IFF: 2/Square Head interrogators, 1/High Pole A transponder
M: 2 Type 40D diesels: 2 props: 4,400 bhp **Electric:** 150 kw
Range: 600/. . . **Fuel:** 25 tons **Crew:** 40 tot.

Remarks: Similar to larger group in the Polish Maritime Brigade of Border Ships that do *not* have Drum Tilt fire-control radars. Names mean "Formidable," "Persistent," "Adroit," "Nimble," "Agile," "Obstinate," "Inflexible," and "Vigilant," respectively. 351 and 352 commissioned 8-2-70.

◆ **8 Pilica class (Project 918)** Bldr: Stocznia Marynarki Wojennej im. Dąbrowszczaków, Gdynia (In serv. 1973–82)

KP 161 to KP 177 series

D: 91 tons (fl) **S:** 28 kts **Dim:** 28.59 × 5.76 × 1.40
A: 2/25-mm 2M-8 or 23-mm ZU-23-2AA (II × 1)—2/533-mm TT—2–4/d.c.
Electron Equipt:
Radar: 1/RN-231 nav.—IFF: High Pole A transponder
M: 3 M50F-4 diesels; 3 props; 3,600 bhp **Crew:** 19 tot.

Pilica-class KP 169—Coast Guard unit Antoni Kaczorowski, 1991

Pilica-class KP 168 M.O.D. Bonn

Remarks: All transferred to the navy in 1991 from the Ministry of the Interior Border Guard. All but the first three have had two 533-mm torpedo tubes added. Some, including KP 173, have a 23-mm twin AA mount vice 25-mm. Two different torpedo tube mounts, removed from discarded P-6-class torpedo boats, are in use; they are angled 7-deg. outboard. Several, including KP 169, have a light towing A-frame at the stern. Five Type 918M sisters serve in the Coast Guard.

MINE WARFARE SHIPS

◆ **8 Krogulec-class minesweepers (Project 206F)** Bldr: Stocznia im Komuny Pariskiy , Gdynia (In serv. 1965–67)

616 Kormoran	620 Tukan	623 Mewa
618 Albatros	621 Flaming	624 Czajka
619 Pelikan	622 Rybitwa	

Tukan (620) French Navy, 6-

D: 424 tons (470 fl) **S:** 18 kts **Dim:** 60.0 (58.2 pp) × 8.0 × 2.1 (hull)
A: 6/25-mm 2M-8 AA (II × 3)—2/d.c. racks—mines
Electron Equipt: Radar: 1/RN-231 **Fuel:** 55 tons
M: 2 Fiat A-230S diesels; 2 props; 3,740 bhp **Range:** 3,200/12
Crew: 6 officers, 24 enlisted

Remarks: Some of these ships had four 23-mm ZSU-23 AA (II × 2) mounted af[t in] place of the original four 25-mm AA. All named for birds. The first three built [with] Cigielski 6AR25 diesels of 1,100 bhp each for 14 kts. Four have been discarded: O[...] (613), *Krogulec* (614), *Jastrząb* (615), and *Czapla* (617).

Note: All remaining Soviet T-43-class (Project 254M long-hull and Project 2[...] short-hull) were discarded 1990–91, the last to go being *Tur* (602), which had [been] employed as a radar trials ship.

◆ **15 (+. . .) Notec-class (Project 207M) coastal minehunter/minesweepers** Bldr: Stocznia Marynarki Wojennej im Dabrowszczakó[w], Gdynia

	L	In serv.		L	In serv.
630 Gopło	16-4-81	13-3-82	638 Sarsko	. . .	1989
631 Gardnó	5-83	31-3-84	639 Necko	. . .	1990
632 Bukowo	. . .	23-6-85	640 Naklo	. . .	2-3-90
633 Dąbie	21-6-85	1986	641 Drużno	. . .	1991
634 Jamno	. . .	1986	642 Mańcza	. . .	1991
635 Mielno	. . .	1987	643	. . .	6-91
636 Wicko	. . .	1987	644	. . .	. . .
637 Resko	. . .	7-88			

Jamno (634) M.O.D. Bonn

Gopło (630)—now has twin 23-mm forward Antoni Kaczo[rowski]

MINE WARFARE SHIPS (continued)

D: 208 tons light (225 fl) **S:** 14 kts **Dim:** 38.20 × 7.00 × 1.78
A: 2/23-mm Wrobel-2MR combination AA/SAM syst. (II × 2)— 2/d.c. racks—2 mine rails (6–24 mines, depending on type)
Electron Equipt:
Radar: 1/RN-231 nav.—IFF: High Pole B transponder
Sonar: SHL-100 and SHL-200 hull-mounted HF mine-location
M: 2 Type M401A diesels; 2 Kort-nozzle props; 2,000 bhp
Range: 700/14; 1,100/9 **Endurance:** 5 days
Crew: 24 tot. (accommodations for 30)

Remarks: GRP hull construction. The first two were initialy fitted with the Type -2PM gun mount until the Wrobel-2MR mount was available. The Project 207D prototype (630) was used for trials with the sonar suite; SHL-100 Flaming-A is a forward-looking mine-avoidance set, while SHL-200 is a side- and aft-looking mine-location set operating at 100 kHz. All are capable of hunting for or sweeping mines in waters 5 to 20 meters deep in sea conditions up to Sea State 3 and winds at 4–5 Beaufort. Equipped with mechanical, acoustic, and magnetic sweep gear.

2 (+. . .) Leniwka-class minesweeping boats (In serv. 1985)

5 626

D: approx. 290 tons (fl) **S:** . . . **Dim:** 25.67 × 7.22 × 2.71
A: . . . **M:** . . .

Remarks: Conversions of Type B-410 192 grt/79 dwt trawlers to determine the feasibility of using this numerous class as auxiliary minesweepers during wartime.

AMPHIBIOUS WARFARE SHIPS

5 Lublin-class (Project 767) landing ships Bldr: Stocznia Północna, Gdańsk

	L	In serv.
1 Lublin	12-7-88	12-10-89
2 Gniezno	7-12-88	23-2-90
3 Krakow	7-3-89	27-6-90
4 Poznan	5-1-90	6-91
5 Toruń	8-6-90	24-5-91

...zno (822) Antoni Kaczorowski, 1990

...n (821) M.O.D. Bonn, 5-90

1,665 tons (fl) **S:** 16.5 kts
...: 95.80 (81.00 pp) × 10.80 × 2.25
8/23-mm Wrobel-2MR combination AA/SAM syst. (II × 4)—12/. . .-mm multi-barrel beach-clearing rockets—mines
...ctron Equipt:
...adar: 1/SRN-7453 nav., 1/SRN-443XTA nav.
3 Cegielski-Sulzer 6ATL 25D diesels; 3 Kort-nozzle props; 3,960 bhp
...tric: 750 kVA tot. (3 ZMiN-Wola 400V, 50 Hz diesel sets)
...ge: 850–1,400/16.25 depending on load
...urance: 5 days
...w: 5 officers, 2 warrant officers, 8 petty officers, 22 enlisted + 135 troops

Remarks: A planned sixth unit was canceled. The 600-m² open cargo deck can accommodate nine 45-ton tanks in one row or two rows of 2.5-meter-wide vehicles for a maximum vehicle load of 465 tons; maximum cargo load is 536 tons. Have hydraulic-snub cargo tie-down system. Vehicle deck has 4.2-m clearance at the ends, and the two-part folding bow ramp is 20 m long when extended. Equipped with an automated ballast system for use when discharging or loading cargo off a beach. Have Decca AD-2 and BRAS radio navaid receivers. In the minelaying rôle, can add a mezzanine deck to increase stowage. The fourth unit was initially equipped with ZU23-2 gun mounts vice the combination gun/missile mounting.

◆ **1 Soviet Polnocny-C-class (Project 776) landing ship** Bldr: Stocznia Północna, Gdańsk (In serv. 1973)

811 Grunwald

Grunwald (811)—with old number 882 M.O.D. Bonn, 6-75

D: 980 tons (1,207 fl) **S:** 18 kts
Dim: 81.30 × 9.30 × 1.20 fwd/2.60 aft
A: 4/30-mm AK-230 AA (II × 2)—2/140-mm RL (XVIII × 2)
Electron Equipt:
Radar: 1/Drum Tilt, 1/Don 2
IFF: 1/Square Head, 1/High Pole A
M: 2 Type 40DM diesels; 2 props; 4,400 bhp **Range:** 1,000/18
Crew: 35 tot. + 135 troops

Remarks: Believed to be the only "Polnocny" remaining in service as an amphibious warfare ship and likely soon to be stricken. Cargo: 180 tons vehicles. Hull has a sharp, reinforced "beak" at the bow to facilitate beaching. The upper deck cannot be used to carry cargo. Ships of this design serve in the Russian Navy, and a modified version with helicopter deck ("Polnocny-D") was built for export.

Note: Of the 22 Project 772, Polnocny-A- and -B- class landing ships listed in the previous edition, only three remained in service as of 11-91, and of those, *Glogów* (809) was to be converted to act as a radar trials ship. Polnocny-B names included: *Lenino* (801), *Studzianki* (802), *Siekierki* (803), *Budziszyn* (804), *Polnochno* (805), *Rablow* (806), *Janów* (807), *Narwik* (808), *Glogów*, and *Ceydynia* (810); Polnocny-A names included: *Odra* (888), *Nysa* (889), *Brda* (890), *Oka* (891), *Bug* (892), *Narew* (893), *San* (894), *Bzura* (897), and *Warta* (898), plus numbers 895, 896, and 899. During 1990, two Polnocny-A were sold to a Dutch buyer (and registered Honduran) and two others were sold abroad for commercial use, while at least four others were to be converted into coastal-service container ships in Poland in 1991.

◆ **3 Dęba-class (Project 716) utility landing craft** Bldr: Stocznia Marynarki Wojennej, Gdynia

851 (In serv. 16-6-88) 852 (In serv. 11-90) 853 (In serv. 1991)

Dęba-class 851 Antoni Kaczorowski, 1988

D: 170 tons (fl) **S:** 20 kts **Dim:** 37.20 (33.60 wl) × 7.27 × 1.67
A: 2/23-mm Wrobel-2MR combination AA/SAM-launcher (II × 1)—mines
Electron Equipt: Radar: 1/SRN-207A nav.
M: 3 Type M401A diesels; 3 props; 3,150 bhp
Range: 500/16 **Fuel:** 9.4 tons **Crew:** 12 tot. + 50 troops

Note: The 4 Marabut- and 15 Eichstaden-class landing craft were stricken 1990–91.

HYDROGRAPHIC SHIPS

◆ **2 modified Finik class (Project 874)** Bldr: Stocznia Północna, Gdańsk (In serv. 2-83)

263 Heweliusz 266 Arctowski

Arctowski (266) Peter Westdijk, 3-91

D: 1,112 tons (fl) **S:** 12 kts **Dim:** 61.30 × 10.80 × 3.27
Electron Equipt: Radar: 1/RN-231 nav.
M: 2 Cegielski-Sulzer 6 AL 25/30 diesels; 2 CP props; 1,920 bhp; 2 150-kw electric auxiliary drive motors
Electric: 675 kVA tot. **Range:** 3,000/10
Crew: 20 tot. (accommodations for 27)

Remarks: 751 grt, 250 dwt. Able to link via chain drag for clearance surveys. Have a bow-thruster, four precision echo-sounders. Compared to Russian Navy sisters, have forecastle extended nearly to stern, no buoy-handling capability. Civilian sisters *Planeta* (launched 21-5-82) and *Zodiak* (launched 28-8-82) are subordinated to the Maritime Agency, Szczecin. Named for an astronomer and an explorer.

◆ **1 Soviet Moma class** Bldr: Stocznia Północna, Gdańsk (In serv. 1973)

Kopernik

Kopernik—with seismic survey gear streamed 1978

D: 1,240 tons (1,800 fl) **S:** 17 kts **Dim:** 73.3 × 11.8 × 3.8
Electron Equipt: Radar: 2/RN-231 nav.
M: 2 Zgoda-Sulzer 6TD48 diesels; 2 CP props; 3,600 bhp
Range: 8,700/11 **Endurance:** 35 days **Crew:** 56 tot.

Remarks: Operated for the Academy of Science. Sisters in Bulgarian and Yugoslav navies. *Piast*-class salvage ships and *Wodnik*-class training ships are very similar. Two others, the *Nawigator* and *Hydrograf,* serve as intelligence collectors. *Kopernik* has 35 m² of laboratory deck area and has been modified for use in seismic survey and oil exploration work. Forward crane removed 1983. Conducted surveys off Mexican coast in 1989 for the Interoceanmetal Consortium. Named for Copernicus.

◆ **2 KH-121 class GRP-hulled hydrographic launches** Bldr: Stocznia Wisła, Gdańsk (In serv. 1988, 1989)

D: . . . tons **S:** . . . kts **Dim:** 18.88 × 4.92 × 1.60
M: 2 diesels; 2 props; 1,000 bhp **Crew:** . . .

◆ **5 MH 111 hydrographic launches** Bldr: Stocznia Rzeczna, Tczew

M-35 M-37 M-38 M-39 M-40

D: . . . tons **S:** 8.6 kts **Dim:** 10.72 × 4.06 × 1.55
M: 1 Wola diesel; 165 bhp **Crew:** 2 + 8 survey party

AUXILIARY SHIPS

◆ **1 ZP-1200-class small replenishment oiler** Bldr: Stocznia Marynarki Woyennej, Gdynia (In serv. 11-3-91)

Z-1 Bałtyk

D: 2,950 tons (fl) **S:** 15.7 kts **Dim:** 84.70 × 13.10 × 4.70
A: 4/23-mm in Wrobel-2MR combination AA/SAM syst. (II × 2)
Electron Equipt: Radar: 1/SRN-7453 nav., 1/SRN-443XTA nav.
M: 2 Cegielski-Sulzer 8ASL 25 diesels; 2 props; 4,025 bhp
Range: 4,250/12 **Crew:** . . . tot.

Remarks: 1,200 dwt. Replenishment stations port and starboard and also able t conduct astern refuelings. Was originally to have been the first of a class of four. "Z stands for *Zbiornikowiec* (tanker).

◆ **3 Moskit-class coastal oilers** Bldr: Stocznia Wroclaw (In serv. 1971–72)

Z-3 Z-8 Z-9

Z-8 Antoni Kaczorowski, 19

D: 700 tons light (1,200 fl) **S:** 10 kts
Dim: 57.7 (54.0 pp) × 9.5 × 3.4
A: 4/23-mm in Wrobel-2MR combination AA/SAM syst. (II × 2)
Electron Equipt: Radar: 1/RN-231 nav.
M: 2 Cegielski-Sulzer diesels; 2 CP props; 600 bhp
Crew: 12 tot.

Remarks: Cargo: 800 tons. Guns occasionally removed. Names associated with th ships, *Krab, Meduza,* and *Slimak,* are unofficial. Wrobel-2MR mounts have repla the twin 25-mm 2M-8 mounts previously installed.

◆ **1 Type 5-class coastal tanker**

Z-5 (In serv. 1960)

Z-5 Antoni Kaczorowski,

D: 400 tons (625 fl) **S:** 9 kts **Dim:** 35.0 × 5.0 × . . .
A: 4/25-mm 2M-8 AA (II × 2)
Electron Equipt: Radar: 1/. . . nav.
M: 1 diesel; 1 prop; 300 bhp **Range:** 1,200/9 **Crew:** 16 tot.

Remarks: Cargo: 180 tons. The guns are not always aboard. Sisters Z-6 and Z-7 stricken 1990–91.

◆ **2 Piast-class salvage ships** Bldr: Stocznia Północna, Gdańsk

281 Piast (In serv. 26-1-74) 282 Lech (In serv. 30-11-74)

Piast (281) M.O.D. Bon

AUXILIARY SHIPS *(continued)*

.ech (282) Antoni Kaczorowski, 1991

D: 1,560 tons (1,732 fl) **S:** 16.5 kts
Dim: 72.6 (67.2 pp) × 12.0 × 4.0
A: 8/25-mm 2M-8 AA (II × 4; not normally mounted)
Electron Equipt: Radar: 2/RN-231
M: 2 Cegielski-Sulzer 6TD48 diesels; 2 CP props; 3,600 bhp
Range: 3,000/12
Crew: 28 officers, 44 enlisted (including 12 officer divers)

emarks: Variation of *Moma* design for salvage and rescue duties. Carry submarine scue bell to port, can tow, and have extensive pump and fire-fighting facilities. Sister *ınguardia* (ex-East German *Otto von Guericke* is in the Uruguayan Navy. *Piast* ployed with UN Coalition forces to the Mideast 12-90 to 20-5-91, armed with four vin 25-mm AA and equipped with Navstar 2000 Global Positioning System receiver, avtex facsimile receiver, and a Kelvin-Hughes collision avoidance system.

3 Gniewko-class (Type R-30) salvage tugs Bldr: Stocznia Marynarki Woyennej, Gdynia

.1 Gniewko (In serv. 29-8-81) R 13 Semko (In serv. . . .)
.2 Bolko (In serv. . . .)

D: 313 tons (365 fl) **S:** 12 kts **Dim:** 32.6 × 8.2 × 3.0
Electron Equipt: Radar: 1/RN-231 nav.
M: 1 Cegielski-Sulzer 6AL 25.30 diesel; 1 Kort-nozzle prop; 1,470 bhp
Range: 4,600/7 **Crew:** . . . tot.

3 Mrówka-class degaussing/deperming tenders (In serv. 1970–71)

-11 SD-12 SD-13

-13 Antoni Kaczorowski, 1991

: 550 tons (fl) **S:** 9 kts **Dim:** 44.6 × 8.2 × 3.0
: 2/25-mm 2M-8 AA (II × 1)
lectron Equipt: Radar: 1/RN-231 nav.
: 1 diesel; 1 prop; 300 bhp **Crew:** 20 tot.

arks: "SD" stands for *Staeja Demagnetyzacyjna* (degaussing station). Name *na"* associated with SD-11 is unofficial.

icebreaker Bldr: P.K. Harris & Sons, Appledore, U.K. (In serv. 1963)

<UN

2,300 tons (fl) **S:** 10 kts
m: 55.06 (50.75 pp) × 13.96 × 4.98 **Crew:** . . .
4 Ruston-Hornsby 920-bhp diesel generators, 4 550-kw motors; 2 props; 3,000 shp

arks: 1,152 grt. Civilian-subordinated harbor icebreaker; manned by the Polish

Polnocny-B-class radar trials ship Bldr: Stocznia Północna, łańsk (In serv. . . .)

Głogów

D: 740 tons (800 fl) **S:** 19 kts **Dim:** 74.0 × 8.9 × 1.9 (max. aft)
A: . . . **Electron Equipt:** Radar: . . .
M: 2 Type 40DM diesels; 2 props; 4,400 bhp **Range:** 900/18
Fuel: 36 tons **Crew:** . . .

Remarks: Former landing ship reported under conversion 1990 as radar trials ship to replace the former minesweeper *Tur*. No details of conversion available.

INTELLIGENCE COLLECTORS

♦ **2 modified Moma class (Type 863)** Bldr: Stocznia Północna, Gdańsk (In serv. 1975–76)

262 Nawigator 263 Hydrograf

Nawigator (262)—cylindrical radome atop bridge R. Neth.N., 6-88

Hydrograf (281)—rounded radomes Gerhard Koop, 7-89

D: 1,467 tons (1,675 fl) **S:** 17 kts **Dim:** 73.3 × 11.2 × 3.8
Electron Equipt: Radar: 2/RN-231 nav.
M: 2 Zgoda-Sulzer 6TD48 diesels; 2 CP props; 3,600 bhp
Range: 8,700/11 **Endurance:** 35 days **Crew:** 56 tot.

Remarks: Crane removed, superstructure lengthened, lattice mainmast as on *Piast* class. Euphemistically described as "navigational training ships." Provision for mounting 8/25-mm AA (II × 4), 2 fwd, 2 aft.

TRAINING SHIPS

♦ **2 Wodnik class (Type 888)** Bldr: Stocznia Północna, Gdańsk

	L	In serv.
251 Wodnik	29-11-75	27-5-76
252 Gryf	13-3-76	26-9-76

D: 1,697 tons (1,820 fl) **S:** 16.8 kts **Dim:** 71.40 × 11.60 × 3.90
A: 4/30-mm AK-230 AA (II × 2)—4/23-mm in Wrobel-2MR combination AA/SAM syst. (II × 2)
Electron Equipt: Radar: 2/RN-231 nav., 1/Drum Tilt f.c.
M: 2 Cegielski-Sulzer 6TD48 diesels; 2 CP props; 3,600 bhp
Range: 7,500/11 **Crew:** 60 men + 13 instructors and 87 cadets

Gryf (252) Leo Van Ginderen, 7-91

TRAINING SHIPS *(continued)*

Wodnik (251) M.O.D. Bonn, 1991

Remarks: Nearly identical to the former East German *Wilhelm Pieck* and similar to the *Luga* and *Oka* in the Soviet Navy. Developed from the *Moma* design. Have latest navigational systems from the West and the U.S.S.R. Names mean "Water Elf" and "Gryphon."

From 12-90 to 5-91, *Wodnik* operated as an unarmed hospital ship in support of UN Coalition forces in the Mideast, reconverting to training ship on return. As a hospital ship, had berths for 84 patients (plus facilities for 30–50 ambulatory patients) and carried 10 medical personnel in addition to an operating crew of 63; to assist her deployment, received new radios, Navstar 2000 Global Positioning system receiver, Navtex facsimile receiver, and Kelvin-Hughes collision-avoidance equipment. Was white-painted, with standard red-cross markings. A temporary helicopter deck was provided aft.

◆ **4 Bryza class (Project OS-1) navigational training craft** Bldr: Stocznia Wisła, Gdańsk

	In serv.		In serv.
K-18 Bryza	1965	712 Kadet	19-7-75
711 Podchorąży	30-11-74	713 Elew	8-4-76

Podchorąży (711) Antonio Kaczorowski, 1991

D: 146.7 tons (fl) **S:** 10.5 kts **Dim:** 28.82 × 6.60 × 1.85
Electron Equipt: Radar: 2/RN-231 nav.
M: 2 Wola diesels; 2 props; 300 bhp
Electric: 84 kw **Range:** 1,100/10
Crew: 11 tot. + 26 midshipmen

Remarks: *Bryza*, with a less elaborate superstructure, displaces 167 tons (fl) and dimensions are 26.82 × 6.00 × 1.80. This class also widely employed by Soviet naval schools and Merchant Marine schools for navigation and seamanship training. 711 serves at the Heroes of the Westerplatte Naval School and was launched 6-4-74.

◆ **1 Type B79 sail-training ship** Bldr: Stocznia Gdańska im. Lenina (In serv. 11-8-82)

Iskra-II

D: 381 tons (498 fl) **S:** 10.2 kts (under power)
Dim: 49.00 (42.70 hull; 36.00 pp) × 8.00 × 3.60
M: 1 Wola 68H12 diesel; 1 prop; 310 bhp; ketch-rigged (1,038 m² sail area)
Crew: 5 officers, 12 petty officers, 45 cadets

Remarks: Has 63 total berths; can also be used for oceanographic research. Operated by the Polish Naval Academy (*Akedemia Marynarki Woyennej*). Sister *Pogoria* is civilian-subordinated, as is the much larger sail-training ship *Dar Mlodziezy*, also completed in 1982. The old naval sail-training ship *Iskra*, renamed *Iotka*, survives as a youth training craft.

◆ **1 SMK-75-class maneuvering training launch**

M-15

Remarks: No data available. Has GAZ-51 diesel engine.

Iskra-II Maritime Photographic, 7-9

MISCELLANEOUS SERVICE CRAFT

◆ **2 Pajak-class torpedo retrievers** Bldr: Stocznia Marynarki Wojennej, Gdynia

K-8 (In serv. 20-2-71) K-11 (In serv. 1971)

Pajak K-11 M.O.D. Bonn, 6

D: 133 tons (fl) **S:** 21 kts
Dim: 34.90 (33.70 wl) × 6.60 (6.00 wl) × 1.60
A: 2/25-mm 2M-8AA (II × 1)
Electron Equipt: Radar: 1/RN-231 nav.
M: 2 M50F-4 diesels; 2 props; 2,400 bhp **Crew:** . . .

Remarks: First unit laid down 30-1-70, launched 20-8-70. Have a 3-ton-capa crane with 8-m radius and a stern recovery ramp. Can stow eight 533-mm torpedoe deck. Names "*Kormoran-I*" and "*Kormoran-II*" are unoffical.

◆ **3 Gniewko class tugs (Type R-30)** Bldr: . . .

R-11 Gniewko (In serv. 29-8-81)
R-12 Bolko (In serv. . . .)
R-13 Semko (In serv. . . .)

D: . . . **S:** . . . **M:** . . .

Remarks: No data available.

Gniewko (R-11) Antoni Kaczorowski,

·IISCELLANEOUS SERVICE CRAFT *(continued)*

◆ **2 Zbyszko-class (Type B-823) salvage tugs** Bldr: Stocznia Ustka, Ustka

	Laid down	L	In serv.
.-14 Zbyszko	5-90	12-90	9-91
:-15 Macko	10-90	2-91	12-91

D: approx. 470 tons (fl) **S:** 11 kts
Dim: 35.00 (30.00 pp) × 8.00 × 3.00
Electron Equipt: Radar: 1/SRN-402X nav.
M: 1 Ceglielski-Sulzer 6AL 20/24D diesel; 1 Kort-nozzle prop; 750 bhp
Electric: 144 kw tot. (3 × Wola SW400 diesel sets)
Range: 3,000/10 **Crew:** . . .

emarks: Operated by the Naval Rescue and Salvage Service. Able to support two vers to 45 m simultaneously and have 100-m-depth decompression chambers. quipped with two DWP-16 fire-fighting water cannon.

1 (+3) Type 960-class harbor tugs Bldr: Gdynska Stocznia Remontowa Nauta, Gdynia (In serv. 1991–92)

-8 H-9 H-10 H-11

D: . . . **S:** 11 kts **Dim:** 27.80 × 8.40 × 3.00
Electron Equipt: Radar: . . .
M: 1 Cegielski-Sulzer 615 L25D diesel; 1 Kort-nozzle prop; 960 bhp

marks: Ordered 1988 to replace the Motyl class and Type H300 tugs. First unit was nched 11-5-91.

4 Bucha-class (Type H900) harbor tugs Bldr: Gdynska Stocznia Remontowa Nauta, Gdynia (In serv. 1981–82)

3 H-4 H-5 H-7

·ha-class H-7 Leo Van Ginderen, 11-88

: 310 tons (fl) **S:** 11 kts **Dim:** 26.3 (25.4 pp) × 7.0 × 3.0
lectron Equipt: Radar: 1/SRN-206 **Electric:** 76 kw
: 1 Cegielski-Sulzer 6AL 20/24H diesel; 1 CP prop; 760 bhp
iel: 20 tons **Crew:** 7 tot.

arks: Class also built for civil use. Bollard pull: 10 tons.

H-1-class (Type 800) harbor tugs Bldr: Gdynska Stocznia emontowa Nauta, Gdynia

In serv. 30-1-70) H-2 (In serv. 28-2-71)

215 tons (fl) **S:** 11 kts **Dim:** 25.5 × 6.8 × 2.8
1 Magdeburg 6NVD48 diesel; Kort-nozzle prop; 800 bhp
nge: 1,500/9 **Crew:** 17 tot.

rks: Bollard pull: 12 tons.

Motyl-class (Type 1500) coastal tugs Bldr: Stocznia Północna, ańsk (In serv. 1962–66)

H-19 H-20

500 tons (fl) **S:** 12.8 kts **Dim:** 31.8 (28.6 pp) × 8.7 × 3.5
1 Zgoda-Sulzer 5TD48 diesel; 1 prop; 1,500 bhp
ctric: 150 kw **Fuel:** 20 tons **Range:** 2,000/12.8
w: 20 tot.

oliat (H300/II)-class harbor tugs Bldr: Gdynska Stocznia ontowa Nauta, Gdynia

H-15 (In serv. 23-2-62) H-16, H-17, H-18 (In serv. 20-1-63)

.12 tons (fl) **S:** 10 kts **Dim:** 21.0 × 5.8 × 2.1
Buckau-Wolff 8 NVD 36 diesel; 1 prop; 300 bhp
ge: 300/9 **Crew:** 6 tot.

ks: Sister H-14 sold commercial 29-1-91 as *Eckor* for use as a diving tender.

Motyl-class tug H-20 M.O.D. Bonn,

◆ **6 M-35/MW-class (Type 306) mooring buoy tenders** Bldr: Stocznia Marynarki Wojennej, Gdynia (In serv. 1973–74)

M-12 M-21 M-22 M-29 M-30 M-36

D: 40 tons (fl) **S:** 9.6 kts **Dim:** 17.8 (15.2 pp) × 4.4 × 1.6
M: 1 Wola DM 150 diesel; 1 prop; 150 bhp **Crew:** 6 tot.

◆ **6 R-34-class diving tenders**

R-32 R-33 R-34 R-35 R-36 R-37

D: 58.5 tons (64.5 fl) **S:** 11 kts **Dim:** 16.8 × 5.5 × 2.4
M: 1 Wola diesel; 1 prop; 300 bhp

Remarks: R-34 entered service 27-1-63.

◆ **1 commander-in-chief's yacht**

	Laid down	L	In serv.
M-1	10-9-69	25-2-70	19-6-70

D: 74.4 tons (fl) **S:** 27.6 kts **Dim:** 28.70 × 5.80 × 1.20
M: 3 Soviet M50-FS diesels; 3 props; 3,600 bhp

Remarks: Steel hull, aluminum superstructure; conference room for 30 persons.

◆ **1 staff motorboat** Bldr: Stocznia Marynarki Wojennej Dzbrowszczaków, Gdynia

M-2 (In serv. 2-2-67)

D: 35 tons **S:** . . . kts **Dim:** 19.50 × 4.47 × 1.00
M: 2 Wola 300 diesel; 2 props; 600 bhp

◆ **4 K-15-class (Type 306) service launches** Bldr: Stocznia Marynarki Wojennej, Gdynia

M-81 (In serv. 20-11-71) M-83 (In serv. 5-11-72)
M-82 (In serv. 6-12-71) M-84 (In serv. 23-10-72)

D: 40 tons (fl) **S:** 9.6 kts **Dim:** 17.8 (15.2 pp) × 4.4 × 1.6
M: 1 Wola DM 150 diesel; 1 prop; 150 bhp **Crew:** 6 tot.

Remarks: Essentially similar to the six Type 306 mooring buoy tenders listed above; employed as personnel launches.

◆ **1 research submersible** Bldr: Stocznia im. Komuny Pariskiy, Gdynia (In serv. 1982)

Geonur II

D: 34 tons (67 sub. fl) **S:** . . . **Dim:** 9.5 × 4.4 × 3.5 (height)

Remarks: Operated jointly with the Institute of Baltic Geodesy. Diving depth: 150 m.

MINISTRY OF THE INTERIOR COAST GUARD (*Straz Graniczna*)

Established 19-5-91 under the Ministry of the Interior from the assets of the former Sea Border Brigade, which had earlier been known as the Border Guard (*Wojska Ochrony Pogranicza*), and several other maritime agencies. Have red stripe with yellow edge, "Straż Graniczna RP," and "Coast Guard" on hull sides.

PATROL BOATS

◆ **2 SKS-40-class fisheries patrol boats** Bldr: Stocznia Wisła, Gdańsk

311 Kaper-1 (In serv. 21-1-91) 312 Kaper-2 (In serv. 3-4-92)

D: 480 tons (fl) **S:** 17 kts **Dim:** 42.50 × 8.38 × 2.80 (3.00 max.)
A: . . . **Electron Equipt:** Radar: 2/. . . nav.
M: 2 diesels; 2 props; 4,790 bhp
Range: 2,600/14 **Endurance:** 8 days **Crew:** 12 tot.

Remarks: Begun for the Maritime Office of Inspections (*Urzed Morski*) but incorporated instead into the new Border Patrol agency. "*Kaper*" means "Privateer." Are to be equipped with one gun mount aft.

POLAND *(continued)*
PATROL BOATS *(continued)*

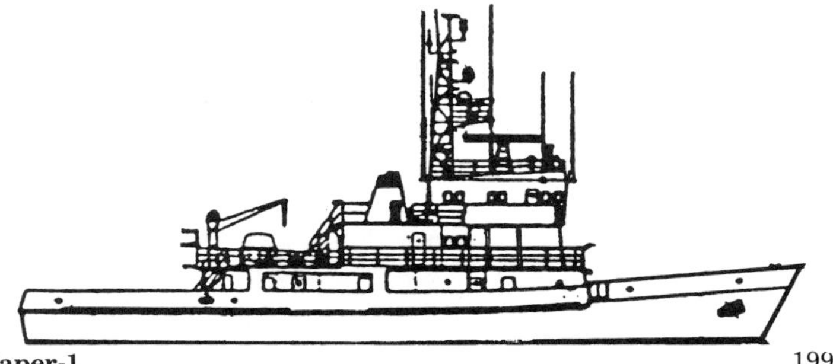
Kaper-1 1990

♦ **5 Obluze class (Project 912)** Bldr: Stocznia Marynarki Wojennej, Gdynia (In serv. 1965–68)

321 Fala 322 Szwiak 323 Zefir 324 Zorza 325 Tecza

Zefir (323) M.O.D. Bonn, 7-91

D: 210 tons (235 fl) **S:** 20 kts **Dim:** 42.0 (39.5 pp) × 5.8 × 2.0 (hull)
A: 4/30-mm AK-230 AA (II × 2)—4 d.c. racks (2 internal)
Electron Equipt:
Radar: 1/RN-231 nav.
Sonar: Tamir-11 hull-mounted HF searchlight
IFF: 1/Square Head interrogator, 1/High Pole A transponder
M: 2 Type 40D diesels; 2 props; 4,000 bhp
Electric: 150 kw **Fuel:** 25 tons **Crew:** 40 tot.

Remarks: Two (including 324) have no 30-mm AA mount aft. Five additional units with more powerful engines and Drum Tilt fire-control radars for the 30-mm AA serve in the Polish Navy.

♦ **3 converted Soviet Osa-I class former missile boats**

301 Gdynia (ex-423) 302 Szczecin (ex-425) 303 Elbląg (ex-426)

D: 168 tons (202.5 fl) **S:** 40 kts (36 sust.)
Dim: 38.6 × 7.6 × 1.8 (2.9 props)
A: 2/25-mm 2M-8 AA (II × 1) **Electron Equipt:** Radar: 1. . . nav.
M: 3 M503A2 diesels; 3 props; 12,000 bhp **Range:** 500/34; 750/25
Crew: . . . tot.

Remarks: Transferred from the navy in 1991 and rearmed to act as fast patrol boats.

♦ **5 Pilica class (Project 918M)**

Remarks: Details as for naval version, except **D:** 86.9 tons, no TT, crew 13 tot.

PATROL CRAFT

♦ **12 Wisloka class** Bldr: Stocznia Wisła, Gdańsk (In serv. early 1970s)

KP-141–152

D: 50 tons (fl) **S:** 12 kts **Dim:** 22.8 × 5.0 × 1.2
A: 2/12.7-mm mg (II × 1) **Electron Equipt:** Radar: 1/. . . nav.
M: 2 Wola 31 ANM diesels; 2 props; 600 bhp **Crew:** 10 tot.

Wisloka-class KP-141 Antoni Kaczorowski, 1991

♦ **12 Project S-3 harbor patrol launches** Bldr: Stocznia Wisła, Gdańsk (In serv. 1990)

K-110-series

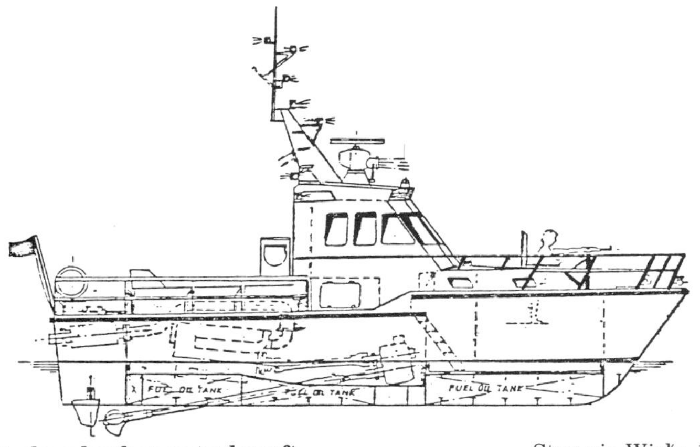
S-3-class harbor patrol craft Stocznia Wisła, 19

D: 21 tons (fl) **S:** 37 kts **Dim:** 11.67 (10.50 pp) × 4.56 × 0.88
A: 2/7.62-mm mg (I × 2) **Electron Equipt:** Radar: . . .
M: 2 . . . diesels; 2 props; 2,000 bhp **Crew:** 4 tot.

Remarks: Harbor patrol craft with GRP hulls. An order for 10 more was canceled 1991.

♦ **3 Type 724 harbor patrol launches** Bldr: Stocznia Marynarki Wojennej, Gdynia

KP-129 (In serv. 1963) KP-130 (In serv. 10-11-63)
KP-131 (In serv. 5-11-63)

D: 18 tons **S:** 11 kts **Dim:** 14.5 × 3.4 × 1.0
M: 1 Wola DVMa diesel; 1 prop; 300 bhp

Remarks: KP-129 to Water Police 25-9-88, returned 1991.

PORTUGAL

Portuguese Republic

Personnel (1991): 15,500, including 1,700 officers and 2,680 *Corpo de Fuzileiro*

Naval Aviation: Five Sea Lynx Mk 95 were ordered 10-90 for delivery in 1993 t a naval aviation organization; the helicopters will carry Bendix 1500 radar and 18 dipping sonars.

Eight Air Force CASA 212 Aviacar light transports (four with photo equipmer equipped for maritime reconnaissance duties. Six ex-Australian P-3B Orions, bished by Lockheed, were purchased 1985; the first was delivered 1-1-88, after m ization by OGMA, to the 601st Squadron at Montijo, and the last delivered termed "P-3P." Five C-130H Hercules transports and 12 SA-330C Puma helicopt used for SAR.

SUBMARINES

Note: Replacements for the *Daphné*-class submarines are to be requested in the 97 Defense Plan.

♦ **3 French Daphné class** Bldr: Dubigeon-Normandy, Nantes

	Laid down	L	In serv.
S 163 Albacora	6-9-65	15-10-66	1-10-67
S 164 Barracuda	19-10-65	24-4-67	4-5-68
S 166 Delfim	14-5-67	23-9-68	1-10-69

Albacora (S 163) Maritime Photographi

UMBARINES *(continued)*

ırracuda (S 164) Pradignac & Léo, 11-90

D: 869 surf./1,043 tons sub. **S:** 13.5 kts surf./16 kts sub.
Dim: 57.75 × 6.76 × 4.56
A: 12/550-mm TT (8 fwd, 4 aft; 12 ECAN E 14 or E 15 torpedoes—no reloads)
Electron Equipt:
Radar: 1/Thompson-CSF DRUA-31search
EW: ARUR, ARUD intercept
Sonar: DUUA-2 active (8.4 kHz), DSUV-2 passive
M: diesel-electric propulsion: SEMT-Pielstick 12PA1 diesels (450 kw); 2 props; 1,200 shp
Range: 2,710/12.5 surf.; 2,130/10 snorkel; 4,300/7.5 snorkel
Crew: 5 officers, 45 enlisted

marks: Sister *Cachalote* (S 165) was purchased by the Pakistani Navy in 1975. The ır suite has been updated. Diving depth: 300 m.

IGATES

3 MEKO 200 class

	Bldr	Laid down	L	In serv.
30 VASCO DA AMA	Blohm + Voss, Hamburg	2-2-89	26-6-89	20-11-90
31 ALVARES ABRAL	Howaldtswerke, Kiel	2-6-89	2-5-90	18-1-91
32 CORTE EAL	Howaldtswerke, Kiel	20-10-89	2-5-90	22-11-91

ıres Cabral (F 331) Stefan Terzibaschitsch, 6-91

Corte Real (F 332) Capt. da Fregata Henrique Alexandre Machado da Silva Fonseca, 11-91

Vasco da Gama (F 330) Peter Voss, 10-90

D: 2,920 tons (3,200 fl) **S:** 31.75 kts (18 kts on diesel)
Dim: 115.90 (109.00 pp) × 14.80 (13.80 wl) × 5.97 (4.10 hull)
A: 8/Harpoon SSM (IV × 2)—1/Mk 29 SAM launcher (VIII × 1, 8 Sea Sparrow missiles)—1/100-mm 55-cal. Mod. 1968 CADAM DP—1/20-mm Mk 15 CIWS gatling AA—6/324-mm Mk 32 Mod 5 ASW TT (III × 2, U.S. Mk 46 Mod. 2 torpedoes)—1/Sea Lynx Mk 95 ASW helicopter
Electron Equipt:
Radar: 1/Kelvin-Hughes 1007 nav., 1/H.S.A. MW-08 Mod. 3 air/surf. search, 1/H.S.A. DA-08 early warning, 2/STIR-18 f.c.
Sonar: Computing Devices Co. SQS-510(V) hull-mounted (6.4–8.0 kHz)
EW: APECS II/AR-700 suite, Mk 36 Mod. 1 SRBOC decoy syst. (VI × 2 Mk 136 RL), SLQ-25 Nixie torpedo decoy
M: CODOG: 2 MTU 12V1163 TB83 diesels (4,420 bhp each), 2 G.E. LM-2500-30 gas turbines (30,000 shp each); 2 Escher-Weiss CP props
Electric: 2,480 kw (4 × 620-kw diesel sets)
Range: 900/31.75; 4,100/18 (2 diesels) **Fuel:** 300 tons
Crew: 23 officers, 44 petty officers, 115 ratings (includes 4 officers, 5 petty officers, and 9 ratings in helo detachment)

Remarks: Ordered 25-7-86. Financed by U.S., Canada, West Germany, Norway, and the Netherlands. Have H.S.A. SEWACO (Sensor Weapon, Control & Command Sys-

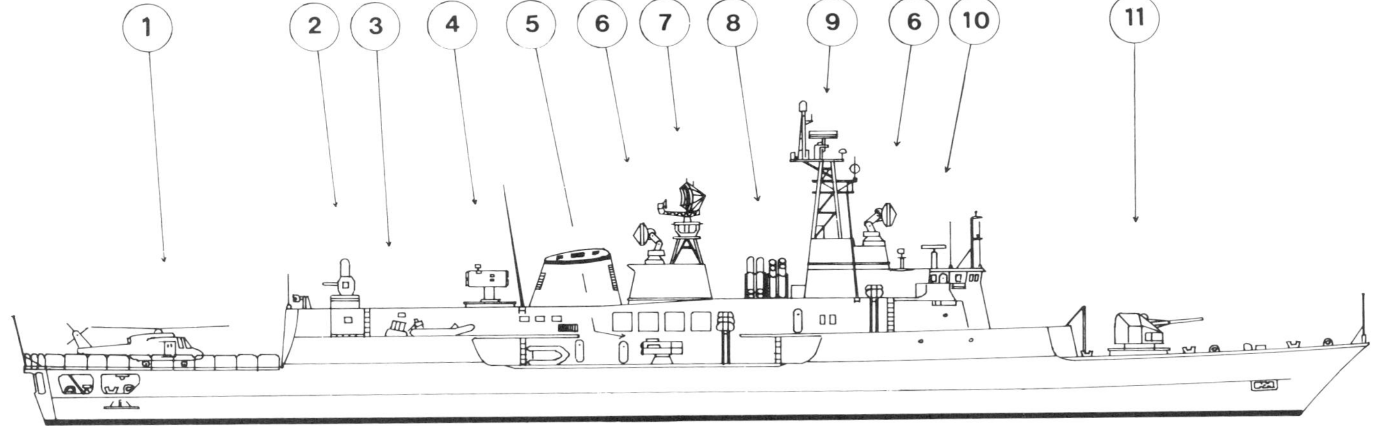

Vasco da Gama (F 330) 1. Sea Lynx Mk 95 helicopter 2. Mk 15 CIWS 3. Mk 136 sextuple RL for Mk 36 SRBOC decoy system 4. Mk 29 launcher for Sea Sparrow 5. triple Mk 32 ASW TT 6. STIR-18 fire-control radars 7. DA-08 early-warning radar 8. Harpoon SSM 9. MW-08 air/surface-search radar 10. Type 1007 navigational radar 11. 100-mm DP gun Robert Dumas

FRIGATES *(continued)*

tem), STACOS tactical command system, and Vespa data-link transponder, NATO LINK 11 and LINK 14 data link, NAUTOS propulsion-control system, Sicom 200 integrated communications suite, and MNS 2000 navigation suite. MW-08 is a short-range 3-D radar based on the H.S.A. SMART. Fitted for later installation of a towed linear hydrophone array (TASS). Have fin stabilizers. Were originally to have had the Creusot-Loire Compact 100-mm gun.

♦ **4 French Commandant Rivière class** Bldr: A.C. de Bretagne, Nantes

	Laid down	L	In serv.
F 480 Comandante João Belo	6-9-65	22-3-66	1-7-67
F 481 Comandante Hermengildo Capelo	13-5-66	29-11-66	26-4-68
F 482 Comandante Roberto Ivens	13-12-66	11-8-67	23-11-68
F 483 Comandante Sacadura Cabral	18-8-67	15-3-68	25-11-69

Comandante Sacadura Cabral (F 483)—Mk 36 SRBOC decoy launchers on platforms abreast mast French Navy, 1990

Comandante Hermengildo Capelo (F 481) Gary Davies, 6-89

Comandante João Belo (F 480) Leo Van Ginderen, 3-91

D: 1,760 tons (2,250 fl) **S:** 25 kts (26.6 max.)
Dim: 103.00 (98.00 pp) × 11.50 × 3.80 (hull)
A: 3/100-mm 55-cal. Model 1953 DP (I × 3)—2/40-mm 60-cal. Bofors AA (I × 2)—1/305-mm ASW mortar (IV × 1)—6/550-mm ASW TT (III × 2; ECAN L5 torpedoes)
Electron Equipt:
Radar: 1/Decca RM 316P nav., 1/Thomson-CSF DRBV-22A air search, 1/Thomson-CSF DRBV-50 surf./air search, 1/Thomson-CSF DRBC-31D f.c.
Sonar: SQS-17A hull-mounted search (12, 13, or 14 kHz), Thomson-Sintra DUBA-3A hull-mounted searchlight attack (22.6–28.6 kHz)
EW: ARBR-10 intercept, Mk 36 SRBOC decoy syst. (VI × 2, Hycor Mk 136 RL)
M: 4 SEMT-Pielstick diesels; 2 props; 16,000 bhp **Electric:** 1,280 kw
Range: 2,300/25; 4,500/15 **Crew:** 14 officers, 183 enlisted

Remarks: Generally similar to units in the French Navy. Major modernization program abandoned, but it is hoped to update them by substituting the Computing Devices Co., Canada, SQS-510(V) sonar for the present suite, U.S. Mk 32 Mod. 5 tubes and Mk 46 Mod. 5 torpedoes for the current mountings, the Argo 700 EW suite for ARBR-10, and the U.S. SLQ-25 Nixie towed torpedo decoy system. F 480 and F 483 were placed in reserve during 1991.

CORVETTES

♦ **4 Baptiste de Andrade class** Bldr: E.N. Bazán, Cartagena, Spain

	Laid down	L	In serv.
F 486 Baptiste de Andrade	1-9-72	13-3-73	19-11-74
F 487 João Roby	1-12-72	3-6-73	18-3-75
F 488 Afonso Cerqueira	10-3-73	6-10-73	26-6-75
F 489 Oliveira e Carmo	1-6-73	22-2-74	28-10-75

Oliveira e Carmo (F 489) Leo Van Ginderen, 7-9

João Roby (F 487) Leo Van Ginderen, 7

D: 1,252 tons (1,348 fl) **S:** 21 kts **Dim:** 84.59 (81.0 pp) × 10.3 × 3.
A: 1/100-mm 55-cal. Model 1968 DP—2/40-mm 60-cal. Bofors AA (I × 2)—6/324-mm Mk 32 ASW TT (III × 2; U.S. Mk 44 and Mk 46 torpedoes)
Electron Equipt:
Radar: 1/Decca TM626 nav., 1/Plessey AWS-2 air search, 1/Thomson-CSF Pollux f.c.
Sonar: Thomson-Sintra Diodon hull-mounted (11, 12, or 13 kHz)
EW: none
M: 2 OEW-Pielstick 12PC2V400 diesels; 2 props; 10,560 bhp
Electric: 1,100 kVA **Range:** 5,900/18
Crew: 11 officers, 111 enlisted

Remarks: Developed version of the *João Coutinho* class with more modern wea and electronics. Helicopter platform. Vega GFCS with CSEE Panda optical bac director for 100-mm gun, two lead-computing directors for 40-mm. Depth-charge removed. Plans to modernize in abeyance for lack of funds. F 486 placed in res during 1991.

♦ **6 João Coutinho class** Bldrs: F 475 to F 477: Blohm + Voss, Hamb F 484, F 485, F 471: E.N. Bazán, Cartagena, Spain

	Laid down	L	In s
F 471 Antonio Enes	10-4-68	16-8-69	18-
F 475 João Coutinho	24-12-68	2-5-69	7-
F 476 Jacinto Candido	10-2-68	16-6-69	10-
F 477 General Pereira D'eca	21-4-69	26-7-69	10-1
F 484 Augusto de Castilho	15-10-68	4-7-69	14-1
F 485 Honorio Barreto	20-2-68	11-4-70	15-

Antonio Enes (F 471) Leo Van Ginderen

꞉ORVETTES *(continued)*

ugusto Castilho (F 484) — Peter Voss, 1-91

D: 1,252 tons (1,401 fl) **S:** 24.4 kts
Dim: 84.59 (81.0 pp) × 10.30 × 3.30
A: 2/76.2-mm 50-cal. U.S. Mk 33 DP (II × 1)—2/40-mm 60-cal. Bofors AA (II × 1)
Electron Equipt:
Radar: 1/Decca TM 626 nav., 1/Microlambda MLA-1B air search, 1/SPG-34 f.c.
Sonar: removed—EW: none
M: 2 OWE-Pielstick 12PC2V280 diesels; 2 props; 10,560 bhp
Electric: 900 kw **Range:** 5,900/8 **Crew:** 9 officers, 84 enlisted

marks: Can also carry 34 marines. Have U.S. Mk 63 Mod. 21 GFCS for the 2-mm mount, Mk 51 Mod. 2 lead-computing optical GFCS for the 40-mm mount. ry 1,200 rounds 76.2-mm. Surpassed 22 kts on trials; F 475 made 25 kts. Moderniza- with SSM and short-range SAM was planned, but funds are not available. ASW ament of one Mk 10 Hedgehog mortar. Two Mk 6 depth-charge mortars and two d.c. s deleted by 1987. F 471 damaged 10-3-87 in ammunition explosion. By 2-91, had the obsolete Microlambda MLA-1B air-search radar replaced by an unidentified F 476 placed in reserve 1991.

TROL BOATS

e: It is hoped to be able to order four seagoing patrol vessels under the 1992–97 nse Plan.

◆ **10 Cacine class** Bldrs: P 1140 to 1143: Arsenal do Alfeite; others: Est. Nav. do Mondego

	L		L
40 Cacine	1968	P 1145 Geba	21-5-69
41 Cunene	1968	P 1146 Zaire	28-11-70
42 Mandovi	1968	P 1147 Zambeze	1-71
43 Rovuma	1968	P 1160 Limpopo	9-4-73
44 Quanza	30-5-69	P 1161 Save	24-10-72

292 tons (310 fl) **S:** 20 kts **Dim:** 44.0 × 7.67 × 2.2
2/40-mm 70-cal. Bofors AA (I × 2)—1/20-mm AA—2/d.c. racks
ectron Equipt: Radar: 1/Kelvin-Hughes Type 1007 nav.
2 Maybach 12V528 diesels; 2 props; 4,400 bhp
nge: 4,400/12 **Crew:** 3 officers, 30 enlisted

rks: P 1144 and later have low bulwarks at the bow. All carry radio signal ion-finding equipment and rigid inflatable inspection dinghies.

e (P 1140)—no bow bulwarks — Leo Van Ginderen, 1990

P 1161) — Leo Van Ginderen, 7-91

◆ **4 São Roque-class former minesweepers** Bldr: Estaleiros Navais da C.U.F., Lisbon

	L	In serv.
M 401 São Roque	15-9-55	6-6-56
M 402 Ribeira Grande	14-10-55	8-2-57
M 403 Lagoa	15-9-55	10-8-56
M 404 Rosario	29-11-55	8-2-56

Rosario (M 404)—and sisters — Leo Van Ginderen, 3-91

D: 394 tons (452 fl) **S:** 15 kts
Dim: 46.33 (42.69 pp) × 8.75 × 2.5
A: 2/20-mm AA (II × 1)
Electron Equipt: Radar: 1/Kelvin-Hughes 14/9 nav.
M: 2 Mirrlees JVSS-12 diesels; 2 props; 2,500 bhp
Fuel: 45 tons **Range:** 2,300/13; 3,000/8
Crew: 4 officers, 43 men

Remarks: All portable sweep gear off-loaded; now used as patrol vessels. Ordered early in 1954 and all launched in 1955. M 401 and M 403 built with U.S. "Offshore" funds as MSC 241 and MSC 242. Similar in appearance to the British "Ton" class. Wooden hulls, fin stabilizers. One 40-mm AA removed in 1972.

PATROL CRAFT

◆ **1 river patrol craft** Bldr: Arsenal do Alfeite (In serv. 9-91)

P . . . Rio Minho

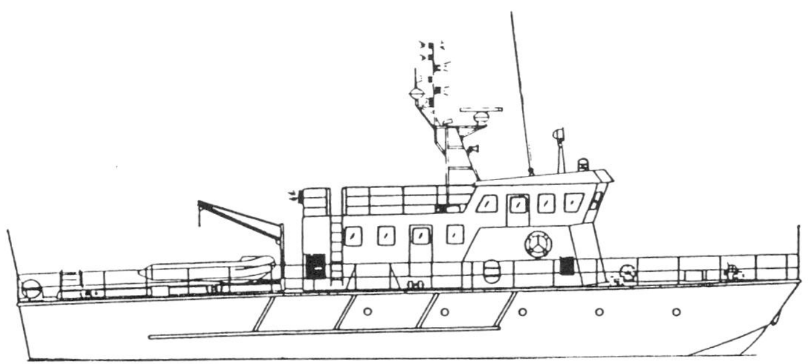

Rio Minho (P . . .) — Portuguese Navy, 1991

D: 57 tons (fl) **S:** 10 kts **Dim:** 20.0 × 5.5 × 0.7
A: 1/7.62-mm mg
Electron Equipt: Radar: 1/Furuno FR-1505 DA nav.
M: 2 Deutz diesels; 2 Schottel waterjets; 332 bhp
Crew: 1 officer, 7 enlisted

Remarks: Replaced the patrol craft *Atria* (P 360) as Rio Minho patrol craft.

◆ **5 Argos class seagoing** Bldr: CONAFI, Vila Real de Santo Antonio, and Arsenal do Alfeite

	In serv.		In serv.
P 1150 Argos	5-91	P 1153 Cassiopeia	10-91
P 1151 Dragão	7-91	P 1154 Hidra	11-91
P 1152 Escorpião	9-91		

D: 84 tons (94 fl) **S:** 28 kts
Dim: 27.20 (25.20 pp) × 5.90 × 1.40
A: 2/12.7-mm mg (I × 2)
Electron Equipt: Radar: Furuno FR-1505 DA nav.
M: 2 MTU 396-series diesels; 2 props; . . . bhp
Range: 200/28; 1,350/15 **Crew:** 1 officer, 7–9 enlisted

PATROL CRAFT *(continued)*

Dragão (P 1151)—under construction; note stern ramp
Leo Van Ginderen, 3-91

Remarks: Hulls for first two delivered to Arsenal do Alfeite early in 1991 for fitting out; other three built entirely at Alfeite. GRP construction with seven watertight compartments, ramp at stern for 4.0-m rigid inflatable inspection boat. Have Tayo VHF-Plus D/F.

◆ **6 Albatroz class** Bldr: Arsenal do Alfeite (In serv. 1974–75)

P 1162 Albatroz P 1164 Andorhina P 1166 Condor
P 1163 Acor P 1165 Aguia P 1167 Cisne

Condor (P 1166) Leo Van Ginderen, 1981

D: 45 tons (fl) **S:** 20 kts **Dim:** 23.6 (21.88 pp) × 5.25 × 1.6
A: 1/20-mm AA—2/12.7-mm mg (I × 2)
Electron Equipt: Radar: 1/Kelvin-Hughes 14/9 nav.
M: 2 Cummins diesels; 2 props; 1,100 bhp
Range: 450/18; 2,500/12
Crew: 1 officer, 7 enlisted

◆ **2 Dom Aleixo class** Bldr: San Jacintho Aveiro

	In serv.
P 1148 Dom Aleixo	6-12-67
P 1149 Dom Jeremias (ex-A 5202)	22-7-67

Dom Jeremias (P 1149) Leo Van Ginderen, 3-91

D: 62.6 tons (67.7 fl) **S:** 16 tons **Dim:** 25.0 × 5.2 × 1.6
A: 1/20-mm AA
Electron Equipt: Radar: Decca RM 316P nav.
M: 2 Cummins diesels; 2 props; 1,600 bhp
Crew: 2 officers, 8 enlisted

Remarks: P 1149 had been used as an inshore survey craft but reverted to patrol boat status in 1989.

◆ **4 harbor patrol craft** Bldr: Cheverton, Cowes, U.K.

UAM 602 Surriada UAM 612 Bonança
UAM 605 Mareta UAM 613 Mar Chão

Bonança (UAM 612) Leo Van Ginderen, 3-9

D: 9 tons (fl) **S:** 20 kts **Dim:** 12.0 × 3.6 × 1.0 **Crew:** 4 tot.
A: small arms **Electron Equipt:** Radar: 1/Decca 110 nav.
M: 2 Volvo Penta TAMD 66B outdrive diesels; 2 props; 426 bhp

Remarks: First pair delivered 5-82, others in 7-82. Intended to patrol on the Tagus the Lisbon area. Glass-reinforced plastic hulls. Have service craft pendant numbers

◆ **28 or more miscellaneous harbor patrol craft**

UAM 611 Bolina

Bolina (UAM 617) Leo Van Ginderen,

D: 15 tons (fl) **S:** 14 **Dim:** 12.57 × 3.64 × 1.10
M: 2 Rolls-Royce Sabre 212 diesels; 2 props; 424 bhp

Remarks: UAM 611 has a British Keith Nelson–built GRP hull.

UAM 608 Maresia

D: . . . **S:** . . . **Dim:** 12.0 × 2.7 × 1.8
M: 2 Rolls-Royce Sabre 212 diesels; 2 props; 424 bhp

UAM 631 Levante

D: . . . **S:** . . . **Dim:** 12.0 × 3.8 × . . .
M: 2 Volvo Penta diesels; 2 props; 520 bhp

Note: Other small harbor patrol launches include 25 for which data are not avail UAM 601 *Baluarte,* UAM 603 *Melides,* UAM *604 Mar de Sesimbra,* UAM 607 UAM 610 *Colfinho,* UAM 614 *Balanço,* UAM 616 *Saltitante,* UAM 617 *Teneb* UAM 618 *Teresa Paula,* UAM 619 *Perraria,* UAM 620 *Capitania,* UAM 621 *Lourenço,* UAM 622 *Salga,* UAM 623 *Serreta,* UAM 624 *Diogo de Teive,* UAM *Comandante Newton,* UAM 626 *Espalamaca,* UAM 627 *Garça,* UAM 628 *Mc* UAM 629 *Mar da Barca,* UAM 630 *Condor,* UAM 632 *Arrábida,* UAM 633 *Catarina,* UAM 634 *Sirocco,* UAM 635 *Brisa,* and UAM 640 *Ciclone.* All are attac various port and harbor facilities.

Ciclone (UAM 640) Leo Van Gindere

MINE COUNTERMEASURES SHIPS

◆ **0 (+4) new-construction deep-sea minesweeper/hunters**
Bldr: . . . . . .

	Laid down	L	In serv.
M	. . . ..	. . .	. . .
M	. . . ..	. . .	. . .
M	. . . ..	. . .	. . .
M	. . . ..	. . .	. . .

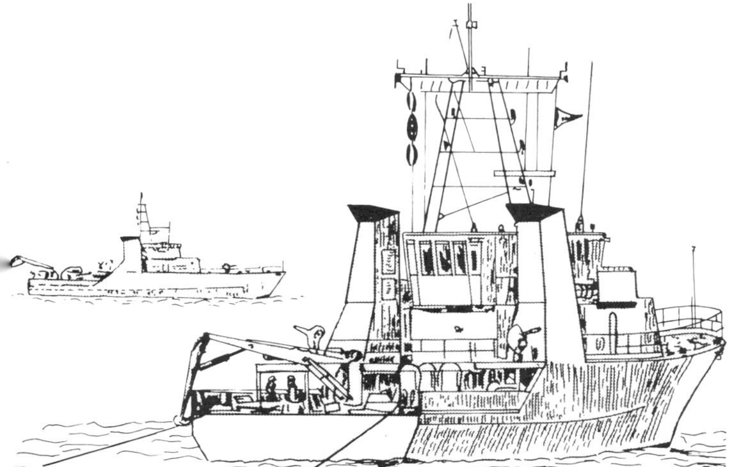

ew mine countermeasures vessel R.Neth.N., 1991

D: 610 tons (fl) **S:** 15 kts (10 kts sweeping)
Dim: 47.0 (43.0 pp) × 9.6 × 3.6
A: 1/20-mm 90-cal. GIAT AA—2/12.7-mm mg (I × 2, for mine disposal)
Electron Equipt:
Radar: 1/. . . . . . nav.—Sonar: . . . . . .
M: 2 . . . . . . diesels; 2 props; 2,200 bhp **Range:** 3,000/12
Crew: 25 tot. + 5 mine-disposal divers

marks: A joint development program with Belgium and the Netherlands. Design tract to Van der Giessen de Noord, the Netherlands, in cooperation with Belgium's ard Polyship placed 11-90; to be ordered 1993. Trials with the Thomson-Sintra erne" minesweeping system intended for this class began in 10-91; the ships may carry the French AP-4 acoustic sweep array and will have an integrated, auto- ed mine countermeasures command and control suite.

PHIBIOUS WARFARE CRAFT

3 Bombarda-class landing craft Bldr: Mondego SY

G 201 Bombarda (In serv. 1969)
G 202 Alabarda (In serv. 1971)
G 203 Bacamarte (In serv. 12-85)

barda (LDG 201)—and sister Leo Van Ginderen, 3-91

285 tons (635 fl) **S:** 11 kts **Dim:** 59.0 (52.88 pp) × 11.91 × 1.6
2/20-mm AA (I × 2)
ectron Equipt: Radar: 1/Decca RM 316P nav.
2 MTU MD 225 diesels; 2 props; 1,000 bhp **Range:** 1,800/8
ew: 2 officers, 18 enlisted

rks: Design based on the World War II British LCT(4).

LDM 400-class landing craft (In serv. 1967–68)

406	LDM 420	LDM 422
418	LDM 421	LDM 423

LDM 423 Pradignac & Léo, 8-88

D: 56 tons (fl) **S:** 9 kts **Dim:** 17.0 × 5.0 × 1.2
A: 1/20-mm AA **M:** 2 Cummins diesels; 2 props; 450 bhp

Remarks: Resemble British LCM(7) class. Gun not usually mounted. Sister LDM 424 stricken 1982.

◆ **3 LDM 100-class landing craft** Bldr: Estaleiros Navais do Mondego (In serv. 1965)

LDM 119 LDM 120 LDM 121

D: 50 tons (fl) **S:** 9 kts **Dim:** 15.25 × 4.37 × 1.17
M: 2 G.M. 6-71 diesels; 2 props; 450 bhp **Range:** 130/9

Remarks: Portuguese-built U.S. LCM(6) class.

HYDROGRAPHIC SHIPS

Note: All survey ships and craft are subordinated to the Hydrographic Institute (*Instituto Hidrográfico*).

◆ **2 Andromeda class** Bldr: Arsenal do Alfeite

	Laid down	L	In serv.
A 5203 Andromeda	1984	12-12-85	1-2-87
A 5205 Auriga	6-84	1986	1-7-87

Andromeda (A 5203)—fitting out Hartmut Ehlers, 12-86

D: . . . **S:** 12 kts **Dim:** 31.50 (28.00 pp) × 7.74 × 2.50
A: none **Electron Equipt:** Radar: 1/Racal-Decca RM 914C nav.
M: 1 MTU 12V396 TC 82 diesel; 1 prop; 1,030 bhp
Electric: 160 kw (1 × 100-kw diesel set, 1 × 60-kw shaft generator)
Range: 1,100/12 **Fuel:** 35.5 tons **Crew:** 3 officers, 14 enlisted

Remarks: Intended to replace the U.K. "Bay"-class survey ship *Alfonso de Albuquerque* (A 526), stricken 1983. Also used for oceanographic research.

◆ **1 ex-U.S. Kellar class** Bldr: Marietta SB Co., Pt. Pleasant, West Virginia

	Laid down	L	In serv.
A 527 Almeida Carvalho (ex-*Kellar*, T-AGS 25)	20-11-62	30-7-64	31-1-69

D: 1,297 tons (1,400 fl) **S:** 13.5 kts
Dim: 63.50 (58.00 pp) × 11.90 × 4.32
Electron Equipt:
Radar: 1/Kelvin-Hughes 14/9 nav., 1/Decca TM 829 nav.
M: 2 Caterpillar D-378 diesels, electric drive; 1 prop; 1,000 shp
Fuel: 211 tons **Crew:** 7 officers, 40 enlisted

HYDROGRAPHIC SHIPS *(continued)*

Almeida Carvalho (A 527) Bernard Prézelin, 7-90

Remarks: Transferred on loan 21-1-72 and purchased outright during 1988. Similar to U.S. *Robert D. Conrad*-class T-AGOR. Sister *S.P. Lee* is operated by the United States Geological Survey.

◆ **2 Coral-class inshore survey/lighthouse tenders**

UAM 801 Coral UAM 802 Hidra

Coral (UAM 801)—outboard *Hidra* (UAM 602) Hartmut Ehlers, 11-86

Remarks: GRP construction. No data available.

◆ **3 inshore survey/lighthouse tenders, former fishing boats**

UAM 803 Actinia UAM 804 Sicandra UAM 805 Fisália

AUXILIARY SHIPS

◆ **1 logistic support ship** Bldr: Howaldtswerke, Kiel (In serv. 1962)

A 5208 São Miguel (ex-*Cabo Verde*, ex-*Sirefjell*)

São Miguel (A 5208) Leo Van Ginderen, 1-91

D: 7,510 tons (8,290 fl) **S:** 14.5 kts
Dim: 108.80 (97.90 pp) × 15.59 × 7.54
Electron Equipt:
Radar: 1/Kelvin Hughes KH1600 nav., 1/Kelvin Hughes 18/12 nav.
M: 1 M.A.N. K62 60/105C, 6-cyl. diesel; 1 prop; 4,050 bhp
Electric: 492 kw **Fuel:** 267 tons **Crew:** 8 officers, 49 enlisted

Remarks: 2,690 grt/3,875 dwt. Cargo ship purchased 8-10-85 for Azores service. Gray hull, white upperworks. Three holds with after hold refrigerated. One 25-ton, six 5-ton, and six 3-ton derricks. A helicopter platform and berthing facilities for embarked troops may be added later. Assisted UN Coalition forces in the Mideast, 1990–91. Not armed.

◆ **1 replenishment oiler** Bldr: Estaleiros Navais de Viana do Castelo

	L	In serv.
A 5206 São Gabriel	1961	27-3-63

São Gabriel (A 5206) Leo Van Ginderen, 6-8

D: 9,000 tons (14,200 fl) **S:** 17 kts
Dim: 146.0 (138.0 pp) × 18.22 × 8.0
Electron Equipt:
Radar: 1/Decca RM 1226C nav., 1/Decca RMS 1230C nav., 1/Westinghouse SPS-6C air search
M: 1 set Pamtreda geared steam turbines; 1 prop; 9,500 shp
Boilers: 2
Range: 6,000/15 **Crew:** 11 officers, 88 enlisted

Remarks: 9,854 grt/9,000 dwt. Two liquid- and one solid-store replenishment statio per side. Helicopter platform aft. Former oiler *Sam Bras* is now an accommodations a fuel-storage hulk.

◆ **1 lighthouse tender and seagoing tug** Bldr: Arsenal do Alfeite

	Laid down	L	In serv.
A 521 Schultz Xavier	2-70	1972	14-7-72

Schultz Xavier (A 521) Portuguese Navy, 1

D: 900 tons **S:** 14 kts **Dim:** 56.1 × 10.0 × 3.8
M: 2 diesels; 1 prop; 2,400 bhp **Range:** 3,000/12.5
Crew: 4 officers, 50 enlisted

◆ **1 sail-training ship** Bldr: Blohm + Voss, Hamburg

	L	In s
A 520 Sagres II (ex-*Guanabara*, ex-*Albert Leo Schlageter*)	30-10-37	1-

Sagres (A 520) Leo Van Gindere

AUXILIARY SHIPS *(continued)*

D: 1,725 tons (1,784 fl) **S:** 10.5 kts (18 sail)
Dim: 90.0 (75.90 hull, 70.4 pp) × 11.9 × 5.2
A: 2/47-mm saluting (I × 2)
Electron Equipt: Radar: 2/Decca . . . nav.
M: 2 M.A.N. diesels; 1 prop; 750 bhp
Range: 5,450/7.5 (power)
Crew: 12 officers, 150 enlisted + . . . cadets

Remarks: Acquired by U.S. Navy as reparations, 1945; sold to Brazil in 1948 and to Portugal in 1962, commissioning on 2-2-62. Sail area: 2,355 m^2. Height of mainmast: 3.3 m. Sisters are U.S. Coast Guard *Eagle* and Russian merchant training *Tovarisch*. Refitted, hull renewed at Arsenal do Alfeite 2-87 to 1988 and again refitted in 1990–91.

◆ **1 sail-training schooner** Bldr: . . . . . ., Lisbon (In serv. 1937)

UAM 201 Creola

Creola (UAM 201) Leo Van Ginderen, 9-91

D: 818 tons (1,055 fl) **S:** . . . kts **Dim:** 67.4 × 9.9 × 4.2
M: 1 diesel; 1 prop; 480 bhp **Crew:** . . .

Remarks: Former four-masted Grand Banks fishing schooner acquired 1976 as a museum by Portuguese Department of Fisheries; turned over to the navy and commissioned for active seagoing training in 1987.

◆ **1 sail-training sloop** (In serv. . . .)

201 Vega (ex-*Arreda*)

D: 60 tons **S:** . . . **Dim:** 19.8 × 4.3 × 2.5

◆ **1 sail-training yacht** (In serv. . . .)

204 Polar (ex-*Anne Linde*)

D: 70 tons **S:** . . . **Dim:** 22.9 × 4.9 × 2.5

Remarks: Acquired in trade for large sail-training ship *Sagres I*, now a museum ship in Hamburg.

SERVICE CRAFT

◆ **U.S. 174-foot-class yard oiler** Bldr: Brunswick Marine, Georgia

	Laid down	L	In serv.
UAM 303 Oeiras (ex-BC-3, ex-YO 3, ex-YO 194)	14-5-45	25-8-45	30-1-46

D: 440 tons light (1,390 fl) **S:** 11 kts
Dim: 53.04 × 9.75 × 3.96
M: 1 G.M. diesel; 1 prop; 800 bhp **Electric:** 120 kw
Fuel: 25 tons **Crew:** 23 tot.

Remarks: Transferred in 4-62. Cargo: 924 tons.

Oeiras (UAM 303)—with old hull number Leo Van Ginderen, 1983

◆ **2 small yard oilers**

UAM 301 Odeleite UAM 302 Odivelas

Remarks: Cargo: 674 tons; no other data available.

◆ **1 catamaran river navigational aid tender** Bldr: San Jacinto, Aveiro

UAM 676 Guia (In serv. . . .)

Guia (UAM 675) Leo Van Ginderen, 3-91

D: 70 tons **S:** 8.5 kts **Dim:** 22.0 × 7.9 × 2.2
M: 1 Deutz SBA 6M 816U diesel; 1 Schottel prop; 350 bhp—1 Harbor Master 50 F76 maneuvering unit (3.5 kts)

Remarks: Subordinated to the Lighthouse Service (*Direcção de Faróis*).

◆ **6 miscellaneous navigational aid tenders**

UAM 675 Berlenga UAM 679 Giralta
UAM 677 Esteiro UAM 780 Santa Maria II
UAM 678 Bugio UAM 681 São Vicente

◆ **1 ex-U.S. Army Design 3004 medium harbor tug** (In serv. 1954)

UAM 914 Nisa (ex-RB 2, ex-ST 1996)

D: 100 tons light (122 fl) **S:** 12 kts **Dim:** 21.31 × 5.94 × 2.50
M: 1 diesel; 1 prop; 600 bhp **Fuel:** 15 tons
Range: 3,500/12 **Crew:** 6 tot.

Remarks: Transferred 2-3-62. Sister RB 1 stricken 1984.

◆ **2 miscellaneous ammunition lighters**

UAM 304 Marateca UAM 305 Mouro

Mouro (UAM 305) Leo Van Ginderen, 3-91

◆ **1 yacht/tender** Bldr: Halmatic, U.K. (In serv. 10-84)

UAM 901 Alva

D: 6.5 tons (fl) **S:** 20 kts **Dim:** 10.62 (9.37 wl) × 3.50 × 0.84
M: 2 Volvo TAMD 60C diesels; 2 props; 420 bhp

Remarks: Glass-reinforced plastic construction. Based at Lisbon and used as C-in-C's yacht. Carries 12 passengers.

◆ **2 miscellaneous personnel launches**

UAM 905 Caia UAM 906 Corgo

Remarks: Both employed as flag officers' barges at Lisbon.

PORTUGAL *(continued)*
SERVICE CRAFT *(continued)*

Alva (UAM 901) Leo Van Ginderen, 3-91

Caia (UAM 905) Leo Van Ginderen, 3-91

♦ **24 miscellaneous port lifeboats**

UAM 650 Aguda UAM 651 Almirante Jaime Afreixo
UAM 652 Almirante Ferreira do Amaral
UAM 655 Comandante Couceiro
UAM 656 Patrão Ezequiel Seabra
UAM 657 Gomes de Amorim
UAM 658 Nossa Senhora de Conceição
UAM 659 Patrão António Faustino
UAM 660 Patrão Quirino Lopes
UAM 661 Patrão Rabumba UAM 662 Patrão Chalandra
UAM 663 Rainha Don Amélia UAM 664 Rei Don Carlos I
UAM 665 Santa Maria UAM 666 Sota Patrão António Crista
UAM 667 Patrão António Simóes UAM 668 Patrão João Rangel
UAM 669 Vila Chão UAM 670 Patrão Henrique Faleiro
UAM 671 Patrão Cesar Martins UAM 672 Patrão João da Silva
UAM 673 Patrão Joaquim Casaca UAM 674 Patrão Joaquim Lopes
UAM 682 Patrão Arnaldo dos Santos

Patrão Joaquim Lopes (UAM 674) Leo Van Ginderen, 1990

Remarks: All subordinated to the Naval Rescue Service (*Instituto de Socorros a Náufragos*).

♦ **3 dockyard service craft**

UAM 851 Cordoaria UAM 853 Romeira UAM 854 Barrocas

Remarks: All attached to the Arsenal do Alfeite. UAM 854 is an accommodations barge.

♦ **1 aquarium service craft**

UAM 852 Albacora II

Remarks: Attached to the Vasco da Gama Aquarium (*Aquário Vasco da Gama*).

♦ **3 personnel ferries**

UAM 908 Paiva UAM 912 Vascão UAM 913 Zezere

Zezere (UAM 913) Hartmut Ehlers, 2-8

Paiva (UAM 908) Leo Van Ginderen, 9-

Remarks: All attached to the Lisbon Naval Base. Also serving the Lisbon Naval B are the following craft for which the functions are not available:

UAM 907 Coura UAM 909 Sorraia UAM 910 Tamega
UAM 911 Tua UAM 915 Nabão UAM 916 Muge

QATAR

State of Qatar

Personnel (1991): 700 total

Aviation: Eight Agusta-built SH-3D Sea King helicopters are in service for se and-rescue duties; of these, two are equipped to launch AM 39 Exocet missiles. Tw Air Force Mirage F-1 EDA and 2 F-1 DDA can also launch Exocets.

GUIDED-MISSILE PATROL BOATS

Note: A new series of guided-missile patrol boats is planned.

♦ **3 French Combattante-III class** Bldr: CMN, Cherbourg

	Laid down	L	In serv.
Q 01 Damsah	6-5-81	17-6-82	10-11-82
Q 02 Al Ghariyah	26-8-81	23-9-82	10-2-83
Q 03 Rbigah	27-10-81	22-12-82	11-5-83

Damsah (Q 01) CMN

QATAR *(continued)*
GUIDED-MISSILE PATROL BOATS *(continued)*

amsah (Q 01) French Navy, 2-83

D: 395 tons (430 fl) **S:** 38.5 kts
Dim: 56.00 (53.00 pp) × 8.16 × 2.15 hull (2.50 max.)
A: 8/MM 40 Exocet SSM—1/76-mm 62-cal. OTO Melara Compact DP— 2/40-mm 70-cal. Breda AA (II × 1)—4/30-mm Emerlec AA (II × 2)
Electron Equipt:
Radar: 1/Decca 1226 nav., 1/Thomson-CSF Pollux search, 1/ Thomson-CSF Castor II f.c.
EW: Racal Cutlass intercept, Dagaie chaff RL
M: 4 MTU 20V538 TB93 diesels; 4 props; 19,300 bhp
Range: 2,000/15 **Crew:** 6 officers, 41 enlisted

marks: Ordered 10-80. Very similar in appearance and equipment to the three gerian units of the class. Two CSEE Panda optical gun directors, with Vega apons-control system. Arrived Qatar in 7-83.

ATROL BOATS

6 103-foot boats Bldr: Vosper Thornycroft, Portchester, U.K.

	In serv.		In serv.
11 Barzan	13-1-75	Q 14 Al Wussail	28-10-75
12 Hwar	30-4-75	Q 15 Fateh al Khatab	22-1-76
13 That Assuari	3-10-75	Q 16 Tariq	1-3-76

eh al Khatab (Q 15) Leo Van Ginderen, 1976

120 tons **S:** 27 kts
m: 32.40 (31.10 pp) × 6.30 × 1.60 (hull)
2/20-mm AA (I × 2)
ectron Equipt: Radar: 1/Decca 1226 nav.
2 Paxman Valenta 16RP200 diesels; 2 props; 6,250 bhp
ew: 25 tot.

arks: Originally had a twin 30-mm AA forward, replaced by single 20-mm AA.

ROL CRAFT

MV-45 class GRP-hulled Bldr: Crestitalia, Ameglia, Italy (In serv. 89)

17 tons (fl) **S:** 32 kts **Dim:** 14.5 × 3.8 × 0.8
1/12.7-mm mg—2/7.62-mm mg (I × 2)
ctron Equipt: Radar: 1/. . . nav.
2 diesels; 2 props; 1,270 bhp **Range:** 275/29 **Crew:** 6 tot.

Polycat 1450 class Bldr: Damen, Gorinchem, Netherlands (In serv. 80)

Q 32 Q 33 Q 34 Q 35 Q 36

Q 32 and a sister Leo Van Ginderen, 1980

D: 18 tons (fl) **S:** 26 kts **Dim:** 14.5 × 4.7 × 1.5 **Crew:** 11 tot.
A: 1/12.7-mm mg **Electron Equipt:** Radar: 1/Decca . . . nav.
M: 2 G.M. 12V71 TI diesels; 2 props; 1,300 bhp **Range:** 650/20

Remarks: Ordered 2-83. Glass-reinforced plastic construction.

♦ **7 P 1200 class** Bldr: Watercraft, Shoreham, U.K. (In serv. 1980)

D: 12.7 tons (fl) **S:** 29 kts **Dim:** 11.9 × 4.1 × 1.1
A: 2/7.62-mm mg (I × 2)
M: 2 Wizeman-Mercedes WM400 diesels; 2 props; 660 bhp
Crew: 4 tot.

♦ **2 45-foot craft** Bldr: Vosper/Keith Nelson

D: 13 tons **S:** 26 kts **Dim:** 13.5 × 3.8 × 1.1
A: 1/12.7-mm mg—2/7.62-mm mg (I × 2)
M: 2 Caterpillar diesels; 2 props; 800 bhp **Crew:** 6 tot.

Remarks: Third unit purchased converted to a pilot boat.

♦ **25 Spear-class craft Mk I and Mk II launches** Bldr: Fairey Marine, Hamble, U.K. (In serv. 1974–77)

Q 71–Q 95

D: 4.3 tons **S:** 26 kts **Dim:** 9.1 × 2.8 × 0.8
A: 3/7.62-mm mg (I × 3) **M:** 2 diesels; 2 props; 290 bhp
Crew: 4 tot.

Remarks: First seven delivered 19-6-74 to 2-75; five more ordered 12-75; three more delivered 30-6-75 to 14-7-75. Ten more delivered 4-77.

SERVICE CRAFT

♦ **1 logistics landing craft** Bldr: . . . , Singapore (In serv. 1987)

Rabha

D: . . . **S:** 9–10 kts **Dim:** 48.8 × . . . × . . .
M: 2 diesels; 2 props; . . . bhp

Remarks: Reported capable of transporting three tanks and 110 troops.

♦ **2 Interceptor class** Bldr: Fairey Marine, Hamble, U.K. (In serv. 28-11-75)

D: 1.25 tons **S:** 35 kts **Dim:** 7.9 × 2.4 × 0.9
M: 2 Johnson outboards; 270 shp **Range:** 150/30
Crew: 3 crew + 10 troops

Remarks: Catamaran GRP hulls. Carry life rafts for SAR duties.

♦ **1 Bulldog-class workboat** Bldr: Fairey Allday Marine, Cowes, U.K. (In serv. 1979)

Remarks: No data available. Up to 30 additional small launches and four Rotork Sea Truck logistics craft may be in service.

ROMANIA

Republic of Romania

Personnel (1991): 7,500 total, 700 of whom are in the Border Guard. There is also a Naval Division of regular troops.

Naval Aviation: Six Soviet Mi-14PL Haze-A land-based ASW helicopters and six Alouette-III shipboard helicopters are in service, operated by the air force.

SUBMARINES

♦ **1 Soviet Kilo class (Project 877E)** Bldr: United Admiralty SY, St. Petersburg

SUBMARINES *(continued)*

521 Delfinul (In serv. 12-86)

D: 2,325 tons surf./3,076 tons sub. **S:** 10 kts surf./17 kts sub.
Dim: 74.3 (70.0 wl) × 10.0 × 6.6
A: 6/533-mm TT (18 torpedoes, or up to 24 mines)—1/9K32M Strela shoulder-launch SAM position
Electron Equipt:
Radar: 1/Snoop Tray-2 search
Sonar: Shark Gill LF active/passive suite, passive hull array
EW: Brick Pulp or Squid Head intercept; Quad Loop D/F
M: 3 Type 2D-42, 1,825-bhp diesel generator sets, electric drive: 1 motor; 1/6-bladed prop; 5,900 shp
Range: 6,000/7 (surf.); 400/3 (sub.)
Crew: 12 officers, 41 enlisted

Remarks: Has anechoic hull coating. Diving depth: 300 m. Probably has some means of auxiliary propulsion, such as low-power (100–150 kw) electric creep motor on the main shaft for low-speed, quiet operations. Diving depth: 250 m. The shoulder-launched SAM position is at the aft end of the sail. Named for Romania's first submarine, commissioned in 1936.

DESTROYER

♦ **1 Muntenia class** Bldr: Mangalia SY No. 2 (In serv. 5-8-85)

Marasesti (ex-*Muntenia*)

Marasesti—fitting out as *Muntenia* Agerpress, 1985

Marasesti—as modified to improve stability Romanian Navy, 1991

D: approx. 6,000 tons (fl) **S:** 28 kts **Dim:** 145.0 × 16.0 × 5.0
A: 8/SS-N-2C SSM (II × 4)—4/76.2-mm 59-cal. AK-276 DP (II × 2)—8/30-mm AK-230 AA (II × 4)—6/533-mm ASW TT (III × 2)—1/RBU-6000 ASW RL (XII × 1)—2/Alouette-III helicopters
Electron Equipt:
Radar: 1/Nayada nav., 1/Strut Curve air/surf. search, 1/Hawk Screech f.c., 2/Drum Tilt f.c.
Sonar: . . .—EW: 2 Watch Dog intercept, 2/RK-16 decoy RL (XVI × 2)
M: 4 M-3 gas turbines; 2 props; 96,000 shp
Range: . . . **Crew:** . . .

Remarks: Reportedly laid down in 1981 and launched by 1983. Laid up shortly after completion and may never have operated. Does not have SA-N-4 SAM system previously estimated but may carry SA-7 Grail point-defense SAMs. Appears likely to have had stability problems and seems to have proved an expensive failure (although there are occasional reports that a second was planned—or even laid down). In a refit still under way in 1991, the four twin SS-N-2 missile launchers were resited one deck lower and the original tower masts replaced by lighter and lower lattice masts in order to improve stability; in addition, the two quintuple-tubed RBU-1200 ASW rocket launchers were replaced by a single RBU-6000 mounted forward of the bridge.

FRIGATES

♦ **5 Tetal class** Bldr: Mangalia SY No. 2

	In serv.
260	1983
261 Vice Admiral Vasile Scodrea	1984
262	1985
263	1987
264	1990

Vice Admiral Vasile Scodrea (261) Romanian Navy, 1991

D: 1,480 tons (1,600 fl) **S:** 24 kts **Dim:** 92.0 × 11.5 × 3.0
A: 260–263: 4/76.2-mm 59-cal. DP (II × 2)—4/30-mm AK-230 AA (II × 2)—4/14.5-mm mg (II × 2)—2/RBU-2500 ASW RL (XVI × 2)—4/533-mm ASW TT (I × 4, fixed); 264: 1/76.2-mm 59-cal. AK-176 DP—4/30-mm AK-230 AA (II × 2)—4/14.5-mm mg (II × 2)—4/533-mm ASW TT (I × 4, fixed)—2/RBU-6000 ASW RL (XII × 2)—helicopter deck
Electron Equipt:
Radar: 1/Nayada nav., 1/Strut Curve surf./air search, 1/Hawk Screech f.c, 1/Drum Tilt f.c.
Sonar: . . . . . . hull-mounted MF
EW: 2 Watch Dog intercept, 2/RK-16 decoy RL (XVI × 2)
M: diesels; 2 props; . . . bhp **Range:** . . . **Crew:** . . .

Remarks: "Tetal" is the NATO code name for this class, which is entirely of Romanian design. First unit laid down 1980. Program slowed by economic problems. The fifth unit substituted later weapons and incorporates a helicopter deck. The Hawk Screech radar director for the 76.2-mm gun mounts has two associated manned target designators on a platform partway up the mast.

Note: The four *Democratia* (German M-40)-class ships previously listed under "corvettes" have been moved to the mine countermeasures category, as it has been found that they are still equipped for minesweeping.

GUIDED-MISSILE PATROL BOATS

♦ **3 Soviet Tarantul I class (Project 1241)** Bldr: Volodarskiy SY, Rybinsk

188 Zborul (In serv. 12-90)
189 Pescarusul (In serv. 12-91)
190 Lastunul (In serv. 12-91)

Zborul (188)—with two Epitrop-class torpedo boats Romanian Navy, 1

D: 385 tons light (455 fl) **S:** 43 kts
Dim: 56.10 (49.50 pp) × 10.20 (9.40 wl) × 2.14 hull (3.59 props)
A: 4/SS-N-2C SSM (II × 2, 2-each P-21 radar-homing and P-22 infrared-homing missiles)—1/76.2-mm 59-cal. AK-176 DP—1/SA-N-8 (MTU-40S) SAM syst. (IV × 1, 12 Strela missiles)—2/30-mm AK-630 gatling AA (I × 2)
Electron Equipt:
Radar: 1/Kivach-2 nav., 1/Plank Shave (Harpun-E) targeting, 1/Bass Tilt (Koral-E/MR123) f.c.
EW: 2/RK-16 decoy RL (XVI × 2)
IFF: 1/High Pole transponder, 1/Square Head interrogator
M: M-15E COGAG plant: 2 DMR-76 cruise gas turbines (4,000 shp each), 2 PR-77 boost gas turbines (12,000 shp each); 2 props; 32,000 shp
Range: 400/43; 2,400/14 **Endurance:** 10 days **Fuel:** 50 tons
Crew: 7 officers, 32 enlisted

Remarks: Unlike Soviet Navy version, have no EW gear. Said to be diffic[ult to] maneuver at low speeds. Are intended to replace the obsolescent Osa-I class[;] additional units may be acquired.

GUIDED-MISSILE PATROL BOATS *(continued)*

◆ 6 ex-Soviet Osa-I (Project 205) class

194 195 196 197 198 199

Romanian Osa-I 199 Romanian Navy, 1991

D: 171 tons (209.5 fl) **S:** 40 kts (36 sust.)
Dim: 38.6 × 7.6 × 1.8 (2.9 props)
A: 4/SS-N-2A Styx SSM (I × 4, P-15 missiles)—1/FASTA HN-4 (SA-N-5) SAM syst. (IV × 1, 8 Strela missiles)—4/30-mm AK-230 AA (II × 2)
Electron Equipt:
Radar: 1/Square Tie surf. search/target designation, 1/Drum Tilt gun f.c.
IFF: 2 Square Head interrogators, 1/High Pole B transponder
M: 3 M503A2 diesels; 3 props; 12,000 bhp
Range: 500/34; 750/25 **Crew:** 4 officers, 18 enlisted

emarks: Built in the U.S.S.R. during the early 1960s, transferred after 1960. All six eem to have been in service in 1991, although there had been reports that two had een discarded; all will probably soon be retired.

ORPEDO BOATS

12 Epitrop class

Bldr: Mangalia SY, Romania (In serv. 1979–. . .)

)1–212

itrop 210 launching torpedo Romanian Navy, 1991

D: 215 tons (fl) **S:** 38 kts **Dim:** 38.60 × 7.60 × 1.85
A: 4/30-mm AK-230 AA (II × 2)—4/533-mm TT (I × 4)
Electron Equipt:
Radar: 1/Pot Drum nav./surf. search, 1/Drum Tilt f.c.
M: 3 M503A diesels; 3 props; 12,000 bhp
Range: 500/35; 750/20 **Crew:** 28 tot.

marks: Design based on Osa class; "Epitrop" is the NATO nickname for the class.

26 Chinese Huchwan-class hydrofoils

Bldr: Dobreta SY, Turnu (In serv. 1973–. . .)

51 to VT 77 JUPITER MARTE

): 39 tons (45 fl) **S:** 50 kts
im: 22.50 × 6.26 (3.80 deck) × 1.15 (1.11 foiling)
: 4/14.5-mm AA (II × 2)—2/533-mm TT
lectron Equipt:
1/Type 756 nav.—IFF: 1/High Pole B transponder
: 3 M50 diesels; 3 props; 3,600 bhp
lectric: 5.6 kw **Range:** 500/30 **Crew:** 11 tot.

anian Huchwan VT 66 Romanian Navy, 1991

Remarks: Three built in China, remainder in Romania. Two, named *Jupiter* and *Marte,* have had the torpedo tubes and hydrofoils removed and are used as search-and-rescue craft. VT = *Vedette Torpedinare* (torpedo boat).

PATROL BOATS

◆ 3 ex-Soviet Poti class

V 31 CAm NICOLAE CRISTESCU V 32 . . . .
V 33 . . . .

CAm Nicolae Cristescu (V 31) Romanian Navy, 1991

D: 400 tons (fl) **S:** 38 kts **Dim:** 59.4 × 7.9 × 2.0 (mean)
A: 2/57-mm 80-cal. AK 257 DP (II × 1)—2/RBU-2500 ASW RL (XVI × 2)—2/533-mm fixed ASW TT (I × 2)
Electron Equipt:
Radar: 1/Don 2 nav., 1/Strut Curve surf./air search, 1/Muff Cob f.c.
Sonar: . . . . . . hull-mounted MF search, HF attack
EW: 2/Watch Dog intercept—IFF: High Pole B transponder
M: CODAG: 2 M503A diesels (4,000 bhp each); 2 gas turbines (20,000 shp each); 2 props mounted in venturi tunnels
Range: 500/37; 4,500/10 **Crew:** 50 tot.

Remarks: Transferred 1970. Have simpler systems than the Soviet units: 533-mm vice 400-mm torpedo tubes, RBU-2500 ASW rocket launchers vice RBU-6000. Gas turbines force air into tubes abaft the propellers in a kind of "waterjet" system. The Muff Cob radar gun director is equipped with a television backup system. The "V" in the pendant number stands for *Vanatore* (chaser). The "*CAm*" in V 31's name stands for "Rear Admiral."

◆ 23 Chinese Shanghai-II class

Bldr: Mangalia SY, Romania (In serv. 1973–. . .)

VS 41 to VS 44 VP 20 to VP 35, VP 38 SATURN VENUS

Romanian Shanghai-II VP 29 Romanian Navy, 1991

D: 123 tons (135 fl) **S:** 28.5 kts **Dim:** 38.78 × 5.41 × 1.55
A: VS 41 series: 1/37-mm 62-cal. AA—2/14.5-mm mg (II × 1)—2/RBU-1200 ASW RL (V × 2)—VP 20 series: 4/14.5-mm mg (II × 2)
Electron Equipt: Radar: 1/Pot Head nav./surf. search
M: 2 M50F-4, 1,200-bhp diesels, 2 12D6, 910-bhp diesels; 4 props; 4,220 bhp
Range: 750/16.5 **Electric:** 39 kw
Endurance: 7 days **Crew:** 36 tot.

Remarks: Units with VP pendants serve the Border Guard; *Saturn* and *Venus,* with only two 14.5-mm machine guns and a large deckhouse aft, serve as search-and-rescue boats. There are mounting positions amidships for two additional gun mounts. In the four equipped as submarine chasers, the RBU-1200 rocket launchers are on the foredeck and the 37-mm mount is aft. VS = *Vanatore de Submarin* (submarine chaser); VP = *Vedette Patrolare* (patrol boat).

◆ 2 ex-Soviet Kronshtadt class

V1 V3

D: 300 tons (330 fl) **S:** 18 kts **Dim:** 52.1 × 6.5 × 2.2 (max.)
A: 1/85-mm DP—1/37-mm 62-cal. AA—6/12.7-mm mg (II × 3)—2/RBU-1200 ASW RL (V × 2)—2/BMB-1 d.c. mortars—2/d.c. racks—mines
Electron Equipt:
Radar: 1/Pot Head nav./surf. search—EW: MF D/F loop
Sonar: Tamir-11 hull-mounted searchlight (25–30 kHz)
M: 3 Type 9D diesels; 3 props; 3,300 bhp **Range:** 3,500/14
Fuel: 20 tons **Crew:** 40 tot.

Remarks: Survivors of three transferred in the 1950s.

PATROL BOATS *(continued)*

Romanian Kronshtadt V 1 Romanian Navy, 1991

MINE WARFARE SHIPS

◆ **2 Cosar-class minelayers** Bldr: . . . SY, Romania (In serv. 1980–82)

271 . . . . 274 . . . .

Cosar-class 271 Romanian Navy, 1991

D: 1,500 tons (fl) **S:** . . . **Dim:** 79.0 × 10.6 × 3.0
A: 1/57-mm DP—4/30-mm AK-230 AA (II × 2)—4/14.5-mm mg (II × 2)—2/RBU-1200 ASW RL (V × 2)—. . . mines
Electron Equipt:
Radar: 1/Nayada nav., 1 Strut Curve surf./air search, 1/Muff Cob f.c., 1/Drum Tilt f.c.
Sonar: probable Tamir-11-derivative hull-mounted searchlight (25–30 kHz)
EW: 2 Watch Dog intercept
M: diesels; 2 props; . . . bhp **Crew:** 75 tot.

Remarks: "Cosar" is the NATO nickname. Also useful as ASW escorts. Share the same hull as the oceanographic research ship *Grigore Antipa* and the rescue tug *Emil Racovita.* The Muff Cob radar/electro-optical director controls the semi-automatic 57-mm gun; the Drum Tilt radar f.c.s. controls the 30-mm AA. There is a helicopter platform above the minelaying deck aft.

◆ **4 Musca-class oceangoing minesweepers** Bldr: Cala de Adocare, Mangalia

	Laid down	L	In serv.
DB 21	1984	. . .	9-86
DB 22	. . .	8-86	12-87
DB 23	1985	. . .	1988
DB 24 Lt Remus Lepoj	1986	. . .	1989

Lt Remus Lepoj (DB 24) Romanian Navy, 1991

D: 660 tons (740 fl) **S:** . . . **Dim:** 59.20 × 9.50 × 2.70
A: 4/30-mm AK-230 AA (II × 2)—8/14.5-mm mg (II × 4)—2/SA-N-5 SAM syst. (IV × 2; . . . Grail missiles)—2/RBU-1200 ASW RL (V × 2)—mines
Electron Equipt:
Radar: 1/Nayada nav. 1/Drum Tilt f.c.
Sonar: Tamir-11-derivative hull-mounted HF searchlight
M: 2 diesels; 2 props; . . . bhp **Range:** . . . **Crew:** 60 tot.

Remarks: Steel-hulled. Similar to Cosar-class minelayers but with lower freeboard. Carry an unusually large number of danbuoy channel markers and may have magnetic and acoustic sweep gear in addition to mechanical sweeping equipment.

◆ **4 German M-40-class minesweepers** Bldr: Galati SY (In serv. 1951)

DB 13 Democratia DB 15 Desrobirea
DB 14 Descatusaria DB 16 Dreptatea

Dreptatea (DB 16) Romanian Navy, 199

D: 637 tons (775 fl) **S:** 17 kts
Dim: 62.30 (57.60 pp) × 8.90 × 2.62
A: 5/37-mm 62-cal. AA (II × 2, I × 1)—4/14.5-mm mg (II × 2)—2/RBU-1200 ASW RL (V × 2)—mines
Electron Equipt:
Radar: 1/Don-2 nav.—IFF: High Pole A transponder
Sonar: Tamir-11-derivative hull-mounted HF searchlight
M: 2 diesels; 2 props; 2,500 bhp
Range: 4,000/10 **Fuel:** 156 tons **Crew:** 80 tot.

Remarks: Begun for German Navy as coal-burning, reciprocating-steam-power ships. Launched postwar. Converted to burn fuel oil on completion. Modernized duri the 1980s with new superstructures, diesel engines in place of the original steam pla ASW ordnance updated. Contrary to previous editions, they retain their mechanic minesweeping equipment.

◆ **12 Soviet T-301-class minesweepers** (In serv. circa 1950)

DR 4–DR 9 DR 17–DR 19 DR 26–DR 28

Romanian T-301 DR 19 Romanian Navy, 1

D: 145.8 tons (160 fl) **S:** 12.5 kts **Dim:** 38.0 × 5.1 × 1.6
A: 2/37-mm AA (I × 2)—4/14.5-m mg (II × 2)—mines
Electron Equipt: Radar: none
M: 3 6-cyl. diesels; 3 props; 1,440 bhp
Range: 2,500/8 **Fuel:** 20 tons **Crew:** 30 tot.

Remarks: Steel-hulled craft with no compound curves to the hull plating. Us river and harbor service. Were originally 24 in service.

AUXILIARY SHIPS

◆ **1 oceanographic research ship** Bldr: Cala de Adocare, Mangalia

Emil Racovita (In serv. 1984)

D: 1,200 tons (fl) **S:** . . . kts **Dim:** 79.0 × 10.5 × 3.0
M: 2 diesels; 2 props; . . . bhp

Remarks: Same basic hull and propulsion as the Cosar-class minelayers an submersible tender/salvage ship *Grigore Antipa.*

◆ **2 Croitor-class small-combatant tenders** Bldr: . . . SY, Roma (In serv. 1980)

281 Constanta 283 . . . .

Constanta (281) Maurizio Brescia,

AUXILIARY SHIPS *(continued)*

Croitor 283 Romanian Navy, 1991

D: 3,500 tons (fl) S: 14 kts Dim: 110.0 × . . . × . . .
A: 2/57-mm DP (II × 1)—2/SA-N-5 SAM syst. (IV × 2)—4/30-mm AK-230 AA (II × 2)—4/14.5-mm mg (II × 2)—2/RBU-1200 ASW RL (V × 2)—1/Alouette-III helicopter
Electron Equipt:
Radar: 1/. . . nav., 1/Strut Curve surf./air search, 1/Muff Cob f.c., 1/Drum Tilt f.c.
Sonar: Tamir-11-derivative hull-mounted HF searchlight
EW: 2 Watch Dog intercept—IFF: 1 High Pole A transponder
M: diesels; 2 props; . . . bhp **Crew:** 150 tot.

Remarks: "Croitor" is the NATO nickname. Helicopter hangar and flight deck aft. Crane forward of bridge tends magazine for torpedoes and missiles. SA-N-5 rack-launchers mounted atop hangar, with ready-service lockers for eight missiles. 281 deployed to the Mediterranean during 10-91, visiting Genoa and Toulon.

1 submersible tender/salvage ship Bldr: Cala de Adocare, Mangalia

Grigore Antipa (In serv. 1980)

Grigore Antipa—note white paint scheme Romanian Navy, 1991

D: 1,200 tons (fl) **S:** . . . **Dim:** 79.0 × 10.6 × 3.0
A: none **Electron Equipt:** Radar: 1/Nayada nav.
M: 2 diesels; 2 props; . . . bhp **Crew:** 60 tot.

Remarks: Same hull and propulsion system as Cosar-class minelayers above. Carries small research submersible at the stern and a submersible decompression chamber beneath a quadrantial gantry to starboard, aft. Equipped to lay a four-point mooring.

3 coastal tankers (In serv. 1971–73)

TM 530 TM 531 TM 532

D: 1,300 tons (fl) **S:** 10 kts **Dim:** 60.0 × 9.2 × 4.1
A: 1/37-mm 62-cal. AA—2/12.7-mm mg (I × 2)
M: 1 diesel; 1 prop; 600 bhp

2 Soviet Roslavl-class ocean tugs Bldr: Galati SY (In serv. 1953–54)

RM 101 Viteasul RM 116 Voinicul

D: 750 tons (fl) **S:** 11 kts **Dim:** 44.5 × 9.5 × 3.5
M: diesel-electric; 2 props; 1,200 bhp **Crew:** 28 tot.

Remarks: RM = *Remorcher de Mare* (seagoing tug).

1 sail-training ship Bldr: Blohm + Voss, Hamburg

	Laid down	L	In serv.
Mircea	15-4-38	22-9-38	16-1-39

D: 1,630 tons (fl) **S:** 12 kts (13 sail)
Dim: 81.28 (67.84 o.a. hull, 62.80 wl) × 12.50 × 5.02
Electron Equipt:
Radar: 1/Decca 202 nav., 1/Nayada nav.
M: 1 MaK 6M 451 AK diesel; 1 prop; 1,100 bhp
Sail area: 1,750 m² tot.
Range: 5,000/. . . on sail and engine; 3,000 engine alone
Crew: 5 officers, 17 warrant officers, 38 enlisted + 120 cadets

Remarks: Three-masted bark. Foremast and mainmast are 44 m above waterline, mizzenmast 39 m. Can carry a total of 23 sails (4 jibs, 6 staysails, 10 square sails, 3 gaff sails). Sister to U.S. Coast Guard *Eagle*, Russian *Tovarisch*, German *Gorch Fock*, and Portuguese *Sagres-II*. Navigation equipment includes a RUMB-16 D/F loop, MEL-25 and DT-700 echo-sounder. Refitted by builder, 1966–67.

Mircea French Navy, 1980

♦ **1 ex-French Friponne-class administrative tender** Bldrs: Brest Dockyard (In serv. 1916–17)

ND 113 Stihi (ex-*Mignonne*)

D: 330 tons (443 fl) **S:** 12 kts **Dim:** 60.9 × 7.0 × 2.5
S: 6/14.5-mm AA (II × 2)
Electron Equipt: Radar: 1/. . . nav.
M: 2 diesels; 2 props; 900 bhp **Range:** 3,000/10
Fuel: 30 tons **Crew:** 50 tot.

Remarks: Used as a headquarters ship. Recently modernized with streamlined superstructures, new armament, etc. Sisters *Dumitrescu* (ND 111, ex-*Friponne*) stricken early 1980s, *Constanta* (ND 113, ex-*Mignonne*) by 1991.

YARDCRAFT

♦ **5 small harbor tugs**

SRS 571 SRS 572 SRS 573 SRS 577 SRS 675

Remarks: No data available.

♦ **5 small fuel lighters**

MM 131 MM 132 MM 133 MM 136 MM 137

Remarks: No data available; are about 25 m o.a.

♦ **4 diving tenders**

♦ **3 accommodations barges**

Oltul Ialomita Siretul

♦ **6 small floating workshops**

♦ **3 fireboats**

Automatice Electronica Energerica

D: 160 tons (fl) **S:** 12 kts **Dim:** 38.0 × 5.5 × 1.4
M: 2 diesels; 2 props; . . . bhp

DANUBE FLOTILLA

♦ **3 Brutar-class monitors** Bldr: . . . (In serv. 1982)

D: 350–400 tons (fl) **S:** . . . **Dim:** 43.0 × 8.0 × 1.5
A: 1/100-mm tank gun—4/14.5-mm mg (II × 2)—1/122-mm BM-21 RL—mines
M: diesels; . . . props; . . . bhp

Remarks: "Brutar" is the NATO nickname. Very low-lying craft; armored tank turret and machine-gun turrets. Barrage rocket launcher has 40 tubes, is hand-loaded.

♦ **18 VB 76 class monitors** Bldr: Dulcea SY (In serv. 1973–76)

VB 76 to VB 93

Cpt. Nicolae Lazar Bogdan (VB 80) Romanian Navy, 1991

D: 85 tons **S:** 17 kts **Dim:** 32.0 × 4.8 × 0.9
A: 1/85-mm—4/14.5-mm AA (II × 2)—2/81-mm mortars (I × 2)
M: 2 diesels; 2 props; 1,200 bhp **Crew:** 25 tot.

Remarks: VB = *Vedeta Blindata* (Armored Boat).

ROMANIA *(continued)*
DANUBE FLOTILLA *(continued)*

◆ **4 VG-class patrol craft** Bldr: Galati SY (In serv. 1954)

VG 14–VG 17

VG class 1971

D: 40 tons (fl) **S:** 18 kts **Dim:** 16.0 × 4.4 × 1.2
A: 1/20-mm AA—1/7.9-mm mg
M: 2 3D12 diesels; 2 props; 600 bhp **Crew:** 10 tot.

◆ **26 river minesweepers** Bldr: Turnu-Severin SY (In serv. 1975–. . .)

VD 141–VD 166

D: 65 tons (fl) **S:** 18 kts **Dim:** 26.0 × 4.0 × 0.8
A: 4/14.5-mm mg (II × 2)—mines
M: 2 M50 diesels; 2 props; 1,200 bhp

Remarks: Replaced the now-discarded Polish TR-40 class. Resemble the VB 76-class monitors.

◆ **3 Braila-class vehicle ferries**

420 421 422

Remarks: Also referred to as "landing craft," but photos show barge-hulled craft with light twin landing ramp forward, cargo king post and derrick amidships and superstructure aft, with craft most suitable for riverine logistics support duties.

◆ **9 SM 165-class patrol/utility craft**

SM 161–SM 169

D: 22 tons **S:** 12 kts **Dim:** 12.2 × 3.0 × 0.9

◆ **5 SD 200-class patrol/utility boats**

SD 270 SD 274 SD 275 SD 277 SD 278

◆ **1 headquarters ship**

REPUBLICA

Remarks: A very old side-wheel paddle boat of about 300 tons (fl). There are also several accommodations and workshop barges assigned to the Danube Flotilla.

RUSSIA

Russian Federation

Note: The former Union of Soviet Socialist Republics ceased to exist on 31 December 1991 and has been replaced by the Commonwealth of Independent States (*Sodruzhestva Nezanvesinykh Gosudarstv*), a loose confederation of former Soviet states that had hoped to have but a single national naval service. The navy of the C.I.S., however, is in fact Russian and will fly as its ensign the Cross of St. Andrew in a decision announced 16-1-92. The assets of the former Soviet Navy are under the general control of Russia, although Ukraine and Azerbaijan have established naval services to use ships and craft transferred from the former Soviet Navy or the KGB Maritime Border Patrol.

On 12-1-92, Ukraine and Russia agreed to divide Black Sea naval assets, and on 24-2-92, it was officially stated that some 42 "ships" had been transferred from among KGB Maritime Border Guard units in the Black Sea (see under Ukraine). By 6-12-91, Georgia, which had not joined the C.I.S., had proclaimed the creation of a navy, but it apparently did not as yet have any ships or craft and had little prospect of obtaining any in the near future. Azerbaijan received a number of former Caspian Sea Flotilla units in 4-92, but, again, which ones had not been anounced at time of writing. The three Baltic republics granted independence during 1991 have not (as yet) joined the C.I.S. and have established their own small navies.

The C.I.S. Navy is plagued by fuel shortages, shortages of personnel as draft evasion increases, and declining material condition. The Baltic and Pacific Ocean Fleets by 12-91 had established entrepreneurial organizations to carry commercial cargoes in naval auxiliaries and to perform other money-making functions in order to raise operating funds and to provide food and housing for naval personnel. By the end of 1991, virtually all overseas-deployed combatants had returned home, although a cruiser and a frigate made a ten-day abbreviated Mediterranean cruise between 5-2-92 and 15-2-92.

Many of the ship names listed below that were assigned prior to the dissolution of the Soviet Union will probably be changed, especially the over sixty "*Komsomolets*" names given to ships theoretically manned by conscripts from Communist Youth Groups; also likely to be changed are former KGB Maritime Border Guard ship names duplicating those of naval ships. The pendant numbers on the sides of Russian combatants are temporary tactical numbers denoting administrative subordination and are changed periodically; for that reason, they are not listed here; alphanumeric auxiliary vessel names, however, are more or less permanent and are listed.

Personnel (12-91): Approximately 442,000 total: 139,000 seagoing, 29,000 "Coastal Force" troops, 9,000 in communications, 58,000 conscripts in training, 122,000 shore establishment, and 85,000 in Naval Aviation. Some 25,000 naval personnel assigned to the KGB-subordinated Maritime Border Guard, including seagoing and shore personnel, were resubordinated to the Ministry of the Interior by the end of 1991 as a result o the disestablishment of separate KGB armed forces after the August 1991 coup attempt; they are included in the seagoing forces total above. In 5-91, a new organizatio called the "Coastal Force" was created to incorporate three understrength former Re Army Motorized Battalions transferred to the navy in 1990, the 12,100-man Nava Infantry, and the 7,000-man Coastal Missile and Artillery Force. Of some 90,00 civilian employees, about 20,000, including a number of women, serve in seagoin positions, chiefly in the Naval Auxiliary Service.

The period of service for naval conscripts, formerly three years, has been reduced t two; a plan to instigate a professional contract enlisted cadre during 1992 may hav fallen by the wayside due to economic difficulties. The net result, when combined with growing shortfall in the conscript draft, will result in further decreases in the man power pool and the combat readiness of the fleet. There are very few women in th uniformed Russian Navy and virtually none in seagoing billets.

On 3-2-92, the newspaper *Izvestiya* announced that the following numbers of ship were in service: 51 strategic submarines, 163 general-purpose submarines (of which 8 were nuclear-powered), 151 warships of over 1,200-tons displacement (including 1 cruisers, 5 of which were aviation-associated), and 87 destroyers and "other escorts 331 coastal patrol units, 298 patrol boats, 1,638 fixed-wing aircraft, and 581 helico ters. The basis for inclusion in the list, however, was not given, and ships in overha may not have been included.

WARSHIPS IN ACTIVE SERVICE OR UNDER CONSTRUCTION AS OF 1 JANUARY 1992

◆ **1 (+1) aircraft carriers**

	L	Tons (fl)	Main armament
1 (+1) KUZNETSOV	1985–88	65,000	30 aircraft, missiles, etc

◆ **243 (+ . . .) combatant submarines**

		Tons (surfaced)	
56 *ballistic-missile* (all nuclear):			
6 Typhoon (nuclear)	1980–89	18,500	20/SS-N-20, . . ./TT
7 Delta-IV (nuclear)	1984–90	10,800	16/SS-N-23, 6/TT
14 Delta-III (nuclear)	1975–	10,600	16/SS-N-18, 6/TT
4 Delta-II (nuclear)	1975	10,550	16/SS-N-8, 6/TT
18 Delta-I (nuclear)	1972–75	9,000	12/SS-N-8, 6/TT
7 Yankee-I (nuclear)	1967–74	7,900	16/SS-N-6, 6/TT
51 (+ . . .) *cruise-missile attack* (42 nuclear):			
7 (+ . . .) Oscar-II (nuclear)	1983–	13,000	24/SS-N-19, 8/TT
2 Oscar-I (nuclear)	1980–82	11,500	24/SS-N-19, 8/TT
6 Charlie-II (nuclear)	1973–	4,300	8/SS-N-9, 6/TT
10 Charlie-I (nuclear)	1968–72	4,000	8/SS-N-7, 6/TT
3 Yankee Notch (nuclear)	. . .	. . .	12/SS-N-24, 6/TT
14 Mod. Echo-II (nuclear)	1960–68	5,000	8/SS-N-3 or SS-N-12, 10/TT
9 Juliett (diesel)	1961–68	3,000	4/SS-N-23, 10/TT
136 (+ . . .) *torpedo attack:* (58 nuclear)			
7 (+ . . .) Akula (nuclear)	1984–. . .	7,500	8/TT
1 (+ . . .) Sierra-II (nuclear)	1989-. . .	6,300	6/TT
2 Sierra-I (nuclear)	1983–86	6,000	6/TT
26 Victor-III (nuclear)	1978–91	4,900	6/TT
7 Victor-II (nuclear)	1972–77	4,500	6/TT
15 Victor-I (nuclear)	1967–74	4,300	6/TT
20 (+ . . .) KILO (diesel)	1980–. . .	2,500	6/TT
18 Tango (diesel)	1972–82	3,000	10/TT
40 Foxtrot (diesel)	1957–74	1,950	10/TT

◆ **23 (+2) cruisers**

		Tons (full load)	
2 aviation:			
1 KIEV (+ 2 in reserve)	1972–82	43,000	Missile launchers, g helicopters
1 MOSKVA	1964	14,590	2/SA-N-3, 1/SUW-N 14 helicopters*

WARSHIPS *(continued)*

21 (+2) guided-missile:			
3 (+1) KIROV (nuclear)	1977–81	28,000	20/SS-N-19, 2/SS-N-14, 12/SA-N-6, 2/SA-N-4, 2/100-mm DP, 10/TT, 3/helos*
3 (+1) SLAVA	1979–89	12,500	16/SS-N-12, 64/SA-N-6, 2/SA-N-4, 2/130-mm, 1 helo*
7 Kara	1971–78	9,700	8/SS-N-14, 2/SA-N-3, 2/SA-N-4, 4/76.2-mm DP, 10/TT, 1 helo*
7 Kresta-II	1967–76	7,700	8/SS-N-14, 2/SA-N-3, 4/57-mm, 10/TT, 1/helo*
1 Kresta-I	1966	7,500	4/SS-N-3, 2/SA-N-1, 4/57-mm, 10/TT, 1/helo*
33 (+10) destroyers			
0 (+1+ . . .) new class	1992?	8,200	. . .
11 (+1) UDALOY	1978–. . .	8,100	8/SS-N-14, 8/SA-N-9, 2/100-mm DP, 4/30-mmAA, 8/533-mm TT, 2/helos, mines*
4 (+9) SOVREMENNYY	1978–	7,850	8/SS-N-22, 2/SA-N-7, 4/130-mm DP, 4/30-mm AA, 4/533-mm TT, 1/helo, mines*
2 Mod. Kashin	1965–72	4,950	4/SS-N-2C, 2/SA-N-1, 4/76.2-mm DP, 5/TT*
6 Kashin	1961–71	4,750	2/SA-N-1, 4/76.2-mm DP, 5/TT*
39 (+ . . .) frigates			
1 (+. . .) NEUSTRASHIMYY	1988–. . .	4,500	4/SA-N-9, 1/100-mm DP. 6/533-mm TT, 1 helo*
7 (+ . . .) Krivak-III	1983–. . .	3,900	1/SA-N-4, 1/100-mm, 8 TT, 1 helo*
1 Krivak-I, -II	1970–81	3,670	4/SS-N-14, 2/SA-N-4, 2/100-mm or 4/76.2-mm DP, 8/TT*
99–101 (+ . . .) corvettes			
Parchim-II	1986–89	950	1/76.2, 4/TT*
(+ . . .) Grisha-V	1984–. . .	1,150	1/SA-N-4, 1/76.2-mm DP, 4/TT*
Grisha-IV	1984(?)	1,150	3/SA-N-9, 2/TT*
Grisha-III	1975–84	1,100	1/SA-N-4, 2/57-mm DP, 4/TT*
Grisha-II	1974–76	1,100	4/57-mm DP, 4/TT*
Grisha-I	1967–73	1,100	1/SA-N-4, 2/57-mm DP, 4/TT*
0 Petya-II	1964–69	1,150	4/76.2-mm DP, 10/TT*
Petya-III	. . .	1,150	4/76.2-mm DP, 3/TT*
166 (+ . . .) patrol combatants			
Dergach	. . .	700	8/SS-N-22, 1/SA-N-4, 1/76.2-mm DP
Tarantul-III	1987–90	455	4/SS-N-22, 1/76.2-mm DP
Tarantul-I, -II	1979–84	455	4/SS-N-2C, 1/76.2-mm DP
Nanuchka-I,-III	1969–91	685	6/SS-N-9, 1/SA-N-4, 1/76.2-mm or 2/57-mm DP
(+ . . .) Pauk-I,-II	1979–	450	1/76.2-mm DP, 4/TT*
IVAN SUSANIN	1975–81	3,400	2/76.2-mm DP
Sorum	1974–. . .	1,656	4/30-mm AA
T-58	1956–61	880	4/57-mm DP*
Mayak	1970–. . .	1,050	2/25-mm AA, TT*

icates additional ASW weapons carried

7 guided-missile and torpedo boats

ver 130 seagoing patrol boats

ver 180 seagoing mine warfare ships

3 amphibious warfare ships

A note on ship class names: The class names used herein are for the most part those used by NATO. Until 1973, Soviet combatants usually did not display names, and thus NATO had devised a series of nicknames based on Russian words (combatants: geographical place names beginning with "K"; small combatants: insects; mine warfare types: diminutives of personal names; amphibious warfare types: reptiles; auxiliaries: rivers). Subsequently, the policy has been to use the actual name of the first ship of a class, as in the West. Often that name is not immediately available, and thus a three-part *interim* nickname is applied. The first syllable denotes the *fleet area* where the class was first identified (BAL = Baltic, BLK = Black Sea, etc.), the second syllable indicates the *type* of ship (COM = combatant, SUB = submarine, AUX = auxiliary, etc.), and the third syllable is a roman numeral indicating the order of discovery within a category. Thus, "BAL-COM-III" would be the third new major combatant discovered under construction in the Baltic. As actual names are learned, they replace the temporary nickname. The Russian Navy itself uses a series of Project Numbers to identify its ships; where available, they have been listed below after the NATO class names.

The Russian Navy has a number of unique ship-type classifications; these are translated, where applicable, in the individual class entries.

WEAPONS AND SYSTEMS

Note: Nuclear warheads have been widely deployed in the past on Soviet Navy weapons, especially submarine-deployed weapons, as witness the presence of nuclear warhead torpedoes aboard the Whiskey-class submarine that ran aground near Karlskrona Naval Base in Sweden 10-81 and aboard the sunken Mike, *Komsomolets*. In 1991 in response to an initiative by U.S. President Bush, it was announced that tactical nuclear weapons would be removed from Soviet (now Russian) warships, with the intent that only strategic ballistic and cruise missiles would have nuclear warheads in the future.

A. MISSILES

◆ Submarine-launched Ballistic Missiles

Note: All have liquid-fuel propulsion, except SS-N-20, which has solid-fuel propulsion. CEP = Circular Error Probable (i.e., half of all launched will fall within this radius).

SS-N-6 (RSM-25) Serb (1968)

Nuclear warhead of about 1 megaton in Mod. 2; Mod. 3 has two re-entry vehicles. Fitted in Yankee-I-class nuclear submarines. Can be launched while submerged. 1,500-m CEP. Mod. 1 and 3 versions obsolete, Mod. 2 probably withdrawn from service by the end of 1992; 192 were in operational service in 10-91.
weight: 14,200 kg length: 9.9 m diameter: 1.50 m
range: Mod. 2—1,600 n.m. (one warhead, 650 kg)

SS-N-8 (RSM-40) Sawfly (1973/77)

Single nuclear warhead of about 1.5 megatons. Fitted in Delta-I and -II nuclear submarines. 1,500-m CEP. Only the Mod. 1 version remains in service. Two-stage weapon with 25.7-ton first stage. 280 were in service as of 10-91.
weight: 33,300 kg length: 13 m diameter: 1.80 m
range: Mod. 1—4,240 n.m. (one 1,100-kilogram warhead)

SS-N-18 (RSM 50) Stingray (1977)

Two-stage missile employed on Delta-III class. CEP estimated at 1,100 m. (Mod. 1). In 10-91, 224 were in operational service. Mods. 2 and 3 no longer in service.
weight: 35,300 kg length: 14.1 m diameter: 1.80 m
range: 3,530 n.m. (3 × 550-kg MIRV warheads)

SS-N-20 (RSM 52) Sturgeon (10-82)

Three-stage weapon with multiple independent reentry-vehicle (MIRV) payload. Used by the Typhoon class. CEP estimated at 500–600 m. Mod. 1 (no longer in service) had 8 MIRV warheads, and the Mod. 2 has 10 MIRV. The first stage weighs 52.8 tons and is 9.5 m long; the second stage is 2.30 m in diameter. As of 10-90, 120 were in operational service. A successor weapon is reported to be in development.
weight: 90,000 kg (including 6,000-kg launch-assist devices)
length: 16.0 m diameter: 2.40 m
range: 4,480 n.m. (10 × 255-kg MIRV warheads)

SS-N-23 (RSM-54) Skiff (1986)

Three-stage weapon originally with up to 10 (Mod. 1) or 4 (Mod. 2) multiple independent reentry-vehicle (MIRV) payload, carried by the Delta-IV class. As of 10-91, 940 Mod. 2 were in operational service. CEP: est. 500 m. The first stage weighs 22,300 kg at launch.
weight: 40,300 kg diameter: 1.90 m length: 14.8 m
range: 4,860 nm (4 × 700-kg MIRV warheads)

◆ Surface-to-Surface Cruise Missiles

SS-N-2A and B Styx (1958/1964)

Soviet designation: P-15. Maximum range: 25 nautical miles. Practical range: 16 nautical miles. Liquid-propulsion rocket with solid booster. I-band active radar guidance in targeting, with infrared *or* radar homing. Altitude can be preset at 100, 150, 200, 250, or 300 m. 500-kg conventional warhead. Installed in Osa-I and Osa-II guided-missile boats. The SS-N-2B has folding wings.
weight: 2,300 kg wingspan: 2.5 m length: 6.5 m speed: Mach 1.3
diameter: 0.8 m

WEAPONS AND SYSTEMS *(continued)*

Twin 57-mm AK-257 57-mm DP ZIF-72 mounts on oiler Berezina

Twin 76.2-mm 59-cal. AK-276 mount on cruiser Kerch'
Eric Grove

SS-N-2b/c Styx launcher on an Osa-II

Triple SS-N-9 Siren launch group on a Nanuchka-I

Muzzle of a quadruple, fixed SS-N-14 quadruple launcher on a Kara
Eric Grove, 1990

Eight SS-N-12 Sandbox launchers abaft 12 vertical-launch silos for the SA-N-9 Gopher SAM system on the carrier Admiral Flota Sovetskogo Soyuza Gorshkov

RBU-1000 ASW rocket launcher

Twin 130-mm DP mount on a Sovremennyy
Leo Van Ginderen, 6-91

Quadruple SS-N-3b Shaddock trainable launcher on a Kynda

Inclined, below-decks SS-N-19 Shipwreck launchers on Kirov

Quadruple SS-N-22 Sunburn launch group on a Sovremennyy
Mike Louagie, 6-91

Quadruple trainable SS-N-14 Silex launcher on a Krivak

Twin, fixed SS-N-12 Sandbox launchers on cruiser Slava

SUW-N-1 launcher and missi on cruiser Moskva

SS-N-2b/c Styx launchers on a Tarantul-II

RBU-6000 ASW rocket launcher on a Krivak; rada above is a Don Kay
Hans J. Vanh

WEAPONS AND SYSTEMS *(continued)*

RBU-12000 ASW rocket launcher

Twin-barreled, trainable decoy rocket launcher on a Kara

Eric Grove

aised SA-N-4 Gecko twin AM launcher on a Krivak RBU-6000 ASW rocket unchers at left)

SA-N-6 Grumble vertical-launch SAM system hatches on Kirov

um Tilt fire-control radar an Osa-II

SA-N-3 Goblet twin SAM launcher on a Kara

Eric Grove

N-6 Grumble vertical-launch SAM silos and their Top Dome radar ctor at right on cruiser Slava

Twin 30-mm AK-230 AA mount on a Stenka

Single 30-mm AK-630 gatling AA on Kirov

Sky Watch phased-array radar below a Strut Pair air/surface-search radar on carrier Admiral Flota Sovetskogo Soyuza Gorshkov; radome is for the Low Ball communications satellite system

Top Steer back-to-back early-warning air-search radar on Sovremennyy

Big Net early-warning radar antenna on a Kashin

Plate Steer back-to-back air-search/3-D radar

CADS-1 combined SA-N-11 SAM launcher/twin 30-mm gatling AA gun close-in weapons system with Hot Flash integral radar; perforated blast shields protect the missile reload hatches (no missiles are uploaded in this view)

WEAPONS AND SYSTEMS *(continued)*

Front Door tracking radar for SS-N-12 SSM on the forward side of Slava's tower mast, below Top Steer back-to-back radar

Top Plate back-to-back early-warning/3-D radar

SA-N-7 Gadfly SAM single-launcher on a Sovremennyy

Top Sail (right) and Head Net-C antennas on a Kresta-II

Top Pair back-to-back early-warning/3-D radar antenna on Slava

Head Net-C air-search radar

Head Net-A air-search radar, above two Don-2 navigational radars

Two Eye Bowl SS-N-14 Silex missile-control radars on a Krivak

Pop Group SA-N-4 SAM system radar director

Peel Group radar director SA-N-1 SAM system

WEAPONS AND SYSTEMS *(continued)*

Front Dome radar director for SA-N-7 system

Top Dome radar director for SA-N-6 system

:uff Cob radar/electro-optical :un director

Bass Tilt radar gun director

:oss Sword radar director for SA-N-9 SAM system

Screen 3-D early-warning radar (left) and Head Lights-C radar :tor for SA-N-3 and SS-N-14 missiles on the cruiser Kerch'

76.2-mm AK-172 DP gun on a Nanuchka-III

Kite Screech 130-mm gun director Alexandre Sheldon-Dupleix

Four SA-N-3 SAM system Goa missiles run up on the twin launch rails on a Moskva-class cruiser; note the elevation of the Head Lights radar director at the right

WEAPONS AND SYSTEMS *(continued)*

SS-N-2C (formerly SS-N-11)(1967)

Maximum range: 45 nautical miles. Radar or infrared terminal-homing versions. 500-kg warhead. In order to employ fully the over-the-horizon maximum range of the SS-N-2C, it is necessary to have a forward observer. The SS-N-2C is carried by the destroyers of the Modified Kashin class, by Tarantul guided-missile corvettes, and by Osa-II missile boats. Widely exported. P-21 version is radar-homing, P-22 is infrared.
weight: 2,500 kg wingspan: 2.5 length: 6.5 m speed: Mach 1.3
diameter: 0.8 m

SS-N-3 Shaddock (A: 1962, B: 1962, C: 1960)

Produced in three versions: SS-N-3A for launch by submarine, with inertial guidance, mid-course correction, and active radar terminal homing: SS-N-3B for Kynda- and Kresta-I-class cruisers, with similar guidance; and SS-N-3C with inertial-only guidance, probably no longer in use from submarines. SS-N-3 is a variant of the SS-C-1 coast-defense missile.
weight: 5,400 kg span: 5 m length: 10.2 m (SS-N-3C: 11.2 m)
diameter: 0.9 m warhead: 1,000 kg
range: SS-N-3A/B: 250 n.m.; SS-N-3C: 350 n.m.

SS-N-7 Starbright (1970)

Used only aboard the Charlie-I-class submarine. Conventional warhead. Launched while submerged. 500-kg conventional or nuclear warhead. Radar homing.
weight: 2,900 kg wingspan: . . . length: 7 m range: 38–43 n.m.
diameter: 0.55 m

SS-N-9 Siren (1969)

Inertial guidance, and active radar or infrared homing to the target. 500-kg conventional or nuclear warhead. Installed in Nanuchka-I- and -III-class guided-missile corvettes and the Sarancha-class hydrofoil. A submerged-launch version is available for Charlie-II submarines.
weight: 3,300 kg wingspan: 1.6 m length: 8.8 m speed: Mach 0.9
diameter: 0.8 m
range: 30 n.m. (60 n.m. with forward observer/video data link)

SS-N-12 Sandbox (1973)

1,000-kg conventional or nuclear warhead. Replacing the SS-N-3 on Echo-II-class submarines and is aboard the *Kiev* class and *Slava*-class cruisers.
weight: 4,800 kg wingspan: 1.8 length: 10.80 m speed: Mach 2.5
diameter: 0.9 m range: 300 n.m.

SS-N-19 Shipwreck (1971)

Conventional or nuclear warhead. Has improved performance characteristics over the SS-N-12 and is carried by the *Kirov*-class cruisers and the Oscar-class nuclear-powered submarines (from which it is submerged-launched). Nuclear or conventional warhead.
weight: 5,000 kg wingspan: 1.6 length: 10.5 m speed: Mach 2.5
diameter: 0.9 m range: 300 n.m.

SS-N-21 Sampson (1988)

A torpedo-tube-launched strategic land target weapon similar in concept to the U.S. Tomahawk. Submerged-launched from submarines, but also developed for surface (SSC-4) and air launch (AS 15 Kent) as well. Employs terrain-following, low-altitude (190–200 m) flight pattern. Probably has a nuclear warhead.
weight: 1,700 kg (2,440 with canister) wingspan: 0.30 m
length: 8.09 m (8.39 canister) speed: Mach 0.7
diameter: 0.51 m (0.65 canister) range: 1,620 n.m.

SS-N-22 Sunburn (1981)

A successor to the SS-N-9, but not, to date, used by submarines. Reportedly flies at "sea-skimming" altitudes to a range of 55–68 n.m. Carried by the *Sovremennyy*-class destroyers and Tarantul-III-class missile boats. Active radar homing.
weight: 3,500 kg wingspan: 1.6 m length: 5.1 m speed: Mach 2.5
diameter: 0.8 m range: 50 n.m.

SS-NX-24 Scorpion (. . .)

Large strategic cruise missile. Used in single Yankee conversion trials submarine and probably intended for a canceled new class. Program probably abandoned.
weight: . . . wingspan: . . . length: 13 m speed: Mach 3.0
diameter: . . . range: 1,600 n.m.

SS-NX-25 . . . . . . (1993?)

Harpoon/Exocet-sized antiship weapon intended to be launched from canisters mounted in quadruple nests. Was to have been carried by the former East German *Sassnitz*-class guided-missile boats (the only tube installation was removed from the prototype and returned to the U.S.S.R. prior to German unification) and on modernized units of the Krivak-class frigates. Has been offered for export. Possibly a surface-launched version of the AS-17 air-launched tactical missile:
weight: 700 kg length: 4.5 m warhead weight: 250 kg range: 54 n.m.

♦ Surface-to-Air Missiles

SA-N-1 Goa (1961)

Twin-launcher. Range: 20,000 m (12 n.m.); interception altitude: 300 to 50,000 feet. Guidance: radar/command. Weight: 400 kg. Conventional warhead, 60 kg. Fitted on Kynda and Kresta-I cruisers, as well as on Kashin-class destroyers. Also has a surface-to-surface capability. Uses Peel Group radar directors. Sixteen per magazine. Obsolescent.

SA-N-3 Goblet (1967)

Twin launcher. Range: 30,000 m (22 n.m.); interception altitude: 300 to 80,000 feet. Guidance: radar/command via Head Lights-series radar director. Weight: 550 kg. Mach 2.5. Conventional warhead, 60 kg. Fitted on Kresta-II and Kara cruisers as well as the *Moskva*-class helicopter cruisers. An improved version has a range of 55,000 m and is on the *Kiev*. Goblet has an anti-surface target capability.

SA-N-4 Gecko (1969)

Twin launcher, retracting into a cylindrical magazine holding 20 missiles on 4 rings of 5. Range: 9,000 m; interception altitude: 30 to 10,000 feet. Guidance: radar command via Pop Group radar director. Conventional warhead. Fitted in Kara and *Kirov* cruisers, Krivak guided-missile frigates, Grisha- and Nanuchka-class corvettes the Sarancha hydrofoil, the landing ship *Ivan Rogov*, and the replenishment ship *Berezina*. Can be used against surface targets. Weight: 125 kg. Launcher designation ZIF-122.

SA-N-5 Grail (1974)

Naval version of SA-7 Grail. Fitted on Pauk- and Tarantul-class corvettes, som Osa-class guided-missile patrol boats, landing ships, some minesweepers, and mar auxiliaries. Employs either a Fasta-4M 4-missile launch rack with operator, or shoulder-launched, singly. IR-homing, visually aimed. 4.4-km range, 7,800-ft altitud Weighs 15 kg with launch tube. Largely superseded by the similar but improv SA-N-8 system.

SA-N-6 Grumble (1981)

A navalized version of the land-based SA-10. Range 80,000 m or greater, altitudes 90,000 ft. Employs vertical launch from 8-missile rotating magazines and reported uses track-via-missile guidance via the Top Dome radar system; each Top Dome c reportedly track six targets simultaneously, provided they are within the same 6 degree radius. Carried by the *Kirov* and *Slava*-class cruisers. Probably also has antiship capability. Land-based version has been offered for export.

SA-N-7 Gadfly (1981)

A navalized version of the land-based SA-11, employing single-armed laun ers. Estimated twenty missiles per magazine. Mach 3 weapon with 28,000-m ra (3,000-m minimum) and usable against targets from 100- to 46,000-ft. altitude. Ope tional on the *Sovremennyy*-class destroyers. Guidance via Front Dome radar track illuminators. Probably has a secondary antiship capability.

SA-N-8 Gremlin (1986?)

A navalized version of the SA-14, the cooled-seeker successor to the SA-7 Grail. U the same Fasta-4M 4-position manned launcher or a shoulder launcher. Slig greater range than SA-N-5, from which it is virtually indistinguishable while in launch tube, which has a slightly larger control section than that of the SA-N-5 lau tube. Weight: 9.9 kg; length: 1.3 m.

SA-N-9 Gopher (1989)

A vertically launched, short-range system intended as a successor to SA-N-4. Car in groups of 8 in 2-m-diameter launch cylinders aboard the *Udaloy*-class destro carriers *Baku* and *Admiral Flota Sovetskogo Soyuza Kuznetsov*, and other new struction. Appears to be sufficient space for two layers of missiles, for a total of 1 launcher. Range 12 km; altitude 19,700-ft maximum/32-ft. minimum. Speed: 85 sec. Missile weighs 32 kg at launch and has a .5-kg warhead.Uses Cross Sword r directors, which have a co-mounted target detection and designation radar, an ill nation radar, and an electro-optical backup feature, and can control two mis simultaneously. Can be used against targets traveling at up to 700-m/sec. Appea have had development problems, as first ships to have carried it completed in 19

SA-N-10 Gimlet (1989)

Lightweight, twin-armed automatic launch system for IR-homing missile (launcher) found only on nuclear-powered auxiliary SSV-33. Believed to use the S (Soviet 9M313, or *Igla*) infrared-homing missile: Weight: 16.65 kg. Range: 3. Altitude: 11,500-ft. maximum/32-ft. minimum. Speed: 680 m./sec.

SA-N-11 . . . (1989)

Missile component of the new multiple gun/missile mounting on the carrier *Ad Flota Sovetskogo Soyuza Kuznetsov*, cruiser *Kalinin*, and frigate *Neustrashimyy* radar-guided missile (possibly navalized SA-19) launched from disposable tube. carries up to 8 missiles, 2/30-mm gatling AA guns, and autonomous Hot Flash s and-track radar system with electro-optical backup. Missiles can be auto-reloade below-deck magazine that probably holds a total of 48 missiles per mount. Also re to by NATO as the CADS-1 (Close Air Defense System-1).

♦ Air-to-Surface Missiles (naval use only)

AS 2 Kipper (1961)

Turbojet propulsion. Inertial guidance or automatic pilot with radar homin 1,000-kg conventional or nuclear warhead. Launched from Badger-C aircraft. O cent and probably removed from service.
weight: 4,200 kg wingspan: 4.8 m length: 9.3 m speed: Mach 1.4–1.6
diameter: 0.87 m range: 115 n.m. high-launch/54 n.m. low-launch

WEAPONS AND SYSTEMS *(continued)*

AS 4 Kitchen (Soviet *Burya*) (1967)

1,000-kg conventional or nuclear warhead. Inertial guidance with radar-terminal homing. In service on Backfire-B and Blinder-B aircraft. Obsolescent and is probably out of service—or soon will be.
weight: 6,400 kg wingspan: 4.8 m length: 11.1 m speed: Mach 2.5–3.5
diameter: 0.87 m range: 240 n.m. high-launch/146 n.m. low-launch

AS 5 Kelt (1965)

Liquid-fueled rocket propulsion. Inertial or autopilot guidance with J-band radar terminal homing. Conventional and nuclear warheads. In service on Badger-C and -G aircraft. Obsolescent and will probably soon be removed from service.
weight: 4,700 kg wingspan: 4.8 m length: 8.5 m speed: Mach 0.7–1.2
diameter: 0.9 m range: 175 n.m. high-launch/90 n.m. low-launch

AS 6 Kingfish (1970)

1000-kg conventional or 350 KT nuclear warhead. In service on Badger-C and -G aircraft, two on each. Obsolescent and will probably soon be out of service.
weight: 4,900 kg wingspan: 2.4 m length: 10.3 m speed: Mach 2.5–3.5
diameter: 0.87 m range: 350 n.m. high-launch/160 n.m. low-launch

AS 7 Kerry (Soviet *Grom*) (late 1970s)

Tactical weapon. Solid-fuel propulsion. Pencil-beam radar terminal homing. 100-kg conventional warhead. Formerly used on carrier-based Yak-38 Forger aircraft and can also be carried by the land-based Su-25 Frogfoot.
weight: 400 kg wingspan: 0.95 m length: 3.5 m speed: Mach 1.0
diameter: 0.305 m range: 6 n.m.

AS 9 Kyle (late 1970s)

Turbojet propulsion. Passive homing on electromagnetic radiation. 150-kg conventional warhead. Can be used by Badger, Backfire, and Fitter-C and Fitter-D aircraft.
weight: 650 kg wingspan: . . . length: 6.0 m speed: Mach 3.0
diameter: 0.5 m range: 60 n.m.

AS 10 Karen (1980)

Solid propulsion. Electro-optical guidance. Conventional warhead of 100 kg. Carried by Fitter-D.
weight: 400 kg wingspan: . . . length: 3.5 m speed: Mach 0.9
diameter: 0.305 m range: 6 n.m.

AS 15 Kent (1986)

Strategic weapon carried by Russian Air Force Bear-H and Blackjack bombers. Air-launched version of the SS-N-21.

Note: The AS 12 Kegler, AS 13, and AS 14 Kedge are tactical missiles used by land-based aircraft. Laser-guided and conventional free-fall bombs in 500, 750, and 1,500-kg sizes are also available.

◆ GUNS

130-mm/70-caliber twin, dual-purpose

Fully automatic; for surface, shore bombardment, and aerial targets. Fitted on *Sovremennyy*-class destroyers, *Slava*-class cruisers, and *Kirov*-class cruisers *Frunze* and *Kalinin*. Water-cooled. Uses Kite Screech radar director with electro-optical backup or local control by on-mount operator.
max. surface range: 28,000 m max. rate of fire: 65/min
muzzle velocity: 950 m/sec weight of mount: 35 tons
arc of elevation: −15° to +85°

[illegible]-mm/55-caliber single-purpose (Soviet U-5 TS)

Armored tank turret-mounted gun on Yaz-class river monitors.
max. rate of fire: 4/min muzzle velocity: 780 m/sec
max. range: 4,800 m arc of elevation: −4° to +17°

[illegible]-mm/70-caliber automatic dual-purpose

Single-barreled, water-cooled gun in an enclosed, manned mounting found on the [illegible]er *Kirov*, *Udaloy*-class destroyers, and *Neustrashimyy*-, Krivak-II-, and -III-class [illegible]es. Uses Kite Screech radar director with electro-optical backup or local control [illegible] on-mount operator.
rate of fire: 80/min max. theoretical range: 15,000 m
max. effective range: 8,000 m projectile weight: 16 kg

[illegible]-mm/56-caliber single dual-purpose (Soviet BU-34)

[illegible]n mount with an open-backed shield. Installed on five Don-class submarine tenders. Once widely employed, but now obsolescent. Uses Wasp Head director with [illegible]scopic rangefinder and Sun Visor ranging radar; can also be locally controlled.
muzzle velocity: 850 m/sec arc of elevation: −5° to +40°
projectile weight: 13.5 kg max. rate of fire: 15/min
max. range: 16,000 m effective range: 10,000 m

[illegible]-mm/59-caliber single automatic dual-purpose (AK-176)

[illegible]y automatic, with on-mount crew. Carried by Grisha-V and Parchim-II cor[illegible], Nanuchka-III, Pauk, and Tarantul-class guided-missile patrol combatants, [illegible]-class guided-missile hydrofoils, etc. Crew of six, with two on mount. Weighs 4 [illegible] Employs Bass Tilt radar/electro-optical director or local, on-mount control.
rate of fire: 120/min
theoretical max. range against surface target: 14,000 m
practical range against aerial target: 6,000 to 7,000 m

76.2-mm/59-caliber twin dual-purpose (AK-276)

Installed on Kara and Kynda cruisers, Kashin destroyers, Krivak-I frigates, Petya corvettes, *Smol'nyy*-class training ships, and *Ivan Susanin*-class patrol icebreakers. Employs either Owl Screech or Hawk Screech radar director, the latter in conjunction with a separate ring-sight target designator.
muzzle velocity: 900 m/sec max. rate of fire: 45/min/barrel
arc of elevation: +80 max. range, AA fire: 10,000 m
effective range, AA fire: 6,000 to 7,000 m projectile weight: 16 kg
muzzle velocity: 980 m/sec.

76.2-mm/48-caliber single-purpose (Soviet D-56 TM)

Tank turret-mounted weapon used on Shmel-class river gunboats; same mount and turret as used by PT-76 amphibious tank.
muzzle velocity: 680 m/sec arc of elevation: −4° to +30°
max. rate of fire: 15/min max. effective range: 800 m

57-mm/70-caliber twin automatic dual-purpose (Soviet AK-257)

Installed on *Moskva*, Kresta-I and Kresta-II cruisers, Grisha corvettes, Nanuchka-I guided-missile patrol combatants, Turya torpedo boats, Ropucha LSTs, Ugra submarine tenders, and the replenishment ship *Berezina*. Now removed from *Boris Chilikin* replenishment ships and *Manych*-class water tankers. Water-cooled barrels. The mount is also referred to as the ZIF-72. Automatic weapon with no on-mount crew. Employs Muff Cob radar/electro-optical or Bass Tilt radar director.
max. rate of fire: 120/min/barrel
max. effective vertical range: 5,000 to 6,000 m

37-mm/63-caliber twin AA (Soviet V-47M)

Installed in twin-barreled mounts. No longer in Russian service but is still widely found on foreign ships, particularly Chinese-built. Obsolescent. Uses either hand-cranked cross-leveling or power cross-leveling. Control by on-mount lead-computing sight. Single-barreled version no longer in use.
muzzle velocity: 880 m/sec arc of elevation: 0° to +85°
max. rate of fire: 160/min/gun max. range: 9,500 m (2,500 m effective)

30-mm/65-caliber single gatling AA (Soviet AK-630)

This gun is in service on *Kiev*-class carriers, Kara and Kresta-II cruisers, and numerous other classes. It is installed in mounts similar to those of the 30-mm AA double-barreled automatic guns, and is designed to fire a great number of rounds at an extremely high rate in order to intercept a cruise missile at a relatively short distance. It has six 30-mm barrels. The often-used incorrect designation "ADMG-630" was a NATO nickname. Controlled by Bass Tilt radar director, with Kolonka-II remote manned sight (on the carrier *Admiral Flota Sovetskogo Soyuza Kuznetsov*, the gun is apparently controlled by the Hot Flash radar system on nearby CADS-1 gun/missile close-in-defense systems; the 30-mm guns on the CADS-1 are a longer-barreled weapon than the AK-630).
muzzle velocity: 1,000 m/sec arc of elevation: −10° to +90°
max. rate of fire: 4,000/min max. range, AA fire: 4,000 m

30-mm/65-caliber twin automatic AA (Soviet AK-230)

Installed in a light mount on several classes of ships—cruisers, destroyers, guided-missile boats, supply ships, etc. Widely exported. Employs Drum Tilt radar director or Kolonka-I remote ringsight director.
mount weight: 1,905 kg. muzzle velocity: 1,050 m/sec
max. rate of fire: 1,000/min/barrel max. range, AA fire: 4,000 m

25-mm/60-caliber twin AA (Soviet 2M-8)

Found on many ships. The manned mount employs two superimposed guns, with on-mount ringsight for control.
muzzle velocity: 900 m/sec arc of elevation: −10° to +83°
max. rate of fire: 150–200/min/gun max. range: 3,000 m

14.5-mm/93-caliber twin machine gun (Soviet 2M-7)

Found in over-and-under twin open mountings (2M-7) and in enclosed side-by-side mounts, the latter on Zhuk-class patrol boats and the nuclear-powered auxiliary SSV-33. Data refer to the older 2M-7 over-and-under manned mounting.
muzzle velocity: 1,000 m/sec arc of elevation: −5C° to +90C°
rate of fire: 150/min/gun max. range: 7,000 m

Note: Also still in use are 1930s-designed twin, over-and-under 12.7-mm machine-gun mounts.

C. ANTISUBMARINE WEAPONS

◆ Missiles

SUW-N-1 system (1967)

Rocket-propelled weapon, installed in *Kiev*-class carriers (not *Baku*) and *Moskva*-class helicopter cruisers. Maximum range: 16 miles. Nuclear warhead. Unguided solid-fuel rocket based on land-based FROG-7 artillery rocket and often referred to as FRAS-1. There may be a variant with a homing torpedo payload.

SS-N-14 Silex (1974)

A solid-propelled aerodynamic cruise missile that drops a 400-mm-diameter parachute-retarded homing torpedo. Maximum range: 30 nautical miles (4 nautical

WEAPONS AND SYSTEMS *(continued)*

miles minimum). Carried by *Kirov*-class cruiser *Kirov,* Kara- and Kresta-class cruisers, *Udaloy*-class destroyers, and Krivak-I- and Krivak-II-class frigates. Can also be used against surface ships. Controlled by Head Lights or Eye Bowl radar directors.

SS-N-15 Starfish (1972)

ASW missile similar to the U.S. Navy's SUBROC. Maximum range: 25 nautical miles. Nuclear warhead. Submerged-launched from submarine torpedo tubes and apparently also surface-launched by the cruisers *Frunze* and *Kalinin* and, possibly, the frigate *Neustrashimyy.* Carried by Victor-I, -II, and -III, Akula-, and Sierra-I- and -II-class nuclear-powered attack submarines. Also usable against surface targets. Uses a 533-mm torpedo tube.

SS-N-16 Stallion (circa 1980)

Derived from the SS-N-15 system but uses a homing torpedo payload in lieu of the nuclear depth bomb. Maximum range: 54 nautical miles. Would also be useful against surface targets. Probably requires the large-diameter 650-mm torpedo tube.

♦ Rockets

Note: RBU = *Raketnaya Bombometnaya Ustanovka* (Rocket Depth-charge Launcher)

RBU-12000 (NATO designation)

A 10-tubed weapon similar in configuration to the RBU-6000 but launches a considerably larger rocket with a range of up to 12,000 m. Found to date on the carriers *Baku* and *Admiral Flota Sovetskogo Soyuza Kuznetsov,* and the cruiser *Kalinin.* Also capable of being used as a torpedo countermeasure.

RBU-6000 (Soviet designation)

Mounts 12 barrels, approximately 1.6 m in length, arranged in a horseshoe and fired in paired sequence. Vertical automatic loading system, loading barrel by barrel. Can be trained and elevated. Maximum range: 6,000 m. Installed in *Kiev*-class carriers, *Slava, Kirov, Moskva,* Kynda, Kresta-I, and Kresta-II cruisers, *Udaloy* and Kashin guided-missile destroyers, Krivak and *Neustrashimyy*-class frigates, and Petya and Grisha-class corvettes. Can also be employed as a torpedo countermeasure. Formerly called "MBU-2500A" by NATO.

RBU-2500 (Soviet designation)

Made up of two horizontal rows of eight barrels each, approximately 1.6 m in length, which can be trained and elevated. Manual reloading. Range: 2,500 m. 21-kg warhead. Carried by Petya-I frigates and *Smol'nyy*-class training ships. Probably also usable as a torpedo countermeasure.

RBU-1200 (Soviet designation)

Made up of two horizontal rows of short, superimposed barrels, three atop two. Tube diameter: 0.250 m; length: 1.400 m; the 70-kg (34-kg warhead) rocket is somewhat shorter. Range: 1,200 m. Tubes elevate but are fixed in train. Installed in T 58- and Pauk-class patrol ships, and Natya-class minesweepers.

RBU-1000 (Soviet designation)

Made up of six barrels arranged in two vertical rows of three and fired in order, with vertical automatic loading. Trainable. Tube diameter: approx. 0.300 m. Length: approx. 1.800 m. Range: 1,000 m. 90-kg rocket with 55-kg warhead. Installed in Kara, Kresta-I, and Kresta-II cruisers, *Sovremennyy* and Kashin destroyers, and the replenishment ship *Berezina.* Appears to have an anti-torpedo function also.

♦ Torpedoes

Type 65: Wake-homing weapon. Launched from Victor-II and later submarines with 65-cm tubes. Probably available in both conventional and nuclear-warhead versions.
Diameter: 650 mm Length: 9.140 m Warhead weight: 900 kg
Speed/range: 50 kt/50 km; 30 kt/100 km

ET-80A: Wire-guided, improved version of the SET-65 with 400-m depth capability. Electric propulsion. For use by submarines and surface ships.
Diameter: 533 mm Length: 7.800 m Warhead weight: 272 kg
Speed/range: 35 kt/15 km; . . ./12 km

53-68: Modernized, nuclear-warhead version of the 53-65 with 100-m launch depth and 300-m maximum operating depth. Straight runner with wakeless HTP fuel propulsion.
Diameter: 533 mm Length: 7.200 m Warhead: 20 kt nuclear
Speed/range: 45 kt/14 km

53-65: Operational in 1968. Wake-homing with closed-cycle thermal propulsion.
Diameter: 533 mm Length: 7.800 m Warhead: 400 kg
Range: 55 kt/14 km; 40 kt/24 km

SET-65: Submarine torpedo with electric propulsion and 400-m operating capability, operational 1967.
Diameter: 533 mm Length: 7.800 m Warhead: 372 kg
Speed/range: 35 kt/10 km; 24 kt/20 km

53-83: Thermal engine-propelled surface and submarine launched wake-homing weapon.

ET-80(66): Nuclear-warhead submarine torpedo with silver-zinc-battery electric propulsion and 300-m operating depth; straight-runner.
Diameter: 533 mm Length: 7.700 m Warhead: 20 kt nuclear
Speed/range: 35 kt/10 km; 20 kt/40 km

ET-80A (SAET-50/SAET-60): ET-80A entered service in 1961 as the first Soviet passive acoustic homing torpedo; Soviet designation was probably SAET-50, while SAET-60 is a higher-performance version that appeared around 1966 and has a range of 15 km at 35 kts and a 400-kg warhead. Both weapons use a 46-cell battery.
Diameter: 533 mm Length: 7.800 m Warhead: 400 kg
Speed/range: 23.3 kt/7.3 km

E53-75, E53-79: Electric torpedoes for air and missile delivery.

53-66: Electric-propelled straight and pattern-running torpedo for surface ship and submarine use.

53-56V, VA: Standard export torpedo-boat weapon, either straight or pattern-running with reciprocating air/steam propulsion. Entered service during 1950s. A nuclear warhead version with 15-kt warhead was developed for Soviet submarine use.
Diameter: 533 mm Length: 7.000 m Warhead weight: 400 kg
Speed/range: 51 kt/4 km; 41 kt/8 km

E45-75A: For S-N-14 and SS-N-16 missile and aircraft delivery; an improved E 45-70 with a 300-m operating depth and electric propulsion. A modified, 4.6-m-long version is also in use that has, presumably, a longer range. E45-75A replaced the slowe[r] E45-70A.
Diameter: 450 mm Length: 3.900 m Warhead: 90 kg
Range: 38 kts/8 km

40-79: Thermal-powered air-dropped or missile payload weapon with active acoustic homing and a maximum depth of around 400 m. Estimated characteristics:
Diameter: 400 mm Length: 3.500 m Warhead: . . .
Range: 35–40 kts/13 km

E40-75A: Surface-ship-launched electric-powered antisubmarine torpedo with pa[s]sive acoustic homing.
Diameter: 400 mm Length: 4.500 m Warhead: 100 kg
Speed/range: 30 kts/14 km

SET-40: Active acoustic homing surface-launched antisubmarine torpedo with ba[t]tery power. Seeker range is 585 m and maximum depth is about 300 m. Entered servi[ce] around 1960, and there are probably improved models now in service.
Diameter: 400 mm Length: 4.500 m Warhead: 100 kg
Speed/range: 28 kts/10 km

♦ Mines

Russia has a vast inventory of air-, surface-, and submarine-launched mines, usi[ng] mechanical (contact), acoustic, magnetic, and, possibly, pressure fuzing. Older min[es] still available include the M12, M16, M26, M31, KB1, MAG, AMAG1, PLT-G, PL-15, KRAB, MIRAB, MKB-3, MAG, and MYaM. Specific details are unavailable for t[he] modern systems, such as the KMD and AMD, which have 300-kg explosive charg[es] and the rocket-propelled rising mines "Cluster Bay" and the deep-water "Cluster Gu[lf]" which have 230 kg of explosives. The RMZ and YaRM mines are small anti-mi[ne] countermeasures and anti-invasion weapons. There may also be stocks of nucle[ar-] armed mines.

D. RADARS

Note: Designations are NATO code names.

♦ Navigation

The most widely used are the X-band Don-2, Spin Trough, Don-Kay, and Pa[lm] Frond. Kivach 3, Mius, and Nayada are used on recent small combatants and au[xi]liaries. Many ships carry two or three navigational sets.

♦ Surface-Search

Most common on small surface combatants are Square Tie (also used for SS-N series cruise-missile target-designation), Pot Head, and Pot Drum. Submarines ca[rry] Snoop Tray, Snoop Slab, Snoop Plate, or Snoop Pair, all operating in the X-band.

♦ Long-Range Air-Search

Big Net: A large L-band (850 MHz) radar fitted on Kresta-I cruisers, and some Ka[shin] destroyers. Its detection range on an aircraft is probably over 100 miles.

Head Net-A: (S-band) Air- and surface-search, obsolescent system once widely [used] but now found only on a few older Kashin-class destroyers.

Head Net-C: Soviet MR-310 or Angora (S-band), consisting of two Head Net-A [an]tennas, mounted back-to-back, one in a horizontal plane, the other inclined. W[idely] used on cruisers and destroyers. The Head Net-series radars use a band that gives [up] to 70-mile detection range on an attack bomber flying at high altitude.

Peel Cone: Air/surface-search combined radar used on Pauk-class subchasers.

Plank Shave: (. . . band) Soviet "Harpoon," found on Tarantul-class missile b[oats]. An apparent successor to Square Tie, acting as air/surface-search and missile t[arget] acquisition and tracking radar.

Plate Steer: (S-band) Combined Top Steer and Strut Curve antennas in back-to[-back] array on fourth and fifth *Sovremennyy*-class destroyers and carriers *Kiev, Ad[miral] Flota Sovetskogo Soyuza Kuznetsov,* and *Admiral Flota Sovetskaya Soyuza Gors[hkov]*.

Slim Net: (S-band) Soviet FUT-N; early-model radar fitted on Petya-class corve[ttes].

Strut Curve: (S-band) Mounted on Petya and early Grisha corvettes.

Strut Pair: (S-band) Mounted on some *Udaloy*-class destroyers and all Gri[sha] corvettes. Employs pulse-compression. Antenna essentially two Strut Curve ref[lectors] back-to-back.

Top Pair: (C/F-band) Three-dimensional; a Top Sail and a Big Net antenna mo[unted] back-to-back; used on *Kirov* and *Slava* classes. Always accompanied by a Top [...] backup radar.

Top Plate: Back-to-back, identical phased-array 3-dimensional radar anten[nas on] *Udaloy*-class destroyers *Marshal Vasilevskiy, Admiral Zakharov,* and later. In [...] the successor to Head Net-C.

Top Steer: (S-band) Back-to-back, 3-dimensional radar antenna using one To[p ...] and one Top Plate antenna; on *Sovremennyy*-class destroyer *Osmotritel'nyy* and

WEAPONS AND SYSTEMS *(continued)*

Top Sail: Soviet Voskhod ("Dawn")(S-band), 3-dimensional radar installed in *Kiev, Moskva,* Kresta-II, and Kara cruisers.

♦ Missile Tracking and Control

Cross Sword: (Ku and X-band) Missile guidance for the SA-N-9 SAM system. Incorporates both detection/tracker radar and illuminator/tracker antennas. Probably has electro-optical backup.

Eye Bowl: (F-band) Smaller version of the command antenna component of Head Lights, installed in the cruiser *Kirov, Udaloy* destroyers, and Krivak frigates (which do not have Head Lights); command radar for the SS-N-14 system.

Front Dome: (X-band) Tracker-illuminator associated with the SA-N-7 SAM system n the *Sovremennyy*-class destroyers (with six) and the trials Kashin, *Provornyy* (with ›ight). Resembles the gun fire-control radar Bass Tilt and is very compact.

ront Door/Front Piece: Front Door is used for tracking the SS-N-12 on *Kiev*-class arriers (where it is mounted at the extreme bow in a retractable mount initially eferred to as "Trap Door"), and *Slava* cruisers (where it is fixed on the mast); Front)oor/Front Piece is used on Echo-II and Juliett submarines (where it is installed in the otating forward portion of the sail, and where the Front Piece component evidently racks the missile in altitude) for SS-N-3 and SS-N-12.

lead Lights: (F-, G-, H-, and D-bands) Mounted on *Kiev* carriers and *Moskva,* Kresta-I and Kara cruisers. Similar to the Peel Group with an assembly of tracking radar for ne target and guidance radar for the missile. Used for guidance for the Goblet missile f the SA-N-3 system and for the surface-to-underwater missiles of the SS-N-14 system. ı several versions, designated "A," "B," and "C," the latter evidently also involved ith the tracking and control of SS-N-14 missiles.

lot Flash: (. . .-band) The multi-antenna radar weapons control system found on the ADS-1 combined SA-N-11 SAM/twin 30-mm gatling AA close-in defense system for ntrolling the guns and providing target designation/illumination to the missiles.

eel Group: (Soviet "Yatogan") On Kynda and Kresta-I cruisers as well as Kashin-ass destroyers. The assembly is made up of two groups of large and small reflectors, in th horizontal and vertical positions, with parabolic design (S-band tracker; X-band acker). Maximum range approximately 30 to 40 miles. Used for guidance of the Goa issile in the SA-N-1 system.

ɔp Group: (F-, H-, and I-bands) Missile guidance for the SA-N-4 system. Upper mponent rotates independently and serves as a target acquisition radar; lower porn is used for missile control and can handle two missiles at once. Latest version pears to have electro-optical backup.

oop Pair: (E-band) Guidance radar for the Shaddock missile of the SS-N-3 system Kynda and Kresta-I cruisers.

p Dome: (X-band) Associated with the SA-N-6 vertically launched SAM system in *Kirov*-class cruisers and the *Azov*. Employs a 4-m-diameter hemispheric radome, ed in elevation, but mechanically steerable in azimuth. Three smaller dielectric lomes are mounted on the face of its mounting pedestal, and there is also a smaller nispheric radome below it. Can reportedly track six targets at once, although bably only if all are within about a 60-degree cone.

Data Links

nth Net: A large parabolic mesh antenna found only in the Kresta-I- and Kynda-s cruisers, probably to receive telemetry from the SS-N-3 cruise missile.

nd Stand: On *Sovremennyy* destroyers, Tarantul-II, and Nanuchka guided-missile batants, and the Sarancha hydrofoil, probably for antiship missile tracking and trol. In large radome. In export ships (and possibly some Soviet installations), nd Stand" covers a Square Tie missile target-acquisition radar, associated with the N-2 Styx family.

ht Bulb: Spherical radomes found only on SS-N-22 Sunburn antiship missile-pped *Sovremennyy*-class destroyers (2) and Tarantul-III missile boats (1); appary performs a data-link function with the missiles.

e: The Russian Navy also employs numerous other data-link systems, for which ils are unavailable. Such data links would include systems permitting aircraft to ide targeting data to surface ships and submarines for over-the-horizon launching tiship missiles.

Gun Fire-Control

Tilt: (C-band) Used with AK-630 gatling gun fitted in *Kiev* carriers, Kara and ta-II cruisers, and Mod. Kildin destroyers, as well as in Grisha-III corvettes, where o controls the twin 57-mm, and on Nanuchka-III corvettes and Matka guided-le patrol boats, where it also controls the 76.2-mm gun.

n Tilt: (C- and X-bands) Installed on Osa missile boats and other ships fitted with m AK-230 twin-barrel AA.

k Screech: (X-band) 76.2-mm DP guns; always found in conjunction with optical or/target designators.

Screech-A, -B: (X- and Ka-bands) 100-mm and new 130-mm twin DP.

Cob: (C-band) For 57-mm AA twin automatic guns. Has t.v. camera attachment.

Screech: (X-band) 76.2-mm DP; improved version of Hawk Screech, does not ssociated manned target designators.

Visor: (X-band) 100-mm DP guns; mounted on Wasp Head directors. Obso-.

NARS

l the late 1950s, the Soviet Navy showed little interest in antisubmarine war-, of course, submarine detection. Most of its ships were equipped with high-ncy sonar (Tamir 11, Pegas, Herkules). New or modernized ships have much-ed sensors.

Surface ships:

Recent sonars (and their NATO nicknames) include the medium-frequency Bull Horn in the Modified Kashin class and the first two *Kiev*-class carriers; Bull Nose medium-frequency in the Kara and Kresta-II classes; the Mare Tail medium-frequency variable-depth sonar in the Mod. Kashin, *Moskva*, Kara, *Slava*, and Krivak classes; the Horse Jaw low-frequency bow-mounted set in the *Kirov* class, 3rd and 4th *Kiev*, and the *Udaloy* class; the Moose Jaw low-frequency set in *Kievs* 1 and 2 and the *Moskva* class; the Horse Tail low-frequency VDS on the *Kirov* class, *Kievs* 3 and 4, and the *Udaloy* class; and the Elk Tail dipping sonar on the Grisha class.

Submarines:

Submarine active sonars have evolved along the same line as Soviet surface-ship sonars, and some of the modern classes have low-frequency active sets. As in the West, Russian submarines are also believed to be equipped with extensive passive hydrophone systems, and the Victor-III, Sierra, Akula, and others tow linear passive arrays deployed from tear-drop-shaped housings atop the vertical rudder or from tubes at the top of the rudder structure.

First-generation nuclear submarines carry the Shark Teeth low-frequency system; the second-generation Typhoon, Delta-IV, Oscar, Victor-III, Sierra, and Akula began receiving the Shark Gill low-frequency active/passive suite in 1978. The Alfa class has a system nicknamed Squid Ram.

Aircraft:

Helicopters (Helix, Hormone, and land-based Haze-A) carry dipping sonars, which are also used aboard smaller ASW patrol craft like the Turya and Stenka classes. Land-based maritime patrol/ASW aircraft (Bear-F, May, Mail) carry an extensive family of sonobuoys.

Sea-based:

Numerous fixed hydrophone arrays are installed to protect Russian naval bases and harbors. The "Cluster Lance" planar arrays are used in the Pacific area.

F. ELECTRONIC WARFARE

The increasing number of radomes of every description that can be seen on Russian ships, especially on the newest and most important types (helicopter and guided-missile cruisers, for example) is an indication of the attention the Russian Navy gives to electronic warfare. NATO code names for the antenna arrays for intercept or for jamming radars include: Side Globe intercept/jamming; Top Hat A intercept; Top Hat B jamming; Bell Thump/Bell Bash intercept/jamming; Bell Shroud/Bell Squat intercept; Rum Tub intercept; Bell Clout intercept; Cage Pot intercept; Sprat Star VHF intercept; Grid Crane VHF-UHF intercept; Site Crane VHF intercept; Watch Dog intercept. Literally hundreds of antennas have received NATO nicknames, and it is not possible to list them all here. The individual antennas are listed by name (where known) on the ship data pages.

Submarines were initially equipped with Stop Light intercept arrays (in effect, a submarine version of Watch Dog covering 1–18 gHz) but now receive Brick Pulp, Brick Spit, etc. On the larger, newer units, there is normally a smaller periscope mast-mounted antenna array and a larger array on its own telescoping mast; on the Typhoon and Akula classes, the principal intercept array, however, is installed around the base of the radar antenna.

Modern ships are equipped with twin-tubed chaff rocket launchers (*Kiev, Moskva,* Kresta-I and -II, Kara, *Berezina*) or 16-tubed fixed chaff rocket launchers (Mod. Kashin, Krivak-I and -II, Tarantul, Pauk, Nanuchka, Matka, etc.). A new, 10-tubed fixed launcher began to appear on the *Udaloy* class in 1989 and is now widely deployed on a variety of classes, some with over ten mounts per ship; the trainable twin-tube or fixed 16-tube launchers are retained.

IFF (Identification Friend or Foe) is taken care of by High Pole A and B transponders and by Square Head or other interrogators. The newer Salt Pot A transponders are slowly replacing High Pole A and B. The modern radars have integral IFF interrogation. TACAN systems include the large Top Knot spherical array on the *Kiev*-class carriers and the various forms of the paired cylindrical Round House array on the *Kirov, Udaloy,* and other classes.

G. COMMUNICATIONS

All Soviet warships are equipped to transmit and receive MF through VHF communications, while submarines have a VLF capability (using towed buoy antennas), and UHF equipment is coming into wider use in surface ships. VHF antennas in use include: Cage Bare, Cage Cone, Cage Stalk, and the older Straight Key. Major warships usually have a Pop Art VHF antenna. Long-range HF communications are handled via the "Vee"-series antennas Vee Cone, Vee Tube, or Vee Bars. Fixed arrangements 9 m long with two identical conical components mounted at 70° to each other in the horizontal plane are termed Vee Cone. Vee Tube uses tubular, 8.6-m-long components at 90° separation, and Vee Bars is the nickname for an open-framework arrangement on the *Kiev* class. Submarines rely on VLF, and an ELF station is building. Tu-142 Bear-J aircraft are equipped with a trailing wire antenna strategic submarine communications system analogous to the U.S. TACAMO system.

H. SATELLITES

The Russians use an ocean surveillance satellite system whose data is transmitted either to ground stations or directly to ships equipped with the SS-N-12 and SS-N-19 cruise-missile systems. The receiving antenna is mounted in a large cylindrical radome termed Punch Bowl. Several cruisers and command auxiliaries have two 4.5-m-diameter Big Ball radomes, associated with the Molniya and Raduga satellite communications systems, although many other ships can apparently also employ communications and navigational satellites.

I. INFRARED AND ELECTRO-OPTICAL SYSTEMS

Cod Eye: in large submarines, is probably a radiometric or optical sextant device for precise navigation.

WEAPONS AND SYSTEMS *(continued)*

Squeeze Box: Installed in *Sovremennyy*-class destroyers and in amphibious ships with 140-mm artillery rocket launchers. Believed to incorporate t.v., laser rangefinder, and infrared sensors and to be used in shore bombardment gun and rocket fire control.

Tee Plinth: Television system installed in large ships in the 1960s and 1970s. Replaced in newer ships by:

Tin Man: A large, stabilized system that may incorporate a laser rangefinder also.

Note: Also in use are smaller, fixed television cameras (Half Cup and Tilt Pot) and periscopic devices mounted atop pilothouses to permit operations in BW/CW warfare conditions and poor weather. The Tall View periscope in the *Sovremennyy* class probably provides the commanding officer with his own view when he is in the command center during combat operations; there are similar "CIC" periscopes in other large surface combatants. All combatant submarines have both a wide field-of-view search periscope and a higher magnification, narrow-view attack periscope.

AIRCRAFT CARRIER

Note: The third through-deck carrier, the 75,000-ton *Ul'yanovsk,* was laid down during 12-88, but reportedly, work began 4-2-92 to break her up on the ways for scrap.

◆ **1 (+1) Kuznetsov class (Project 1143.5)** Bldr: Nosenko SY 444, Nikolayev

	Laid down	L	In serv.
Admiral Flota Sovetskogo Soyuza Kuznetsov (ex-*Tbilisi,* ex-*Leonid Brezhnev, ex-Riga*)	6-11-83	5-12-85	21-1-91
Varyag (ex-*Riga*)	6-12-85	4-12-88	1996?

Admiral Flota Sovetskogo Soyuza Kuznetsov—en route her Northern Fleet base PH2 Paul Vise, USN, 12-91

Admiral Flota Sovetskogo Soyuza Kuznetsov—note longer takeoff run up ski jump possible from the port side PH2 Paul Vise, USN, 12-91

D: 60,000 tons (67,000 fl) **S:** 32 kts
Dim: 302.0 × 73.0 (68.5 flight deck, 39.7 wl) × 10.4 (mean hull)
Air Group: 24/Su-27 Flanker interceptors; 9–12/Helix-A and -C helicopters
A: 16/SS-N-19 Shipwreck SSM—24/SA-N-9 VLS SAM (VIII × 24; 384 Siren missiles)—8/CADS-1 CIWS (VIII × 8; 384 SA-N-11 missiles; 2/30-mm gatling AA per mount also)—6/30-mm AK-630 gatling AA (I × 6)—2/RBU-12000 ASW RL (X × 2)
Electron Equipt:
Radar: 3/Palm Frond nav., 2/Strut Pair 2-D air search, 1/Sky Watch 3-D air search (4 arrays, *see* Remarks), 1/Top Plate 3-D air search, 4/Cross Sword f.c., 8 Hot Flash f.c. (on CADS-1 mounts)
Sonar: LF hull-mounted—TACAN: Cake Stand
EW: 4 each of 3 new intercept antenna groups, 3/Cross Loop D/F loops, 2/Wine Flask intercept, 1/Bell Slam intercept, several other intercept antennas, 8/Foot Ball jammers, numerous unidentified intercept/jamming, 2/twin-tube trainable decoy RL, 10/10-tube decoy RL
E/O: 1/Bob Tail telescoping, 3 Tin Man t.v./IR/laser, 5 fixed t.v., 4 optical periscopes
M: 4 sets geared steam turbines; 4 props; 200,000 shp
Boilers: 8, turbopressurized **Range:** . . ./. . . . . .
Crew: 200 officers, 1,300 enlisted (*see* Remarks)

Admiral Flota Sovetskogo Soyuza Kuznetsov
PH2 Paul Vise, USN, 12-

Stern view of Admiral Flota Sovetskogo Soyuza Kuznetsov—sho the white-painted landing-path indicator, the semicircular VTOL air lift engine spray deflector recessed into the stern, and the two personnel gangways in stowed position; the white stripe passes throug dielectric cover over the auto-landing radar system antenna.
Boris Lemachko,

Admiral Flota Sovetskogo Soyuza Kuznetsov—while still weari name *Tbilisi* Boris Lemachko

AIRCRAFT CARRIER *(continued)*

Admiral Flota Sovetskogo Soyuza Kuznetsov Tass, 1990

ral Flota Sovetskogo Soyuza Kuznetsov—note the open hatch in the eyes of the ship for two television surveillance cameras PH2 Paul Vise, USN, 12-91

AIRCRAFT CARRIER *(continued)*

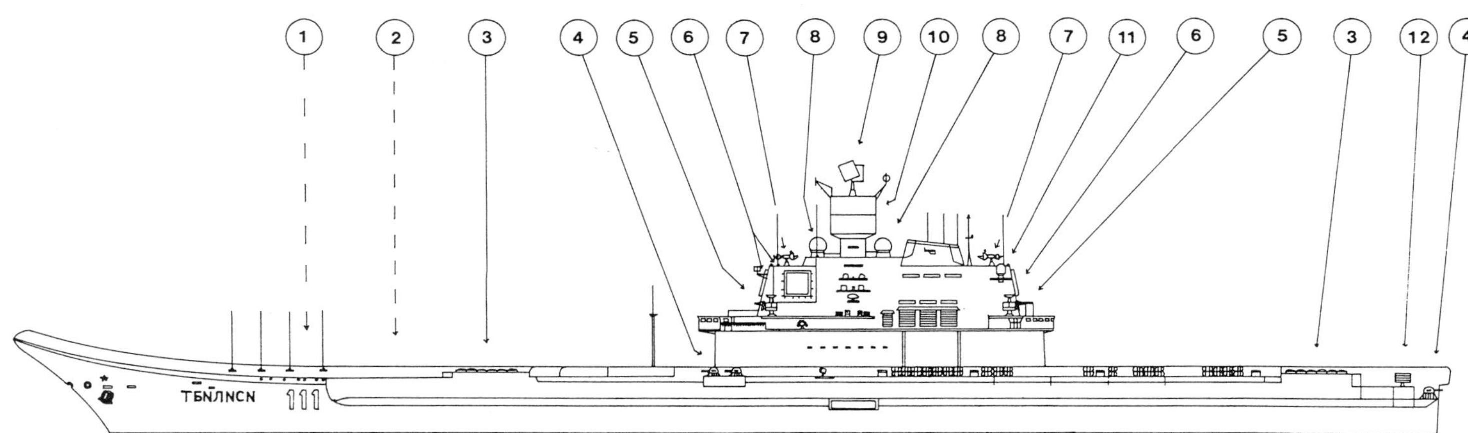

Admiral Flota Sovetskogo Soyuza Kuznetsov 1. location of SS-N-19 Shipwreck cruise-missile installation, recessed into the flight deck with 12 flush hatches in two rows of six 2. CADS-1 defensive system location, port side forward 3. SA-N-9 Gopher vertical-launch SAM groups (6 on each quarter) 4. deck landing mirror system 5. Cross Sword radar directors for SA-N-9 6. Sky Watch 3-D/early-warning radar planar arrays 7. Strut Pair air/surface-search radar 8. Low Ball SATCOMM system antenna radomes 9. Top Plate 3-D/air-search radar 10. Cake Stand TACAN system 11. Punch Bowl satellite missile targeting data-link system radomes 12. RBU-12000 ASW/torpedo countermeasures rocket launcher
Robert Dumas

Remarks: According to Soviet press, design began in 1974 for what was intended to be a "defensive" aircraft carrier. Admiral of the Fleet Vladimir Chernavin has stated that the ships have a "main role as platforms for fighter aircraft able to provide long-range cover for our vessels when shore-based fighters are unable to help. This defensive function is enshrined in the new aircraft carrier, *Tbilisi*." (*Pravda*, 19-10-89). Subsequently, Chernavin stood corrected in a 22-10-89 *Pravda* article that stated, "*Tbilisi* falls within the category of heavy aircraft-carrying cruiser (*tyazholiy avionosnyy kreyser*) and not within that of aircraft carriers . . ." Thus, the ship is intended to carry interceptor fixed-wing aircraft with no ground or ship attack rôle. Initial sea trials for the ship began between 19-10-89 and 24-10-89, and on 22-11-89 it was reported that Su-27 Flanker, MiG-29 Fulcrum, and Su-25UT trainer Frogfoot aircraft had performed arrested landings and ski-jump takeoffs. The crew total listed above as that being aboard in 12-91 in a Russian publication may not include the air group personnel.

The first ship's name was changed for the third time on 4-10-90, and she deployed from the Black Sea bound for the Northern Fleet to serve as flagship on 2-12-91 without an air group — which was officially stated still to be in training at a Crimean facility (probably Saki).

Whether *Varyag* will be completed is uncertain, but with the ship nearly complete by the end of 1991, it is likely that the investment will not be wasted; in mid-1-92, however, it was officially stated that she would be mothballed incomplete until the Russian financial position improved. In mid-February, it was announced that Northern Fleet servicemen had volunteered funds to complete her ($522 million was said to be needed) and that she would complete in 1996. By March, however, rumors were rampant that she was to be sold abroad, perhaps to India or China. The name was changed late in 1990 to commemorate the stricken Pacific Ocean Fleet Kynda-class cruiser *Varyag*, a traditional Russian Navy warship name, and on 15-12-91, it was officially stated that *Varyag* was destined for service with the Pacific Ocean Fleet.

The air group capabilities of the ships are limited by the provision of a 12-degree exit ski-jump bow for takeoff by high-performance fixed-wing fighter aircraft; apparently the Russians have experienced difficulty in developing steam catapults. Aircraft accommodations are apparently also limited by a 150-m-long but narrow hangar and by the installation of twelve inclined launch tubes for SS-N-19 missiles, which take up space that could have been employed for additional aircraft stowage; there are very few flight deck aircraft tiedown positions, and it is likely that all aircraft are intended to be hangared at once (unlike in U.S. carriers, where only about a third can be in the hangar at one time). Provision of a spray-reduction recess in the center of the transom stern indicates that the ship was at least at one time intended to be able to accommodate VTOL (vertical take off or landing) fighters like the Yak-38 Forger and the canceled Yak-141 Freestyle.

The aircraft landing system employs four cross-deck wires spaced at 14-m intervals near the after end of the 220-m, 5.5° angled deck, and aircraft are guided to the deck by an automatic radar-controlled landing system; there is also a mirror landing system, as in U.S. Navy carriers. Aircraft take off down the ramp from any of three detent positions (two with a 105-m run and one to port with a 195-m run), where they are held firmly in check until full engine afterburner thrust is developed. A great many objects protrude above the flight deck, including decoy rocket launchers, a fixed navigational light mast to starboard, and a number of fire-fighting foam cannon. There are but two semi-outboard elevators 20 m long by 15 m wide and capable of lifting about 40 tons.

The air group will apparently not be large—as few as a dozen "interceptors" have been mentioned by Russian official sources and might reasonably be expected to include two 9- or 12-plane squadrons of Su-27 Flanker interceptor aircraft and a half-dozen Helix helicopters. Provision was made to operate the apparently-canceled Yak-41 V/STOL ground-attack follow-on to the Yak-38 Forger. The Su-25UT flown from the *Tbilisi* in initial trials is a two-seat trainer, but it should not be difficult to develop a navalized version of the standard Su-25 Frogfoot ground-attack aircraft. Although the MiG-29K naval version of the Fulcrum fighter has been under development for use as an interceptor from this class, it has lagged the Su-27 by several years and may now not be put into production; the MiG-29 reportedly requires only a 105-m takeoff run up the carrier's ski-jump.

The propulsion plant is believed to be essentially a duplicate of the plant used in the *Kiev* class, using standard Soviet vertical turbopressurized boilers. Reported to be 27 decks from keel up and to have over 3,000 compartments. There are two deck-edge elevators to starboard. Appears to trim down by the stern by about two meters.

The shipboard armament suite, aside from the dozen SS-N-19 Shipwreck antis missiles, is strictly short-range self-defense and is the heaviest such ever installed any ship. The six individual AK-630 gatling guns are presumably controlled by CADS-1 CIWS fire-control systems, as there are no separate Bass Tilt radars for the The SA-N-9 silo launchers are arranged in groups of six and the CADS-1 systems paired to cover the four "Corners" of the ship. The RBU-12000 ASW rocket launch are installed aft primarily as torpedo countermeasures.

The electronics suite includes an unusually (even by Soviet standards) diverse extensive array of electronic warfare antennas, not all of which have yet recei NATO nicknames. Satellite communications antenna systems include two Low commuications arrays and two Punch Bowl over-the-horizon targeting data recep antennas. The Sky Watch four-panel fixed planar array three-dimensional air-sea radar is evidently not a success and may not be operational.

AVIATION CRUISERS

◆ 1 Modified Kiev class (Project 1143.4)

Bldr: Chernomorskiy (Nosenko) SY 444, Nikolayev

	Laid down	L	In s
ADMIRAL FLOTA SOVETSKOGO SOYUZA GORSHKOV (ex-*Baku*)	12-78	19-4-82	

Admiral Flota Sovetskogo Soyuza Gorshkov—only *Kiev*-seri with 12 SSN-12 missile launchers, in two rows of eight and four
U.S. Nav

AVIATION CRUISERS *(continued)*

dmiral Flota Sovetskogo Soyuza Gorshkov—as *Baku,* with 11 Ka-26 elix helicopters on deck LT P.J. Azzolina, U. S. Navy, 6-88

Admiral Flota Sovetskogo Soyuza Gorshkov French Navy, 6-88

miral Flota Sovetskogo Soyuza Gorshkov M.O.D.U.K., 1989

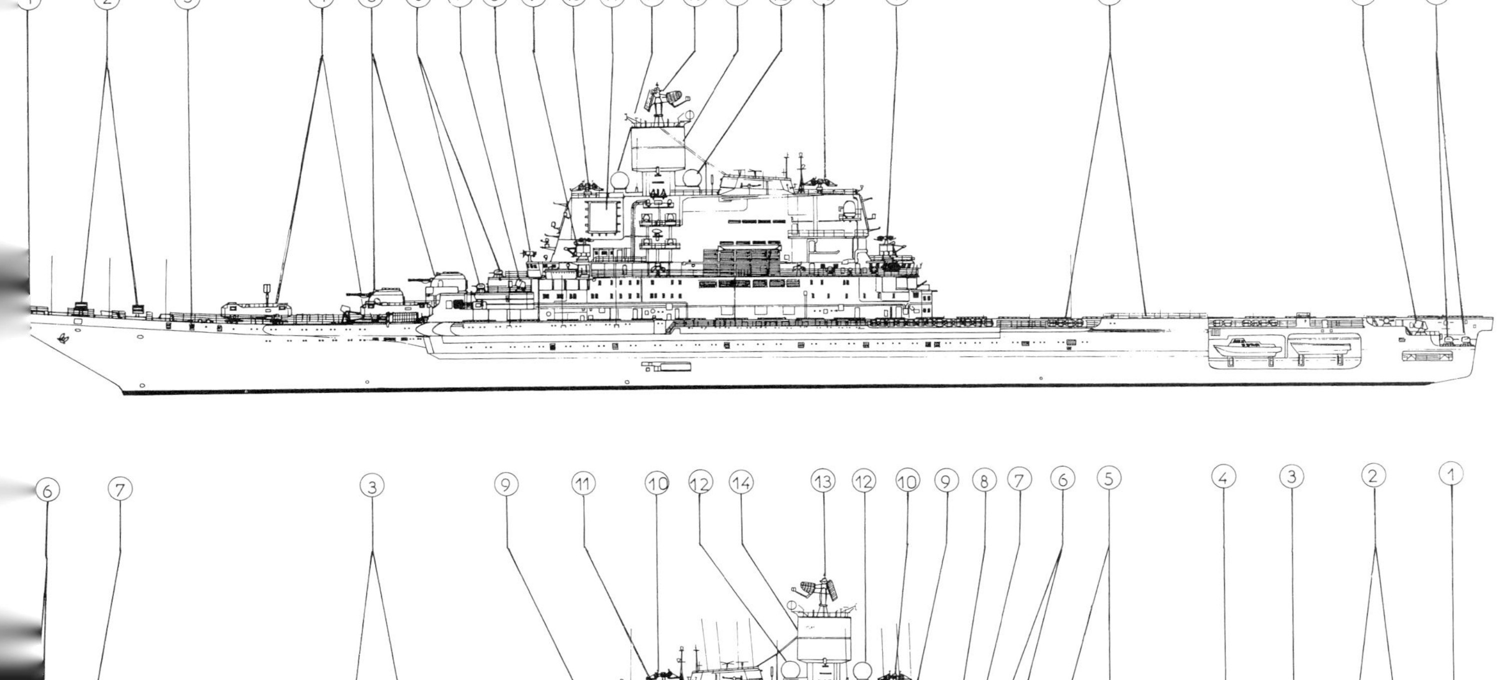

al Flota Sovetskogo Soyuza Gorshkov 1. Trap Door-C guidance radar for SS-N-12 missiles 2. RBU-12000 ASW/torpedo-countermeasures rocket ers 3. SA-N-9 Gopher vertical-launch SAM groups port and starboard 4. SS-N-12 Sandbox antiship missile launchers 5. 100-mm DP guns 6. AK-ling AA guns 7. Bass Tilt radar director for the AK-630 AA guns 8. Kite Screech radar director for the 100-mm guns 9. Cross Sword radar director SA-N-9 missiles 10. Strut Pair air/surface-search radars 11. Sky Watch 3-D early-warning radar 12. Low Ball SATCOMM system antenna s 13. Plate Steer 3-D/air-search radar 14. Cake Stand cylindrical TACAN array

AVIATION CRUISERS *(continued)*

Admiral Flota Sovetskogo Soyuza Gorshkov—still under old name *Baku* French Navy, 6-90

Admiral Flota Sovetskogo Soyuza Gorshkov—island, showing similarity of equipment to that of the larger *Kuznetsov* French Navy, 6-90

D: 38,000 tons (45,000 fl) **S:** 31.5 kts
Dim: 273.0 (249.5 wl) × 53.0 (32.7 wl) × 12.00 mean hull
Air Group: 13/Yak-38 Forger fighters—17 Ka-27PL Helix-A ASW helos—2/Ka-32PS Helix-D SAR-utility helo—3 Ka-25 Hormone-B targeting helo—1/Ka-25PL Hormone-A ASW helo (on initial deployment, *see* Remarks)
A: 12/SS-N-12 Sandbox SSM (II × 6, no reloads)—24/SA-N-9 VLS SAM silos (VIII × 24; 384 Gopher missiles)—2/100-mm 70-cal. DP (I × 2)—8/30-mm AK-630 gatling AA (I × 8)—2/RBU-12000 ASW RL (X × 2)
Electron Equipt:
Radar: 3/Palm Frond (nav.), 2/Strut Pair (air/surf. search), 1/Plate Steer (3-D air search), 1/Sky Watch (phased-array 3-D; 4 panels), 4/Cross Sword (SA-N-9 dir.), 1/Kite Screech (100-mm f.c.), 4/Bass Tilt (30 -mm f.c.), 1/Trap Door C (SS-N-12 f.c.), 2/Fly Trap (landing aid)
Sonar: Horse Jaw LF hull-mounted, Horse Tail LF VDS
EW: 8/Foot Ball-series intercept, 8/Wine Flask jammers, 2/Cage Pot intercept, 4/Bell Bash jammers, 4/Bell Thump jammer, 2/ trainable decoy RL (II × 2)
TACAN: 1/Cake Stand
IFF: 4/Watch Guard . . ., 2/Salt Pot A transponder (interrogation by radars)
E/O: 3/Tin Man, 4/Tilt Pot fixed t.v., 2 bridge periscopes
M: 4 sets geared steam turbines; 4 props (4-bladed); 200,000 shp
Boilers: 8, turbopressurized **Fuel:** 7,000 tons
Range: 4,000/30; 13,500/18
Crew: 300 officers, 1,300 men (incl. air group)

Remarks: *General:* Required nearly 10 years to construct and fit out, in large part because of the large number of new systems not found in the preceding three *Kiev*-class units, which have the same hull and propulsion plant. Left the Black Sea 8-6-88 and operates in the Northern Fleet. A number of the systems evident on the ship are apparently trials installations for the *Kuznetsov* class, which may account for the delay in her completion. Was originally intended to carry the Yak-141 Freestyle V/STOL fighter. Name changed 4-10-90.

Hull: Appears to draw quite a bit more than the *Kievs*, due to new systems; like them she trims down by the stern. Port forward gun sponson eliminated; the angled portion of the flight deck has been lengthened by 5 m at its forward end, in consequence. A single, movable air-deflector plate is mounted to improve airflow over the deck, and the deck edges have been rounded more extensively. The aircraft deck park area is larger, through the elimination of several weapons positions. Two inboard aircraft elevators (19 × 10 m and 19 × 5 m) and three weapons elevators to the flight deck are fitted.

Weapons: The SS-N-12 missiles are disposed in one row of four paired tubes and one row of two paired tubes, separated by a traversing reload skid; unlike the preceding trio, there is no elevator to a reload magazine, and a Soviet article indicates that she has a larger aircraft hangar than the original three. No long-range air defense SAM system is fitted; the 8-celled SA-N-9 vertical launch silos are disposed 12 forward of the SS-N-12 installation, 6 in a row on the port side of the angled deck aft, and two rows of 3 to starboard of the after elevator, while the 4 Cross Sword radar detection/track/ directors are mounted port and starboard above the bridge and abaft the island. Two single 100-mm mounts forward replace twin 76.2-mm mounts fore and aft of the island. Two new "RBU-12000" ASW rocket launchers replace the RBU-6000 launchers on the forecastle, and there are no torpedo tubes nor SUW-N-1 ASW RL; RBU-12000 can also be used as a torpedo countermeasure. AK-630 gatling guns replace the twin AK-230 mounts and are differently disposed. The air group listed is that aboard during the ship's initial deployment to her new home port; subsequently, it appears that the Yak-38 Forger has been retired, leaving the ship and her half-sisters as helicopter carriers only.

Electronics: In place of Top Sail and Top Steer, *Admiral Gorshkov* carries the Sky Watch fixed planar phased-array radar mounted on the island sides to give 360-degree coverage; it may not be entirely satisfactory, as the Soviet press reported difficulties with the ship's radars. A secondary 3-D radar, Plate Steer, is mounted above the 9-meter-high cylindrical array for the Cake Stand TACAN-cum-air control system antenna. In addition to the systems listed, there are 5 D/F loop arrays (Cross Loop, Park Plinth, High Ring, 2 Prim Wheel) and numerous whip, wire, and cage/VHF communications antennas. Low Ball SATCOMM antenna radomes are mounted fore and aft of the Cake Stand tower, while 2 Punch Bowl satellite data link radomes flank the island; there are also two Pert spring satellite communications antennas.

♦ 2 Kiev class (Projects 1143 and 1143M—in reserve)

Bldr: Chernomorskiy (Nosenko) SY 444, Nikolayev

	Laid down	L	In serv.
KIEV	9-70	31-12-72	5-75
NOVOROSSIYSK	10-75	4-12-78	9-82

D: 36,000 tons (43,000 fl) **S:** 32 kts
Dim: 273.0 (249.5 wl) × 53.0 (32.70 wl) × 9.5 (12.0 max.)
Air Group: 12–13/Forger-A/B VTOL fighters—14–17/Ka-25PL Hormone-A or Ka-27PL Helix-A and Hormone-B or Helix C helicopters (*see* Remarks)
A: 8/SS-N-12 SSM (II × 4, 16 Sandbox missiles)—2/SA-N-3 SAM systems (II × 2; 72 Goblet missiles)—2/SA-N-4 SAM systems (II × 2, 40 Gecko missiles, not in *Novorossiysk*)—4/76.2-mm 59-cal. DP (II × 2)—8/30-mm gatling AA (I × 8)—10/533-mm TT (V × 2)—1/ SUW-N-1 ASW RL (II × 1)—2 RBU-6000 ASW RL (XII × 2)
Electron Equipt:
Radar: 1/Don Kay nav., 2/Don-2 nav. (*Novorossiysk:* 3 Palm Frond vice Don Kay and Don-2), 1/Top Sail 3-D air search, 1/Plate Steer air search, 2/Head Lights-C (SA-N-3 f.c.), 2/Pop Group (SA-N-4 f.c., not in *Novorossiysk*), 2/Owl Screech (76.2-mm f.c.), 4/Bass Tilt (30-mm f.c.), 1/Trap Door (SS-N-12 f.c.) (*Novorossiysk* also: 2 Strut Pair 2-D air search)
Sonar: First two: Moose Jaw LF and Bull Horn MF hull-mounted, Mare Tail MF VDS; *Novorossiysk:* Horse Jaw LF hull, Horse Tail LF VDS
EW: 8/Side Globe intercept (not in *Novorossiysk*), 4/Top Hat A, 4/Top Hat B, 4/Rum Tub, 4/Bell Bash, 4/Bell Thump, 4/Bell Nip, 2/ Bell Clout, 2/trainable decoy RL (II × 2)
TACAN: Top Knot—IFF: High Pole B or Salt Pot transponder
M: 4 sets geared steam turbines; 4 props; 200,000 shp
Boilers: 8, turbopressurized
Fuel: 7,000 tons **Range:** 4,000/30; 13,500/18
Crew: 300 officers, 1,300 enlisted (incl. air group)

Kiev French Navy

AVIATION CRUISERS *(continued)*

Novorossiysk U.S. Navy photo, 1987

Novorossiysk U.S. Navy photo, 1987

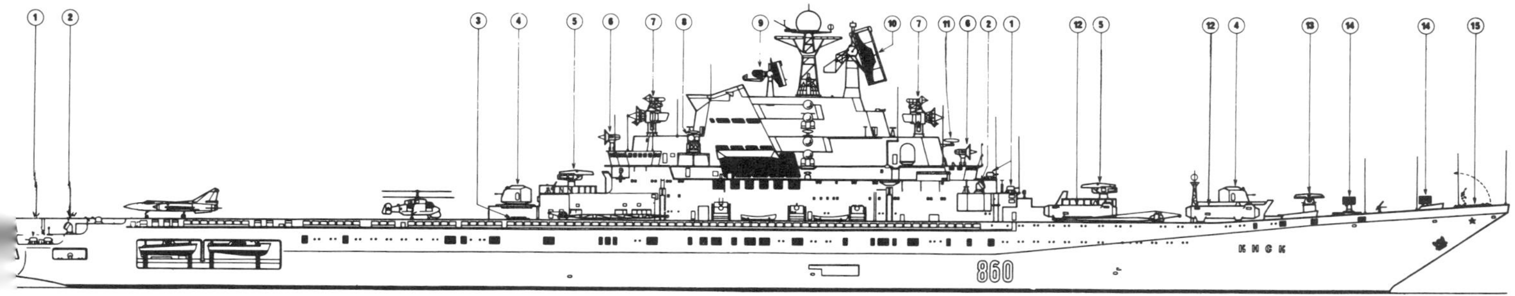

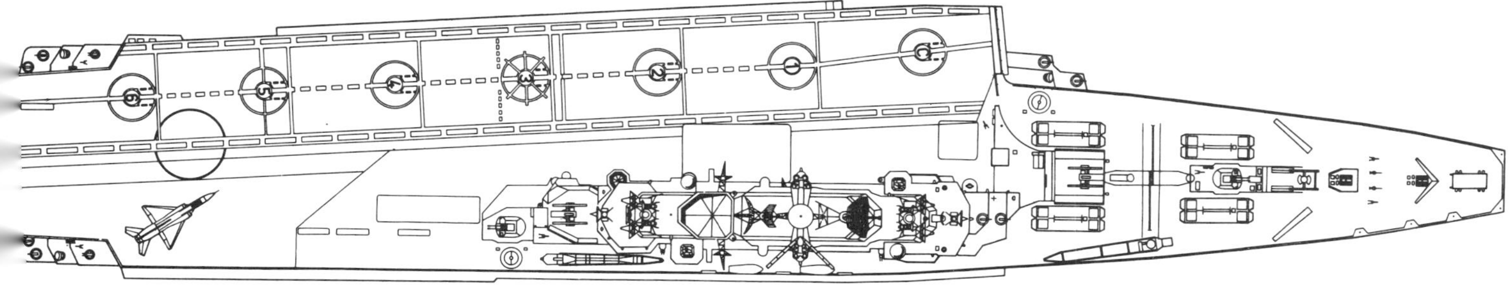

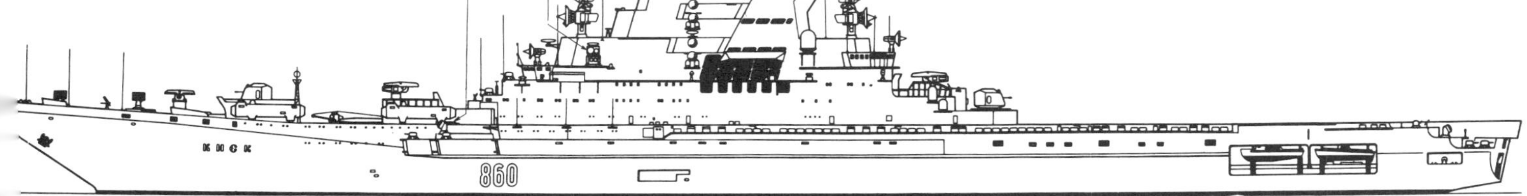

Kiev 1. AK-630 gatling AA guns 2. Bass Tilt radar director for AK-630 guns 3. SA-N-4 SAM launcher 4. twin 76.2-mm 59-cal. DP guns 5. SA-N-3 Goa SAM launcher 6. Owl Screech radar director for 76.2-mm guns 7. Head Lights radar directors for SA-N-3 SAM system 8. Pop Group radar director for SA-N-4 SAM system 9. Plate Steer air-search radar (drawing shows Top Steer originally installed) 10. Top Sail early-warning radar 11. Don-2 navigational radar 12. twin launchers for SS-N-12 Sandbox antiship missiles 13. SUW-N-1 ASW rocket launcher 14. RBU-6000 ASW rocket launchers 15. Trap Door tracking radar for SS-N-12 missiles (*Note:* Plan view shows flight deck configuration as completed in 1976; the angled-deck centerline stripe is now straight at its forward end, and the two after ammunition elevators have been combined into a single 12.5-m-long lift.)

AVIATION CRUISERS *(continued)*

Kiev—dark, ribbed recess in transom stern below centerline of the angled flight deck is intended to act as a deflector for the spray generated by the lift engines of Yak-38 Forger VTOL fighters when landing
French Navy, 6-87

Novorossiysk—with nine Yak-38 Forger VTOL fighters and one Ka-26 Hormone helicopter on deck
U.S. Navy photo, 4-85

Remarks: *General:* The Russian Navy's designation for the *Kiev* class is now *Tyazholyy Avionesushchiy Kreyser* (Heavy Aviation Cruiser), formerly *Bolshoy Protolovadochnyy Kreyser* (Large Antisubmarine Cruiser), although sister *Minsk* was referred to briefly as a *Taktycheskoye Avionosnyy Kreyser* (Tactical Aircraft-Carrying Cruiser) on her initial deployment. The ships have capabilities for ASW, sea-control, and sea-denial missions. The hull is unusual in having a counter stern that sweeps up several meters above the waterline before meeting the transom. The variable-depth sonar is deployed through doors on the centerline of the transom stern; the black-painted, ribbed recess to port of the VDS housing is a spray deflector to prevent spray from entering air intakes of Forger V/STOL aircraft while landing. *Kiev* is in the Northern Fleet, the other in the Pacific. Sister *Minsk* (completed 2-78) out of service at Vladivostok since 1989–90, reportedly because of severe engineering problems, was sold for scrap in 3-92; in 2-92, it had been stated in the Russian press that all three might have to be scrapped due to their poor material condition and the probable lack of access to their building yard in Ukraine for the specialized and extensive repairs needed. In fact, with no likelihood of ever receiving fixed-wing aircraft again, they are essentially useless. Reported 5-92 that *Kiev* may be cannibalized to repair *Admiral Flota Sovetskogo Soyuza Gorshkov*.

Minsk was refitted in 1981–82 at Vladivostok with an extended port forward sponson supporting the 30-mm gatling guns, a rounded leading edge to the flight deck, and a number of blast deflector or wind deflection plates erected on the forecastle abaft the SS-N-12 launchers; all these changes should improve air flow over the flight deck (which has been given an additional V/STOL landing spot) and should prevent sea damage to the guns. The third unit, *Novorossiysk* (Project 1143M), has the deflectors and rounded deck edge, but retains the original sponson configuration. *Kiev* entered the Black Sea in 1982 to undergo her first major overhaul and emerged in 1985 with fewer alterations than expected, although air-flow baffles had been added. These ships are hampered by their low freeboard and have a noticeable squat at the stern when moving at higher speeds. There is an enormous bow bulge to accommodate the hull-mounted sonar transducer.

Novorossiysk lacks the SA-N-4 SAM system, instead having blanking plates over what will eventually be six SA-N-9 vertical-launch installations abaft the island and six forward to port; there are two empty Cross Sword director platforms on the superstructure. The ship showed a number of electronics array differences from the first two, including the elimination of the eight-radome Side Globe array and the substitution of six new t.v./electro-optical devices ("Tin Man") for the Tee Plinth devices formerly used.

The ships have a retractable, spherical Bob Tail radio sextant antenna abaft the stack; all have microwave aircraft landing systems. The Vee Bars long-range HF communications antenna is fitted, as are satellite communications equipment (two Punch Bowl antennas) and a very extensive VLF through UHF communications suite.

Aviation features: The flight deck portion of the upper deck is angled about 4.5° to port of the centerline axis of the ship and is about 185 m long by 20 m wide; the deck is angled not to permit rolling takeoffs but to provide an obstruction-free flight area. To protect against the hot exhaust of the Forger vertical takeoff and landing aircraft, the flight areas were originally partially covered with a mosaic of refractory tiles, now removed. There are two elevators to the hangar deck: one (19.20 m × 10.35 m) beside the stack, the other (18.50 m × 4.70 m) abaft the island. Four small ammunition elevators are connected by an on-deck rail system. With the reported retirement of the Yak-36 Forger VTOL fighter in 1991 and the failure of the successor Yak-141 Freestyle to enter production, the ships are now effectively reduced to service as helicopter carriers and may be able to carry more Ka-26 and Ka-27 airframes than listed above.

Armament: The SS-N-12 missiles are launched from four twin, non-trainable elevating tubes. In order to use the full over-the-horizon range of the missiles, a forward located, target-designation observer platform has to be used. On the *Kiev* class, that requirement is met by the Hormone-B helicopter, which carries a radar giving a range of 100 nautical miles with the helicopter at an altitude of 4,000 feet. The ship can also use target information relayed by satellite, using the two receiving antennas in the Punch Bowl radomes. There are eight missiles in the launch tubes, plus sixteen reloads raised from a below-decks magazine by a centerline elevator between the launch-tube sets and aligned with the launchers for loading by a traversing system.

AVIATION CRUISER

◆ **1 Moskva class (Project 1123)**
Bldr: Chernomorskiy (Nosenko) SY 444, Nikolayev

	Laid down	L	In serv.
Moskva	1962	1964	7-67

D: 11,200 tons (14,590 fl) **S:** 31 kts (29 sonar down)
Dim: 189.0 (179.0 wl) × 34.1 (flight deck), 23.0 (wl) × 8.50 (13.00 sonar down)
Air Group: 12/Ka-27PL Helix-A ASW helicopters, 2/Ka-27PS Helix-SAR/utility helicopters
A: 2/SA-N-3 SAM systems (II × 2; 44 Goblet missiles)—4/57-mm AK 257 DP (II × 2)—1/SUW-N-1 ASW RL (II × 1; 18 Type 82-P rockets)—2/RBU-6000 ASW RL (XII × 2)
Electron Equipt:
Radar: 3/Don-2 nav., 1/Top Sail 3-D air search, 1/Head Net-C air search, 2/Head Lights-A SA-N-3 f.c., 2/Muff Cob gun f.c.
Sonar: 1/Moose Jaw LF hull-mounted, 1/Mare Tail MF VDS
EW: 8/Side Globe intercept, 2/Top Hat, 2 Bell Clout jammer, 2/Bell Slam jammer, 2/Bell Tap jammer, 2/trainable chaff RL (II × 2
E/O: 2/Tee Plinth trainable t.v., 4 Tilt Pot fixed t.v., 2/bridge periscopes
IFF: 2 Salt Pot transponders, interrogation via search radars
M: 2 sets geared steam turbines; 2 props; 100,000 shp
Boilers: 4, turbopressurized **Range:** 4,500/29; 14,000/12
Crew: 840 tot.

Moskva
U.S. Navy,

Moskva—acting as host for a sports festival
Tass

AVIATION CRUISERS (*continued*)

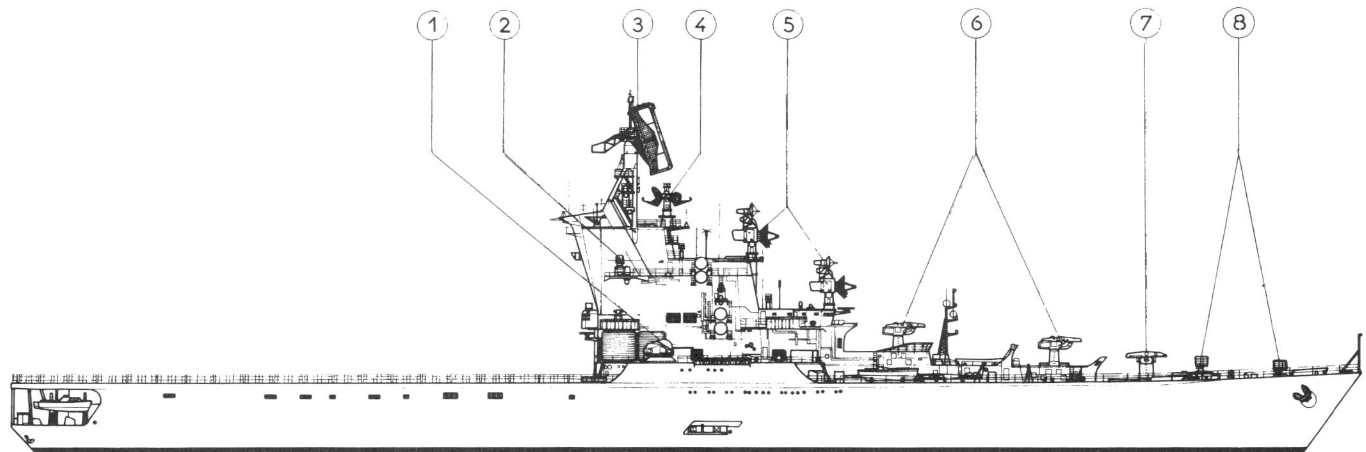

Moskva 1. twin 57-mm AK-257 DP gun mount 2. Muff Cob radar director for 57-mm guns 3. Top Sail 3-D early-warning radar 4. Head Net-C air-search radar 5. Head Lights radar directors for the SA-N-3 Goa SAM system 6. SA-N-3 Goa SAM launchers 7. SUW-N-1 ASW rocket launcher 8. RBU-6000 ASW/torpedo-countermeasures rocket launchers

marks: Soviet type designation: *Protivolodochnyy Kreyser* (Antisubmarine uiser). Flight deck 86 × 34 m. Two elevators to hangar aft, plus small hangar for two licopters at forward end of flight deck, between the stack uptakes. The *Moskva* was efly modified to test the Yak-38 Forger-A aircraft (first flight from *Moskva:* 18-11-, which were for use aboard the *Kiev*-class carriers. Both ships had their ten 533-mm W TT removed and the side embrasures plated in during the mid-1970s. The huge ar dome is retractable within the hull. Fin stabilizers fitted. Hull trims down about by the bow, and the ship is a poor sea boat. Sister *Leningrad* (completed 1968) was icken around 6-91, and *Moskva* (which had not deployed for over eight years until a ef Mediterranean cruise just prior to the withdrawal of the Soviet Mediterranean *hadra* in 12-91) will reportedly follow in 1992; both spent their careers attached to Black Sea Fleet. Only two were ever planned, but a 12-meter-longer version was igned and canceled shortly after construction had started.

MARITIME AVIATION (*MORSKAYA AVIATSIYA*)

aval aviation, which dates from 1919, is an integral part of the Russian Navy, in ch approximately 75,000 personnel are involved, but its organization and ranks are same as those of the Russian air forces. Aircraft are part of the four naval fleets thern, Baltic, Black Sea, and Pacific Ocean) and are under the direct control of the manders of those fleets. According to the Soviet Ministry of Defense, the air arm some 1,143 combat aircraft in 1988, while the U.S. Navy stated in 1-92 that the was 1,875 as of 7-91, with much of the difference probably stemming from the e numbers of Flogger, Fitter, Frogfoot, and Fencer land-based tactical aircraft sferred to the navy during 1989–90 to avoid CFE limitations. Current first-line e aircraft totals are estimated to be:

fixed-wing:
eeconnaissance: 50 Bear-D; 55 Badger-A, -C, -D, -E, -F; 12 Fencer-E
ectronic warfare: 77 Badger-H, -J; 14 Coot-A, -B; 5 Cub
ombers: 150 Backfire-B, -C; 145 Badger-A, -C, -G
ttack fighters: 170 Fitter-A, -C, -D; 50 Flogger, 5 Fulcrum, 5 Flanker, 50 Frogfoot,) Fencer
rial refueling: 50 Badger-A
SW: 65 Bear-F; 45 May; 90 Mail

elicopters:
SW: 75 Hormone-A; 100 Helix-A; 100 Haze-A (land-based)
get designation: 25 Hormone-B
ne countermeasures: 25 Haze-A
iscellaneous: Hook, Hip-C; Helix-B, -D; Haze-B; Hormone-C; etc.

ition, some 480 fixed-wing aircraft and helicopters (training, transport, experi-l, etc.) are believed to be available. All Tu-22 Blinder reconnaissance aircraft ombers are believed to have been retired, and the numbers of Tu-16 Badger ts listed above are in actuality probably fewer, as these by-now ancient aircraft ginning to be retired.

COMBAT AIRCRAFT

In the following entries, the "operational radius" is roughly 60 percent of the given by one-half of the range. The aircraft are arranged alphanumerically by -bureau designation.

D-WING AIRCRAFT:

Cub electronic warfare aircraft Design Bureau: Antonov

: 1960 **Max. weight:** 28 tons **Wingspan:** 38 m
gth: 37 m
ines: 4 Ivchenko AI-20K turboprops (4,000 shp each)
ed: 420 kts max. **Operational radius:** . . .

ks: A small number of An-12 transports have been equipped with various antennas for electronic reconnaissance duties.

Mail antisubmarine patrol amphibian Design Bureau: Beriev

Be-12 Mail ASW amphibian U.S. Navy, 1990

IOC: 1966 **Max. weight:** 31 tons **Wingspan:** 29.5 m
Length: 30.2 m
Engines: 2 Al-20D turboprops (4,190 shp each)
Speed: 330 kts at 40,000 ft; 315 kts at sea level (170 kts cruise)
Operational radius: 1,100 km at 170 kts
Armament: torpedoes, depth charges, sonobuoys, mines
Equipment: navigation radar, MAD, sonobuoy processor, etc.

Remarks: Amphibian. Seaplane capabilities apparently seldom used.

Be-42 Mermaid search-and-rescue/ASW amphibians
Design Bureau: Beriev

IOC: 1992 **Max. weight:** 86 tons **Wingspan:** 42 m
Length: 42 m
Engines: 2 Soloviev D-30KVP turbofans (12,000-kg thrust each); 2 RD-36/35 auxiliary turbojets (2,500-kg thrust each)
Speed: 430 kts (297 kts cruise)
Operational radius: 1,650 km at 297 kts
Armament: torpedoes, depth charges, sonobuoys
Equipment: MAD; both: radar, etc.

Be-42 Albatros ASW amphibian prototype 9-91

FIXED-WING AIRCRAFT *(continued)*

Be-42 Albatros ASW amphibian prototype 9-91

Remarks: The two prototypes were referred to as the A-40 Albatros. A rescue version will be able to land in the open sea to rescue up to 54 persons. The Be-42 will probably replace the aging Be-12 Mail, although not in as large a number; it may have a dipping sonar for use while afloat on the ocean surface. The first 20 of the ASW version were ordered during 3-92. Also offered for foreign sale, the aircraft is available as the Be-200 for civilian purposes.

Il-20 Coot-A electronic warfare aircraft Design Bureau: Ilyushin

Il-20 Coot-A electronics warfare aircraft U.S. Navy, 1989

IOC: 1978 **Max. weight:** 64 tons **Wingspan:** 37.42 m
Length: 35.90 m
Engines: 4 Ivchenko AI-20M turboprops (4,300 shp each)
Speed: 364 kts (337 kts cruise) **Operational radius:** 1,100 km
Equipment: Side-looking radar in 10.3-m-long by 1.2-m-deep gondola, cameras

Remarks: The airframe was developed from that of the Il-18 Coot transport and is similar to that of the Il-38 May ASW aircraft.

Il-38 May antisubmarine patrol aircraft Design Bureau: Ilyushin

IOC: 1968 **Max. weight:** 63.5 tons **Wingspan:** 37.5 m
Length: 39.5 m
Engines: 4 Ivchenko AI-20 turboprops (5,200 shp each)
Speed: 380 kts at 30,000 ft (313 kts cruise)
Operational radius: 3,300 km (12 hours)
Armament: 7,000 kg torpedoes, depth charges, sonobuoys, etc.
Equipment: Wet Eye surveillance radar, MAD boom, sonobuoy processor, etc.

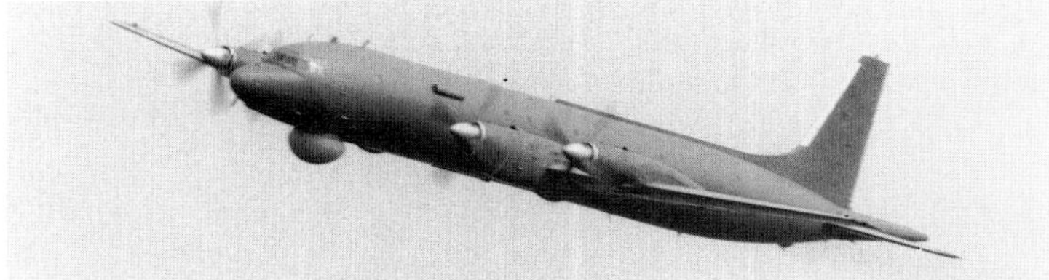

Il-38 May ASW patrol aircraft French Navy, 6-90

Il-38 May ASW patrol aircraft U.S. Navy, 1990

Remarks: Airframe developed from the Il-18 transport, but wings moved farther forward on fuselage. Numbers slowly decreasing; several sold to India.

MiG-23 Flogger-B fighter-bomber Design Bureau: Mikoyan

MiG-23 Flogger strike aircraft U.S. Navy, 199

IOC: 1980 **Max. weight:** 18.9 tons
Wingspan: 13.95 m (7.77 m fully swept)
Length: 15.88 m
Engine: 1 Tumanskiy R-29B turbojet (12,500-kg thrust)
Speed: Mach 2.35 max. (Mach 1.2 at sea level)
Operational radius: 900 km low-low-low; 1,300 km high-low-high
Armament: 6 stores positions for bombs, rockets, and ASMs; 2/23-mm cannon

Remarks: Transferred from Soviet Air Force 1989–90. The similar MiG-23 Flogger interceptors formerly based at Cam Ranh Bay for air defense were returned home 1990 and probably returned to the air force.

MiG-29K Fulcrum-D shipboard interceptor Design Bureau: Mikoya

IOC: 1993? **Max. weight:** 18.5 tons (15.24 tons normal)
Wingspan: 11.36 m (8.0 m folded) **Length:** 17.32 m
Engines: 2 Tumanskiy RD-33K turbojets (5,040-kg dry thrust/ 8,300-kg afterburner each)
Speed: Mach 2.35 max.; Mach 1.06 at sea level
Operational radius: 630 km max.
Armament: 6/AA-8 Aphid, AA-10 Alamo, or AA-11 Archer missiles 1/30-mm gatling cannon
Equipment: Look-down/shoot-down doppler radar with 54 n.m. ran IR sensor, laser ranging, Sirena-3 radar warning

Remarks: Only about five prototypes had been completed by the end of 1991, ar the aircraft is stated to be several years behind the competing Su-27K Flanker s board interceptor, it may not go into production, especially as the performance ov is not as good as the Su-27K. Has 55,800-ft max. altitude. Range is 2,900 km with t 1,500-liter external tanks. Requires only a 240-m takeoff run on level ground. M mum load factor is 9 g. Height is 4.73 m

Su-17/20 Fitter-C, -H fighter-bomber Design Bureau: Sukhoi

IOC: 1971/76 **Max. weight:** 17.75 tons
Wingspan: 13.5 m (10.0 fully swept)
Length: 18.5 m
Engine: 1 Lyulka AL-21F turbojet (11,000-kg thrust)
Speed: Mach 1.8 at 50,000 ft (1,160 kts); Mach 1.05 at sea level
Operational radius: 400 km low-low-low; 800 km high-low-high
Armament: 3,500 kg bombs or 32/57-mm rockets or AA-2, AA-8, AS-7, or AS-10 missiles; 2/30-mm cannon
Equipment: Mapping and ranging radar; laser rangefinder; autop

Remarks: Transferred from the Soviet Air Force; for use in maritime strike based in the Baltic and Pacific areas.

Su-24 Fencer-E maritime reconnaissance fighter-bomber
Design Bureau: Sukhoi

IOC: 1985 **Max. weight:** 41 tons
Wingspan: 17.5 m (10.5 m fully swept) **Length:** 21.3 m
Engines: 2 Lyulka AL-21F-3 turbojets (11,000-kg thrust each)
Speed: Mach 2.2 (1,425 kts)/Mach 1.2 at sea level
Operational radius: 322 km low-low-low; 1,300 high-low-high
Armament: 8 AS-7, -10, -11, -12, or -13 missiles; 1/30-mm cannon
Equipment: cameras

Remarks: Fencer-E reconnaissance fighters are based in the Baltic Fleet ar U.S. Navy has stated that the Russian Navy now also has an unspecified nun Fencer-A, -B, and -D strike fighters, probably transferred from the Soviet Air F 1989–90 to avoid CFE limitations. Variable geometry, swing-wing design.

Su-24 Fencer strike aircraft U.S. Do

FIXED-WING AIRCRAFT *(continued)*

Su-25 Frogfoot strike aircraft Design Bureau: Sukhoi

IOC: 1978 **Max. weight:** 14.6 tons **Wingspan:** 14.36 m
Length: 15.55 m
Engines: 2 Tumanskiy R-195 turbojets (4,500-kg thrust each)
Speed: Mach 0.8 (520 kts)
Operational radius: 750 km low-low-low; 1,250 km high-low-high
Armament: 1,000 kg normal bombs or 8 AS-8 missiles

-25K Frogfoot naval trainer landing on Kuznetsov U.S. DoD, 11-89

marks: Land-based, former Soviet Air Force aircraft transferred 1989–90. Weight pty is 9.5 tons, and they can be flown at up to 17.6 tons. Ferry range is 2,095 km, and ximum altitude is 23,000 ft. Early versions had the Tumanskiy R-13-300 turbojet of 36-kg thrust. One reported lost to accident 27-11-91 in Pacific area by Russian ss. A navalized carrier familiarization version of the two-seat Su-28 Frogfoot iner with R-95 turbojets was tested aboard the carrier *Admiral Flota Sovetskogo uza Kuznetsov* in 11-89 but may not have been procured in quantity.

-27K Flanker shipboard interceptor Design Bureau: Sukhoi

OC: 1992? **Max. weight:** 30 tons
Vingspan: 14.70 m (10.00 folded) **Length:** 21.93 m
Engines: 2 Lyulka AL-31F turbojets (12,475-kg thrust each)
Speed: Mach 2.35 max. (1,550 kts); Mach 1.1 at sea level
Operational radius: 1,500 km (4,000-km max. ferry range)
rmament: 10 AA-8, -9, -10, or -11 missiles; 1/30-mm gatling cannon
quipment: track-while-scan, look-down/shoot-down radar with 130-km range

7K Flanker shipboard interceptor Tass, 1990

Flanker 2-seat side-by-side trainer Tass, 1990

ks: Only about five prototypes had been produced by end-1991 for service *Kuznetsov*-class carriers, including a single side-by-side, two-seat trainer ver- at could later be developed into a shipboard strike aircraft. The navalized r has folding wings and an upward-folding radome for carrier stowage, canard s, no "stinger" protruding from the aft end, a tail-hook (which eliminates one osition), upgraded engines, ten-tons internal fuel capacity for 4,000-km ferry and an aerial refueling capability.

Tu-16 Badger-A aerial refueling aircraft Design Bureau: Tupolev

IOC: 1953 **Max. weight:** 75 tons **Wingspan:** 33.0 m
Length: 36.5 m
Engines: 2 AM-3M turbojets (9,550-kg thrust each)
Speed: 535 kts at 22,000 ft; 445 kts at sea level
Operational radius: 4,800 km
Armament: up to 7/23-mm cannon
Equipment: navigation and bombing radar; tailgun radar; ECM gear on some

Remarks: Wing-tip hose dispensers for refueling; retain a secondary bombing capability (3,800-kg total). Despite obsolescence, have not begun to be replaced by the Il-76 tanker.

Tu-16 Badger-C maritime strike aircraft Design Bureau: Tupolev

IOC: 1960 **Max. weight:** 75 tons
Wingspan: 33.0 m **Length:** 36.5 m
Engines: 2 AM-3M turbojets (9,550-kg thrust each)
Speed: 535 kts at 22,000 ft; 445 kts at sea level
Operational radius: 3,200 km without refueling
Armament: 2 AS-6 Kingfish; 6/23-mm cannon
Equipment: Puff Ball navigation and bombing radar; 1 Bee Hind tail radar

Remarks: Formerly could carry the now-obsolete AS-2 Kipper antiship missile. Likely to be retired soon.

Tu-16 Badger-G maritime strike aircraft Design Bureau: Tupolev

Tu-16 Badger-G strike aircraft French Navy, 1990

IOC: 1965 **Max. weight:** 75 tons **Wingspan:** 33.0 m
Length: 36.5 m
Engines: 2 AM-3M turbojets (9,550-kg thrust each)
Speed: 535 kts at 22,000 ft; 445 kts at sea level
Operational radius: 3,200 km without refueling
Armament: 2 AS-5 Kelt or AS-6 Kingfish antiship missiles; 6–7/23-mm cannon
Equipment: Short Horn navigational and bombing radar; doppler radar; Bee Hind tail radar

Remarks: Will probably soon be retired.

Tu-16 Badger-D, -E, -F, -H, -J reconnaissance and EW aircraft Design Bureau: Tupolev

IOC: 1960s **Max. weight:** 75 tons **Wingspan:** 33.0 m
Length: 36.5 m
Engines: 2 AM-3M turbojets (9,550-kg thrust each)
Speed: 535 kts at 22,000 ft; 445 kts at sea level
Operational radius: 3,200 km without refueling
Armament: 6–7/23-mm cannon
Equipment: Puff Ball navigation and bombing radar; tail radar; EW/ECM/ECCM

Tu-16 Badger-D U.S. Navy, 1989

Remarks: Different versions for ELINT, photoreconnaissance, etc. Should be phased out soon. Badger-E is for aerial photography; Badger-F is an ELINT aircraft with numerous radomes and other antennas; Badger-H has two radomes below the forward fuselage and one aft; and Badger-J has a canoe radome beneath the fuselage.

Tu-22M Backfire-B, -C medium-range bomber Design Bureau: Tupolev

IOC: 1974 **Max. weight:** 121.5 tons
Wingspan: 34.45 m (26.2 fully swept)

FIXED-WING AIRCRAFT *(continued)*

Length: 40.2 m
Engines: 2 Kuznetsov NK-144 turbojets (24,00-kg thrust each)
Speed: Mach 2.0 at 50,000 ft, max./Mach 1.3 at 3,000 ft
Operational radius: Supersonic: 3,485/2,250 km with/without refueling;
Subsonic: 6,300/5,320 km with/without refueling
Armament: 12,000 kg bombs or 2 AS-4, AS-6, or AS-9 missiles, or mines; 2/23-mm cannon (twin)
Equipment: Down Beat navigation and bombing radar; optical bombsight; Fan Tail tailgun radar

Tu-22M Backfire-B bomber U.S. Navy, 1990

Tu-22M Backfire-B bomber U.S. Navy, 1990

Remarks: Variable-geometry swept wing. Has ECM and ECCM gear. Backfire-C has raked engine air inlets and, presumably, more powerful engines. Naval Aviation units carry no refueling probes. One reported lost in the Tatar Straits on 23-11-89.

Tu-95 Bear-D reconnaissance bomber Design Bureau: Tupolev

IOC: 1965 **Max. weight:** 162 tons
Wingspan: 50.0 m **Length:** 45.0 m
Engines: 4 Kuznetsov NK-12MV turboprops (15,000 shp each); 4/8-bladed counterrotating props
Speed: 450 kts at 25,000 ft; 440 kts at sea level
Operational radius: 9,500 km/8,300 km with/without aerial refueling
Armament: 8,000 kg bombs, 2/23-mm cannon (twin)
Equipment: Big Bulge-A surveillance radar; tailgun radar; extensive ECM/ECCM suite

Tu-95 Bear-D reconnaissance bomber U.S. Navy, 7-91

Tu-95 Bear-D reconnaissance bomber U.S. Navy, 1989

Tu-142 Bear-F, -J ASW/communications aircraft
Design Bureau: Tupolev

IOC: 1970/1984 **Max. weight:** 188 tons
Wingspan: 51.1 m **Length:** 49.5 m
Engines: 4 Kuznetsov NK-12MV turboprops (15,000 shp each); 4/8-bladed counterrotating props
Speed: 450 kts at sea level
Operational radius: 6,000 km (Bear-F)
Armament: 2/23-mm cannon (twin); Bear-F also: 8,000 kg torpedoes, air-dropped stores
Equipment: Bear-F: Wet Eye surveillance radar; Bear-J: trailing-wire VLF comms antenna and probable SATCOMM and NAVSAT systems; both have ECM/ECCM suites

Tu-142 Bear-F Mod. IV ASW patrol aircraft U.S. Navy, 7-

Tu-142 Bear-J communications relay aircraft U.S. Navy, 4-

Remarks: The Bear-F antisubmarine patrol aircraft may remain in low-level prod tion and has been exported to India. Bear-J is intended for communications relay submerged submarines in a rôle analogous to that of the U.S. E-6A TACAMO.

Yak-38 Forger A shipboard VTOL fighter-bomber
Design Bureau: Yakolev

Yak-38 Forger-A VTOL fighter in new gray paint scheme
M.O.D. U.K.,

IOC: 1976 **Max. weight:** 10.3 tons
Wingspan: 7.0 m **Length:** 15.5 m
Engines: 1 Mikulin-Soyuz R27V-300 lift/cruise engine (7,650-kg thrust); 2 Koliesov RD-36-35-FVR lift engines (3,500-kg thrust each)
Speed: 648 kts max.
Operational radius: 200 km (680-km max. range)
Armament: 2/AS-7 Kerry or AA-8 Aphid missiles; 32/57-mm rock bombs; 2/23-mm cannon
Equipment: Passive radar warning system; laser rangefinder; autolanding system; no radar

Remarks: Believed to have been retired in 1990, but data retained here for refe Only about 100 single-seat Forger-A attack and two-seat Forger-B operational tr were built, and their performance was marginal at best. Could not perform r takeoff, limiting load potential, and seldom operated out of line-of-sight of their n ships.

Yak-141 Freestyle shipboard V/STOL fighter-bomber
Design Bureau: Yakolev

Yak-141 Freestyle V/STOL fighter prototype Yakolev

COMBAT AIRCRAFT *(continued)*

IOC: . . . **Max. weight:** 19.5 tons
Wingspan: 10.00 (5.90 folded) **Length:** 18.30 m **Height:** 5.00 m
Engines: 1 Tumanskiy R79 lift/cruise turbojet (15,500-kg thrust); 2 Kolesov R-41 or RD lift-only turbojets (4,000 kg each)
Speed: 970 kts max.
Operational radius: 417 km VTOL mode; 600 km V/STOL mode
Armament: 2,600 kg stores, including AA-10 Atoll and AA-11 missiles
Equipment: Slot Back look-down/shoot-down doppler radar with 54 n.m. range, IR sensor, laser ranging, Sirena-3 radar warning

Remarks: Intended as the replacement for the Yak-38, but delays and increases in cost caused Soviet Navy to withdraw support. One of the two flying prototypes crashed 5-11-91 aboard the carrier *Admiral Flota Sovetskogo Soyuza Gorshkov* while on company-funded trials. Now unlikely to be procured. Aircraft is 26 percent carbon fiber composite by empty weight. Ceiling is 49,200 ft., and the aircraft is 5.00 m high.

HELICOPTERS:

Ka-25 Hormone A, -B, -C ASW/targeting/utility helicopter
Design Bureau: Kamov

Ka-25 Hormone-A ASW helicopter 7-91

Ka-25 Hormone-B targeting helicopter U.S. DoD, 1986

Ka-25 Hormone-C utility helicopter French Navy, 6-90

IOC: 1967 **Max. weight:** 7.5 tons **Rotor dia.:** 16 m
Length: 10 m fuselage
Engines: 2 Glushenkov GTD 3 BM turboshafts (905 shp each)
Speed: 124 kts max.; 105 kts cruise
Operational radius: 175 km (1.5–2 hrs.)
Armament: Hormone-A: 1,000 kg total, torpedoes and/or depth charges, sonobuoys
Equipment: Hormone-A: Oka-2 dipping sonar, radar; Hormone-B: Short Horn targeting radar, video data link

Remarks: Developed for the *Moskva* and other 1960s-built classes; now being replaced by the Ka-27 series. Hormone-C is a blanket designation for various utility/SAR/reconnaissance versions.

Ka-27PL Helix-A antisubmarine helicopter Design Bureau: Kamov

Ka-27PL Helix-A ASW helicopter RN, 5-90

Ka-29TB Helix-B assault helicopter—note rocket pod 1987

Ka-27PS Helix-D search-and-rescue helicopter French Navy, 6-90

IOC: 1980
Max. weight: 11.0 tons (Ka-29TB: 12 tons; Ka-32T: 12.6 tons)
Rotor dia.: 15.90 m **Length:** 11.30 m (12.23 rotors deployed)
Engines: 2 Isotov TV3-117BK turboshafts (2,225 shp each)(Ka-29TB: TV-3117VK, 2,300 shp each)

COMBAT AIRCRAFT *(continued)*

Speed: 143 kts (124 kts with 5,000-kg payload)
Operational radius: 375 km (2–2.5 hrs)
Armament: Ka-27PL: 2 torpedoes or depth charges; Ka-29TB: 1/7.62-mm gatling gun, 8/AT-6 Spiral anti-tank missiles, 2/80-mm rocket pods (20 each) or 2/57-mm rocket pods (32 each), 8–10 troops

Remarks: Various versions by maker's designation include: Ka-27L transport, Ka-27PL ASW (Helix-A), Ka-27PS search-and-rescue (Helix-D), Ka-28 export version of Ka-27PL, Ka-29 combat transport, Ka-29TB Naval Infantry transport (Helix-B), Ka-32T civil transport/naval utility, Ka-32S civilian search-and-rescue.

Mi-8 Hip-C transport helicopter Design Bureau: Mil

IOC: 1967 **Max. weight:** 12 tons **Rotor dia.:** 21.3 m
Length: 18.3-m fuselage
Engines: 2 Isotov TV-2-117A turboshafts (1,620 shp each)
Speed: 125 kts max. (100 kts cruise) **Operational radius:** 220 km
Equipment: 4,000 kg cargo or 12 troops

Mi-14PL Haze-A, Mi-14BT Haze-B antisubmarine/mine countermeasures helicopters Design Bureau: Mil

Mi-14PL Haze-A ASW helicopter 6-89

IOC: 1978 **Max. weight:** 14 tons (11.55 empty)
Rotor dia.: 21.294 m
Length: 25.315 m (18.356 fuselage) **Height:** 6.936 m
Engines: 2 Isotov TV-3-117A turboshafts (2,200 shp each)
Speed: 124 kts max. **Operational radius:** 225 km (2.5 hrs)
Armament: Mi-14PL: 2,000 kg stores: 2 torpedoes or . . . depth charges (2,000 kg max.)
Equipment: Mi-14PL: Oka-2 dipping sonar, APM-60 towed MAD

Remarks: Land-based; rotors do not fold. Also in use are small numbers of Mi-14ES Hip-C search-and-rescue helicopters. Mi-14BT mine countermeasures version tows various arrays, including hydrofoil sled magnetic countermeasures gear at up to 25 kts or a 50-kg acoustic sweep array.

Note: For training, experimental/developmental, and support duties, Russian Naval Aviation also employs Il-62 Classic, Il-76 Candid, Il-18 Coot, An-14 Cub, Tu-154M Careless, and . . . Crusty aircraft, as well as examples of the first-line aircraft described above.

SUBMARINES

Note: Nuclear-powered submarines are built at the Northern Machine-building Factory, Severodvinsk (formerly Molotovsk), on the White Sea near Arkhangelsk; at Komsomolsk-na-Amur in the Far East; at the Krasnoye Sormovo Shipyard at Nizhniy Novgorod (formerly Gorkiy) on the Volga; and at the United Admiralty Shipyard in St. Petersburg (comprising the former Sudomekh and Admiralty Shipyards). According to Russian press and periodical writings, Admiralty and Krasnoye Sormovo are to cease building submarines in the near future.

Most modern Russian submarines have an anechoic hull coating that absorbs the echoes of sonars and thus reduces the intensity of reflected echoes. The rubber-compound anechoic tiles come in several thicknesses and are frequently missing, accounting for the odd random rectangular depressions seen on the outer hulls of many Russian submarines (apparently, Russian adhesives technology is deficient).

Exotic propulsion systems, such as magnetohydrodynamic drive, electromagnetic drive, or the use of compliant coatings to improve boundary layer flow, etc., have yet to find use on an actual Russian submarine class.

BALLISTIC-MISSILE SUBMARINES (NUCLEAR-POWERED)

(Soviet Type: PLARB—*Podvodnaya Lodka Atomnaya Raketnaya Ballisticheskaya* = Nuclear-powered Ballistic Missile Submarine)

◆ **7 Delta-IV (Del'fin) class (Project 667BDRM)**
Bldr: Severodvinsk SY (In serv. 1985–1991)

D: 10,800 tons (surf.)/13,500 tons (sub.)
S: 24 kts (sub.)/20 kts (surf.) **Dim:** 164.0 × 12.0 × 8.7
A: 16/SS-N-23 (RSM-54) Skiff ballistic missiles—6/533 and 650-mm TT (bow, 18 torpedoes and/or SS-N-15 or SS-N-16 missiles)
Electron Equipt:
Radar: 1/Snoop Tray
Sonar: Shark Gill LF active/passive, towed array
EW: Brick Pulp intercept, Park Lamp DF
E/O: Cod Eye radio sextant, 2 periscopes
M: 2 pressurized-water nuclear reactors, geared steam turbines; 2/7-bladed props; 50,000 shp
Endurance: 90 days **Crew:** 20 officers, 90 enlisted

Delta-IV class—later unit without camera fairing aft French Navy, 199

Delta-IV class M.O.D. U

Remarks: First unit launched 2-84, operational by 1985. Second launched 1985, t in 1986, fourth during 1-87, fifth in 2-88, sixth in 1-89, seventh in 1990; additional u were expected, but production has reportedly come to a halt, at least tempora Design is a further elongation of the early-1960s Yankee design and is distinguish from Delta-III by fewer limber-holes, towed passive hydrophone array dispenser atop rudder and, on the first unit only, a camera housing at aft end of the mi turtledeck. Believed capable of operating under the ice pack. Have Pert Sp SATCOMM antenna. According to the Russian press, one unit suffered a mis launch failure during 9-91. All seven are in the Northern Fleet, based at Olen'ya

◆ **6 Typhoon (Tayfun) class (Project 941)** Bldr: Severodvinsk SY serv. 1983–1990)

TK-12 TK-13 TK-17 TK-202 TK-208 TK-. . .

Typhoon class M.O.D., U.K.

Typhoon in dry dock—note shrouded propellers, prominent keels

BALLISTIC-MISSILE SUBMARINES (NUCLEAR-POWERED)
continued)

yphoon class—first unit, with camera fairings aft M.O.D. U.K., 1989

hoon class—later unit, with no camera fairings but with more ninent safety line tracks on deck forward M.O.D. U.K., 5-90

18,500 tons surf. (25,000 sub.)
25 kts (sub.)/20 kts (surf.)
m: 171.0 × 24.0 × 12.5 (approx.)
20/SS-N-20 (RSM-52) Sturgeon ballistic missiles— 6/533-mm and/ or 650-mm bow TT (. . . torpedoes, SS-N-15 and SS-N-16 missiles)
ectron Equipt:
Radar: 1/Snoop Pair—Sonar: Shark Gill LF active/passive
EW: Rim Hat intercept (on Snoop Pair mast), Park Lamp DF
E/O: Cod Eye radiometric sextant, 2 periscopes
2/330–360 MW pressurized-water nuclear reactors—2/1,090-bhp diesel generator sets for emergency propulsion; 2/shrouded 6-bladed props; 90,000 shp
durance: 90 days **Crew:** 150 tot.

rks: World's largest submarines. Evidently intended to operate beneath the ice pack, breaking through to launch. The first Typhoon launched two missiles 15 sec. in 10-82. Design incorporates two parallel pressure hulls within the ull, with the massive sail being an additional pressure vessel. Forward location nissile tubes is unique.

first, laid down in 1975, was launched in 9-80, commenced trials 6-81, and l service 1983. The second launched 9-82, commenced trials 6-83, and entered in 1984. The third was launched 12-83 and began trials at the beginning of he fourth was launched at the end of 1984, the fifth at the end of 1986, and the 1989; no additional units are expected. All are based at Nerpich'ya on the Kola ıla about 200 km east of Murmansk.

irst unit began a modernization refit in 1991 that "may include fitting the class e SS-N-20 follow-on missile," according to the U.S. Department of Defense. All o large hatches abaft the sail for deploying towed communications buoys; on the it only, abaft the hatches are pyramidal protrusions that probably house televi- neras for watching the buoys as they are deployed and recovered. Flanking the probable crew escape modules. Hull has massive bilge keels to reduce rolling, sual feature in a modern submarine. The Rim Hat EW intercept array sur- the base of the Snoop Pair back-to-back radar antenna.

◆ **14 Delta-III (Kal'mar) class (Project 667BDR)**
Bldr: Severodvinsk SY (In serv. 1975–82)

60 Let Velikyo Oktyabr 13 others

Delta-III class—a unit that had just completed a transfer to the Pacific Ocean Fleet U.S. Navy, 9-90

Delta-III class—showing the massive casing M.O.D. U.K., 1987

D: 10,600 tons (surf.)/13,250 tons (sub.) **S:** 24 kts (sub.)
Dim: 155.5 × 12.0 × 8.6
A: 16/SS-N-18 (RSM-50 Stingray) SLBM—6/533-mm TT fwd (18 torpedoes and/or SS-N-15 missiles)
Electron Equipt:
Radar: 1/Snoop Tray
Sonar: Shark Teeth LF active/passive array, towed array in some
EW: Brick Pulp or Brick Group intercept, Park Lamp D/F
E/O: Cod Eye radiometric sextant, 2 periscopes
M: 2 pressurized-water nuclear reactors, steam turbines; 2/5-bladed props; 50,000 shp
Endurance: 90 days **Crew:** 20 officers, 90 enlisted

Remarks: Two went into service in 1975, four in 1976, two in 1977, two in 1978, and three in 1979–81; the 13th was launched 3-4-81, the 14th in 12-81. Have higher "turtledeck" than Delta-II to accommodate the longer SS-N-18 tubes. Have towed VLF communications buoys and Pert Spring SATCOMM antenna. Normal diving depth limitation is believed to be 360 m. Being backfitted with towed passive linear sonar arrays, as on the Delta-IV class, from which they are becoming difficult to distinguish. Three are based at Yagel'naya and two at Olen'ya in the Northern Fleet, and units are also employed by the Pacific Fleet.

◆ **4 Delta-II (Murena-M) class (Project 667BD)**
Bldr: Severodvinsk SY (In serv. 1974–75)

Delta-II class French Navy, 6-90

BALLISTIC-MISSILE SUBMARINES (NUCLEAR-POWERED)
(continued)

Delta-II class—with (fore to aft) periscope, D/F loop, snorkel intake, comms mast, and EW intercept array telescoping masts raised
M.O.D. U.K., 1989

D: 10,500 tons (surf.)/13,200 tons (sub.) **S:** 24 kts (sub.)
Dim: 155.5 × 12.0 × 8.6
A: 16/SS-N-8 (RSM-40) Sawfly SLBM—6/533-mm TT fwd (18 torpedoes and SS-N-15 missiles)
Electron Equipt:
Radar: 1/Snoop Tray—Sonar: Shark Teeth LF active/passive array
EW: Brick Pulp or Brick Group intercept, Park Lamp D/F
E/O: Cod Eye radiometric sextant, 2 periscopes
M: 2 pressurized-water nuclear reactors, steam turbines; 2/5-bladed props; 50,000 shp
Endurance: 90 days **Crew:** 20 officers, 90 enlisted

Remarks: Lengthened version of Delta-I, so as to carry four more SS-N-8 submarine-launched ballistic missiles. All have Pert Spring SATCOMM antennas. All operate in the Northern Fleet, based at Yagel'naya.

◆ 18 Delta-I (Murena) class (Project 667B)
Bldr: Severodvinsk SY and Komsomolsk SY (In serv. 1973–76)

Delta-I class—note unique "double step" to missile bay casing
M.O.D. U.K., 1989

Delta-I class—note SATCOMM, HF comms, and Snoop Tray radar antenna masts raised, only 12 missile tubes in casing M.O.D. U.K., 1990

Delta-I class M.O.D. U.K., 1990

D: 9,000 tons (surf.)/11,300 tons (sub.) **S:** 25 kts (sub.)
Dim: 140.0 × 12.0 × 8.6
A: 12/SS-N-8 (RSM-40) Sawfly SLBM—6/533-mm TT fwd. (18 torpedoes and SS-N-15 missiles)
Electron Equipt:
Radar: 1 Snoop Tray—Sonar: Shark Teeth LF active, passive arrays
EW: Brick Pulp or Brick Group intercept, Park Lamp D/F
E/O: Cod Eye radiometric sextant, 2 periscopes
M: 2 pressurized-water nuclear reactors, steam turbines; 2/5-bladed props; 50,000 shp
Endurance: 90 days **Crew:** 20 officers, 90 enlisted

Remarks: One entered service in 1972, four in 1973, six in 1974, two in 1975, two in 1976, and three in 1977. Distinguished from later, longer Delta-II and -III by stepped turtleneck abaft sail. All have Pert Spring SATCOMM antennas. Nine are based in the Northern Fleet at Ostrovnoy and nine are in the Pacific Ocean Fleet.

◆ 7 Yankee-I (Navaga) class (Project 667A)
Bldrs: Severodvinsk SY and Komsomolsk SY (In serv. 1967–74)

Yankee-I class sail area and missile casing—note SATCOMM anten periscope, D/F loop, and communications masts raised
French Navy, 6

Yankee-I class—note that this unit has a small sonar array at the to of the sail vice the bridge windows found on most units of th
M.O.D. U.K

BALLISTIC-MISSILE SUBMARINES (NUCLEAR-POWERED) (*continued*)

Yankee-I class French Navy, 1990

D: 7,900 tons (surf.)/9,600 tons (sub.) **S:** 26 kts
Dim: 130.0 × 12.0 × 8.6
A: 16/SS-N-6 (RSM-25) Serb SLBM—6/533-mm TT (18 torpedoes)
Electron Equipt:
Radar: 1/Snoop Tray—Sonar: 1 Shark Teeth LF active/passive array
EW: Stop Light intercept, Brick Group intercept, Park Lamp D/F
E/O: Cod Eye radiometric sextant, 2 periscopes
M: 2 pressurized-water nuclear reactors, steam turbines; 2/5-bladed props; 50,000 shp
Endurance: 90 days **Crew:** 20 officers, 90 enlisted

Remarks: A total of 34 were completed: two in 1967, four in 1968, six in 1969, eight in 1970, six in 1971, five in 1972, two in 1973, and one in 1974. To date, 27 (including one converted to Yankee-II configuration to launch the solid-fueled SS-N-17 SLBM) have had their missile tubes deactivated in compliance with the U.S.–Soviet strategic arms limitations agreements, including six during 1991; the remaining SLBM-configured units are expected to be deactivated shortly. In 10-91, four operated from Yagel'naya in the Northern Fleet and three from Rybachiy in the Pacific Ocean Fleet.

Several "defanged" Yankees have been converted for other functions: one served as a trials platform for the SS-NX-24 strategic cruise missile, one has been converted as a trials platform for submarine acoustic systems, and three have been converted to launch the SS-N-21 strategic cruise missile; more of the latter version may be under conversion. Most, however, are to be scrapped due to their age and the cost of converting and modernizing them.

One Yankee-I (K-219) was lost at sea east of Bermuda on 6-10-86 after a fire and explosion in the missile-bay area. Yankees have a towed VLF buoy antenna and the Pert Spring SATCOMM antenna. Yankee patrols off the coasts of the United States ceased in late 1987, and the few remaining submarines now have a European/Far East "theatre attack" rôle.

Note: All Hotel-II-class nuclear-powered ballistic-missile submarines have been discarded. The sole Yankee-II ("Navaga-M") conversion submarine was discarded during 1991. The last Golf-II diesel-powered ballistic-missile submarine was decommissioned in the Baltic on 1-10-90 and may be employed as a museum exhibit.

CRUISE-MISSILE ATTACK SUBMARINES (NUCLEAR-POWERED)

Soviet Type: PLARK—*Podvodnaya Lodka Atomnaya Raketnaya Krylataya* = Nuclear-Powered Cruise-Missile Submarine)

◆ 7 (+ . . .) Oscar-II class (Project 949A)
Bldr: Severodvinsk SY (In serv. 1986–. . .)

D: 15,000 tons (surf.)/18,000 tons (sub.) **S:** 33 kts (sub.)
Dim: 154.0 × 18.0 × 10.0
A: 24/SS-N-19 SSM —6/533- and 650-mm TT fwd (24 SS-N-15/16 missiles and/or torpedoes)
Electron Equipt:
Radar: 1/Snoop Pair (with Rim Hat intercept array)
Sonar: Shark Gill LF active; passive array; towed array
EW: Rim Hat, Bald Head intercept, . . . D/F
E/O: 2 periscopes
M: 2 pressurized-water reactors, steam turbines; 2/7-bladed props; 90,000 shp
Crew: 130 total

Oscar-II class—one of two that deployed to the Pacific Ocean Fleet in 1991 U.S. Navy, 9-91

Oscar-II class—unit that deployed to the Pacific Ocean Fleet in 9-90 U.S. Navy, 9-90

Oscar-II class—emphasizing the broad length-to-beam ratio of this class; raised casing abaft sail surrounds hatch for comms buoy M.O.D. U.K., 1990

Remarks: Lengthened version of Oscar-I; reason undetermined. The first unit was launched during 1985 and entered service 7-86, the second was launched in 1986, the third in 1987, the fourth in 1988, the fifth and sixth in 1990, and one in 1991. A total of 12 are expected to be built. Two units of the class were transferred to the Pacific Ocean Fleet in 10-91; the others operate in the Northern Fleet.

The SS-N-19 missile tubes are arranged in two rows of 12 flanking the pressure hull and are fixed at an elevation of about 40 degrees; six doors cover each row. The submarines require about three years to build. To achieve their maximum combat usefulness, the submarines must employ their Punch Bowl antenna to receive radar satellite targeting data; also have a Pert Spring SATCOMM antenna. All have a towed linear passive hydrophone array, with the cable deploying from the top of the vertical stabilizer at the stern. A towed VLF communications buoy is housed in the hump abaft the sail; it is deployed via a double-doored 7.5 × 2.5-m hatch. Normal diving depth is believed to be around 500 m.

◆ 2 Oscar-I class (Project 949)
Bldr: Severodvinsk SY (In serv. 1982–83)

D: 13,900 tons (surf.)/16,700 tons (sub.) **S:** 33 kts (sub.)
Dim: 146.0 × 18.0 × 10.0
A: 24/SS-N-19 SSM—6/533- and 650-mm TT fwd (24 SS-N-15 and SS-N-16 missiles, and/or 16 torpedoes)
Electron Equipt:
Radar: 1/Snoop Head—EW: Rim Hat, Bald Head intercept; . . . D/F
Sonar: Shark Gill LF active, passive; 2nd unit: towed array
E/O: 2 periscopes
M: 2 pressurized-water nuclear reactors, steam turbines; 2/7-bladed props; 90,000 shp
Crew: 130 tot.

CRUISE-MISSILE ATTACK SUBMARINES (NUCLEAR-POWERED) *(continued)*

Oscar-I class—second unit, with towed hydrophone array facilities M.O.D. U.K., 1987

Oscar-I class—first unit, without towed array U.S. D.O.D., 1988

Remarks: The first was launched in 4-80, the second in 12-82. The missile tubes are mounted in two rows of twelve, abreast the sail, fixed in elevation at about 40 degrees, with doors opening through the outer hull, as on the Charlie-I and -II classes. The missiles are launched while the submarine is submerged, using targeting data from a forward observer or from radar satellite targeting, with data received by the Punch Bowl antenna. Six outer hatch doors each cover two tubes. The tubes provide a 3.5-m standoff between the outer hull and the pressure hull. A towed antenna is dispensed from a tube at the top of the rudder on the second unit. Carry the Pert Spring SATCOMM antenna. Both are in the Northern Fleet.

Note: The single Papa-class (Project 741) nuclear-powered cruise-missile submarine was discarded during 1991.

◆ **6 Charlie-II class (Project 670M)** Bldr: Krasnaya Sormova SY, Nizhniy Novgorod (ex-Gorkiy)(In serv. 1973–1982)

Charlie-II class U.S. Navy

Charlie-II class—bow and sail area M.O.D. U.K., 1989

Charlie-II class—note "collar" at base of sail M.O.D. U.K., 1989

D: 4,300 tons (surf.)/5,500 tons (sub.) **S:** 24 kts (sub.)
Dim: 103.0 × 10.0 × 8.0
A: 8/SS-N-9 SSM—6/533-mm TT fwd (12 SS-N-15 missiles or torpedoes)
Electron Equipt:
Radar: 1/Snoop Tray—Sonar: Shark Teeth LF active/passive array
EW: Brick Spit intercept, Brick Pulp intercept, Park Lamp D/F
M: 1 pressurized-water nuclear reactor, steam turbines; 1/5-bladed prop; 15,000 shp
Crew: 85 tot.

Remarks: All in Northern Fleet. One in service in each of the years 1973, 1974, 197[illegible] 1979, 1980/81, and 1982. The additional 9-m length over the Charlie-I comes betwee[illegible] the missile tubes and the sail. Have VLF comms-buoy housing abaft the sail. Th[illegible] SS-N-9 missiles are fired while the submarine is submerged. The need for acoust[illegible] identification of targets and the relatively slow speed of the Charlie-I and -II class[illegible] limit their tactical usefulness.

◆ **10 Charlie-I class (Project 670)** Bldr: Krasnaya Sormova SY, Nizhni Novgorod (ex-Gorkiy) (In serv. 1968–72)

Charlie-I class—note missile tube outer hatches Siegfried Breyer collect[illegible]

Charlie-I class—the Indian Navy's leased *Chakra* U.S. Navy

CRUISE-MISSILE ATTACK SUBMARINES (NUCLEAR-POWERED) *(continued)*

Charlie-I class U.S. Navy, 1990

D: 4,000 tons (surf.)/5,000 tons (sub.) **S:** 24 kts (sub.)
Dim: 94.0 × 10.0 × 8.0
A: 8/SS-N-7 SSM—6/533-mm TT fwd. (12 SS-N-15 missiles and/or torpedoes)
Electron Equipt:
Radar: 1/Snoop Tray—Sonar: Shark Teeth LF active/passive arrays
EW: Brick Spit and Brick Pulp intercept, Park Lamp D/F
M: 1 pressurized-water nuclear reactor, steam turbines; 1/5-bladed prop; 15,000 shp
Crew: 80 tot.

Remarks: In service at the rate of about two a year between 1968 and 1973. "Collar" structures being added at the forward base of the sail, apparently to smooth water flow. Diving depth: 400 m normal/600 m max. One sank 6-83 in the Pacific; subsequently raised, but sank again and was not returned to service. One, leased to India 5-1-88 for three years under the name *Chakra*, was returned to the Soviet Pacific Fleet in 1-91; due to its reported poor condition while in Indian service, it may not be retained much longer. The missiles are submerged-launched from eight tubes inclined about 40° and mounted in two rows flanking the pressure hull forward of the sail. Due to the missile's short range, the need to determine targets acoustically, and their relatively slow speed, the submarines have limited tactical utility.

3 (+ . . .) Yankee Notch class Bldr: Severodvinsk SY

D: 9,400 tons (surf.)/11,500 tons (sub.) **S:** 27 kts (sub.)
Dim: 142.0 × 13.0 × 8.6
A: 40/SS-N-21 Sampson cruise missiles (*see* Remarks)—6/533-mm TT fwd (18 SS-N-15 missiles and/or torpedoes)
Electron Equipt:
Radar: 1/Snoop Tray—EW: . . .
Sonar: Shark Gill LF active/passive, passive array
M: 2 pressurized-water nuclear reactors, steam turbines; 2/5-bladed props; 50,000 shp
Endurance: 90 days **Crew:** 20 officers, 90 enlisted

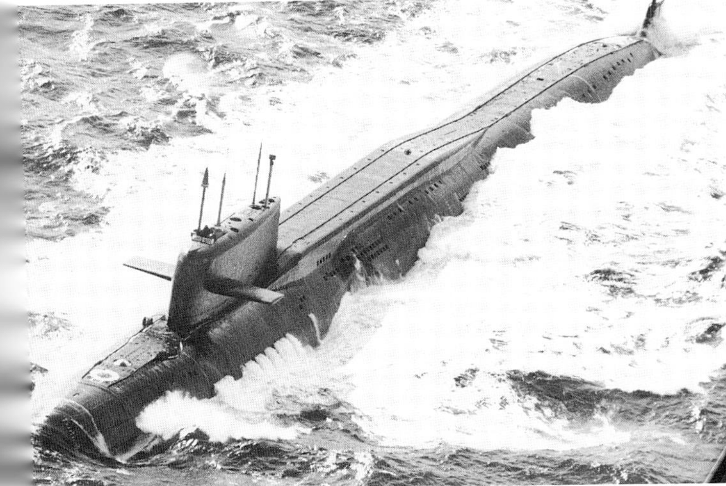

Yankee Notch class M.O.D. U.K.

Yankee Notch class M.O.D. U.K., 1990

Yankee Notch Class M.O.D. U.K., 1990

Remarks: First conversion completed around 1987, second shortly thereafter, and third in 1991. Reworked Yankee-I-class SSBNs with new midbody having horizontal tubes exiting via a "notch" on either beam; the number of launch tubes is unknown but is at least four. The sail has been reconfigured and lengthened by 3 m to 20 m overall. "Yankee Notch" is a *strategic* submarine in the Western sense, in that the SS-N-21 Sampson missiles are targeted against land vice ship targets. Missiles are launched while the submarine is submerged. Conversion project nickname may be "*Andromeda*" or "*Grushcha.*"

◆ **14 Modified Echo-II class (Project 675M)** Bldr: Severodvinsk SY and Komsomolsk SY (In serv. 1960–67)

Modified Echo-II class M.O.D. U.K., 1990

CRUISE-MISSILE ATTACK SUBMARINES (NUCLEAR-POWERED)

(continued)

Modified Echo-II with SS-N-12—note Front Door/Front Piece antenna deployed at forward end of sail, bulge on sail side, and relocated hinge bulge at forward end of the second missile-tube pair U.S. Navy, 1980

D: 5,000 tons (surf.)/6,000 tons (sub.) **S:** 20/23 kts
Dim: 115.0 × 9.0 × 7.5
A: 8/SS-N-12 SSM (II × 4)—6/533-mm TT fwd (18 torpedoes)—4/400-mm TT aft (no reloads)
Electron Equipt:
Radar: 1/Snoop Tray search, 1/Front Piece missile-height tracking, 1/Front Door missile tracking
Sonar: Shark Teeth LF active/passive arrays, including Feniks
EW: Squid Head or Brick Pulp intercept, Quad Loop D/F
M: 2 pressurized-water nuclear reactors, steam turbines; 2/4-bladed props; 30,000 shp
Crew: 90 tot.

Remarks: Of the original 29 built, 14 have been modified to launch SS-N-12 in place of the SS-N-3 originally carried; they have a bulge on either side of the sail and a bulge at the forward ends of the missile tubes abreast the sail and have been equipped with the Punch Bowl satellite targeting reception antenna. The Echo-II must be surfaced to launch, the tubes elevating in pairs to fire. The forward part of the sail rotates 180° to expose the Front Door/Front Piece missile-tracking radars.

On 26-6-89 an Echo-II suffered a nuclear-propulsion-related accident north of Norway. Examination of the damage has resulted in a decision to retire all "first generation" nuclear submarines "ahead of schedule." It is believed that by the end of 1991, all unmodified Echo-IIs had been discarded and that the surviving Modified Echo IIs will probably be stricken during the next two years. One other Echo-II has been disarmed as a research submarine—see later page.

CRUISE-MISSILE ATTACK SUBMARINES (DIESEL-POWERED)

(Soviet Type: PLRK = *Podvodnaya Lodka Raketnaya Krylataya* = Cruise-Missile Submarine)

◆ **9 Juliett class (Project 651)** Bldr: Krasnaya Sormova SY, Nizhniy Novgorod (ex-Gorkiy) (In serv. 1961–63)

Juliett class—with tug alongside forward Boris Lemachko, 1989

Juliett class U.S. Navy, 1987

Juliett class—with after pair of SS-N-3 Shaddock missile tubes raised U.S. Navy, 3-87

D: 3,000 tons (surf.)/3,750 tons (sub.) **S:** 14 kts (surf.)/14 kts (sub.)
Dim: 90.0 × 10.0 × 7.0
A: 4/SS-N-3A SSM (II × 2)—6/533-mm TT fwd (12 torpedoes)—4/400-mm TT aft (no reloads)
Electron Equipt:
Radar: 1/Snoop Slab or Snoop Plate search, 1/Front Piece missile-height tracking, 1/Front Door missile tracking
Sonar: 1/MF active/passive arrays—EW: Stop Light intercept
M: 2 diesels, electric drive; 2 props; 5,000 shp
Range: 9,000/7 (snorkel) **Crew:** 80 tot.

Remarks: Fifteen originally constructed. In 1981, three were transferred to the Baltic; two more followed in 1989, and a sixth in 1991. Missiles are in paired tubes elevating to fire while on the surface, as on the Echo-II class. One ("Modified Juliett") has been equipped with SS-N-12 missiles and the Punch Bowl satellite targeting reception antenna. Two were discarded prior to 1989, and two more Northern Fleet units entered the Baltic late in 1989 for probable scrapping. Units have also been operational in recent years in the Black Sea and Pacific Ocean Fleets, whose units appeared to have been discarded during 1990–91. The others will probably be discarded soon also.

ATTACK SUBMARINES (NUCLEAR-POWERED)

(Soviet Type: PLA—*Podvodnaya Lodka Atomnaya* = Nuclear-Powered Submarine)

◆ **7 (+ . . .) Akula (Project 671)** Bldr: Komsomolsk SY, Komsomolsk-na-Amur and Severodvinsk SY (In serv. 1985–. . .)

BARS PANTERA PUMA 4 others

Akula class M.O.D. U.K., 19

Akula class U.S. D.O.D., 1

Akula class U.S. Navy,

Akula class M.O.D. U.K

ATTACK SUBMARINES (NUCLEAR-POWERED) *(continued)*

D: 7,500 tons (surf.)/10,000 tons (sub.)
S: 25 kts (surf.)/35 kts (sub.)
Dim: 113.0 (107.0 wl) × 13.0 × 10.0
A: 2/650-mm TT fwd—6/533-mm TT (. . . SS-N-15, -16, and -21 missiles, torpedoes, mines)
Electron Equipt:
Radar: Snoop Pair search
Sonar: Shark Gill LF active/passive, passive array, towed LF linear hydrophone array
EW: Amber Light intercept, Rim Hat intercept, Park Lamp D/F
M: 2 pressurized-water nuclear reactors, steam turbines; 1/7-bladed prop; 45,000 shp
Crew: about 90 tot.

Remarks: First unit launched 7-84; the second in 1986, the third in 1987, the fourth in 1988 (at Severodvinsk, for the Northern Fleet), the fifth during 1989, and one each during 1990 and 1991 (*Puma*). Named units above were built at Northern Machine-building Factory, Severodvinsk; *Pantera* was commissioned during late 1-91. Production is expected to continue at both building yards, with an average completion rate of one per year.

Differs from the smaller Sierra in having a longer, more streamlined sail. Broader hull than preceding Victor series indicates probable use of "rafted" (sound-isolated) propulsion plant to greatly reduce radiated noise. *Akula* means "shark" in Russian; the NATO nickname was chosen because all the letters of the phonetic alphabet had been used to name earlier classes. Steel hull vice titanium on Sierra. Have Pert Spring SATCOMM antenna. The Snoop Pair radar and Rim Hat intercept array are on the same telescoping mast. All have a pod-mounted towed linear hydrophone array dispenser. Recent units have environmental sensor arrays on the casing forward of the sail for probable "non-acoustic" means of submarine detection. Soviet press (*Moskva Rabochaya Tribuna*, 24-1-91, pg. 46) stated that Akulas can dive to 1 km, but that may have been an exaggeration!

1 (+ . . .) Sierra-II class (Project 945B) and 2 Sierra-I class (Project 945A) Bldr: Krasnaya Sormova SY, Nizhniy Novgorod (ex-Gorkiy)(In serv. 1984–. . .)

[Sie]rra class R. Nor. A.F., 1984

[Sierr]a class—second unit, with extension at the base of the aft end of the [sail;] note the vee-shaped fairing in the middle of the sail that covers the [detac]hable crew rescue pod M.O.D. U.K., 1989

Sierra class R. Nor. A.F., 1984

D: Sierra-I: 6,050 tons (surf.)/7,600 tons (sub.); Sierra-II: 6,350/7,900 tons
S: 34–36 kts (sub.) **Dim:** 107.0 (Sierra-II: 112.0) × 12.5 × 7.4
A: 4/650-mm TT—2/533-mm TT (. . . SS-N-15, -16, -21 missiles, torpedoes, and/or mines)
Electron Equipt:
Radar: 1/Snoop Pair search
Sonar: LF suite, towed passive hydrophone array
EW: Rim Hat intercept, Park Lamp D/F
M: 2 pressurized-water nuclear reactors; 1/7-bladed prop; 45,000 shp
Crew: 70 tot.

Remarks: First unit launched 7-83 at Gorkiy and transferred via river/canal system to Severodvinsk for completion. Second unit, with low extension to aft end of sail, reported on trials 1987. The third was launched during 5-89. The third unit (Sierra-II) is 5 m longer and has a 6-m-longer sail. Also known as the "Barrakuda" class.

Differ from Akulas in having a blunter sail shape; probably have the same propulsion plant as Akula, optimized for radiated noise reduction. Have a titanium pressure hull. Carry environmental sensors on the sail for probable "non-acoustic" submarine detection and are equipped with a mast-mounted Pert Spring communications satellite antenna.

Note: The single Mike-class nuclear-powered attack submarine, *Komsomolets*, was lost as a result of fire and resultant flooding in the Barents Sea on 7-4-89 in 1,500-m-deep water; plans to raise the submarine have not borne fruit. The five Alfa-class liquid-metal reactor-powered attack submarines were withdrawn from service in 1990–91; while they were the world's fastest submarines, they had also presented numerous engineering reliability problems.

◆ **26 Victor-III class (Project 671PTM)** Bldrs: Admiralty SY, St. Petersburg, and Komsomolsk SY (In serv. 1978–1983, 1985–91)

Victor-III class French Navy, 6-90

Victor-III class—note pod housing towed linear hydrophone array atop vertical stabilizer M.O.D. U.K., 1990

ATTACK SUBMARINES (NUCLEAR-POWERED) *(continued)*

Victor-III—unit with housing forward of sail for two horizontal launch tubes, probably for the SS-N-21 Sampson strategic cruise missile 1990

Victor-III M.O.D. U.K., 1989

D: 4,900 tons (surf.)/6,000 tons (sub.) **S:** 30 kts (sub.)
Dim: 104.0 × 10.0 × 7.0
A: 4/650-mm TT—2/533-mm TT (24 SS-N-15 and/or SS-N-16 missiles, torpedoes, and/or up to 36 mines)
Electron Equipt:
Radar: 1/Snoop Tray-2 search—EW: Brick Pulp intercept, Park Lamp D/F
Sonar: Shark Gill LF active/passive, towed linear array
M: 2 pressurized-water nuclear reactors, steam turbines; 1/tandem 8-bladed prop; 30,000 shp (plus 2 small props for maneuvering)
Crew: 85 tot.

Remarks: Further lengthened over basic Victor-I; distinguished by large teardrop-shaped pod atop vertical stabilizer to house a towed linear passive hydrophone array system. Launchings resumed at St. Petersburg in 7-85 with the 21st unit; the 22nd was launched in the spring of 1987, the 23rd in 6-88, and one each year through 1991, when the program is believed to have ended. Construction may have continued as a means of maintaining force level while the more sophisticated Akula and Sierra classes are being built at a slower rate due to cost and complexity. Later units were Project 671 PTMK.

Have a towed VLF communications buoy, deployed from the casing abaft the sail. One unit has a 10-m fairing on deck forward of the sail containing two horizontal launch tubes in what is probably a trials installation for the SS-N-21 Sampson strategic cruise missile. Most employ an unusual 8-bladed propeller, consisting of two tandem 4-bladed props oriented 22.5° apart and co-rotating; others have a standard 7-bladed prop. Have Pert Spring SATCOMM antenna. Several have had environmental sensors installed on the foredeck and on the sail as part of an apparent "non-acoustic" submarine detection suite.

Dimensions and performance above appeared in a Soviet publication and are believed to be accurate; diving depth was given as 400 m.

♦ 7 Victor-II class (Project 671PT)
Bldr: Admiralty SY, St. Petersburg (In serv.1972–78)

Victor-II class—sail detail: both periscopes, Snoop Tray radar, Park Lamp D/F loop, and comms whip masts raised French Navy, 1990

Victor-II class M.O.D. U.K., 1988

Victor-II class—with bowplanes extended M.O.D., U.K., 19

D: 4,500 tons (surf.)/5,900 tons (sub.) **S:** 30 kts
Dim: 100.0 × 10.0 × 7.0
A: 6/533-mm TT (24 SS-N-15 missiles, torpedoes and/or up to 36 mines)
Electron Equipt:
Radar: Snoop Tray-2 search—Sonar: Shark Teeth LF active/passiv
EW: Brick Pulp and Brick Spit intercept, Park Lamp D/F
M: 2 pressurized-water nuclear reactors, steam turbines; 1/5-bladed prop (plus 2 small props for maneuvering); 30,000 shp
Crew: 80 tot.

Remarks: One went into service in each of the years 1972, 1974, and 1975, two 1976, and one each in 1977 and 1978. Longer than Victor-I, without pronounced hu on forward casing. Have a VLF comms-buoy housing within the casing abaft the s Some may have 8-bladed propellers as on the Victor-III class. Diving depth: 400 m

♦ 15 Victor-I class (Projects 671, 671M)
Bldr: Admiralty SY, St. Petersburg (In serv. 1968–75)

50 Let SSR 14 others

D: 4,300/5,100 tons **S:** 30 kts **Dim:** 95.0 × 10.0 × 7.0
A: 6/533-mm TT (24 SS-N-15 missiles, torpedoes, and/or up to 36 mines)
Electron Equipt:
Radar: 1/Snoop Tray-1 search
Sonar: Shark Teeth LF active/passive arrays
EW: Brick Pulp and Brick Spit intercept, 1/Park Lamp D/F
M: 2 pressurized-water nuclear reactors, steam turbines; 1/5-bladed prop; 30,000 shp (2 small, 2-bladed props for slow speeds)
Crew: 80 tot.

Victor-I class M.O.D., U.K.

ATTACK SUBMARINES (NUCLEAR-POWERED) *(continued)*

Victor-I class—note the characteristic "hump" to the casing forward of the ail that distinguishes the Victor-I from the Victor-II M.O.D., U.K., 1990

ctor-I class—with water cascading from the two rows of torpedo tubes d the centerline torpedo loading hatch M.O.D. U.K., 1989

marks: Completed two per year between 1968 and 1975. Diving depth: 400 m max. rating. Distinguishable from later Victor-II by "hump" to casing between the bow l the sail. One named *50 Let SSR*. One Pacific Ocean Fleet unit was irreparably naged during nuclear recoring operations on 10-8-85 at Chazma Bay, near Vladitok, and was subsequently discarded.

TACK SUBMARINES (DIESEL-POWERED)

iet Type: PL—*Podvodnaya Lodka* = Submarine)

20 (+ . . .) Kilo class (Project 877) Bldr: Komsomolsk-na-Amur SY, United Admiralty SY, St. Petersburg, and Krasnaya Sormova SY, Nizhniy Novgorod (ex-Gorkiy)(In serv. 1980–. . .)

class U.S. Navy, 1989

Kilo class Leo Van Ginderen, 1991

Kilo class U.S. Navy, 6-91

D: 2,325 tons (surf.)/3,076 tons (sub.)
S: 10 kts (surf.)/17 kts (sub.)
Dim: 74.3 (70.0 wl) × 10.0 × 6.6
A: 6/533-mm TT (18 SS-N-15 missiles, torpedoes, and up to 24 mines)—1/SA-N-5/8 SAM syst.
Electron Equipt:
Radar: 1/Snoop Tray-2 search
Sonar: Shark Gill LF active/passive suite, passive hull array
EW: Brick Pulp or Squid Head intercept; Quad Loop D/F
M: 3/1,825-bhp diesel generator sets, electric drive: 1 motor; 1/6-bladed prop; 5,900 shp
Range: 6,000/7 (surf.); 400/3 (sub.) **Crew:** 12 officers, 41 enlisted

Remarks: First unit launched 9-80, entering service 4-82. The second launched 8-81, and the third and fourth during 1983. In 1984, three were launched, including the first unit for export. In 1985 four (two for export) were launched, and in 1986 three of the four launched were for export. In 1987 and 1988, two of the four launched each year were for export, while in 1989 and 1990, only one of the four launched each year was for export. Three were launched in 1991 (of which one or two were for export), but subsequent production is expected to average only one per year for the Russian Navy and one for export. Foreign customers (Project 877E) have been India (eight delivered, with more possibly on order), Algeria (2), Poland (1), Romania (1), and Iran (2 or 3). Syria and, less likely, Libya are possible future customers. Units built at United Admiralty Shipyard are believed all to have been for export. Most Russian Navy units are in the Pacific Ocean Fleet.

Have anechoic hull coating like larger nuclear submarines. The shoulder-launched SA-14 SAM launch position is located in the after portion of the sail. Data above apply to the Polish unit but are probably typical for the class. Diving depth: 300 m. Probably have some means of auxiliary propulsion, such as low-power (100–150 kw) electric creep motor on the main shaft for low-speed, quiet operations.

◆ **18 Tango Class (Project 641B)** Bldr: Krasnaya Sormovoa SY, Nizhniy Novgorod (ex-Gorkiy) (In serv. 1972–82)

Gorkovskiy Komsomolets Magnitogorskiy Komsomolets
16 others

Tango class U.S. Navy, 1989

ATTACK SUBMARINES (DIESEL-POWERED) *(continued)*

Tango class—running nearly awash U.S. Navy, 6-90

Tango class French Navy, 6-90

Tango class French Navy, 1990

D: 3,100 tons (surf.)/3,900 tons (sub.) **S:** 20 kts (surf.)/16 kts (sub.)
Dim: 91.5 × 9.0 × 7.0
A: 10/533-mm TT (6 fwd, 4 aft—24–28 SS-N-15 missiles, torpedoes, and/or mines)
Electron Equipt:
Radar: 1/Snoop Tray-1 or -2 search
Sonar: Shark Teeth LF active/passive suite; passive hull array
EW: Brick Pulp and Brick Spit intercept, Quad Loop D/F
M: 3 diesels, electric motors; 3 props; 6,000 shp
Endurance: 20,000/11 (surf.); 380/3 (sub.)
Crew: 12 officers, 50 enlisted

Remarks: Also known as the "*Som*" class. Two entered service in 1972, and roughl[y] two per year were built. Hull sheathed in anechoic sonar-absorbent rubber compound[.] Have significantly greater battery capacity than the Foxtrot class, and greater interna[l] volume provides more space for weapons reloads. Previous figure of "22" built wa[s] incorrect. EW arrays vary; some have Squid Head. All but one believed to be i[n] Northern Fleet; one is in the Black Sea Fleet.

◆ **40 Foxtrot class (Project 641)** Bldr: Admiralty/Sudomekh SY, St. Petersburg; Severodvinsk SY (In serv. 1957–68)

Bryanskiy Komsomolets	Ul'yanovskiy Komsomolets
Chelyabinskiy Komsomolets	Vladimirskiy Komsomolets
Kuibishevskiy Komsomolets	Yaroslavskiy Komsomolets
Magnitogorskiy Komsomolets	33 others

Foxtrot class—late-construction limber-hole pattern, with folding I[...] whip raised U.S. Navy, 7-[...]

Foxtrot class . . . ., 1[...]

Foxtrot class—early-construction limber-hole pattern French Nav[y]

ATTACK SUBMARINES (DIESEL-POWERED) *(continued)*

xtrot class French Navy, 6-90

): 1,957 tons (surf.)/2,485 tons (sub.)
;: 15.5 kts (surf.)/18 kts (sub.)
)im: 91.30 (89.70 pp) × 7.50 × 6.00
\: 10/533-mm TT (6 fwd, 4 aft—22 torpedoes or 44 mines)
:lectron Equipt:
Radar: 1/Snoop Tray-1 search—Sonar: 1/MF active; passive arrays
EW: 1/Stop Light intercept; Quad Loop D/F
/I: 3 Type 37D or Type 42 diesels of 2,000/1,825 bhp, 3 electric motors; 3/5 or 6-bladed props; 5,400 shp (sub.)
tange: 20,000/8 (surf.); 11,000/8 (snorkel); 36/18 (sub.); 380/2 (sub.)
:ndurance: 70 days **Fuel:** 360 tons (527 max.)
:rew: 12 officers, 70 enlisted

narks: Foxtrot is a "long-range" submarine, and the design is a development of of the now-stricken Zulu class, with a large bow passive sonar array added and a e streamlined sail. Between 1967 and 1983, 17 were built for export at St. Peters- ;: 8 to India, 6 to Libya, and 3 to Cuba. Poland has received 2 ex-Soviet units on . Several Soviet Navy units have been lost. Early units are obsolescent, based on ned 27-year service life for this class, and at least 20 had been discarded or lost by .

ew size listed is maximum accommodations; in recent years most have run with as as 9 officers and 50 enlisted. Names listed above will probably change with the emberment of the former Communist Youth League (Komsomol).

:: During 1989–91, Whiskey class (Project 613) submarines were disposed of in numbers in foreign scrapyards, and by 1991, none were left in Soviet Navy ce.

XILIARY SUBMARINES (NUCLEAR-POWERED)

Xray class Bldr: United Admiralty SY (Sudomekh Division), St. etersburg (In serv. 1983)

. . . **S:** . . . **Dim:** 39.6 × 3.0 × . . .
probably none **Electron Equipt:** . . .
: 1 nuclear reactor; . . . **Crew:** . . .

arks: Reportedly analogous to the U.S. Navy's NR-1 and intended for oceano- ic research purposes.

◆ **2 Uniform class** Bldr: United Admiralty SY (Sudomekh Division), St. Petersburg

D: 2,000 tons (sub.) **S:** . . . **Dim:** 73.0 × 7.0 × . . .
A: . . . **M:** nuclear reactor; . . . prop; . . . shp **Crew:** . . .

Remarks: Apparently intended for research or special operations. The first Soviet single-hulled nuclear-powered submarines. First launched 6-82, second in 4-88.

◆ **1 Yankee-class missile trials conversion** Bldr: Severodvinsk SY (In serv. pre-1974)

Yankee-conversion cruise-missile trials submarine—artist's conception U.S. D.O.D., 1987

D: 10,550 tons (surf.)/13,650 tons (sub.) **S:** 23 kts (sub.)
Dim: 153.0 × 18.0 × 9.0
A: 12/SS-NX-24 SSM—6/533-mm TT fwd (18 SS-N-15 missiles and/or torpedoes)
Electron Equipt:
Radar: 1/Snoop Tray—EW: . . .
Sonar: Shark Teeth LF active, Shark Gill active/passive, passive array
M: 2 pressurized-water reactors, steam turbines; 2/5-bladed props; 50,000 shp
Endurance: 90 days **Crew:** 20 officers, 90 enlisted

Remarks: Converted from a Yankee-I that had had the SS-N-6 ballistic-missile system deleted in compliance with SALT agreements. Relaunched 12-82 as trials submarine for the SS-NX-24 cruise-missile system. Addition of cruise missiles apparently greatly added to the ship's beam, reducing speed and maneuverability. Development of the SS-NX-24 strategic cruise missile has ceased, and the submarine will probably soon be discarded.

◆ **1 Yankee class** Bldr: Severodvinsk SY (In serv. pre-1974)

D: 8,000/10,100 tons **S:** 27 kts (sub.)
Dim: 134.0 × 12.0 × 9.0
A: probably none
Electron Equipt:
Radar: 1/Snoop Tray—EW: . . .
Sonar: submarine suite trials arrays
M: 2 pressurized-water nuclear reactors, steam turbines; 2/5-bladed props; 45,000 shp
Endurance: 90 days **Crew:** 20 officers, 80 enlisted

AUXILIARY SUBMARINES (NUCLEAR-POWERED) *(continued)*

Yankee-class sonar trials submarine French Navy, 6-90

Remarks: Unique conversion of a former ballistic-missile submarine. Completed alterations 1984, lengthened by 4 m to accommodate Shark Gill low-frequency sonar suite. Subsequent photography has revealed that the ship is equipped with a variety of submarine sensor systems for trials purposes and that the equipment includes a pod atop the vertical stabilizer to accommodate a towed linear passive hydrophone array; there is also a second towed array dispenser tube just below the pod. Mounted on either side of the forward edge of the sail are what appear to be fixed torpedo front-end bodies, indicating possible use for trials of torpedo seeker systems. The new sonar equipment mounted at the bow is believed to have required removal of the torpedo tubes.

♦ **1 converted Echo-II class**

D: 5,000 tons (surf.)/6,000 tons (sub.)
S: 20 kts (surf.)/23 kts (sub.) **Dim:** 115.0 × 9.0 × 7.5
A: 6/533-mm TT (fwd)—4/400-mm TT (aft)
Electron Equipt:
Radar: 1/Snoop Tray-1—Sonar: . . .—EW: . . .
M: 2 pressurized-water nuclear reactors, steam turbines, 2 props; 30,000 shp
Crew: . . .

Remarks: One Echo-II-class nuclear-powered cruise-missile submarine has been modified for an unknown research purpose. The eight tubes for SS-N-3A missiles have been removed. May be intended for special operations with *Spetsnaz* sabotage swimmers.

Note: The single Hotel-class nuclear-powered ballistic-missile submarine converted to serve as a submarine sensor suite trials ship has probably been retired as part of the general layup of first-generation Soviet nuclear-powered submarines.

AUXILIARY SUBMARINES (DIESEL-POWERED)

♦ **1 Beluga-class trials submarine** Bldr: United Admiralty SY (Sudomekh Division), St. Petersburg (In serv. 1987)

SS-533

D: 2,000 tons (surf.)/2,500 (sub.) **S:** 12 kts (surf.)/30+ kts (sub.)
Dim: 62.0 × 8.7 × 6.0 **A:** none
M: diesel-electric, possible closed-cycle air-independent propulsion system; 1 prop; est. 5,300 shp
Crew: . . .

Beluga sail area—note sensor head to port below sail *International Defense Review,* 1991

Beluga-class trials submarine *International Defense Review,* 199

Remarks: Experimental submarine with hull form like that of Alfa, but with a low sail. Not armed or intended for combat service. May have a closed-cycle diesel-power air-independent propulsion system for trials. Double-hulled, as indicated by t limber-hole pattern extending well forward to the bow. By 1991 was attached to t Black Sea Fleet.

♦ **1 Lima-class research submarine (Project 18-40)** Bldr: Admiralty SY (Sudomekh Division), St. Petersburg (In serv. 1978)

BS-555

Lima-class trials submarine Boris Lemachko, 19

D: 2,000 tons (surf.)/2,400 tons (sub.)
S: 12 kts (surf.)/12 kts (sub.) **Dim:** 86.0 × 9.5 × 7.4 **A:** none
Electron Equipt:
Radar: Snoop Tray search—Sonar: *see* Remarks
M: diesels, electric drive; 1 prop; 2,500 shp **Crew:** . . .

Remarks: Sail, set well aft on unusually bulky hull, has forward extension hou an active sonar transducer and has fixed radar mast. There is also an integral b mounted sonar transducer array. Returned to the St. Petersburg area in 1989 a having served since completion in the Black Sea.

♦ **2 India-class salvage submarines (Project 940)** Bldr: Komsomolsk SY, Komsomolsk-na-Amur (In serv. 1979–80)

BS-498 BS-. . .

Pacific Fleet India—with two salvage submersibles in their doc wells J.M.S.

Pacific Fleet India U.S. Navy

AUXILIARY SUBMARINES (DIESEL-POWERED) *(continued)*

D: 3,900 tons (surf.)/4,800 tons (sub.)
S: 15 kts (surf.)/15 kts (sub.)
Dim: 106.0 × 10.0 × 7.0 **A:** probably none
Electron Equipt:
Radar: Snoop Tray—Sonar: MF and HF active/passive suite
EW: Squid Head and Stop Light intercept, Quad Loop D/F
M: 2 diesel generator sets; 2 props; 4,000 shp—bow-thruster
Crew: . . .

Remarks: Hull designed for surface cruising. Probably do not have armament, con-idering function and the narrow hull configuration forward. Originally carried two 1-m salvage/submarine-rescue submersibles in wells on after casing; the Pacific Fleet nit had been re-equipped with 12.1-m craft by 1987. One unit remains in Pacific, the ther transited the Arctic to the Northern Fleet, 1980.

◆ **4 Bravo-class target-training submarines (Project 690)** Bldr: Komsomolsk SY, Komsomolsk-na-Amur (In serv. 1968–70)

S-622 SS-638 SS-. . . SS-. . .

avo class M.O.D. U.K.

vo class—at Vladivostok Leo Van Ginderen, 2-92

: 2,400 tons (surf.)/2,900 tons (sub.)
14 kts (surf.)/16 kts (sub.)
im: 70.1 × 9.8 × 7.3 **A:** none
lectron Equipt:
Radar: 1/Snoop Tray
Sonar: active bow array, passive array
EW: . . .
: diesel-electric drive; 1 prop; 4,500 shp **Crew:** 65 tot.

arks: Configured as "hard" targets for torpedo-firing training, they may also a training role. Bow shape and low location of sonar window may indicate that are not armed. Units stationed in the Northern, Pacific Ocean, and Black Sea to provide target services.

Romeo-class (Project 633) torpedo systems trials ıbmarine Bldr: . . . (In serv. 1959-61)

ified Romeo Leo Van Ginderen, 8-91

D: 1,350 tons surf./1,760 tons sub. **S:** 15.2 kts surf./12 kts sub.
Dim: 78.60 × 6.70 × 4.95
A: 2/650-mm TT fwd—2/533-mm TT aft (*see* Remarks)
Electron Equipt:
Radar: 1/Snoop Plate
Sonar: Tamir 5 L active, Feniks passive
M: diesel-electric: 2 Type 37D diesels, 2,400 bhp each; 2 props; 2,700 shp—2 electric creep motors: 100 shp
Endurance: 60 days **Range:** 14,000/9 surf.; 350/9 sub.
Crew: 6 officers, 36 enlisted

Remarks: First noted 1991 but probably converted some years ago, a Romeo-class diesel attack submarine modified by the addition of a massive structure atop the bow to accommodate what are probably two 650-mm torpedo tubes for trials purposes; the structure appears to be free-flooding and thus contains no reload facilities for the tubes. The forward six 533-mm torpedo tubes have probably been deleted, but the stern pair may have been retained. The new structure appears to extend the overall length by about 2 meters. Revised characteristics above are estimated.

MIDGET SUBMARINES

◆ **2 Losos class (Soviet Project 865)**
Bldr: United Admiralty SY, St. Petersburg

MS-520 (In serv. 12-88) MS-521 (In serv. 1991?)

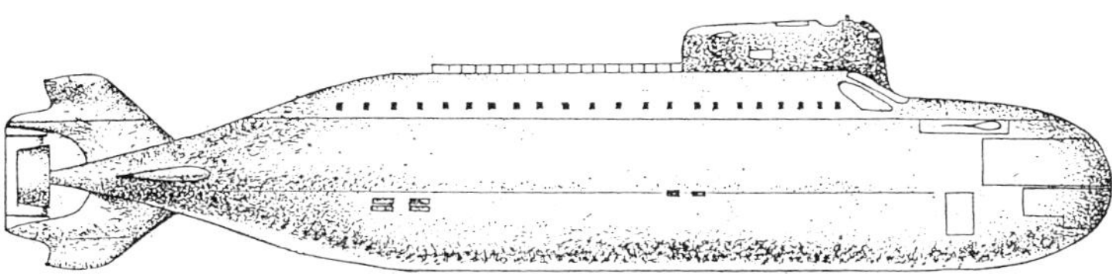

Losos class *Izvestiya,* 1-92

D: 219 tons (sub.) **S:** 6.5 kts (sub.) **Dim:** 28.0 × 4.0 × . . .
A: 2/533-mm TT (2 torpedoes)—*see* Remarks
M: 1 diesel, electric drive; 1 prop; . . . shp
Range: 540/. . . surf.; 60/6.5 sub. **Endurance:** 10 days
Crew: 3 + 3 combat swimmers

Remarks: The subject of caustic press commentary. The craft are said to be too heavy, too difficult to operate, and unable to meet hovering requirement, and no more are to be built. Said to have made 170 trips to sea between them, but never more than 10 n.m. from Liepaja. Intended to dive to 200 m and to act as special forces transports, salvage craft, or submarine rescue units, as well as to serve as combatant submarines. The weapons-stowage area beneath the casing atop the pressure hull is said have interchangeable torpedo tubes, rescue equipment, or a manipulator for handling objects on the bottom. They are either to be stored ashore for future use or relegated as museum exhibits.

Note: A number of small submersibles for clandestine operations by *Spetsnaz* forces are also in service. Some are probably similar to the salvage submersibles carried by the India class. Many other small submersibles, Soviet and foreign-built, are used for military and civilian research purposes.

GUIDED-MISSILE CRUISERS (NUCLEAR-POWERED)

◆ **3 (+1) Kirov class (Project 1144)** Bldr: Baltic SY, St. Petersburg, Russia

	Laid down	L	In serv.	Fleet.
Admiral Ushakov (ex-*Kirov*)	1973	26-12-77	9-80	Northern
Admiral Lazarev (ex-*Frunze*)	1-78	23-5-81	8-84	Pacific
Admiral Nakhimor (ex-*Kalinin*)	5-83	29-4-86	12-88	Northern
Petr Velikiy (ex-*Yuri Andropov*)	24-4-86	4-89	1993	. . . . . .

Admiral Ushakov (as Kirov)—note recess at stern for VDS door French Navy, 6-90

GUIDED-MISSILE CRUISERS (NUCLEAR-POWERED) *(continued)*

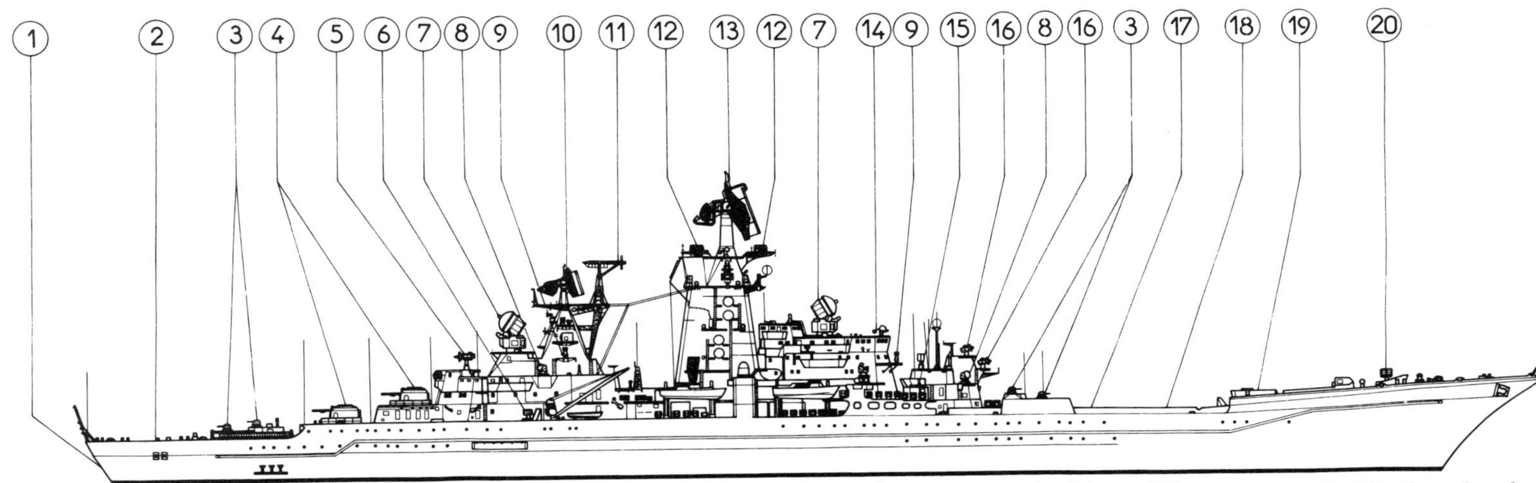

Admiral Ushakov 1. variable-depth sonar 2. helicopter pad 3. 30-mm AK-630 gatling AA guns 4. 100-mm DP gun mounts 5. Kite Screech radar director for 100-mm guns 6. RBU-1000 ASW RL 7. Top Dome radar director for SA-N-6 8. Bass Tilt radar director for 30-mm AA 9. Tin Man optronic device 10. Top Steer radar 11. Vee Tube HF comms antenna 12. Round House TACAN 13. Top Pair 3-D early-warning radar antenna 14. Palm Frond navigational radar 15. SA-N-4 SAM launcher 16. Eye Bowl radar director for SS-N-14 17. SS-N-19 cruise-missile launchers 18. SA-N-6 vertical SAM launch silos 19. twin SS-N-14 ASW/SSM launcher 20. RBU-6000 ASW RL Drawing: Capitaine de Frégate L. Gassier

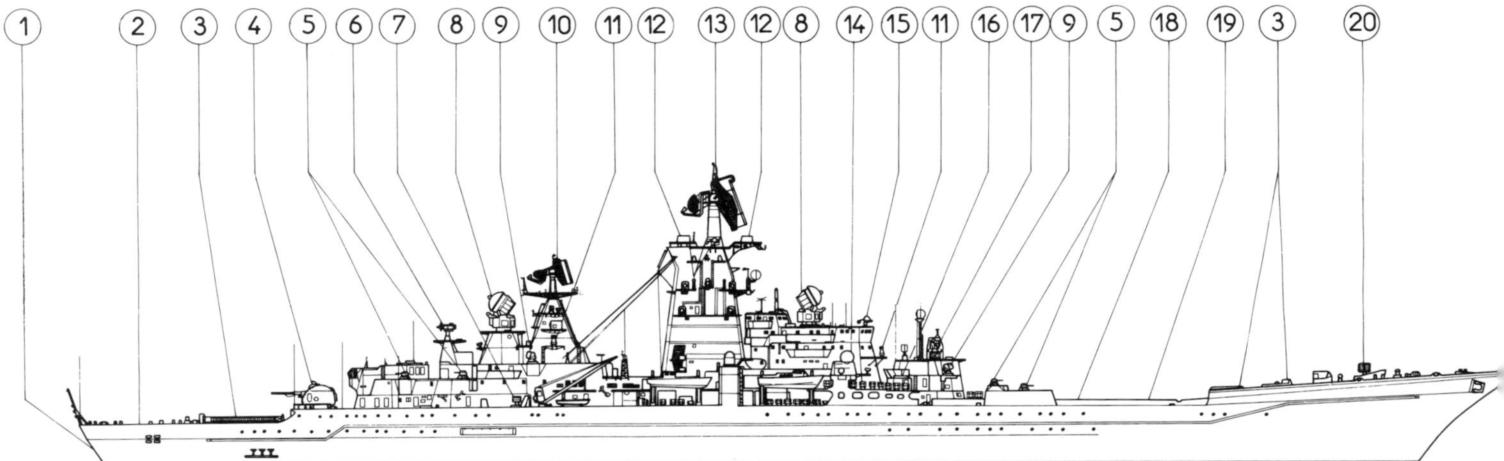

Admiral Lazarev 1. variable-depth sonar 2. helicopter pad 3. SA-N-9 vertical-launch SAM silos 4. twin 130-mm DP gun mount 5. 30-mm AK-6 gatling AA 6. Kite Screech radar director for 130-mm guns 7. RBU-1000 ASW RL 8. Top Dome radar director for SA-N-6 9. Bass Tilt radar director 30-mm AA 10. Top Steer radar antenna 11. Tin Man optronic device 12. Round House TACAN 13. Top Pair 3-D early-warning radar antenna 14. B Ball SATCOMM antenna radome 15. Palm Frond navigational radar 16. SA-N-4 SAM launcher 17. Pop Group track-while-scan radar director SA-N-4 18. SS-N-19 cruise-missile launchers 19. SA-N-6 vertical SAM launch silos 20. RBU-6000 ASW RL Drawing: Capitaine de Frégate L. Gassi

Admiral Ushakov French Navy,

GUIDED-MISSILE CRUISERS (NUCLEAR-POWERED) *(continued)*

Admiral Nakhimov 7-91

Admiral Nakhimov U.S. Navy, 1-91

Admiral Lazarev—two Ka-27PL Helix-A and one Ka-25 Hormone-B helos on deck, elevator up and hangar doors open U.S. Navy, 1990

Admiral Ushakov—superstructure detail, showing plethora of antennas French Navy, 12-89

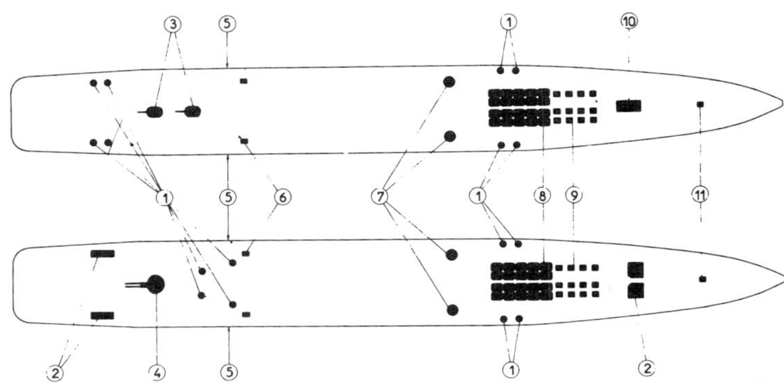

Ushakov (top) and Lazarev compared 1. 6-barreled 30-mm gatling AA 2. provision for SA-N-9 silos (8 missiles each) 3. 100-mm single-mount DP 4. 130-mm twin-mount DP 5. quintuple torpedo tubes 6. RBU-1000 ASW RL (6-tubed) 7. SA-N-4 twin SAM launchers (20 missiles each) 8. SS-N-19 inclined cruise-missile launch-tube hatches 9. SA-N-6 vertical-launch SAM hatches (8 missiles to each position) 10. twin SS-N-14 ASW missile launcher 11. RBU-6000 ASW RL (12-tubed) *Kalinin* resembles *Frunze* but has no torpedo tubes or AK-630 gatling guns; instead, six SA-N-11/30-mm gatling AA mounts are installed (four aft, two forward).

Admiral Lazarev U.S. Navy, 7-91

D: 24,300 tons (28,300 fl) **S:** 30 kts
Dim: 252.0 (230.0 wl) × 28.0 (24.0 wl) × 11.0 (max.)
A:
Ushakov: 20/SS-N-19 Shipwreck SSM (20 inclined tubes)—12/SA-N-6 vertical SAM launchers (96 Grumble missiles)—2/SA-N-4 SAM syst. (II × 2, 40 Gecko missiles)—2/100-mm DP (I × 2)—8/30-mm AK-630 gatling AA (I × 8)—1/SS-N-14 ASW cruise-missile launcher (II × 1, 14–16 missiles)—10/533-mm TT (V × 2)—1/RBU-6000 ASW RL (XII × 1)—2/RBU-1000 ASW RL (VI × 2)—2/Helix-A helicopters—1/Hormone-B helicopter
Lazarev: 20/SS-N-19 Shipwreck SSM (20 inclined tubes)—12/SA-N-6 vertical SAM launchers (96 Grumble missiles)—provision for 16/SA-N-9 vertical SAM launchers (VII × 2; 256 missiles—not yet operational)—2/SA-N-4 SAM syst. (II × 2, 40 Gecko missiles)—2/130-mm DP (II × 1)—8/30-mm AK-630 gatling AA (I × 8)—10/533-mm TT (V × 2; 10 torpedoes and/or SS-N-15 missiles)—1/RBU-6000 ASW RL (XII × 1)—2/RBU-1000 ASW RL (VI × 2)—2/Helix-A and 1/Hormone-B helicopters
Nakhimov: 20/SS-N-19 Shipwreck SSM (20 inclined tubes)—12/SA-N-6 vertical SAM launchers (96 Grumble missiles)—2/SA-N-4 SAM systems (II × 2; 40 Gecko missiles)—provision for 16/SA-N-9 vertical SAM launchers, not yet operational (VIII × 16, 256 missiles)—6/CADS-1 point-defense syst. (VIII × 6, each with 2/30-mm gatling AA; est. 192 SA-N-11 missiles)—2/130-mm DP—10/533-mm TT (V × 2; 10 torpedoes and/or SS-N-15 missiles)—1/RBU-12000 ASW RL (X × 1)—2/RBU-1000 ASW RL (VI × 2)—2/Helix-A and 1/Hormone-B helicopters

Electron Equipt:
Ushakov:
Radar: 3/Palm Frond nav., 1/Top Pair 3-D early warning, 1/Top Steer 3-D air search, 2/Top Dome SA-N-6 f.c., 2/Pop Group SA-N-4 f.c., 2/Eye Bowl SS-N-14 f.c., 1/Kite Screech 100-mm f.c., 4/Bass Tilt 30-mm, 1/Fly Screen landing aid
Sonar: Horse Jaw bow-mounted LF, Horse Tail LF VDS
EW: 8/Side Globe, 4/Rum Tub, 10/Bell-series, 2/chaff RL (II × 2)
TACAN: 2/Round House—SATCOMM: 2/Punch Bowl
IFF: interrogation by radars, Salt Pot transponder—E/O: 4/Tin Man
Lazarev:
Radar: 3/Palm Frond nav., 1/Top Pair 3-D early warning, 1/Top Steer 3-D air search, 2/Top Dome SA-N-6 , 2/Pop Group SA-N-4 f.c., 1/Kite Screech 130-mm f.c., 4/Bass Tilt 30-mm f.c., 1/Fly Screen landing aid, provision for 2 Cross Sword SA-N-9 f.c.

GUIDED-MISSILE CRUISERS (NUCLEAR-POWERED) *(continued)*

Sonar: Horse Jaw bow-mounted LF, Horse Tail LF VDS
EW: 8/Wine Flask, 10/Bell-series, 2/chaff RL (II × 2)
TACAN: 2/Round House—SATCOMM: 2/Low Ball, 2/Punch Bowl
IFF: interrogation by radars, Salt Pot transponder—E/O: 4/Tin Man

Kalinin:
Radar: 3/Palm Frond nav., 1/Top Pair 3-D early warning, 1/Top Plate 3-D air search, 2/Top Dome SA-N-6 f.c., 2/Pop Group SA-N-4 f.c., 1/Kite Screech, 6/Hot Flash CADS-1 f.c., 1/Fly Screen landing aid, provision for 2/Cross Sword SA-N-9 f.c.
Sonar: Horse Jaw bow-mounted LF, Horse Tail LF VDS
EW: 8/Foot Ball, 4/Bell Bash, 4/Bell Nip, 4/Bell Push, 4/Bell Thumb, 2/decoy RL (II × 2)
E/O: 4 Tin Man—TACAN: 2/Round House
SATCOMM: 2 Punch Bowl, 2/Low Ball
IFF: 2/Long Head interrogators, interrogation also by radars, 2/Salt Pot transponders

M: CONAS (Combined Nuclear And Steam turbine): 2 nuclear reactors + 2 oil-fired boilers, steam turbines; 2 props; 140,000 shp
Range: effectively unlimited **Fuel:** 2,500 tons
Endurance: 60 days **Crew:** 82 officers, 610 enlisted

Remarks:
General: The *Kirov* class are the world's largest "cruisers" and might best be termed "battlecruisers." Also known in Russia as the *"Orlan"* (Eagle) class. The type-designation applied has been RKR—*Raketnyy Kreyser* (Missile Cruiser) or, on occasion, *Atomnaya Raketnyy Kreyser*. The ships are capable of independent operations, due to the virtual autonomy conveyed by the nuclear-propulsion system, but would also make ideal escorts for the new carriers. The *Ushakov* and *Lazarev* differ considerably in armament and sensors, and *Nakhimov*, laid down some years later, differs further still. *Lazarev* deployed to the Pacific in 9-10-85, while *Ushakov* and *Nakhimov* are in the Northern Fleet. The fourth unit will probably resemble the *Nakhimov* configuration but have the SA-N-9 SAM system installed as completed. A fifth unit was laid down in 1989, but work halted almost immediately, and the components were scrapped in 11-89. *Ushakov* had a minor nuclear power-related accident while on a Mediterranean deployment, 1-90, and has not deployed since. Displacement, dimensional, horsepower, and other data above modified to conform with published Russian data. The names were changed 5-92.

Hull: On *Ushakov*, the high forecastle shelters the reloadable SS-N-14 ASW cruise-missile launcher within a redoubt or cul-de-sac. A long, raised strake down either side of the hull acts as an external hull stiffener, as on smaller Russian warships. The helicopter hangar is beneath the forward portion of the fantail, with an elevator delivering the aircraft to the flight deck. The steeply raked stern has a 9-m broad centerline recess for the VDS installation, whose door when closed is raked forward past the vertical. The screws appear to be mounted unusually far forward. Two solid-stores replenishment stations are fitted: one amidships to port, and one folding station forward to port, abreast the SA-N-6 system; both employ the sliding-stay, constant-tension concept. Oil and water replenishments are handled at stations on either beam abreast the Kite Screech radar. The forward transfer gear is considerably more compact on *Lazarev* and *Nakhimov*.

Propulsion: The two circular reactor access hatches can be seen amidships, just abaft the enormous twin exhaust uptakes for the unusual CONAS (Combined Nuclear And Steam) propulsion system. The oil-fired boilers provide steam to completely separate turbines, which are geared to the same drive shafts as the nuclear-supplied turbines. One stack probably serves the oil-fired boilers, while the other serves to ventilate the reactor spaces. Speed on reactors alone (90,000 shp) would be about 24 kts.

Armament: The launch tubes for the 20 SS-N-19 antiship missiles are buried within the hull at a fixed angle of 40–45-degree elevation, in four rows of five, forward of the superstructure. Before these are the 12 vertical launchers for SA-N-6; each has a door, beneath which is a rotating magazine containing 8 missiles. Targeting data for the SS-N-19, with its 300-nautical-mile maximum range, can come either from a Hormone-B helicopter embarked on the ship, or from satellites, via the Punch Bowl satellite communications antennas on either side of the ship. In *Ushakov* only, the ASW cruise-missile system is the only *reloadable* SS-N-14 installation in a Russian ship, employing a magazine forward of the launcher, buried within the forecastle. The official publication *Morskoy Sbornik* has stated that *Lazarev* and *Nakhimov* have "rocket torpedoes" in place of SS-N-14, a presumed reference to the SS-N-15 missile system, originally developed for submarine use; *Nakhimov* was incorrectly stated in the last edition not to have torpedoes. The gatling gun mounts are paired and located so as to cover all four quadrants; each pair is served by a Bass Tilt radar director and a manned, Kolonka-2 ringsight backup director. *Lazarev* and *Nakhimov* have a single twin 130-mm gun mount in place of the two 100-mm mounts and lack the SS-N-14 system; instead, eight SA-N-9 launchers will eventually be installed within the forecastle, while eight more are to be located flanking the helicopter elevator, four per side (the gatling guns are mounted on the aft superstructure). The two Cross Sword directors for SA-N-9 are yet to be mounted in *Lazarev* and *Nakhimov* and are intended to be positioned abaft the after Kite Screech and between the two Pop Group directors forward; the SA-N-4 installation may be a temporary stopgap. *Nakhimov* has the new RBU-12000 ASW rocket launcher vice RBU-6000 and mounts the new CADS-1 combined twin long-barrel 30-mm gun and octuple, reloadable SA-N-11 missile system vice the 30-mm AK-630 mounts.

Electronic equipment: As might be expected, the communications antenna array is extensive and diverse and includes satellite communications equipment and long-range HF gear. There are four stabilized Tin Man electro-optical sensors, covering all four quadrants, as well as several smaller remote t.v. cameras. Two Bob Tail radiometric sextant antennas are housed in spherical enclosures. A Fly Screen microwave landing-approach radar is mounted on a starboard platform on the after tower mast. The Horse Tail VDS employs a lens-shaped "fish" about 4 m in diameter to house the transducer and has a twin boom-mounted empennage with horizontal and vertical control surfaces. In addition to a low-frequency bow-mounted sonar, there is probably a medium-frequency set for fire-control purposes (including depth determination) for the RBU-series rocket launchers (which also have a torpedo countermeasures function). *Frunze* lacks the large Vee Tube HF communications antenna but has port-and-starboard Low Ball SATCOMM antenna radomes; she has a newer model EW suite also. (The devices listed here as Wine Flask have also been referred to as "Modified Football"; they appear to be combined receiver/jammers.) *Nakhimov's* electronics antenna suite is further updated; both she and *Lazarev* have provision for later installation of Cross Sword radar directors for the SA-N-9 system fore and aft.

GUIDED-MISSILE CRUISERS

◆ **3 (+1) Slava class (Project 1164)** Bldr: 61 Kommuna SY, Nikolayev, Ukraine

	Laid down	L	In serv.	Fleet
SLAVA ("Glory")	1976	1979	1982	Black Sea
MARSHAL USTINOV (ex-*Admiral Lobov*)	1978	1981	1986	Northern
CHERVONA UKRAINA ("Heart of the Ukraine")	1979	7-83	1989	Pacific
ADMIRAL LOBOV (ex-*Komsomolets*)	. . .	15-8-90	1993	. . . . . .

Chervona Ukraina—note Top Plate radar in place of Top Steer
U.S. Navy, 10-

Chervona Ukraina U.S. Navy,

Marshal Ustinov U.S. Navy

GUIDED-MISSILE CRUISERS *(continued)*

Chervona Ukraina — French Navy, 10-90

Marshal Ustinov — U.S. Navy, 7-91

Marshal Ustinov — French Navy, 10-90

Marshal Ustinov — Dr. Giorgio Arra, 7-91

D: 9,000 tons (11,500 fl) **S:** 30 kts
Dim: 186.0 × 21.0 × 9.0 (max.)
A: 16/SS-N-12 Sandbox SSM (II × 8)—8/SA-N-6 vertical-launch SAM groups (VIII × 8, 64 Grumble missiles)—2/SA-N-4 SAM syst. (II × 2, 40 Gecko missiles)—2/130-mm 70-cal. DP (II × 1)—6/30-mm AK-630 gatling AA (I × 6)—10/533-mm TT (V × 2)—2/RBU-6000 ASW RL (XI × 2)—1/Ka-25 Hormone-B helicopter
Electron Equipt:
Radar: 3/Palm Frond nav., 1/Top Pair 3-D early warning, 1/Top Steer (*Chervona Ukraina:* Top Plate) 3-D air search, 1/Top Dome SA-N-6 f.c., 2/Pop Group SA-N-4 f.c., 1/Kite Screech 130-mm f.c., 3/Bass Tilt 30-mm f.c., 1/Front Door-C SS-N-12 tracking
Sonar: Bull Nose hull-mounted LF, Horse Tail MF VDS
EW: 8/Side Globe, 4/Rum Tub, 2/Bell Crown, 2/Bell Push, . . ./Bell-series, 2/trainable RL (II × 2)(*Chervona Ukraina* also: 12/10-tubed, fixed decoy RL)

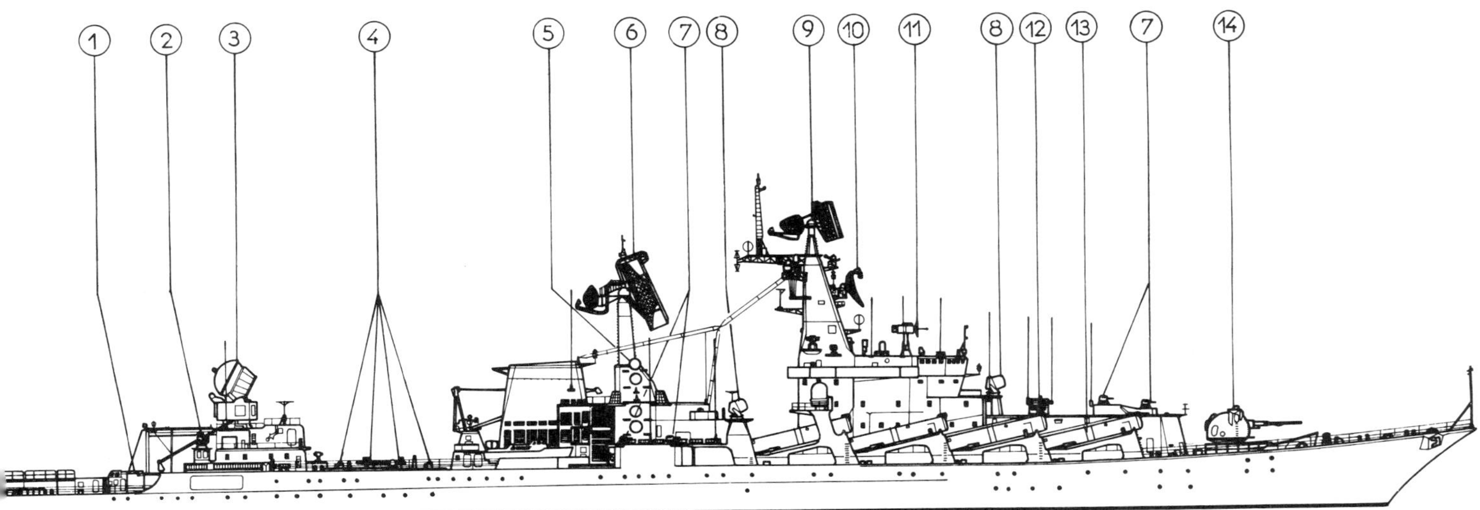

a 1. SA-N-4 launchers port and starboard 2. Pop Group radar director for SA-N-4 3. Top Dome radar director for SA-N-6 launchers 4. SA-N-6 cal SAM launchers 5. Side Globe electronic-warfare antennas 6. Top Pair 3-D early-warning radar 7. 30-mm gatling AA 8. Bass Tilt 30-mm 9. Top Steer 3-D air-search radar 10. Front Door/Front Piece tracking radar for SS-N-12 11. Kite Screech fire-control radar for 130-mm DP gun nt 12. RBU-6000 ASW RL 13. SS-N-12 antiship missile tubes 14. twin 130-mm DP gun mount — Drawing: Capitaine de Frégate L. Gassier

GUIDED-MISSILE CRUISERS *(continued)*

E/O: 2/Tee Plinth (*Slava* only)—SATCOMM: 2/Punch Bowl data link
IFF: 1/Salt Pot-A and 1/Salt Pot-B transponder, interrogation by radars
M: COGOG: 4 boost gas turbines, 25,000 shp each; 2 cruise gas turbines, 8,000 shp each; 2 props; 100,000 shp max.
Range: 2,000/30; 9,000/15
Electric: 4 gas-turbine sets; 6,000 kw
Endurance: 30 days
Crew: 38 officers, 416 enlisted (*see* Remarks)

Remarks: Initially referred to by the NATO code name "Blk-Com-1" and later, briefly, as the "Krasina" class. Typed *Raketnyy Kreyser* (Missile Cruiser) by the Soviet Navy. Fitted as flagships, in which rôle they carry up to 27 additional officers and 24 additional enlisted. *Slava* first deployed from the Black Sea on 15-9-83. Unusual in having considerable equipment that is not the latest of its type in Russian service, including the main battery, nuclear-capable SS-N-12 missile system. The Russians have referred to these ships as having an 11,000-ton displacement, probably meaning "normal" vice standard or full load; data in the listing above have been revised to match published Russian figures. *Admiral Lobov* is said to be the last combatant warship to be launched from 61 Kommuna Shipyard, and it is probable that only four ships were planned; the fourth will probably be delayed in completion by the economic turmoil in Ukraine or even abandoned. *Chervona Ukraina* arrived at her home port of Petropavlovsk on the Kamchatka Peninsula in 11-90 and has been stated to be suffering from a lack of material support. A canceled fifth unit was to have been named *Oktyabrskaya Revolutsiya*.

Only one Top Dome director is fitted for the SA-N-6 system, limiting its flexibility. The torpedo tubes are mounted behind shutters in the ships' sides, near the stern. The hangar floor is one-half deck below the flight deck, which is reached via an inclined ramp, the helicopter being maneuvered by a chain-haul system. Each of the paired stack uptakes incorporates one cruise-turbine exhaust, two boost-turbine exhausts, and two gas-turbine generator exhausts. In *Chervona Ukraina,* the Top Steer paired radar is replaced by Top Plate, and additional decoy rocket launchers have been fitted. In all, the officer accommodations are opulent by Western standards, even to the extent of installing a waterfall-equipped below-decks swimming pool and a sauna, but enlisted quarters are spartan; in general, the ships contain a great deal of flammable material and appear to have a lack of damage-control features.

◆ 1 Modified Kara class   Bldr: 61 Kommuna SY, Nikolayev, Ukraine

	Laid down	L	In serv.	Fleet
Azov	1972	1974	1977	Black Sea

Azov Pradignac & Léo, 6-91

Azov—note Top Dome aft Pradignac & Léo, 6-91

Azov French Navy, 6-91

D: 6,700 tons light (8,565 fl)
S: 32 kts (30 sust.; 18 on cruise turbines)
Dim: 173.40 (162.00 pp) × 18.50 (16.80 wl) × 5.74 (hull)
A: 8/SS-N-14 Silex ASW/antiship (IV × 2)—4/SA-N-6 vertical SAM launchers (VI × 4, 24 Grumble missiles)—1/SA-N-3 SAM system (II × 1, 36 Goblet missiles)—2/SA-N-4 SAM systems (II × 2, 40 Gecko missiles)—4/76.2-mm DP (II × 2)—4/30-mm AK-630 gatling AA (I × 4)— 4/533-mm TT (II × 2)—2/RBU-6000 ASW RL (XII × 2)—2/RBU-1000 ASW RL (VI × 2)—1/Ka-27PL Helix-A ASW helicopter
Electron Equipt:
Radar: 1/Don-2 nav., 2/Don Kay nav., 1/Top Sail 3-D early warning, 1/Head Net-C air search, 1/Top Dome SA-N-6 f.c., 1/Head Lights-C SA-N-3/SS-N-14 f.c., 2/Pop Group SA-N-4 f.c., 2/Owl Screech 76.2-mm f.c., 2/Bass Tilt 30-mm f.c.
Sonar: Bull Nose hull-mounted MF, Mare Tail MF VDS
EW: 8/Side Globe, 2/Bell Clout, 2/Bell Slam, 2/Bell Tap, 2/trainable decoy RL (II × 2)
IFF: interrogation by radars, 1/Pot-A and 1/Salt Pot-B transponder
M: COGOG: 4 boost gas turbines, 30,000 shp each; 2 cruise gas turbines, 8,000 shp each; 2 props; 120,000 shp max.
Electric: 5,000 kw **Endurance:** 30 days
Range: 3,000/32; 6,500/18 **Fuel:** 1,830 tons
Crew: 43 officers, 278 enlisted (accommodations for 330 enlisted)

Remarks: The fourth hull in the Kara series, *Azov* was modified as trials ship for t SA-N-6 vertical-launch SAM system. The SA-N-6 installation replaces the aft SA-N-3 launcher, magazine, and associated Head Lights-C guidance radar and appea to use a different launcher arrangement than that on the *Kirov* and *Slava* classes: la rectangular hatches cover each launch group. Because of restricted space, it w possible to fit only two twin torpedo tubes instead of the normal quintuple mounts.

◆ 6 Kara class (Project 1134B)   Bldr: 61 Kommuna SY, Nikolayev, Ukraine

	Laid down	L	In serv.	Fleet
Nikolayev	1969	1971	1973	Pacific
Ochakov	1970	1972	1975	Black Sea
Kerch'	1971	1973	1976	Black Sea
Petropavlovsk	1973	1975	1978	Pacific
Tashkent	1975	1976	1979	Pacific
Vladivostok (ex-*Tallin*)	1976	1977	1980	Black Sea

Kerch'—with Flat Screen 3-D air-search radar Boris Lemachko,

Kerch' Tas

GUIDED-MISSILE CRUISERS *(continued)*

Ochakov U.S. Navy, 1987

Petropavlovsk—with higher hangar, small Round House TACAN dome, and no RBU-1000 U.S. Navy, 3-82

Tashkent U.S. Navy, 1987

D: 6,700 tons light (8,565 fl)
S: 32 kts (30 sust., 18 on cruise turbines)
Dim: 173.40 (162.00 pp) × 18.50 (16.80 pp) × 5.74 (hull)
A: 8/SS-N-14 SSM (IV × 2, 8 Silex missiles)—2/SA-N-3 systems (II × 2, 72 Goblet missiles)—4/SA-N-4 (II × 2, 40 Gecko missiles)—4/76.2-mm 59-cal. DP (II × 2)—4/30-mm AK-630 gatling AA (I × 4)—10/533-mm TT (V × 2)—2/RBU-6000 ASW RL (XII × 2)—2/RBU-1000 ASW RL (VI × 2; not on *Petropavlovsk*)—1/Ka-27PL Helix-A helicopter
Electron Equipt:
Radar: 1/Don-2 or Palm Frond nav., 2/Don-Kay nav., 1/Top Sail (*Kerch':* Flat Screen) 3-D early warning, 1/Head Net-C air search, 2/Head Lights-C SA-N-3/SS-N-14 f.c., 2/Pop Group SA-N-4 f.c., 2/Owl Screech 76.2-mm f.c., 2/Bass Tilt 30-mm f.c., *Petropavlovsk* only: 1/Fly Screen landing aid
Sonar: Bull Nose hull-mounted MF, Mare Tail MF VDS
EW: 8/Side Globe, 2/Bell Clout, 2/Bell Slam, 2/Bell Tap (or 4/Rum Tub), (*Petropavlovsk, Kerch':* 4/Rum Tub vice Bell-Series), 2/decoy RL (II × 2)
IFF: 1/Salt Pot transponder (interrogation by search radars)
TACAN: *Petropavlovsk* only: 2/Round House—E/O: 2/Tee Plinth t.v.

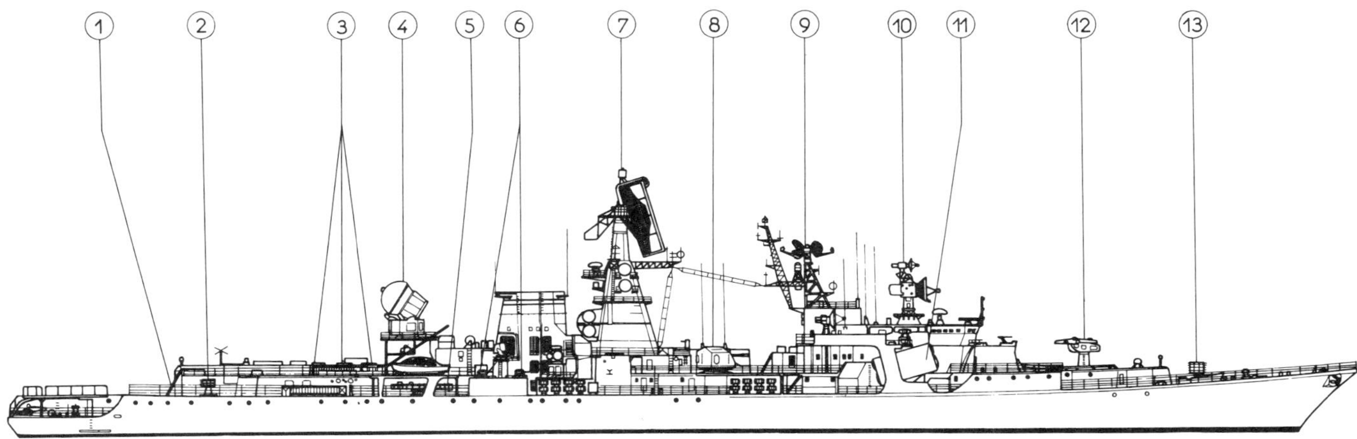

Azov 1. helicopter hangar 2. RBU-1000 ASW RL (VI × 2) 3. SA-N-6 Grumble vertical-launch SAM area 4. Top Dome guidance radar 5. 533-mm torpedo tubes (II × 2) 6. 30-mm AK-630 6-barreled gatling AA 7. Top Sail 3-D air-search radar 8. 76.2-mm 59-cal. DP (II × 2) 9. Head Net-C air/surface-search radar 10. Head Lights-C guidance radar 11. SS-N-14 Silex antisubmarine/antiship missile launchers (IV × 2) 12. SA-N-3 Goblet SAM launcher 13. RBU-6000 ASW RL (XII × 2)
Drawing: Capitaine de Frégate L. Gassier

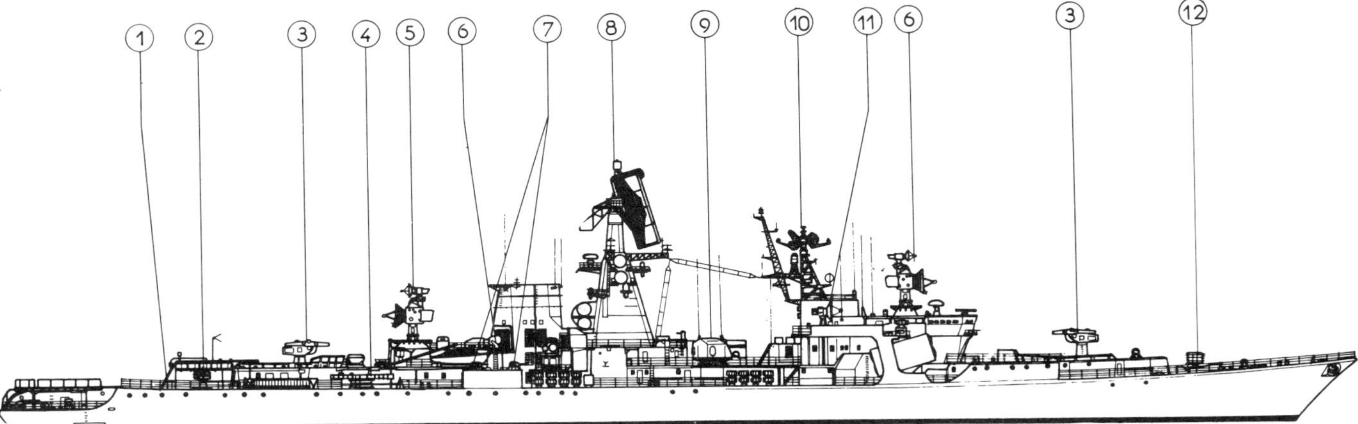

Nikolayev 1. helicopter hangar 2. RBU-1000 ASW RL (VI × 2) 3. SA-N-3 Goblet SAM launcher 4. 533-mm TT (V × 2) 5 and 6. Head Lights-C guidance radars 7. 30-mm AK-630 6-barreled gatling AA (I × 4) 8. Top Sail 3-D air-search radar 9. 76.2-mm 59-cal. DP (II × 2) 10. Head Net-C air/surface-search radar 11. Owl Screech gun-control radar (2) 12. RBU-6000 ASW RL (XII × 2)
Drawing: Capitaine de Frégate L. Gassier

GUIDED-MISSILE CRUISERS *(continued)*

M: COGOG: 4 boost gas turbines, 30,000 shp each; 2 cruise gas turbines; 8,000 shp each; 2 props; 120,000 shp max.
Electric: 5,000 kw **Endurance:** 30 days
Range: 3,000/32; 6,500/18 **Fuel:** 1,830 tons
Crew: 43 officers, 278 enlisted (accommodations for 330 enlisted)

Remarks: Type designation: *Bol'shoy Protivolodochnyy Korabl'* (Large Antisubmarine Ship), a type considered by the Russians to be more in the destroyer than the cruiser category; the commanding officers are normally commander-equivalents. Pacific Ocean Fleet units *Nikolayev* and *Tashkent* returned to the Black Sea for probable overhauls in the late 1980s and have not yet re-emerged.

Petropavlovsk has two cylindrical Round House TACAN arrays abreast the helicopter hangar, which is 1 m higher than on the other ships; in consequence, she has no RBU-1000 rocket launchers. *Ochakov* was in collision with the Kashin-class destroyer *Strogiy* in 10-86. The last three built have incomplete EW suites, having been equipped to take four Rum Tub, as on *Petropavlovsk* and *Kerch'*. *Nikolayev* is unique in having Square Head IFF interrogators on either side of the stack. SA-N-3, SA-N-4, and SS-N-14 can also be used against surface targets, and the RBU-weapons have a counter-torpedo capability. As in the Kresta-II class, the helicopter hangar is at main-deck level, the helicopter being raised to flight-deck level by means of an inclined elevator. *Kerch'* received a new rotating phased planar array 3-D air-search radar in place of Top Sail during an overhaul that ended by early 1989. Revised data based on Russian official figures. Carry 4,300 rounds 76.2-mm ammunition, 144 RGB-60 rockets for the RBU-1,000, 8,000 rounds 30-mm ammunition.

◆ **7 Kresta-II class (Project 1134A)** Bldr: Severnaya Zavod (ex-Zhdanov SY), St. Petersburg, Russia

	L	In serv.	Fleet
Admiral Makarov	1970	8-72	Northern
Khabarovsk (ex-*Marshal Voroshilov*)	1970	5-73	Pacific
Admiral Oktyabr'skiy	1971	11-73	Pacific
Admiral Isachenkov	1972	9-74	Northern
Marshal Timoshenko	1973	9-75	Northern
Vasily Chapaev	1975	10-76	Pacific
Admiral Yumashev	1976	1-78	Northern

Admiral Oktyabr'skiy U.S. Navy, 8

Admiral Makarov French Navy,

Admiral Yumashev M.O.D. U.

GUIDED-MISSILE CRUISERS *(continued)*

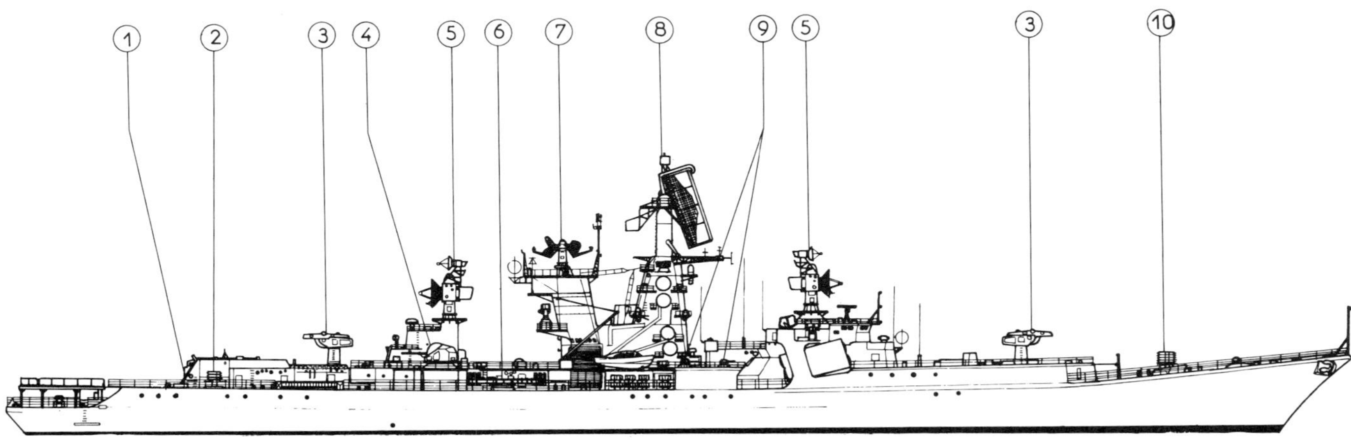

Kresta-II class 1. helicopter hangar 2. RBU-1000 ASW RL (VI × 2) 3. SA-N-3 SAM launcher (II × 2) 4. 57-mm DP (II × 2) 5. Head Lights-C missile-guidance radars 6. 533-mm TT (V × 2) 7. Head Net-C air/surface-search radar 8. Top Sail 3-D air-search radar 9. 30-mm 6-barreled gatling AA 10. RBU-6000 ASW RL (XII × 2) (*Note:* Drawing applies to *Marshal Voroshilov* and *Admiral Oktyabr'skiy*; the others have a two-level deckhouse between the tower mast and the bridge superstructure.)
Drawing: Capitaine de Frégate L. Gassier

…niral Makarov—superstructure detail: note extra deckhouse abaft …ge, no Bass Tilt directors for 30-mm guns, unique underway …enishment equipment above stowed brow French Navy, 6-90

…: 5,600 tons light (7,535 fl) **S:** 32 kts
…im: 159.00 (148.00 pp) × 16.80 (16.20 wl) × 6.3 max. (5.84 hull)
…: 8/SS-N-14 SSM (IV × 2, 8 Silex missiles)—2/SA-N-3 SAM systems (II × 2, 48 Goblet missiles)—4/57-mm AK-257 DP (II × 2)—4/30-mm AK-630 gatling AA (I × 4)—2/RBU-6000 ASW RL (XII × 2)—2/RBU-1000 ASW RL (VI × 2)—10/533-mm TT (V × 2)—1/Ka-25 Hormone-A or Ka-27PL Helix-A helicopter

Electron Equipt:
Radar: 1/Don-2 nav., 2/Don-Kay, nav. 1/Top Sail 3-D early warning, 1/Head Net-C air search, 2/Head Lights-C SA-N-3/SS-N-14 f.c., 2/Muff Cob 57-mm DP, 2/Bass Tilt 30-mm f.c. (not in *Adm. Nakhimov* or *Adm. Makarov*)
Sonar: Bull Nose hull-mounted MF—E/O: 2/Tee Plinth
EW: 8/Side Globe, 1/Bell Clout, 2/Bell Slam, 2/Bell Tap, 2/decoy RL (II × 2)
IFF: 1/High Pole B, 1/High Pole A transponder (interrogation by search radars)

M: 2 sets TV-12 geared steam turbines; 2 4-bladed props; 91,000 shp
Boilers: 4, turbopressurized, 640 kg/cm^2, 500°C
Fuel: 1,830 tons **Range:** 1,600/32; 5,200/18
Crew: 33 officers, 310 enlisted

Remarks: Type designation: BPK—*Bol'shoy Protivolodochnyy Korabl'* (Large Anti-submarine Ship); normally commanded by commander-equivalents. The first ship of the class, *Kronshtadt,* reported in Soviet press to have spent *seven* years in overhaul and still to have emerged with many deficiencies in 1989, was stricken in 1991, as was the second-oldest unit, *Admiral Isakov,* and the third oldest, *Admiral Nakhimov.* The name of *Marshal Voroshilov* was changed to *Khabarovsk* in 1991; on 20-11-90, the ship had collided near Vladivostok with the merchant ship *Gorets,* suffering some damage.

The first four units did not have Bass Tilt radar gun directors and controlled their 30-mm AA with Kolonka-2 lead-computing optical directors only. The three final units and *Admiral Makarov* have larger forward superstructure, the area between the tower foremast and the bridge being filled in by a two-level deckhouse. *Admiral Makarov* has prototype solid-stores equipment to port and prototype underway refueling equipment to starboard. SA-N-3 and SS-N-14 can also be used against surface targets. Have fin stabilizers. The helicopter hangar is one deck lower than the flight deck and is reached by means of an inclined elevator, as on the Kara class. *Adm. Oktyabr'skiy* has Square Head IFF interrogators flanking the bridge wings, possibly as a primitive TACAN system for the helicopter. Carry 144 rockets for the RBU-6000, 60 for the RBU-1000, 2,000 rounds 57-mm ammunition.

◆ **1 Kresta-I class (Project 1134)** Bldr: Severnaya Zavod (ex-Zhdanov SY), St. Petersburg, Russia

	L	In serv.	Fleet
ADMIRAL ZOZULYA	10-65	3-67	Baltic

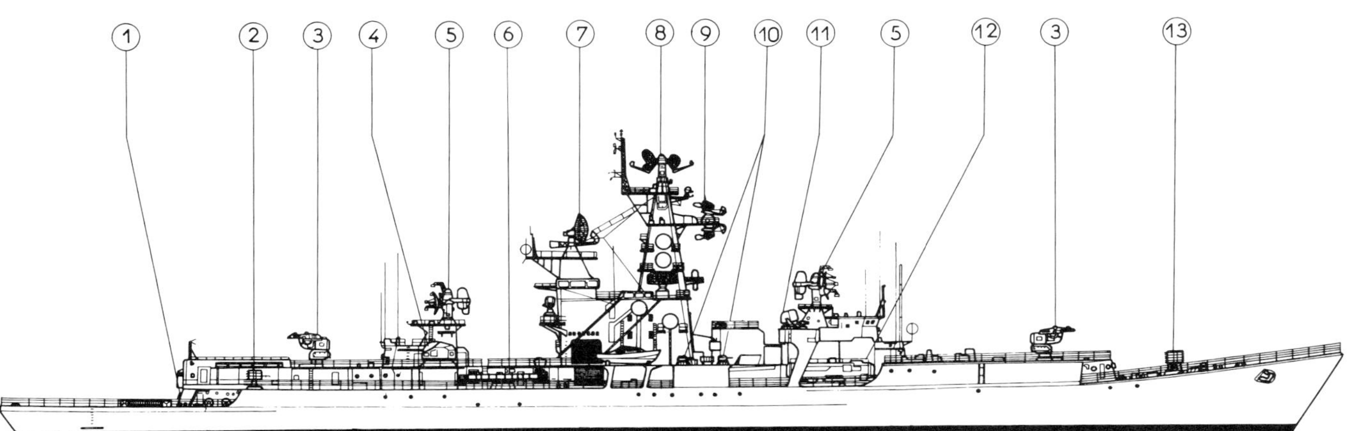

Vitse-Admiral Drozd 1. helicopter hangar 2. RBU-1000 ASW RL (VI × 2) 3. SA-N-1 SAM launchers (II × 2) 4. 57-mm DP (II × 2) 5. Peel Group guidance radars for SA-N-1 6. 533-mm TT (V × 2) 7. Big Net air-search radar 8. Head Net-C air/surface-search radar 9. Scoop Pair guidance radar for SS-N-3B 10. 30-mm 6-barreled gatling AA (I × 4) 11. Bass Tilt f.c. radar for 30-mm AA 12. SS-N-3B Shaddock SSM launchers (II × 2) 13. RBU-6000 ASW RL (XII × 2) Drawing: Capitaine de Frégate L. Gassier

GUIDED-MISSILE CRUISERS *(continued)*

Vitse-Admiral Drozd (now stricken)—with gatling AA guns, Bass Tilt fire-control radars, and enlarged superstructure; *Admiral Zozulya* is probably quit similar French Navy, 2-8

D: 5,400 tons light (7,400 fl) **S:** 32 kts
Dim: 155.5 (148.5 wl) × 16.8 (16.2 wl) × 5.8 (6.5 max.)
A: 4/SS-N-3B Shaddock SSM (II × 2)—2/SA-N-1 SAM systems (II × 2, 32 Goa missiles)—4/57-mm AK-257 DP (II × 2)—4/30-mm AK-630 gatling AA (I × 4)—2/RBU-6000 ASW RL (XI × 2)—2/RBU-1000 ASW RL (VI × 2)—10/533-mm TT (V × 2)—1/Ka-25 Hormone-B helicopter
Electron Equipt:
Radar: 2/Palm Frond nav., 1/Don Kay nav., 1/Big Net early warning, 1/Head Net-C air search, 1/Scoop Pair SS-N-3 tracking, 2/Peel Group SA-N-3 f.c., 2/Muff Cob 57-mm f.c., 2/Bass Tilt 30-mm f.c.
Sonar: Herkules hull-mounted MF—E/O: 2/Tee Plinth t.v.
EW: 8/Side Globe, 2/Bell Clout, 2/Bell Slam, 2/Bell Tap, 2/Bell Strike, 2/Fig Jar, 2/decoy RL (II × 2)
Electron Equipt: IFF: 2/High Pole B or Salt Pot transponders
M: 2 sets Type TV-12 geared steam turbines; 2 4-bladed props; 91,000 shp
Boilers: 4, turbopressurized, 640 kg/cm², 500° C
Range: 1,600/32; 5,200/18 **Fuel:** 1,830 tons
Crew: 380 tot.

Remarks: Type designation: RKR—*Raketnyy Kreyser* (Missile Cruiser). Based on the Kynda class, but have a better-balanced mixture of weapons. Two Pacific Fleet sisters, *Sevastopol* and *Vladivostok,* were retired late 1990; *Sevastopol* was scrapped in India 6-91 and *Vladivostok* in 1-92. Northern Fleet unit *Vitse-Admiral Drozd* was retired by the end of 1991 and towed away for scrap in 1-92. *Admiral Zozulya* completed an overhaul and modernization in the Baltic late in 1991 and will probably be retained for several more years.

The surface-to-surface launchers, fitted on each side of the superstructure forward under the bridge wings, are elevated to fire, but cannot be trained. No SS-N-3 missile reloads. Installation of gatling guns abaft the Shaddock launchers and construction of a new deckhouse between the gatling guns altered the silhouette of the *Vitse-Admiral Drozd* in 1976 and *Admiral Zozulya* during an overhaul completed in 1991. Has two Plinth Net data-link antennas for the SS-N-3 Shaddock system. Carries 2,000 rounds 57-mm ammunition, 144 RGB-60 ASW rockets, 60 RGB-10 ASW rockets. See addenda for photo.

Note: Of the four Kynda-class (Project 58) guided-missile cruisers, Pacific Ocean Fleet unit *Varyag* was stricken in 7-90 and her name conferred on the new aircraft carrier; the cruiser was to become a museum, funds permitting. Baltic Fleet sister *Groznyy,* Black Sea Fleet sister *Admiral Golovko,* and Pacific Ocean Fleet sister *Admiral Fokin* are believed to have been discarded by the end of 1991.

GUIDED-MISSILE DESTROYERS

♦ 0 (+1+ . . .) Project 1155.1 Bldr: Yantar Zavod, Kaliningrad

	Laid down	L	In serv.	Fleet
. . . .	. . .	. . .	1993	. . . . . .

D: 6,700 tons (8,100 fl) **S:** 32 kts
Dim: 164.0 (150.0 wl) × 19.3 (17.8 wl) × 6.2 (8.0 max.)
A: 8/. . . . . . SSM (IV × 2)—8/SA-N-9 vertical SAM launchers (VIII × 8, 64 missiles)—2/130-mm 70-cal. DP (II × 1)—2/CADS-1 CIWS (2/30-mm gatling AA, 8/SA-N-11 SAM per mount; 96 missiles)—2/RBU-6000 ASW RL (XII × 2)—8/533-mm TT (IV × 2)—mines—2/Ka-27PL Helix-A ASW helicopters
Electron Equipt:
Radar: 3/Palm Frond nav., 1/Top Plate 3-D air search, 1/Strut Pair air/surf. search; all: 2/Eye Bowl SS-N-14 f.c., 1/Kite Screech 100-mm f.c., 2/Cross Sword SA-N-4 f.c., 2/Hot Flash CADS-1 f.c.—1/Fly Screen helo landing control
Sonar: . . . . . . bow-mounted LF, ... LF VDS
EW: . . . . . . intercept, ... jammers, 4/Half Cup IR detection, 2/trainable decoy RL (II × 2), 10/fixed decoy RL (X × 10)
TACAN: 2/Round House—IFF: 1/Salt Pot-B, 1/Salt Pot-C transponder
M: COGAG: 2 cruise gas turbines (12,100 shp each), 2 boost gas turbines (24,300 shp each); 2 props; 72,800 shp max.
Electric: 6,000 kw **Endurance:** 30 days **Range:** 6,000/20
Crew: 29 officers, 220 enlisted

Remarks: In the fall of 1991, the U.S. Department of Defense announced that "t first unit of a new destroyer program based on a modified *Udaloy* hull . . . should rea the fleet in 1992. . ." and that it would carry a twin 130-mm dual-purpose gun mou in place of the two single 100-mm mounts of the *Udaloy* class, have two or more CADS close-in weapons systems, and mount a new sonar suite. Completion has probably si been delayed by the economic and social turmoil within Russia. The above data provisional. Originally intended for the KGB Maritime Border Guard; first unit to h been named *Chebanenko,* second *Kucherov.*

♦ 11 Udaloy class (Project 1155) Bldrs: A: Yantar Zavod, Kaliningra Kaliningradskiy Oblast; B: Severnya Zavod (ex-Zhdanov), St. Petersburg, Russia

	Bldr	Laid down	L	In serv.	Fleet
Udaloy ("Daring")	A	1978	9-79	1981	Northe
Vitse-Admiral Kulakov	B	1978	5-80	4-82	Northe
Marshal Vasil'yevskiy	A	1979	1981	1983	Northe
Admiral Spiridonov	A	1981	1983	1985	Pacific
Admiral Tributs	B	1982	1984	1986	Pacific
Marshal Shaposhnikov	A	1983	1985	8-85	Pacific
Simferopol	A	1983	1986	1987	North
Admiral Levchenko	B	1984	1987	1988	North
Admiral Vinogradov	A	1984	1987	1988	Pacifi
Admiral Kharlamov	A	1984	1988	1989	North
Admiral Pantaleyev	A	1986	1990	1991	. . . .

Admiral Vinogradov—late unit, with four twin 12.7-mm mg (twc pilothouse, two abreast hangar) U.S. Navy

Vitse-Admiral Kulakov—initial version with no SA-N-9 insta narrow helo deck, and two Strut Curve radars; Helix-A ASW deck French Nav

GUIDED-MISSILE DESTROYERS *(continued)*

Admiral Pantaleyev—the last *Udaloy* to be completed, on trials; note use of shaded pendant number, as on U.S. Navy ships 9-91

Simferopol Dr. Giorgio Arra, 7-91

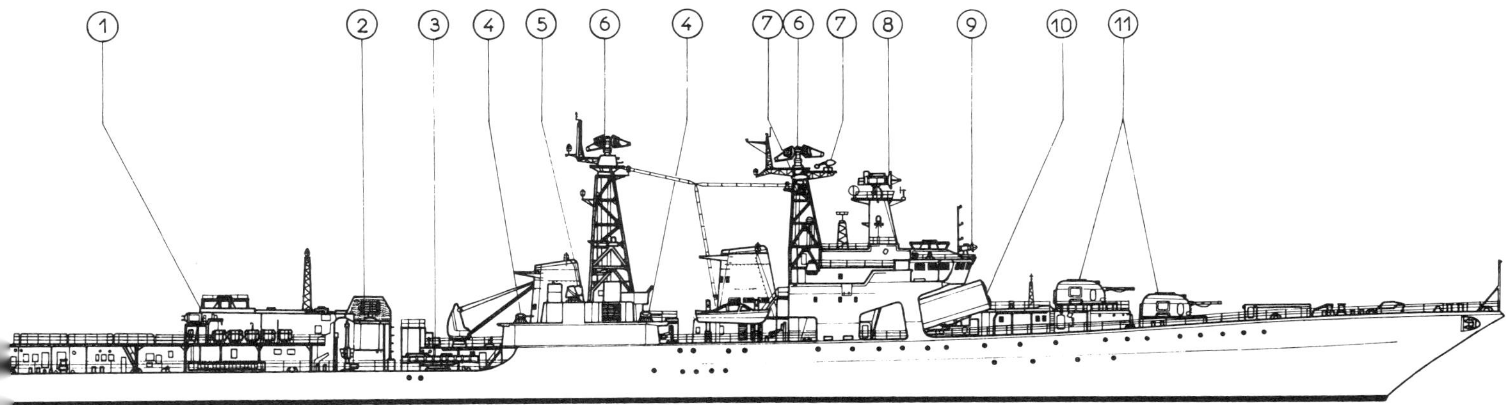

Udaloy and Vitse-Admiral Kulakov 1. helicopter hangar (2 Helix-A) 2. RBU-6000 ASW RL 3. 533-mm ASW TT (IV × 2) 4. 30-mm AK-630 gatling AA 5. Bass Tilt control radar for 30-mm AA 6. Strut Pair air/surface-search radars 7. Palm Frond navigational/surface-search radars 8. Kite Screech radar gunfire-control director (100-mm guns) 9. Eye Bowl radar directors (SS-N-14 missiles) 10. SS-N-14 missiles (IV × 2) 11. 100-mm DP guns Drawing: Capitaine de Frégate L. Gassier

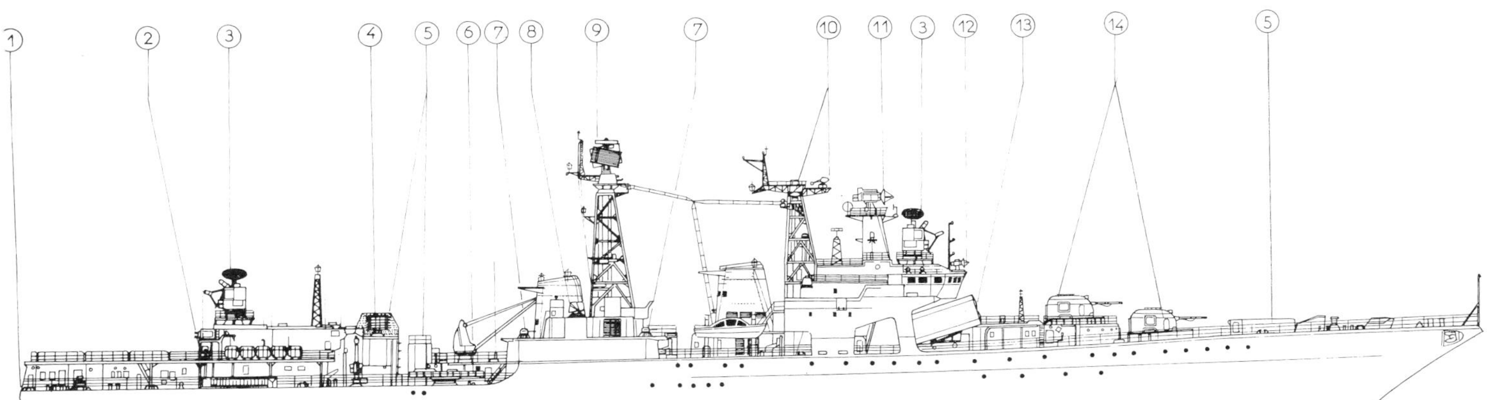

Later Udaloy-class units 1. Horse Tail VDS emplacement 2. helicopter hangar 3. Cross Sword radar for SA-N-9 (position above bridge vacant in *Admiral Spiridonov, Admiral Tributs)* 4. RBU-6000 ASW RL 5. SA-N-9 VLS silo locations (2 between the RBU-6000 RL, 2 in the small deckhouse abaft the stores crane, and 4 within the forecastle, forward of the 100-mm gun mounts) 6. quadruple 533-mm TT 7. 30-mm AK-630 gatling AA 8. Bass Tilt radar for 30-mm AA 9. Top Plate 3-D radar 10. Palm Frond navigational radars 11. Kite Screech radar for the 100-mm guns 12. Eye Bowl radar for SS-N-14 13. SS-N-14 cruise-missile launchers 14. 100-mm dual-purpose guns (*Note*: Final 6 have Strut Pair air/surface-search radar atop foremast also.) Drawing: Capitaine de Frégate L. Gassier

ral Tributs—mid-series unit with Cross Sword aft only, Top Plate aft and no Strut Pair Mike Louagie, 5-90

GUIDED-MISSILE DESTROYERS *(continued)*

Marshal Vasel'yevskiy—still without SA-N-9 SAM system and Cross Sword guidance radars; note Top Plate atop after mast, empty position atop foremast, Ka-27PL Helix-A helo on deck French Navy, 6-90

Udaloy—the first unit, still without SA-N-9 SAM systems after first major overhaul French Navy, 6-90

Simferopol—8th unit completed, fully equipped Dr. Giorgio Arra, 7-91

D: 6,700 tons (8,100 fl) **S:** 32 kts
Dim: 164.0 (150.0 wl) × 19.3 (17.8 wl) × 6.2 (8.0 max.)
A: 8/SS-N-14 Silex SSM (IV × 2)—0 or 8/SA-N-9 vertical SAM launchers (VIII × 8, 64 missiles; *see* Remarks)—2/100-mm 70-cal. DP (I × 2)— 4/30-mm AK-630 gatling AA (I × 4)—2/RBU-6000 ASW RL (XII × 2)— 8/533-mm TT (IV × 2)—mines—2/Ka-27PL Helix-A ASW helicopters— *Adm. Vinogradov* also: 8/12.7-mm mg (II × 4)
Electron Equipt:
Radar: 3/Palm Frond nav.; *Udaloy, V. Adm. Kulakov:* 2/Strut Pair air/surf. search; others: 1/Top Plate 3-D air search (*M. Shaposhnikov* and later also: 1/Strut Pair); all: 2/Eye Bowl SS-N-14 f.c., 1/Kite Screech 100-mm f.c., 0, 1, or 2/Cross Sword SA-N-4 f.c. (*see* Remarks), 2/Bass Tilt 30-mm f.c., 1/Fly Screen helo landing control
Sonar: Horse Jaw bow-mounted LF, Horse Tail LF VDS
EW: 2/Bell Shroud, 2/Bell Squat, 4 Bell Crown, 2/decoy RL (II × 2)
TACAN: 2/Round House—IFF: 1/Salt Pot-B, 1/Salt Pot-C transponder
M: COGAG: 2 cruise gas turbines (12,100 shp each), 2 boost gas turbines (24,300 shp each); 2 props; 72,800 shp max.
Electric: 6,000 kw **Endurance:** 30 days **Range:** 6,000/20
Crew: 29 officers, 220 enlisted

Remarks: The former Zhdanov Shipyard was renamed Severnaya Zavod (North SY on 8-2-89. Initally had NATO nickname "Bal-Com-3" class. Type designation BPK–*Bol'shoy Protivolodochnyy Korabl'* (Large Antisubmarine Ship). *Admiral Tributs* had serious shipyard fire at Vladivostok on 18-7-91. *Admiral Pantalayev,* the final unit c the class, commenced trials in the Baltic during 7-91. *Admiral Zakharov,* complete 1984, suffered an explosion and fire 17-2-92 off Vladivostok and was sold for scrap th following month.

Provision was made for installation of the SA-N-9 vertically launched SAM systen four on the raised portion of the forecastle, two more disposed athwartships in the sma deckhouse between the torpedo tubes, and two arranged fore and aft in the deckhous between the RBU-6000 ASW RL mounts. Each rotating cylinder can hold 8 missiles, f a total of 64, and there may be a second layer of missiles, as in larger ships with t system. *Admiral Zakharov* was the first ship to actually have the operational SA-N system installed, with two Cross Sword–equipped radar directors mounted in mid-19 (one later removed); as of 1991, no ship completed without SA-N-9 had had it backf ted: the first two ships still lacked the VLS and Cross Sword directors, the third ship h the VLS but no directors, units 5–7 have all VLS but only one Cross Sword, a *Simferopol* and later are fully equipped. All carry four antiship and four antisubmari torpedoes in the 533-mm tubes; there are no reloads.

This is the first BPK design to carry two ASW helicopters. The two hangars are si by side and use inclined elevator ramps to raise the aircraft to the flight deck; hangar roofs slide forward in two segmented sections to clear the rotors. From the th unit on (Project 1155R), the helicopter deck is wider, extending to the sides of the sh Two Round House TACAN radomes are mounted on yards on the after mast, while Fly Screen microwave landing-control radar is beside the starboard hangar. The E suite is incomplete, with several empty platforms on the after mast, except for *Simfe pol,* which has four Foot Ball on the after mast. *Vitse-Admiral Kulakov* has four H Cup infrared detection arrays, apparently intended to detect the exhausts of inbo antiship missiles and aircraft.

The first two ships, with two Strut Pair, lack a height-finding capability. *Mars Vasil'yevskiy* was the first to have a Top Plate back-to-back phased-array 3-D ra atop the after mast, and, beginning with *Simferopol,* a Strut Pair is again mounted a the foremast. *Udaloy* completed an overhaul in the Baltic in 12-89 and returned to Northern Fleet without receiving the SA-N-9 SAM system or any significant elect ics antenna update. *Admiral Vinogradov* deployed to the Pacific Ocean Fleet in 8 with four old-model twin 12.7-mm machine-gun mounts, two abreast the forward en the hangar and two atop the bridge.

◆ 14 (+9) Sovremennyy class (Project 956)

Bldr: Severnaya Zavod, St. Petersburg, Russia

	Laid down	L	In serv.	Fleet
Sovremennyy ("Modern")	1976	11-78	1981	North
Otchayannyy ("Merciless")	1977	3-80	1982	North
Otlichnyy ("Perfect")	1978	3-81	1983	North
Osmotritel'nyy ("Circumspect")	1979	4-82	1984	Pacifi
Bezuprechnyy ("Irreproachable")	1980	8-83	7-85	North
Boyevoy ("Militant")	1981	8-84	1986	Pacifi
Stoykiy ("Steadfast")	1982	8-85	1987	Pacifi
Okrylennyy ("Inspiring")	1983	6-86	1988	North
Burnyy ("Fiery")	1983	1-87	1989	Pacif
Gremyashchiy ("Thunderous")	1984	1987	1989	North
Bystryy ("Speedy")	1984	1987	1989	Pacif
Rastoropnyy ("Prompt")	1985	1988	1990	Nort
Bezboyaznennyy ("Intrepid")	1986	2-89	5-90	Paci
Bezuderzhannyy ("Tenacious")	6-86	11-89	13-7-91	Nort
Bespokoynyy ("Restless")	1987	1990	1992	. . .
Moskovskiy Komsomolets	1988	1991	1993	. . .
Besstrashnyy ("Fearless")	1988	. . .	1994	. . .
Vazhnyy ("Eminent")	1989	. . .	1994	. . .
Vdumchivyy ("Thoughtful")	1989	. . .	1995	. . .
. . . . (". . . . . .")	1990	. . .	1996	. . .
. . . . (". . . . . .")	1990	. . .	1996	. . .
. . . . (". . . . . .")	1991	. . .	1997	. . .
. . . . (". . . . . .")	1992	. . .	1998	. . .

Osmotritel'nyy—4th unit, with Plate Steer radar U.S. Nav

UIDED-MISSILE DESTROYERS *(continued)*

oikyy—7th unit French Navy, 1990

zboyaznennyy—13th unit, with Top Plate radar atop foremast Mike Louagie, 6-91

oyaznennyy—superstructure detail Leo Van Ginderen, 6-91

Bystryy—with Top Plate radar Frank Pletscher, 6-90

Gremyashchiy PH3(AC) Stephen L. Batiz, USN, 4-90

Bezuprechnyy—with Plate Steer 3-D radar Maritime Photographic, 7-90

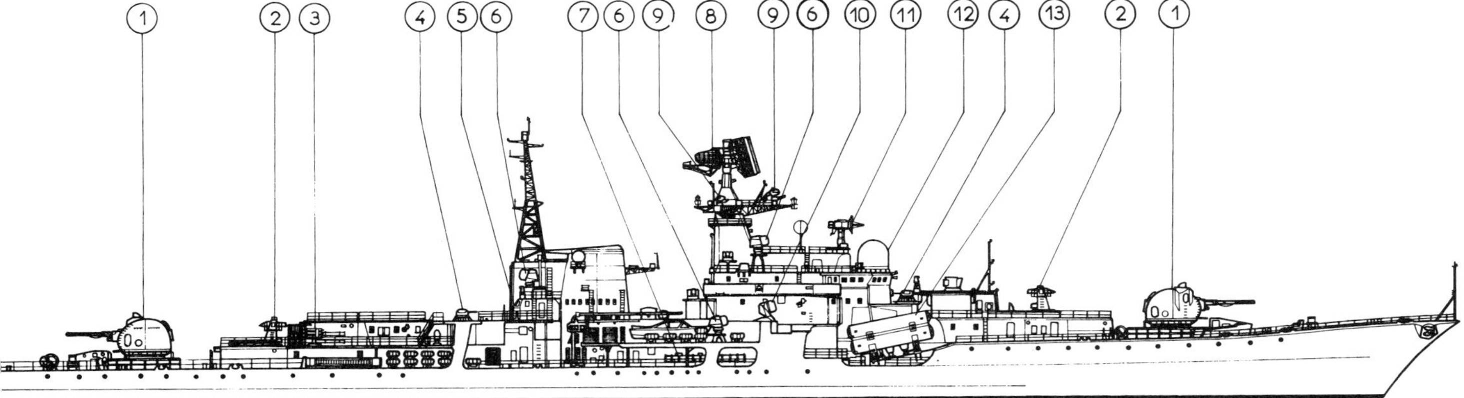

mennyy class—first three units 1. 130-mm dual-purpose guns (II × 2) 2. SA-N-7 SAM launcher (I × 2) 3. RBU-1000 ASW . 30-mm AK-630 gatling AA guns 5. telescoping helicopter hangar (shown in retracted position) 6. Front Dome radar directors for the 7 system 7. 533-mm TT (II × 2) 8. Top Steer 3-D air-search radar (later ships have Plate Steer or Top Plate) 9. Palm Frond navigational/ e-search radars 10. Bass Tilt radar directors for the 30-mm gatling AA 11. Kite Screech radar director for the 130-mm guns 12. Band Stand e (SS-N-22 SSM-associated) 13. SS-N-22 SSM (IV × 2) Drawing: Capitaine de Frégate L. Gassier

GUIDED-MISSILE DESTROYERS *(continued)*

Boyevoy U.S. Navy, 7-

Otchayannyy—2nd unit, with Top Steer radar atop foremast French Navy, 6-90

Okrylennyy—with Top Plate 3-D radar U.S. Navy, 4-90

D: 6,300 tons (7,850 fl) **S:** 32 kts
Dim: 155.7 (145.0 wl) × 16.8 (12.2 wl) × 6.0 (8.8 max.)
A: 8/SS-N-22 Sunburn SSM (IV × 2)—2/SA-N-7 SAM systems (I × 2, 40 Gadfly missiles)—4/130-mm 70-cal. DP (II × 2)—4/30-mm AK-630 gatling AA (I × 4)—4/533-mm TT (II × 2)—2/RBU-1000 ASW RL (VI × 2)—mines—1/Ka-25 Hormone-B helicopter (not usually carried)
Electron Equipt:
Radar: 3/Palm Frond nav., 1 Top Steer early warning (*Osmotritel'nyy, Bezuprechnyy:* Plate Steer; *Boyevoy* and later: Top Plate), 6/Front Dome SA-N-7 f.c., 1/Kite Screech 130-mm f.c., 2/Bass Tilt 30-mm f.c.
Sonar: 1/. . . . . . MF hull-mounted
EW: 2/Bell Shroud, 2/Bell Squat, 4/Foot Ball, 2/decoy RL (II × 2) (later units also: 8/10-tubed decoy RL)
E/O: 1/Squeeze Box, 1/Tall View periscope, 2/Watch Box bridge periscopes
IFF: 2/Salt Pot-A/B, 1/High Pole B transponder, interrogation by radars

M: 2 sets TV-12 geared steam turbines; 2/4-bladed props; 91,000 shp
Boilers: 4 turbopressurized, 640 kg/cm², 500° C
Electric: 4,800 kw
Range: 1,600/32; 5,200/18 **Fuel:** 1,830 tons
Crew: 25 officers, 296 enlisted (accommodations for 38 officers, 330 enlisted)

Remarks: Type designation: *Bol'shoy Protivolodochnyy Korabl'* (Large Antis marine Ship). Design derived from the Kresta-I and -II series built at the same s yard (renamed from Zhdanov SY on 8-2-89); uses similar hull form and same pulsion plant. Formerly called the "Bal-Com-2" class by NATO. Primarily intended surface warfare tasks, including antiship, shore bombardment, and antiair defense; minimal ASW capability is primarily for self-defense. *Gremyashchiy* was laid dow the *Vedushchiy,* the name being changed to commemorate a retiring Kanin-class u The name *Moskovskiy Komsomolets* has probably been changed. Two other units o class were assigned to a yard in Nikolayev for construction; *Vnushitel'nyy* launched 17-10-87 but abandoned, and the other does not seem to have been begu

The SS-N-22 antiship missile system is probably capable of ranges of not more 120 nautical miles, as there are no satellite receiving radomes of the Punch Bowl t the Hormone-B helicopter (which is seldom carried) can provide targeting data fo missiles, and the ships also have the large Band Stand radome associated with mi targeting for the SS-N-9 in the Nanuchka class. There are also two small sphe Light Bulb radomes on the sides of the stack that might be missile-associated. twin-tubed chaff launchers are at the extreme stern, while *Okrylennyy* and later eight additional 10-tubed fixed launchers (six on the bridge, two aft).

The 130-mm guns are of a new, fully automatic, water-cooled model, capable of A surface fire. The helicopter hangar is partially telescoping, extending aft from the structure, and the helicopter facilities are less elaborate than in other contemp Russian classes, with no support or weapons stowage for an ASW helicopter prov Squeeze Box is believed to be an optronic gunfire-control director combining a rangefinder, low light-level television, and infrared devices. *Sovremennyy* had Foot Ball EW antennas, but the positions remained empty through the fifth *Boyevoy* and later have four Foot Ball and four Bell-series antennas.

◆ 2 Modified Kashin class (Project 61M, MP)

Bldr: 61 Kommuna SY, Nikolayev, Ukraine

	In serv.		In
SMYSHLENNYY ("Clever")	1968	SDERZHANNYY ("Cautious")	

Smyshlennyy French Nav

ɜUIDED-MISSILE DESTROYERS *(continued)*

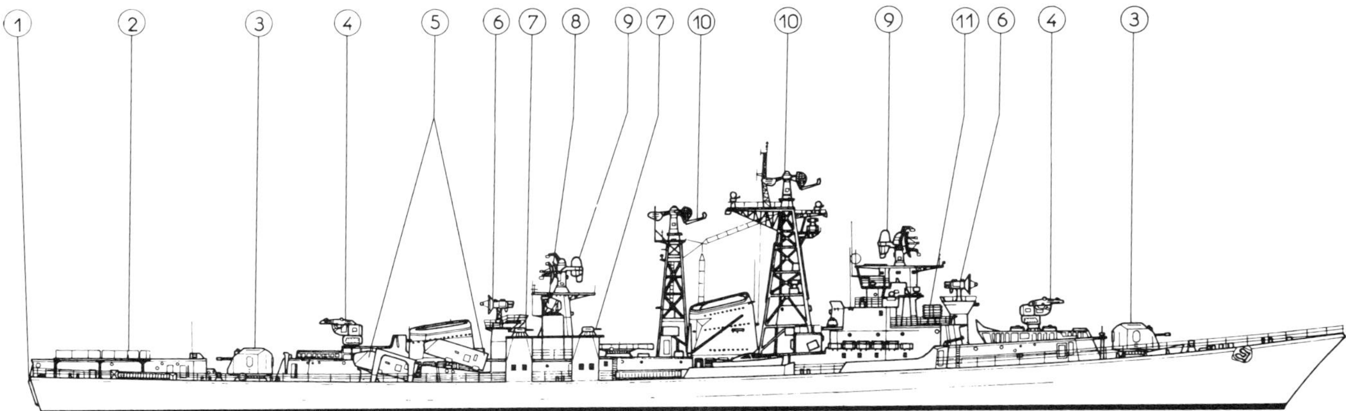

Modified Kashin 1. variable-depth sonar housing 2. helicopter platform 3. 76.2-mm DP (II × 2) 4. SA-N-1 Goa SAM launchers (II × 2) 5. SS-N-2C SSM (I × 4) 6. Owl Screech gun-control radars 7. 30-mm 6-barreled gatling AA (I × 4) 8. Bass Tilt control radars for 30-mm AA 9. Peel Group guidance radars for SA-N-1 10. locations for Head Net-C (forward) and Big Net (aft) air-search radars (incorrectly shown as 2 Head Net-A—the original fit on *Ognevoy*) Drawing: Capitaine de Frégate L. Gassier

ıyshlennyy 22 Flot., French Navy, 2-86

: 3,950 tons (4,950 fl) **S:** 35 kts **Dim:** 146.0 × 15.8 × 4.8 (hull)
: 4/SS-N-2C SSM (I × 4)—2/SA-N-1 SAM syst. (II × 2, 32 Goa missiles)—4/76.2-mm 59-cal. DP (II × 2)—4/30-mm AK-630 gatling AA (I × 4)—5/533-mm TT (V × I)—2/RBU-6000 ASW RL (XII × 2)
lectron Equipt:
Radar: 2/Don-Kay nav., 1/Head Net-C air search, 1/Big Net early warning, 2/Peel Group SA-N-1 f.c., 2/Owl Screech 76.2-mm f.c., 2/Bass Tilt 30-mm f.c.
Sonar: Bull Horn hull-mounted MF, Mare Tail MF VDS
E/O: 2/Tee Plinth t.v., 4/Tilt Pot fixed t.v., 2/Watch Box bridge periscopes
EW: 2/Bell Squat, 2/Bell Shroud, 4/decoy RL (XVI × 4)
IFF: 1/Salt Pot transponder, interrogation by radars
: 4 M-3 gas turbines, 2 props; 96,000 shp (72,000 sust.) **Fuel:** 836 tons
ange: 1,000/35; 3,500/18 **Crew:** 280 tot.

arks: Type designation: BPK—*Bol'shoy Protivolodochnyy Korabl'* (Large Anti-ıarine Ship), having briefly been listed as "Large Missile Ships." Six conversions completed from 1973 onward, with *Sderzhannyy* built to the new configuration; *hlennyy* completed conversion in 1974. Hull lengthened by 2 meters, helicopter ɔrm raised above new VDS installation, gatling guns added in place of two RBU-ASW rocket launchers. New EW gear and radars; *Ognevoy*, the first converted, lly retained original two Head Net-A air-search radars, but later received the ard fit. Sister *Smel'yy* transferred to Poland 12-87, *Ognevoy* scrapped in Turkey in , *Slavnyy* was stricken during 1991, and *Stroynyy* was scrapped in Turkey in 1-91. wo survivors are in the Northern Fleet and Black Sea Fleet, respectively.

Kashin class (Project 61) Bldrs: 61 Kommuna SY, Nikolayev, ıkraine (except *Obraztsovyy:* Severnaya Zavod, St. Petersburg, Russia)

	In serv.	Fleet
ꜱNYY KAVKAZ ("Red Kavkaz")	1967	Black Sea
ɪTEL'NYY ("Decisive")	1-68	Black Sea
LIVYY ("Intelligent")	9-69	Black Sea
NYY KRYM ("Red Crimea")	9-70	Black Sea
ɔBNYY ("Capable")	8-71	Pacific
YY ("Swift")	8-72	Black Sea

3,550 tons light (4,510 fl) **S:** 35 kts
n: 144.00 (132.00 pp) × 15.80 (14.00 wl) × 4.45 (hull)
2/SA-N-1 SAM syst. (II × 2, 32 Goa missiles)—4/76.2-mm 59-cal. DP (II × 2)—5/533-mm TT (V × I)—2/RBU-6000 ASW RL (XII × 2)— 2/RBU-1000 ASW RL (VI × 2)—mines
ctron Equipt:
adar: 2/Don-Kay or Palm Frond nav., 1/Head Net-C air search, 1/Big Net early warning, 2/Peel Group SA-N-1 f.c., 2/Owl Screech 76.2-mm f.c. (*Obraztsovyy:* 2/Head Net-A vice Head Net-C and Big Net, 2/Don-2 nav.)
Sonar: Bull Nose hull-mounted MF, Wolf Paw hull-mounted HF f.c.
E/O: 2/Tee Plinth t.v., 4/Tilt Pot fixed t.v., 2/Watch Box bridge periscopes
EW: 2/Watch Dog intercept
IFF: 1/Salt Pot transponder, interrogation by radars
M: 4 M-3 gas turbines; 2 props; 96,000 shp (72,000 sust.)
Electric: 2,400 kw (4 gas-turbine-powered generators)
Range: 1,000/35; 3,500/18 **Fuel:** 836 tons
Crew: 22 officers, 244 enlisted

Krasnyy Kavkaz Pradignac & Léo, 6-91

Krasnyy Kavkaz Leo Van Ginderen, 6-91

Krasnyy Krym Leo Van Ginderen, 8-91

GUIDED-MISSILE DESTROYERS *(continued)*

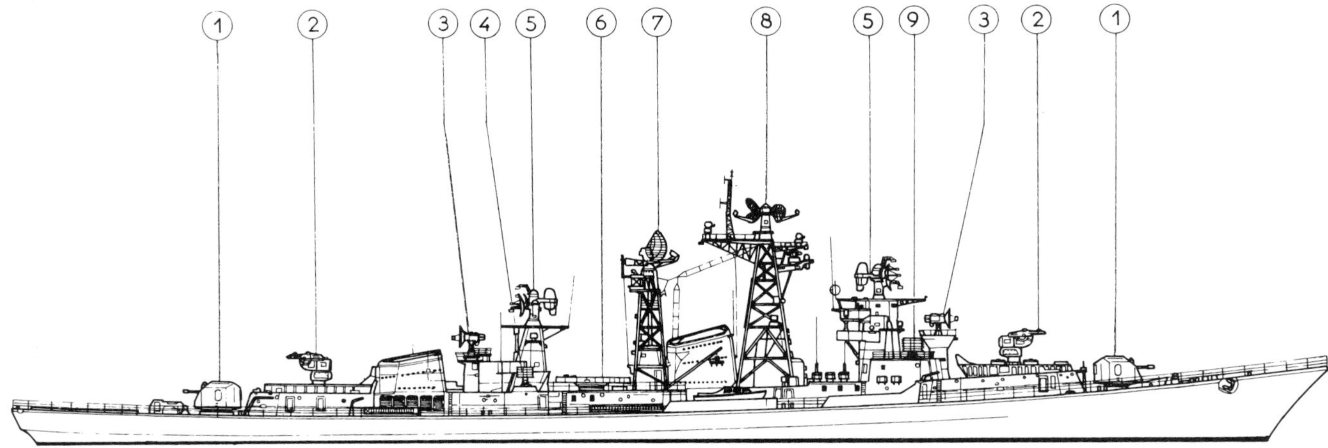

Kashin class 1. 76.2-mm DP guns (II × 2) 2. SA-N-1 Goa SAM system 3. Owl Screech gunfire-control radar 4. Peel Group guidance radars for SA-N-1 5. RBU-1000 ASW RL (VI × 2) 6. 533-mm TT (V × 1) 7. Big Net air-search radar 8. Head Net-C air/surface-search radar 9. RBU-6000 ASW RL (XII × 2) Drawing: Capitaine de Frégate L. Gassier

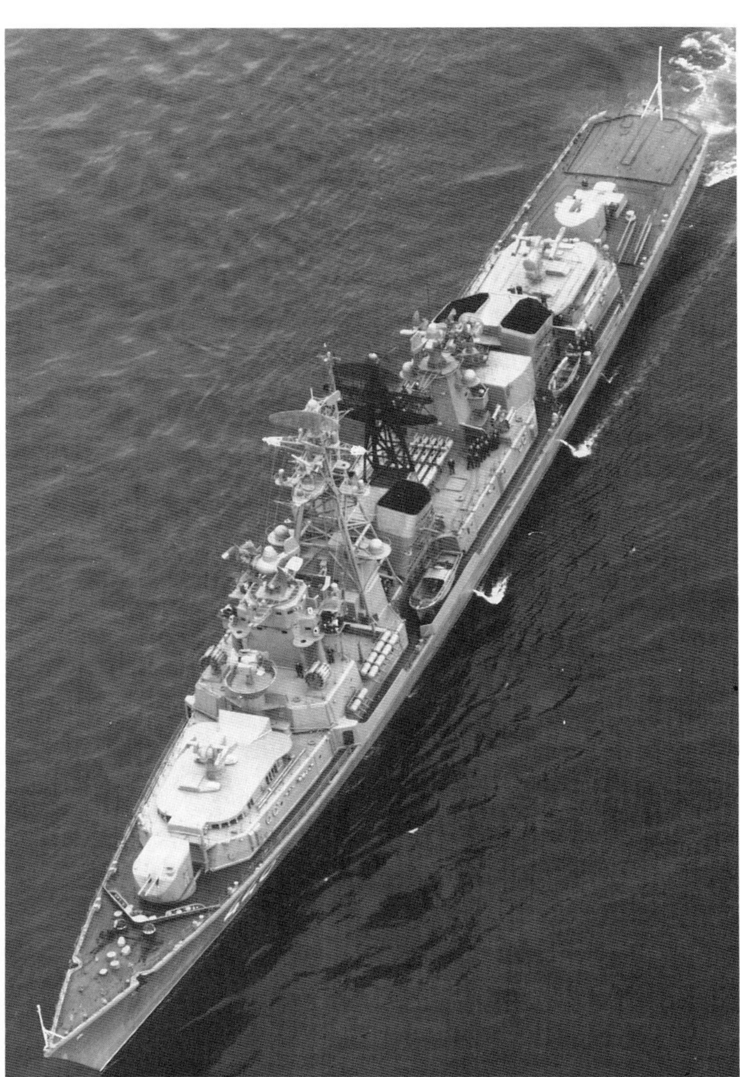

Obraztsovyy—now stricken U.S. Navy, 6-84

Remarks: Type designation: *Bol'shoy Protivolodochnyy Korabl'* (Large Antisubmarine Ship). Of 20 originally completed 1962 to 1973, six were converted or completed to the "Modified Kashin" design (see above), *Otvazhnyy* sank 31-8-74 following explosion and fire, *Provornyy* was converted as trials ship for the SA-N-7 SAM system and stricken circa 1990, and five have been stricken for scrap in 1990–91: *Komsomolets Ukrainyy, Soobrazitel'nyy, Obraztsovyy, Odarennyy, Steregushchiy,* and *Strogiy.* The only surviving Pacific Fleet unit, *Sposobnyy,* returned to the Black Sea in the late 1980s for a probable refit and has not re-emerged. The survivors are likely to be stricken shortly. Could make 39 kts when new.

The early-construction units were completed with two Head Net-A search radars and the later units with one Head Net-C and one Big Net. *Obraztsovyy* has additional EW radomes on the masts nicknamed "Guard Dog." The ships have retractable gyro stabilizers. The fantail is cleared as a landing platform, but helicopters are rare carried. These were the world's first all-gas-turbine-powered large warships, but th are now antiquated and lack adequate self-defense and EW equipment. Carry 2,4 rounds 76.2-mm ammunition, 192 RGB-60 rockets for RBU-6000, 48 RGB-10 rock for RBU-1000, 5 torpedoes.

Note: All older destroyers of the Kanin (ex-Krupnyy) (Project 1157), Kotlin (Proj 56), and *Skoryy* (Project 30-*bis*) series have been stricken or converted for other dut such as barracks hulks. Also stricken by 1990 was the *Provornyy,* a Kashin modifie serve as trials ship for the SA-N-7 SAM system. The majority of the stricken ships w sold to foreign scrap dealers during 1989–91.

FRIGATES

◆ **1 (+1 +. . .) Neustrashimyy class (Project 1154.0)**
Bldr: Yantar SY, Kaliningrad, Kaliningrad Oblast

	Laid down	L	In serv.	Fl
Neustrashimyy ("Undaunted")	1986	1988	1991	. .
Nepristupnyy ("Unassailable")	1988	1991	. . .	. .

Neustrashimyy—with VDS door open

Neustrashimyy

RIGATES *(continued)*

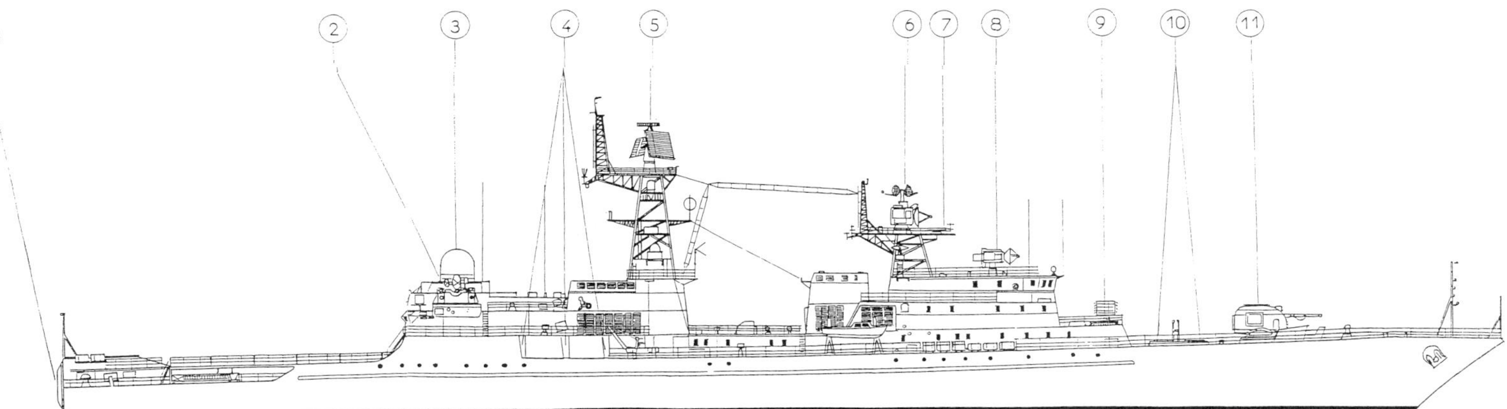

eustrashimyy 1. Variable-depth sonar housing 2. CADS-1 point-defense systems (port and starboard) 3. Cross Dome air-search/target designation dar 4. 533-mm torpedo tubes (3 per side) 5. Top Plate 3-D air search radar 6. Cross Sword guidance radar 7. Palm Frond navigational radars 8. Kite reech fire-control radar for 100-mm gun 9. RBU-6000 ASW rocket launcher 10. SA-N-9 vertical-launch SAM launchers 11. 100-mm DP gun
Drawing: Capitaine de Frégate L. Gassier

trashimyy 12-90

rashimyy 12-90

Neustrashimyy—Note that the VDS housing at the stern is higher than the helicopter deck 12-90

Neustrashimyy 12-90

D: 4,000 tons (4,500 fl) **S:** 32 kts
Dim: 130.0 × 15.5 (14.7 wl) × 4.9 mean hull (5.6 max.)
A: 4/SA-N-9 VLS SAM silos (32 missiles)—1/100-mm DP—2/CADS-1 CIWS (2/30-mm gatling AA and 8/SA-N-11 missiles each; 96 missiles)—6/533-mm TT (I × 6, 16 SS-N-15 missiles or torpedoes)—1/RBU-6000 ASW RL (XII × 1)—1/Ka-27PL Helix-A helicopter—mines
Electron Equipt:
Radar: 1/Nayada nav., 2/Palm Frond nav., 1/Top Plate 3-D air search, 1/Cross Dome (Positiv-E) target designation, 1/Cross Sword SA-N-9 f.c., 1/Kite Screech 100-mm f.c., 2/Hot Flash CADS-1 f.c.
Sonar: . . . . . . bow-mounted LF, ... LF VDS
EW: 2/Foot Ball-A intercept, 2/Half Hat-B intercept, 1/Cage Flask intercept, 2/Bell Squat jammer, 2/16-tubed decoy RL, 8/10-tubed decoy RL
IFF: 2/Salt Pot transponders, interrogation by radars
M: COGAG: 2 cruise gas turbines (12,100 shp each), 2 boost gas turbines (24,300 shp each); 2 props; 72,800 shp max.
Electric: 4,000 kw **Range:.** 700/30; 3,900/20; 4,500/16
Endurance: 30 days **Crew:** 200 tot.

Remarks: *Neustrashimyy* began sea trials during 12-89 and was still in a trials status a year later. The design is apparently the production successor to the Krivak series and is optimized for ASW. Third and fourth units, which will probably not be completed, were to have been named *Tuman* ("Snow Leopard") and *Nepokornyy* ("Unruly").

Special care has been taken in the design to reduce radar and infrared emissions. The above-water hull form has a flat flare over its entire length while the low superstructure has each level broken by flat convex planes to disburse radar returns. The stacks feature complex eductors and are shaped to reduce radar return; the after stack (just abaft the mainmast) is so low as to be barely higher than the hangar. The effectiveness

FRIGATES *(continued)*

of the signature-reduction effort is spoiled somewhat, however, by the design of the lattice mast and the usual plethora of bulky antennas.

The six torpedo tubes flanking the hangar are fixed at about a 15-degree outboard angle and can launch the SS-N-15 antisubmarine missile as well as wire-guided torpedoes. The sonar suite appears to be identical to that on the modernized Krivak-I-class frigates *Zharkiy* and *Leningradskiy Komsomolets*; there is no provision for a towed linear passive hydrophone array. The use of a single older RBU-6000 vice the longer-ranged RBU-12000 ASW rocket launcher is surprising; it can also function as a torpedo countermeasure system. There are no bridge periscopes as in other modern Russian designs.

◆ **7 (+1+. . .) Krivak-III class (Project 1135P)**
Bldr: Kamysh-Burun SY, Kerch', Ukraine

	In serv.	Fleet
Menzhinskiy	8-84	Pacific
Dzerzhinskiy	8-85	Pacific
Imeni XXVII Syezda K.P.S.S.	2-87	Pacific
Imeni 70-Letiya Vuk KGB	4-88	Pacific
Imeni 70-Letiya Pogranvoysk	4-89	Pacific
Kedrov	10-90	Pacific
Vorovskiy	8-91	Pacific
Kirov	. . .	. . . . .

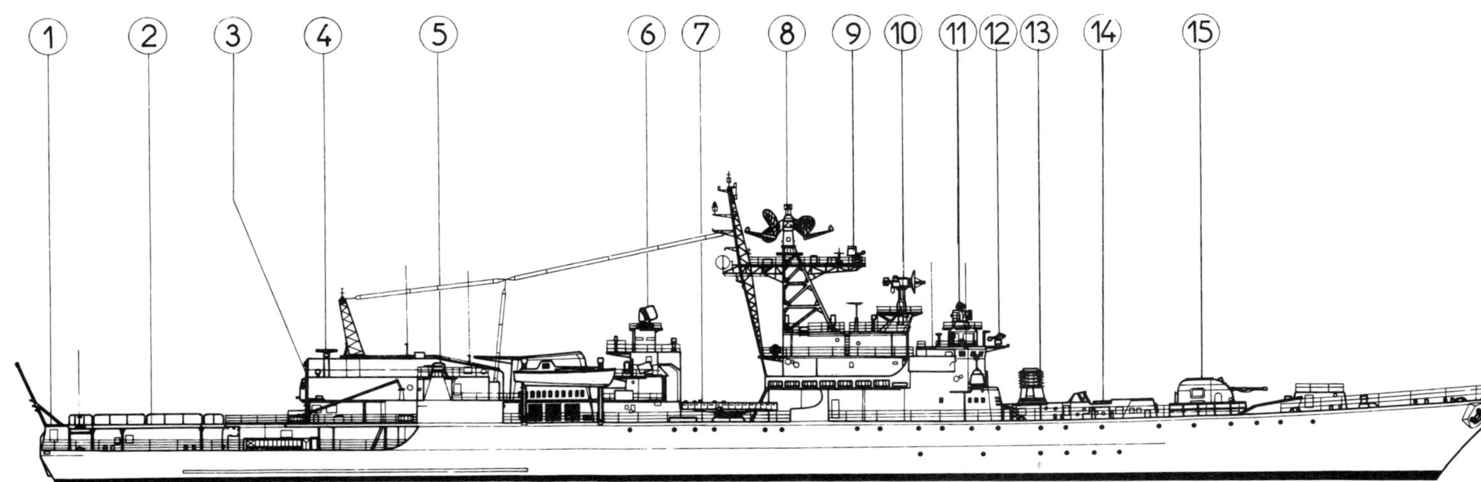

Krivak-III 1. variable-depth sonar housing 2. helo deck 3. helo hangar 4. Spin Trough radar for helo control 5. 30-mm gatling AA 6. Bas Tilt radar director for 30-mm AA 7. quadruple 533-mm TT 8. Head Net-C air-search radar (Top Plate after first two) 9. Don-Kay nav. radar 10. Kite Screech radar director for 100-mm gun 11. Pop Group track-while-scan radar for SA-N-4 12. Palm Frond nav. radar 13. RBU-6000 ASW RL 14. twin SA-N-4 launcher 15. 100-mm DP Drawing: Capitaine de Frégate L. Gassier

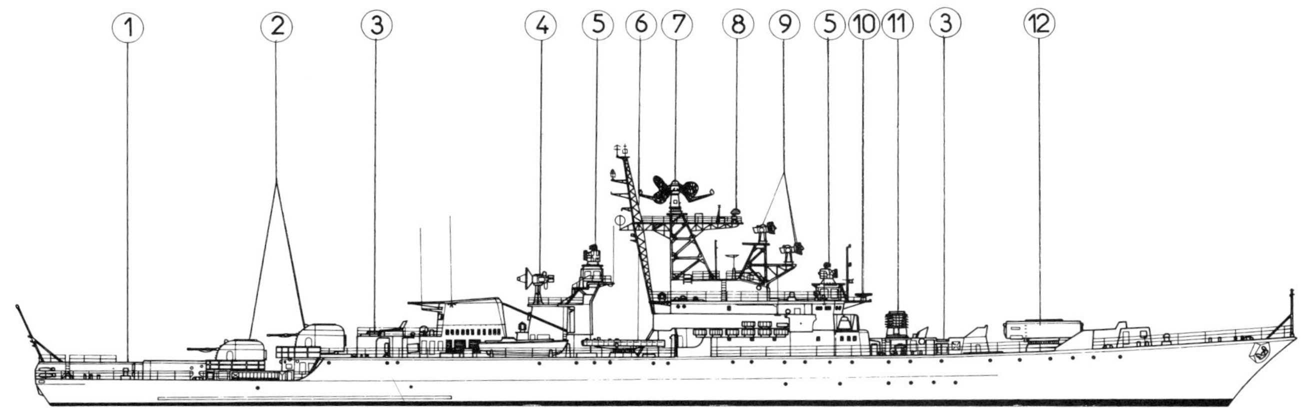

Krivak-II 1. variable-depth sonar housing 2. single 100-mm DP mounts 3. twin SA-N-4 launcher 4. Kite Screech radar director for 100-mm guns 5. Pop Group track-while-scan radar director for SA-N-4 6. quadruple 533-mm TT 7. Head Net-C air-search radar 8. Don-Kay or Palm Frond nav. radar 9. Eye Bowl radar directors for SS-N-14 10. Spin Trough nav. radar 11. RBU-6000 ASW RL 12. quadruple SS-N-14 launcher Drawing: Capitaine de Frégate L. Gassier

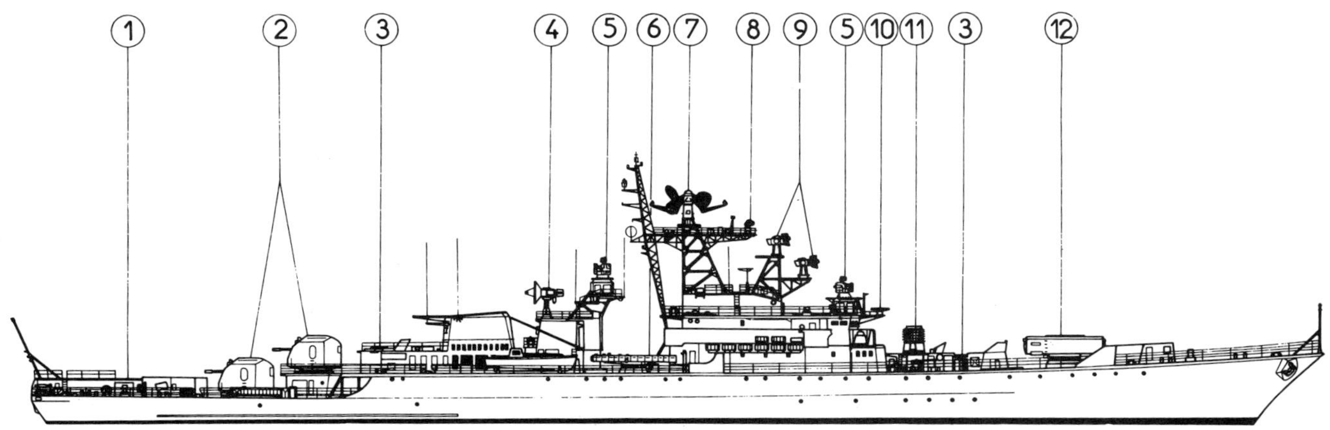

Krivak-I 1. variable-depth sonar housing 2. twin 76.2-mm DP 3. twin SA-N-4 launcher 4. Owl Screech radar director for 76.2-mm DP 5. Pop Group track-while-scan radar directors for SA-N-4 6. quadruple 533-mm TT 7. Head Net-C air-search radar 8. Don-Kay or Palm Frond nav. radar 9. Eye Bowl radar directors for SS-N-14 10. Spin Trough nav. radar 11. RBU-6000 ASW RL 12. quadruple SS-N-14 launcher Capitaine de Frégate L. Gassier

FRIGATES *(continued)*

Kedrov French Navy, 10-90

rov U.S. Navy, 11-90

i 70-Letiya Pogranvoysk J.M.S.D.F./*Ships of the World*, 1991

hinskiy—with Head Net-C air-search radar 1984

D: 3,300 tons light (3,900 fl) **S:** 30 kts (29 sust.)
Dim: 124.2 (116.9 pp) × 14.2 (13.2 wl) × 4.9 (hull)
A: 1/SA-N-4 SAM syst. (II × 1, 20 Gecko missiles)—1/100-mm DP—2/30-mm AK-630 gatling AA (I × 2)—2/RBU-6000 ASW RL (XII × 2)—8/533-mm TT (IV × 2)—1/Ka-27 Helix-A helicopter—mines
Electron Equipt:
Radar: 1/Palm Frond nav., 1/Don-Kay nav., 1/Spin Trough nav., 1/Head Net-C air search (3rd ship and later: Top Plate 3-D air search), 1/Pop Group SA-N-4 f.c., 1/Kite Screech 100-mm f.c., 1/Bass Tilt 30-mm f.c.
Sonar: Bull Nose hull-mounted MF, Mare Tail MF VDS
EW: 2/Bell Shroud, 2/Bell Squat, 4/fixed decoy RL (XVI × 4)
IFF: 1/Salt Pot transponder, 1/High Pole B transponder
M: COGOG: 2 cruise gas turbines (12,100 shp each), 2 boost gas turbines (24,300 shp each); 2 props; 48,600 shp max.
Range: 700/29; 3,900/20; 4,500/16 **Fuel:** 800 tons
Crew: 20 officers, 200 enlisted

Remarks: Revised version of basic Krivak design for KGB Maritime Border Guard service in the Far East. Typed PSKR—*Pogranichnyy Storozhevoy Korabl'* (Border Patrol Ship). First two named for prominent KGB "heroes." *Menzhinskiy* deployed from the Black Sea 7-9-84, bound for the Pacific, and *Dzerzhinskiy* followed a year later. The name for the third unit means "In Honor of the 27th Anniversary of the Communist Party of the Soviet Union"; the fourth "In Honor of the 70th Anniversary of the KGB"; the fifth, "In Honor of the 70th Anniversary of the Border Patrol"; the sixth is named for Mikhail Sergeyevich Kedrov (1878–1941), a pioneer member of the NKVD and later a member of the Soviet supreme court; the seventh is named for a World War II–era KGB leader. More are believed building, although the basic design is well over 20 years old. Eighth unit may not be completed, names for all likely to change.

The addition of a helicopter facility (with simple deck-transit system) and helicopter weapons reload magazines cost two gun mounts and one SA-N-4 position aft, while the Krivak-I/II SS-N-14 dual-purpose missile system was replaced by a 100-mm gun, more useful for the patrol mission of these ships. Two six-barreled gatling guns were added to improve close-in defense. *Imeni XXVII Syezda K.P.S.S.* and later units substitute Top Plate for the Head Net-C air/surface-search radar. These ships have a significantly greater displacement than earlier Krivak variants. The Spin Trough radar is mounted atop the helicopter hangar and probably serves in flight control.

♦ 11 Krivak-II class (Project 1135M)

Bldr: Yantar Zavod, Kaliningrad, Kaliningradskiy Oblast

	In serv.	Fleet
Rezvyy ("Lively")	1975	Northern
Rezkiy ("Brusque")	1976	Pacific
Razitel'nyy ("Wrathful")	1977	Black Sea
Grozyashchiy ("Dissuasive")	1977	Pacific
Neukrotimyy ("Indomitable") (ex-*Komsomolets Litviy*, ex-*Neukrotimyy*)	1978	Baltic
Bessmennyy ("Vigilant")	1978	Northern
Gromkiy ("Thunderous")	1979	Northern
Gordelivyy ("Trustworthy")	1979	Pacific
R'yanyy ("Spirited")	1980	Pacific
Revnostnyy ("Roaring")	1980	Pacific
Pytlivyy ("Curious")	1982	Black Sea

Rezkiy U.S. Navy, 6-90

Bessmennyy PH1 Lowe, USN, 7-89

FRIGATES *(continued)*

Neukrotimyy Hartmut Ehlers, 6-90

Neukrotimyy Peter Voss, 6-90

Neukrotimyy—bridge detail French Navy, 3-89

Razitel'nyy U.S. Navy, 4-90

Gromkiy French Navy, 3-87

D: 3,255 tons light (3,440 fl) **S:** 30.6 kts
Dim: 124.2 (116.9 wl) × 14.2 (13.2 wl) × 4.6 (hull)
A: 4/SS-N-14 Silex SSM (IV × 1)—2/SA-N-4 SAM systems (II × 2, 40 Gecko missiles)—2/100-mm DP (I × 2)—2/RBU-6000 ASW RL (XII × 2)—8/533-mm TT (IV × 2)—mines
Electron Equipt:
Radar: 1/Palm Frond or Don-Kay nav., 1/Spin Trough or Don-2 nav. 1/Head Net-C air search, 2/Eye Bowl SS-N-14 f.c., 2 Pop Group SA-N-4 f.c., 1/Kite Screech 100-mm f.c.
Sonar: Bull Nose hull-mounted MF, Mare Tail MF VDS
EW: 2/Bell Shroud, 2/Bell Squat, 4/decoy RL (XVI × 4)
IFF: 1/Salt Pot transponder, interrogation by radars
M: COGOG: 2 cruise gas turbines of 12,100 shp each and 2 boost gas turbines of 24,300 shp each; 2 props; 48,600 shp max.
Range: 700/30; 3,900/20; 4,500/16 **Fuel:** 800 tons
Crew: 26 officers, 173 enlisted (240 total accommodations)

Remarks: Type designation: SKR—*Storozhevoy Korabl'* (Patrol Ship), forme BPK—*Bol'shoy Protivolodochnyy Korabl'* (Large Antisubmarine Ship). The VDS ho ing at the stern is somewhat larger than on the Krivak-Is, but the principal differer is substitution of two single 100-mm for the two twin 76.2-mm guns. The chaff/de rocket launchers were moved from the stern to the 01 level, abreast the aft SA-N launcher. *Revnostnyy* has four 4-tubed decoy RL mounted between the torpedo tubes, addition to her normal chaff RL system. *Neukrotimyy* was renamed in 1988 for Communist Youth League of Lithuania but renamed in 1990 when that state manded independence. Ships of this class have operated with as few as 18 officers 162 enlisted.

◆ **20 Krivak-I class (Project 1135)** Bldrs: A: Severnaya Zavod (ex-Zhdanov SY), St. Petersburg, Russia; B: Yantar Zavod, Kaliningrad, Kaliningradskiy Oblast; C: Kamysh-Burun SY, Kerch'

	Bldr	In serv.	Fleet
Bditel'nyy ("Vigilant")	B	1970	Baltic
Dostoynyy ("Dignified")	C	1971	Northe
Bodryy ("Brave")	B	1971	Baltic
Svirepyy ("Ferocious")	B	1971	Baltic
Sil'nyy ("Powerful")	B	1972	Baltic
Doblestnyy ("Valorous")	C	1972	Northe
Storozhevoy ("Guarding")	B	1973	Pacific
Razumnyy ("Sensible")	B	1973	Pacific
Druzhnyy ("Amicable")	A	1975	Baltic
Deyatel'nyy ("Active")	C	1975	Black S
Zharkyy ("Passionate")	B	1975	Northe
Retivyy ("Zealous")	A	1976	Pacific
Leningradskiy Komsomolets	A	1976	Northe
Letuchiy ("Flying")	A	1977	Pacific
Bezzavetnyy ("Conscientious")	C	1978	Black
Pylkiy ("Ardent")	A	1979	Baltic
Zadornyy ("Provocative")	A	1979	Baltic
Bezukoriznennyy ("Irreproachable")	C	1980	Black
Ladnyy ("Friendly")	C	1980	Black
Poryvistyy ("Impetuous")	C	1982	Pacifi

Bditel'nyy—with forecastle extended Mike Louag

Zharkiy—with enlarged VDS housing U.S. Na

RIGATES *(continued)*

eningradskiy Komsomolets—as modernized with new VDS, Half Plate radar, and provision for SS-N-25 missiles 5-91

ryvistyy—the newest Krivak-I, with bow sonar partly exposed U.S. Navy, 6-90

Dostoynyy French Navy, 6-90

toynyy—superstructure detail French Navy, 6-90

Bditel'nyy Leo Van Ginderen, 6-91

y Gilbert Gyssels, 11-87

FRIGATES *(continued)*

D: 3,075 tons (3,575 fl) **S:** 30.6 kts
Dim: 124.2 (116.9 wl) × 14.2 (13.2 wl) × 4.5 (hull)
A: 4/SS-N-14 Silex SSM (IV × 1)—2/SA-N-4 SAM systems (II × 2, 40 Gecko missiles)—4/76.2-mm DP (II × 2)—2/RBU-6000 ASW RL (XII × 2)—8/533-mm TT (IV × 2)—mines (*Leningradskiy Komsomolets:* provision for 8/SS-N-25 SSM (IV × 2), no RBU-6000)
Electron Equipt:
Radar: 1/Don-2 or Spin Trough nav., 1/Don-Kay or Palm Frond nav., 1/Head Net-C (*Leningradskiy Komsomolets:* Half Plate) air search, 2/Eye Bowl SS-N-14 f.c., 2/Pop Group SA-N-4 f.c., 1/Owl Screech 76.2-mm f.c.
Sonar: Bull Nose hull-mounted MF, Mare Tail MF VDS (*Zharkiy* and *Leningradskiy Komsomolets:* LF hull-mounted, LF VDS)
EW: 2/Bell Shroud, 2/Bell Squat, 4/decoy RL (XVI × 4) (*Leningradskiy Komsomolets, Bodry:* 8-18/10-tubed decoy RL)
IFF: 1/High Pole B or Salt Pot transponder, interrogation by radars
M: COGOG: 2 cruise gas turbines of 12,100 shp each and 2 boost gas turbines of 24,300 shp each; 2 props; 48,600 shp max.
Range: 700/30; 3,900/20; 4,500/16 **Fuel:** 800 tons
Crew: 26 officers, 172 enlisted (240 total accommodations)

Remarks: In 1978 Krivak-I and Krivak-II classes were rerated from BPK (*Bol'shoy Protivolodochnyy Korabl'*—large ASW ship) to SKR (*Storozhevoy Korabl'*—patrol ship), a demotion prompted perhaps by their limited endurance at high speeds, speed, and size. Pacific Fleet sister *Razyashchiy,* completed in 1974, was stricken in 1991.

Bodryy has been equipped with ten 10-tubed chaff RL, *replacing* the original four 16-tubed. *Zharkiy* has had her VDS housing enlarged, and the chaff RL relocated as on the Krivak-II class. *Bditel'nyy* and *Doblestnyy* have had their forecastle decks extended aft slightly, reason unknown.

Leningradskiy Komsomolets emerged from a Baltic-area refit in 5-91 with an enlarged VDS housing as on *Zharkiy,* the RBU-6000 ASW rocket launchers replaced by as-yet-vacant racks for two quadruple SS-N-25 antiship cruise-missile launchers, the Head Net-C air-search radar replaced by Half Plate atop a new lattice foremast with an additional deckhouse level at its base, and eight 10-tubed fixed decoy rocket launchers added to the four 16-tubed launchers already mounted; also added were six Half Cup infrared detectors, and the navigational radar suite now consists of two Palm Frond. The "Project 1135.2" update will probably be performed on other selected units of the class, resources permitting. The bow appears to have been lengthened slightly, possibly indicating installation of a new bow sonar as well.

Note: The single Koni-class (Project 1159) frigate in Soviet service, *Del'fin,* was transferred to Bulgaria in 1-90. All remaining Riga (Project 50)-class frigates had been discarded by the end of 1991, and most had either been scrapped abroad or were on offer for scrap.

CORVETTES

◆ **12 Parchim-II class**
Bldr: Peenewerft, Wolgast, Germany (In serv. 1986–89)

Parchim-II class M.O.D., Bonn, 6-90

MPK 217(247)—Parchim-II class Hartmut Ehlers, 3-92

D: 790 tons (910 fl) **S:** 24 kts
Dim: 75.20 (69.00 pp) × 9.80 (9.00 wl) × 2.65 hull (4.40 max.)
A: 1/76.2-mm 59-cal. AK-176 DP—1/30-mm AK-630 gatling AA— 2/SA-N-5/8 SAM syst. (IV × 2, 24 Grail or Gremlin missiles)—4/533-mm TT (II × 2)—2/RBU-6000 ASW RL (XII × 2)—2/d.c. racks (12 d.c.)—mines
Electron Equipt:
Radar: 1/Spin Trough nav., 1/Cross Dome ("Positiv-E") air search, 1/Bass Tilt gun f.c.
Sonar: MF hull-mounted, HF dipping
EW: 2 Watch Dog intercept, 2/decoy RL (XVI × 2)
IFF: 1/High Pole A, 1/High Pole B transponder, interrogation by radar
M: 3 Type M504A-3 diesels; 3 props (centerline: CP); 14,250 bhp
Range: 1,200/20; 2,500/12 **Endurance:** 10 days
Crew: 9 officers, 71 enlisted

Remarks: Type designation: MPK—*Malyy Protivolodochnyy Korabl'* (Small Antisu marine Ship). An improved version of the East German Navy's Parchim, with lat armament and a new 75-n.m.-ranged radar mounted in a radome. As this design inferior in all respects to the current-production, Russian-built Grisha-V, its acqu sition may have been a form of aid to the East German shipbuilding industry. T dipping sonar deploys through a door on the starboard side of the main deck superstru ture. The d.c. racks exit through ports in the stern. All operate in the Baltic Fle where they have replaced Mirka- and Petya-class units.

◆ **21 (+ . . .) Grisha-V class (Project 1124EhM)** Bldr: Leninskaya Kuznitsa SY, Kiev; Khabarovsk SY; Kamysh-Burun SY, Kerch'; Zelenodolsk S (In serv. 1985–. . .)

Arkhangel'skiy Komsomolets	Leninskaya Kuznitsa
Brestskiy Komsomolets	Poryvistyy
Kievskiy Komsomolets	16 others

Grisha-V class—KGB unit with Strut Pair radar U.S. Navy, 8

Grisha-V class—with Half Plate-B radar, SA-N-4 launcher raised U.S. Navy,

Detail of Grisha-V—showing lengthened torpedo tubes for wire-gui and shoulder-fired SAM launch positions just forward of the stack; not 10-tubed decoy rocket launchers on bridge, RBU-6000 to port only Plate-B search radar French Nav

CORVETTES *(continued)*

ɪrisha-V class—naval unit with Strut Pair radar French Navy, 6-90

ɪsha-V class M.O.D., U.K., 5-90

D: 910 tons (1,200 fl) **S:** 31 kts
Dim: 71.6 (66.9 wl) × 9.8 × 3.7 hull
A: 1/SA-N-4 SAM system (II × 1, 20 Gecko missiles)—1/76.2-mm 59-cal. AK-176 DP—1/30-mm AK-630 gatling AA—2/SA-N-5/8 SAM positions (I × 2, 24 Grail or Gremlin, shoulder-launched)—4/533-mm TT (II × 2)—1/RBU-6000 ASW RL (XII × 1)—2/d.c. racks (6 d.c. each) or mines
Electron Equipt:
Radar: 1/Don-2 nav., 1/Strut Pair, (late units: Half Plate-B) air/surf. search, 1/Pop Group SA-N-4 f.c., 1/Bass Tilt gun f.c.
Sonar: Bull Nose hull-mounted MF, Elk Tail MF dipping
EW: 2/Watch Dog intercept, 2/decoy RL (XVI × 2)
IFF: 1/Square Head interrogator, 1/High Pole A, 1/High Pole B transponder
M: CODAG: 1/19,000-shp gas turbine, 2 twin Type M504 diesels (10,000 bhp each); 3 props; 39,000 bhp
Range: 450/30; 4,000/18 **Crew:** 60 tot.

ɴarks: Type designation: MPK—*Malyy Protivolodochnyy Korabl'* (Small Antisub-ine Ship). The latest production variant of the basic Grisha substitutes the Strut radar for Strut Curve and a 76.2-mm gun for the twin 57-mm mount, with one J-6000 ASW RL removed as weight compensation (the surviving mount is carried ne port position). Two launch positions for shoulder-fired point-defense SAMs have added at the break of the 01 level superstructure, just forward of the stack. Just t the mast is a Kolonka-2 backup ringsight director for the 30-mm gun. The torpedo s have been modified to launch wire-guided torpedoes. The dipping sonar is housed ne after superstructure, lowering through the hull between the starboard and erline propeller shafts.

ɪme of these ships, probably including *Poryvistiy,* were built for the KGB Border rd. Recent construction units have substituted the Half Plate-B radar (one half of ɔack-to-back Top Plate 3-D radar) for Strut Pair. Still building at the rate of four year, a quarter century after the first Grisha-I was begun. There are units in all fleet areas.

Grisha-IV class Bldr: . . . (In serv.: circa 1984)

: 860 tons (1,150 fl) **S:** 31 kts
ɪm: 71.6 (66.9 wl) × 9.8 × 3.6 (hull)
: 3/SA-N-9 VLS SAM silos (VIII × 3, 24 missiles)—1/30-mm AK-630 gatling AA—2/RBU-6000 ASW RL (XII × 2)—2/533-mm TT (I × 2)—2/d.c. racks (12 d.c.) or mines
ectron Equipt:
Radar: 1/. . . nav., 1/Cross Sword SA-N-9 f.c., 1/Bass Tilt gun f.c.
Sonar: Bull Nose hull-mounted MF, Elk Tail MF dipping
EW: 2/Watch Dog intercept—IFF: . . .
. . . **Range:** . . . **Crew:** . . .

ɪrks: A one-of-a-kind trials ship for the SA-N-9 vertically launched SAM system new propulsion system. No photos available. Probably in the Black Sea Fleet.

◆ **31 Grisha-III class (Project 1124M)** Bldr: Zelenodolsk SY; Leninskaya Kuznitsa SY, Kiev; Kamysh-Burun SY, Kerch'; Komsomolsk SY (In serv. 1975–85)

Bditel'nyy	Komsomolets Gruzii
Kievskiy Komsomolets	Odesskiy Komsomolets
Komsomolets Armenii	Orlovskiy Komsomolets
Komsomolets Bashkirii	Reshitel'nyy
Komsomolets Latviy	Smel'yy
Komsomolets Moldavii	20 others

Grisha-III class M.O.D., Bonn, 1990

Grisha-III class M.O.D., U.K., 5-90

Smel'yy—a KGB Border Guard Grisha-III with boat to port beside stack U.S. Navy, 1985

D: 860 tons (1,150 fl) **S:** 31 kts
Dim: 71.6 (66.9 wl) × 9.8 × 3.6 (hull)
A: 1/SA-N-4 SAM syst. (II × 1, 20 Gecko missiles)—2/57-mm AK-257 DP (II × 1)—1/30-mm AK-630 gatling AA—2/RBU-6000 ASW RL (XII × 2)—4/533-mm TT (II × 2)—2/d.c. racks (12 d.c.) or mines
Electron Equipt:
Radar: 1/Don-2 nav., 1/Strut Curve air/surf. search, 1/Pop Group SA-N-4 f.c., 1/Bass Tilt gun f.c.
Sonar: Bull Nose hull-mounted MF, Elk Tail MF dipping
EW: 2 Watch Dog intercept
IFF: 1 High Pole A, 1 High Pole B transponder, interrogation by radar
M: CODAG: 1/19,000 shp gas turbine, 2 twin Type M504 diesels (10,000 bhp each); 3 props; 39,000 shp
Range: 450/30; 4,000/18 **Crew:** 60 tot.

Remarks: Soviet type designation: MPK—*Malyy Protivolodochnyy Korabl'* (Small Antisubmarine Ship). Bass Tilt, which is atop a small deckhouse to port on the aft superstructure, has been substituted for Muff Cob radar fire control, while a gatling gun has been mounted in the space occupied by Muff Cob in the Grisha-I and -II.

CORVETTES *(continued)*

Depth-charge racks can be mounted on the aft end of the mine rails. Several Pacific Fleet units serve the KGB Maritime Border Guard, including *Smel'yy, Bditel'nyy,* and *Reshitel'nyy*; at least one, *Smel'yy,* has had an extra boat added to port of the stack, stowed on an 01-level platform. Some KGB names duplicate Russian Navy names and may have since been changed. Some may have 2 SA-N-5/8 SAM launch positions, as on Grisha-V.

♦ **10 Grisha-II class (Project 1124P)**
Bldrs: Zelenodolsk SY (In serv. 1974–. . .)

Ametist	Brilliant	Dozornyy	Izumrud
Nadezhnyy	Premernyy	Provornyy	Predanyy
Prozorlivyy	Rubin	Sapfir	Zhemchug

Grisha-II class—57-mm guns fore and aft — Tass, 1990

Grisha-II class — French Navy, 6-90

D: 850 tons (1,100 fl) **S:** 30–31 kts
Dim: 71.6 (66.9 wl) × 9.8 × 3.5 (hull)
A: 4/57-mm AK-257 DP (II × 2)—2/RBU-6000 ASW RL (XIII × 2)—4/533-mm TT (II × 2)—2/d.c. racks (12 d.c.) or mines
Electron Equipt:
Radar: 1/Don-2 nav., 1/Strut Curve air/surf. search, 1/Muff Cob f.c.
Sonar: Bull Nose hull-mounted MF, Elk Tail MF dipping
EW: 2/Watch Dog intercept—IFF: 1/High Pole B transponder
M: CODAG: 1/15,000- or 19,000-shp gas turbine, 2 twin M503 (8,000 bhp each) or twin M504 (10,000 bhp each) diesels; 3 props; 31,000 or 39,000 shp (*see* Remarks)
Range: 450/30; 4,000/18 **Crew:** 60 tot.

Remarks: Soviet type designation: PSKR—*Pogranichnyy Storozhevoy Korabl'* (Border Patrol Ship). Were built for the KGB Maritime Border Guard but may now be naval (with names changed, in some instances). A second twin 57-mm was substituted for SA-N-4 forward, and the Pop Group missile-control radar was not installed. At least one Black Sea Fleet unit has had a boat added to port of the stack, stowed on a new 01-level platform; the after twin 57-mm DP was removed as weight compensation on that unit. Early units probably had the lower horsepower plant, with later construction employing the Grisha-III plant. Two from the above list of names were transferred to Bulgaria in 1990.

♦ **14 Grisha-I class (Project 1124)** Bldrs: Zelenodolsk SY; Leninskaya Kuznitsa SY, Kiev; Kamysh-Burun SY, Kerch'; Khabarovsk SY (In serv. 1968–74)

Grisha-I class — M.O.D., U.K., 5-9

Grisha-I class—with enlarged stack casing — French Navy, 19

Grisha-I—with standard stack casing — U.S. Navy,

D: 850 tons (1,100 fl) **S:** 30 kts
Dim: 71.6 (66.9 wl) × 9.8 × 3.5 (hull)
A: 1/SA-N-4 SAM syst. (II × 1, 20 Gecko missiles)—2/57-mm AK- DP (II × 1)—2/RBU-6000 ASW RL (XII × 2)—4/533-mm TT (II × 2)—2/d.c. racks (6 d.c. each) or mines
Electron Equipt:
Radar: 1/Don-2 nav., 1/Strut Curve air/surf. search, 1/Pop Grou SA-N-4 f.c., 1/Muff Cob gun f.c.
Sonar: 1/Bull Nose hull-mounted MF, 1/Rat Tail HF dipping
EW: 2/Watch Dog intercept
IFF: 1/High Pole B, 1/High Pole A transponder

CORVETTES *(continued)*

M: CODAG: 2/twin M503 diesels; 1/15,000-shp gas turbine; 3 props; 31,000 shp
Range: 450/30; 4,000/18 **Crew:** 60 tot.

Remarks: More specialized for ASW than the earlier Petya and Mirka "patrol ships." Type designation: MPK—*Malyy Protivolodochnyy Korabl'* (Small Antisubmarine Ship). The full name for the Khabarovsk Shipyard is *Sudostroitel'nyy Zavod Imeni 60 Letiya Oktyabrya* (Shipbuilding Works Named in Honor of the 60th Anniversary of the October Revolution). A plate has been added forward of the Muff Cob fire-control radar to protect personnel on the bridge from its radiation. The dipping sonar is housed beneath a hump to starboard on the after deckhouse, deploying through the hull bottom between the starboard and centerline propeller shafts. A few Grisha-Is are subordinated to the KGB Maritime Border Guard. One Northern Fleet Grisha-I was discarded in 1991.

◆ **2 Petya-III class (Project 159AE)** (In serv. . . .)

A: 4/76.2-mm 59-cal. DP (II × 2)—3/533-mm TT (III × 1)—4/RBU-2500 ASW RL (XVI × 4)—2/d.c. racks—mines

Remarks: Other details as for Petya-II class. These are export versions of the Petya, which for some reason were never delivered. Probably have Strut Curve air-search radars. Units with this configuration were exported to Ethiopia, India, Syria, and Vietnam.

◆ **8–10 Petya-II class (Project 159A)** Bldrs: Yantar Zavod, Kaliningrad, Kaliningradskiy Oblast; Khabarovsk SY (In serv. 1964–69)

tya-II class M.O.D., U.K., 6-89

D: 950 tons (1,150 fl) **S:** 29 kts
Dim: 81.8 (78.0 pp) × 9.2 × 2.9 (hull)
A: 4/76.2-mm 59-cal. AK-276 DP (II × 2)—2/RBU-6000 ASW RL (XII × 2)—10/400-mm ASW TT (V × 2)—2/d.c. racks—mines
Electron Equipt:
Radar: 1/Don-2 nav., 1/Strut Curve air/surf. search, 1/Hawk Screech f.c.
Sonar: 1/Herkules hull-mounted HF, 1/HF helo dipping sonar (on some)
EW: 2/Watch Dog intercept—IFF: 1/High Pole B transponder
M: CODAG: 2/15,000-shp gas turbines + 1/6,000-bhp Type 61V-3 diesel; 3 props (CP on centerline); 36,000 shp—2/electric auxiliary props
Range: 450/29 (diesel + gas turbine); 1,800/16 (diesel)
Crew: 8 officers, 84 enlisted

Remarks: Type designation: SKR—*Storozhevoy Korabl'* (Patrol Ship). Some have carried helicopter dipping sonars in temporary installations amidships. The diesel drives the centerline CP prop and can drive the ships at up to 16 kts. Two small electrohydraulic maneuvering propellers are mounted at the extreme stern and can produce 3 kts. Have fin stabilizers. The teardrop-shaped sonar dome adds 1.5 m to the navigational draft. One Black Sea Fleet Petya-I or -II carried a twin SUW-N-1 ASW RL on the bow in place of the gun mount in 1976. Six standard Petya-IIs were transferred to Ethiopia and Vietnam during 1983–84. About half of the class are believed now to have been discarded, and the rest will likely soon follow.

Note: The remaining 7 Petya-I-class (Project 159) corvettes are believed to have been discarded by 1989, followed by the Mirka-I (Project 35) and Mirka-II class (Project 35M) and all 11 Modified Petya-I (Project 159M) corvettes in 1990–91.

PATROL SHIPS

◆ **6 Ivan Susanin-class (Project 97-17) patrol icebreakers**
Bldr: Admiralty SY, St. Petersburg (In serv. 1975–81)

AYSBURG	IMENI XXVI SYEZDA K.P.S.S.
DUNAY	NEVA
IMENI XXV SYEZDA K.P.S.S.	VOLGA

Volga U.S. Navy, 5-90

ya-II class U.S. Navy, 9-83

PATROL SHIPS *(continued)*

Imeni XXVI Syezda K.P.S.S. M.O.D., U.K., 5-90

D: 3,400 tons (fl) **S:** 14.5 kts **Dim:** 70.0 (62.0 pp) × 18.3 × 6.5
A: 2/76.2-mm 59-cal. AK-276 DP (II × 1)—2/30-mm AK-630 gatling AA (I × 2)
Electron Equipt:
Radar: 2/Don-Kay nav., 1/Strut Curve air/surf. search, 1/Owl Screech 76.2-mm f.c.
IFF: 1/High Pole B transponder
M: 3 Type 13D100 diesels, electric drive; 2 props; 5,400 shp
Electric: 1,000 kw **Range:** 5,500/12.5; 13,000/9.4
Fuel: 550 tons
Crew: 9 officers, 33 enlisted (accommodations for 140 tot.)

Remarks: Built for KGB Maritime Border Guard use and designated as *Pogranichnyy Storozhevoy Korabl'* (Border Patrol Ship). Two sisters, disarmed and painted with black hulls and white superstructures, serve as naval auxiliaries: *Ivan Susanin* and *Ruslan*. The 30-mm gatling AA guns are controlled only by two Kolonka-2 ringsight directors. Have a helicopter deck aft but no hangar. *Dunay* and *Neva*, the last two built, also have two positions for shoulder-launching Grail or Gremlin surface-to-air missiles.

Note: The old patrol icebreaker *Purga* was towed to India for scrapping in 8-90.

♦ **18 Sorum-class armed tugs** Bldr: Yaroslavl SY, Russia (In serv. 1974-. . .)

Amur	Primorsk
Bug	Primorye
Brest	Sakhalin
Chukotka	Ural
Kaluga	Viktor Kingisepp
Kamchatka	Yan Berzin'
Kareliya	Yenisey
Ladoga	Zabaykalye
Neman	Zapolyare

Yan Berzin' 7-91

Zapolyare M.O.D., U.K., 6-89

Yenisey French Navy, 19

D: 1,210 tons (1,656 fl) **S:** 14 kts **Dim:** 58.3 × 12.6 × 4.6
A: 4/30-mm AK-230 AA (II × 2)
Electron Equipt: Radar: 2/Don-2 nav.—IFF: 1/High Pole B
M: 2 Type 5-2D42 diesels, electric drive; 1 prop; 1,500 shp
Fuel: 322 tons **Range:** 6,720/13 **Crew:** 35 tot.

Remarks: Armed units of a standard naval/commercial seagoing tug, used by K(Maritime Border Guard for patrol duties. Typed PSKR—*Pogranichnyy Storozhe Korabl'* (Border Patrol Ship). Retain all towing, firefighting, and salvage facilities.

♦ **1 or more Mayak class (Project 502)** Bldr: . . . (In serv. 1967–197
D: 1,050 tons (fl) **S:** 11 kts **Dim:** 54.2 (50.4 pp) × 9.3 × 3.6
A: 2/25-mm 2M-8 AA (II × 1)—4/RBU-1200 ASW RL (V × 4)—4/400-mm ASW TT (fixed)—2/d.c. racks (6 d.c. each)
Electron Equipt: Radar: 1/Spin Trough—Sonar: HF, hull mounted
M: 1 Karl Liebnecht 8NVD48 diesel; 1 prop; 800 bhp
Range: 9,400/11 **Crew:** 60 tot.

Mayak patrol ship 321 U.S. Navy,

Remarks: Late-model Mayak-class trawlers converted while under constructi act as inexpensive, long-endurance patrol units. Originally thought to have intended for training, but Russian writings and observed operations indicate tha are considered to be combatants, despite low speed. One Pacific Ocean Fleet unit, 525, was stricken during 1991.

♦ **3 T-58-class (Project 264M) radar pickets, former minesweepers** (In serv. 1957–61)
D: 760 tons (880 fl) **S:** 17 kts **Dim:** 70.0 × 9.1 × 2.5
A: 2/57-mm DP (II × 1)—4/30-mm AK-230 AA (II × 2)—2/SA-N-ξ syst. (IV × 2, 16 SA-7 Grail missiles)—2/d.c. racks (6 d.c. each)
Electron Equipt:
Radar: 1/Spin Trough nav., 1/Strut Curve air/surf. search, 1/Big Net early warning, 1/Muff Cob gun f.c.
Sonar: HF hull-mounted—EW: 2/Watch Dog intercept
IFF: High Pole transponder, interrogation by radars
M: 2 diesels; 2 props; 4,000 bhp **Range:** 2,500/13.5
Crew: 100 tot.

PATROL SHIPS *(continued)*

'-58-class patrol ship French Navy, 5-90

58-class patrol ship M.O.D., U.K., 5-90

marks: First unit conversion completed 1979 at Sredniy Neva SY, near St. Peters-'g; the second in 1981, the third around 1983–84. Considering the small number verted, the age of the hulls, and the pace of the program, these ships are probably ended for a specialized range-security role, rather than as classical "radar pickets." val-operated. Will probably soon be stricken.

IDED-MISSILE PATROL COMBATANTS

1 Dergach-class (Project 1239) surface effect ship

Bldr: Kamysh-Burun SY, Kerch' (In serv. 1989)

UCH ("Sealion")

ıch—showing rubber bow air seal; note that the ship is under way with nain-propulsion propeller struts folded up out of the water 1990

Sivuch Boris Lemachko, 1990

Sivuch—note propeller struts in raised position 1990

D: 700 tons (fl) **S:** 60 kts (?) **Dim:** 64.50 × 17.00 × 3.05
A: 8/SS-N-22 Sunburn SSM (IV × 2)—1/SA-N-4 SAM syst. (II × 1, 20 Gecko missiles)—1/76.2-mm 59-cal. AK-176 DP—2/30-mm AK-630 gatling AA (I × 2)
Electron Equipt:
Radar: 1/ Cheese Cake nav., 1/ Cross Dome air/surf. search, 1/Pop Group SA-N-4 f.c., 1/Bass Tilt gun f.c.
EW: 2/Foot Ball-A intercept, 2/Half Hat-B intercept, 2/10-tubed decoy RL
IFF: 1/Square Head interrogator, 1/High Pole B transponder
M: 3 gas turbines for propulsion and lift; 4/4-bladed props (paired two per strut); 36,300 shp—2 auxiliary propulsors
Range: . . ./. . . **Crew:** 60 tot.

Remarks: Rigid sidewall-type surface effect ship, the largest ever built. The only unit constructed to date serves in the Black Sea Fleet; further production is unlikely. The ship has a Band Stand Radome and two Light Bulb data-link radomes, equipment associated with the SS-N-22 supersonic, sea-skimming missile system; in this unit, Band Stand may conceal a target detection/designation radar. Cross Dome is known as Positiv-E in Russia and is said to have a range of about 90 n.m. There are two Kolonka-2 ringsight backup directors for the gatling guns. The propellers are mounted in tandem at the end of struts that can be swung completely out of the water; there are therefore probably small, diesel-powered hull-mounted propellers for harbor maneuvering.

♦ 1 Utka-class Wing-in-Ground-Effect craft

Bldr: . . . (In serv. 1988?)

D: 400 tons (fl) **S:** 250 kts (cruise)
Dim: 75.0 × 41.0 (span) × . . .
A: 6/SS-N-22 Sunburn SSM (II × 3) **Electron Equipt:** 1/. . .
M: 8 turbojet engines mounted on forward canard
Range: 900/. . . **Crew:** . . .

Utka class—artist's impression U.S. DoD, *Soviet Military Power,* 1988

GUIDED-MISSILE PATROL COMBATANTS *(continued)*

Remarks: A missile-armed equivalent to the Orlan amphibious warfare WIG. Believed to be the prototype for a series to have been built during the 1990s. A wing-in-ground-effect craft uses the extra lift of its large wing, achieved when it is in close proximity to the surface, about 10 m. The craft can possibly fly like a normal aircraft, although uneconomically. Has a seaplane-like hull. The engines can probably swivel to provide additional lift at takeoff.

◆ **16 Tarantul-III class (Project 1141.1MP)** Bldrs: Sudostroitel'noye Obyedineniye "Almaz," Petrovskiy SY, St. Petersburg, and Sredniy Neva SY, Kolpino; Vladivostokskiy Sudostroitel'nyy Zavod (Ulis), Vladivostok (In serv. 1987–90)

Tarantul-III class—at Vladivostok Leo Van Ginderen, 10-91

Tarantul-III class—in the Baltic M.O.D., Bonn, 1990

Tarantul-III class M.O.D., Bonn, 4-89

D: 385 tons light (455 fl) **S:** 44 kts
Dim: 56.10 (49.50 pp) × 10.20 (9.40 wl) × 2.14 hull (4.0 props)
A: 4/SS-N-22 Sunburn SSM (II × 2)—1/76.2-mm 59-cal. AK-176 DP—1/SA-N-8 SAM syst. (IV × 1, 12 Gremlin missiles)—2/30-mm AK-630 gatling AA (I × 2)
Electron Equipt:
Radar: 1/Kivach-3 nav., 1/Band Stand target detection/designation, 1/Bass Tilt (Koral-E/MR 123) gun f.c.
EW: 2/Half Hat-B intercept, 2/Foot Ball-A intercept, 2/RK-16 decoy RL (XVI × 2)
IFF: 1 or 2/Square Head, 1/High Pole B transponder
M: CODAG: 2 PR-76 gas turbines (12,000 shp each), 2 Type M504 diesels (5,000 bhp); 2 props; 34,000 bhp
Range: 400/43; 1,600/14 **Fuel:** 50 tons
Crew: 7 officers, 32 enlisted

Remarks: Although a prototype Tarantul appeared in the early 1980s configured with four SS-N-22 supersonic, sea-skimming missiles, not until 1987 was what appears to be a production version sighted. The propulsion system also differs from that of earlier Tarantuls. A Light Bulb probable missile data-link antenna radome is located atop a vertical lattice mast. The antenna beneath the Band Stand radome apparently provides targeting and guidance for the SS-N-22 SSM. There is a backup lead-computing optical director aft for the six-barreled 30-mm gatling guns. In addition to the project number, they are also known as the "*Molniya-1*" project.

Names known to be applied to units of either the Tarantul-III or Tarantul-II classes include: *Poltavskiy Komsomolets, Kuybyshevskiy Komsomolets,* and *Krasnodarskiy Komsomolets.*

◆ **19 Tarantul-II class (Project 1141.1M)** Bldrs: Sudostroitel'noye Obyedineniye "Almaz," Petrovskiy SY, St. Petersburg, and Sredniy Neva SY, Kolpino; Vladivostokskiy Sudostroitel'nyy Zavod (Ulis), Vladivostok (In serv. 1981–86)

Tarantul-II—Band Stand atop bridge, Light Bulb atop raked mas M.O.D., Bonn, 6-8

Tarantul-II class M.O.D., Bonn, 19

D: 385 tons light (455 fl) **S:** 43 kts
Dim: 56.10 (49.50 pp) × 10.20 (9.40 wl) × 2.14 hull (4.0 props)
A: 4/SS-N-2C SSM (II × 2)—1/76.2-mm 59-cal. AK-176 DP—1/SA-N-8 SAM syst. (IV × 1, 12 Gremlin missiles)—2/30-mm AK-630 gatling AA (I × 2)
Electron Equipt:
Radar: 1/Kivach-3 nav., 1/Band Stand target detection and trackin 1/Bass Tilt (Koral-E/MR 123) gun f.c.
EW: no intercept, 2/RK-16 decoy RL (XVI × 2)
IFF: 1/Square Head interrogator, 1/High Pole B transponder
M: M-15E COGAG plant: 2 DMR-76 cruise gas turbines (4,000 shp each), 2 PR-77 boost gas turbines (12,000 shp each); 2 props; 32,000 shp
Range: 400/43; 2,400/14 **Fuel:** 50 tons **Electric:** 500 kw tot.
Crew: 7 officers, 32 enlisted **Endurance:** 10 days

Remarks: The initial large-scale production variant of the Tarantul design for Soviet Navy. The cruise gas turbines exhaust through a stack, while the high-sp turbines exhaust through the transom stern, adding their residual thrust to the pulsive power; all four are employed simultaneously for maximum power. There two 200-kw and one 100-kw diesel generator sets.

A Light Bulb probable missile data-link antenna has been added at the masth while the Band Stand radome appears to conceal a missile target acquisition guidance radar. There are four unoccupied positions for EW antennas. Some rounds of 76.2-mm and 6,000 rounds of 30-mm ammunition are carried.

◆ **2 Tarantul-I class (Project 1241.1)** Bldr: Sudostroitel'noye Obyedineniye "Almaz," Petrovskiy SY, St. Petersburg, Russia (In serv. 1979–

Tarantul-I class—upper missile-tube doors open M.O.D., Bonn,

GUIDED-MISSILE PATROL COMBATANTS *(continued)*

Tarantul-I class prototype 1979

D: 385 tons light (455 fl) **S:** 43 kts
Dim: 56.10 (49.50 pp) × 10.20 (9.40 wl) × 2.14 hull (4.0 props)
A: 4/SS-N-2C SSM (II × 2)—1/76.2-mm 59-cal. AK-176 DP—1/SA-N-8 SAM syst. (IV × 1, 12 Gremlin missiles)—2/30-mm AK-630 gatling AA (I × 2)
Electron Equipt:
Radar: 1/Kivach-3 nav., 1/Plank Shave (Harpun-E) targeting, 1/Bass Tilt (Koral-E/MR 123) f.c.
EW: 2/Half Hat-B intercept, 2/Foot Ball-A intercept, 2/RK-16 decoy RL (XVI × 2)
IFF: 1/High Pole transponder, 1/Square Head interrogator
M: M-15E COGAG plant: 2 DMR-76 cruise gas turbines (4,000 shp each), 2 PR-77 boost gas turbines (12,000 shp each); 2 props; 32,000 shp
Range: 400/43; 2,400/14 **Fuel:** 50 tons **Electric:** 500 kw tot.
Crew: 7 officers, 32 enlisted **Endurance:** 10 days

Remarks: Typed RKA—*Raketnyy Kater* (Missile Boat). Two prototype Tarantul-I etained for trials and training. Others, all for export to Poland (4), East Germany (5), nd India (5), have been built at Volodarskiy SY, Rybinsk; India is also building the esign. There are minor differences in cruise gas-turbine stack configuration, and only ne has the EW intercept sensor suite.

20 Nanuchka-III class (Project 1234.1) Bldrs: Sudostroitel'noye Obyedineniye "Almaz," Petrovskiy SY, St. Petersburg; Vladivostokskiy Sudostroitel'nyy Zavod (Ulis), Vladivostok (In serv. 1977–1991)

ISBERG ("Iceberg")	PASSAT ("Tradewind")
EYSER ("Geyser")	PRIBOY ("Surf")
OMSOMOLETS MORDOVII (ex-*Zeb'*)	PRILIV ("Tidesurge")
	PURGA ("Blizzard")
VEN ("Downpour")	RADUGA ("Rainbow")
ETEOR ("Meteor")	RASSVET ("Dawn")
IRAZH ("Mirage")	TUCHA ("Stormcloud")
OROZ ("Frost")	URUGAN ("Hurricane")
AKAT ("Counter-recoil")	VETER ("Wind")
TLIV ("Ebbtide")	VIKHR ("Whirlwind")
	ZARYA ("Daybreak")

D: 685 tons (fl) **S:** 32 kts
Dim: 59.0 × 12.6 × 2.4 (3.1 max.)
A: 6/SS-N-9 Siren SSM (III × 2)—1/SA-N-4 system (II × 1, 20 Gecko missiles)—1/76.2-mm AK-176 DP—1/30-mm AK-630 gatling AA (VI × 1)
Electron Equipt:
Radar: 1–2/Nayada nav. (not in all), 1/Peel Pair nav./surf. search (not in all), 1/Band Stand target designation, 1/Pop Group SA-N-4 f.c., 1/Bass Tilt gun f.c.
EW: 2/Half Hat-B intercept, 2/Foot Ball-A intercept, 2/RK-16 decoy RL (XVI × 2)
IFF: 1/High Pole transponder, 1/Square Head interrogator
M: 3 M517 diesels; 3 props; 30,000 bhp
Range: 900/30; 2,500/12 (1 engine) **Crew:** 60 tot.

marks: Type designation: MRK—*Malyy Raketnyy Korabl'* (Small Missile Ship). single 76.2-mm DP was substituted for the twin 57-mm AA aft, the gatling gun is he position occupied by Muff Cob in the Nanuchka-I, and Bass Tilt is situated atop a deckhouse abaft the mast. The pilothouse is higher and the superstructure is arged. The 30-mm gatling gun is off centerline, to starboard. Two Fish Bowl or Light radomes on the mast are believed to house SS-N-9 missile data-link antennas. ercept arrays vary considerably. Early units had Peel Pair target designation and king radar atop the mast; later units lack the Peel Pair and add two Light Bulb sile data-link antenna radomes on the sides of the mast and one or two Nayada igational radars; recent units also have four 10-tubed fixed decoy rocket launchers ddition to the two 16-tubed launchers.

Northern Fleet unit completed in 1987, sometimes referred to as the nuchka-IV," substitutes two sextuple racks for an unidentified missile for the N-9 SSM.

ven' ("Downpour"), launched 12-5-91, is the last to be built, according to the sian press, which said that the hull of another was broken up on the ways at the ovskiy facility. All are named for meteorological or natural phenomena.

The "Nanuchka-IV"—with racks for unidentified missiles
M.O.D., U.K., 5-90

Nanuchka-III class—with Light Bulb arrays on mast, no Peel Pair radar French Navy, 6-90

Nanuchka-III—with Fish Bowl radomes above EW intercept arrays on mast and Peel Pair atop mast platform French Navy, 6-90

Nanuchka-III class—Band Stand atop higher pilothouse than Nanuchka-I; unit has Fish Bowl and Peel Pair antennas 7-89

GUIDED-MISSILE PATROL COMBATANTS *(continued)*

♦ **17 Nanuchka-I class (Project 1234)** Bldrs: Sudostroitel'noye Obyedineniye "Almaz," Petrovskiy SY, St. Petersburg, Russia (In serv. 1969–76)

Briz ("Breeze")	Shtorm ("Storm")
Buran ("Snowstorm")	Smerch ("Waterspout")
Grad ("Hail")	Tsiklon ("Cyclone")
Grom ("Thunder")	Tayfun ("Typhoon")
Burya ("Gale")	Vikhr' ("Whirlwind")
Metel ("Snowstorm")	Volnya ("Wave")
Molniya ("Lightning")	Zarnitsa ("Summer Lightning")
Shkval ("Squall")	

Nanuchka-I—with Spin Trough radar antenna at highest point on mast Ivan Chernikov, 1987

Nanuchka-I class M.O.D., Bonn, 4-73

D: 675 tons (fl) **S:** 32 kts **Dim:** 59.0 × 12.6 × 2.4 (3.1 max.)
A: 6/SS-N-9 Siren SSM (II × 3)—1/SA-N-4 SAM system (II × 1, 20 Gecko missiles)—2/57-mm AK-257 DP (II × 1)
Electron Equipt:
Radar: 1/Peel Pair nav./surf. search, 1/Band Stand target designation, 1/Pop Group SA-N-4 f.c., 1/Muff Cob gun f.c.
EW: 4/. . . intercept, 2/RK-16 decoy RL (XVI × 2)
IFF: 1/High Pole transponder, 1/Square Head interrogator
M: 3 M517 diesels; 3 props; 30,000 bhp
Range: 900/30; 2,500/12 (1 engine) **Crew:** 60 tot.

Remarks: Type designation: MRK—*Malyy Raketnyy Korabl'* (Small Missile Ship). Named for meteorological phenomena. Reported to be poor sea boats with very unreliable engines. Early units have separate blast shields abaft the SS-N-9 launchers; they have smaller engine air intakes and may employ paired M503 diesels for 24,000-bhp total, 30 kts max. Band Stand is associated with target designation for the SS-N-9 missiles. New EW antennas are being added near the top of the mast. The similar Nanuchka-II (Project 1234E), for export, has four SS-N-2C missiles; units were built for Algeria (3), India (3), and Libya (4). One, named *Musson*, lost 3-87.

GUIDED-MISSILE PATROL BOATS

♦ **16 Matka-class (Project 206MP) semi-hydrofoils**
Bldr: Sudostroitel'noye Obyedineniye"Almaz" (Sredniy Neva), Kolpino (In serv. 1978–81)

Matka class at speed—on foils M.O.D., Bonn, 8-84

Matka class hull-borne—note low freeboard U.S. Navy, 198[illegible]

D: 225 tons (260 fl) **S:** 36 kts
Dim: 40.0 × 12.0 (7.6 hull) × 2.1 (hull; 3.2 foils)
A: 2/SS-N-2C Styx SSM (I × 2)—1/76.2-mm 59-cal. AK-176 DP—1/30-mm AK-630 gatling AA
Electron Equipt:
Radar: 1/Cheese Cake nav., 1/Plank Shave target detection/tracking, 1/Bass Tilt gun f.c.
EW: no intercept equipment, 2/RK-16 decoy RL (XVI × 2)
IFF: 1/High Pole B, 1/Square Head
M: 3 M504 diesels; 3 props; 15,000 bhp
Range: 400/36; 650/25 **Crew:** 30 tot.

Remarks: Essentially a missile-armed version of the Turya-class hydrofoil torpe[illegible] boat, with larger superstructure, 76.2-mm gun forward, and missiles and gatling gu[illegible] aft. Construction proceeded very slowly. Use Plank Shave targeting radar, larger th[illegible] Square Tie. Appear to be overloaded, and construction ceased in favor of the Tarant[illegible] series. Positions for EW intercept antennas remain empty. Project number may ha[illegible] been changed to 1149.

♦ **25 or fewer Osa-II class (Project 205M)** (In serv. 1966–70)

Amurskiy Komsomolets	Kirovskiy Komsomolets
Michurinskiy Komsomolets	Tambovskiy Komsomolets
up to 21 others	

Osa-II class—under tow 1[illegible]

Osa-II class U.S. Navy,

D: 215 tons (245 fl) **S:** 35 kts
Dim: 38.6 × 7.6 × 2.0 hull (3.1 props)
A: 4/SS-N-2B/C Styx SSM (I × 4)—4/30-mm AK-230 AA (II × 2)
Electron Equipt:
Radar: 1/Square Tie surf. search/target-detection, 1/Drum Tilt gun f.c.
IFF: 1/High Pole B transponder, 2/Square Head interrogators
M: 3 M504 diesels; 3 props; 15,000 bhp
Range: 500/34; 750/25 **Crew:** 4 officers, 24 enlisted

Remarks: Type designation: RKA—*Raketnyy Kater* (Missile Cutter). Some have been given SA-N-5/8 systems aft, with the quadruple, manned launcher a[illegible] four-round missile locker. Widely exported during 1970s and 1980s, primarily new-built units. Some reports indicate that they are mediocre sea boats and th[illegible] engines are very temperamental. Numbers beginning to decline, and most shoul[illegible] be discarded.

GUIDED-MISSILE PATROL BOATS *(continued)*

◆ **25 or fewer Osa-I class (Project 205)** (In serv. 1959–66)

D: 171 tons (209.5 fl) **S:** 38 kts
Dim: 38.6 × 7.6 × 1.8 hull (2.9 props)
A: 4/SS-N-2 Styx SSM (I × 4)—4/30-mm AK-230 AA (II × 2)—1/SA-N-5/8 SAM syst. (IV × 1, 4 Grail/Gremlin missiles) in some
Electron Equipt:
Radar: 1/Square Tie surf. search/target-designation, 1/Drum Tilt gun f.c.
IFF: 1/High Pole B transponder, 2/Square Head interrogators
M: 3 M503A2 diesels; 3 props; 12,000 bhp
Range: 500/34; 750/25 **Crew:** 4 officers, 24 enlisted

sa-I class—quadruple SA-N-5/8 launcher abaft Drum Tilt radar 7-90

sa-I class—in the Neva River, St. Petersburg Ivan Chernikov, 1987

marks: Originally built at Petrovskiy SY, St. Petersburg, but other yards were also olved in the program. Type designation: RKA—*Raketnyy Kater* (Missile Cutter). ese small craft can launch their missiles in a Force-4 sea (2-m waves). Many of them e been transferred to other navies. Some have been built as, or converted to, targets. Bogomol, Stenka, Matka, Turya, and Mol classes (an export torpedo boat, *see* nalia) all use Osa hulls and propulsion plants. Numbers already considerably re-ed, and most should be discarded shortly.

RPEDO BOATS

29 Turya class (Project 206) semi-hydrofoils
Bldrs: Sudostroitel'noye Obyedineniye"Almaz," Petrovskiy SY, St. Petersburg, and Sredniy Neva SY, Kolpino; Vladivostokskiy Sudostroitel'nyy Zavod (Ulis), Vladivostok (In serv. 1973–79)

ya class—showing helicopter dipping sonar housed on starboard ter M.O.D., Bonn, 5-73

Turya class M.O.D., Bonn

D: 215 tons (250 fl) **S:** 35 kts
Dim: 39.0 × 7.6 (12.5 over foils) × 2.0 (4.0 over foils)
A: 2/57-mm AK-257 AA aft (II × 1)—2/25-mm 2M-8 AA (II × 1)—4/533-mm TT (I × 4)
Electron Equipt:
Radar: 1/Pot Drum surf. search, 1/Muff Cob gun f.c.
Sonar: 1/Hormone helicopter, dipping
IFF: 1/High Pole-B transponder, 1/Square Head interrogator
M: 3 M504 diesels; 3 props; 15,000 bhp
Range: 400/36; 650/25 **Crew:** 24 tot.

Remarks: Russian nickname, "*Shtorm*"-class. Fixed hydrofoils forward only; stern planes on water surface. Have Osa-II-class hull and propulsion. The dipping sonar is housed in a sponson over the starboard quarter. The torpedo tubes can evidently launch both anti-ship and anti-submarine torpedoes. Some units have received a single 14.5-mm heavy machine gun amidships, just forward of the Muff Cob director; one also has a possible Cheese Box radar atop the mast. Nine of this class, without dipping sonar, have been delivered to Cuba since 1-79, and others have been exported to Vietnam, Kampuchea, and the Seychelles.

ANTISUBMARINE PATROL BOATS

◆ **2 (+ . . .) Mukha class hydrofoils**
Bldr: Yuzhnaya Tochka Zavod, Feodosiya, Ukraine (In serv. 1989-. . .)

Mukha class Boris Lemachko collection, 1990

D: 320 tons (400 fl) **S:** 45 kts
Dim: 50.0 (46.3 wl) × 13.0 (8.5 hull) × . . .
A: 1/76.2-mm 59-cal. AK-176 DP—2/30-mm AK-630 gatling AA (I × 2)—8/400-mm ASW TT (IV × 2)
Electron Equipt:
Radar: 1/Don-2 nav., 1/Peel Cone nav./surf. search, 1/Bass Tilt f.c.
Sonar: . . . . . .—EW: no intercept equipment, 2/RK-16 decoy RL (XVI × 2)
IFF: 1/Square Head interrogator, High Pole transponder
M: COCOG: 1 Type DMR-76 cruise gas turbine (4,000 shp), 2 Type PR-77 boost gas turbines (12,100 shp each); 2 props; 24,000 shp max.
Range: . . ./. . . **Crew:** 30 tot.

Remarks: A production version of the 1978-vintage Babochka prototype, with heavier armament. A true hydrofoil, with fixed foils fore and aft. Probably has both hull-mounted and dipping sonars. Initial units in the Black Sea Fleet.

◆ **2 (+. . .) Svetlyak class (Project 1144.0)** Bldrs: Vladivostokskiy Sudostroitel'nyy Zavod (Ulis), Vladivostok (In serv. 1989–. . .); . . . . . .

Svetlyak class—in the Black Sea Boris Lemachko collection, 1991

ANTISUBMARINE PATROL BOATS *(continued)*

Svetlyak class—in the Far East *Ships of the World*, 6-89

D: 370 tons (fl) **S:** 30+ kts **Dim:** 50.0 × . . . × . . .
A: 1/76.2-mm AK-176 DP—1/30-mm AK-630 gatling AA—2/400-mm ASW TT (I × 2)—2/d.c. racks (12 d.c.)
Electron Equip:
Radar: 1/Peel Cone nav./surf. search, 1/Bass Tilt f.c.
Sonar: . . .—EW: . . .—IFF: . . .
M: 2 M517 diesels; 2 props; 20,000 bhp
Range: . . . **Crew:** 60 tot.

Remarks: Design tailored to extended patrolling. Semi-planing hull with low spray chine forward. Probably successor to Pauk production for KGB Maritime Border Guard use. Larger than the similar Muravey, but is not hydrofiol-equipped. Initial units built for service in the Far East, but likely to be introduced in other fleet areas as well.

◆ **14 Muravey-class hydrofoils (Project 133)**
Bldr: Yuzhnaya Tochka Zavod, Feodosiya, Ukraine (In serv. 1982–90)

Muravey class 1988

Muravey class M.O.D., Bonn, 1988

D: 180 tons (230 fl) **S:** 45+ kts
Dim: 40.0 × 7.6 × 1.9 (hull)
A: 1/76.2-mm 59-cal. AK-176 DP—1/30-mm AK-630 gatling AA—2/400-mm ASW TT (I × 2); 2 d.c. racks (12 d.c.)
Electron Equipt:
Radar: 1/Peel Cone nav./surf. search, 1/Bass Tilt gun f.c.
Sonar: hull-mounted?, HF dipping at stern
IFF: Salt Pot transponder
M: 2 PR-77 gas turbines; 2 props; 24,000 shp
Range: . . . **Crew:** 20 tot.

Remarks: First reported 1983. Also known as the "*Antares*" class in Russia. Built for the KGB Maritime Border Guard. Use fixed, fully submerged foil system. The dipping sonar deploys through a hatch in the transom stern. There is a Kolonka-2 ringsight backup director for the 30-mm gatling gun aft. Used in Baltic and Black Sea fleets.

◆ **35 Pauk-I class (Project 1241.2)** Bldr: Yaroslavl SY: Vladivostokskiy Sudostroitel'nyy Zavod (Ulis), Vladivostok (In serv. 1980–. . .)

Gregoriy Kuropyatnikov Gregoriy Gnatenko
33 others

Pauk-I class—high pilothouse version, with Half Hat EW arrays mast Boris Lemachko, 7-

Pauk-I class—high pilothouse version Hartmut Ehlers, 3

Pauk-I class—low pilothouse version M.O.D., Bonn,

Pauk-I class—low pilothouse version U.S. Navy,

A modified Pauk—with Cross Dome search radar and 2/533-mm KGB Border Guard service Leo Van Ginderen

ANTISUBMARINE PATROL BOATS *(continued)*

D: 385 tons (455 fl) **S:** 32 kts
Dim: 58.5 (49.5 pp) × 10.2 (9.4 wl) × 2.14 hull (4.0 props)
A: 1/76.2-mm AK-176 DP—1/SA-N-8 SAM syst. (IV × 1, 12 Gremlin missiles)—1/30-mm AK-630 gatling AA—2/RBU-1200 ASW RL (V × 2)—4/400-mm ASW TT (I × 4)—2/d.c. racks (12 d.c.)
Electron Equipt:
Radar: 1/Spin Trough nav., 1/Peel Cone nav./surf. search, 1/Bass Tilt f.c.
Sonar: MF hull-mounted, MF dipping, HF dipping
IFF: 2/Square Head, 1/High Pole B
EW: 2/Half Hat-B intercept (not in all); 2/chaff RL (XVI × 2)
M: 2 M517 diesels; 2 props; 20,000 bhp
Range: 2,000/20 **Fuel:** 50 tons
Crew: 7 officers, 32 enlisted

Remarks: Type designation: MPK—*Malyy Protivolodochnyy Korabl'* (Small Antisubmarine Ship), and apparently intended to replace the Poti class. Also known as the *"olnaya-2"* class. Most are/were operated by the KGB Maritime Border Guard. This class uses same hull as Tarantul-class missile corvette but has ASW armament vice SS-N-2C missiles and an all-diesel propulsion plant vice Tarantul's COGAG/CODAG system. One Pauk-I was transferred to Bulgaria in 1990.

A large housing for a dipping sonar system projects 2 m out from the stern. A variant first noted in 1982 in the Baltic has the pilothouse one-half deck higher. There is a Kolonka-2 backup ringsight director for the single gatling AA gun; Bass Tilt can control both the 76.2-mm and 30-mm guns. The main engines are probably the same diesels as used in the Nanuchka class. A helicopter-type dipping sonar installation, housed in a cabinet on the starboard side near the stern, has been added on a few, possibly indicating that the larger dipping sonar is not fully effective.

The Pauk-II variant, for export, has the pilothouse mounted farther forward, carries Cross Dome ("Positiv-E") radar atop the mast, and has only two torpedo tubes; one been transferred to Cuba and four to India, which at one time planned to build its own as well. At least one has been retained for Russian Navy use.

1 Babochka class (Project 1141)
Bldr: Yuzhnaya Tochka Zavod, Feodosiya (In serv. 1978)

ALEKSANDR KYNAKOVICH

Aleksandr Kynakovich 1978

D: 400 tons (fl) **S:** 50 kts
Dim: 50.0 × 13.0 (8.5 hull) × . . .
A: 2/30-mm AK-630 gatling AA (VI × 2)—8/400-mm ASW TT (IV × 2)
Electron Equipt:
Radar: 1/Don-2 nav., 1/Peel Cone nav./surf. search, 1/Bass Tilt f.c.
Sonar: . . .
M: CODOG: 2 cruise diesels, 3 gas turbines; 3 props; 36,300 shp (max.)

Remarks: Experimental prototype ASW hydrofoil with fixed, fully submerged foils fore and aft. The torpedo tubes are mounted, two on two, on either side of the forecastle between the forward gatling gun and the superstructure. The Mukha class is the production version.

13 Stenka class (Project 205P)
Bldrs: Sudostroitel'noye Obyedineniye "Almaz," Petrovskiy SY, St. Petersburg (In serv. 1967–90)

Stenka class—with Peel Cone navigational radar
Boris Lemachko Collection, 1990

Stenka class—also with Peel Cone 1991

D: 170 tons (210 fl) **S:** 36 kts **Dim:** 39.5 × 7.6 × 1.8
A: 4/30-mm AK-230 AA (II × 2)—4/400-mm ASW TT—2/d.c. racks (12 d.c.)
Electron Equipt:
Radar: 1 Pot Drum or Peel Cone nav./surf. search, 1/Drum Tilt gun f.c.
Sonar: 1/Hormone-A helicopter dipping type
IFF: 1/High Pole B transponder, 2/Square Head interrogators
M: 3 M503A diesels; 3 props; 12,000 bhp
Range: 550/34; 750/25 **Crew:** 22 tot.

Remarks: Soviet type designation: PSKR—*Pogranichnyy Storozhevoy Korabl'* (Border Patrol Ship). Built for the Maritime Border Guard of the KGB. Construction continued for over 20 years, although at a low rate in recent years, and new units continued to enter service to replace early craft being discarded. Recent units have Peel Cone navigational radar vice Pot Drum, and some may have 5,000-bhp M504 diesels. Only a small number have been exported: four to Cuba and possibly some to Vietnam.

Note: All remaining Poti-class (Project 204) small antisubmarine ships are believed to have been discarded by the end of 1991.

PATROL CRAFT

◆ 30 or more Zhuk class (Project 199)
Bldr: . . . (In serv. 1975–. . .)

Zhuk class Boris Lemachko

D: 42 tons (50 fl) **S:** 35 kts **Dim:** 24.0 × 5.9 × 1.0 (1.6 props)
A: 2/14.5-mm mg (II × 1)
Electron Equipt: Radar: 1/Spin Trough nav.
M: 2 M420 diesels; 2 props; 3,000 bhp **Fuel:** 8 tons
Range: 530/16 **Crew:** 13 tot. **Endurance:** 13 days

Remarks: Over 110 have been exported, most armed with a side-by-side turreted gun mount; non-export units have one (or occasionally two) over-and-under gun mounts. Also known as the *"Grif"* (Griffon) class in Russia. Have two 21-kw and one 6-kw generator sets. A new 54.5-ton, 28.6-m export version is offered.

RIVERINE CRAFT

Note: The U.S.S.R. maintained a number of river gunboats on the Lower Danube, on the Amur and Ussuri river systems in the Far East, and possibly elsewhere. In addition to gunboats, the riverine forces have a few support craft, including the administrative flagship of the Danube River Flotilla, *Dunay* (SSV-10, ex-*Prut,* PS 10, ex-Romanian *Grafinul,* ex- Austrian . . .): 360 tons, 49 m overall, diesel-powered, equipped with 2/45-mm saluting cannon.

Dunay—flagship of the Danube Flotilla, with two 45-mm saluting cannon abreast stack, twin 14.5-mm mg forward Erwin Seiche, 4-85

RIVERINE CRAFT *(continued)*

◆ **21 Yaz-class (Project 1208) river monitors**
Bldr: . . . (In serv. 1981– . . .)

KHABAROVSKIY KOMSOMOLETS 60-LET VChK 19 others

Yaz class *Ships of the World,* 1991

D: 400 tons (fl) **S:** 14–16 kts
Dim: 55.0 (52.5 wl) × 9.0 × 1.4
A: 2/115-mm tank guns in turrets (I × 2)—2/30-mm AK-630 gatling AA (I × 2)—4/14.5-mm mg (II × 2)—mines
Electron Equipt:
Radar: 1/Spin Trough or Kivach nav., 1/Bass Tilt f.c.
EW: 1/twin-tube decoy/illumination RL
IFF: High Pole transponder, Square Head interrogator
M: . . . diesels; 2 props; . . . bhp **Crew:** 60 tot.

Remarks: Low-freeboard monitors for the Amur River Flotilla. All assigned to the Amur River Flotilla of the Maritime Border Guard. *60-Let VChK* means "60th Anniversary of the *Cheka.*" The rocket launcher amidships is the same auto-loading device employed on major, seagoing combatants; in these ships, it probably launches illumination rockets rather than chaff.

◆ **7 (+ . . .) Vosh class** Bldr: . . . (Far East) (In serv. 1980– . . .)

D: 180 tons (250 fl) **S:** 18 kts **Dim:** 42.0 × 7.0 × 1.0
A: 1/76-mm, 48-cal. low-angle—6/14.5-mm mg (II × 3)
M: 2 diesels; 2 props; . . . bhp

◆ **8 (+ . . .) Pivyaka class** Bldr: . . . (Far East) (In serv. 1980– . . .)

D: 230 tons (fl) **S:** . . . **Dim:** 38.5 × 6.5 × . . . **M:** . . .

Remarks: Like Vosh class, intended for duty with the Amur River Flotilla to police the border with China. No characteristics data available.

◆ **79 Shmel-class gunboats (Project 1204)** (In serv. 1967–74)

Shmel class—with a Yaz-class monitor in the background
Leo Van Ginderen, 1990

Shmel class Erwin Seiche, 4-85

D: 60 tons (fl) **S:** 22 kts **Dim:** 28.3 × 4.6 × 0.9
A: 1/76.2-mm, 48 cal., fwd in a tank turret—2/25-mm 2M-8 AA (II × 1) aft—5/7.62-mm mg (I × 5)—1/122-mm RL (XVIII × 1)—mines
M: 2 M50F-4 diesels; 2 props; 2,400 bhp
Range: 240/20; 600/10 **Crew:** 15 tot.

Remarks: Type designation: AKA—*Artilleriyskiy Kater* (Artillery Cutter). Not all these craft have a rocket launcher. An early version has a twin machine-gun mount aft that resembles a tank turret. One 7.62-mm is mounted coaxially with the 85-mm gun; the others fire through slits in the sides of the open-topped redoubt forward of the artillery RL. Four transferred to Kampuchea, 1984–85. Many are maintained in reserve, and two Pacific Ocean Fleet units were stricken during 1991, and the numbers are likely to diminish through the mid-1990s.

MINE WARFARE SHIPS

Note: Four or more Polnocny-class landing craft were converted as assault minesweepers, carrying two radio-controlled boats to tow line-charge, inshore-obstacle-clearance systems into place. The ships remain capable of landing vehicles and are listed with the amphibious ships.

◆ **3 Alesha-class (Project 317) minelayers**
Bldr: Nosenko Zavod 444, Nikolayev, Ukraine (In serv. 1967–69)

PRIPYAT' VYCHEGDA SUKHONA

Vychegda—the first Alesha U.S. Navy, 199

Vychegda J.M.S.D.F., 10-

D: 2,900 tons (3,500 fl) **S:** 17 kts
Dim: 97.0 (91.5 wl) × 14.0 (13.0 wl) × 5.4
A: 4/57-mm AA (IV × 1)—300 mines
Electron Equipt:
Radar: 1/Don-2 nav., 1/Strut Curve air/surf. search, 1/Muff Cob f.c
IFF: 1/High Pole B
M: 4 diesels; 2 props; 8,000 bhp
Range: 4,000/16; 8,500/8 **Crew:** 190 tot.

Remarks: Can also be used as netlayers, minesweeper tenders, and command sh The second and third ships had two king posts and booms vice the forward crane. In Baltic, Pacific Ocean, and Northern Fleets, respectively.

◆ **1 (+ . . .) Gorya-class (Project 1260) mine countermeasures vessel**
Bldr: Sudostroitel'noye Obyedineniye "Almaz" (Sredniy Neva), Kolpino

	Laid down	L	In serv.
ZHELEZNYAKOV	1984	12-85	1988

Zheleznyakov M.O.D., Bonn,

Zheleznyakov M.O.D., Bonn

MINE WARFARE SHIPS *(continued)*

D: 950 tons (1,100 fl) **S:** 16 kts **Dim:** 66.5 (61.3 wl) × 11.0 × 3.2
A: 1/76.2-mm 59-cal. AK-176 DP—1/30-mm AK-630 gatling AA— 2/SA-N-8 SAM syst. (IV × 2; 16 Gremlin missiles)—*possible* 2/RBU-1200 ASW RL (V × 2; *see* Remarks)
Electron Equipt:
Radar: 1/Nayada nav., 1/Palm Frond nav., 1/Bass Tilt f.c.
Sonar: HF minehunting
EW: no intercept arrays, 2/RK-16 decoy RL (XVI × 2)
IFF: 1/Salt Pot transponder, 2/Square Head interrogators
M: 2 diesels; 2 props; 5,000 bhp **Crew:** 60 tot.

Remarks: First, and to date only, unit of a new metal-hulled combined minehunter/minesweeper design possibly intended to succeed the Natya class in production. First unit was transferred to the Black Sea Fleet during 8-89. The very cramped mine countermeasures working area accommodates several standard acoustic mine countermeasures devices. The sliding doors at the 02 level on the hull sides aft may cover either RBU-1200 ASW rocket launchers or be used to deploy some form of sweep or countermeasures gear. The 76.2-mm gun is limited to 180° in horizontal train.

• **1 Natya-II-class minehunter** Bldr: Sudostroitel'noye Obyedineniye "Almaz" (Sredniy Neva), Kolpino (In serv. 1982)

Natya-II class—deckhouse on stern, no 25-mm AA or ASW RL
French Navy, 7-85

Natya-II class U.S. Navy, 8-85

D: 780 tons (880 fl) **S:** 16.5 kts
Dim: 61.0 (57.6 wl) × 10.2 × 3.3 hull
A: 4/30-mm AK-230 AA (II × 2)—2/SA-7 Grail or SA-14 Gremlin shoulder-launch SAM positions (8 missiles)
Electron Equipt:
Radar: 1/Don-2 nav.—IFF: 3/Square Head interrogators, 1/High Pole B
Sonar: HF minehunting
M: 2 diesels; 2 props; 5,000 bhp
Range: 1,800/16, 5,200/10 **Crew:** 40 tot.

Remarks: Single-unit prototype believed intended for trials with a minehunting system deployed from a deckhouse on the fantail that replaced the standard Natya countermeasures winch. Retains articulated sweep gear davits at the stern, but countermeasures gear is visible on deck. Omitted were the normal ASW RL and two 25-mm AA. Transferred to the Black Sea Fleet in 7-85.

• **36 Natya-I-class (Project 266M) minesweepers**
Bldr: Sudostroitel'noye Obyedineniye "Almaz" (Sredniy Neva), Kolpino; Khabarovsk SY (In serv. 1970–1980, 1991)

...iral Pershin
...lerist
...antnik
...list
...triy Lysov
Padist
Paravan
Pulemetchik
Pylemyetnik
Radist
Ehlektrik
Ivan Maslov
Kazarskiy
Kharkovskiy Komsomolets
Komendor
Kontradmiral Khoroshkin
Kontradmiral Persin
Kurskiy Komsomolets (ex-*Navodchik*)
Mashinist
Miner
Motorist
Rulevoy
Schitshchik
Signal'shchik
Snayper
Svyazist
Torpedist
Turbinist
Vakulenchuk
Vitse-Admiral Zhukov
Vsevolod Vishnevskiy
Zaryad
Zenitchik
3 others

New Natya Variant—with single AK-630 gatling guns, no Drum Tilt radar or 25-mm AA, one of two transferred to the Pacific in 1991
J.M.S.D.F., 6-91

Early Natya-I—with gooseneck sweep-gear davits aft, no SAM positions
Leo Van Ginderen, 1987

Late Natya-I—with articulated davits, SAM positions at aft end of superstructure
J.M.S.D.F., 1991

Late Natya-I U.S. Navy, 1977

MINE WARFARE SHIPS *(continued)*

D: 780 tons (880 fl) **S:** 17 kts
Dim: 61.0 (57.6 wl) × 10.2 × 3.3 hull
A: 4/30-mm AA AK-230 AA (II × 2)—4/25-mm 2M-8AA (II × 2)—most: 2/SA-N-5/8 SAM syst. (IV × 2, 16 Grail/Gremlin missiles)—2/RBU-1200 ASW RL (V × 2)—mines (2 new units: 2/30-mm AK-630 gatling AA (I × 2)—2/SA-N-8 SAM syst (IV × 2, 16 Gremlin missiles)—2/RBU-1200 ASW RL (V × 2)—mines
Electron Equipt:
Radar: 1–2/Don-2 nav., 1/Drum Tilt f.c. (not in 2 new units)
Sonar: HF hull-mounted
IFF: 1/High Pole B transponder, 2/Square Head interrogators
M: 2 diesels: 2 props; 5,000 bhp
Range: 1,800/16; 5,200/10 **Crew:** 8 officers, 70 enlisted

Remarks: Type designation: MT—*Morskoy Tral'shchik* (Seagoing Minesweeper). Equipped also to serve as ASW escorts, with the RBU-1200 rocket launchers also used for detonating mines. Post-1980 production was for export, with one unit with no ASW ordnance or minesweeping gear delivered to Syria in 1985 as a training ship, and 12 for India, 8 for Libya.

Early units had rigid davits aft; on later units they are articulated. Stem cut back sharply below waterline, as in T-43 and Yurka classes. Low magnetic signature, aluminum-steel alloy hull. Two SA-N-5/8 quadruple launchers have been added to a number of units of the class, just abaft the lattice mast. Some also have an extra navigational radar atop the pilothouse. Sweep gear includes SEMP-3 magnetic and MPT-3 mechanical arrays and a net trawl deployed over the stern ramp.

In 1991, four units of a new variant, with single 30-mm AK-630 gatling guns substituted for the twin 30-mm AK-230 mounts but without 25-mm guns, Drum Tilt fire control radar, or net trawl facilities, were completed. Two were transferred from the Baltic to the Pacific Ocean Fleet, and one each were transferred to Ethiopia and Yemen.

◆ **35 Yurka-class (Project 266) fleet minesweepers**
Bldrs: Sudostroitel'noye Obyedineniye "Almaz" (Sredniy Neva), Kolpino; Khabarovsk SY; Kamysh-Burun Zavod, Kerch', Ukraine (In serv. 1962–69)

Gafel' J. Mazlov' Komsomolets Belorussiy
Navodchik Yevgeniy Nikonov Semen Roshal' 29 others

Yurka class—with two SA-N-5/8 SAM systems
Leo Van Ginderen, 1991

Yurka class Leo Van Ginderen, 1990

D: 400 tons (460 fl) **S:** 16 kts **Dim:** 52.0 × 9.3 × 2.0
A: 4/30-mm AK-230 AA (II × 2)—20 mines
Electron Equipt:
Radar: 1 or 2 Don-2 nav., 1/Drum Tilt f.c.
Sonar: Tamir-11 hull-mounted HF
IFF: 1/High Pole B transponder, 2–3/Square Head interrogators
M: 2 diesels; 2 props; 4,000 bhp **Range:** 2,000/14; 3,200/10
Crew: 45–50 tot.

Remarks: Type designation: MT—*Morskoy Tral'shchik* (Seagoing Minesweeper). Low magnetic signature, aluminum-steel alloy hull. Four transferred to Egypt in 1969, one to Vietnam in 1979. Several have received two SA-N-5/8 SAM systems (IV × 2, 16 Grail/Gremlin missiles). Early units are being discarded; a number of ships of this class are believed already to be in reserve, and five were offered for scrap during 1991. Another was lost 19-8-89 in the Black Sea after an explosion.

◆ **67 (+ . . .) Sonya-class (Project 1265) coastal minesweepers**
Bldrs: Petrozavodsk SY; Vladivostokskiy Sudostroitel'niy Zavod (Ulis SY), Vladivostok (In serv. 1973–. . .)

Aleksey Lebedev
Astrakhanskiy Komsomolets
Kolomenskiy Komsomolets
Komsomolets Latviy
Orenburgskiy Komsomolets
Sevastopolskiy Komsomolets (ex-*Komsomol'skiy Telegraf*)
Yakhut
60 others

Sonya class M.O.D., Bonn, 199

Sonya variant with two single 30-mm gatling guns 19

D: 350 tons (400 fl) **S:** 15 kts **Dim:** 48.5 × 7.3 × 1.9
A: 2/30-mm AK-230 AA (II × 1)—2/25-mm 2M-8 AA (II × 1)
Electron Equipt:
Radar: 1/Spin Trough nav.—Sonar: HF hull-mounted
IFF: 1/High Pole B transponder, 2/Square Head interrogators
M: 2 diesels; 2 props; 2,400 bhp **Range:** 1,600/14; 3,000/10
Crew: 5–6 officers, 26 enlisted

Remarks: Type designation: BT—*Basovyy Tral'shchik* (Base Minesweeper). A known as the "*Yakont*" class in Russia. Wooden construction with glass-reinfor plastic hull sheathing. Several have received one SA-N-5/8 quadruple SAM syst abaft the boat, to starboard. Carry acoustic, magnetic, and mechanical sweep eq ment. The 25-mm mount is aimed by the operator, while the 30-mm mount is contro by a Kolonka-1 ringsight director. Several have been refitted with two 30-mm AK- gatling AA in place of the original armament.

Two transferred to Cuba in 1980, two more in 1985; others have gone to Bulgaria Syria (1), and Vietnam (2). One Northern Fleet was declared for scrap in 1991.

◆ **20–30 Vanya-I and -II class (Project 257D, 257DM, 257DT) coastal minesweepers** Bldrs: Petrozavodsk SY; Vladivostokskiy Sudostroitel'niy Zavod (Ulis SY), Vladivostok (In serv. 1961–73)

D: 200 tons (245 fl) **S:** 14 kts **Dim:** 39.9 × 7.5 × 1.8 hull
A: 2/30-mm AK-230 AA (II × 1)
Electron Equipt:
Radar: 1/Don-2 nav.—IFF: 1/High Pole A transponder
M: 1 diesel; 1 prop; 2,400 bhp **Range:** 1,400/14; 2,400/10
Crew: 30 tot.

Remarks: Type designation: *Basovyy Tral'shchik* (Base Minesweeper). Wooden struction. One (Project 257DT) was converted to a minehunter, armed with a 25-mm Type 2M-8 AA, equipped with two boats for mine-disposal divers, and Don-Kay radar in place of Don-2. The gun mount is controlled by a remote Kolon ringsight director. The last three built (Project 257DM) were classed as "Vanya-I NATO; they are 1 meter longer, have a larger diesel exhaust pipe amidships, and heavier-capacity davits at the stern. A number have been exported, and large num have been discarded.

Note: Of the two units of the unsuccessful Zhenya coastal minesweeper class (Pr 1252, or "Almaz"), BT-251 blew up on 19-8-89, and the other was discarded by 19

MINE WARFARE SHIPS *(continued)*

'anya class Leo Van Ginderen, 1991

2 (+. . .) **Lida-class inshore minesweepers** Bldr: Sudostroitel'noye Obyedineniye "Almaz" (Sredniy Neva), Kolpino (In serv. 1990-. . .)

ida class M.O.D., Bonn, 1991

D: 130 tons **S:** 11 kts **Dim:** 31.0 × 6.5 × 1.5
A: 1/30-mm AK-630 gatling AA—mines
Electron Equipt: Radar: 1/. . . . . . nav.
M: 2 diesels; 2 props; 900 bhp **Range:** . . ./. . .
Crew: 12–14 tot.

marks: New design first sighted in the Baltic in 1991 and probably intended as the ccessor to the Yevgenya class. Probably of glass-reinforced plastic construction and y have an SA-N-8 point-defense SAM system.

48 Yevgenya-class (Project 1258) inshore minesweepers
Bldr: Sudostroitel'noye Obyedineniye "Almaz" (Sredniy Neva), Kolpino (In serv. 1970–76)

D: 80 tons (90 fl) **S:** 11 kts **Dim:** 26.2 × 6.1 × 1.5
A: 2/14.5-mm AA (II × 1)
Electron Equipt:
Radar: 1/Spin Trough nav.—IFF: High Pole B transponder
M: 2 diesels; 2 props; 600 bhp **Range:** 300/10
Crew: 1 officer, 9 enlisted (+ 2–3 clearance divers)

vgenya class M.O.D., Bonn, 1991

Remarks: Glass-reinforced plastic hull. Production since 1976 believed all for export; some foreign units armed with one twin 25-mm 2M-8 AA. Employ a television minehunting system useful to 30-m depths that dispenses marker buoys to permit later disposal of mines. Also known as the "*Korchund*" class in Russia.

◆ **2 or more Pelikan-class (Project 1206T) air-cushion vehicle minesweepers**
Bldr: Yuzhnaya Tochka Zavod, Feodosiya, Ukraine (In serv. 1986-. . .)

D: 100 tons (fl) **S:** . . . **Dim:** 26.0 × 13.0 × . . .
A: . . . **Electron Equipt:** Radar: . . .
M: . . . **Crew:** . . . tot.

Remarks: No other data available. Apparently built for trials, and no series production has ensued. One may have been lost in 1990.

◆ **2 Andryusha-class (Project 1256) magnetic mine countermeasures ships** Bldr: . . . . . . (In serv. 1975–76)

ALTAYSKIY KOMSOMOLETS KOMSOMOLETS ESTONIY

Andryusha class M.O.D., Bonn, 1991

D: 320 tons **S:** 15 kts **Dim:** 47.8 × 8.5 × 3.0 **A:** none
Electron Equipt:
Radar: 1/Spin Trough nav.—IFF: High Pole B
M: 2 diesels; 2 props; 2,200 bhp **Crew:** 40 tot.

Remarks: Wooden or plastic hulls. Large cable ducts running down both sides indicate probable role in sweeping magnetic mines or in simulating larger ships for magnetic mine trials. Prominent stack for gas-turbine generator; diesel engines exhaust through hull sides. Provision was made for installing a twin 30-mm AK-230 AA mount on the forecastle. Also known as the "*Topaz*" class in Russia. Both operate in the Baltic Fleet. The listed names may have been changed or eliminated.

◆ **1 Baltika-class auxiliary minesweeper**
Bldr: Leninskaya Kuznitsa SY, Kiev, Ukraine (In serv. 1978)

D: 210 tons (235 fl) **S:** 9.5 kts
Dim: 25.50 (22.00 pp) × 6.80 × 2.45
A: 2/14.5-mm AA (II × 1)
Electron Equipt: Radar: 1/Spin Trough nav.
M: 1 ChISP 18/22 (6NVD-26-2A) diesel; 1 prop; 300 bhp
Electric: 25 kw **Range:** 1,350/9.5 **Crew:** 5–10 tot.

Remarks: 108 grt/145 nrt, small stern-haul purse-seiner fishing boat acquired circa 1980–81, apparently for testing the feasibility of rapidly converting the several hundred civilian craft of this class to simple wire-sweep minesweepers in time of war.

Note: The first unit of a new, small minesweeping-boat class was delivered late in 1991 and was, according to the Russian press, of poor quality. The design may be intended as a successor to the thoroughly obsolescent K-8 class below; no data available.

◆ **15–20 K-8-class (Project 361T) minesweeping boats**
Bldr: Stocznia Północna, Gdańsk, Poland (In serv. 1954–59)

D: 19.4 tons (26 fl) **S:** 12 kts **Dim:** 16.9 × 3.2 × 0.8
A: 2/14.5-mm AA (II × 1) **Electron Equipt:** Radar: none
M: 2 Type 3D6 diesels; 2 props; 300 bhp **Electric:** 80 kw
Range: 300/9 **Crew:** 6 tot.

K-8 class

MINE WARFARE SHIPS *(continued)*

Remarks: Wooden construction. Tow, but do not carry, wire sweep or self-powered solenoid arrays. Long overdue for retirement, but a few are maintained in reserve.

Note: The four small Olya-class (Project 1259/ "*Malakhit*") minesweeping boats completed in the mid-1970s are believed to have been discarded.

◆ **1 or more Tanya-class mine countermeasures drones** Bldr: Sudostroitel'noye Obyedineniye "Almaz" (Sredniy Neva), Kolpino (In serv. . . .)

D: 80 tons **S:** 12 kts **Dim:** 26.5 (25.0 wl) × 4.50 × 1.50
A: none **M:** 1 diesel; 1 prop; 300 bhp

Remarks: Little available data. In effect, a Russian version of the German "Troika" concept.

◆ **11 Ilyusha-class (Project I-376) mine-countermeasures drones** Bldr: Sudostroitel'noye Obyedineniye "Almaz" (Sredniy Neva), Kolpino (In serv. 1970s)

Ilyusha class M.O.D. Bonn

D: 80 tons (85 fl) **S:** 12 kts **Dim:** 26.2 × 5.8 × 1.5
A: none
Electron Equipt:
Radar: 1/Spin Trough nav.—IFF: High Pole B
M: 1 diesel; 1 prop; 300 bhp **Crew:** 6 tot. for transit

Remarks: Radio-controlled while operating, but can be manned for transit. Stream sweep arrays over stern through five chocks; may also dispense line-charge mine-disposal arrays. Also known as the "*Yaroslavets*" class in Russia.

◆ **several dozen non-self-propelled mine countermeasures craft**

D: 25 tons (fl) **Dim:** 12.0 × 4.0 × 1.5

Towed mine-countermeasures craft 1977

Remarks: A towed equivalent to the Ilyusha class, with an internal cable reel and winch to deploy magnetic sweep arrays or explosive line-charge arrays. In addition to these craft, specially equipped Mi-14BT Haze-B helicopters can tow "Volga"-class sports hydrofoils equipped with noise and electric-field generators, and there are also large numbers of towed magnetic-field-generating barges that resemble small submersibles.

AMPHIBIOUS WARFARE SHIPS

◆ **3 Ivan Rogov-class (Project 1174) landing ships**
Bldr: Yantar Zavod, Kaliningrad

	L	In serv.
Ivan Rogov	1976	1978
Aleksandr Nikolayev	. . .	11-82
Mitrofan Moskalenko	1988	12-89

D: 11,000 tons (13,000 fl) **S:** 23 kts
Dim: 158.0 × 24.0 × 8.2

A: 1/SA-N-4 SAM syst. (II × 1, 20 Gecko missiles)—2/76.2-mm 59-cal. DP (II × 1)—2/SA-N-5/8 SAM syst. (IV × 2; 16–20 Grail/Gremlin missiles)—4/30-mm AK-630 gatling AA (VI × 4)—1/122-mm BM-21 automatic bombardment RL (XL × 1, 720 BM-21 rockets)—4/Ka-29TB Helix-B helicopters—3/Lebed air-cushion landing craft or 6 Ondatra-class LCM.
Electron Equipt:
Radar: 2/Palm Frond nav. (*I. Rogov:* 2/Don-Kay), 1/Head Net-C air search (*Moskalenko:* Top Plate), 1/Owl Screech 76.2-mm gun f.c., 1/Pop Group SAN-4-f.c., 2/Bass Tilt 30-mm gun f.c., *Moskalenko* also: 1/Fly Screen helicopter landing control
EW: first two: 2 (*A. Nikolayev:* 3)/Bell Shroud intercept, 2/Bell Squat jammer; *Moskalenko:* no intercept or jammers, 4/RK-16 decoy RL (XVI × 4), 10/10-tubed decoy RL
IFF: 1/High Pole B, 1/Salt Pot-B transponder; *Moskalenko* also: 2 Long Head interrogators
TACAN: *Moskalenko:* 2/Round House—E/O: 1/Squeeze Box
M: 2 gas turbines; 2 props; 48,600 shp
Range: 8,000/20; 12,500/14 **Crew:** 200 crew + 525 troops

Mitrofan Moskalenko Leo Van Ginderen, 19

Ivan Rogov—with bow door partially open Boris Lemachko, 1

Mitrofan Moskalenko M.O.D., Bonn,

Aleksandr Nikolayev French Navy,

.MPHIBIOUS WARFARE SHIPS *(continued)*

emarks: Soviet type designation: BDK—*Bol'shoy Desantnyy Korabl'* (Large Land-.g Ship). The second unit apparently suffered construction delays. The third was not .id down until 1987 but was built much more quickly. No more ships of this class are .xpected. The first two are now in the Pacific Ocean Fleet, and *Mitrofan Moskalenko* ›erates in the Northern Fleet. Also known as the "*Yedinorog*" class in Russia.

Equipped with bow doors and articulating ramp leading to a vehicle cargo deck in the .rward part of the hull, while a stern door provides access to a floodable docking well .tended to accommodate up to three Lebed air-cushion landing craft or six Ondatra-.ass landing craft. The massive superstructure incorporates a helicopter hangar, with . steep ramp leading downward to a helicopter pad on the foredeck, and doors aft .ading to a second helicopter platform over the stern. There are also hydraulically .ised ramps leading from the upper deck forward of the superstructure to both the bow .ors and the docking well. The BM-22 rocket launcher has a range of 20 km; each .cket produces 356 shrapnel fragments.

Cargo capacity: 1,600 tons maximum; capable of transporting an entire naval infan-.y battalion and its vehicles, including 10 tanks, 30 armored personnel carriers, and .ucks. The ability to use helicopters, to beach, and to deploy air-cushion vehicles gives .versatility unmatched by any other amphibious-warfare ship; this is combined with . organic shore fire-bombardment capability and very extensive command, control, .d surveillance facilities. The hull has a pronounced bulb projecting forward below .e waterline.

3 Ropucha-II-class tank landing ships Bldr: Stocznia Północna, Gdańsk, Poland (In serv. 5-90, 2-91, 4-91)

.e first Ropucha-II 5-91

.t Ropucha-II on trials—note gatling guns and Bass Tilt radar aft, .ier lattice mast, stern door M.O.D., Bonn, 5-90

.: 3,500 tons normal (4,080 fl) **S:** 17.8 kts
.im: 112.70 × 15.00 × 4.00 (aft)
.: 1/76.2-mm 59-cal. AK-176 DP—2/30-mm AK-630 gatling AA (I × 2)—2/122-mm BM-21 bombardment RL (XL × 2; 360 rockets)
.ectron Equipt:
Radar: 2/Don-2 nav., 1/Cross Dome (Positiv-E) surf./air search, 1/ Bass Tilt gun f.c.
.FF: 1/Salt Pot-B transponder, interrogation via Cross Dome radar
.E/O: 1/Squeeze Box surveillance/f.c., 2/bridge periscopes
.: 2 diesels; 2 props; 10,000 bhp **Range:** 3,500/16
.ew: 7 officers, 64 enlisted + 190 troops

.arks: Variant of the basic Ropucha design substituting later defensive arma- and sensors. No more are expected. The first unit was turned over to the former .R. in 12-90.

.4 Ropucha-class (Project 775) tank landing ships
.ldr: Stocznia Północna, Gdańsk, Poland (In serv. 1975–78, 1982–87)

.ksandr Shabalin	Bobruysk	Konstantin Ol'shanskiy
.ar' Kunikov	Zemlyansk	19 others

Pacific Ocean Fleet Ropucha-I with bow doors open and ramp extended—note crane forward, an unusual feature U.S. Navy, 7-90

Ropucha-I—with bow beaching "spur" exposed U.S. Navy, 4-91

Konstantin Ol'shanskiy—one of several Ropucha-Is with two BM-21 barrage rocket launchers forward M.O.D., Bonn, 1-90

BDK-47—early-version Ropucha-I Leo Van Ginderen, 9-91

D: 3,500 tons normal (4,080 fl) **S:** 17.8 kts
Dim: 112.70 × 15.00 × 4.00 (aft)
A: 4/57-mm 70-cal. AK-257 DP (II × 2)—some: 4/SA-N-5/8 syst. (IV × 4; 32 Grail/Gremlin missiles)—6 also: 2/122-mm BM-21 bombardment RL (XL × 2, 360 rockets)
Electron Equipt:
Radar: 2/Don-2 or Palm Frond nav., 1/Strut Curve surf./air search, 1/Muff Cob gun f.c.
IFF: 1/High Pole B or Salt Pot-B transponder, interrogation by radar
M: 2 diesels; 2 props; 10,000 bhp **Range:** 3,500/16
Crew: 7 officers, 64 enlisted + 190 troops

Remarks: Soviet type designation: BDK—*Bol'shoy Desantnyy Korabl'* (Large Landing Ship). Bow and stern doors permit roll-on/roll-off loading. Cargo capacity: 450 tons; usable deck space: 600 m². The hull has a moulded depth of 8.60 m amidships and is equipped with a "beak" bow projection to aid in beaching. There are both bow and stern doors. No vehicle cargo is carried on the upper deck, the hatch serving for loading by crane and for ventilation when vehicle motors are running.

The six units in the group built 1982–87 have angled hances to the corners of the main-deck superstructure, a stern ramp with no external web reinforcing, and reinforcing gussets around the forward 57-mm gun platform. Several have received 4/SA-N-5/8 quadruple launchers for point-defense SAMs. Although the entire class was intended to receive two barrage rocket launchers on the forecastle, only the six most recently completed actually carry the weapons. Although equipped to receive the accompanying Squeeze Box electro-optical rangefinder/director, none of the ships yet has it. One unit was transferred to the People's Democratic Republic of Yemen in 1979.

AMPHIBIOUS WARFARE SHIPS *(continued)*

♦ 14 Alligator-class (Project 1171) tank-landing ships

Bldr: Yantar Zavod, Kaliningrad (In serv. 1964–77)

Aleksandr Tortsev*	Nikolay Vilkov*
Donetskiy Shakhter*	Nikolay Obyekov
Ilya Azarov*	Petr Il'ichyev*
Komsomolets Kareliyy	Sergei Lazo
Krasnaya Presnya*	Tomskiy Komsomolets
Krymskiy Komsomolets*	Voronezhskiy Komsomolets
Nikolay Fil'chenkov*	50 Let Shefstva V.L.K.S.M.*

Sergei Lazo—with no 122-mm rocket launcher, but with three SA-N-5/8 SAM launchers J.M.S.D.F., 6-89

Komsomolets Kareliyy—early unit with three cranes, 2/14.5-mm mg (I × 2) abaft stack, no SA-N-5/8 French Navy, 2-86

Nikolay Fil'chenkov—late unit with 2 twin 25-mm AA aft, 122-mm rocket launcher forward French Navy, 2-85

D: 3,400 tons (4,700 fl) **S:** 18 kts
Dim: 112.8 × 15.3 × 4.4 (aft)
A: 2/57-mm 70-cal. DP (II × 1)—*N. Fil'chenkov, N. Vilkov* also: 4/25-mm 2M-8 AA (II × 2)—starred units: 1/BM-21, 122-mm RL (XL × 1, 360 rockets)
Electron Equipt:
Radar: 2/Don-2 and/or Spin Trough nav.—IFF: 1/High Pole B transponder
E/O: starred units: 1/Squeeze Box surveillance/f.c.
M: 2 diesels; 8,000 bhp **Range:** 9,000/16; 14,000/10
Crew: 75 crew + 300 troops

Remarks: Soviet type designation: BDK—*Bol'shoy Desantnyy Korabl'* (Large Landing Ship). The design evolved continually during the time these ships were built. Also known as the "*Nosorog*" class in Russia.

Have ramps fore and aft. Their hoisting equipment varies (one or two 5-ton cranes, one 15-ton crane), as does their armament: later ships also have a BM-21, 40-tubed, 140-mm rocket launcher forward for shore bombardment, the last two have four 25-mm AA (II × 2) aft, and some are equipped with two or three SA-N-5/8 launchers for Grail or Gremlin point-defense SAMs (IV × 2 or 3). Cargo capacity is about 600 tons for beaching, twice that in freighting service; can carry about two dozen tanks, plus lighter vehicles on upper decks. Some of the older units have probably been placed in reserve or even been discarded.

♦ 24 Polnocny-series medium landing ships

Bldr: Stocznia Północna, Gdańsk, Poland (In serv. 1961–73)

Polnocny-B class—with 4/SA-N-5/8 launchers, no 30-mm AA aft U.S. Navy, 5

Polnocny-B—with side troughs for line charges and 2 chutes aft launching tow boats; unit also has 4 SA-NA5/8 SAM launchers J.M.S.

Polnocny-C class—note longer superstructure M.O.D.,

9 C (Project 773) version:

D: 980 tons (1,207 fl) **S:** 18 kts
Dim: 81.3 × 9.3 × 1.2 fwd/2.6 aft
A: 4/30-mm AK-230 AA (II × 2)—2/140-mm barrage RL (XVIII × —4/SA-N-5/8 systems (IV × 2, 32 Grail or Gremlin missiles)
Electron Equipt:
Radar: 1/Spin Trough nav., 1/Drum Tilt f.c.
IFF: 1/Square Head interrogator, 1/High Pole B transponder
M: 2 Type 40DM diesels; 2 props; 4,400 bhp
Range: 1,000/18; 3,000/14 **Crew:** 40 crew, plus 120 troops

15 B (Project 771) version:

D: 740 tons (800 fl) **S:** 18 kts
Dim: 74.0 × 8.9 × 1.2 fwd/2.4 aft
A: 2 or 4/30-mm AK-230 AA—2/140-mm barrage RL (XVIII × 2)-4/SA-N-5/8 systems (IV × 4; 32 Grail or Gremlin missiles)
Electron Equipt:
Radar: 1/Spin Trough, 1/Drum Tilt
IFF: 1/Square Head, 1/High Pole B
M: 2 Type 40D diesels; 2 props; 5,000 bhp
Range: 900/18; 1,500/14 **Crew:** 40 tot. + 60 troops

Remarks: Soviet type designation: SDK—*Srednyy Desantnyy Korabl'* (M Landing Ship). "A" version had convex bow form; "B" has concave bow flare longer and has additional accommodations. All "A"-version (Project 770) units b discarded, and the numbers of the "B"-version are declining through strikir transfers. Only export-version Type D have helicopter decks.

Have a bow door only, and the hull has a "beak" projecting forward be waterline at the bow to aid in beaching. Hatches to upper deck are for loadi ventilation only. Cargo: about 180 tons in B-model, 250 tons in C.

Most have now been equipped with two or four point-defense SAM syste Polnocny-Bs that have 30-mm AA mounts aft have heightened stacks. "Troug Polnocny-A and -B were line-charge layers for beach-defense minefield clearan carried two small remote-controlled motor boats to tow the line charges.

MPHIBIOUS LANDING CRAFT

3 Orlan-class (Project 904) wing-in-ground effect craft
Bldr: . . . (In serv. 1986– . . .)

lan class *Sudostroyenie,* 1-91

an class—note 23-mm cannon atop cockpit Sukhoi, 1991

: 125 tons normal (140 fl) **S:** 190 kts
im: 58.0 × 31.5 span × 1.0 (at rest)
: 1/23-mm AA
lectron Equipt: Radar: 1/Curl Stone nav., 1/. . . search
: 1/ Kuznetsov NK-12 turboprop (14,795 ehp) driving contra-rotating 8-bladed airscrew; 2 Kuibyshev NK-8 turbojets (23,150-lb thrust each) for lift/thrust
ange: 1,080/146
rew: 6 tot. + 100–150 troops and/or several vehicles

arks: Wing-in-ground (WIG) effect craft designed by Sukhoi Bureau to take ntage of cushion of air generated by blowing beneath a broad-chord wing at low de. The Soviet term is "Ekranoplan." Soviet data on the craft vary, and a commer- ersion is offered with a 110-ton normal takeoff weight/125 tons maximum. The oottom has at least six hydroplane steps to aid in getting airborne, and when in , they leave a marked tip-vortex spray wake on the sea surface. The craft re- dly suffer greatly from corrosion due to their operating environment, and the am seems to have stalled. They are operated from a Caspian Sea base and are still ly experimental. A fourth unit was reportedly lost. The proposed commercial n is known as the "Type A-90-150."
cargo bay is 25.0 × 3.3 × 3.0 m high, and maximum payload is 28 tons. The nose to starboard just abaft the gun mount to permit troop and vehicle egress. The -mounted navigational radar appears to be the same as the set on the Pomornik The WIG should normally fly at an altitude of 5–15 m but can rise out of ground for brief periods. The lift-turbine exhausts swivel to direct air beneath the wings eoff. Overall vehicle height is said to be 16.0 m.

(+ . . .) Pomornik class (Project 1232.2) air-cushion vehicles
dr: Sudostroitel'noye Obyedineniye "Almaz," Dekabristov SY, St. Petersburg nits 1 and 3); Yuzhnaya Tochka SY, Feodosiya (unit 2) (In serv. 1986–91)

350 tons (fl) **S:** 55 kts **Dim:** 57.0 × 21.0 × 12.0 high
2/SA-N-8 SAM syst. (IV × 2, 16 Gremlin missiles)—2/30-mm AK-630 gatling AA—2/122-mm retractable artillery RL (XXII × 2)
ctron Equipt:
adar: 1/Curl Stone-B nav.; 1st unit: 1/Cross Dome (Positiv-E) air/surf. search; later units: 1/Bass Tilt gun f.c.
FF: 2/Salt Pot A/B transponders
/O: 1/Quad Look surveillance/f.c.
5 NK-12 gas turbines (12,100 shp each; 2 to power lift fans); 3 ducted airscrew propellers, 4 lift fans; 36,300 shp propulsion
ge: . . . **Crew:** 40 crew + 220 troops

Pomornik class—first unit with Cross Dome radar M.O.D., Bonn, 1990

Pomornik class—later unit, with Bass Tilt *Tass,* 1991

Pomornik class—second unit with rocket launcher raised U.S. Navy, 7-89

Remarks: The vehicle deck can hold up to five armored amphibious personnel transport vehicles or PT-76 light tanks plus a detachment of infantry. Have small bow and stern ramps. Too large for shipboard transportation, and are intended for short-range independent assault operations. Production may have ceased. Also known as the "*Zubr*" (Bison) class in Russia.

Three of the gas-turbine engines are mounted on pylons and drive airscrew propellers; they are equipped with exhaust thrust diverters to enhance mobility. The lift-fan gas turbines are mounted near the stern in the wing compartments and exhaust through the stern. The modified Squeeze Box electro-optical device has no weather cover, as in other installations; there is also a television camera mounted just below the pilothouse. The navigational radar is mounted within a lozenge-shaped radome. The retractable artillery rocket launchers are located near the bow in the hull wing-walls and are reloaded below decks. While the first unit (which may not have the barrage rocket launchers) had the Cross Dome, 75-n.m.-ranged air/surface-search radar atop the superstructure, later units carry a Bass Tilt radar director for the 30-mm gatling AA guns in that position.

♦ 6 (+ . . .) Tsaplya-class air-cushion vehicle landing craft
Bldr: Yuzhnaya Tochka SY, Feodosiya, and Ussuri SY, Khabarovsk (In serv. 1982–1989)

D: 80 tons (115 fl) **S:** 70 kts **Dim:** 31.20 × 13.00 × . . .
A: 2/30-mm AK-630 gatling AA (II × 2)—4/14.5-mm mg (II × 2)
Electron Equipt: Radar: 1/Curl Stone-B nav.
M: 2 PR-77 gas turbines; 2/3.5-m-dia. airscrew props; 8,000 shp
Crew: 6 tot. + 80–160 troops

Remarks: Class reportedly can carry 45 tons of cargo: one amphibious tank plus 80 troops, or 160 troops, or 25 tons of stores and 160 soldiers, or 225 soldiers. Appears to be a Lebed successor. First unit delivered 1982, second in 1987, third in 1988, sixth in 1990. In the Far East are operated on the Amur–Ussuri River system. The twin 14.5-mm machine-gun mounts flank the 5.5 m long by 5.0 m wide bow ramp. The cargo deck has about 130 m² useful space. There are two lift fans, probably also powered by the main-propulsion gas turbines. The gatling guns and 14.5-mm cannon appear to be controlled by Kolonka-2 ringsight directors on platforms abaft the pilothouse.

AMPHIBIOUS LANDING CRAFT *(continued)*

Tsaplya—at speed Siegfried Breyer

A camouflaged Tsaplya—with a Gus ACV in the background on the Amur River *Ships of the World,* 1-92

◆ **2 Utenok-class air-cushion vehicle landing craft**
Bldr: Yuzhnaya Tochka SY, Feodosiya (In serv. 1982)

D: 70 tons (fl) **S:** 65 kts **Dim:** 26.3 × 13.0 × . . .
A: 2/30-mm AK-230 AA (II × 1)
M: 2 gas turbines; 2 airscrew props; . . . shp

Remarks: Can carry one 45-ton T-72/T-80 tank plus 80 troops. Apparently unsuccessful, as only two were built.

◆ **19 Lebed-class (Project 1206) air-cushion vehicle landing craft**
Bldr: . . . (In serv. . . .)

Lebed class Boris Lemachko

Lebed class—as deck cargo on a merchant ship U.S. Navy, 1985

D: 70 tons (fl) **S:** 50 kts **Dim:** 24.8 × 10.8 × . . .
A: 1/14.5-mm mg **M:** 3 gas turbines; 2 props
Range: 100/50 **Crew:** 2 officers, 6 enlisted

Remarks: Broad bow ramp, ducted props, control cab to starboard, gun mount ato Can carry one or two PT-76 light tanks or 120 troops or about 35 tons of cargo. Al known as the "*Kalmar*" class in Russia.

◆ **20 Aist-class (Project 1232) air-cushion vehicle landing craft**
Bldr: Sudostroitel'noye Obyedineniye "Almaz," Dekabristov SY, St. Petersburg (In serv. 1971–1986)

Aist class—early unit with single gun mount atop pilothouse M.O.D., Bo

Aist class at rest—late unit with Drum Tilt, 2 gun mounts M.O.D., B

D: 220 tons (fl) **S:** 45 kts **Dim:** 47.8 × 17.5 × 0.3
A: 4/30-mm AK-230 AA (II × 2)
Electron Equipt:
Radar: 1/Spin Trough nav., 1/Drum Tilt f.c.
IFF: 1/High Pole B interrogator, 1/Square Head interrogator
M: 3 NK-12 gas turbines; 4 props; 2 lift fans; 24,000 shp propulsion
Range: 100/45; 208/40 **Crew:** 8 tot. + up to 220 troops

Remarks: Can carry four PT-76 light tanks or one medium tank and 220 troops. units also carry 2/SA-N-5/8 SAM syst. (IV × 2) and chaff RL (XVI × 2). Early unit soon have reached the end of their useful lives, if that has not already happened.

◆ **20 Gus-class (Project 1205) air-cushion vehicle landing craft**
Bldr: Sudostroitel'noye Obyedineniye "Almaz," Dekabristov SY, St. Petersbu (In serv. 1970–74)

Gus class *Tass*

D: 27.2 tons (fl) **S:** 57.5 kts **Dim:** 21.3 × 7.1 × 0.2 (at rest)
A: none **M:** 3 gas turbines; 2 props; 1 lift fan; 2,340 shp
Range: 185/50; 200/43 **Crew:** 3 tot. + 24 troops

Remarks: A training version with two pilot positions is also in service. Twelve have been scrapped, and the others should soon be discarded. Also known as the class in Russia.

MPHIBIOUS LANDING CRAFT *(continued)*

16 Ondatra-class (Project 1176) landing craft (In serv. 1978–79)

D: 90 tons (140 fl) **S:** 10 kts **Dim:** 24.2 × 5.0 × 1.5
A: none **M:** 2 diesels; 2 props; 600 bhp **Crew:** 4 tot.

ndatra class 1979

marks: Built for use aboard the *Ivan Rogov*-class landing ships. Cargo well is about × 3.8 m.

te: All Vydra-class utility landing craft and T-4-class landing craft are believed to ve been discarded.

AVAL AUXILIARIES

OMMAND SHIPS

8 Vytegrales class (Project 596P)
Bldr: Zhdanov Zavod, St. Petersburg (In serv. 1963–66)

SHERON (ex-*Tosnales*)	DONBASS (ex-*Kirishi*)
SKUNCHAK (ex-*Vostok-4*)	SEVAN (ex-*Vyborgles*)
URIYA (ex-*Suzdal*)	TAMAN' (ex-*Vostok-3*)
KSON (ex-*Vagales*)	YAMAL (ex-*Svirles*)

sheron—under modification Leo Van Ginderen, 10-90

nal—standard unit Leo Van Ginderen, 3-91

9,650 tons (fl) **S:** 16 kts
m: 121.9 (114.0 pp) × 16.7 × 7.3 **A:** none
ectron Equipt:
Radar: 2/Don-2 nav., *Donbass* only: 1/Big Net early warning
IFF: 1/High Pole B transponder
TACAN: *Apsheron* only: 2/Round House
: 1 Burmeister & Wain 950 VTBF 110 diesel; 1 prop; 5,200 bhp
nge: 7,380/14.5 **Fuel:** 462 tons **Crew:** 90 tot. (naval)

arks: Originally built as merchant timber carriers, then converted as space-support ships by the addition of more communications facilities and a helicopter rm over the stern—consequently losing access to the after hold. Now used as fleet y ships and flagships. Seven sisters were converted to serve the Academy of ces as satellite-tracking ships. A deckhouse has been built over hold number forward of the superstructure in *Dikson, Taman, Dauriya,* and *Baskunchak*. In *Apsheron* completed an extensive refit and alteration at Sevastopol and was ped with a 13 × 11.5 × 6 m hangar for two helicopters and new electronics ding 2 Palm Frond radars in place of Don-2, Round House helicopter-control AN, and Fly Screen helicopter landing-control radar antennas.

SUBMARINE TENDERS

◆ **7 Ugra-class (Project 1886) command tenders**
Bldr: Black Sea SY, Nikolayev (In serv. 1963–72)

EVGENIY OSIPOS	IVAN KOLYSHKIN	IVAN KUCHERENKO
IVAN VAKHRAMEYEV	TOBOL	VLADIMIR EGOROV
VOLGA		

Ivan Kolyshkin—unique unit with hangar French Navy, 1978

Tobol 7-91

Volga—with taller after mast, topped by Vee Cone HF COMMS antenna French Navy, 4-83

D: 6,750 tons (9,600 fl) **S:** 17 kts **Dim:** 145.0 × 17.7 × 6.4
A: 8/57-mm 70-cal. AK-257 DP (II × 4)—most: 2/SA-N-5/8 SAM syst. (IV × 2, 16 Grail or Gremlin missiles)
Electron Equipt:
Radar: 1–3 Don-2 nav., 1/Strut Curve surf./air search, 2/Muff Cob f.c.
EW: 4/Watch Dog intercept
IFF: 2/Salt Pot-A/B transponders, 2/Square Head interrogators
M: 4 diesels; 2 props; 8,000 bhp **Range:** 21,000/10
Crew: 450 tot.

Remarks: Soviet type designation: PB—*Plavuchaya Baza* (Floating Base). One modified version was built for India, as *Amba*. Can support eight to twelve diesel submarines at sea with supplies, fuel, provisions, water, and spare torpedoes and can offer repair services. This class and the Don class have frequently been used as flagships for deployed forces. Two Northern Fleet units were offered for scrap late in 1991.

One 10-ton and two 6-ton cranes are fitted. *Ivan Kolyshkin* (Project 1886M) has a tall helicopter hangar, while the others have only a landing platform. *Ivan Kucherenko* and *Volga* have a Vee Cone HF communications antenna. Sisters *Gangut* and *Borodino* are configured as training ships for naval officer cadets and do not serve submarines—*see* Training Ships.

◆ **6 Don-class (Project 310) command tenders**
Bldr: Black Sea SY, Nikolayev (In serv. 1958–61)

DMITRIY GALKIN	FYODOR VIDYAEV
KAMCHATSKIY KOMSOMOLETS	MAGADANSKIY KOMSOMOLETS
MAGOMED GADZHIEV	VIKTOR KOTEL'NIKOV

D: 6,730 tons (9,000 fl) **S:** 20 kts
Dim: 140.0 × 17.6 × 6.4 (6.8 max.)
A: 4/100-mm 56-cal. BU-34 DP (I × 4)—8/57-mm AA (II × 2)—*see* Remarks
Electron Equipt:
Radar: 1 or 2/Don-2 nav., 1/Slim Net surf./air search, 1/Sun Visor gun f.c., 2/Hawk Screech gun f.c. (for 57-mm mounts)—*see* Remarks
Sonar: . . . hull-mounted HF—EW: 2/Watch Dog intercept
IFF: 1/Salt Pot-A or High Pole B transponder, 2/Square Head interrogator
M: 4 Type 37D diesels; 2 props; 8,000 bhp
Range: 21,000/10 **Crew:** 300 tot.

SUBMARINE TENDERS *(continued)*

Kamchatskiy Komsomolets—fully armed version with 4/100-mm, 4 twin 57-mm, and 4 twin 25-mm gun mounts U.S. Navy, 5-

Magadanskiy Komsomolets—no 100-mm guns, large helo deck J.M.S.D.F, 6-86

Dmitriy Galkin—Vee Cone aft, lattice foremast U.S. Navy, 6-88

Viktor Kotel'nikov—Big Ball SATCOMM radomes, small helo platform aft 11-90

Remarks: Soviet type designation: PB—*Plavuchaya Baza* (Floating Base). Can serve as logistic support for a flotilla of eight to twelve diesel submarines. *Viktor Kotel'nikov's* after 100-mm mounts were replaced by a helicopter platform, while the *Magadanskiy Komsomolets* has always had a very large helicopter platform aft and has never carried any 100-mm guns; the ship had Low Ball SATCOMM antennas fitted aft in 1984. *Magomed Gadzhiev* received a very similar Low Ball installation in 1989 but retains all four 100-mm guns. *Fyodor Vidyaev* has eight 25-mm (II × 4) also, but no Hawk Screech; she and *Dmitriy Galkin* have been fitted with a Vee Cone antenna for long-range communications. A bow lift-hook of 100-ton capacity is fitted, as are one 10-ton, two 5-ton, and two 1-ton cranes. All are used as flagships. One other unit was transferred to Indonesia, and the others are likely to be stricken by the mid-1990s.

MISSILE AND AMMUNITION TRANSPORTS

◆ 1 Aleksandr Brykin-class ballistic-missile transport (Project 1826)

Bldr: United Admiralty SY, St. Petersburg (In serv. 1987)

Aleksandr Brykin

D: 14,000 tons (fl) **S:** 16 kts **Dim:** 155.0 (142.0 wl) × 24.0 × 6.5
A: 4/30-mm AK-630 gatling AA (I × 4)—2/SA-N-8 SAM syst. (IV × 2; 16 Gremlin missiles)

Electron Equipt:
Radar: 2/Nayada nav., 1/Half Plate-A air search, 2/Bass Tilt f.c.
EW: 2/Bell Shroud intercept, 2/Bell Squat jammer, 2/RK-16 chaff RL (XVI × 2), 2 or more/10-tubed decoy RL (X × . . .)
IFF: 1/Salt Pot-B transponder, interrogation via Half Plate-A rad
M: 2 diesels, electric drive; 1 prop; . . . shp—bow-thruster
Range: . . . **Crew:** 140 tot.

Aleksandr Brykin M.O.D., Bonn,

Aleksandr Brykin M.O.D., Bonn

Remarks: Intended to transport 16 SS-N-20 missiles for the Typhoon class possibly, SS-N-23 for the Delta-IV. Missiles are stowed vertically in a large served by a 75-ton crane. There are also two 5–10-ton cranes amidships. Also kn the *"Lira"* class in Russia. In Northern Fleet.

◆ 3 Amga-class ballistic-missile transports (Project 1791)

Bldr: Krasnoye Sormovo SY, Nizhniy Novgorod (ex-Gorkiy)

Amga (In serv. 1973) Vetluga (In serv. 1976)
Daugava (In serv. 1981)

D: 4,500 tons (5,500 fl) **S:** 12 kts
Dim: 102.0 × 17.7 × 4.4 (*see* Remarks)
A: 4/25-mm 80-cal. 2M-8 AA (II × 2)
Electron Equipt:
Radar: 1/Don-2 nav.—IFF: 1/High Pole B transponder
M: 2 diesels; 2 props; 4,000 bhp
Range: 4,500/12 **Crew:** 60 tot.

[MI]SSILE AND AMMUNITION TRANSPORTS *(continued)*

[Ve]tluga J.M.S.D.F, 11-90

[Da]ugava J.M.S.D.F., 1981

[Rem]arks: One 55-ton crane with a reach of 34 meters. Have ice-reinforced hulls. [Inte]nded to transport ballistic missiles for strategic submarines. *Vetluga* is 6 m longer [than] *Amga*; *Daugava* is 113.0 m long, displaces 6,200 tons (fl), and has a different [hull]e, with solid sides. *Vetluga* and *Daugava* are in the Pacific Fleet; *Amga* is in the [Nort]hern Fleet.

[♦ 7] Lama-class cruise-missile transports (Project 323)

[B]ldr: Black Sea SY, Nikolayev (In serv. 1963–79)

[GEN]ERAL RYABIKOV	PM-868	PM-946	PM-873 (ex-PM-877)
[VOR]ONEZH (PM-872)	PM-150	PM-938	

[Gen]eral Ryabikov French Navy, 9-90

[Voro]nezh (PM-872)—forward 57-mm mount deleted AO3 Howard, USN, 7-89

[PM-8]73 (ex-PM-877) in reserve at Sevastopol Leo Van Ginderen, 10-90

PM-150—with twin 57-mm DP aboard Leo Van Ginderen, 10-91

D: 4,500 tons (fl) **S:** 14 kts **Dim:** 112.8 × 14.9 × 4.4
A: 2, 4 or 8/57-mm DP (IV × 1 or 2, or II × 2)—2 or 4/SA-N-5/8 SAM syst. (IV × 4, 16 or 32 Grail or Gremlin missiles)—*Voronezh* & one other also: 4/25-mm 80-cal. 2M-8 AA (II × 2)
Electron Equipt:
Radar: 1/Don-2 nav., 1/Slim Net or Strut Curve surf./air search, 1 or 2/Hawk Screech or 2/Muff Cob f.c.
IFF: 1/High Pole B transponder, 2/Square Head interrogators
M: 2 diesels; 1 prop; 4,000 bhp
Crew: 240 tot. (420 in missile boat tenders)

Remarks: PM—*Plavuchaya Masterskaya* (Floating Workshop) and PB—*Plavuchaya Baza* (Floating Base). Vary greatly in equipment. Intended to transport cruise missiles for submarines and surface units. *Voronezh* (PM-872) and PM-873 have larger missile-stowage areas and smaller cranes, carry open 57-mm DP mounts (II × 2, aft), and four 25-mm AA (II × 2), but have no fire-control radar; both had lost their forward twin 57-mm mounts by 1986, but the mount was restored on PM-873 by 1990. These serve Nanuchka-class corvettes and Osa-class patrol boats. All have two 20-ton (10-ton on missile-boat tenders) precision cranes. *General Ryabikov*, completed 1979, has an enclosed, automatic 57-mm AK-257 gun mount and four SA-N-5/8 systems. Two are in the Northern Fleet, three (including *General Ryabikov, Voronezh*, and the other SS-N-2-series missile tender) are in the Black Sea Fleet, and two (including PM-150) are in the Pacific Fleet.

♦ 1 converted Yuniy Partizan-class ammunition ship

Bldr: Turnu-Severin SY, Romania (In serv. 1976)

VITSE-ADMIRAL FOMIN (ex-*Pinega*)

Vitse-Admiral Fomin Boris Lemachko

D: 3,800 tons (fl) **S:** 12.9 kts
Dim: 88.75 (80.25 pp) × 12.8 × 4.6
A: 4/14.5-mm mg (II × 2)
Electron Equipt:
Radar: 1/Don-2 nav.—IFF: 1/High Pole A transponder
M: 1 Cegielski-Sulzer 8 TAD 36 diesel; 1 prop; 2,080 bhp
Electric: 306 kw **Range:** 4,000/12
Fuel: 125 tons **Crew:** . . .

Remarks: Former naval cargo ship of 2,079 grt/2,150 dwt, one of 24 sisters (20 civilian) originally intended as container vessels. Reappeared 1-86 with forecastle deck extended past forward hold, sides raised by two decks abreast number three hold, and a single electrohydraulic crane having replaced the original king posts and three 10-ton booms.

♦ 2 Modified Andizhan-class ammunition ships

Bldr: Neptunwerft, Rostock, East Germany (In serv. 1960–61)

VENTA VILYUY

Venta J.M.S.D.F., 4-88

MISSILE AND AMMUNITION TRANSPORTS *(continued)*

Vilyuy U.S. Navy, 7-89

D: 6,740 tons (fl) **S:** 13.5 kts
Dim: 104.0 × 14.4 × 6.6 **A:** none
Electron Equipt:
Radar: 2/Don-2 nav.
IFF: 1/High Pole B transponder, 1/Square Head interrogator
M: 1 diesel; 1 prop; 1,890 bhp **Range:** 6,000/13.5
Crew: 60 tot.

Remarks: Converted from cargo ships during the 1970s. Large crane forward, two small cranes and a helicopter deck aft. Forward holds can accommodate ten SS-N-9 cruise missiles and twenty SA-N-1 or SA-N-3 surface-to-air missiles, as well as other ammunition. Helicopter pad aft used mostly for volleyball.

◆ **2 MP-6-class missile transports** Bldr: Hungary (In serv. 1959–60)

BUREYA KHOPER

Bureya—long forward hatch to missile hold J.M.S.D.F., 4-88

D: 2,100 tons (fl) **S:** 10.5 kts
Dim: 74.7 (70.1 pp) × 11.3 × 4.4
Electron Equipt: Radar: 1/Don-2 nav.
M: 2 Buchau-Wolff 6 NVD 48 diesels; 1 prop; 800 bhp
Range: 3,300/9 **Crew:** 40 tot.

Remarks: Former medium landing ships, resembling engines-aft coastal freighters. Bow doors welded shut circa 1960, when they were adapted as cargo vessels. Subsequently modified to transport SS-N-5 ballistic missiles. *Khoper* in the Northern Fleet and *Bureya* in the Pacific.

◆ **2 Melitopol-class missile transports** Bldr: . . . , U.S.S.R. (In serv. 1952–55)

INDIRKA FORT SHEVERENKO

D: 1,200 tons (fl) **S:** 11.3 kts **Dim:** 57.6 × 9.0 × 4.3
Electron Equipt: Radar: 1/Don-2 nav. **Range:** 2,500/10.5
M: 1 Type 6DR 30/40 diesel; 1 prop; 600 bhp **Crew:** 30 tot.

Remarks: Converted late 1970s from small, engines-aft coastal cargo vessels. Have one long hold. All cargo-handling gear removed. In Baltic Fleet. Three sisters have served as survey vessels.

◆ **10 or more Muna-class small munitions transports**
Bldr: Nakhodka SY (In serv. 1960s)

VTR-81	VTR-82	VTR-83	VTR-84	VTR-85
VTR-86	VTR-91	VTR-92	VTR-94	VTR-148

D: 680 tons (fl) **S:** 11 kts **Dim:** 51.0 × 8.5 × 2.7
Electron Equipt:
Radar: 1/Spin Trough nav.—IFF: High Pole A transponder
M: 1 diesel; 1 prop; 600 bhp **Crew:** 20 tot.

VTR-94 Boris Lemach

VTR-92 6

Remarks: Built in several different configurations, some as torpedo transports, ot to carry surface-to-air missiles. When deployed out of area, have born VTR (Voyen Transport—Military Transport)-series pendants, but in home waters often seen MBSS *(Morskaya Barzha Samokhodnaya Sukhogruznaya*—Seagoing Self-Prop Dry Cargo Lighter)-series pendants. Usually have a single electric crane positi between two or four small holds. Two have been converted into coastal survey ves see later page.

REPAIR SHIPS

◆ **3 (+1) Malina class** Bldr: Black Sea SY, Nikolayev

PM-12 (In serv. 1991) PM-16 (In serv. 1992?)
PM-63 (In serv. 1984) PM-74 (In serv. 1985)

PM-74 J.M.S.D.F.,

PM-12 French Navy

D: 8,000 tons (12,000 fl) **S:** 12 kts
Dim: 137.0 (123.0 wl) × 21.0 × 6.0
A: none
Electron Equipt:
Radar: 2/Palm Frond nav. (PM-12: 2/Nayada)
IFF: 1/High Pole B transponder
M: 4 diesels; 1 prop; 8,000 bhp **Crew:** 380 tot.

EPAIR SHIPS *(continued)*

marks: PM—*Plavuchaya Masterskaya* (Floating Workshop). Second unit began als in the spring of 1985, third in 11-90. Unusual hull form with no curved surfaces, licates not intended to move very often. Intended to serve nuclear-powered sub-arines, as evidenced by the mooring pockets along the hull sides and the two large, ecialized reactor recoring cranes. PM-12 is assigned to the Northern Fleet, as is 1-63; PM-74 was delivered to the Pacific Fleet late in 1985.

29 Amur class

Bldr: A. Warski SY, Szczecin, Poland (In serv. 1968–78, 1981–88)

1-5	PM-9	PM-10	PM-15	PM-34	PM-37	PM-40
1-49	PM-52	PM-56	PM-59	PM-64	PM-69	PM-73
1-75	PM-81	PM-82	PM-86	PM-92	PM-94	PM-97
1-129	PM-138	PM-139	PM-140	PM-156	PM-161	PM-163
1-164						

1-64—early series LSPH K. Degener, R.A.N., 12-90

-129—early series French Navy, 1990

-56—second series, with additional accommodations Skyfotos, 4-88

9—fourth series, squared-off stack, new cranes M.O.D., Bonn, 2-90

PM-97—fourth series, with new cranes, squared-off stack J.M.S.D.F., 1988

D: 4,000 tons (5,490 fl) **S:** 12 kts
Dim: 121.7 × 17.0 × 5.1 **A:** none
Electron Equipt:
Radar: 1/Don-2 nav.—IFF: 1/High Pole B transponder
M: 2 diesels; 1 prop; 4,000 bhp **Range:** 13,200/8
Crew: 210 tot., plus up to 210 passengers (PM-5 and later: 300 total)

Remarks: PM—*Plavuchaya Masterskaya* (Floating Workshop). Enlarged version of the Oskol class. Two 5-ton cranes. Construction resumed 1980–82, with PM-5 of the new series having a long deckhouse in the forecastle. Early units do not have the passenger facilities. Serve surface ships and submarines with basic repair facilities and spare parts. The fourth series, which includes PM-59, PM-69, PM-86, PM-92, and PM-97, have only two new-style cranes, an extra deckhouse atop the superstructure forward of the stack, squared-off stacks, and a slightly flattened face to the forward side of the bridge superstructure. There are a great many minor variations.

◆ **12 Oskol class** Bldr: A. Warski SY, Szczecin, Poland (In serv. 1964–67)

PM-2	PM-20	PM-21	PM-24	PM-26	PM-28
PM-51	PM-62	PM-68	PM-146	PM-148	PM-477

PM-146—flush-decked Oskol French Navy, 1991

PM-24—the armed Oskol 10-90

PM-26—note brow at stern 2-91

REPAIR SHIPS *(continued)*

D: 2,500 tons (3,000 fl) **S:** 12 kts **Dim:** 91.4 × 12.2 × 4.0
A: PM-24 only: 2/57-mm 70-cal. DP (II × 1)—4/25-mm 80-cal. 2M-8 AA (II × 2)
Electron Equipt:
Radar: 1 or 2/Don-2—IFF: 1/High Pole A transponder
M: 2 diesels; 1 prop; 4,000 bhp **Range:** 9,000/8
Crew: 60 tot.

Remarks: PM—*Plavuchaya Masterskaya* (Floating Workshop). Most have a well deck forward of the bridge; PM-146 is flush-decked. All have one or two 3.4-ton cranes. PM-28 was deployed to Yemen at Aden during the late 1980s but returned to the Black Sea in 1991.

◆ **5 Dnepr class (Project 734)** Bldr: Black Sea SY, Nikolayev (In serv. 1960–64)

PM-17 PM-22 PM-30 PM-130 PM-135

PM-17 1960

D: 4,500 tons (5,300 fl) **S:** 11 kts
Dim: 113.3 (100.0 pp) × 16.5 × 4.4
Electron Equipt:
Radar: 1/Don-2 nav.—IFF: 1/High Pole A transponder
M: 1 diesel; 1 prop; 2,000 bhp **Range:** 6,000/8.3
Crew: 420 tot.

Remarks: PM—*Plavuchaya Masterskaya* (Floating Workshop). Have one 150-ton bow hoist, one king post, and one crane. Equipment varies from ship to ship. PM-130 and -135, the last two units (Modified Dnepr class), are flush-decked. Intended to serve submarines. Can be armed with 2/57-mm AA (II × 1). Not seen since initial delivery voyages. Received criticism in Soviet naval press when new; early units may have been discarded.

GENERATOR SHIPS

◆ **4 Tomba class** Bldr: A. Warski SY, Szczecin, Poland

ENS-244 (In serv. 1975) ENS-254 (In serv. 1974)
ENS-348 (In serv. 1978) ENS-357 (In serv. 1977)

ENS-254 R. Neth. N., 1991

D: 4,400 tons (5,800 fl) **S:** 12 kts
Dim: 107.0 (98.0 wl) × 17.0 × 5.0
Electron Equipt:
Radar: 1/Don-2 nav., 1/Spin Trough nav.—IFF: 1/High Pole B transponder
M: 1 diesel; 1 prop; 4,500 bhp **Range:** 7,000/12
Crew: 50 tot.

Remarks: ENS—*Elektrostantsiye Nativatel'noye Sudno* (Electric Power Station and Steam-Source Ship). Two stacks and a "mack" on the forecastle, all containing diesel-engine exhausts, while the stack amidships also has the uptake from a large boiler. Two 3.5-ton cranes. PM-254 differs in having a short mainmast, while the others have a tall pole mast. PM-244 and -254 are in the Northern Fleet, the others in the Pacific Ocean Fleet.

SUBMARINE RESCUE SHIPS

◆ **2 (+ 1) El'brus (Project 537) class** Bldr: 61 Kommuna SY, Nikolayev

	L	In serv.		L	In serv.
El'brus	1977	1981	Alagaz	1984	1988
Ayudag	. . .	. . .			

Alagaz French Navy, 198

El'brus U.S. Navy, 1-

D: 20,000 tons (fl) **S:** 17 kts **Dim:** 175.0 × 25.0 × 7.5
A: provision for 4/30-mm AK-630 gatling AA (I × 4) or 8/30-mm AK-230 AA (II × 4)
Electron Equipt:
Radar: 1/Don-2 nav., 2/Don-Kay nav.—IFF: 2/Salt Pot-C transponders
M: 4 diesels; 2 props; . . . bhp **Range:** . . .
Crew: 420 tot.

Remarks: Icebreaking hull. Large hangar aft of stack holds two or four salvage-a rescue submersibles, which are moved forward on rails for launching by extenda overhead gantry cranes on either side. Hangar for one Hormone or Helix helicopt with hangar door dropping to form a ramp leading to the helicopter flight deck. Can and retrieve a four-point moor. The 3-ton crane on port quarter has very long fold arm. Have submersible decompression and observation chambers, fire-fighting equ ment. Far and away the world's largest and most elaborate submarine salvage-a rescue ships.

El'brus made one brief deployment in 12-81 to 1-82 and then returned to the Bl Sea, not emerging again until 5-84, again briefly. *Alagaz* was under constructior early as 3-83 and deployed to the Pacific Ocean Fleet on completion, but *El'b* remains in the Black Sea. *Ayudag* reported under construction in the Russian p during 1991 but, under present economic conditions, may not be completed.

◆ **1 Nepa class (Project 530)** Bldr: Black Sea SY, Nikolayev (In serv. 1970)

Karpaty

Karpaty R. Neth. N.,

D: 9,800 tons (fl) **S:** 16 kts
Dim: 129.5 × 19.2 × 6.4 **A:** none
Electron Equipt:
Radar: 2/Don-2 nav.—IFF: 1/High Pole B transponder
M: 2–4 diesels; 2 props; 8,000 bhp
Range: 8,000/14 **Crew:** 270 tot.

Remarks: Has a 600-ton lift hook supported by horns extending over the sterr others beneath the hull. Very large all-purpose salvage ship with submarine-r equipment, including several rescue bells and observation chambers. Has opera Baltic Fleet since early 1980s.

◆ **7 Prut class (Project 527)**
Bldr: Nosenko/Chernomorskiy SY, Nikolayev (In serv. 1960–68)

Altay (ex-SS-22) Zhiguli (ex-SS-25)
Beshtach SS-21
Ehpron (ex-SS-26) SS-83 (ex-SS-24)
Vladimir Trefol'ev (ex-SS-87)

SUBMARINE RESCUE SHIPS *(continued)*

hpron Boris Lemachko, 6-91

-21 Leo Van Ginderen, 8-90

D: 2,800 tons (3,300 fl) **S:** 20 kts
Dim: 90.2 × 14.3 × 5.5
Electron Equipt:
Radar: 1–2/Don-2 nav.—IFF: High Pole A transponder
M: 4 diesels; 2 props; 8,000 bhp
Range: 10,000/16 **Crew:** 120 tot.

marks: SS—*Spasitel'noye Sudno* (Rescue Ship). One derrick, two or three special riers for rescue chambers, submersible decompression chamber for divers, and vage observation bells. Four anchor buoys are stowed on inclined racks on the after k. One unit was armed for a while with four 57-mm AA (IV × 1) controlled by a Muff b radar director, long since removed. SS-21, SS-26, SS-83, *Beshtau,* and *Vladimir folev* have quadripod foremasts, smaller moorings buoys; others have tripod fore-sts. Sister SS-44 lost during early 1970s, and SS-23 was scrapped around 1987.

up to 11 Modified T-58-class (Project 532A) Bldr: . . . (In serv. late 1950 to mid-1960s)

ZBEK	VALDAY	ZANGEZUR	SS-35	SS-47	SS-51
IBINY	POLKOVO	SS-30	SS-40	SS-50 (ex-*Shakhter*)	

30 Hartmut Ehlers, 3-92

: 815 tons (930 fl) **S:** 17 kts **Dim:** 71.7 × 9.6 × 2.7
lectron Equipt:
Radar: 1/Don-2, 1/Spin Trough nav.—IFF: 1/High Pole A transponder
Sonar: 1/Tamir-11 hull-mounted HF searchlight
: 2 diesels; 2 props; 4,000 bhp **Range:** 2,500/12
ew: 60 tot.

arks: SS—*Spasitel'noye Sudno* (Rescue Ship). Minesweepers altered while under ruction. *Kazbek* was laid down 21-11-62, launched 12-8-64, and commissioned 65. *Valday* reported in Soviet press late 1989 to be a training ship for the St. sburg Naval Base, while *Zangezur* serves as frogman training support ship at Sevastopol. Sister *Gidrolog* served as an intelligence collector until struck, early 1980s. Another was transferred to India. Some of the units listed above have probably been stricken.

Lift rig overhanging the stern to handle divers' gear and submersible decompression chamber. Rescue diving chamber to port, amidships. Can be armed with one 37-mm AA.

FLEET REPLENISHMENT SHIPS

Note: The Soviet press reported the launch in 1-89 of a new "naval tanker" named *Vladimir Peregudov;* no data available. If actually a navy vessel, would be first new replenishment ship since *Kaliningradneft* class below. The only armed underway replenishment ship is the naval-manned *Berezina;* all others are crewed by the civilian Naval Auxiliary Service.

◆ **2 Kaliningrad class** Bldr: Rauma-Repola, Rauma, Finland

VYAZ'MA (ex-*Katun*) (In serv. 5-83) ARGUN (ex-*Kallavere*) (In serv. 7-83)

Argun U.S. Navy, 1987

D: 8,700 tons (fl) **S:** 14 kts
Dim: 115.5 (112.0 pp) × 17.0 × 6.5
Electron Equipt:
Radar:1/Okean-A nav., 1/Okean-B nav.
M: 1 Russkiy/Burmeister & Wain 5 DKRP 50/110-2 diesel; 1 prop; 3,850 bhp
Electric: 805 kw **Range:** 5,000/14
Crew: 12 officers, 28 unlicensed (all civilians)

Remarks: 4,821 grt/5,873 dwt. Last two built of a class that had over two dozen units delivered to the U.S.S.R. Ministry of Fisheries from 1979 to 1982. Originally completed 12-82 and 11-82, respectively. *Argun,* which operates with the Pacific Ocean Fleet, was on charter for civilian operations during 1991–92.

Three liquid replenishment stations (one each side, plus astern); no underway solids replenishment. Carry 5,750 m^3 (5,350 tons) liquid cargo in ten tanks, 80 m^3 dry cargo in one hold within the forecastle. Two cargo pumps have combined 400 m^3/hr capacity. Have a 1,600-ton water-ballast capacity.

◆ **1 Berezina class (Project 1859)**
Bldr: 61 Kommuna SY, Nikolayev (In serv. 1978)

BEREZINA

Berezina—with Tango-class sub alongside U.S. Navy, 1990

Berezina French Navy, 1991

FLEET REPLENISHMENT SHIPS *(continued)*

D: 15,000 tons (36,000 fl) **S:** 21 kts
Dim: 210.0 × 25.0 × 10.0
A: 1/SA-N-4 SAM system (II × 1, 20 Gecko missiles)—4/57-mm 70-cal. AK-257 DP (II × 2)—4/30-mm AK-630 gatling AA (VI × 4)—2/RBU-1000 ASW RL (VI × 2)—2/Ka-25 Hormone-C or Ka-32T Helix helicopters
Electron Equipt:
Radar: 1/Don-2 nav., 2/Don-Kay nav., 1/Strut Curve surf./air search, 1/Pop Group SAM f.c., 1/Muff Cob gun f.c., 2/Bass Tilt gun f.c.
Sonar: . . .—IFF: 1/Salt Pot-C transponder, interrogation via Strut Curve
EW: 2/Bell Shroud intercept, 2/Bell Squat jammer, 2/trainable decoy RL (II × 2)
M: 2 diesels; 2 props; 54,000 bhp **Range:** 10,000/21
Endurance: 90 days
Crew: 24 officers, 290 enlisted (naval)

Remarks: Soviet type designation: VTR—*Voyenyy Transport* (Military Transport). The largest multipurpose underway replenishment ship yet built for the Russians and the only one currently armed. No additional units are expected. *Berezina* was involved in a serious collision in the Sea of Marmara on 15-5-86.

Can refuel over the stern and from single constant-tension stations on either side, amidships. Solid replenishment is by two sliding-stay, constant-tension transfer rigs on either side. Vertical replenishment is by two utility helicopters hangared in the after superstructure. There are four 10-ton stores-handling cranes to supply ships moored alongside. Cargo: approx. 16,000 tons of fuel oil and diesel fuel, 500 tons fresh water, and 1,500–2,000 tons of provisions, munitions, and combat spares. Can accommodate up to about 600 personnel in order to transport spare crews for submarines, for which mooring pockets are provided along the ship's side. The RBU-1000 rocket launchers are aboard principally as torpedo countermeasures.

◆ 6 Boris Chilikin class (Project 1559) Bldr: Baltic SY, St. Petersburg (In serv. 1971–78)

Boris Butoma	Dnestr	Ivan Bubnov
Boris Chilikin	Genrikh Gasanov	Vladimir Kolyachitskiy

Dnestr Leo Van Ginderen, 1990

Boris Chilikin 6-89

D: 8,700 tons light (24,500 fl) **S:** 17 kts
Dim: 162.3 × 21.4 × 11.5
Electron Equipt:
Radar: 2/Don-Kay nav.—IFF: 1/High Pole B transponder
M: 1 diesel; 1 prop; 9,600 bhp **Range:** 10,000/16.6
Crew: 75 tot. (civilians)

Remarks: 16,300 dwt. Soviet type designation: VTR—*Voyenyy Tanker* (Military Tanker). Naval version of the merchant *Velikiy Oktyabr* class. Equipment varies: early units had solid-stores, constant-tension rigs on both sides forward; later units, only to starboard, with liquids to port. All have port and starboard liquid-replenishment stations amidships and can replenish liquids over the stern. Cargo: 13,500 tons liqu (fuel oil, diesel, water); 400 tons ammunition; 400 tons provisions; 400 tons stores. T *Ivan Bubnov* and *Genrikh Gasanov* were completed in merchant colors, without gu Strut Curve air/surface-search radar, or Muff Cob fire-control radars; that equipme was removed from the other ships by the end of the 1970s, although several retair their gun houses for a short period.

◆ 4 Dubna class Bldr: Rauma-Repola, Rauma, Finland

Dubna (In serv. 1974)	Pechenga (In serv. 1978)
Irkut (In serv. 12-75)	Sventa (In serv. 4-79)

Dubna U.S. Navy, 7

Dubna French Navy,

D: 4,300 tons light (11,100 fl) **S:** 16 kts
Dim: 130.1 (126.3 pp) × 20.0 × 7.2
Electron Equipt:
Radar: 2/Don-2 nav.—IFF: none
M: 1 Russkiy 8DRPH 23/230, 8-cyl. diesel; 1 prop; 6,000 bhp
Electric: 1,485 kVA **Fuel:** 1.056 m³ **Range:** 8,000/15
Crew: 60 tot. (civilians)

Remarks: 6,022 grt/6,500 dwt. Soviet type designation: VTR—*Voyenyy Tanker* tary Tanker). Cargo: 4,364 m³ heavy fuel oil; 2,646 m³ diesel fuel; 140 m³ cargo v 537 m³ refrigerated provisions; 810 m³ dry stores. Twenty-seven cargo tanks transfer one-ton loads from constant-tension stations forward. Liquid replenish from one station on port and starboard, amidships, and over the stern. Addi berths for "turnover crews." Original commercial Okean-series radars were rep

◆ 5 Altay class Bldr: Rauma-Repola, Rauma, Finland (In serv. 1969–7

Ilim	Izhora	Kola	Yegorlik	Yel'nya

Yel'nya U.S. Navy

D: 2,183 light (2,228 fl) **S:** 14.2 kts
Dim: 106.0 (97.0 pp) × 15.0 × 6.7
Electron Equipt:
Radar: 2/Don-2 nav.—IFF: 1/High Pole A transponder
M: 1 Valmet-Burmeister & Wain BM-550 VTBN-110 diesel; 3,250 (2,900 sust.)
Electric: 650 kw **Range:** 8,600/12
Crew: 60 tot. (civilians)

Remarks: 3,670 grt/5,045 dwt. All have an underway replenishment capabi frame king post added forward since 1975, permitting them to refuel one ship a on either beam. Also able to replenish over stern. Differ in details, heights of ma More than two dozen sisters served in the Soviet merchant marine. *Izhora* suff explosion and fire 17-9-91 while in refit at Vladivostok.

FLEET REPLENISHMENT SHIPS *(continued)*

◆ **1 Sofia class** Bldr: Admiralty SY, St. Petersburg (In serv. 1963)

AKHTUBA (ex-*Khanoi*)

Akhtuba Leo Van Ginderen, 1-91

D: 62,600 tons (fl) **S:** 17 kts
Dim: 230.50 (217.50 pp) × 31.10 × 11.85
Electron Equipt:
Radar: 2/Don-2 nav.—IFF: 1/High Pole A transponder
M: 2 sets Kirov steam turbines; 1 prop; 19,000 shp
Boilers: 2
Electric: 1,870 kw tot. (2 × 750-kw turbogenerators, 1 × 100 and 1 × 270-kw diesel sets)
Range: 20,900/17 **Crew:** 70 tot. (civilians)

Remarks: 32,841 grt/49,385 dwt. Taken over for naval service in 1969. Carries 44,500 tons of liquid cargo (53,751 m³) in 20 tanks. Ice-strengthened hull. Can refuel over the stern only; primarily used to refuel other tankers. Based in the Pacific Ocean Fleet and had often served on Indian Ocean deployment until the navy left that area in 1991.

3 Olekhma and Pevek classes Bldr: Rauma-Repola, Rauma, Finland

OLEKHMA IMAN ZOLOTOI ROG

Olekhma—modified for underway replenishment French Navy, 4-83

Iman—unmodified U.S. Navy, 2-86

D: 6,700 tons (fl) **S:** 14 kts **Dim:** 105.0 × 14.8 × 6.8
Electron Equipt:
Radar: 1/Don-2 nav.—IFF: 1/High Pole A transponder
M: 1 Burmeister & Wain diesel; 2,900 bhp
Range: 7,900/13.6 **Crew:** 40 tot.

Remarks: 3,300 grt/4,400 dwt. All built in the mid-1960s. *Zolotoi Rog* belongs to the *Pevek* class and differs only slightly as built. *Olekhma* was modernized in 1978 with a frame abaft the bridge to permit underway fueling of one ship at a time on either side. The other two have not been similarly upgraded. Predecessor to the *Altay* design, with conventional "three-island" tanker layout. The *Zolotoi Rog* differs only slightly. All can refuel over the stern. Good candidates for scrapping.

Uda class Bldr: Vyborg SY (In serv. 1962–64)

DUNAY KOIDA LENA SHEKSNA TEREK VISHERA

D: 7,100 tons (fl) **S:** 17 kts
Dim: 122.0 × 15.8 × 6.3 **A:** removed
Electron Equipt:
Radar: 2/Don-2 nav.—IFF: High Pole A transponder
M: 2 diesels; 2 props; 8,000 bhp
Range: 4,000/17 **Crew:** 85 tot. (civilians)

Lena—with two refueling positions amidships French Navy, 5-88

Koida—with only one bipod refueling king post U.S. Navy, 2-84

Remarks: Soviet type designation: VTR—*Voyenyy Tanker* (Military Tanker). Equipped to carry eight 57-mm AA (IV × 2), *Dunay, Vishera, Sheksna,* and *Lena* have been equipped with a second A-frame king post for liquid replenishment, amidships. Three transferred to Indonesia during the early 1960s and later scrapped.

◆ **3 Kazbek class** Bldr: Admiralty SY, St. Petersburg, or Kherson SY

ALATYR' DESNA VOLKHOV

Desna French Navy, 1991

D: 16,250 tons (fl) **S:** 14 kts **Dim:** 145.5 × 19.24 × 8.5
Electron Equipt:
Radar: 2/Don-2 nav.—IFF: 1/High Pole A transponder
M: 2 Russkiy Dizel diesels; 2 props; 4,000 bhp
Range: 18,000/14 **Crew:** 46 tot. (civilians)

Remarks: Soviet type designation: VTR—*Voyenyy Tanker* (Military Tanker). Built in the mid-1950s. 8,230 grt/11,800 dwt. Carry 11,600 tons of fuel. The three naval units can be distinguished from their civilian sisters because they have two tall king posts and an A-frame king post to support fueling hoses before the bridge, and working decks were added over the cargo decks before and abaft the bridge. Merchant units of this class were among those most frequently used to support naval forces but have now mostly been scrapped. Despite age, however, the three Naval Auxiliary Service units are still in use.

OILERS

◆ **2 Baskunchak class**
Bldr: Kamysh-Burun SY, Kerch' (In serv. 1964–68)

IVAN GOLUBETS SOVETSKIY POGRANICHNIK

D: 2,940 tons (fl) **S:** 13.2 kts
Dim: 83.6 (74.0 pp) × 12.0 × 4.9
Electron Equipt: Radar: 1/Don-2 nav.
M: 1 Type 8DR 43/61 W diesel; 2,220 bhp
Electric: 325 kw **Fuel:** 124 tons
Range: 5,000/12.6 **Crew:** 30 tot. (KGB/naval)

OILERS *(continued)*

Ivan Golubets Boris Lemachko, 7-91

Sovetskiy Pogranichnik J.M.S.D.F., 7-90

Remarks: 1,768 grt/1,660 dwt. Cargo: 1,490 tons (9,993 bbl.) Subordinated to the KGB Maritime Border Guard, in the Pacific area. One sister, *Usedom*, was formerly in East German Navy; others in Soviet merchant marine. *Sovetskiy Pogranichnik* (Soviet Border Guard) is believed to be the correct name for the unit previously listed here as *"Ukhta,"* now believed to be the civil unit *Ukhta*. Have ice-reinforced hulls and are used to support outlying posts.

♦ **4 Konda class** Bldr: Sweden (In serv. mid 1950s)

Konda Rossoch' Soyana Yakhroma

Yakhroma French Navy, 1-90

D: 1,980 tons (fl) **S:** 12 kts **Dim:** 69.0 × 10.0 × 4.3
Electron Equipt:
Radar: 1–2/Don-2 and/or Spin Trough nav.
M: 1 diesel; 1,600 bhp **Range:** 2,470/10 **Crew:** 26 tot.

Remarks: 1,117 grt/1,265 dwt. Can refuel over the stern.

WATER TANKERS

♦ **2 Manych class** Bldr: Vyborg SY

Manych (In serv. 1971) Tagil (In serv. 1977)

D: 7,800 tons (fl) **S:** 18 kts
Dim: 115.8 × 15.8 × 6.7 **A:** removed
Electron Equipt:
Radar: 2/Don-Kay nav.; *Manych* also: 1/Strut Curve surf./air search, 2/Muff Cob f.c.
M: 2 diesels; 2 props; 9,000 bhp **Range:** 11,500/12
Crew: 90 tot. (civilian)

Manych U.S. Navy, 1982

Tagil Leo Van Ginderen, 11-

Remarks: Reported in the Soviet press to be unsuccessful in their designed rôle small replenishment oilers to carry fuel and solid stores for submarines. *Manych* w assigned as a water tender to support the Mediterranean Squadron. Her two tw AK-272 automatic 57-mm gun mounts were removed in 1975. *Tagil* was complet without armament.

♦ **Up to 14 Voda class** Bldr: . . . (In serv. 1950s)

Abakan	MVT-9	MVT-17	MVT-21	MVT-138
Sura	MVT-10	MVT-18	MVT-24	MVT-428
MVT-6	MVT-16	MVT-20	MVT-134	

Sura Leo Van Ginderen,

Abakan U.S. Navy,

D: 2,100 tons (3,100 fl) **S:** 12 kts **Dim:** 81.5 × 11.5 × 4.3
Electron Equipt:
Radar: 1 or 2/Don-2 or Spin Trough or Kivach nav.
M: 2 diesels; 2 props; 1,600 bhp **Range:** 3,000/10
Crew: 40 tot. (civilian)

Remarks: MVT—*Morskoy Vodnyy Tanker* (Seagoing Water Tanker). Several ha working deck over the cargo tank area. A number are likely to have been scrapp most Soviet Navy steam-powered warships (which, because of inadequate evapo design, required frequent boiler feedwater make-up) have been stricken.

SPECIAL LIQUIDS TANKERS

♦ **2 Belyanka class** Bldr: Karamaki SY, Vyborg

Amur (In serv. 1987) Pinega (In serv. 1988)

D: approx. 10,000 tons (fl) **S:** 15.4 kts (loaded)
Dim: 130.30 (119.00 pp) × 17.30 × 6.93
A: none **Electron Equipt:** Radar: 2/Kivach nav.
M: 1 Russkiy Dizel 5DKRN 62/140-3 diesel; 1 prop; 6,100 bhp
Electric: 1,500 kw **Crew:** . . . (civilian)

Remarks: Built on *Pioner Moskvyy*-class timber-carrier/container-ship me cargo hulls (as used by the *Mikhail Rudnitskiy*-class salvage tenders, q.v.) tended as waste nuclear-reactor plant coolant-water collection, and, possibly ment ships. Cargo capacity: 4,000 m^3. Have been employed to dump highly radi waste liquids into the Kara Sea, east of Novaya Zemlya.

♦ **6 Luza class** Bldr: Sredniy Neva SY, Kolpino (In serv. 1960s)

Alambay	Barguzin	Kana
Aragvy	Don	Selenga

IAL LIQUIDS TANKERS *(continued)*

Leo Van Ginderen, 8-91

1,900 tons (fl) **S:** 12 kts **Dim:** 62.5 × 10.7 × 4.3
ctron Equipt: Radar: 1/Don-2 nav.
1 diesel; 1,000 bhp **Range:** 2,000/11
w: 20 tot. (civilian)

ks: Carry volatile liquids, probably missile fuel. Three sisters have been n, *Oka, Sasima,* and *Yenisey,* and additional units may have been discarded.

/ala class (In service: early 1960s)

.1 TNT-12 TNT-19 TNT-25 TNT-29

12—Vala class

3,100 tons (fl) **S:** 14 kts **Dim:** 76.2 × 12.5 × 5.0
1 diesel; 1,000 bhp **Range:** 2,000/11
w: . . . (civilian)

ks: Carry waste liquids from nuclear-propulsion plants. Some have carried mm mg (II × 1). May all have been discarded.

ONNEL TRANSPORT

Mikhail Kalinin class

r: Mathias Thesen Werft, Wismar, East Germany (In serv. 1963)

N (ex-*Nadezhda Krupskaya*)

n U.S. Navy, 1988

6,400 tons (fl) **S:** 18 kts **Dim:** 122.2 × 16.0 × 5.1
ctron Equipt:
adar: 2/Don-2 nav., 1/Spin Trough nav.
2 M.A.N. 6-cyl. diesels; 2 props; 8,000 bhp **Range:** 8,100/17
w: . . . tot. (civilian)

ks: 5,260 grt/1,354 dwt. Former passenger-cargo ship used to rotate crews on n the Mediterranean Squadron. Can carry 340 passengers, 1,000 tons of dry

O SHIPS

Cargo ships are usually referred to as VTR—*Voyenyy Transport* (Military ort). The eight *Vytegrales*-class former timber carriers formerly listed in this have been redesignated command ships and moved to the head of the "Auxil- ection.

Anadyr-class float-on/float-off heavy lift ship Bldr: Wärtsilä, o, Finland (In serv. 10-88)

YR

Anadyr M.O.D., Bonn, 7-90

Anadyr M.O.D., Bonn, 3-90

ANADYR

D: approx. 30,000 tons (fl) **S:** 20 kts
Dim: 226.1 (pp) × 30.0 × 6.5 (13.0 flooded)
Electron Equipt: Radar: 2/Spin Trough nav.
M: 4 Wärtsilä Vasa diesels; 2 props; 32,600 bhp—bow- and stern-thrusters
Range: . . ./. . . **Crew:** 70 tot. (naval)

Remarks: 34,151 grt/12,765 dwt. A very large combination float-on/float-off cargo and container ship for which there seems to be little use; appears to have been an expensive mistake. Remained in the Baltic after completion until transferred to the Pacific Ocean Fleet in 1990 after a refit in Sweden. The 128.0-m-long by 13.0-m-wide by 5.5-m-high cargo well is covered by a portable deck and reportedly was intended for the transport of submarines (although there are now few submarines in the Russian fleet that would fit). A 120-ton-capacity crane travels on rails on the wing-walls and is used to handle the alternative 868 TEU (Twenty-foot Equivalent Unit) cargo-container load. Forward of the cargo well is a flight deck and hangar for two helicopters. The cargo well is closed at the stern by a 60-ton-capacity ramp, allowing the well-deck to be used for vehicle cargo.

◆ **11 Neon Antonov class** Bldr: . . . (In serv. 1978–87)

DVINA, IRBIT, IVAN LEDNEV, IVAN SUDSOV, IVAN YEVTEYEV, MIKHAIL KONOVALOV, NEON ANTONOV, NIKOLAY SIPYAGIN, NIKOLAY STARSHINOV, SERGEY SUDYESKIY, VYACHESLAV DENISOV

Sergey Sudyeskiy Boris Lemachko, 5-91

D: 5,200 tons (fl) **S:** 17 kts
Dim: 95.10 (87.20 pp) × 14.70 × 5.50
A: 2/30-mm AK-230 AA (II × 1)—4/14.5-mm mg (II × 2)—2/SA-7 Grail or SA-14 Gremlin shoulder-launched SAM positions
Electron Equipt:
Radar: 2/Palm Frond or 1/Don-Kay and 1/ Spin Trough or Don-2 nav.
IFF: 1/High Pole B transponder
M: 2 diesels; 1 prop; 7,000 bhp **Range:** 8,750/14
Crew: 40 tot. (KGB or naval)

Remarks: Specialized supply ships for remote garrisons of the KGB Maritime Border Guard in the Pacific area. Built in the Far East. Carry one or two small landing craft aft. Initially appeared without armament, but now all seem to have weapons installed. *Irbit* and *Dvina* are naval-subordinated and are also armed.

◆ **1 Amguema class** Bldr: Okean SY, Nikolayevsk (In serv. 1975)

YAUZA

D: 11,290 tons (fl) **S:** 15 kts
Dim: 133.10 (123.00 pp) × 18.80 (18.50 wl) × 7.60 max.
Electron Equipt:
Radar: 2/Don-2 nav.—IFF: 1/High Pole A transponder
M: 4 1,800-bhp diesels, electric drive; 1 prop; 7,200 shp
Range: 10,000/15 **Crew:** 54 tot. (civilian)

CARGO SHIPS *(continued)*

Yauza 1976

Remarks: 6,280 dwt. Passenger-cargo ship: can break .6-m ice. Numerous merchant sisters. Two 60-ton, two 10-ton, and six 5-ton cranes.

♦ 3 Yuniy Partizan class
Bldr: Turnu-Severin SY and Oltenitza SY, Romania (In serv. 1975–78)

PECHORA TURGAY UFA

Turgay 11-80

D: 3,947 tons (fl) **S:** 12.9 kts
Dim: 88.75 (80.25 pp) × 12.8 × 5.2
Electron Equipt:
Radar: 1/Don-2 nav.—IFF: 1/High Pole A transponder
M: 1 Cegielski-Sulzer 8 TAD 36 diesel; 1 prop; 2,080 bhp
Electric: 306 kw **Range:** 4,000/12
Fuel: 125 tons **Crew:** 25 tot. (civilian)

Remarks: 2,079 grt/2,150 dwt. Small container ships. Three 10-ton cranes, one of which can be rigged to lift 28 tons. Cargo: 3,200 m^3. Originally intended to be able to carry 58 standard cargo containers. Twenty sisters are civilian. Naval sister *Pinega* converted to a missile transport and renamed *Vitse-Admiral Fomin.*

♦ up to 8 Keyla class
Bldr: Hungary (In serv. 1960–66)

MEZEN'	PONOY	TULOMA	USSURI
ONEGA	TERIBERKA	UNZHA	YERUSLAN

D: 832 tons light (2,042 fl) **S:** 12 kts
Dim: 78.5 (71.4 pp) × 10.5 × 4.6
Electron Equipt:
Radar: 1 or 2/Don-2 or Spin Trough nav.
M: 1 Lang 8 LD315RF diesel; 1 prop; 1,000 bhp
Electric: 300 kw **Range:** 4,200/10.7
Fuel: 72 tons **Crew:** 26 tot. (civilian)

Mezen' French Navy, 9-90

Remarks: 1,296 grt/1,280 dwt. Carry 1,100 tons of cargo. One 10-ton, six 2 cranes. Sister *Ritsa* converted as an intelligence collector during the 1970s.

♦ 2 Andizhan class
Bldr: Neptunwerft, Rostock, East Germany (In serv. 1959–60)

ONDA POSET

Onda

D: 6,739 tons (fl) **S:** 13.5 kts
Dim: 104.2 (95.8 pp) × 14.4 × 6.6
Electron Equipt: Radar: 1/Don-2 nav.
M: 2 Gorlitzer-Sulzer 8SV55 MA diesels; 1 prop; 2,500 bhp
Electric: 550 kw **Range:** 6,000/13.5
Fuel: 238 tons diesel/150 tons heavy oil
Crew: 43 tot. (civilian)

Remarks: 3,368 grt/4,324 dwt. Cargo: 3,954 tons. Sister *Yemetsk* stricken. Two sisters are now missile transports; other sisters served in merchant service. entered naval service around 1978, *Onda* in 1980–81. Have one 40-ton, one 18-to eight 3-ton cranes. Will probably soon be discarded.

♦ up to 3 MP-6-class former landing ships
Bldr: . . . . . . SY, Hungary (In serv. 1959–60)

BIRA IRGIZ VOLOGDYA

Bira Hartmut Ehlers

D: 2,100 tons (fl) **S:** 10.5 kts
Dim: 74.7 (70.1 pp) × 11.3 × 4.4
Electron Equipt: Radar: 1/Don-2 nav.
M: 2 Buchau-Wolff 6 NVD 48 diesels; 1 prop; 800 bhp
Range: 3,300/9 **Crew:** 40 tot. (civilians)

Remarks: Deleted in error from the last edition; they remained in service i despite obsolescence. Bow doors welded closed during the 1960s, when it was r that they were unsatisfactory as amphibious warfare ships. *Vologdya* has one serving all three hatches; the other two have six 2.5-ton derricks. Two sisters, and *Khoper,* serve as missile transports.

Note: The remaining *Leninskiy Komsomol*-class cargo ship, *Samara,* was sold for scrap during 1990.

PROVISIONS SHIPS

♦ 8 Mayak class
Bldr: Dnepr SY, Kiev (In serv. 1971–76)

BUZULUK	LAMA	NEMAN	ULMA
ISHIM	MIUS	RIONI	VYTEGRA

Ishim J.M.S.D.F.,

ROVISIONS SHIPS *(continued)*

D: 1,050 tons (fl) **S:** 11 kts **Dim:** 54.3 × 9.3 × 3.6
Electron Equipt: Radar: 1/Spin Trough nav.
M: 1 diesel; 800 bhp **Range:** 9,400/11
Crew: 29 tot. (civilian)

marks: 690 grt. Former trawlers. Refrigerated fish holds are used to carry pro-ions. *Lama* has two lifeboats and lacks bulwarks around the stern. Some may have ·n retired 1987–89. Other naval sisters operate as intelligence collectors and ASW ·rol ships.

)ORING TENDERS

8 Kashtan class Bldr: Neptunwerft, Rostock

L-140 (In serv. 1990) KIL-168 (In serv. 5-10-90)
L-143 (In serv. 1989) KIL-498 (In serv. 1990)
L-158 (In serv. 1989) KIL-926 (In serv. 1988)
L-164 (In serv. 1989) KIL-927 (In serv. 1988)

·-168 French Navy, 6-91

164 M.O.D., U.K., 5-90

6,200 tons (fl) **S:** 13.75 kts
n: 113.00 (97.92 pp) × 18.22 × 3.71
ctron Equipt: Radar: 1/Mius nav., 1/Don-2 nav.
2 Karl Liebnecht 8-cyl. diesel generator sets, electric drive; 2 props; 2,990 shp—bow-thruster
nge: . . ./. . . **Crew:** 78 tot. (civilian)

rks: 4,400 grt/1,000 dwt. Have 100-ton West German Stülcken heavy-lift gan-stern for lifting mooring buoys and for salvage assignments, a 12-ton electrohy-: crane to starboard, and a 60-ton boom amidships. Like the preceding Sura class ich this design is an obvious development), they probably also have a liquid-:apacity. KIL-926 and KIL-140 are based in the Baltic; KIL-168, KIL-498, and 27 are home-ported at Vladivostok; KIL-158 operates in the Black Sea; and 13 and KIL-164 are home-ported at Murmansk.

Sura class Bldr: Neptunwerft, Rostock, East Germany (In serv. 1965–1976–78)

KIL-21 KIL-23 KIL-29 KIL-32
KIL-22 KIL-27 KIL-31 KIL-33

:,370 tons (3,150 fl) **S:** 13 kts
: 87.0 (68.0 pp) × 14.8 × 5.0
tron Equipt: Radar: 2/Don-2 nav.
w: 60 tot. (civilian)
4 diesels, electric drive; 2 props; 2,240 shp
ge: 4,000/10

KIL-31 M.O.D., U.K., 5-90

KIL-2 M.O.D., U.K., 6-88

Remarks: 2,366 grt. KIL—*Kilektor* (Mooring Tender). Can carry 890 tons of cargo in hold amidships. Stern rig, which can lift 60 tons, is used for buoy-handling and salvage. Can also carry several hundred tons of cargo fuel. One has been used to transport two Gus-class amphibious air-cushion personnel landing craft. Mooring buoys are stowed amidships and moved aft for handling by the stern gallows rig via a chain-haul system. There are also a 5-ton electric crane to port and a heavy-lift boom amidships, the latter tending the buoy stowage holds. The diesel propulsion generator plant is forward.

CABLE LAYERS

◆ **2 Biriusa class** Bldr: Wärtsilä, Turku, Finland

	L	In serv.		L	In serv.
Biriusa	29-11-85	4-7-86	Kem'	23-11-85	23-10-86

Kem' U.S. Navy, 1988

D: 2,370 tons (fl) **S:** 11.8 kts
Dim: 86.10 (78.70 pp) × 12.6 × 3.10
Electron Equipt: Radar: 1/. . . nav. **Crew:** 48 tot. (civilian)
M: diesel-electric: 2 Wärtsilä Vasa 8R22 diesels; 2 swiveling Schottel props; 1,700 shp—bow tunnel-thruster

Remarks: 2,650 grt. Ordered 1-85. Lengthened version of *Emba* class, with more powerful engines, carrying twice as much cable (600 tons; 518 m^3 coiled, in two cable tanks) and equipped with a gantry over the bow cable. Have three bow cable sheaves, 2-m diameter, and two 2-m-diameter cable drums. Propellers swivel through 360 degrees. Have a bow-thruster. Both in Pacific Ocean Fleet.

◆ **3 Emba class** Bldr: Wärtsilä SY, Turku, Finland

Emba (In serv. 5-80) Nepryadva (L: 24-4-81) Setun (L: 29-4-81)

D: 2,050 tons (fl) **S:** 11.8 kts
Dim: 75.90 (68.50 pp) × 12.60 × 3.10
Electron Equipt: Radar: 1/. . . nav. **Crew:** 38 tot. (civilian)
M: diesel-electric: 2 Wärtsilä Vasa 6R22 diesels; 2 shrouded Schottel props; 1,360 shp—bow tunnel-thruster

Remarks: 1,910 grt. Cargo: 300 tons cable. Intended for use in shallow coastal areas, rivers, and harbors.

CABLE LAYERS *(continued)*

Setun Wärtsilä, 4-81

◆ **8 Klazma class** Bldr: Wärtsilä SY, Turku, Finland

	In serv.		In serv.
DONETS	1968	INGURI	1978
TAVDA	1977	YANA	1962
INGUL	1962	KATUN'	1973
TSNA	1968	ZEYA	1970

Ingul—early unit VF-111, U.S. Navy, 1985

Inguri—late unit Leo Van Ginderen, 3-91

D: 6,920 tons (fl) **S:** 14 kts
Dim: 130.4 (120.0 pp) × 16.0 × 5.75
Electron Equipt: Radar: 2/Don-2 nav.
M: 5 1,000-bhp Wärtsilä 624TS diesels, electric drive; 2 props; 4,400 shp
Range: 12,000/14 **Fuel:** 250 tons **Crew:** 110 tot. (civilian)

Remarks: Soviet type designation: KS—*Kabel'noye Sudno* (Cable Ship). 5,760 grt/3,750 dwt. *Ingul* and *Yana,* the first built, have four 2,436-bhp diesels, a longer forecastle, and are 5,645 grt/3,400 dwt (6,810 tons fl). All have ice-strengthened hulls. In the later units, the diesel engines drive five 680-kw generators, which provide power for propulsion and for all auxiliary functions. All cable machinery built by Submarine Cables, Ltd., Great Britain. *Katun'* carries 1,850 m^3 of cable and displaces 7,885 tons (fl), drawing 5.76 m; she capsized while fitting out. The others have three cable tanks totaling 1,600 m^3. *Ingul* refitted in Japan 1978, receiving new Dowty paired-wheel cable gear. All have a 500-shp electric active rudder and a bow-thruster.

Plans to replace these ships with eight larger, 4,000-dwt cable layers to be built in Finland appear to have foundered with the collapse of the U.S.S.R.

FLEET TUGS

◆ **2 MB 330-class seagoing tugs**
Bldr: Jurong SY, Singapore (In serv. 3-91)

M-330 MB-331

D: approx. 1,180 tons (fl) **S:** . . . kts
Dim: 47.90 (42.00 pp) × 10.80 × 4.00
Electron Equipt: Radar: . . . .
M: 2/1,400-bhp diesel generator sets, electric drive; 2 props; 2,000 shp
Range: . . ./. . . **Crew:** 24 tot.

Remarks: 741 grt/232 dwt. Have 30-ton bollard pull capacity.

◆ **1 Neftegaz-class (Project B-92) oilfield tug/supply vessel**
Bldr: A. Warski SY, Szczecin, Poland

ILGA (In serv. 4-11-83)

Ilga M.O.D., U.K., 8-

D: 2,800 tons (fl) **S:** 15 kts
Dim: 81.5 (71.5 pp) × 16.3 (15.0 wl) × 5.4
Electron Equipt: 2/Nayada nav.
M: 2 Sulzer-Zgoda diesels; 2 CP props; 7,200 bhp
Range: . . . **Fuel:** 533 tons **Crew:** 25 tot. (civilian)

Remarks: 2,372 grt/1,396 dwt. One of a class of 33 oilfield supply tugs ordered in 19 Cargo: up to 600 tons dry cargo on deck plus 1,000 m^3 liquid cargo. Can act as a tug has four fire-fighting water monitors. Has a bow-thruster. Broad, level fantail round-down stern would permit the ship to be adapted rapidly for minelaying. *Ilga* carried a large missile-range telemetry tracking antenna aft and operates in Northern Fleet.

◆ **10 Goryn class**
Bldr: Rauma-Repola, Finland (In serv. 1977–78, 1982–83)

MB-18 (ex-*Berezinsk*) MB-30 MB-31 MB-32 MB-35 MB-36 MB-38 MB-61 MB-105 (ex-*Baykalsk*) MB-119 (ex-*Bilbino*)

D: 2,240 tons (2,600 fl) **S:** 13.5 kts
Dim: 63.50 × 14.30 (14.00 wl) × 5.10
Electron Equipt: Radar: 2/Don-2 nav.
Crew: 40 tot. (civilian)
M: 1 Russkiy Type 67N diesel; 3,500 bhp **Range:** . . .

MB-35—second series

MB-105—first series J.M.S.D.F

'LEET TUGS *(continued)*

Remarks: Soviet type designation: MB—*Morskoy Buksir* (Seagoing Tug). 1,600 grt. 5-ton pull. For ocean towing, salvage, and fire-fighting. Sister *Bolshevetsk* lost 2-79 off apan. Later units have a Type 671 diesel and produce 43 tons bollard pull. Second eries of ten began with MB-30, launched 15-12-81, and ended with MB-108, delivered -83. The two series can be distinguished visually by the overlapping rubbing strakes t the forecastle break in the early units and the sloping connecting strake in late nits. Four others have been redesignated as rescue tugs (SB—*Spastel'noye Buksir*): B-365 (ex-MB-29), SB-522 (ex-MB-62), SB-523 (ex-MB-64), and SB-524 (ex-MB-108).

22 (+ . . .) Sorum class

Bldr: Yaroslavl SY, U.S.S.R. (In serv. 1974–. . .)

IB-4	MB-25	MB-31	MB-61	MB-100	MB-304
IB-6	MB-26	MB-37	MB-70	MB-110	MB-307
IB-13	MB-28	MB-56	MB-76	MB-148	
'B-19	MB-30	MB-58	MB-99	MB-236	

B-61—with commercial SATCOMM antenna J.M.S.D.F., 1991

3-4—also with SATCOMM antenna M.O.D., Bonn, 7-89

D: 1,210 tons (1,656 fl) **S:** 14 kts
Dim: 58.3 × 12.6 × 4.6
Electron Equipt:
Radar: 2/Don-2 nav.—IFF: 1/High Pole B transponder
M: 2 Type 5-2D42 diesels, electric drive; 1 prop; 1,500 shp
Range: 6,720/13 **Fuel:** 322 tons **Crew:** 35 tot. (civilian)

narks: MB means *Morskoy Buksir* (Seagoing Tug). A modified version with larger erstructure and an A-frame king post aft is used by the Ministry of Fisheries as a ue tug, prominently displaying *Spastel'* (Rescue) on the black hull sides; named the *az* class, it includes *Almaz, Kapitan Beklemishev,* and *Ametist.* Sixteen armed ions of the design serve the KGB Maritime Border Guard as patrol ships (see under ettes on an earlier page), and another, OS-72, is a trials ship. Russian Naval iliary Service units are unarmed but do have blanking plates for two twin 30-mm mounts forward. MB-110, the most recent to be completed, departed the Baltic 1-92.

up to 45 Okhtenskiy class

Bldr: Petrozavod SY, St. Petersburg (In serv. 1958–early 1960s)

160—Okhtenskiy class Leo Van Ginderen, 3-92

MB-176 J.M.S.D.F., 1991

D: 663 tons light (926 fl) **S:** 13.3 kts
Dim: 47.3 (43.0 pp) × 10.3 × 5.5
Electron Equipt:
Radar: 1–2/Don-2 or Spin Trough nav.—IFF: 1/High Pole A transponder
M: diesel-electric: 2 Type D5D50 diesels; 1 prop; 1,500 shp
Electric: 340 kw **Range:** 7,800/7
Fuel: 197 tons **Crew:** 30 tot. (civilian)

Remarks: Several had a twin 57-mm DP gun mount (II × 1) and were operated by the KGB Maritime Border Guard for use as patrol ships. Units with names are civilian; naval units have MB—*Morskoy Buksir* (Seagoing Tug) or SB—*Spastel'noye Buksir* (Rescue Tug) hull numbers; the latter carry an "unsinkable" lifeboat or divers' workboat to port and are submarine-associated. A total of 63 were built. Soviet name: *Goliat* class. Bollard pull: 27 tons initial/17 sustained.

MB-241—a unit of a hitherto unreported seagoing tug class of about 900–1,000 tons displacement, moving a floating crane at Murmansk in 1990, assisted by a Tugur-class yard tug Leo Van Ginderen

SALVAGE AND RESCUE SHIPS

◆ **2 Nikolay Chiker-class salvage tugs**

Bldr: Hollming SY, Rauma, Finland

	Laid down	L	In serv.
SB-131 NIKOLAY CHIKER	28-5-87	19-4-88	12-4-89
SB-135 FOTIY KRYLOV	24-8-87	9-9-88	30-6-89

D: approx. 8,000 tons (fl) **S:** 18.5 kts (cruise)
Dim: 98.80 × 19.45 × 6.90
A: none **Electron Equipt:** Radar: 2/. . . nav.
M: 4 Wärtsilä Vasa 12V32 diesels; 2 Kort-nozzle CP props; 24,480 bhp—1,360-shp bow tunnel-thruster
Electric: 3,640 kw (2 × 1,200-kw shaft gen.; 2 × 620-kw diesel sets)
Range: 11,000/18 **Endurance:** 50 days
Crew: 51 crew (civilian), 20 passengers

Fotiy Krylov (SB-135) M.O.D., Bonn, 1989

SALVAGE AND RESCUE SHIPS *(continued)*

Nikolay Chiker (SB-131) M.O.D., U.K., 5-90

Remarks: 7,300 grt. World's most powerful salvage tugs. *Nikolay Chiker,* in Northern Fleet, is named for Engineer Rear Admiral Nikolay Chiker, a former head and principal proponent of the Soviet Naval Salvage Service. Have platform forward for an 11-ton helicopter, four water/foam fire monitors whose pumps have a combined 2,000 m^3/hr. capacity, three portable fire pumps, floating a.c. and d.c. power cables, a 200-kg dry cargo/personnel transfer system, a capacity to support two divers working at up to 60-m depth, two 32-ton and two 10-ton salvage winches, two 400-ton cable/chain stoppers aft, three telescoping electrohydraulic cranes (2 × 8 ton, 1 × 3 ton), two 150-ton and one 60-ton towing winches, and a capacity for up to 14 km of towing cable. Bollard pull is 250 tons. Have elaborate navigation and salvage control equipment and are equipped to operate under severe (−25°C) arctic conditions. *Nikolay Chiker* serves the Northern Fleet, *Fotiy Krylov* the Pacific Ocean Fleet.

♦ 4 Pionier Moskvyy-class salvage submersible tenders
Bldr: Vyborg SY

Mikhail Rudnitskiy (In serv. 1979)
Giorgiy Koz'min (In serv. 1980)
Georgiy Titov (In serv. 1983)
Sayany (In serv. 1984)

Sayany—with longer forecastle and poop, additional white-painted superstructure U.S. Navy, 11-86

Georgiy Titov—standard unit Boris Lemachko, 5-90

D: 8,500 tons (10,700 fl) **S:** 15.75 kts
Dim: 130.3 (119.0 pp) × 17.3 × 6.93
A: none **Electron Equipt:** Radar: 2/Don-2 nav.
M: 1 5DKRN 62/140-3 diesel; 1 prop; 6,100 bhp
Electric: 1,500 kw **Range:** 12,000/15.5 **Crew:** 120 tot.

Remarks: Soviet type: *Sudno-baze Podvodnikh Issledovaniy* (underwater research support ship). Modification of a standard merchant timber-carrier/container-ship design, retaining two holds. The after hold has two superstructure levels built over it, and the small hold forward has been plated over. Retain two 40-ton and two 20-ton boon and have had heavy-cable fairleads cut in the bulwarks fore and aft and a number boat booms added to starboard.

Titov has a larger superstructure built over number three hold than do the first tw and carries two Pisces submersibles with 2,000-m depth capability. *Mikhail Rudnitsk* carries a Poisk-2, three-man submersible, plus underwater search and exploratio equipment. *Sayany,* painted in white and gray, has had the forecastle and poop deck extended, the deckhouse amidships one deck higher, and a two-level deckhouse ov the forward hold area: she appears intended for some research role. Equipped with bo and stern-thrusters and can be attached to a four-point salvage moor.

First three carry the ensign of the Naval Salvage and Rescue Service and are nam for important developers of research/salvage submersibles; *Sayany* may be employ in research with submersibles. Operate one salvage submersible, stowed in hold nu ber two. *Mikhail Rudnitskiy* serves in the Black Sea Fleet, *Giorgiy Titov* in the Nort ern Fleet, and the other two in the Pacific Ocean Fleet.

♦ 4 Sliva-class salvage tugs
Bldr: Rauma-Repola Uusikaupunki SY, Finland

	Laid down	L	In serv.
SB-406	. . .	6-7-83	20-2-84
SB-408	. . .	28-10-83	5-6-84
SB-921	17-8-84	28-12-84	5-7-85
SB-922	31-8-84	3-5-85	20-12-85

SB-921 Leo Van Ginderen,

SB-408 J.M.S.D.F.

D: 3,400 tons (fl) **S:** 16 kts
Dim: 69.20 (60.10 pp) × 15.40 × 5.10
Electron Equipt: Radar: 2/. . . nav.
M: 2 SEMT-Pielstick/Russkiy Dizel 6PC 2.5 L400 (TS HN40/46) diesels; 2 CP props; 7,800 bhp—bow-thruster
Crew: 43 crew + 10 salvage party (all civilian)

Remarks: 2,050 grt/810 dwt. Ice-reinforced hull. Able to support divers to 60 m four water monitors. One 60- and one 30-ton winch. Unique 350-m floating powe to support vessels in distress. Five-ton electrohydraulic crane. Second pair o 4-84. Bollard pull: 90 tons. The similar icebreaking rescue ships of the *Stroptivy* (described at the end of this chapter) are civilian-subordinated. During 1991, S operated under the name *Shakhter* (Miner).

♦ 4 Goryn-class rescue tugs
Bldr: Rauma-Repola, Finland (In serv 1982–83)

SB-365 (ex-MB-29) SB-521 (ex-MB-62)
SB-522 (ex-MB-64) SB-524 (ex-MB-108)

D: 2,240 tons (2,600 fl) **S:** 13.5 kts
Dim: 63.50 × 14.30 (14.00 wl) × 5.10
Electron Equipt: Radar: 2/Don-2 nav.
Crew: 40 tot. (civilian)
M: 1 Russkiy Type 67N diesel; 3,500 bhp **Range:** . . .

ALVAGE AND RESCUE SHIPS *(continued)*

-522 J.M.S.D.F., 11-90

marks: SB—*Spastel'noye Buksir* (Rescue Tug). Former fleet tugs redesignated as vage tugs. Change in designation appears to have been administrative only; no ange to characteristics. During 1988 began carrying "Spastel" (rescue) painted on hull sides. All but SB-365 are in Pacific Ocean Fleet. In 1991, SB-521 operated as ordinated to the Kamchatskiy Shipping Company of Petropavlovsk.

4 Ingul-class (Project 1452) salvage tugs
Bldr: United Admiralty SY, St. Petersburg

MIR (In serv. 1975) MASHUK (In serv. 1972)
ATAU (In serv. 1984) KARABAKH (In serv. 1988)

shuk *Ships of the World*, 1990

: 3,200 tons (4,050 fl) **S:** 20 kts (18.75 cruise)
im: 92.79 × 15.63 × 5.90
lectron Equipt:
Radar: 2/Don-2 nav.–
IFF: 1/High Pole B transponder, 1/Square Head interrogator
: 2 type 58D-4R diesels; 2 props; 9,000 bhp
lectric: 1,040 kw (4 × 240-kw, 1 × 80-kw diesel sets)
ange: 9,000/18.7 **Crew:** 120 tot. (civilian)

arks: Two sisters, *Yaguar* and *Bars* (2,781 grt/1,140 dwt), are in the merchant ne and have 35-man crews, plus bunks for 50 rescued personnel. Very powerful with constant-tension highline personnel rescue system, salvage pumps, fire-ng equipment, and complete diving gear, capable of supporting divers to 60-m s. Have a 94-ton bollard pull. Large bulbous bow. *Karabakh,* completed 14 years the first ship, has INTELSAT SATCOMM equipment and may have more elabo-salvage capabilities.

Pamir class Bldr: Gävle, Sweden (In serv. 1958)

TAN ALDAN

n French Navy, 1-83

D: 1,443 tons (2,240 fl) **S:** 17.5 kts
Dim: 78.0 × 12.8 × 4.0
Electron Equipt: Radar: 2/Don-2 nav.
M: 2 M.A.N. G10V 40/60 diesels; 2 CP props; 4,200 bhp
Range: 15,200/17.5; 21,800/12 **Crew:** . . . tot. (civilian)

Remarks: 1,443 grt. One 10-ton and two 1.5-ton booms. Carry fixed fire pumps with 2,600 tons/hour capacity and portable pumps with 1,650 tons/hour capacity. Can support divers to a depth of 90 m, and have decompression chambers and powerful air compressors. Two sisters, the *Gidrograf* and *Peleng,* were intelligence collectors. *Agatan* refitted 1981 in Sweden.

◆ **4 Okhtenskiy-class rescue tugs**
Bldr: Petrozavod SY, St. Petersburg (In serv. 1958–early 1960s)

SB-3 SB-4 KODOR SB-5 SB-15

SB-5 LCDR Cihlar, PatRon 24, USN, 7-89

D: 663 tons light (926 fl) **S:** 13.3 kts
Dim: 47.3 (43.0 pp) × 10.3 × 5.5
Electron Equipt:
Radar: 1–2/Don-2 or Spin Trough nav.—IFF: 1/High Pole A transponder
M: diesel-electric: 2 Type D5D50 diesels; 1 prop; 1,500 shp
Electric: 340 kw
Range: 7,800/7 **Fuel:** 197 tons **Crew:** 30 tot. (civilian)

Remarks: Characteristics essentially identical to the general fleet-tug version, except that they are equipped to support divers. SB-5 is in the Black Sea Fleet. SB—*Spastel'noye Buksir,* rescue tug.

◆ **2 Orel class** Bldr: Valmet SY, Turku, Finland (In serv. late 1950s)

SB-38 SB-43

SB-38 R. Neth. N., 8-88

D: 1,200 tons (1,760 fl) **S:** 15 kts **Dim:** 61.3 × 11.9 × 4.5
Electron Equipt: Radar: 1/Don or Don-2 nav.
Crew: 37 tot. (civilian)
M: 1 M.A.N. G5Z52/70 diesel; 1,700 bhp **Range:** 13,000/13.5

Remarks: SB—*Spastel'noye Buksir* (Rescue Tug). Several civilian sisters, including the *Stremitel'nyy* and *Strogyy,* serve the fishing fleet. SB-38 is in the North Sea Fleet, SB-43 in the Pacific Ocean Fleet.

◆ **1 salvage lifting ship, ex-submarine rescue ship**
Bldr: De Schelde, Vlissingen, the Netherlands (L: 1913)

KOMMUNA (ex-*Volkhov*)

SALVAGE AND RESCUE SHIPS *(continued)*

Kommuna U.S. Navy, 1975

D: 2,450 tons **S:** 10 kts **Dim:** 96.0 × 20.4 × 4.7
A: none **Electron Equipt:** 1/. . . nav.
M: 2 diesels; 2 props; 1,200 bhp **Fuel:** 82 tons
Range: 1,700/6 **Crew:** . . .

Remarks: Although "retired" during 1978, *Kommuna* was stated officially to be still in service during 1992. Catamaran-hulled vessel intended to raise sunken submarines by means of four 250-ton-capacity lifting rigs above and between the hulls. As few Soviet submarines remain that could be retrieved by the ship, it is assumed that she is employed as a submersible support ship. Was overhauled 5-50 to 7-51 by builder in the Netherlands. In Black Sea Fleet.

Note: The 14 large (2,299-ton) salvage and fire-fighting vessels of the *Vikhr* series, although on occasion referred to by the NATO nickname "Iva class," are civilian-subordinated and operate in support of offshore oilfields, although they would have obvious value as naval auxiliaries in wartime; the 13th unit, *Vikhr-13,* was launched 25-11-86 at Stocznia Północna, Gdańsk, and the last was completed in 1987. Data include:

Vikhr-4 M.O.D., U.K., 6-88

D: 2,299 tons (fl) **S:** 16 kts **Dim:** 72.30 × 14.30 × 4.56
M: 2 Cegielski-Sulzer 16 AV 25/30 diesels; 2 CP props; 5,880 bhp—2/500 shp side-thrusters
Range: 2,500/12
Crew: 26 ship's company, 18 rescue team + 50 evacuees

Remarks: 317 dwt. Have water, foam, and chemical fire-fighting systems.

SEAGOING FIRE BOATS

◆ **11 Katun class** Bldr: U.S.S.R. (In serv. 1970–1981)

PZHS-64	PZHS-92	PZHS-98	PZHS-123
PZHS-124	PZHS-209	PZHS-279	PZHS-282
PZHS-551	PZHS-. . .	PZHS-. . .	

D: 1,016 tons (fl) **S:** 17 kts **Dim:** 62.6 × 10.2 × 3.6
Electron Equipt:
Radar: 1/Don-2 nav.—IFF: 1/High Pole B transponder
M: 2 Type 40DM diesels; 2 props; 4,000 bhp
Range: 2,200/16 **Crew:** 32 tot. (civilian)

Dunay (PZHS 123)—Katun class Leo Van Ginderen, 199

Remarks: Originally PDS—*Pozharno-Degazatsionnoye Sudno* (Fire-Fighting a Decontamination Ship); this designation later revised to PZHS—*Pozharnoye Sud.* (Fire-Fighting Ship). Extensive fire-fighting gear, including extendable boom. Pow ful pumps. There are several civilian sisters, including the *General Gamidov.* PZHS- completed 1981, is approx. 3 m longer and has an extra level to the superstructu designated "Katun II" by NATO.

Note: See also harbor fireboat entries on page 604.

HOSPITAL SHIPS

◆ **4 Ob' class (Project B-320)** Bldr: A. Warski SY, Szczecin, Poland

Ob' (In serv. 1980)	Yenisey (In serv. 1981)
Svir (In serv. 1989)	Irtysh (In serv. 10-8-90)

Ob' French Navy, 1

Irtysh J.M.S.D.F., 1

D: 9,500 tons (11,977 fl) **S:** 20 kts
Dim: 152.80 (142.00 pp) × 19.40 × 5.2
Electron Equipt: Radar: 3/Don-2 nav. (*Irtysh:* 3/Nayada nav.)
M: 2 diesels; 2 props; . . . bhp
Crew: 208 crew + 200 medical personnel

Remarks: Have civilian crews but carry uniformed naval medical personnel. 488 beds, 7 operating rooms. The hangar aft can accommodate a Hormone-C or He utility helicopter. Bow-thrusters fitted. Intended to "provide medical and recreat facilities." Are also employed as personnel transports. There are a physical th facility, two gymnasiums, two pools, a library, and a 100-seat auditorium. The are on offer for charter for humanitarian purposes. Second pair are "Project B-82 implying a modification to the basic design; external differences are minor. *Irtys* the Pacific Ocean Fleet.

◆ **20 SK-620-class ambulance craft**
Bldr: Wisla SY, Gdańsk, Poland (In serv. 1978–81)

D: 236 tons (fl) **S:** 12 kts **Dim:** 33.0 × 7.4 × 2.0
Electron Equipt: Radar: 2/Mius navigational
M: 2 diesels; 2 props; 570 bhp **Crew:** 14 tot. + 18 patients

Remarks: Pendant numbers in the SK-600 (SK—*Sanitarnyy Kater* = Clinic C series, although some (like the unit illustrated) appear to be operated by or f Maritime Border Guard. White-painted.

IOSPITAL SHIPS *(continued)*

K-620 class U.S. Navy, 1987

TELLIGENCE COLLECTORS (AGI)

ote: A few of the Soviet ships of this type, often designated ELINT (electronic telligence) or SIGINT (signal intelligence) collectors, look like trawlers; most, such the *Primor'ye* and the Bal'zam class, are obviously configured for their roles. No etense is made that the AGIs are anything but intelligence collectors, which detect d analyze radio and other electromagnetic signals. Most now have pendant numbers the *Sudno Svyazyy* (communications vessel) series, and names have mostly been leted. A few hull numbers are still in the once widely used GS—*Gidrograficheskoye dno* (hydrographic vessel) series. By the end of 1991, very few were deployed; the S. East Coast station was vacated in 1-92, and no intelligence collector had operated the West Coast since 1989.

1 Kapusta-class intelligence collection/range instrumentation ship Bldr: Baltic SY, St. Petersburg

	Laid down	L	In serv.
SV-33	5-81	5-83	8-89

V-33 J.M.S.D.F., 9-89

D: 32,000 tons (41,000 fl) **S:** 27 kts
Dim: 265.0 (253 wl) × 29.6 × 9.0
A: 2/76.2-mm 59-cal. AK-176 DP (I × 2)—4/SA-N-10 SAM syst (IV × 4, . . . SA-14 Gremlin missiles)—4/30-mm AK-630 gatling AA—8/14.5-mm mg (II × 4)—1/Ka-32 Helix-D helicopter
Electron Equipt:
Radar: 3/Palm Frond nav., 1/Top Plate 3-D air search, 2/Bass Tilt f.c., 6/Owl Perch tracking, 4/Mad Hack (*see* Remarks), 1/Fly Screen (helo control)
Telemetry/Space Comms: 2/Low Ball SATCOMM, 1/Ship Bowl, 1/Quad Leaf; 1/Punch Bowl
Sonar: probable hull-mounted MF and passive arrays
EW: extensive arrays, including: 1/Trawl Net, 2/Soup Cup, 1/Cage Box, 1/Cake Tin, . . ./Foot Ball, etc.
E/O: 4/Tin Man, 4/Spot Pot—TACAN: 2/Round House
IFF: 1/Long Head interrogator, 2/Salt Pot transponders
M: CONAS (Combined-Nuclear-and-Steam): 2 pressurized-water reactors, 2 or 4 conventional boilers, 4 sets geared turbines; 4 props; 98,800 shp
Range: Essentially unlimited **Endurance:** 6 months
Crew: 940 tot. (naval)

Remarks: The world's first nuclear-powered naval auxiliary. Initially nicknamed Bal-Aux-2 by NATO, now called "Kapusta" (Cabbage), which seems inappropriate for so significant a ship. Appears to combine the peacetime functions of intelligence collection, space communications, and missile-range re-entry vehicle tracking with a possible wartime role as a major command, control, and communications facility. Despite the size and importance of the ship, however, the weapons/countermeasures suite has no ASW systems, nor are there any chaff/decoy rocket launchers. The SA-N-10 system, the only ship installation to date, appears to be an auto-loading, remote-controlled successor to the manned SA-N-5/8 systems.

The Mad Hack possible planar radar array differs significantly from the Sky Watch radar on the carriers *Baku* and *Tbilisi* but is also found on the *Primorye*-class intelligence collector SSV-501; two of the 12-sided panels face broadside on the amidships tower/mast, one faces aft on the same structure (directly into extensive superstructure), and one lies on deck to starboard beside the tower, facing vertically. The enormous 30-m-diameter radome above the pilothouse, Ship Bowl, may also cover a radar antenna.

Three canvas tents between the forward and amidships tower/masts (the original inflatable covers having been replaced) probably cover stabilized precision theodolite camera tracking arrays, as on the *Marshal Nedelin*-class missile-range tracking ships. The after tower/mast contains the uptakes for the conventional steam component of the engineering plant and supports an extensive suite of ELINT/SIGINT antennas. The nuclear reactors are paired athwartships just forward of the amidships tower/mast.

Although SSV-33 ran extensive trials in the Baltic as early as 1-88, the ship did not deploy to her Pacific Ocean Fleet operational base until 8-89. No second unit is expected, and the first unit does not appear to have operated since delivery.

♦ **1 (+ 1) Kamchatka class** Bldr: Chernomorskoy SY, Nikolayev

	L	In serv.
SSV-679 Kamchatka (ex-SSV-391)	8-85	11-87

D: 5,500 tons (fl) **S:** 18 kts **Dim:** 107.0 × 18.0 × 6.0
A: 2/30-mm AK-630 gatling AA (I × 2)—2/SA-N-8 SAM syst. (IV × 2; 16 SA-14 Gremlin missiles)—2/Ka-32 Helix-D helicopters
Electron Equipt:
Radar: 3/Palm Frond nav., 1/Fly Screen landing aid
Sonar: *see* Remarks
EW: *see* Remarks—TACAN: 2/Round House
M: 2 or 4 diesels; 1 prop; 6–8,000 bhp
Range: . . ./. . . **Crew:** 180 tot.

-33 U.S. Navy, 8-89

INTELLIGENCE COLLECTORS (AGI) *(continued)*

Kamchatka (SSV-679) U.S. Navy, 8-90

Remarks: Although numbered in the SSV-*Sudno Svyazyy* (communications vessel) series normally assigned to electronic-intelligence collection vessels, she has no visible ELINT or SIGINT antennas beyond an HFD/F loop. The tall tower/mast may house the hoisting mechanism for an acoustic array deployed through the bottom of the hull. During the ship's delivery voyage to the Pacific in Nov.–Dec. 1987, the name *Kamchatka* was painted out. The helicopter facility is unusually elaborate for a Soviet auxiliary; a Fly Screen microwave landing aid antenna is mounted atop the hangar, and a ground control cab is to port of the twin hangar. The gatling AA guns do not have radar directors; optical lead-computing directors are mounted within nearby enclosed cupolas (indicating that the ship is intended to operate in a cold climate). A second unit is reported to be under construction.

♦ **7 Vishnaya class (Project 864)** Bldr: Stocznia Północna, Gdańsk

SSV-520 (In serv. 1985) SSV-169 (In serv. 1987)
SSV-208 (In serv. 1987) SSV-175 (In serv. 1988)
SSV-535 (In serv. 1987) SSV-231 (In serv. 4-89)
SSV-201 (In serv. 1987)

D: 2,700 tons (fl) **S:** 18 kts **Dim:** 91.50 (85.0 wl) × 14.50 × 4.0
A: 2/30-mm AK-630 gatling AA (I × 2)—2/SA-N-5/8 SAM systems (IV × 2, . . . Grail or Gremlin missiles)
Electron Equipt:
Radar: 2/Nayada nav.
Sonar: 1/HF dipping sonar, possible hull-mounted passive arrays
EW: 1/Ring Web, 2/Sprat Star, 1/Grid Wheel, 4/Cage Flask, 2/Soup Cup, 1/Prim Wheel, 2 HFD/F loops
M: 2 diesels: 2 props; 9,000 bhp **Range:** . . . **Crew:** 160 tot.

SSV-175—with one hemispheric radome M.O.D., Bonn, 2-90

SSV-231—with two spherical radomes; note door centerline in transom stern French Navy, 10-90

SSV-535—with parabolic dish antenna, no radomes J.M.S.D.F., 12-

Remarks: SSV-520 on first deployment lacked an extensive intelligence-collect antenna suite, other than MF, HF, and VHF D/F gear. Two large circular rad foundations indicate planned later installation of satellite communications anten like those on the Bal'zam class, of which they appear to be a reduced edition. Ante suites vary: SSV-201 has a hemispherical radome above the pilothouse, and SSV- has a deckhouse between the two circular platforms. There are two lead-comput directors for the 30-mm guns mounted forward. The point-defense SAM launchers aft. SSV-208, -535 in the Pacific; SSV-201, -231 in the Black Sea Fleet; others in Northern and Baltic Fleets.

♦ **4 Al'pinist class** Bldr: Yaroslavl SY, U.S.S.R. (In serv. 1981–82)

GS-7 GS-8 GS-19 GS-39

GS-39—with forecastle extended to stern

GS-7—forecastle extended, but ending short of stern J.M.S.D.F.,

D: 1,202 tons (fl) **S:** 12.5 kts **Dim:** 53.70 (46.20 pp) × 10.50 × 4
A: GS-19, GS-39: 2/SA-N-8 SAM syst. (IV × 2; 16 SA-14 Gremlin missiles)
Electron Equipt: Radar: 1/Don-2 nav.
M: 1 Type 8NVD48-2U diesel; 1 CP prop; 1,320 bhp
Electric: 450 kw **Range:** 7,600/12.5
Fuel: 162 tons **Crew:** 60 tot.

Remarks: Selected from a class of several hundred 322-dwt stern-haul tra modified as intelligence collectors. The 218-m^3 former fish hold may provide elec and/or additional accommodations spaces. Have a bow-thruster. The Russian also uses an *Al'pinist* in an experimental role (OS-104, see later page), and seve used in oceanographic research. During 1988 GS-19 and GS-39 had their for decks extended to the stern, SA-N-8 launchers added fore and aft, and their co antenna suites greatly enhanced: a series of planar antennas surround the s upper-deck level, and an elaborate VHD/F array surmounts the after goalpos GS-7 has had the forecastle extended, but not all the way to the stern. G equipped with a Stop Light submarine-type intercept array, GS-34 carries two Dog intercept arrays, and GS-7 has a Squid Head submarine-type antenna GS-19 and GS-39 are in the Baltic Fleet, the others are in the Pacific Ocean F

INTELLIGENCE COLLECTORS (AGI) *(continued)*

◆ **4 Bal'zam class** Bldr: Yantar Zavod 820, Kaliningrad

SSV-80 (In serv. 1983) SSV-493 (In serv. 1982)
SSV-516 (In serv. 1980) SSV-571 (In serv. 1988)

SSV-493—in all-gray paint scheme U.S. Navy, 1-91

SV-571—with white superstructure U.S. Navy, 8-90

D: 5,400 tons (fl) **S:** 22 kts **Dim:** 105.5 × 15.5 × 5.8
A: 1/30-mm AK-630 gatling AA—2/SA-N-5/8 syst. (IV × 2, 16 Grail or Gremlin missiles)
Electron Equipt:
Radar: 2/Don-Kay nav.
Sonar: hull-mounted MF, possible passive arrays, HF dipping
EW: 2/Cage Pot, 1/Twin Wheel D/F, 1/Log Maze D/F, 1/Fir Tree, 1/Wing Fold, 1/Trawl Net, 2/Sprat Star, 1/Cross Loop A MFD/F, 1/High Ring-C HFD/F, 1/Park Plinth VHD/F
M: 2 diesels; 2 props; 9,000 bhp **Range:** 7,000/16 **Crew:** 220 tot.

emarks: SSV—*Sudno Svyazyy* (Communications Vessel). Built-for-the-purpose telligence-collection-and-processing ships, wholly military in concept. The two herical radomes probably house satellite transmitting and receiving antennas. iere are numerous intercept and direction-finding antenna arrays. Have Prim Wheel d Soup Cup satellite antennas. Equipped to refuel under way and to transfer solid rgo and personnel via constant-tension rigs on either side of the after mast. There is ly a remote Kolonka-2 pedestal director for the gatling gun, no radar GFCS. SSV-516 d -571 operate in the Atlantic, the other two in the Pacific.

1 converted Yug class Bldr: Stocznia Północna, Gdańsk (In serv. 5-78)

V-704 (ex-SSV-328, ex-*Yug*)

D: 2,700 tons (fl) **S:** 15 kts **Dim:** 82.50 (75.80 pp) × 13.50 × 4.10
A: 4/14.5-mm mg (II × 2)
Electron Equipt:
Radar: 2/Don-2 nav.—IFF: 1/High Pole B transponder
Sonar: HF dipping sonar(?)
EW: 2/Watch Dog, 1/HFD/F loop, 1/. . .
M: 2 Cegielski-Sulzer 8TD48 diesels; 2 CP props; 4,400 bhp (3,600 sust.)
Electric: 1,920 kVA tot. **Fuel:** 343 tons
Endurance: 40 days **Range:** 9,000/12 **Crew:** 80 tot.

V-704—with previous hull number U.S. Navy, 11-89

Remarks: Conversion from an existing Black Sea Fleet oceanographic research ship completed summer 1989. Forecastle deck extended to stern, and sides plated in; 01- and 02-level superstructures also extended aft, presumably to allow for an increase in accommodations and for electronics spaces. Had few intercept antennas as initially sighted. Large radome on cylindrical stalk between the stack and the foremast is also found on the giant SSV-33. The machine gun mounts are mounted abaft the boats. SSV-704 is in the Northern Fleet.

◆ **6 Primor'ye class (Project 394)**
Bldr: . . . SY, U.S.S.R. (In serv. 1969–73)

SSV-464 (ex-*Zabaykal'ye*) SSV-502 (ex-*Zakarpat'ye*)
SSV-465 (ex-*Primor'ye*) SSV-590 (ex-*Krym*)
SSV-501 (ex-*Zaporozh'ye*) SSV-591 (ex-*Kavkaz*)

SSV-501—with Mad Hack arrays U.S. Navy, 1991

SSV-502—with "Christmas Tree" intercept array mast amidships U.S. Navy, 4-90

SSV-591—with rounded radome forward AOAN Morvant, USN, 9-89

INTELLIGENCE COLLECTORS (AGI) *(continued)*

SSV-464—with van-mounted parabolic dish antenna aft U.S. Navy, 19

D: 2,600 tons (3,700 fl) **S:** 13 kts **Dim:** 84.7 × 14.0 × 5.5
A: . . ./Grail/Gremlin shoulder-launched SAM
Electron Equipt:
Radar: 2/Don-Kay—EW: *see* Remarks
M: 2 diesels; 1 prop; 2,000 bhp **Range:** 12,000/13; 18,000/12
Crew: 160 tot.

Remarks: Although these ships resemble small passenger liners, they are modified versions of the *Mayakovskiy*-class stern-haul factory trawler. All given SSV—*Sudno Svyazyy* (Communications Vessel) pendants, and names deleted, 1979–81. Carry hand-held Grail/Gremlin SAMs. SSV-590 and SSV-591 have lost the forward stump masts, and have a rounded radome in place of the original angular structure forward. SSV-464 and SSV-465 have had the aft rectangular radome replaced by a portable van surmounted by a parabolic dish antenna and have had the after king posts deleted. SSV-501 has the same "Mad Hack" planar array that appears on the nuclear-powered SSV-33 and has operated extensively off the U.S. East Coast; the visible faces of the four "antennas" are actually plasticized fabric. SSV-502 has a very complex direction-finding array amidships nicknamed "Christmas Tree."

◆ **9 Moma class (Project 861)**
Bldr: Stocznia Północna, Gdańsk, Poland (In serv. 1968–74)

Ekvator	SSV-472 (ex-*Il'men*)	SSV-509 (ex-*Pelorus*)
Kil'din	SSV-474 (ex-*Vega*)	SSV-512 (ex-*Arkhipelag*)
Yupiter	SSV-506 (ex-*Nakhodka*)	SSV-514 (ex-*Seliger*)

SSV-514—with log periodic array aft, VHD/F loop on extended deckhouse forward U.S. Navy, 1991

SSV-506—with tripod-reinforced mainmast, light pole mast forward U.S. Navy, 8-91

Liman—still with crane forward, and with van on deck abaft crane fo dation U.S. Navy, 6

Kil'din—unmodified unit with ELINT vans aft U.S. Navy, 1

Ekvator—crane deleted, 2-level ELINT facility aft U.S. Navy,

NTELLIGENCE COLLECTORS (AGI) *(continued)*

D: 1,260 tons (1,540 fl) **S:** 16 kts **Dim:** 73.3 (64.2 pp) × 10.8 × 3.9
A: 2/SA-N-5/8 SAM systems (IV × 2, 16 Grail or Gremlin missiles) in most
Electron Equipt: Radar: 2/Don-2 nav.
M: 2 Zgoda-Sulzer 6TD48 diesels; 2 CP props; 3,600 bhp [Fuel: 220 tons]
Range: 8,000/11 **Crew:** 80–120 tot.

ɛemarks: Ex-survey ship/navigational buoy tenders. *Yupiter,* SSV-472, SSV-474, SV-509, and SSV-512 have new superstructures added in the area forward of the ridge and also have new masts. The others are much less modified, most having only a ɛw canvas-covered antennas atop the bridge and "vans" containing support equipment. SSV-472 carried a submarine-type EW intercept antenna atop her bridge in 983–1986, as did SSV-474 in 1988. *Yupiter* carries a 9-m-long by 4-m-high radome top an enlarged deckhouse aft.

8 Mayak class Bldr: . . . (In serv. 1967–70)

NEROYD	GIRORULEVOY (ex-GS-536)	KHERSONES	KURS
.URSOGRAF	LADOGA	GS-239	GS-242

ʖ-239 9-91

-242 4-90

: 1,050 tons (fl) **S:** 11 kts **Dim:** 54.2 × 9.3 × 3.6
lectron Equipt:
Radar: 1–2/Don-2 and/or Spin Trough nav.
: 1 8NVD48 diesel; 800 bhp **Range:** 9,400/11 **Crew:** 40 tot.

ıarks: GS—*Gidrograficheskoye Sudno* (Hydrographic Survey Ship), an interest-uphemism. These ships vary greatly in appearance and in equipment carried. carry hand-held Grail or Gremlin missiles launched from two railed positions either at the bow and stern or atop the deckhouse amidships. *Ladoga* carried 5-mm mg (II × 2) in 1980, since removed, but added to *Kursograf.* The ships have employed almost exclusively in home waters in recent years, and some may have discarded.

ɜ converted Nikolay Zubov-class former oceanographic ships
ldr: A. Warski SY, Szczecin, Poland (In serv. 1963–68)

-468 (ex-*Gavril Sarychev*)	SSV-503 (ex-*Khariton Laptev*)
-469 (ex-*Semyen Chelyushkin*)	

SSV-469—original short forecastle U.S. Navy, 1989

SSV-503 U.S. Navy, 1989

D: 2,200 tons (3,020 fl) **S:** 16.5 kts **Dim:** 90.0 × 13.0 × 4.7
Electron Equipt:
Radar: 2/Don-2 nav.—IFF: 1/High Pole B transponder
M: 2 Zgoda-Sulzer 8TD48 diesels; 2 props; 4,800 bhp
Endurance: 60 days **Range:** 11,000/14
Crew: 160 tot. (SSV-469: 100 tot.)

Remarks: Former oceanographic research ships. SSV-468 and SSV-501 have been extensively altered: their forecastle decks have been extended to the stern and the sides plated in, and an extra deck has been added to the superstructure. SSV-503 had an additional deckhouse added aft in 1988–89. All three have launch positions for SA-7 Grail or SA-14 Gremlin shoulder-launched SAMs. SSV-469 formerly carried a Strut Curve surface/air-search radar. SSV-468 and SSV-469 operate in the Pacific; SSV-503 is assigned to the Northern Fleet. All three are likely soon to be discarded.

◆ **1 converted Keyla-class cargo ship**
Bldr: Turnu-Severin SY, Hungary (In serv. between 1959 and 1968)

RITSA

Ritsa U.S. Navy, 1988

D: 950 tons light (1,900 fl) **S:** 12 kts
Dim: 78.50 (71.40 pp) × 10.50 × 4.50
A: none **Electron Equipt:** Radar: 2/Don-2 nav.
M: 1 Lang 8LD315Rf diesel; 1 prop; 1,000 bhp
Range: 4,200/10.7 **Fuel:** 72 tons **Crew:** 80 tot.

Remarks: Converted mid-1970s from a three-hatch cargo vessel. Deckhouse built over hold 3, hold 2 plated over, and only the forward two 2.5-ton derricks retained to handle small boats. Collection antenna suite is not very elaborate (a canvas-covered "ELINT hut" at the stern, and HFD/F loop and two small intercept arrays on the A-frame foremast), although the communications suite was enhanced. May serve as a training ship for ELINT operators and is assigned to the Black Sea Fleet. Has deployed from the Black Sea only rarely.

◆ **1 converted Pamir-class former rescue tug**
Bldr: Gävle, Sweden (In serv. 1958)

SSV-477 (ex-*Peleng,* ex-*Pamir*)

INTELLIGENCE COLLECTORS (AGI) *(continued)*

SSV-477 U.S. Navy, 1986

D: 1,443 tons (2,300 fl) **S:** 17.5 kts **Dim:** 78.0 × 12.8 × 4.0
Electron Equipt: Radar: 2/Don-2 nav.
M: 2 M.A.N. G10V 40/60 diesels; 2 CP props; 4,200 bhp
Range: 15,200/17.5; 21,000/12 **Crew:** 120 tot.

Remarks: Former rescue tug, with sisters *Agatan* and *Aldan* still serving in that capacity. Sister SSV-480 (ex-*Gidrograf*) has been stricken. SSV-477 has been heavily modified as an intelligence collector, with extra deckhouse levels, the forecastle extended, and numerous collection arrays added. Has three launch positions for SA-7 Grail or SA-14 Gremlin shoulder-launched SAMs. Assigned to the Pacific Ocean Fleet.

♦ up to 7 Okean trawler class
Bldr: . . . Sy, East Germany (In serv. 1962–67)

Ekholot	Reduktor	Zond
Linza	Repiter	
Lotlin' (GS-319)	Travers	

Lotlin' Gerhard Koop, 1989

Reduktor 10-9(

D: 700 tons (fl) **S:** 11 kts **Dim:** 50.8 × 8.9 × 3.7
A: 2/SA-N-5/8 SAM positions (I × 2, 16 Grail or Gremlin missiles)
Electron Equipt: Radar: 1–2/Don-2 nav.
M: 1 diesel; 1 prop; 540 bhp
Range: 7,900/11 **Crew:** 60 tot.

Remarks: Appearances vary greatly, many having had their poop decks extende well forward of the bridge superstructure and their port sides plated in. Sister *Alidada, Ampermeter, Barograf, Barometr, Deflektor, Gidrofon, Krenometr,* and *Teo dolit* have not been sighted in many years and almost certainly been discarded; th others will probably soon follow.

Note: All of the older Lentra-class intelligence collectors were retired prior to 198(The four Mirnyy-class converted whale-catchers formerly used as intelligence co lectors in the Mediterranean, *Bakan, Lotsman, Val,* and *Vertikal,* have been replace by Vishnaya-class ships and have probably been discarded.

OCEANOGRAPHIC-RESEARCH SHIPS

Note: The only units included here are those known to be subordinated to the Russia Navy. There are in addition nearly 300 research ships under the control of civilia agencies, primarily the Ministry of Science and the Ministry of Fisheries. Some of th civilian ships also perform research in support of military aims. All naval units a painted white.

♦ 2 Sibiryakov-class (Type B970)
Bldr: A. Warski SY, Sczcecin, Polan

	Laid down	L	In serv.
Sibiryakov	8-88	5-8	97-90
Romuald Mukhlevich	1988	1990	12-91

Sibiryakov U.S. Navy, 7

D: 2,700 tons (fl) **S:** 16 kts
Dim: 100.00 (85.00 pp) × 17.00 × 5.68
Electron Equipt: Radar: . . .—Sonar: . . .
M: 2 Cegielski-Sulzer diesels (3,200 bhp each), electric drive; 4 propulsors; 5,100 shp—bow-thruster
Range: . . .
Crew: 48 tot. + 52 scientists/technicians

Remarks: 1,950 dwt. Ordered 1-89 to explore for mineral resources at depths u 6,000 m. Can carry two 18-ton submersibles and have 14 laboratories. For cruis there are two 1,080-kw electric motors, while for precision maneuvering, there are 810-kw propulsors. Delivery of the second delayed by the poor condition of the Rus economy; a third may have been ordered and later canceled.

♦ 17 Yug class (Project 862)
Bldr: Stocznia Północna, Gdańsk, Poland (In serv. 5-78 to 6-9-83)

Donuzlav	Pluton
Gals	Senezh
Gidrolog	Strelets
Gorizont	Stvor
Mangyshlak	Tayga
Marshal Golovani	Vitze-Admiral Vorontsov (ex-*Briz*)
Nikolay Matusevich	Vizir
Pegas	Zodiak
Persey	

·CEANOGRAPHIC-RESEARCH SHIPS *(continued)*

›rizont U.S. Navy, 8-91

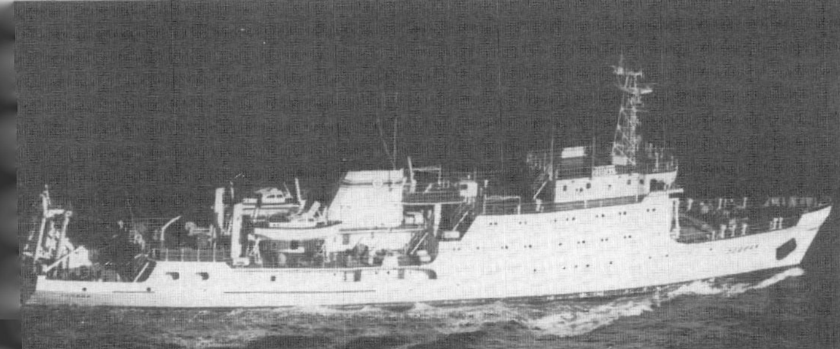
›liak—with gantry at stern U.S. Navy, 1986

·olay Matusevich French Navy, 1-90

: 2,500 tons (fl) **S:** 15.6 kts
im: 82.50 (75.80 pp) × 13.50 × 3.97
lectron Equipt:
Radar: 2/Don-2 nav.—IFF: 1/High Pole B transponder
: 2 Zgoda-Sulzer 8TD48 diesels; 2 CP props; 4,400 bhp (3,600 sust.)—2 100-kw low-speed electric motors—300-shp bow-thruster
lectric: 1,920 kVA **Range:** 9,000/12 **Fuel:** 343 tons
ndurance: 40 days
rew: 8 officers, 38 unlicensed (civilian), 20 scientists + 4 spare

arks: Class name ship *Yug* converted to intelligence collector; *Briz* renamed -*Admiral Voronov* in 1989. Stated intended for: "Complex oceanographic re-h; exploration of the sea bed and sampling of soils; gravimetric studies; hydro-ıic and geophysical research, including the removal and implanting of oceano-ıic buoys; collection of navigational and hydrographic data; and inshore ›graphic surveys by [use of the embarked two Type 727 glass-reinforced plastic-d] cutters."
adrantial davit over stern ramp, with 4-ton lift. Two 5-ton booms and several ›ographic davits. Have three echo-sounders, six laboratories. Deck reinforcements ‹ 25-mm AA (II × 3). *Zodiak* fitted about 1985 with large gantry at stern to handle ›ed object and main deck superstructure extended.

Akademik Krylov class (Project 856)
·dr: A. Warski SY, Szczecin, Poland (In serv. 1974–79)

·RAL VLADIMIRSKIY LEONID DEMIN
›EMIK KRYLOV LEONID SOBELYEV
KRUZENSHTERN MIKHAIL KRUPSKIY

6,600 tons (9,100 fl) **S:** 20.4 kts **Dim:** 147.0 × 18.6 × 6.3
·ctron Equipt:
Radar: 3/Don-2 nav.—IFF: 1/High Pole B transponder
4 diesels; 2 props; 16,000 bhp **Endurance:** 90 days
nge: 23,000/15.4 **Crew:** 90 tot. (civilian)

Admiral Vladimirskiy—blunt stern J.M.S.D.F., 11-90

Mikhail Krupskiy—blunt stern, large radome amidships French Navy, 3-85

Remarks: The largest ships of their type in any navy. Equipped with helicopter hangar and flight deck, two survey launches, and twenty-six laboratories totaling 900 m². *Leonid Demin* and *Mikhail Krupskiy* were delivered in 1978 and 1979, respectively, and, because they have pointed sterns, are about 2.5 m longer, as is *Leonid Sobelyev*. *Admiral Vladimirskiy* has carried two Post Lamp gun/torpedo fire-control radars, one atop the forward superstructure and one on the foremast—both offset to starboard. *Akademik Krylov* has a small hemispherical radome before the stack, while *Mikhail Krupskiy* has carried a large, spherical dome in the same position.

◆ 1 Vladimir Kavrayskiy class, icebreaker-hulled
Bldr: Admiralty SY, St. Petersburg (In serv. 1974)

VLADIMIR KAVRAYSKIY

Vladimir Kavrayskiy U.S. Navy, 1991

D: 3,900 tons (fl) **S:** 15.4 kts
Dim: 70.00 (65.70 wl) × 18.20 × 6.40
Electron Equipt:
Radar: 2/Don-2 nav.—IFF: 1/High Pole B transponder
M: Type 13D100 diesels, electric drive; 2 props; 4,800 shp
Endurance: 60 days **Range:** 5,500/12.5; 13,900/9.4
Crew: 60 tot. (civilian)

Remarks: Greatly modified version of the *Dobrynya Nikitich* icebreaker class for Arctic research. Has helicopter deck but no hangar, a survey launch, nine laboratories totaling 180 m², one 8-ton crane, two 3-ton booms, and a hold capacity of 200 m³. The *Otto Schmidt*, completed in 1979 and subordinated to the Academy of Sciences, differs in appearance but is of similar design. The civilian research icebreakers *Georgiy Sedov* and *Petr Pakhtusov*, also subordinated to the Academy of Science, are units of the *Dobrynya Nikitich* class with very few external alterations.

◆ 4 Abkhaziya class
Bldr: Mathias Thiesen Werft, Wismar, East Germany (In serv. 1971–73)

ABKHAZIYA ADZHARIYA BASHKIRIYA MOLDAVIYA

D: 5,460 tons (7,500 fl) **S:** 21 kts
Dim: 124.7 × 17.0 × 6.4
Electron Equipt: Radar: 3/Don-2 nav.
M: 2 M.A.N. K6Z 57/80 diesels; 2 props; 8,000 bhp
Endurance: 60 days **Range:** 20,000/16 **Crew:** 85 tot.

OCEANOGRAPHIC-RESEARCH SHIPS *(continued)*

Moldaviya U.S. Navy, 2-86

Bashkiriya U.S. Navy, 1990

Remarks: Military version of the Academy of Science's *Akademik Kurchatov* class, with helicopter deck, telescoping hangar, Vee Cone communications antenna, stern-mounted A-frame lift gear, two survey launches, and twenty-seven laboratories totaling 460 m^2.

♦ 8 Nikolay Zubov class (Project 850)

Bldr: A. Warski SY, Szczecin, Poland (In serv. 1963–68)

ALEKSEY CHIRIKOV
ANDREY VIL'KITSKIY
BORIS DAVYDOV
FADDEY BELLINGSGAUZEN
FYODOR LITKE
NIKOLAY ZUBOV
SEMEN DEZHNEV
VASILIY GOLOVNIN

Nikolay Zubov—early unit with small platform aft Leo Van Ginderen, 6-91

Faddey Bellingsgauzen—late unit with large platform aft French Navy, 3-90

D: 2,200 tons (3,020 fl) **S:** 16.5 kts
Dim: 90.0 × 13.0 × 4.7
Electron Equipt:
Radar: 2/Don-2 or Palm Frond nav.—IFF: 1/High Pole B transponder
M: 2 Zgoda-Sulzer 8TD48 diesels; 2 props; 4,800 bhp
Endurance: 60 days **Range:** 11,000/14
Crew: 50 tot. (civilian)

Remarks: Considerable variation from ship to ship. Can carry four survey launche but usually have only two. Nine laboratories, totaling 120 m^2. Two 7-ton and two 5-to booms, nine 0.5–1.2-ton oceanographic-equipment davits, 600-m^3 total capacity in tw holds. The after platform, *not* for helicopters, is larger in the later ships. Three othe serve as intelligence collectors. Nearing the end of their useful lives.

♦ 1 Nevel'skoy class

Bldr: . . . SY, Nikolayev (In serv. 1962)

NEVEL'SKOY

Nevel'skoy—as modified J.M.S.D.F., 11-

D: 2,350 tons (fl) **S:** 17 kts **Dim:** 83.8 × 15.2 × 3.8
Electron Equipt: Radar: 2/Don-2 nav. **Crew:** 45 tot.
M: 2 diesels; 2 props; 4,000 bhp **Range:** 10,000/11

Remarks: The only naval oceanographic research ship, other than the *Vladi Kavrayskiy*, built in the Soviet Union; apparently the prototype for the *Nikolay Zu* design. In the Pacific Fleet. Between 1983 and 1987 refitted and given an additional bipod mast forward of the stack and an extensive horizontal lattice array running fr the stack to the stern. Appears to be involved in low-frequency radio or radar propa tion studies.

♦ 3 Polyus class

Bldr: Neptunwerft, Rostock, East Germany (In serv. 1962–64)

BAYKAL BALKHASH POLYUS

Baykal (Balkhash similar) U.S. Navy,

Polyus U.S. Navy,

D: 4,560 tons (6,900 fl) **S:** 14.2 kts
Dim: 111.6 × 14.4 × 6.3
Electron Equipt:
Radar: 2/Don-2 nav. (*Balkhash:* 2/Palm Frond)
M: 4 diesels, electric drive; 1 prop; 4,000 shp
Endurance: 75 days **Range:** 25,000/12.3
Crew: 120 tot. (civilian)

Remarks: Seventeen laboratories, totaling 290 m^2. *Polyus* has less-extensiv perstructure, different mast arrangement. *Balkhash* and *Baykal* have a oceanographic-equipment gantry at the stern and a small "hangar" for towed se or submersibles. All three likely soon to be stricken.

NAVIGATIONAL AID TENDER/HYDROGRAPHIC-SURVEY SHIPS

Note: Ships of the Finik, Moma, Biya, Kamenka, and Samara classes are used as hydrographic-survey ships and as navigation tenders, handling buoys, marking channels, etc. They set and retrieve the 2,000 buoys and 4,000 spar buoys that are taken up for the winter months. Most can carry from two to six navigation buoys. In addition, they are equipped to take basic oceanographic and meteorological samplings. The Russian Navy's Hydrographic Service has the task not only of surveying Russian and overseas waters, but of maintaining no less than 600 lighthouses, 150 noise beacons, and 8,000 navigation buoys.

◆ 24 Finik class (Project 872)

Bldr: Stocznia Północna, Gdańsk, Poland (In serv. 1979–81)

GS-44	GS-87	GS-278	GS-301	GS-398	GS-402
GS-47	GS-265	GS-280	GS-388	GS-399	GS-403
GS-84	GS-270	GS-296	GS-392	GS-400	GS-404
GS-86	GS-272	GS-297	GS-397	GS-401	GS-405

GS-401 Leo Van Ginderen, 10-91

GS-265 French Navy, 3-90

D: 1,200 tons (fl) **S:** 13 kts
Dim: 61.30 × 11.80 (10.80 wl) × 3.27
Electron Equipt:
Radar: 2/Don-2 nav.—IFF: 1/High Pole B transponder
M: 2 Cegielski-Sulzer diesels; 2 CP props; 1,920 bhp—2/75-kw electric motors for quiet, 6-kt operations—130-kw bow-thruster
Electric: 675 kVA **Endurance:** 15 days **Range:** 3,000/13
Crew: 5 officers, 23 unlicensed (civilian)

Remarks: GS—*Gidrograficheskoye Sudno* (Hydrographic Vessel). Intended for navigational buoy-tending and survey, for which four echo-sounders are fitted. Up to three glass 3-dwt utility landing craft can be stowed on the buoy working deck, beneath the 7-ton crane. Have hydrological, hydrographic, and cartographic facilities. Also, one for East Germany and four for Poland (two civilian).

◆ 19 Moma class (Project 861)

Bldr: Stocznia Północna, Gdańsk, Poland (In serv. 1967–74)

ANADYR	CHELEKEN	MORZHOVETS
ANDROMEDA	EL'TON	OKEAN
ANTARES	KOLGUEV	RYBACHIY (ex-*Odograf*)
ANTARKTIKA	KRIL'ON	SEVER
ARKA	LIMAN	TAYMYR
ASKOL'D	MARS	ZAPOLAR'YE
BEREZAN		

Kril'on M.O.D., U.K., 6-89

Cheleken French Navy, 1-90

Rybachiy—armed unit, with deckhouse in place of crane J.M.S.D.F., 8-90

D: 1,260 tons (1,540 fl) **S:** 16 kts
Dim: 73.3 (64.2 pp) × 10.8 × 3.9
Electron Equipt:
Radar: 2/Don-2 nav.—IFF: 1/High Pole A transponder
M: 2 Zgoda-Sulzer 6TD48 diesels; 2 CP props; 3,600 bhp
Endurance: 35 days **Range:** 8,700/11
Crew: 56 tot. (civilian)

Remarks: Carry one survey launch and a 7-ton crane, and have four laboratories, totaling 35 m^2. *Rybachiy* (ex-*Odograf*) has a deckhouse in place of the crane and may be involved in naval-related oceanographic research; the ship is armed with 4/12.7-mm mg (II × 2) forward and 2/SA-N-5 or SA-N-8 SAM systems (IV × 2; 16 Grail or Gremlin missiles) aft and probably has a naval crew. Sisters in Polish, Bulgarian, and Yugoslav navies. Nine more serve as intelligence collectors. Sister *Anadyr'* is presumed to have been stricken circa 1988, as her name has been given to a large naval cargo ship.

◆ 14 Biya class

Bldr: Stocznia Północna, Gdańsk, Poland (In serv. 1972–76)

GS-182	GS-193	GS-198	GS-204	GS-208	GS-214	GS-271
GS-192	GS-194	GS-202	GS-206	GS-210	GS-269	GS-273

GS-214—note crane at forecastle break M.O.D., Bonn, 7-91

GS-271 Leo Van Ginderen, 3-91

NAVIGATIONAL AID TENDER/HYDROGRAPHIC-SURVEY SHIPS *(continued)*

D: 750 tons (fl) **S:** 13 kts **Dim:** 55.0 × 9.2 × 2.6
Electron Equipt: Radar: 1/Don-2 nav.
M: 2 diesels; 2 CP props; 1,200 bhp **Endurance:** 15 days
Range: 4,700/11 **Fuel:** 90 tons **Crew:** 25 tot. (civilian)

Remarks: GS—*Gidrograficheskoye Sudno* (Hydrographic Survey Ship). Similar to Kamenka class, but have longer superstructure and less buoy-handling space; one survey launch; one 5-ton crane. Laboratory space: 15 m². One unit transferred to Guinea-Bissau, one (GC-186) to Cuba in 1980, and one to Cape Verde in 1980.

◆ **11 Kamenka class**
Bldr: Stocznia Północna, Gdańsk, Poland (In serv. 1968–72)

GS-66	GS-103	GS-203
GS-74	GS-107	GS-207
GS-78	GS-108 (ex-*Vernier*)	GS-211
GS-82	GS-113 (ex-*Bel'bek*)	

Kamenka class—note crane in center of working deck M.O.D., Bonn, 9-85

D: 703 tons (fl) **S:** 13.7 kts **Dim:** 53.5 × 9.1 × 2.6
Electron Equipt: Radar: 1/Don-2 nav.
M: 2 diesels; 2 props; 2 CP props; 1,765 bhp
Range: 4,000/10 **Crew:** 40 tot. (civilian)

Remarks: GS—*Gidrograficheskoye Sudno* (Hydrographic Survey Ship). Similar to Biya class, but have more facilities for stowing and handling buoys. No survey launch. One 5-ton crane. One sister formerly served in the East German Navy.

◆ **15 Samara class**
Bldr: Stocznia Północna, Gdańsk, Poland (In serv. 1962–64)

Azimut	Gradus	Tropik
Deviator	Kompas	Vaygach
Gigrometr	Pamyat' Merkuriya	Vostok
Glubometr	Rumb (GS-118)	Zenit
Gorizont	Tura (ex-*Globus*)	GS-275 (ex-*Yug*)

Gradus—standard unit M.O.D., Bonn, 7-89

Vaygach—with deckhouse in working deck M.O.D., U.K

Tura—forecastle extended to increase accommodations

D: 1,050 tons (1,276 fl) **S:** 15.5 kts
Dim: 59.0 × 10.4 × 3.8
Electron Equipt: Radar: 2/Don-2 nav.
M: 2 Zgoda-Sulzer 5TD48 diesels; 2 CP props; 3,000 bhp
Endurance: 25 days **Range:** 6,200/11
Crew: 45 tot. (*Tura:* 140 tot.)

Remarks: Have one survey launch and 15 m² of laboratory space. The T[ura] (ex-*Globus*) had her forecastle extended to her superstructure in 1978 and her 7-to[n] removed; able to accommodate 120 personnel, she was used for training foreig[n] at Poti in the Black Sea. *Deviator* served briefly as an intelligence collector. V[aygach] has a large deckhouse surrounding the base of the buoy crane.

COASTAL SURVEY SHIPS

◆ **2 Vinograd class** Bldr: Rauma-Repola SY, Savonlinna, Finland
GS-525 (In serv. 12-11-85) GS-526 (In serv. 17-12-85)

GS-525 Rauma-Repola

D: 450 tons (fl) **S:** 10 kts **Dim:** 32.30 (28.60 pp) × 9.60 × 2.60
Electron Equipt: Radar: 1/Mius nav.
M: 2 Baykal 300 diesels; 2 props; 598 bhp
Crew: 20 tot. (civilian)

Remarks: Although these small ships were at one time listed by NATO as [intelli]gence collectors, it is obvious from their equipment and appearance that they p[erform] the survey mission for which they were built. Have small side-scan sonars tha[t deploy] from recesses on the hull sides amidships.

COASTAL SURVEY SHIPS *(continued)*

◆ **2 converted Muna-class former ammunition lighters**
Bldr: Nakhodka SY (In serv. 1960s)

GIROSKOP UGLOMER

Uglomer M.O.D., Bonn, 7-90

D: 680 tons (fl) **S:** 11 kts **Dim:** 51.0 × 8.5 × 2.7
Electron Equipt: Radar: 1/Spin Trough nav.
M: 1 diesel; 1 prop; 600 bhp **Crew:** 40 tot.

Remarks: *Uglomer* extensively converted at a Baltic-area shipyard to serve as a coastal survey ship and deployed under tow to the Pacific Ocean Fleet in 7-90; *Giroskop* completed a similar conversion in 1991 and remains in the Baltic. A small deckhouse covers the former forward ammunition hold area, while two king posts with derricks were stepped forward of the pilothouse. The original electric crane was retained.

◆ **several GPB-480-class inshore-survey craft** Bldr: U.S.S.R. (In serv. 1960s)

GPB-480, GPB-767, etc.

GPB-767—GPB-480 class French Navy, 8-79

D: 120 tons (fl) **S:** 12 kts **Dim:** 29.0 × 5.0 × 1.7
Electron Equipt: Radar: 1/Spin Trough nav.
M: 1 diesel; 450 bhp
Endurance: 10 days **Range:** 1,600/10 **Crew:** 15 tot.

Remarks: GPB—*Gidrograficheskoye Pribezhnyy Bot* (Coastal Hydrographic Survey Boat). VM on the diving-tender version stands for *Vodolaznyy Morskoy* (Seagoing Diving Tender). Same hull and propulsion as the Nyryat-I-class diving tenders. The chartthouse/laboratory is 6 m², and there are two 1.5-ton derricks. Most employ a dual side-looking mapping sonar system using transducers mounted on swinging-arm davits amidships. The smaller GPB-710 class is carried aboard the larger survey and oceanographic ships listed above:

D: 7 tons (fl) **S:** 10 kts for 150 nautical miles
Dim: 11.0 × 3.0 × 0.7.

MISSILE-RANGE INSTRUMENTATION SHIPS

◆ **2 Marshal Nedelin class** Bldr: United Admiralty SY, St. Petersburg

MARSHAL NEDELIN (In serv. 1984)
MARSHAL KRYLOV (In serv. 1989)

D: 24,000 tons (fl) **S:** 20 kts **Dim:** 213.0 × 27.1 × 7.7
Electron Equipt:
Radar: 3/Palm Frond nav., 1/Strut Pair surf./air-search (*M. Krylov:* Top Plate), 1/Fly Screen helo control, 1/End Tray balloon tracking, 1/Ship Globe tracking
IFF: 2/Salt Pot and 1/High Pole transponders, interrogation via Strut Curve
TACAN: 2/Round House
M: 2 gas turbines; 2 props; 54,000 shp **Range:** . . .
Crew: 200 tot.

Marshal Nedelin U.S. Navy, 8-89

Marshal Krylov U.S. Navy, 7-90

Remarks: Possibly intended to begin replacement of the aged *Desna-* and *Sibir'*-class range-tracking ships, but equipped also to serve in a space-tracking and communications role. Named for pioneer leaders of the Soviet ballistic-missile program; first ship named for Chief of Soviet Missile Forces, Marshall Mitrofan Nedelin, killed in a missile explosion in 1960 at Baikonur. Tracking antennas include 1/Quad Leaf, 3/Quad Wedge, 4/Quad Rods, and 6/telemetry reception arrays. Twin hangars accommodate 2/Ka-32 Helix-D utility helicopters. Hull has a bulbous bow form. Foundations for 6/30-mm gatling AA and 3/Bass Tilt radar directors are present. Has a swimming pool just abaft the stack. Both operate in the Pacific Fleet. A reported third ship of the class, *Akademik Nikolay Pilyugin,* is actually of quite a different design and is civilian-subordinated.

◆ **2 Desna class** Bldr: Warnow Werft, Warnemünde (In serv. 1963)

CHAZHMA (ex-*Dangera*) CHUMIKAN (ex-*Dolgeschtchel'ye*)

D: 14,065 tons (fl) **S:** 15 kts
Dim: 139.50 (134.50 wl) × 18.0 × 7.9
Electron Equipt:
Radar: 2/Don-2 nav., 1/Head Net-C surf./air search, 1/Ship Globe tracking
EW: 2/Watch Dog intercept
M: 1 M.A.N.-Dieselmotor Rostock K72 70/120A3 diesel; 1 prop; 5,400 bhp
Range: 9,000/13 **Crew:** 240 tot.

Remarks: Heavily modified cargo ships. Tracking radar in large dome atop the bridge, with three tracking directors mounted forward. Hormone helicopter with hangar aft. Vee Cone communications antennas atop the stack. Were only ships with Head Net-B radar (both reflectors in the same plane), now replaced by Head Net-C in both. Based in the Pacific at Petropavlovsk on the Kamchatka Peninsula. Both likely soon to be stricken.

Chazhma U.S. Navy, 8-89

MISSILE-RANGE INSTRUMENTATION SHIPS *(continued)*

Chazhma U.S. Navy, 8-89

◆ **3 Sibir' class** Bldr: A. Warski SY, Szczecin, Poland (In serv. 1958)
Chukotka Sakhalin Spassk (ex-*Suchan*)

Chukotka—with Big Net radar U.S. Navy, 1986

Spassk U.S. Navy, 8-89

D: 7,800 tons (fl) **S:** 12 kts **Dim:** 108.2 × 14.6 × 7.2
Electron Equipt:
Radar: 2/Don-2 nav., 1/Head Net-C surf./air-search (*Chukotka:* Big Net), two tracking sets
M: triple-expansion reciprocating steam; 1 prop; 2,300 ihp
Boilers: 2 **Range:** 11,800/12 **Crew:** 240 tot.

Remarks: Converted (circa 1960) *Donbass*-class cargo ships. Originally, only *Chukotka* was flush-decked; the others had a well-deck forward. Now all are flush-decked. All carry one Ka-25 Hormone-C helicopter, but have no hangar. Now carry two tracking radars forward, two Quad Rods telemetry trackers, and an optical tracking device on the forecastle. Have a swimming pool to starboard, forward. All are in the Pacific Ocean Fleet, based at Petropavlovsk on the Kamchatka Peninsula. Sister *Sibir'* scrapped 1-91, and the others will probably soon follow.

SHIP SIGNATURE-MEASUREMENT SHIPS

◆ **14 or more Onega class** Bldr: . . . (In serv. 9-73–. . .)

GKS-52 GKS-224 SFP-95 SFP-177 SFP-295 SFP-340 SFP-511
GKS-83 GKS-286 SFP-173 SFP-283 SFP-322 SFP-372 SFP-562

D: 1,925 tons (fl) **S:** 16 kts **Dim:** 81.0 × 11.0 × 4.2
Electron Equipt: Radar: 1/Don-2 nav.
M: 2 diesels; 1 or 2 props; 8,000 bhp **Crew:** 120 tot.

Remarks: GKS—*Gidroakusticheskoye Kontrol'noye Sudno* (Hydro-acoustic Monitoring Ship)—indicates that these ships are successors to the T-43-class noise-monitoring ships. SFP—*Sudno Fizicheskiy Poley* (Physical Fields Measuring Vessel)—indicates different mission and sensors. SFP ships have the helicopter platform farther forward, abutting the stack, and have lattice vice pylon masts. SFP-173 and SFP-177 were delivered in 1991.

SFP-177 Leo Van Ginderen, 10-

SFP-295 J.M.S.D.F., 6-

◆ **17 Modified T-43 class** Bldr: Various (In serv. mid-1950s)
GKS-11 through GKS-24, GKS-26, GKS-42, GKS-45

GKS-12 Leo Van Ginderen, 1

GKS-17—note deckhouse forward of stack Leo Van Ginderen,

D: 500 tons (570 fl) **S:** 14 kts **Dim:** 58.0 × 8.6 × 2.3
Electron Equipt:
Radar: 1/Don-2 or Spin Trough nav.
IFF: 1/High Pole A transponder
M: 2 Type 9D diesels; 2 props; 2,200 bhp **Crew:** 77 tot.

Remarks: GKS—*Gidroakusticheskoye Kontrol'noye Sudno* (Hydro-acoustic Mo ing Ship)—indicates that these ships measure the radiated noise of other ships, i ing submarines, by laying hydrophone arrays via the numerous small davits they aft. One 37-mm AA gun can be installed on the forecastle. At least two (GKS-2 have been stricken, and many of the others listed above have probably also discarded or relegated to service as berthing hulks.

DEGAUSSING/DEPERMING SHIPS

◆ **18 (+ . . .) Bereza class (Project 130)**
Bldr: Stocznia Północna, Gdańsk, Poland (In serv. 1985–. . .)

SR-23 SR-137 SR-478 SR-560 SR-939
SR-59 SR-216 SR-479 SR-569 SR-. . .
SR-74 SR-245 SR-541 SR-570
SR-120 SR-253 SR-548 SR-938

)EGAUSSING/DEPERMING SHIPS *(continued)*

R-939 French Navy, 1-90

-568 Leo Van Ginderen, 10-91

): 2,094 tons (fl) **S:** 15.5 kts **Dim:** 69.50 × 13.80 × 4.0
lectron Equipt:
Radar: 1/Kivach nav.
IFF: 1/High Pole B transponder
I: 2 Cegielski-Sulzer 8TD48 diesels; 2 CP Kort-nozzle props; 4,400 bhp (3,600 sust.)—bow-thruster
lectric: . . . **Range:** . . . **Crew:** 50 tot. (civilian)

narks: SR—*Sudno Razmagnichivanya* (Deperming Vessel). Design appears to be ed on that of the *Yug*-class oceanographic ship, with the forecastle raised one deck ier. A large crane is fitted aft to handle deperming cables. One sister delivered to garia in mid-1989. Why the Soviet Navy was simultaneously acquiring two quite erent classes of deperming tenders is not understood. At least two more were ding at the time of the collapse of the Soviet Union.

21 (+ . . .) Pelym class (Project 1799) Bldr: Khabarovsk SY (In serv. 1971–. . .)

26	SR-180	SR-221	SR-280	SR-. . .
70	SR-191	SR-222	SR-281	
77	SR-203	SR-233	SR-407	
111	SR-215	SR-241	SR-409	
179	SR-218	SR-276	SR-455	

:6—latest version, with forecastle deck extended to stern Boris Lemachko, 1990

1,300 tons (fl) **S:** 16 kts **Dim:** 65.5 × 11.6 × 3.4
ectron Equipt: Radar: 1/Don-2 nav.
2 diesels; 2 props; 4,000 bhp
nge: 4,500/12 **Crew:** 40 tot. (civilian)

rks: Numbers in the SR—*Sudno Razmagnichivanya* (Deperming Vessel) se- pparently intended to replace the aged Sekstan and Korall classes. One trans- to Cuba in 1982. Late units have a tripod mast aft to support radio antenna early ships had an aerial spreader on the stack. The most recent variant has the stle deck extended right aft to the stern to provide stowage for a rectangular raft nown function.

SR-241—mid-series version, with tripod mast aft M.O.D., Bonn, 7-86

SR-222—early unit, with tripod on stack J.M.S.D.F., 6-85

ICEBREAKERS

Note: The Russian Navy has far and away the largest and most powerful icebreaker fleet in the world. Its civilian component includes the atomic-powered *Arktika* class. The two types, patrol and support, that the navy operates are both based on the same civilian design and are among the very few conventionally driven icebreakers in service to be designed and built in the former U.S.S.R.

◆ **2 Ivan Susanin-class (Project 97-17) port icebreakers**
Bldr: Admiralty SY, St. Petersburg

IVAN SUSANIN (In serv. 1974) RUSLAN (In serv. 1981)

Ivan Susanin 1983

D: 3,400 tons (fl) **S:** 14.5 kts
Dim: 70.0 (62.0 pp) × 18.3 × 6.5
Electron Equipt:
Radar: 2/Don-Kay nav.—IFF: 1/High Pole B transponder
M: 3 Type 13D100 diesels, electric drive; 2 props; 5,400 shp
Electric: 1,000 kw **Range:** 5,500/12.5; 13,000/9.4
Fuel: 550 tons **Crew:** 140 tot.

Remarks: Based on the *Dobrynya Nikitich* and *Vladimir Kavrayskiy* design. Sisters *Aysberg*, *Dunay*, *Imeni XXV Syezda K.P.S.S.*, and *Imeni XXVI Syezda K.P.S.S.* remain armed and were operated by the KGB Maritime Border Guard as PSKR—*Pogranichnyy Storozhevoy Korabl'* (Border Patrol Ship). Helicopter deck aft, but no hangar. Both had their guns and Owl Screech and Strut Curve radars removed, were repainted black and white, and are operated as naval icebreakers.

◆ **6 Dobrynya Nikitich-class (Project 97) port icebreakers**
Bldr: Admiralty SY, St. Petersburg (In serv. 1959–74)

BURAN	IL'YA MUROMETS	PURGA
DOBRYNYA NIKITICH	PERESVET	SADKO

D: 2,940 tons (fl) **S:** 14.5 kts **Dim:** 67.7 × 18.3 × 6.1
Electron Equipt:
Radar: 1–2/Don-2 nav.
IFF: 1/High Pole B transponder
M: 3 13D100 diesels, electric drive; 3 props (1 fwd); 5,400 shp
Range: 5,500/12; 13,000/9.4 **Crew:** 80 tot.

ICEBREAKERS *(continued)*

Sadko U.S. Navy, 9-91

Il'ya Muromets U.S. Navy, 6-90

Remarks: More than twenty of this class were built, the remainder being civilian. *Peresvet, Purga, Sadko,* and *Vyuga* were armed with 2/57-mm AA (II × 1) and 2/25-mm AA (II × 1), now removed. Resemble the *Ivan Susanin* class, but have much less superstructure and an open fantail rigged for ocean towing. Later units do not have a bow propeller but have the same shaft horsepower. The name *Purga* is also carried by a Maritime Border Guard patrol icebreaker. Pacific Ocean Fleet sister *Vyuga* was stricken 1991.

TRAINING SHIPS

◆ **3 Smol'nyy class (Project 887)** Bldr: A. Warski SY, Szczecin, Poland (In serv. 1976–78)

Khasan Perekop Smol'nyy

Smol'nyy Skyfotos, 8-85

Perekop Pradignac & Léo, 6-91

D: 8,500 tons (fl) **S:** 20 kts **Dim:** 138.00 × 18.60 × 6.00
A: 4/76.2-mm 59-cal. AK-276 DP (II × 2)—4/30-mm AK-230 AA (II × 2)—RBU-2500 ASW RL (XII × 2)
Electron Equipt:
Radar: 1/Don-Kay nav., 2/Don-2 nav., 1/Spin Trough nav., 1/Head Net-C surf./air search, 1/Owl Screech f.c., 1/Drum Tilt f.c.
Sonar: hull-mounted MF search, searchlight HF attack
EW: 2/Watch Dog intercept
IFF: 1/Salt Pot transponder, interrogation via Head Net-C radar
M: 2 16-cylinder diesels; 2 props; 30,000 bhp **Range:** 12,000/15
Crew: 40 officers, 126 enlisted + 270–300 cadets

Remarks: Built to relieve the *Sverdlov*-class cruisers that were formerly used for cadet training. Carry six rowboats aft for exercising the cadets. Have similar navigational training facilities to the Ugra-class training ships. Because of their armament and endurance, could be used as convoy escorts in an emergency. *Khasan* collided with and sank Turkish torpedo boat *Melten* on 25-9-85.

◆ **2 Ugra class (Project 1889U)**
Bldr: Chernomorskoy Zavod, Nikolayev (In serv. 1970–71)

Borodino Gangut

Borodino U.S. Navy, 7-9

Gangut M.O.D., Bonn, 19

D: 6,900 tons (9,650 fl) **S:** 17 kts **Dim:** 145.0 × 17.7 × 6.4
A: 8/57-mm 7-cal. AK-257 automatic DP (II × 4)
Electron Equipt:
Radar: 4/Don-2 nav., 1/Strut Curve surf./air search, 2/Muff Cob f.c
Sonar: . . .—EW: 4/Watch Dog intercept
IFF: 1/High Pole B transponder, interrogation via Strut Curve rad
M: 4 diesels; 2 props; 8,000 bhp
Range: 21,000/10 **Crew:** 300 crew + 400 cadets

Remarks: Soviet type designation: *Uchebnoye Sudo* (Training Ship), hence the "U the project number. Similar to the submarine-tender version, but have accom dations and training facilities in place of workshops, magazines, storerooms, etc. larged after deckhouse incorporates navigation-training space, including nume duplicate navigator's positions. No helicopter facilities. *Borodino* serves the Pa Ocean Fleet, *Gangut* the Black Sea Fleet.

◆ **2 Modified Polish Wodnik class (Project 888)**
Bldr: Stocznia Północna, Gdańsk, Poland (In serv. 1977)

Oka Luga

Oka M.O.D., Bonn, 1

D: 1,500 tons (1,750 fl) **S:** 17 kts **Dim:** 72.0 × 12.0 × 4.0
Electron Equipt: Radar: 3/Don-2 nav.
M: 2 Cegielski-Sulzer 6TD48 diesels; 2 CP props; 3,600 bhp
Electric: 594 kw **Range:** 7,500/11
Crew: 58 tot. + 90 cadets

Remarks: Used for navigation training. Similar to Polish and former East Ge units of the *Wodnik* class, but have slightly larger superstructures, pilothouse on higher, and are not armed. Based on the Moma design. Both in Baltic Fleet.

◆ **. . . (+ 2) UK-3 class (Polish Project TS-39) training cutters**
Bldr: Stocznia Wisla, Gdańsk, Poland (In serv. 1982-. . .)

TRAINING SHIPS *(continued)*

K-3-class UK-3/9 Siegfried Breyer

K-3-class training craft Petrushka Leo Van Ginderen, 1991

D: 341 tons (fl) **S:** 10.5 kts
Dim: 39.41 (36.00 pp) × 8.80 × 2.15
Electron Equipt: Radar: 2/Mius nav.
M: 2 diesels; 2 props; 570 bhp
Crew: 13 tot. + 30 instructors and students

marks: Delivery of first of a second series, planned for 1991, was halted by the lapse of the Soviet Union; a second was ordered during 4-91. Resemble the SK-620-ss hospital cutters. Hull numbers are in the UK (*Uchebniy Kater*—Training Cutter) ies.

25 Polish Bryza (Project OS-1)-class training cutters
Bldr: Stocznia Wisla, Gdańsk, Poland (In serv. 1970s)

D: 146.7 tons (fl) **S:** 10.5 kts **Dim:** 28.82 × 6.60 × 1.85
Electron Equipt: Radar: 2/. . . nav.
M: 2 Wola diesels; 2 props; 300 bhp
Electric: 84 kw **Range:** 1,100/10
Crew: 11 tot. + 26 students

narks: Used at various naval training centers for basic navigation and maneuver-training. Some also used by merchant marine training academies.

CHT

1 ex-German naval yacht Bldr: H.C. Stülcken Sohn, Hamburg

	Laid down	L	In serv.
GARA (ex-*Nadir*, ex-*Hela*)	23-11-37	28-12-38	16-10-40

D: 2,113 tons (2,520 fl) **S:** 21 kts (19.3 sust.)
Dim: 99.80 (92.50 wl) × 12.70 (12.20 wl) × 3.70 (4.05 max.)
Electron Equipt:
Radar: 1/Spin Trough nav., 1/Don-2 nav.
M: 2 M.A.N. Type W9Vu 40/46 diesels; 2 props; 8,360 bhp
Range: 2,000/15 **Fuel:** 188 tons **Crew:** 224 tot.

arks: Built as a fleet tender (i.e., yacht) for the German Navy; acquired 1946 as rations by the U.S.S.R. Refitted in Greece 1983 and in 1989. Little changed from nal appearance. Used as yacht for C-in-C Russian Fleet and for commander, Black Fleet.

: Each fleet commander also has a high-speed yacht of about 80-ton displacement.

ALS SHIPS AND CRAFT

acoustic systems trials barge
Bldr: United Admiralty SY, St. Petersburg

KAL (L: 31-1-91)

. . . tons **Dim:** 100.0 × 30.0 × . . .

Remarks: Intended for service on Lake Ladoga near St. Petersburg as an underseas sensors and weapons trials support barge and to serve as repair tender for smaller auxiliaries associated with the program. Incorporates a floating dry dock.

◆ **1 Modified Sorum-class tug** Bldr: Yaroslavl SY

OS-572 (In serv. 1987)

OS-572 M.O.D., U.K., 6-89

D: 1,250 tons (1,696 fl) **S:** 14 kts **Dim:** 59.1 × 12.6 × 4.6
Electron Equipt:
Radar: 2/Don-2 nav.—IFF: 1/Salt Pot transponder
Sonar: towed linear passive hydrophone array
M: 2 Type 5-2D42 diesels, electric drive; 1 prop; 1,500 shp
Range: 6,700/13 **Fuel:** 322 tons **Crew:** 60 tot.

Remarks: Built as a trials platform, apparently for towed passive linear hydrophone (towed array) research and development. Forecastle deck extended to stern, where a raised poop houses the array. The support/deployment structure for the towed array projects past the original stern. No provision for armament.

◆ **1 or more Al'pinist class** Bldr: Yaroslavl SY (In serv. 1980s)

OS-104

OS-104 J.M.S.D.F, 1985

D: 1,200 tons (fl) **S:** 13 kts **Dim:** 53.7 (46.2 pp) × 10.5 × 4.3
Electron Equipt: Radar: 1/Don-2 nav., 1/. . . nav.
M: 1 Type 8NVD48-2U diesel; 1 CP prop; 1,320 bhp
Fuel: 162 tons **Electric:** 450 kw **Range:** 7,600/13 **Crew:** . . .

Remarks: Modification of a 322-dwt stern-haul trawler. Gallows crane at stern resembles those used to handle submersible decompression chambers on T-58-class submarine-rescue ships. Forecastle has been extended aft and supports two-level deckhouse on starboard side. OS-104 is in the Pacific Ocean Fleet.

◆ **5 Potok class** Bldr: . . . (In serv. 1978–. . .)

OS-100 OS-138 OS-145 OS-225 OS-. . .

S-225

TRIALS SHIPS AND CRAFT *(continued)*

Potok class—with missile launcher on deckhouse at stern 1986

D: 750 tons (860 fl) **S:** 17 kts **Dim:** 71.0 × 9.1 × 2.5
A: 1/533-mm TT, 1/400-mm TT
Electron Equipt: Radar: 1/Don-2 nav.
M: 2 diesels; 2 props; 4,000 bhp **Range:** 5,000/12 **Crew:** 40 tot.

Remarks: OS—*Opitnoye Sudno* (Experimental Vessel). The design closely resembles the T-58-class minesweeper, but the forecastle extends well aft. The trainable torpedo tubes are on the bow. A large crane aft is presumably used for retrieval. These ships were replacements for modified T-43-class minesweepers that had been used in torpedo trials since the 1950s. One Potok was employed with trials for the SA-N-10 point-defense SAM system.

Note: There are probably a number of additional ships of various classes with OS—*Opitnoye Sudno* (Experimental Vessel)—pendants, either built for the purpose or former combatants or auxiliaries adapted for specific trials duties.

TARGET SERVICE CRAFT

♦ up to 9 Osa-class target-control boats

Osa target controller Leo Van Ginderen, 10-91

Remarks: Have Osa hull and propulsion. Used to operate craft shown below by remote control. Carry Square Tie surface-search/target acquisition radar and a High Pole B IFF transponder. Communications antennas have been enhanced to provide for radio control.

♦ up to 8 Modified Osa-class missile targets

KTs-897—Osa mobile target, with nets strung between the masts, radar corner reflectors at bow and stern, and two heat generators amidships 8-80

Remarks: KTs—*Kontrol'naya Tsel'* (Controlled Target). Have Osa hull and pr[o]pulsion. Crew departs when ship is in operation. Equipped with radar corner reflecto[rs] to strengthen target and two heat-generator chimneys to attract infrared homi[ng] missiles.

♦ 20 more Shelon-class torpedo retrievers

Bldr: . . . (In serv. 1978–. . .)

Shelon class torpedo retriever—canvas covers twin 25-mm AA moun[t on] foredeck French Navy,

Shelon class—note dipping sonar installation on starboard quarter M.O.D., U.K.

D: 270 tons (fl) **S:** 24 kts **Dim:** 41.0 × 6.0 × . . .
Electron Equipt:
Radar: 1/Spin Trough nav.—IFF: 1/High Pole B
Sonar: 1/Oka-1 helicopter dipping-type
M: 2 M504 diesels; 2 props; 10,000 bhp **Crew:** 40 tot.

Remarks: High-speed hull with a covered torpedo-recovery ramp aft. Has re[placed] most of the old Poluchat-I-class torpedo retrievers.

A variant of the Shelon-class torpedo-retriever design was sighted during 1983 under tow from the Black Sea to Vladivostok. Unlike earlier units it does not h[ave a] slope to the weapons-recovery area of the after portion of the deckhouse; it has no [. . .] in the deckhouse roof and no recovery hatch through the transom stern. The func[tion of] the craft, which has a crew of about 30, is unknown.

♦ up to 40 Poluchat-I-class torpedo retrievers

D: 90 tons (fl) **S:** 18 kts **Dim:** 29.6 × 6.1 × 1.9
A: 2/14.5-mm AA (II × 1) in some
Electron Equipt:
Radar: 1/Spin Trough nav.—IFF: 1/High Pole A transponder
M: 2 M50 diesels; 2 props; 2,400 bhp
Range: 450/17; 900/10 **Crew:** 20 tot.

'ARGET SERVICE CRAFT *(continued)*

oluchat-I torpedo retriever TL-850 M.O.D., U.K., 6-89

emarks: Carry numbers in the TL—*Torpedolov* (Torpedo Retriever) series. Built in e 1950s. Recovery ramp aft. Some configured as patrol boats. Many exported abroad, d a number have probably been scrapped.

ARGET BARGES

7-m target barge—with two heat-generator arrays to attract IR-homing ssiles; target arrays can be altered as needed Gerhard Koop, 1985

meter catamaran gunnery-terget barge M.O.D., U.K., 6-88

mer Khabarov-class cargo ship—in use as a missile target barge U.S. Navy, 6-90

'ING TENDERS

2 Yelva class (In serv. 1973–. . .)

143 VM-146 VM-154 VM-266 VM-268 VM-413
414 VM-416 VM-420 VM-425 VM-807 VM-809

: 295 tons (fl) **S:** 12.4 kts **Dim:** 40.90 (37.00 pp) × 8.00 × 2.07
ectron Equipt: Radar: 1/Spin Trough nav.
: 2 Type 3D12A diesels; 2 props; 600 bhp **Electric:** 200 kw
nge: 1,870/12 **Endurance:** 10 days **Crew:** 30 tot.

arks: Can support seven divers at once to 60 m. Have a built-in decompression ber; some (but not all) also have a submersible decompression chamber. Replaced minesweepers built for the role. Several exported and a number are in Russian ıse. Russian class name: *Krab-M*.

VM-268, Yelva class Gerhard Koop, 1985

♦ **several Flamingo class** (In serv. late 1970s)

D: 42 tons (fl) **S:** 12 kts **Dim:** 21.20 × 3.93 × 1.40
Electron Equipt: Radar: 1/Lotsiya nav. (not always fitted)
M: 1 Type 3D12A diesel; 1 prop; 300 bhp **Electric:** 12 kw
Range: 200/12 **Endurance:** 5 days **Crew:** 3 tot. + 5 divers

Flamingo class, configured as a workboat—PO-2 workboat in background 1991

PO-2 class PSK 676 Leo Van Ginderen, 1991

Remarks: Also produced in a workboat version with a full-load displacement of 54.0 tons, a maximum speed of 11 knots, and a capacity for 27 passengers or 17 tons of cargo. Developed from the PO 2/Nyryat-2 design but not built in as large numbers; also rail-transportable. The diving launch version can support divers to 45 m.

♦ **several Nyryat-1 class** (In serv. late 1950s–mid 1960s)

D: 120 tons (fl) **S:** 12 kts **Dim:** 29.0 × 5.0 × 1.7
Electron Equipt: Radar: 1/Spin Trough nav.
M: 1 diesel; 1 prop; 450 bhp **Endurance:** 10 days
Range: 1,600/10 **Crew:** 15 tot.

Remarks: Carry VM—*Vodolaznyy Morskoy* (Seagoing Diving Tender)—pendants. Same hull used for GPB-480-class inshore survey craft. Many exported.

♦ **several Nyryat-2 class** (In serv. 1950s)

VM-9, Nyryat-1 class—Black Sea Fleet C-in-C's yacht in background Antonio Scrimali, 1990

DIVING TENDERS *(continued)*

Nyryat-1 644—modified as a personnel tender U.S. Navy, 9-90

D: 50 tons (fl) **S:** 9 kts **Dim:** 21.0 × 4.5 × . . .
Electron Equipt: Radar: 1/Spin Trough nav. or none
M: 1 Type 3D6 diesel; 1 prop; 150 bhp **Crew:** 10 tot.

Remarks: Uses same hull as PO-2-class utility launch; distinguishable by bulwarks to hull at bow and stern. Hundreds of PO-2 hulls were built; many were exported, and a great many have been discarded. Are rail-transportable.

FIREBOATS

♦ **9 Morkov (PZhK-415)-class fireboats**
Bldr: . . . U.S.S.R. (In serv. 1984–85)

PZhK-415 PZhK-1514 PZhK-1544 PZhK-1547 PZhK-1859 etc.

D: 320 tons (fl) **S:** 12.5 kts **Dim:** 36.53 × 7.80 × 2.20
Electron Equipt: Radar: 1/Spin Trough nav.
M: 2 Type ZKD 12N-520 diesels; 2 CP props; 1,040 bhp
Range: 450/12.5 **Electric:** 400 kw **Crew:** 20 tot.

Remarks: Four fire-fighting water monitors, two with 220 m^3/hr. capacity and two of 500 m^3/hr., driven by two 750 m^3/hr diesel-powered pumps. Foam and Freon extinguishing systems. Water curtain to protect boat. Can also be used for towing. Resemble large harbor tugs.

♦ **. . . Pozharnyy-I-class fireboats** (In serv. 1950s)

D: 180 tons (fl) **S:** 17 kts **Dim:** 35.0 × 6.2 × 2.0
M: 2 Type M50F-1 diesels; 2 props; 1,800 bhp

HARBOR TUGS

Note: Three new harbor tugs for the former Soviet Navy were ready for delivery from Poland in 9-91 but could not be transferred because they had not been paid for; no characteristics available.

♦ **. . . Stividor class** Bldr: . . .

RB-325 Boris Lemachko

D: 340 tons (fl) **S:** 12 kts **Dim:** 30.0 × 8.3 × 3.2
M: 2 diesels; 2 Kort-nozzle props; 1,200 bhp

Remarks: Successor design to *Prometey* class; probably also built at Petrozavod SY, St. Petersburg. Have two firefighting water monitors.

♦ **100+ Prometey-class large harbor tugs**
Bldr: Petrozavod SY, St. Petersburg; Gorokhovets SY (In serv. 1971–1980s)

D: 319 tons (fl) **S:** 12 kts **Dim:** 29.8 (28.2 pp) × 8.3 × 3.2
Electron Equipt: Radar: 1/Spin Trough
M: 2 Type 6D30/50-4 diesels; 2 Kort-nozzle props; 1,200 bhp
Electric: 50 kw **Range:** 1,800/12 **Fuel:** 30 tons **Crew:** 3–5 tot.

Remarks: Known to NATO as the "Saka" class. Some have been exported. Also in civil use. Have 14-ton bollard pull, ice-strengthened hull. Over 100 built since 1971.

Prometey-class RB-202 198

♦ **26 Sidehole-II-class harbor tugs**
Bldr: Petrozavod SY, St. Petersburg (In serv. 1970s)

Civilian unit of Sidehole-II class Leo Van Ginderen, 19

D: 197 tons (fl) **S:** 10 kts **Dim:** 24.2 × 7.0 × 3.4
Electron Equipt: Radar: 1/Spin Trough nav.
M: 2 Type 6 CHN25/34 diesels; 2 vertical cycloidal props; 900 bhp

Remarks: Russian class name: *Peredovik.* Also in civil use. Bollard pull: 10.5 to Naval units have RB—*Rednyy Buksir* (Roadstead Tug) pendants.

♦ **30 Sidehole-I-class harbor tugs** (In serv. 1960s)

D: 183 tons (fl) **S:** 9 kts **Dim:** 24.4 × 7.0 × 3.3
Electron Equipt: Radar: 1/Spin Trough
M: 2 Type 6 CH25/34 diesels; 2 vertical cycloidal props; 600 bhp

♦ **several Tugur-class harbor tugs** (In serv. 1950s)

D: 300 tons (fl) **S:** 12 kts **Dim:** 30.7 × 7.7 × 2.3
M: 1 set triple-expansion reciprocating steam; 1 prop; 500 ihp
Boilers: 2, watertube **Crew:** . . . tot.

Remarks: Despite age and obsolescent design, a number are still in use at Russ naval bases. Originally burned coal, but were probably later altered to burn oil.

FUEL LIGHTERS

♦ **. . . Toplivo-2 class** Bldr: U.S.S.R. and Egypt (In serv. 1958–1975)

D: 466 tons (1,180 tons fl) **S:** 10 kts
Dim: 54.26 (49.40 pp) × 7.40 × 3.10
Electron Equipt: Radar: 1/Spin Trough nav.
M: 1 Russkiy Dizel 6 DR30/50-5-2 diesel; 1 prop; 600 bhp
Electric: 250 kw **Fuel:** 19 tons **Range:** 1,500/10 **Crew:** 24 to

PUS-1—Toplivo-2-class water tanker Leo Van Ginderen,

‍JEL LIGHTERS *(continued)*

'N-96—Toplivo-2-class fuel tanker French Navy, 11-86

‍marks: 308 grt/508 dwt. Four cargo tanks, totaling 606 m. Built in several versions ‍uding fuel-oil lighter, water lighter, and diesel-fuel lighter. Final series built at ‍xandria, Egypt, with deliveries terminated by Soviet expulsion. Fully seagoing if ‍uired.

. . . Toplivo-3 class (In serv. 1950s)

‍): 1,300 tons (fl) S: 9 kts Dim: 53.0 × 10.0 × 3.0
‍M: 1 diesel; 1 prop; 300 bhp

‍narks: Low-freeboard, low-superstructure harbor craft. There are probably a few ‍e smaller (450-ton fl) Toplivo-1-class harbor fuel lighters remaining, but a number ‍nits of both classes have been stricken.

‍COMMODATIONS BARGES

‍up to 57 Bolva series
‍Bldr: Valmet Oy, Helsinki, Finland (In serv. 1960–84)

‍HTUBA	Michurinsk	Tosna
‍ROID	Mologa	Tura
‍JGAVA	Naryn	Vava
‍JYA	Olensk	Vazuza
‍SH	Olonka	Veksa
‍H	Saida	Venta
‍TRA	Samarga	Viga
‍ANGA	Sayma	Vorkuta
‍M	Severnaya	Vuoksa
‍LAS	Sungai	Zapolyare
‍S	Tagil	up to 25 others

‍s—Bolva-III class with auditorium aft Valmet, 1978

‍6,500 tons (fl) **Dim:** 113.5 (110.9 pp) × 13.8 × 2.8
‍ew: 374–394 total berthing

‍arks: 4,448 grt/1,000 dwt. First series of 8 Bolva-I built 1960–63, second series of ‍lva-II built 1963–72, with hangar-like auditorium built atop superstructure aft. ‍-III built 1971–. . . , with 62 completed. The last three were ordered in 1983. ‍went to civilian service. Sister *Salgir* was transferred to Bulgaria in 1989, and at ‍one has been sold to a European customer for commerical use as a floating hotel.

. . Vyn-class (In serv. 1960s)

‍3,000 tons (fl) **Dim:** 92.0 × 13.4 × 4.6
‍ew: approx. 200

‍rks: Converted from cargo barges built in Finland in the late 1940s to early ‍. One was based in Somalia during the mid-1970s. Apparently support sub‍es, as there is a torpedo-loading hatch. Pendant numbers in the PKZ—‍*chiya Kazarma* (Floating Barracks) series. A considerable number have been ‍ded, and only a handful probably remain in use.

‍ELLANEOUS SERVICE CRAFT

‍nuclear support barge Bldr: Rauma-Repola, Savonlinna, Finland
‍A-1 (In serv. 9-86)

‍1,700 tons (fl) **Dim:** 63.00 × 12.00 × 2.30

‍rks: Launched 21-3-86. Intended to provide radiation-hazard disposal, decon‍ation, laboratory services, and refit assistance to nuclear-powered ships at ‍ansk. There are large numbers of other classes of service barges.

♦ 1 historical relic, former armored cruiser

	Bldr	Laid down	L	In serv.
Avrora	New Admiralty SY, St. Petersburg	6-97	5-00	1903

Avrora Maritime Photographic, 5-91

D: 6,732 tons normal (7,271 fl) **S:** 19 kts
Dim: 126.83 (123.47 wl) × 16.63 × 7.30 max
A: 14/130-mm low-angle (I × 14)—5/45-mm AA (I × 5)
M: 3 sets vertical triple-expansion steam; 3 props; 13,000 ihp
Boilers: 20 Belleville-Dolgolenko
Range: 1,200/18; 1,778/10 **Fuel:** 800 tons coal (732 normal)
Electric: 3 generators **Crew:** 129 officers, 318 enlisted

Remarks: Famous as the ship that fired the signal starting the Bolshevik Revolution, on 25-10-17. Used for training between World Wars I and II; damaged during WW II. A museum since 1948, with over 19 million visitors to date. Underwent massive restoration at Zhdanov SY, St. Petersburg, essentially receiving a new 32-mm hull plating intended to last for several centuries; refloated early 1987 and rededicated 25-10-87. Data above pertain to the ship in 1917.

MINISTRY OF FISHERIES

FISHERIES PATROL SHIPS

♦ 4 Komandor-class fisheries protection ships
Bldr: Danyard, Frederikshavn, Denmark

	L	In serv.
Komandor	. . .	8-89
Shkiper Gyek	4-89	20-12-89
Herluf Bidstrup	8-89	2-90
Manchzhur	4-5-90	6-7-90

Komandor Danyard, 1989

Shkiper Gyek 10-90

FISHERIES PATROL SHIPS *(continued)*

D: 2,425 tons (fl) **S:** 20 kts (19.2 cruising)
Dim: 88.90 (82.20 wl) × 13.60 × 4.70 (mean)
A: none—1/Ka-32S Helix-D SAR helicopter
Electron Equipt: Radar: 3/. . . nav. (1 Furuno)
M: 2 Russkiy-Pielstick 6 PC 2.5 L400 diesels; 1/4-bladed CP prop; 7,786 bhp—1/500-shp bow-thruster
Electric: 1,840 kw (1 × 600-kw shaft gen., 2 × 620-kw diesel sets)
Range: 7,000/19.2 **Crew:** 42 tot.

Remarks: 2,800 grt/534 dwt. Ordered 11-11-87. Operated for and by the Russian Ministry of Fisheries in the Northern Pacific area. The helicopter is stored in a two-deck-high hangar beneath the flight deck, which is 14 m long and has folding sides to increase its width. Have Blohm + Voss folding fin stabilizers. Carry two unsinkable GRP lifeboats and two rigid inflatables—one for inspection duties.

CIVILIAN SPACE-EVENT SUPPORT SHIPS

Note: The ships listed below are subordinated to the Academy of Sciences and are primarily intended to provide communications relay services with manned satellites.

♦ 0 (+1) Akademik Nikolay Pilyugin class
Bldr: United Admiralty SY, St. Petersburg

	Laid down	L	In serv.
AKADEMIK NIKOLAY PILYUGIN	15-4-88	1991	. . .

D: . . . tons (fl) **S:** . . . kts **Dim:** . . . × . . . × . . .
Electron Equipt: Radar: . . .
M: . . . . . . **Crew:** . . .

Remarks: Probably intended to replace the aged *Kosmonavt Vladimir Komarov.* Will have three Ship Bowl and two Ship Shell stabilized communications dishes. Incorrectly described as a modified version of the naval *Marshal Nedelin* class in the previous edition. Completion may be delayed or canceled as a result of the economic chaos in Russia.

♦ 4 Kosmonavt Pavel Belyayev class
Bldr: Zhdanov SY, St. Petersburg

	In serv.	Conv.
KOSMONAVT GEORGIY DOBROVOLSKIY (ex-*Semyon Kosinov*)	1968	1978
KOSMONAVT PAVEL BELYAYEV (ex-*Vytegrales*)	1963	1977
KOSMONAVT VIKTOR PATSEYEV (ex-*Nazar Gubin*)	1968	1978
KOSMONAVT VLADISLAV VOLKOV (ex-*Yeniseiles*)	1964	1977

D: 9,100 tons (fl) **S:** 16 kts
Dim: 121.8 (113.0 pp) × 16.7 × 7.3
Electron Equipt:
Radar: 1/Don-2 nav., 1/Okean nav., 1/Mod. Kite Screech tracking
M: Bryansk-Burmeister & Wain 950 VTBF 110 diesel; 1 prop; 5,200 bhp
Fuel: 350 tons **Range:** 7,400/15
Crew: 56 tot. + 70–80 technicians

Kosmonavt Viktor Patseyev U.S. Navy, 4-90

Kosmonavt Vladislav Volkov Leo Van Ginderen, 3-90

Remarks: 4,482 grt/2,010 dwt. Conversions from *Vytegrales*-class timber ca performed at the building yard. Named for cosmonauts killed on missions. Have stabilized Quad Spring communications array amidships and three smaller sa communications arrays. Based at St. Petersburg.

♦ 1 Kosmonavt Yuriy Gagarin class
Bldr: Baltic SY, St. Petersb

KOSMONAVT YURIY GAGARIN (In serv. 12-71)

Kosmonavt Yuriy Gagarin Leo Van Ginderen

D: 53,500 tons (fl) **S:** 18 kts
Dim: 231.7 (213.9 pp) × 31.1 × 10.0
Electron Equipt: Radar: 1/Don-Kay nav., 1/Okean nav.
M: 2 sets geared steam turbines, electric drive; 1 prop; 19,000 shp
Boilers: 2 **Range:** 24,000/17.7
Crew: 160 tot. + 180 scientists/technicians

Remarks: 32,291 grt/31,300 dwt. A *Sofiya*-class tanker hull adapted prior struction. Has two 27-m-diameter Ship Shell and two 12.5-m diameter Ship stabilized communications dishes, two Vee Tube HF, and four Quad Ring arrays and stern-thrusters. Three swimming pools, 300-seat theater; gymnasium. Endu 120 days. Home port: Odessa.

♦ 1 Akademik Sergey Korolev class
Bldr: Chernomorskiy SY, Nikolayev

AKADEMIK SERGEY KOROLEV (In serv. 1970)

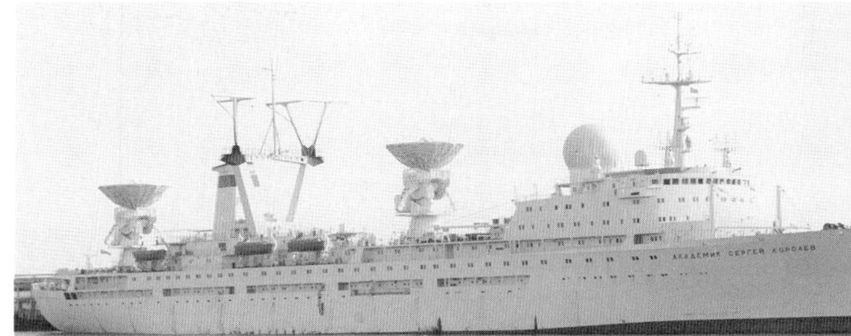
Akademik Sergey Korolev French Navy

D: 21,465 tons (fl) **S:** 17 kts
Dim: 181.9 (167.9 pp) × 25.0 × 7.9
Electron Equipt:
Radar: 1/Okean nav., 1/Don-2 nav.
M: 1 Bryansk-Burmeister & Wain diesel; 1 prop; 12,000 bhp
Range: 22,500/17 **Crew:** 188 tot. + 170 technicians

Remarks: 17,114 grt/7,067 dwt. Has 80 "laboratories." Space communicatio tennas include two Ship Bowl and one Ship Globe and four Quad Ring.

Note: The four *Borovichi*-class space-event support ships, *Borovichi, Kegostro zhovets,* and *Nevel,* were sold 12-89 for scrapping.

♦ 1 Kosmonavt Vladimir Komarov class
Bldr: Kherson SY (In serv. 1966)

KOSMONAVT VLADIMIR KOMAROV (ex-*Genichevsk*)

Kosmonavt Vladimir Komarov U.S. Navy

IAN SPACE-EVENT SUPPORT SHIPS *(continued)*

.7,500 tons (fl) **S:** 17.5 kts **Dim:** 155.7 (146.4 pp) × 22.3 × 8.6
tron Equipt: Radar: 2 Don Kay nav.
1 Bryansk-Burmeister & Wain diesel; 1 prop; 9,000 bhp
ge: 16,700/17.5 **Fuel:** 1,656 tons **Crew:** 254 tot.

ks: 13,935 grt/7,065 dwt. Converted from a *Poltava*-class bulk carrier at Baltic ingrad, completing 7-67. Hull amidships widened by full-height bulges. Was to gun conversion 1989 at Baltic SY to an environmental research ship, but work been accomplished by late spring 1992, when she made a trip to the Mideast to e the Russian space program.

CIVILIAN SCIENTIFIC RESEARCH SHIPS

hips listed below are subordinated to a variety of scientific organizations. Many military-related research. Major fisheries research ships are presented, but a mber of smaller trawlers are omitted for reasons of space. Ships are presented rse order of class introduction. Many of the older units, particularly those y involved in fisheries-related research, will probably be offered for scrap in the ure. The Russian economic situation forced a significant reduction in scientific ionary cruising during 1991 that is likely to continue for some time.

to construct several units of the 3,442-grt Polish B-865-class oceanographic sign have apparently been put on hold; the ships would have been capable of nd would have had dimensions of 83.6 × 15.0, with a crew of 64.

+1) research icebreaker Bldr: Masa Yard, Helsinki

. . . . (In serv. 1993?)

grt research icebreaker Masa Yard, 1991

18,000 tons (fl) **S:** . . . kts **Dim:** . . . × . . . × . . .
diesel-electric; 2 props; . . . shp

ks: 8,700 grt. Builder reports planned for completion in 1993, but contract may een canceled due to state of Russian finances. Intended for the Ministry of y.

+1) Aleksey Maryshev class
r: Hollming, Rauma and Turku, Finland

	Laid down	L	In serv.
SEY MARYSHEV	8-1-90	30-3-90	1991
R KOTTSOV	3-90	28-5-90	1991
. . . .	5-90	. . .	. . .

sey Maryshev Leo Van Ginderen, 1991

1,570 tons **S:** 13.9 kts
n: 64.90 (61.54 pp) × 12.92 × 3.60
ctron Equipt: Radar: 3/. . . nav.
2 Wärtsilä 8R22 HFO diesels; 1 CP prop; 3,500 bhp—bow-thruster
ctric: 750 kw (3 × 250-kw diesel sets) **Crew:** 40 tot.

rks: 557 dwt. Ordered 3-6-89 for use as hydrographic survey ships. Have a hold forward served by an 8-ton-capacity electric crane and generally resemble navigational aids tenders. Carry a small landing craft as a tender and also have two lifeboats, a rigid-inflatable boat and a smaller boat stowed aft. Third unit possibly canceled.

◆ **1 small research ship** Bldr: . . . (In serv. 1990)

TSIKLON

D: 190 tons (fl) **S:** 9.5 kts
Dim: 26.50 (22.00 pp) × 6.60 × 2.06
Electron Equipt: Radar: . . . . . .
M: 1 Russkiy Dizel 6ChNSP 18/22 diesel; 1 prop; 224 bhp
Range: . . ./. . . **Crew:** . . . tot.

Remarks: 115 grt/24 dwt. Home-ported at Izmail near the mouth of the Danube in Ukrainian territory; may have been taken over by Ukraine.

◆ **2 Professor Fedinskiy class** Bldr: Rauma-Repola, Savonlinna, Finland

	L	In serv.
PROFESSOR FEDINSKIY	11-4-87	1-3-89
PROFESSOR RYABINKIN	24-8-87	28-6-89

D: approx. 580 tons (fl) **S:** 11 kts
Dim: 49.80 (46.40 pp) × 10.50 × 2.00
Electron Equipt: Radar: . . .—Sonar: . . .
M: 2 diesels, electric drive; 2 rudder-props; 1,114 shp
Fuel: 95 tons **Crew:** 30 tot.

Remarks: 920 grt. Ordered 28-2-85 for hydrographic research.

◆ **1 small geophisical research ship** Bldr: . . .

PROFESSOR PAVLOVSKIY

D: 206 tons (fl) **S:** 12 kts
Dim: 28.80 (25.25 pp) × 6.12 × 2.05
Electron Equipt: Radar: . . . . . .
M: 1 Ruskiy Dizel 12ChSP 15/18 diesel; 1 Ruskiy diesel 6ChSP 15/18 diesel; 1 prop; . . ./. . . bhp
Range: . . ./. . . **Crew:** . . . tot.

Remarks: 155 grt/21 dwt.

◆ **1 Mir-class sail-research training ship**
Bldr: Stocznia Gdańsk, Poland (L: 30-7-89)

PALLADA

Pallada U.S. Navy, 1991

D: 2,986 tons (fl) **S:** 17 kts
Dim: 108.6 (105.5 hull) × 14.0 × 6.6
Electron Equipt: Radar: 1/. . . nav.
M: 2 Cegielski-Sulzer 8AL 20/24 diesels; 2 props; 1,140 bhp
Crew: 30 officers, 23 unlicensed + 90 trainees

Remarks: 2,062 grt. Three-masted sail-training bark adapted for training in oceanographic research techniques. Ordered 7-85. Sisters *Mir*, *Druzhba*, and *Khersones* are in merchant marine training service. Tallest mast: 49.5 m.

◆ **2 Akademik Sergei Vavilov class** Bldr: Hollming, Rauma, Finland

	Laid down	L	In serv.
AKADEMIK SERGEI VAVILOV	18-8-86	16-12-86	17-2-88
AKADEMIK IOFFE	27-2-87	28-8-87	10-2-89

CIVILIAN SCIENTIFIC RESEARCH SHIPS *(continued)*

Akademik Sergei Vavilov Leo Van Ginderen, 4-89

Akademik Ioffe—note sails stowed amidships Leo Van Ginderen, 7-89

D: 6,600 tons **S:** 15 kts
Dim: 117.10 (110.50 pp) × 18.20 × 5.90
Electron Equipt: Radar: 1/Okean, 1/. . . nav.
M: 2 Pielstick/Russkiy Dizel 6PC2.5 L400 (6ChN-40/60) diesels; 2 CP props; 6,800 bhp—2 Aquamaster 800-shp drop-down azimuthal thrusters aft—bow-thruster
Electric: 6,100 kVA tot. (2 × 2,000 kVA shaft generators, 2 × 1,050 diesel sets)
Range: 20,000/15 **Crew:** 75 tot. + 52 scientists and technicians

Remarks: Ordered 13-5-85. Intended for ocean floor sampling and physical oceanography. One 12-ton A-frame gantry aft, five oceanographic cranes to starboard. Have Krupp-Atlas hull-mounted deep-sea echo-sounder/bottom profiler, Hollming Echos XD bottom-mapping system, NAVAC LBL acoustic positioning system, Hollming NETOS data-acquisition network, WETOS weather station, Loran-C, Omega, and doppler log. Both have INTELSAT SATCOMM. Have a total of 20 laboratories, including meteorological, cosmic ray and radar sounding, hydrological, hydrochemical, radiometric, geological, and geophysical facilities.

Akademik Ioffe is equipped with hollow semi-cylindrical, hydraulically raised "sails" for use during silent operations. *Akademik Sergei Vavilov* was offered for Baltic tourist cruising during 1991, and it is apparent that funds to operate these ships in their designed rôle are lacking.

♦ 1 Antarctic research ship Bldr: Rauma-Repola, Savonlinna, Finland

	Laid down	L	In serv.
Akademik Fedorov	29-8-86	27-2-87	8-87

D: 16,200 tons (fl) **S:** 16 kts **Dim:** 141.2 × 23.5 × 8.5
Electron Equipt: Radar: 2/Okean-series nav.
M: 2 Wärtsilä Vasa R32, 6-cyl. 11,222-hp diesels, electric drive; 1 prop; 16,000 shp—1,700-hp bow-thruster
Range: 20,000/16 **Endurance:** 80 days
Crew: 90 crew + 160 scientists/passengers

Akademik Fedorov Leo Van Ginderen, 1991

Remarks: 12,660 grt/7,200 dwt. Operated for the Arctic and Antarctic Institu Intended as replacement for *Mikhail Somov* as Antarctic expedition and supply sh Ordered 12-85. Can operate in up to 1.8-m-thick ice. Helicopter deck, with hangar one Ka-32S Helix-D. Two 50-ton and two 10-ton cranes. Carries one ramped land craft. Commenced initial Antarctic cruise 12-87.

♦ 7 Vadim Popov class Bldr: Laivateollisuus SY, Turku, Finland

	Laid down	L	In serv.
Vadim Popov	15-10-85	3-86	6-10-86
Viktor Buynitskiy	21-11-85	15-4-86	30-11-86
Pavel Gordienko	14-2-86	25-6-86	2-87
Vasiliy Lominadze	15-4-86	31-10-86	5-5-87
Igor Maksimov	25-6-86	17-3-87	7-10-87
Ivan Petrov	8-86	15-6-87	9-88
. . . .	27-10-87	12-11-88	1989

Ivan Petrov M.O.D., U.K.,

D: approx. 960 tons (fl) **S:** 12 kts
Dim: 49.90 (44.50 pp) × 10.00 × 3.50
Electron Equipt: Radar: 2/. . . nav.
M: 1 Wärtsilä Vasa 824-TS diesel; 1 prop; 1,340 bhp
Range: . . . **Electric:** 500 kw (2 × 250-kw diesel sets)
Crew: 21 tot. + 7 scientists/technicians (35 tot. accommodations)

Remarks: 886 grt. First four ordered 1-9-85, others on 16-5-86. Intended for hyd teorological reporting and for supply of remote weather stations in the Far East. a small beachable cargo launch forward, atop cargo hold. Have a 5-ton crane for

♦ 5 Iskatel'-2 class Bldr: Stocznia Wisla, Gdańsk, Poland

	L	In serv.
Iskatel'-2	16-12-85	11-86
Iskatel'-3	16-12-86	12-87
Iskatel'-4	. . .	1988
Iskatel'-5	. . .	. . .
Iskatel'-6	. . .	. . .

Iskatel'-4 French Nav

D: 742 tons (fl) **S:** 11.9 kts **Dim:** 49.30 (44.50 pp) × 18.20 × 1
Electron Equipt: Radar: 1/. . . nav.
M: 2 Cegielski-Sulzer 6 AL 20/24 diesels; 2 CP Kort-nozzle props; 1,140 bhp
Range: . . ./. . . **Endurance:** 10 days **Fuel:** 53.6 m^3
Electric: 600 kVA **Crew:** 15 tot. + 10 scientists

ꞮIVILIAN SCIENTIFIC RESEARCH SHIPS *(continued)*

ꞮRemarks: 600 grt. Catamaran design, using Polish *Nadezhnyy*-class trawler hull. ntended for seismological/geophysical research in shallow water in the Barents, Kara, nd Baltic seas and the Sea of Okhotsk, as part of the "Shel'f" program for offshore oil xploration. Aluminum alloy deckhouse. Equipped with both a towed hydrophone rray, with a capacity of 3,200 m of 51-mm array cable, and a pneumatic pulsator rray. Not certain whether the last two were ever built.

◆ **2 modified Akademik Aleksey Krylov class** Bldr: Okean SY, Nikolayev, Ukraine

ᴀᴋᴀᴅᴇᴍɪᴋ Nɪᴋᴏʟᴀʏ Aɴᴅʀᴇʏᴇᴠ (In serv. 10-86)
ᴀᴋᴀᴅᴇᴍɪᴋ Bᴏʀɪs Kᴏɴsᴛᴀɴᴛɪɴᴏᴠ (In serv. 3-89)

kademik Boris Konstantinov—note door at stern Peter Voss, 6-89

ademik Nikolay Andreyev—with black hull M.O.D., U.K., 6-89

): 11,600 tons (fl) **S:** 15 kts **Dim:** 142.7 (128.0 pp) × 17.5 × 7.2
Ɛlectron Equipt:
Radar: 1/Palm Frond nav., 1/Okean-A nav., 1/Okean-B nav.
M: 2 Russkiy Dizel Type 58D-6R diesels; 2 CP props; 9,000 bhp—bow- and stern-thrusters
Ɛlectric: . . . **Range:** 15,000/15 **Crew:** 117 crew + 32 scientists

narks: *Andreyev:* 9,363 grt/2,060 dwt; *Konstantinov:* 9,433 grt/2,150 dwt. An rged, lengthened version of *Akademik Aleksey Krylov*. *Andreyev* has a pronounced ous bow and facilities to starboard for handling two large submersible devices. *stantinov* also has a large hangar structure at the extreme stern for deploying an stic sensor. *Andreyev* has had her hull painted black since she originally was pleted; *Konstantinov* is all white. Both are home-ported at St. Petersburg.

2 Bavenit class Bldr: Hollming, Rauma, Finland

	Laid down	L	In serv.
ENIT	1-2-85	. . .	20-5-86
ERIT	8-5-85	17-1-86	17-12-86

nit M.O.D., U.K., 6-89

D: 5,300 tons **S:** 12.75 kts **Dim:** 85.80 (75.40 pp) × 16.80 × 5.60
Electron Equipt: Radar: . . .
M: 4 Russkiy Dizel EG-74/2 (1,700 hp) diesels, electric drive; 2 Aquamaster rudder-props; 6,000 shp
Range: 8,000/12 **Crew:** 65 tot. **Endurance:** 56 days

Remarks: 2,000 dwt. Ordered 13-4-84 for the Arctic Complex Marine Geology Expedition of the Ministry of the Oil and Gas Industry. Able to drill to 200-m depths in waters up to 300 m deep, using a 35-m derrick drill support amidships. A-frame trawl gantry at the stern. Ice-reinforced hulls. Two 1,360-hp bow-thrusters plus the two U.S.-supplied Aquamaster, 360°-pivoting props give a dynamic position-keeping capability.

◆ **9 Akademik Fersman-class (Type B-93) geophysical research ships** Bldr: A. Warski SY, Szczecin, Poland

	L	In serv.
Aᴋᴀᴅᴇᴍɪᴋ Fᴇʀsᴍᴀɴ	24-1-85	5-86
Aᴋᴀᴅᴇᴍɪᴋ Sʜᴀᴛsᴋɪʏ	19-7-85	1986
Aᴋᴀᴅᴇᴍɪᴋ Sᴇɪsᴋʟʏ	14-12-85	1986
Aᴋᴀᴅᴇᴍɪᴋ Lᴀᴢᴀʀᴇᴠ	1986	1986
Zᴇᴘʜʏʀ (ex-*Akademik Gubkin*)	24-3-87	1988
Aᴋᴀᴅᴇᴍɪᴋ Nᴀʟɪᴠᴋɪɴ	4-87	1988
Aᴋᴀᴅᴇᴍɪᴋ Nᴀᴍᴇᴛᴋɪɴ	12-7-87	1988
Aᴋᴀᴅᴇᴍɪᴋ Kʀᴇᴘs	1-88	1989
Aᴋᴀᴅᴇᴍɪᴋ Nᴇᴍᴄʜɪɴᴏᴠ	27-2-88	1989

Akademik Lazarev—standard unit M.O.D., U.K., 6-88

Akademik Nemchinov—sides plated in to stern Hans J. Verhöfen, 1991

Akademik Nametkin M.O.D., U.K., 4-90

D: 3,250 tons (fl) **S:** 14.5 kts **Dim:** 81.85 (73.50 pp) × 14.80 × 5.00
Electron Equipt:
Radar: 2/. . . nav.—Sonar: 6-km-long seismic array
M: 1 Zgoda-Sulzer 6 ZL 40/48 diesel; 1 Kort-nozzle CP prop; 4,200 bhp—bow-thruster
Electric: 2,760 kVA (1 × 1500-kVA shaft alternator, 2 × 630-kw diesel sets)
Range: 12,000/14.5 **Fuel:** 700 m^3 heavy oil, 170 m^3 diesel
Crew: 31 tot. + 29 scientists

CIVILIAN SCIENTIFIC RESEARCH SHIPS *(continued)*

Remarks: 2,833 grt/1,313 dwt. A series of ships to support the "Shel'f" research program to search for offshore gas and oil deposits. Ice-strengthened hulls, stern ramp for towing seismic array. Bow-thruster. Geophysical, gravimetric, and chemical laboratories. JMR-4A NAVSAT receiver, Krupp-Atlas DESO-20 echo-sounder, Syledis radiogeodetic receiver, EC-1010 computer. *Akademik Gubkin* was registered under the Panamanian flag in 1991 and renamed; she is still under Russian ownership and is on offer for charter.

♦ 2 modified Yelva-class diving tenders

GIDROBIOLOG (In serv. 1985) IMPULS (In serv. 1988)

Gidrobiolog—note diving chamber to port, aft Antonio Scrimali, 1990

D: 295 tons (fl) **S:** 12.4 kts **Dim:** 40.90 (37.00 pp) × 8.00 × 2.07
Electron Equipt: 1/Spin Trough nav.
M: 2 type 3D12A diesels; 2 props; 600 bhp
Electric: 200 kw **Range:** 1,870/12 **Endurance:** 10 days
Crew: 13 tot. + 7 scientists

Remarks: 168 grt. *Gidrobiolog* operates in the Black Sea for the Moscow State University as a training ship in physical and biological oceanography. *Impuls* operates for the Institute of Geology (*Yuzhmorgeologiya*) in the Far East. They are equipped with a side-scan sonar and retain the divers' decompression chamber.

♦ 9 modified Pulkovskiy Meridian trawler class

Bldr: Chernomorskiy SY, Nikolayev, Ukraine

	In serv.
MORSKOY GEOLOG	1983
AKADEMIK ALEKSANDR KARPENSKIY	1984
GEOLOG PETR ANTROPOV	1984
AKADEMIK ALEKSANDR SIDORENKO	18-6-85
GEOLOG FERSMAN	1986
SEVMORGEOLOGIYA	1989
GELENDZHIK	2-90
XVII SYEZD PROFSOYUZOV	1990
PROFESSOR LOGACHEV	1990

Akademik Aleksandr Karpenskiy French Navy, 1990

Sevmorgeologiya—note davits to port for submersible and stern lift for submersible equipment Leo Van Ginderen, 3-90

D: 5,620–5,700 tons (fl) **S:** 17 kts (15.5 sust.)
Dim: 104.50 (94.00 pp) × 16.00 × 5.90
Electron Equipt: Radar: 1/Don-2 nav., 1/Okean-A nav.
M: 2 Zgoda-Sulzer 6L52511PV diesels; 1 CP prop; 6,900 bhp (later units: 2 Russkiy Dizel-Pielstick 6PC2L 400 diesels; 7,004 bhp)—all except *Morskoy Geolog:* bow- and stern-thrusters
Electric: 450 kw **Range:** 8,800/14.5 **Fuel:** 1,450 tons
Endurance: 90 days **Crew:** 52 tot. + 40 scientists

Remarks: Registered tonnages vary: *Professor Logachev* is 4,504 grt/1,592 dw *Syezd Profsoyuzov* is 3,385 grt/1,405 dwt; *Akademik Aleksandr Sidorenko* and *M Geolog* are 4,430 grt/1,730 dwt. Part of a class of two dozen or more stern-haul trawlers built since 1974 and adopted while under construction for hydrogec research. Have 13 laboratories totaling 300 m^2 and 14 oceanographic winches greatly from unit to unit in equippage and in configuration, especially in the are stern.

♦ 4 Akademik Boris Petrov class

Bldr: Hollming, Rauma, Finlar

	Laid down	L	In serv
AKADEMIK BORIS PETROV	7-4-83	7-7-83	29-6-84
AKADEMIK M.A. LAVRENT'YEV	18-8-83	28-10-83	12-10-84
AKADEMIK NIKOLAY STRAKHOV	9-11-83	3-2-84	14-5-85
AKADEMIK OPARIN	. . .	1-2-85	29-11-85

Akademik Oparin J.M.S.D.F

Akademik Nikolay Strakhov Leo Van Ginderen

D: 2,550 tons (fl) **S:** 15.5 kts **Dim:** 75.45 (68.00 pp) × 14.70 ×
Electron Equipt: Radar: 1/Okean-A nav., 1/. . . nav.
M: 2 SEMT-Pielstick/Russkiy Dizel 6PC 2.5 L400 diesels; 1 CP pr 3,500 bhp—bow-thruster
Range: 15,000/14.75
Crew: 41 tot. + 26 scientists (74 tot. accommodations)

Remarks: First three ordered 17-6-82 for the Academy of Sciences Vernadski tute for Geochemistry and Analytical Chemistry. Second trio ordered 28-6- there have been no reports on progress on 5th and 6th units, and they were ev canceled. Intended to conduct geophysical and hydrophysical research worldwid thruster; bulbous forefoot to bow. Carry MARISAT SATCOMM system. Sh assymetric, with portside plated in, starboard open along main deck for v equipment. The first three carry large seismic cable reels at stern, to starboar A-frame quadrantial davit, and have an open stern working space, while on *Ak Oparin* the forecastle deck extends to the stern.

♦ 1 geological research catamaran

Bldr: . . . SY, Vladivostok (In serv. 10-83)

GEOLOG PRIMOR'YE

D: 791 tons (fl) **S:** 9 kts **Dim:** 85.8 (75.3 pp) × 18.2 × 5.6
M: 2 diesels; 2 props; 1,200 bhp—2/1,150-hp bow-thrusters

Remarks: Intended for mineral resources research. Able to four-point moor.

♦ 5 Modified Akademik Shuleykin class

Bldr: Laivateollisuus, Turku, Finland

	In serv.
AKADEMIK GAMBURTSEV	20-12-83
AKADEMIK GOLITSYN	22-2-84
PROFESSOR POLCHAKOV	7-4-84
GEOLOG DMITRIY NALYVKIN	14-2-85
PROFESSOR GAGARINSKIY	1989

IVILIAN SCIENTIFIC RESEARCH SHIPS *(continued)*

olog Dmitriy Nalyvkin M.O.D., U.K., 6-89

ademik Golytsin M.O.D., U.K., 6-88

: 2,554 tons (fl) **S:** 14 kts **Dim:** 74.50 (64.3 pp) × 14.70 × 4.50
lectron Equipt: Radar: 1/Okean-M4 nav., 1/Okean-B nav.
: 2 S.E.M.T.-Pielstick 6PC2.5 L400 diesels; 2 CP props; 3,500 bhp
lectric: 600 kVA **Range:** 14,000/12 **Endurance:** 50 days
rew: 31–38 crew + 31–38 scientists

arks: 1,650 grt/600 dwt. Constitute second and third group of the *Akademik eykin* class, lengthened, broadened, and re-engined. First four are configured for stry of Geology for seismic survey duties and can carry a remote-controlled sub-ible robot. Have 200-shp bow-thruster, Decca Arkas autopilot, Rumb MFD/F loop, -M2B echo-sounder, ELAC ENIF deep echo-sounder, ELAC bottom profiler, Fur-oppler log, 1EL-2 electromagnetic log, and Furuno FSN-200 NAVSAT receiver; e fitted with INTELSAT SATCOMM.
e similar *Ar'nold Veymer*, and *Professor Gagarinskiy* are members of a third group ed 1-80 that are configured for general oceanography. *Ar'nold Veymer* was subor-ed to the Estonian S.S.R. Academy of Sciences; she was launched 14-2-86 and ferred to Estonia in 1991 under the name *Livonia*. Two others to the same design canceled.

Akademik Shuleykin class Bldr: Laivateollisuus, Turku, Finland

	In serv.
DEMIK SHULEYKIN	1982
ESSOR PAVEL MOLCHANOV	1982
DEMIK SHOKALSKIY	1982
ESSOR KHROMOV	1983
ESSOR MUL'TANOVSKIY	7-83

emik Shuleykin Leo Van Ginderen, 8-87

Professor Mul'tanovskiy M.O.D., U.K., 6-88

D: 2,140 tons (fl) **S:** 14 kts **Dim:** 71.60 (64.30 pp) × 12.80 × 4.85
Electron Equipt: Radar: 1/Okean M4 nav.; 1/Okean-B nav.
M: 2 Gor'kiy Type G-74 diesels; 2 CP props; 3,120 bhp
Electric: 600 kVA **Range:** 14,000/12 **Endurance:** 50 days
Crew: 38 crew + 38 scientists

Remarks: 1,800 grt/620 dwt. Academy of Sciences hydrometeorological reporting ships, equipped for cold-weather operations. Home ports: *Shuleykin* at St. Petersburg, *Shokalskiy* and *Khromov* at Vladivostok, *Molchanov* at Murmansk, and *Mul'tanovskiy* at St. Petersburg.

♦ **1 Akademik Aleksey Krylov class**
Bldr: Okean SY, Nikolayev, Ukraine

AKADEMIK ALEKSEY KRYLOV (In serv. 1981)

Akademik Aleksey Krylov Ben Sullivan, 7-91

Akademik Aleksey Krylov French Navy, 6-90

D: 9,920 tons (fl) **S:** 16 kts **Dim:** 124.7 (110.0 pp) × 17.5 × 7.2
Electron Equipt:
Radar: 1/Okean-A nav., 1/Okean-B nav., 1/Palm Frond nav.
M: 2 Type 58D-6R diesels; 2 CP props; 9,000 bhp
Electric: 3,600 kw **Range:** 10,000/16
Crew: 117 tot. + 32 scientists

Remarks: 6,358 grt/1,930 dwt. Originally intended to support a 13.4-m submersible, hangared amidships, with a large door and internal handling gantry to port. The submersible weighs 10 tons and can dive to 1,500 m. In 1991, was carrying the *Del'fin* and *Uran-1* submersibles. The ship has bow- and stern-thrusters, with a "Zaliv" automated control system. Home-ported at Sevastopol. In 1991, was transferred to the "EKOLAS" organization for conducting ecological studies. Lengthened, modified half-sisters *Akademik Nikolay Andreyev* and *Akademik Boris Konstantinov* are described above.

CIVILIAN SCIENTIFIC RESEARCH SHIPS *(continued)*

♦ 7 modified Al'pinist class

Bldr: Yaroslavl' SY

RIFT (In serv. 1982)
DIORAT (In serv. 1983)
GIDROBIOLOG (In serv. 1983)
DIABAZ (In serv. 1983)
GIDRONAVT (In serv. 1983)
GIDROOPTIK (In serv. 1988)
POLYGON (In serv. 1989)

Gidrooptik *Sudostroenniye,* 1988

D: 1,185 tons (fl) **S:** 12.5 kts
Dim: 53.65 (46.20 pp) × 10.51 × 4.90
Electron Equipt: Radar: 1/Spin Trough nav.
M: 1 Type 8NVD48-2U diesel; 1 CP prop; 1,320 bhp
Electric: 778 kw **Range:** 6,900/12 **Endurance:** 20 days
Crew: 26 crew + 11 scientists

Remarks: First three are *Al'pinist*-class stern-haul trawlers modified while under construction to carry and support a manned submersible beneath a traveling double gantry crane amidships. Employed on oceanography, hydrology, and marine ecology research by the Ministry of Fisheries. Equipped with bow- and stern-thrusters. In late 1983 *Rift,* designed for the *Tinro-2* submersible, was carrying the *Argus* submersible and a *Zvuk*-4M towed drone submersible.

Diorat and *Diabaz* are used for geophysical research and have a 15-m drill tower for the 9-ton ZIF-1200 drill in place of the submersible facility. *Polygon,* which displaces 1,250 tons (fl), operates for the Ministry of Geology, southern Production Association for Marine Geological Operations and is equipped to drill 100-m cores; she carries an ES/011 computer and the SNF-10 underwater navigation system.

Gidrooptik, as the name implies, is equipped to study the optical properties of seawater and has an observation cabin extending forward from the bow; her length is 56.15 m overall, displaces 1,149 tons full load, has a range of 7,600 n.m., is equipped with bow and stern tunnel-thrusters, and carries a crew of 19 plus 10 scientists.

♦ 3 Vityaz' class

Bldr: Adolf Warski SY, Szczecin, Poland

VITYAZ' (In serv. 1981)
AKADEMIK ALEKSANDR NESMEYANOV (In serv. 1982)
AKADEMIK ALEKSANDR VINOGRADOV (In serv. 1983)

Akademik Aleksandr Vinogradov U.S. Navy, 1991

Akademik Aleksandr Nesmeyanov U.S. Navy, 8-90

D: 5,700 tons (fl) **S:** 16 kts
Dim: 110.90 (100.00 pp) × 16.60 × 5.70
Electron Equipt:
Radar: 2/Don-2 nav., 1/Okean-series nav.
M: 2 Zgoda-Sulzer 6ZL140/48 diesels; 2 CP props; 6,400 bhp
Endurance: 60 days **Electric:** 925 kVA
Range: 16,000/16 **Crew:** 61 crew + 65 scientists

Remarks: 4,940 grt/1,810 dwt. Operated by the Academy of Sciences for s research, exploring for exploitable natural materials to 10,000-m depths. Ha laboratories. Carry the *Argus* submersibles: 8 tons, 600-m diving depth, 3-kt. speed, crew of three, with an eight-hour powered endurance. *Vityaz'* also car submersible decompression chamber for three divers. Cargo holds total 477 m^3 ity. *Vityaz'* home-ported at Novorossiysk in the Black Sea, *Nesmeyanov* and *Vir dov* at Vladivostok.

♦ 1 Akademik Keldysh class

Bldr: Hollming SY, Rauma, Finland

AKADEMIK MSTISLAV KELDYSH (In serv. 12-80)

Akademik Mstislav Keldysh M.O.D., U.K.

Akademik Mstislav Keldysh Leo Van Ginderen,

D: 5,500 (fl) **S:** 16 kts
Dim: 122.20 (113.00 pp) × 17.80 × 5.40
M: 4 Wärtsilä Vasa 824TS diesels; 2 props; 5,840 bhp—bow-thrust
Range: 20,000/16 **Crew:** 65 crew + 65 scientists

Remarks: 5,543 grt/1,832 dwt. Operated by the Academy of Sciences for ge purpose oceanography. Has 17 internal laboratories and can carry 4 contain laboratories. Home-ported at Kaliningrad. Originally carried two *Pisces*-class re submersibles, capable of descending to 2,000 m with a crew of three; refitted 1 carry two Rauma-Repola-built submersibles *Mir-1* and *Mir-2:* 18.6 tons, 7.80 × 3.45 (high) meters, three hydraulic motors (1 × 12-kw aft, 2 × 3.6-kw swiveli sides) for 1.5 kts, crew of three; capable of diving to 6,000 m. The *Mirs* are c beneath new shelters built to starboard aft. *Keldysh* has two data-storage comp Magnavox SATCOMM receiver, and other sophisticated navigational gear. P tank anti-rolling system. Bow-thruster and a 360°-rotatable Aquamaster ster pulser.

♦ 1 modified Dobrynya Nikitich class Arctic research ship

Bldr: United Admiralty SY, St. Petersburg

OTTO SCHMIDT (In serv. 17-7-79)

D: 2,528 tons (3,650 fl) **S:** 14.8 kts
Dim: 73.00 (62.00 pp) × 18.60 × 6.60
Electron Equipt:
Radar: 1/Okean-series nav., 1/Don-2 nav.
M: 3 Type 13D100 diesels, electric drive; 2 props; 5,440 shp
Electric: 1,875 kw **Range:** 11,000/14 **Endurance:** 60 days
Crew: 32 tot. + 20 scientists (accommodations for 65 tot.)

Otto Schmidt Leo Van Ginderen

LIAN SCIENTIFIC RESEARCH SHIPS *(continued)*

·ks: 2,828 grt/1,095 dwt. Operated by the Arctic/Antarctic Scientific Research te. Can break 60-cm ice at 2-kt speeds; 50 days endurance. Has 14 laboratories. val research icebreaker *Vladimir Kavrayskiy* has the same hull and propulsion, wo standard units of the *Dobrynya Nikitich* class, *Petr Pakhtusov* and *Georgiy* are also employed on research tasks as needed. Home-ported at Murmansk.

ea-mining research ship Bldr: . . . , U.S.S.R.

1 (In serv. 1976)

. . . **S:** 16.5 kts **Dim:** 62.6 × 10.5 × 3.1
2 12-cyl. diesels; 2 props; . . . bhp
nge: . . . **Crew:** . . .

rks: 669 grt/193 dwt. Built to test ocean-shelf mining techniques to 100-m . Has a 5-ton crane.

Antarctic research and supply ship Bldr: Kherson SY, Ukraine

AIL SOMOV (In serv. 1975)

ail Somov Peter Voss, 12-88

5,000 tons (11,290 fl) **S:** 15 kts
n: 133.1 (123.3 pp) × 18.8 (18.5 wl) × 7.6
ctron Equipt: Radar: 2/Don-2 nav.
2 diesels, electric drive; 2 props; 7,150 shp
nge: 10,000/16.4 **Crew:** 54 tot.

rks: 6,280 dwt. Operated by the Arctic and Antarctic Institute. Essentially *guema*-class icebreaking passenger/cargo ship intended for annual resupply to Soviet research stations in the Antarctic. Has helicopter deck above stern, RSAT SATCOMM. Commercial sisters, including *Kapitan Myshevskiy* in 1983, lso been used for Antarctic resupply on occasion. *Somov* was replaced as prin- ntarctic expedition ship by *Akademik Fedorov* in 1987. Became entrapped in ice ut was freed.

Valerian Uryvayev class Bldr: Khabarovsk SY

	In serv.		In serv.
'VO	1982	MORKSOY GEOFIZIK	1975
	1982	POISK	1974
ZIYE ZELENTSY*	1978	PROFESSOR FEDYNSKIY	1982
'IZIKH	1983	PROFESSOR GAGARINSKIY	1990
LS	1988	REZONANS	1980
'EL'	1977	VALERIAN URYVAYEV*	1974
DOVATEL'	1977	VEKTOR	1980
	1990	VSEVLOD BEREZKIN*	1975
ITOV*	1980	VULKANOLOG	1976
JL	1981	VYACHESLAV FROLOV*	1979
		YAKOV GAKKEL*	1975

Titov—hydromet version, king posts at stern Leo Van Ginderen, 1991

Kern—quadrantial gantry crane at stern U.S. Navy, 1991

Morskoy Geofizik—king posts abaft stack J.M.S.D.F., 8-90

Professor Gagarinskiy—cable winch at stern J.M.S.D.F., 8-90

D: 1,050 to 1,124 tons (fl) **S:** 11 kts
Dim: 54.80 to 55.60 × 9.50 × 4.27
Electron Equipt:
Radar: 1/Don-2 nav., 1/End Tray on * units
M: 1 Karl Liebnecht diesel; 1 CP prop; 880 bhp
Electric: 450 kw
Range: 10,000/11 **Endurance:** 40 days
Crew: 20–25 tot. + 12–15 technicians/scientists

Remarks: Registered tonnages differ; 697 grt/350 dwt is typical. Those operated for the Institute of Hydrometeorology (*) are equipped to mount an End Shield radiosonde balloon-tracking radar. Others operate for the Arctic and Antarctic Institute or the Academy of Sciences. *Vulkanolog* operates for the Institute of Vulkanology, Petropavlovsk. Have eight laboratories. Some have twin king posts at the stern, and others have the king posts just abaft the stack. Sister *Rudolf Samoylovich* was transferred to Lithuania in 11-91. Are home-ported as follows: *Berezkin, Kern,* and *Zelentsy* at Murmansk; *Titov* in the Baltic, *Issledovatel', Modul. Vektor,* and *Gakkel* in the Black Sea area, *Elm* in the Caspian, and the remainder in the Far East.

♦ 3 modified Passat-class weather-reporting ships
Bldr: A. Warski SY, Szczecin, Poland (In serv. 1971)

ERNST KRENKEL' (ex-*Vikhr*)
VIKTOR BUGAYEV (ex-*Poriv*)
GEORGIY USHAKOV (ex-*Schkval*)

D: 4,200 tons (fl) **S:** 16 kts
Dim: 100.1 (88.4 pp) × 14.8 × 5.1
Electron Equipt:
Radar: 2/Don-2 nav., 1/End Tray balloon-tracking
M: 2 Cegielski-Sulzer diesels; 2 CP props; 4,800 bhp
Electric: 1,089 kw **Range:** 15,000/16 **Fuel:** 652 tons
Crew: 110 tot. + 63 scientists/technicians

Remarks: 3,311 grt/1,450 dwt. Improved version of the *Passat*-class hydrometeorological reporting ships. Facilities for launching and tracking radiosonde balloons and rockets. All home-ported in the Black Sea at Odessa. Fitted with Magnavox NAVSAT receivers.

CIVILIAN SCIENTIFIC RESEARCH SHIPS *(continued)*

Viktor Bugayev Leo Van Ginderen, 12-87

Ernst Krenkel Leo Van Ginderen, 10-86

◆ **1 shipbuilding structural materials testing ship**
Bldr: Chernomorskiy SY, Nikolayev, Ukraine (In serv. 1970)

IZUMRUD

Izumrud French Navy, 1-91

Izumrud Leo Van Ginderen, 10-91

D: 5,170 tons (fl) **S:** 14 kts
Dim: 99.40 (90.00 pp) × 14.00 × 5.40
Electron Equipt:
Radar: 1/Don-2 nav., 1/Okean-series nav.
M: 4 diesels, electric drive; 1 prop; 4,000 shp
Range: . . ./. . .
Crew: 110 tot. + 40 scientists/technicians

Remarks: 3,862 grt/2,640 dwt. A modified version of the *Tavriya*-class passe cargo vessel design, built for the Ministry of Shipbuilding for trials with struc concepts, materials coatings, navigation systems, and communications systems. tions of the superstructure are made from glass-reinforced plastic. Low Sieve radar has been removed. Has Vee Cone-series long-range HF radio antenna. rectly deleted from previous edition.

◆ **19 Dmitriy Ovtsyn class** Bldr: Laivateollisuus SY, Abo, Finland

	In serv.		In se
DMITRIY LAPTEV	1970	PROFESSOR BOGOROV*	[illegible]
DMITRIY OVTSYN	1970	PROFESSOR KURENTSOV*	[illegible]
DMITRIY STERLEVGOV	1971	PROFESSOR SHTOKMAN*	[illegible]
EDUARD TOLL	1972	PROFESSOR VODYANITSKIY*	[illegible]
FEDOR MATISEN*	1976	SERGEY KRAVKOV	[illegible]
GEORGIY MAKSOMOV*	1977	STEPAN MALYGIN	[illegible]
IVAN KIREYEV*	1977	VALERIAN ALBANOV	[illegible]
NIKOLAY KOLOMEYTSEV	1972	VLADIMIR SUKHOTSKIY	[illegible]
NIKOLAY YEVGENOV	1974	YAKOV SMIRNITSKIY*	[illegible]
PAVEL BASHMAKOV*	1977		

D: 1,650 to 1,675 tons (fl) **S:** 16 kts (12 sust.)
Dim: 68.75 (60.00 pp) × 11.9 × 4.20 to 4.50
Electron Equipt:
Radar: varies: 2/Don-2, or 1/Okean, or 1/Don, 1/Don-2 nav
M: 1 Humboldt-Klockner-Deutz RBV6M358 diesel; 1 CP prop; 2,200 bhp
Electric: 595 kw **Range:** 9,700/13.5 **Fuel:** 180 tons
Endurance: 30 days **Crew:** up to 35 tot. + up to 25 scientists

Nikolay Kolomeytsev—first series James W. Goss/NAVPIC,

Professor Bogorov—second series Leo Van Ginderen,

Pavel Bashmakov—second series M.O.D., U.K.,

LIAN SCIENTIFIC RESEARCH SHIPS *(continued)*

arks: 1,130 to 1,150 grt/295 dwt. Ships delivered 1976 and later (*) are con- d a second series, but are very similar. Fourteen are subordinated to the Ministry Maritime Fleet for hydrographic survey and seismic survey duties, the remain- the Academy of Sciences or to the Hydrometeorological Institute (units with essor" names). *Bogorov* built at Turku. Equipment varies, but most carry DESO- d ELAC ENIF echo-sounders; Decca Sea-Fix and Hi-Fix radio navigation gear; a, Transit, and Tsykada NAVSAT receivers. Can also carry seismic, gravimetric, ydrographic survey equipment.

3 Agat class Bldr: . . . (In serv. 1969–79)

T	Gidrolog	Monatsit	Tantal
anavt	Granat	Morion	Topaz
ll	Ilmenit	Pluton	Tsirkon
ey	Kartesh	Radon	Uran
	Kvarts	Rutil	Yantar
termik	Metan	Shel'f	

'f Leo Van Ginderen, 9-83

350 tons (fl) **S:** 9.5 kts **Dim:** 34.0 × 7.1 × 2.6
ectron Equipt: Radar: 1/. . . nav.
: 1 Karl Liebnecht 8-cyl. diesel; 1 prop; 300 bhp
ectric: 411 kw **Endurance:** 7 days
ange: 1,600/9 **Crew:** . . .

arks: 166 grt/35 dwt. A general-purpose oceanographic tender version of the *vrennyy*-class seiner fishing boat. Subordination about equally divided between inistry of Geology, Academy of Sciences, and the Hydrometeorological Institute.

2 Atlantik-I* and -II-class fisheries research ships
ldr: Volkswerft, Stralsund, East Germany (In serv. 1968–72)

a*	Gerakl'	Professor Sergey Dorofeyev
emida	Kamenskoye	Professor Mesyatsev
ika	Milogradvo	Shantar
ent	Professor	Zond

fessor Sergey Dorofeyev Leo Van Ginderen, 5-87

: 2,240 tons (3,360 fl) **S:** 13.7 kts
im: 82.2 (73.0 pp) × 13.6 × 5.0
ectron Equipt: Radar: 2/Don-2 nav.
: 2 Karl Liebnecht diesels; 2 CP prop; 2,350 bhp
ectric: 1,660 kw **Fuel:** 600 tons
ange: . . . **Crew:** 85 tot.

arks: Average 2,242 grt/1,025 dwt. Stern-haul factory trawlers adapted for ries-related oceanographic research; subordinated to the Ministry of Fisheries. a 75-hp bow-thruster. Will probably be scrapped shortly.

Passat-class hydrometeorological reporting ships
ldr: A. Warski SY, Szczecin, Poland

	In serv.		In serv.		In serv.
sson	1968	Volna	1968	Priboy	1969
sat	1968	Okean	1969	Priliv	1970

Priboy Leo Van Ginderen, 5-90

Musson U.S. Navy, 9-90

D: 4,145 tons (fl) **S:** 16 kts
Dim: 96.9 (88.4 pp) × 13.8 × 5.3
Electron Equipt:
Radar: 2/Don-2 nav., 1/End Tray balloon-tracker
M: 2 Cegielski-Sulzer or Zgoda-Sulzer 8TD48 diesels; 2 CP props; 4,800 bhp
Electric: 800 kw **Range:** . . ./. . .
Endurance: 45 days
Crew: 50–55 tot. + 50–60 scientists and technicians

Remarks: 3,284 grt/1,170 dwt. B-88 design, with 23 laboratory spaces. Have End Tray radiosonde tracking antenna aft and can launch weather balloons and atmospheric probe rockets. 45-day endurance. Subordinated to the Hydrometeorological Institute. Home-ported: Vladivostok, except *Musson, Passat:* Odessa; *Priliv:* Baltic. Vee-series HF antenna atop foremast on *Priboy, Priliv, Okean,* and *Volna.*

◆ **1 Sever class** Bldr: Chernomorskiy SY, Nikolayev, Ukraine

Sever (In serv. 1967)

Sever J.M.S.D.F., 7-90

D: 1,780 tons (2,530 fl) **S:** 13.1 kts **Dim:** 71.0 (64.0 pp) × 13.1 × 5.0
Electron Equipt: Radar: 1/Don-2 nav.
M: 3 diesels, electric drive; 1 CP prop; 3,000 shp
Range: 11,000/13 **Endurance:** 50 days
Fuel: 350 tons **Crew:** 51 tot.

Remarks: 1,940 grt/706 dwt. Operated by the Ministry of Geophysics in geological oceanography studies. Was originally the prototype for a class of stern-haul trawlers, but no others were built. Operates in the Black Sea.

◆ **1 modified Nereida-class trawler** Bldr: Khabarovsk SY

Akademik Petrovskiy (ex-*Moskovskiy Universitet*) (In serv. 1966)

CIVILIAN SCIENTIFIC RESEARCH SHIPS *(continued)*

Akademik Petrovskiy French Navy, 1984

D: 922 tons (fl) **S:** 11 kts **Dim:** 54.1 (52.8) × 9.3 × 3.7
Electron Equipt: Radar: 1/Don-2 nav., 1/Spin Trough nav.
M: 1 diesel; 1 CP prop; 780 bhp
Range: 10,000/11 **Crew:** 41 crew + 10 scientists

Remarks: 577 grt/277 dwt. Operated by Moscow State University for studies in oceanology, hydrobiology, ichthyology, and seismology. Modernized and renamed 1970. Large numbers of this class (unmodified) and the very similar Mayak class perform fisheries research duties.

◆ 7 Akademik Kurchatov class
Bldr: Mathias Thiesen Werft, Wismar, East Germany (In serv. 1966–68)

Akademik Kurchatov
Akademik Korolev
Akademik Shirshov
Akademik Vernadskiy
Dmitriy Mendeleyev
Professor Vize
Professor Zubov

Dmitriy Mendeleyev Leo Van Ginderen, 5-89

Professor Vize—hydrometeorological reporting ship with Vee-Cone HF antenna atop foremast Leo Van Ginderen, 11-88

Akademik Shirshov—with twin radomes abaft stack J.M.S.D.F., 8-90

D: 6,986 tons (fl) **S:** 18.3 kts **Dim:** 124.2 (110.0 pp) × 17.0 × 6.1
Electron Equipt: Radar: 2/Don or Don-2 nav., 1 or 2/tracking
M: 2 Halberstadt-M.A.N. 6KZ 57/60 diesels; 2 props; 8,000 bhp—2/190-shp bow-thrusters—300-shp Pleuger active rudder
Electric: 1,840 kw **Range:** 20,000/18 **Fuel:** 1,415 tons
Crew: 80 tot. + 74 scientists & technicians

Remarks: 5,460 grt/1,986 dwt (*D. Mendeleyev:* 5,560 grt). Vary considerably i equipment. *Kurchatov, Vernadskiy,* and *Mendeleyev* subordinate to the Academy Sciences, the others to the Hydrometeorological Institute. The weather ships original had radiosonde balloon- and rocket-launching facilities. End Tray tracking radar, an two theodolite trackers, one of which was a converted naval Wasp Head directo (*Shirshov* has two side-by-side tracking radars in radomes amidships and a new type tracking radar aft—now removed—as did *Korolev*. The other three have a large cra aft for handling oceanographic gear and small submersibles; they also carry one Er Tray. The weather ships also have Vee Bars HF antennas atop the foremast.

Korolev and *Mendeleyev* have an Okean-series navigational radar in lieu of o Don-2. Unlike their naval half-sisters of the *Abkhaziya* class, these ships have helicopter facilities. *Vernadskiy* has MGI 4206 oceanic internal wave-measuri equipment, which uses three towed paravane-deployed sensors, plus a fourth deploy directly from the hull. Most now have an INTELSAT SATCOMM receiver. *Dmitr Mendeleyev* was modified 1991 to handle two *Rift* submersibles (15 tons, 7.5 m lon capable of diving to 4,000 m) and was equipped with a multi-beam mapping son *Akademik Vernadskiy* was used for radar propagation trials with a Decca 110 radar 1989.

Home ports: *Korolev, Mendeleyev,* and *Shirshov* at Vladivostok, *Vernadskiy* in t Black Sea, and the others in the Baltic.

◆ 4 Tropik-A class
Bldr: V.E.B. Volkswerft, Stralsund, East Germany

	In serv.		In serv.
Kallisto	1964	Pegas	1963
Nauka	1966	Raduga	1966

Kallisto Leo Van Ginderen,

D: approx. 3,000 tons (fl) **S:** 12.5 kts
Dim: 79.8 (71.0 pp) × 13.2 × 5.2
Electron Equipt: Radar: 2/Don-2 nav.
M: 2 Karl Liebnecht 8-cyl. diesels; 1 prop; 1,680 bhp
Electric: 1,080 kw **Range:** . . ./. . . **Fuel:** 400 tons
Crew: 42 tot. + 29 scientists

Remarks: 2,435 grt/988 dwt. Former stern-haul factory trawlers. Approximate sisters operate as fishing boats. *Pegas* operates for the Academy of Sciences, *Kallis* the Oceanographic Science Research Institute, and the other two for the Minist Fisheries. Will likely soon be stricken.

◆ 3 modified Bologoe-class trawlers
Bldr: Leninskaya Kuznitsa SY, Kiev (In serv. 1963)

Akademik A. Kovalevskiy
Yuriy Godin
Akademik Archangel'skiy

Akademik A. Kovalevskiy Leo Van Ginderen,

CIVILIAN SCIENTIFIC RESEARCH SHIPS *(continued)*

D: 580 tons (fl) **S:** 10 kts **Dim:** 43.6 × 7.6 × 3.0
Electron Equipt: Radar: 1/Spin Trough nav.
M: 1 Karl Liebnecht diesel; 1 prop; 450 bhp
Range: . . ./. . . **Crew:** 35 tot. + 13 scientists

Remarks: 416 grt/142 dwt. Greatly modified versions of a standard side-trawler design. *Ak. Archangel'skiy* and *Godin* perform seismic and geophysical studies in the Black Sea and Mediterranean under the Ministry of Geology and Geophysics Institute, respectively. The less extensively modified *Ak. A. Kovalevskiy* performs general oceanography in the same area. All three are due for replacement.

◆ **1 small research ship** (In serv. 1962)

PROFESSOR KOLESNIKOV

Professor Kolesnikov French Navy, 7-90

D: . . . tons **S:** 10 kts **Dim:** 74.0 × 9.6 × . . .
M: 2 diesels; 1 prop; 1,660 bhp **Crew:** 606 tot.

Note: The ex-passenger vessel *Ayu-Dag* is presumed to have transferred to the Estonian flag in 1991, as she operated for the Estonian Academy of Sciences.

◆ **1 ex-Norwegian seismic research ship**
Bldr: A.M. Liasen SY, Alesund (In serv. 1962)

SHEL'F II (ex-*Longva*)

D: approx. 1,400 tons (fl) **S:** 13 kts
Dim: 63.0 (57.9 pp) × 10.0 × 4.2
Electron Equipt: Radar: 3/nav.
M: 1 Klockner-Humboldt-Deutz diesel; 1 prop; 1,500 bhp
Electric: 360 kw **Range:** . . /. . . **Fuel:** 249 tons **Crew:** 52 tot.

Remarks: 793 grt. Purchased 1977 for oil exploration. Very elaborately equipped, including data-storage computers. Has passive tank stabilization, bow-thruster.

◆ **10 Mayakovskiy class** Bldr: Chernomorskiy (Nosenko) SY, Nikolayev

	In serv.		In serv.
A. I. VOYEYKOV	1959	IKHTIANDER	1973
AKADEMIK BERG	1963	ODISSEY	1970
AKADEMIK KNIPOVICH	1964	POSEIDON	1971
ARGUS	1969	PROFESSOR DERYUGIN	1967
EKVATOR	1968	SKIF	1969

A. I. Voyeykov—hydrometeorological ship Leo Van Ginderen, 1-87

D: approx. 3,600 tons (fl) **S:** 13 kts **Dim:** 84.7 (78.1 pp) × 14.0 × 5.7
Electron Equipt: Radar: 2/Don-2 nav.
M: 2 Russkiy Dizel diesels; 1 CP prop; 2,000 bhp
Electric: 800 kw **Range:** 18,000/12 **Crew:** 53 tot. + 37 scientists

Remarks: Average 3,220 grt/1,287 dwt. Stern-haul fish-factory trawlers adapted for research purposes. *Voyeykov*, with stern ramp plated up, operates for the Hydrometeorological Institute and has an End Tray radiosonde tracking radar. The remainder support fisheries research for the Ministry of Fisheries. *Odissey* and *Ikhtiander* have an internal hangar opening through the port side of the hull to launch a *Sever-II* or *Tinro-2* research submersible. *Deryugin, Argus,* and *Poseidon* carry a *Sever-I* submersible, launched via crane. *Skif and Ekvator* are essentially unmodified from the fishing-boat version. The six *Primorye*-class intelligence collection ships were built on the same hull. Sister *Persey-III* sold 1991 for scrap, and the others are likely soon to follow.

Note: The research ship *Mikhail Lomonosov* was transferred to non-oceanographic duties in 1990 and is probably available for scrap. Acoustic research vessels *Petr Lebedev* and *Sergey Vavilov* were scrapped in India in mid-1991.

◆ **2 Korall-class sailing vessels**
Bldr: Laivateollisuus SY, Turku, Finland

POLYARNYY ODISSEY (In serv. 1950) ZARYA (In serv. 9-52)

Zarya Leo Van Ginderen, 12-83

D: approx. 600 tons (fl) **S:** 8 kts **Dim:** 52.5 (42.5 pp) × 9.0 × 3.1
Electron Equipt: Radar: 1/Spin Trough
M: 1 Halberstadt 6NVD36 diesel; 1 prop; 300 bhp
Range: 4,000/8 **Crew:** 35 tot. + 10 scientists

Remarks: 333 grt/78 dwt. Among the last survivors of a large class of wooden-hulled sealer schooners built as war reparations, a number of which were adapted by the Soviet Navy as deperming tenders. *Zarya* has been made as completely non-magnetic as is possible and is used in gravimetric and ocean-current research by the Academy of Sciences, Institute of Earth Magnetism, Ionospheric, and Radio Wave Propagation; home-ported at Murmansk. Refitted 1984–85. *Polyarnyy Odissey* operates for the Northern Branch of the Geographical Society of Russia. It is hoped to replace *Zarya* with a new non-magnetic sailing vessel.

CIVILIAN ICEBREAKERS

Note: Because of their importance to the Russian Navy in keeping Arctic sea lanes open, the Ministry of the Merchant Marine's icebreakers are listed here. There is little doubt that they would come under naval jurisdiction in wartime, and, in fact, the nuclear-powered icebreaker *Arktika* (ex-*Leonid Brezhnev*, ex-*Arktika*), *Sibir,* and *Rossiya* were heavily armed during initial sea trials. Naval-subordinated icebreakers are listed in the Russian Navy section.

NUCLEAR-POWERED ICEBREAKERS

◆ **2 Taymyr class** Bldr: Wärtsilä, Helsinki/Baltic SY, St. Petersburg

	L	In serv.		L	In serv.
TAYMYR	10-4-87	18-8-89	VAYGACH	26-2-88	15-7-90

Taymyr Wärtsilä, 3-89

D: 20,480 tons (23,460 fl) **S:** 22 kts (18.5 continuous)
Dim: 150.2 (140.8 wl) × 29.2 (28.0 wl) × 8.1 mean (9.0 max.)
Electron Equipt: Radar: 1/Okean nav., 1/. . . nav.
M: 1 Type KLT-40M, 171 megawatt pressurized-water reactor, 4 steam generators, 2 steam turbines, 2 Siemens 18.4 MW alternators, 3 Stromberg electric motors; 3 props; 52,000 shp (48,000 sust.)

NUCLEAR-POWERED ICEBREAKERS *(continued)*

Electric: 13,350 kw (3 × 2,650-kw Stromberg, powered by Wärtsilä Vasa 16V22 diesels; 2 × 2,000-kw steam turbogenerators); 1 × 1,000-kw diesel set; 2 × 200-kw diesel sets)
Crew: 117 crew + helicopter crew and medical personnel

Remarks: Ordered 1984 for shallow-water work in Arctic estuaries. Delivered under own power to St. Petersburg for installation of the reactor, employing temporary steam generators mounted on the helicopter deck, *Taymyr* on 7-4-88 and *Vaygach* on 6-3-89. Can also operate on the electric power generated by auxiliary boilers driving the three 2,650-kw turboalternators. Were originally to have been able to break 2-m ice continuously on 74,000 shp, but design was cut back to breaking 1.8-m ice. Hangar for one Ka-32 Helix-D utility helicopter. Two 3-ton Hagglunds cranes. Bollard pull: 400 kilo-Newton.

◆ 4 (+2) Arktika class Bldr: Baltic SY, St. Petersburg

	Laid down	L	In serv.
Arktika (ex-*Leonid Brezhnev*, ex-*Arktika*)	1971	12-72	12-74
Sibir'	1973	2-76	1977
Rossiya	. . .	2-11-83	12-12-85
Sovetskiy Soyuz (ex-*Leonid Brezhnev*)	11-83	25-9-86	9-1-90
Oktyabrskaya Revolutsiya	31-10-86	4-10-89	1992–93
Ural	4-10-89	. . .	1994–96

Sovetskiy Soyuz M.O.D., Bonn, 2-90

Sibir' M.O.D., U.K., 6-89

D: *Arktika* and *Sibir'*: 19,300 tons light (23,460 fl); others: 23,625 (fl)
S: 20.5 kts (15 service)
Dim: *Arktika* and *Sibir'*: 148.00 (136.00 pp) × 30.00 (28.00 wl) × 11.00; others: 150.00 (136.00 pp) × 30.00 (28.00 wl) × 11.00
Electron Equipt:
Radar: 1/Okean nav., 1/Don-2 nav., 1/Head Net-C surf./air search (*Rossiya* and later: Top Plate)
M: 2 pressurized-water reactors, turbogenerators, electric drive; 3 props; 75,000 shp
Electric: 11,400 kw (5 × 2,000-kw turbogenerators; 1 × 1,000-kw diesel set; 2 × 200-kw)
Crew: 141 tot. + 6 air group, 35 passengers

Remarks: 18,172 grt/4,096 dwt. *Arktika*, renamed 1982, was armed during her trials period with 8/76.2-mm 59-cal. AK-276 DP (II × 4, controlled by 2/Hawk Screech radar GFCS) and 8/30-mm AK-230 AA (II × 4, controlled by 2/Drum Tilt radar GFCS); these were removed before the ship left the Baltic. *Rossiya* and subsequent units are equipped to accommodate a single 76.2-mm 59-cal. AK-176 automatic DP gun and Bass Tilt radar GFCS forward. Propulsion power is distributed 37,500 hp on the centerline shaft and 18,750 hp on each of the outboard shafts. Each shaft is driven by two 8,800-kw a.c./8,100-kw d.c. motors. *Rossiya* and the fourth unit have heated waterline ice-strakes and improved, corrosion-resistant hull-steel alloys. *Rossiya* began dock trials 8-85. All have seven watertight compartments. Cinema, library, "nature hall," and 7.5 × 3.0-m pool fitted. There is a hangar and flight deck for two Helix-D (Ka-32) ice-reconnaissance helicopters. *Arktika* traveled to the North Pole in 8-87, the surface ship to do so. *Arktika* renamed *Brezhnev* after his death, restored to ori name, 1985, when the fourth unit was named *Brezhnev;* fourth unit, subsequ renamed, began sea trials 10-12-89. The name for the fifth unit will reported changed, and it is likely that *Sovetskiy Soyuz* will be renamed as well. *Ural,* v construction was announced during 12-88, may be of a new or modified design, horsepower of 90,000 was initially reported.

In 1-92, it was announced that *Arktika* and *Sibir'* were to be used as static power-generating stations for the city of Nakhodka, providing some 165 MW of el power; there was, however, considerable public pressure against the scheme. The demotion probably means that both are in need of unaffordable overhauls.

Note: The world's first nuclear-powered surface ship, the icebreaker *Lenin,* was drawn from service during 12-89; it was stated that her hulk may be employed floating power station in the Arctic.

SEAGOING ICEBREAKERS

◆ 4 Kapitan Sorokin class Bldr: Wärtsilä, Helsinki, Finland

	In serv.		In serv.
Kapitan Sorokin	1977	Kapitan Dranitsyn	2-12-80
Kapitan Nikolayev	1978	Kapitan Khlebnikov	1981

Kapitan Sorokin—with new bow Peter Voss, 1

Kapitan Dranitsyn—unmodified Leo Van Ginderen,

D: *K. Dranitsyn, K. Khlebnikov:* 10,699 tons light (14,790 fl); *K. Sorokin:* 17,000 (fl); *K. Nikolayev:* 15,200 (fl)
S: 19 kts (16 kts service)—*K. Sorokin:* 16.2 kts; *K. Nikolayev:* 16.22 kts
Dim: *K. Dranitsyn, K. Khlebnikov:* 132.4 (122.5 pp) × 26.5 (25.6 wl 8.5; *K. Sorokin:* 138.0 (130.2 pp) × 30.5 (25.6 amidships) × 8. *K. Nikolayev:* 134.8 (125.9 pp) × 26.5 × 8.5
M: 6 Wärtsilä-Sulzer 9ZL 40/48 diesel generator sets, electric drive; props; 24,848 shp (22,300 sust.)
Electric: 4,900 kw **Range:** 10,700/16 **Fuel:** 3,666 tons
Crew: 11 officers, 65 unlicensed

Remarks: As built: 10,609 grt/4,225 dwt. Equipped with the Wärtsilä bubbler sy to keep the hull bottom ice-free. Helicopter pad, no hangar. All personnel accom dated in the superstructure. Considered to be "shallow-draft" ships. Equipped to form salvage and towing operations. Capable of breaking 1.4-m ice continuo *Kapitan Sorokin* and *Kapitan Nikolayev* received new bows during 1990–91, *Soro* Thyssen-Waas bow as fitted to *Mudyug,* and *Nikolayev* a modified version design Wärtsilä. *Sorokin* can now break 2.25-m ice continuously, *Nikolayev* 2.0-m ice. Co sion of *Sorokin* began 1-7-90; trials with her new bow began 4-91.

SEAGOING ICEBREAKERS *(continued)*

◆ **3 Yermak class** Bldr: Wärtsilä, Helsinki, Finland

YERMAK (In serv. 4-7-74) ADMIRAL MAKAROV (In serv. 6-75)
KRASIN (In serv. 2-76)

Admiral Makarov Wärtsilä, 1975

D: 13,280 tons light (20,241 fl) **S:** 19.5 kts
Dim: 135.8 (130.0 pp) × 26.0 (25.8 wl) × 11.0
M: 9 Wärtsilä-Sulzer 12 ZN 40/48-3,050 diesel generator sets, electric drive; 3/4-bladed props; 36,500 shp
Electric: *see* Remarks **Range:** 29,300/14 **Fuel:** 5,750 tons
Crew: 146 tot.

Remarks: 12,231 grt/7,441 dwt. Russia's most powerful conventional icebreakers. [C]an break 6-m ice or maintain 2 kts through 1.8-m ice. Have Wärtsilä bubbler system, [h]elicopter pad. Electrical power taken from propulsion generators. *Krasin* refitted 1-84 [t]o 3-84 by Böttcher and Gröning, Hamburg; re-engined. *Krasin* should not be confused [w]ith the nineteenth century icebreaker *Krasin,* which is maintained as a relic at St. [P]etersburg.

◆ **5 Moskva class** Bldr: Wärtsilä, Helsinki, Finland

[M]OSKVA (In serv. 1960) MURMANSK (In serv. 1968)
[L]ENINGRAD (In serv. 1962) VLADIVOSTOK (In serv. 1969)
[K]IEV (In serv. 1966)

[Le]ningrad J.M.S.D.F., 1990

D: 13,290 tons (15,360 fl) **S:** 18.3 kts
Dim: 122.1 (112.4 pp) × 24.5 (23.5 wl) × 9.5
M: 8 Wärtsilä-Sulzer 9MH51, 2,160-kw generator sets, electric drive; 3/4-bladed props; 26,300 shp
Range: 20,000/14 **Fuel:** 5,200 tons **Crew:** 116 tot.

[Re]marks: 9,427 grt/4,221 dwt. Have heeling tanks, capable of shifting 480 tons of [wa]ter in two minutes. Can carry two ice-reconnaissance helicopters. 60-ton bollard-[pul]l towing capacity. *Leningrad* was overhauled at Yokohama in 1969–70 and re-[en]gined; she will no doubt be renamed shortly.

[M]EDIUM ICEBREAKERS

◆ **1 modified Mudyug class** Bldr: Wärtsilä, Helsinki, Finland

[MU]DYUG (In serv. 29-10-82)

D: 7,775 tons (fl) **S:** 17.45 kts
Dim: 111.36 (89.80 pp) × 22.20 × 6.50
Electron Equipt: Radar: 1/Don-2 nav., 1/Okean-series nav.
M: 4 Wärtsilä Vasa 8R32 heavy-oil diesels; 2 KaMeWa CP props; 12,400 bhp
Electric: 2,530 kw **Range:** . . . **Fuel:** 690 m^3
Crew: 34 tot. (43 accommodations)

[Re]marks: 5,342 grt. Modified at Thyssen Nordseewerke, Emden, 28-7-86 to 29-10-86 [with] new 1,150-ton Thyssen/Waas flat-form bow and Jastran water hull-lubrication [and] thruster system. Icebreaking capability improved with 50 percent power saving. [Fue]l tankage also increased. The modifications add 1 knot to maximum icebreaking [spe]ed. Can break 1.4-m ice at 6 knots, using 9,500 shp. Change to hull form imparted no [ope]n-water speed penalty. During icebreaking, broken ice is pushed beneath ice [alon]gside, leaving a clear path astern—unlike clogged path left by conventional ice-[brea]kers. Helo deck added during trials, later removed.

Mudyug Skyfotos, 8-89

◆ **2 Mudyug class** Bldr: Wärtsilä, Helsinki, Finland

MAGADAN (In serv. 12-82) DIKSON (In serv. 17-3-83)

Dikson—compare to view of *Mudyug* M.O.D., U.K., 6-88

D: 5,558 tons light (6,210 fl) **S:** 17.45 kts (16.5 sust.)
Dim: 92.00 (88.49 hull, 78.50 wl) × 21.40 (20.00 wl) × 6.50
M: 4 Wärtsilä Vasa 8R32 heavy-oil diesels; 2 CP props; 12,400 bhp—*see* Remarks
Electric: 2,530 kw **Range:** 15,000/16.5 **Crew:** 34 tot.
Fuel: 1,902 tons heavy oil, 388 tons diesel

Remarks: Approx. 4,400 grt. Have Wärtsilä air-bubbler system. Intended for use in the Barents, Baltic, and Sea of Okhotsk. Have 91.7-ton bollard pull. Unusual in not employing electric drive. Have three 800-kw ship's service generators. Can break .5-m ice. Propulsion plant restricted to 9,380-shp total output because of main engine-to-shaft compatibility problems.

◆ **12 Dobrynya Nikitich class** Bldr: Admiralty SY, St. Petersburg

	In serv.		In serv.
AFANASIY NIKITIN	1962	YURIY LISYANSKIY	1965
KHARITON LAPTEV	1962	PETR PAKHTUSOV	1966
VASILIY POYARKOV	1963	GEORGIY SEDOV	1967
YEROFEY KHABAROV	1963	FEDOR LITKE	1970
IVAN KRUZHENSHTERN	1964	IVAN MOSKVITIN	1971
SEMEN CHELYUSHKIN	1965	SEMEN DEZHNEV	1971

D: 2,675–2,940 tons (fl) **S:** 14.5 kts (12.0 service)
Dim: 67.7 (62.0 pp) × 18.3 × 6.1
Electron Equipt: Radar: 1 or 2/Don-2 nav.
M: 3 Type 13D100 diesel generator sets; 3/3-bladed props (1 fwd); 5,400 shp
Range: 5,500/12 **Fuel:** 600 tons **Crew:** 39 tot.

MEDIUM ICEBREAKERS *(continued)*

Afanasiy Nikitin Leo Van Ginderen, 5-90

Ivan Kruzhenshtern Leo Van Ginderen, 7-90

Remarks: 2,305 grt/1,092 dwt typical. Seven sisters serve in the Russian Navy. *Petr Pakhtusov* and *Georgiy Sedov* have been employed on occasional scientific voyages by the Academy of Sciences. The specially built research icebreakers *Otto Schmidt* (civilian) and *Vladimir Kavrayskiy* (naval) are variants of this design, as are the *Ivan Susanin*-class patrol icebreakers. Ships of this class are often used as ocean tugs in summer months. *Vasily Pronchishchev* suffered fire 28-1-89; three died; she was sold to Portugal for scrap. Sister *Vladimir Rusanov* scrapped 5-88.

◆ **3 Kapitan Belousov class** Bldr: Wärtsilä, Helsinki, Finland

Kapitan Belousov (In serv. 1954) Kapitan Melekhov (In serv. 1956)
Kapitan Voronin (In serv. 1955)

Kapitan Belousov

D: 5,360 tons (fl) **S:** 16.5 kts **Dim:** 83.20 (77.10 pp) × 19.40 × 7.0
M: 6 Wärtsilä diesel generator sets, electric drive; 4 props (2 fwd); 10,600 shp
Range: 10,000/14.8 **Fuel:** 1,025 tons **Crew:** 120 tot.

Remarks: 3,377 to 3,710 grt/1,308 to 1,423 dwt. The U.S.S.R.'s first post–W.W. II icebreakers; primarily for harbor and thin-ice work, hence forward-mounted pair of propellers. Can break 1.2-m ice.

RIVER ICEBREAKERS

◆ **9 Kapitan Yevdokimov class** Bldr: Wärtsilä, Helsinki, Finland

Kapitan Yevdokimov (In serv. 31-3-83)
Kapitan Babichev (In serv. 30-6-83)
Kapitan Borodkin (In serv. 13-11-83)
Kapitan Chudinov (In serv. 9-9-83)
Kapitan Evdokimov (In serv. 1983)
Avraamiy Zavenyagin (In serv. 12-4-84)
Kapitan Metsayk (In serv. 8-84)
Kapitan Demidov (In serv. 22-11-84)
Kapitan Moshkin (In serv. 14-5-86)

Kapitan Yevdokimov Leo Van Ginderen,

D: 2,200 tons (fl) **S:** 13.5 kts (12 kts service)
Dim: 76.50 × 16.60 × 2.50
M: 4 Wärtsilä Vasa 12V22B, 1,640-hp diesel generator sets, electri drive; 4 props (2 fwd); 5,170 shp
Crew: 25 tot.

Remarks: 1,500 grt. Remarkably shallow draft. Intended to clear Arctic r Equipped with Wärtsilä bubbler system and a sewage-treatment plant. Ninth o 27-6-84 and launched 12-7-85.

◆ **6 Kapitan Chechkin class** Bldr: Wärtsilä, Helsinki, Finland

	In serv.		In serv.
Kapitan Bukayev	1978	Kapitan Krutov	1978
Kapitan Chadayev	1978	Kapitan Plakhin	1977
Kapitan Chechkin	1977	Kapitan Zarubin	1978

Kapitan Krutov Wärtsilä,

D: 2,240 tons (fl) **S:** 14 kts **Dim:** 77.60 (73.90 pp) × 16.30 × 3.3
M: 3 Wärtsilä diesels, electric drive; 3 props; 6,300 shp
Electric: 330 kw **Range:** . . . **Crew:** 28 tot.

Remarks: Approx. 1,600 grt. Capable of breaking 1-meter-thick ice; have air-b systems. Service speed 10 kts.

◆ **3 Kapitan M. Izmaylov class** Bldr: Wärtsilä, Helsinki, Finland (In serv. 1976)

Kapitan A. Radzhabov Kapitan M. Izmaylov
Kapitan Kosolabov

Kapitan A. Radzhabov Leo Van Ginderen

RUSSIA *(continued)*
RIVER ICEBREAKERS *(continued)*

D: 2,048 tons (fl) **S:** 14 kts **Dim:** 56.3 (52.2 pp) × 16.3 × 4.2
M: 4 Wärtsilä Vasa 824TS diesels, 2/4-bladed props; 5,330 bhp
Range: 5,000/14 **Fuel:** 380 tons **Crew:** 24 tot.

Remarks: 1,362 grt/354 dwt. Endurance: 15 days.

ICEBREAKING RESCUE SHIPS

◆ **7 Stroptivyy class** Bldr: Wärtsilä, Helsinki, Finland

	In serv.		In serv.
STROPTIVYY	30-11-79	SUVOROVETS	1982
STAKHANOVETS	29-2-80	FOBOS	29-4-83
SIBIRSKIY	2-7-80	DEYMOS	31-5-83
SPRAVEDLIVYY	1982		

Stakhanovets Leo Van Ginderen, 10-91

D: 4,200 tons (fl) **S:** 15 kts **Dim:** 72.70 × 18.00 × 6.50
Electron Equipt: Radar: 1/Okean-A nav.
M: 2 Wärtsilä-Pielstick 6PC2.5 L400 diesels; 2 CP props; 7,600 bhp—bow-thruster
Range: . . ./. . . **Crew:** 40 crew + 12 rescued/passengers

Remarks: Icebreaker-hulled rescue and salvage ships built to support the Arctic fishing fleet. Can perform salvage, fire-fighting, repair, and towing duties; four fire monitors. Have two 5-ton and two 3-ton cranes, divers' support facilities, extensive welding/cutting capability, and medical facilities.

Note: The Soviet Union had over 400 ice-capable civilian cargo and fishing vessels; most of them remain on the Russian registry.

ST. KITTS

State of Saint Christopher-Nevis

Note: Achieved full independence 8-83; the formerly associated island of Anguilla remains a British dependent.

ST. CHRISTOPHER-NEVIS COAST GUARD

Personnel (1992): 35 tot.

PATROL BOAT

◆ **1 U.S. 110-ft. Commercial Cruiser design**
Bldr: Swiftships, Inc., Morgan City, Louisiana (In serv. 7-85)

C-253 STALWART

Stalwart (C-253) Norman Polmar, 10-89

D: 99.8 tons (fl) **S:** 24 kts (22 cruise) **Dim:** 33.53 × 7.62 × 2.13
A: 2/12.7-mm mg (I × 2)—2/7.62-mm mg (I × 2)
Electron Equipt: Radar: 1/. . . nav.
M: 4 G.M. 12V71 TI diesels; 4 props; 2,400 bhp
Range: 1,800/15 **Fuel:** 31,608 liters **Crew:** 11 tot.

Remarks: Aluminum construction. Acquired with U.S. financial assistance.

PATROL CRAFT

◆ **1 Spear-class patrol craft** Bldr: Fairey Marine, U.K. (In serv. 10-9-74)

RANGER I

D: 4.3 tons (fl) **S:** 30 kts **Dim:** 9.1 × 2.8 × 0.8
A: 2/7.62-mm mg (I × 2)
M: 2 Ford Mermaid diesels; 2 props; 360 bhp **Crew:** 2 tot.

◆ **1 Whaler utility craft** Bldr: Boston Whaler, Rockland, Mass.

RANGER II

D: 1.5 tons light (2 fl) **S:** 40 kts **Dim:** 6.81 × 2.26 × . . .
M: 2 gasoline outboards, 360 bhp **Range:** 167/40 **Crew:** 2 tot.

Remarks: Received in 1990 from U.S. Government. Foam-core GRP construction. Replaces locally built craft with same name.

ST. LUCIA

State of Saint Lucia

COAST GUARD

PATROL CRAFT

◆ **1 U.S. 65-ft. Commercial Cruiser design**
Bldr: Swiftships, Inc., Morgan City, Louisiana (In serv. 3-5-84)

P-02 DEFENDER

Defender (P-02) Swiftships, 5-84

D: 35 tons (fl) **S:** 23 kts **Dim:** 19.96 × 5.59 × 1.52
A: small arms **Electron Equipt:** Radar: 1/Raytheon 1210 nav.
M: 2 G.M. 12V71 TI diesels; 2 props; 1,350 bhp
Electric: 20 kw **Range:** 500/18 **Crew:** 6 tot.

Remarks: Aluminum construction. Ordered 9-11-83 with U.S. financial aid. Blue hull, white superstructure.

◆ **1 patrol launch** Bldr: Phoenix Marine Enterprises, Hialeah, Florida

P-06 VIGILANT II (In serv. 5-90)

D: 5 tons (fl) **S:** 30 kts **Dim:** 8.8 × 3.1 × 0.7
M: 2 Volvo Turbo diesels; 2 props; 400 bhp **Crew:** 3 tot.

Remarks: GRP construction. Replaced the Buhler-built *Vigilant.*

◆ **2 Whaler launches** Bldr: Boston Whaler, Rockland, Mass. (In serv. 7-88)

P-03 ALPHONSE P-04 REYNOLDS

D: 1.5 tons light (2 fl) **S:** 36 kts **Dim:** 6.70 × 2.00 × 0.60
M: 2 Johnson V6, 2.5-liter gasoline outboards; 310 bhp **Crew:** 2 tot.

ST. VINCENT

State of Saint Vincent and the Grenadines

MARINE WING, POLICE FORCE

Personnel (1992): 3 officers, 37 enlisted

PATROL BOATS AND CRAFT

♦ **1 120-ft. Commercial Cruiser class**
Bldr: Swiftships, Inc., Morgan City, La.

SVG-01 CAPTAIN MULZAC (L: 6-6-86; in serv. 13-6-87)

Captain Mulzac (SVG-01) Swiftships, 1987

D: 101 tons light (. . . fl) **S:** 21 kts **Dim:** 35.56 × 7.62 × 2.10
A: 2/12.7-mm mg (I × 2)—2/7.62-mm mg (I × 2)
Electron Equipt: Radar: 1/Raytheon 1010 nav.
M: 4 G.M. 12V71 TI diesels; 4 props; 2,700 bhp
Range: 1,800/15 **Crew:** 4 officers, 10 enlisted

Remarks: Ordered 8-86, with U.S. financial aid. Aluminum construction. Former oilfield pipe carrier, converted for patrol duties.

♦ **1 patrol craft** Bldr: Vosper Thornycroft, Portchester (In serv. 23-2-81)

SVG-05 GEORGE MCINTOSH

George McIntosh (SVG-05) Leo Van Ginderen, 3-84

D: 70 tons (fl) **S:** 24.5 kts **Dim:** 22.86 × 7.43 × 1.64
A: 1/20-mm Oerlikon AA
Electron Equipt: Radar: 1/Decca . . . nav.
M: 2 Caterpillar 12V D348 TA diesels; 2 props; 1,840 bhp
Electric: 24 kw **Range:** 600/21; 1,000/11
Crew: 3 officers, 8 enlisted

Remarks: Glass-reinforced plastic, Keith Nelson–designed hull.

♦ **2 8.2-m patrol craft** Bldr: Buhlers Yachts, Ltd.

SVG-06 LARKAI SVG-07 BRIGHTON

D: 6 tons (fl) **S:** 23 kts **Dim:** 8.20 × 2.95 × 0.90
M: 2 Johnson gasoline outboards, 310 bhp **Crew:** 3 tot.

Remarks: Original Perkins diesel removed 1989–90 when the craft were converted to use gasoline outboards, gaining 4 kts maximum speed.

SÃO TOME AND PRINCIPE

Republic of São Tome and Principe

Personnel (1991): 50 to 75 total

PATROL BOATS AND CRAFT

Note: One Soviet Zhuk-class patrol boat was delivered in 1983 but has been inoperable since at least 1988. Several other small patrol craft are reportedly available; no details available.

♦ **2 Soviet Zhuk-class patrol boats**

D: 48 tons (60 fl) **S:** 34 kts **Dim:** 24.0 × 5.0 × 1.2 (1.8 props)
A: 4/14.5-mm mg (II × 2)
Electron Equipt: Radar: 1/Spin Trough nav.
M: 2 M50F-4 diesels; 2 props; 2,400 bhp
Range: 700/28; 1,100/15 **Fuel:** 10 tons **Crew:** 12 tot.

Remarks: One, delivered 1983, was inoperable by 1988 but was refitted in 1990. Th other was provided as a gift fom Angola in 4-90.

♦ **1 U.S. 2810-V Protector-class patrol craft**
Bldr: SeaArk Marine, Monticello, Arkansas

FALCÃO (In serv. 11-1-92)

D: . . . tons (fl) **S:** 38 kts **Dim:** 8.69 × 3.56 × 0.56
A: small arms **Electron Equipt:** Radar: 1/Furuno . . . nav.
M: 2 Volvo AQAD 41/290 outdrive diesels; 2 props; 400 bhp
Crew: 4 tot.

Remarks: U.S. donation. Aluminum construction. Formally dedicated 20-1-92. Sar class employed by U.S. Coast Guard on Lake Champlain.

Note: Also in use is a 6.7-m riverine patrol craft equipped with a 12.7-mm mg a capable of 13 kts.

SAUDI ARABIA

Kingdom of Saudi Arabia

Personnel (1991): 10,200 total, including 1,200 Marines.

Naval Aviation: 18 SA-365 F/AS Dauphin-2 for ship- and shore-based ASW and s attack, and 4 SA-365N Dauphin-2 configured for search-and-rescue duties, with Omera DRB 32 search radar. The Frontier Force, Coast Guard, and Police Divisio the Ministry of the Interior share six SA-332F1 Super Puma helicopters equipped w AM 39 missiles or a 20-mm cannon and six AS-332B1 troop transports. Six additic Super Pumas were ordered 11-90.

SA-365 Dauphin 2 helicopter:
Rotor diameter: 13.29 m — Weight: light: 1,850 kg/max.: 3,900 kg
Fuselage length: 11.41 m — Speed: 130 kts max.
Height: 4 m — Endurance: 2 hours with 4/AS-15; 3 hours with 2/AS-15
Radius of action: 100 nautical miles with 4/AS-15; 140 nautical mile with 2/AS-15
Propulsion: 2 Turbomeca "Arriel" 1C turbines, 710 shp each.
Armament: 2 or 4 Aérospatiale AS-15 antiship missiles or 2 Mk 36 ASW torpedoes.

The AS-15 missile has a range of 15 km, weighs 96 kg, and is 2.16 m long. helicopter carries an "Agrion-15" frequency-agile, pulse-doppler radar to provide sile targeting and to permit the helicopter to provide mid-course guidance upo information to the ship-launched Otomat Mk 2 ("Erato") missiles, which have a r of 90 nautical miles, weigh 780 kg, and carry a 210-kg warhead.

SA-365 F/AS Dauphin—launching AS-15 missile S.N.I.A.S.,

SUBMARINES

♦ **0 (+10) diesel-electric** Bldr: . . .

Remarks: Saudi Arabia has plans to purchase between six and ten submarines initial bids requested by 12-86. Designs being considered are the Dutch *W Zeeleeuw* and *Moray* classes, the Vickers Type 2400, the West German IKL Swedish Kockums Type 471, a French design, and an Italian design. The *Moray* d had reportedly been chosen late 1989, but no contracts had been let as of 3-92. R that Saudi Arabia had actually ordered small submarines and/or midget subm from South Korea appear to be incorrect.

GUIDED-MISSILE FRIGATES

♦ **0 (+3) F-3000 class** Bldr: DCAN, Lorient

	Laid down	L	In serv.
. . . .	. . .	. . .	. . .
. . . .	. . .	. . .	. . .
. . . .	. . .	. . .	. . .

ED-MISSILE FRIGATES *(continued)*

3,800 tons fl **S:** 28 kts **Dim:** 125.0 × 13.8 × 4.0
3/MM-40 Exocet or Otomat SSM (IV × 2)—1/Aster-15 SAM vertical launch group (16 missiles)—2/Sadral point-defense SAM syst. (VI × 2, . . . Mistral missiles)—1/100-mm 55-cal. Compact DP—4 tubes for F17P wire-guided ASW torpedoes—1/SA-365FF/AS Dauphin helicopter
ctron Equipt:
adar: 1/Decca 1226 nav., 1/DRBC-26C air search, 1/Arabel target designation, 1/. . . f.c.
onar: Thomson-Sintra Sphérion hull-mounted
W: Thomson-CSF Janet or ESD Salamandar intercept, 2/Dagaie decoy RL
4 SEMT-Pielstick 16 PA 6 BTC diesels; 2 CP props; 31,800 bhp
ge: . . ./. . . **Fuel:** . . . **Crew:** . . .

rks: Project definition contract granted to France 11-6-89; no order placed as of nitially planned to deliver the first unit around 1-95 and the last in 1998. The teristics above are provisional. May initially have Crotale SAM and later be with the longer-ranged Aster-30 SAM.

Al Madinah class

	Bldr	Laid down	L	In serv.
L MADINAH	Arsenal de Lorient	15-10-81	23-4-83	4-1-85
OFOUF	CNIM, La Seyne	14-6-82	24-6-83	31-10-85
BHA	CNIM, La Seyne	7-12-82	23-12-83	4-4-86
AIF	CNIM, La Seyne	1-3-83	25-5-84	29-8-86

2,000 tons (2,250 normal, 2,610 fl) **S:** 30 kts
: 115.00 (106.50 pp) × 12.50 wl × 3.40 (4.65 over sonar)
8/Otomat Mk 2 "Erato" SSM (IV × 2)—1/Crotale EDIR SAM syst. (VIII × 1; 26 total missiles)—1/100-mm 55-cal. Compact DP—4/40-mm Breda AA (II × 2)—4 tubes for F17P wire-guided torpedoes—1/Dauphin-2 ASW/antiship helicopter
ctron Equipt:
adar: 2/Decca TM 1226 nav., 1/Sea Tiger (DRBV-15) air search, 1/Castor IIC f.c., 1/DRBC-32E f.c. (on Crotale launcher); 1/helo control
onar: Thomson-Sintra TSM 2630 (Diodon) hull-mounted, TSM 2630 (Sorel) VDS
W: Thomson-CSF DR 4000S intercept syst., Janet jammer, Telegon VI D/F, 2/Dagaie decoy RL
4 SEMT-Pielstick 16 PA 6 BTC diesels; 2 props; 32,500 bhp
ctric: 2,560 kw (4 × 480-kw diesel sets; 2 × 320-kw diesel sets)
nge: 6,500/18; 8,000/15 **Fuel:** 370 tons
durance: 30 days
w: 15 officers, 50 petty officers, 114 enlisted

rks: Ordered 10-80 as part of the "Sawari" program, under which France ed the U.S. as principal naval equipment supplier. Very complex ships, with new, untried equipment. Have an NBC warfare defense citadel.
e Thomson-CSF TAVITAC computer data system, with two Type 15M 125F ters, six display consoles, E7000 tactical table; similar to French Navy's SENIT- backup, there are two CSEE optronic directors. The Otomat missiles have the O (Extended Range of Targeting) feature, using the TAVITAC data system and pter-derived target data. Retractable fin stabilizers fitted. Alcatel Type DLA o f.c.s. 702 arrived 7-85 in Saudi Arabia, 708 on 17-1-87 with the final Dauphin-2 pter.
l is a VDS version of the Diodon sonar; both operate at 11, 12, or 13 kHz. Carry ds 100-mm ammunition, 6,300 rds 40-mm. There are two CSEE optical gun ors. There are 13 main watertight bulkheads to the hull.

Hofouf (704) Gilbert Gyssels, 6-85

Taif (708) Pradignac & Léo, 11-86

Al Madinah (702) DCAN, 4-84

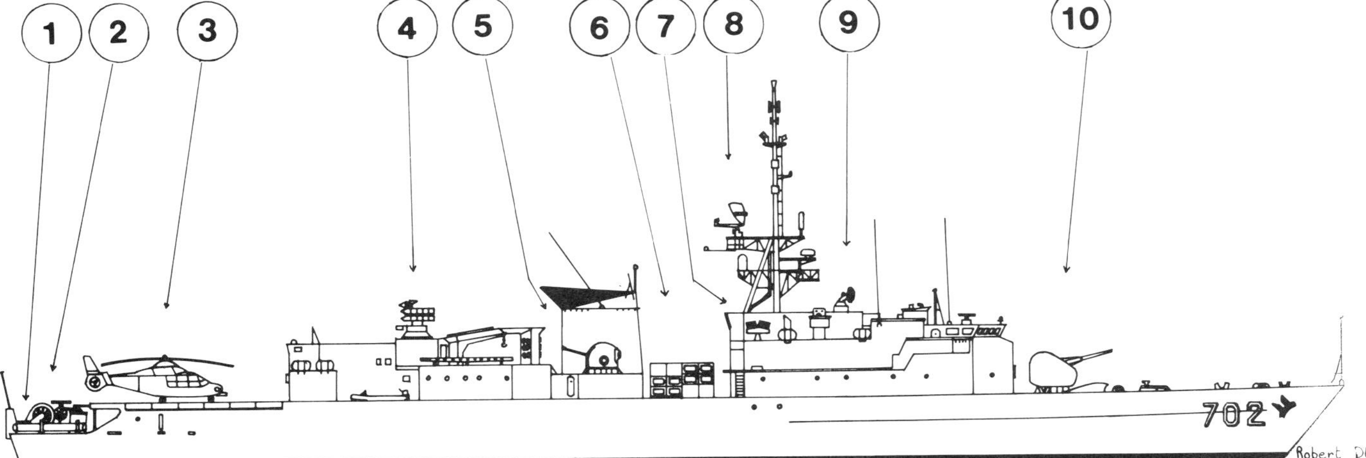

Al Madinah (702) 1. stern torpedo tubes 2. Sorel variable-depth sonar 3. Dauphin helicopter 4. Crotale EDIR SAM launcher 5. twin 40-mm Breda AA 6. Otomat SSM launchers 7. Dagaie decoy launcher 8. Sea Tiger search radar 9. Castor-IIC radar director 10. 100-mm Compact gun Robert Dumas

GUIDED-MISSILE CORVETTES

◆ **4 U.S. PCG class** Bldr: Tacoma Boatbuilding, Tacoma, Washington

	Laid down	L	In serv.
612 Badr (ex-PCG 1)	30-5-79	26-1-80	28-9-81
614 Al-Yarmook (ex-PCG 2)	13-12-79	13-5-80	10-5-82
616 Hitteen (ex-PCG 3)	19-5-80	5-9-80	12-10-82
618 Tabuk (ex-PCG 4)	22-9-80	18-6-81	10-1-83

Badr (612) Leo Van Ginderen, 1989

Al-Yarmook (614) Dr. Giorgio Arra, 1983

D: 903 tons (1,038 fl)
S: 30 kts on gas turbine, 21 kts on diesels
Dim: 74.68 × 9.60 × 2.59
A: 8/Harpoon SSM (IV × 2)—1/76-mm 62-cal. U.S. Mk 75 DP—1/20-mm Mk 15 Phalanx CIWS—2/20-mm AA (I × 2)—1/81-mm mortar—2/40-mm Mk 19 grenade launchers—6/324-mm Mk 32 ASW TT (III × 2)
Electron Equipt:
Radar: 1/SPS-55 nav./surf. search, 1/SPS-40B air search, 1/Mk 92 f.c.
Sonar: SQS-56 (Raytheon DE-1160B) hull-mounted (5.6, 7.5, 8.4 kHz)
EW: SLQ-32 (V)1 intercept, Mk 36 SRBOC decoy syst. (VI × 2, Mk 137 RL)
M: CODOG: 1 G.E. LM-2500 gas turbine (23,000 shp); 2 MTU 12V652 TB91 diesels (3,058 bhp tot.); 2 CP props
Electric: 1,200 kw **Range:** 4,000/20
Crew: 7 officers, 51 enlisted

Remarks: Ordered 30-8-77. Have fin stabilizers. Program completed well behind schedule, with the ships considerably overweight. Have one Mk 24 optical target designator, Mk 309 ASW f.c.s. All based at Jubail on the Persian Gulf.

GUIDED-MISSILE PATROL BOATS

◆ **9 U.S. PGG class** Bldr: Peterson Builders, Sturgeon Bay, Wisconsin

	Laid down	L	In serv.
511 As-Siddiq (ex-PGG 1)	30-9-78	22-9-79	15-12-80
513 Al-Farouq (ex-PGG 2)	12-3-79	17-5-80	22-6-81
515 Abdul-Aziz (ex-PGG 3)	19-10-79	23-8-80	3-9-81
517 Faisal (ex-PGG 4)	4-3-80	15-11-80	23-11-81
519 Khalid (ex-PGG 5)	27-6-80	28-3-81	11-1-82
521 Amr (ex-PGG 6)	21-10-80	13-6-81	21-6-82
523 Tariq (ex-PGG 7)	10-2-81	23-9-81	16-8-82
525 Oqbah (ex-PGG 8)	8-5-81	12-12-81	18-10-82
527 Abu Obaidah (ex-PGG 9)	4-9-81	3-4-82	6-12-82

D: 425 tons (495 fl) **S:** 34 kts on gas turbine, 16 kts on diesels
Dim: 58.02 × 8.08 × 1.95
A: 4/Harpoon SSM (II × 2)—1/76-mm 62-cal. U.S. Mk 75 DP—1/20-mm Mk 15 Phalanx CIWS—2/20-mm AA (I × 2)—1/81-mm mortar—2/40-mm Mk 19 grenade launchers

Electron Equipt:
Radar: 1/SPS-55 nav./surf. search, 1/Mk 92 fire-control system
EW: SLQ-32 (V)1 intercept, Mk 36 SRBOC decoy syst. (VI × 2, M 137 RL)
M: CODOG: 1 G.E. gas turbine (23,000 shp); 2 MTU 12V652 TB91 diesels (3,058 bhp tot.); 2 CP props
Electric: 800 kw **Range:** 600/30; 2,900/14
Crew: 5 officers, 33 enlisted

Oqbah (525) JO1 (AW) Joseph F. Lancaster, USN

As-Siddiq (511)—bow detail French Navy,

Remarks: Ordered 16-2-77. Fin stabilizers fitted. Delivered behind schedule considerably over designed displacement. Have one Mk 24 optical target design transmitter. The Gulf War delayed a planned modernization program. Two bas the Red Sea, the others in the Persian Gulf at Jubail.

TORPEDO BOATS

◆ **3 German Jaguar class (Type 141)**
Bldr: Lürssen, Vegesack (In serv. 1969)

Al Dammam Khybar (ex-*Yarmaq*) Makkah (ex-*Meccah*)

Khybar

D: 170 tons (210 fl) **S:** 40 kts **Dim:** 42.62 × 7.10 × 2.39
A: 2/40-mm 70-cal. Bofors AA (I × 2)—4/533-mm fixed TT (I × 4)
Electron Equipt: Radar: 1/. . . nav.
M: 4 Maybach 16-cyl. diesels; 4 props; 12,000 bhp
Crew: 3 officers, 33 men **Range:** 500/39; 1,000/32

Remarks: Refitted 1976 by builders. Used for training and are nearing the e their useful lives; one is reportedly in reserve, and the others rarely leave the p

PATROL CRAFT

◆ **0 (+ 17) U.S. 77-ft. class**
Bldr: Trinity-Equitable SY, New Orleans, La. (In serv. 2-92 -. . .)

D: 56.4 tons (fl) **S:** 28 kts
Dim: 23.66 × 6.06 × 1.01 hull (1.76 props)
A: 2/25-mm Mk. 38 Chain-Gun (I × 2)—2/7.62-mm mg (I × 2)
Electron Equipt: Radar: 1/Raytheon SPS-64(V)11

:OL CRAFT *(continued)*

2 G.M. 16V92 TAB diesels; 2 props; 2,800 bhp
tric: 70 kw (2 × 35 kw) **Range:** 600/24, 1,200/. . .
l: 18,950 liters
urance: 5 days **Crew:** 1 officer, 7 enlisted

ks: Ordered 12-90. Aluminum construction. A 4-m rigid inflatable boat d by a 40-bhp outboard motor is stowed amidships. Sisters serve in the Philip-avy.

WARFARE SHIPS

+5) U.K. Sandown-class minehunters
r: Vosper Thornycroft, Woolston

	Laid down	L	In serv.
L JAWF (ex-*Inverness*)	. . .	2-8-89	21-12-91
IAQRA	3-90	15-5-91	1992
L KHARG	4-90	. . .	. . .
NIZAH	. . .	. . .	. . .
L RASS	. . .	. . .	. . .
L BAHAIN	. . .	. . .	. . .

wf (420) James W. Goss/NAVPIC, 1-91

wf (420) Leo Van Ginderen, 4-91

378 tons light (465 fl) **S:** 15 kts (13 sust.)/6.5 hunting
: 52.50 (50.00 pp) × 10.50 (9.00 wl) × 2.30
2/30-mm Emerlec (II × 1)
ctron Equipt:
adar: 1/Kelvin-Hughes Type 1007 nav.
onar: 1/Plessey 2093 variable-depth minehunting
W: . . . intercept, Mk 36 RBOC decoy RL (VI × 2, Mk 137 RL)
2 Paxman Valenta 6 RPA 200-E diesels; 2 Voith-Schneider 16 G.S. 5-bladed vertical cycloidal props; 1,500 bhp (1,360 sust.)—2/200-shp electric motors (7 kt max)—2 Schottel electric bow-thrusters
ctric: 750 kw (3 × 250-kw) Mawdsley generator; 3 Perkins V8-250G diesels driving (335 bhp each)
nge: 3,000/12 **Crew:** 7 officers, 40 enlisted

rks: Ordered 3-12-88. Six more were ordered spring 1991, then canceled at the sion of the Gulf War. GRP construction. Differ from RN version in having gun raised one-half deck. The sonar uses a variable-depth vertical lozenge-shaped body lowered beneath the hull; it has search, depth-finder, classification, and survey modes. The ships have the RN Remote-Controlled Mine Disposal System using two French PAP-104 Mk 5 submersibles and carry mine-disposal divers. y NAUTIS-M navigation/minehunting data system. Also have Racal Hyperfix, 4, and Navigator Mk 21 radio navaids. The guns are controlled by a Contraves) optronic director. Capable of dealing with mines to 200 m depths.

U.S. MSC 322-class minesweepers
dr: Peterson Builders, Sturgeon Bay, Wisconsin

	Laid down	L	In serv.
ADDIRIYAH (ex-MSC 322)	12-5-76	20-12-76	6-7-78
AL-QUYSUMAH (ex-MSC 323)	24-8-76	26-5-77	15-8-78
AL-WADEEAH (ex-MSC 324)	28-12-76	6-9-77	7-9-78
SAFWA (ex-MSC 325)	5-3-77	7-12-77	20-10-78

Safwa (418) Leo Van Ginderen, 1984

D: 320 tons (407 fl) **S:** 14 kts
Dim: 46.63 × 8.29 × 4.06 max.
A: 2/20-mm AA Mk 67 (II × 1)
Electron Equipt:
Radar: SPS-55 nav./surf. search
Sonar: SQQ-14 VDS minehunting HF
M: 2 Waukesha E1616 diesels; 2 props; 1,200 bhp
Electric: 2,150 kw **Crew:** 4 officers, 35 enlisted

Remarks: Ordered 30-9-75. Longer than standard U.S. export coastal minesweepers. Wooden construction. Have a 1,750-kw sweep current generator. Used primarily as patrol boats and played very little part in clearing Iraqi-laid mines during and after the Gulf War.

AMPHIBIOUS WARFARE CRAFT

♦ **4 U.S. LCU 1646 class**
Bldr: Newport SY, Newport, Rhode Island (In serv. 1976)

212 AL-QIAQ (ex-SA 310) 216 AL-ULA (ex-SA 312)
214 AS-SULAYEL (ex-SA 311) 218 AFIF (ex-SA 313)

D: 173 tons (403 fl) **S:** 11 kts
Dim: 41.07 × 9.07 × 2.08
A: 2/20-mm AA (I × 2)
Electron Equipt: Radar: 1/LN-66 nav.
M: 4 G.M. 6-71 diesels; 2 Kort-nozzle props; 900 bhp
Electric: 80 kw **Range:** 1,200/10
Crew: 2 officers, 12 enlisted + 20 passengers

Remarks: Standard units of the class, with cargo capacity rated at 168 tons on the open 30.5 × 5.5-m cargo deck; have ramps fore and aft. Used as logistics transports.

♦ **4 landing craft (LCM)**
Bldr: Schlichting Werft, Travemünde, West Germany (In serv. 1982)

201 202 203 204

D: 26 tons (light) **S:** . . . **Dim:** 16.5 × 4.0 × . . .
M: 2 diesels; 2 props; . . . bhp

♦ **8 U.S. LCM(6)-class landing craft**
Bldr: Marinette Marine, Marinette, Wisconsin

	In serv.		In serv.
212	7-77	220 DHEBA	7-80
214	7-77	222 UMLUS	7-80
216	7-77	224 AL LEETH	7-80
218	7-77	226 AL QUONFETHA	7-80

D: 24 tons (57.5 fl) **S:** 13 kts **Dim:** 17.07 × 4.37 × 1.14
A: 2/40-mm Mk 19 grenade launchers
M: 2 G.M. 6V71 diesels; 2 props; 450 bhp
Range: 130/9 (loaded) **Crew:** 5 tot.

Remarks: Cargo: 30 tons or 80 troops. Cargo well: 11.9 × 3.7.

AUXILIARIES

♦ **2 underway replenishment oilers** Bldr: CN la Ciotat, Marseille

	Laid down	L	In serv.
902 BORAIDA	13-4-82	22-1-83	29-2-84
904 YUNBOU	9-10-83	20-10-84	29-8-85

Yunbou (904) DCN, 1985

AUXILIARIES *(continued)*

Boraida (902) Leo Van Ginderen, 8-84

D: 10,500 tons (trials) **S:** 20.5 kts
Dim: 135.0 × 18.7 × 7.0
A: 4/40-mm 70-cal. AA (II × 2)—2/SA-365N Dauphin-2 helicopters
Electron Equipt: Radar: 2/Decca . . . nav.
M: 2 SEMT-Pielstick 14 PC 2.5V400 diesels; 2 CP props; 13,200 bhp
Electric: 3,400 kw **Range:** 7,000/17 **Endurance:** 30 days
Crew: 140 tot. + 55 cadets

Remarks: Ordered 10-80 as part of the "Sawari" program. Design is a reduced version of the French *Durance* class. Act as training ships as well as replenishment vessels. Cargo includes 4,350 tons diesel fuel; 350 tons aviation fuel; 140 tons potable water; 100 tons provisions; 100 tons munitions; and 70 tons spares. One replenishment station per side, plus over-the-stern refueling. Can transfer 1.7-ton solid loads. Have electrical, mechanical, and metal workshops. Two CSEE Naja directors for the 40-mm AA. The helicopters can also carry ASW and antiship weapons. 902 left France 3-8-84 for Saudi Arabia.

◆ **1 ex-Iraqi presidential yacht**
Bldr: Elsinore SB & Eng., Denmark (L: 10-80; In serv. 1981)

Al Yamana (ex-*Qadissayat Saddam*)

Al Yamana Elsinore SY, 1980

D: 1,660 tons (fl) **S:** 19.3 kts **Dim:** 82.00 × 13.00 × 3.30
M: 2 MTU 12V1163 TB82 diesels; 2 CP props; 6,000 bhp
Electric: 1,095 kVA

Remarks: 2,282 grt. Because of the Iran-Iraq War, was never delivered to Saddam Hussein, who gave it as a present to King Fahd in 1988. Can carry 56 passengers (74 additional on short cruises). Sperry retractable fin stabilizers. 300-hp bow-thruster. Helicopter deck aft above swimming pool.

◆ **1 royal yacht** Bldr: Helsingor Vaerft, Denmark (In serv. 12-83)

Abdul Aziz

Abdul Aziz—white with blue funnels Walles Foto, 5-84

D: approx. 5,200 tons (fl) **S:** 22 kts
Dim: 147.00 (126.00 pp) × 18.00 × 4.90
M: 2 Lindholmen-Pielstick 12 PC 2-5V400 diesels; 2 props; 15,600 bhp
Fuel: 640 tons **Crew:** 65 crew, plus 4 royalty, plus 60 passengers

Remarks: Delivered by builders 4-83 to Vosper Shiprepairers, Southampton, for final fitting out and ran post-outfitting trials 15-5-84. Stern ramp leading to vehicle garage. Swimming pool. Helicopter hangar forward, beneath the forecastle.

Note: The royal yacht *Al Riyadh* was sold 1990.

◆ **1 Jetfoil-type hydrofoil royal yacht tender** Bldr: Boeing, Sea

Al Aziziah (In serv. 8-85)

D: 115 tons (fl) **S:** 46 kts
Dim: 27.4 (foils down) × 9.1 × 1.9 hull (5.2 foils down at rest/2.0 foiling)
A: 2/20-mm G.E. Sea Vulcan gatling AA (I × 2), with 2 Stinger missiles co-mounted
Electron Equipt: Radar: 1/. . . nav.
M: 2 Allison 501-KF20A gas turbines; 2 Rocketdyne R-20 waterjet pumps; 9,000 shp (7,560 sust.)—2 G.M. 8V92 TI diesels; 2 props 900 bhp for hull-borne cruise
Range: 890/40; 1,500/15 (hull-borne)
Fuel: 33 tons **Crew:** . . .

Remarks: Aluminum construction. Subcontracted to Boeing by Lockheed. Has a morgen HSV-20NCS electro-optical GFCS with Mk 35 Mod. L3 electro-optical si the gun mounts. Acts as tender and escort craft for the larger yachts.

◆ **1 salvage tug** Bldr: Hayashikane, Shimonoseki (In serv. 1978)

13 Jeddah

D: 350 tons **S:** 12 kts **Dim:** 34.4 × . . . × . . .
M: 2 diesels; 800 bhp

◆ **2 U.S. YTB 760-class tugs** (In serv. 15-10-75)

EN 111 Tuwaig (ex-YTB 837) EN 112 Dareen (ex-YTB 838)

D: 291 tons (356 fl) **S:** 12 kts **Dim:** 33.22 × 9.30 × 4.14
A: 2/20-mm AA (I × 2)
Electron Equipt: Radar: 1/LN-66 nav.
M: 1 Fairbanks-Morse 38D8Q diesel; 1 prop; 2,000 bhp
Electric: 120 kw **Range:** 2,000/10 **Crew:** 4 officers, 8 enlisted

Remarks: 25-ton bollard pull. Intended for target towing, fire fighting, torpedo ery, and local patrol duties.

COAST GUARD

PATROL BOATS

◆ **4 Al Souf-class shallow-draft** Bldr: Blohm + Voss, Hamburg

	In serv.		In serv.
351 Al Jouf	15-6-89	353 Hail	20-8-89
352 Turaif	15-6-89	354 Najran	20-8-89

Turaif (352) Hartmut Ehlers

D: 210 tons (fl) **S:** 38 kts
Dim: 38.80 (36.20 pp) × 7.90 × 1.90
A: 2/20-mm Oerlikon GAM-801 AA (I × 2)—2/12.7-mm mg (I × 2)
Electron Equipt:
Radar: 1/Decca RM 1290A nav., 1/Decca ARPA S-1690 surf. sear
M: 3 MTU 16V538 diesels; 3 props; 11,260 bhp
Electric: 321 kVA tot. **Range:** 1,900/15
Crew: 4 officers, 16 enlisted

Remarks: Ordered 9-86. Steel hulls, aluminum superstructures. Have a 300 min fire-fighting monitor and carry a radio direction-finder. Two based at Jiddah Persian Gulf and two at Damman on the Red Sea.

◆ **2 CGV-26 "Explorer" class**
Bldr: Abeking & Rasmussen, Lemwerder, Germany

	Laid down	L	In serv.
Al Jubatel	1-3-86	3-87	4-87
Salwa	1-3-86	3-87	4-87

D: 80 tons (95 fl) **S:** 40+ kts
Dim: 26.60 (23.00 pp) × 6.50 × 1.80 (props)
A: 2/20-mm Oerlikon GAM-B01 AA (I × 2)—2/12.7-mm mg (I × 2
Electron Equipt: Radar: 1/Decca . . . nav.
M: 2 MTU 16V396 TB94 diesels; 2 props; 6,340 bhp
Range: 1,100/. . . **Crew:** 4 officers, 8 enlisted

Remarks: Ordered 11-8-85. Steel construction. Reduced version of builder's S. class for Turkey.

ꞩAUDI ARABIA *(continued)*
ᴾATROL BOATS *(continued)*

.l Jubatel Abeking & Rasmussen, 1987

.ATROL CRAFT

40 Naja 12 class Bldr: Simonneau S.A. Marine, Fontenay-le-Comte, France (In serv. 1988–89, 1991)

D: 7.5 tons (fl) **S:** 50 kts
Dim: 12.80 (10.20 pp) × 4.00 × 0.50
A: 1/20-mm GIAT F-2 AA—2/7.62 GIAT mg (I × 2)
Electron Equipt: Radar: 1/Furuno . . . nav.
M: 4 OMC gasoline outboard motors; 1,200 shp
Range: 350/35 **Fuel:** 1,700 liters **Crew:** 4 tot.

›marks: First group of 20 ordered 6-6-88, second in 10-90. Of the first group, one was ›t during delivery and replaced by the builder. Aluminum construction. Delivered to ›udi Arabia by air.

15 Scorpion class Bldrs: Originally 25 units, of which 20 units: Bayerische Schiffsbau, Erlenbach; and 5 units: Arminias Werft, Bodenwerder, West Germany (In serv. 1979, except last 10: 28-2-81)

9–164

Peter Voss, 5-82

): 33 tons (fl) **S:** 25 kts **Dim:** 17.14 (15.6 pp) × 4.98 × 1.40
\: 2/7.62-mm mg **Electron Equipt:** Radar: 1/Decca RM 914
I: 2 G.M. 12V71 TI diesels; 2 props; 1,300 bhp (1,050 sust.)
ℜange: 200/20 **Crew:** 7 tot.

›narks: Ten sisters have been discarded, despite brief service.

12 Rapier class
Bldr: Halter Marine, New Orleans, La. (In serv. 1976–77)

–138

›: 26 tons (fl) **S:** 28 kts **Dim:** 15.24 × 4.57 × 1.35
.: 2/7.62-mm mg (I × 2)
lectron Equipt: Radar: 1/. . . nav.
I: 1 G.M. 12V71 TI diesel; 2 props; 1,300 bhp
lectric: 20 kw **Crew:** 1 officer, 8 enlisted

ier class Halter Marine, 1976

◆ **43 C-80 class** Bldr: Northshore Yacht Yard, U.K. (In serv. 1975–77)

D: 2.8 tons (fl) **S:** 20 kts **Dim:** 8.9 × 2.9 × 0.6 **A:** 1/7.62-mm mg
M: 1 Caterpillar diesel; Castoldi waterjet; 210 bhp **Crew:** 3 tot.

◆ **10 Huntress class** Bldr: Fairey Marine, Hamble, U.K. (In serv. 1976)

D: 4 tons (fl) **S:** 20 kts
Dim: 7.1 × 2.7 × 0.8 **Crew:** 4 tot.
A: 1/7.62-mm mg **M:** 1 diesel; 180 bhp **Range:** 150/20

◆ **10 (+ 20) Type SAH-2000 hovercraft**
Bldr: Slingsby, U.K. (In serv. 1991–92)

Remarks: Small air-cushion vehicles armed with 1/12.7-mm mg. Have Kevlar armor. Up to 20 additional planned.

◆ **8 SRN.6 Mod. 8 hovercraft**
Bldr: British Hovercraft, Cowes (In serv.: 6 in 1981, 2 in 1-82)

Two Saudi Coast Guard SRN.6 Mod. 8 British Hovercraft, 1981

D: 17 tons (fl) **S:** 50–55 kts **Dim:** 18.3 × 8.5 × . . .
A: small arms **Electron Equipt:** Radar: 1/Decca . . .
M: 1 Rolls-Royce Gnome gas turbine; 1 lift-fan, 1 airscrew; 1,060 shp

Remarks: Payload: 6 tons. Endurance: 6 to 11 hours. Carry 1,200 liters fuel internally, plus two 450-liter deck tanks. Eight similar SRN.6 of an earlier model, delivered 1970, have been discarded.

◆ **8 harbor patrol craft** Bldr: Yokohama Yacht, Japan, 1972

D: . . . **S:** 20 kts **Dim:** 10.5 × 3.0 × . . .
M: 2 diesels; 2 props; 280 bhp

Note: There are also several hundred small boats: 200 of 5.1-m length with 40-hp engines, and 100 of 4.2-m length with 20-hp engines.

AUXILIARIES AND SERVICE CRAFT

◆ **1 training ship** Bldr: Bayerische Schiffsbau, Erlenbach, West Germany

TEBUK (In serv. 12-77)

D: 600 tons (750 fl) **S:** 20 kts
Dim: 60.0 (55.5 pp) × 10.0 × 2.50
A: 1/20-mm Oerlikon GAM-B01 AA
Electron Equipt: Radar: 1/Decca TM 1226 nav.
M: 2 MTU 16V538 TB81 diesels; 2 props; 5,260 bhp (4,800 sust.)
Range: 2,400/18; 3,900/12 **Electric:** 1,040 kVA
Crew: 24 crew + 36 trainees

◆ **3 ramped personnel launches** Bldr: Rotork, U.K. (In serv. 1991)

AL FAISAL AL HAMZA AL HASSHIM

D: 9 tons (fl) **S:** 28 kts **Dim:** 12.7 × 3.2 × 0.9
M: 2 diesels; 2 props; 240 bhp **Crew:** 3 + 28 troops

◆ **3 small fuel lighters**—27 m overall

AL FORAT DAJLAH . . . .

◆ **2 yachts**

AL DERIYAH PROMINEUT

◆ **5 barges**

◆ **4 motor dhows**

SENEGAL

Republic of Senegal

Note: The "confederation" with The Gambia did not affect military forces and was dissolved 30-9-89.

Personnel (1992): 700 total

Naval Aviation: One Canadian de Havilland DHC-6-300M Twin Otter for maritime patrol.

PATROL BOATS

◆ **1 Osprey 55 design** Bldr: Danyard A/S, Frederikshavn, Denmark

	Laid down	L	In serv.
Fouta	11-86	3-87	1-6-87

Fouta French Navy, 1987

D: 500 tons (fl) **S:** 20.2 kts; 19 sust.
Dim: 54.75 (50.83 pp) × 10.30 (9.15 wl) × 2.55
A: 1/20-mm AA—1/12.7-mm mg
Electron Equipt:
Radar: 1/Furuno FR-1411 nav., 1/Furuno FR-1221 nav.
M: 2 M.A.N. Alpha 12V.23/30-DVO diesels; 2 CP props; 4,960 bhp
Electric: 359 kw **Range:** 4,500/16 **Fuel:** 95 tons
Crew: 4 officers, 34 enlisted + 8 trainees

Remarks: Ordered early 1986. Thornycroft Giles "short, fat ship" hull. Near-sisters in Danish, Moroccan, Greek, and Burmese service. Used for 200-n.m. economic zone and fisheries patrol, and financed by the Ministry of Equipment rather than the navy. Armed after delivery. No helicopter facility. Berths for 20 rescued personnel. A stern docking well holds a 6.5-m Watercraft RI-22 inspection/rescue boat. Senegal hopes to rearm the boat with a 40-mm AA.

◆ **1 French PR 72 MS class** Bldr: SFCN, Villeneuve-la-Garenne

	Laid down	L	In serv.
P 773 N'jambuur	5-80	23-12-80	9-81

N'jambuur (P 773) SFCN, 1981

D: 381 tons light (451 fl) **S:** 30 kts
Dim: 58.70 (54.0 pp) × 8.22 × 2.18
A: 2/76-mm 62-cal. OTO Melara Compact (I × 2)—2/20-mm Type F2 AA (I × 2)
Electron Equipt: Radar: 1/Decca 1226 nav.
M: 4 AGO 195V16 RVR diesels; 4 props; 12,800 bhp
Range: 2,500/16 **Crew:** 39 tot. plus 7 passengers

Remarks: Can be equipped later with 4 Exocet SSM. Has two CSEE Naja optical GFCS.

◆ **3 PR-48 class** Bldr: SFCN, Villeneuve-la-Garenne

	Laid down	L	In serv.
Saint Louis	20-4-70	5-8-70	1-3-71
Popenguine	12-73	22-3-74	10-8-74
Podor	12-75	20-7-76	13-7-77

Saint Louis 19

D: 240 tons (avg.) **S:** 23 kts **Dim:** 47.5 (45.5 pp) × 7.1 × 2.5
A: 2/40-mm AA (I × 2)—2/7.62-mm mg (I × 2)
Electron Equipt: Radar: 1/Decca 1226 nav.
M: 2 AGO V12 CZSHR diesels; 2 props; 6,240 bhp
Range: 2,000/16 **Crew:** 3 officers, 22 enlisted

◆ **2 Chinese Shanghai-II class**

Banjul Cuajur

D: 121 tons (131 fl) **S:** 28.5 kts (26 sust.)
Dim: 38.78 × 5.41 × 1.49 (hull: 1.554 full load)
A: 6/25-mm 2M-8 AA (II × 3)
Electron Equipt: Radar: 1/Furuno 1505 nav.
M: 2 M50F-4 (Chinese Type L12-180) 1,200-bhp, and 2/12D6 (Chines Type L12-180Z) 910-bhp diesels; 4 props; 4,200 bhp
Electric: 39 kw **Range:** 750/16.5
Endurance: 7 days **Crew:** 34 tot.

Remarks: Received as a gift of the Peoples' Republic of China on 2-2-89 after refit China. Were constructed during the late 1970s. The standard Shanghai-II armame two twin 37-mm and two twin 25-mm AA had been altered, a Japanese comme radar was substituted for the original Pot Head, and the fantail has been left cle accommodate an inspection dinghy.

PATROL CRAFT

◆ **3 "Interceptor" class**
Bldr: Turbec Ltd., St. Catharines, Quebec, Canada

Senegal II Siné Saloum II Casamance II

Casamance II Leo Van Ginderen,

D: 52 tons (62 fl) **S:** 32 kts **Dim:** 26.5 × 5.81 × . . .
A: 2/20-mm AA (I × 2)
Electron Equipt: Radar: 1/LN-66 nav.
M: 2 diesels; 2 props; 2,700 bhp **Crew:** . . .

Remarks: In service 2-79, 7-79, and 10-79, respectively. Used for fisheries-prot patrol.

◆ **2 British Tracker 2 class**
Bldr: Fairey Marine, Cowes, U.K. (In serv. 1978)

P 3 Challenge P 4 Champion

D: 31.5 tons (fl) **S:** 29 kts **Dim:** 19.25 × 4.98 × 1.45
A: 1/20-mm Oerlikon AA—2/7.62-mm mg (I × 2)
Electron Equipt: Radar: 1/Decca 110 nav., 1/. . . nav.
M: 2 G.M. Detroit Diesel 12V71 TI diesels; 2 props; 1,290 bhp
Range: 650/20 **Crew:** 11 tot.

Remarks: GRP construction. Air-conditioned. Were returned to Senegal in 9 The Gambia.

AMPHIBIOUS WARFARE SHIPS

◆ **1 French EDIC 700-class tank landing craft**
Bldr: SFCN, Villeneuve-la-Garenne

	Laid down	L	In serv.
841 Karabene	23-4-85	6-3-86	23-6-86

ENEGAL *(continued)*
MPHIBIOUS WARFARE SHIPS *(continued)*

D: 410 tons light (730 fl) **S:** 12 kts
Dim: 59.00 (52.90 pp) × 11.90 × 1.69 (max.)
A: 2/20-mm AA (I × 2)—1/81-mm mortar
Electron Equipt: Radar: 1/Decca 1226 nav.
M: 2 UNI UD30.V12 diesels; 2 props; 1,400 bhp (1,040 sust.)
Range: 1,800/8 **Crew:** 18 tot.

:marks: Ordered 3-6-85 to replace sister *Faleme* (ex-EDIC 9095), on loan from ance since 7-1-74. Cargo: 340 tons, carried in 28.50 × 8.0 vehicle well: eleven trucks five light tanks. Arrived in Senegal 8-86.

:te: U.S. LCM (6)-class landing craft *Djomboss* and *Douloulou,* transferred 7-69, ve been discarded.

ERVICE CRAFT

1 training craft

RAME JEAN (ex-*Raymond Sarr*)

marks: A former fishing vessel, acquired 1978. Of 18 tons displacement.

2 French Oiseau-class tugs

GRETTE IBIS

D: 200 tons (fl) **S:** 9 kts **Dim:** 18.4 × 5.7 × 2.5
M: 1 Poyaud diesel; 250 bhp **Range:** 1,700/9

marks: On loan from the French Navy; *Aigrette* arrived 1990.

CUSTOMS SERVICE

ATROL CRAFT

4 LVI 85S class Bldr: Aresa, Barcelona (In serv. 1987)

IBRIL N'DIAYE GORÉE DJILOR

D: 3.4 tons (fl) **S:** 18 kts **Dim:** 8.5 × . . . × . . .
Electron Equipt: Radar: 1/Decca 110 nav.
M: . . . **Crew:** 3–4 tot.

marks: GRP construction. Had been ordered in 1979!

3 Type DS 01 Bldr: Celayo, Bilbao, Spain (In serv. 1-82)

D: 26 tons (fl) **S:** 20 kts **Dim:** 16.0 (13.3 pp) × 4.8 × 1.6
A: 1/12.7-mm mg **Electron Equipt:** Radar: 1/Decca 110 nav.
M: 2 G.M. 5V71 TI diesels; 2 props; 870 bhp **Crew:** 8 tot.

SEYCHELLES

ublic of Seychelles

sonnel (1992): Approximately 200 tot.

al Aviation: 1 Britten-Norman BN-42 B/T Maritime Defender for surveillance, 1 child Merlin twin-engine light transport, 2 Super Rallye light planes, and 2 HAL ak (Alouette-III) helicopters.

TROL BOATS AND CRAFT

modified Soviet Turya-class patrol boat

DASTER

210 tons (240 fl) **S:** 38 kts **Dim:** 38.60 × 7.60 × 2.00
2/57-mm AK-257 DP (II × 1)—2/25-mm 2M-8 AA (II × 1)
ectron Equipt:
Radar: 1/Pot Drum surf. search, 1/Muff Cob f.c.
IFF: High Pole B transponder, Square Head interrogator
3 Type M504 diesels; 3 props; 15,000 bhp
nge: 400/38; 650/25 **Crew:** 24 tot.

arks: Delivered 21-6-86 without the standard hydrofoils, 4/533-mm TT, or dip-sonar installation. Essentially an Osa hull. Has no ASW weapons or sensors.

FPB 42 class Bldr: C.N. Picchiotti, Viareggio, Italy (In serv. 10-1-83)

ANDROMACHE

240 tons (268 fl) **S:** 28 kts
m: 41.80 × 8.00 × 2.50 (props; 1.70 hull)
1/20-mm Oerlikon AA—2/7.62-mm mg (I × 2)
ectron Equipt: Radar: 2/Furuno . . . nav.
2 Paxman Valenta 16 RP200 CM diesels; 2 props; 6,800 bhp (5,700 sust.)
nge: 3,000/16 **Crew:** 3 officers, 19 enlisted

rks: Ordered 8-10-81. Also used as a personnel transport. Refitted 1985–86 in A long-projected second unit may have been ordered during 1991.

Andromache (605) Carlo Martinelli, 9-86

♦ **1 ex-French Sirius-class former minesweeper**
Bldr: Seine Maritime (In serv. 13-6-56)

TOPAZ (ex-*Croix du Sud*)

D: 400 tons (44 fl) **S:** 15 kts
Dim: 46.40 (42.70 pp) × 8.55 × 2.50
A: 1/40-mm 60-cal. Bofors AA—1/20-mm Oerlikon AA
Electron Equipt: Radar: 1/Decca 1226 nav.
M: 2 SEMT-Pielstick diesels; 2 props; 2,000 bhp
Range: 3,000/10 **Crew:** 37 tot.

Remarks: Transferred minus mine-countermeasures equipment in 1-79; retired 1987 but refitted and recommissioned early 1990. Wooden construction.

♦ **2 Soviet Zhuk class**

CONSTANT (In serv. 17-10-81) FORTUNE (In serv. 6-11-82)

Constant and Fortune French Navy, 8-85

D: 60 tons (fl) **S:** 34 kts **Dim:** 24.0 × 5.0 × 1.8 (props)
A: 4/14.5-mm mg (II × 2)
Electron Equipt: Radar: 1/Spin Trough nav.
M: 2 M50F-4 diesels; 2 props; 2,400 bhp
Range: 700/28; 1,100/15 **Fuel:** 10 tons **Crew:** 17 tot

Note: The small patrol boat *Junon* was stricken in 1991.

AUXILIARY

♦ **1 medium landing ship** Bldr: A.C. de la Perrière, France

	Laid down	L	In serv.
5 JUIN	7-4-78	19-9-78	11-1-79

D: 350 tons (855 fl) **S:** 9 kts **Dim:** 58.2 × 11.37 × 1.9
M: 2 Poyaud A12 150M diesels; 2 props; 880 bhp
Range: 2,000/9

Remarks: Owned by the government but generally operated in local commercial service. Bow ramp. Cargo: 272 tons.

SIERRA LEONE

Republic of Sierra Leone

Personnel (1992): 158 total

FISHERIES PROTECTION SHIP

◆ **1 former Canadian fisheries protection ship**
Bldr: Canadian Vickers, Montreal, Quebec, Canada (In serv. 1959)

MARITIME PROTECTOR (ex-*Arctic Prowler,* ex-*0081-2,* ex-*Cygnus*)

D: . . . tons (fl) **S:** . . . kts
Dim: 46.64 (43.29 wl) × 8.65 × . . .
Electron Equipt: Radar: . . .
M: 2 Fairbanks-Morse diesels; 2 props; 1,600 bhp

Remarks: 524 grt. Contract service provided beginning in 1991 by Maritime Protection Services (Sierra Leone), Ltd., to combat poaching on the rich fishing grounds off Sierra Leone. Civilian crew. Had been built for the Canadian Coast Guard.

PATROL BOATS AND CRAFT

◆ **1 U.S. 110-ft. Commmercial Cruiser-class patrol boat**
Bldr: Swiftships, Inc., Morgan City, La. (In serv. 1-90)

FARANDUGU

D: 99.8 tons (fl) **S:** 24 kts **Dim:** 33.53 × 7.62 × 2.13
A: 2/12.7-mm mg **Electron Equipt:** Radar: 1/. . . nav.
M: 4 G.M. 12V71 TI diesels; 4 props; 2,400 bhp
Range: 1,800/15 **Fuel:** 31,608 liters **Crew:** 11 tot.

Remarks: Ordered 10-87 under the U.S. Foreign Military Sales program. Aluminum construction.

◆ **2 Chinese Shanghai-II-class patrol boats**

MOA MAIMBANA

D: 122.5 tons (134.8 fl) **S:** 28.5 kts
Dim: 38.78 × 5.41 × 1.49 hull
A: 2/37-mm V-47M AA (I × 2)—4/25-mm 2M-8 (II × 2)
Electron Equipt: Radar: 1/Pot Head surf. search
M: 2 L12-180 (1,200-bhp) diesels, and 2 Type 12180Z (910-bhp) diesels; 4 props; 4,220 bhp
Electric: 39 kw **Range:** 750/16.5
Endurance: 7 days **Crew:** 36 tot.

Remarks: Delivered 3-87 as replacements for three sisters transferred 1976 and no longer in service. Lack the normal aft twin 37-mm AA found on this class; replaced by davits for inflatable inspection boat.

◆ **2 Cat 900S-class patrol craft**
Bldr: Cougar Holdings, Hamble, U.K. (In serv. 5-88)

D: 7.4 tons (fl) **S:** 40 kts **Dim:** 10.40 × 2.89 × 0.78
A: 1/7.62-mm mg
Electron Equipt: Radar: 1/Decca . . . nav.
M: 2 Volvo Penta ADAQ 41A diesel outdrives; 400 bhp
Range: 250/30 **Crew:** 4 tot.

Remarks: Kevlar resin hull construction.

◆ **1 patrol and pilot-service boat** Bldr: Halmatic, UK (In serv. 1987)

D: 13.5 tons (fl) **S:** 23 kts **Dim:** 12.30 × 3.40 × 1.00
A: 1/7.62-mm mg
Electron Equipt: Radar: 1/Decca . . .
M: 2 Volvo Penta TAMD 70E diesels; 2 props; 530 bhp
Range: . . ./. . . **Crew:** . . .

Remarks: GRP construction. Primarily a pilot boat. A second pilot boat was delivered during 1991 by Swansea Maritime, U.K.; no data available.

AMPHIBIOUS WARFARE SHIPS

◆ **3 Pompoli-class landing ships** Bldrs: Shikoku DY, Japan (first two); Kegoya SY, Japan (*Kallondo*) (In serv. 14-5-80)

POMPOLI GULAMA KALLONDO

D: 634 tons (fl) **S:** 13 kts **Dim:** 55.0 × 11.6 × 1.5
A: . . . **Electron Equipt:** Radar: . . .
M: 1 Yanmar diesel; 1 prop; . . . bhp **Range:** 1,540/12
Crew: 6 officers, 7 men + 262 troops

Remarks: Ferry-like craft suitable for river and coastal service; ramps fore and aft. Can carry up to 31 small vehicles.

SINGAPORE

Republic of Singapore

Personnel (1992): Approximately 4,500 total

Naval Aviation: The Singapore Air Force 125 Squadron has 22 AS-332M Super Pu helicopters equipped for ASW, 18 Bell UH-1H helicopters, 6 AS-350B Écureuil lig helicopters, and 20 AS-550 Fennec attack helicopters (10 with Helitow anti-tank/sh missiles and 20-mm rocket pods, 10 in utility configuration). The air force also opera 4 E-2C Hawkeye radar surveillance aircraft and some 50 A-4 Skyhawk fight bombers capable of maritime strike. Eight F-16A/B fighters were delivered in 19 The Singapore Navy ordered four Fokker 50 maritime patrol aircraft in 1991 delivery in 1994–95. In addition to tracking aerial contacts, the Hawkeyes are capa of providing over-the-horizon targeting data for Harpoon missiles aboard naval uni

GUIDED-MISSILE PATROL BOATS

Note: Bids requested 10-4-92 for six (with option for six more) 44–55-m patrol bo with Harpoon SSM, OTO Melara 76-mm gun, ASW TT; to order 9-92.

◆ **6 MGB 62 class**
Bldr: P 88: Lürssen, Vegesack, Germany; others: Singapore SB & Eng., Jurong

	L	In serv.
P 88 VICTORY	8-6-88	18-8-90
P 89 VALOUR	10-12-88	18-8-90
P 90 VIGILANCE	27-4-89	18-8-90
P 91 VALIANT	22-7-89	25-5-91
P 92 VIGOUR	1-2-89	25-5-91
P 93 VENGEANCE	23-2-90	25-5-91

Victory (P 88) R.A.N.,

Vigour (P 92) R.A.N

ED-MISSILE PATROL BOATS *(continued)*

50 tons normal (600 fl) **S:** 35 kts
62.95 (59.90 pp) × 9.30 × 2.60
/Harpoon SSM (IV × 2)—1/76-mm 62-cal. OTO Melara Super
apid DP—4/12.7-mm mg (I × 4)—6/324-mm ILAS-3 ASW TT (III
2; 6/A244 torpedoes)
tron Equipt:
dar: 1/ Decca . . . nav., 1/H.S.A. ZW-06 surf./air search, 1/BEAB
9LV 200 f.c.
nar: Thomson-Sintra Salmon VDS
V: Rafael SEWS intercept/jammer suite, 2 Plessey Shield decoy
RL (VI × 2)
MTU 20V538 TB93 diesels; 4 props; 18,740 bhp
tric: 408 kw **Range:** 700/34; 4,000/16
v: 4 officers, 36 enlisted

ks: Same hull as pair for Bahrain, but without helicopter facilities. Intended to a SAM system aft, possibly French modular Crotale (IV × 1), Israeli Barak, or M with 21-cell Mk 49 launcher. First unit ordered 6-86. P 88 began trials 9-88. raeli NATACS command system. Are receiving rudder roll-stabilization sys- ve experienced stability problems due to the weight of the large tower mast e and are to be reconfigured. They constitute 188 Squadron. Transferred to the astal Command 10-91 for anti-piracy, fisheries protection, and search-and- uties.

PB 45 class Bldrs: P 76, P 77: Lürssen, Vegesack, Germany; others: gapore SB & Eng., Jurong

	In serv.		In serv.
EA WOLF	1972	P 79 SEA TIGER	1974
EA LION	1972	P 80 SEA HAWK	1975
EA DRAGON	1974	P 81 SEA SCORPION	1975

ragon (P 78)—with Gabriel and Harpoon French Navy, 1991

ion (P 77)—with no Gabriel, more elaborate EW suite French Navy, 1991

225 tons (252 fl) **S:** 38 kts
: 44.90 (42.30 wl) × 7.00 × 2.48
4/Harpoon SSM (II × 2)—2/Gabriel I SSM (I × 2; not on P 77)—1/
57-mm 70-cal. Bofors SAK-57 Mk 1 DP—1/40-mm 70-cal. Bofors
AA—2/12.7-mm mg (I × 2)
ctron Equipt:
adar: 1/Decca TM 626 nav., 1/H.S.A. WM-28 f.c.
W: Rafael SEWS intercept/jammer suite
4 MTU 16V538 diesels; 4 props; 14,400 bhp
ge: 2,000/15 **Crew:** 5 officers, 36 enlisted

ks: Ordered in 1970. Two multiple 57-mm flare launchers on 57-mm mount. 504 rounds 57-mm, 1,008 rounds 40-mm. Intercept equipment on tripod topmast 1980–81. These craft were to transfer to a new Naval Reserve force on com- of the MGB 62 class. Four Harpoon SSM replaced the former Gabriel triple, trainable SSM mount aft; P 80 first to convert, in 1988, P 76, the last, in early 1991. P 77 has a larger superstructure, additional mast, and no Gabriel missile positions; she carries a Racal Cygnus jammer.

PATROL BOATS

◆ **3 110-foot, "Type A"**
Bldr: Vosper Thornycroft, Portsmouth, U.K. (P 70, P 72: Singapore)

	L	In serv.
P 69 INDEPENDENCE	15-7-69	8-7-70
P 70 FREEDOM	18-11-69	11-1-71
P 72 JUSTICE	20-6-70	23-4-71

Freedom (P 70) George R. Schneider, Jr., 3-87

D: 100 tons (130 fl) **S:** 30 kts
Dim: 33.4 (31.46 pp) × 6.4 × 1.71
A: 1/40-mm 70-cal. Bofors AA—1/20-mm Oerlikon AA—2/
12.7-mm mg (I × 2)
Electron Equipt: Radar: 1/Decca TM 626 nav.
M: 2 MTU 16V538 diesels; 2 props; 7,200 bhp **Electric:** 100 kw
Range: 1,100/15 **Crew:** 3 officers, 16 enlisted

Remarks: Ordered 21-5-68. Two 50-mm flare RL on 40-mm shield sides.

◆ **3 110-foot, "Type B"**
Bldr: Vosper Thornycroft, Portsmouth, U.K. (P 73, P 74: Singapore)

	L	In serv.
P 71 SOVEREIGNTY	25-11-69	2-71
P 73 DARING	1970	18-9-71
P 74 DAUNTLESS	6-5-71	7-71

Dauntless (P 74) Leo Van Ginderen, 3-83

D: 100 tons (130 fl) **S:** 32 kts **Dim:** 33.4 × 6.4 × 1.71
A: 1/76.2-mm 50-cal. Bofors low-angle—1/20-mm Oerlikon AA
Electron Equipt:
Radar: 1/Decca TM 626 nav., 1/H.S.A. M-26 f.c.
M: 2 MTU 16V538 diesels; 2 props; 7,200 bhp
Range: 1,000/15 **Crew:** 3 officers, 16 enlisted

Remarks: Gun- and fire-control system as on the Norwegian *Storm* class. The 76.2-mm gun is for surface fire only.

Note: The modified British "Ford"-class patrol boat *Panglima* was stricken during 7-91.

◆ **1 ex-French craft**
Bldr: Deggendorfer Werft, West Germany (In serv. 1955)

P 75 ENDEAVOR

D: 184 tons (fl) **S:** 20 kts
Dim: 40.9 × 7.6 × 2.4 **Range:** 800/8
A: 2/20-mm Oerlikon AA (I × 2)
Electron Equipt: Radar: 1/Decca . . . nav.
M: 2 Maybach diesels; 2 props; 2,000 bhp **Crew:** 24 tot.

PATROL BOATS *(continued)*

Remarks: Purchased on 30-9-70 from Malaysia. Low freeboard. Used for training and as a diving tender.

PATROL CRAFT

◆ **12 "Swift" class** Bldr: Singapore SB & Eng., Jurong (In serv. 20-10-81)

P 11 Swift Knight	P 18 Swift Combatant
P 12 Swift Lancer	P 19 Swift Challenger
P 14 Swift Swordsman	P 20 Swift Cavalier
P 15 Swift Warrior	P 21 Swift Conqueror
P 16 Swift Archer	P 22 Swift Centurion
P 17 Swift Warlord	P 23 Swift Chieftain

Swift Chieftain (P 23) Leo Van Ginderen, 1989

D: 45.7 tons (fl) **S:** 33 kts (31 sust.)
Dim: 22.7 (20.0 pp) × 6.2 × 1.6 (3.0 props)
A: 1/20-mm Oerlikon GAM-B01 AA—2/7.62-mm mg (I × 2)
Electron Equipt: Radar: 1/Decca 1226 nav.
M: 2 Deutz SBA-16M816 diesels; 2 props; 2,660 bhp
Electric: 2 generators **Range:** 550/20; 900/10 **Fuel:** 8.6 tons
Crew: 3 officers, 9 enlisted

Remarks: All commissioned same date; first unit launched 8-6-80. Design based on Australian de Havilland "Capricornica" design. Provision for installing two Gabriel SSM. Aluminum construction. Carry two tons fresh water. Transferred to the new Coastal Command 10-91 for anti-piracy, fisheries protection, and search-and-rescue duties.

MINE WARFARE SHIPS

◆ **0 (+ 4) Swedish Landsort-class minehunters**
Bldr: Karlskronavarvet, Karlskrona, Sweden (*see* Remarks)

	Laid down	L	In serv.
M	. . .	. . .	. . .
M	. . .	. . .	. . .
M	. . .	. . .	. . .
M	. . .	. . .	1995

D: 310 tons (360 fl) **S:** 15 kts
Dim: 47.50 (45.00 pp) × 9.60 × 2.30
A: 1/40-mm AA—2/7.62-mm mg (II × 2)—mines (portable rails)
Electron Equipt:
Radar: 1/. . . nav.—Sonar: Thomson-Sintra TSM 2022
M: 4 Saab-Scania DSI-14 diesels; 2 Voith-Schneider vertical cycloidal props; 1,440 bhp
Electric: 585 kVA **Range:** 2,500/12
Crew: 7 officers, 32 enlisted

Remarks: Glass-reinforced-plastic construction, based on Swedish Coast Guard's TV 171. Ordered 4-91, with option for two more. Hulls will be built in Sweden and outfitted in Singapore.

Will have Nobeltech 9LV100 optronic director for the gun. Y-shaped portable mine-rail arrangement, with single laying-point. Will have the Thomson-CSF TSM 2061 mine-countermeasures information system with IBIS plot. To carry two PAP 105 Mk 5 remote-controlled mine-disposal vehicles. Will have 2 × 225-kVA, 1 × 135-kVA diesel generator sets, all mounted on the upper deck to reduce noise signature.

Note: The last ex-U.S. *Redwing*-class minesweeper, *Jupiter* (M 101, ex-*Thrasher*, MSC 203) was discarded during 1990. The new diving tender *Mercury* is intended to perform route survey duties during peacetime.

AMPHIBIOUS WARFARE SHIPS

◆ **5 ex-U.S. LST 542 class** Bldrs: L 201: American Bridge, Ambridge, Pa.; L 203: Missouri Valley Bridge & Iron, Evansville, Indiana; others: Chicago Bridge and Iron, Seneca, Illinois

	Laid down	L	In serv.
L 201 Endurance (ex-*Holmes County,* LST 836)	11-9-44	29-10-44	25-11-44
L 202 Excellence (ex-T-LST 629)	13-4-44	8-7-44	28
L 203 Intrepid (ex-T-LST 579)	4-5-44	22-6-44	2
L 204 Resolution (ex-T-LST 649)	19-7-44	6-10-44	26-
L 205 Persistence (ex-T-LST 614)	28-1-44	6-5-44	2

Persistence (L 205) Leo Van Ginderen

Excellence (L 202)—helo deck aft, only 1/40-mm AA Mike Louagi

D: 1,653 tons light (4,080 fl) **S:** 11.6 kts
Dim: 99.98 (96.32 pp) × 15.24 × 4.29
A: 3/40-mm AA (I × 3)—2/7.62-mm mg (I × 2)
Electron Equipt:
Radar: 1/Decca 626 nav., 1/. . . nav.
M: 2 G.M. 12-567A diesels; 2 props; 1,800 bhp
Electric: 300 kw **Range:** 19,000/9
Crew: 5 officers, 60 enlisted

Remarks: L 201 loaned 1-7-71 and purchased 5-12-75; the others were purchas the U.S. 4-6-76. L 202 through L 205 mistakenly deleted from last edition. Thre sisters purchased same date were later sold commercially, without entering Sir Navy service: ex-T-LST 117, T-LST 276, and *Chase County* (T-LST 532). L 20 helicopter platform at the stern in place of the two aft 40-mm guns. Cargo-h equipment varies: L 202 and L 205 have king posts and cargo booms before the b 201 and L 203 do not. All have MARISAT SATCOMM equipment. All carry t LCVP landing craft in Welin davits abreast the bridge. *Sister Perseverence* ex-T-LST 632) stricken 1990 for cannibalization, and L 203 is in reserve.

◆ **4 RPL 60-class utility landing craft**

	Bldr	Laid down	L	In serv.
RPL 60	North SY, Singapore	. . .	11-85	1986
RPL 61	North SY, Singapore	. . .	11-85	1986
RPL 62	Singapore SY & Eng.	5-85	10-85	2-11-85
RPL 63	Singapore SY & Eng.	5-85	10-85	2-11-85

RPL 61 Hartmut Ehler

D: 151 tons **S:** 10 kts **Dim:** 36.0 (33.0 pp) × 8.5 × 2.5
Crew: 6 tot. **A:** none **Electron Equipt:** Radar: 1/. . .
M: 2 Deutz diesels; 2 props; 860 bhp

Remarks: Differ in detail, by builder. Can carry 450 standing troops or two A tanks. Painted green. Ordered 28-2-85. Cargo deck: 26.5 × 6.6 m.

◆ **4 RPL 54-class landing craft**
Bldr: Vosper Thornycroft, Singapore (In serv. 1968–69)

RPL 54 RPL 55 RPL 56 RPL 57

IIBIOUS WARFARE SHIPS *(continued)*

4 Hartmut Ehlers, 1-89

i0 tons light (150 fl) **S:** 10 kts
.: 27.0 × 6.9 × 1.3 **M:** 2 diesels; 2 props; 650 bhp
.ge: 300/10 **Crew:** 9 tot.

ks: RPL 54 and 55 formerly named *Ayer Chawan* and *Ayer Merban*. Cargo: 40 ·go, or 20 tons fuel and one tank.

Utility landing craft RPL 41 (ex-*Brani*) and RPL 42 (ex-*Berlayer*) were stricken 9.

'iger 40 hovercraft Bldr: Singapore SB & Eng. (In serv. 1987)

40 prototype Singapore SB & Eng., 1987

l2.3 tons (fl) **S:** 35 kts
: 16.50 × 6.00 × 3.65 (high) **A:** 2/12.7-mm mg (I × 2)
4 Deutz diesels (2 for lift-fans, 2 for propellers): 760 bhp
ıge: 175/35 **Crew:** 2 tot. + 35 troops

'ks: Privately funded prototype. Cargo: 3 tons. Hovers at up to 0.8 m. Two airscrews aft, two lift-fans. Aluminum construction.

ersonnel landing craft Bldr: . . . (In serv. . . .)

–EP 07

'ks: No data available; have a bow ramp.

5 Hartmut Ehlers, 1-89

♦ **2 ALC-1800-class personnel tenders**
Bldr: Le Comte, Vianen, the Netherlands (L: 16-10-85; In serv. 1-11-85)

FL 1 FL 2

Remarks: No data available. Ordered 10-4-85 and laid down 12-6-85 and 4-7-85, respectively.

♦ **450 assault-personnel landing craft** Bldr: Singapore SB & Eng.

D: . . . **S:** 12 kts **Dim:** 5.3 × 1.8 × 0.7 (moulded depth)
M: 1 outboard motor; 50 shp **Crew:** 12 troops

Remarks: Army-subordinated, man-portable craft.

SERVICE CRAFT

♦ **1 route-survey and diving tender**
Bldr: Singapore Technologies-Marine, Jurong

	L	In serv.
A 102 Jupiter	3-4-90	1-6-90

Jupiter (A 102) Singapore SB & Eng., 6-90

D: 170 tons (fl) **S:** 14.25 kts
Dim: 35.70 (33.50 wl) × 7.10 × 2.30 (props)
A: 1/20-mm Oerlikon GAM-B01 AA—2/12.7-mm mg (I × 2)
Electron Equipt: Radar: 1/Decca . . . nav.
M: 2 Deutz-MWM TBD 234 V12 diesels; 2 props; 1,360 bhp—azimuth thruster
Electric: 345-kw tot. (3 × 115-kw diesel sets)
Range: 200/14.5; 288/4 on steerable thruster
Crew: 5 officers, 28 enlisted + divers

Remarks: Sophisticated multipurpose craft capable of performing mine-clearance route survey work, acting as a diving tender, or assisting in salvage operations. Carries a towed side-scan high-resolution sonar and has an underwater data-logging system and precision navigation equipment. To assist divers, has a two-man decompression chamber and two high-pressure compressors. Carries a 10-man rigid inflatable dinghy with a 60-bhp engine, handled by a 1.5-ton crane. Will carry remotely operated vehicles to assist in developing minehunting techniques. Designed with German assistance. Replaces *Mercury* (M 102, ex-*Whippoorwill*, MSC 207), stricken 1990.

♦ **1 oil-fuel lighter** Bldr: Siong Huat SY, Singapore (In serv. 1-9-87)

Jolly Rodger II

D: 800 dwt **S:** . . . **Dim:** . . . × . . . × . . .
M: 2 MWM TPK-6K diesels; 2 props; 2,060 bhp

Remarks: Laid down 8-6-87, launched 11-8-87.

MARINE POLICE

PATROL CRAFT

♦ **8 PT 12 class** Bldr: Singapore SB & Eng., Jurong

	L	In serv.		L	In serv.
PT 12	. . .	21-1-89	PT 16	21-1-89	3-89
PT 13	. . .	21-1-89	PT 17	. . .	3-89
PT 14	. . .	21-1-89	PT 18	. . .	4-89
PT 15	21-1-89	3-89	PT 19	. . .	4-89

PT 12, 13, and 14 Singapore SB & Eng., 1-89

SINGAPORE *(continued)*
PATROL CRAFT *(continued)*

D: 21 tons (fl) **S:** 30+ kts **Dim:** 14.80 × 4.23 × 1.20
A: 2/7.62-mm mg (I × 2)
Electron Equipt: Radar: 1/Decca . . . nav.
M: PT 12–15: 2 M.A.N. D2840 LE diesels; 2 props; 1,252 bhp
PT 16–19: 2 MTU 12V183 TC91 diesels; 2 props; 1,182 bhp
Range: 310/22 **Fuel:** 2,000 liters **Crew:** 4 tot.

Remarks: Updated version of PT 1 class. Two from the final four are configured as "command boats" and have air-conditioned seating for 10 passengers.

♦ **11 PT 1 class** Bldr: Singapore SB & Eng., Jurong

	Laid down	L	In serv.
PT 1	21-7-83	19-12-83	14-1-84
PT 2	25-7-83	6-1-84	17-2-84
PT 3	28-7-83	16-1-84	13-3-84
PT 4	1-8-83	23-3-84	6-4-84
PT 5	15-9-83	23-4-84	15-5-84
PT 6	30-9-83	14-5-84	1-6-84
PT 7	11-10-83	30-5-84	19-6-84
PT 8	14-10-83	16-6-84	5-7-84
PT 9	21-12-83	4-7-84	1-8-84
PT 10	6-1-84	23-7-84	24-8-84
PT 11	19-1-84	10-8-84	5-9-84

PT 1 Leo Van Ginderen, 9-88

D: 20 tons **S:** 30 kts **Dim:** 14.54 × 4.23 × 1.20 (props)
A: 1/7.62-mm mg
Electron Equipt: Radar: 1/Decca . . . nav.
M: 2 M.A.N. D2542 MLE diesels; 2 props; 1,076 bhp
Range: 310/22 **Fuel:** 2,600 liters **Crew:** 7 tot.

Remarks: Aluminum construction. Four sisters built for Singapore Customs (CE 5–CE 8, delivered 6-2-87) and seven built for Brunei.

♦ **24 PX 10 class** Bldr: Sembawang SY (In serv. 1981)

PX 10–33

PX 13 Leo Van Ginderen, 9-88

D: . . . **S:** 32 kts **Dim:** 11.2 × . . . × . . .
M: 2 MTU diesels; 2 props; 770 bhp

♦ **37 PC 32 class**
Bldr: Vosper Thornycroft, Singapore (In serv. 1978–79, . . .)

PC 32 to PC 65

D: 2 tons (fl) **S:** 35 kts **Dim:** 6.5 × 2.5 × 0.46
A: small arms
M: 2 Johnson outboards; 280 bhp **Crew:** 4 tot.

Remarks: PC 32 to PC 51 delivered 1978–79; second series began building late 1980s.

PC 35 John Bouvi

CUSTOMS SERVICE

PATROL CRAFT

♦ **18 GP-50-class pilot boats** Bldr: Cheoy Lee SY, Kowloon, Hong

GP 40–57

Remarks: Delivered 1989–90; no data available.

♦ **4 PT 1 class** Bldr: Singapore SB & Eng., Jurong (In serv. 6-2-87)

CE 5 CE 6 CE 7 CE 8

Remarks: Data identical to Singapore Police sisters.

♦ **4 CE 1 class** Bldr: Vosper Thornycroft Pty., Singapore

CE 1 CE 2 CE 3 CE 4

CE 3 Hartmut Ehle

Remarks: Aluminum construction. No data available.

Note: The Singapore Ports Authority operates three small hydrographic surv *Mata Ikan* (103 tons, built 1967), and *Discovery* and *Investigator* (31 tons, bui

SOLOMON ISLANDS

Republic of the Solomon Islands

Personnel (1992): 10 officers, 40 constables

ROYAL SOLOMON ISLANDS POLICE SERVICE

Note: Ship names are prefaced by "RSIPV" (Royal Solomon Islands Police V

PATROL BOATS AND CRAFT

♦ **2 ASI 315 design** Bldr: Australian SB Ind. (WA), Pty., Ltd., South
Coogie

ION ISLANDS *(continued)*
)L BOATS AND CRAFT *(continued)*

	Laid down	L	In serv.
ᴀ	12-9-87	19-5-88	3-9-88
ɪ	23-1-91	. . .	2-11-91

3) Leo Van Ginderen, 5-92

55 tons (fl) **S:** 21 kts
31.50 (28.60 wl) × 8.10 × 2.12
/12.7-mm mg (I × 3)
tron Equipt: Radar: 1/Furuno 1011 nav.
Caterpillar 3516 diesels; 2 props; 2,820 bhp
urance: 10 days **Range:** 2,500/12
: 27.9 tons **Electric:** 116 kw
v: 1 officer, 4 noncommissioned, 9 constables

ks: "Pacific Patrol Boat" design for Australian foreign aid program. First unit 3-10-85. Carry a 5-m aluminum boarding boat. Extensive navigational suite, g Furuno FSN-70 NAVSAT receiver, 525 HF/DF, 120 MH/HF/DF, FE-881 nder and DS-70 doppler log. Sisters in Papua New Guinea, Vanuatu, Fiji, and Samoan, etc., service.

-150 class Bldr: Australian Marine Services Assoc., North Fremantle
o (ex-*Pioneer*) (In serv. 1984)

02) Leo Van Ginderen, 1991

. . **S:** 26 kts **Dim:** 26.0 × 7.9 × 1.9 × . . .
mall arms
tron Equipt: 1/. . . nav. **Range:** 520/20; 1,100/12
2 Caterpillar 3412 V-12 diesels; 2 props, 1,500 bhp

ks: Glass-reinforced plastic demonstration patrol boat purchased 1984 after sales tour.

arpentaria class
: De Havilland Marine, Homebush Bay, Australia
ᴀɢɪ (In serv. 30-3-79)

27 tons (fl) **S:** 27 kts **Dim:** 16.0 × 5.0 × 1.2
w: 8 tot. **A:** 2/7.62-mm mg (I × 2)
tron Equipt: Radar: 1/Decca 110 nav.
2 G.M. 12V71 TI diesels; 2 props; 1,120 bhp
ge: 700/22

ks: Operated by the Department of Fisheries for fisheries patrol.

Tulagi (01) Leo Van Ginderen, 1984

SERVICE CRAFT

◆ **2 27-m landing craft** Bldr: Carpenter Boatyard, Suva (ordered 1980)

Lɪɢᴏᴍᴏ III (L: 24-2-81) Uʟᴜsᴀɢʜᴇ (L: 26-3-81)

D: 195 grt/105 dwt **S:** 9 kts **Dim:** 27.0 × . . . × . . .
M: 2 diesels; 2 props; . . . bhp

◆ **2 oceanographic research craft** Bldr: Murakima (L: 10-8-81)

Sᴏʟᴏᴍᴏɴ Aᴛᴜ Sᴏʟᴏᴍᴏɴ Kᴀʀɪǫᴜᴀ

Remarks: 140 grt, 9 kts; no other data available.

SOMALIA

Somali Democratic Republic

Personnel (1991): 600 total

Note: Virtually all craft are in very poor condition.

GUIDED-MISSILE PATROL BOATS

◆ **2 ex-Soviet Osa-II class** (transferred 12-75)

Osa-II class—under tow to Somalia 1976

D: 205 tons (240 fl) **S:** 35 kts **Dim:** 38.6 × 7.6 × 2.0
A: 4/SS-N-2 Styx SSM—4/30-mm AK-230 AA (II × 2)
Electron Equipt:
Radar: 1/Square Tie surf. search/target designation, 1/Drum Tilt f.c.
IFF: 2 Square Head interrogators, 1/High Pole B transponder
M: 3 M504 diesels; 3 props; 15,000 bhp
Range: 500/34; 750/25 **Crew:** 30 tot.

TORPEDO AND PATROL BOATS

◆ **4 Soviet Mol class**

Somali Mol class—without torpedo tubes 1976

SOMALIA *(continued)*
TORPEDO AND PATROL BOATS *(continued)*

Somali Mol class—with torpedo tubes 1976

D: 170 tons (205 fl) **S:** 38 kts **Dim:** 39.0 × 7.6 × 1.7
A: 4/30-mm AK-230 AA (II × 2)—two units: 4/533-mm TT (I × 4)
Electron Equipt:
Radar: 1/Pot Head surf. search, 1/Drum Tilt f.c.
IFF: 1/Square Head interrogator, 1/High Pole B transponder
M: 3 M504 diesels; 3 props; 15,000 bhp
Range: 450/34; 700/20 **Crew:** 25 tot.

Remarks: Newly built units transferred one in 12-76, two in 1-77, and one in 2-77. Two did not have torpedo tubes. Boats with tubes are approximately 215 tons (fl), 36 kts max.

Note: All Soviet-supplied Poluchat-1-class patrol boats are believed to have been discarded by 1991.

AMPHIBIOUS WARFARE CRAFT

♦ **2 ex-Soviet T-4-class landing craft** (transferred 1968–69)

D: 70 tons (fl) **S:** 10 kts **Dim:** 19.0 × 4.3 × 1.0
M: 2 Type 3D12 diesels; 2 props; 600 bhp **Crew:** 5 tot.

Remarks: In marginal condition at best. Two others discarded by 1991.

SOUTH AFRICA

Republic of South Africa

Personnel (1991): 4,000 total, plus 1,000 National Service and 500 Citizens Force personnel

Naval Aviation: An air force detachment is available to assist the navy. Ten SA-330E/H/J Puma helicopters can operate from the replenishment ship *Tafelberg,* With the striking of the Shackleton long-range maritime patrol aircraft in 1984 and 18 Piaggio P 166 maritime patrol aircraft in 1990 and the arms embargo preventing replacements, two C-47 transports equipped with radars have been pressed into service. Two SafAir L-100 Hercules have been chartered for search-and-rescue and pollution-control duties. Also retired in 1990 were all remaining Wasp and Super Frélon helicopters; in 1991, the last six Buccaneer maritime strike aircraft were retired.

SUBMARINES

♦ **3 French Daphné class** Bldr: Dubigeon, Nantes

	Laid down	L	In serv.
S 97 Maria Van Riebeeck	14-3-68	18-3-69	22-6-70
S 98 Emily Hobhouse	18-11-68	24-10-69	25-1-71
S 99 Johanna Van Der Merwe	24-4-69	21-7-70	21-7-71

D: 869 surf./1,043 sub. tons **S:** 13/15.5 kts
Dim: 57.75 × 6.75 × 4.5
A: 12/550-mm TT (8 fwd, 4 aft; 12 E 15 and L4/5 torpedoes—no reloads)
Electron Equipt:
Radar: Thomson-CSF Calypso-II—EW: Timnex 4 CH(V)2 intercept
Sonar: Thomson-Sintra DUUA-2 active (8.4 kHz), Thomson-Sintra DUUX-2 passive ranging, Thomson-Sintra DSUV-2 passive search
M: SEMT-Pielstick 12PA4-135 diesels, 2 450-kw generator sets, electric drive; 2 props; 2,600 bhp
Range: 4,300/7.5 (snorkel) **Crew:** 6 officers, 41 enlisted

Maria Van Riebeeck (S 97) Leo Van Ginderen, 10-87

Emily Hobhouse (S 98) S.A.N

Remarks: Modernization with new sonar and combat data systems by Trivett Durban, began 1986; S 98 completed 1-89 and S 99 in late 1990, at which time S placed in reserve. Diving depth: 300 m. New communications suites, periscop new data displays are to be added during mid-1990s refits. Are expected to be r in service to 2005, by which time they will be thoroughly obsolete. Two emb *Agosta*-class submarines ordered from France in 1975 were sold by France to Pa

Note: There continue to be plans to build submarines in South Africa at Durb plans for an IKL design were reportedly acquired from West Germany's aldtswerke in mid-1986. Funding for such an ambitious undertaking is not av however.

FRIGATES

Note: Plans to construct a new 1,400–1,500-ton-frigate design in South Afri been held in abeyance, due to the embargo on arms-related imports and ec conditions. The last U.K. *Whitby*-class frigate, *President Pretorius* (F 145), was in reserve in 1986 and is unlikely ever to see further service; sister *President S* 147), to reserve 1981, was sunk as a missile target on 29-4-91.

GUIDED-MISSILE PATROL BOATS

♦ **9 Israeli Reshev ("Minister") class**
Bldrs: P 1561–P 1563: Israeli SY, Haifa; others: Sundock Austral, Durban

	L	In serv.
P 1561 Jan Smuts	2-77	9-77
P 1562 P.W. Botha	9-77	12-77
P 1563 Frederick Creswell	1-78	6-78
P 1564 Jim Fouche	9-78	12-78
P 1565 Franz Frasmus	3-79	7-79
P 1566 Oswald Pirow	9-79	4-3-80
P 1567 Hendrik Mentz	26-3-82	11-2-83
P 1568 Kobie Coetzee	3-9-82	11-2-83
P 1569 Magnus Malan	27-3-86	4-7-86

Jan Smuts (P 1561) Leo Van Gindere

ED-MISSILE PATROL BOATS *(continued)*

ster" class S.A.N., 1990

15 tons (450 fl) **S:** 32 kts **Dim:** 58.10 × 7.60 × 2.60
/Skorpioen SSM (I × 6)—2/76-mm 62-cal. OTO Melara Compact
P (I × 2)—2/20-mm AA (I × 2)—2/12.7-mm mg (I × 2)
tron Equipt:
dar: 1/Thomson-CSF THD-1040 Neptune surf./air search,
1/Selenia RTN-10X Orion f.c.
V: Elta MN-53 intercept, 4 chaff RL
MTU 16V956 TB91 diesels; 4 props; 14,400 bhp
ge: 1,500/30; 3,000/20; 5,000/15 **Crew:** 6 officers, 41 enlisted

ks: First six ordered 1974. A second six were ordered 15-11-77, three of which ver laid down; equipment, including weapons and electronics, had been bought 1. Carry 500 rds 76-mm ammunition. Skorpioen is a license-built version of the Gabriel II antiship missile. All named for former Ministers of Defense. The *rank Chappel* has also been reported, and the name *Magnus Malan* for P 1569 is ain. P 1561 recommissioned 3-11-85, P 1502 on 4-7-86, both from reserve, where d reposed since about 1982. P 1569 originally launched 25-11-82, then placed in P 1568 completed major refit 7-88. P 1561 and P 1567 journeyed to Taiwan in 4-91, P 1567 and P 1568 were placed in reserve. All are expected to have been d by around 2000 (they have been heavily stressed by the heavy seas around frica), but it is now planned to retain them until at least 2005; a modernization n to be started in 1992 will incorporate a new communications suite, improved nodern target designation system using a computerized combat data system, s-control update, and new fuzing for 76-mm ammunition.

OL CRAFT

+ . . .) T 2210-class hydrofoils

: T-Craft International, Capetown (In serv. 1991)

T 2211 T 2212

. . tons (fl) **S:** 41 kts (38 sust.) **Dim:** 22.00 × . . . × . . .
./20-mm AA—unguided rockets
tron Equipt: Radar: 1/. . . nav.
2 MTU 12V183 TB92 diesels; 2 waterjets; 2,000 bhp
ge: 525/30 **Crew:** 2 + 15 troops

ks: Trials with prototype summer 1991. Unusual catamaran hull form with ils, for naval police use. Have a helmet-mounted sight for the 20-mm gun. nal units may be ordered.

Namicurra class

r: . . . , South Africa (In serv.1980–81)

–Y 1530

curra class S.A.N., 1984

5 tons (fl) **S:** 30 kts **Dim:** 9.0 × . . . × . . .
1/12.7-mm mg—2/7.62-mm mg **M:** 2 diesels **Crew:** 4 tot.

rks: Radar-equipped, glass-reinforced plastic-hulled harbor craft, which can be ansported on trailers.

WARFARE SHIPS

"River" class minehunters

rs: Abeking & Rasmussen, Lemwerder, Germany

	In serv.		In serv.
M 1499 Umkomaas	1986	M . . . Umzinkulu	1987
M 1212 Umhloti	1986	M 1213 Umgeni	1987

"River"-class minehunter S.A.N., 1990

D: 380 tons (fl) **S:** 15 kts **Dim:** 48.00 × 8.50 × 2.30
A: 1/20-mm Oerlikon GAM-B01 AA—2/12.7-mm mg (I × 2)
Electron Equipt:
Radar: 1/Decca nav.
Sonar: 1/Simrad . . . hull-mounted, 1/Klein towed side-looking
M: 2 MTU diesels; 2 props; . . . bhp
Range: . . ./. . . **Crew:** 7 officers, 30 enlisted

Remarks: Built in West Germany as "hydrographic survey ships" and delivered to Sandock Austral Shipyard, Durban, in 1981 for outfitting. Sufficient equipment was purchased to oufit a total of 12, but no work has begun on building additional units. Also employ some equipment removed from discarded "Ton"-class minehunters, including two French PAP-104 remote-controlled submersibles per ship. Were designed to carry Thomson-CSF DUBM-21 minehunting sonar, but it was apparently not fitted. Have a mine-disposal divers' rigid inflatable boat aft and a decompression chamber. Wooden construction.

♦ 3 British "Ton"-class minesweepers and 1 minehunter*

	Bldr	L
M 1210 Kimberley (ex-*Stratton*)*	Dorset Yacht	29-7-57
M 1214 Walvisbaai (ex-*Packington*)	Harland & Wolff, Belfast	3-7-58
M 1215 East London (ex-*Chilton*)	Cook, Welton & Gemmell	15-7-57
M 1498 Windhoek	John I. Thornycroft, Woolston	28-6-57

Walvisbaai (M 1214) Leo Van Ginderen, 1989

D: 370 tons (425 fl) **S:** 15 kts (cruising)
Dim: 46.33 (42.68 pp) × 8.76 × 2.5
A: 1/40-mm 60-cal. Bofors AA—2/20-mm Oerlikon AA (not in M 1210)—2/7.62-mm mg (I × 2)
Electron Equipt:
Radar: 1/Type 978 nav. (M 1210: 1/Type 1006)
Sonar: M 1210 only: 1/Type 193M HF minehunting (100–300 kHz)
M: 2 Paxman Deltic 18A-7A; 2 props; 3,000 bhp **Fuel:** 45 tons
Range: 2,300/13; 3,000/8 **Crew:** 27 tot. (M 1210: 36 total)

Remarks: M 1210, converted as minehunter, with Type 193M minehunting sonar, Type 1006 radar, two PAP-104 remote-controlled minehunting devices, and mine-disposal diver facilities. All now have enclosed bridges and tripod masts.

M 1214 had been redesignated a patrol boat in 1977–78, retaining most sweep gear as P 1559; she was redesignated a minesweeper in the early 1980s and in 1990–92 was undergoing a major refit intended to extend her life by up to 15 years. M 1210 began a life-extension refit in 11-90. The rehabilitations are expected to keep the ships operating for another 15–20 years. Six sisters stricken 1987: minesweepers *Johannesburg* (M 1207, ex-*Castleton*) and *Durban* (M 1499), minehunters *Port Elizabeth* (M 1212, ex-*Dumbleton*) and *Mosselbaai* (M 1213, ex-*Oakington*), and patrol boats *Pretoria* (P 1556, ex-*Dunkerton*) and *Kaapstad* (P 1557, ex-*Hazelton*); *Pretoria* and *Durban* are maintained as museum exhibits.

AUXILIARY SHIPS

♦ 1 U.K. Hecla-class hydrographic ship/intelligence collector

	Bldr	Laid down	L	In serv.
A 324 Protea	Yarrow, Scotstoun	20-7-70	14-7-71	23-5-72

Protea (A 324)—white hull, buff stack and mast S.A.N., 1990

D: 2,750 tons (fl) **S:** 15.5 kts (14 sust.)
Dim: 79.25 (71.63 pp) × 14.94 × 4.90
A: 2/20-mm Oerlikon AA (I × 2)
Electron Equipt:
Radar: 1/Type 1006 nav.
EW: *see* Remarks.
M: 4 Paxman Ventura 1,280-bhp diesels; electric drive; 1 prop; 2,000 shp
Range: 12,000/11.5; 20,000/9 **Fuel:** 570 tons
Crew: 17 officers, 112 enlisted

Remarks: Ordered 7-11-69. Hull reinforced for navigating in ice. Bow-thruster and anti-roll tanks fitted. Has been equipped for electronic surveillance duties. No longer carries a Wasp helicopter.

Note: The 245-grt Danish trawler *Margit Rye* was purchased in 1989 for use as an intelligence collector and agent infiltration ship by the now-disbanded Civil Cooperative Bureau; the ship was laid up at Durban by 1992.

♦ 1 fleet replenishment ship Bldr: Dorbyl Marine, Durban

	Laid down	L	In serv.
A 301 Drakensberg	8-84	24-4-86	11-11-87

Drakensberg (A 301) Leo Van Ginderen, 7-91

Drakensberg (A 301) Leo Van Ginderen, 7-91

D: 6,000 tons light (12,500 fl) **S:** 20+ kts
Dim: 157.00 (147.00 pp) × 20.00 × 7.90
A: 4/20-mm GAM-B01 AA (I × 4)—2 Puma helicopters (S.A.A.F.)
Electron Equipt: Radar: 1/. . . nav. **Endurance:** 90 days
M: 2 diesels; 1 CP prop; 16,320 bhp **Crew:** 10 officers, 86 enlisted

Remarks: Largest ship ever built in South Africa. Now used for patrol and SAR and is, by default, South Africa's most capable naval ship. Ordered 22-9-84. complete 6-87. Can carry 5,500 tons cargo fuel, 750 tons dry stores. Helicopter fore and aft, hangar aft only. One dual refueling/solid transfer station on each and capable of over-the-stern refueling. Three-month endurance. Equipped wit thruster.

♦ 1 fleet replenishment ship
Bldr: Nakskovs Skibsvaerft, Denmark (L: 20-6-58)

A 243 Tafelberg (ex-Danish tanker *Annam*)

Tafelberg (A 243) S.A.N.

D: approx. 27,000 tons (fl) **S:** 15 kts **Dim:** 170.6 × 21.9 × 9.2
A: 2/40-mm 70-cal. Bofors AA (I × 2)—2/20-mm Oerlikon GAM-B AA (I × 2)
Electron Equipt: Radar: 2/. . . nav.
M: 1 Burmeister & Wain diesel; 1 prop; 8,420 bhp **Crew:** 100 tot

Remarks: 12,499 grt/18,980 dwt (prior to 1984). Purchased and refitted in D 1965–67. Two refueling stations and one solid-stores transfer station per side. M ized 1983 to 16-7-84, with flight deck amidships, a hangar for two Puma helicop search-and-rescue duties, and a hospital facility; one refueling station per side d Can carry four Namicurra-class patrol craft. Temporarily laid up in reserve 1986 for lack of funds. Traveled to Taiwan in 6-90 and to South America in During a 6-month refit in 1993, a classroom for 60 cadets is to be added.

SERVICE CRAFT

♦ 1 torpedo-recovery and diver-training ship
Bldr: Dorman Long, Durban

P 3148 Fleur (In serv. 3-12-69)

Fleur (P 3148) Leo Van Ginderen

D: 220 tons (257 fl) **S:** 14 kts **Dim:** 35.0 × 7.5 × 3.4
M: 2 Paxman-Ventura diesels; 2 props; 1,400 bhp
Crew: 4 officers, 18 enlisted

Remarks: Ramp at stern for torpedo recovery. Has a divers' decompression ch Refitted by 1981 with fantail area enlarged, new stacks. Acts as tender to t marines.

Note: The training craft *Navigator* was stricken 1990.

♦ 1 seagoing tug

	Bldr	L	In serv.
De Mist	Dorman Long, Durban	21-12-78	12-78

D: 275 grt **S:** 12.5 kts **Dim:** 34.3 (32.3 pp) × 7.8 × 3.4
M: 2 Mirrlees-Blackstone ESL-8-MGR diesels; 2 props; 2,440 bhp

♦ 1 large harbor tug

	Bldr	L	In serv.
De Neys	Globe Engineering, Capetown	7-69	23-7-69

D: 282 tons (fl) **S:** 11.5 kts **Dim:** 28.6 (27.0 wl) × 8.1 × 3.6
M: 2 Lister-Blackstone ERS-8-M diesels; 2 Voith-Schneider vertic cycloidal props; 1,268 bhp
Crew: 10 tot.

Remarks: 14-ton max. bollard pull.

H AFRICA *(continued)*
ICE CRAFT *(continued)*

ys S.A.N., 1978

rge harbor tug Bldr: Globe Engineering, Capetown (L: 12-61)

ORDE

orde S.A.N., 1978

170 grt **S:** 9 kts **Dim:** 34.2 × 8.2 × . . .
2 Lister-Blackstone ERS-8-M diesels; 2 Voith-Schneider vertical cycloidal props; 1,268 bhp

EA RESCUE BOATS

airey Tracker class

r: Groves & Gutteridge, Cowes, U.K. (In serv. 1973)

PASELBERG

31 tons (fl) **S:** 29 kts **Dim:** 19.25 × 4.98 × 1.45
2 G.M. 12V71 diesels; 2 props; 1,120 bhp
ge: 650/20 **Crew:** 11 tot.

ks: Sister P 1554 discarded by 1990.

erman-built Bldr: Krogerwerft, Rendsburg (In serv. 1961–62)

1 S.A.N., 1978

67 tons (73 fl) **S:** 30 kts **Dim:** 28.8 (27.9 pp) × 5.0 × 1.6
1/12.7-mm mg **Electron Equipt:** Radar: 1/Decca 707 nav.
2 Maybach 12-cyl. diesels; 2 props; 3,000 bhp
nge: 600/25 **Crew:** 8 tot.

rks: Sister P 1552 wrecked and lost 1990.

DEPARTMENT OF TRANSPORT

Antarctic survey and supply ship

	Bldr	Laid down	L	In serv.
HAS	Mitsubishi, Shimonoseki	14-6-77	30-9-77	31-1-78

Agulhas Leo Van Ginderen, 1-86

D: 3,035 dwt **S:** 14 kts **Dim:** 109.2 (100.0 pp) × 18.0 × 5.8
M: 2 Mirrlees-Blackstone K-6 Major diesels; 1 prop; 6,000 bhp
Range: 8,200/14 **Crew:** 40 crew + 92 scientists/passengers

Remarks: Formerly manned by the South African Navy, but since 1989 has had a civilian crew. Twin helicopter hangar. Red hull, white upperworks.

SPAIN

Spanish State

Personnel (1991): 39,800 total (4,050 officers), plus 8,300 Naval Infantry (595 officers), and about 9,000 civilians

Naval Aviation: 7 AV-8S Matador, 2 TAV-8S 2-seat Matador, and 11 EAV-8B Harrier V/TOL fighter-bombers were in service. The EAV-8Bs are to be backfitted with the APG-65 radar. Eight additional AV-8Bs are to be procured to replace the AV-8S Matadors in the mid-1990s.

The *Arma Aerea de la Armada* also operates 6 SH-60B Seahawk, 11 Augusta-Bell 212 (with SS-12 missiles; 4 AB-212 are also equipped with Elettronica "Gufo" 2000 EW intercept gear), 10 Sikorsky SH-3D/G Sea King (with AS-12 missiles), 3 SH-3D AEW conversions, and 10 Hughes 369-HM(500M) Cayuse helicopters, plus 2 Cessna Citation-II, 2 Piper Comanche PA-24, and 2 Piper Twin Comanche PA-30 liaison aircraft. Six more SH-60B are being sought, and three more SH-3D/G helicopters are to be converted to AEW configuration.

In 1991, the *Grupo Aeronavale Alfa* had 7 squadrons, all based at Rota: 3 Sq. (10 AB-212 helicopters), 4 Sq. (2 PA-24, 2 PA-30, and 2 Citation-II light transports), 5 Sq. (10 SH-3D/G ASW helicopters, 3 SH-3AEW helicopters), 6 Sq. (10 Hughes-500 training helicopters), 8 Sq. (7 AV-8S, 2 TAV-8S Matador), 9 Sq. (11 EAV-8B Harrier), and 10 Sq. (6 SH-60B Seahawk ASW helicopters).

The Spanish Air Force performs a maritime surveillance role, using 2 P-3A, 5 P-3B, and 4 P-3C Orion. Twelve CASA C-212 Aerocar with APS-128 radars are used for search-and-rescue work. Boeing is to update 2 P-3A, 5 P-3B to P-3C standard, adding APS-134(V) radar. Air Force F/A-18 Hornet fighter-bombers are equipped for maritime strike with Harpoon missiles.

The search-and-rescue service (*Servicio de Busqueda y Salvamento*) received 3 Fokker F-27 SAR aircraft in 1979 for coastal surveillance; they carry Litton APS-504V radar. Ten AS.332F Super Puma helicopters for rescue duties and two configured as VIP transports were delivered 21-1-84.

EAV-8B Harrier-II McDonnell Douglas, 1988

AV-8S Matador Lcdr. John Leenhouts, USN, 6-88

NAVAL AVIATION *(continued)*

SH-3G Sea King Stefan Terzibaschitsch, 9-89

AB-212 Stefan Terzibaschitsch, 9-89

SH-60B on Victoria (F 82) Stefan Terzibaschitsch, 9-89

WEAPONS AND SYSTEMS

Except for naval guns, which are domestically designed and manufactured, most of the weapon systems in use are of American or French make. Twenty-five U.S. Harpoon missiles were ordered 1985 for delivery 1987–90; 55 Harpoons had been delivered earlier. In 1988, 4 *truck*-launched Harpoon systems, plus air-launched Harpoons for Spanish Air Force F/A-18 Hornets, were ordered. Also in 1988, 231 Mk 46 Mod. 5 ASW torpedoes were ordered from the USA to supplement Mk 46 Mod. 2 delivered earlier. A total of 500 Mk 46 Mod. 5 torpedoes was available in 1991. In 12-91, 800 Mistral short-range SAMs were ordered for the Spanish Marines and Army.

The Meroka antiaircraft/antimissile point-defense system consists of two rows of six 20-mm Oerlikon guns:

Length: 120 calibers	Round Weight: 320 gr. all-up
Maximum effective range: 2,000 m	Projectile Weight: 102 gr.
Maximum rate of fire: 9,000 rd/min./mount	Muzzle velocity: 1,200 m/sec.

Meroka uses a Lockheed Electronics AN/VPS-2 Sharpshooter I-band monopulse radar on the mount, with target designation by the ship's Selenia RAN-12L/X or RAN-11L/X search radar and a Selenia PDS-10 TDS console. Current models carry 720 rounds on-mount; later versions will have 2,160 rounds. Twenty mounts have been ordered.

The ABCAS (*Arma de Bajo Coste Anti-Submarina*) deck-mounted ASW rocket launcher is in development; it will fire 24 hollow-charge warhead rocket depth-charges to a range of 1,000 to 8,000 m.

Spain is developing its own electronic warfare and electro-optical systems. The MSP-2000 electro-optical fire-control system will employ a German Type 282 co-mounted radar.

AIRCRAFT CARRIER

◆ **1 Modified U.S. Sea Control Ship design**

Bldr: E.N. Bazán, el Ferrol

	Laid down	L	I
R 11 Principe de Asturias (ex-*Canarias*, ex-*Almirante Carrero Blanco*)	8-10-79	22-5-82	3

Principe de Asturias (R 11) Pradignac & Le

Principe de Asturias (R 11) Maritime Photograph

Principe de Asturias (R 11) French Nav

RAFT CARRIER (continued)

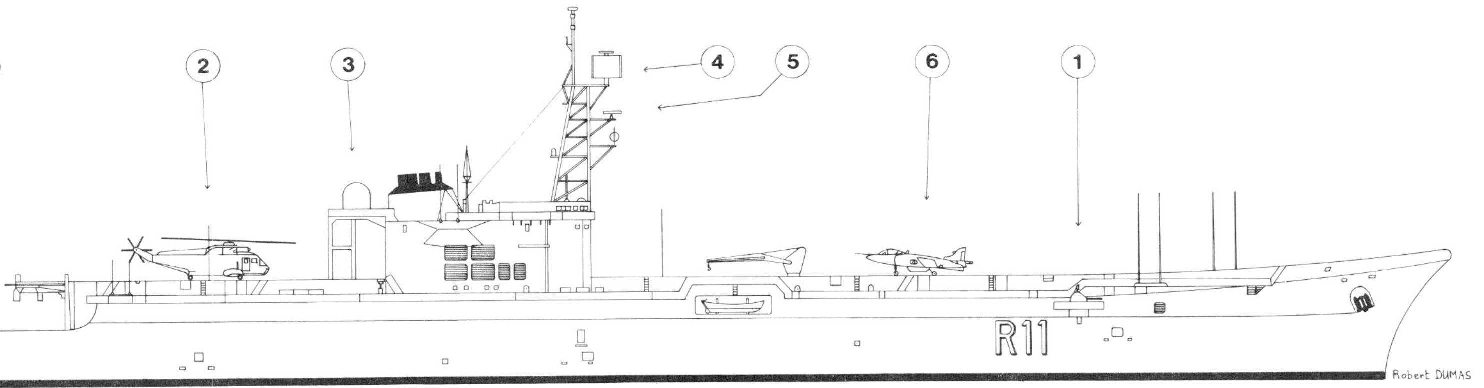

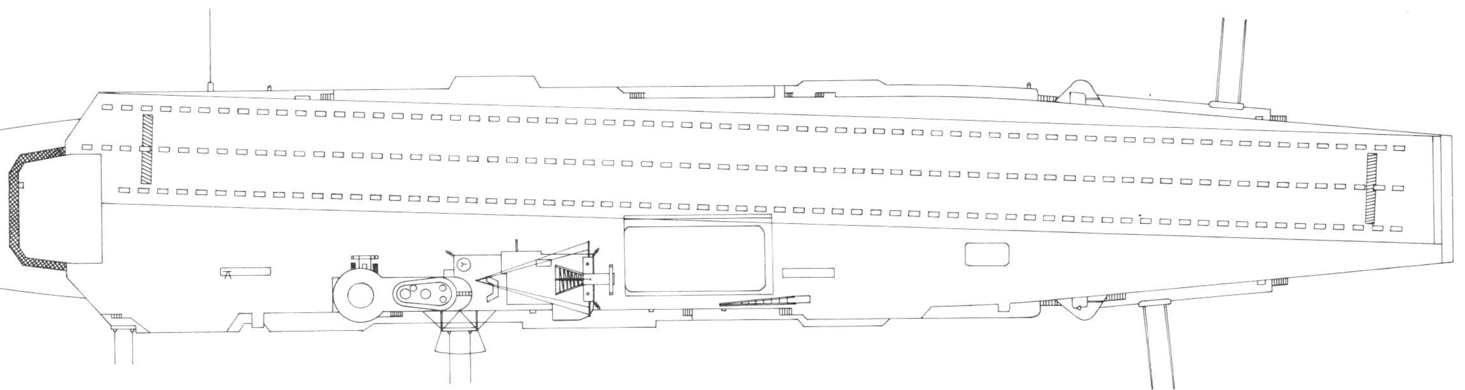

ipe de Asturias (R 11) 1. Meroka 20-mm CIWS 2. Sea King helo 3. SPN-35 air-control radar 4. SPS-52D 3-D radar 5. SPS-55 surface-search 6. EAV-8S Matador V/STOL fighter Drawing by Robert Dumas

cipe de Asturias (R 11) Leo Van Ginderen, 2-92

16,200 tons (fl) **S:** 26.27 kts

m: 195.1 (187.5 pp) × 24.4 (30.0 flight deck) × 6.7

r Group: 6–8 EAV-8B Harrier V/STOL fighters, 12–14 SH-60B, SH-3D/G, and AB-212 helicopters

4/Meroka 20-mm CIWS (XII × 4)

ectron Equipt:

Radar: 1/SPS-55 surf. search, 1/SPS-52D 3-D air search, 1/SPN-35A air control, 1/RAN-11 L/X target designation, 4/VPS-2 f.c.

TACAN: URN-25

EW: Nettunel intercept, Mk 36 Mod. 2 SRBOC decoy syst. (VI × 6, Mk 137 launchers), SLQ-25 Nixie towed torpedo decoy syst.

: 2 G.E. LM-2500 gas turbines; 1 CP prop; 46,400 shp (plus 2/800-shp retractable Pleuger auxiliary props, electric drive to 5 kts)

ectric: 7,500 kw (3 Allison 501-K17 gas turbine-driven 2,500-kw sets)

nge: 6,500/20

ew: 810 total: 100 officers, 145 senior petty officers, 565 enlisted

arks: Ordered 29-6-77. Design is essentially that of the final version of the U.S. 's Sea Control Ship concept, with a 12-degree ski-jump bow added. A second ship is g-term goal. Is flagship of Aviation Group Alfa.
e flight deck is 175.3 × 29 m and is served by two elevators, one at the extreme aft Takeoff pattern angled to starboard. Has two pair Denny-Brown fin stabilizers. 11 and LINK 14 data link and U.S. Fleet SATCOMM are installed. Has U.S. ie/Masker bubbler noise suppression system. The Tritan combat data system oys 2 Unisys UYK-3 and 2 UYK-20 computers. Has U.S. UPX-25 and UPX-28 IFF ment, "Raylass" navigation system with Magnavox MX1105 NAVSAT/Omega ver, and 2 Sperry HK inertial navigation systems (SINS).

In a 1990 refit, a parallel fuel distribution system with 37,000 m^3 tank capacity was installed to permit carrying a fuel load of 40 percent aviation fuel/60 percent DFM propulsion fuel. At the same time, the island superstructure was enlarged to port at its aft end to incorporate a briefing room, the flying control central was enlarged, accommodations for 6 additional officers and 30 additional enlisted were added, and the SPS-52C radar was updated to SPS-52D.

SUBMARINES

◆ 0 (+4) "Submarino Biparto" (S 80) program

Bldr: E.N. Bazán, Cartagena

	Laid down	L	In serv.
S	1999	. . .	2003
S	. . .	. . .	. . .
S	. . .	. . .	. . .
S	. . .	. . .	. . .

D: 2,800–2,900 tons (sub.) **S:** 12 kts surf./25 kts sub.

Dim: 76.0 × 7.8 × . . .

A: 6/533-mm bow TT (20 tot. F 17 Mod. 2 torpedoes and Sub-Harpoon or SM 39 Exocet SSM)

Electron Equipt: Radar: . . .—Sonar: . . .—EW: Manta XL intercept

M: diesel-electric: . . . **Range:** 10,500/. . .

Endurance: 70 days **Fuel:** 210 tons **Crew:** 35 tot.

Remarks: Intended to replace *Daphné* class. Cooperative design effort between Bazán and DCN, France. Diving depth: 300 m. The first unit is to be ordered around 1995, and a preliminary design study was under way in 1992.

◆ 4 Agosta (S 70) class

Bldr: E.N. Bazán, Cartagena

	Laid down	L	In serv.
S 71 GALERNA	5-9-77	5-12-81	22-1-83
S 72 SCIROCO	27-11-78	13-11-82	5-12-83
S 73 MISTRAL	30-5-80	14-11-83	5-6-85
S 74 TRAMONTANA	18-12-81	30-11-84	27-1-86

D: 1,230/1,490/1,750 tons **S:** 12 kts (surf.)/20.5 kts (sub.)

Dim: 67.90 × 6.80 × 5.40

A: 4/550-mm bow TT (20 F 17, E 18, and L 5 torpedoes)

Electron Equipt:

Radar: 1/DRUA-33—EW: Manta XL intercept

Sonar: Thomson-Sintra DUUA-2A/2B active, Thomson-Sintra DSUV-22 passive search and attack, S 71, 72: Thomson-Sintra DUUX-2A ranging, S 73, 74: DUUX-5

SUBMARINES *(continued)*

M: 2 SEMT-Pielstick 16 PA4 185 diesel generator sets, 850 kw each; 4,600-shp main engine; 1/23-kw cruising engine; 1 prop
Fuel: 185 tons **Range:** 17.5/1 hr. (sub.); 8,500/9 (snorkel)
Endurance: 45 days **Crew:** 8 officers, 53 enlisted

Tramontana (S 74) Luciano Grazioli, 2-89

Galerna (S 71) James W. Goss/NAVPIC, 5-89

Remarks: See also *Agosta* class in France section. As with the *Daphné* class, built with French technical assistance. Agreement signed 6-2-74; first two ordered 9-5-75, second pair 29-6-77. Can dive to 300 m. In lieu of 11 torpedoes, 19 mines can be carried. S 71 refitted 12-86 to 12-87. S 72 in collision with destroyer *Valdes,* 10-85; repaired. All to get INISEL/MEL Manta EW suite during mid-life refits beginning 1994 with S 71. S 72 and S 73 ran trials during spring 1991 with the Thomson-Sintra clip-on DSUV-62 towed passive linear hydrophone array.

♦ 4 French Daphné (S 60) class Bldr: E.N. Bazán, Cartagena

	Laid down	L	In serv.
S 61 Delfin	13-8-68	25-3-72	3-5-73
S 62 Tonina	2-3-70	3-10-72	10-7-73
S 63 Marsopa	19-3-71	15-3-74	12-4-75
S 64 Narval	24-4-72	14-12-74	22-11-75

Tonina (S 62) Luciano Grazioli, 3-90

D: 865/1,042 tons **S:** 12.5/15.5 kts **Dim:** 57.78 × 6.75 × 4.60
A: 12/550-mm TT (8 fwd, 4 aft; 12 F17 Mod. 2 wire-guided and L5 Mod. 3/4 active/passive-homing torpedoes, or 12 mines in lieu of torpedoes)
Electron Equipt:
Radar: 1/DRUA-33A—EW: VR-1B(J) intercept
Sonar: Thomson-Sintra DUUA-2A and DUUA-1D active, Thomson-Sintra DSUA-22 passive search and attack (*see* Remarks)
M: 2 SEMT-Pielstick PA1 450-kw diesel generators; 2 props; 2,000 bhp
Range: 4,300/7.5 snorkel; 2,710/12.5 surf.
Crew: 6 officers, 41 enlisted

Remarks: Built with French technical assistance; agreement made on 16-7-6 ing depth: 300 m. Beginning with S 61 refitted during late 1980s with DU forward (retain DUUA-1D aft), DSUV-22 passive sonar, and updated torpe control system; have large bow sonar dome, like French Navy *Daphnés*. A completed by end-1988. Are to remain in service until at least 2003.

Note: U.S. *Gearing*-class destroyers *Gravina* (D 62; ex-*Furse,* DD 882) and *Blas* (D 65, ex-*Noa,* DD 841) were stricken 30-9-91; sisters *Mendez Nuñez* (D 63, ex- DD 889) and *Langara* (D 65, ex-*Leary,* DD 879) were stricken 3-4-92.

FRIGATES

Note: Spain remained as a partner in the NATO frigate (NFR-90) program a U.K., France, and Italy departed in 9-89 but withdrew 1-90. Plans had called first NFR-90 to be built in Spain, for delivery in 1998 and for a total of five to be b the Spanish Navy. Current plans call for the construction of five F 110 frigat ordered between 1998 and 2002, with the first to be delivered in 2003 in additio four F 100 units below. The F 110 design may be prepared in conjunction w Netherlands, but it is more likely that the program will be canceled.

♦ 0 (+ 4) F 100 design Bldr: E.N. Bazán, El Ferrol

	Laid down	L	In serv.
F	. . .	. . .	1997
F	. . .	. . .	. . .
F	. . .	. . .	. . .
F	. . .	. . .	2001

D: 3,000 tons (fl) **S:** . . . kts **Dim:** . . . × . . . × . . .
A: 16 vertical-launch missile cells–. . .
M: . . . **Range:** . . ./. . . **Crew:** . . .

Remarks: Although it had been hoped to lay the keel for the first unit of this 12-93, there appears to have been little progress on the design effort to da funding is not yet available. The first unit was to have been delivered in mid-1 the last in the fall of 2001. Would be helicopter-capable and would have four w fire-control channels.

♦ 4 (+2) U.S. Oliver Hazard Perry class Bldr: E.N. Bazán, El F

	Laid down	L	In serv
F 81 Santa Maria (ex-*Navarra*)	22-5-82	24-11-84	12-10-86
F 82 Victoria (ex-*Murcia*)	16-8-83	23-7-86	11-11-87
F 83 Numancia (ex-*Léon*)	8-1-86	29-1-87	17-11-89
F 84 Reina Sofia (ex-*América*)	12-10-87	19-7-89	30-10-90
F 85	1992	. . .	1995
F 86	1993	. . .	1996

Santa Maria (F 81) French Navy

Victoria (F 82) Leo Van Ginderen

Numancia (F 83) Leo Van Ginderen

TES (continued)

851 tons light (4,017 fl) **S:** 30 kts max.
138.80 (125.90 wl) × 13.72 × 4.52 (8.60 sonar dome)
Mk 13 Mod. 4 missile launcher (8 Harpoon SSM and 32 Standard M-1 MR SAM)—1/76-mm 62-cal. OTO Melara Compact DP (U.S. k 75)—1/20-mm Meroka Mod. 2 AA system—6/324-mm Mk 32 od. 5 ASW TT (III × 2)—1/SH-60B Seahawk LAMPS-III SW helo
ron Equipt:
lar: 1/Decca . . . nav.,1/Raytheon SPS-64(V) nav., 1/Raytheon SPS-49 air search, 1/Selenia RAN-12 L/X target designation, 1/Mk 92 Mod. 2 track-while-scan gun/missile f.c., 1/STIR missile f.c., 1/VPS-2 Meroka f.c.
ar: 1/Raytheon DE 1160 hull-mounted MF, Gould SQR-19 TASS
: Elettronica Nettunel active/passive system, Mk 36 Super RBOC decoy syst. (VI × 2 Mk 137 RL), SLQ-25 Nixie torpedo decoy syst.
CAN: URN-25
Fiat-G.E. LM-2500 gas turbines; 1 CP prop; 41,000 shp—/350-shp retractable, rotatable electric auxiliary propulsion 1otors
tric: 4,000 kw (4 × 1,000-kw Kato-Allison 114-DOOL diesel sets)
ge: 5,000/18 **Fuel:** 587 tons **Crew:** 13 officers, 189 enlisted

s: Although the first three were officially ordered on 29-6-77, little progress le until 1981 on construction, the new carrier *Principe de Asturias* taking 1ce. The fourth unit ordered 19-6-86. Fifth and sixth authorized 6-89 and 26-10-89, but work has been delayed because of payment disputes. Plans to ditional units have been dropped in favor of the F 100/F 110 frigate programs. four form the 41st Escort Squadron and are assigned to Aviation Group Alfa as

ave the longer hull used in U.S. FFG 36–61. Similar to latest U.S. version r close-defense AA gun system and different radar and EW suite. Have Saturn COMM gear. Sonar essentially the same as the U.S. Navy's SQS-56. Have elicopter deck-handling system to handle SH-60B LAMPS-III helicopters; F 83 r completed with SSQ-28 LAMPS-III data link, backfitted to others.
NATO LINK-11 data-link equipment and Prairie-Masker bubble noise reduc-em. Although twin hangars can accommodate two SH-60B, only one per ship is as only six were procured. The final pair will have the updated Mk 92 Mod. 6 fire-control system and a Spanish-developed combat direction system.
ning with refits to start 1994, all are to receive two INSEL/FABA DORNA *ón detiro Optrónica y Radárica NAval)* directors with radar tracker, infrared laser rangefinder, and high-definition t.v. in place of the original U.S. target tion sights atop the pilothouse.

escubierta class Bldr: E.N. Bazán, Cartagena (F 35, 36: El Ferrol)

	Laid down	L	In serv.
ESCUBIERTA	16-11-74	8-7-75	18-11-78
ANA	18-7-75	26-1-76	30-6-79
FANTA ELENA	26-1-76	14-9-76	12-4-80
FANTA CRISTINA	14-9-76	19-4-77	24-11-80
AZADORA	14-12-77	17-10-78	20-7-81
ENCEDORA	1-5-78	27-4-79	27-3-82

a Elena (F 33) Carlo Martinelli, 10-90

lora (F 35)—with 4 Harpoon SSM French Navy, 1990

D: 1,363 tons (1,575 fl) **S:** 26 kts
Dim: 88.88 (85.80 pp) × 10.40 × 3.90
A: 2 or 4/Harpoon SSM (I or II × 2)—1/Mk 29 SAM launcher (VIII × 1; 24 Sea Sparrow missiles)—1/76-mm 62-cal. OTO Melara DP—2/40-mm 70-cal. AA (I × 2)—1/375-mm Bofors ASW RL (II × 1)—6/324-mm Mk 32 ASW TT (III × 2)
Electron Equipt:
Radar: 1/H.S.A. ZW-06/2 surf. search, 1/H.S.A. DA-05/2 surf./air search, 1/H.S.A. WM-25 track-while-scan f.c.
Sonar: Raytheon 1160C hull-mounted MF
EW: Elettronica Beta intercept, Mk 36 SRBOC decoy syst. (VI × 2, Mk 137 RL), SLQ-25 Nixie torpedo decoy syst.
M: 4 MTU-Bazán 16MA956 TB91 diesels; 2 CP props; 18,000 bhp
Electric: 1,810 kw **Range:** 6,100/18 **Fuel:** 250 tons
Crew: 10 officers, 106 enlisted

Remarks: Design evolved from the Portuguese Navy's *João Coutinho* class, built by same yard. The first four were ordered on 7-12-73, the others on 25-5-76. Form the 21st Escort Squadron.

Harpoon missiles added 1988–89 amidships. All are scheduled to get 1/20-mm Meroka in place of upper 40-mm, and two chaff launchers. Plans for backfitting Raytheon Type 1167 VDS have been abandoned. Have fin stabilization, plus U.S. Prairie-Masker bubble system to reduce radiated noise below the waterline. Can accommodate 30 troops. Carry 600 rounds 76-mm-gun ammunition. Have H.S.A. SEWACO weapons-control system. The WM-25 radars are being upgraded with new front-end amplifiers and signal processors, and the Canopus EW suite is to replace Beta. An auxiliary gas-turbine generator set has been added amidships for use during passive sonar search. Sisters *Centinella* (F 37) and *Serviola* (F 38) were sold to Egypt in 1982, prior to completion; another sister was built for Morocco.

◆ **5 Baleares class** Bldr: E.N. Bazán, El Ferrol

	Laid down	L	In serv.
F 71 BALEARES	31-10-68	20-8-70	24-9-73
F 72 ANDALUCIA	2-7-69	30-3-71	23-5-74
F 73 CATALUÑA	20-8-70	3-11-71	16-1-75
F 74 ASTURIAS	30-3-71	13-5-72	2-12-75
F 75 ESTREMADURA	3-11-71	21-11-72	10-11-76

Estremadura (F 75) Ben Sullivan, 5-91

Andalucia (F 72) Leo Van Ginderen, 5-90

Cataluña (F 73) Leo Van Ginderen, 7-91

FRIGATES *(continued)*

Asturias (F 74)—showing stern torpedo tubes Bernard Prézelin, 5-90

D: 3,015 tons (4,177 fl) **S:** 27/28 kts
Dim: 133.59 (126.5 pp) × 14.33 × 4.6 (7.01 over sonar)
A: 4/Harpoon SSM (II × 2)—1/Mk 22 guided-missile launcher (16 Standard SM-1 MR SAM)—1/127-mm 54-cal. Mk 42 DP—2/20-mm Meroka CIWS (XII × 2)—1/Mk 116 ASROC ASW RL (VIII × 1, plus reloads)—4/324-mm Mk 32 fixed ASW TT (I × 4)—2/fixed Mk 25 ASW TT for Mk 37 torpedoes
Electron Equipt:
Radar: 1/Decca 1226 nav., 1/SPS-10 surf. search, 1/SPS-52B 3-D air search, 1/RAN-12L/X target-designation, 2/VPS-2 Meroka f.c., 1/SPG-51C SAM f.c., 1/SPG-53B gun/SAM f.c.
Sonar: Raytheon 1160B bow-mounted MF, SQS-35A VDS
EW: Elettronica Nettunel intercept, Mk 36 SRBOC decoy syst. (VI × 4 Mk 137 RL), SLQ-25 Nixie torpedo decoy syst.
TACAN: SRN-15A
M: 1 set Westinghouse geared steam turbines; 1 prop; 35,000 shp
Boilers: 2 Combustion-Engineering; 84 kg/cm², 510° C
Electric: 3,000 kw **Range:** 4,500/20 **Fuel:** 750 tons
Crew: 15 officers, 241 enlisted

Remarks: Built with American aid (agreement of 31-5-66) as U.S. DEG 7 to DEG 11. Form the 31st Escort Squadron. To be replaced by the F 110 class begining in 2002.

The Mk 74 missile fire-control system can use both the Mk 73 director (with SPG-51C radar) and Mk 68 director (with SPG-53B) to control two Standard missiles; the Mk 68 is also used to control the 127-mm gun. The ships have the Mk 114 digital ASW computer to control ASROC and ASW-torpedo firing. Forty-one ASW torpedoes of the Mk 44/46 and Mk 37 wire-guided types can be accommodated. The Mk 32 torpedo tubes are built into the port and starboard sides of the after superstructure and are oriented to a 45-degree angle outboard of the centerline. The two Mk 25 tubes are built into the stern, facing aft. Can accommodate 8 Harpoon SSM (IV × 2), but normally carry only four.

An initial modernization completed by 1987 in all saw the addition of Harpoon missiles, SRN-15A TACAN, TRITAN-1 combat data system, upgraded missile fire control with Mk 152 digital computer, and NATO LINK 11 capability. The second round of modernizations completed 1988–91 saw two Meroka CIWS and their Selenia RAN-12 target-detection radar added, updated the EW suite (including the addition of decoy RL), and substituted the Raytheon 1160B sonar for the original SQS-23; the SQS-35A variable-depth sonar was also updated, and the Tritan-1 combat data system was installed (see entry for the carrier *Principe de Asturias*). All now have the Saturn 3S SATCOMM system, and the boilers have been renovated and converted to burn diesel fuel.

F 73 was damaged by an explosion during refit at El Ferrol 30-5-90.

CORVETTES

◆ **4 Serviola-class (Type B-215) patrol ships** Bldr: E.N. Bazán, El Ferrol

	Laid down	L	In serv.
P 71 Serviola	7-10-89	10-5-90	22-3-91
P 72 Centinella	19-1-90	30-10-90	24-9-91
P 73 Vigia	6-6-90	12-4-91	2-92
P 74 Atalaya	30-10-90	8-91	8-92

Serviola (P 71) Dr. Giorgio Arra, 2-92

Serviola (P 71) Spanish Navy

D: 826 tons (1,103 fl) **S:** 20 kts
Dim: 68.65 (63.00 wl) × 10.40 × 3.40
A: 1/76.2-mm 50-cal U.S. Mk 26 DP—2/12.7-mm mg (I × 2)
Electron Equipt: Radar: 1/ARPA nav., 1/Decca 2459F/I nav.
M: 2 Bazán-MTU 16V956 TB91 diesels; 2 CP props; 7,500 bhp
Electric: 468 kw tot. (3 Bazán-M.A.N. R6V 16/18 diesel sets)
Range: 8,000/12 **Fuel:** 247 tons **Endurance:** 30 days
Crew: 8 officers, 34 enlisted + 6 spare berths

Remarks: Ordered 2-89 for use as offshore patrol vessels to replace the *Atrevida* A planned fifth unit has been deferred. Design based on the "Aquila" class Mexican Navy. Originally referred to as the "Milano" class while under constr and were to have been numbered PA 01 through PA 04 (*Patrulleros de Altura*).

Platform for an AB-212-sized helicopter, but no hangar. Non-retractable bilizers. Carry two rigid inflatable inspection boats. Carry three 80-m³/hr fire-fi pumps. Have 200 rounds 76.2-mm and 7,000 rounds 12.7-mm ammunition aboa 76.2-mm gun, from surplus stocks, is controlled by an Alcor-C optronic dire locally.

◆ **2 Atrevida class** Bldr: E.N. Bazán, Cartagena (P 65: Cádiz)

	Laid down	L	In serv.
P 61 Atrevida	26-6-50	2-12-52	25-4-53
P 65 Villa de Bilbao	18-3-53	19-2-58	2-9-60

Villa de Bilbao (P 65) Leo Van Ginderen

D: 977 tons (1,136 fl) **S:** 16–17 kts
Dim: 75.5 (68.0 pp) × 10.2 × 2.64 (4.08 max.)
A: 1/76.2-mm 50-cal. U.S. Mk 26 DP—3/40-mm 70-cal. Bofors AA (I × 3)
Electron Equipt: Radar: 2/Decca 1226 nav.
M: 2 Sulzer diesels; 2 props; 3,000 bhp
Range: 8,000/10 **Fuel:** 100 tons **Crew:** 9 officers, 123 enlisted

Remarks: Being replaced by the *Serviola* class. P 61 and P 65 were to be stric 1979, but were refitted and employed in patrolling between Gibraltar and the ies. *Diana* (P 63) stricken in 1972; *Princesa* (P 62) and *Nautilus* (P 64) on 28-2-9 other two are to be stricken by the end of 1992.

Tandem machinery arrangement. Electronic equipment and weapons mode with U.S. aid during the 1970s. Can carry twenty mines. ASW ordnance and removed 1980 when redesignated PA, *Patrullero de Altura*. Have a single computing director for the 40-mm AA; the 76.2-mm mount has a rangefinde Redesignated *Patrullero* in 1986, and now carry a semi-rigid inflatable inspectio on the stern. There is no exhaust stack, the engines exhausting through the hull.

PATROL BOATS

◆ **1 Cormoran class** Bldr: E.N. Bazán, El Ferrol

	L	In serv.
P 41 Cormoran (ex-P 53)	10-85	28-12-89

D: 300 tons (374 fl) **S:** 33 kts **Dim:** 56.60 × 7.59 × 1.97 (hull)
A: 1/40-mm 70-cal. Bofors AA—1/20-mm Oerlikon AA
Electron Equipt: Radar: 1/Raytheon 1620/6 nav.
M: 3 Bazán-MTU MA 16V956 TB 91 diesels; 3 props; 13,500 bhp
Range: 2,000/15 **Crew:** 5 officers, 27 enlisted

Remarks: Begun on speculation for foreign sale but remained unpurchased accepted by the Spanish Navy in 1989. A second hull was also laid down. Has bee for patrol in Straits of Gibraltar area and for trials with new equipment. May first of three units of the class for the Philippines if the proposed order is consum At one time or another, it was also reported that this class had been sold to Ven and Mexico, but no firm orders materialized. Has an Alcor-C optronic director 40-mm gun.

)L BOATS *(continued)*

ran (P 41) Leo Van Ginderen, 4-92

azaga class Bldr: P 01: Lürssen, Vegesack, Germany; others: E.N. án, La Carraca, Cádiz

	L	In serv.		L	In serv.
AZAGA	30-9-74	14-6-75	P 04 VILLAMIL	15-5-75	26-4-77
LSEDO	8-1-75	28-2-77	P 05 BONIFAZ	15-5-75	11-7-77
ADARSO	8-1-75	10-7-76	P 06 RECALDE	16-10-75	15-12-77

le (P 06) Pradignac & Léo, 5-89

75 tons (397 fl) **S:** 29.7 kts **Dim:** 57.4 (54.4 pp) × 7.60 × 2.70
/76-mm 62-cal. OTO Melara DP—1/40 mm 70-cal. Bofors AA—
/20-mm AA (I × 2)
tron Equipt: Radar: 1/Raytheon 1620/6 nav., 1/H.S.A. M 22 f.c.
2 MTU MA-16V956 TB91 diesels; 2 props; 7,780 bhp
tric: 405 kVA tot. **Range:** 2,260/27; 4,200/17 **Fuel:** 112 tons
w: 4 officers, 35 enlisted

ks: P 01 and P 03 were commissioned with a U.S. Mk 22, 76.2-mm gun instead TO Melara 76-mm. Space reserved for addition of six 324-mm Mk 32 ASW tubes and a small, high-frequency sonar. Carry 300 rounds of 76-mm, 1,472 of 40-mm, and 3,000 rounds of 20-mm. Redesignated PC = *Patrulleros Ca-* in 1980, and plain *Patrulleros* in 1986. P 03 conducted Meroka CIWS sea trials with the 12-barreled 20-mm gun in place of the 76-mm mount. P 02 is used for collection. The WM-22 radars will be upgraded with new front-end amplifiers nal processors by 1995.

arcelo class

rs: P 11: Lürssen, Vegesack, Germany; others; E.N. Bazán, La Carraca, iz

	L	In serv.		L	In serv.
ARCELO	6-10-75	26-3-76	P 14 ORDONEZ	10-9-76	7-6-77
AYA	16-12-75	23-12-76	P 15 ACEVEDO	10-9-76	14-7-77
AVIER	16-12-75	1-4-77	P 16 CANDIDO PEREZ	3-3-77	25-11-77
ROGA					

10 tons (134 fl) **S:** 36.5 kts
: 36.2 (43.2 pp) × 5.8 × 1.75 (2.15 props)
/40-mm 70-cal. Bofors AA—1/20-mm AA—2/12.7-mm mg (I × 2)
tron Equipt: Radar: 1/Raytheon 1620/6 nav.
2 Bazán-MTU 16V538 TB90 diesels; 2 props; 7,320 bhp
(6,120 sust.)
tric: 220 kVA tot. **Range:** 600/33.5; 1,200/16
l: 18 tons **Crew:** 3 officers, 16 enlisted

r Quiroga (P 13) Antonio Scrimali, 1990

Remarks: Lürssen FPB 36 design. Carry 750 rounds 40-mm, 2,500 rounds 20-mm ammunition. Redesignated *Patrulleros* from *Patrulleros Cañaneros* in late 1986. Designed to be armed with two 533-mm torpedo tubes if required.

FISHERIES PATROL BOATS

Note: The following units were designated PVZ—*Patrulleros de Vigilancia de Zona* in 9-80 and are operated by the Navy on behalf of the Ministry of Commerce for 200-nautical-mile economic zone patrol. All were redesignated plain *Patrulleros* in late 1986.

♦ 10 Anaga class Bldr: E.N. Bazán, San Fernando, Cádiz

	L	In serv.		L	In serv.
P 21 ANAGA	14-2-80	30-1-81	P 26 MEDAS	15-12-80	16-10-81
P 22 TAGOMAGO	14-2-80	30-1-81	P 27 IZARO	15-12-80	9-12-81
P 23 MAROLA	. . .	4-6-81	P 28 TABARACA	15-12-80	30-12-81
P 24 MOURO	. . .	14-7-81	P 29 DEVA	24-11-81	3-6-82
P 25 GROSA	15-12-80	15-9-81	P 30 BERGANTIN	24-11-81	30-7-82

Mouro (P 24) Bernard Prézelin, 7-91

Izaro (P 27) Leo Van Ginderen, 8-90

D: 296.5 tons (350 fl) **S:** 20 kts **Dim:** 44.4 (40.0 pp) × 6.6 × 2.6
A: 1/76.2-mm 50-cal. U.S. Mk 22 DP—1/20-mm AA—2/7.62-mm mg (I × 2)
Electron Equipt: Radar: 2/Decca 1226 nav.
M: 1 Bazán-MTU 16V956 diesel; 1 CP prop; 4,800 bhp
Range: 4,000/15 **Crew:** 3 officers, 22 enlisted

Remarks: Ordered 22-7-78. P 21 laid down 4-79. P 30 originally numbered PVZ 210. Carry rescue and fire-fighting equipment.

♦ 4 Conejera class Bldr: E.N. Bazán, San Fernando, Cádiz

	L	In serv.
P 31 CONEJERA (ex-LVE 1)	9-81	31-12-81
P 32 DRAGONERA (ex-LVE 2)	9-81	31-12-81
P 33 ESPALMADOR (ex-LVE 3)	11-1-82	10-5-82
P 34 ALCANADA (ex-LVE 4)	10-2-82	10-5-82

D: 85 tons (fl) **S:** 25 kts **Dim:** 32.15 (30.0 pp) × 5.30 × 1.42
A: 1/20-mm Oerlikon Mk 10 AA—1/12.7-mm mg
Electron Equipt: Radar: 1/. . . nav.
M: 2 Bazán-M.A.N. V8V16/18 TLS diesels; 2 props; 2,800 bhp
Range: 1,200/15 **Crew:** 12 tot.

Remarks: Ordered 1978; first two laid down 20-12-79. Jointly funded by the Navy and the Ministry of Commerce. Aluminum construction. A planned further six were not built.

FISHERIES PATROL BOATS *(continued)*

Espalmador (P 33) Stefan Terzibaschitsch, 5-89

◆ **3 U.S. Adjutant-class former minesweepers**

	Bldr	L	In serv.
P 51 NALON (ex-M 21, ex-MSC 139)	South Coast Co., Newport Beach, Cal.	22-11-52	16-2-54
P 52 ULLA (ex-M 24, ex-MSC 265)	Adams Yacht, Quincy, Mass.	28-1-56	24-7-58
P 54 TURIA (ex-M 27, ex-MSC 130)	Hiltebrand Drydock, Kingston, N.Y.	14-7-54	1-6-55

Nalon (P 51) Maritime Photographic, 7-90

D: 355 tons (384 fl) **S:** 12 kts **Dim:** 43.0 (41.5 pp) × 7.95 × 2.55
A: 2/20-mm AA (II × 1)
Electron Equipt: Radar: 1/Decca TM 626 or RM 914
M: 2 G.M. 8-268A diesels; 2 props; 1,200 bhp
Range: 2,500/10 **Fuel:** 40 tons **Crew:** 2 officers, 35 enlisted

Remarks: Redesignated as fisheries patrol boats 9-80; all portable minesweeping gear removed. Two others redesignated PVZ have been returned to mine-warfare duties: *Miño* (PVZ 53/M 25) and *Sil* (PVZ 55/M 29).

◆ **2 small fisheries patrol boats** Bldr: Ast. Viudes, Barcelona

	In serv.		In serv.
P 81 TORALLA	29-4-87	P 82 FORMENTOR	23-6-89

D: 56 tons (78 fl) **S:** 19.75 kts **Dim:** 28.50 (25.00 wl) × 6.50 × 1.45
A: 1/12.7-mm mg
Electron Equipt:
Radar: 1/Decca RM 1070 nav., 1/Decca RM 270 nav.
M: 2 Bazán-MTU 8V396 TB93 diesels; 2 props; 2,200 bhp
Range: 1,000/12 **Crew:** 13 tot.

Toralla (P 81) Viudes, 1987

Remarks: GRP-sheathed wooden hulls. A planned third was not ordered.

Note: The fisheries protection ship *Salvora* (ex-PVZ 11, ex-W 32, ex-*Virge Almudena,* ex-*Mendi Eder*) was stricken 10-90. The former Ministry of Agri Fisheries, and Food fisheries support ship *Chilreu* was transferred to the navy see addenda for data.

PATROL CRAFT

◆ **21 P 101 class** Bldr: Aresa, Arenys del Mar, Barcelona (In serv. 19

P 101, 102, 104–114, 116–123 (ex-PVC 11–19, 110–123 series)

P 106 Peter Voss,

D: 16.9 tons (21.7 fl) **S:** 26 kts **Dim:** 15.90 (13.7 pp) × 4.36 ×
A: 1/12.7-mm mg **Electron Equipt:** Radar: 1/Decca 110 nav.
M: 2 Baudouin-Interdiesel DNP-8 MIR diesels; 2 props; 768 bhp
Electric: 12 kVA tot. **Range:** 430/18 **Fuel:** 2.2 tons
Crew: 2 officers, 4–5 enlisted

Remarks: Ordered 13-5-77. Jointly funded by the Navy and the Ministry o merce. Originally numbered LVC 1–LVC 23. Glass-reinforced plastic constr P 121–123 have supercharged engines producing 1,024 bhp and a maximum s 27 kts and were completed 1981–82. Sister P 103 stricken 1990; P 115 lost to f 1991.

Notes: The former Spanish Customs patrol craft P 126 (ex-PVC 41, ex-*Roquer* at her moorings at Ceuta in 1990 and was not repaired.

◆ **1 glass-reinforced plastic patrol craft** Bldr: Ast. Viudes, Barc

P 124 (ex-PVC 21, ex-V 33) (L: 24-3-77)

D: 20.3 tons (25 fl) **S:** 27 kts **Dim:** 16.06 × 4.30 × 0.97
A: 1/12.7-mm mg **Electron Equipt:** Radar: 1/Decca 110 nav.
M: 2 M.A.N. D-2542-MTE diesels; 2 props; 1,100 bhp
Range: 700/18 **Crew:** 9 tot.

◆ **25 P 202 class** Bldr: Rodman, Vigo (In serv. 1978–80)

P 203, P 204, P 206–210, P 212–218, P 220–230 (ex-PVI 12–18, 110– series)

P 217—old number Leo Van Ginderen,

D: 3 tons (4.2 fl) **S:** 18 kts **Dim:** 9.0 × 3.1 × 0.8
A: 1/7.62-mm mg **Electron Equipt:** Radar: *see* Remarks
M: 2 Ebro MH-58 inboard/outboard diesels; 2 props; 240 bhp
Range: 120/18 **Crew:** 6 tot.

Remarks: Formerly LVI 1–20, redesignated 9-80. Ten units stationed at no ports have Decca 060 radar; the others have none. PVI = *Patrullero de Vigi Interior;* redesignated again 1986. PVI 19 lost 1984, PVI 11 stricken 1986, P 1987, P 205 and one other sunk by terrorists 8-90; another unit of the class 14-2-91. The similar P 125 (ex-PVC 31) was stricken 1988.

OL CRAFT *(continued)*

231 class Bldr: E.N. Bazán, La Carraca, Cádiz (In serv. 1963–64)
235 (ex-PVI 21–25, ex-LPI 1–5)

Peter Voss, 10-89

7.2 tons (25 fl) **S:** 13 kts **Dim:** 14.04 × 4.57 × 1.0
/7.62-mm mg (II × 1) **Electron Equipt:** Radar: none
Gray Marine 64HN9 diesels; 2 props; 450 bhp **Crew:** 8 tot.

ks: Copy of U.S. "45-foot picket boat." Wooden construction.

.S. Coast Guard 83-foot design Bldr: E.N. Bazán, Cádiz

	In serv.		In serv.
ex-PAS 11)	24-3-65	P 313 (ex-PAS 13)	13-9-65
ex-PAS 12)	21-4-65		

—old number, ASW weapons now removed 1969

49 tons (63 fl) **S:** 15 kts **Dim:** 25.4 (23.8 pp) × 4.9 × 2.0
1/20-mm AA—2/7.62-mm mg (I × 2)
ctron Equipt: Radar: 1/Decca . . . nav.
2 diesels; 2 props; 800 bhp **Crew:** 15 tot.

ks: Wooden hull. Based on U.S.C.G. WPB design. Formerly designated PAS = *ero de Antisubmarino.* ASW equipment removed by 1988.

iver patrol boat Bldr: Bazán, La Carraca, Cádiz (In serv. 11-1-63)
CABO FRADERA (ex-PVI 01, ex-V 22)

28 tons **S:** 10 kts **Dim:** 17.80 × 4.20 × 0.82
1/7.62-mm mg **M:** diesel; 280 bhp **Crew:** 9 tot.

rks: For use on the Rio Miño border with Portugal. To be stricken soon.
River patrol craft P 236 (ex-PVI 31, ex-V 22) and P 237 (ex-PVI 32, ex-V 6) were n 1990.

E WARFARE SHIPS

+4+4+4) GRP construction minehunters Bldr: E.N. Bazán, rtagena

	L	In serv.
. . . .	. . .	. . .
. . . .	. . .	. . .
. . . .	. . .	. . .
. . . .	. . .	. . .
. . . .	. . .	. . .
. . . .	. . .	. . .
. . . .	. . .	. . .
. . . .	. . .	. . .

530 tons (fl) **S:** 12 kts
n: 54.00 (51.00 wl) × 10.70 × . . .
1/. . . AA
ctron Equipt: Radar: 1/. . . nav.—Sonar: . . .

M: 4 MTU 8V396-series diesels; 2 props; . . . bhp—2/200-shp electric motors (7-kt max.)
Electric: 750 kw (3 Maudsley 250-kw gen., 335-bhp Perkins V8-2506 diesels driving)
Range: 2,000/12 **Crew:** 7 officers, 26 enlisted (40 accomm.)

Remarks: Vosper Thornycroft design selected 1989 but not ordered as of 3-92 for lack of authorization of funds in 1992 Budget. Instead, a Bazán design, based on Vosper's concepts, was selected. First four ordered 3-92. Hulls to be built at El Ferrol and fitted out at Cartagena. Sonar may be Plessey 2093. Will carry two SAES remotely operated minehunting submersibles. Despite delays, it is still hoped to deliver the first unit in 10-96. Will be ordered in two groups of four, with another eight to be added later.
Program replaces the indigenous "Cazador" program. The ships will replace the overaged U.S.-built units described below.

◆ 4 ex-U.S. Aggressive-class minesweepers

	Bldr	L	In serv.
M 41 GUADALETE (ex-PVZ 41, ex-M 41, ex-*Dynamic,* MSO 432)	Colbert Boatworks, Stockton, Cal.	17-12-52	15-12-53
M 42 GUADALMEDINA (ex-*Pivot,* MSO 463)	Wilmington Boatworks, Wilmington, Cal.	9-1-54	12-7-54
M 43 GUADALQUIVIR (ex-*Persistent,* MSO 491)	Tacoma Boat, Tacoma, Wash.	23-4-55	3-2-56
M 44 GUADIANA (ex-*Vigor,* MSO 473)	Burgess Boat, Manitowoc, Wisc.	24-6-53	8-11-54

Guadalmedina (M 42) Leo Van Ginderen, 1990

D: 665 tons (780 fl) **S:** 14 kts **Dim:** 52.75 × 10.70 × 3.88 (4.2 max.)
A: 1/20-mm Oerlikon Mk 10 AA—2/12.7-mm mg (I × 2)
Electron Equipt:
Radar: 1/Decca RM 1226 nav., 1/Decca TM 626 nav.
Sonar: SQQ-14 variable-depth HF minehunting (100–300 kHz)
M: 4 Packard diesels; 2 CP props; 2,280 bhp
Range: 2,000/12; 3,000/10 **Crew:** 6 officers, 65 enlisted

Remarks: Modernized 1969–70. Loaned 1-7-71, except M 44 on 4-4-72. All purchased in 8-74. Equipped for mechanical, magnetic, and acoustic sweeping. *Guadelete* (M 41, ex-MSO 432) redesignated PVZ 41 in 9-80, redesignated M 41 late 1981. M 44, equipped as a flagship, has no 20-mm AA. SPS-5C radars have been replaced by a second navigational set. To be retired 1992–95.

◆ 8 ex-U.S. Adjutant, MSC 268*, and Redwing-class minesweepers

	Bldr	L	In serv.
M 21 JUCAR (ex-M 23, ex-MSC 220)	Bellingham SY, Bellingham, Wash.	24-1-55	22-6-56
M 22 EBRO (ex-M 26, ex-MSC 269)*	Bellingham SY, Bellingham, Wash.	8-11-57	19-12-58
M 23 DUERO (ex-M 28, ex-*Spoonbill,* MSC 202)	Tampa Marine, Tampa, Fla.	3-8-54	16-6-59
M 24 TAJO (ex-M 30, ex-MSC 287)*	Tampa Marine, Tampa, Fla.	1-5-56	9-7-59
M 25 GENIL (ex-M 31, ex-MSC 279)*	Tacoma Boat, Tacoma, Wash.	8-8-58	11-9-59
M 26 ODIEL (ex-M 32, ex-MSC 288)*	Tampa, Marine, Tampa, Fla.	3-9-58	9-10-59
M 27 SIL (ex-PVZ 55, ex-M 29, ex-*Redwing,* MSC 200)	Tampa Marine, Tampa, Fla.	29-4-54	16-6-59
M 28 MIÑO (ex-PVZ 53, ex-M 25, ex-MSC 266)	Adams Yacht, Quincy, Mass.	14-4-56	25-10-56

D: 355 tons (384 fl) **S:** 12 kts **Dim:** 43.00 (41.50 pp) × 7.95 × 2.55
A: 2/20-mm Oerlikon AA (II × 1)
Electron Equipt:
Radar: 1/Decca TM 626 or RM 914 nav.
Sonar: UQS-1D hull-mounted (100 kHz)
M: 2 G.M. 8-268A diesels; 2 props; 1,200 bhp
Range: 2,500/10 **Fuel:** 40 tons **Crew:** 2 officers, 35 enlisted

MINE WARFARE SHIPS *(continued)*

Ebro (M 22)—MSC 268 class, with short bulwarks Carlo Martinelli, 4-89

Duero (M 23)—Redwing class, with long bulwarks, mast aft Carlo Martinelli, 4-89

Remarks: Originally a group of twelve, transferred under MAP: two in 1954, one in 1955, three in 1956, one in 1958, two in 1959, and three in 1960. *Llobregat* (M 22, ex-MSC 143) was stricken on 4-7-79 after a fire. M 21 and M 23 have a mast well astern of the stack; the others have only a small davit beside the stack. MSC 268-class ships were 43.9 m overall by 8.51 max. beam and had 4 G.M. 6-71 diesels; 2 props; 900 bhp. Five sisters were redesignated PVZ in 9-80 and had portable sweep gear removed; two were redesignated minesweepers in 1984: M 27 and M 28.

AMPHIBIOUS WARFARE SHIPS

Note: Plans announced 10-91 called for the construction of two dock landing ships (LPD) and five tank landing ships (LST) to replace existing units. The first would be an LPD to be laid down in 1994 in cooperation with the Netherlands. Earlier plans had called for the construction of five 20,000-ton dock landing ships, each to carry 1,500 troops each, the first to deliver in 2002. The joint Spanish-Dutch design in its preliminary stages is intended to displace 9,000 tons full load, be 140 m long by 21 m beam, and to carry 600 troops and six helicopters.

♦ 2 ex-U.S. Paul Revere-class transports
Bldr: New York SB Corp., Camden, N.J.

	L	In serv.
L 21 CASTILLA (ex-*Paul Revere,* LPA 248, ex-*Diamond Mariner*)	13-2-54	3-9-58
L 22 ARAGÓN (ex-*Francis Marion,* LPA 249, ex-*Prairie Mariner*)	11-4-53	6-7-61

D: 10,704 light (16,838 fl) **S:** 22.5 kts
Dim: 171.80 (160.94 pp) × 23.24 × 7.32
A: 8/76.2-mm 50-cal. Mk 33 DP (II × 4)
Electron Equipt:
Radar: 1/LN-66 nav., 1/SPS-10 surf. search, 1/SPS-12 air search (L 22: SPS-40)
EW: WLR-1 intercept, ULQ-6 deception jammer, Mk 36 SRBOC decoy syst. (VI × 2, Mk 137 RL)
M: 2 sets G.E. geared steam turbines; 1 prop; 22,000 shp
Boilers: 2 Combustion-Eng. (L 22: Foster-Wheeler); 42.3 kg/cm², 467° C
Electric: 2,400 kw **Range:** 10,000/22; 17,000/14
Crew: 28 officers, 424 enlisted + troops: 96 officers, 1,561 enlisted

Remarks: Mariner-class C4-S-1A merchant ships converted to troop transports, L 21 by Todd Shipyard, San Diego, and L 22 by Bethlehem Steel, Baltimore. Have a helicopter platform. Can carry 7 LCM(6) and 16 LCVP. Four Mk 63 gunfire-control systems removed between 1977 and 1978, but intercept and jamming equipment retained. Prior to transfer had served the U.S. Naval Reserve Force. Were sold to Spain: L 21 on 17-1-80, and L 22 on 11-7-80. TACAN removed from L 21. Chaff/decoy RL added to both, 1989. L 22 is flagship of the Amphibious Command.

Castilla (L 21) Dr. Maurizio del Pret

Aragón (L 22) Pradignac & L

♦ 2 ex-U.S. Terrebonne Parish-class tank landing ships
Bldrs: L 11: Bath Iron Works; L 12: Christy Corp., Sturgeon Bay, Wisc.

	L	
L 11 VELASCO (ex-*Terrebonne Parish,* LST 1156)	9-8-52	2
L 12 MARTIN ALVAREZ (ex-*Wexford County,* LST 1168)	. . .	

Velasco (L 11) Peter Vos

D: 2,590 tons (6,225 fl) **S:** 13 kts **Dim:** 117.35 × 16.7 × 3.7
A: 6/76.2-mm 50-cal. Mk 33 DP (II × 3)
Electron Equipt:
Radar: 1/Decca TM 626 nav., 1/Decca 1229 nav., 2/Mk 34 f.c.
M: 4 G.M. 16-278A diesels; 2 props; 6,000 bhp **Electric:** 600 kw
Fuel: 1,060 tons **Range:** 6,000/9 **Crew:** 115 tot.

Remarks: Transferred on loan 29-10-71 and purchased outright on 1-11-76. modations for 395 troops. Cargo: 2,200 tons. Carry two LCVP to starboard LCPL to port. Two Mk 63 radar GFCS. Sister *Conde del Venadito* (L 13, ex-*To County,* LST 1159) stricken 1990.

Note: The three "Pelicano"-class utility landing craft were redesignated as au in 1986 and are found on a later page.

♦ 2 ex-U.S. LCU 1466-class utility landing craft
Bldr: Kingston Dry Dock Const. Co., Kingston, N.Y. (L: 4-55)

L 71 (ex-LCU 11, ex-LCU 1471) L 72 (ex-LCU 12, ex-LCU 1491)

:IBIOUS WARFARE SHIPS *(continued)*

80 tons (347 fl) **S:** 8 kts **Dim:** 35.08 × 10.36 × 1.60 (aft)
/20-mm AA (I × 2) **Electron Equipt:** 1/. . . nav.
Gray Marine 64YTL diesels; 3 props; 675 bhp
tric: 40 kw tot. **Range:** 1,200/6 (700/7 loaded)
: 11 tons **Crew:** 6 crew + 8 troops

ks: Transferred in 6-72. Cargo: 160 tons. Formerly LCU 1, 2.

xperimental air-cushion vehicle landing craft
: Chaconsa, Murcia
6 (In serv. 1985)

36 Chaconsa, 1985

2 tons (36 fl) **S:** 60 kts (50 cruise)
: 25.17 × 11.04 × 9.50 (high)
one **Electron Equipt:** . . . **Fuel:** 12,500 l.
2 Avco-Lycoming gas turbines; 2 airscrew props; 5,000 shp
ge: 145/45 **Electric:** 30 kVA **Crew:** 3 crew + 70 troops

ks: Ordered 12-82 for the Marine Infantry, which also operates the 400-kg, -kt trials hovercraft *Furtivo.* VCA 36 is able to transport 14 tons of cargo or 3 over trucks, plus 70 troops. Further trials canceled 1992 for lack of funds. Cargo tment: 18.65 × 2.60 m. There are two centrifugal lift-fans. The Navy also s Chaconsa's VCA-3 hovercraft, a 4-ton test craft completed 1978 and powered 220-shp Dodge gasoline engines.

J.S. LCM(8)-class landing craft Bldr: First 6: Oxnard Boat, Cal. serv. 1975); others: E.N. Bazán, San Fernando (In serv. 1989)

86 (ex-LCM 81–86) L 87 L 88

wearing old number 1975

58.8 tons (116 fl) **S:** 10 kts **Dim:** 22.40 × 6.42 × 1.83 (aft)
2 G.M. 6-71 diesels; 2 props; 600 bhp
nge: 150/9.2 (loaded) **Fuel:** 2.4 tons **Crew:** 5 tot.

rks: First six transferred 7-75 to 9-75. Formerly E 81–86; two others built in Carry up to 53.5-tons cargo.

U.S. LCM(6)-class landing craft Bldr: First six: Lukens Steel, tsburgh, Pa.; others: E.N. Bazán, San Fernando

61 through LCM 66 LCM 601 through LCM 608

24 tons (56 fl) **S:** 10.2 kts **Dim:** 17.07 × 4.37 × 1.52 (props)
2 Gray Marine 64HN9 or G.M. 6V71 diesels; 2 props; 330 bhp
nge: 130/10 **Crew:** 3 tot. + 80 troops

rks: First eight transferred on 23-12-74. LCM 601 completed 28-12-84; LCM 1-2-85, LCM 603–608 in 1985–86. Cargo: 34 tons.

LCP Mk 7 personnel landing craft
dr: Ast. y Talleres Ferrolanos S.A. (In serv. 1987)

11.77 tons (fl) **S:** . . . **Dim:** . . . × . . . × . . . **M:** . . .

rks: First two delivered 2-87, third in 3-87.

◆ **42 ex-U.S. LCVP**

D: 13 tons (fl) **S:** 9 kts **Dim:** 11.0 × 3.2 × 1.1 (aft)
M: 1 Gray Marine 64HN9 diesel; 1 prop; 225 bhp **Range:** 110/9

Note: Above totals reflect landing craft on hand before the transfer of LPA 248 and LPA 249, which retain their nine LCM(6) and eleven LCVP each. Most LCVP are aboard larger ships. Also used by the Spanish Naval Infantry are 16 LVTP-7 tracked amphibious armored personnel carriers, 2 LVTC-7 amphibious vehicle command craft, and one LVTR-7 amphibious recovery vehicle.

AUXILIARY SHIPS

◆ **0 (+1) BES-50 proposed experimental air-cushion vehicle**
Bldr: Chaconsa, Murcia

D: 350 tons (fl) **S:** 50 kts **Dim:** 55.00 × 14.50 × 1.00
A: 8/Harpoon SSM (IV × 2)—2/40-mm AA (I × 2)—1/helicopter
Electron Equipt: Radar: . . .
M: CODOG: 2 gas turbines, 2 diesels for lift/2 for propulsion
Range: 1,000/50; 3,000/12 (diesel) **Crew:** . . .

Remarks: Proposed expansion on BES-16, below, and in turn to be the prototype for "BES-95," a 95.0 × 20.4-m, 2,000-ton, 50-kt combatant with 16 vertical missile launchers, 1/76-mm OTO Melara DP, 6/324-mm ASW TT (III × 2), a Meroka CIWS, and a LAMPS-III helicopter, powered by four LM-2500 gas turbines or four diesels in a CODOG arrangement driving waterjets. The BES-50 had not been ordered as of 4-92; if ordered, would take about six years to construct.

◆ **1 experimental air-cushion vehicle**
Bldr: Chaconsa, Murcia (In serv. 25-7-88)

BES-16

D: 16 tons (fl) **S:** 35 kts
Dim: 16.78 × 5.40 × 0.75 (0.30 on cushion)
M: 2 Isotta-Fraschini propulsion diesels; 2 Castoldi 06 w/j waterjets; 900 bhp; 1 VM HRI 492 lift-fan diesel; 3 centrifugal fans; 110 bhp
Range: 222/35 **Fuel:** 1,300 liters **Crew:** 3 tot.

Remarks: Aluminum construction, launched 16-4-88. BES = *Buque de Efecto Superficie.* Joint design Chaconsa-Bazán.

◆ **1 Antarctic oceanographic ship** Bldr: E.N. Bazán, San Fernando

	Laid down	L	In serv.
A 33 HESPÉRIDES (ex-*Mar Antarctico*)	1989	12-3-90	1991

Hespérides (A 33)—red hull/white superstructure Bazán, 1991

D: 1,943 tons (2,710 fl) **S:** 15 kts
Dim: 82.50 (77.77 pp) × 14.33 × 4.42
Electron Equipt: Radar: 2/. . . nav.—Sonar: *see* Remarks
M: 2 Bazán-M.A.N. B&W 14V 20/27 diesels (1,904 bhp each) 2 Bazán-M.A.N. B&W 7L 20/27 diesels (884 bhp each) in two generator set pairs; 2 A.E.G. 1,400-kw electric motors; 1 prop; 3,800 shp—350 shp bow- and stern-thrusters
Range: 12,000/13 **Endurance:** 120 days
Crew: 9 officers, 30 enlisted + 30 scientists

Remarks: Ordered 7-88. Paid for by Ministry of Foreign Affairs; operated by Navy. Intended for geophysical, magnetic, and biological research. Began sea-trials 19-6-91. Icebreaker bow for antarctic duties. Helicopter deck and telescopic hangar for one Agusta-Bell 212. Diver support to 200 m. Twelve laboratories total 330 m^2. In addition to the main generator complexes, also has a 120-kw emergency diesel generator set. The Norwegian Simrad-supplied sonar/echo-sounder suite includes: An EM-12 deep-sea multi-beam echo-sounder (13 kHz/11,000-m depth); EM-1000 multi-beam echo-sounder (95 kHz/5,800-m depth); EK-500 fisheries research echo-sounder (38, 120, and 200 kHz); EA-500 hydrographic echo-sounder (12 and 200 kHz); SL-490 obstacle-avoidance sonar (49 kHz); and VD-280 towed transducer platform—all except the last with transducers in a 12 × 3-meter keel dome. There is a complete automated data reduction and storage system.

◆ **4 Castor-class survey ships** Bldr: E.N. Bazán, La Carraca, Cádiz

	L	In serv.		L	In serv.
A 21 CASTOR	5-11-64	1-12-66	A 23 ANTARES	5-3-73	21-11-74
A 22 POLLUX	5-11-64	15-12-66	A 24 RIGEL	5-3-73	21-11-74

D: 354.5 tons (383.4 fl) **S:** 11.5 kts
Dim: 38.36 (33.8 pp) × 7.60 × 3.10
Electron Equipt: Radar: 1/Raytheon 1620 nav.
M: 1 Echevarria-B & W Alpha 408-26VO diesel; 1 prop; 800 bhp
Range: 3,000/11.5 **Fuel:** 22.5 tons **Crew:** 4 officers, 34 enlisted

AUXILIARY SHIPS *(continued)*

Castor (A 21) Hartmut Ehlers, 10-86

Remarks: Produced in pairs, the later units having full main-deck bulwarks. A 21 and A 22 have one 720-bhp Sulzer diesel. Have Raydist navigation system, Omega receivers, three echo-sounders, and a Hewlett-Packard 2100A computer. Redesignated A 21–24 from AH 21–24 in 1986.

◆ **2 Malaspina-class hydrographic ships**
Bldr: E.N. Bazán, La Carraca, Cádiz

	L	In serv.		L	In serv.
A 31 Malaspina	14-8-73	21-2-75	A 32 Tofiño	22-12-73	23-4-75

Tofiño (A 32) Leo Van Ginderen, 7-87

D: 820 tons (1,090 fl) **S:** 15 kts **Dim:** 57.7 (51.4 pp) × 11.7 × 3.64
A: 2/20-mm AA (I × 2)
Electron Equipt: Radar: 1/Raytheon 1620/6XB nav.
M: 2 San Carlos-MWM TbRHS-345-6I diesels; 2 CP props; 2,700 bhp
Electric: 780 kVA **Range:** 3,140/14.5; 4,000/12
Crew: 9 officers, 53 enlisted

Remarks: Have Magnavox satellite navigation system, Omega, Raydist, three echo-sounders, side-scanning mapping sonar Mk 8, and a Hewlett-Packard 2100 AC computer. Formerly AH 31, 32; redesignated 1986.

◆ **1 supply ship, ex-merchant refrigerated cargo ship**
Bldr: Eriksbergs M/V AB, Göteborg, Sweden (In serv. 5-53)

A 01 Contramaestre Casado (ex-*Thanasis K.*, ex-*Fortuna Reefer*, ex-*Bonzo*, ex-*Bajamar*, ex-*Leeward Islands*)

Contramaestre Casadi (A 01) Leo Van Ginderen, 4-92

D: approx. 5,300 tons (fl) **S:** 16 kts
Dim: 104.20 (96.12 pp) × 14.36 × 6.11
A: none
Electron Equipt: Radar: 1/Decca 626 nav., 1/Decca TM 1226 na
M: 1 Eriksberg 7-cyl. heavy-oil diesel; 1 prop; 3,600 bhp
Range: 18,600/16 **Fuel:** 727 tons
Electric: 660 kw **Crew:** 72 tot.

Remarks: 2,272-grt/2,743-dwt refrigerated cargo ship impounded for smuggl turned over to the Spanish Navy to supply the Canary Islands; commissioned 1 Four cargo holds. Two 5-ton derricks. Helicopter platform at stern.

◆ **0 (+1) joint Netherlands-Spanish replenishment oiler**
Bldr: E.N. Bazán, El Ferrol

	Laid down	L	In serv.
A . . . Mar del Sud	1992	. . .	1994

Mar del Sud (A . . .)—artist's rendering R.Neth.N./Olling

D: 17,050 tons (fl) **S:** 21 kts **Dim:** 175.00 × 23.7 × 8.00
A: 2/20-mm Meroka CIWS (XII × 2)—2/20-mm Oerlikon AA (I × 2)—3/. . . helicopters
Electron Equipt:
Radar: . . .
EW: . . . intercept, Mk 36 RBOC decoy syst. (VI × 2, Mk 137 R
M: diesel-electric: 2 Bazán-M.A.N. diesels, 2 motors; 2 props; . . .
Range: 13,000/22
Crew: 136 crew + 25 air complement, 70 spare berths

Remarks: Ordered 2-92. Joint design between Netherlands' Nevesbu and Bazán design bureaus under agreement signed 11-88. Will have two alongs plenishment stations, VERTREP position forward. Cargo deadweight: 10,30 including around 9,000 tons fuel, plus repair capability. Some reports give crew total plus 20 air group and 100 passengers.

◆ **1 replenishment oiler** Bldr: E.N. Bazán, el Ferrol

	Laid down	L	In serv.
A 11 Mar del Norte	16-11-89	3-10-90	3-6-91

Mar del Norte (A 11) Leo Van Gindere

Mar del Norte (A 11) Leo Van Ginderen

D: 13,237 tons (fl) **S:** 16 kts
Dim: 123.21 (115.00 pp) × 19.50 × 7.96
A: none **Electron Equipt:** Radar: . . .
M: 1 Bazán-M.A.N. 18V 40/54A diesel; 1 prop; 11,250 bhp

LIARY SHIPS *(continued)*

ctric: 2,520 kW tot. (4 × Bazán-MTU V8V 16/18 TL diesels driving)
ıge: 10,000/15
w: 11 officers, 14 chief petty officers, 105 enlisted

rks: Commercial-design tanker ordered 12-88 as an interim replacement for the *Teide* until the new full-service replenishment ship being developed in coopera-th the Netherlands is ready. Helicopter platform aft and VERTREP positions d aft. Cargo: 7,498 tons distillate fuel, 1,746 tons JP-5, 2,878 tons water, 10 tons ons + five 20-foot refrigerated containers. Has three 120 m^3/hr cargo pumps and on/day distiller. Provision was made for later installation of a Meroka CIWS aft ır Mk 137 decoy RL.

Two merchant tankers were chartered 12-88 from the Spanish state-owned um company CAMPSA for two years for use as replenishment ships until the above were completed; they remain available for future use.

ommercial tankers
lr: Ast. Españoles S. A., Puerto Real, Cádiz (In serv. 1979)

EON   CAMPONUBLA

approx. 28,000 tons (fl) **S:** 14 kts
n: 166.02 (156.01 pp) × 24.24 × 9.30
1 Sulzer 6RND 68 6-cyl. diesel; 1 prop; 9,900 bhp
ctric: 1,500 kw tot. (1 × 1,00 kw, 1 × 500 kw) **Range:** . . ./. . .
el: 1,275 tons heavy oil, 284 tons diesel **Crew:** . . .

rks: 12,040 grt/22,227 dwt. Received Canadian-manufactured underway re-nment equipment for naval service.

rescue and salvage tugs
lr: Duro Felguera, Gijon (In serv. 24-3-75)

MAR CARIBE (ex-*Amatista*)   A 102 MAR ROJO (ex-*Amapola*)

1,860 tons (fl) **S:** 13.5 kts
n: 58.48 (52.61 pp) × 11.86 × 4.21
none **Electron Equipt:** Radar: 2/. . . nav.
2 Echevarria-Burmeister & Wain Alpha 18V 23/30 diesels; 2 props; 4,860 bhp—bow-thruster
ctric: 660 kw (3 × 220 kw diesel sets)
nge: 6,000/10 **Fuel:** 361 tons **Crew:** 44 tot.

rks: Former oilfield supply tugs purchased and commissioned 14-12-88. Have bollard pull. A 101 is assigned to the amphibious forces. A 102 completed sion at Cartagena Navy Yard as a diving tender and diving training ship in 1-91; en equipped to support divers to 200 m and carries a 600-m-capable Vosma rsible that will later be replaced by a deep-submergence submarine rescue e. A 102 also equipped with a dynamic positioning system and a high-frequency avoidance sonar.

submarine rescue, salvage ship, and diving tender
dr: E.N. Bazán, La Carraca, Cádiz (In serv. 8-8-64)

POSEIDÓN (ex-AS 01, ex-BS 1, ex-RA 6)

idón (A 12) Leo Van Ginderen, 7-89

951 tons (1,107 fl) **S:** 15 kts
m: 55.90 (49.80 pp) × 10.00 × 4.80
4/20-mm Oerlikon AA (II × 2)
ectron Equipt: Radar: 1/Decca TM 626 nav., 1/. . . nav.
2 Sulzer diesels; 1 CP prop; 3,200 bhp
nge: 4,640/14 **Crew:** 60 tot.

arks: Near sister to AR ocean tugs *Cádiz* and *Ferrol*. Can support a frogman and has a 300-meter-depth rescue bell. Equipped for fire fighting, towing, and alvage pumps.

seagoing tugs Bldr: Astilleros Atlantico, Santander (In serv. 1978)

MAHÓN (ex-*Circos*)   A 52 LAS PALMAS (ex-*Somiedo*)

1,437 tons (fl) **S:** 14 kts **Dim:** 41.0 × 11.6 × 5.5
2/12.7-mm mg (I × 2)
ectron Equipt: Radar: 2/Decca . . . nav.
2 AESA-Sulzer 16 ASV 25/30 diesels; 2 props; 7,744 bhp
nge: 27,000/12 (A 52) **Crew:** 6 officers, 39 enlisted

Mahón (A 51) Dr. Giorgio Arra, 2-92

Las Palmas (A 52)—white superstructure, red hull, after conversion as Antarctic research ship Peter Voss, 10-89

Remarks: 700 dwt. Former oilfield support tugs purchased from Compañía Hispano Americana de Offshore SA and commissioned 30-7-81. Redesignated from AR 51 and 52 in 1986. A 52 modified 1988 to serve as Antarctic exploration ship, with bow strengthened, space for two scientific vans on fantail, additional fuel tankage, and accommodations for 22 scientists; will be relieved during 1992 in that rôle by the new *Hespérides* and may be sold.

◆ **2 Cádiz-class ocean tugs** Bldr: E.N. Bazán, La Carraca, Cádiz

	L	In serv.
A 42 CÁDIZ (ex-AR 42, ex-AR 44, ex-R 4)	20-7-62	25-3-64
A 43 FERROL (ex-AR 43, ex-AR 45, ex-R 5)	14-9-62	11-4-64

Cádiz (A 42) Leo Van Ginderen, 4-92

D: 951 tons (1,069 fl) **S:** 15 kts **Dim:** 55.9 (49.8 pp) × 10.0 × 4.0
A: 4/20-mm AA (II × 2)
Electron Equipt: Radar: 1/Decca TM 626 nav.
M: 2 Sulzer diesels; 1 CP prop; 3,200 bhp
Range: 4,640/14 **Crew:** 49 tot.

Remarks: Improved version of AR 41 design, similar to A 12. Can carry and lay twenty-four mines.

AUXILIARY SHIPS *(continued)*

◆ **1 seagoing tug** Bldr: E.N. Bazán, Cartagena (In serv. 9-7-55)

A 41 Cartagena (ex-AR 41, ex-*Valen*)

Cartagena (A 41) Carlo Martinelli, 5-91

D: 757 tons (1,039 fl) **S:** 15 kts **Dim:** 56.1 × 10.1 × 3.9
A: 2/20-mm AA (I × 2)—up to 24 mines
Electron Equipt: 2/Decca RM . . . nav.
M: 2 Bazán-Sulzer diesels; 1 CP prop; 3,200 bhp
Range: 5,500/15 **Crew:** 49 tot.

Note: The royal yacht *Azor* (A 91) was placed up for sale in 10-90.

◆ **1 sail-training ship** Bldr: Ast. Echevarrieta, Cádiz

	Laid down	L	In serv.
A 71 Juan Sebastian de Elcano	24-11-25	5-3-27	17-8-28

Juan Sebastian de Elcano (A 71) Leo Van Ginderen, 2-88

D: 3,420 tons (3,754 fl) **S:** 10 kts **Dim:** 94.11 × 13.6 × 6.95
A: 2/37-mm saluting cannon (I × 2)
Electron Equipt: Radar: 2/Decca TM 626 nav.
M: 1 Sulzer diesel; 1 prop; 1,500 bhp
Range: 13,000/8 **Fuel:** 230 tons **Crew:** 224 tot. + 80 cadets

Remarks: Four-masted topsail schooner, 2,467-m² sail area. Renumbered from A 01 in 1986, but number is not borne. Also in use at the Naval Academy are the ketch *Arosa* (A 72, 40 tons, in serv. 1-4-81), schooner *La Graciosa* (A 74, in serv. 1988), and cutter *Hispania* (A 63, in serv. 1988).

SERVICE CRAFT

◆ **5 navigational training tenders** Bldr: . . ., Cartagena (In serv. 1982)

A 81 Guardiamarina Barrutia
A 82 Guardiamarina Salas
A 83 Guardiamarina Godinez
A 84 Guardiamarina Rull
A 85 Guardiamarina Chereguini

D: 90 tons (fl) **S:** 12.5 kts **Dim:** 21.89 × 5.10 × 1.52
A: none **Electron Equipt:** Radar: 1/Halcon 948
M: 2 MTU diesels; 2 props; 800 bhp **Range:** 1,000/. . .
Crew: . . . tot. + 1 instructor and 12–21 cadets

Remarks: A 81 in service 14-9-82; A 84, 85 delivered 6-84. Tenders to the Naval School. Have Magnavox NAVSAT receiver, Decca 21 Navigator. Formerly numbered YE 01–05 and AI 01–05.

Guardiamarina Salas (A 82)—old number Spanish Navy

◆ **1 yard oiler** Bldr: E.N. Bazán, San Fernando (In serv. 1980)

Y 231 (ex-YPF 21, ex-PP 6)

D: 523 grt **S:** 10.8 kts **Dim:** 34.0 × 7.0 × 3.0
M: 1 diesel; 1 prop; 600 bhp **Cargo:** 300 tons

◆ **1 yard oiler** Bldr: E.N. Bazán, San Fernando (In serv. 1980)

Y 232 (ex-YPF 31, ex-PP 23)

D: 830 grt **S:** 10.7 kts **Dim:** 42.8 × 8.4 × 3.1
M: 1 diesel; 1 prop; 600 bhp **Cargo:** . . . tons

◆ **2 YPF 3-class yard oilers**
Bldr: E.N. Bazán, Cartagena (In serv. 1956–60)

Y 233 (ex-YPF-51, ex-YPF 3, ex-PP 3)
Y 235 (ex-YPF-53, ex-YPF 5, ex-PP 5)

Remarks: Sister Y 234 stricken 1992.

D: 510 grt **S:** 10 kts **Dim:** 37.0 × 6.8 × 3.0
M: 1 diesel; 1 prop; . . . bhp

◆ **1 diesel-fuel lighter** Bldr: E.N. Bazán, Cartagena (In serv. 1981)

Y 254 (ex-YPG 41)

D: 214 grt **S:** 10.7 kts **Dim:** 24.0 × 5.5 × 2.2
M: 1/M.A.N. diesel; 1 prop; 400 bhp **Cargo:** 100 tons

◆ **1 diesel-fuel lighter** Bldr: E.N. Bazán, Cádiz (In serv. 1980)

Y 255 (ex-YPG 51)

D: 520 grt **S:** . . . **Dim:** 34.0 × 7.0 × 2.9
M: 1 diesel; prop; . . . bhp **Cargo:** . . .

◆ **3 YPG 21-class diesel-fuel lighters**
Bldr: E.N. Bazán, Cádiz (In serv. 1963–65)

Y 237 (ex-YPG 22) Y 252 (ex-YPG 21) Y 253 (ex-YPG 23)

D: 337 grt **S:** 10.7 kts **Dim:** 34.3 × 6.2 × 2.3
M: 1 diesel; 1 prop; 220 bhp **Cargo:** 100 tons

◆ **2 YPG 01-class diesel-fuel lighters**
Bldr: E.N. Bazán, El Ferrol (In serv. 1956, 1959)

Y 251 (ex-YPG 11, ex-YPG 01) Y 236 (ex-YPG 13, ex-YPG 03)

D: 200 grt **S:** 10 kts **Dim:** 34.0 × 6.0 × 2.7
M: 1 diesel; 1 prop; . . . bhp **Cargo:** 193 tons

Remarks: Formerly numbered in the PB series. Sister YPG 02 stricken 1982.

◆ **1 large water tanker**
Bldr: E.N. Bazán, San Fernando (In serv. 16-10-81)

A 66 Condestable Zaragoza (ex-AA 41, ex-AA 32, ex-A 32)

Condestable Zaragoza (A 66)—old number Spanish Navy

D: 895 tons (fl) **S:** 10.8 kts **Dim:** 48.8 (42.85 pp) × 8.40 × 3.35
M: 1 diesel; 1 prop; 700 bhp **Cargo:** 600 tons **Crew:** 16 tot.

/ICE CRAFT *(continued)*

arge water tanker Bldr: E.N. Bazán, San Fernando (In serv. 1981)

/ARINERO JARANA (ex-AA 31, ex-A 31)

535 tons (fl) **S:** 10.8 kts **Dim:** 34.0 × 7.0 × 3.03
1 diesel; 1 prop; 600 bhp **Cargo:** 300 tons

\-7-class large water tankers
r: Bazán, La Carraca (all in serv. 6-62)

/AQUINISTA MACIÁS (ex-AA 21, ex-A 9; L: 25-10-58)
TORPEDISTA HERNANDEZ (ex-AA 22, ex-A 10; L: 10-10-58)
FOGONERA BAÑOBRE (ex-AA 23, ex-A 11; L: 5-3-62)

edista Hernandez (A 63)—old number Spanish Navy, 1984

610 tons (fl) **S:** 9 kts **Dim:** 44.78 (41.00 pp) × 7.55 × 2.95
1 diesel; 1 prop; 700 bhp **Range:** 1,000/8 **Crew:** 17 tot.

rks: Cargo: 350 tons. Named 1982. Launched 25-10-58, 10-10-58, and 5-3-62, ctively.

large water tanker Bldr: E.N. Bazán, La Carraca (In serv. 1-4-51)

CONTRAMAESTRE CASTELLO (ex-AA 06, ex-A 6)

1,860 tons (fl) **S:** 8 kts **Dim:** 64.05 × 9.60 × 4.80
1 set triple-expansion steam; 1 prop; 800 ihp **Boilers:** 2
ew: 27 tot. **Cargo:** 1,000 tons

small water tankers Bldr: E.N. Bazán, Cádiz (In serv. 1965)

1 (ex-YA 01, ex-AB 1) Y 273 (ex-YA 03, ex-AB 3)
2 (ex-YA 02, ex-AB 2)

337 grt **S:** 10.7 kts **Dim:** 34.3 × 6.2 × 2.5
1 diesel; 1 prop; 220 bhp **Cargo:** 200 tons **Crew:** 8 tot.

non-self-propelled fuel-oil barge (In serv. . . .)

2 (ex-YPFN 31)

arks: Sister Y 201 (ex-YPFN 11) stricken 1988.

non-self-propelled diesel-fuel barge (In serv. . . .)

1 (ex-YPGN 01)

"Pelicano"-class logistics support craft
ldr: E.N. Bazán, La Carraca, Cádiz

	L	In serv.
(ex-LCT 6)	10-11-65	6-12-66
(ex-LCT 7)	10-2-66	30-12-66
(ex-LCT 8)	10-11-66	30-12-66

Leo Van Ginderen, 1992

D: 279 tons (710 fl) **S:** 9.5 kts
Dim: 59.00 (52.9 pp) × 11.90 × 1.86
A: 1/20-mm Oerlikon AA—2/12.7-mm mg (I × 2)—1/81-mm mortar
Electron Equipt: Radar: 1/Decca 404 nav.
M: 2 Bazán-M.A.N. R6V16/18 TLS diesels; 2 props; 1,060 bhp
Electric: 25 kw **Range:** 1,500/9.5 **Crew:** 17 tot. + 35 troops

Remarks: In service in 12-66. Cargo: 300 tons. Formerly BDK 6–8. Design based on the French EDIC-type utility landing craft. Redesignated as logistics support craft in 1986.

◆ **1 gate craft** (In serv. 1959–60)

Y 611 (ex-YBPN 01, ex-YPB 01)

D: 140 tons (fl) **Dim:** 22.3 × 8.7 × 0.8 **M:** non-self-propelled

Remarks: Sisters YPB 02, 03 discarded. Antisubmarine harbor net tender; winches self from point to point for mobility.

◆ **4 netlaying barges** (In serv. 1959–60)

Y 361 (ex-YDS 01) Y 363 (ex-YDS 04)
Y 362 (ex-YDS 02) Y 364 (ex-YDS 05)

D: 140 tons **Dim:** 22.3 × 8.7 × 0.8 **M:** non-self-propelled

Remarks: Sister YDS 03 stricken 1984. Originally PR 1, 2, 4, 5.

◆ **1 harbor-defense support tug** (In serv. 1960)

Y 364 (ex-YDS 15)

D: . . . **S:** . . . **Dim:** 28.0 × 8.5 × 0.7
M: 1 diesel; 1 prop; . . . bhp

Remarks: Handles the former YPB-series gate craft and former YDS-series netlaying barges. Sisters YDS 13, 14 stricken 1984, YDS 11, 12, 21, 22 by 1986.

◆ **2 large torpedo retrievers** Bldr: E.N. Bazán, . . . (In serv. 1961–63)

Y 372 (ex-YTM 13) Y 373 (ex-YTM 14)

D: 178 tons (190 fl) **S:** 7 kts **Dim:** 30.9 × 6.6 × 1.4
A: 50 small mines **M:** 1 diesel; . . . bhp **Crew:** 8 tot.

◆ **1 small torpedo retriever** Bldr: E.N. Bazán, . . . (In serv. 1963)

Y 374 (ex-YTM 21)

D: 98 tons **S:** 7 kts **Dim:** 33.4 × 6.2 × 1.3
A: 79 small mines **M:** diesels; . . . bhp

◆ **2 large diving tenders** Bldr: E.N. Bazán, Cartagena (In serv. 13-4-81)

Y 562 NEREIDA (ex-YBZ 11) Y 563 PROSERPINA (ex-YBZ 12)

D: 103.5 tons (fl) **S:** 9 kts **Dim:** 21.5 × 5.9 × 2.9
M: 1 Sulzer diesel; 1 prop; 200 bhp

◆ **1 small diving tender** Bldr: . . . (In serv. 9-9-82)

Y 579 (ex-YBZ 61)

D: 8 tons **S:** 12 kts **Dim:** 11.0 × 4.0 × 0.8
M: diesels; waterjets

◆ **2 small diving tenders** Bldr: Ferrolanos, La Grana

Y 583 (ex-YBZ 83, in serv. 30-6-86)
Y 584 (ex-YBZ 84, in serv. 11-6-86)

Remarks: No data available.

◆ **1 small diving tender** (In serv. 15-6-83)

Y 580 (ex-YBZ 71)

D: 13.7 tons **S:** 7 kts **Dim:** 10.9 × 3.8 × 0.8
M: 1 diesel; 70 bhp

◆ **1 non-self-propelled diving platform**

Y 565 (ex-YBZN 31)

◆ **3 coastal tugs** Bldr: E.N. Bazán, El Ferrol

Y 116 (ex-YRR 21, ex-YRR 71) (In serv. 10-4-81)
Y 117 (ex-YRR 22, ex-YRR 72) (In serv. 1-6-81)
Y 119 (In serv. 11-87)

D: 422 tons (fl) **S:** 12.4 kts **Dim:** 28.0 × 8.0 × 3.8
M: 2 diesels; 2 vertical cycloidal props; 1,500 bhp
Range: 3,000/10

◆ **3 YRR 53-class coastal tugs**
Bldr: E.N. Bazán, Cartagena (In serv. 1967)

Y 113 (ex-YRR 14, ex-YRR 53, ex-RR 53)
Y 114 (ex-YRR 15, ex-YRR 54, ex-RR 54)
Y 115 (ex-YRR 16, ex-YRR 56, ex-RR 56)

D: 227 tons (320 fl) **S:** 12 kts **Dim:** 27.8 × 7.0 × 2.6
M: 1 diesel; 1 prop; 1,400 bhp **Crew:** 13 tot.

◆ **2 YRR 50-class coastal tugs**
Bldr: E.N. Bazán, Cartagena (In serv. 1963)

Y 111 (ex-YRR 11, ex-YRR 31, ex-RR 50)
Y 112 (ex-YRR 13, ex-YRR 33, ex-RR 52)

SERVICE CRAFT *(continued)*

D: 205 tons (300 fl) **S:** 10 kts **Dim:** 27.8 × 7.0 × 2.5
M: 1 diesel; 1 prop; 800 bhp **Crew:** 13 tot.

◆ **1 large harbor tug** Bldr: E.N. Bazán, . . . (In serv. 29-9-88)

Y 118

Y 118 Bazán, 9-88

D: 220 tons **S:** 14 kts **Dim:** 22.5 × 7.5 × . . .
M: 2 MTU diesels; 2 Voith-Schneider 21 Gil/135 vertical cycloidal props; 1,768 bhp (1,560 sust.)

◆ **2 large harbor tugs** Bldr: E.N. Bazán, Cartagena (In serv. 1981)

Y 141 (ex-YRP 11) Y 142 (ex-YRP 12)

D: 229 tons (fl) **S:** 11 kts **Dim:** 28.0 × 7.5 × 3.4
M: 1 diesel; 1 prop; 950 bhp

◆ **1 large harbor tug** Bldr: S. España d. C.N. Cádiz (In serv. 1965)

Y 146 (ex-YRP 61)

Y 146—old number Leo Van Ginderen, 10-84

D: 173 tons (fl) **S:** 10 kts
Dim: 23.3 × 6.0 × 2.9 **M:** 1 diesel; 825 bhp

Remarks: Entered naval service 27-10-83.

◆ **1 U.S. Army Design 3004 medium harbor tug** (In serv. 27-12-61)

Y 143 (ex-YRP 41, ex-RP 40, ex-. . .)

D: 100 tons light (122 fl) **S:** 12 kts **Dim:** 21.31 × 5.94 × 2.50
M: 1 diesel; 1 prop; 600 bhp **Range:** 3,500/12
Fuel: 15 tons **Crew:** 6 tot.

◆ **1 small harbor tug** Bldr: E.N. Bazán, San Fernando (In serv. 14-4-87)

Y 147

Y 147 Peter Voss, 10-89

D: 87 tons (fl) **S:** 10 kts **Dim:** 16.5 × . . . × . . .
M: 1 diesel; 400 bhp

Remarks: Ordered 18-12-85; launched 25-2-87. Has one water monitor f fighting.

◆ **10 YRP 01-class small harbor tugs** (In serv. 1965–67)

Y 131–141 (ex-YRP 01–09, 012)

D: 65 tons (fl) **S:** 8 kts **Dim:** 18.45 × 4.72 × 1.53
M: 1 diesel; 1 prop; 300 bhp

Remarks: Sister YRP 010 stricken 1984, YRP 011 stricken 6-7-82.

◆ **3 submarine-support push-tugs**

Y 171 (ex-YRS 01)(In serv. 3-11-82) Y 173 (ex-YRS 03) (In serv. 6-8
Y 172 (ex-YRS 02) (In serv. 5-85)

D: 10.5 tons (fl) (Y 172, 173: 9.8 tons) **S:** 11 kts
Dim: 8.3 (Y 172, 173: 9.5) × . . . × . . .
M: 2 diesels; 2 waterjets; 400 bhp

◆ **1 suction dredge** Bldr: IHC, the Netherlands (In serv. 2-12-81)

Y 441 (ex-YDR 11)

D: 150 tons (fl) **S:** . . . **Dim:** 25.2 × 5.8 × 1.0
M: 1 diesel; 530 bhp

◆ **5 personnel launches** Bldr: Rodman, Vigo (In serv. 1980–81)

Y 531–535 (ex-QF 01–05)

Y 535 Leo Van Ginderen

D: 3 tons (4.2 fl) **S:** 18 kts **Dim:** 9.0 × 3.1 × 0.8
M: 2 Volvo-Penta inboard/outboard diesels; 2 props; 240 bhp
Range: 120/18

Remarks: GRP construction. Similar to patrol craft P 202–230.

◆ **13 U.S. LCP(L)-class former personnel landing craft** (In serv. 1943–44)

Y 572–Y 584

D: 10.2 tons (fl) **S:** 19 kts **Dim:** 10.91 × 3.42 × 1.07
M: 1 G.M. 8V71N diesel; 1 prop; 350 bhp

Remarks: Transferred 10-58 and in 1971. Wooden construction. Redesigna service craft in 1986.

◆ **5 miscellaneous VIP personnel launches**

Y 538 (ex-QF 31, ex-V 31) Y 537 (ex-LVC 79, ex-*Cynosure*)
Y 536 (ex-. . .) Y 539 (ex-QF 32, ex-V 32) Y 540 (ex-. . .)

Remarks: Former small patrol craft and yachts. Y 536 is 21.1 tons, 12.8 × 3.5 can make 12 kts.

◆ **18 miscellaneous personnel launches**

Y 501–Y 518

Remarks: Six different designs, from 2.9 to 17.5 tons (fl). Four ordered 11-6-8 Ferrolanos, La Grana, as YQP 16–19.

◆ **1 barracks barge**
Bldr: Pullman Std. Car Co., Chicago, Ill. (In serv. 1944)

Y 601 (ex-YFCN 01, ex-LSM 329, 331, or 343)

D: 1,095 tons (fl) **Dim:** 62.03 (59.89 wl) × 10.52 × 2.54

Remarks: Former medium landing ship, transferred 5-60. Hulked and emplo an accommodations ship.

◆ **1 large floating crane** (In serv. 1929)

Y 381 Sansón (ex-YGR 11)

D: 589 tons (fl) **Dim:** 31.2 × 16.5 × 3.2 **Capacity:** 100 tons

◆ **3 miscellaneous floating cranes** (In serv. 1954)

Y 382 (ex-YGR 21) Y 383 (ex-YGR 22) Y 384 (ex-YGR 23)

D: 470–490 tons (fl) **Dim:** 22.5 × 14.0 × 3.0 **Capacity:** 30 ton

ERVICE CRAFT *(continued)*

2 miscellaneous floating cranes (In serv. 1953–54)

385 (ex-YGR 31) Y 386 (ex-YGR 33)

D: 272 tons **Dim:** 19.0 × 11.7 × 2.4
Capacity: 15 tons

39 miscellaneous barges

202, 211, 301–305, 307–323, 331, 332, 341–346, 351–354, 365, 411, 412

marks: Formerly barges, fuel barges, water barges, pontoons, etc., with YGC, ;G, YGP, YGT-series pendant numbers. Y 365 is a pontoon barge ordered 30-12-85 d launched 25-9-86 at the Cartagena Naval Dockyard.

CUSTOMS SERVICE *(Servicio de Vigilancia Aduanera)*

te: All carry *"Aduanes"* (Customs) on hull sides. Also in use are four CASA 212 ritime patrol aircraft and four helicopters.

JSTOMS PATROL SHIP

1 former oilfield supply ship Bldr: De Waal, Zaltbommel, the Netherlands

NDOR-III (ex-*Smit Lloyd Cairo*)

D: approx. 1,600 tons (fl) **S:** 14 kts
Dim: 59.75 (53.52 pp) × 11.31 × 4.32
Electron Equipt: Radar: 2/. . . nav.
M: 2 De Industrie-Alphen 6D7HD diesels; 2 CP props; 2,700 bhp
Electric: 270 kw (2 × 135 kw) **Crew:** 12 tot.

marks: Captured while smuggling and appropriated as the Customs Service's gest unit in 6-91. Carries two fast "interceptor" boats aft on the open-stowage cargo k.

STOMS PATROL CRAFT

1 Cat 2100-class catamaran-hulled
Bldr: Cougar Holdings, Hamble, U.K. (In serv. 1991)

2100 for Spanish customs—model Cougar Holdings, 1990

: . . . tons **S:** 52 kts **Dim:** 22.0 × . . . × . . .
: 2 MTU 16V396 TB94 diesels; 2 props; 3,480 bhp—1 Ford Sabre cruise diesel; 2 waterjets; 350 bhp

6 R-46-class waterjet-powered
ldr: Polyships, Vigo (In serv. 1986–90)

–HJ XII, ALBATROS-I–ALBATROS-IV

: 14 tons (17 fl) **S:** 65 kts **Dim:** 17.00 (14.55 pp) × 4.00 × 1.00
small arms **Electron Equipt:** Radar: 1/. . . nav.
: 2 MWM Deutz TBD-234-V12 diesels; 2 Riva Calzoni IRC 41.DL waterjets; 2,970 bhp
nge: 400/. . . **Crew:** 5 tot.

arks: GRP construction. A 9-m prototype was also built, and two smaller R-38 were ordered during 1988. Albatros-I was delivered 19-7-89, followed by three s in the same series.

Alcaravan class Bldr: J. Roberto Rodriguez, Vigo (In serv. 1984–87)

RAVAN-I–V

85 tons (fl) **S:** 28 kts **Dim:** . . . × . . . × . . .
2 diesels; 2 props; 3,920 bhp

Alcaravan-III Fouad Sadek, 1988

♦ **1 wooden, 32-meter class** Bldr: Chantiers Navals de l'Estérel, Cannes

AGUILA (In serv. 1974)

D: 80 tons (fl) **S:** 30 kts **Dim:** 32.0 × 5.8 × 1.6
A: 1/20-mm AA **Electron Equipt:** Radar: 1/Decca 926
M: 2 MTU 820Db diesels; 2,750 bhp **Crew:** 16 tot.

Aguila—with VA 2 Fouad Sadek, 1988

♦ **5 Aguilucho class** Bldr: J. Roberto Rodriguez, Vigo

AGUILUCHO (In serv. 1974) GAVILAN-III (In serv. 8-7-82)
GAVILAN-I (In serv. 1976) GAVILAN-IV (In serv. 1987)
GAVILAN-II (In serv. 1976)

Aguilucho class Stefan Terzibaschitsch, 5-89

D: 45 tons (fl) **S:** 30 kts **Dim:** 26.1 × 5.1 × 1.3
A: 1/20-mm AA **M:** 2 MTU 820Db diesels; 2 props; 2,750 bhp
Range: 750/30 **Crew:** 14 tot.

Remarks: *Aguilucho* is 26.1 m o.a., *Gavilan-III* is 32.0 m, *Gavilan-IV* has 3,920 bhp for 28 kts.

♦ **6 22-meter patrol craft** (In serv. 1980–83)

ALCA GERIFALTE HALCON-II
HALCON-III MILANO NEBLI-II

S: 17 kts (*Alca:* 10, *Gerifalte:* 12, *Halcon-II:* 32 kts)
M: diesel, 3,200 bhp

SPAIN *(continued)*
CUSTOMS PATROL CRAFT *(continued)*

◆ **1 16.5-meter patrol craft**

COLIMBO

D: 36 tons **S:** 20 kts **Dim:** 16.5 × . . . × . . . **M:** 850 bhp

◆ **13 LVR-class patrol craft**

LVR 1 to LVR 13
Dim: 11.4 × . . . × . . . **S:** 14 kts

Note: Other Customs Service names reported that have not been equated to the classes above include *Polviera* (L: 1989), *Cormoran, Alcotan-IV, Keita,* and *Zarati.*

SPANISH ARMY
GUARDIA CIVIL SERVICIO MARITIMA

The *Guardia Civil* has been given port security responsibilities and plans to expand its afloat forces to a total of 12 30-meter, 36 18-meter, and 39 12-meter patrol boats, supported by some 2,000 personnel. The initial units were established 9-91 with 194 men and 6 women at Corunna, Santander, Murcia, and Barcelona; five 18-meter and seven 12-meter boats were to be assigned by 12-91. The prototype Guardia Civil GRP-hulled 12-meter craft was completed 6-91 by E.N. Bazán, San Fernando:

New Guardia Civil 12-meter-class patrol craft

D: . . . tons **S:** 40+ kts **Dim:** 11.90 × 4.0 × 0.7
M: 2 Bazán-M.A.N. diesels; 2 Hamilton waterjets; 1,200 bhp

Earlier craft taken over for *Guardia Civil del Mar* service are:

◆ **4 Salvamar-I class** Bldr: Polyships, Vigo (In serv. 1990)

SALVAMAR-I SALVAMAR-II SALVAMAR-III SALVAMAR-IV

D: 8 tons (fl) **S:** 30 kts **Dim:** 11.00 (9.00 pp) × 3.90 × 0.60
M: 2 Fiat-AIFO 8061-SRM 27 diesels; 2 props; 540 bhp
Range: 135/20 **Crew:** 4 tot.

SRI LANKA

Republic of Sri Lanka

Personnel (1991): 7,000 men, including 500 officers (plus 1,000 tot. Volunteer Naval Force, including 100 officers and 89 Naval Reservists, with 12 officers)

Naval Aviation: One Beech Super King Air was acquired 1986 by the air force for maritime surveillance. Six Bell 214 helicopters were ordered 7-90 for maritime patrol and attack duties, land-based.

PATROL BOATS

◆ **2 large patrol boats** Bldr: Colombo Dockyard

	Laid down	L	In serv.
P 601 JAYESAGARA	5-82	26-5-83	9-12-83
P 602 SAGARAWARDENE	7-82	20-11-83	4-6-84

Jayesagara (P 601) R.A.N., 5-90

D: 330 tons (fl) **S:** 15 kts **Dim:** 39.80 × 7.00 × 2.20
A: 2/25-mm 60-cal. Soviet 2M-8 AA (II × 1)—2/14.5-mm mg (II × 1)
Electron Equipt: Radar: 1/. . . nav.
M: 2 M.A.N. 8L 20/27 diesels; 2 props; 2,040 bhp
Electric: 220 kw **Range:** 3,000/11 **Crew:** 4 officers, 48 enlisted

Remarks: First two ordered 31-12-81; three more authorized 8-84 but not buil[t]. Intended as "offshore patrol boats."

◆ **8 Chinese Shanghai-II class**

P 3140 SURAYA	P 3145 JAGATHA	P 320 RANASURU
P 3141 WEERAYA	P 3146 RAKSHAKA	P 321 RANAWIRU
	P 3147 RANAKAMI	P 322 RANARISI

Weeraya (P 3141) Sri Lanka Navy, 19

D: 122.5 tons (135 fl) **S:** 28.5 kts **Dim:** 38.78 × 5.41 × 1.55
A: 2/37-mm 63-cal. V-47M AA (II × 1)—2/25-mm 60-cal. 2M-8 AA (II × 1)—4/14.5-mm mg (II × 2)
Electron Equipt: 1/Furuno 825D nav.
M: 2 M50F-4 1,200-hp diesels; 2 12D6, 910-bhp diesels; 4 props; 4,220 bhp
Electric: 39 kw **Range:** 750/16.5
Endurance: 7 days **Crew:** 34 tot.

Remarks: First five transferred in February 1972 and in 1975; *Jagatha* and *Rakshc* transferred 1980, commissioning 30-11-80. Three more were delivered 11-90. Sis *Daksaya* stricken 1983, *Balawitha* (P 3144) in 1991. Originally armed with 4/37-m AA (II × 2) and 4/25-mm AA (II × 2) and equipped with Pot Head radars. P 3 refitted and rearmed 1985.

PATROL CRAFT

◆ **39 outboard-powered** Bldr: Consolidated Marine Eng., Sri Lanka

P 111–149 (In serv. 1988-90)

P 149 Sri Lanka Navy, 1

D: 5 tons (fl) **S:** 26 kts **Dim:** 13.4 × 3.0 × 0.5
A: 1/12.7-mm mg **M:** 2 Yamaha D343 K diesels; 2 props; 324 bhp
Crew: 5 tot.

Remarks: Like the "Seaguard" class below, designed to operate from the t "deckship" command vessels. Wooden construction.

◆ **10 "Seaguard" class** Bldr: . . . (In serv. 1988)

P 101–110

D: 3.5 tons **S:** 30 kts **Dim:** 12.8 × 2.4 × 0.5
A: 1/12.7-mm mg **M:** 2 outboard motors; 280 bhp **Crew:** 4 tot.

◆ **3 Killer class** Bldr: Korea SB & Eng., Pusan (In serv. 2-88)

P 373 P 374 P 375

D: 56 tons (fl) **S:** 40 kts **Dim:** 23.0 × 5.4 × 1.8
A: 2/20-mm AA (I × 2)—2/12.7-mm mg (I × 2)
Electron Equipt: Radar: 1/Decca . . . nav.
M: 2 MTU 8V396 TB93 diesels; 2 props; 3,400 bhp **Crew:** 12 tot.

Remarks: Ordered 10-86. A planned additional three were not ordered.

◆ **9 Cougar Cat 900 patrol craft**
Bldr: Cougar Marine, Netley, U.K. (in serv. 1984–85)

P 101–109

D: 4.5 tons (fl) **S:** 40–42 kts
Dim: 10.40 × 2.89 × 0.78 (0.48 at speed)
A: 1/20-mm AA or several mg **Range:** 150/32 **Crew:** 3–8 tot.
M: 2 Volvo Penta AQAD41 diesels; 2 Type 290P outdrives; 400 bhp

ROL CRAFT *(continued)*

—Cougar Cat 900 class Sri Lanka Navy, 1990

rks: First unit, purchased 1984 for evaluation in operations from mother ships, 20 m o.a. Glass-reinforced plastic construction. Eight more ordered 1-85 and ed by 10-85.

Israeli Dvora and Super Dvora classes
lr: Israeli Aircraft Ind., Bir Shiva (In serv. 1985–88)

–458 P 463–468

—Super Dvora class Sri Lanka Navy, 1990

47 tons (fl) **S:** 36 kts **Dim:** 21.62 × 5.49 × 0.94 (1.82 props)
2/20-mm Oerlikon AA (I × 2)—2/12.7-mm mg (I × 2)
ctron Equipt: Radar: 1/Decca 926
2 MTU 12V331 TC81 diesels; 2 props; 2,720 bhp
ctric: 30 kw **Range:** 700/32 **Crew:** 8–10 tot.

rks: First six ordered late 1984. Aluminum construction. Second six, of "Super version, ordered 10-86, have MTU 12V396 TB93 diesels, are 22.4 m overall.

P 445 class Bldr: Colombo Dockyard

L	In serv.		L	In serv.
. . .	20-9-82	P 448	27-8-82	1982
. . .	17-9-82	P 449	20-9-82	1982
15-6-82	1982			

40 tons (44 fl) **S:** 22 kts **Dim:** 20.0 (18.3 pp) × 5.1 × 1.3
2/12.7-mm mg (I × 2)
ctron Equipt: Radar: 1/Decca . . . nav.
2 DDA-G.M. 12V71 TI diesels; 2 props; 1,300 bhp
el: 10 tons **Range:** 1,600/14 **Crew:** 10 tot.

rks: Improved version of the *Pradeepa* class. Steel construction. Provision for ing 1/20-mm AA.

P 201 class
lr: Colombo Dockyard (P 201–205 in serv. 1981–82; P 211 in 6-86)

P 202 P 205 P 211

15 tons (22 fl) **S:** 20 kts **Dim:** 13.73 × 3.63 × 0.90
1/12.7-mm mg **M:** 2 G.M. 8V71 TI diesels; 2 props; 800 bhp
ctric: 1 kw **Range:** 450/14 **Fuel:** 2.5 tons
w: 1 officer, 5 enlisted

rks: Also employed for Customs inspection. Sister P 203 sank 1989.

Pradeepa class Bldr: Colombo DY (In serv. 1980–81)

P 232 P 233 P 234 P 235 P 236

—Pradeepa class Sri Lanka Navy, 1990

D: 40 tons (44 fl) **S:** 19 kts **Dim:** 19.5 × 4.9 × 1.1
A: 2/20-mm AA (I × 2)
M: 2 G.M. 8V71 TI diesels; 2 props; 800 bhp
Range: 1,200/14 **Crew:** 10 tot.

Remarks: Hull numbers originally P 431–436; first unit was at one time named *Pradeepa.*

♦ **5 Belikawa class** Bldr: Cheverton, Cowes, U.K.

P 221 P 222 P 223 P 224 P 225

P 224—Belikawa class Sri Lanka Navy, 1990

D: 22 tons (fl) **S:** 23.6 kts **Dim:** 17.0 × 4.5 × 1.2
A: 3/7.62-mm mg (I × 3)
M: 2 G.M. 8V71 TI diesels; 2 props; 800 bhp
Range: 790/18; 1,000/12.2 **Crew:** 7 tot.

Remarks: In service between 4-77 and 10-77. GRP construction. Originally intended for Customs duties but used as patrol craft. Originally named *Belikawa, Diyakawa, Korawakka, Seruwa, and Tarawa,* respectively; hull numbers were originally P 421–425.

AUXILIARY SHIPS

♦ **3 small patrol craft tender/command ships**
Bldr: Chung Wah SB & Eng. Co., Ltd., Hong Kong (L: 1976–77; in serv. 9-8-84)

P 714 Abheetha (ex-*Carinia*) P 715 Edithara (ex-*Francisca*)
P 716 Wickrama (ex-*Delicia*)

Abheetha (P 714) Sri Lanka Navy, 1990

D: 2,628 tons (fl) **S:** 11 kts **Dim:** 76.66 (71.17 pp) × 17.07 × 3.81
Electron Equipt:
Radar: 1/Furuno FR1011 nav., 1/. . . nav., 1/Selesmar nav., 1/Selescan nav.
A: 2/25-mm 60-cal. AA (II × 1)—8/14.5-mm mg (II × 4)
M: 2 Deutz SBA 12M528 diesels; 2 CP props; 3,000 bhp
Electric: 315 kw **Range:** 5,000/11 **Fuel:** 202 tons **Crew:** 50 tot.

Remarks: Former 1,550-grt/4,318-dwt "deckship" container carriers with no below-decks cargo capacity and a 30-ton traveling crane. Had a stern ramp to weather deck for vehicle cargo. Purchased 6-84 for use as mother ships for small patrol craft.

♦ **1 command ship/ patrol craft tender**
Bldr: Bijker's Aannemings, Gorinchem (In serv. 1959)

A 526 . . . (ex-*Kota Rukun,* ex-*Mercury Cove,* ex-*Tijmanuc*)

D: 6,300 tons (fl) **S:** 13.75 kts **Dim:** 99.45 × 15.65 × 6.84
A: 1/12.7-mm mg
Electron Equipt: Radar: 1/Furuno FR 1011 nav., 1/Decca 110 nav.
M: 1 Werkspoor diesel; 1 prop; 3,600 bhp
Electric: 450 kw (3 × 150 kw)
Range: 14,600/. . . **Fuel:** 448 tons **Crew:** 50 tot.

Remarks: Former 3,350 dwt, 4-hold general cargo vessel purchased 17-9-84. Intended to act as mother ship for small patrol craft. Typed "Surveillance Command Tender," vice the designation "Surveillance Command Ship" used for the trio above. Placed in service 19-10-84.

SRI LANKA *(continued)*

SERVICE CRAFT

♦ **2 utility landing craft** Bldr: Vosper Pty, Singapore (In serv. 21-12-87)

A 537 KANDULA A 538 PABBATHA

Pabbatha (A 538) Vosper-QAF, 1987

D: 200 tons (fl) **S:** 8 kts **Dim:** 33.00 (30.00 pp) × 8.00 × 1.50
A: 2/20-mm Oerlikon AA—2/12.7-mm mg
Electron Equipt: 1/. . . nav.
M: 2 Caterpillar 3408 TA diesels; 2 props; 762 bhp
Range: 1,800/8 **Crew:** 2 officers, 10 enlisted

Remarks: Built on speculation, 1983; purchased 10-85.

♦ **2 Chinese Yuqin-class landing craft** (In serv. 6-91)

D: 60 tons light (110 fl) **S:** 11.5 (9.5 loaded) kts
Dim: 24.1 × 5.2 × 1.1 **A:** 2/14.5-mm mg (II × 2)
M: 2 Type 12V50 diesels; 2 props; 600 bhp

♦ **2 catamaran personnel transports** Bldr: International Catamarans, Hobart, Tasmania (In serv. 20-12-87)

A 540 HANSAYA (ex-*Offshore Pioneer*)
A 541 LIHINAYA (ex-*Offshore Pride*)

Hansaya (A 540) Sri Lanka Navy, 1988

D: 153.2 tons (fl) **S:** 32 kts **Dim:** 30.00 × 11.20 × 2.34
A: 1/20-mm Oerlikon AA—2/12.7-mm mg (I × 2)
Electron Equipt: Radar: 1/. . . nav.
M: 2 MTU diesels; 2 props; . . . bhp **Crew:** 2 officers, 10 men

Remarks: 169 grt. Cargo: 60 tons or 120 troops. Acquired 1-86 and converted by Sing Koon Seng SY, Singapore, when they were lengthened 5 m and had additional superstructure added. Originally built as oilfield supply boats.

♦ **1 fuel lighter**

MADERA OYA

Remarks: No data available.

Note: Training for the Sri Lankan Navy is carried out aboard the commercial cargo ship *Lanka Kanthi,* operated by the Sri Lanka Shipping Corporation.

SUDAN

Democratic Republic of the Sudan

Personnel (1991): 500 total

Aviation: Two CASA Aviocar C-212-200 were ordered 6-84 for Maritime Patrol duties.

Note: Due to operating conditions and the withdrawal of traditional sources of aid, the material condition of the units of the Sudanese fleet is rapidly declining. A number of patrol craft are no longer operable, and all auxiliaries have been discarded.

PATROL BOATS

♦ **2 ex-Iranian** Bldr: Abeking & Rasmussen, Germany (In serv. 1970)

KADER (ex-*Shahpar*) KARARI (ex-*Shakram*)

D: 80 tons (fl) **S:** 28 kts **Dim:** 22.9 × 5.0 × 1.8
A: 3/20-mm AA (I × 3)
Electron Equipt: Radar: 1/Decca 202 nav.
M: 2 MTU diesels; 2 props; 2,200 bhp **Range:** 1,220/21
Crew: 3 officers, 16 enlisted

Remarks: Built for the Iranian Navy, transferred to the Iranian Coast Guard i and to Sudan the same year. In very poor condition. Sister *Shekan* has been balized.

PATROL CRAFT

♦ **4 Yugoslav Type 15 patrol craft** Bldr: . . . (In serv. 5-89)

501 KURMUK 502 QAYSAN 503 RUMBEK 504 MAYOM

Qaysan (502) French Navy

D: 19.5 tons (fl) **S:** 16 kts **Dim:** 16.87 × 3.90 × 0.65 (0.70 props)
A: 1/20-mm AA—2/7.62-mm mg (I × 2)
Electron Equipt: Radar: none
M: 2 diesels; 2 props; 330 bhp **Range:** 160/12 **Crew:** 6 tot.

Remarks: Design originally intended for riverine and lake use by Yugoslavia; Yugoslavian Navy, units do not have a radar. Were a gift; intended for use on th

Note: The four ex-Iranian 40-ft. patrol craft, *Fijab, Halote, Maroub, and Salak* been discarded.

SURINAME

Republic of Suriname

Personnel (1989): 160 total.

Naval Aviation: The air force uses four Britten-Norman BN-42 B/T Maritim fender aircraft for coastal patrol.

PATROL BOATS AND CRAFT

♦ **3 32-meter** Bldr: De Vries, Aalsmeer, the Netherlands

P 401 (In serv. 6-11-76) P 402 (In serv. 3-5-77) P 403 (In serv. 1-11

P 403

INAME *(continued)*
ROL BOATS AND CRAFT *(continued)*

127 tons (140 fl) **S:** 17.5 kts **Dim:** 32.0 × 6.5 × 1.7
2/40-mm AA (I × 2)—2/7.62-mm mg (I × 2)
ctron Equipt: Radar: 1/Decca 110 nav.
2 Paxman 12 YHCM diesels; 2 props; 2,110 bhp
nge: 1,200/13.5 **Crew:** 15 tot.

22-meter Bldr: Schottel, Warmond, the Netherlands

I (In serv. 2-76) C 303 (In serv. 11-76)

65 tons (70 fl) **S:** 13.5 kts **Dim:** 22.0 × 4.7 × . . .
1/12.7-mm mg—2/7.62-mm mg (I × 2)
ctron Equipt: Radar: 1/Decca 110 nav.
2 Dorman 8JT diesels; 2 props; 560 bhp
nge: 650/13.5 **Crew:** 8 tot.

rks: Sister C 302 cannibalized for spares.

12.6-meter river patrol craft Bldr: Schottel, Warmond, the etherlands (In serv. 1975)

01 Bahadoer RP 202 Fajablow RP 203 Korangon

15 tons (20 fl) **S:** 14 kts **Dim:** 12.6 × 3.8 × 1.1
1/12.7-mm mg **M:** 1 Dorman 8JT diesel; 280 bhp
nge: 350/10 **Crew:** 4 tot.

small hydrographic survey craft

oeni Litani

arks: Owned by the Ministry of Economic Affairs and operated by the navy. *eni,* launched 1962, displaces 80 tons; *Litani,* launched in 1958, displaces 70 tons.

WEDEN

dom of Sweden

onnel (1991): 9,150 total: 3,100 men of the regular Navy and Coastal Artillery, *ding* officers, petty officers, enlisteds, and civilians with permanent status, plus national service men available for immediate service and 3,500 reserves. Some conscripts receive annual naval training.

e Coastal Artillery has 3,900 personnel (2,800 conscripts). Its five regiments te 75-, 120- and 152-mm fixed coast defense gun batteries, 40-mm AA guns, nm mortars, and Carl Gustav anti-tank missiles. The Bofors 120-mm Karin towed and RBS-15 and RBS-17 missiles are being introduced into service.

l Aviation: 350 personnel. 27 helicopters: 10 Agusta Bell 206-A JetRanger -6), and 17 Vertol 107 (3 HKP-4B for minesweeping and 14 HKP-4C for rescue ASW, with 6 depth charges or up to 4 Type 422 torpedoes, AS-380 dipping sonar). of the 14 HKP-4C were transferred from the Air Force in 1984–86. A Cessna 404 with a prototype side-looking radar (SLAR) was delivered 6-83. Of three CASA 2-200 Aviocar light transports ordered 16-12-85, two are for the Coast Guard, and or the navy as a TP-89 maritime surveillance aircraft. A Fairchild Metro-III light port with an Ericsson side-looking radar in a 10.7-m radome began trials in 1987 wedish Air Force use in maritime surveillance; in 1991, trials began in the same aft with the Ericsson Eriye maritime surveillance radar.

-4 (Vertol 107) Royal Swedish Navy

P-6 (Agusta-Bell 206-A) Royal Swedish Navy

WEAPONS AND SYSTEMS

Most of the electronic equipment in use in the Swedish Navy is of Dutch design (for example, LW-03 air-search radars, H.S.A. fire-control radars) manufactured locally or of wholly Swedish design and construction. Svenska Phillips Electronics AB (PEAB) was purchased by Bofors in the late 1980s and became BEAB (Bofors Electronik A/B); in 6-91, BEAB has been merged with Ericsson, and its products are now marketed under the trade-name "NobelTech." Bofors itself has been combined with FFV under the new company name Swedish Ordnance, but the "Bofors" trade name has been kept for 40-mm and 57-mm naval guns.

A. Missiles

◆ The U.S. Laser-Hellfire missile is being procured as the RBS-17 for coastal defense service between 1989–95; 25 battalions with RBS-17 are being formed to replace 32 battalions with French wire-guided SS-11 missiles. The first 700 RBS-17 missiles were ordered 6-87, with initial deliveries in 6-89.

Length: 1.625 m Range: 5+ km
Weight: 48 kg (71 with launcher)

◆ The Saab RB-08A, a surface-to-surface missile based on the CT-30 of the S.N.I.A.S., is in use in the coastal defense batteries.

Length: 5.7 m Wingspan: 3.6 m
Diameter: 0.65 m Weight: 9,000 kg
Max range: 70 nautical miles

◆ The infrared-homing Norwegian Penguin Mk 2 missile is in use on board the *Hugin*-class patrol boats, where it is called the RB-12. It has a 120-kg warhead.

Length: 3.0 m Weight: 340 kg
Diameter: 280 mm Speed: Mach 0.7
Wingspan: 1.4 m Max. range: 30 km at an altitude of 60–100 m

◆ The Saab RBS-15 became operational in 1985. The missile has a solid rocket booster and a turbojet sustainer. A sea-skimmer, it has a terminal-homing guidance system. The RBS-15F is launched from air force Viggen jet fighters, and a vertical submerged-launched RBS-17 version may be developed for the *Västergötland*-class submarines.

Length: 4.350 m Weight: 598 kg (770 kg with booster)
Diameter: 0.500 m Speed: Mach 0.8
Wingspan: 0.85 m (folded) Range: 80–100 km at an altitude of 10–20 m
Wingspan: 1.4 (extended) Range: 10–20 m

◆ The RBS-70 shoulder-launched SAM entered development in 1983 as a weapon for surface combatants in a version known as the RBS-70 SLM. Is replacing Swedish Army and Coast Artillery 40-mm AA during 1990–92. The weapon is also being offered as an add-on to the H.S.A.-Phillips LIOD optronic director, with four launch tubes co-mounted. The RBS-90, now being offered, is basically RBS-70 Mk II with a night sight.

Length: 1.735 m Range: 5–6 km
Weight: 25 kg Altitude: 3 km
Diameter: 152 mm Launcher weight: 150 kg (loaded)

B. Guns

◆ 57-mm single-barrel automatic SAK 57 Mk 2

Entered service aboard *Stockholm* in 1985. Trials with the weapon took place 1981–82 on the *Hugin*-class missile boat *Mjölner.* Also purchased by Canada. Carries 120 rounds ready service within the low, streamlined gunhouse, automatically loading clips of 20 rounds each.

Mount weight: 6 tons Shell weight:
Train speed: 55°/sec AA: 5.8 kg (projectile: 2.4 kg)
Elevation: −10°/+85° Surface fire: 6.8 kg
Muzzle velocity: 1,020 m/sec. Range: 14,000 m max. horizontal
Max. rate of fire: 220 rounds/min

◆ 57-mm single-barrel automatic SAK 57 Mk 1

Installed on the *Hugin*-class missile boats, the *Spica* and *Spica-II* torpedo boats.

Mount weight (without ammunition): 6 tons Elevation: −10°/+75°
Train speed: 55°/sec Max. rate of fire:
Elevation speed: 20°/sec 200 rounds/min

◆ 40-mm single-barrel semi-automatic L70

World-standard weapon, by Bofors. Mk 2 proximity fuze now offered. A new mounting, the 3.7-ton "Trinity" with 1.025 m/sec muzzle velocity, a 4-km range, and a 330-rpm firing rate from a 100-round magazine; fitted with an integral radar, the "Trinity" fires a .975-kg 3-P (Programmed Proximity Prefragmented) round with 1,000 tungsten pellets. Basic version, E1, has on-mount radar and laser range finder; "E1 Optronic" lacks the radar; "S1" uses a remote-control director and has no on-mount operator.

Characteristics for the standard Bofors L70 gun mount include:
Barrel length: 70 caliber Effective range: 4 km
Muzzle velocity: 1005–1025 m/sec. Training rate: 85°/sec.
Elevation/depression: + 90/−10°
Weight: 2.8 to 3.3 tons without ammunition

C. Torpedoes—Underwater Division, Swedish Ordnance (formerly FFV Ordnance), Motala

◆ Types 61/62 series

The wire-guided Type 61 is used for antisurface duties from surface ships and submarines. The weapon entered service in 1977, and is now delivered in the Type 613 version, with a wakeless hydrogen peroxide engine.

Length: 7,025 mm Weight: 1,765 kg Range: 30,000 m
Diameter: 533.4 mm Warhead: 240 kg

The Type 617 is a 6.98-m-long export version weighing 1,850 kg and having a 20,000-m range. The Type 62 (also known as the "Type 2000"), now under development, is an improved Type 61 with a range of up to 45 km and speeds of up to 60 kts; it will be carried by the new A 19 submarines for use against surface and submarine targets.

WEAPONS AND SYSTEMS *(continued)*

♦ Type 42 series

The lightweight Type 42 torpedo is wire-guided and has acoustic homing, for use by submarines, surface ships, and aircraft against submarines. It was developed from the similar Type 41, which is still in service. The current Type 422 entered Swedish service in 1983; a reduced-charge warhead is available for peacetime use against intruders. The 2.645-m long Type 431 improved ASW torpedo was to enter service in 1987; the initial examples, however, were not ordered until late 1991 as the "Type 43X2" and will now enter service in 1993 on the *Göteborg* class; Type 43X0 is the export version. In the interim, some 50 Whitehead A-244 lightweight torpedoes were ordered from Italy in 1990.

Data for the Type 422 include:
Length: 2,600 mm (2,440 mm without wire-guidance attachment)
Diameter: 400 mm   Warhead: 50 kg
Weight: 298 kg   Range: 20,000 m (10,000 at high speed)

D. ASW Weapons

The Malin small depth charge and Elma harassment device (renamed the ASW-600 in 1990) are available for helicopter and surface-ship use. Elma is a rocket launcher firing 100-mm-dia. charges to ranges of 250–300 m in patterns of 9, 18, 27, or 36 grenades when installed in the normal 4-unit suite. Each grenade weighs 4.2 kg and has a shaped-charge warhead. A shallow-water (10-m minimum) version entered service in 1986, followed by chaff and IR decoy rounds. A longer-ranged version of Elma with a larger rocket engine is in development, as is a decoy round called EWS-900E.

The Bofors 375-mm ASW rocket launcher, no longer in Swedish Navy service, is widely used in foreign navies in 2-, 4-, or 6-tubed versions. Two types of rockets are furnished: the Erika, with ranges from 600–1,600 m and the Nelli, with ranges from 1,600–3,600 m. The SR-375 twin-tubed launcher has a 24-round auto-loading magazine.

E. Sensors

The Ericsson Sea Giraffe series C-band radars are offered for export in various models and provide for air and surface search via two separate channels. The digital, pulse-compression radar is offered at 15–60-kw power with differing antenna gains.

Seven sets of U.S. Klein sidescan high-frequency sonars were purchased in 1984 to assist in locating intruding submarines.

Note: In the ship-name and hull-number lists below, also given is a three-letter condensed form of the ship's name used when pendant numbers have been painted out.

SUBMARINES

Note: The next generation of submarines is expected to enter service around 2005 and is being designed under the rubric "Submarine 2000." It will incorporate Stirling-cycle air-independent propulsion, possibly as a prime mover, and will have a low-r.p.m. propeller, television camera vice a periscope, and X-form stern controls. One concept from Kockums, known as "Flounder," would have a squashed cross section and be capable of bottoming; it may be able to operate small, unmanned submersibles.

♦ 0 (+3) Gotland class (Type A-19)   Bldr: Kockums, Mälmo

	Symbol	Laid down	L	In serv.
Gotland	Gld	1991	1994	1996
Halland	Hnd	1992	1995	1997
Uppland	Urd	1993	1996	1998

Gotland class, Type A-19—showing Stirling-engine section to be added   Kockums, 1991

D: 1,300 tons (sub.) **S:** 12 kts (surf.)/20 kts (sub.)
Dim: 52.50 × 6.06 × 5.60 (surf.)
A: 6/533-mm TT (12 Type 613 torpedoes)—3/400-mm TT (6 Type 422 or 43X2 torpedoes)—22 mines in external belt
Electron Equipt:
Radar: 1/Terma . . .—EW: MEL Manta intercept
Sonar: Atlas CSU-90 suite (panoramic passive attack, passive intercept, LF flank arrays)
M: 2 Hedemora V12A/15-Ub (VA 185) diesels (1,800 bhp each); 2 Jeumont-Schneider 760-kw generators; 1 ASEA electric motor; 1/5-bladed prop; 1,800 shp—2 Stirling V4-275R 75-kw generator sets
Range: . . ./. . . **Crew:** 20 tot.

Remarks: Ordered 28-3-90, although not funded until the 1992 Budget. Order placed 5-9-91 to incorporate Stirling-cycle external-combustion engines in the generator sets. Work began on hull sections for first unit in 1990. Plans to construct two more abandoned. Design is essentially an updated A-17 with Stirling-cycle air-independent auxiliary low-speed propulsion and improved electronics.

♦ 4 Västergötland class (Type A-17)   Bldrs: Kockums, Malmö, and Karlskrona Varvet, Karlskrona

	Symbol	Laid down	L	In serv.
Västergötland	Vgd	10-1-83	17-9-86	27-11-87
Hälsingland	Hgd	1-1-84	31-8-87	20-10-88
Södermanland	Söd	1985	12-4-88	21-4-89
Östergötland	Ögd	1986	9-12-88	10-1-90

Södermanland (Söd)   Gilbert Gyssels

Östergötland (Ögd)   Leo Van Ginderen

Västergötland (Vgd)   Peter Voss

D: 990 tons light, 1,070 surfaced (1,140 sub.)
S: 12 kts (surf.)/20 kts (sub.) **Dim:** 48.50 × 6.06 × 5.60 (surf.)
A: 6/533-mm TT (12 Type 613 torpedoes)—3/400-mm TT (6 Type torpedoes)—22 mines in external belt

MARINES (continued)

ctron Equipt:
adar: 1/Terma . . .—EW: Argo intercept
onar: Atlas CSU-83 suite (DBQS-21, including flank arrays, towed array)
2 Hedemora V12A/15-Ub (VA 185) diesels (1,080 bhp each); 2 Jeumont-Schneider 760-kw generators; 1 ASEA electric motor; 1/5-bladed prop; 1,800 shp
ew: 20 tot. (25 accommodations)

rks: Design by Kockums under 17-4-78 contract. Ships ordered 8-12-81, with ms building the mid-bodies and Karlskrona building the bows and sterns. *Öster-d* collided with a tanker 7-11-89 while on trials; repaired.
torpedo tubes are arranged with the row of six 533-mm tubes above the three 400-mm tubes, with separate reload magazine compartments. Plans to equip with four vertical tubes for antiship missiles (a submerged-launch version of the 5) in the sail have been abandoned. Very low reserve buoyancy—7 percent. Bow mounted on sail, cruciform stern control surfaces. Five spare berths for trainees udor 84-cell lead-acid batteries. Two main watertight compartments. Two Barr oud periscopes. Use Ericsson IPS-17 combat data/fire-control system. Have an oic hull coating. *Västergötland* has a prototype t.v. mounted on a telescoping n lieu of one periscope.

Näcken (Type A-14) class

	Symbol	Bldr	Laid down	L	In serv.
KEN	NÄK	Kockums, Malmö	11-72	17-4-78	25-4-80
D	NAJ	Karlskrona	9-73	6-12-78	5-12-80
UN	NEP	Kockums, Malmö	3-74	13-8-79	26-6-81

1,030 surf. (fl)/1,125 tons (*Näcken:* approx. 1,300 tons sub.)
10 kts (surf.)/20 kts (sub.) **Dim:** 49.5 (*Näcken:* 57.5) × 5.7 × 4.1
6/533-mm TT (8 Type 61B or 613 torpedoes or mines)—2/400-mm TT (4 Type 422 or 431 torpedoes)—mines
ectron Equipt:
Radar: 1/Terma . . .—EW: Argo intercept
Sonar: Atlas CSU-83 suite (DBQS-21)
diesel-electric: 1 MTU 16V652 MB, 1,800-bhp diesel; 1 Jeumont-Schneider generator; 1 ASEA motor; 1 5-bladed prop; 1,500 shp—*Näcken* only: 2 Stirling V4-275 air-independent 75-kw generators
ectric: 150 kw (Scania diesel) **Crew:** 5 officers, 14 enlisted

ad (Naj) Peter Voss, 8-90

tun (Nep) Leo Van Ginderen, 1991

Näcken (Näk)—with Stirling AIP Kockums, 11-88

Remarks: Ordered at the end of 1972. Have an anechoic hull coating. The 168-cell Tudor electric-battery installation is mounted on shock absorbers. Two Kollmorgen periscopes. An Ericsson IDPS central data system furnishes, in addition to tactical information, data on the main engines; it uses two Censor 932 computers. Stern planes are x-configuration; bow planes on the sail. *Näcken* and *Neptun* were launched by cranes. Diving depth: 300 m (500-m collapse). Kockums developed a "mine-girdle" removable minelaying magazine for this and other Swedish submarine classes. All three are to be upgraded insofar as possible to Type A-17 standard, with new sonar suite and automated torpedo-launching.

Näcken began conversion at Kockums 11-87 to install two United Stirling Type 4-275R Stirling-cycle engines, each generating 75 kw. Relaunched 6-9-88, the submarine began trials 23-11-88 and recommissioned 11-4-89. During conversion, an 8-meter section containing the Stirling engines, liquid oxygen tanks, and auxiliary machinery was added. Using the closed-cycle plant, *Näcken* can remain submerged for over two weeks. All are to receive a Plessey towed passive sonar array.

◆ 5 Sjöormen (Type A-11B) class

	Symbol	Bldr	Laid down	L	In serv.
SJÖORMEN	SOR	Kockums, Malmö	1965	25-1-67	31-7-67
SJÖLEJONET	SLE	Kockums, Malmö	1966	29-6-67	16-12-68
SJÖHUNDEN	SHU	Kockums, Malmö	1966	21-3-68	25-6-69
SJÖBJÖRNEN	SBJ	Karlskronavarvet	1967	6-8-68	28-2-69
SJÖHASTEN	SJÄ	Karlskronavarvet	1966	9-1-68	15-9-69

Sjölejonet (Sle) Hartmut Ehlers, 4-89

Sjöorman (Sor) Leo Van Ginderen, 10-86

D: 1,130 tons (surf.)/1,400 tons (sub.) **S:** 10 kts (surf.)/20 kts (sub.)
Dim: 50.5 × 6.1 × 5.1
A: 4/533-mm TT (8 Type 613 torpedoes or mines)—2/400-mm TT (4 Type 422 ASW torpedoes)
M: diesel-electric: 4 Hedemora-Pielstick V12A2, 525-bhp diesel generator groups, 1 ASEA electric motor; 1 5-bladed prop; 1,500 shp
Endurance: 21 days **Crew:** 7 officers, 11 enlisted

Remarks: Maximum diving depth 150 meters. Four battery compartments. Stern planes are x-configuration; bow planes on the sail. One unit given turbocharged (vice supercharged) diesels, 1982. Modernized 1984–85 with Ericsson IBS-A17 combat data/fire-control system, Krupp-Atlas CSU-3-2 sonar suites. Two are to receive mid-life modernizations under FY 87–91 planning: both are to receive the Plessey Hydra sonar array, with 129-m towed array, 457-m tow cable, and improved hull-mounted sensors, including Atlas flank arrays and a new fire-control system. The other three will be replaced by the A-19 class.

Note: The four remaining *Draken*-class (A-11) submarines have been stricken; *Vargen* was sunk for use as a rescue training vehicle and sonar target in 2-90, *Nordkaparen* will be a museum exhibit, and *Delfinen* and *Springaren* will probably be scrapped.

SUBMARINES *(continued)*

◆ **1 intruder simulation midget submarine** Bldr: K.A. Johanssons AB

SPIGGEN-II (L: 19-6-90)

D: 12 tons (surf.)/14 tons (sub.) **S:** 6–10 kts (surf.)/3–5 kts (sub.)
Dim: 11.0 × 1.7 × 2.7 (high) **A:** none
M: 1 Volvo Penta diesel, electric drive; 1 prop; . . . shp
Range: 27/5 (sub.) **Endurance:** 24 hrs. **Crew:** 2 tot.

Remarks: Intended to simulate the intruder submersibles believed to violate Swedish waters. Named for a British-built "X-Craft" midget submarine operated by the Swedish Navy after World War II. Began trials 1-91. Diving depth: 100 m.

◆ **1 Mala-class swimmer-delivery vehicle** Bldr: Brodosplit, Split, Yugoslavia (In serv. 1-85)

R 2 STOR KLAS

D: 1.4 tons **S:** 4.4 kts **Dim:** 4.90 × 1.22 × 1.32 high (1.70 over fins)
A: 2/50-kg limpet mines **M:** 1 electric motor; 1 prop; 6 shp
Range: 18/4.4; 23/1.7 **Crew:** 2 tot.

Remarks: Aluminum and Plexiglas free-flooding hull. Diving depth: 60 m max. Also purchased was a two-man chariot, R 1, *Lille Klas,* with a range of 8 n.m. at 2.5 kts; the device is 3.7 m long and weighs 145 kg without riders. Both craft are intended to assist in the search for submarine intruders and to act as training targets.

◆ **1 salvage and rescue submersible** Bldr: Kockums, Malmö (L: 17-4-78)

URF

D: 52 tons (surf.) **S:** 3 kts **Dim:** 13.9 × 43.2 × 2.9 **Crew:** 3 tot.

URF Leo Van Ginderen, 4-90

Remarks: URF is an acronym for *Ubats Raddnings Farkost* (Submarine Rescue Craft). Has a depth capability of 460 meters and can accommodate up to 25 persons rescued from a bottomed submarine. Based at the Naval Diving Center, Berga. Can be towed at up to 10 kts to the scene of an accident. Lock-out capability to support two divers to 300 meters. Pressure hull of HY 130 steel; collapse depth 900 meters. Two projected sisters not built.

GUIDED-MISSILE PATROL BOATS

◆ **1 signature-suppression trials air-cushion vehicle**
Bldr: Karlskronavarvet, Karlskrona

	L	In serv.
SMYGE	3-91	. . .

Smyge Karlskronavarvet, 1991

Smyge Karlskronavarvet

D: 140 tons (fl) **S:** 50 kts
Dim: 30.40 (27.00 wl) × 11.40 × 1.9 (0.70 on cushion)
A: provision for: 2/RBS-15 SSM—1/40-mm 70-cal. Bofors Trinity AA—1/400-mm ASW TT
Electron Equipt:
Radar: 1/. . . nav.—Sonar: *see* Remarks
M: 2 MTU 16V396 TB94 diesels; 2 KaMeWa VSD63 waterjets; 5,550 bhp—2 Saab DSI-14 diesels; 2 lift-fans; 1,250 bhp
Electric: 144 kw tot. (2 × 72-kw diesel sets)
Range: . . ./. . . **Crew:** 6 officers, 8 enlisted

Remarks: Unique trials craft to test radar, noise, and infrared signature-red techniques. Name means "Stealth." External hull shaped in flat planes to reduce return and coated with radar-absorbent. Rigid-sidewall catamaran configuratio bow and stern flexible air seals. Will also be used to test sonar equipment l through center well, both for ASW and minehunting, and will also test the remotely operated vehicle for minehunting. The missile launchers are buried decks amidships and the torpedo tube exits the stern. The 40-mm AA, in a sp shaped gunhouse, will be placed forward. Later, a retractable or removable mast substituted. Intended to provide data for a possible future generation of much craft, the 40-meter YSM for mine countermeasures and patrol duties, and the 60 YSS, which would be configured as a missile boat.

◆ **2 (+2) Göteborg class (KKV-90 design)** Bldr: Karlskronavarve

	Symbol	Laid down	L	In serv.
K 21 GÖTEBORG	GBG	10-2-86	12-4-89	15-2-90
K 22 GÄVLE	GLE	10-9-88	12-8-89	1-2-91
K 23 KALMAR	KMR	10-9-88	1-11-90	2-92
K 24 SUNDSVALL	SVL	10-3-89	29-11-91	7-92

D: 380 tons (425 fl) **S:** 32 kts
Dim: 57.0 (50.0 wl) × 8.0 (7.3 wl) × 1.93
A: 8/RBS-15 SSM (II × 4)—1/57-mm Bofors 70-cal. SAK57 Mk 2 DP—1/40-mm 70-cal. Bofors AA—4/400-mm ASW TT (Type 4: torpedoes)—4/Elma ASW RL (IX × 4)—mines
Electron Equipt:
Radar: 1/Terma PN-612 nav., 1/NobelTech Pilot surf. search, 2/ 400 f.c.
Sonar: Simrad SS 304 Spira hull-mounted (34 kHz), Thomson-C TSM 2643 Salmon dismountable VDS (MF)
EW: MEL Sceptre intercept/deception syst., IR detector, NobelT 9CM-300 decoy RL (XXXII × 2)
M: 3 MTU 16V396 TB94 diesels; 3 KaMeWa 80-S62/6 waterjets; 8,640 bhp (6,390 sust.)
Range: . . . **Electric:** 855 kVA (3 × 285-kVA diesel sets)
Crew: 7 officers, 36 enlisted

Göteborg (K-21, Gbg) Gilbert Gyssels

Gävle (K-22, Gle)—without missiles Royal Swedish Navy

)ED-MISSILE PATROL BOATS *(continued)*

)org (K-21, Gbg) Royal Swedish Navy, 1990

rks: First four ordered 1-12-85; two others, to have been requested later in will not be ordered (were to have been named *Helsingborg* and *Härnösand*). ered to be "corvettes." An expanded version of the *Stockholm* design, intended to the remaining Spica-I missile boats. K 21 began sea trials late 11-89.
NobelTech 9LV 450 gunfire-control system uses the ARTE-726E gun-control , RCI-400 missile fire-control, TORPE torpedo-control, 9AU-300 ASW fire- and 9CM-300 EW-control systems. The two 9LV 200 Mk 3 optronic directors)-mounted television, IR, laser, and 9GR-400 radars. The four fixed ASW TT are ed on the starboard side, two firing aft, two forward, for wire-guided Type 431 orpedoes. K 23 has two Whitehead ILAS-3 triple ASW torpedo tubes for A-244 oes vice single tubes for the as-yet-unavailable Type 431 torpedo. Steel hull, ıum superstructures. Have fin stabilizers. Infrared, radar, and noise signature ssion measures incorporated.

Stockholm class (Spica III/YA-81 design)
lr: Karlskronavarvet, Karlskrona

	Symbol	Laid down	L	In serv.
STOCKHOLM	STO	1-8-82	24-8-84	1-3-85
MALMÖ	MMÖ	14-3-83	21-3-85	10-5-85

ıö (K-12, Mmö) Leo Van Ginderen, 1990

kholm (K-11, Sto)—with 48 mines aboard
Royal Swedish Navy, 1990

D: 290 tons (320 fl) **S:** 32 kts (20 kts on diesels)
Dim: 50.5 (46.6 wl) × 7.5 (6.8 wl) × 2.0 (hull)
A: 8 RBS-15 SSM (II × 4)—1/57-mm Bofors 70-cal. SAK 57 Mk 2 DP—1/40-mm 70-cal. Bofors L70 AA—2/533-mm TT—4 Elma ASW RL (IV × 4)—mines
Electron Equipt:
Radar: 1/Terma PN-612 nav., 1/Ericsson Sea Giraffe 50HC surf./air search, 1/NobelTech 9LV200 Mk 2
Sonar: Simrad SS 304 Spira hull-mounted (34 kHz); Thomson-CSF TSM 2642 Salmon dismountable MF VDS
EW: Saab-Scania EWS-905 intercept; 2 NobelTech Philax decoy RL (XXXII × 2)
M: CODAG 1 Allison 570KF, 7,170-shp (6,000 sust.) gas turbine; 2 MTU 16V396 TB93 diesels (2,095 bhp each); 3 CP props; 11,360 shp
Electric: 648 kw **Range:** . . . **Crew:** 7 officers, 33 enlisted

Remarks: Considered to be "corvettes." Armament suite interchangeable, the RBS-15 missiles being replaceable by two more torpedo tubes, four 400-mm ASW torpedo tubes, and/or mine rails. Have the Ericsson MARIL weapons-control system, with an SRA Censor 932E computer. A 6-cell 57-mm rocket flare launcher is mounted before the bridge. The 9LV300 gunfire-control system incorporates a 9LV200 radar director forward and a 9LV100 optronic director on the aft face of the mainmast. During 1986–87 K 11 conducted trials with the Plessey COMTASS towed linear sonar array, and in 1989 with the Bofors Trinity 40-mm AA mounting with Ericsson Eagle K-band doppler tracking radar.

◆ **16 Hugin class** Bldrs: Bergens Mekanske Verksted, Norway (P 154–158 subcontracted to Westermoen, Mandal, Norway)

	Symbol	L	In serv.
P 151 HUGIN	HUG	3-6-77	3-7-78
P 152 MUNIN	MUN	3-10-77	3-7-78
P 153 MAGNE	MAG	9-1-78	12-10-78
P 154 MODE	MOD	8-8-78	12-1-79
P 155 VALE	VAL	3-10-78	26-4-79
P 156 VIDAR	VID	6-3-79	10-8-79
P 157 MJÖLNER	MJÖ	12-6-79	24-10-79
P 158 MYSING	MYS	18-9-79	14-2-80
P 159 KAPAREN	KAP	8-8-79	7-8-80
P 160 VÄKTAREN	VÄK	12-12-79	19-9-80
P 161 SNAPPHANEN	SNA	18-3-80	14-1-81
P 162 SPEJAREN	SPE	13-5-80	21-3-81
P 163 STYRBJÖRN	SYB	8-80	26-10-81
P 164 STARKODDER	STA	1-81	24-8-81
P 165 TORDÖN	TÖN	3-2-81	26-10-81
P 166 TIRFING	TIR	17-9-81	21-1-82

D: 120 tons (150 fl) **S:** 35 kts **Dim:** 36.53 (33.6 pp) × 6.20 × 1.60
A: 2–6 Penguin Mk 32 (I × 6)—1/57-mm 70-cal. Bofors SAK 57 Mk 1 DP—24 mines or 2/d.c. racks in lieu of missiles—4 Elma ASW RL (IX × 4)
Electron Equipt:
Radar: 1/Terma Scanter 009 nav., 1/NobelTech 9LV200 Mk 2 f.c. system
Sonar: 1/Simrad SQ-3D/SF hull-mounted searchlight-type (24 kHz)
EW: Saab-Scania EWS-905 intercept
M: 2 MTU 20V672 TB90 diesels; 2 props; 7,200 bhp
Electric: 200 kVA **Range:** 550/35 **Crew:** 3 officers, 19 enlisted

Styrbjörn (P 163, Syb) Leo Van Ginderen, 1990

Vale (P 155, Val) Piet Sinke, 9-90

GUIDED-MISSILE PATROL BOATS *(continued)*

Remarks: Can carry six Norwegian Penguin Mk 2 (Swedish RB-12) SSM (I × 6), but normally mount only two. Engines came from discarded *Plejad*-class torpedo boats. Carry 103-mm rocket flare launchers on either side of the 57-mm gun mount. The NobelTech 9LV200 Mk 2 fire-control system employs separate search and tracking radars. P 157 carried the prototype SAK 57 Mk 2 57-mm DP gun, but mounted within the original high gunhouse. Saab-Scania EWS-905 "Doughnut" passive intercept EW systems have been added, with the toroidal radome mounted just below the search antenna for the 9LV200 system. Receiving Roll-Nix rudder roll-control system.

Twelve units of the class are to be re-engined and provided with a low-speed loiter engine, a variable-depth sonar set, and the longer-ranged Elma ASW RL now in development. The other four will be reclassified as patrol boats. Class prototype *Jägeren* (V 150, ex-P 150, ex-P 151) reclassified as a patrol boat in 1989.

◆ **12 Spica-II class** Bldr: Karlskronavarvet and Götaverken

	Symbol	L	In serv.
R 131 NÖRRKOPING	NKG	16-11-72	5-11-73
R 132 NYNÄSHAMN	NYN	24-4-73	8-9-73
R 133 NORTÄLJE	NTÄ	18-9-73	1-8-74
R 134 VARBERG	VAB	2-2-74	13-6-74
R 135 VÄSTERÅS	VOS	15-5-74	25-10-74
R 136 VÄSTERVIK	VÄS	2-9-74	15-1-75
R 137 UMEÅ	UMÅ	13-1-75	15-5-75
R 138 PITEÅ	PIT	12-5-73	13-9-75
R 139 LULEÅ	LUL	19-8-75	28-11-75
R 140 HALMSTAD	HSD	28-11-75	9-4-76
R 141 STRÖMSTAD	SSD	26-4-76	13-9-76
R 142 YSTAD	YSD	3-9-76	10-12-76

Strömstad (R 141, Ssd) Gilbert Gyssels, 8-90

Ystad (R 142, Ysd) Gilbert Gyssels, 8-90

D: 190 tons (230 fl) **S:** 40.5 kts **Dim:** 43.6 × 7.1 × 1.6 (2.4 props)
A: 2/RBS-15 SSM—1/57-mm 70-cal. Bofors SAK-57 Mk 1 DP—2/533-mm TT—4/Elma ASW RL (IX × 4)
Electron Equipt:
Radar: 1/Terma Scanter 009 nav., 1/Sea Giraffe 50HC surf./air search, 1/NobelTech 9LV200 Mk 1 f.c. syst.
Sonar: Simrad ST-240 dismountable VDS (24 kHz)
EW: Saab-Scania EWS-905 intercept, 2 NobelTech Philax decoy RL (XXXII × 2)
M: 3 Rolls-Royce Proteus gas turbines; 3 props; 12,900 shp
Crew: 7 officers, 20 enlisted

Remarks: All re-equipped for the Saab RBS-15 cruise missile during 1982–85. Two missiles are normally carried, and up to six 533-mm torpedo tubes for wire-guided Type 61 torpedoes. The fire-control system is an analog version of the digital system used in the *Hugin* class. Mines can be substituted for the missiles and the torpedo tubes, the forward-most of which must be swung out several degrees before firing. The M 880 (SRA) weapons-control system permits over-the-horizon targeting data to ceived from a helicopter. All have six rails for 103-mm rocket radar flares on the 5 gun mount. The sonar, when mounted, can be towed at up to 12 kts. The Elma rocket launchers can also launch decoy rockets. The gas turbines exhaust throu transom to provide residual thrust for added speed.

R 140 conducted trials 1987 with the NobelTech Pilot low-detectable radar in p the Sea Giraffe. Pendant numbers painted out on all in 1989. R 140 conducted 1987 with the then-PEAB "Pilot" low-detectable radar, and R 137 conducted trial a new weapons control system in 1990–91. R 132 and R 139 collided 14-11-91 both were making 35 kts; one killed. Units of this class are to begin disposal in

PATROL BOATS

◆ **3 Dalerö class** Bldr: Djupviks Varvet, Rönnäng

	Symbol	In serv.
V 09 DALERÖ	DAL	21-9-84
V 10 SANDHAMN	SAN	5-12-84
V 11 OSTHAMMAR	OST	1-3-85

Dalerö (V 09, Dal) Djupviks,

D: 50 tons (fl) **S:** 30 kts **Dim:** 23.40 × 5.10 × 1.05
A: 1/40-mm 70-cal. Bofors L70 AA—2/7.62-mm mg (I × 2)—mine
Electron Equipt: Radar: 1/Terma TM 610 nav.
M: 2 MTU 8V396 TB83 diesels; 3 props; 2,100 bhp
Electric: 60 kw **Crew:** 3 officers, 4 enlisted + 3 passengers

Remarks: Ordered 28-2-83 in lieu of further torpedo-boat-to-patrol-boat conve Are equipped with G.E.C. AQS-928 sonobuoy processors.

◆ **1 modified Hugin class** Bldrs: Bergens Mekanske Verksted, Berg Norway (In serv. 8-6-72)

V 150 JÄGAREN (ex-P 150, ex-P 151)

D: 120 tons (150 fl) **S:** 20 kts **Dim:** 36.53 (33.6 pp) × 6.20 × 1.
A: 1/40-mm 70-cal. Bofors L 70 AA—mines
Electron Equipt: Radar: 1/ Terma Scanter 009 nav.
M: 2 Cummins KTA 50-M diesels; 2 props; 2,800 bhp
Electric: 200 kVA **Range:** 550/35 **Crew:** 3 officers, 12 enliste

Remarks: Was prototype for *Hugin* class but carried Penguin Mk 1 missile briefly. Re-engined and re-armed 1988 and relegated to patrol and trials dut 10-90 conducted trials with Rockwell Crossbow stabilized weapons/sensor mo with RBS-70 SAM and RBS-17 SSM.

◆ **4 Skanör class** Bldr: Naval Dockyard, Stockholm (In serv. 1958–59

	Symbol	Recommissioned
V 05 ÖREGRUND (ex-T 47)	ÖRE	14-1-83
V 06 SLITE (ex-T 48)	SLI	15-4-83
V 07 MARSTRAND (ex-T 50)	MAR	16-5-83
V 08 LYSEKIL (ex-T 52)	LYS	13-6-83

Lysekil (V 08, Lys) Mike Louagie

PATROL BOATS *(continued)*

D: 40 tons (44.5 fl) **S:** 27 kts (25 sust.)
Dim: 23.0 × 5.9 × 1.2 (1.4 props)
A: 1/40-mm 70-cal. Bofors L 70 AA—mines
Electron Equipt: Radar: 1/Terma Scanter 009 nav.
M: 2 MTU 8V396 TB83 diesels; 2 props; 2,100 bhp **Crew:** 12 tot.

Remarks: Converted 1981–83 by Djupviks Varvet; original three gasoline engines replaced for safety and economy. Conversion of four more canceled in favor of building the three *Dalerö*-class patrol boats. Have one six-railed 57-mm rocket flare launcher on the bow. Are equipped with G.E.C. AQS-928 sonobuoy processors. Sisters *Skanör* (V 01) and *Smyge* (V 02) were stricken 1989 and *Arild* (V 03, ex-T 45) and *Viken* (V 04, ex-T 4) in 1991.

◆ **1 Hanö-class former minesweeper** Bldr: Karlskronavarvet (In serv. 1954)

V 55 Ornö (ex-M 56)

D: 270 tons **S:** 14.5 kts **Dim:** 42.0 (40.0 pp) × 7.0 × 2.7
A: 2/40-mm 70-cal. Bofors L 70 AA (I × 2)—mines
Electron Equipt: Radar: 1/Terma Scanter 009 nav.
M: 2 Nohab diesels; 2 props; 910 bhp **Crew:** 25 tot.

Remarks: Redesignated as patrol craft on 1-1-79. Used primarily for training. Has one six-railed 57-mm rocket flare launcher. Sisters *Hanö* (V 51) and *Utö* (V 56), stricken 1980, *Sturkö* (V 54) in 1987, *Tärnö* (V 52) in 1989, and *Tjurkö* (V 53) in 1991.

MINE WARFARE SHIPS

Note: The Coastal Artillery Service has a large number of specialized minelayers and amphibious warfare units capable of laying mines, all described on later pages. Most surface combatants and all submarines can also be used to lay mines.

◆ **1 fleet minelaying/training ship** Bldr: Karlskronavarvet, Karlskrona

	Symbol	Laid down	L	In serv.
M 04 Carlskrona (ex-*Karlskrona*)	Ckr	1980	28-5-80	19-3-82

Carlskrona (M 04, Ckr) Leo Van Ginderen, 1-90

D: 3,300 tons (3,550 fl) **S:** 20 kts
Dim: 105.70 (97.50 pp) × 15.2 × 4.00
A: 2/57-mm 70-cal. Bofors Mk 1 DP (I × 2)—2/40-mm 70-cal. Bofors L 70 AA (I × 2)—105 mines
Electron Equipt:
Radar: 1/Terma Scanter 009 nav., 1/Raytheon . . . nav., 1/Sea Giraffe 50HC surf./air search, 2/NobelTech 9LV200 Mk 2 f.c. (9LV400 system)
Sonar: Simrad SQ3-D/SF hull-mounted searchlight type (24kHz)
EW: . . . intercept, 2/NobelTech Philax decoy RL (XXXII × 2)
M: 4 Nohab-Polar F212-D825, 12-cyl. diesels; 2 CP props; 10,560 bhp
Electric: 2,570 kVA
Crew: as minelayer: 118 tot.; as training ship: 50 + 136 cadets, 46 instructors

Remarks: Ordered 25-11-77 to replace cadet training ship *Alvsnäbben,* which, in the event, expired before her completion. Name changed to honor the Swedish king. Intended to act as a mine countermeasures ship support tender and submarine torpedo and target in peacetime, when not conducting the annual Cadet Training Cruise. Hull reinforced below waterline to permit exercise torpedo hits; there are 14 watertight compartments. A bow-thruster is fitted. Has two complete combat information centers (CIC), one duplicating that of a *Hugin* and one duplicating a *Spica-II.* Extensive navigational systems, including Decca Navigator and Omega receivers. Raised helicopter deck above fantail. There are two lead-computing optical directors to control the 40-mm AA, and two radar/optronic 9LV200 Mk 2 directors for the 57-mm guns. Has a -Nix rudder roll-control, providing a 40 percent reduction in roll.

◆ **2 Älvsborg-class minelayers** Bldr: Karlskronavarvet

	Symbol	Laid down	L	In serv.
M 02 Älvsborg	Äbg	16-11-68	11-11-69	10-4-71
M 03 Visborg	Vbg	16-10-73	22-1-75	6-2-76

D: 2,660 tons (fl) (M 03: 2,450 fl) **S:** 16 kts
Dim: 92.4 (83.3 pp) × 14.7 × 4.0
A: 3/40-mm 70-cal. Bofors L 70 AA (I × 3)—300 mines
Electron Equipt:
Radar: 1/Terma Scanter 009 nav., 1/Raytheon . . . nav. , 1/Ericsson Sea Giraffe 50HC surf./air search,1/NobelTech 9LV 200 f.c.
EW: . . . intercept, 2/NobelTech Philax decoy RL (XXXII × 2)
M: 2 Nohab-Polar 12-cyl. diesels; 1 CP prop; 4,200 bhp
Electric: 1,200 kw
Crew: 95 tot. (M 02: + 205 submarine crew/staff; M 03: + 158 flag staff)

Visborg (M 03, Vbg) Leo Van Ginderen, 9-91

Älvsborg (M 02, Äbg) Peter Voss, 8-90

Remarks: M 02 is used as a submarine tender in peacetime and has accommodations for 205 submarine crewmembers. M 03 is equipped as Flagship, Coastal Fleet, and has accommodations for 158 flag staff. Each has a helicopter deck. Radar suite expanded 1977–78. Originally were equipped with an H.S.A. M-22 radar gun fire-control system. An intercept array is mounted on the mast just forward of the stack. Have two triple 103-mm flare rocket launchers. M 02 is being used for further trials with the Bofors Trinity 40-mm CIWS; it has replaced one of the regular 40-mm mountings.

◆ **6 (+ 1) Landsort (M80)-class coastal minesweeper/hunters** Bldr: Karlskronavarvet, Karlskrona

	Symbol	Laid down	L	In serv.
M 71 Landsort	Ldo	5-10-81	22-11-82	19-3-84
M 72 Arholma	Arh	13-2-82	10-10-84	23-11-84
M 73 Koster	Ksr	1-9-84	16-1-86	30-5-86
M 74 Kullen	Kln	1-1-85	15-8-86	3-7-87
M 75 Vinga	Vin	27-4-86	14-8-87	22-11-87
M 76 Ven	Ven	15-5-87	18-8-88	12-12-88
M 77 Ulvön	Uln	2-1-88	10-89	1992

Ven (M 76, Ven) Peter Voss, 9-90

Arholma (M 72, Arh) Mike Louagie, 9-90

MINE WARFARE SHIPS *(continued)*

D: 310 tons (360 fl) **S:** 15 kts **Dim:** 47.50 (45.00 pp) × 9.60 × 2.30
A: 1/40-mm 70-cal. Bofors AA—RBS-70 shoulder-launched SAM—2/7.62-mm mg (I × 2)—4/Elma ASW RL (IX × 4)—mines (portable rails)
Electron Equipt:
Radar: 1/Terma Scanter 009 nav.
Sonar: Thomson-CSF TSM 2022 variable-depth minehunting (250–525 kHz)
EW: 2/NobelTech Philax decoy RL (XXXII × 2)
M: 4 Saab-Scania DSI-14 diesels; 2 Voith-Schneider vertical cycloidal props; 1,440 bhp
Electric: 468 kw tot. (2 × 180 kw alternators, 1 × 108 kw alternator)
Range: 2,000/12 **Crew:** 7 officers, 32 enlisted

Remarks: Glass-reinforced plastic construction, based on Swedish Coast Guard's TV 171. First pair ordered 25-2-81. Next four ordered 31-1-84; one more in 10-88. Plans to order an eighth canceled.

Have Y-shaped portable mine-rail arrangement, with single laying-point. 9MJ-400 computerized integrated navigational/mine system. NobelTech 9LV-100 gun control system with TVT-100 optronic director. Carry two SUTEC "Sea Owl" remote-controlled mine-disposal vehicles, as well as controlling up to three SAM, glass-reinforced plastic, self-propelled magnetic/acoustic catamaran minesweeping devices. Diesel generator sets, all mounted on the upper deck to reduce noise signature. M 75 conducted trials with the "Trinity" 40-mm AA mount.

◆ 3 SAM-class radio-controlled mine countermeasures craft
Bldr: Karlskronavarvet, Karlskrona

SAM 01 (In serv. 29-3-83) SAM 02 (In serv. 29-3-83)
SAM 04 (In serv. 26-5-83)

SAM 02 Leo Van Ginderen, 1990

D: 15 tons (20 fl) **S:** 8 kts **Dim:** 18.0 × 6.10 × 0.70 (1.60 prop)
M: 1 Volvo-Penta TAMD 70D diesel; 1 Schottel shrouded prop; 210 bhp
Range: 330/7

Remarks: The catamarans also automatically lay eight swept-channel danbuoy markers. An eventual total of 20 SAMs is planned. Sisters SAM 03 and SAM 05 sold to the U.S. Navy for use in the Persian Gulf, 3-91.

◆ 3 Arkö-class coastal minesweepers
Bldrs: M 57, M 67: Karlskrona; M 68: Hälsingborg

	L	In serv.		L	In serv.
M 57 Arkö	21-1-57	1958	M 68 Blidö	1964	1964
M 67 Nämdö	1964	1964			

D: 285 tons (300 fl) **S:** 14.5 kts **Dim:** 44.4 × 7.5 × 2.5 (3.0 prop)
A: 1/40-mm 70-cal. Bofors L 70 AA—1/RBS-70 SAM position—mines
Electron Equipt: Radar: 1/Terma Scanter 009 nav.
M: 2 MTU 12V493 diesels; 2 props; 1,000 bhp
Crew: 25 tot.

Blidö (M 68)—curved strake variant Peter Voss, 4-91

Remarks: Wooden-hulled construction. M 68 has a curved rubbing-strake line along the hull side; in M 57 and M 67 there are two strakes, paralleling the hull sheer. Have one six-railed 57-mm rocket flare launcher. Sisters *Karlsö* (M 59), *Iggö* (M 60), and *Aspö* (M 63) stricken 1984; *Vinö* (M 65) and *Vallö* (M 66) in 1985; *Styrsö* (M 61), *Hasslö* (M 64), and *Spåro* (M 58) in 1989; and *Skaftö* (M 62) in 1990.

◆ 1 former fishing boat
Bldr: Karlskronavarvet (In serv. 1981)

M 50 Rörö (ex-*Astrid-II*)

Rörö (M 50) Leo Van Ginderen, 11-

D: approx. 450 tons (fl) **S:** 9 kts **Dim:** 27.41 × 7.83 × 3.50
A: 1/20-mm Oerlikon AA **Electron Equipt:** Radar: 2/. . . nav.
M: 1 8-cylinder diesel; 1 CP prop; 460 bhp **Crew:** 10 tot.

Remarks: 177-grt glass-reinforced plastic-hulled fishing boat taken over 1990. Although given mine-warfare-series pendant number, is referred to as a patrol boat and may be used on fisheries protection duties.

◆ 3 Gåsston-class inshore minesweepers

	Symbol	Bldr	L	In serv.
M 31 Gåssten	Gsn	Knippla SY	11-72	16-11-73
M 32 Norsten	Nsn	Hellevikstrands SY	4-73	12-10-73
M 33 Viksten	Vsn	Karlskronavarvet	18-4-74	1-7-74

Norsten (M 32, Nsn)—wooden hull Leo Van Ginderen,

Viksten (M 33, Vsn)—GRP hull Leo Van Ginderen,

D: 120 tons (M 33: 130 tons) **S:** 11 kts
Dim: 23.0 (M 33: 25.3) × 6.6 × 3.7 **A:** 1/20-mm Oerlikon AA
Electron Equipt: Radar: 1/Terma Scanter 009 nav.
M: 1 diesel; 1 prop; 460 bhp **Crew:** 9 tot.

WARFARE SHIPS *(continued)*

ks: The hull of M 33 is made of glass-reinforced plastic; she was intended to s the prototype for a new class of 300-ton, 43-meter coastal minesweepers that t built. The other two are built of wood. The 20-mm AA gun has replaced the 60-cal. originally carried.

illöga-class inshore minesweepers Bldr: . . . (In serv. 1964)

ILLÖGA (GIL) M 48 RÖDLÖGA (RÖD) M 49 SVARTLÖGA (SVA)

10 tons (135 fl) **S:** 9 kts **Dim:** 22.0 × 6.5 × 1.4
/20-mm Oerlikon AA
tron Equipt: Radar: 1/Terma Scanter 009 nav.
1 diesel; 1 prop; 380 bhp **Crew:** 10–12 tot.

ks: Wooden-hulled trawler type, similar to *Hisingen* class, but with bluffer es forward and a higher pilothouse. Have had similar modifications.

isingen-class inshore minesweepers Bldr: . . . (In serv. 1960)

HISINGEN (HIS) M 45 DÄMMAN (DÄM)
BLACKAN (BLA) M 46 GALTEN (. . .)

an (M 45, Däm) Leo Van Ginderen, 8-87

30 tons (150 fl) **S:** 9 kts **Dim:** 24.0 × 6.5 × 1.4
/20-mm Oerlikon AA
tron Equipt: Radar: 1/Terma Scanter 009 nav.
1 diesel; 1 prop; 380 bhp **Crew:** 10–12 tot.

ks: Wooden-hulled fishing boats. A 20-mm AA has replaced the original 60-cal. AA in all. All received new deckhouse amidships in 1987.

15-class inshore minesweepers (All L: 1941)

M 22 M24 M25

Gilbert Gyssels, 9-85

70 tons (93 fl) **S:** 12–13 kts **Dim:** 27.7 × 5.05 × 1.4 (2.0 props)
1/20-mm Oerlikon AA
diesels; 1 prop; 320–430 hp **Crew:** 10 tot.

ks: Wooden hulls. M 21, M 22, M 25 are used as tenders for mine-clearance The gun is not normally mounted. No radar. Sisters M 15 and M 16 were n during 1984, as were *Lommen* (A 231, ex-M 17) and *Spoven* (A 232, ex-M 18); nd M 26 stricken in 1989.

nine-clearance divers' support craft Bldr: . . .

SKREDSVIK (ex-. . . . . .)

ks: Characteristics not available. Leased from the Swedish Coast Guard.

◆ **1 mine-countermeasures support ship** Bldr: Drypool Group, Ltd., Cochrane SY, Selby, Scotland (In serv. 1973)

A 261 ÜTO (ex-*Smit Manila*, ex-*Seaford*, ex-*Seaford Challenger*)

Üto (A 261) Leo Van Ginderen, 6-89

D: 1,800 tons (fl) **S:** 14 kts
Dim: 55.91 (49.00 pp) × 12.27 (11.80 wl) × 4.57
A: 2/20-mm Oerlikon AA (I × 2)
Electron Equipt: Radar: 2/. . . nav.
M: 2 Mirrlees Blackstone EZ SL 16M diesels; 2 CP props; 5,000 bhp
Electric: 600 kw (3 × 200-kw diesel sets)
Crew: 35 officers, 30 enlisted (including mine-warfare staff)

Remarks: Former 791-grt/1,040-dwt oilfield support tug/salvage and diving tender converted as a mine-countermeasures craft tender and command ship for mine-countermeasures operations by Pan-United Shipyard, Singapore; commissioned 4-89. Has one 30-ton crane.

AUXILIARIES

◆ **1 intelligence collection ship** Bldr: Karlskronavarvet

	Symbol	Laid down	L	In serv.
A 201 ORION	ORI	23-4-82	30-11-83	7-6-84

Orion (A 201, Ori) Hans J. Vanhöfen, 1991

D: 1,400 tons (fl) **S:** 15 kts **Dim:** 61.3 × 11.0 × 4.2 **A:** none
Electron Equipt:
Radar: 1/Terma Scanter 009 nav., 1/Raytheon . . . nav.—EW: . . .
M: 2 Hedemora V8A/135 diesels; 1 CP prop; 1,840 bhp
Crew: 35 tot.

Remarks: Ordered 25-6-81. Expected to last 30 years. Signal collection antennas beneath a large glass-reinforced plastic radome atop full length of the superstructure. In collision with Soviet minesweeper, 26-10-85. Has MARISAT SATCOMM antenna atop after lattice mast, helicopter platform at stern.

◆ **1 roll-on/roll-off cargo ship** Bldr: Lindenau Werft, Kiel (In serv. . . .)

A . . . . (ex-*Feederchief*, ex-*Modo Gorthon*)

D: approx. 6,500 tons (fl) **S:** 13.5 kts
Dim: 118.17 (110.78 pp) × 15.40 × 4.95
A: . . . **Electron Equipt:** Radar: . . .
M: 1 MaK 12-M453C diesel; 1 prop; 3,960 bhp
Range: 6,000/13.5 **Fuel:** 276 tons **Crew:** . . .

Remarks: 1,813 grt. Purchased 12-91, purpose unreported. Former ramped vehicle cargo vessel intended for Baltic service.

◆ **1 coastal tanker** Bldr: D. W. Kremer Sohn, Elmshorn, West Germany

	Symbol	In serv.
A 228 BRANNAREN (ex-*Indio*)	BRA	1965

AUXILIARIES *(continued)*

Brannaren (A 228, Bra) Royal Swedish Navy, 1972

D: 655 tons (857 fl) **S:** 11 kts
Dim: 61.71 (56.76 pp) × 8.6 × 3.57 **A:** none
Electron Equipt: Radar: 1/Terma Scanter 009 nav.
M: 1 MAK 6 Mu 51 diesel; 1 prop; 800 bhp **Crew:** . . . tot.

Remarks: Eight cargo tanks totaling 1,170 m^3. Purchased in 1972.

◆ **1 submarine rescue and salvage ship** Bldr: Karlskronavarvet

	Symbol	L	In serv.
A 211 Belos	Bel	15-11-61	29-5-63

Belos (A 211, Bel) Peter Voss, 8-90

D: 965 tons (1,000 fl) **S:** 13 kts **Dim:** 62.3 (58.0 pp) × 11.2 × 4.0
Electron Equipt: Radar: 2/. . . nav.
M: 2 Mercedes-Benz MB 820b diesels; 2 props; 1,200 bhp
Crew: . . . tot.

Remarks: Well-equipped for underwater search: decompression chamber, active rudder, underwater television, and a small helicopter deck. Modernized in 1979–80 to support the URF submarine-rescue submersible. Has rescue bell to starboard, divers' stage/observation platform to port. Also acts as tender to the Mala-class swimmer delivery craft *Stor Klas.*

SERVICE CRAFT

◆ **4 Ejdern-class sonobuoy monitoring boats** Bldr: Djupviks Varvet, Tjörn

B 01 Ejdern (In serv. 23-4-91)
B 02 Krickan (In serv. 1991)
B 03 Svartan (In serv. 1991)
B 04 Viggen (In serv. 1991)

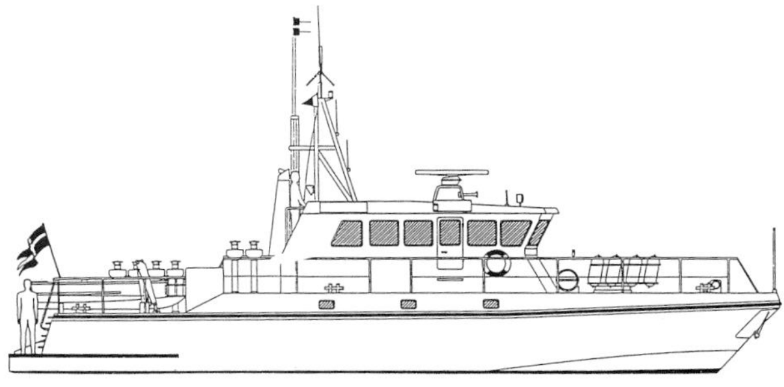
Ejdern class Djupviks, 1991

D: 34 tons (fl) **S:** 15 kts **Dim:** 19.00 (17.40 pp) × 4.98 × 1.00
A: 1/20-mm Oerlikon AA **Electron Equipt:** Radar: 1/. . . nav.
M: 2 Volvo Penta TAMD-122A diesels; 2 props; 800 bhp
Crew: 3 officers, 7 enlisted

Remarks: Aluminum construction. Equipped to deploy six recoverable hydrop[hones] for use in detecting intruders in Swedish waters. Have G.E.C. AQS-928 son[ar] acoustic data processors. Gun not normally mounted.

◆ **1 harbor tanker** Bldr: Asiverken, Åmål (In serv. 4-59)

A 229 Eldaren (ex-*Brotank*)

D: 231 grt/320 dwt **S:** 8 kts **Dim:** 37.22 (34.14 pp) × 6.53 × 2.9
M: 2 Volvo Penta 6-cyl. diesels; 1 CP prop; 420 bhp **Crew:** . . . t[ot.]

Remarks: Purchased 5-81 from commercial service.

◆ **1 small water tanker** (L: 1959)

A 217 Fryken (Fry)

D: 307 tons **S:** 10 kts **Dim:** 34.4 (32.0 pp) × 6.1 × 2.9
M: 1 diesel; 1 prop; 370 bhp **Crew:** . . . tot.

Remarks: Sister *Merlanda* (A 313) stricken 1991.

◆ **1 torpedo- and missile-recovery craft** Bldr: Lundervarv-Ooverkstads AB, Kramfors

	Symbol	L	In serv.
A 248 Pingvinen	Pin	26-9-73	3-75

Pingvinen (A 248, Pin) Leo Van Ginderen,

D: 191 tons **S:** 13 kts **Dim:** 33.0 × 6.1 × 1.8
Electron Equipt: Radar: 1/Terma Scanter 009 nav.
M: 2 MTU 12V493 diesels; 2 props; 1,040 bhp **Crew:** . . . tot.

◆ **1 torpedo- and missile-recovery craft** (L: 9-63)

A 247 Pelikanen (Pel)

Pelikanen (A 247, Pel) Gilbert Gyssels

D: 130 tons **S:** 15 kts **Dim:** 33.0 × 5.8 × 1.8
Electron Equipt: Radar: 1/Terma Scanter 009 nav.
M: 2 MTU 12V493 diesels; 2 props; 1,040 bhp **Crew:** . . . tot.

◆ **1 torpedo-recovery craft** (L: 1951)

A 246 Hägern (Häg)

ICE CRAFT *(continued)*

n (A 246, Häg) Gilbert Gyssels, 8-90

0 tons **S:** 10 kts **Dim:** 29.0 × 5.4 × 1.6
tron Equipt: Radar: 1/Terma Scanter 009 nav.
2 diesels; 2 props; 480 bhp **Crew:** . . . tot.

ials craft (In serv. 1970)

URD (ex-*Capella*)

3 tons (90 fl) **S:** 8 kts **Dim:** 27.0 × 5.6 × 2.8
2 diesels; 200 bhp

mmunition lighters

ATB 1 A 342 ATB 2

(A 341) John Jedrlinic, 6-88

240 tons (fl) **S:** 10 kts **Dim:** 30.4 × 6.0 × 2.0
mines **Electron Equipt:** Radar: 1/Terma Scanter 009 nav.
1 diesel; 1 prop; . . . bhp **Crew:** 4 tot.

ks: 70 grt. Cargo capacity: 100 tons.

nine transport lighter (L: 1940)

MINÖREN (MÖN)

170 tons (fl) **S:** 9 kts **Dim:** 31.8 × 6.2 × 2.2
2 diesels; 1 prop; 240 bhp

ks: Mahogany hull; can also lay mines. Sister *Fällaren* (A 236) stricken 91.

aundry ship (L: 1961)

SIGRUN

n (A 256) Royal Swedish Navy, 1974

D: 250 tons **S:** 11 kts **Dim:** 32.0 × 6.8 × 3.6
M: 1 diesel; 1 prop; 320 bhp

Remarks: Probably the world's only camouflaged self-propelled floating laundry.

◆ **1 M 15-class general-purpose tender** (L: 1941)

A 242 SKULD (ex-M 20)

Skuld (A 242) Maritime Photographic, 6-92

D: 70 tons (fl) **S:** 13 kts **Dim:** 26.0 × 5.0 × 1.4
M: 2 diesels; 2 props; 410 bhp

Remarks: Wooden-hulled former minesweeper used for mine-warfare trials; new deckhouse added abaft original pilothouse. Sisters *Lommen* (A 231, ex-M 17) and *Spoven* (A 232, ex-M 18) stricken 1984. Four others still serve in a mine-countermeasures role.

◆ **2 sail-training schooners** Bldr: Naval Dockyard, Stockholm (L: 1947, 1948)

S 01 GLADAN (GAD) S 02 FALKEN (FAK)

D: 220 tons **S:** . . . kts **Dim:** 42.5 (28.3 pp) × 7.27 × 4.2
M: 1 diesel auxiliary; 1 prop; 50 bhp; sail area: 512 m^2

Falken (S 02, Fak) Maritime Photographic, 7-90

◆ **4 naval reserve training craft** (In serv. 1954–60)

SVK 1 SVÄRDET (ex-Tv 228) SVK 3 PILEN (ex-Tv 230)
SVK 2 SPJUTET (ex-Tv 226) SVK 4 BÅGEN (ex-Tv 234)

D: 12 tons **S:** 20 kts **Dim:** 14.0 × 3.4 × 1.2
A: 1/20-mm AA **M:** 1 Volvo Penta diesel; 1 prop; . . . bhp

Pilen (SVK 3) Hartmut Ehlers, 5-90

SERVICE CRAFT *(continued)*

Remarks: Acquired from Swedish Coast Guard in 1983. Wooden construction. Gun not normally mounted. SVK 14 is slightly larger: 15.2 × 3.6 × 1.2.

◆ **3 diving tenders** Bldr: Storebro Bruks AB (In serv. 1980)

D: 7 tons (fl) **S:** 24 kts **Dim:** 10.35 × 3.30 × 1.0
Electron Equipt: Radar: 1/Decca 091 nav.
M: 2 Volvo Penta TAMD 60C diesels; 2 props; 370 bhp

Remarks: Fold-down door at stern. 1.7-ton useful load.

◆ **2 range safety boats** Bldr: Storebro Bruks AB (In serv. 1980)

Remarks: Data as for diving-tender version above.

◆ **3 personnel launches** Bldr: Storebro Bruks AB (In serv. 1980)

1290 1300 1310

Personnel launch 1300 Gilbert Gyssels, 8-90

D: 5.5 tons (fl) **S:** 24 kts **Dim:** 9.30 × 3.30 × 1.0
M: 2 Volvo Penta TAMD 60C diesels; 2 props; 370 bhp

Remarks: Builder's Type 31 design; glass-reinforced plastic construction. Can carry 25 personnel or 6 stretchers. Can reach 27 kts in light condition.

TUGS

◆ **2 Herkules-class icebreaking tugs** Bldr: Åsiverken, Åmål

A 323 Herkules (L: 1969) A 324 Hera (L: 1971)

D: 127 tons **S:** 11.5 kts **Dim:** 21.4 × 6.9 × 3.7
M: diesels; 615 bhp

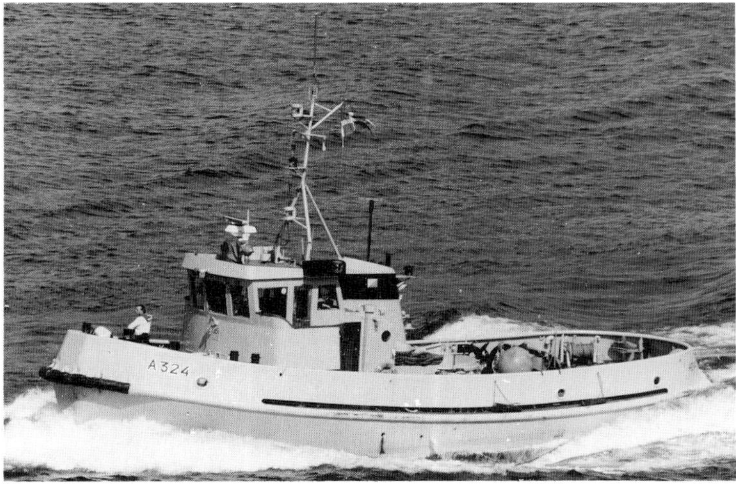

Hera (A 324) Gilbert Gyssels, 8-90

◆ **2 Achilles-class icebreaking tugs** Bldr: Åsiverken, Åmål

A 251 Achilles (L: 1962) A 252 Ajax (L: 1963)

D: 450 tons **S:** 12 kts **Dim:** 35.5 (33.15 pp) × 9.5 × 3.9
Electron Equipt: Radar: 1 or 2/Decca 1226C nav.
M: diesels; 1,650 bhp

◆ **2 Hermes-class icebreaking tugs** (L: 1953–57)

A 253 Hermes (Hem) A 322 Heros (Her)

D: 185 tons **S:** 11 kts **Dim:** 24.5 (23.0 pp) × 6.8 × 3.6
M: diesel; 600 bhp

Remarks: Sister *Hector* (A 321) stricken 1991.

Achilles (A 251, Als) Hartmut Ehlers,

◆ **6 small harbor tugs/tenders** Bldr: Lundevarv (In serv. 1978–79)

A 751–756

D: 42 tons (fl) **S:** 9.5 kts **Dim:** 15.5 × 5.0 × 2.7 **M:** 1 diesel

Björkö (A 754) Leo Van Ginderen,

Remarks: Can break thin ice. Carry 40 passengers. Sisters 701–705 are used Coast Artillery; see photo on later page. 754 named *Björkö*; others may now als names.

◆ **3 miscellaneous small tugs**

	Symbol	In serv.	D (fl)	Kts.
A 326 Hebe	. . .	1969	34	9 (210 bhp)
A 327 Passop	Pas	1957	25	9
A 330 Atlas	Atl	1975	35	9

MINISTRY OF TRANSPORT

ICEBREAKERS

Note: All Swedish icebreakers are owned by the Ministry of Transport, b manned and administered by the Swedish Navy. In 1984, it was decided to p nently arm all seagoing icebreakers.

◆ **1 (+1) Oden class** Bldr: Götaverken, Arendel

	Laid down	L	In serv.
Oden	19-10-87	5-8-88	29-1-89

Oden Royal Swedish Navy,

REAKERS *(continued)*

0,300 tons (12,900 fl) **S:** 17 kts free (3 kt through 1.8-m ice)
: 107.70 (93.20 pp) × 31.00 max. (29.40 over "reamers"; 25.00 wl) × 7.00 (8.50 max.)
rovision for 4/40-mm Bofors AA (I × 4)—mines
tron Equipt: Radar: 2/. . . nav.
4 Cegielski-Sulzer 8ZAL-40S diesels, geared drive; 2 shrouded props; 24,480 bhp—bow- and stern-thrusters
tric: 4,800 kw (4 NEBB 1,200-kw alternators, Sulzer AT-25H diesels, 1,750 bhp each, driving)
ge: 30,000/13 **Fuel:** 3,380 m^3 heavy oil, 990 m^3 diesel
w: 28 tot. + 21 spare berths

ks: *Oden* ordered 1-87. 3,850 dwt. Unique hull form, designed by Canadian Drilling Co., is nearly rectangular in plan form and has a barge-like bow.)-ton towing winch, 10-ton crane, and 390 m^2 helicopter deck aft. Carry up to ^{3} ballast water and have a heeling pump system, hull wash, and jet-mister to ı ice conditions. Can be equipped as a minelayer. Will be available for Arctic-commercial charter in summer. A second unit, to be named *Thule,* is planned not yet been funded.

innish Urho class Bldr: Wärtsilä, Helsinki, Finland

Laid down	L	In serv.
10-5-73	27-11-73	21-10-74
. . .	3-6-74	30-9-75
12-2-76	3-9-76	26-10-77

-with guns mounted Leo Van Ginderen, 1-90

',900 tons (9,500 fl) **S:** 19 kts
: 104.6 (99.0 pp) × 23.8 × 7.8
/40-mm AA (I × 4)—3 mine rails
liesel-electric drive: 5 Wärtsilä-Pielstick 5,000-bhp diesels, 4 Strömberg electric motors; 4 props; 22,000 shp
w: 16 officers, 38 enlisted

ks: Two props forward, two aft. Helicopter platform. All personnel live and y work above the main deck. Given permanent gun armament, mine rails, and ilities for two helicopters: *Frej* in 10-83, others in 1984. Guns mounted atop and forward of pilothouse.

le class Bldr: Wärtsilä, Helsinki, Finland

L	In serv.
1-6-73	12-12-73

Leo Van Ginderen, 1989

D: 1,550 tons (fl) **S:** 14 kts **Dim:** 46.0 × 13.0 × 5.0
A: 1/40-mm 70-cal. Bofors L 70 AA (not normally aboard)
M: 2 diesels, electric drive; 2 props; 4,750 shp
Crew: 8 officers, 24 enlisted

Remarks: Built for service on Lake Vänern in central Sweden, also used for hydrographic survey in summer.

♦ **1 modified Tor class** Bldr: Wärtsilä, Helsinki, Finland

	L	In serv.
NJORD	2-10-68	10-69

Njord—with guns mounted and 50 mines aboard Mike Louagie, 9-86

D: 5,150 tons (5,686 fl) **S:** 18 kts
Dim: 86.45 (79.45 pp) × 21.18 × 6.9
A: 3/40-mm 70-cal. Bofors L 70 AA (I × 3)—mines
M: diesel-electric propulsion: 4 Sulzer 9MH-51 diesels; Strömberg electric motors, 2 fwd (3,400 kw each), 2 aft (2,200 kw each); 4 props; 13,620 shp

Remarks: Three lead-computing directors installed for the 40-mm AA guns.

♦ **1 Tor class** Bldr: Wärtsilä, Turku, Finland

	L	In serv.
TOR	25-5-63	31-1-64

Tor Wärtsilä

D: 4,980 tons (5,290 fl) **S:** 18 kts **Dim:** 84.4 × 20.42 × 6.2
A: 3/40-mm 70-cal. Bofors L 70 AA (I × 3)
M: diesel-electric propulsion: 4 Sulzer 9MH-51 diesels, 4 Strömberg electric motors; 4 props; 11,200 shp.

Remarks: The Finnish *Tarmo* is similar. Two propellers fwd, two aft.

♦ **1 harbor icebreaker/navigational aids tender** Bldr: Åsiverken AB, Åmål

BALTICA (In serv. 1982)

D: 1,238 tons (fl) **S:** 15 kts **Dim:** 54.9 (50.0 pp) × 12.0 × 3.7 (mean)
Electron Equipt: Radar: 1/Decca "Arpa," 1/Decca "Clearscan"
M: 2 Hedemora V16A/12 diesels; 1 CP prop; 3,520 bhp
Electric: 1,375 kVA **Fuel:** 140 tons **Crew:** 12 tot.

Remarks: 857 grt/252 nrt. Two 300-hp tunnel side-thrusters. Twelve-ton electrohydraulic crane serving combination buoy hold/workshop. Can tow at 50-ton bollard pull. Capable of operating in light ice conditions. Civilian-manned.

HYDROGRAPHIC SHIPS

Note: Swedish hydrographic ships are operated by the Navy, but are owned by the Ministry of Transport. The icebreaker *Ale* also performs survey tasks.

♦ **1 catamaran-hulled survey ship** Bldr: Oskarshamns SY (In serv. 28-6-85)

NILS STRÖMKRONA (NSA)

D: 175 tons **S:** 12 kts **Dim:** 29.0 × 10.0 × 1.6
M: 4 Saab-Scania diesels; 2 props; 1,732 bhp
Crew: 5 officers, 9 enlisted

Remarks: Built to replace 1894-vintage unit with the same name. Each aluminum-construction hull has 3.9-m beam.

HYDROGRAPHIC SHIPS *(continued)*

◆ **1 seagoing survey ship** Bldr: Falkenbergs Varvet

	Symbol	Laid down	L	In serv.
JOHAN NORDENANKAR	JNO	1977	1-11-79	1-7-80

D: 2,000 tons (fl) **S:** 15 kts **Dim:** 73.0 (64.0 pp) × 14.0 × 3.8
Electron Equipt: Radar: 1/Raytheon Raycas, 1/Decca . . .
M: 2 Hedemora V16A/12 diesels; 2 KaMeWa CP props; 3,520 bhp
Electric: 2,246 kVA **Crew:** 14 officers, 50 enlisted

Remarks: Acts as mother ship for eight small survey craft that act in teams. Data collected by the launches are telemetered to the ship and collected via the Krupp-Atlas computer. There are three sets of davits per side, with three additional boats in an internal hangar. Ship very maneuverable, with 700-hp drop-down bow-thruster, which can also drive the ship at 4.5 kts, and a Becker KSV flap-rudder; turning radius 150 m. Navigation equipment includes Decca Navigator, Magnavox NAVSAT receiver, Decca Sea Fix, Syledis Ranger, Syledis Miniranger, and eight echo-sounders. Passive tank stabilization. Helo platform aft. Hull red, superstructure white.

◆ **1 coastal survey boat** Bldr: Djupviks, Rönnäng (In serv. 10-82)

JACOB HÄGG (JHÄ)

D: 130 tons (fl) **S:** 16.5 kts **Dim:** 36.50 × 7.50 × 1.65
M: 4 Saab-Scania DSI-14 diesels; 2 props; 1,684 bhp (1,300 sust.)

Remarks: Aluminum construction. The same builder also delivered a 42-ton, 400-hp hydrographic survey launch in 1983. The former "lead boats" No. 1 and No. 94 were named *Sirius* and *Kompass* in 1982, respectively, and now operate independently.

Note: Coastal survey boat *Anders Bure* discarded by 1991. Also operated by the Ministry of Transport are the lightships *Fyrbjorn* and *Fyrbyggaren,* the geological research ship *Altair,* and the oceanographic research ship *Argos.* The polar support ship *Stena Arctica* (ex-*Columbialand*) has on occasion been chartered for arctic research.

Argos Leo Van Ginderen, 4-90

COASTAL ARTILLERY SERVICE

The Coastal Artillery Service has 3,900 active personnel (2,800 conscripts) and 3,000 reservists. In addition to the craft described below, it operates 75-mm, 120-mm, and 152-mm coast-defense artillery, 40-mm AA guns, 120-mm mortars, and Carl Gustav anti-armor missiles. The *Kustartilleriet* is receiving 120-mm Bofors Karin mobile artillery, RBS-15, and RBS-17 antiship missiles. Organized into five regiments and subordinated to the Navy, the Coast Artillery also has a 265-man ranger battalion. A major expansion and reorganization into six amphibious coastal-defense squadrons, each with 800 personnel, was canceled 2-91.

PATROL CRAFT

◆ **0 (+ 4) Bevakningsbåt 2000 class** Bldr: Djupviks Varv, Tjörn (In serv. 1992–93)

D: 45 tons (51 fl) **S:** 28 kts **Dim:** 21.85 (19.73 pp) × 5.40 × 1.05
A: 2/12.7-mm mg (I × 2) **Electron Equipt:** Radar: 1/. . . nav.
M: 2 MWM TBD 234 V16 diesels; 2 waterjets; 2,100 bhp **Crew:** 4 tot

Remarks: Ordered 1991 to begin replacement of the Type 72 class. Design based on same builder's Kbv 290 for the Swedish Coast Guard. Aluminum alloy construction.

◆ **17 Type 72 class**

61 to 77

Eggskar—Type 72 class Leo Van Ginderen, 1-91

D: 28 tons (30 fl) **S:** 19 kts **Dim:** 21.1 × 4.6 × 1.3
A: 1/20-mm Oerlikon AA—8/depth charges—mines
Electron Equipt: Radar: 1/Decca RM914C nav.
M: 3 diesels; 3 props; . . . bhp

Remarks: Built in two series, nos. 61 to 70 in 1960–61 and nos. 71 to 77 in 1... the second group can achieve 22 kts on their more powerful engines. Known na... correlated to hull numbers) are *Eggskar* and *Skifteskar*; the others are prob... named.

MINELAYERS

◆ **1 MUL 20 class** Bldr: Åsiverken, Åmål

	Symbol	L	In serv.
MUL 20 FURUSUND	FUR	16-12-82	10-10-83

Furusund (MUL 20, Fur) Royal Swedish Na...

D: 225 tons (245 fl) **S:** 11 kts **Dim:** 32.4 (30.0 pp) × 8.4 × 1.8
A: 1/20-mm Oerlikon AA—2/7.62-mm mg (I × 2)—24 tons mine...
Electron Equipt: Radar: 1/Decca RM 1226C nav.
M: 2 Saab-Scania GASI-14 diesels (335 bhp each), ASEA 300 kV... electric drive; 2 props; 420 shp + 1/125-hp maneuvering pro...
Electric: 73 kw **Crew:** 24 tot. (10 peacetime)

Remarks: Ordered 23-6-81. An ultimate total of ten was planned, but the... went bankrupt after only the one was completed, and no more were ordered.

◆ **8 MUL 12-class mine planters** (In serv. 1952–56)

MUL 12 ARKOSUND (ARK)	MUL 16 FÄRÖSUND (FÄR)
MUL 13 KALMARSUND (KSD)	MUL 17 SKRAMSÖSUND (SMD)
MUL 14 ALNÖSUND (ALN)	MUL 18 ÖRESUND (ÖSD)
MUL 15 GRUNDSUND (GRU)	MUL 19 BÅRÖSUND (BÅR)

Öresund (MUL 18, Ösd) Hartmut Ehl...

D: 200 tons (245 fl) **S:** 10.5 kts **Dim:** 31.18 (29.0 pp) × 7.62 ×...
A: 1/40-mm 60-cal. Bofors L 60 AA—26 tons mines
Electron Equipt: Radar: 1/Decca RM 1226C nav.
M: 2 Nohab or Saab-Scania diesels; 2 props; 460 bhp

Remarks: These craft are used for placing and maintaining controlled mi... Given names 1985–86.

◆ **1 coastal mine planter** (L: 1946)

MUL 11 KALVSUND (KVD)

D: 200 tons (fl) **S:** 10 kts **Dim:** 30.1 (27.0 pp) × 7.21 × 3.65
A: 2/20-mm (I × 2)—21 tons mines
M: 2 Atlas diesels; 1 prop; 300 bhp

:LAYERS *(continued)*

ɜund (MUL 11, Kvd) Leo Van Ginderen, 11-91

ıe-class former utility landing craft (L: 1944)

r (ex-*Balder,* 325)(Fro)

135 tons **S:** 8.5 kts **Dim:** 28.0 × 8.0 × 1.8
1/20-mm Oerlikon AA—1/7.62-mm mg—. . . mines
2 diesels

rks: Retyped circa 1990 and renamed. Three sisters remain typed as utility
g craft (see below).

501-class minelaying launches (L: 1969–71)

ırough 542

15 tons (fl) **S:** 14 kts **Dim:** 14.6 × 4.2 × 0.9 **A:** 12 mines
ctron Equipt: Radar: 1/Decca RM 914C nav.
2 diesels; 2 props; . . . bhp **Crew:** 7 tot.

Leo Van Ginderen, 9-90

small minelaying craft Bldr: Marinvarvet, Fårösund

-1881 (In serv. 4-7-83) 1882–1884 (In serv. 23-1-84)

rks: Displace 2.5 tons; waterjet-powered: 20 kts. Ordered 27-11-82.

The 80 201-series personnel landing craft can also be fitted to lay mines.

DING CRAFT

Grim-class utility landing craft Bldr: Åsiverken, Åmål

Grim Heimdal

Hartmut Ehlers, 5-90

D: 340 tons (fl) **S:** 12 kts **Dim:** 36.0 × 8.5 × 2.6
A: 2/20-mm Oerlikon AA (I × 2)
Electron Equipt: Radar: 1/. . . nav.
M: 2 diesels; 2 props; 800 bhp **Crew:** . . . tot + 325 troops

Remarks: *Grim* was launched in 1962, *Bore* and *Heimdal* in 1967. Car ferry design: bow hinges upward to permit extending ramp. Can be adapted to lay mines, and two 20-mm AA can be installed.

◆ **2 Sleipner-class utility landing craft** (In serv. 1959–60)

A 333 Skagul (Ska) A 335 Sleipner (Sle)

D: 275 tons (335 fl) **S:** 10 kts **Dim:** 35.0 × 8.5 × 2.9
A: none **M:** 2 diesels; 2 props; 640 bhp

Remarks: Ferry-type, similar to the *Grim* class. Can be adapted to lay up to 100 tons of mines. Now considered to be auxiliaries and normally used as ferries.

◆ **3 Ane-class utility landing craft** (L: 1943–45)

A 324 Ane A 326 Loke A 327 Ring

Loke (A 326) Leo Van Ginderen, 7-87

D: 135 tons **S:** 8.5 kts **Dim:** 28.0 × 8.0 × 1.8
A: 1/20-mm Oerlikon AA—1/7.62-mm mg **M:** 2 diesels

Remarks: Equipped with bow and stern ramps. Can be adapted to lay mines. Now considered to be auxiliaries and normally used as ferries. Sister *Balder* (325) renamed *Frost* and reclassified as a minelayer.

◆ **1 (+ 13) Trossbåt-class vehicle/personnel landing craft** (In serv. 1-91)

D: 45 tons (fl) **S:** 15 kts loaded **Dim:** 23.00 × 5.40 × 1.10 light
A: 1/12.7-mm mg—mines (on portable rails)
M: 2 Saab-Scania 8V DSI-14 diesels; 2 Alumina waterjets; 340 bhp
Crew: 3 tot. + 17 troops

Remarks: With funding reductions, planned additional units may not be built. Cargo: 15 tons on 14.0 × 4.5-m deck area or 2 m^3 water and 9 tons cargo or 8 m^3 diesel fuel or 7 m^3 and no deck cargo. Has folding bow ramp and a small crane. Considered to be capable of operating in light ice. *Trossbåt* means "Support Boat."

◆ **1 99-class landing craft** Bldr: Wico Oy, Helsinki (In serv. 6-87)

99

D: 20 tons (35 fl) **S:** 23.5 kts light/18 with 5 tons cargo
Dim: 21.80 × 5.00 × . . . **Crew:** . . .
M: 2 Saab-Scania DSI 14 diesels; 2 props; 970 bhp

Remarks: Foam sandwich GRP construction. Cargo: 5 tons deck cargo, 4,000 liters fresh water and 2,000 liters diesel fuel in double bottom. Six-ton electrohydraulic crane, bow ramp. Was not selected for further production.

◆ **0 (+ 63 + 105) Stridsbåt-90H-class fast personnel landing craft** Bldrs: 815–846: Dockstavarvet, Docksta; 847–877: Gotlands Varv (In serv. 1-93–5-96)

815—877

D: 13.2 tons light (18 fl) **S:** 30+ kts
Dim: 14.90 (13.00 wl) × 3.80 × 0.80
A: 1/30-mm fixed Aden gun—1/12.7-mm mg—1/7.62-mm mg—provision for: RBS-17 Hellfire SSM, 1/81-mm mortar, 4 mines, or 6 depth charges
Electron Equipt: Radar: 1/Decca RD360 nav.
M: 2 Saab-Scania 8V DSI-14 diesels; 2 FF Jet FF 450 waterjets; 1,256 bhp
Range: . . ./. . . **Crew:** 3 tot. + 21 troops

Remarks: Production order placed 23-1-92, with work to be shared by the two yards above (Gotland Varvet is a subsidiary of Djupviks). Option for 105 more in contract. Will deliver at five-week intervals. Like prototype series, are of aluminum construction. The 30-mm Aden gun is now mounted to starboard of the disembarkation ramp, co-mounted with a 7.62-mm mg for aiming (the 12.7-mm mg is mounted on a training ring atop the troop compartment). These craft will replace the 300-series personnel landing craft.

LANDING CRAFT *(continued)*

♦ **7 (+ 7) Stridsbåt-90H class** Bldr: Dockstavarvet, Docksta

	In serv.		In serv.
801 HELGE	4-10-89	808	1992
802 HELGA	14-12-89	809	1992
803	21-5-91	810	1992
804	21-5-91	811	1992
805	22-8-91	812	1992
806	16-10-91	813	1992
807	10-12-91	814	1992

Helge (801) Dockstavarvet, 1991

803 Maritime Photographic, 6-92

D: 13.2 tons (18 fl) **S:** 35 or 40 kts **Dim:** 16.50 × 4.50 × 0.82
A: 1/30-mm fixed Aden gun—1/12.7-mm mg—4 mines or 6 depth charges—provision for RBS-17 Hellfire SSM or 81-mm mortar
Electron Equipt: Radar: 1/Decca 110 (802: Furuno 800) nav.
M: *Helge:* 2 Saab-Scania 8V DSI-14 diesels; 2 waterjets; 1,080 bhp *Helga* and 803–814: 2 Saab-Scania 8V DSI-14 diesels; 2 waterjets; 1,256 bhp
Range: . . ./. . . **Crew:** 3 crew + up to 20 troops

Remarks: First two were pre-production prototypes, based on DVA.115 below. Aluminum construction. 14-m^3 troop compartment (with disembarkation ramp). 801's hull has 20° deadrise to Vee-bottom; 802 has 26° deadrise. 803 through 814 ordered 21-6-90, based on 801 hull form and 802 propulsion plant; they have Decca RD 360 radars. Work on 803–814 began 10-12-90.

♦ **1 DVA.115-class raiding craft** Bldr: Djupviks, Tjörn/Rönnäng

344 (L: 1-7-86; in serv. 1-11-86)

D: . . . **S:** 40 kts (35.4 sust.) **Dim:** 11.64 × 3.80 × 0.63
A: 1/30-mm Aden gun—1/81-mm mortar—1/12.7-mm mg—4 mines or 6 d.c.
Electron Equipt: Radar: 1/. . . nav.
M: 2 Volvo Penta TAMD 71 outdrive diesels; 2 props; 700 bhp
Range: 180/35.4 **Crew:** 3 tot. + 7 to 9 troops

Remarks: GRP construction. Ordered 1-4-86. Also referred to as Stridsbåt 90M class by builder. Has bow ramp atop Vee-form hull. Payload: 3 tons. Trials with Aden gun fixed forward in troop compartment, 1988, and the craft can also carry an RBS-17 missile aft.

♦ **1 M 85-class large personnel landing craft** Bldr: Marinvarvet, Fårösund

81 TJELVAR 7 (In serv. 31-7-85)

D: 55 tons (65 fl) **S:** 20 kts **Dim:** 28.40 (24.00 pp) × 5.60 × 0.80
A: 2 or 3/7.62-mm mg (I × 2 or 3)—mines
Electron Equipt: Radar: 1/. . . nav. **Crew:** 4 tot. + 45 troops
M: 3 Saab-Scania DSI-14 diesels; 3 waterjets; 1,350 bhp

Remarks: Enclosed troop compartment, ramps on either side of bow. Aluminum prototype replacement design for 201 series. Ordered 27-7-84; laid down 5-12-84. As many as 140 were to have been built, but the design was unsuccessful.

♦ **19 vehicle landing craft** Bldrs: Djupviks, Tjörn; Oskarhamms; Marinvarvet, Fårösund (In serv. 1978–87)

601–612, 651–657

D: 20 tons (53 fl) **S:** 8–10 kts **Dim:** 21.0 (20.0 pp) × 7.2 × 0.7
A: none **Electron Equipt:** Radar: 1/Decca RM 914C nav.
M: 2 Saab-Scania DSI-11/40-M20 diesels; 2 Schottel props; 340 bhp
Cargo: 25 tons deck cargo or 30 tons liquid **Crew:** . . .

Remarks: The prototype was delivered in 1978: classified as "support boats" (*Trossbåt*). No. 603 delivered 2-4-84 by Marinvarvet; Nos. 604, 605 delivered 1-10-84 by Djupviks. No. 607 in service 1-9-86; 608 on 22-9-86, 609 on 12-3-87, 610 on 27-4-86; 612, 655–57 delivered 1987. Some carry names.

604 Hartmut Ehlers

♦ **72 201-series large personnel landing craft** Bldrs: Lundevar Verkstads and Marinteknik, Oregrund (In serv. 1957–77)

200, 207, 208, 211–217, 219–226, 228, 230–239, 241–276, 277–284

281 Leo Van Ginderen

D: 31 tons (fl) **S:** 17 kts **Dim:** 21.4 × 4.2 × 1.3
A: 2 or 3/6.5-mm mg (II × 1, I × 1)—mines
Electron Equipt: Radar: 1/Decca RM 914C nav.
M: 3 Saab-Scania 6 DS-11 diesels; 3 props; 705 bhp
Crew: 5 crew, 40 troops

Remarks: 266 through 269 have Volvo Penta diesels. Patrol-boat-like bow c permit extension of ramp from troop compartment below decks. Twin machine port, plus single mount aft in some. Mine rails can be laid from the pilothouse c stern. 210 was re-engined 1984 by Djupviks with two Saab-Scania DSI-14 dies steerable hydraulic drives; 950 hp; pilot program for a class-wide rehabilitation. ning to be retired.

♦ **24 personnel landing craft**

	L	D	S	Horsepower
370	1981	. . . tons	. . . kts	560 hp
337–354	1970–73	6 tons	21 kts	225 hp
332–336	1967	5.4 tons	25 kts	225 hp

352 Gilbert Gyssel

Remarks: The prototype of what was to have been a new series, number 37 delivered 2-9-81; the craft is powered by two Volvo Penta TAMD 70 diesel through 330 stricken 1984, 331 by 1991.

♦ **2 TF.700 raiding craft** Bldr: Task Force Boats, U.K. (In serv. 199C

D: . . . tons **S:** 42 kts **Dim:** 7.00 × 2.30 × . . .
M: 2 Suzuki outboards; 280 bhp **Crew:** 10 commandos

Remarks: With 1,690-kg payload, can make 30 kts; 42 kts reached with 300

♦ **56 outboard-powered canoes**

Remarks: Intended for the amphibious battalion (*Amfibiebatalion*).

ANDING CRAFT *(continued)*

5 support tenders Bldr: Djupviks, Tjörn (In serv. 1982–85)
1–705

Hartmut Ehlers, 4-85

): 42 tons **S:** 9.5 kts **Dim:** 15.5 × 5.0 × 2.7
I: 1 diesel; 1 prop; . . . bhp

narks: Can be used to transport cargo, personnel, to plant mines, or as tugs. warks at bow open to permit debarking personnel over a beach. Several sisters e the Swedish Navy proper.

12 support tenders
–412

narks: Wooden-hulled utility tenders. Number in service not available. Powered single diesel; have a Decca RM914C radar.

Hartmut Ehlers, 5-90

COAST GUARD

onnel (1991): 580 total.
Swedish Coast Guard, organized in 1638, became independent from the Swedish ms Service on 1-7-88. It now is responsible for fisheries regulation, customs , pollution and dumping monitoring and cleanup, other environmental consider-, and merchant traffic regulation. The Coast Guard is organized into four Regions, with a total of 15 Districts; each District has two to four stations. All units now have blue-painted hulls with a yellow diagonal stripe. None are armed.

In addition to some 130 boats and craft, it also operates four CASA C-212-200 Aviocar patrol aircraft with side-looking radar (SLAR), one Cessna 402C, and four BO-105 helicopters.

All boat pendants changed 7-88 from "Tv"—*Tullverket* (Central Customs Office) prefix to "Kbv"—*Kustbevakning* (Coast Guard).

ish Coast Guard CASA C-212-200 CASA, 1991

PATROL BOATS

◆ **1 modified Finnish Tursas class** Bldr: Rauma Oy, Uusikaupunki, Finland

Kbv 181 Gotland (In serv. 30-11-90)

D: 800 tons (fl) **S:** 16 kts **Dim:** 56.00 (49.80 pp) × 10.20 × 4.00
Electron Equipt:
Radar: 2/Decca . . . nav.
Sonar: Simrad Subsea hull-mounted HF searchlight-type
M: 2 Wärtsilä Vasa 8R22 diesels; 2 props; 3,800 bhp—bow-thruster
Electric: 700 kw tot. **Range:** . . ./. . . **Fuel:** 82 m^2 **Crew:** 11 tot.

Remarks: Ordered 10-89 to replace *Nynäshamn* (Kbv 172) as flagship and command vessel for search-and-rescue and oil-spill cleanup operations. Lengthened over the Finnish prototype in order to accommodate a second hold to stow oil-soil cleanup gear. Can be armed with one 20-mm Oerlikon AA. Can make 12 kts through 0.2-m ice.

◆ **2 Kbv 171 class** Bldr: Karlskronavarvet, Karlskrona

	L	In serv.
Kbv 171 Karlskrona	11-79	3-9-80
Kbv 172 Nynäshamn	13-9-80	10-81

Nynäshamn (Kbv 172) Hartmut Ehlers, 4-85

D: 375 tons (fl) **S:** 20 kts **Dim:** 49.90 (46.00 pp) × 8.52 × 2.40
Electron Equipt:
Radar: 2/Decca . . . nav.
Sonar: Simrad Subsea hull-mounted HF searchlight type
M: 2 Hedemora V16A/15 diesels; 2 KaMeWa CP props; 4,480 bhp
Electric: 340 kVA **Range:** 500/20; 3,000/12 **Crew:** 14 tot.

Remarks: Class "A" cutters. Kbv 171 lengthened by 6 m in 1981; Kbv 172 longer as completed. Helicopter platform, bow-thruster. Glass-reinforced plastic sandwich hull construction, originally developed for the not-built M 70-class naval minesweeper. Fire monitor can be replaced by a 40-mm gun, and mine rails can be fitted. Both have Roll-Nix rudder roll-control system. Kbv 172 was replaced in active service by the new *Gotland* (Kbv 180) in 1990 and laid up; she may be transferred to the Swedish Navy.

PATROL CRAFT

◆ **0 (+ 16) Kbv 301 class** Bldr: Djupviks, Tjörn/Rönnäng (In serv. 1993–97)

Kbv 301–316

D: . . . tons (fl) **S:** 38 kts **Dim:** 20.0 × . . . × . . .
Electron Equipt: Radar: 1/. . . nav.
M: 2 MWM TBD-234-V16 diesels; 2 FF-Jet waterjets; 2,120 bhp
Range: . . ./. . . **Crew:** 4 tot.

Remarks: Design evolved from Kbv 290. Aluminum alloy construction.

◆ **1 Kbv 290 class** Bldr: Djupviks, Tjörn/Rönnäng (In serv. 6-12-90)

Kbv 290

D: 45 tons (51 fl) **S:** 28 kts **Dim:** 21.85 (19.73 pp) × 5.40 × 1.05
Electron Equipt: Radar: 1/. . . nav.
M: 2 MWM TBD 234 V16 diesels; 2 props; 2,120 bhp
Range: . . ./. . . **Fuel:** 5,000 liters **Crew:** 4 tot.

Remarks: Aluminum construction. Intended as prototype for new class to replace older patrol craft.

◆ **4 Kbv 103 class** Bldr: Djupviks, Tjörn (In serv. 1972–73)

Kbv 102 Kbv 103 Simrishamn Kbv 104 Kbv 105

D: 53 tons (fl) **S:** 22 kts **Dim:** 26.72 × 5.23 × 1.13
M: 2 MTU 8V331 TC82 diesels; 2 props; 1,866 bhp
Electric: 60 kVA **Range:** 1,000/15 **Fuel:** 11 tons **Crew:** 6 tot.

PATROL CRAFT *(continued)*

Kbv 102 7-90

Remarks: Class "A" cutters. Aluminum construction. Three sisters were built for the Liberian Coast Guard. Kbv 103 and 105 re-engined 1987 with two Cummins KTA 38M diesels.

◆ **1 Kbv 101 class** Bldr: Karlskronavarvet (In serv. 1969)

Kbv 101

D: 50 tons (fl) **S:** 22 kts **Dim:** 24.90 × 5.00 × 1.10
M: 2 MTU 8V331 TC82 diesels; 2 props; 1,866 bhp
Electric: 60 kVA **Range:** 1,000/15 **Fuel:** 11 tons **Crew:** 6 tot.

◆ **8 Kbv 271 class** (In serv. 1974–77) Bldr: 275, 276: Djupviks, Rönnäng; 277–278: Lunde Varv & Verkstads, Ramvik; others: . . .

Kbv 271–Kbv 278

D: 20 tons (fl) **S:** 20 kts **Dim:** 19.2 × 4.0 × 1.3
M: 2 Volvo Penta TAMD 120A diesels; 2 props; 700 bhp
Electric: 46.5 kw **Crew:** 5 tot.

Remarks: Aluminum construction. Kbv 271, 272: 18.7 × 4.0 × 1.4. Class "B" cutters.

Kbv 274 Maritime Photographic, 6-92

◆ **7 Kbv 281 class** Bldr: Djupviks, Tjörn/Rönnäng

Kbv 281 (In serv. 1979)
Kbv 282 (In serv. . . .)
Kbv 283 (In serv. 1979–80)
Kbv 284 (In serv. 30-1-84)
Kbv 285 (In serv. 2-5-84)
Kbv 286 (In serv. 21-8-86)
Kbv 287 (In serv. 12-2-87)

Kbv 286—without flying bridge Hartmut Ehlers, 5-90

D: 37 tons (42 fl) **S:** 30+ kts **Dim:** 21.85 × 5.00 × . . .
Electron Equipt: 2/Decca . . . nav.
M: 2 Cummins KTA 38M diesels; 2 props; 2,100 bhp **Crew:** 5 tot.

Remarks: Class "B" cutters. Aluminum construction. Kbv 286, 287 ordered 1-9-8[illegible] Kbv 286 launched 14-6-86, Kbv 287 on 25-1-87; they lack the flying bridge atop th[illegible] pilothouse of the other five.

◆ **21 Kbv 236-class aluminum-hulled class "D" cutters** (In serv. 1961–72)

Kbv 236–238, Kbv 240–250, Kbv 255–261

D: 17 tons **S:** . . . **Dim:** 16.2 × 3.7 × . . .

Kbv 238—with two radars Hartmut Ehlers, 5-

Remarks: Kbv 250 has an enlarged pilothouse and no open bridge. Kbv 238 has tri mast on forecastle.

◆ **1 Kbv 234-class aluminum-hulled, Class "B"** (In serv. 1960)

Kbv 234

D: 15 tons (fl) **S:** . . . **Dim:** 15.2 × 3.6 × . . .

◆ **4 Kbv 251-class aluminum-hulled, Class "B"** (In serv. 1958–61)

Kbv 251 Kbv 252 Kbv 253 Kbv 254

D: 12 tons (fl) **S:** . . . **Dim:** 15.0 × 3.7 × . . .

◆ **26 miscellaneous speedboats** (In serv. 1962–79)

Kbv 314, 315, 317, 318, 341, 350, 356, 360, 363, 365, 366, 368, 369, 371 374, 381–385, 388–391

Kbv 317—alongside Kbv 283 Hartmut Ehlers,

◆ **6 inflatable boats** (In serv. 1971–75)

Kbv 602, 661–665

◆ **5 iceboats** (In serv. 1965–72)

Kbv 801, Kbv 804–807

Dim: 5.0 × 2.0

POLLUTION-CONTROL SHIPS AND CRAFT

Note: Class A anti-pollution units are described as "Depôt Ships"; Class B ar[illegible] Trucks"; Class C are "Base Ships"; and Class D are catamarans.

◆ **1 Class A** Bldr: Lunde Varv & Verkstads, Ramvik

Kbv 06 (L: 24-3-85)

D: 450 tons (fl) **S:** 15 kts **Dim:** 37.35 (33.70 pp) × 8.80 × . . .
M: 2 Cummins KTA-2300M diesels; 2 rudder props; 2,100 bhp
Fuel: 30.5 tons **Crew:** 6 tot.

Remarks: Similar to Kbv 04 design; ordered 12-84.

LUTION-CONTROL SHIPS AND CRAFT *(continued)*

Class A Bldr: Lunde, Ramvik

)4 (In serv. 1980)

450 tons (fl) **S:** 12 kts **Dim:** 35.5 × 8.0 × 3.0
2 diesels; 2 props; 1,200 bhp **Electric:** 224 kVA **Crew:** 10 tot.

rks: Helipad on fantail, 200-hp bow-thruster, 30-kt workboat, 80-m^3 oil-nment tanks, 500-m^3 containment boom stowage, oil-spill skimming equipment, ghting gear.

Class A miscellaneous "depôt ships"

	In serv.	D:	Dim:
)1 (ex-*Falkland*)	1960	190 tons (fl)	26.0 × 6.7 × . . .
)2 Mäkläppan	1973	260 tons (fl)	33.0 × 7.2 × . . .
)3 Rivöfjord (ex-*ngoon*)	1960	300 tons (fl)	40.0 × 6.46 × 3.52

fjord (Kbv 03) James W. Goss/NAVPIC, 3-90

läppan (Kbv 02) Hartmut Ehlers, 5-90

rks: Kbv 01, bought 1971 and rebuilt by Djupviks, Rönnäng, is powered by one diesel, 595 bhp, for 11 kts. Kbv 03, bought 1973 and rebuilt by Djupviks, was nened 6.0 m in 1987 by Dockstvarvet AB.

Kbv 050 class, Class B oil spill-cleanup boats Bldr: Lunde, amvik

050 (In serv. 20-9-83) Kbv 051 (In serv. 6-83)

340 tons (fl) **S:** . . . **Dim:** 32.6 × 8.5 × . . . **M:** diesels

rks: Enlarged version of Kbv 045 class.

051—deploying oilspill boom Leo Van Ginderen, 4-90

♦ **5 Kbv 050 class, Class B oil spill-cleanup boats** Bldr: Lunde, Ramvik (In serv. 1980–83)

Kbv 045 Kbv 046 Kbv 047 Kbv 048 Kbv 049

D: 133 tons (230 fl) **S:** 11 kts **Dim:** 28.9 (24.80 pp) × 6.5 × 1.9
M: 2 Saab-Scania DST-11 diesels; 2 props; 540 bhp
Electric: 300 kw **Fuel:** 18 tons **Crew:** 4 tot.

Kbv 048 Leo Van Ginderen, 1-92

Remarks: Resemble landing craft, with bow ramp. Have 110-m tanks for recovered oil. Hydraulic thrusters fore and aft. Stowage for 800-m oil-spill-containment booms. Endless belt-type oil-recovery device.

♦ **3 Kbv 041 class, Class B oilspill-cleanup boats** Bldr: Karlstad Varv, Karlstad (In serv. 1972)

Kbv 041 Kbv 042 Kbv 043

D: 70 tons (fl) **S:** 11 kts **Dim:** 18.4 × 5.4 × . . .
M: 2 diesels; 2 props; 450 bhp

Kbv 042 Hartmut Ehlers, 4-85

♦ **1 Class B oilspill-cleanup boat** Bldr: Djupviks, Rönnäng (In serv. 1976)

Kbv 044 Måseskjar

D: 76 tons (100 fl) **S:** 12 kts **Dim:** 25.0 × 6.0 × 1.5
M: 2 Volvo Penta diesels; 2 props; 580 bhp

♦ **1 Class B oilspill-cleanup boat** Bldr: . . . (In serv. 1974)

Kbv 059

D: 22 tons (fl) **S:** . . . **Dim:** . . . × . . . × . . . **M:** . . .

♦ **3 Kbv 011 class, Class C**

Kbv 011 (In serv. 1974) Kbv 012 (In serv. 1970)
Kbv 014 (In serv. 1971)

D: 50 tons (fl) **S:** . . . **Dim:** 25.0 × 5.1 × . . .

Remarks: Wooden construction.

SWEDEN *(continued)*
POLLUTION-CONTROL SHIPS AND CRAFT *(continued)*

Måseskjar (Kbv 044) Leo Van Ginderen, 9-90

♦ **1 Kbv 015 class, Class C** (In serv. 1971)
Kbv 015

D: 140 tons (fl) **S:** . . . **Dim:** 23.0 × 5.5 × . . .

♦ **1 Class D1 catamaran** Bldr: Djupvik, Tjörn (In serv. 8-6-82)
Kbv 020

Kbv 020 Leo Van Ginderen, 8-86

D: 60 tons (fl) **S:** 27 kts **Dim:** 27.6 × 9.2 × 1.5
M: 2 MTU 12V396 TB82 diesels; 2 props; 2,600 bhp

Remarks: Drum-type skimmer mounted forward between the hulls can recover up to 40 tons/hr., or a belt-type cleaner can recover 10–20 tons/hr. Design is Westermoen of Norway's Type 88.

♦ **3 miscellaneous Class D2 catamarans**

	In serv.	D:	Dim:
Kbv 021, 022	1973	30 tons (fl)	14.0 × 7.0
Kbv 023	1975	30 tons (fl)	16.5 × 7.5

Kbv 023—catamaran oilspill-cleanup boat Hartmut Ehlers, 5-90

♦ **6 Class E shore-cleaning boats** (In serv. 1979–1982)
Kbv 0701-712 series

D: 9 tons **S:** . . . **Dim:** 9.0 × 3.1 × . . .

Kbv 0711 Hartmut Ehlers,

♦ **7 miscellaneous Class G oilspill-storage lighters**

	In serv.	D:	Dim:
Kbv 061	1974	300 tons (fl)	28.8 × 6.3 × . . .
Kbv 062	1975	140 tons (fl)	12.0 × 6.0 × . . .
Kbv 063	1974	250 tons (fl)	28.8 × 6.3 × . . .
Kbv 064	1981	. . .	. . .
Kbv 065	1983	450 dwt	33.0 × 10.0 × 2.5
Kbv 068	1979	400 tons (fl)	30.6 × 6.8 × . . .
Kbv 069	1980	360 tons (fl)	30.6 × 6.7 × . . .

Remarks: Kbv 065 is a former tank barge at Göteborg, has 15 cargo tanks an carry vehicles on deck; built by Kalmar Fartygsreparationer AB, Kalmar.

♦ **4 Class H small craft** (In serv. 1973–75)
Kbv 031–Kbv 034

D: 6 tons (fl) **S:** . . . **Dim:** 7.5 × 2.5 × . . .

♦ **1 Class J seasled** (In serv. 1979)
Kbv 036

Dim: 11.8 × 4.6

♦ **20 miscellaneous Class K workboats** (In serv. 1971–82)
Kbv 080–Kbv 099

D: 0.8 to 1.0 tons (fl) **S:** . . . **Dim:** 5.8 to 6.5 × 2.4 to 2.7 × . . .

SWITZERLAND

Swiss Confederation

SWISS ARMY

PATROL CRAFT

♦ **11 Patrouillenboat 80 class** Bldr: Müller AG, Spiez (In serv. 1978

Antares, Aquarius, Castor, Mars, Orion, Perseus, Pollux, Satu Sirius, Uranus, Venus

P 80 class Jürg Kürs

TZERLAND *(continued)*
ROL CRAFT *(continued)*

: 5.9 tons (fl) **S:** 35 kts **Dim:** 10.7 × 3.3 × 0.9 (0.6 hull)
. 2/12.7-mm M3 mg (I × 2) **Electron Equipt:** Radar: 1/. . . nav.
: 2 Volvo Penta AQ 260A gasoline engines; 2 props; 560 shp
ew: 6 tot.

arks: Glass-reinforced plastic construction, wooden superstructure. Replaced a p of wooden-hulled craft built in 1942. Employed on Lakes Constance, Geneva, and giore. *Aquarius* completed 1978, *Pollux* in 1984, rest in 1981.

: Six 11-meter patrol craft were ordered 3-91 from Reliance Workboats, Laver-, U.K., for the Swiss Police; all delivered 5-91.

YRIA

an Arab Republic

onnel (1991): approximately 3,700 total, plus 2,500 reserves

al Aviation: Helicopters: 3 Kamov Ka-25 Hormone-A ASW and 20 Mi-14PL -A ASW

: Coast-defense batteries of SSC-1b Shaddock and SSC-3 Styx missiles have been sferred from the former U.S.S.R. They are mounted on vehicles.

MARINES

: Although rumored during 1988, no Kilo-class submarines had been delivered as 92.

Soviet Romeo class Bldr: Baltic SY, Leningrad (In serv. 1957–60)

an Romeo Leo Van Ginderen, 11-86

: 1,319 tons (surf.)/1,712 tons (sub.) **S:** 15.2 kts (surf.)/13 kts (sub.)
im: 76.60 × 6.70 × 4.95
: 8/533-mm TT (6 fwd, 2 aft; 14 torpedoes or 28 mines)
lectron Equipt:
Radar: 1/Snoop Plate—EW: Stop Light intercept
Sonar: MF active, passive
: 2 Type 37D diesels (2,000 bhp each), 2 electric motors; 2 shrouded props; 2,700 shp; 2 electric creep motors; 100 shp
ange: 14,000/surf; 350/9 sub. **Endurance:** 60 days
rew: 56 tot.

arks: First pair transferred 11-85, with the third arriving 12-86. Also transferred 1-86 was a Whiskey-class submarine converted as a battery-charging hulk to ort these ships. Diving depth: 300 m. Have 224 cell, 6,600 amp./hr. batteries. d at Tartous.

RVETTES

2 ex-Soviet Petya-III class

. . . . 14 . . . .

rian Petya-III No. 14 6th Flot., French Navy, 10-83

D: 950 tons (1,150 fl) **S:** 29 kts
Dim: 81.8 (78.00 pp) × 9.2 × 2.97 (mean hull)
A: 4/76.2-mm 59-cal. AK-276 DP (II × 2)—3/533-mm TT (III × 1)—4/RBU-2500 ASW RL (XVI × 4)—2/d.c. racks—mines
Electron Equipt:
Radar: 1/Don-2 nav., 1/Strut Curve surf./air search, 1/Hawk Screech f.c.
Sonar: hull-mounted HF search and attack sets
IFF: 2/Square Head interrogators, 1/High Pole B transponder
M: CODAG: 2 gas turbines (15,000 shp each); 1 Type 61V3 diesel (6,000 bhp); 3 props; 36,000 shp—2 auxiliary props; 100 shp
Range: 450/29; 4,800/10 **Crew:** 8 officers, 84 enlisted

Remarks: Transferred 1975; may have been newly built. Standard export version, with triple 533-mm TT substituted for Soviet Navy quintuple 400-mm mount. Based at Tartous.

GUIDED-MISSILE PATROL BOATS

♦ **8 ex-Soviet Osa-II class**

D: 215 tons (240 fl) **S:** 35 kts **Dim:** 38.6 × 7.6 × 2.0
A: 4/SS-N-2B Styx P-20/21 SSM (I × 4)—4/30-mm AK-230 AA (II × 2)
Electron Equipt:
Radar: 1/Square Tie surf. search/target designation, 1/Drum Tilt f.c.
IFF: 2/Square Head interrogators, 1/High Pole B transponder
M: 3 M504 diesels; 3 props; 15,000 bhp
Range: 500/34; 750/25 **Crew:** 28–30 tot.

Syrian Osa-II 6th Flot., French Navy, 10-83

Remarks: Two transferred 1978, four in 1979, two in 1982, two in 5-84, two in 1985; four had been deleted by 1987. The pair delivered in 1984 were each equipped with one 16-tubed decoy rocket launcher.

♦ **6 ex-Soviet Osa-I class**

D: 171 tons (209.5 fl) **S:** 38 kts
Dim: 38.60 × 7.60 × 1.80 (2.90 props)
A: 4/SS-N-2A Styx P-15 missiles (I × 4)—4/30-mm AK-230 AA (II × 2)
Electron Equipt:
Radar: 1/Square Tie surf. search/target designation, 1/Drum Tilt f.c.
IFF: 2/Square Head interrogators, 1/High Pole B transponder
M: 3 M503A2 diesels; 3 props; 12,000 bhp **Range:** 500/34; 800/25
Crew: 28–30 tot.

Syrian Osa-I 6th Flot., French Navy, 10-83

SYRIA *(continued)*
GUIDED-MISSILE PATROL BOATS *(continued)*

Remarks: Transferred 1966; two others were sunk during the Arab–Israeli War, October 1973.

PATROL BOAT

♦ **1 Soviet Natya class**

Syria's Natya (transfer No. 642) 21st Flot., French Navy, 1-85

D: 750 tons (850 fl) **S:** 18 kts
Dim: 61.0 × 10.2 × 3.3 (mean hull)
A: 4/30-mm AK-230 AA (II × 2)—4/25-mm 2M-8 AA (II × 2)
Electron Equipt:
Radar: 1/Spin Trough nav., 1/Drum Tilt f.c.
IFF: 2/Square Head interrogators, 1/High Pole A transponder
M: 2 diesels; 2 props; 5,000 bhp
Range: 1,800/16; 5,200/10 **Crew:** 60 tot.

Remarks: Transferred 26-1-85; probably was newly built. Not equipped with any of the normal Natya-class seagoing minesweeper mine-countermeasures equipment, winches, cranes, etc., nor does she have the standard 2/RBU-1200 ASW rocket launchers or mine rails.

♦ **2 ex-Libyan** Bldr: Müller Verft, Hameln, Germany (In serv. 1-78)

Jihad Salam

D: 120 tons (fl) **S:** 27 kts **Dim:** 37.0 × 6.2 × . . .
A: *see* Remarks **Electron Equipt:** Radar: 1/. . . nav.
M: 2 MTU diesels; 2 props; . . . bhp
Range: 1,100/27 **Crew:** 21 tot.

Remarks: Originally ordered for Lebanon but sold to Libya 1-78 when Lebanon could not pay. Transferred to the Palestine Liberation Front 8-81 and based in Syria. Have probably been rearmed and placed under Syrian control; originally had two twin Hispano-Suiza 20-mm GCM A02 AA mounts.

PATROL CRAFT

♦ **9 Soviet Zhuk class**

D: 48 tons (60 fl) **S:** 34 kts **Dim:** 24.0 × 5.0 × 1.2 (1.8 props)
A: 4/14.5-mm mg (II × 2)
Electron Equipt:
Radar: 1/Spin Trough nav.—IFF: 1/High Pole A transponder
M: 2 M50F-4 diesels; 2 props; 2,400 bhp
Range: 700/28; 1,100/15 **Fuel:** 10 tons **Crew:** 12 tot.

Remarks: Three delivered 12-83, three in 12-84, three in 1-85. Based at Tartous.

MINE WARFARE SHIPS AND CRAFT

♦ **1 Soviet T-43-class fleet minesweeper**

504 Hittin

D: 500 tons (570 fl) **S:** 14 kts **Dim:** 58.0 × 8.6 × 2.3 (hull)
A: 4/37-mm AA (II × 2)—8/12.7-mm mg (II × 4)—2/d.c. mortars—mines
Electron Equipt:
Radar: 1/. . . nav.—Sonar: Tamir-11 hull-mounted HF searchlight type
IFF: 2/Square Head interrogators, 1/High Pole A transponder
M: 2 Type 9D diesels; 2 props; 2,200 bhp
Range: 2,000/14; 3,200/10 **Fuel:** 70 tons **Crew:** 75 tot.

Remarks: Transferred 1962; sister *Yarmouk* lost in the October 1973 war.

♦ **1 Soviet Sonya-class coastal minesweeper** Bldr: Petrozavodsk SY

D: 350 tons (400 fl) **S:** 15 kts **Dim:** 48.5 × 7.3 × 1.9 (hull)
A: 2/30-mm AK-230 AA (II × 1)—2/25-mm 2M-8 AA (II × 1)
Electron Equipt:
Radar: 1/Spin Trough nav.—Sonar: HF hull-mounted
IFF: 1/High Pole B transponder, 2/Square Head
M: 2 diesels; 2 props; 2,400 bhp
Range: 1,600/14; 3,000/10 **Crew:** 40 tot.

Remarks: Wooden construction, with hull sheathed in GRP. Arrived in Syria 1-86.

♦ **2 ex-Soviet Vanya-class coastal minesweepers**

775 Kadisia 776 Yarmouk

D: 200 tons (245 fl) **S:** 16 kts **Dim:** 39.9 × 7.5 × 1.8
A: 2/30-mm AA (II × 1)—mines
Electron Equipt: Radar: 1/Don-2 nav.—Sonar: none
M: 1 diesel; 1 prop; 2,200 bhp
Range: 1,400/14; 2,400/10 **Crew:** 30 tot.

Remarks: Transferred 12-72. Wooden construction; glass-reinforced plastic-shea hull.

♦ **5 Soviet Yevgenya-class inshore minesweepers** Bldr: Sredniy Neva SY, Kolpino

D: 80 tons (90 fl) **S:** 11 kts **Dim:** 26.2 × 6.1 × 1.5
A: 2/14.5-mm mg (II × 1)
Electron Equipt:
Radar: 1/Spin Trough nav.—IFF: 1/High Pole B transponder
M: 2 diesels; 2 props; 600 bhp **Range:** 300/10 **Crew:** 10 tot.

Remarks: Glass-reinforced plastic construction. Use television minehunting sy to 30-m depths. First unit transferred 1978, second in 1981, the third and fourth ar on 15-2-85, and the fifth on 19-1-86. Last two delivered had tripod masts.

AMPHIBIOUS WARFARE SHIPS

♦ **3 Soviet Polnocny-B-class medium landing ships** Bldr: Stocz Północna, Gdańsk

D: 740 tons (800 fl) **S:** 18 kts **Dim:** 74.0 × 8.9 × 1.9
A: 4/30-mm AK-230 AA (II × 2)—2/140-mm barrage RL (XVIII ×
Electron Equipt:
Radar: 1/Spin Trough nav., 1/Drum Tilt f.c.
IFF: 1/Square Head interrogator, 1/High Pole B transponder
M: 2 Type 40D diesels; 2 props; 5,000 bhp
Range: 900/18; 1,500/14 **Crew:** 40 crew + 100 troops

Remarks: Transferred from U.S.S.R. 15-1-84, two in 2-85. Cargo: about 180 tons also have 2 or 4/SA-N-5 point-defense SAM stations (IV × 2 or 4).

AUXILIARIES AND SERVICE CRAFT

♦ **1 training ship/transport** Bldr: Stocznia Północna SY, Gdańsk (In 1989)

Al Assad

D: 3,500 tons (fl) **S:** 16 kts **Dim:** 105.00 × 17.20 × 4.00 **A:** no
Electron Equipt: Radar: . . . **M:** 2 diesels; 2 props; . . . bhp

Remarks: Ordered at the beginning of 1984 and launched 8-2-87. Combination ing ship and vehicle and personnel transport. Based at Latakia.

♦ **1 Soviet Sekstan-class degaussing tender** (In serv. 1949–55)

D: 400 tons (fl) **S:** 11 kts **Dim:** 41.0 × 9.3 × 4.2
M: 1 diesel; 1 prop; 400 bhp **Range:** 1,200/10.5 **Crew:** 24 tot.

Remarks: Transferred 12-83. Wooden construction.

♦ **1 Soviet Nyryat-1-class diving tender**

D: 120 tons (fl) **S:** 12 kts **Dim:** 29.0 × 5.0 × 1.7
Electron Equipt: Radar: 1/Spin Trough nav.
M: 1 diesel; 1 prop; 450 bhp **Range:** 1,600/10 **Crew:** 15 tot.

♦ **3 survey launches** Bldr: ARCOR, La Teste, France (In serv. 1985)

D: . . . **S:** 25 kts **Dim:** 9.80 (8.50 pp) × 3.40 × 0.90
M: 2 Volvo Penta AQAD-40 diesels; 310 bhp **Range:** 300/. . .
Crew: 4 tot.

Remarks: Ordered 12-84. Glass-reinforced plastic construction.

♦ **1 ex-Soviet Whiskey-class battery-charging barge**

D: approx. 1,100 tons (fl) **Dim:** 76.0 × 6.3 × 4.8
Electric: approx. 2,800 kw (2 Type 37D, 2,000-bhp diesels)

Remarks: Former submarine, with tubes sealed, propellers removed, etc., us support of the Romeo-class submarines. Transferred by 11-86. Based at Tartous.

TAIWAN

Republic of China

Personnel (1991): 37,000 total navy, plus 31,000 marines; plus 45,000 naval re ists, 35,000 marine reservists

Naval Aviation: Naval Helicopter Group has 12 Hughes 500MD/ASW ar Sikorsky S-70CM1 helicopters for land-based use (the 500MDs occasionally a ployed aboard destroyers; the S-70CM1s will be used aboard the new frigates) S-70CM1 helicopter is an export version of the U.S. Navy SH-60B Seahawk a equipped with APS-143 radar, ASN-150 tactical navigation system, ALR-606 gear, one or two ARR-84 99-channel sonobuoy receivers, and MAD gear. The MD have ASQ-81(V)2 MAD gear and can lift one torpedo.

NAVAL AVIATION *(continued)*

The 439th Composite Wing of the ROCAF has 32 Grumman S-2E Trackers in two squadrons based at Pintung; two Trackers modernized by Grumman to S-2T standard with Garrett TPE-331-15AW turboprops, AQS-902F digital sonobuoy processor, ARR-84 99-channel sonobuoy receiver, DIFAR and CODAR capability, Litton APS-504 radar, ASQ-504 MAD, and AAS-40 FLIR (in place of the former searchlight) were delivered 8-91, and the other 30 aircraft are being modernized by Chungshan Institute of Science and Technology at Taichung. Thirty of the S-2Ts will be ASW configured, the other two for EW. The marines also have several light liaison aircraft and helicopters. The air force ordered four E-2T conversions from surplus U.S. E-2B Hawkeye radar picket aircraft, for delivery 1993 with APS-138 radar.

Unmodified S-2E Trackers of 34 Squadron Chien Chung, 8-91

S-2E Tracker, with turbine engines *Defense Technology,* 1991

Five S-70CM1 Seahawk helicopters *Defense Technology,* 1991

McDonnell Douglas 500MD helicopter *Defense Technology,* 1991

Coastal Defenses: Land-based mobile batteries with Hsiung Feng-II anti ship missiles are maintained on the islands of Quemoy, Matsu, Tung-Ying, Chu-Kwang, and Wu-Chiu off the Chinese mainland.

Hsiung Feng II missile at launch *Defense Technology,* 1989

Note: Almost all ships, weapons, and electronics systems currently in use originated in the United States, the principal exception being the Hsiung Feng antiship missile, a copy of the Israeli Aviation Industries' Gabriel II, and the CR-201 (King Fen) 16-tubed 127-mm decoy rocket launcher of Taiwanese design.

The Hsiung Feng II, developed by the Chungshan Institute of Science and Technology, resembles the U.S. Harpoon and has a range of over 80 km. Powered by a turbojet, it has a mid-course guidance provision and an active radar *plus* IR seekers. The weapon is capable of air, surface, and land launch and will be adapted for submarine launch. Hsiung Feng means "Proud Wind."

Some 200 Indonesian-built, West German-designed SUT wire-guided torpedoes were ordered in 1988 for use by submarines.

The Chang Bai phased-array radar system has been developed for land use with U.S. assistance and may be adapted for shipboard employment; if not, U.S.-supplied systems will be aboard new frigates.

In 1989, 88 U.S. Standard SM-1 surface-to-air missiles were acquired for use aboard modernized *Gearing*-class destroyers.

SUBMARINES

◆ **0 (+4) German Type 209/1400** Bldr: Howaldtswerke, Kiel

D: 1,310 tons surf./1,460 sub. **S:** 11.0/21.5 kts
Dim: 61.20 × 6.25 × 5.50
A: 8/533-mm TT (bow) (14 torpedoes or . . . mines)
Electron Equipt:
Radar: Thomson-CSF Calypso search—EW: . . . intercept
Sonar: Krupp-Atlas CSU-83/1 suite
M: 4 MTU 12V493 A280 AG diesels (600 bhp each), 4/405-kw generator sets, 1 Siemens electric motor; 1 prop; 5,000 shp
Range: 8,200/8 snorkel; 230/8, 400/4 sub.
Endurance: 50 days **Crew:** 30 tot.

Remarks: Contract several times reported to have been signed during 1991, although unconfirmed. Would all be built in Germany as a means to obtain submarines more quickly than the proposed complementary construction of Dutch-designed submarines in Taiwan. If the Dutch program cannot be consummated, another six Type 209 may be built in Taiwan. Program replaces 2-89 letter-of-intent to co-produce the larger German Type 2000.

Diving depth: 320 m. Two 240-cell batteries. Two periscopes (1 search, with EW; one attack).

◆ **2 modified Dutch Zwaardvis class** Bldr: First two: Wilton Fijenoord, Schiedam; others: China Shipbuilding, Keelung

	Laid down	L	Delivered	In serv.
793 HAI LUNG	12-82	4-10-86	9-10-87	9-10-87
795 HAI HU	. . .	20-12-86	9-4-88	4-7-88

Hai Hu (795) *Defense Technology,* 4-91

SUBMARINES *(continued)*

Hai Lung (793) *Defense Technology,* 1991

D: 2,376 tons(surf.)/2,660 tons (sub.) **S:** 11 kts (surf.)/20 kts (sub.)
Dim: 66.92 × 8.40 × 6.70
A: 6/533-mm TT fwd (28 SUT and Mk 37 wire-guided torpedoes)
Electron Equipt:
Radar: 1/H.S.A. ZW-06—EW: Elbit TIMNEX 4 CH V2 (2–18 gHz) intercept
Sonar: H.S.A. SIASS integrated system
M: 3 Brons/Stork-Werkspoor 12 ORUB 215 diesels (1,350 bhp each); 2 922-kw Holec DG.110/47/90 alternator groups, 1 3,800-kw motor; 1 5-bladed prop; 5,100 shp sub./1,400 surf.
Range: 10,000/9 (surf.) **Fuel:** 310 tons
Crew: 8 officers, 59 enlisted

Remarks: First two ordered late 1980 over mainland China's protests. Design also referred to as "Sea Dragon" class, as names mean "Sea Dragon" and "Sea Tiger," respectively. Request for two more (and option for fifth and sixth) turned down by Dutch government in 1984, due to Chinese pressure. The first submarine left the Netherlands for Taiwan as deck cargo on a heavy-lift ship on 28 October 1987; the second arrived via deckship on 28-6-88.

Although the Dutch parliament on 14-2-92 rejected permission for RDM, Rotterdam, to assist in the construction of four additional units in Taiwan, the rejection was contingent on improved Netherlands trade with mainland China being evident by 1-6-92; if not, permission for the submarine program will be given. The second increment will presumably have some updated systems.

Highly automated design. SINBADS-M, 8-target track data system, Sperry Mk 29 Mod. 2A inertial navigation system. Two 196-cell batteries. Diving depth: 240 m. Torpedoes are ex-Dutch Navy.

♦ **2 ex-U.S. Guppy II class**

	Bldr	Laid down	L	In serv.
736 Hai Shih (ex-*Cutlass,* SS 478)	Portsmouth, NSY, Portsmouth, NH	22-7-44	5-11-44	17-3-45
794 Hai Pao (ex-*Tusk,* SS 426)	Cramp SB, Philadelphia	23-8-43	8-7-45	11-4-46

Hai Pao (794) or Hai Shih (736) *Defense Technology,* 1986

D: 1,517 tons (std.)/1,870 tons fl (surf.)/2,440 tons (sub.)
S: 18 kts (surf.)/16 kts (sub.) **Dim:** 93.57 × 8.33 × 5.18
A: 10/533-mm TT (6 fwd, 4 aft; 22 torpedoes)
Electron Equipt:
Radar: 1/SS-2—EW: WLR-1, WLR-3 intercept
Sonar: BQR-2B passive, BQS-4C active (7 kHz), DUUG-1B sonar intercept
M: diesel-electric propulsion: 4 Fairbanks-Morse 38D8Q diesels; 2 electric motors; 4,610 bhp (surf.)/5,200 shp (sub.)
Range: 10,000/10 (surf.); 95/5 (sub.) **Fuel:** 330 tons
Crew: 11 officers, 70 enlisted

Remarks: Transferred 12-4-73 and 18-10-73, for ASW training. Four 126-cell batteries. Source of torpedoes uncertain: may use old Japanese or U.S. Mk 14 World War II–era straight-runners, U.S. Mk 37 or NT-37C homing torpedoes, or U.K. Mk 24 Tigerfish; tubes were welded shut at time of delivery but were reportedly made operational again.

DESTROYERS

♦ **12 ex-U.S. Gearing FRAM-I class**

7 Wu Chin III conversions:

	Bldr	Laid down	L	In serv.
912 Chien Yang (ex-*James E. Kyes,* DD 787)	Todd Pacific SY, Seattle	27-12-44	4-8-45	8-2-46
921 Liao Yang (ex-*Hanson,* DD 832)	Bath Iron Wks, Bath, Maine	7-10-44	11-3-45	11-5-45
923 Shen Yang (ex-*Power,* DD 839)	Bath Iron Wks, Bath, Maine	26-2-45	30-6-45	13-9-45
925 Te Yang (ex-*Sarsfield,* DD 837)	Bath Iron Wks, Bath, Maine	15-1-45	27-5-45	31-7-45
927 Yun Yang (ex-*Hamner,* DD 718)	Federal SB, Newark, N.J.	5-4-45	24-11-45	11-7-46
928 Chen Yang (ex-*Johnston,* DD 821)	Consolidated Steel, Orange, Texas	6-5-45	19-10-45	10-10-46
929 Shao Yang (ex-*Hollister,* DD 788)	Todd Pacific SY, Seattle	18-1-45	9-10-45	29-3-46

3 Wu Chin II conversions:

	Bldr	Laid down	L	In serv.
915 Han Yang (ex-*Herbert J. Thomas,* DD 833)	Bath Iron Wks, Bath, Maine	30-10-44	25-3-45	29-5-4
920 Lai Yang (ex-*Shelton,* DD 790)	Todd Pacific SY, Seattle	31-5-45	8-3-46	21-6-4
924 Kai Yang (ex-*Richard B. Anderson,* DD 786)	Todd Pacific SY, Seattle	1-12-44	7-7-45	26-10-4

1 Wu Chin I conversion:

	Bldr	Laid down	L	In serv.
926 Sui Yang (ex-*Leonard K. Mason,* DD 852)	Bethlehem SY, Quincy, Mass.	8-6-45	4-1-46	28-6-4

1 unconverted

	Bldr	Laid down	L	In serv.
930 Tse Yang (ex-*Hawkins,* DD 873)	Consolidated Steel, Orange, Texas	14-5-44	7-10-44	10-2-4

Sui Yang (926)—the only Wu Chin I conversion Leo Van Ginderen, 6

Tse Yang (930)—unmodified *Defense Technology,*

DESTROYERS *(continued)*

Liao Yang (921)—a Wu Chin III conversion *Defense Technology,* 1990

Lai Yang (920)—Wu Chin II conversion Raymond Cheung, 3-91

Liao Yang (921)—Wu Chin III conversion *Defense Technology,* 10-91

D: varies; typical: 2,425–2,500 tons (3,465–3,540 fl)
S: 31 kts (Wu Chin III: 27 kts)
Dim: 119.03 (116.74) × 12.52 × 4.61–4.65 (6.50–6.54 over sonar)
A: Wu Chin III conversions :
10/Standard SM-1 MR SAM/SSM (III × 2, II × 2)—1/76-mm 62-cal. OTO Melara DP—2/40-mm 70-cal. Bofors AA (I × 2)—1/20-mm Mk 15 CIWS—1/Mk 112 ASROC ASW RL (VIII × 1, no reloads)—6/324-mm Mk 32 ASW TT (III × 2)—1/MD-500 helicopter
Tse Yang (930):
4/127-mm 38-cal. Mk 30 DP (II × 2)—1/Mk 112 ASROC ASW RL (VIII × 1, 9 reloads)—4–6/12.7-mm mg (I × . . .)—6/324-mm Mk 32 ASW TT (III × 2)—1/MD-500 helicopter
Wu Chin I and II conversions:
5/Hsiung Feng SSM (III × 1, I × 2)—2/127-mm 38-cal. Mk 30 DP (II × 1)—1/76-mm 62-cal. OTO Melara DP—1/Sea Chaparral SAM syst. (IV × 1, 16 RIM-72C missiles)—2/40-mm 70-cal. Bofors AA (I × 2)—926 only: 1/Mk 112 ASW RL (VIII × 1, no reloads)—6/324-mm ASW TT (III × 2)—1/MD-500 helicopter

Electron Equipt: Radar:
Wu Chin III conversions: 1/SPS-58A surf./air search, 1/H.S.A. DA-08/2 air search, 1/H.S.A. STIR-18 missile f.c., 1/Westinghouse HW-160 gun f.c.
Tse Yang (930): 1/SPS-10 or SPS-58A surf./air search, 1/SPS-40 air search, 1/Mk 25 gun f.c.
Wu Chin II conversions: 1/Elbit EL/M-2208 surf. search, 1/SPS-40 air search, 1/RTN-10X f.c.
Wu Chin I conversion (926): 1/SPS-58A surf./air search, 1/SPS-29 air search, 2/R.C.A. HR-76 C5 f.c.
Sonar (all): Raytheon DE-1191 (updated SQS-23) hull-mounted (4.5/5.0/5.5 kHz)
EW: Wu Chin I, III conversions: Chang Feng III active/passive suite; unconverted and Wu Chin II ships: WLR-1 intercept, some: ULQ-6 jammer; all: 4/King Fen decoy RL (XVI × 4); Wu Chin III ships also: 1 AS-899A D/F

M: 2 sets G.E. geared steam turbines; 2 props; 60,000 shp
Boilers: 4 Babcock & Wilcox; 43.3 kg/cm², 454° C
Electric: 1,200 kw **Range:** 1,500/31; 5,800/12
Fuel: 720 tons **Crew:** 275 tot.

Remarks: 912, 920, and 921 were transferred 18-4-73. 915 transferred 6-5-74, 924 on 10-6-77, 925 and 923 on 1-10-77, and 922 on 10-3-78. 927 and 928 were purchased (without ASROC) on 27-2-81, while 929 and 930 were purchased 17-4-83. Another unit, *Tsao Yang* (916, ex-*Rowan,* DD 782) was lost 22-8-77 while under tow to Taiwan for activation. 915, at time of transfer, was unusual in having extra superstructure and an extra gas turbine generator; used for NBC-warfare defense trials by the U.S. Navy during 1963–64, she had a sealed air system, extra air-conditioning, and lacked an ASROC launcher at time of transfer (two twin 40-mm AA with Mk 51 Mod. 2 directors were in the ASROC position).

Wu Chin III ships received the Honeywell H 930 weapons-control systems, with an H.S.A. STIR-1.8 fire-control radar substituted for the original Mk 37 director with Mk 25 radar; the system can track 24 air, surface, and underwater targets simultaneously while controlling attacks on 4, with an 8-second response time. All 127-mm mounts were deleted, and an OTO Melara 76-mm mount was substituted forward. On the fantail, two sets of triple fixed box-launchers for U.S. Standard SM-1 MR surface-to-air missiles (which can also be used against surface targets) are positioned fore and aft of a U.S. Mk 15 CIWS; two twin Standard box-launchers are located forward of the bridge. The DA-08/2 air-search radar (which uses the antenna for the LW-05 radar) is located atop the foremast, and the SPS-58A radar (which uses an SPS-10 radar antenna) is located on the former air-search radar platform. A new lattice aftermast carries the HW-160 radar and the various arrays for the Chang Feng III EW suite, which was derived from the Hughes SLQ-31. The 40-mm AA are mounted to port at the aft corner of the hangar structure (necessitating deletion of the ASROC reload magazine) and on a raised platform forward of the whaleboat to starboard; Raytheon DE-1191 sonar is a digital, transistorized update to the SQS-23. Also received a Taiwanese-made SATCOMM system. All are believed to have completed conversion by 10-91 except *Te Yang* (925), on which work was in progress; prior to conversion, 925 had lacked the after 127-mm mount but had a larger helicopter facility for two BO-105s.

The Wu Chin II ships were updated with assistance from Israeli Aircraft Industries and have the Elbit NTCCS (Naval Tactical Command and Control System), which can track 12 underwater, surface, and air targets simultaneously and attack 3 with a 20-second response time; the ships retain the forward twin 127-mm mount. The 76-mm gun is located in "B" position before the bridge, and a triple, trainable Hsiung Feng I SSM launcher replaced the aft 127-mm mount. Two single, fixed Hsiung Feng I launch containers are located atop the hangar. None has an ASROC launcher, the space between the stacks being occupied by a deckhouse flanked by the two 40-mm AA.

The sole Wu Chin I update, *Sui Yang,* employs equipment originally ordered for the stricken *Sumner*-class destroyers *Hsiang Yang* and *Po Yang* (the spare equipment set is used in a shore training facility). The original air-search radar, SPS-29, was relocated lower on a new lattice foremast, which is topped by the radome for the forward R.C.A. HR-76 C5 fire-control radar, and a new lattice aftermast carries the EW suite and the other HR-76 C5 radar. The Hsiung Feng I missiles are situated as in the Wu Chin II *Gearing* FRAM Is, and the Sea Chaparral SAM launcher is on the fantail. A Kollmorgen Mk 35 optical periscopic gunsight replaces the optics and Mk 25 radar of the original Mk 37 director, which is now fixed in position.

Tse Yang (930) is not included in any of the modification programs; reason unknown.

♦ 2 ex-U.S. Gearing FRAM-II class

1 Wu Chin II conversion:

	Bldr	Laid down	L	In serv.
907 Fu Yang (ex-*Ernest G. Small,* DD 838)	Bath Iron Wks, Bath, Maine	30-1-45	14-6-45	21-8-45

1 Wu Chin I conversion:

	Bldr	Laid down	L	In serv.
911 Dang Yang (ex-*Lloyd Thomas,* DD 764)	Bethlehem Steel, San Francisco	26-3-44	5-10-45	21-3-47

Fu Yang (907)—Wu Chin II conversion R.O.C.N., 1987

DESTROYERS *(continued)*

Dang Yang (911)—Wu Chin I conversion *Defense Technology,* 1988

D: 2,425 tons (3,477 fl) **S:** 32 kts
Dim: 119.03 (116.74 wl) × 12.52 × 4.61 (6.54 over sonar)
A: 907: 5/Hsiung Feng SSM (III × 1, I × 2)—1/Sea Chaparral SAM syst. (IV × 1, 16 RIM-72C missiles)—4/127-mm 38-cal. Mk 30 DP (II × 2)—1/76-mm 62-cal. OTO Melara DP—2/40-mm 70-cal. Bofors AA (I × 2)—2/Mk 11 Hedgehog ASW mortars (XXIV × 2)—6/324-mm Mk 32 ASW TT (III × 2)
911: 5/Hsiung Feng SSM (III × 1, I × 2)—2/127-mm 38-cal. Mk 30 DP (II × 1)—1/76-mm 62-cal. OTO Melara DP—2/40-mm 70-cal. Bofors AA (I × 2)—6/324-mm Mk 32 ASW TT (III × 2)—1/MD-500 helicopter
Electron Equipt:
Radar: 907: 1/SPS-58A surf./air search, 1/SPS-37 air search, 2/RCA HR-76 C5 f.c.
911: 1/Elta EL/M-2208 surf. search, 1/SPS-6B air search, 1/RTN-10X f.c.
EW: 907: Argo AR 680/681 intercept/jammer suite, AS-899 D/F, 4/King Fen decoy RL (XVI × 4)
911: WLR-1 and WLR-3 intercept, ULQ-6 deceptive jammer, 4/King Fen decoy RL (XVI × 4)
Sonar: Raytheon DE 1191 hull-mounted (4.5/5.0/5.5 kHz)
TACAN: SRN-15 (not in 907)
M: 2 sets G.E. geared steam turbines; 2 props; 60,000 shp
Boilers: 4 Babcock & Wilcox; 43.3 kg/cm², 454° C
Electric: 1,200 kw **Range:** 1,600/31; 6,100/12
Fuel: 720 tons **Crew:** 275 tot.

Remarks: *Dang Yang,* completed as an ASW destroyer (DDE), finished FRAM-II modernization in 11-61 and was transferred to Taiwan on 12-10-72. *Fu Yang,* transferred in 2-71, completed FRAM-II modernization as a radar picket destroyer in 8-61; her SPS-30 height-finding radar was removed before transfer. *Fu Yung* acts as fleet flagship and has been modernized with the Honeywell H 930 Mod. 1 weapons-control system, with two R.C.A. HR-76 C5 f.c. radars, five Hsiung Feng SSM, an OTO Melara 76-mm DP, a Chaparral point-defense SAM system, the Mk 37 director converted to carry a Kollmorgen Mk 35 periscopic sight, SPS-58 substituted for SPS-10, and new EW equipment. *Dang Yang* was modernized with Israeli assistance, receiving an Israeli-made official Galileo OGR 7/2 optronic GFCS in place of the Mk 37, a Selenia RTN-10X radar on the reinforced mainmast (for SSM control), and the Elta EL/M-2208 radar in place of the SPS-10; the SPS-6C air-search radar received a new solid-state transmitter, greatly improving its performance.

♦ 2 ex-U.S. Allen M. Sumner FRAM-II class—Wu Chin I conversions

	Bldr	Laid down	L	In serv.
914 Lo Yang (ex-*Taussig,* DD 746)	Bethlehem Steel, Staten Isl., N.Y.	30-8-43	25-1-44	20-5-44
917 Nan Yang (ex-*John W. Thomason,* DD 760)	Bethlehem Steel, San Francisco	21-11-43	30-9-44	11-10-45

Nan Yang (917) R.O.C.N., 1987

D: 2,350 tons (3,220 fl) **S:** 33 kts
Dim: 114.63 (112.52 wl) × 12.52 × 4.4 (5.9 over sonar)
A: 5/Hsiung Feng I SSM (III × 1, I × 2)—1/Sea Chaparral point-defense SAM system (IV × 1; 16 RIM-72C missiles)—2/127-mm 38-cal. Mk 30 DP (II × 1)—1/76-mm 62-cal. OTO Melara Compact DP—2/40-mm 70-cal. Bofors AA (I × 2)—2/Mk 11 Hedgehog ASW spigot mortars (XXIV × 2)—6/324-mm Mk 32 ASW TT (III × 2)—1/MD-500 helicopter
Electron Equipt:
Radar: 1/SPS-58A surf./air search, 1/SPS-29 air search, 2 R.C.A. HR-76 C5 f.c.
Sonar: Krupp-Atlas DSQS-21CZ hull-mounted
EW: Argo AR 680/681 intercept/jammer suite, AS-899 D/F, 4/King Fen decoy RL (XVI × 4)
TACAN: SRN-15
M: 2 sets geared steam turbines: 2 props; 60,000 shp
Boilers: 4 Babcock & Wilcox; 43.3 kg/cm², 454° C
Electric: 1,200 kw **Range:** 1,000/32
Fuel: 500 tons **Crew:** 275 tot.

Remarks: Both transferred on 6-5-74, having completed FRAM-II modernization i 9-62 and 1-60, respectively. Rebuilt by mid-1985 with "B" 127-mm mount replaced b 76-mm gun, aft 127-mm mount by triple, trainable SSM launcher. The manned Se Chaparral launcher is at the extreme stern. The Honeywell H930 weapons-contr system is supported by two Westinghouse radars mounted on new lattice masts and ca track eight surface and air targets simultaneously: the old Mk 37 GFCS director retained without its Mk 25 radar, but with a Kollmorgen Mk 35 electro-optical syste added. The SQS-29 series sonar has been replaced by a German set.

♦ 1 ex-U.S. Allen M. Sumner class—Wu Chin I-conversion

	Bldr	Laid down	L	In serv
906 Huei Yang (ex-*English,* DD 696)	Federal SB, Kearny, N.J.	19-10-43	27-2-44	4-5-4

Huei Yang (906)—Wu Chin I conversion *Defense Technology,* 1

D: 2,200 tons (3,300 fl) **S:** 33 kts
Dim: 114.63 (112.52 wl) × 12.52 × 4.4 (hull)
A: 5/Hsiung Feng I SSM (III × 1, I × 2)—1/Sea Chaparral SAM system (IV × 1, 16 RIM-72C missiles)—4/127-mm 38-cal. Mk 30 DP (II × 2)—1/76-mm 62-cal. OTO Melara DP—2/40-mm 70-cal. Bofors AA (I × 2)—6/324-mm Mk 32 ASW TT (III × 2)—2/Mk 11 Hedgehog ASW spigot mortars (XXIV × 2)—1/d.c. rack
Electron Equipt:
Radar: 1/SPS-58A surf./air search, 1/SPS-6C air search; 2/R.C.A. HR-76 C5 f.c.
Sonar: Krupp-Atlas DSQS-21CZ hull-mounted MF
EW: Argo AR-680/681 intercept/jammer suite, AS-899 D/F, 4/Kin Fen decoy RL (XVI × 4)
M: 2 sets geared steam turbines; 2 props; 60,000 shp
Electric: 1,000 kw
Boilers: 4 Babcock & Wilcox; 43.3 kg/cm², 454° C
Range: 1,000/32; 4,400/11 **Fuel:** 500 tons **Crew:** 275 tot.

Remarks: Transferred in 9-70. Received "Wu Chin I" conversion, with the Honey H 930 Mod. 2 weapon-control system and two R.C.A. HR-76 C5 radars and a morgen Mk 35 periscopic sight in place of the Mk 25 radar in the Mk 37 director, w is now fixed. An OTO Melara 76-mm mount replaced the "B" twin 127-mm mount, the Sea Chaparral launcher is atop the after superstructure.

"Tien Shi"-conversion half-sisters *Heng Yang* (902, ex-*Samuel N. Moore,* DD *Hua Yang* (903, ex-*Bristol,* DD 857), and *Yuen Yang* (905, ex-*Haynsworth,* DD were retired in 1991. Two additional Tien Shi units (which were to have receive Chin I upgrades) were stricken earlier: *Hsiang Yang* (901, ex-*Brush,* DD 745) ar 1984, and *Po Yang* (910, ex-*Maddox,* DD 731) around 1985. Both were in poor condi

♦ 4 ex-U.S. Fletcher class

Bldrs: 918: Bethlehem Steel, Staten Island; others: Bethlehem, San Francis

	Laid down	L	In
908 Kwei Yang (ex-*Twining,* DD 540)	21-11-42	11-7-43	1-
909 Chiang Yang (ex-*Mullany,* DD 528)	15-1-42	12-10-42	23-
918 An Yang (ex-*Kimberly,* DD 521)	27-7-42	4-2-43	24-
919 Kun Yang (ex-*Yarnell,* DD 541)	5-12-42	25-7-43	30-

TROYERS *(continued)*

ernized Fletcher—with 3 127-mm DP, no 76-mm DP
Defense Technology, 1986

Yang (908)—with 76-mm gun *Defense Technology, 1985*

2,100 tons (3,036 fl) **S:** 35 kts
m: 114.65 (112.52 wl) × 11.99 × 4.39 (5.38 over sonar)
3/Hsiung Feng SSM (III × 1)—1/Sea Chaparral SAM system (IV × 1, 16 RIM-72C missiles)—3/127-mm 38-cal. Mk 30 DP (I × 3; 908, 909: 2/127-mm DP (I × 2) and 1/76-mm 62-cal. OTO Melara Compact DP)—2/40-mm 70-cal. Bofors AA (I × 2)—6/324-mm Mk 32 ASW TT (III × 2)—2/Mk 11 Hedgehog ASW spigot mortars (XXIV × 2)—1/d.c. rack; 919 also: 1/mine rail
ectron Equipt:
Radar: 1/SPS-10 or SPS-58A surf./air search, 1/SPS-66 surf. search, 2/R.C.A. R-76 C5 f.c.
Sonar: Krupp-Atlas DSQS-21CZ hull-mounted MF
EW: Argo AR 680/681 intercept/jammer suite, AS-899 D/F, 4/King Fen decoy RL (XVI × 4)
2 sets geared steam turbines; 2 props; 60,000 shp
ectric: 880 kw **Boilers:** 4 Babcock & Wilcox; 43.3 kg/cm², 454° C
nge: 860/35; 4,700/13 **Fuel:** 512 tons **Crew:** 275 tot.

arks: *An Yang* transferred in 6-67; *Chiang Yang* in 10-71; *Kun Yang* in 6-68; *Yang* in 10-71. Sea Chaparral is a manned mounting for launching Redeye seeking, short-range SAMs; it replaced a twin 40-mm antiaircraft mount. All four have received the Wu Chin I modernization with the Honeywell H 930 weapons-control system, two R.C.A. HR-76 C5 f.c. radars, the Mk 37 f.c.s. converted with the Kollmorgen Mk 35 periscopic sight and, on *Kwei Yang* and *Chiang Yang*, the superfiring 127-mm DP forward replaced by a 76-mm mount. Seatime is kept to a minimum, as the ships have exceeded their useful hull lives.

FRIGATES

Note: In addition to the Kwang Hua-series frigates and the FL-3000 program, Taiwan is continuing to negotiate with Germany for the possible production in Taiwan of up to ten smaller frigates of the MEKO-140 class.

◆ 0 (+6 + 10) Kwang Hua II (FL-3000/PF) class

Bldr: DCAN, Lorient, and China SB, Keelung

	Laid down	L	In serv.
1001	...	...	...
1003	...	...	...
1005	...	...	...
1006	...	...	...
1007	...	...	...
1008	...	...	...

FL-3000 (PF) class—French Navy version DCAN, 1991

D: 3,800 tons fl **S:** 28 kts **Dim:** 125.00 × 13.80 × 4.00
A: 8/Hsiung Feng II SSM (IV × 2)—1/76-mm 62-cal. OTO Melara Compact DP—. . ./. . . ASW TT—1/helicopter
Electron Equipt:
Radar: 1/. . . nav., 1/. . . air search, 1/. . . f.c.
Sonar: . . . hull-mounted
EW: . . . intercept, 4/King Fen (CR-201) decoy RL (XVI × 4)
M: 4 SEMT-Pielstick 16 PA 6 BTC diesels; 2 CP props; 31,800 bhp
Range: 7,000/15 **Fuel:** . . . **Crew:** approx. 160 tot.

Remarks: Project definition contract granted to France 11-6-89; after delays caused by protests by mainland China, the program was recast as one whereby France will deliver the first six hulls (without weapons or sensors) in prefabricated sections each to Taiwan for assembly and fitting out. Contract signed 27-9-91. The first is to deliver from France in 3-96 and the last in 1998. Up to ten more would be built entirely in Taiwan. The characteristics above are provisional. Under the original concept, the ships would have had the French TAVITAC combat data system and the DSUV-61 towed passive linear hydrophone array.

◆ 0 (+1 + 4) Kwang Hua I/PFG-2 Batch II class

Bldr: China Shipbuilding Corp., Kaohsiung

	Laid down	L	In serv.
1110 Tien Tan	5-97	3-98	10-99

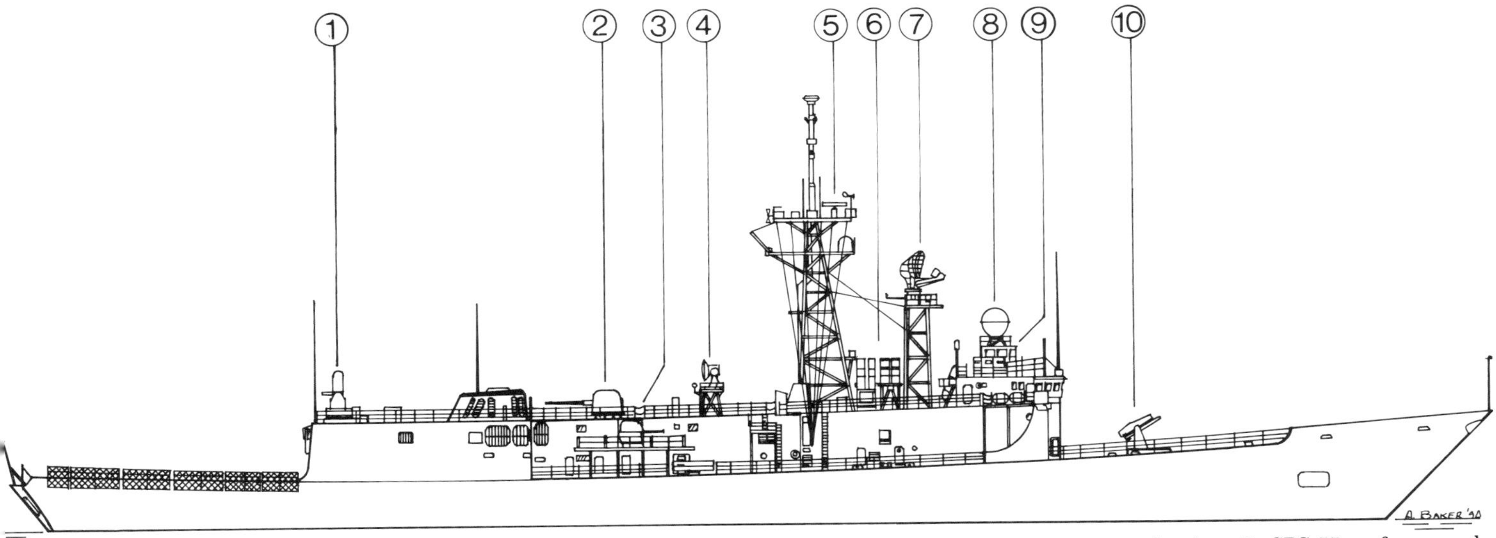

ung Kung (1101) 1. Mk 15 CIWS 2. 76-mm 62-cal. DP 3. 40-mm 70-cal. Bofors AA 4. STIR-24 weapons-control radar 5. SPS-55 surface-search r 6. Hsiung Feng II missile launchers 7. SPS-49(V)5 air-search radar 8. Mk 92 Mod. 6 weapons-control radar 9. SLQ-32(V)5 EW antenna 10. Mk od. 4 missile launcher
A. D. Baker III

FRIGATES *(continued)*

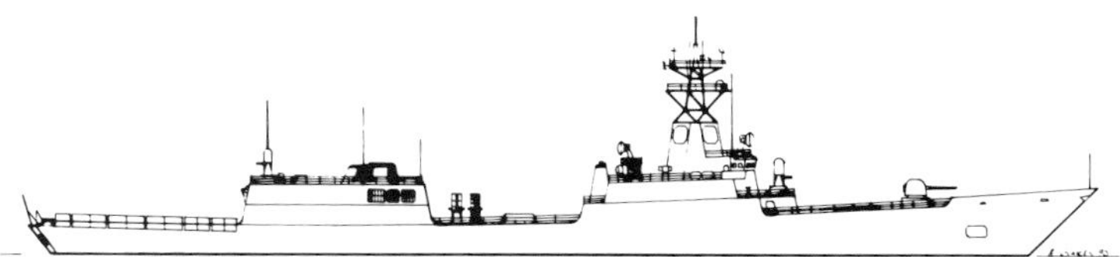

Tien Tan (1110)—conjectural drawing A. D. Baker III, 1990

D: approx. 4,300 tons (fl) **S:** 28 kts
Dim: 144.00 (132.00 wl) × 13.72 × 5.70 (8.60 max.)
A: 8/Hsiung Feng II SSM (IV × 2)—82/Tien Kung I or Standard SM-1 SAM (Mk 41 VLS, forward)—16/NATO Sea Sparrow SAM (*see* Remarks)—1/76-mm 62-cal. OTO Melara DP—2/40-mm 70-cal. Bofors AA (I × 2)—2/20-mm Mk 15 CIWS (I × 2)—6/324-mm ASW TT (III × 2)—1/Sikorsky S-70 helicopter
Electron Equipt:
Radar: 1/SPS-55 surf. search, 1/G.E. ADAR-2N "Mini-Aegis" or Raytheon CMAR + phased-array air search, 2/H.S.A. STIR-24
Sonar: Raytheon DE 1160B hull-mounted MF
EW: Chang Feng III intercept, 4/King Fen decoy RL (XVI × 4)
M: 2 G.E. LM-2500 gas turbines; 2 CP props; 55–60,000 shp
Electric: . . . kw **Range:** 4,200/20 **Fuel:** 600+ tons **Crew:** . . .

Remarks: First two ordered 8-5-89, but now apparently only 1110 will be built to this configuration; four more planned, but may be canceled in favor of additional units of the FL-3000 class. An updated, enlarged PFG-2, modified by adding a 5.18-m plug (in 1991, it was proposed to increase the plug to 15.6 m, increasing the displacement to well over 4,500 tons to permit fitting 48 VLS cells). The 76-mm gun will be mounted on the bow, forward of the Mk 41 VLS launch group. A second Mk 15 CIWS will be mounted forward of the bridge. A four-faced phased-array radar will replace SPS-49, and two STIR-24 f.c. radars will be fitted. In place of one of the two helicopter hangar positions, a Martin Marietta "Quad Pack" (4 Mk 41 VLS cells subdivided to total 16 launch positions) will be fitted. The UNISYS "Advanced Combat System," with a distributed data architecture, will be accommodated in a main and an auxiliary combat information center (CIC) that have been moved from the superstructure to below the main deck. The amidships superstructure, where the 76-mm gun is located in the first group of ships, will be one deck lower and will be topped by the Hsiung Feng II missile launch canisters. The 40-mm AA listed may not be carried. A towed passive sonar array (TASS) may be added later. To the twin-screw propulsion system may be added two cruise gas turbines in a COGOG arrangement. The mast will be a raked GRP structure.

◆ **0 (+7) Kwang Hua I/PFG-2 Batch I class** Bldr: China SB Corp., Kaohsiung

	Laid down	L	In serv.
1101 Cheung Kung	2-12-90	27-10-91	7-5-93
1103 Cheng Ho	3-11-91	27-9-92	7-4-94
1105 Chi Kuang	4-10-92	29-8-93	7-3-95
1106 Yueh Fei	5-9-93	31-7-94	7-2-96
1107 Tzu I	8-94	6-95	1-97
1108 Pan Chao	7-95	5-96	12-97
1109 Chang Chien	6-96	4-97	11-98

Kwang Hua/PFG-2 Batch I class P. K. Hsu/Gibbs & Cox, 1989

D: approx. 3,100 tons light (4,200 fl) **S:** 29 kts
Dim: 138.80 (125.90 wl) × 13.72 × 5.70 (8.60 max.)
A: 8/Hsiung Feng II SSM (IV × 2)—1/Mk 13 Mod. 4 guided-missile launch syst. (I × 1; 40 Standard SM-1 MR SAM)—1/76-mm OTO Melara DP—2/40-mm 70-cal. Bofors AA (I × 2)—1/20-mm Mk 15 CIWS—6/324-mm Mk 32 ASW TT (III × 2)—1 or 2/Sikorsky S-70 helicopters
Electronic Equipt:
Radar: 1/SPS-55 surf. search, 1/SPS-49(V)5 air search, 1/Mk 92 Mod. 6 f.c., 1/H.S.A. STIR-24 missile f.c.
Sonar: Raytheon DE-1160B hull-mounted MF; provision for TAS
EW: SLQ-32(V)5 with Sidekick jammer; Mk 36 SRBOC decoy sy (VI × 2)
M: 2 G.M. LM-2500 gas turbines; 1 CP prop; 41,000 shp—2 drop-d electric propulsors; 720 shp
Electric: 3,000 kw (3 × 1,000-kw diesel alternator sets)
Range: 4,200/20; 5,000/18 **Fuel:** 587 tons + 64 tons helicopter f
Crew: . . .

Remarks: The first 8 of a planned 12 were ordered 8-5-89; of these, 7 are to slightly modified version of the "long-hulled" U.S. Navy *Oliver Hazard Perry* Construction of the first two will be aided by "kits" supplied by Bath Iron Works, will also assist with the remainder. Design by Gibbs & Cox. Originally only fou to have been built to the basic design, but development of the phased-array rad vertically launched SAM for the "Batch II," updated variant has lagged. A hold-down and transfer system will be installed. The towed linear passive sonar (TASS) may be the French Thomson-Sintra DSBV-61A; the first ship to have stalled at completion will be *Chi Kuang* (1105), which will also be the first of the c have a data link. Named for Chinese maritime heroes.

◆ **0 (+ 3 + 3) ex-U.S. Knox class**

	Bldr	Laid down	L	In
. . . . (ex-*Brewton*, FF 1086)	Avondale SY,	2-10-70	24-7-71	8
. . . . (ex-*Robert E. Peary*, ex-*Conolly*, FF 1073)	Lockheed SB, Seattle, Wash.	20-12-70	23-6-71	2
. . . . (ex-*Kirk*, FF 1087)	Avondale SY Westwego, LA	4-12-70	25-9-71	9

Brewton (FF 1086)—in U.S. Navy service John Bouvia

D: 3,075 tons light (4,260 fl) **S:** 27+ kts
Dim: 134.0 (126.5 wl) × 14.33 × 4.60 (7.55 over sonar)—*see* Rema
A: 1/127-mm 54-cal. Mk 42 DP—1/20-mm Mk 15 CIWS—1/Mk 116 ASROC system (VIII x 1)—4/324-mm Mk 32 fixed ASW T 1/. . . . . ASW helicopter
Electron Equipt:
Radar: 1/LN-66 or SPS-53 nav., 1/SPS-67 surf. search, 1/SPS-4 air search, 1/SPG-53 gun f.c.
Sonar: 1/SQS-26CX hull-mounted (3.5 kHz), SQS-35(V) VDS (13 kHz), SQR-18A towed hydrophone array
EW: SLQ-32(V)1 or 32(V)2 intercept, Mk 36 SRBOC decoy syst. (VI × 2, Mk 137 RL)
TACAN: SRN-15
M: 1 set Westinghouse geared steam turbines; 1 prop; 35,000 shp
Boilers: 2 Babcock & Wilcox or Combustion Eng. 84 kg/cm², 510°
Electric: 3,000 kw **Range:** 4,300/20 **Fuel:** 750 tons
Crew: 17–20 officers, 255–265 enlisted (in U.S. Navy service)

Remarks: To transfer on lease on decommissioning from the U.S. Navy on 7-8-92, and 6-8-93, respectively. Three more may be transferred later.
The ASROC system has an automatic reloading magazine beneath the bridg poon missiles will not be transferred with the ships. The ASW torpedo tubes ar in the forward end of the hangar superstructure, aimed outboard at an angle of 4 SQS-35 towed VDS transducer body and hoist was modified to permit towi SQR-18A TACTASS. All carry a Mk 68 gunfire-control system with SPG-53A, radar. Have Mk 114 ASW fire-control system. Anti-rolling fin stabilizers fitted Prairie-Masker bubbler system fitted to hulls and propellers to reduce radiate Received the ASWTDS (ASW Tactical Data System) during the 1980s.

◆ **1 ex-U.S. Rudderow class** Bldr: Bethlehem Steel, Hingham, Mas

	Laid down	L	In serv.
827 Tai Yuan (ex-*Riley*, DE 579)	20-10-43	29-12-43	13-3-44

D: 1,420 tons (1,920 fl) **S:** 24 kts **Dim:** 93.27 × 11.24 × 3.40
A: 2/127-mm 38-cal DP (I × 2)—4/40-mm 60-cal. AA (II × 2)—4/20-mm Oerlikon AA (I × 4)—1/Mk 11 Hedgehog ASW spigot mortar (XXIV × 1)—6/324-mm Mk 32 ASW TT (III × 2)—2/M d.c. racks—mines
Electron Equipt:
Radar: 1/. . . nav., 1/SPS-6 air search, 1/Mk 26 f.c.
Sonar: . . . hull-mounted
M: turbo-electric drive: 2 sets G.E. steam turbogenerators; 2 moto props; 12,000 shp

ATES (continued)

lers: 2 Foster-Wheeler D-type; 31.7 kg/cm², 399° C
ctric: 1,140 kw **Range:** 1,100/24; 5,000/12
l: 354 tons **Crew:** 200 tot.

rks: Transferred, after modernization, on 10-7-69; purchased outright in 3-74. nverted to fisheries patrol ship in 1989 as reported in last edition; retained ent listed above through 1991. Depth-charge racks are bolted to mine rails.

Of the six *Crosley*- and three *Charles Lawrence*-class former high-speed trans- onverted to frigates that were listed in the previous edition, four have been ed and the others are listed under the Customs Service entry.

VETTES

It is planned to order from 10 to 16 missile corvettes (PCEG) of about 1,250 tons ement to augment ASW capabilities. The first two would be built in Europe and t in Taiwan.

x-U.S. Auk-class former minesweepers

rs: *Wu Sheng:* Savannah Machine & Foundry, Ga; others: American SB, veland, Ohio

	Laid down	L	In serv.
NG JIN (ex-*Steady*, F 118)	17-11-41	6-6-42	16-11-42
HU YUNG (ex-*Waxwing*, F 389)	24-5-44	10-3-45	6-8-45
U SHENG (ex-*Redstart*, F 378)	14-6-44	18-10-45	4-4-45

Yung (870) *Ships of the World,* 1988

890 tons (1,250 fl) **S:** 18 kts
n: 67.39 (65.53 pp) × 9.80 × 3.30
2/76.2-mm 50-cal. Mk 26 DP (I × 2)—4/40-mm 60-cal. AA (II × 2)—4/20-mm AA (II × 2)—1/Mk 11 Hedgehog ASW spigot mortar (XXIV × 1)—3/324-mm Mk 32 ASW TT (III × 1)—2/Mk 9 d.c. racks
ctron Equipt:
Radar: 1/Decca . . . nav.
Sonar: SQS-17 hull-mounted (12/13/14 kHz)
2 G.M. 12-278A diesels; 2 props; 3,532 bhp
ctric: 360 kw **Fuel:** 216 tons **Crew:** 80 tot.

rks: After conversion to corvettes, transferred as follows: *Chu Yung* in 11-65, *Jin* in 3-68, and *Wu Sheng* in 7-65. *Chu Yung* was fitted with mine rails in 1975. se they have exceeded their hull lives, are used very sparingly.

DED-MISSILE PATROL BOATS

0 Hai Ou class Bldr: China SB, Kaohsiung (In serv. 1980–84)

G 1 through FABG 50

Ou-class FABG *Defense Technology,* 4-91

Two Hai Ou class maneuvering *Defense Technology,* 10-85

D: 47 tons (fl) **S:** 36 kts **Dim:** 21.62 × 5.49 × 0.94 (1.82 props)
A: 2/Hsiung Feng I SSM (I × 2)—2/12.7-mm mg (I × 2)
Electron Equipt:
Radar: 1/LN-66 nav., 1/R.C.A. CS/SPG-24 missile target designation
EW: WD-2A intercept, 4 AV-2 decoy RL
M: 2 MTU 12V331 TC81 diesels; 2 props; 2,720 bhp
Electric: 30 kw **Range:** 700/32 **Crew:** 8 tot.

Remarks: Design based closely on the Israeli Dvora class; project name means "Sea-gull." Have Kollmorgen Mk 35 optical sight, four AV-2 chaff RL (I × 4). The fire-control radar is a variant of the HR-76 C2 used on destroyers. Early units had a pylon mast and the missile launchers situated near the stern; late units (the majority) have a lattice mast and the missile launchers located closer to amidships, with an unoccupied mounting ring for a 20-mm AA near the stern. All attached to the Hai Chiao (Sea Dragon) division, home-ported at Makung in the Pescadores Islands since 9-89.

◆ 2 Lung Chiang class

	Bldr	In serv.
601 LUNG CHIANG	Tacoma Boatbldg, Tacoma, Wash.	15-5-78
602 SUIKIANG	China SB, Kaohsiung	1982

Suikiang (602) 1990

GUIDED-MISSILE PATROL BOATS *(continued)*

D: 218 tons (250 fl) **S:** 40 kts **Dim:** 50.14 (46.94 pp) × 7.60 × 2.26
A: 4/Hsiung Feng I SSM—1/76-mm 62-cal. OTO Melara DP—2/30-mm Emerlec AA (II × 1)—2/12.7-mm mg (I × 2)
Electron Equipt:
Radar: 1/SPS-58A surf./air search, 1/RAN-11L/X (NA 10 system) f.c. (583: *see* Remarks)
EW: WD-2A intercept, 4 AV-2 decoy RL (I × 4)
M: CODOG: 3 G.M. 12V149 TI diesels (3,600 shp), 3 AVCO-Lycoming TF-40A gas turbines; 3 CP props; 15,000 shp
Range: 700/40 (gas turbines), 1,900/30 (3 diesels); 2,700/12 (1 diesel)
Crew: 5 officers, 30 enlisted

Remarks: Design is a variation of Tacoma Boatbuilding (U.S.) PSMM Mk-5 design. Prototype built in U.S. with follow-on unit to be built in Taiwan. Second unit is of revised design, with the R.C.A. HR-76 C5 fire-control radar and fin stabilizers; a planned six additional were canceled.

PATROL BOATS AND CRAFT

Note: Twelve 300-ton submarine chasers are planned, with the first two to be built in Europe and the remainder in Taiwan. In 7-90, it was announced that a ten-unit 34-meter-long class of patrol boats, an enlarged version of the class below, was to be built.

◆ **22 32-meter class** Bldr: China SB, Kaohsiung (In serv. 1987–. . .)

PCC 1-series

32-meter class *Defense Technology,* 12-90

D: 100 tons (143 fl) **S:** 40 kts **Dim:** 32.10 × 9.00 × 1.80
A: 1/40-mm 60-cal. Mk 3 AA—2/12.7-mm mg (I × 2)—2/d.c. racks
Electron Equipt:
Radar: 1/Decca . . . nav.—Sonar: . . . hull-mounted HF
M: 3 MTU 12V396 TB93 diesels; 3 props; 5,760 bhp
Range: . . . **Fuel:** 36 tons **Crew:** 3 officers, 13 enlisted

Remarks: Designed by Vosper-QAF, Singapore. Intended for harbor and coastal patrol service. Some are assigned to the Coastal Patrol Command and have a Gemini dinghy on davits aft.

◆ **14 Taiwanese-built** Bldr: . . .

D: . . . **S:** 32 kts **Dim:** 12.8 × . . . × . . .
A: 1/12.7-mm mg **Electron Equipt:** Radar: 1/. . . nav.
M: 2 G.M. diesels; 2 Arneson surface-piercing outdrives; 1,300 bhp
Range: 400/. . .

Remarks: GRP construction, C. Raymond Hunt design. Program reported 1987.

◆ **6 (+ . . .) Vosper design** Bldr: prototype: Vosper Pty., Singapore; others: . . . ., Taiwan

Prototype 21-m patrol craft Vosper, 1986

D: 28 tons (fl) **S:** 40+ kts **Dim:** 21.00 (16.60 wl) × 4.80 × 1.00
A: 1/20-mm AA—2/7.62-mm mg
Electron Equipt: Radar: 1/Decca 170 nav.
M: 2 G.M.-Stewart & Stevenson 16V92 TMAB diesels; 2 Arneson A 14 surface-piercing outdrives; 2,700 bhp
Electric: 18 kw **Range:** 400/. . . **Crew:** . . .

Remarks: Aluminum construction. Program delayed by 1986–87 insolvency since-reorganized Vosper Pty.; series craft built in Taiwan.

◆ **7 PBC-series** Bldr: China Shipbuilding Corp., Kaohsiung (In serv. 1

PBC 5501 through PBC 5507

PBC 5506 and PBC 5507 Martin Chung,

D: . . . **S:** 40 kts **Dim:** 26.2 × . . . × . . . **A:** 1/20-mm AA
M: 3 Isotta Fraschini diesels; 3 Castoldi waterjets; 3,000 bhp

Remarks: Used mainly for fisheries patrol and counterinsurgency missions; h large searchlight atop the pilothouse.

◆ **10 aluminum-hulled** Bldr: China Shipbuilding Corp., Kaohsiung

PBC 3521-series

PBC 3521 Chien Chung,

D: 55 tons (fl) **S:** 25 kts **Dim:** 15.0 × . . . × . . .
A: 2/12.7-mm mg (I × 2) **M:** 2 diesels; waterjet drive

Remarks: Date from 1971. Originally mounted a 40-mm Mk 3 AA but were gunned.

MINE WARFARE SHIPS

◆ **4 (+8) MWW 50-class minehunters** Bldr: Abeking & Rasmussen, Lemwerder, West Germany

	L	In serv.
. . . . (ex-*Explorer-I*)	4-90	1990
. . . . (ex-*Explorer-II*)	. . .	1990
. . . . (ex-*Explorer-III*)	. . .	5-91
. . . . (ex-*Explorer-IV*)	. . .	5-91

D: . . . **S:** 15 kts **Dim:** 49.00 × 10.80 × 2.80
A: 1/40-mm Bofors L-70 AA—2/20-mm AA (I × 2)
Electron Equipt:
Radar: . . .—Sonar: Simrad SA950 hull-mounted (95 kHz)
M: 2 MTU 8V396-series diesels; 2 props; 2,000 bhp
Range: 3,500/15 **Crew:** . . .

ɪINE WARFARE SHIPS *(continued)*

:plorer-II—on trials Peter Voss, 7-90

plorer-III—with mechanical sweep gear added *China Times,* 1-92

ɪarks: Reported ordered 1989 to begin the long-overdue replacement of the obso-ent U.S.-built units listed below. Were delivered without armament or mine-ɪtermeasures equipment in blue hull/white superstructure paint scheme and let-d "CPC Offshore" on sides for the China Petroleum Corporation, which ostensibly ·red them as "multi-purpose offshore vessels," intended to "support to oilrigs, ɪnographic research, firefighting, pollution control, and search-and-rescue." ·den hull construction. By late 1991 had been fitted with mechanical sweep equip-t but still did not have armament; may also employ Gaymarine "Pluto" remotely ·ated vehicles. Up to eight more are planned.

10 ex-U.S. and ex-Belgian Adjutant, MSC 268*, and MSC 289† :oastal minesweeper classes

	Bldr	In serv.
Yung Chou (ex-MSC 278)*	Tacoma Boat, Wash.	7-59
Yung Chen x-*Maaseick,* ex-MSC 78)	Adams Yacht, Quincy, Mass.	7-53
Yung An (ex-MSC 123)	. . . . . .	6-55
Yung Sui (ex-*Diksmuide,* ·-MSC 65)	H. B. Nevins, N.Y.	2-54
Yung Lo (ex-MSC 306)†	Dorchester Bldrs., N.J.	4-66
Yung Nien (ex-MSC 277)*	Tacoma Boat, Wash.	5-59
Yung Shan (ex-*Lier,* ex-SC 63)	H. B. Nevins, N.Y.	7-53
Yung Fu (ex-*Diest,* :-*Macaw,* ex-MSC 77)	Adams Yacht, Quincy, Mass.	5-53
Yung Jen (ex-*St. Niklaas,* -MSC 64)	H. B. Nevins, N.Y.	2-54
Yung Hsin (ex-MSC 302)†	Dorchester Bldrs., N.J.	3-65

ɪ Chou (423)—MSC 268 class, wearing old number 1979

Yung Lo (469)—MSC 289 class, wearing old number 1970

D: 320 tons (378 fl) **S:** 12.5 kts **Dim:** 43.0 (41.5 wl) × 7.95 × 2.55
A: 2/20-mm Oerlikon AA (II × 1)
Electron Equipt:
Radar: 1/Decca 45 or 707 nav.
Sonar: UQS-1D (100 kHz)
M: 2 G.M. 8-268A diesels; 2 props; 1,200 bhp (MSC 268 class: 4 G.M. 6-71 diesels; 2 props; 890 bhp)
Range: 2,500/12 **Fuel:** 40 tons **Crew:** 40 tot.

Remarks: Wooden hulls. All transferred on completion except ex-Belgian ships, which were transferred in 11-69. Have a variety of configurations, the ex-MSC 268 having a different propulsion scheme and the ex-MSC 289 class having a lower bridge and taller stack. Sister *Yung Ping* (ex-MSC 140) stricken 1982; *Yung Chi* (497, ex-*Charleroi,* ex-MSC 152), *Yung Ching* (432, ex-*Eekloo,* ex-MSC 101), and *Yung Ju* (457, ex-MSC 300) stricken by 1991. Several others soon to follow, as all are in poor condition.

◆ **1 ex-U.S. minesweeping boat**

MSB 12 (ex-U.S. Navy MSB 4, ex-U.S. Army . . .)

D: 39 tons (fl) **S:** 12 kts **Dim:** 17.5 × 4.6 × 1.25
M: 2 Packard diesels; 2 props; 600 bhp **Crew:** 6 tot.

Remarks: Built in 1945 and transferred in 12-61. Wooden hull.

◆ **8 ex-U.S. minesweeping launches**

MSML 1	MSML 3	MSML 5	MSML 6
MSML 7	MSML 8	MSML 11	MSML 12

D: 24 tons (fl) **S:** 8 kts **Dim:** 15.29 × 3.96 × 1.31
M: 1 diesel; 1 prop; 60 bhp **Range:** 800/8 **Crew:** 4 tot.

Remarks: Built between 1943 and 1945, and converted from personnel launches before transfer in 3-61. Wooden hulls.

AMPHIBIOUS WARFARE SHIPS

◆ **1 command ship** Bldr: Dravo Corp., Neville Island, Pittsburgh, Pa.

	L	In serv.
219 Kao Hsiung (ex-*Chung Hai,* LST 229, ex-*Dukes County,* LST 735)	11-3-44	26-4-44

Kao Hsiung (219)—wearing old number 1968

D: 1,650 tons (4,080 fl) **S:** 11 kts **Dim:** 99.98 × 15.24 × 3.4
A: 8/40-mm 60-cal. Bofors AA (II × 2, I × 4)—4/20-mm Oerlikon AA (II × 2)
Electron Equipt: Radar: 1/SPS-10 surf. search, 1/SPS-12 air search
M: 2 G.M. 12-567A diesels; 2 props; 1,700 bhp **Range:** 15,000/9

Remarks: Transferred in 5-57, converted to command ship in 1964, with additional communications gear and radars. Retains bow doors. Current equipment and status uncertain.

◆ **1 ex-U.S. Cabildo-class dock landing ship**
Bldr: Gulf SB, Chickasaw, Ala.

	Laid down	L	In serv.
618 Chen Hai (ex-*Fort Marion,* LSD 22)	15-9-44	22-5-45	29-1-46

D: 4,790 tons (9,375 fl) **S:** 15.6 kts
Dim: 139.52 (138.38 wl) × 22.0 × 5.49
A: 2/Sea Chaparral point-defense SAM syst. (VI × 2)—12/40-mm 60-cal. Bofors AA (IV × 2, II × 2)

AMPHIBIOUS WARFARE SHIPS *(continued)*

Electron Equipt: Radar: 1/LN-66 nav., 1/SPS-5 surf. search
M: 2 sets geared steam turbines; 2 props; 9,000 shp
Boilers: 2; 30.6 kg/cm², 393° C **Range:** 8,000/15
Fuel: 1,758 tons **Crew:** 326 crew + several hundred troops

Remarks: Transferred by sale on 15-4-77, having been stricken from the U.S. Navy in 10-74. Modernized under FRAM-II program 12-59 to 4-60. Helicopter platform over 119.5 × 13.4-meter docking well, which can accommodate three LCUs, eighteen LCMs, or thirty-two amphibious armored troop carriers.

♦ 13 ex-U.S. LST 1 and LST 542-class tank landing ships

From among:

	Bldr	In serv.
201 Chung Hai (ex-LST 755)	American Br., Ambridge, Pa.	29-7-44
203 Chung Ting (ex-LST 537)	Missouri Valley B & I, Evansville, Ind.	9-2-44
204 Chung Hsing (ex-LST 557)	Missouri Valley B & I, Evansville, Ind.	5-5-44
206 Chung Chi (ex-LST 1017)	Bethlehem, Fore River, Mass.	12-4-44
205 Chung Chien (ex-LST 716)	Jeffersonville B & M, Ind.	18-8-44
208 Chung Shun (ex-LST 732)	Dravo, Pittsburgh, Pa.	10-4-44
209 Chung Lien (ex-LST 1050)	Dravo, Pittsburgh, Pa.	3-4-45
210 Chung Yung (ex-LST 574)	Missouri Valley B & I, Evansville, Ind.	26-6-44
216 Chung Kuang (ex-LST 503)	Jeffersonville B & M, Ind.	14-12-43
217 Chung Suo (ex-*Bradley County,* LST 400)	Newport News SB & DD, Va.	7-1-43
221 Chung Chuan (ex-*Wan Tu,* ex-LST 640)	Chicago B & I, Seneca, Ill.	18-9-44
222 Chung Sheng (ex-LST(H) 1033)	Chicago B & I, Seneca, Ill.	4-44
223 Chung Fu (ex-*Iron County,* LST 840)	American Br., Ambridge, Pa.	11-12-44
225 Chung Chiang (ex-*San Bernardino County,* LST 1110)	Missouri Valley B & I, Evansville, Ind.	7-3-45
226 Chung Chih (ex-*Sagadohoc County,* LST 1091)	American Br., Ambridge, Pa.	6-4-45
227 Chung Ming (ex-*Sweetwater County,* LST 1152)	Dravo, Pittsburgh, Pa.	13-4-45
228 Chung Shu (ex-LST 520)	Chicago B & I, Seneca, Ill.	28-2-44
229 Chung Wan (ex-LST 535)	Missouri Valley B & I, Evansville, Ind.	4-2-44
230 Chung Pang (ex-LST 578)	Missouri Valley B & I, Evansville, Ind.	15-7-44
231 Chung Yeh (ex-*Sublette County,* LST 1144)	Chicago B & I, Seneca, Ill.	28-5-45

Chung Yeh (231) 1990

D: 1,653 tons (4,080 fl) **S:** 11.6 kts **Dim:** 99.98 × 15.24 × 3.40
A: several: 2/76.2-mm 50-cal. DP (I × 2)—6–8/40-mm 60-cal. AA (II × 2, or I × 2 or 4)—4–8/20-mm AA (II × 4)
M: 2 G.M. 12-567A diesels; 2 props; 1,700 bhp **Electric:** 300 kw
Range: 15,000/9 **Fuel:** 569 tons **Crew:** 100–125 tot.

Remarks: Six transferred in 1946, two in 1947, *Chung Shu* in 1948, seven in 1958, *Chung Yun* in 1959, *Chung Kuang* in 1960, *Chung Yeh* in 1961, and two subsequently. All extensively rebuilt during the late 1960s, in many cases becoming almost new ships; re-engined at the same time. Most have four pairs of Welin davits, while *Chung Chih, Chung Yung, Chung Sheng,* and *Chung Shu* have six, and *Chung Chien* has two; each pair of davits handles one LCVP. Five or more have two 76.2-mm guns. *Chung Chih* (ex-216, ex-LST 279) was stricken in 1978. Sister *Chung Cheng* (224, ex-*Lafayette County,* LST 859), stricken 1989, may become a museum exhibit in the U.S.A. Between 1984 and 1991, seven others had also been stricken and laid up at Kaohsiung along with *Chung Cheng.*

♦ 4 ex-U.S. LSM 1-class medium landing ships

	Bldr	L	In serv.
637 Mei Lo (ex-LSM 362)	Brown SB, Houston, Tex.	9-12-44	11-1-45
649 Mei Chin (ex-LSM 155)	Charleston NY, S.C.	19-6-44	26-7-44
659 Mei Ping (ex-LSM 471)	Brown SB, Houston, Tex.	17-2-45	23-2-45
694 Mei Sung (ex-LSM 457)	Western Pipe & Steel, San Pedro, Cal.	28-1-45	28-3-45

D: 1,095 tons (fl) **S:** 12.5 kts
Dim: 62.03 (59.89 wl) × 10.52 × 2.54 (max.)
A: 4/40-mm 60-cal. Bofors AA (II × 2)—2/20-mm Oerlikon AA (I × 2)
M: *Mei Lo, Mei Ping:* 2 Fairbanks-Morse 38D8Q × 10 (others: 2 G.M. 16-278A) diesels; 2 props; 2,800 bhp
Electric: 240 kw **Range:** 5,000/7 **Fuel:** 165 tons **Crew:** 60 tot.

Remarks: *Mei Sung* and *Mei Chin* transferred in 1946, *Mei Ping* in 11-56, and *Mei L* in 5-62. Have been extensively overhauled; original cylindrical pilothouse and bridg replaced with larger, rectangular structure, and twin 40-mm added aft.

♦ 6 ex-U.S. LCU 1466-class utility landing craft

Bldr: Ishikawajima, Harima, Japan

488 Ho Shan (ex-LCU 1596)	491 Ho Meng (ex-LCU 1599)
489 Ho Chuan (ex-LCU 1597)	492 Ho Mou (ex-LCU 1600)
490 Ho Seng (ex-LCU 1598)	493 Ho Shou (ex-LCU 1601)

D: 347 tons (fl) **S:** 8 kts **Dim:** 35.08 × 10.36 × 1.6 (max.)
A: 4/20-mm AA (II × 2)
M: 3 Gray Marine 64/65YTL diesels; 3 props; 675 bhp
Range: 1,200/6 **Fuel:** 11 tons **Crew:** 14 tot.

Remarks: Built under Offshore Procurement Program. In service in 3-55. Cargo: 1 tons.

♦ 16 ex-U.S. LCU 501 (LCT(6))-class utility landing craft

	In serv.
401 Ho Chi (ex-LCU 1212)	16-8-44
402 Ho Huei (ex-LCU 1218)	25-8-44
403 Ho Yao (ex-LCU 1244)	22-9-44
404 Ho Deng (ex-LCU 1367)	12-10-44
405 Ho Feng (ex-LCU 1397)	26-10-44
406 Ho Chao (ex-LCU 1429)	8-12-44
407 Ho Teng (ex-LCU 1452)	20-10-44
481 Ho Shun (ex-LCU 1225)	4-9-44
482 Ho Tsung (ex-LCU 1213)	17-8-44
484 Ho Chung (ex-LCU 849)	7-8-44
485 Ho Chang (ex-LCU 512)	7-9-43
486 Ho Cheng (ex-LCU 1145)	11-5-44
494 Ho Chun (ex-LCU 892)	27-7-44
495 Ho Yung (ex-LCU 1271)	19-8-44
496 Ho Chien (ex-LCU 1278)	22-7-44
SB1 Ho Chie (ex-LCU 700)	18-4-44

Ho Feng (405) *Defense Technology,*

D: 143 tons (309 fl) **S:** 10 kts **Dim:** 36.3 (32.0 wl) × 9.96 × 1.14
A: 2/20-mm Oerlikon AA (I × 2)—2/12.7-mm mg (I × 2)
M: 3 G.M. 6-71 diesels; 3 props; 675 bhp **Electric:** 20 kw
Crew: 10 tot.

Remarks: Six transferred between 1946 and 1948, the others between 1958 and *Ho Chie* has served in an auxiliary role since delivery.

♦ 250 U.S. LCM(3)- and LCM(6)-class landing craft

Bldrs: U.S. and Taiwan

D: 62 tons (fl) **S:** 9 kts **Dim:** 17.07 × 4.37 × 1.07
A: 1/20-mm AA or 12.7-mm mg in some
M: 2 Gray Marine 64HN9 diesels; 2 props; 450 bhp
Range: 130/9 **Crew:** 9 tot.

Remarks: LCM(3) are 56 tons (fl), 15.38 m overall. Cargo: LCM(3): 30 tons, LC 34 tons.

HIBIOUS WARFARE SHIPS *(continued)*

(3) adapted as workboat — Fu S. Mei, 10-91

bout 120 U.S. LCVP class

13 tons (fl) **S:** 9 kts **Dim:** 10.9 × 3.21 × 1.04
2/7.62-mm mg (I × 2) **M:** 1 Gray Marine 64HN9 diesel; 225 bhp
nge: 110/9 **Crew:** 3 tot.

P 1902—armed with 2 7.62-mm mg — *Defense Technology*, 11-84

rks: Many attached to LSTs. Wooden construction. Cargo: 36 troops or 4 tons. 25 to 30 were built in Taiwan in the 1970s, known as Type 272. Some are ɔed with radar and two 7.62-mm mg for use as beach reconnaissance craft.

bout 20 20-ft. UDT/patrol craft

-series

3 tons (fl) **S:** . . . kts **Dim:** 6.10 × . . . × . . .
1/7.62-mm mg **Electron Equipt:** Radar: 1/. . . nav.
diesels

series — *Defense Technology*, 11-84

arks: GRP-hulled craft intended to carry underwater demolition teams to heads and to act as patrol craft during amphibious landings. Were in service by

bout 15 commando assault boats

2001-series

ARP 2001-series commando boats — *Defense Technology*, 11-84

D: 2 tons (fl) **S:** . . . kts **Dim:** 4.6 × . . . × . . . **Crew:** 4 tot.
A: 1/7.62-mm mg **M:** 1 Chrysler 115 gasoline outboard; 115 bhp

Note: Also in service are some 717 LVT-5 tracked amphibious armored personnel carriers.

AUXILIARY SHIPS

Note: Hydrographic survey vessels *Bien Dou*, *Chiu Lien* (563, ex-*Geronimo*, ATA 207), and *Lien Chang* (466, ex-LSIL 1017) have either been transferred to a civilian agency or, in the latter case, stricken.

◆ **1 (+ . . .) underway-replenishment ship** — Bldr: China SB, Keelung

	Laid down	L	In serv.
530 Wu Yi	4-88	4-3-89	23-6-90

Wu Yi (530) — *Military Technology*, 1991

Wu Yi (530) — Chien Chung, 12-91

D: 7,700 tons light (17,000 fl) **S:** 21 kts
Dim: 162.12 × 22.00 × 8.60
A: 1/Sea Chaparral SAM syst. (IV × 1; 16 RIM-72C missiles)—2/40-mm 70-cal. Bofors AA (II × 1)—2/20-mm Oerlikon GAM-B01 AA (I × 2)
Electron Equipt: Radar: . . .—TACAN: SRN-15
M: 2 Mitsubishi-M.A.N. 14-cyl. diesels; 2 props; 25,000 bhp
Range: 9,200/10 **Crew:** . . .

Remarks: Designed in U.S. by Rosenblatt & Son. Additional units planned. Helicopter deck at stern capable of handling two CH-47 or S-70CM1-sized helicopters. Capable of underway replenishment on both sides; has four fueling and two solids transfer stations. Carries 9,300 tons of fuel and water, 600 tons munitions and provisions. Largest naval unit yet built in Taiwan. Reportedly, the hull was found to be warped after launch and has a permanent list, the ship is underpowered, and there are gearbox and steering equipment problems.

◆ **1 offshore-island support tanker**

	Bldr	In serv.
512 Wan Shou	Ujina SB, Hiroshima, Japan	1-11-69

AUXILIARY SHIPS *(continued)*

Wan Shou (512) 1970

D: 1,049 tons light (4,150 fl) **S:** 13 kts **Dim:** 86.5 × 16.5 × 5.5
A: 2/40-mm 60-cal. Bofors Mk 3 AA (I × 2)—2/20-mm AA (I × 2)
M: 1 diesel; 1 prop; 2,100 bhp **Fuel:** 230 tons **Crew:** 70 tot.

Remarks: No underway-replenishment capability. Cargo: 2,600 tons.

◆ **2 ex-U.S. Patapsco-class support tankers**
Bldr: Cargill Inc., Savage, Minn.

	Laid down	L	In serv.
507 Hsin Lung (ex-*Elkhorn,* AOG 7)	7-9-42	15-5-43	12-2-44
515 Lung Chuan (ex-*Endeavor,* ex-*Namakagon,* AOG 53)	1-8-44	4-11-44	10-5-45

Hsin Lung (507) and Lung Chuan (515) Martin Chung, 2-92

D: 1,850 tons light (4,335 fl) **S:** 14 kts
Dim: 94.72 (89.0 wl) × 14.78 × 4.78
A: 2/76.2-mm 50-cal. DP (I × 2)—4/20-mm Oerlikon AA (I × 4)
M: 2 G.M. 16-278A diesels; 2 props; 3,300 bhp **Electric:** 460 kw
Range: 6,670/10 **Fuel:** 295 tons **Crew:** 124 tot.

Remarks: Former gasoline tankers. Cargo: 2,040 tons. *Hsin Lung* transferred on 1-7-72, and *Lung Chuan* on 29-6-71 after serving in the New Zealand Navy as Antarctic supply ship since 5-10-62. Used for supplying offshore islands. Purchased outright 19-5-76. Sister *Chang Pei* (378, ex-*Pecatonia,* AOG 57) stricken 1989.

◆ **5 large transports** Bldr: Tsoying Naval SY

524 . . . . (In serv. 11-88)
525 Wu Kang (In serv. 2-85)
526 . . . . (In serv. 11-88)
527 . . . . (In serv. 11-88)
529 . . . . (In serv. 1990)

Wu Kang (525) *Defense Technology,* 12-85

D: 3,040 tons (fl) **S:** . . . **Dim:** 101.0 × 17.0 × . . .
A: 1/ Sea Chaparral point-defense SAM syst. (VI × 1)—2/40-mm 60-cal. Bofors Mk 3 AA (I × 2)
Electron Equipt: Radar: 1/. . . nav.
M: 2 diesels; 2 props; . . . bhp—bow-thruster

Remarks: Transports to serve Quemoy and Matsu garrisons. Stern truncated to fit small berthing area; do *not* have stern vehicle ramp. Can carry over 600 passengers. Later units have smaller cargo cranes. Class has replaced LSTs used in transport and supply service.

◆ **1 transport** Bldr: China SB, Keelung

523 Yuen Feng (In serv. 1983)

D: . . . **S:** . . . **Dim:** 110.0 × . . . × . . .
A: 2/20-mm AA (I × 2) **M:** 1 diesel; . . . bhp

Remarks: Passenger-cargo ship with accommodations for 500 troops.

◆ **1 transport**

	Bldr	L	In serv.
522 Ling Yuen	China SB, Keelung	27-1-75	15-8-75

D: 4,000 tons (fl) **S:** . . . **Dim:** 100.2 × 14.6 × 5.0
A: 2/20-mm AA (I × 2)—2/12.7-mm mg (I × 2)
M: 1 6-cylinder diesel; 1 prop; . . . bhp **Crew:** 55 tot.

Remarks: 2,510 dwt/3,040 grt. Can carry 500 troops.

Note: U.S. *Achelous*-class former repair ship *Wu Tai* (520, ex-*Sung Shan,* ex-ARL 3, ex-LST 490), which had been converted for use as a transport 1973–stricken 1991.

◆ **1 ex-U.S. Army 427-class intelligence collector**
Bldr: Higgins, New Orleans, La. (In serv. 21-12-44)

359 Yung Kang (ex-*Mark,* AKL 12, ex-AG 143, ex-Army FS 214)

Yung Kang (359)—wearing old number

D: 693 tons (899 fl) **S:** 12 kts **Dim:** 54.86 (52.37 wl) × 9.75 × 3
A: 2/20-mm AA (I × 2) **M:** 2 G.M. 6-278A diesels; 2 props; 1,000
Electric: 225 kw **Range:** 4,000/11 **Fuel:** 100 tons **Crew:** 37

Remarks: Built as an aircraft maintenance ship for the U.S. Army Air Forces. ferred to the U.S. Navy on 30-9-47 and to Taiwan on 1-6-71. Sold outright on 1 Now has intelligence-gathering equipment.

◆ **1 ex-U.S. Amphion-class repair ship** Bldr: Tampa SB, Tampa,

	Laid down	L	In serv.
521 Yu Tai (ex-*Cadmus,* AR 14)	30-10-44	5-8-45	23-4-46

Yu Tai (521) Leo Van Ginderen

D: 7,826 tons light (14,490 fl) **S:** 16.5 kts
Dim: 149.96 (141.73 pp) × 21.18 × 8.38
Electron Equipt: Radar: 1/SPS-5 surf. search
A: 1/127-mm 38-cal. DP—6/40-mm 60-cal. AA (II × 3)—4/20-mm (I × 4)
M: 1 set Westinghouse geared steam turbines; 1 prop; 8,500 shp
Boilers: 2 Foster-Wheeler D-type; 30.6 kg/cm², 399° C
Electric: 3,600 kw **Fuel:** 2,430 tons **Crew:** 920 tot.

Remarks: Transferred on 15-1-74. Employed as support ship during cadet tr cruises to South Africa. Carries three LCVP.

◆ **1 ex-U.S. Diver-class salvage ship** Bldr: Basalt Rock Co., Napa

	Laid down	L	In serv.
324 Tai Hu (ex-*Grapple,* ARS 7)	8-9-42	31-12-42	16-12-43

UXILIARY SHIPS *(continued)*

D: 1,530 tons (1,900 fl) **S:** 14.8 kts
Dim: 65.08 (63.09 wl) × 11.89 × 4.29
A: 2/20-mm AA (I × 2) **Electron Equipt:** Radar: 1/SPS-53 nav.
M: 4 Cooper-Bessemer GSB-8 diesels, electric drive; 2 props; 3,060 shp
Electric: 460 kw **Range:** 9,000/14; 20,000/7
Fuel: 283 tons **Crew:** 85 tot.

marks: Transferred on 1-12-77.

4 ex-U.S. Cherokee-, Abnaki-* and Achomawi†- class fleet tugs
Bldrs: *Ta Tung, Ta Wan, Chien Chung:* United Eng., Alameda, Cal.; others: Charleston SB & DD, Charleston, S.C.

	Laid down	L	In serv.
2 TA HAN (ex-*Tawakoni,* ATF 114)*	19-5-43	28-10-43	15-9-44
3 TA TUNG (ex-*Chickasaw,* ATF 83)	14-2-42	23-7-42	4-2-43
) TA WAN (ex-*Apache,* ATF 67)	8-11-44	8-5-45	12-12-45
3 . . . . (ex-*Wenatchee,* ATF 118)*	12-1-44	7-9-44	24-3-45
. . . . (ex-*Achomawi,* ATF 148)†	15-1-44	10-9-44	11-11-44

aki-class tug 563 Chien Chung, 2-92

1,235 tons (1,675 fl) **S:** 15 kts
m: 62.48 (59.44 wl) × 11.73 × 4.67
1/76.2-mm DP—2/12.7-mm mg
ectron Equipt: Radar: 1/. . . nav.
4 G.M. 12-278 diesels, electric drive; 1 prop; 3,000 shp (*see* Remarks)
ectric: 260–400 kw **Fuel:** 295 tons **Range:** 6,500/16; 15,000/8
ew: 85 tot.

arks: *Ta Tung* transferred 1-66 (purchased on 19-5-75), *Ta Wan* on 30-6-74, and *an* on 1-6-78. *Chien Chung* and ex-*Achomawi* were purchased 20-6-91 unarmed the U.S. Maritime Administration along with ex-*Narragansett* (ATF 88), which is used for cannibalization spares. *Ta Han* and *Chien Chung* have Busch-Sulzer 39 diesels and only a small exhaust pipe. Sister *Ta Tai* (551, ex-*Shakori,* ATF 162) aground 15-3-87, was salved, and was later sunk as a missile target.

ex-U.S. Sotoyomo-class ocean tugs
dr: Levingston SB, Orange, Tex.

	Laid down	L	In serv.
'A TENG (ex-*Cahokia,* ATA 186)	16-8-44	18-9-44	24-11-44
'A PENG (ex-*Mahopac,* ATA 196)	24-11-44	21-12-44	6-3-45

435 tons (835 fl) **S:** 13 kts **Dim:** 43.59 (40.74 wl) × 10.31 × 4.01
1/76.2-mm DP—2/20-mm AA (I × 2)
ctron Equipt: Radar: 1/. . . nav.
2 G.M. 12-278A diesels, electric drive; 1 prop; 1,500 shp
ctric: 120 kw **Fuel:** 158 tons **Crew:** 45 tons

rks: *Ta Sueh* transferred in 4-62, and *Ta Teng* on 29-3-72 after serving the U.S. rce since 1971. Sister *Chiu Lien* was an oceanographic research ship, and *Ta* 357, ex-*Tonkawa,* ATA 176) was stricken 1991.

SERVICE CRAFT

Note: U.S. 174-ft-class yard oiler *Szu Ming* (504, ex-YO 198), for some years in reserve, was stricken by 1991.

◆ **6 ex-U.S. Navy YTL 422-class small harbor tugs**

YTL 8 (ex-ST-2002) YTL 10 (ex-ST-2008) YTL 12 (ex-YTL 584)
YTL 9 (ex-ST-2004) YTL 11 (ex-YTL 454) YTL 14 (ex-YTL 585)

D: 70 tons (80 fl) **S:** 8 kts **Dim:** 20.3 × 5.18 × 2.4
M: 1 diesel; 1 prop; 375 bhp

Remarks: YTL 8 to YTL 10 transferred in 3-62, YTL 11 in 8-63, YTL 12 and YTL 14 in 7-64. First three are former U.S. Army units built during World War II.

Note: There are also a large number of other small tugs and service craft in service for which no information is available.

◆ **1 ex-U.S. ARD 12-class floating dry dock**
Bldr: Pacific Bridge, Alameda, Cal.

FO WU 6 (ex-*Windsor,* ARD 22)

Dim: 149.86 × 24.69 × 1.73 (light) **Capacity:** 3,500 tons

Remarks: In service 4-44, transferred on 19-5-76; purchased 1981.

◆ **1 ex-U.S. ARD 2-class floating dry dock**
Bldr: Pacific Bridge, Alameda, Cal.

FO WU 5 (ex-ARD 9)

Dim: 148.03 × 21.64 × 1.75 (light) **Capacity:** 3,500 tons

Remarks: In service 9-43, transferred on 12-1-77; purchased outright 1981.

◆ **2 ex-U.S. floating dry docks** Bldr: V. P. Loftis, Wilmington, N.C.

HAY TAN (ex-AFDL 36) HAN JIH (ex-AFDL 34)

Dim: 73.15 × 19.69 × 1.3 (light) **Capacity:** 1,000 tons

Remarks: In service 5- and 6-44, transferred in 3-47 and 7-59.

◆ **1 ex-U.S. floating dry dock**

KIM MEN (ex-AFDL 5)

Dim: 60.96 × 19.5 × 1.04 **Capacity:** 1,000 tons

Remarks: Built in 1944, transferred in 1-48.

MARITIME SECURITY POLICE COASTAL PATROL COMMAND

Established 1990 under the Ministry of the Interior Civil Police to patrol coastal waters, harbors, and river mouths. In time of war would switch to naval subordination. Seven detachments are maintained at Tamshui, Hsinchu, Suao, Wuchi, Makung, Anping, and Kaohsiung. Duties include interdiction of illegal immigrants, countering smuggling, and fisheries protection within territorial waters. The 1992 growth plan includes one 800-ton, two 400-ton, one 200-ton, and one 100-ton patrol boats. Several naval 32-meter-class patrol boats have also been assigned to the Coastal Patrol Command.

PATROL BOATS AND CRAFT

◆ **12 60-foot patrol boats** (In serv. late 1980s-. . .)

PP-601 through PP-612

Remarks: Armed with one 7.62-mm mg and have two Decca navigational radars.

PP-601 *Defense Technology,* 4-89

◆ **6 (+ 4) 50-ft. harbor patrol boats** (In serv. late 1980s)

PP-501 through PP-506

Remarks: Armed with one 7.62-mm mg and have a Decca navigational radar.

PATROL BOATS AND CRAFT *(continued)*

PP-501 and PP-502 *Defense Technology,* 4-89

◆ **12 (+ 18) M-4 Jet-Boat riverine patrol craft**

PP-301 through PP-312

PP-309 *Defense Technology,* 4-89

Remarks: Employed for harbor and river-mouth anti-smuggling patrol. Gasoline outboard-propelled.

CUSTOMS SERVICE

Subordinate to the Ministry of Finance in peacetime and to the navy in time of war.

PATROL SHIPS

◆ **0 (+ 2) Ho Hsing class** Bldr: China Shipbuilding, Keelung

509 Ho Hsing (In serv. 1992) 510 Wei Hsing (In serv. 1992)

Ho Hsing class Korea-Tacoma, 1990

D: 1,795 tons (fl) **S:** 22 kts **Dim:** 82.29 × 11.59 × 4.14
A: . . . **Electron Equipt:** Radar: 2/. . . nav.
M: 2 MTU 16V1163 TB93 diesels; 2 CP props; 13,122 bhp—bow-thruster
Electric: 1,050 kw tot. (3 × 350 kw diesel alternator sets)
Range: 7,000/16 **Fuel:** 290 tons **Crew:** 18 officers, 62 enlisted

Remarks: Ordered 11-1-90. Planned to deliver both 1-7-91 but were delayed by German embargo on the engines. Nearly complete *Ho Hsing* capsized 18-8-91 in a typhoon. Will receive light machine-gun armament. Have accommodations for two senior personnel in addition to listed crew. Very similar to U.S. Coast Guard *Bear*-class 270-ft cutters, but carry no heavy armament and substitute four high-speed interceptor craft in individual davits (two per side) for the helicopter facility. The eight interceptor craft were delivered 7-91 from Hood Military Vessels of the United States: 12.19-m overall, six crew, two 300-bhp Cummins diesels driving Arneson outdrives for 35 kts, range: 382 nautical miles at 35 kts; 466 nautical miles at 30 kts.

◆ **2 Mou Hsing class** Bldr: Wilton-Fijenoord, Schiedam, the Netherlands

	L	In serv.		L	In serv.
Mou Hsing	13-2-88	14-6-88	Fu Hsing	13-2-88	14-6-88

D: 700 tons (850 fl) **S:** 28 kts (25 sust.) **Dim:** 66.10 × 9.60 × 3.22
A: . . . **Electron Equipt:** Radar: 2/. . . nav.
M: 3 MTU 16V538 TB93 diesels; 3 props; 13,200 bhp (11,040 sust.)
Range: . . . **Crew:** 54 tot.

Mou Hsing Piet Sinke, 4

Remarks: Ordered 4-86. Replaced U.S. *Admirable*-class former minesweepers.

◆ **1 Yun Hsing class** Bldr: China SB, Keelung

Yun Hsing (In serv. 28-12-87)

D: 900 tons (fl) **S:** 24 kts **Dim:** 65.0 × 10.0 × 2.9
A: 1/40-mm 60-cal. Bofors Mk 3 AA
Electron Equipt: Radar: 2/. . . nav.
M: 1 Sulzer 12 SA 25 diesel; 1 prop; . . . bhp **Crew:** . . . tot.

Remarks: Somewhat resembles the larger Dutch-built *Mou Hsing* class. Carrie inspection boats in davits.

◆ **2 Chin Hsing class** Bldr: China SB, Kaohsiung

Chin Hsing (In serv. 23-5-85) Pao Hsing (In serv. 11-86)

D: 550 tons (fl) **S:** 24 kts **Dim:** 57.8 × 7.8 × 2.1
A: 1/40-mm 60-cal. Bofors Mk 3 AA—1/20-mm Oerlikon AA
Electron Equipt: Radar: 2/. . . nav.
M: 2 M.A.N. 12V 25/30 diesels; 2 props; 7,200 bhp **Crew:** 40 tot.

Remarks: A flush-decked design resembling South Korean Coast Guard "Sea W but somewhat smaller. Replace three U.S. PC 461-class patrol ships. *Chin* launched 26-12-84.

◆ **5 ex-U.S. Crosley and ex-U.S. Charles Lawrence-class former high-speed transports**

	Bldr:	Laid down	L	In
Chung Shan (ex-*Blessman,* APD 48, ex-DE 69)	Bethlehem Steel, Hingham, Mass.	23-3-43	19-6-43	19
Shou Shan (ex-*Kline,* APD 120, ex-DE 687)	Bethlehem Steel, Quincy, Mass.	27-5-44	27-6-44	18-
and three others				

Shou Shan—disarmed

D: 1,680 tons (2,150 fl) **S:** 22 kts **Dim:** 93.27 × 11.24 × 3.96 (
A: removed; *see* Remarks **Electron Equipt:** Radar: . . .
M: turbo-electric drive: 2 G.E. steam turbogenerators; 2 motors; 2 props; 12,000 shp
Boilers: 2 Babcock & Wilcox, Foster-Wheeler, or Combustion Engineering; 31.7 kg/cm^2, 399° C
Electric: 1,140 kw **Range:** 1,800/22; 5,000/13
Fuel: 364 tons **Crew:** . . .

.N (continued)
)L SHIPS (continued)

s: In addition to the *Charles Lawrence*-class unit listed above, the five sur- me from among the six *Crosley* and three *Charles Lawrence*-class former ɘd transports listed in the previous edition: *Tien Shan* (815, ex-*Kleinsmith*, , ex-DE 718), *Yu Shan* (832, ex-*Kinzer*, APD 91, ex-DE 232), *Hua Shan* (833, *d W. Wolf*, APD 129, ex-DE 713), *Fu Shan* (ex-*Truxtun*, APD 98, ex-DE 282), *in* (837, ex-*Kline*, APD 120, ex-DE 687), and *Tai Shan* (838, ex-*Register*, APD 233) of the *Crosley* class and *Wen Shan* (834, ex-*Gantner*, APD 42, ex-DE 60) *Shan* (836, ex-*Bull*, APD 78, ex-DE 693). All have been disarmed except or some light machine guns and are assigned to the Customs Service Coastal mmand.
in transferred in 4-62; *Hua Shan* in 5-65; *Fu Shan* and *Shou Shan* in 3-66; *Wen* 5-66; *Lu Shan* in 8-66; *Tai Shan* in 10-66; *Tien Shan* in 6-67; and *Chung Shan* All were sold outright except *Tien Shan*, which, because she was on loan, was fied by the addition of a second 127-mm mount aft until after her purchase in others all received the second gun in lieu of a cargo hold and derrick, g about 1970. In some, Welin davits were retained amidships, but only two original four) landing craft were carried, to save topweight; these have now aced by small speedboats for inspection purposes in the five survivors. The *osley*-class ships have low navigating bridges, the other ships have high ones. one was modernized with a Sea Chaparral point-defense SAM system (16 missiles) aft but with no upgrade to other weaponry or sensors. Sisters *Heng* -*Raymond W. Herndon*, APD 121) and *Lung Shan* (ex-*Schmitt*, APD 76) were in 1976, and *Kang Shan* (ex-*George W. Ingram*, APD 43) was stricken in 1978. the ships listed in the first paragraph were stricken 1988–90 and another by .

)L BOATS AND CRAFT

welve 560-ton offshore patrol boats are planned to improve anti-infiltration -smuggling capabilities. In addition to the boats listed below, up to 11 others e been transferred by the navy in 1990.

sun Hsing class Bldr: China SB, . . .

ISING (In serv. 15-12-86)

39 tons (fl) **S:** . . . kts **Dim:** 44.5 × 7.5 × 1.7
. . **Electron Equipt:** . . .
MTU 16V396 TB93 diesels; 3 props; 8,160 bhp
/: . . . tot.

vedish-built Bldr: Boghammar Marine, Stockholm (In serv. 1979)

5 tons (fl) **S:** 50 kts **Dim:** 11.30 × 2.30 × 0.90
nall arms **Range:** 500/40 **Crew:** 3–5 tot.
Volvo Penta TAMD-70E diesels; 2 outdrive props; 600 bhp

s: Aluminum construction. Sisters to craft used by Iranian Revolutionary

uminum-hulled Bldr: China SB, Kaohsiung

NG (In serv. 28-2-79) HAI AN (In serv. 18-3-79)
ENG (In serv. 1979)

. . **S:** . . . **Dim:** 26.0 × 5.6 × 2.7
/20-mm Oerlikon GAM-B01 AA
MTU 8V331 TC81 diesels; 2 props; . . . bhp

imitar-class aluminum-hulled
: Halter Marine, New Orleans (In serv. 1977)

EI HAI . . .

ei Kalter Marine, 1986

'0 tons **S:** 19 kts **Dim:** 23.77 × 5.56 × 1.52 **A:** . . .
2 G.M. 12V71 TI diesels; 2 props; 1,350 bhp
tric: 60 kw **Range:** . . ./. . . **Crew:** . . . tot.

TANZANIA

United Republic of Tanzania

Note: Craft listed below also include units assigned to the semi-autonomous island of Zanzibar.

Personnel (1991): Approximately 700 total

PATROL BOATS

◆ **3 Chinese Shanghai-II class**

JW 9861 series

Two Tanzanian Shanghai-II patrol boats A. Zioko, 10-84

D: 122.5 tons (135 fl) **S:** 28.5 kts **Dim:** 38.78 × 5.41 × 1.55
A: 4/37-mm 63-cal. AA (II × 2)—4/25-mm 60-cal. AA (II × 2)
Electron Equipt: Radar: 1/Pot Head surf. search
M: 2 M50F-4, 1,200-bhp diesels; 2 12D6, 910-bhp diesels; 4 props; 4,220 bhp
Electric: 39 kw **Endurance:** 7 days
Range: 750/16.5 **Crew:** 36 tot.

Remarks: Seven transferred 1970–71, but by 1991, only one was operable. Two replacements were delivered 6-92.

TORPEDO BOATS

◆ **4 Chinese Huchuan class** Bldr: Hudung SY, Shanghai

JW 9841 JW 9842 JW 9843 JW 9844

JW 9842 1976

D: 39 tons (45 fl) **S:** 50 kts **Dim:** 22.50 × 3.80 × 1.146
A: 4/14.5-mm mg (II × 2)—2/533-mm TT (I × 2)
Electron Equipt: Radar: 1/Skin Head surf. search
Electric: 5.6 kw **M:** 3 M50 diesels; 3 props; 3,600 bhp
Range: 500/30 **Crew:** 11 tot.

Remarks: Transferred 1975. Unlike most Chinese Navy Huchuans, these craft have no hydrofoils. Gun mounts are fore and aft, while on most units of this class both mounts are aft. All four were operational in 1991.

PATROL CRAFT

◆ **1 Yugoslav Type 16 class** (In serv. late 1980s)

D: 23 tons (fl) **S:** 15 kts **Dim:** 17.00 × 3.60 × 0.85 mean
A: 1/20-mm AA—2/7.62-mm mg (I × 2)
Electron Equipt: Radar: 1/Decca 110 nav.
M: 2 diesels; 2 props; 464 bhp **Range:** 340/15 **Crew:** 7 tot.

Remarks: Steel hull, wooden decking. Can also transport up to 30 troops for short distances.

◆ **5 North Korean Kimjin class** (In serv.: 2 in 9-87, 3 in 2-88)

D: 35 tons (fl) **S:** 35 kts **Dim:** 18.3 × 3.4 × 1.7
A: 4/14.5-mm mg (II × 2) **Electron Equipt:** Radar: 1/. . . nav.
M: 2 M50F diesels; 2 props; 2,400 bhp
Range: 220/20 **Crew:** 10 tot.

◆ **1 or more "Seneca" class** Bldr: Crestitalia, Ameglia, Italy
(In serv. . . .)

TANZANIA *(continued)*
PATROL CRAFT *(continued)*

D: 7.8 tons (fl) **S:** 32 kts **Dim:** 12.0 × 3.8 × 0.5
A: . . . **M:** 2 G.M. diesels; 2 Castoldi waterjets; 864 bhp
Range: 220/28 **Fuel:** 0.6 tons **Crew:** 5 tot.

Remarks: GRP construction, delivered post-1980.

◆ **4 patrol craft** Bldr: Vosper Thornycroft, U.K.

D: 70 tons **S:** 24.5 kts **Dim:** 22.9 × 6.0 × 1.5
A: 2/20-mm AA (I × 2) **M:** 2 diesels; 2 props; 1,840 bhp
Range: 800/20 **Crew:** 11 tot.

Remarks: The first two units were delivered 6-7-73, the last two in 1974. Glass-reinforced plastic construction; Keith Nelson design. All four assigned to Zanzibar.

◆ **4 Chinese Yu Lin-class**

Changa Kasa Ngisi Nyangumi

D: 9.8 tons (fl) **S:** 25 kts **Dim:** 13.0 × 2.9 × 1.1
A: 2/12.7-mm mg (I × 2) **M:** 1 diesel; 1 prop; 300 bhp

Remarks: Transferred by the Chinese People's Republic in 11-66. These craft operate on Lake Victoria Nyanza for the Marine Police.

SERVICE CRAFT

◆ **1 coastal survey craft**
Bldr: Bayerische Schiffsbau, West Germany (In serv. 1979)

Utafiti

D: 33 tons (fl) **S:** 14 kts **Dim:** 19.05 × . . . × 1.0
Electron Equipt: Radar: 1/Decca 060 nav.
M: 2 Caterpillar diesels; 2 props; 456 bhp
Range: 250/12 **Crew:** 6 tot.

Remarks: Has Atlas DESO 10 echo-sounder. Steel hull, aluminum superstructure.

THAILAND

Kingdom of Thailand

Personnel (1991): 25,000 total (including 900 in Naval Air Arm), plus 26,000 marines

Naval Aviation: Available are: 2 Fokker F-27-400M and 3 Fokker F-27-200 Maritime, 3 Dornier Do-228, 9 Nomad Searchmaster, and 2 Cessna T-337 Skymaster for maritime surveillance; 2 CL-215 amphibians; 20 C-46 and C-47 transports; 10 Cessna 0-1 Bird Dog observation aircraft; 14 U-17 Skywagon utility aircraft, 2 Lake L-A4 Skimmer training amphibians; and 12 Bell 214 ST, 3 Bell UH-1H, and 10 Bell 212 helicopters.

Plans exist to acquire a naval tactical fighter wing with 30 or more U.S. A-7E Corsair-II fighter-bombers. Nine Harbin Zhi-9 (Dauphin copy) helicopters were ordered 3-92 for shipboard and land-based use. Three refurbished U.S. P-3A Orion maritime reconnaissance aircraft may be acquired to replace 8 retired S-2F Trackers.

Naval Systems: Fourteen Marconi Stingray ASW torpedoes were ordered 9-84 for the F-27 Maritime and for the new U.S.-built corvettes. The F-27 aircraft are equipped to launch U.S. Harpoon missiles. Ten MM 38 Exocet SSM coast-defense batteries ordered 1986. The fleet operates a wide variety of equipment from a large number of national suppliers, complicating logistics and tactical employment.

FRIGATES

◆ **0 (+2) Chinese Type 25T** Bldr: Hudong SY, Shanghai

	Laid down	L	In serv.
621 Naresuan	11-91	1993	1995
622 Taksin	1992	1994	1996

D: 2,500 tons (2,900 fl) **S:** 25.5 kts **Dim:** 119.0 × 13.0 × 3.80
A: 8/Harpoon RGM-84A SSM (IV × 2)—1/Mk 29 SAM launcher × 1, 16 Sea Sparrow missiles)—1/127-mm 54-cal. U.S. Mk 45 (II × 1)—4/37-mm 63-cal. AA (II × 2)—6/324-mm Mk 32 Mod ASW TT (III × 2)—2/RBU-1200 ASW RL (V × 2)—2/Zhi-9 helicopters
Electron Equipt:
Radar: 2/Raytheon SPS-64(V)5 nav., 1/SPS-49 air search, 1/U. 92 f.c., 1/U.S. Mk 91 SAM f.c., 1/STIR-18 gun f.c.
Sonar: Raytheon DE-1160C hull-mounted LF (5.6/7.5/8.4 kHz)
EW: U.S. SLQ-32(V)2 intercept, Mk 36 SRBOC decoy syst. (VI Mk 137 RL)
M: CODOG: 2 G.E. LM-2500 gas turbines (25,000 shp each) or 2 20V1163 TB 83 diesels (8,000 bhp each/7,385 bhp sust.); 2 CP props
Range: 4,000/18 **Endurance:** 15 days **Crew:** 150 tot.

Remarks: Ordered 9-89. How the ships are to be completed without U.S. comp not known, and many systems may have to be installed post-delivery. Desi enlarged version of the Jangwei frigate hull and will incorporate many syst features not previously employed in a Chinese-built ship. There will be a he hangar, and weight and space are reserved for later installation of a vertical launch group forward of the bridge.

◆ **3 (+ 1) Chinese Jianghu III class (Type 053T and 053HT)**
Bldr: Zhonghua SY, Shanghai

	Laid down	L	In serv.
455 Chao Phraya	4-89	24-6-90	5-4-91
456 Bangpakong	1989	24-7-90	20-7-91
457 Kraburi	1990	28-12-90	16-1-92
458 Saiburi	1990	29-6-91	7-92

Kraburi (457) *Battlefield Week*

Chao Phraya (455) R.T.N

Chao Phraya (455) R.T.N

[F]RIGATES *(continued)*

[D]: 1,586 tons (1,865 fl) **S:** 31 kts (trials)
[D]im: 103.20 × 10.83 × 3.10 (hull)
[A]: C-801 SSM (II × 2)—4 (457, 458: 2)/100-mm 56-cal. DP (II × 1 or 2)—8/37-mm 63-cal. AA (II × 4)—2/RBU-1200 (EDS2-5A) ASW RL (V × 2)—1/d.c. rack
[E]lectron Equipt:
Radar: 1/Decca RM 1290A nav., 1/MX-902 (Type 354) air search, 1/Square Tie missile (Type 352) f.c., 1/Type 343 gun f.c., 1/Type 341 f.c.
Sonar: Type E-5 HF bow-mounted searchlight-type
EW: Elettronica Newton-Beta suite (Type 211 intercept, Type 318 noise jammer, Type 521 deception jammer), 2/. . . chaff RL
[M]: 2 MTU 20V1163 TB83 diesels; 2 props; 16,000 bhp (14,730 sust.)
[R]ange: 2,500/18 **Endurance:** 15 days
[E]lectric: 1,600 kw (4 MTU 8V396-series diesel sets)
[C]rew: 22 officers, 146 enlisted

[Rem]arks: First two ordered in 7-88, with delivery for first to be within 30 months and [...]in 42 mos. Second pair ordered 8-89. Will be employed primarily for anti-piracy and [...]ne police functions. In most respects, are identical to Chinese units at time of [deli]very, except for substitution of West German diesels for the usual license-built [...]T-Pielstick 12 PA6 engines. Plans to modernize the ships with Western weapons [...]sensors have been dropped.
[Th]e ASW suite, including the rocket launchers, sonar, and 2KJ-5 display console, is [desi]gnated SJD-5. The EW suite employs Type 923 omni-directional antennas for the [Type] 521 deception jammer, and Type 981 omnidirectional and Type 929 directional [ante]nnas, all mounted on the mast and superstructure sides; the equipment is of [Itali]an design, license-built in China. The 100-mm guns are controlled by the Wok Won [(Typ]e 343) radar director atop the pilothouse, while the Type 341 radar aft provides [...]e inputs to the 37-mm guns, which are aimed via ringsights and are arranged to [...]r one quadrant for each mount. The 100-mm guns have a rate of fire of 25 rounds [per m]inute, a range of 16 km, and employ a French-designed autoloader. 457 and 458 [have] a helicopter platform raised above the fantail at forecastle level and omit the after 100-mm gun mount; there is no hangar.

[...] **"Yarrow frigate" class** Bldr: Yarrow, Scotstoun, Glasgow, Scotland

	Laid down	L	In serv.
[...]akut Rajakumarn	11-1-70	18-11-71	7-5-73

[Mak]ut Rajakumarn (7)—prior to modernization R.A.N., 1981

[D:] 1,650 tons (1,900 fl) **S:** 26 kts (gas turbines)/18 kts (diesel)
[Di]m: 97.56 (92.99 pp) × 10.97 × 5.5 (over sonar)
[A:] 2/114-mm 55-cal. Vickers Mk 8 DP—2/40-mm 70-cal. Bofors L70 AA (I × 2)—6/324-mm STW-1 ASW TT (III × 2)—2/d.c. mortars, 1/d.c. rack
[Ele]ctron Equipt:
[R]adar: 1/H.S.A. ZW-06 surf. search, 1/H.S.A. DA-05 surf./air search, 1/H.S.A. WM-22 f.c.
[S]onar: Krupp-Atlas DSQS-21C hull-mounted MF
[E]W: Racal . . . intercept
[M:] CODOG: 1 Rolls-Royce Olympus TBM 3B gas turbine (23,125 shp), 1 Crossley-Pielstick 12 PC2V diesel (6,000 bhp); 2 CP props
[Ele]ctric: 2,200 kw tot. **Range:** 1,000/25; 4,000/18
[Cre]w: 16 officers, 124 enlisted

[Rema]rks: Ordered 21-8-69. Similar to the Malaysian *Rahmat* but longer and more [heavil]y armed. Highly automated. The WM-22 track-while-scan radar controls the [...]m guns. Modernized 1985–88 after a serious fire in 2-84: new sonar, air-search [...]Sea Cat missile launcher and director deleted, Limbo ASW mortar replaced by [...]T (with U.K. Stingray torpedoes). Plans calling for further modernization, with [...]-mm gun replaced by U.S. Harpoon missiles and either a Mk 29 launcher for Sea [...]w short-range SAMs or a Mk 15 20-mm Phalanx gatling CIWS, appear to have [...]anceled. Suffered another serious fire in 1990 and was out of service through [...]when repaired, will probably become fleet training ship.
[...] U.S. *Cannon*-class frigate *Pin Klao* (3, ex-*Hemminger*, DE 746) was stricken in [...]ng of 1991; U.S. *Tacoma*-class frigates *Tachin* (1, ex-*Glendale*, PF 36) and [...] (2, ex-*Gallup*, PF 47) were also stricken in 1991 to provide crews for the new [...]e-built frigates.

CORVETTES

◆ **2 U.S. PFMM Mk 16 class** Bldr: Tacoma Boatbldg., Tacoma, Wash.

	Laid down	L	In serv.
1 Ratanakosin	6-2-84	11-3-86	26-9-86
2 Sukhothai	26-3-84	20-7-86	19-2-87

Ratanakosin (1) George R. Schneider, Jr., 12-86

Sukhothai (2) Dr. Giorgio Arra, 11-86

D: 840 tons normal (960 fl) **S:** 26 kts
Dim: 76.82 × 9.55 × 2.44 (hull)
A: 8/Harpoon RGM-84A SSM (IV × 2)—1/Albatros SAM system (VIII × 1, 24 Aspide missiles)—1/76-mm 62-cal. OTO Melara Compact DP—2/40-mm 70-cal. Breda AA (II × 1)—2/20-mm Oerlikon GAM-B01 AA (I × 2)—6/324-mm Mk 32 ASW TT (III × 2, 6 Stingray torpedoes)
Electron Equipt:
Radar: 1/Decca 1226 nav., 1/H.S.A. ZW-06 surf. search, 1/H.S.A. DA-05 surf./air search, 1/H.S.A. WM-25 Mod. 41 f.c., 1/H.S.A. LIROD-8 f.c.
Sonar: Krupp-Atlas DSQS-21C hull-mounted MF
EW: Elettronica Newton intercept; 1/Dagaie chaff RL
M: 2 MTU 20V1163 TB83 diesels; 2 props; 16,000 bhp (14,730 sust.)
Electric: . . . **Range:** 3,000/16 **Crew:** 15 officers, 72 enlisted

Remarks: Ordered 9-5-83. Plans to build a third ship in Thailand canceled. Enlarged version of Saudi Arabian PCG class. Have H.S.A. Mini-SADOC weapons control, H.S.A. LIROD-8 optronic backup director for the 76-mm gun, radar, infrared, and low light-level t.c. sensors. A Dutch Goalkeeper 30-mm CIWS may be installed later.

◆ **2 ex-U.S. PF 103 class**

	Bldr	Laid down	L	In serv.
5 Tapi (ex-PF 107)	American SB, Toledo, Ohio	1-4-70	17-10-70	1-11-71
6 Khirirat (ex-PF 108)	Norfolk SB & DD, Va.	18-2-72	2-6-73	10-8-74

D: 893 tons light (1,172 fl) **S:** 20 kts
Dim: 84.04 × 10.06 × 3.05 (4.27 sonar)
A: 1/76-mm 62-cal. OTO Melara Compact DP—1/40-mm 70-cal. Bofors L70 AA—2/20-mm AA (I × 2)—2/12.7-mm mg (I × 2)—6/324-mm Mk 32 ASW TT (III × 2, 6 Mk 46 Mod. 2 torpedoes)—1/Mk 9 d.c. rack

CORVETTES *(continued)*

Electron Equipt:
Radar: 1/Raytheon . . . nav., 1/SPS-6C air search, 1/H.S.A. WM-25 f.c.
Sonar: 1/Krupp-Atlas DSQS-21C hull-mounted MF
M: 2 Fairbanks-Morse 38D8⅛-10 diesels; 2 props; 5,300 bhp
Electric: 750 kw tot. **Range:** 2,400/18 **Fuel:** 110 tons
Crew: 16 officers, 124 enlisted

Khirirat (6) R.A.N., 5-90

Khirirat (6) Leo Van Ginderen, 5-90

Remarks: Ordered 27-6-69 and 26-6-71, respectively. Patterned after the Italian-built *Pattimura* class for Indonesia; four sisters built for the Iranian Navy. *Tapi* completed modernization in 1983 with the OTO Melara gun replacing the forward U.S. 76.2-mm mount, a Bofors 40-mm on a raised bandstand replacing the aft 76.2-mm mount, two single 20-mm AA replacing the original twin 40-mm mount, an H.S.A. WM-25 track-while-scan radar director being mounted above the bridge, and a new sonar in place of the original U.S. SQS-17A; a Hedgehog ASW spigot mortar was removed. *Khirirat* received similar modernization in 1985–87, and both received further updates to the communications suites in 1988–89.

GUIDED-MISSILE PATROL BOATS

◆ **3 Ratcharit class** Bldr: C.N. Breda, Venice, Italy

	L	In serv.		L	In serv.
4 Ratcharit	30-7-78	10-8-79	6 Udomet	28-9-78	21-2-80
5 Witthayakom	2-9-78	12-11-79			

Ratcharit (4) U.S. Navy, 5-80

D: 235 tons light (270 fl) **S:** 36 kts
Dim: 49.80 (47.25 pp) × 7.50 × 1.68 (hull)
A: 4/MM 38 Exocet SSM (II × 2)—1/76-mm 62-cal. OTO Melara Compact DP—1/40-mm 70-cal. Breda-Bofors AA
Electron Equipt:
Radar: 1/Decca 1226 nav., 1/H.S.A. M-25 track-while-scan f.c.
EW: Decca RDL-2 intercept
M: 3 MTU MD20 V538 TB91 diesels; 3 CP props; 13,500 bhp
Electric: 440 kw **Range:** 650/36; 2,000/15
Crew: 7 officers, 38 enlisted

Remarks: Ordered 23-7-76. Builder's BMB 230 design. Can make 30 kts on engines.

◆ **3 Prabrarapak class**
Bldr: Singapore SB & Eng. Co., Jurong, Singapore

	L	In serv.		L	In s
1 Prabrarapak	29-7-75	28-7-76	3 Suphairin	20-2-76	1-:
2 Hanhak Sattru	28-10-75	6-11-76			

Hanhak Sattru (2) Dr. Giorgio Arra,

D: 224 tons (260 fl) **S:** 41 kts **Dim:** 44.9 × 7.0 × 2.1 (2.46 props
A: 5/I.A.I. Gabriel I SSM (III × 1, I × 2)—1/57-mm 70-cal. Bofors Mk 1 AA—1/40-mm 70-cal. Bofors L70 AA—2/12.7-mm mg (I ×
Electron Equipt:
Radar: 1/Decca TM 626 nav., 1/H.S.A. WM-28 track-while-scan
EW: Decca RDL-2 intercept
M: 4 MTU 16V538 TB92 diesels; 4 props; 14,000 bhp
Electric: 405 kVA **Range:** 500/38.5; 1,500/16
Crew: 5 officers, 36 enlisted

Remarks: Similar to the Singapore Navy's Lürssen FPB-45-design boats; built license. 103-mm rocket flare launch rails are mounted on the 57-mm mount.

PATROL BOATS

◆ **2 (+1) Khamronsin class**

	Bldr	Laid down	L	In
1 Longlom	Royal Thai NDY, Bangkok	15-3-88	8-8-89	
2 Khamronsin	Ital Thai, Bangkok	16-3-88	15-8-89	
3 Thayanchon	Ital Thai, Bangkok	20-4-88	7-12-89	

D: 362 light (475 fl) **S:** 25 kts
Dim: 62.0 (56.7 pp) × 8.26 × 2.50 (hull)
A: 1/76-mm 62-cal. OTO Melara Compact DP—2/30-mm 70-cal. AA (II × 1)—2/12.7-mm mg (I × 2)—6/324-mm Plessey PMW ASW TT (III × 2; Stingray torpedoes)—1/d.c. rack—mines
Electron Equipt:
Radar: 1/Decca 1226 nav., 1/MUSL AWS-4 surf./air search
Sonar: Krupp-Atlas DSQS-21C hull-mounted MF
EW: . . .
M: 2 MTU 12V1163 TB93 diesels; 2 CP props; 7,340 bhp
Range: 2,500/15 **Fuel:** . . . **Crew:** 6 officers, 51 enlisted

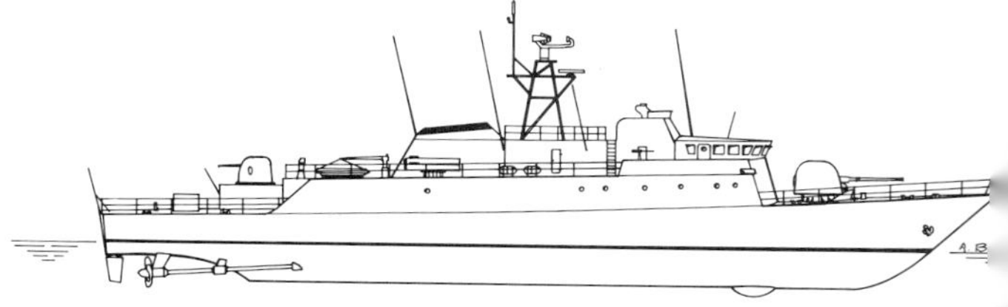

Khamronsin class A. D. Baker I

.TROL BOATS *(continued)*

narks: First three ordered 29-9-87; a fourth in a simplified version was ordered in) for the Marine Police. Up to four more may be ordered later. Variant of Vosper rnycroft "Vita" strike craft with reduced power and no missile armament. Have Sea her 1A Mod. 2 optronic (t.v./IR/laser) GFCS, Plessey NAUTIS-P combat-data sys- Depth-charge racks and mine rails are portable and would not normally be inted. Some difficulties have been experienced during construction, and the first were not fully operational at the beginning of 1992.

6 PSMM Mk 5 class Bldr: Ital Thai SY, Samutprakarn, Bangkok

	Laid down	L	In serv.
ATTAHIP	15-1-82	27-7-83	16-9-83
LONGYAI	. . .	9-3-84	5-84
AKBAI	. . .	25-5-84	7-84
ATANG	. . .	26-10-84	14-10-85
HEPA	. . .	1985	17-4-86
HAI MUANG	. . .	12-85	17-4-86

: 270 tons (300 fl) **S:** 22 kts
im: 50.14 (47.22 wl) × 7.30 × 1.58 (1.80 props)
: 1/76.2-mm 50-cal. U.S. Mk 26 DP—1/40-mm 60-cal. Mk 3 AA—2/20-mm AA (I × 2)—2/12.7-mm mg (I × 2)
lectron Equipt: Radar: 1/Decca 1226 nav.
: 2 MTU 16V538 TB91 diesels; 2 props; 6,840 bhp
lectric: 420 kw **Range:** 2,500/15 **Fuel:** 80 tons **Crew:** 56 tot.

arks: First four ordered 9-9-81, others on 27-12-83 and 31-8-84. Of Thai design. Italian NA-18 optronic GFCS. Final three may have 76-mm OTO Melara Com- DP in place of the obsolescent U.S. 76.2-mm mount.

MV 400 design Bldr: C.N. Breda, Puerto Marghera, Venice, Italy

	Laid down	L	In serv.
ONBURI	15-8-81	7-6-82	22-2-83
NGKHLA	15-9-81	6-9-82	16-7-83
UKET	15-12-81	3-2-83	13-1-84

ket (3) U.S. Navy, 8-86

et (3) French Navy, 7-87

400 tons (450 fl) **S:** 30 kts
m: 60.40 (57.50 pp) × 8.80 × 1.95 (hull)
2/76-mm 62-cal. OTO Melara Compact DP (I × 2)—2/40-mm 70-cal. Breda-Bofors AA (II × 1)—2/12.7-mm M2 mg (I × 2)

Electron Equipt:
Radar: 1/H.S.A. ZW-06 surf. search, 1/H.S.A. WM-22 Mod. 61 track-while- scan f.c., 1/H.S.A. LIROD-8 radar/optronic f.c.
EW: Elettronica Newton intercept, 4/Breda chaff RL (VI × 4)
M: 2 MTU 20V538 TB92 diesels; 3 CP props; 15,000 bhp (12,600 sust.)
Electric: 800 kw **Range:** 900/29; 2,500/18
Crew: 7 officers, 35 enlisted

Remarks: Ordered 11-79, originally for delivery in 1982, but that slipped considerably. First unit delivered 29-11-82 by shipyard. Able to accommodate antiship missiles, but none were to be installed at delivery. Steel hull, aluminum-alloy superstructure.

◆ **7 T 93 class** Bldr: Royal Thai Naval Dockyard, Bangkok

T 93 (L: 1973) T 94 (In serv. 16-9-81) T 95 (In serv. 1981)
T 96 (In serv. 1982) T 97 (In serv. 16-9-83) T 98 (In serv. 1984)
T 99 (In serv. 5-87)

T 95 1983

D: 117 tons (125 fl) **S:** 25 kts
Dim: 34.00 (32.00 wl) × 5.70 × 1.40 (1.65 props)
A: 2/40-mm 60-cal. Mk 3 AA (I × 2)—2/12.7-mm mg (I × 2)
Electron Equipt: Radar: 1/Decca . . . nav.
M: 2 MTU 12V538 TB81 diesels; 2 props; 3,300 bhp
Crew: 23–25 tot.

Remarks: Revised version of T 91 design. T 99 has 20-mm aft, vice 40-mm. Have Sea Archer Mk 1A optronic directors.

◆ **2 T 91 class** Bldr: Royal Thai Naval Dockyard, Bangkok

T 91 (L: 1965) T 92 (L: 1973)

T 92 Dr. Giorgio Arra, 1976

D: 87.5 tons **S:** 25 kts **Dim:** 31.8 × 5.36 × 1.5
A: 2/40-mm 60-cal. Mk 3 AA (I × 2)—2/12.7-mm mg (I × 2)
Electron Equipt: Radar: 1/Decca . . . nav.
M: 2 MTU diesels; 2 props; 3,300 bhp **Range:** 700/21
Crew: 21 tot.

Remarks: T 91 has a longer superstructure and no spray strakes on the hull sides forward, and only one 40-mm AA gun. Both refitted 1984–85.

Note: The 10 U.S. PGM 71-class patrol boats, T 11 through T 19 and T 110, were stricken 1989–90. U.S. PC 461-class large patrol boats *Sarasin* (1, ex-PC 495), *Phali* (4, ex-PC 1185), *Sukrip* (5, ex-PC 1218), *Tongliu* (6, ex-PC 616), and *Liulom* (7, ex-PC 1253) were stricken 1990–91.

PATROL CRAFT

◆ **18 (+. . .) T 213 class** Bldr: Ital Thai Development Co., Bangkok

	In serv.		In serv.		In serv.
T 213	29-8-80	T 219	16-9-81	T 225	28-3-84
T 214	29-8-80	T 220	16-9-81	T 226	28-3-84
T 215	29-8-80	T 221	16-9-81	T 227	1984
T 216	26-3-81	T 222	16-9-81	T 228	1984
T 217	26-3-81	T 223	16-9-81	T 229	1990
T 218	26-3-81	T 224	19-11-81	T 230	1990

D: 34 tons (fl) **S:** 22 kts (18 sust.) **Dim:** 19.8 × 5.3 × 1.5
A: 1/20-mm Oerlikon GAM-B01 AA—1/12.7-mm mg—1/81-mm mortar
Electron Equipt: Radar: 1/Decca 110 nav.
M: 2 MTU 8V396-series diesels; 2 props; 1,300 bhp
Crew: 1 officer, 7 enlisted

PATROL CRAFT *(continued)*

T 216—alongside T 92 1981

Remarks: Aluminum construction. Intended for fisheries protection duties.

◆ **3 ex-U.S. Sea Spectre PB Mk III class**
Bldr: Peterson Builders, Sturgeon Bay, Wisconsin

T 210 T 211 T 212

D: 28 tons (36.7 fl) **S:** 30 kts (22 sust.)
Dim: 19.78 × 5.50 × 1.80 (props)
A: 2/20-mm Oerlikon AA (I × 2)—2/12.7-mm mg (I × 2)—2/7.62-mm mg (I × 2)—1/81-mm mortar
Electron Equipt: Radar: 1/Raytheon 1500B Pathfinder nav.
M: 3 G.M. 8V71 TI diesels; 3 props; 1,800 bhp **Endurance:** 3 days
Range: 450/20; 2,000/. . . **Crew:** 1 officer, 8 enlisted

Remarks: Transferred 1975. Aluminum construction.

◆ **9 ex-U.S. Swift Mk II-class inshore patrol craft**
Bldr: Swiftships Inc., Morgan City, Louisiana

T 21 through T 29

D: 22.5 tons (fl) **S:** 25 kts (20 sust.) **Dim:** 15.64 × 4.14 × 1.06
A: 2/12.7-mm mg (II × 1)—1/12.7-mm mg/81-mm mortar combined mount
Electron Equipt: Radar: 1/Raytheon 1500B Pathfinder nav.
M: 2 G.M. 6V53 N diesels; 2 props; 860 bhp **Range:** 400/24
Crew: 1 officer, 7 enlisted

Remarks: Transferred 1968–70. Aluminum construction. Will probably soon be stricken.

Note: The unsuccessful Hysucat 18-class prototype catamaran patrol boat T 231, all 37 U.S. PBR Mk II river patrol craft, and the three remaining U.S. 36-foot RPC-class river patrol craft were stricken 1989–90.

MINE WARFARE SHIPS

◆ **1 mine-countermeasures support ship**

	Bldr	L	In serv.
1 Thalang	Royal Thai NDY, Bangkok	. . .	4-8-80

D: 1,000 tons (fl) **S:** 12 kts **Dim:** 55.7 × 10.0 × 3.1
A: 1/40-mm 60-cal. Bofors Mk 3 AA—2/20-mm AA (I × 2)—2/12.7-mm mg (I × 2)—mines
Electron Equipt: Radar: 1/Decca TM 1226 nav.
M: 2 MTU diesels; 2 props; 1,310 bhp **Crew:** 77 tot.

Remarks: Designed by Ferostaal, Essen, Germany. Has two 3-ton cranes and carries four sets of spare mine-countermeasures equipment for transfer to minesweepers. Also capable of use as a minelayer and can stream a mechanical minesweeping array.

◆ **2 M 48-class mine hunter/sweepers**
Bldr: Friedrich Lürssen Werft, Vegesack, Germany

2 Bangrachan (In serv. 29-4-87) 3 Nhongsarhai (In serv. 17-11-87)

Bangrachan (2) Lürssen, 1987

Nhongsarhai (3) Peter Voss, 1

D: 414 tons light (444.3 fl) **S:** 18 kts
Dim: 48.00 (45.70 pp) × 9.30 × 2.75
A: 3/20-mm AA Oerlikon GAM-B01 (I × 3)—mine rails
Electron Equipt:
Radar: 1/Decca 1229 nav.
Sonar: Krupp-Atlas DSQS-11H hull-mounted
M: 2 MTU 16V396 TB83-DB51L diesels; 2 CP props; 3,223 bhp—auxiliary diesel low-speed (7-kt) propulsion
Range: 3,100/12 **Electric:** 620 kw **Crew:** 7 officers, 33 enlisted

Remarks: First ordered 31-8-84, second 5-8-85 with option for two more. Used marily as patrol boats. Have had problems with stability, and the ineffective s system may be replaced with Atlas DSQS-11M.

Composite hull construction: non-magnetic metal framing with wooden skin. Kr Atlas MWS-80R mine-countermeasures system. Carry two Gaymarine Pluto rer controlled minehunting/disposal submersibles, plus mechanical, magnetic, and a tic sweep gear. Use a removable generator module when sweeping, and carry SD mechanical sweep gear. Standard generator suite: 2 × 275 kVA, 2 × 150 kVA. (7,600 rounds 20-mm, 30 mine-disposal charges. Have Becker flap rudders, Mot "MiniRanger" navigational positioning system.

◆ **4 ex-U.S. MSC 289-class minesweepers**

	Bldr	In
5 Ladya (ex-MSC 297)	Peterson, Sturgeon Bay, Wis.	14-1
6 Bangkeo (ex-MSC 303)	Dorchester SB, Camden, N.J.	9
7 Tadindeng (ex-MSC 301)	Tacoma Boat, Wash.	23
8 Don Chedi (ex-MSC 313)	Peterson, Sturgeon Bay, Wis.	17

Bangkeo (6) Ross Gillett

D: 330 tons (362 fl) **S:** 13 kts **Dim:** 44.32 × 8.29 × 2.6
A: 2/20-mm AA (II × 1)
Electron Equipt:
Radar: 1/Decca 1226 nav.—Sonar: UQS-1D hull-mounted (100
D: 4 G.M. 6-71 diesels; 2 props; 1,000 bhp (880 sust.)
Range: 2,500/10 **Crew:** 7 officers, 36 enlisted

Remarks: Transferred on completion. Wooden construction. Minesweepers engined and reactivated from reserve, 1987–88, but all need replacement. Ca Mk 4(V), Mk 6, and Type Q2 mine-countermeasures equipment.

◆ **8 Chinese Type 312 drone minesweepers**

D: 46.95 tons (fl) **S:** 11.5 kts **Dim:** 20.94 × 4.20 (3.90 wl) × 1.
M: 1 Type 12-150C diesel; 1 CP prop; 300 bhp **Range:** 150/11.5

INE WARFARE SHIPS *(continued)*

marks: Ordered 1988 at "friendship price." Intended to be operated by radio control range of 3 n.m., but can be manned. Electric propulsion during operations: 1–5 kts. sel generator amidships powers integral electromagnet for magnetic sweeping and oisemaker for activating acoustic mines. All equipment shock-mounted. Laser cision navigation system. Poor seakeeping limits use to rivers and sheltered waters.

5 ex-U.S. 50-foot motor-launch minesweepers

MS 6 to MLMS 10

D: 21 tons (fl) **S:** 8 kts **Dim:** 15.29 × 4.01 × 1.31
A: 2/7.62-mm mg (I × 2) **M:** 1 Navy DB diesel; 1 prop; 50 bhp
Range: 150/8 **Crew:** 6 tot.

narks: Transferred 1963–64. Wooden-hulled former personnel launches, con-ted before transfer. Employed on the Chao Phraya River.

PHIBIOUS WARFARE SHIPS

0 (+ 1) dock landing ship

Bldr: E.N. Bazán, El Ferrol, Spain

	Laid down	L	In serv.
. . . .	. . .	. . .	. . .

: 13,000 tons (fl) **S:** 26 kts (sust.)
im: 173.00 × 30.50 (22.50 wl) × 6.30
: none
lectron Equipt: Radar: . . .
: CODOG: 2 Bazán-MTU 16V1163 TB91 diesels, 2 LM-2500 gas turbines; 2/5-bladed props; 60,000 shp max.—1,000-bhp bow-thruster
lectric: 3,330 kw (4 × 770 kw, 1 × 250 kw)
ange: 10,000/12
rew: 455 ship's company, plus 600 troops

arks: Ordered 28-3-92 and will be manned by a civilian crew. Intended for ster relief duties in peacetime. Long-range plans call for arming the ship after ery and equipping her with Harrier-type V/STOL fighter-bombers. Program ces a more elaborate design to have been ordered from Bremer-Vulkan in Ger-y that was canceled in 7-91. A second unit may be ordered later.
to five CH-47-sized helicopters can be accommodated. Will carry three 18.5-m ing craft, launched via a stern docking well equipped with a 40-ton traveling e crane. Design based loosely on the Spanish Navy carrier *Principe de Asturias* with twin-screw propulsion and a docking well. The contract may be canceled ding to 7-92 reports.

(+2) PS 700 class

	Bldr	Laid down	L	In serv.
HANG	Ital Thai SY, Bangkok	. . .	14-4-87	9-10-87
RIN	Bangkok Dock Co.	1987	1988	1992
. . .	Bangkok Dock Co.	1989	. . .	. . .

6: 3,540 tons (4,235 fl); 7: 4,520 tons (fl) **S:** 16 kts
m: 6: 103.00 (91.65 pp) × 15.65 × 3.52 (7: 109.00 overall)
1/40-mm 70-cal. Bofors L70 AA—2/20-mm Oerlikon GAM-B01 AA (I × 2)—2/12.7-mm mg (I × 2)
ectron Equipt: Radar: 1/Decca 1226, 1/. . .
2 MTU 20V1163 TB62 diesels; 2 CP props; 9,600 bhp
nge: 4,000/14; 7,000/12
ew: 52 crew + 339 troops (7: 354 troops)

arks: License-built French Normed design, built with technical assistance from Tacoma SY. 2,045 dwt. Cargo: 850 tons. (Up to 13 50-ton tanks, 6 2-ton trucks.) ing draft 2.88 m at 1,162 dwt. Use Sea Archer Mk 1A Mod. 2 optronic (low-light aser, IR) f.c.s. for 40-mm. Helicopter deck aft, 17-m bow ramp. Program well d schedule. Third ordered 1987; six total planned.
second unit was delayed after launch to include a 6-m hull "plug" to provide ent space for the ship to accommodate a 354-man Thai troop battalion.

ex-U.S. LST 542-class tank-landing ships

	Bldr	L	In serv.
ANG (ex-*Lincoln Cty.*, T 898)	Dravo, Pittsburgh	25-11-44	29-12-44
NGAN (ex-*Stark Cty.*, T 1134)	Chicago Br. & Iron, Ind.	16-3-45	7-4-45
TA (ex-*Stone Cty.*, T 1141)	Chicago Br. & Iron, Ind.	18-4-45	9-5-45
THONG (ex-*Dodge Cty.*, T 722)	Jefferson Br. & Mach. Co., Ind.	21-8-44	13-9-44

1,625 tons (4,080 fl) **S:** 11 kts **Dim:** 99.98 × 15.24 × 4.36
8/40-mm 60-cal. Bofors AA (II × 2, I × 4)—2 also: 2/20-mm AA (I × 2)—all: 4/12.7-mm mg (I × 4)
ctron Equipt: Radar: 1/Decca 1229 nav.
2 G.M. 12-567A diesels; 2 props; 1,700 bhp **Electric:** 300 kw
nge: 15,000/9 **Fuel:** 569 tons **Crew:** 80 tot. + 348 troops

Pangan (3) J. Perrichet, 4-89

Chang (2)—with reinforced bow plating U.S. Navy, 8-86

Remarks: *Chang* was transferred in 8-62, *Pangan* in 5-66, *Lanta* on 12-3-70, and *Prathong* on 17-12-75. *Chang* has a reinforced bow and waterline, originally intended for Arctic navigation. Sister *Anthong* (1, ex-U.S. LST 294) discarded. Cargo: 1,230 tons maximum/815 tons beaching. Two Mk 51 Mod. 2 lead-computing directors for twin 40-mm AA.

♦ 2 ex-U.S. LSM 1-class medium landing ships

Bldr: 1: Pullman Standard Car Mfg. Co., Chicago; 3: Brown SB, Houston, Tex.

	Laid down	L	In serv.
1 KUT (ex-LSM 338)	17-8-44	5-12-44	10-1-45
3 KRAM (ex-LSM 469)	27-1-45	17-2-45	17-3-45

Kut (1) Ross Gillett, 1989

D: 743 tons (1,095 fl) **S:** 12.5 kts **Dim:** 62.03 × 10.52 × 2.54
A: 2/40-mm 60-cal. Bofors AA (II × 1)—4/20-mm AA (I × 4)
Electron Equipt: Radar: 1/Raytheon 1500B Pathfinder nav.
M: 2 Fairbanks-Morse 38D8Q diesels; 2 props; 2,800 bhp
Range: 2,500/12 **Crew:** 6 officers, 85 enlisted + 50 troops

Remarks: *Kut* transferred in 10-46, *Kram* on 25-5-62. Have a Mk 51 Mod. 2 optical lead-computing director for the 40-mm mount. Cargo: 452 tons. Past due for replacement; sister *Phai* (2, ex-LSM 333) stricken 1990.

Note: U.S. LCI(M) 351-class infantry landing ship *Satakut* (2, ex-LCI(M) 739) was stricken during 1991.

♦ 1 ex-U.S. LSSL 1-class support landing craft

Bldr: Commercial Iron Works, Portland, Oregon

	Laid down	L	In serv.
3 NAKHA (ex-*Himiwari*, ex-LSSL 102)	13-1-45	3-2-45	17-2-45

D: 233 tons (387 fl) **S:** 14 kts **Dim:** 48.16 × 10.52 × 2.54
A: 1/76.2-mm 50-cal. Mk 22 DP—4/40-mm 60-cal. Bofors AA (II × 2)—4/20-mm AA (I × 4)—4/12.7-mm mg (I × 4)—4/81-mm mortars (I × 4)

AMPHIBIOUS WARFARE SHIPS *(continued)*

Electron Equipt: Radar: 1/Raytheon 1500B Pathfinder nav.
M: 8 G.M. 6-71 diesels; 2 CP props; 1,320 bhp
Electric: 120 kw **Range:** 3,500/12.5 **Fuel:** 84 tons **Crew:** 60 tot.

Remarks: Transferred to Japan in 7-59 and to Thailand in 10-66 on return to U.S. control. Used mainly as a tender to small patrol craft. Likely soon to be stricken.

◆ **5 Thong Kaeo-class utility landing craft** Bldr: Royal Thai Naval Dockyard, Bangkok

7 Thong Kaeo (In serv. 23-12-82)
8 Thonglang (In serv. 19-4-83)
9 Wang Nok (In serv. 16-9-83)
10 Wang Nai (In serv. 11-11-83)
11 . . . . . . (In serv. 1986)

Wang Nok (9) U.S. Navy, 8-86

D: 193 tons (396 fl) **S:** 10 kts **Dim:** 41.0 × 9.0 × 2.1
A: 2/20-mm AA (I × 2)—2/7.62-mm mg (I × 2)
Electron Equipt: Radar: 1/. . . nav.
M: 2 G.M. 16V71N diesels; 2 props; 1,400 bhp **Range:** 1,200/10
Crew: 3 officers, 29 enlisted

Remarks: Based on U.S. LCU 1626 class. First four ordered 1980, fifth ordered 1984. Cargo: 143 tons, with 30.5 × 5.5-m vehicle deck.

◆ **5 ex-U.S. LCU 501-class utility landing craft**

	Bldr	L	In serv.
1 Mataphon (ex-LCU 1260)	Quincy Barge, Ill.	29-7-44	8-9-44
2 Rawi (ex-LCU 800)	Mt. Vernon Br. Co., Oh.	14-6-44	16-6-44
3 Adang (ex-LCU 861)	Darby, Kansas City, Kans.	15-2-44	22-2-44
4 Phe Tra (ex-LCU 1089)	Quincy Barge, Ill.	10-5-44	10-6-44
6 Talibong (ex-LCU 753)	Quincy Barge, Ill.	30-3-44	10-5-44

D: 134 tons (309 fl) **S:** 10 kts **Dim:** 36.3 × 9.96 × 1.14
A: 4/20-mm AA (II × 2) **M:** 3 G.M. 6-71 diesels; 3 props; 675 bhp
Range: 1,200/7 **Fuel:** 10.5 tons **Crew:** 13 tot.

Remarks: Transferred 10-46 to 11-47. Used as logistics transports on the Chao Phraya River. Cargo: 150 tons. Sister *Kolum* (5, ex-LCU 904) stricken 1984. Long overdue for replacement.

◆ **24 ex-U.S. LCM(6)-class landing craft**

L 14–16 L 61–68 L 71–78 L 81–82 L 85–87

D: 24 tons (56 fl) **S:** 9 kts **Dim:** 17.11 × 4.27 × 1.17
M: 2 Gray Marine 64HN9 diesels; 2 props; 330 bhp
Range: 130/9 **Crew:** 5 tot.

Remarks: Transferred 2-65 to 4-69. Cargo capacity: 34 tons.

◆ **12 ex-U.S. LCVP-class landing craft**

L 51–59; L 510–512

D: 12 tons (fl) **S:** 9 kts **Dim:** 10.9 × 3.21 × 1.04
M: 1 Gray Marine 64HN9 diesel; 1 prop; 225 bhp
Range: 110/9 **Crew:** 3 + 39 troops

Remarks: Transferred 3-63. Eight LCVPs are carried aboard the four Thai LSTs.

◆ **4 armored riverine personnel transports**
Bldr: Bangkok Dock Co., Ltd. (In serv. 1984)

L 40 L 41 L 42 L 43

D: 10 tons (fl) **S:** 25 kts **Dim:** 12.0 × 3.0 × 1.0
M: 2 Ford Sabre diesels; 2 props; . . . bhp **Crew:** . . . tot. + 35 troops

Remarks: Based on a GRP-hulled prototype constructed in 1968; may have waterjets vice propellers.

◆ **3 Type 1000 TD hovercraft personnel transports** Bldr: Griffon Hovercraft, U.K. (In serv. 1990)

D: . . . tons (fl) **S:** 33 kts **Dim:** 8.4 × 3.8 × . . .
M: 1 Deutz BF 6L913C diesel; 1 shrouded airscrew/1 lift-fan; 190 bhp
Range: 200/27 **Crew:** 2 + 9 troops or 1,000 kg cargo

HYDROGRAPHIC SHIPS

◆ **1 oceanographic research and survey ship**
Bldr: Royal Thai Naval Dockyard, Bangkok

	Laid down	L	In serv.
. . . Suk	27-8-79	16-9-81	3-9-82

Suk Leo Van Ginderen, 5

D: 1,400 tons (1,526 fl) **S:** 15 kts **Dim:** 62.9 × 11.0 × 4.1
A: 2/20-mm AA (I × 2)—2/7.62-mm mg (I × 2)
Electron Equipt: Radar: 1/Decca TM 1226 nav.
M: 2 MTU diesels; 2 props; 2,400 bhp **Crew:** 58 tot.

Remarks: Used primarily in oceanographic research.

◆ **1 oceanographic research ship** Bldr: C. Melchers, Bremen, Germa

	Laid down	L	In serv.
11 Chandhara	27-9-60	17-12-60	1961

Chandhara (11) R. Starcevich, 1

D: 870 tons (997 fl) **S:** 13 kts **Dim:** 70.0 (61.0 pp) × 10.5 × 3.0
A: 1/40-mm 60-cal. Bofors Mk 3 AA—1/20-mm Oerlikon AA
M: 2 Klöckner-Humboldt-Deutz diesels; 2 props; 1,090 bhp
Range: 10,000/10 **Crew:** 8 officers, 60 enlisted

Remarks: Built as a training ship and has also served as a royal yacht.

◆ **2 inshore survey craft**
Bldr: Lürssen, Vegesack, Germany (In serv. 1956)

D: 96 tons (fl) **S:** 12 kts **Dim:** 29.0 × 5.5 × 1.5
M: 2 diesels; 2 props; . . . bhp **Crew:** 8 tot.

Remarks: May be named *Oceanographic 1* and *Oceanographic 2*; there is also an small research ship named *Oceanographic 3*.

AUXILIARIES

◆ **1 small underway-replenishment oiler**

	Bldr	L	In serv.
2 Chula	Singapore Slipway & Eng.	24-9-80	1981

D: 2,000 tons (fl) **S:** 14 kts **Dim:** 67.0 × 9.5 × 4.35
A: 2/20-mm AA (I × 2)
Electron Equipt: Radar: 1/Decca 1226 nav.
M: 2 MTU 12V396 TC62 diesels; 2 props; 2,400 bhp
Crew: 7 officers, 32 enlisted

Remarks: 960 dwt. Cargo: 800 tons, transferred by means of an electrohydraulic supporting the hose.

Note: British *Algerine*-class minesweeper *Phosamton* (1, ex-*Minstrel*), long use training ship, was discarded during 1991, as was the *Tachin*-class training f *Maeklong* (3).

◆ **1 navigational buoy tender** Bldr: Royal Thai Naval Dockyard, Bangkok (In serv. 18-1-79)

. . . Suriya

D: 690 tons light (960 fl) **S:** 12 kts
Dim: 54.2 (47.3 pp) × 10.0 × 3.0 **A:** 2/20-mm AA (I × 2)
M: 2 MTU diesels; 1 prop; 1,310 bhp **Electric:** 300 kw
Range: 3,000/12 **Crew:** 12 officers, 48 enlisted

UXILIARIES *(continued)*

marks: One 10-ton derrick serves short, very low freeboard working deck forward. rgo capacity: 270 tons.

te: Manned by the Thai Navy is the motor yacht *Visud Sakorn,* a rakish-looking rman-built vessel of about 750 tons (fl) owned by the Thai Communications Author- no data available.

RVICE CRAFT

3 Samed-class harbor oilers
Bldr: Royal Thai Naval Dockyard, Bangkok

PROET (In serv. 16-1-70) 10 CHIK (In serv. 1970)
SAMED (In serv. 15-12-70)

oet (9) Ross Gillett, 1989

: 360 tons (485 fl) **S:** 9 kts **Dim:** 39.0 (36.6 pp) × 6.1 × 2.8
: 1 diesel; 500 bhp **Crew:** 20 tot.

narks: Proet differs slightly in appearance from the other two. All designed to nt 2/20-mm AA (I × 2) but do not carry them. No radar. Cargo: 210 tons.

1 Charn-class water tanker
Bldr: Royal Thai Naval Dockyard, Bangkok

HUANG (L: 14-1-65)

: 355 tons (485 fl) **S:** 11 kts **Dim:** 42.0 × 7.5 × 3.1
: 1 G.M. diesel; 500 bhp **Crew:** 29 tot.

arks: Near-sister *Charn* stricken during 1984. Can carry one 20-mm AA. No r.

: Refrigerated provisions transport *Kled Keo* (7) was stricken during 1989–90.

2 Rang-class coastal tugs Bldr: Singapore SB & Eng. (In serv. 9-80)

NG (L: 12-6-80) 5 RIN (L: 14-6-80)

g (6) Ross Gillett, 1989

250 tons (300 fl) **S:** 12 kts **Dim:** 32.3 × 9.0 × . . .
1 MWM TBD 441V/12K diesel; 1 prop; 2,100 bhp
ctric: 233 kw **Range:** 1,000/10 **Crew:** 16 tot.

rks: Bollard pull: 22 tons. Have two fire-fighting monitors.

ex-Canadian small harbor tugs
dr: Central Bridge Co., Trenton, Ontario (In serv. 1943–44)

JENG BADEN 3 MARIN VICHAI

63 grt **S:** 8 kts **Dim:** 19.8 × 5.0 × 1.8 **M:** 1 diesel; 240 bhp

rks: Acquired in 1953.

ROYAL THAI MARINE POLICE

orms duties analogous to those of a coast guard and operates a large number of boats and craft. A number of the newer and larger units are listed below. The Thai Marine Police has absorbed the former Customs Service fleet.

PATROL BOATS

◆ **0(+ 2) modified Khamronsin class** Bldr: Ital Thai Marine, Bangkok

. . . . (In serv. 1992) . . . . . . (In serv. . . .)

D: 362 light (475 fl) **S:** 25 kts
Dim: 62.0 (56.7 pp) × 8.26 × 2.50 (hull)
A: 1/30-mm/82-cal. Breda AA—2/20-mm Oerlikon GAM-B01 AA (I × 2)
Electron Equipt: Radar: 1/Decca 1226 nav.
M: 2 Deutz-M.W.M. BV 16M 628 diesels; 2 CP props; 9,980 bhp
Range: 2,500/15 **Fuel:** . . . **Crew:** 6 officers, 51 enlisted

Remarks: Simplified version of Thai Navy patrol boat. First unit ordered in 9-89 and second in 1991. Variant of Vosper Thornycroft "Vita" strike craft with reduced power and no missile armament.

◆ **2 Damrong Rachanuphat-class seagoing patrol boats**
Bldr: Schiffwerft Hameln, Germany (In serv. 1975)

1802 DAMRONG RACHANUPHAT 1803 LOPBURI RAMAS

Lopburi Ramas (1803) Leo Van Ginderen, 2-88

D: 430 tons (fl) **S:** 23 kts **Dim:** 56.7 × 8.1 × 2.4
A: 1/76.2-mm 50-cal. Mk 26 DP—2/20-mm AA (I × 2)
M: 4 MTU diesels; 2 props; 4,400 bhp

◆ **2 Chasanyabadee class**
Bldr: Sumidagawa, Tokyo, Japan (In serv. . . .)

1101 CHASANYABADEE 1103 PHROMYOTHEE

D: 130 tons (fl) **S:** 32 kts **Dim:** 34.0 × 5.8 × 2.8
A: 1/20-mm Oerlikon AA
Electron Equipt: Radar: 1/Decca . . . nav.
M: 3 Ikegai diesels; 3 props; 4,050 bhp

◆ **1 Chawengsak Songkram class**
Bldr: Yokohama Yacht, Japan (In serv. 1975)

1102 CHAWENGSAK SONGKRAM

Chawengsak Songkram (1102) U.S. Navy, 8-86

D: 190 tons (fl) **S:** 32 kts **Dim:** 37.0 (35.5 pp) × 6.80 × 1.50
A: 2/20-mm Oerlikon AA (I × 2)
Electron Equipt: Radar: 1/. . . nav.
M: 4 Ikegai diesels; 2 props; 5,400 bhp **Crew:** 4 officers, 12 enlisted

THAILAND *(continued)*
PATROL BOATS *(continued)*

PATROL CRAFT

♦ **1 Sriyanont class** Bldr: Ital Thai Marine, Bangkok (In serv. . . .)

901 Sriyanont

D: 52 tons (fl) **S:** 23 kts **Dim:** 27.4 × 4.9 × 2.0
A: 2/20-mm Oerlikon AA (I × 2)—2/7.62-mm mg (I × 2)
Electron Equipt: Radar: 1/Decca . . . nav.
M: 2 Deutz SBA 16M 816CH diesels; 2 props; . . . bhp

♦ **1 (+ . . .) 24.6-meter class** Bldr: Marsun, Bangkok (In serv. 27-3-91)

802

D: 60 tons (fl) **S:** 38 kts **Dim:** 24.60 × 6.00 × 1.10 **Crew:** 12 tot.
A: . . . **Electron Equipt:** Radar: 1/. . . nav.
M: 2 G.M. Detroit Diesel 16V149 TI diesels; 2 props; 4,000 bhp

Remarks: Kevlar/GRP sandwich hull. Launched 11-2-91.

♦ **3 U.S. Cutlass class**
Bldr: Halter Marine, New Orleans, La. (In serv. 1978)

807 Phra Ong Chao Khamrop | 809 Ram Inthra
808 Picharn Pholakit

D: 34 tons (fl) **S:** 25 kts **Dim:** 19.66 × 5.18 × 1.12
A: 1/20-mm Oerlikon AA—2/7.62-mm mg (I × 2)
M: 3 G.M. 12V71 TI diesels; 2 props; 1,530 bhp
Fuel: 2.7 tons **Crew:** 15 tot.

♦ **3 27-meter class** Bldr: Tecnautic, Bangkok (In serv. 1984)

810 811 812

812—27-meter class U.S. Navy, 8-86

D: 50 tons (fl) **S:** 27 kts **Dim:** 27.00 × 5.85 × 1.90
A: 1/20-mm Oerlikon AA—2/7.62-mm mg (I × 2)
M: 3 Isotta-Fraschini diesels; 3 Castoldi 07 waterjets; 2,500 bhp

♦ **5 19.5-meter class** Bldr: Ital Thai Marine, Bangkok (In serv. 1987–90)

625 626 627 628 629

629—19.5-meter class John Bouvia, 1990

D: 42 tons (fl) **S:** 27 kts **Dim:** 19.5 × 5.3 × 1.5
A: 1/12.7-mm mg **Electron Equipt:** Radar: 1/. . . nav.
M: 2 M.A.N. D2842LE diesels; 2 props; 1,520 bhp

♦ **17 18-meter class** Bldr: Tecnautic, Bangkok (In serv. 1983–19-2-86)

608–624

D: 30 tons (fl) **S:** 27 kts **Dim:** 18.30 × 4.45 × 0.90
A: 1/12.7-mm mg **Electron Equipt:** Radar: 1/. . . nav.
M: 2 Isotta-Fraschini ID 368V diesels; 2 Castoldi 07 waterjets; 1,930 bhp

♦ **2 17.4-meter class** Bldr: Marsun, Bangkok (In serv. . . .)

539 540

D: 30 tons (fl) **S:** 25 kts **Dim:** 17.4 × 4.9 × 0.9
A: 1/12.7-mm mg **Electron Equipt:** Radar: 1/. . . nav.
M: 2 G.M. Detroit Diesel 12V71 TI diesels; 2 props; 1,500 bhp

♦ **26 16.6-meter class** Bldrs: 513–533: Sumidigawa, Tokyo, Japan; others: Captain Co., Bangkok, Thailand (In serv. 1978–79)

513–538

522—16.6-meter class U.S. Navy,

D: 18 tons (fl) **S:** 23 kts **Dim:** 16.5 × 3.8 × 0.70
A: 1/12.7-mm mg **M:** 2 Cummins diesels; 800 bhp

♦ **26 12.2-meter class** Bldr: Camcraft, Crown Point, Louisiana, U.S.A.

415–440

D: 13 tons (fl) **S:** 25 kts **Dim:** 12.2 × 3.7 × 1.0
A: small arms **M:** 2 G.M. diesels; 2 props; 540 bhp

♦ **1 11.5-meter GRP-hulled prototype**
Bldr: SEAT Co., Bangkok (In serv. 1990)

. . .

D: . . . tons (fl) **S:** 60 kts (57 sust.) **Dim:** 11.58 × 2.73 × . . .
M: 5 gasoline outboard motors; 1,000 bhp

♦ **38 11.3-meter river patrol craft** Bldr: . . .

300-series

D: 5 tons (fl) **S:** 25 kts **Dim:** 11.3 × 3.4 × . . .
A: small arms **M:** 2 . . . diesels; 2 props; . . . bhp

♦ **22 Typhoon-class rigid inflatable boats**
Bldr: Task Force Boats, U.K. (In serv. 1990–91)

Remarks: Two 225-bhp Johnson gasoline outboards: 50 kts (40 kts with 12 aboard).

TOGO

Republic of Togo

Personnel (1991): 110 total

PATROL BOATS

♦ **2 wooden-hulled** Bldr: C. N. de l'Estérel, Cannes, France

P 761 Kara (L: 18-5-76) | P 762 Mono (L: 1976)

D: 80 tons (fl) **S:** 30 kts **Dim:** 32.00 × 5.80 × 1.50
A: 1/40-mm 60-cal. Bofors Mk. 3 AA—1/20-mm Oerlikon AA
Electron Equipt: Radar: 1/Decca 916 nav.
M: 2 MTU 12V493 diesels; 2,700 bhp **Range:** 1,500/15
Crew: 1 officer, 17 enlisted

(continued)

OL BOATS (continued)

(P 762) French Navy

ONGA

m of Tonga

MARITIME DEFENSE DIVISION
TONGAN DEFENSE SERVICE

nel (1991): 10 officers, 8 cadets, 92 enlisted, plus Royal Tongan Marines: 3 1 cadet, 47 enlisted

OL BOATS AND CRAFT

SI 315 design

: Australian SB Ind. (WA) Pty. Ltd., South Coogie, Australia

	Laid down	L	In serv.
'OEA NEIAFU	30-1-89	. . .	30-10-89
'OEA PANGAI	2-10-89	. . .	30-6-90
'OEA SAVEA	2-90	. . .	23-3-91

Savea (P 203) Leo Van Ginderen, 10-91

65 tons (fl) **S:** 21 kts **Dim:** 31.50 (28.60 wl) × 8.10 × 2.12
/12.7-mm mg (I × 2)
tron Equipt: Radar: 1/Furuno 1101 nav.
Caterpillar 3516 diesels; 2 props; 2,820 bhp
ge: 2,500/12 **Fuel:** 27.9 tons **Endurance:** 10 days
tric: 116 kw **Crew:** 4 officers, 9 enlisted

ks: Craft were originally to have been assigned to Fiji. Aluminum construc- istralian government "Pacific Patrol Boat" grant-aid design, donated to a of Southwest Pacific island states. Carry a 5-m aluminum boarding boat. ve navigational suite, including Furuno FSN-70 NAVSAT receiver, 525 120 MH/HF/DF, FE-881 echo-sounder, and DS-70 doppler log. P 203 is addi- equipped to perform hydrographic survey work.

berglass-hulled Bldr: Brooke Marine, Lowestoft, U.K.

NGAHAU KOULA (In serv. 10-3-73)
NGAHAU SILIVA (In serv. 10-5-74)

D: 15 tons (fl) **S:** 21 kts **Dim:** 13.7 × 4.0 × 1.2
A: 2/12.7-mm mg (I × 2)
Electron Equipt: Radar: 1/Koden MD306 nav.
M: 2 Cummins KT2300M diesels; 2 props; 700 bhp
Range: 800/20; 1,000/18 **Crew:** 7 tot.

Remarks: Names mean "Golden Arrow" and "Silver Arrow."

AUXILIARIES

◆ **1 ex-German Army Mannheim-class utility landing craft**
Bldr: Schiffs und Motorenwerke AG, Mannheim (In serv. 1960)

TOFUA

D: 89 tons light (200 fl) **S:** 9 kts **Dim:** 27.40 × 7.20 × 1.20
M: 2 M.W.M. RHS 578A diesels; 2 props; 432 bhp
Crew: 2 officers, 7 enlisted

Remarks: Transferred as a gift from Germany, 1991. Cargo: 70 tons (90 max.). Of limited utility due to low freeboard and lack of protected vehicle/cargo deck.

◆ **1 Australian-built U.S. LCM(8)-class landing craft**
Bldr: North Queensland Eng., Cairns

C 315 LATE (ex-Australian Army 1057)

D: 34 tons light (116 fl) **S:** 12 kts **Dim:** 22.70 × 6.41 × 1.37
Electron Equipt: Radar: 1/Koden MD305 nav.
M: 2 G.M. 12V71 diesels; 2 props; 600 bhp **Range:** 480/10

Remarks: Transferred to Tonga 1-9-82. Cargo: 55 tons. Has been fitted with a pilot-house and navigational radar.

◆ **2 Sea Truck utility craft** Bldr: Rotork, U.K.

FANGAILIFUKA (In serv. 29-9-83) 'ALO-I-TALAU (In serv. 25-3-85)

D: 5.4 tons (fl) **S:** 25 kts **Dim:** 12.7 × 2.3 × 0.60
Electron Equipt: Radar: 1/Decca 060 nav.
M: 2 Volvo Penta AQAD 40 diesels; 2 outdrives; 560 bhp
Range: 85/. . . **Crew:** 3 tot.

Remarks: GRP construction, bow-ramp. First is builder's model PBF 512, second is an LSC 512. Transferred to the custody of the governors of Ha'apaik and Vavau Islands, respectively, in 1-91, but can be recalled for Tongan Navy service if needed.

◆ **1 royal yacht**

TITILUPE

Remarks: 10.4-m glass-reinforced plastic craft capable of 8 kts; also used in patrol work.

◆ **6 4.90-meter aluminum utility launches**

Remarks: Powered by 30-bhp outboard motors.

TRINIDAD AND TOBAGO

Republic of Trinidad and Tobago

COAST GUARD

Personnel (1991): 45 officers, 600 enlisted

Aviation: The Coast Guard operates one Twin Beech maritime surveillance aircraft and two Cessna light aircraft. The Air Division of the National Security Forces operates two SA.341G Gazelle and two Sikorsky S-76 helicopters for surveillance and rescue service.

PATROL BOATS

Note: Funds permitting, it is intended to order a 350-ton, 55-meter seagoing patrol boat from Sweden's Karlskrona; powered by two diesels, the boat would have a helicopter platform. Trinidad and Tobago may also receive a former U.S. Coast Guard 82-ft. "Point"-class patrol boat during 1992.

◆ **2 CG 40 class** Bldr: Karlskrona Varvet, Karlskrona, Sweden (Both in serv. 15-6-80)

CG 5 BARRACUDA CG 6 CASCADURA

D: 210 tons (fl) **S:** 32 kts (27 sust.) **Dim:** 40.60 × 6.70 × 1.70
A: 1/40-mm 70-cal. Bofors L70 AA—1/20-mm Oerlikon AA
Electron Equipt: Radar: 1/Decca TM 1226 nav.
M: 2 Paxman Valenta 16RP200 diesels; 2 props; 8,000 bhp
Range: 2,200/15 **Crew:** 22 tot. (plus 9 spare berths)

Remarks: Ordered 8-78. Have an optronic GFCS for the 40-mm AA; rescue dinghy carried on stern. Have HF and VHF D/F gear, pollution spill control equipment. Refitted 1988–89.

PATROL BOATS *(continued)*

Barracuda (CG 5) Leo Van Ginderen, 1-84

PATROL CRAFT

Note: During 1992, it is hoped to obtain two 9.45-meter patrol craft from the United States. In addition to the craft listed below, Bowen Boat Co., Port-of-Spain, delivered two small 50-kt drug interdiction craft during 6-91.

♦ **2 Wasp 20-m class** Bldr: W. A. Souter & Sons, Cowes (In serv. 12-82)

CG 31 Kairi (ex-*Sea Bird*) CG 32 Moriah (ex-*Sea Dog*)

Moriah (CG 32) Trinidad & Tobago C. G., 1989

D: 32 tons (fl) **S:** 36 kts (30 sust.) **Dim:** 20.0 × 5.0 × 1.5
A: 2/7.62-mm mg (I × 2) **Electron Equipt:** Radar: 1/Decca 150 nav.
M: 2 G.M. 16V92 TI diesels; 2 props; 2,400 bhp
Range: 450/30 **Crew:** 2 officers, 4 enlisted

Remarks: Aluminum hulls. Ordered 30-9-81.

♦ **5 Wasp 17-m-class patrol craft**
Bldr: W. A. Souter & Sons, Cowes, U.K. (In serv. 27-8-82)

CG 27 Plymouth CG 28 Caroni CG 29 Galeota CG 30 Moruga
CG 35 Cadros (ex-*Sea Erne*)

Plymouth (CG 27) Leo Van Ginderen, 1-84

Cadros (CG 35) Trinidad & Tobago C.G., 1989

D: 19.25 tons (fl) **S:** 28 kts (25 sust.)
Dim: 16.76 (13.90 wl) × 4.20 × 1.40 **A:** 2/7.62-mm mg (I × 2)
Electron Equipt: Radar: 1/Decca 150 nav.
M: 2 Stewart and Stevenson-G.M. 8V92 MTI diesels; 2 props; 1,300 bhp
Range: 500/18 **Crew:** 2 officers, 4–6 enlisted

Remarks: Glass-reinforced plastic construction. Ordered 8-81. CG-35, ex-Ma lice, transferred 30-6-89, has slightly larger pilothouse.

♦ **1 fiberglass-hulled** Bldr: Watercraft, Shoreham, U.K. (In serv. 1

CG 37 Carenaga (ex-*Sea Dragon*)

Carenaga (CG 37) Trinidad & Tobago C. C

D: 14.9 tons (fl) **S:** 23.5 kts **Dim:** 13.7 × 4.1 × 1.2 **Crew:** 4
A: 2/7.62-mm mg (I × 2) **Electron Equipt:** Radar: 1/Decca 1
M: 2 G.M. 8V92 diesels; 2 props; 700 bhp **Range:** 360/18

Remarks: Former Marine Police unit, transferred 30-6-89.

♦ **1 locally built launch** Bldr: Tugs & Lighters, Inc., Port-of-Spain

CG 36 Speyside (ex-*Sea Hawk*)

D: 12 tons (fl) **S:** 22 kts **Dim:** 10.9 × 3.9 × 1.2
A: 1/7.62-mm mg
M: 2 G.M. Detroit Diesel 6V71 diesels; 2 props; 460 bhp
Range: 400/20 **Crew:** 6 tot.

Remarks: Former Marine Police unit transferred 30-6-89.

Note: Of the two "Sword"-class patrol boats listed in the previous edition, (GC 34) burned and sank 24-9-90, and *Matelot* (GC 33) was discarded 1991. T craft *Fort Chacon* (CG 9) was retired in 1991.

SERVICE CRAFT

♦ **1 inshore survey craft** (In serv. 1985)

Meridian

Remarks: 75 tons (full load); crew: 2 officers, 3 enlisted; no other data avail

♦ **1 service launch**
Bldr: Tugs & Lighters, Ltd., Port-of-Spain (In serv. 1977)

A 02 El Tucuche (ex-CG 25)

D: 22.5 tons (fl) **S:** 24 kts **Dim:** 16.7 × 4.7 × 1.2
A: 1/7.62-mm mg **Electron Equipt:** Radar: 1/Decca 150 nav.
M: 2 G.M. 8V71 diesels; 2 props; 600 bhp **Range:** 400/20
Crew: 6 tot.

♦ **1 service launch**
Bldr: Tugs & Lighters, Ltd., Port-of-Spain (In serv. 15-8-76)

A 01 Naparima (ex-CG 26)

D: 21.4 tons **S:** 10 kts **Dim:** 15.2 × 4.9 × 2.4 **Crew:** 6 tot.
M: 2 G.M. 6V71 diesels; 2 props; 460 bhp **Range:** 400/10

♦ **6 miscellaneous launches**

A 04 Reform A 05 Rehab A 06 Cocrico (ex-*Redeem*)
A 07 Semp (ex-*Recover*) A 08 Fireboat (ex-*Relay*)
A 09 Egret (ex-*Review*)

Remarks: A 04 and A 05 transferred from Prison Authority, A 06 and A ferred from Port Authority, A 08 transferred from Fire Services, and A 09 tra from Immigration—all on 30-6-89.

IDAD AND TOBAGO *(continued)*
ICE CRAFT *(continued)*

n (A 04) Trinidad & Tobago C.G., 1989

UNISIA

lic of Tunisia

nel (1991): 4,500 total (including 700 conscripts)

Germany delivered four ex-East German Kondor-I-class patrol minesweepers Bremse-class patrol craft in 7-92; see addenda for names and data.

ATE

.S. Savage-class former radar picket

r: Consolidated Steel Corp., Orange, Texas

	Laid down	L	In serv.
DAKH (ex-*President Bourguiba*, *Thomas J. Gary*, DER 326)	15-6-43	21-8-43	27-11-43

h (E 7) Leo Van Ginderen, 7-89

1,590 tons (1,850 fl) **S:** 19 kts
: 93.27 (91.50 wl) × 11.22 × 4.27 (hull)
2/76.2-mm 50-cal. Mk 34 DP (I × 2)—2/20-mm Oerlikon AA
I × 2)—6/324-mm Mk 32 Mod. 5 ASW TT (III × 2)
ctron Equipt:
adar: 1/SPS-10 surf. search, 1/SPS-29 air search, 1/Mk 34 f.c.
onar: SQS-29 hull-mounted MF
4 Fairbanks-Morse 10-38D8⅛ reversible diesels; 2 props;
6,080 bhp
ctric: 580 kw tot. **Range:** 11,500/11
l: 310 tons **Crew:** 169 tot.

ks: Transferred 27-10-73. Had been reported for sale in 1988, but is still in ; a replacement is sought, but funds are not available. Had been converted to a picket in 1957. Prior to transfer to Tunisia, the SPS-8 height-finding radar, N, WLR-1 EW suite, Mk 15 Hedgehog ASW spigot mortar, and one depth-charge ere removed. Has Mk 63 f.c.s. forward (Mk 34 radar mounted on forward gun and Mk 51 Mod. 2 lead-computing f.c.s aft for 76.2-mm guns. Suffered major fire that will probably force retirement.

GUIDED-MISSILE PATROL BOATS

Note: Bids requested 1988 for six 55-m guided-missile patrol boats; in 9-90, bids were requested for 100-ton and 450-ton patrol boats.

◆ 3 Combattante-III class Bldr: CMN, Cherbourg, France

	Laid down	L	In serv.
P 501 La Galite	26-5-82	16-6-83	27-2-85
P 502 Tunis	28-9-82	27-10-83	28-3-85
P 503 Carthage	6-1-83	24-1-84	29-4-85

Carthage (P 503) French Navy, 9-89

D: 395 tons (425 fl) **S:** 38.5 kts
Dim: 56.80 (53.00 pp) × 8.16 × 2.15 (2.50 props)
A: 8/MM 40 Exocet SSM (IV × 2)—1/76-mm 62-cal. OTO Melara Compact DP—2/40-mm 70-cal. Breda AA (II × 2)—4/30-mm Oerlikon AA (II × 2)
Electron Equipt:
Radar: 1/Thomson-CSF Triton-S surf./air search, 1/Thomson-CSF Castor-IIB gun f.c.
EW: . . . intercept, 1/Dagaie decoy RL
M: 4 MTU 20V538 TB93 diesels; 4 props; 19,300 bhp
Electric: 405 kVA **Range:** 700/33; 2,800/10 **Crew:** 35 tot.

Remarks: Ordered 27-6-81. Have Thomson-CSF Vega II control system for missiles, 76-mm and 40-mm guns; two CSEE Naja optronic directors for the 30-mm AA; CSEE Sylosat navigational system.

PATROL BOATS AND CRAFT

◆ 3 French P 48 class Bldr: SFCN, Villeneuve-la-Garenne

	L	In serv.
P 301 Bizerte	20-11-69	10-7-70
P 302 Horria (ex-*Liberté*)	19-2-70	10-70
P 304 Monastir	25-6-74	25-3-75

Bizerte (P 301) Leo Van Ginderen, 7-89

D: 250 tons (fl) **S:** 22 kts **Dim:** 48.0 (45.5 pp) × 7.1 × 2.25
A: 2/40-mm 70-cal. Bofors AA (I × 2)—2/20-mm AA (I × 2)—8/SS-12 wire-guided missiles (IV × 2)
Electron Equipt: Radar: 1/Decca TM 1226 nav.
M: 2 MGO MB-839 Db diesels; 2 props; 4,000 bhp
Range: 2,000/16 **Crew:** 4 officers, 30 enlisted

◆ 2 103-foot class Bldr: Vosper Thornycroft, Portchester, U.K.

	L	In serv.
P 205 Tazarka	19-7-76	27-10-77
P 206 Menzel Bourguiba	19-7-76	27-10-77

D: 100 tons (125 fl) **S:** 27 kts **Dim:** 31.29 (28.95 pp) × 6.02 × 1.98
A: 2/20-mm AA (I × 2) **Electron Equipt:** Radar: 1/Decca 916 nav.
M: 2 MTU diesels; 2 props; 4,000 bhp
Range: 1,500/14 **Crew:** 24 tot.

TUNISIA *(continued)*
PATROL BOATS AND CRAFT *(continued)*

Tazarka (P 205) Leo Van Ginderen, 10-77

◆ **2 Chinese Shanghai-II class** (In serv. 2-5-77)

P 305 Gafsa   P 306 Amilcar

Gafsa (P 305) 1978

D: 122.5 tons (135 fl) **S:** 28.5 kts **Dim:** 38.78 × 5.41 × 1.55
A: 4/37-mm 63-cal. AA (II × 2)—4/25-mm AA (II × 2)
Electron Equipt: Radar: 1/. . . nav.
M: 4 MTU 8V331 TC92 diesels; 4 props; 4,260 bhp (3,540 sust.)
Range: 800/17 **Crew:** 38 tot.

Remarks: Re-engined and refitted at Socomena SY, Bizerte, completing 12-84.

◆ **4 French 32-meter class** Bldr: CN de l'Estérel, Cannes

	In serv.
P 201 Istiklal (ex-French VC 11)	1957
P 202 Joumhouria	1-61
P 203 Al Jala	11-63
P 204 Remada	7-67

Istiklal (P 201) 1970

D: 60 tons (82 fl) **S:** 28 kts **Dim:** 31.45 × 5.75 × 1.7
A: 2/20-mm AA (I × 2)
Electron Equipt: Radar: 1/Decca 1226 nav.
M: 2 MTU 12V493 diesels; 2 props; 2,700 bhp
Range: 1,400/15 **Crew:** 3 officers, 14 enlisted

Remarks: Wooden construction. P 201 was launched on 25-5-57 and transferred in 3-59.

◆ **6 French 25-meter class** Bldr: CN de l'Estérel, Cannes (In serv. 1961–63)

V 101 through V 106

D: 38–39 tons **S:** 23 kts **Dim:** 25.0 × 4.75 × 1.25 **Crew:** 11 tot.
A: 1/20-mm AA **M:** 2 G.M. 12V71 TI diesels; 2 props; 940 bhp
Range: 900/16 **Electron Equipt:** Radar: 1/Decca 1226 nav.

V 101 Leo Van Gindere

Remarks: V 107 and V 108 were transferred to the Fisheries Administrati armed, in 1971, as *Sabeq el Bahr* (T 2) and *Jaouel el Bahr* (T 3); T 3 was lost 7

AUXILIARY SHIPS

◆ **1 ex-U.S. Sotoyomo-class oceangoing tug**
Bldr: Gulfport Boilers & Welding Works, Port Arthur, Tex.

	Laid down	L	I
. . . Ras Adar (ex-*Zealand*, ex-*Pan America*, ex-*Ocean Pride*, ex-*Oriana*, ex-BAT 1)	16-3-42	15-8-42	13

D: 570 tons (835 fl) **S:** 13 kts
Dim: 43.59 (41.0 pp) × 10.31 × 4.01 **A:** none
M: 2 G.M. 12-278A diesels, electric drive; 1 prop; 1,500 shp
Electric: 90 kw **Fuel:** 171 tons **Crew:** 45 tot.

Remarks: Built under Lend-Lease, transferred to Great Britain on 22-12- turned and sold commercially in 1946. Purchased for Tunisia from Dutch com late 1960s. BAT-series had larger superstructure than standard *Sotoyomo* cl were considered to be ocean rescue tugs.

◆ **1 diving tender**

Kerkennah (In serv. 1948)

D: 653 grt **S:** 10 kts **Dim:** 53.95 × 9.75 × 2.75
M: diesel-electric; . . . props; . . . shp
Crew: 4 officers, 20 enlisted, 4 civilians

CUSTOMS

◆ **10 Tunisian-built patrol craft** Bldr: Socomena, Bizerte

Assad Ibn Fourat (L: 25-2-86; in serv. 2-3-86)
9 others (In serv. by 1989)

D: 32 tons (fl) **S:** 28 kts **Dim:** 20.5 × 4.7 × 1.3
A: 1/12.7-mm mg—2/7.62-mm mg (I × 2) **Crew:** 8 tot.
M: 2 diesels; 2 props; 1,000 bhp **Range:** 500/20

Remarks: GRP construction, built with South Korean assistance.

◆ **4 GRP construction**
Bldr: ARESA, Arenys del Mar, Barcelona (In serv: 2 in 1981, 2 in 1983)

D: . . . **S:** . . . **Dim:** 23.0 × . . . × . . .
A: . . . **M:** . . .

NATIONAL GUARD

◆ **4 patrol craft** Bldr: SBCN, Loctudy, France (In serv. 1988–89)

D: . . . **S:** 35 kts **Dim:** 13.0 × . . . × . . .
A: . . . **M:** 2 . . . diesels; 2 props; 800 bhp

TURKEY

Republic of Turkey

Personnel (1991): 59,700 naval (including 900 Naval Aviation); 4,000 r 70,000 naval reserve

Naval Aviation: The naval air arm, organized in 1972, consists of 8 S-2A and Tracker land-based ASW airplanes, 3 AB-204 helicopters, and 9 AB-212 helic

WEAPONS AND SYSTEMS

Most weapons and systems are of U.S. origin, some from West Germany. Bri Skua antiship missiles have been purchased for use by AB-212 helicopters. In license was obtained from Marconi Underwater Systems to build 40 Mk 24 Tigerfish wire-guided submarine torpedoes to begin replacement of German S SST-4 and U.S. Mk 37 torpedoes. Ten U.S. Mk 48 submarine torpedoes were or 1990, and the Turkish Navy also has a considerable number of AGM-84 launched Harpoon antiship missiles and will be receiving Sub-Harpoon missile the mid-1990s. Old U.S. Mk 23 submarine torpedoes are also still in inventor

?PONS AND SYSTEMS (*continued*)

ish S-2E Tracker — Turkish Navy, 1991

sh AB-212 helicopter — Turkish Navy, 1991

uard Close-In Weapons System—Contraves/Oerlikon

point-defense system, employed only by the Turkish Navy, employs three Sea quadruple 25-mm AA with a combined rate of fire of 3,200 rounds per minute. practical range of about 2,000 m, the mountings can depress to −15° and elevate 7°, with extremely rapid elevation and traversing. In the MEKO-200 class, the ounts are controlled by two Siemens Albis radar-electro-optical directors. Suf- ready-service ammunition is carried on-mount for 18 engagements.

IARINES

+2+4) West German Type 209/1400 class — Bldr: Gölcük NSY

	Laid down	L	In serv.
Preveze	27-7-89	10-91	1994
Sakarya	4-4-90	1993	1995
. . . . . .	. . .	. . .	. . .
. . . . . .	. . .	. . .	. . .

1,464 tons (surf.)/1,586 tons (sub.) **S:** 11.0 (surf.)/21.5 kts (sub.)
ı: 61.20 × 6.25 × 5.50
8/533-mm bow TT (14 Mk 24 Mod. 2 Tigerfish torpedoes, Sub-Harpoon SSM, and/or mines)
ctron Equipt:
adar: . . .—EW: Racal Porpoise intercept suite
onar: Krupp-Atlas CSU-83/1 suite (with flank and towed passive arrays)
4 MTU 12V493 A280 AG diesels (600 bhp each), 4/405-kw generator sets, 1 Siemens electric motor; 1 prop; 5,000 shp
ıge: 8,200/8 snorkel; 230/8, 400/4 sub. **Endurance:** 50 days
w: 30 tot.

rks: Enlarged version of standard IKL 1400 design. First two of planned six d 12-11-87; authorization of two more expected by 1994. Building with How-erke technical assistance. Diving depth: 320 m. Two 240-cell batteries. Two ırgen periscopes (1 search, with EW; one attack). All will have a new command ntrol system from Atlas Electronik.

German Type 209/1200 — Bldrs: S 347, S 348, S 349; Howaldtswerke, el; S 350 and later: Gölcük NSY

	Laid down	L	In serv.
Atilay	1-12-72	23-10-74	23-7-75
Saldiray	2-1-73	14-2-75	21-10-75
Batiray	11-6-75	24-10-77	20-7-78
Yildiray	1-5-76	20-7-77	20-7-81
Doganay	21-3-80	16-11-83	16-11-85
Dolunay	16-11-83	21-7-88	21-7-89

Saldiray (S 348)—note low casing forward — Hartmut Ehlers, 10-91

Batiray (S 349)—note high hull casing forward for bow sonar — Lt. P. J. Azzolina, USN, 4-88

D: 1,000 tons (std.)/1,180 tons (surf.)/1,285 sub.
S: 11.5 kts (surf.)/22 kts (sub.)
Dim: 55.90 × 6.30 × 5.50 **A:** 8/533-mm bow TT (14 SUT, SST-4, and Mk 37 torpedoes, and/or mines)
Electron Equipt:
Radar: 1/Thomson-CSF Calypso-II search
EW: Racal Porpoise suite
Sonar: Krupp-Atlas CSU-3 suite: AN526 passive/AN407AS active, DUUX-2 telephone
M: 4 MTU 12V493 TY60 diesels (600 bhp each); 4/405-kw generator sets; 1 Siemens electric motor, 5,000 shp
Range: 7,800/8 surf.; 11,300/4 (surf.); 28/20 (sub.); 460/4 (sub.)
Fuel: 185 tons
Endurance: 50 days **Crew:** 6 officers, 27 enlisted

Remarks: A total of 12 were planned, with 9 to be built in Turkey with assistance from Howaldtswerke, but a larger design is now being built. First two have H.S.A. M8 torpedo fire control and Thomson-CSF DR 2000 EW, others have H.S.A. SINBADS and Racal Porpoise. Two Kollmorgen periscopes (search 'scope with EW array). All are to be updated with a new combat data/weapons-control system, funds permitting. Have four 120-cell lead-acid batteries, delivering 11,500 amp./hr. and weighing 257 tons. Diving depth: 250 m.

◆ **2 ex-U.S. Tang class** — Bldr: Portsmouth Naval Shipyard, Portsmouth, New Hampshire

	Laid down	L	In serv.
S 342 Hizir Reis (ex-*Gudgeon*, SSAG 567)	20-5-50	11-6-52	21-11-52
S 343 Piri Reis (ex-*Tang*, SS 563)	18-4-49	19-6-51	25-10-52

Piri Reis (S 343) — Turkish Navy, 1991

D: 1,975 tons (surf.)/2,600 tons (sub.) **S:** 15.5 kts (surf.)/16 kts (sub.)
Dim: 87.50 × 8.33 × 5.70
A: 8/533-mm TT (6 fwd for Mk 48 and Mk 23 torpedoes, 2 short aft for Mk 37 torpedoes)
Electron Equipt:
Radar: 1/BPS-12 search—EW: WLR-1 intercept
Sonar: BQS-4 passive/active, BQG-4 (PUFFS) passive-ranging
M: 3 Fairbanks-Morse 38D8 $^{1}/_{8}$ × 10 diesels; 2 Westinghouse motors; 2 props; 3,430 bhp surf./5,600 shp sub.
Range: 7,600/15; 17/9 submerged
Crew: 11 officers, 75 enlisted

Remarks: S 343 leased for five years 8-2-80, ex-SSAG 567 leased 30-9-83; both purchased outright 6-8-87. Have Mk 106, Mod. 18, torpedo f.c.s. Aft tubes can fire Mk 37 torpedoes only.

SUBMARINES *(continued)*

♦ **2 ex-U.S. Guppy-III class** Bldr: Electric Boat Co., Groton, Connecticut

	Laid down	L	In serv.
S 333 Ikinci Inönü (ex-*Corporal,* SS 346)	27-4-44	1-4-45	8-8-45
S 341 Canakkale (ex-*Cobbler,* SS 344)	3-4-44	1-4-45	9-11-45

Ikinci Inönü (S 333) Hartmut Ehlers, 10-87

D: 1,975 tons (surf.)/2,450 tons (sub.) **S:** 17.2 kts (surf.)/14.5 kts (sub.)
Dim: 99.52 × 8.33 × 5.18
A: 10/533-mm TT (6 fwd, 4 aft: 24 Mk 23 and Mk 37 torpedoes or up to 40 mines)
Electron Equipt:
Radar: 1/SS-2A search—EW: WLR-1 intercept
Sonar: BQG-4 (PUFFS) passive ranging, BQR-2B passive
M: 4 G.M. 16-278A diesels (1,625 bhp each), diesel-electric drive; 2 props; 6,500 bhp surf./5,000 shp sub.
Range: 10,000–12,000/10 (surf.); 95/5 (sub.)
Crew: 8 officers, 78 enlisted

Remarks: Transferred on 21-11-73. Lengthened by 3.6 meters in 1962 at Philadelphia (S 341) and Charleston (S 333) in order to accommodate Sperry-Raytheon passive-ranging sonar equipment. Two 126-cell batteries. Direct diesel drive on surface.

♦ **5 ex-U.S. Guppy-IIA class** Bldrs: S 345: Electric Boat Co.,Groton, Conn.; others: Portsmouth Naval Shipyard, Portsmouth, New Hampshire

	Laid down	L	In serv.
S 335 Burak Reis (ex-*Sea Fox,* SS 402)	2-11-43	28-3-44	13-6-44
S 336 Murat Reis (ex-*Razorback,* SS 394)	9-9-43	27-1-44	3-4-44
S 338 Uluç Ali Reis (ex-*Thornback,* SS 418)	5-4-44	7-7-44	13-10-44
S 340 Çerbe (ex-*Trutta,* SS 421)	22-5-44	18-8-44	16-11-44
S 346 Birinci Inönü (ex-*Threadfin,* SS 410)	18-3-44	26-6-44	30-8-44

Uluç Ali Reis (S 338) Hartmut Ehlers, 6-90

Çerbe (S 340)—showing "stepped" sail Hartmut Ehlers, 10-85

D: 1,525 tons (std.)/1,848 tons (surf.)/2,440 tons (sub.)
S: 17.4 kts(surf.)/14 kts (sub.), 9.4 kts (snorkel)
Dim: 93.36 × 8.33 × 5.04
A: 10/533-mm TT (6 fwd, 4 aft: 24 Mk 23 and Mk 37 torpedoes or 40 mines)
Electron Equipt:
Radar: 1/SS-2A search—EW: WLR-1 intercept
Sonar: BQR-2B passive, BQS-4 active
M: 3 Fairbanks-Morse 38D8$^1/_8$ × 10 (S 345: G.M. 16/278A) diesels, electric drive; 2 props; 3,430 bhp surf./5,200 shp sub.
Range: 10,000/10 (surf.); 95/5 (sub.) **Fuel:** 330 tons
Crew: 8–9 officers, 76 enlisted

Remarks: S 335 was transferred in 12-70, S 336 in 11-70, S 338 on 24-8-73, S 6-72, and S 346 on 15-8-73. S 336 and S 338 were at one time while in U.S. equipped as "hard" targets for ASW training. S 340 is the only operational e "Guppy" to retain the original stepped sail. Sisters *Oruç Reis* (S 337, ex-*Pomf* 391) and *Preveze* (S 345, ex-*Entemedor,* SS 340) stricken 1987.

DESTROYERS

Note: Turkey declined a U.S. offer of up to four *Charles F. Adams* (DDG 2 guided-missile destroyers in 1991.

♦ **2 ex-U.S. Carpenter class**

	Bldr	Laid down	L	In
D 346 Alcitepe (ex-*Robert A. Owens,* DD 827)	Bath Iron Works, Bath, Maine	29-10-45	15-7-46	5-
D 347 Anitepe (ex-*Gemlik,* ex-*Anitepe,* ex-*Carpenter,* DD 825)	Consolidated Steel, Orange, Tex.	30-7-45	30-12-45	15-

Alcitepe (D 346) Hartmut Ehlers,

Alcitepe (D 346) U.S. Navy

D: 2,425 tons (3,540 fl) **S:** 34 kts
Dim: 119.03 × 12.52 × 4.61 (6.40 over sonar)
A: 2/127-mm 38-cal. Mk 30 DP (II × 1)—2/76.2-mm 50-cal. Mk 3 (II × 1)
2/35-mm 90-cal. Oerlikon AA (II × 1)—1/Mk 112 ASROC AS (VIII × 1, 6 reloads)—6/324-mm Mk 32 ASW TT (III × 2, Mk Mod. 2 torpedoes)— 1/d.c. rack (12 d.c.)
Electron Equipt:
Radar: 1/. . . nav., 1/SPS-10 surf. search, 1/SPS-40 air search, 1/Mk 35 f.c.
Sonar: SQS-23 hull-mounted LF
EW: WLR-1 intercept, 4/decoy RL (XX × 4)
M: 2 sets G.E. geared steam turbines; 2 props; 60,000 shp
Boilers: 4 Babcock & Wilcox; 43.3 kg/cm^2, 454° C
Electric: 1,200 kw tot. **Range:** 1,500/31; 5,800/12
Fuel: 720 tons **Crew:** 14 officers, 260 enlisted

Remarks: D 347 leased 20-2-81, ex-DD 827 on 16-2-82; both purchased outr 6-8-87. Name for D 347 changed two weeks after transfer. Variant of the design, originally optimized for ASW. Completed FRAM-I modernizations 1 taining high bridges. Have Mk 56 radar GFCS, tripod mast aft, larger hanga structure than *Gearing* FRAM-I. Twin 76.2-mm placed on fantail, twin 35-mm after transfer. The GFCS for the 35-mm mount has not been identified; the 7 mount is locally controlled. Both ships can handle an AB-212 helicopter, hangar is too small to accept the aircraft. ULQ-6 deception jammer gear h removed.

ROYERS *(continued)*

x-U.S. Gearing FRAM-I class

	Bldr	Laid down	L	In serv.
YÜCETEPE *Orleck,* DD)	Consolidated Steel, Orange, Tex.	18-11-44	12-5-45	15-9-45
ASTEPE *Meredith,* 890)	Consolidated Steel, Orange, Tex.	27-1-45	28-6-45	31-12-45
KILIÇ ALI A (ex- *ert H. Card,* DD)	Consolidated Steel, Orange, Tex.	26-1-45	9-11-45	26-10-46
PIYALE A (ex- *ke,* DD 842)	Bath Iron Wks., Bath, Maine	9-4-45	8-9-45	28-11-45
M. FEVZI KMAK (ex- *rles H. an,* DD 853)	Bethlehem Steel, Quincy, Mass.	27-9-45	15-3-46	12-9-46
GAYRET *Eversole,* 789)	Todd SY, Seattle, Wash.	28-2-45	8-1-46	10-7-46
ADATEPE *orrest* , DD 872)	Bethlehem, Staten Isl., N.Y.	6-6-45	17-1-46	28-6-46

stepe (D 348)—with both 127-mm mounts forward, twin 35-mm on l, and working helo facility French Navy, 1991

evzi Cakmak (D 351)—with four Harpoon Hartmut Ehlers, 10-89

et (D 352)—twin 35-mm AA fore and aft Hartmut Ehlers, 10-91

etepe (D 345)—firing ASROC; note EW radome on foremast Turkish Navy, 1991

D: 2,425 tons (3,600 fl) **S:** 32 kts
Dim: 119.03 × 12.49 × 4.56 (6.4 over sonar)
A: D 351, 352 only: 8/Harpoon SSM (IV × 2)—all: 4/127-mm 38 cal. Mk 30 DP (II × 2)—2 or 4/35-mm 90-cal. Oerlikon AA (II × 1)—2/12.7-mm mg (I × 2)—1/Mk 112 ASROC ASW RL (VIII × 1; 17 missiles)—6/324-mm Mk 32 ASW TT (III × 2)—1/Mk 9 d.c. rack (12 d.c.)
Electron Equipt:
Radar: 1/Decca . . . nav., 1/SPS-10 surf. search, 1/SPS-40 (D 345, 348–50: SPS-29) air search, 1/Mk 25 (D 345, 351–353: 1/. . . f.c. also)
Sonar: SQS-23 hull-mounted LF
EW: WLR-1, WLR-3 intercept, ULQ-6 deceptive jammer (not in D 348), 4/chaff RL (XX × 4)
M: 2 sets geared steam; 2 props; 60,000 shp **Electric:** 1,200 kw tot.
Boilers: 4 Foster-Wheeler and/or Babcock & Wilcox, 43.3 kg/cm^2, 454° C
Range: 2,400/25; 4,800/15 **Fuel:** 720 tons
Crew: 14 officers, 260 enlisted

Remarks: D 351 was transferred on 29-9-73, D 352 on 11-7-73, and D 353 on 27-3-71. All three originally received a twin 40-mm mount just before the bridge (with Mk 51 Mod. 2 optical director) and a twin 35-mm antiaircraft gun on the former DASH drone helicopter deck in the mid-1970s; the 40-mm mount has since been replaced by a second twin 35-mm mount in all three. D 351 has four Babcock & Wilcox boilers, while the other pair have two Babcock & Wilcox and two Foster-Wheeler boilers. All have chaff RL atop former hangar, two saluting guns fwd. GFCS include Mk 37 for 127-mm DP, 1 Mk 51 Mod. 2 for the 40-mm mount, and an unidentified radar GFCS (antenna atop after mast) for the 35-mm AA.

D 348 was purchased 20-3-80 for cannibalization, but was instead refurbished and recommissioned 20-7-81; she has both 127-mm mounts forward, the twin 35-mm AA on the fantail, and retains the helo deck, as does D 345.

D 349 and D 350 were leased for five years 5-6-80 and formally recommissioned 30-7-81. Because of their status they were not drastically altered, although one depth-charge rack, the twin 35-mm AA, and chaff RL were added. D 345 leased 1-10-82, recommissioning 29-3-83; purchased outright (with D 349, D 350) on 6-8-87. *McKean* (DD 784), previously damaged in a collision, transferred 1982 for cannibalization.

D 351 and D 352 received Harpoon missiles in 1986, mounted on the former helicopter deck, forward of the aft 35-mm AA mount. Plans to fit four with vertical-launch Sea Sparrow SAM and two H.S.A. STIR-24 radar directors have been canceled. Only D 345 and D 348 now have operational helicopter platforms.

♦ 1 ex-U.S. Gearing FRAM-II class

Bldr: Bethlehem Steel, San Pedro, Cal.

	Laid down	L	In serv.
D 354 KOCATEPE (ex-*Norris,* DD 859)	29-8-44	25-2-45	9-6-45

Kocatepe (D 354) Hartmut Ehlers, 10-91

D: 2,390 tons (3,480 fl) **S:** 32 kts
Dim: 119.03 × 12.49 × 4.6 (6.54 over sonar)
A: 4/127-mm 38-cal. DP (II × 2)—2/35-mm 90-cal. Oerlikon AA (II × 1)—4/40-mm 60-cal. Bofors AA (II × 2)—1/Mk 15 trainable Hedgehog ASW spigot mortar (XXIV × 1)—6/324-mm Mk 32 ASW TT (III × 2)—1/Mk 9 d.c. rack (12 d.c.)
Electron Equipt:
Radar: 1/Decca . . . nav., 1/SPS-10 surf. search, 1/SPS-40 air search, 1/Mk 25 f.c., 1/. . . f.c.
Sonar: 1/SQS-23 hull-mounted LF
EW: WLR-1 intercept, ULQ-6 deception jammer, 4/decoy RL (XX × 4)
M: 2 sets geared steam turbines; 2 props; 60,000 shp
Electric: 1,200 kw
Boilers: 4 Babcock & Wilcox; 43.3 kg/cm^2, 454°C
Range: 2,400/25; 4,800/15 **Fuel:** 720 tons
Crew: 14 officers, 260 enlisted

Remarks: A previous *Kocatepe* (ex-*Harwood,* DD 861) was lost on 21-7-74 when mistakenly bombed by the Turkish Air Force. She was replaced by the *Norris* (DD 859), which had been transferred on 7-7-74 for cannibalization spares. Two single 40-mm AA were mounted on former DASH drone helicopter deck in 1974, and two twin 40-mm AA were added on the upper deck between the stacks in 1977. In 1980, had a twin Oerlikon 35-mm AA substituted for the two single 40-mm aft and SPS-40 substituted for SPS-6D radar. Has Mk 37 radar GFCS for the 127-mm guns and an unidentified radar system to control the 35-mm mount; the 40-mm mounts are controlled by Mk 51 lead-computing optical directors abreast the forward stack. Sister *Tinaztepe* (D 355) badly damaged in collision 2-5-84 and laid up, awaiting possible (but increasingly unlikely) restoration.

DESTROYERS *(continued)*

◆ 1 ex-U.S. Allen M. Sumner FRAM-II class

Bldr: Federal SB, Kearny, N.J.

	Laid down	L	In serv.
D 356 ZAFER (ex-*Hugh Purvis*, DD 709)	23-5-44	17-12-44	1-3-45

Zafer (D 356) French Navy, 1990

D: 2,200 tons (3,300 fl) **S:** 33 kts
Dim: 114.76 × 12.49 × 4.39 (5.79 over sonar)
A: 6/127-mm 38-cal. DP (II × 3)—4/40-mm 60-cal. Bofors AA (II × 2)—2/35-mm 90-cal. Oerlikon (II × 1)—2/Mk 11 fixed Hedgehog ASW spigot mortars (XXIV × 2)—6/324-mm Mk 32 ASW TT (III × 2)—1/Mk 9 d.c. rack (12 d.c.)
Electron Equipt:
Radar: 1/Decca . . . nav., 1/SPS-10 surf. search, 1/SPS-29 air search, 1/Mk 25 f.c., 1/. . . f.c.
Sonar: SQS-29 series hull-mounted MF
EW: WLR-1 intercept, ULQ-6 deceptive jammer, 4/decoy RL (XX × 4)
M: 2 sets geared steam turbines; 2 props; 60,000 shp
Electric: 1,200 kw tot.
Boilers: 4 Babcock & Wilcox; 43.3 kg/cm^2, 454° C
Range: 800/32; 4,300/11 **Fuel:** 650 tons
Crew: 15 officers, 260 enlisted

Remarks: Transferred on 15-2-72. In 1977, two twin 40-mm AA with two Mk 51 Mod. 2 optical GFCS were added amidships; also has Mk 37 radar GFCS for 127-mm DP. Twin 35-mm AA replaced two single 40-mm AA on former helicopter flight deck in 1979; an unidentified f.c. radar antenna is mounted atop the after mast.

◆ 1 ex-U.S. Robert H. Smith-class destroyer minelayer

Bldr: Bethlehem Steel, San Pedro, California

	Laid down	L	In serv.
DM 357 MUAVENET (ex-*Gwin*, MMD 33, ex-DD 772)	31-10-43	9-4-44	30-9-44

Muavenet (DM 357) French Navy, 1990

D: 2,250 tons (3,375 fl) **S:** 34 kts **Dim:** 114.76 × 12.49 × 4.4 (hull)
A: 6/127-mm 38-cal. DP (II × 3)—2/76.2-mm 50-cal. Mk 33 DP (II × 1)—12/40-mm 60-cal. Bofors AA (IV × 2; II × 2)—2/Mk 11 Hedgehog ASW spigot mortars (XXIV × 2)—6/324-mm Mk 32 ASW TT (III × 2)—1/Mk 9 d.c. rack (12 d.c.)—. . ./mines
Electron Equipt:
Radar: 1/Decca . . . nav., 1/SPS-10 surf. search, 1/SPS-40 air search, 1/Mk 25 f.c., 1/SPG-34 f.c.
Sonar: . . . hull-mounted—EW: WLR-1 intercept, 4 decoy RL (XX × 4)
M: 2 sets geared steam turbines; 2 props; 60,000 shp
Electric: 900 kw tot.
Boilers: 4 Babcock & Wilcox; 43.3 kg/cm^2, 454° C
Range: 4,600/15 **Fuel:** 494 tons **Crew:** 274 tot.

Remarks: Transferred on 22-10-71 after reactivation and modernization. Fire-control equipment includes 1 Mk 37 radar GFCS for 127-mm guns, Mk 63 radar GFCS for the 76.2-mm mount, and two Mk 51 Mod. 2 optical GFCS for 40-mm AA. Mine rails on either side of main deck of what is basically an *Allen M. Sumner*-class destroyer. Survivor of a U.S. Navy class of twelve. Modernized with new radars and arma 1982–83, SPS-40 replacing SPS-6, a twin 76.2-mm mount replacing the after qu ple 40-mm mount, etc. Original sonar suite replaced with probable SQS-29-seri

FRIGATES

◆ 0 (+2+2) MEKO 200 TN "Track II"-class guided-missile friga

	Bldr	Laid down	L	In serv.
F 244	Blohm + Voss, Hamburg	. . .	4-93	1995
F 245	Gölçük NSY	10-91	11-93	1996

MEKO 200 TN Track II Blohm + Voss,

D: 3,100 tons (3,495 fl) **S:** 31.75 kts (20 on diesel)
Dim: 115.50 (107.20) × 14.80 (13.80 wl) × 5.97 (4.10 hull)
A: 8/Harpoon SSM (IV × 2)—1/Mk 29 SAM launcher (VIII × 1, 16 Sea Sparrow SAM)—1/127-mm 54-cal. Mk 45 Mod. 2 DP—12/25-mm GM 25-52 AA (IV × 3)—6/324-mm Mk 32 Mod. 5 ASW TT—1/AB-212 helicopter with Sea Skua missiles
Electron Equipt:
Radar: 1/Decca 2040 BT ARPA nav., 1/Plessey AWS-9 (Dolphin) surf. search, 1/. . . air search, 1/H.S.A. STIR-24 SAM f.c. 1/H.S.A. STIR-18 gun f.c., 2/H.S.A. TMX f.c.
Sonar: Raytheon SQS-56 (DE 1160) hull-mounted MF
TACAN: URN-25
EW: Racal Cutlass B1 intercept, Racal Scorpion B jammer, Mk 3 SRBOC decoy RL syst. (VI × 4, Hycor Mk 137 launchers)
M: CODOG: 2 MTU 12V1163 TB83 diesels (6,530 bhp each), 2 G.E. LM-2500-30 gas turbines (30,000 shp each); 2 CP props; 13,060 bhp/60,000 shp
Electric: 2,480 kw (4 × 620-kw MTU 8V396-series diesel alternat sets)
Range: 900/31.75; 4,100/18 (2 diesels) **Fuel:** 300 tons **Crew:** . .

Remarks: First two of planned four ordered 2-90. To have H.S.A. combat data s with two Oerlikon-Contraves X-band radar trackers for Sea Sparrow and th Guard CIWS. The weapons-control system also incorporates a GEC-Marconi FL a Ferranti laser-rangefinder. First steel cut for F 244 on 5-11-91. In addition to ha different propulsion system, these ships also substitute later electronics. Will be for later substitution of the Mk 48 vertical-launch group for 16 Sea Sparrow miss place of the octuple Mk 29 launcher.

◆ 4 MEKO 200-class guided-missile frigates

	Bldr	Laid down	L	In
F 240 YAVUZ	Blohm + Voss, Hamburg	31-5-85	7-11-85	17
F 241 TURGUT REIS	Howaldtswerke, Kiel	20-9-85	30-5-86	4
F 242 FATIH	Gölçük NSY	1-1-86	24-4-87	22
F 243 YILDIRIM	Gölçük NSY	24-4-87	22-7-88	21

Fatih (F 242) French Navy,

ATES *(continued)*

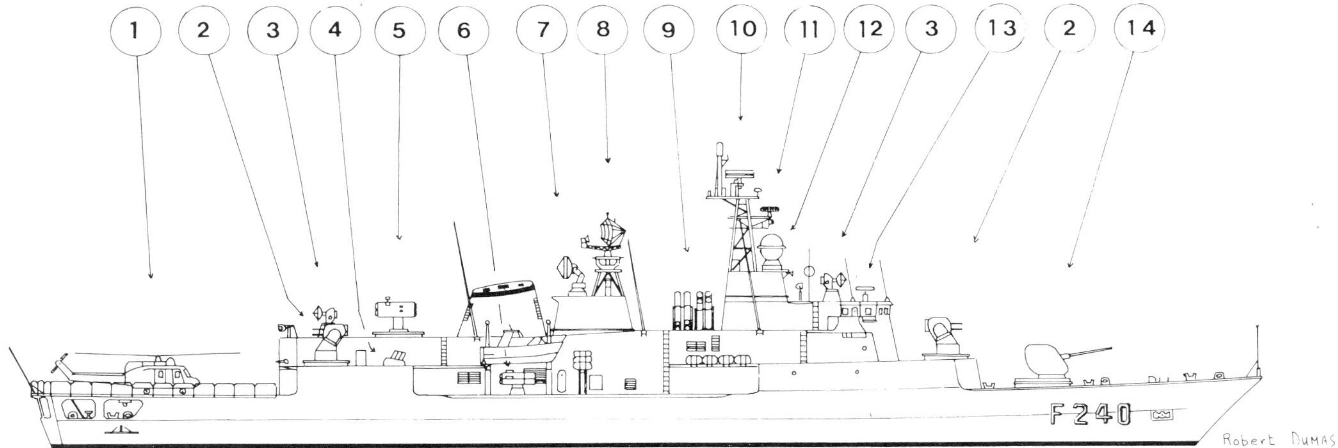

Yavuz (F 240) 1. AB-212 helicopter 2. Siemens Albis Radar/optronic director 3. Sea Zenith 25-mm CIWS mount 4. Mk 137 decoy RL 5. MK 29 Sea Sparrow SAM launcher 6. MK 32 triple ASW TT 7. STIR radar director 8. DA-08 search radar 9. Harpoon missiles 10. WM-25 track-while-scan radar director 11. 127-mm Mk 45 DP

ut Reis (F 241) Mike Louagie, 5-90

rim (F 243) Hartmut Ehlers, 10-91

2,700 tons (2,994 fl) **S:** 27 kts (18 cruise)
n: 110.50 (102.20 pp) × 13.25 × 3.94 (mean hull)
8/Harpoon SSM (IV × 2)—1/Mk 29 SAM launcher (VIII × 1, 16 Sea Sparrow missiles)—1/127-mm 54-cal. Mk 45 Mod. 1 DP—12/25-mm Sea Zenith GM 25 AA (IV × 3)—6/324-mm Mk 32 Mod. 5 ASW TT (III × 2)—1/AB-212 helicopter with Sea Skua missiles and Sea Spray radar
ctron Equipt:
Radar: 1/Decca TM 1226 nav., 1/Plessey AWS-6 (Dolphin) surf./air search, 1/H.S.A. DA-08 air search, 1/H.S.A. WM-25 track-while-scan missile/gun f.c., 1/H.S.A. STIR-24 SAM f.c., 2/Siemens Albis TMK-CW optronic f.c.
Sonar: Raytheon SQS-56 (DE 1160) hull-mounted MF
TACAN: H.S.A. Vesta
EW: H.S.A. Rapids/Ramses suite, Mk 36 SRBOC decoy RL syst. (VI × 2, Hycor Mk 137 launchers), SLQ-25 towed torpedo decoy syst.
4 MTU 20V1163 TB93 diesels; 2 CP props; 40,000 bhp
ectric: 1,440 kw tot.
nge: 4,000/20 **Fuel:** 380 tons **Crew:** 26 officers, 154 enlisted

arks: Ordered 4-83, with Blohm + Voss supplying technical assistance in con-ing two in Turkey. The Contraves quadruple 25-mm Sea Guard AA gun system ced the earlier-proposed single U.S. Vulcan-Phalanx AA. Have the H.S.A. OS-TU data system. Have fin stabilizers. Albis, by Siemens, is a laser-radar-nic f.c. director for the Sea Zenith guns. Name of F 241 changed 14-2-88.

Berk class Bldr: Golçük Naval Shipyard

	Laid down	L	In serv.
8 Berk	9-3-67	25-6-71	12-7-72
9 Peyk	18-1-68	7-6-72	24-7-75

Peyk (D 359) Hartmut Ehlers, 10-87

D: 1,450 tons (1,950 fl) **S:** 25 kts
Dim: 95.15 × 11.82 × 4.40 (5.50 over sonar)
A: 4/76.2-mm 50-cal. Mk 33 DP (II × 2)—2/Mk 11 fixed Hedgehog ASW spigot mortars (XXIV × 2)—6/324-mm Mk 32 ASW TT (III × 2)—1/Mk 9 d.c. rack
Electron Equipt:
Radar: 1/Decca TM 1226 nav., 1/SPS-10 surf. search, 1/SPS-40 air search, 2/SPG-34 f.c.
Sonar: 1/SQS-11 hull-mounted HF (25.5 kHz)—EW: WLR-1 intercept
M: 4 Fiat-Tosi 16-cyl., 800-rpm, Type 3-016-RSS diesels; 1 prop; 24,000 bhp
Range: 3,600/22; 10,000/9 **Fuel:** 220 tons **Crew:** 175 tot.

Remarks: Based on the U.S. *Claud Jones* class, but more heavily armed. Can carry an AB-212 helicopter but have no hangar. Two Mk 63 GFCS, with the SPG-34 radars mounted on the gun mounts.

♦ **2 ex-German Köln (Type 120) class** Bldr: H. C. Stülcken, Hamburg

	Laid down	L	In serv.
D 360 Gelibolu (ex-*Gazi Osman Paşa*, ex-*Karlsruhe*, F 223)	15-12-58	24-10-59	15-12-62
D 361 Gemlik (ex-*Emden*, F 221)	15-4-58	21-3-59	24-10-61

Gemlik (D 361) Turkish Navy, 1991

FRIGATES *(continued)*

D: 2,425 tons (2,970 fl) **S:** 30 kts (20 on diesels)
Dim: 109.83 (105.00 pp) × 10.50 × 4.61
A: 2/100-mm 55-cal. Mod. 1953 DP (I × 2)—6/40-mm 70-cal. Bofors AA (II × 2, I × 2)—2/375-mm Bofors ASW RL (IV × 2)—4/533-mm ASW TT (I × 4)—2/d.c. racks (6 d.c. each)—up to 82 mines
Electron Equipt:
Radar: 1/Kelvin-Hughes 14/9 nav., 1/H.S.A. SGR-103 surf. search, 1/H.S.A. DA-08 surf./air search, , 2/H.S.A. M 44 f.c., 1/H.S.A. M 45 f.c.
Sonar: 1 Krupp-Atlas PAE/CWE hull-mounted MF search/HF attack
EW: . . . intercept, 2/decoy RL (XX × 2)
M: CODAG: 4 M.A.N. 16-cyl., 3,000-bhp diesels, 2 Brown-Boveri 13,000-shp gas turbines; 2 CP props; 38,000 hp max.
Electric: 2,700 kw **Range:** 900/30; 2,900/22 **Fuel:** 361 tons
Crew: 17 officers, 193 enlisted (in German service)

Remarks: D 360 transferred 28-3-83 at Gölçük; D 361 transferred 23-9-83. Made 33 kts on original trials. Carry 72 rockets for the ASW RL. D 361 had a serious engine-room fire in 1989 but has been repaired. Sister *Lübeck* (F 224) transferred 1-12-88, was to have been activated but has been employed instead for cannibalization spares; *Braunschweig* (F 225) sold to Turkey 6-6-89 and delivered 4-7-89 for cannibalization.

GUIDED-MISSILE PATROL BOATS

◆ **8 (+2+2) German FPB 57 class** Bldrs: P 340: Lürssen, Vegesack, W. Germany; others: Taşkizak Naval Dockyard, Istanbul

	Laid down	L	In serv.
P 340 DOGAN	2-6-75	16-6-76	15-6-77
P 341 MARTI	1-7-75	30-6-77	28-7-78
P 342 TAYFUN	1-12-75	19-7-79	19-7-79
P 343 VOLKAN	. . .	11-8-80	25-7-80
P 344 RÜZGAR (ex-*Gurbet*)	30-7-81	. . .	17-12-84
P 345 POYRAZ	. . .	17-12-84	7-2-86
P 346 GURBET	. . .	24-7-87	22-7-88
P 347 FIRTINA	. . .	31-5-88	23-10-88
P 348 . . .	. . .	. . .	1994
P 349 . . .	. . .	. . .	. . .

Firtina (P 347)—with 2 Harpoon aboard Hartmut Ehlers, 11-90

Tayfun (P 342) Turkish Navy, 1991

D: 353 tons (398 fl) **S:** 36.5 kts
Dim: 58.1 (54.4 pp) × 7.62 × 2.83
A: 8/Harpoon SSM (IV × 2)—1/76-mm 62-cal. OTO Melara Compact DP—2/35-mm 90-cal. Oerlikon AA (II × 1)—2/7.62-mm mg (I × 2)
Electron Equipt:
Radar: P 340–347: 1/Decca TM 1226 nav., 1/H.S.A. WM-28-41 f.c.
P 348–349: 1/. . . nav., 1/Plessey AWS-6 (Dolphin) surf./air search, 1/ Siemens Albis TMX-CW f.c.
EW: P 340–347: MEL SUSIE-1 intercept, 2 decoy RL (XX × 2)
M: 4 MTU 16V956 TB91 diesels; 4 props; 18,000 bhp (16,000 sust.)
Electric: 405 kVA **Range:** 700/35; 1,600/32.5; 3,300/16
Endurance: 12 days
Crew: 5 officers, 33 enlisted (P 348, 349: 45 tot.)

Remarks: The 76-mm mount has a manned local control cupola. Carry 300 r 76-mm, 2,750 rounds 35-mm. Steel hulls, aluminum superstructures. Usually only four Harpoon. P 346 and P 347 have H.S.A. LIOD optronic gun directors an the local control system for the 76-mm gun. P 348 and 349, ordered 3-91, wil H.S.A. STACOS Mod. 4 combat data systems, LIOD optronic directors, and helicopter beacon, and later radars; will also have NBC warfare defensive citad least two more beyond P 349 are planned.

◆ **8 Kartal-class guided-missile and torpedo boats**
Bldr: Friedrich Lürssen Werft, Vegesack, Germany (In serv. 1967–71)

P 321 DENIZ KUSU	P 324 KARTAL	P 328 SIMSEK
P 322 ATMACA	P 326 PELIKAN	P 329 KARSIGA
P 323 SAHIN	P 327 ALBATROS	

Karsiga (P 329) Hartmut Ehlers

Kartal class launching Penguin Turkish Navy,

D: 184 tons (210 fl) **S:** 42 kts **Dim:** 42.8 × 7.14 × 2.21
A: 2/40-mm 70-cal. Bofors AA (I × 2)—2/Penguin Mk 1 SSM—2/ 533-mm TT—4/mines
Electron Equipt: Radar: 1/Decca TM 1226 nav.—EW: . . . inter
M: 4 MTU 16V538 diesels; 4 props; 12,000 bhp
Range: 500/39; 1,000/32 **Crew:** 39 tot.

Remarks: Similar to the German *Jaguar* class. Wooden planking; steel and metal keel and frames; aluminum-alloy superstructure. Can be fitted as fast gu or minelayers (four mines). All now carry two Penguin IR-homing antiship m Sister *Melten* (P 325) cut in two by Soviet naval training ship *Khasan* 25-9-85 a No longer carry spare torpedoes.

TORPEDO BOATS

◆ **6 ex-German Jaguar class (Type 140)** Bldrs: P 336: Krögerwe Rendsburg; others: Lürssen,Vegesack

	L		
P 331 TUFAN (ex-*Storch*)	16-11-59	P 334 YILDIZ (ex-*Wolf*)	21
P 332 KILIÇ (ex-*Pinguin*)	4-7-60	P 335 KALKAN (ex-*Löwe*)	8-
P 333 MIZRAK (ex-*Häher*)	9-1-60	P 336 KARAYEL (ex-*Tiger*)	21

Kalkan (P 335) Hartmut Ehlers

D: 184 tons (210 fl) **S:** 42 kts **Dim:** 42.62 × 7.1 × 2.21 (props)
A: 2/40-mm 70-cal. Bofors AA (I × 2)—4/533-mm TT or 2/TT and mines
Electron Equipt: Radar: 1/Kelvin-Hughes 14/9 nav.
M: 4 MTU 16V538 diesels; 4 props; 12,000 bhp
Range: 500/39; 1,000/32 **Crew:** 39 tot.

Remarks: Transferred 1975–76. The *Alk, Iltis,* and *Reiher* were transferred same time to be cannibalized for the maintenance of the six in service. Similar to class but shorter deckhouse with stepped face. Sisters *Firtina* (P 330, ex-*Pelikan* (P 332, ex-*Pinguin*), and *Yildiz* (P 334, ex-*Wolf*) were stricken 8-6-82, but the lat have since been refitted for further service, as have the others. Two reload tor carried for forward tubes.

Note: Six former West German *Zobel*-class torpedo boats were purchased in 1 spares.

ATROL BOATS

1 German PB 57 class

Bldr: Taşkizak Naval DY, Istanbul (In serv. 30-7-76)

140 Girne

irne (P 140)—large radar at masthead now gone, mast raised Hartmut Ehlers, 3-83

D: 341 tons (399 fl) **S:** 29.5 kts **Dim:** 58.1 (54.4 pp) × 7.6 × 2.8
A: 2/40-mm 70-cal. Bofors AA (I × 2)—2/12.7-mm mg (I × 2)—4/Mk 20 Mousetrap ASW RL (IV × 4)—2/Mk. 6 d.c. mortars—2/Mk. 9 d.c. racks (9 d.c. each)
Electron Equipt:
Radar: 1/Decca TM 1226 nav.
Sonar: Plessey PMS 26 hull-mounted MF
M: 2 MTU 16V956 TB91 diesels; 2 props; 9,000 bhp
Electric: 405 kVA **Range:** 2,200/28; 4,200/16
Crew: 3 officers, 27 enlisted

marks: Same basic design as the Spanish *Lazaga*-class patrol boats, but with nter armament. Design by Lürssen. Construction program canceled after one unit. e CSEE Naja optronic gun director. Single 40-mm Bofors replaced twin 40-mm aft 1982, and by 1988 the mast had been raised and a second radar deleted.

1 ex-U.S. Asheville class

Bldr: Peterson Builders, Sturgeon Bay, Wisc.

	L	In serv.
39 Bora (ex-*Surprise*, PG 97)	15-11-68	24-9-69

ra (P 339) Hartmut Ehlers, 5-83

: 225 tons (240 fl) **S:** 40 kts (16 on diesels)
im: 50.14 (46.94 pp) × 7.28 × 2.9
: 1/76.2-mm 50-cal. Mk 34 DP—1/40-mm 60-cal. Bofors Mk. 3 AA—4/12.7-mm mg (II × 2)
lectron Equipt: Radar: 1/SPS-53 nav., 1/SPG-50 f.c.
: CODAG: 1 LM-1500 Mk 7 gas turbine (12,500 shp); 2 Cummins 875V12 diesels (725 bhp each); 2 props; 13,950 hp max.
ange: 325/35; 1,700/16 **Fuel:** 50 tons **Crew:** 25 tot.

arks: Leased on 28-2-73 and purchased 6-8-87. Mk 63 radar GFCS, with SPG-50 r on 76.2-mm gun mount. Sister *Yildirim* (P 338, ex-*Defiance*, PG 95) lost through sion 11-4-85 near Lesbos.

2 AB 25 class

Bldr: Gölçük Naval SY (In serv. 1967–70)

5 AB 25	P 128 AB 28	P 131 AB 31	P 134 AB 34
6 AB 26	P 129 AB 29	P 132 AB 32	P 135 AB 35
7 AB 27	P 130 AB 30	P 133 AB 33	P 136 AB 36

0 (P 130) Hartmut Ehlers, 1-92

D: 150 tons (170 fl) **S:** 22 kts **Dim:** 40.24 × 6.4 × 1.65
A: 1/40-mm 60-cal. Bofors Mk. 3 AA—1/20-mm Oerlikon AA—2/12.7-mm mg (I × 2)—2/Mk 20 Mousetrap ASW RL (IV × 2)—4/d.c. release racks
Electron Equipt:
Radar: 1/Decca . . . nav.—Sonar: Plessey PMS-26 hull-mounted MF
M: 2 SACM-AGO V16CSHR diesels; 2 props; 4,800 bhp; 2 cruise diesels; 300 bhp

Remarks: Fourteen others are assigned to the Marine Police. Built with French assistance. AB 35 and 36, delivered two years later than others, have a lower hull knuckle forward and bow bulwarks. Cruise diesels are geared to the main shafts. Hull numbers revised 1-1-91; had been P 1225–1236.

◆ 4 ex-U.S. PGM 71 motor gunboats

Bldr: Peterson Builders, Sturgeon Bay, Wisc.

	L	In serv.
P 121 AB 21 (ex-PGM 104)	4-5-67	8-67
P 122 AB 22 (ex-PGM 105)	25-5-67	9-67
P 123 AB 23 (ex-PGM 106)	7-7-67	10-67
P 124 AB 24 (ex-PGM 108)	14-9-67	5-68

AB 23 (P 123)—with old number Hartmut Ehlers, 10-89

D: 104 tons (144 fl) **S:** 17 kts **Dim:** 30.81 × 6.45 × 1.83
A: 1/40-mm 60-cal. Bofors Mk 3AA—4/20-mm AA (II × 2)—2/Mk 20 Mousetrap ASW RL (IV × 2)—2/d.c. racks (4 d.c.)
Electron Equipt:
Radar: 1/Raytheon 1500B nav.—Sonar: SQS-17A hull-mounted MF
M: 8 G.M. 6-71 diesels; 2 props; 2,040 bhp **Electric:** 30 kw
Range: 1,000/12 **Fuel:** 16 tons **Crew:** 30 tot.

Remarks: Two single 12.7-mm mg have been removed. First three handed over 12-67. Hull numbers revised 1-1-91; had been P 1221–1224.

◆ 6 ex-U.S. PC 1638-class antisubmarine patrol boats

Bldrs: P 116: Gölçük Naval SY; others: Gunderson Bros., Portland, Ore.

	L	In serv.
P 111 Sultan Hisar (ex-PC 1638)	1964	5-64
P 112 Demir Hisar (ex-PC 1639)	9-7-64	22-4-65
P 113 Yar Hisar (ex-PC 1640)	14-5-64	9-64
P 114 Ak Hisar (ex-PC 1641)	14-5-64	3-12-64
P 115 Sivri Hisar (ex-PC 1642)	5-11-64	6-65
P 116 Koc Hisar (ex-PC 1643)	12-64	7-65

Sivri Hisar (P 115) Hartmut Ehlers, 10-88

Yar Hisar (P 113) Hartmut Ehlers, 1-90

PATROL BOATS *(continued)*

D: 325 tons (477 fl) **S:** 19 kts **Dim:** 52.9 × 7.0 × 3.1 (hull)
A: 1/40-mm 60-cal. Bofors Mk 3 AA—4/20-mm Oerlikon AA (II × 2)—1/Mk 15 trainable Hedgehog ASW spigot mortar (XXIV × 1)—4/Mk 6 d.c. mortars—1/Mk 9 d.c. rack (9 d.c.)
Electron Equipt:
Radar: 1/Decca TM 1226 nav.—Sonar: SQS-17A hull-mounted MF
M: 2 Alco 169 × 10A T diesels; 2 props; 4,800 bhp
Range: 5,000/10 **Fuel:** 60 tons **Crew:** 5 officers, 60 enlisted

Remarks: Design based on the U.S. PC 461 class of World War II.

PATROL CRAFT

♦ 1 modified German KW 15 class Bldr: Schweers, Bardenfleth

P 145 Caner Gönyeli (In serv. early 1960s)

D: 56 tons (fl) **S:** 19 kts **D:** 26.7 × 4.7 × 1.7
A: 2/20-mm 70-cal. Oerlikon AA (I × 2)
Electron Equipt: Radar: 1/Decca . . . nav.
M: 2 diesels; 2 props; 1,250 bhp **Crew:** 10–14 tot.

Remarks: Employed as harbor patrol craft at Girne in North Cyprus, under Turkish control. Strongly resembles Turkish Coast Guard units of the KW 15 class but appears to be somewhat smaller.

♦ 4 ex-U.S. Coast Guard 83-foot class
Bldr: U.S.C.G. Yard, Curtis Bay, Md.

P 109 LS 9 P 110 LS 10 P 111 LS 11 P 112 LS 12

LS 12 (P 112)—old number — Selçuk Emre, 1988

D: 63 tons **S:** 18 kts **Dim:** 25.3 × 4.25 × 1.55
A: 1/20-mm Oerlikon AA—2/Mk 20 Mousetrap ASW RL (IV × 2)
Electron Equipt: Radar: 1/SO-2—Sonar: QBE-3
M: 4 G.M. 6-71 diesels; 2 props; 900 bhp **Crew:** 15 tot.

Remarks: Transferred on 25-6-53. Wooden hulls. Radars and sonars are obsolete U.S. World War II–era equipment. Former Turkish hull numbers P 339, P 308, P 309, and P 310; hull numbers revised again 1-1-91 from P 1209–1212.

Note: Nine mine-disposal divers' tenders of the MTB 1 class and the various net tenders also carry patrol-series pendant numbers.

MINE WARFARE SHIPS

Note: The destroyer *Muavenet* (D 357) is also a minelayer when required, and the ex-German *Köln*-class frigates and two *Rhein*-class tenders also have mine rails.

♦ 1 (+1) Osman Gaşi class minelayer/landing ships
Bldr: Taşkizak Naval Dockyard, Istanbul

	Laid down	L	In serv.
N^{L} 125 Osman Gaşi	5-7-89	20-7-90	10-92
N^{L} 126 Orhan Gaşi	7-91	. . .	10-94

D: 3,773 tons (fl) **S:** 17 kts **Dim:** 105.0 × 16.1 × 4.8
A: 2/40-mm 70-cal. Bofors AA (I × 3)—2/35-mm 90-cal. Oerlikon AA (II × 1)
Electron Equipt: Radar: 1/. . . nav.
M: 4 MTU 8V396-series diesels; 2 props; 10,000 bhp
Range: 4,000/15 **Crew:** . . .

Remarks: To have 50 percent more capacity than *Saruçabey* class, carrying 900 troops and 15 tanks. To carry four LCVP-type landing craft and will have a helicopter platform, amphibious warfare command facilities, and full NBC warfare protection. A third unit is planned.

♦ 2 Saruçabey-class minelayer/landing ships
Bldr: Taşkizak Naval Dockyard, Istanbul

	Laid down	L	In serv.
N^{L} 123 Saruçabey (ex-*Karaçebey*)	25-7-80	30-7-81	26-7-84
N^{L} 124 Karamürselbey	26-7-83	26-7-84	27-7-85

Karamürselbey (N^{L} 124) — French Navy, 198

D: 2,600 tons (fl) **S:** 14 kts **Dim:** 92.0 × 14.0 × . . .
A: 3/40-mm 70-cal. Bofors AA (I × 3)—4/20-mm Oerlikon AA (II × 2)—150 mines
Electron Equipt: Radar: Decca TM 1226 nav.
M: 3 diesels; 3 props; 4,320 bhp **Crew:** . . .

Remarks: Enlarged version of *Çakabey*, with raised forecastle and larger superstru ture, helicopter deck aft. Two LCVP stowed on deck amidships, handled by lar articulated crane. Have two mine embarkation ports on each side at tank-deck le that can also be used to disembark troops into craft alongside. Can carry 11 tanks, trucks, and 600 troops. Minelaying ports in stern.

♦ 1 Çakabey-class minelayer/landing ship Bldr: Taşkizak NDY, Istanbul

	Laid down	L	In serv.
N^{L} 122 Çakabey (ex-L 405)	. . .	3-6-77	25-7-80

Çakabey (N^{L} 122) — Hartmut Ehlers, 4

D: 1,600 tons (fl) **S:** 14 kts **Dim:** 77.3 (74.3 pp) × 12.0 × 2.3
A: 4/40-mm 70-cal. Bofors AA (II × 2)—8/20-mm AA (II × 4)—150 mines
Electron Equipt: Radar: 1/Decca TM 1226 nav.
M: 3 diesels; 3 props; 4,320 bhp **Crew:** . . .

Remarks: Redesignated as a minelayer/landing ship in 1980. Originally planned class of four. As a landing ship, N 112 can carry 400 troops, 9 U.S. M-48 tanks, an jeeps. Carries two LCVP in davits. Deck cleared forward as a helicopter platform. disembarkation ports on each side, at tank-deck level.

♦ 2 ex-German, ex-U.S. LST 542-class minelayer/tank landing shi
Bldrs: N^{L} 120: Missouri Valley Bridge & Iron, Evansville, Ind.; N^{L} 121: American Bridge Co., Ambridge, Pa.

	Laid down	L	In s
N^{L} 120 Bayraktar (ex-L 403, ex-*Bottrop*, ex-*Saline County*, LST 1101)	22-11-44	3-1-45	26-
N^{L} 121 Sancaktar (ex-*Bochum*, ex-*Rice County*, LST 1089)	20-12-44	17-2-45	14-

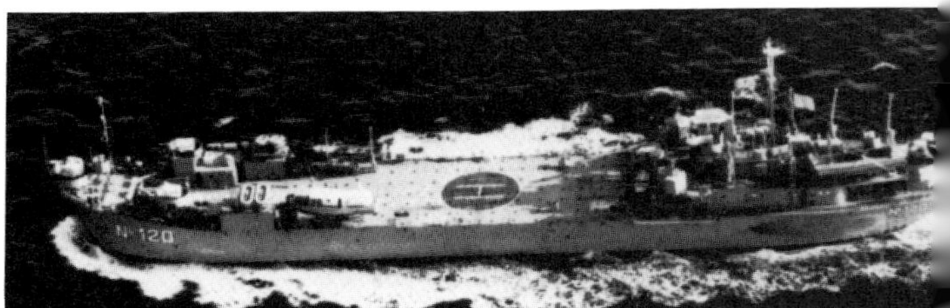
Bayraktar (N^{L} 120)

D: 3,640 tons (4,140 fl) **S:** 11 kts
Dim: 101.37 × 15.28 × 3.98 (max.)
A: 6/40-mm 60-cal. Bofors AA (II × 2, I × 2)—mines
Electron Equipt: Radar: 1/Kelvin-Hughes 14/9 nav.
M: 2 G.M. 16-567A diesels; 2 props; 1,700 bhp
Electric: 860 kw **Range:** 15,000/9 **Crew:** 60 tot.

Remarks: N^{L} 120 was transferred to West Germany on 6-2-64 and to Turk 13-12-72; N^{L} 121 to West Germany on 23-1-64 and to Turkey on 12-12-72. Conve minelayers while in German service. Six rails on the upper deck, tapering to two stern, have been removed, but there remain four rails below decks, exiting thr broadened stern. Four two-ton mine-handling cranes added. Bow doors ret Redesignated as amphibious ships 1974–75, but again placed in mine-warfare ca 1980.

WARFARE SHIPS *(continued)*

anish Falster-class minelayer Bldr: Frederikshavn DY, mark

	Laid down	L	In serv.
NUSRET (ex-N 108, ex-MMC 16)	1962	1964	16-9-64

t (N 110)—wearing old number

,880 tons (fl) **S:** 16.5 kts **Dim:** 77.0 (72.5 pp) × 12.8 × 3.4
/76.2-mm 50-cal. Mk 33 DP (II × 2)—400 mines
tron Equipt:
dar: 1/. . . nav., 1/Selenia RAN-7S surf./air search, 2/SPG-34 f.c.
2 G.M. 16-567D3 diesels; 2 CP props; 4,800 bhp
: 130 tons **Crew:** 130 tot.

ks: Paid for by the U.S.A. Two Mk 63 radar GFCS systems, with SPG-34 radars un mounts. Four sisters in Danish Navy service.

oastal minelayers Bldr: Brown Shipbuilding, Houston, Texas

	Laid down	L	In serv.
MORDOGAN (ex-MMC 11, SM 484)	17-2-45	10-3-45	15-4-45
MERSIN (ex-*Vale*, ex-MMC 13, SM 494)	11-3-45	31-3-45	8-5-45
MÜREFTE (ex-*Vidar*, ex-MMC 14, SM 492)	3-3-45	24-3-45	1-5-45

fte (N 105) Hartmut Ehlers, 10-90

'43 tons (1,100 fl) **S:** 12.5 kts **Dim:** 62.0 × 10.52 × 2.54
/40-mm 60-cal. Bofors AA (II × 3)—5/20-mm Oerlikon AA (I ×)—400 mines
tron Equipt: Radar: 2/. . . nav.
2 G.M. 16-278A (N 104: Fairbanks-Morse 38D8$^1/_8$ x 10) diesels; 2 props; 2,800 bhp
ge: 2,500/12 **Fuel:** 60 tons **Crew:** 70 tot.

ks: Former U.S. LSM 1-class medium landing ships. In 10-52, after conversion tal minelayers, the first was transferred to Turkey, the other two to Norway; N 1 N 105 were returned to U.S. control in 1960, then reassigned to Turkey. Four two forward, two aft, for the loading of mines. Two minelaying rails. Originally r twin 40-mm AA and six 20-mm AA. Sisters *Meriç* (ex-MMC 12, ex-LSM 490) *rmaris* (N 103, ex-MMC 10, ex-LSM 481) stricken in 1987–88.

nine planter Bldr: Higgins Inc., New Orleans, La. (L: 1958)

MEHMETCIK (ex-YMP 3)

540 tons (fl) **S:** 10 kts **Dim:** 39.62 × 10.67 × 3.05
. . mines **Electron Equipt:** Radar: 1/Decca 45 nav.
2 G.M. 6-71 diesels; 2 props; 600 bhp **Crew:** 22 tot.

ks: Paid for by the U.S. Military Aid Program. Used to place and tend con- minefields. The 40-mm AA formerly carried has been removed.

+ 6) NATO Tripartite-class minehunters Bldr: Lorient Arsenal
. . . . , Turkey

535 tons (605 fl) **S:** 15 kts on main engine, 7 kts while hunting
: 51.6 (47.1 pp) × 8.96 × 2.49 hull (3.50 max.)
1/20-mm 80-cal. GIAT-20/F2 AA—2/12.7-mm mg (I × 2)
ctron Equipt:
adar: 1/Decca 1229 nav.
onar: DUBM 21B hull-mounted minehunting

M: 1 Brons-Werkspoor A RUB 215V12 diesel; 1 CP prop, 1,900 bhp—2 ACEC electric maneuvering props, 120 shp each; bow-thruster
Electric: 750 kw **Range:** 3,000/12
Crew: 5 officers, 23 petty officers, 21 ratings

Mehmetcik (N 115) Selçuk Emre, 1988

Remarks: Design selected and letter-of-intent signed with France 10-91, but no contract has yet resulted and shortage of funds may prevent ordering for several years. Ultimately, up to 14 units are desired. Prototype would be built in France, others in Turkey.

Hull built of glass-reinforced polyester plastic. Dutch, Belgian, and French units have the EVEC 20 automatic plotting table and Decca HiFix and Syledis radio precision navigation equipment, two PAP-104 remote-controlled minehunting submersibles, and a six-man portable decompression chamber module at the aft end of the forecastle deck. Turkish units may employ the U.S. SQQ-32 or British Type 2093 sonar, Pinguin B3 minehunting submersibles, and U.S. SYQ-13 or British Nautis-M control system.

♦ **6 ex-German French Mercure-class coastal minesweepers**
Bldr: C.N. Amiot (CMN), Cherbourg

	Laid down	L	In serv.
M 520 KARAMÜRSEL (ex-*Wörms*)	19-3-58	30-1-60	30-4-60
M 521 KEREMPE (ex-*Detmold*)	19-2-58	17-11-59	20-2-60
M 522 KILIMLI (ex-*Siegen*)	18-4-58	29-3-60	9-7-60
M 523 KOZLU (ex-*Hameln*)	20-1-58	20-8-59	15-10-59
M 524 KUSADASI (ex-*Vegesack*)	20-12-57	21-5-59	19-9-59
M 525 KEMER (ex-*Passau*)	19-5-58	25-6-60	15-10-60

Kilimli (M 522) Hartmut Ehlers, 9-90

D: 366 tons (383 fl) **S:** 14.5 kts **Dim:** 44.62 (42.5 pp) × 8.41 × 2.55
A: 2/20-mm Oerlikon AA (II × 1)
Electron Equipt:
Radar: 1/Decca 707 nav.—Sonar: Simrad . . . hull-mounted
M: Mercedes-Benz MB-820 Db diesels; 2 CP props; 4,000 bhp
Electric: 520 kw **Crew:** 40 tot.

Remarks: These ships were built for the German Navy, placed in reserve in 1963, and stricken on 31-12-73. Transferred to Turkey between 6-75 and 10-75, except M 525, in 1979. Wooden construction. M 520 has been employed for minehunting trials since 1987 and is equipped with a sonar; the others had Simrad mine-avoidance sonars added post-1988.

♦ **12 ex-U.S. Adjutant- , MSC 268(*)- , and MSC 289(†)-class coastal minesweepers** Bldrs: M 507: Hiltebrant DD, Kingston, N.Y.; M 508: Stephen Bros.; M 509: South Coast Co., Newport Beach, Cal.; M 510 to M 513: Bellingham SY, Bellingham, Wash.; M 514, M 515: Dorchester Builders, Dorchester, N.J.; M 516 to M 518: Peterson Builders, Sturgeon Bay, Wisc.

	L	In serv.
M 507 SEYMEN (ex-*De Panne*, ex-MSC 131)	. . .	28-10-55
M 508 SELÇUK (ex-*Pavot*, ex-MSC 124)	. . .	6-54
M 509 SEYHAN (ex-*Renoncule*, ex-MSC 142)	. . .	8-54
M 510 SAMSUN (ex-MSC 268)*	6-9-57	30-9-58
M 511 SINOP (ex-MSC 270)*	4-1-58	2-59
M 512 SÜRMENE (ex-MSC 271)*	1958	27-3-59

MINE WARFARE SHIPS *(continued)*

	L	In serv.
M 513 Seddul Bahr (ex-MSC 272)*	1958	5-59
M 514 Silifke (ex-MSC 304)†	21-11-64	9-65
M 515 Saros (ex-MSC 305)†	1-5-65	2-66
M 516 Sigaçik (ex-MSC 311)†	12-6-64	6-65
M 517 Sapanca (ex-MSC 312)†	14-9-64	26-7-65
M 518 Sariyer (ex-MSC 315)†	21-4-66	8-9-67

Selçuk (M 508)—Adjutant class Hartmut Ehlers, 7-91

Sinop (M 511)—MSC 268 class Hartmut Ehlers, 12-86

Sigaçik (M 516) Hartmut Ehlers, 10-90

D: 300 tons (392 fl) **S:** 14 kts **Dim:** 43.0 (41.5 pp) × 7.95 × 2.55
A: 2/20-mm Oerlikon AA (II × 1)
Electron Equipt:
Radar: 1/Decca 1226 or 707—Sonar: UQS-1D hull-mounted (100 kHz)
M: 2 G.M. 8/268A diesels; 2 props; 1,200 bhp
Range: 2,500/10 **Crew:** 4 officers, 34 enlisted

Remarks: M 507 was returned to the U.S.A. by Belgium in 1970, and M 508 and M 509 were returned by France on 23-3-70, then transferred to Turkey. The MSC 268 class have four G.M. 6-71 diesels; two props; 880 bhp. The MSC 289 class have lower superstructure, taller stacks, and two Waukesha L-1616 diesels of 600 bhp each; **Dim:** 44.32 × 8.29 × 2.55.

◆ **4 ex-Canadian Bay-class coastal minesweepers**
Bldr: Davie SB, Lauzon, Quebec

	L
M 530 Trabzon (ex-*Gaspé*)	20-5-53
M 531 Terme (ex-*Trinity*)	31-7-53
M 532 Tirebolu (ex-*Comax*)	24-4-52
M 533 Tekirdag (ex-*Ungava*)	12-11-51

Terme (M 531) Hartmut Ehlers,

D: 390 tons (412 fl) **S:** 16 kts **Dim:** 50.0 (46.05 pp) × 9.21 × 2.
A: 1/40-mm 60-cal. Bofors AA—2/12.7-mm mg (I × 2)
Electron Equipt: Radar: 1/Decca TM 1226 nav.
M: 2 G.M. 12-278A diesels; 2 props; 2,400 bhp
Electric: 940-kw sweep/plus 690-kw ship's service
Range: 4,000/10 **Fuel:** 52 tons **Crew:** 44 tot.

Remarks: Transferred under U.S. Military Aid Program on 19-5-58. Wood-p skin on steel frame. M 533 has been equipped with an EW intercept antenna arr all now have 2/12.7-mm mg far forward on the forecastle. The 40-mm gun is in a War II–era U.K. "Boffin" mounting.

◆ **4 ex-U.S. Cape-class inshore minesweepers**
Bldr: Peterson Builders, Sturgeon Bay, Wis.

	L	In serv.
M 500 Foca (ex-MSI 15)	23-8-66	8-67
M 501 Fethiye (ex-MSI 16)	7-12-66	9-67
M 502 Fatsa (ex-MSI 17)	11-4-67	10-67
M 503 Finike (ex-MSI 18)	11-67	12-67

Fatsa (M 502) Hartmut Ehlers

D: 203 tons (239 fl) **S:** 12.5 kts **Dim:** 34.06 × 7.14 × 2.4
A: 2/12.7-mm mg (I × 2)
Electron Equipt: Radar: 1/. . . nav.
M: 4 G.M. 6-71 diesels; 2 props; 960 bhp **Electric:** 120 kw
Range: 1,000/9 **Fuel:** 20 tons **Crew:** 20 tot.

Remarks: Transferred on completion. Wooden construction. Machine-gun mou atop pilothouse and abaft stack; actual guns normally stowed below.

◆ **2 ex-U.S. 64-foot distribution-box minefield tenders**

Y 1148 Samandira L 1 Y 1149 Samandira L 2

D: 72 tons (fl) **S:** 9.5 kts **Dim:** 19.58 × 5.72 × 1.83
A: 1 Gray Marine 64HN9 diesel; 1 prop; 225 bhp **Crew:** 6 tot.

Remarks: Transferred in 1959. Wooden construction.

◆ **8 MTB 1-class mine-warfare support tenders**
Bldr: . . ., U.K. (In serv. 1942)

P 312 Dalgiç 2 (ex-MTB 2) P 315 MTB 5 P 318 MTB 8
P 313 MTB 3 P 316 MTB 6 P 319 MTB 9
P 314 MTB 4 P 317 MTB 7

D: 70 tons **S:** 20 kts **Dim:** 21.8 × 4.2 × 2.6
A: 1/12.7-mm mg or 20-mm AA in some **M:** 2 diesels; 2,000 bhp

Remarks: First unit redesignated diver support boat in 1983; others are general-purpose tender/supply craft at mine-warfare bases. Sister MTB 10 s 1987 and diver support conversion *Dalgiç 1* (P 311, ex-MTB 1) in 1990.

WARFARE SHIPS *(continued)*

: 2 (P 312) Hartmut Ehlers, 7-84

HIBIOUS WARFARE SHIPS AND CRAFT

The *Çakabey* (N^L 112), *Bayraktar* (N^L 120), and *Sancaktar* (N^L 121), formerly .s landing ships, are now listed as minelayers; they can still be employed in ious landings, as can units of the the *Saruçabey* (N^L 123) and *Osman Gaşi* (N^L isses.

x-U.S. Terrebonne Parish–class tank landing ships
r: Christy Corp., Sturgeon Bay, Wisc.

	L	In serv.
ERTUGRUL (ex-*Windham County,* LST 1170)	22-5-54	15-12-54
SERDAR (ex-*Westchester County,* LST 1167)	18-4-53	10-3-54

r (L 402) Hartmut Ehlers, 10-85

2,590 tons (5,786 fl) **S:** 15 kts
: 117.35 (112.77 pp) × 17.06 × 5.18
3/76.2-mm 50-cal. Mk 33 DP (II × 3)
ctron Equipt: Radar: 1/Decca TM 1226 nav., 2/Mk 34 f.c.
4 G.M. 16-268A diesels; 2 CP props; 6,000 bhp **Electric:** 600 kw
l: 874 tons **Crew:** 116 tot. + 395 troops

ks: L 401 leased in 6-73 and L 402 in 8-74; both purchased 6-8-87. Cargo: 2,200 an carry four LCVPs in Welin davits. Two Mk 63 radar GFCS.

(+ . . .) Ç 139-class utility landing craft Bldr: Taşkizak Naval kyard

L		L		L
8-84	Ç 144	25-7-85	Ç 149	21-7-90
8-84	Ç 145	21-7-89	Ç 150	7-91
9-84	Ç 146	21-7-89	Ç 151	7-91
25-7-85	Ç 147	21-7-89	Ç 152	7-91
25-7-85	Ç 148	21-7-90		

Hartmut Ehlers, 6-86

D: 280 tons light (600 fl) **S:** 10 kts (8.5 kts loaded)
Dim: 60.16 × 11.58 × 1.25 (aft)
A: 2/20-mm Oerlikon AA (I × 2)—2/12.7-mm mg (I × 2)
Electron Equipt: Radar: 1/Decca TM 1226 nav.
M: 2 MTU 8V396 TE-series diesels; 2 props; 1,240 bhp
Range: 600/10 (light); 1,100/8 (loaded) **Crew:** . . . tot.

Remarks: Developed from the the Ç 107 design, but with greater length, greater moulded depth amidships, and larger superstructure. Can carry 100 troops and 6 M-48 tanks.

◆ **15 Ç 107-class utility landing craft**
Bldr: Gölçük Naval SY (In serv. 1966–81)

Ç 109 Ç 110 Ç 117 Ç 118 Ç 122 Ç 123 Ç 124 Ç 126
Ç 127 Ç 128 Ç 132 Ç 133 Ç 135 Ç 137 Ç 138

Ç 132 Turkish Navy, 1991

D: 260 tons light (580 fl) **S:** 10 kts (8.5 kts loaded)
Dim: 56.56 × 11.58 × 1.25 (aft)
A: 2/20-mm AA (I × 2)—2/12.7-mm mg (I × 2)
Electron Equipt: Radar: 1/Decca . . . nav.
M: 3 G.M. 6-71 diesels; 3 props; 900 bhp (675 sust.)
Range: 600/10 (light); 1,100/8 **Crew:** . . . tot.

Remarks: Design based on British LCT(4) design. Libya received Ç 134 from Turkish inventory in 12-79, and Ç 129 and Ç 130 in 1983. Ç 137 and Ç 138 were launched 21-3-80 and commissioned 20-7-81. Can carry 100 troops and 5 M-48 tanks. Superstructure configurations vary: Ç 121 and later have mg platform atop pilothouse. Ç 136 lost in storm 30-1-85. Ç 107, 108, 111–116, 121 retired by 1991.

◆ **12 Ç 205-class utility landing craft**
Bldr: Taşkizak Naval Dockyard, Istanbul (In serv. 1965–66)

Ç 205 through Ç 216

Ç 206 Selçuk Emre, 1986

D: 320 tons (405 fl) **S:** 10 kts **Dim:** 44.3 (40.8 wl) × 8.8 × 1.7
A: 2/20-mm AA (I × 2) **Electron Equipt:** Radar: 1/Decca . . . nav.
M: 2 G.M. 6-71 diesels; 2 props; 600 bhp (450 sust.) **Crew:** . . . tot.

Remarks: Up to eight may have been retired by end-1991. Design similar to U.S. Navy LCU 1626 class, but freeboard higher at bow and pilothouse moved well forward. Have ramps at bow and stern.

◆ **20 U.S. LCM(8)-class landing craft**
Bldr: Taşkizak Naval Dockyard, Istanbul (In serv. 1965–66)

Ç 301 through Ç 320

Ç 308 Hartmut Ehlers, 10-89

AMPHIBIOUS WARFARE SHIPS AND CRAFT *(continued)*

D: 56 tons (113 fl) **S:** 9 kts **Dim:** 22.43 × 6.42 × 1.6
A: 2/12.7-mm mg (I × 2)
M: 4 G.M. 6-71 diesels; 2 props; 660 bhp **Range:** 140/9 **Crew:** 5 tot.

HYDROGRAPHIC SHIPS

◆ **1 oceanographic research and hydrographic survey ship**
Bldr: Gölçük NSY (L: 17-11-83; in serv. 7-84)

A 594 Çubuklu (ex-Y 1251)

Çubuklu (A 594) Hartmut Ehlers, 8-87

D: 512 tons (600 fl) **S:** 11 kts **Dim:** 40.40 (36.40 wl) × 9.60 × 3.20
A: 2/20-mm AA (I × 2) **Electron Equipt:** Radar: 1/. . . nav.
M: 1 MWM diesel; 1 CP prop; 1,004 bhp (820 sust.) **Crew:** 39 tot.

Remarks: Carries one survey launch to port. Forecastle side plating extends to abaft the boat installation on port side. Received Qubit (Australia) integrated navigation data-processing system in 1990–91.

◆ **2 ex-U.S. 52-foot inshore-survey craft** (In serv. 1966)

Y 121 Mesaha 1 Y 122 Mesaha 2

Mesaha 2 (Y 122)—with old number Selçuk Emre, 1988

D: 31.7 tons (37.6 fl) **S:** 10 kts **Dim:** 15.9 × 4.45 × 1.3
M: 2 G.M. 6-71 diesels; 2 props; 330 bhp **Range:** 600/10
Crew: 10 tot.

INTELLIGENCE COLLECTOR

◆ **1 West German Type 422B converted trawler** Bldr: Unterweser, Bremerhaven

	L	In serv.	Converted
A 590 Yunus (ex-*Alster*, A50, ex-*Mellum*)	21-11-60	21-3-61	19-10-71

Yunus (A 590) Hartmut Ehlers, 10-91

D: 1,187 tons (1,497 fl) **S:** 15 kts
Dim: 72.83 (68.35 pp) × 10.50 × 5.60
A: . . .
Electron Equipt: Radar: 1/Kelvin-Hughes 14/7 nav.—EW: . . .
M: 1 Klöckner-Humboldt-Deutz 8-cyl., 1,800-bhp diesel, electric d
1 KHD 8-cyl. auxiliary diesel, electric drive, 400 shp; 1 prop
Range: . . . **Crew:** 90 total

Remarks: Transferred 2-89; sister *Oker* (A53, ex-*Hoheweg*) transferred to 12-2-88. Converted 1970 to act as intelligence collector by Blohm + Voss.

OILERS

◆ **1 (+1) replenishment oiler** Bldr: Gölçük Naval SY, Istanbul

	L	In serv.
A 580 Akar	16-11-83	24-4-87

Akar (A 580) Turkish Navy

D: 19,350 tons (fl) **S:** 15 kts **Dim:** 145.1 × 22.8 × 8.4
A: 2/76.2-mm 50-cal. Mk 34 DP (II × 1)—2/40-mm 70-cal. Bofors (I × 2)—2/20-mm AA (I × 2)
Electron Equipt:
Radar: 1/Decca . . . nav. , 1/Decca 1226 nav., 1/Mk 34 f.c.
M: 1 diesel; 1 prop; 6,500 bhp **Crew:** 329 tot.

Remarks: 15,000 dwt. Underway replenishment capability. Has helicopter pl Construction suspended for several years after launching. Has U.S. Mk 63 GFC SPG-34 radar) for the twin U.S. Mk 34 76.2-mm gun mount. A sister is planne

◆ **1 transport tanker** Bldr: Taşkizak Naval Dockyard

	L	In serv.
A 570 Taşkizak	28-7-83	1-8-84

Taşkizak (A 570) Hartmut Ehler

D: 1,440 tons (fl) **S:** 13 kts **Dim:** 64.6 × 9.4 × 3.5
A: 1/40-mm 60-cal. Bofors AA—2/20-mm Oerlikon AA (I × 2)
Electron Equipt: Radar: 1/Decca . . . nav.
M: 1 diesel; 1 prop; 1,400 bhp **Crew:** 57 tot. **Cargo:** 1,000 dw

◆ **1 replenishment oiler** Bldr: Taşkizak NDY, Istanbul (L: 7-69)

A 573 Binbaşi Saadettin Gürçan

Binbaşi Saadettin Gürçan (A 573) Leo Van Ginderen

RS (continued)

1,505 tons (4,680 fl) **S:** 16 kts **Dim:** 89.7 × 11.8 × 5.4
1/40-mm 60-cal. Bofors AA—2/20-mm Oerlikon AA (I × 2)
ctron Equipt: Radar: 1/Decca TM 1226 nav.
4 G.M. 16-567A diesels, electric drive; 2 props; 4,400 shp
w: . . . tot.

rks: One liquid-replenishment station on each side. Primarily used as a trans-nker.

Turkish-designed transport oiler Bldr: Gölçük Naval Shipyard

ALBAY HAKKI BURAK (In serv. 1964)

y Hakki Burak (A 572) Hartmut Ehlers, 3-88

1,800 tons (3,740 fl) **S:** 16 kts **Dim:** 83.73 × 12.25 × 5.49
2/40-mm 60-cal. Bofors AA (I × 2)
ctron Equipt: Radar: 1/Decca 707 nav.
4 G.M. 16-567A diesels, electric drive; 2 props; 4,400 shp
w: 88 tot.

rks: One liquid-replenishment station on each side. Primarily a transport r.

ex-German Bodensee-class transport oiler
dr: Lindenau-Werft, Kiel

	Laid down	L	In serv.
5 INEBOLU (ex-*Bodensee*, ex-*Unkas*)	24-8-55	19-11-55	11-2-56

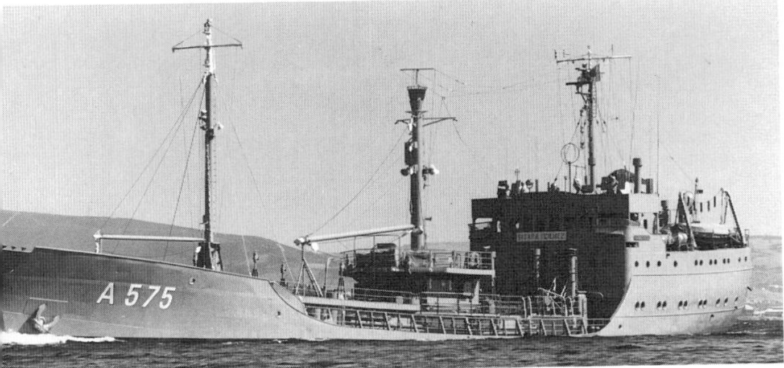

olu (A 575) Hartmut Ehlers, 5-86

1,237 tons (1,840 fl) **S:** 13.5 kts
m: 67.1 (61.2 pp) × 9.84 × 4.27
2/20-mm AA (I × 2)
ectron Equipt: Radar: 1/Kelvin-Hughes 14/9 nav.
: 1 MaK 6-cyl. diesel; 1 prop; 1,050 bhp **Electric:** 238 kVA
nge: 6,240/12 **Crew:** 21 tot.

arks: Former merchant tanker acquired on 26-3-59 for the West German Navy; ferred to Turkey on 25-8-77. Cargo: 1,231 tons. One replenishment station, usable her side.

Turkish-designed transport oiler
ldr: Taşkizak Naval Dockyard, Istanbul

1 YUZBASI TOLÜNAY (ex-*Taşkizak*)

: 2,500 tons (3,500 fl) **S:** 14 kts **Dim:** 79.0 × 12.4 × 5.9
: 2/40-mm 60-cal. Bofors AA (I × 2)
lectron Equipt: Radar: 1/Kelvin-Hughes 14/9 nav.
: 2 Atlas-Polar diesels; 2 props; 1,900 bhp **Crew:** . . . tot.

arks: Launched on 22-8-50. Has one alongside-replenishment station and can nish over the stern.

Yuzbasi Tolünay (A 571)—with *Pinar*-class water tanker Y 1216 (now Y 116) alongside Hartmut Ehlers, 3-84

WATER TANKERS

♦ **2 Van-class water tankers**
Bldr: Gölçük Naval Shipyard (In serv. 1969–70)

A 597 VAN (ex-Y 1208) A 598 ULABAT (ex-Y 1209)

Van (A 597) Hartmut Ehlers, 9-91

D: 900 tons (1,250 fl) **S:** 10 kts **Dim:** 53.1 × 9.0 × 3.0
A: 1/20-mm AA **Electron Equipt:** Radar: 1/Decca 707 nav.
M: 1 diesel; 1 prop; 650 bhp **Crew:** . . . tot.

Remarks: Cargo: 700 tons. Reclassified as auxiliaries from service craft on 1-1-91.

♦ **1 ex-German FW 1-class water tanker**
Bldr: Schichau, Bremerhaven

	Laid down	L	In serv.
A 591 SÖGÜT (ex-Y 1217, ex-*FW 2*)	5-4-63	3-9-63	4-1-64

Sögüt (A 591)—with old number Hartmut Ehlers, 11-85

D: 598 tons (647 fl) **S:** 9.5 kts **Dim:** 44.03 (41.4 pp) × 7.8 × 2.63
M: 1 MWM 12-cyl. diesel; 1 prop; 230 bhp **Electric:** 130 kVA
Range: 2,150/9 **Fuel:** 15 tons **Crew:** 12 tot.

Remarks: Transferred on 3-12-75. Cargo: 343 tons of fresh water. Reclassified as an auxiliary from service craft on 1-1-91.

TENDERS AND REPAIR VESSELS

♦ 2 ex-German Rhein-class tenders

	Bldr	L	In serv.
A 577 SOKULLU MEHMET PAŞA (ex-*Isar,* A 54)	Blohm + Voss, Hamburg	14-7-62	25-1-64
A 579 CEZAYIRLI GAZI HASAN PAŞA (ex-*Ruhr,* A 64)	Schlieker, Hamburg	18-8-60	2-5-64

Sokullu Mehmet Paşa (A 577) Leo Van Ginderen, 8-86

Cezayirli Gazi Hasan Paşa (A 579) Hartmut Ehlers, 6-90

D: A 579: 2,370 tons (2,740 fl); A 577: 2,330 tons (2,930 fl)
S: 20 kts (22 trials)
Dim: A 579: 98.18 (92.80 pp) × 11.80 × 3.90
A 577: 98.80 (92.80 pp) × 11.80 × 3.95
A: 2/100-mm 65-cal. Mod. 1953 DP (I × 2)—4/40-mm 70-cal. Bofors AA (I × 4)—70 mines
Electron Equipt:
Radar: 1/. . . nav., 1/H.S.A. SGR-103 surf. search, 1/ H.S.A. SGR-105 air search, 2/H.S.A. M 45 f.c.
M: 6 Maybach (A 577: Mercedes-Benz 839Db) diesels (A 577: electric drive); 2 props; 11,400 bhp (A 577: 11,000 shp)
Electric: 2,250 kw **Range:** 2,500/16 **Fuel:** 334 tons
Crew: 98 tot. (accommodations for 40 officers, 170 enlisted)

Remarks: A 579, transferred on 15-11-76, was built as a Type 401 small combatant tender, but was employed as a training ship in the West German Navy; she continues in this latter role in the Turkish Navy. A 577, transferred on 30-9-82, is configured as a Type 402 mine-countermeasures support ship and had been in reserve since 1968. A 579 has CP props. Both have two M4 directors for the 100-mm guns and can be employed as minelayers or escorts, if required.

♦ 2 tenders, ex-West German Angeln-class cargo ships

Bldr: Ateliers et Chantiers de Bretagne, Nantes, France

	Laid down	L	In serv.
A 586 ÜLKÜ (ex-*Angeln,* ex-*Borée*)	17-4-54	9-10-54	20-1-55
A 588 UMURBEY (ex-*Dithmarschen,* ex-*Hebé*)	20-10-54	7-5-55	17-11-55

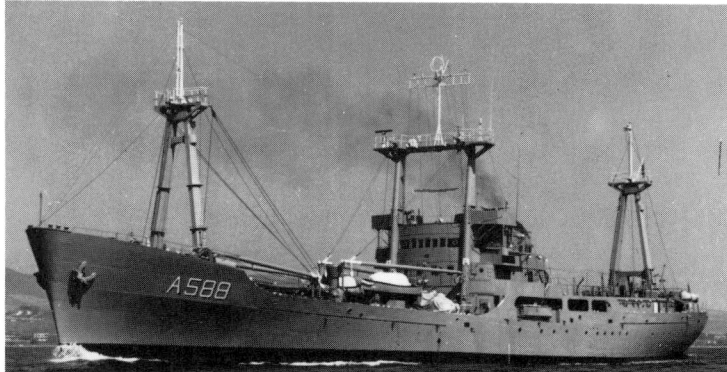

Umurbey (A 588) Hartmut Ehlers, 5-86

D: 2,998 tons (4,089 fl) **S:** 19 kts
Dim: 90.53 (84.5 pp) × 13.32 × 6.2
A: 2/20-mm Oerlikon AA (I × 2)
Electron Equipt: Radar: 1/Kelvin-Hughes 14/9 nav.
M: 2 SEMT-Pielstick 6-cyl. diesels; 1 prop; 3,000 bhp
Electric: 335 kw **Range:** 3,660/15 **Crew:** 57 tot.

Remarks: Former French merchant cargo ships acquired for the West German on 27-11-59 and 19-12-59, respectively. A 586 was transferred to Turkey on 28-3-7 A 588 on 6-10-76. A 586 is used as a patrol-boat tender and A 588 as a subm tender. A 588's displacement is 3,098 tons (4,189 fl). Cargo: A 586, 2,665 tons; 2,670 tons. Six 2.5-ton derricks, three holds.

♦ 1 ex-U.S. Portunus-class patrol-boat tender

Bldr: Bethlehem Steel, Hingham, Mass.

	Laid down	L	In serv.
A 581 ONARAN (ex-*Alecto,* AGP 14, ex-LST 977)	12-12-44	15-1-45	8-2-45

Onaran (A 581) Dr. Giorgio Arra,

D: 4,100 tons (fl) **S:** 11.6 kts **Dim:** 99.98 × 15.24 × 3.4
A: 8/40-mm 60-cal. Bofors AA (IV × 2)—8/20-mm Oerlikon AA (I
Electron Equipt: Radar: 1/. . . nav.
M: 2 G.M. 12-278A diesels; 2 props; 1,800 bhp **Electric:** 500 kw
Range: 9,000/9 **Fuel:** 590 tons **Crew:** 291 tot.

Remarks: Transferred in 11-52. Retains bow doors. Superstructure enlarged transfer.

♦ 1 ex-U.S. Achelous-class submarine tender

Bldr: Bethlehem Steel, Hingham, Mass.

	Laid down	L	In ser
A 582 BAŞARAN (ex-*Patroclus,* ARL 19, ex-LST 955)	22-9-44	22-10-44	13-11-4

Başaran (A 582) Hartmut Ehlers,

Remarks: Former landing-craft repair ship. Data as for *Onaran,* above, e **Electric:** 420 kw; **Fuel:** 621 tons. Has less superstructure than *Onaran.*

♦ 1 ex-U.S. Dixie-class destroyer tender

Bldr: Tampa SB, Tampa,

	Laid down	L	In serv
A 576 DERYA (ex-*Piedmont,* AD 17)	1-12-41	7-12-42	5-1-4

D: 9,450 tons light (17,190 fl) **S:** 18 kts
Dim: 161.70 × 22.33 × 7.80
A: 3/40-mm 60-cal. Bofors AA (I × 3)—6/20-mm Oerlikon AA (I ×
Electron Equipt: Radar: 1/LN-66 nav., 1/SPS-10 surf. search
M: 2 sets geared steam turbines; 2 props; 11,000 shp
Electric: 3,600 kw
Boilers: 4 Babcock & Wilcox; 28.4 kg/cm², 282° C
Range: 12,200/12 **Fuel:** 3,680 tons **Crew:** approx. 1,200 tot.

Derya (A 576) Hartmut Ehlers,

)ERS AND REPAIR VESSELS *(continued)*

·ks: Leased 18-10-82 and recommissioned 29-3-83; purchased 6-8-87. Modern- rly 1960s under FRAM program to serve as repair tender to missile-equipped :xtensive workshops, spares capacity. Two 20-ton cranes. Small helicopter deck. ›nal armament added since transfer.

AND BOOM TENDERS

›x-U.S. AN 103-class net tender
ır: Krögerwerft, Rendsburg, Germany
AG 5 (ex-AN 104)

(P 305) Leo Van Ginderen, 5-87

680 tons (975 fl) **S:** 12.8 kts
ı: 52.50 (48.50 hull) × 10.60 × 3.70
1/40-mm 70-cal. Bofors AA—3/20-mm Oerlikon AA (I × 3)
ctron Equipt: Radar: 1/Decca TM 1226 nav.
1 M.A.N. G7V 40/60 diesel; 1 prop; 1,470 bhp
nge: 6,500/10.8 **Fuel:** 134 tons **Crew:** 5 officers, 45 enlisted

rks: Sister to *Thetis* in the Greek Navy. Built with U.S. Offshore Procurement Can carry 1,600 rounds 40-mm, 25,200 rounds 20-mm ammunition.

ex-U.S. AN 93-class net tender Bldr: Bethlehem Steel, Staten ıand, N.Y.

	L	In serv.
; AG 6 (ex-Dutch *Cerberus,* ex-AN 93)	5-52	10-11-52

; (P 306) Hartmut Ehlers, 5-84

780 tons (902 fl) **S:** 12.8 kts
ɪm: 50.29 (44.50 pp) × 10.20 × 3.20
1/76.2-mm 50-cal. Mk 26 DP—4/20-mm Oerlikon AA (I × 4)
ectron Equipt: Radar: 1/Decca TM 1226 nav.
2 G.M. 8-268A diesels, electric drive; 1 prop; 1,500 shp
ınge: 5,200/12 **Crew:** 48 tot.

arks: Prototype of a class also built in France and Italy. Transferred to the erlands in 12-52 and returned 17-9-70; transferred to Turkey the same day.

ex-U.S. Aloe-class net tender
ldr: Marietta Mfg. Co., Pt. Pleasant, W. Va.

	Laid down	L	In serv.
4 AG 4 (ex-*Larch,* AN 21, ex-YN 16)	18-10-40	2-7-41	13-12-41

560 tons (805 fl) **S:** 12.5 kts **Dim:** 49.73 (44.5 wl) × 9.3 × 3.56
: 1/76.2-mm 50-cal. Mk 26 DP—4/20-mm Oerlikon AA (I × 4)
: 2 Alco 538-6 diesels, electric drive; 1 prop; 620 shp
ıectric: 120 kw **Fuel:** 80 tons **Crew:** 48 tot.

arks: Transferred in 5-46.

AG 4 (P 304) Leo Van Ginderen, 6-82

◆ **1 ex-British "Bar"-class net tender** Bldr: Blyth DD & SB Co., U.K.

	Laid down	L	In serv.
P 301 AG 1 (ex-*Barbarian*)	10-6-37	21-10-37	16-4-38

AG 1 (P 301) Selçuk Emre, 6-80

D: 750 tons (1,000 fl) **S:** 11.7 kts **Dim:** 52.96 × 9.8 × 4.62
A: 1/76.2-mm 50-cal. Mk 26 DP **M:** 2 diesels; 1 prop; . . . bhp
Range: 3,100/10 **Fuel:** 214 tons **Crew:** 32 tot.

Remarks: Transferred in 1947. Sisters *AG 2* (ex-*Barbette*) and *AG 3* (ex-*Barfair*) were stricken in 1975. Original reciprocating steam propulsion plant replaced by diesels in the 1960s. Has no radar. Oldest active ship in the Turkish Navy.

SALVAGE SHIPS AND SEAGOING TUGS

◆ **1 ex-U.S. Bluebird-class submarine-rescue ship**
Bldr: Charleston SB & DD Co., Charleston, S.C.

	Laid down	L	In serv.
A 584 KURTARAN (ex-*Bluebird,* ASR 19, ex-*Yurok,* ATF 164)	23-6-45	15-2-46	28-5-46

Kurtaran (A 584) Hartmut Ehlers, 10-89

D: 1,294 tons (1,760 fl) **S:** 16 kts
Dim: 62.48 (59.44 pp) × 12.19 × 4.88
A: 1/76.2-mm 50-cal. Mk 26 DP
Electron Equipt: Radar: 1/. . . nav.
M: 4 G.M. 12-278A diesels, electric drive; 1 prop; 3,000 shp
Electric: 600 kw **Range:** 6,500/16; 15,000/8
Fuel: 300 tons **Crew:** 100 tot.

Remarks: Transferred 15-8-50. Begun as an *Achomawi*-class fleet tug, but altered while under construction, wooden fenders adding .5 meters to the beam. Carries a McCann rescue diving bell and four 4-point moor marking buoys.

SALVAGE SHIPS AND SEAGOING TUGS *(continued)*

◆ **1 ex-U.S. Chanticleer-class submarine-rescue ship**
Bldr: Moore Shipbuilding and Drydock Co., Oakland, Cal.

	Laid down	L	In serv.
A 585 Akin (ex-*Greenlet,* ASR 10)	15-10-41	12-7-42	29-5-43

Akin (A 585) French Navy, 1988

D: 1,770 tons (2,321 fl) **S:** 15 kts
Dim: 76.61 (73.15 pp) × 12.8 × 4.52
A: 1/40-mm 60-cal. Bofors Mk 3 AA—4/20-mm Oerlikon AA (II × 2)
Electron Equipt: Radar: 1/Decca TM 1226 nav.
M: 4 Alco 539 diesels, electric drive; 1 prop; 3,000 shp
Electric: 460 kw **Fuel:** 235 tons **Crew:** 85 tot.

Remarks: Loaned on 12-6-70 and purchased outright on 15-2-73. Carries McCann rescue diving bell and four marker buoys. Can also be used for general salvage duties.

◆ **1 ex-U.S. Diver-class salvage ship** Bldr: Basalt Rock Co., Napa, Cal.

	Laid down	L	In serv.
A 589 Işin (ex-*Safeguard,* ARS 25)	5-6-43	20-11-43	31-10-44

Işin (A 589) Hartmut Ehlers, 5-83

D: 1,480 tons (1,970 fl) **S:** 14.8 kts
Dim: 65.08 (63.09 pp) × 12.5 × 4.0
A: 2/20-mm AA (I × 2)
Electron Equipt: Radar: 1/. . . nav.
M: 4 Cooper-Bessemer GSB-8 diesels, electric drive; 2 props; 3,000 shp
Electric: 460 kw **Fuel:** 300 tons **Crew:** 97 tot.

Remarks: Leased 28-9-79; purchased 6-8-87. Wooden fenders add .6 meter to beam.

◆ **1 ex-U.S. Cherokee-class fleet tug** Bldr: United Eng. Co., Alameda, Cal.

	Laid down	L	In serv.
A 587 Gazal (ex-*Sioux,* ATF 75)	14-2-42	27-5-42	6-12-42

Gazal (A 587) Hartmut Ehlers, 3-88

D: 1,235 tons (1,675 fl) **S:** 16.5 kts
Dim: 62.48 (59.44 pp) × 11.73 × 4.67
A: 1/76.2-mm 50-cal. Mk 26 DP—2/20-mm Oerlikon AA (I × 2)
M: 4 G.M. 12-278 diesels, electric drive; 1 prop; 3,000 shp
Electric: 260 kw
Range: 6,500/16; 15,000/8 **Fuel:** 300 tons **Crew:** 85 tot.

Remarks: Transferred on 30-10-72 and purchased outright on 15-8-73. Can b for salvage duties. Similar to submarine rescue ship *Kurtaran* (A 584), but has and no wooden fenders.

SERVICE CRAFT

Note: On 1-1-91, pendant numbers were changed, 1100 in effect being subtracte the previous number in the former 1200-series.

◆ **3 small yard oilers**
Bldr: Taşkizak Naval Dockyard, Istanbul (In serv. 1970s)

Y 131 H 500 Y 132 H 501 Y 133 H 503

H 501 (Y 132)—with old number Hartmut Ehlers,

D: 300 tons **S:** 11 kts **Dim:** 33.6 × 8.5 × 1.8
M: 1 G.M. 6-71 diesel; 1 prop; 225 bhp **Cargo:** 150 tons

◆ **1 small water tanker** Bldr: Gölçük Naval SY (L: 1979)
Y 140
D: 850 tons (fl) **S:** 10 kts **Dim:** 51.8 (46.8 pp) × 8.1 × . . .
M: 1 diesel; 1 prop; 480 bhp **Cargo:** 530 dwt

◆ **4 Pinar-3-class small water tankers**
Bldr: Taşkizak Naval Dockyard, Istanbul

Y 113 Pinar 3 Y 114 Pinar 4 Y 115 Pinar 5 Y 116 Pinar 6

Pinar 5 (Y 115)—alongside *Muavenet* (DM 357) Hartmut Ehlers,

D: 300 tons **S:** 11 kts **Dim:** 33.6 × 8.5 × 1.8
M: 1 G.M. 6-71 diesel; 1 prop; 225 bhp **Cargo:** 150 tons

◆ **1 small water tanker** Bldr: Gölçük Naval Shipyard (In serv. 1958)
Y 112 Pinar 2
D: 1,300 tons (fl) **S:** 10 kts **Dim:** 51.0 × 8.5 × . . .
A: none **M:** 1 diesel; 1 prop; . . . bhp **Crew:** 11 tot.

Pinar 2 (Y 112)—with old number Hartmut Ehlers,

ICE CRAFT *(continued)*

mall water tanker Bldr: Meentzer SY, Neth. (In serv. 1938)

PINAR 1 (ex-*Istanbul*)

90 tons (fl) **S:** . . . **Dim:** . . . × . . . × . . .
1 diesel; 240 bhp

1 (Y 111)—with old number Hartmut Ehlers, 3-86

mall water tanker

MEHMET KAPTAN

ks: No data available.

Kanarya-class cargo lighters
r: Taşkizak Naval Dockyard, Istanbul (In serv. 1972–74)

KANARYA Y 157 KARADENIZ ERIĞLISI
SARKÖY Y 165 ECEABAT

bat (Y 165)—with old number Leo Van Ginderen, 8-86

823 tons (fl) **S:** 10 kts **Dim:** 50.7 (47.4 pp) × 8.0 × . . .
1/20-mm AA **Electron Equipt:** Radar: 1/. . . nav.
1 diesel; 1 prop; 1,440 bhp

rks: 500 dwt. Moulded depth: 3.6 m.

Salopa-class stores lighters

31–1043 SALOPA 1–13

pa 13 (Y 1043) Hartmut Ehlers, 7-90

rks: No data available.

Layter-class lighters

11–1016 LAYTER 1–6

ter 2 (Y 1012) Hartmut Ehlers, 4-86

♦ **7 pontoon barges**

Y 1061–1067 PANTON 1–7

♦ **3 personnel ferries**

Y 1096 IŞÇI TAŞITI 1 Y 1097 IŞÇI TAŞITI 2 Y 1110 IŞÇI TAŞITI 3

♦ **2 Cephane-class ammunition lighters**

Y 1195 CEPHANE 2 Y 1197 CEPHANE 3

Remarks: Sister *Cephane 1* (Y 1194) stricken 1987.

♦ **1 small ammunition lighter**

Y 1196 BEKIRDERE

♦ **7 small danbuoy layers**

Y 1141–1147 SAMANDIRA MOTORU 1–7

♦ **1 training craft, former minelayer** Bldr: Gölçük NSY (In serv. 1938)

Y 1101 ATAK

Atak (Y 1101) Hartmut Ehlers, 5-82

D: 350 tons (500 fl) **S:** 13 kts **Dim:** 44.0 × 7.4 × 3.6
M: 1 Atlas-Polar diesel; 1 prop; 1,025 bhp

Remarks: Tender to Naval Academy.

♦ **3 ex-U.S. non-self-propelled gate craft**
Bldr: Weaver SY, Orange, Texas (In serv. 1960–61)

Y 101 KAPI I (ex-YNG 45) Y 103 KAPI III (ex-YNG 47)
Y 102 KAPI II (ex-YNG 46)

D: 325 tons (fl) **Dim:** 33.5 × 10.4 × 1.5

♦ **2 ex-U.S. APL 41-class barracks barges**

	Bldr	L
Y 1204 YUZBAŞI NASIT ÖNGEREN (ex-APL 47)	Puget Sound Bridge & Dredge, Seattle, Wash.	5-1-45
Y 1205 BINBAŞI METIN SÜLÜS (ex-APL 53)	Tampa SB, Tampa, Fla.	3-3-45

D: 2,660 tons (fl) **Dim:** 79.6 × 14.99 × 2.59
Electric: 300 kw **Crew:** 650 tot.

Remarks: Y 1204 was leased in 10-72, Y 1205 in 12-74; both purchased 6-8-87. Non-self-propelled.

♦ **1 Darica-class seagoing tug/torpedo retriever**
Bldr: Taşkizak Naval Dockyard

	L	In serv.
Y 1125 DARICA	27-7-87	30-7-90

D: 750 tons (fl) **S:** 14 kts **Dim:** 40.9 × 9.8 × 3.9
M: 2 ABC diesels; 2 props; 4,000 bhp **Range:** 2,500/14

Remarks: Oilfield tug-supply-type vessel, with open fantail for recovering and stowing torpedoes; is also equipped for fire fighting and salvage.

♦ **2 Doğanarslan-class large coastal tugs**
Bldr: Taşkizak Naval Dockyard

Y 1123 DOĞANARSLAN (In serv. 25-7-85)
Y 1128 ÖZGEN (In serv. 1987)

D: . . . **S:** . . . **Dim:** . . . × . . . × . . .
A: . . . **M:** . . .

Remarks: No data available; appear to be about 600–800 tons (fl), 1,200 bhp.

♦ **2 Öncü-class coastal tugs** Bldr: Gölçük Naval Shipyard (In serv. 1953)

Y 1120 ÖNCÜ Y 1124 ÖNDER

D: 500 tons **S:** 12 kts **Dim:** 40.0 × 9.1 × 4.0
A: 2/20-mm AA (I × 2)—2/12.7-mm mg (I × 2)
M: diesel; 1 prop; . . . bhp

SERVICE CRAFT *(continued)*

Doğanarslan (Y 1123) Hartmut Ehlers, 10-89

Önder (Y 1124) Hartmut Ehlers, 10-89

♦ **1 coastal tug**

Y 1122 Kuvvet (In serv. 2-62)

D: 390 tons **S:** . . . **Dim:** 32.1 × 7.9 × 3.6

Remarks: Built in Turkey with U.S. Grant Aid funds.

♦ **2 ex-U.S. Army 3004-design medium harbor tugs**

Y 1229 Kudret (ex-LT . . .) Y 1134 Ersen Bayrak (ex-LT . . .)

Kudret (Y 1229)—alongside APL 41-class barracks barge
Hartmut Ehlers, 5-81

D: 100 tons (122 fl) **S:** 12 kts **Dim:** 21.31 × 5.94 × 2.50
M: 1 diesel; 1 prop; 600 bhp **Range:** 3,500/12 **Crew:** 6 tot.

Remarks: Built during the early 1950s, transferred in 6-71.

♦ **2 Turkish-designed harbor tugs** Bldr: Denizcilik, Bançusi (In serv. 1976)

Y 1130 Güven Y 1132 Atil

D: 300 grt **S:** . . . **Dim:** 32.8 × 8.9 × . . . **M:** diesels; 250 bhp

Remarks: Sister *Doğanarslan* (Y 1133) stricken 1984.

♦ **2 ex-U.S. small harbor tugs**

Y 1117 Sonduren (ex-YTL 751) Y 1121 Yedekci (ex-YTL 155)

D: 70 tons (80 fl) **S:** 8 kts **Dim:** 20.1 × 5.5 × 2.4
M: 1 Atlas diesel; 1 prop; 375 bhp **Crew:** 4 tot.

Remarks: Transferred in 5-54 and 11-57.

♦ **2 miscellaneous small tugs**

Y 1118 Kepez Y 1119 Akbas

Remarks: No data available.

♦ **38 push tugs** (do not have Y-pendants)

Katir 1–13

Push Tug 38 Hartmut Ehlers,

♦ **1 ex-German Type 430 torpedo retriever** (L: 13-9-65)

Y . . . . (ex-TF 107, Y 873)

D: 56 tons (63.5 fl) **S:** 17 kts **Dim:** 25.22 × 5.40 × 1.60
M: 1 MWM diesel; 1 prop; 1,000 bhp **Crew:** 6 tot.

Remarks: Ex-TF 107 stricken from German Navy 31-8-89 and transferred to T 4-9-89.

♦ **1 ex-U.S. 72-ft.-class torpedo retriever** (In serv. 1950s)

Y 1052 (ex-. . .)

D: 53 tons (fl) **S:** 18 kts **Dim:** 22.17 × 5.18 × 1.68
M: 2 G.M. diesels; 2 props; 1,000 bhp
Range: 450/18 **Crew:** 6 tot.

Remarks: Wooden construction. Can carry up to 10.8-tons of weapons retriev stern ramp.

♦ **2 miscellaneous torpedo retrievers**

Y 1051 Torpito Tender 1 Y 1102 Ikmal

♦ **1 ex-U.S. floating crane** Bldr: Odenback SB, Rochester, N.Y. (In se 14-8-51)

Y 1023 Algarna III (ex-YD 185)

D: 1,200 tons (fl) **Dim:** 36.6 × 13.7 × 2.7

Remarks: Transferred in 9-63.

♦ **3 miscellaneous floating cranes**

Y 1021 Algarna I Y 1022 Levent Y 1024 Turgut Alp

Remarks: No data available, except Y 1022: 600-ton lift.

♦ **1 dredge**

Y 1029 Tarak—**D:** 200 tons

♦ **16 miscellaneous service launches**—no data available.

Y 1181–Y 1193, Y 1198–Y 1200 Mavna 1–Mavna 16

Mavna 9 (Y 1189) Hartmut Ehlers,

CE CRAFT *(continued)*

-U.S. ARD-12-class floating dry dock
Pacific Bridge, Alameda, Cal. (In serv. 10-43)

HAVUZ 7 (ex-ARD-12)
49.86 × 24.69 × 1.73 (light) **Lift capacity:** 3,500 tons
s: Launched in 1943 and loaned in 11-71; purchased 6-8-87.

iscellaneous floating dry docks

	Capacity (tons)		Capacity (tons)
HAVUZ 1	16,000	Y 1085 HAVUZ 5	400
HAVUZ 2	12,000	Y 1086 HAVUZ 6	3,000
HAVUZ 3	2,500	Y . . .	700
HAVUZ 4	4,500	Y . . .	3,500

3 (Y 1083) Carlo Martinelli, 10-89

ks: Y 1083 was built in Turkey in 1958 with U.S. funds; **Dim:** 116.5 × 26.4 × . These docks are named in sequence *Havuz I* to *Havuz VI*. A new three-section dry dock was completed late in 1980. During 7-89, Taşkizak NDY delivered a -capacity dock, while Gölçük delivered a 3,500-ton-capacity dock on 21-7-89.

iscellaneous officers' yachts
9 HALAS Y 1092 ACAR Y 1103 GÜL Y . . . KAPLAN

an Hartmut Ehlers, 7-91

ks: *Kaplan* is a wooden-hulled former U.S. 63-ft. air-sea rescue craft.

MINISTRY OF THE INTERIOR COAST GUARD *(SAHIL GÜVENLIK)*

nnel (1991): approx. 1,200 total, headed by a Turkish Navy rear admiral

The Coast Guard was formed in 7-82 from the former naval police *(Jandarma)*. 12 AB-212 helicopters assigned for search-and-rescue duties. Future plans call construction of 10 250-ton and 14 70-ton patrol boats to replace older units now vice. The planned construction of the Lürssen/Singapore Shipbuilding 200T class kizak in the late 1980s did not materialize.

ROL BOATS

SG 71 class Bldr: Taşkizak Naval Dockyard

(In serv.: 25-7-85) SG 72 (L: 25-7-85) SG 73 (L: . . .)
(L: 24-7-87)

210 tons (fl) **S:** 40 kts (35 sust.) **Dim:** 36.60 × 8.60 × 1.90
1/40-mm 60-cal. Bofors Mk 3 AA—2/7.62-mm mg (I × 2)
ctron Equipt: Radar: 1/Decca TM 1226 nav.
3 SACM (UNI) AGO V16 CSHR diesels; 3 CP props; 12,000 bhp
nge: 450/35; 1,000/20 **Crew:** 24 tot.

rks: Lengthened version of SAR-33 class, with longer superstructure.

SG 74 Hartmut Ehlers, 10-89

◆ **10 SAR-33 class** Bldrs: J 61: Abeking & Rasmussen, Lemwerder, West Germany; others: Taşkizak Naval Dockyard, Istanbul (In serv. 1978–84)

SG 61–SG 70 (ex-J 61–J 70)

SG 62 French Navy, 1990

D: 150 tons (170 fl) **S:** 40 kts **Dim:** 33.00 (29.50 wl) × 8.60 × 1.85
A: 1/40-mm AA—2/76.2-mm mg (I × 2)
Electron Equipt: Radar: 1/Decca TM 1226 nav.
M: 3 SACM-AGO V16CSHR diesels; 3 CP props; 12,000 bhp
Electric: 300 kw **Fuel:** 18 tons
Range: 450/35; 1,000/20 **Crew:** 23 tot.

Remarks: SG 61 was launched on 12-12-77 and SG 62 in 7-78; SG 65 through SG 67 in service 30-7-81. Wedge-shaped hull design of remarkable seaworthiness and steadiness at high speeds in heavy weather. Turkey was also to have built 14 units of this class for Libya, but the contract was canceled circa 1986.

◆ **14 AB 25 class**
Bldr: Taşkizak Naval Dockyard, Istanbul (In serv.1972–78)

SG 21–34

SG 24 Turkish Navy, 1991

D: 170 tons (fl) **S:** 22 kts **Dim:** 40.24 × 6.4 × 1.65
A: 2/40-mm Bofors Mk 3 AA (I × 2)—2/12.7-mm mg (I × 2)
Electron Equipt: Radar: 1/Decca TM 1226 nav.
M: 2 SACM-AGO V16 CSHR diesels; 2 props; 4,800 bhp; 2 cruise diesels; 300 bhp

Remarks: Twelve sisters are operated by the Turkish Navy. Some have one 40-mm AA aft and one 20-mm AA forward. Built with French assistance.

PATROL CRAFT

◆ **6 14.6-m class** Bldr: Taşkizak Naval Dockyard, Istanbul

SG 51–56

D: 25 tons (fl) **S:** 18 kts **Dim:** 14.6 × 3.5 × 1.1
A: 1/12.7-mm mg **Electron Equipt:** Radar: 1/. . . nav.
M: 2 diesels; 2 props; 700 bhp **Crew:** 6 tot.

Remarks: First three completed 20-7-90, others in 7-91. One sister built for Turkish Republic of Cyprus.

◆ **8 German KW 15 class** Bldr: Schweers, Bardenfleth, Germany (In serv. 1961–62)

SG 12–SG 16 SG 18–SG 20

TURKEY *(continued)*
PATROL CRAFT *(continued)*

SG 16 Hartmut Ehlers, 7-86

D: 59.5 tons (69.6 fl) **S:** 25 kts **Dim:** 28.9 × 4.7 × 1.42
A: 1/40-mm 60-cal. Bofors Mk 3AA—2/20-mm Oerlikon (I × 2)
M: 2 MTU 12-cyl. diesels; 2 props; 2,000 bhp
Range: 1,500/19 **Fuel:** 8 tons **Crew:** 15 tot.

Remarks: Sisters in German Navy.

◆ **9 ex-U.S. 45-ft Picket Boat class**

SG 41–48, 50

SG 44 Hartmut Ehlers, 6-86

D: 15 tons (fl) **S:** 18 kts **Dim:** 13.94 × 4.17 × 1.10
A: 2/7.62-mm mg (II × 2)
Electron Equipt: Radar: 1/Decca . . . nav.
M: 2 G.M. Gray Marine 64HN9 diesels; 2 props; 450 bhp
Range: 200/18 **Crew:** 5 tot.

Remarks: Wooden-hulled. Transferred during the 1950s. SG 49 has been stricken.

◆ **2 miscellaneous small transports**

SG 101 SG 104

SG 104 Hartmut Ehlers, 10-89

SG 103 Hartmut Ehlers, 10-85

Remarks: SG 104 built 1978, Hasköy SY, Istanbul. SG 101 is smaller and o 104 has 2/7.62-mm mg (I × 2).

Note: Also in service are utility craft SG 102, "dispatch boat" SG 103, and yac

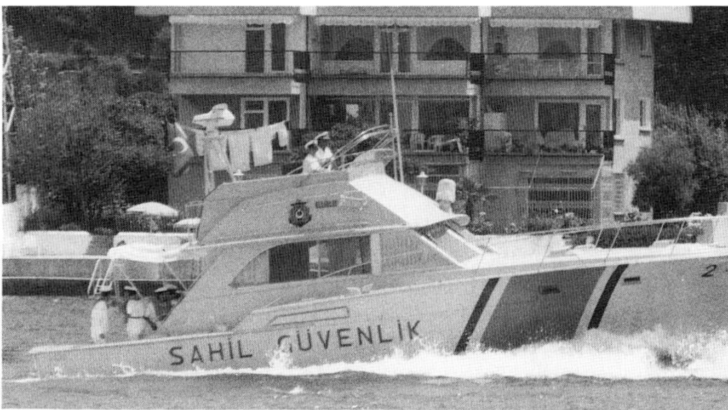

SG 2 Hartmut Ehle

TURKS AND CAICOS

British Protectorate

POLICE

PATROL CRAFT

◆ **1 M 160 class** Bldr: Halmatic, U.K. (In serv. 9-89)

Sea Quest

Sea Quest Mike Louagi

D: 17.3 tons (fl) **S:** 27+ kts
Dim: 15.40 (12.20 pp) × 3.86 × 1.15 **A:** 1/7.62-mm mg
Electron Equipt: Radar: 1/Decca 370BT nav.
M: 2 G.M. 6V92 TA diesels; 2 props; 1,100 bhp (770 sust.)
Range: 300/20 **Fuel:** 2,700 l **Crew:** 6 tot.

Remarks: Sister to Virgin Islands' *Ursula.* Carries rigid inflatable ins dinghy aft.

◆ **1 Dagger class** Bldr: Fairey Marine, Cowes (In serv. 6-86)

Turks & Caicos Dagger Fairey

JRKS AND CAICOS *(continued)*
ATROL CRAFT *(continued)*

D: 12 tons (fl) **S:** 24 kts **Dim:** 12.2 × 3.4 × 1.1
A: 1/7.62-mm mg **Electron Equipt:** Radar: 1/Decca . . . nav. **M:** 2 Perkins T.6354.4 diesels; 2 props; 440 bhp
Range: 540/20 **Crew:** 6 tot.

marks: GRP construction. Based at Grand Turk.

TUVALU

te: Acquisition of an Australian grant-aid ASI 315-class patrol boat is still under sideration, but none had been ordered as of 4-92.

1 patrol boat Bldr: Richards, U.K. (In serv. 1991)

VANGA

D: . . . tons **S:** . . . kts **Dim:** . . . × . . . × . . . **A:** . . .
M: 2 Mirrlees-Blackstone ESL-2 Mk 1 diesels; . . . props, 1,325 bhp

narks: No further information available.

UKRAINE

e: Soon after achieving independence at the end of 1991, Ukraine laid claim to the re former Soviet Black Sea Fleet, most of whose ships and aircraft were based on ainian soil. The Commonwealth of Independent States, however, declared the fleet e a "strategic" asset of the entire C.I.S. and hence not available. Ukraine was ally offered 42 former KGB Maritime Border Guard patrol craft (which, it appears, actually transferred) to a separate Ukrainian Maritime Border Guard.
n 3-8-92, agreement was reached to *share* the remaining floating assets of the ner Soviet Black Sea Fleet until 1995 when a decision on their disposition is to be hed. In addition, however, a Black Sea Fleet Petya-II-class corvette defected to aine on 21-7-92, and on 26-7-92, a 6,000-ton auxiliary begun at Nikolayev for the et Navy as an "intelligence ship" was launched or commissioned by Ukraine as the hip of its navy and named *Slavutich.*
ne order-of-battle of the Ukrainian Navy was not available at time of closing for s, but the former KGB units transferred probably included examples of the Stenka, lak, and Muravey classes of seagoing patrol boats, Danube River Flotilla riverine are craft of the Shmel-class based at Izmail near the mouth of the Danube, and, bly, Grisha II-class corvettes. Characteristics for these units can be found in the ia chapter.

UNITED ARAB EMIRATES

onnel (1991): 120 officers, 1,680 enlisted

l Aviation: Two Britten-Norman BN-2 Islander Maritime Defender for patrol s, eight Aérospatiale AS-332 Super Puma helicopters with AS 39 Exocet antiship les, eight Aérospatiale SA-316B Alouette-III light helicopters.

Incorporating the former Defense Force Sea Wing of the Abu Dhabi National se Force, the UAE Navy was formed on 1 February 1978 as part of the federated of Abu Dhabi, Ajman, Dubai, Fujairah, Ras al Khaimah, Sharjah, and Umm al an. The merchant marines of these states are also combined into a single adminis- e unit. Several of these nation states, including Abu Dhabi and Dubai, also e separate Customs Services with their own patrol craft (which see).

GATES

The U.A.E. Navy during 1992 has been discussing the acquisition of two frig- ith foreign shipbuilders.

DED-MISSILE CORVETTES

German FPB 62 class Bldr: Friedrich Lürssen Werft, Vegesack

1 . . . . . . (In serv. 10-91) CM 02 . . . . . . (In serv. 10-91)

560 tons (630 fl) **S:** 34.7 kts (32.25 sust.)
n: 62.95 (59.90 pp) × 9.30 × 2.60
8/MM 40 Exocet SSM (IV × 2)—1/Crotale Modulaire SAM syst. (VIII x1)—1/76-mm 62-cal. OTO Melara Super Rapid DP—1/ 30-mm Goalkeeper CIWS—1/Alouette-III helicopter

Electron Equipt:
Radar: 1/Decca TM 1226 nav., 1/Ericsson Sea Giraffe 50HC surf./ air search, 1/BEAB 9LV 200 f.c., 1/Thomson-CSF DRBC-51C f.c., 1/H.S.A. Goalkeeper f.c. array
EW: Racal Cutlass RDL-2 intercept, Cygnus jammer, 2/Dagaie decoy RL
M: 4 MTU 16V538 TB92 diesels; 4 props; 15,600 bhp
Electric: 408 kw **Range:** 4,000/16
Fuel: 120 tons **Crew:** 43 tot.

First U.A.E. FPB 62 on trials Peter Voss, 10-89

U.A.E. FPB 62 Leo Van Ginderen, 1990

Remarks: Ordered mid-1987, along with modified FPB-38 class below. Launched during 1989. Have a helicopter deck with integral elevator to hangar below, as in similar Bahraini navy units. In these ships, the elaborate weapons-control array includes the BEAB 9LV radar/optronic system for the 76-mm gun (which in this class is linked to a Sea Giraffe surveillance radar rather than to the usual 9GA 209 radar), a separate DRBC-51C radar/optronic director abaft the tower mast for the Crotale SAM system, and the self-contained track-while-scan radar array of the Goalkeeper close-in weapons system. In addition, a CSEE NAJIR optronic backup director with t.v. and infrared sensors and a laser rangefinder for the 76-mm gun is mounted on the bridge just forward of the tower mast. A third ship may be ordered at a later date.

GUIDED-MISSILE PATROL BOATS

♦ **2 German FPB-44 class** Bldr: Friedrich Lürssen Werft, Vegesack

P 4401 Mubarraz (In serv. 2-91) P 4402 Makasib (In serv. 2-91)

Mubarraz (P 4401) Peter Voss, 10-89

GUIDED-MISSILE PATROL BOATS *(continued)*

Makasib (P 4402) Peter Voss, 8-90

D: 210 tons (235 fl) **S:** 33 kts
Dim: 44.0 (41.50 pp) × 7.0 × 2.2 (props)
A: 4/MM 40 Exocet (II × 2)—1/76-mm 62-cal. OTO Melara Super Rapid DP—1/Sadral SAM syst. (VI × 1, . . . Mistral missiles)
Electron Equipt:
Radar: 1/Decca TM 1226 nav., 1/Ericsson Sea Giraffe 50 air/surf. search, 1/BEAB 9LV200 M.3 f.c.
EW: Racal Cutlass RDL-2 intercept, 1/Cygnus jammer
M: 2 MTU 20V538 TB92 diesels; 2 props; 10,200 bhp
Electric: 405 kVA **Range:** 500/38; 1,600/16
Crew: 5 officers, 35 enlisted

Remarks: Order placed mid-1987. Arrived in U.A.E. waters 5-91. Are an enlarged version of Lürssen's FPB-38 design rather than being further units of the TNC-45 class. A third and fourth unit may be ordered later.

The Sadral installation is the first export of the French system, which, in these ships, is controlled by a C.S.E.E. NAJIR optronic director abaft the mast. In order to accommodate the point-defense SAM system and the enhanced EW suite (whose spherical radome for the Cygnus jammer is mounted on the mast), a second gun position was sacrificed. A Bofors 57-mm rocket flare/chaff launcher is mounted amidships.

◆ **6 German TNC-45-class** Bldr: Friedrich Lürssen Werft, Vegesack

	In serv.		In serv.
P 4501 Baniyas	11-80	P 4504 Shaheen	4-81
P 4502 Marban	11-80	P 4505 Saqar	6-81
P 4503 Rodqum	4-81	P 4506 Tarif	6-81

Rodqum (P 4503) French Navy, 1986

D: 231 tons (259 fl) **S:** 41.5 kts
Dim: 44.90 (42.30 pp) × 7.00 × 2.46 (props)
A: 4/MM 40 Exocet (II × 2)—1/76-mm 62-cal. OTO Melara Compact DP—2/40-mm 70-cal. Breda AA (II × 1)—2/7.62-mm mg (I × 2)
Electron Equipt:
Radar: 1/Decca TM 1226 nav., 1/Ericsson Sea Giraffe 50 surf./air search, 1/BEAB 9LV 200 Mk 2 f.c. system
EW: Decca Cutlass RDL-2 intercept, 1/Dagaie decoy RL
M: 4 MTU 16V538 TB92 diesels; 4 props; 15,600 bhp (13,000 sust.)
Electric: 405 kVA **Range:** 500/38.5; 1,600/16
Crew: 5 officers, 27 enlisted

Remarks: The radar director is equipped with low light-level t.v. and an infrared tracker and has an associated search radar atop the mast. There is a C.S.E.E. Panda optical director for the 40-mm mount. Carry 350 rds 76-mm, 1,800 rds 40-mm, and 6,000 rds mg ammunition.

PATROL BOATS

◆ **6 U.K. 110-foot class** Bldr: Vosper Thornycroft, Portsmouth, U.K.

	L		L
P 1101 Ardhana	7-3-75	P 1104 Al Ghulian	16-9-75
P 1102 Zurara	13-6-75	P 1105 Radoom	15-12-75
P 1103 Murban	15-9-75	P 1106 Ghanadhah	1-3-76

Ardhana (P 1101) French Navy, 19

D: 110 tons (140 fl) **S:** 29 kts **Dim:** 33.5 (31.5 pp) × 6.4 × 1.7
A: 2/30-mm 75-cal. BMARC/Oerlikon A32 AA (II × 1)—1/20-mm 80-cal. BMARC/Oerlikon A 41A AA
Electron Equipt: Radar: 1/Decca TM 1226 nav.
M: 2 Ruston-Paxman Valenta RP200M diesels; 2 props; 5,400 bhp
Range: 1,800/14 **Crew:** 26 tot.

Remarks: Originally operated by Abu Dhabi prior to the establishment of the U.A fleet. Have two U.K. 51-mm rocket flare launchers.

PATROL CRAFT

◆ **3 Kawkab-class** Bldr: Keith Nelson, Bembridge, U.K.

P 561 Kawkab (In serv. 7-3-69) P 562 Thoaban (In serv. 7-3-69)
P 563 Baniyas (In serv. 27-12-69)

Kawkab (P 561) Vosper,

D: 25 tons (32 fl) **S:** 17.52 (15.84 pp) × 4.72 × 1.37
A: 2/20-mm 80-cal. Oerlikon AA (I × 2)
Electron Equipt: Radar: 1/Decca RM 916 nav.
M: 2 Caterpillar diesels; 2 props; 750 bhp **Electric:** 24 kw
Range: 445/15 **Endurance:** 7 days **Crew:** 2 officers, 9 enlisted

Remarks: Glass-reinforced plastic construction. Used for coastal patrol, hydrogr surveys, and surveillance of petroleum leases. Designed by Keith Nelson, t division of Vosper. Freshwater evaporator provides 900 liters daily.

◆ **3 fast patrol craft** Bldr: Boghammar, Stockholm (In serv. 1986)

D: 5.5 tons (fl) **S:** 50 kts **Dim:** 13.00 × 2.66 × 0.90
M: 2 Volvo Penta TAMD-70E diesels; 2 outdrive props; 600 bhp
Range: 500/35 **Crew:** 3–5 tot.

Remarks: Purchased by Abu Dhabi specifically for the defense of the Sultan's and are not part of the U.A.E. armed forces.

AUXILIARIES AND SERVICE CRAFT

◆ **1 repair tender** Bldr: Singapore Slipway (In serv. 6-83)

Baracuda

D: approx. 1,400 tons (fl) **S:** 12 kts **Dim:** 58.0 × 12.0 × 4.0
M: 2 Ruston-Paxman RKCM diesels; 2 props; 6,000 bhp

◆ **1 diving tender** Bldr: Crestitalia, Ameglia, La Spezia, Italy

D 1051 (In serv. 7-87)

D: 100 tons (fl) **S:** 27 kts **Dim:** 31.35 × 6.90 × 1.20
Electron Equipt: Radar: 1/. . . nav. **M:** 2 MTU 12V396 TB93 diesels; 2 props; 3,950 bhp
Range: 432/18 **Crew:** 6 tot.

Remarks: Lengthened version of the *Mario Marino* class built for the Italiar Ordered 12-85. GRP construction. Intended to support combat swimmers, as w provide diving support services. Decompression chamber. A second may be ord

◆ **1 seagoing tug** Bldr: Richard Dunston, Hessle, U.K.

A 3501 Annad (In serv. 4-89)

LIARIES AND SERVICE CRAFT *(continued)*

Crestitalia, 1987

d (A 3501) R. Van der Hoek, 1989

'95 tons (fl) **S:** 14.4 kts **Dim:** 35.00 (31.25 pp) × 9.80 × 4.15
:tron Equipt: Radar: 1/Decca RM 2070/4 BT nav.
2 Caterpillar 3606TA diesels; 2 Liaaen CP props; 4,200 bhp—Jastrum bow-thruster (3-ton thrust)
:tric: 206 kw (2 × 103 kw Siemens/Mercedes-Benz OM421 diesel sets)
ge: 2,500/14 **Fuel:** 143 tons **Crew:** 3 officers, 10 enlisted

·ks: 400 grt. Fully equipped berthing/coastal tug with secondary fire fighting, and salvage capabilities. Bollard pull: 55 tons. The bow-thruster is powered by a Caterpillar 3406TA diesel. Towing winch with 400 m of 40-mm cable, 5-ton 1. Two 600 m³/hr pumps for the three 200 m³/hr and one 400 m³/hr fire and foam rs. Extensive navigational and communications systems. Can transport two rd containers on fantail.

ogistics landing craft Bldr: Vosper-QAF, Singapore (Both L: 10-88, in serv. 12-88)

NAH Dayyinah

. . . **S:** . . . **Dim:** 54.0 × . . . × . . .
2 MTU diesels; 2 props; . . . bhp

rks: 350 dwt; can carry four medium tanks and have a large crane. Can also ort fuel and water cargo. Built at Argos Engineering Pty facilities, under lease.

ogistics landing craft Bldr: Siong Huat, Singapore

:YI (In serv. 4-8-87)

650 tons (fl) **S:** 11 kts **Dim:** 50.0 × 11.0 × 2.8
2 diesels; 2 props; 1,248 bhp **Range:** 1,800/11
:w: 10 tot.

ogistics landing craft Bldr: Siong Huat, Singapore

HA II (L: 17-4-87)

100 tons (fl) **S:** 9 kts **Dim:** 40.0 × 10.0 × 1.0
2 diesels; 2 props; 730 bhp **Crew:** 6 tot.

workboats Bldr: Cheverton, Cowes, U.K. (In serv. 1975)

A 272

3.3 tons **S:** 8 kts **Dim:** 8.2 × 2.7 × 0.8
1 Lister-Blackstone RMW3 diesel; 150 bhp

rks: Glass-reinforced plastic construction.

The 2,150-grt cable ship *Etisalat,* ordered 1989 from Wärtsilä, Helsinki, is a n unit, not owned by any of the U.A.E. governments. The ship, delivered 11-90 by ilä's successor company, Masa Yards, was launched 25-3-90: 2,150 grt. Dim: (62.91 pp) × 13.21 × 2.50; M: 2 × 1,920-bhp diesels, 2 × 1,368-kw alternator sets, 650-shp electric propulsion motor.

COAST GUARD

Note: The Coast Guard operates under the Ministry of the Interior.

PATROL CRAFT

♦ **4 Type 23GC class** Bldr: C.N. Baglietto, Varazzo, Italy (In serv. 1986–87)

U.A.E. Coast Guard 23GC class Carlo Martinelli, 8-90

D: 40 tons light/44.50 standard (48 fl) **S:** 41.8 kts (38 sust.)
Dim: 23.00 (20.00 wl) × 5.50 × 1.17
A: 1/20-mm 80-cal. Oerlikon AA—2/7.62-mm mg (I × 2)
Electron Equipt: Radar: 1/. . . nav.
M: 2 MTU 12V396 TB93 diesels; 2 props; 3,560 bhp (2,960 sust.)
Range: 700/20 **Fuel:** 7,500 liters **Endurance:** 4 days
Electric: 64 kVA **Crew:** 9 tot.

Remarks: Design derived from Italian Customs *Meattini* class. Aluminum-magnesium alloy hull and superstructure. First unit, paid for by Dubai, delivered 3-86. Second, paid for by Abu Dhabi, delivered 5-86. Third and fourth, paid for by Dubai, delivered 14-7-87 and 9-87.

♦ **9 U.K. 45-ft Mk-II class** Bldr: Watercraft, Ltd., U.K. (In serv. 1982–83)

D: 10 tons (fl) **S:** 26 kts **Dim:** 13.90 × 4.26 × 1.14
A: 1/7.62-mm mg
Electron Equipt: Radar: 1/Decca 202 nav.
M: 2 M.A.N. D2542 MLE diesels; 2 props; 1,300 bhp **Crew:** 5 tot.

Remarks: Glass-reinforced plastic construction. Ordered 2-82.

♦ **9 P 1200 class** Bldr: Watercraft, Ltd., U.K. (In serv. 1979–81)

D: 10 tons (fl) **S:** 29 kts **Dim:** 11.90 (10.16 wl) × 4.08 × 1.06
A: 2/7.62-mm mg (I × 2) **Electron Equipt:** Radar: 1/Decca 202 nav.
M: 2 MTU diesels; 2 props; 800 bhp **Range:** 300/20 **Crew:** 4 tot.

Remarks: Glass-reinforced plastic hulls. First ten delivered 1979–80; seven more ordered, 1980. By 1991, eight had been retired.

♦ **6 Spear-class police patrol craft** Bldr: Fairey Marine, Hamble, U.K.

D: 10 tons **S:** 26 kts **Dim:** 9.1 × 2.75 × 0.84 **A:** 2/12.7-mm mg
M: 2 Perkins T 6-354 diesels; 2 props; 580 bhp **Crew:** 3 tot.

Remarks: Subordinate to the Marine Police. In service in 8-74, 9-74, and 1-75. Fiberglass hull.

Note: The six *Dhafeer*-class Marine Police patrol craft had been retired by 1991.

CUSTOMS SERVICES

Note: Several of the component states of the United Arab Emirates operate their own Customs Service patrol craft. Dubai (listed elsewhere) has two U.S. Swiftships 19.8-m Commercial Cruisers, while Sharjah received from Halter Marine, Moss Point, Mississippi, in 1987, two customs patrol boats:

D: . . . **S:** 24 kts **Dim:** 23.77 × 5.64 × 1.42
M: 2 G.M. 12 V71 TI diesels; 2 props; 1,350 bhp

Remarks: Modified oilfield-crew boat design.

Units assigned to the joint U.A.E. Customs Service include:

♦ **16 P-63A patrol craft** Bldr: Camcraft, New Orleans, La. (In serv. 9-78)

D: 50 tons (fl) **S:** 25 kts **Dim:** 19.2 × 5.5 × 1.5
A: 1/20-mm 80-cal. Oerlikon AA
M: 2 G.M. 12V71 TI diesels; 2 props; 1,400 bhp **Crew:** 8 tot.

♦ **5 P-77A patrol craft** Bldr: Camcraft, New Orleans, La. (In serv. 9-75)

753 754 755 756 757

D: 70 tons (fl) **S:** 25 kts **Dim:** 23.4 × 5.5 × 1.5
A: 1/20-mm 80-cal. Oerlikon AA **M:** 2 G.M. 12V71 TI diesels; 2 props; 1,400 bhp **Range:** 750/25

UNITED KINGDOM

United Kingdom of Great Britain and Northern Ireland

Personnel (1-92): 54,850 total Royal Navy (including about 9,000 officers), 7,410 Royal Marines (including about 600 officers), 2,500 Royal Fleet Auxiliary (including 1,100 officers), 2,090 Royal Navy Auxiliary Service (RNXS), 5,750 Royal Naval Reserve (RNR), and about 1,500 Royal Maritime Auxiliary Service (RMAS) civilians. There are about 70,000 civilian administrative and dockyard employees.

Naval Aviation: First line aircraft include 39 Sea Harrier FRS.1 V/STOL fighters, 72 Sea King HAS.5/6 ASW helicopters, 10 Sea King AEW.2A AEW helicopters, 28 Sea King HC.2 troop-carrying helicopters, and 78 Sea Lynx HAS.3 light shipboard helicopters. Major land-based maritime aircraft operated by the Royal Air Force include 28 Nimrod MR.2 maritime patrol aircraft, 3 Nimrod R.2 EW aircraft, and 24 Buccaneer S.2 maritime strike fighters. A more complete listing of aircraft, organization, and characteristics is found in the Naval Aviation section following the aircraft carrier listing.

WEAPONS AND SYSTEMS

A. MISSILES AND BOMBS

♦ strategic ballistic missiles

Trident 2D-5 Bldr: Lockheed

U.S. missile with a delivery vehicle and payload of British design and manufacture, with an independent trajectory capability (MIRV). The agreement for the acquisition of Trident was signed 14–15 July 1980. The submarines to carry Trident will not be ready until the mid-1990s; 80 Trident missiles are being acquired, and they will have British-built A-90 warheads. The missiles will be serviced at King's Bay, Georgia, in the U.S.A.

Polaris A-3TK

The nuclear-powered ballistic-missile submarines of the *Resolution* class employ Polaris A-3 missiles with a payload package of entry vehicles of British design and manufacture. The payload is designated Chevaline and is composed of six 150-kT warheads with greatly improved penetration aids. Chevaline employs post-boost guidance to improve accuracy and entered service late in 1982, the missile thus being typed Polaris A-3TK. About 70 missiles are available.

Length: 9.84 m — Propulsion: 2-stage solid-rocket (36,000 kg initial thrust)
Diameter: 1.37 m
Weight: 15,870 kg — Range: 2,500 n.m.

♦ surface-to-air missiles

Sea Dart (GWS.30) Bldr: British Aerospace Dynamics Group

Medium-range system (35 miles, interception altitudes from 100 to 60,000 ft)

Length: 4.40 m — Diameter: 0.42 m
Wingspan: 0.91 m — Weight: 550 kg
Propulsion: solid-propellant booster, ramjet sustainer — Warhead: 22.7 kg, expanding-rod
Guidance: Semi-active homing
Speed: Mach 2.5–3.0
Fire control: Type 909 radar

Sea Dart missiles on Invincible (R 05) Peter Voss, 10-90

Mk 30 Mod. 2 launcher on the *Sheffield* and *Invincible* classes. Improveme low-altitude capability and response time are being made. 1,000 delivered by 198 with G.Mk 39 A1 fragmentation warheads ordered 3-86. 500 had been fired b 1986. The Type 909 fire-control radars were updated under 5-87 contract with Ma

Sea Wolf (GWS.25/26) Bldr: British Aerospace Dynamics Group

Short-range point-defense missile system (5,000 m)

Length: 1.9 m — Wingspan: 0.56 m — Warhead: 13.4 kg
Diameter: 0.3 m — Weight: 82 kg
Guidance: radar — Speed: Mach 2.5
Fire control: Marconi Type 910 pulse-doppler radar, which permits c of two-missile salvos, or by electro-optical tracker

GWS.25 fitted on Type 22-series frigates and four *Leander* class in a tra launcher containing six missiles (total weight with missiles: 3,500 kg). Target de tion is via the combined Type 967-968 radar. The GWS.25 Mod. 3 fire-control s employing the Marconi Type 911 (ex-805SW) search-and-track radar, with D Blindfire guidance and upgraded features to the Type 967-968 radar is installed *Brave* and later Type 22-class frigates. The GWS.26 vertical-launch version is c by the Type 23 frigates and *Fort Victoria*-class replenishment vessels. Pla a lightweight, four-cell launcher for backfitting to Type 42-class destroye *Invincible*-class carriers have been abandoned.

Sextuple Sea Wolf launcher Leo Van Ginderen,

Sea Cat (GWS.20, 22, and 24) Bldr: Short Bros. and Harland

Length: 1.47 m — Weight: 68 kg
Diameter: 0.2 m — Range: 5,300 m (max.)
Wingspan: 0.65 m — Speed: Mach 0.6
Propulsion: 2-stage solid propellant
Guidance: GWS.22 or GWS.24 radar, or GWS.20 optical system; command-guidance for all versions

The 3,000-kg quadruple launcher is standard, although a three-missile, 1,: launcher has been exported. System is obsolescent and cannot engage supe targets.

Javelin (GWS. . . .) Bldr: Short Bros. and Harland

The Royal Navy began purchasing the hand-held Javelin (successor to Blowp 6-84 and conducted initial at-sea firings shortly thereafter in HMS *Phoebe*. Guid semi-autonomous, line-of-sight. The weapon is issued to deployed units of all ty terminal defense. The 12.7-kg Javelin missile is 1.4 m long, has a range of 4,000 employs a two-stage rocket motor.

The projected successor to Javelin is Starstreak, a Mach 0.4 missile with a ra 7 km, 1.27 m long; a 24-tubed launcher with an autonomous radar targeting offered for development as "Seastreak."

Note: The Royal Marines employ mobile Rapier area-defense SAMs. Older Bl shoulder-launched SAMs are still carried aboard warships deploying to dan areas and are used by the Royal Marines.

♦ surface-to-surface missiles

The Royal Navy has purchased the MM 38 Exocet as the GWS.50 system (see F section for characteristics). It is employed on the *Amazon, Broadsword, Boxer* c and *Leander* class.

Two twin trailer-mounted MM 38 Exocet launchers built by Vosper Thornycr maintained at Gibraltar by Royal Navy personnel.

In August 1977, it was announced that the U.S. Sub-Harpoon system wo bought for use from all nuclear attack submarines. 300 have been purchased tional Harpoons have been procured for use on R.A.F. Nimrod aircraft. Harpoon the GWS.60 system for surface launching, is carried aboard Type 23/"Duke"- ar 22/*Cornwall*-class frigates.

ISSILES AND BOMBS *(continued)*

arpoon antiship missile launchers, Goalkeeper CIWS, and DLA a Gnat decoy launchers on Cornwall (F 99) Dr. Giorgio Arra, 2-90

air-to-surface missiles

a Skua (CL 834) Bldr: British Aerospace Dynamics Group

eveloped for use by Lynx helicopters, which can carry two or four. An export face-ship version has been developed for small combatant use, with initial trial nches conducted late 1988. Single-stage solid-fuel propulsion.

ngth: 2.50 m — Wingspan: 0.72 m
ameter: 0.25 m — Weight: 145 kg
ed: Mach 0.8 — Range: 15,000 m
idance: semi-active — Warhead: 20 kg high explosive

a Eagle (P3T) Bldr: British Aerospace Dynamics Group

eveloped from the Anglo-French, television-guided Martel. Sea Eagle is intended use as an antiship weapon by carrier-based Sea Harrier V/STOL aircraft as well as and-based Tornado GR-1 and Buccaneer attack aircraft. Using active radar guid-e, it employs the French Microturbo/Toulouse TRI-60 engine for propulsion. First al launchings took place in the spring of 1981. First launching of a shipboard sion 3-87, using solid boosters developed for Indian Sea King helicopters, but no s have developed. (Indian Navy Sea Harrier and Indian Air Force Javelin fighters carry the weapon.) It has also been sold to Malaysia for use on Hawk 100 and Hawk light attack aircraft.

ngth: 4.0 m — Weight: 600 kg
meter: 0.4 m — Range: 36+ km shipboard/250 km air-launch
ngspan: 1.2 — Speed: Mach 0.85

bombs

0- and 1,000-lb conventional bombs are carried on *Invincible*-class carriers for use ea Harrier fighter-bombers; tactical nuclear weapons are no longer carried.

air-to-air missiles

ewinder-1B (AIM-9L) Bldr: Philco-Ford

frared-homing, solid-fueled, Mach 2.5 lightweight weapon employed with Sea rier V/STOL aircraft aboard *Invincible*-class carriers. The weapon was to be aced by the U.S. AMRAAM (AIM-120A).

gth: 2.90 m — Weight: 84.4 kg
meter: 0.127 m — Range: 12 nautical miles
ngspan: 0.61 m — Speed: Mach 2.5

UNS

: A new medium-caliber gun is being sought for use on future Royal Navy major ace combatants. An improved 114-mm Mk 8, the U.S. FMC 127-mm Mk 45, and a lightweight OTO Melara 127-mm mount are being considered., as is a proposed mm 52-caliber weapon from VSEL, the N155-2000, with a 30-km range (40 km base-bleed).

mm Mk 8 Bldr: Vickers (VSEL)

e-barreled, automatic, dual-purpose; has a muzzle brake.

gth of barrel: 55 calibers — Rate of fire: 25 round/min
of elevation: −10° + 53° — Shell weight: 21.0 kg
imum effective range in surface fire: 23,000 m
imum effective range in antiaircraft fire: 6,000 m

ht gun mount with glass-reinforced plastic housing. Installed on the *Sheffield*- destroyers, and "Duke," *Amazon*- and *Cornwall*-class frigates.

114-mm Mk 6 Bldr: Vickers (VSEL)

Double-barreled, 45-caliber, semi-automatic, dual-purpose; phased out of Royal Navy service in 1992, but is still found on Leander-class frigates in the Indian, New Zealand, and Chilean navies. Uses variable-fuzed shells with proximity and point-detonating fuzes of variable sensitivity.

Muzzle velocity: 850 m/sec — Rate of fire: 10–12 rounds/min/barrel
Maximum effective range in surface fire: 17,000 m
Maximum effective range in antiaircraft fire: 6,000 m

76-mm Compact Bldr: OTO Melara (Italy)

Lightweight weapon installed only in the three remaining *Peacock*-class Hong Kong patrol boats. See Italian section for characteristics. The 80-round/minute version is in use by the Royal Navy.

40-mm Bofors

These 60-caliber guns are used on single Mk 7 and Mk 9 powered mounts; rate of fire on these obsolete weapons is only about 120 rpm. Hand-operated Mk 3 mountings are aboard the "River"-class minesweepers.

30-mm twin Bldr: Oerlikon/BMARC

Twin GCM-A02 mounts. Eight mounts procured 1982 from BMARC as emergency close-defense weapons for *Sheffield*-class destroyers, and additional mounts acquired later. Optical lead-computing sights.

30-mm DS-30B single Bldr: BMARC

A stabilized single mounting for the Mauser/BMARC 30-mm gun. Twenty-five were ordered 9-84 for the "Duke"-class frigates and to begin replacing old 40-mm mounts; by 7-90, 63 total had been ordered. Has 160 rounds ready service on mount. Rate of fire: 650 rpm. Muzzle velocity: 1,080 m/sec.

DS-30B 30-mm AA mount Defence Systems, 1989

30-mm Goalkeeper (SGE-30) Bldr: H.S.A., the Netherlands

General Electric GAU-8A, 30-mm gatling gun in EX-30 mounting co-mounted with H.S.A. radar detect-and-track fire-control system. Six mounts ordered 1984 for close defense in the *Cornwall*-class frigates; nine more ordered 2-86 for the *Invincible* class. See details in Netherlands section.

20-mm Oerlikon Bldr: BMARC

Large numbers of single-barrel GAM-B01 mountings procured 1982–83 to augment close defense on a variety of classes. An 85-caliber weapon with 1,000-rpm firing rate and optical, lead-computing sight on mount. In addition, standard World War II–era Mk 4 Oerlikon mountings remain in use aboard destroyers and frigates.

BMARC-Oerlikon GAM-B02 20-mm AA mount James W. Goss/NAVPIC, 8-90

GUNS *(continued)*

20-mm Phalanx Mk 15 Bldr: General Dynamics (U.S.)

Six U.S. Mk 15 Mod. 0 CIWS (Close-In Weapon System) mounts purchased 5-82 for use on the *Invincible*-class carriers. Additional mountings have since been ordered for the Type 42 class. A total of 30 mounts is planned. Uses six-barreled G.E. Vulcan gatling gun; see U.S. section for details.

7.62-mm machine guns

Standard NATO 7.62-mm light machine guns, having been found very useful in the Falklands War for disrupting low-level air attack, have been added in considerable numbers to frigates and destroyers, using simple pintle mountings. Also, for close defense against air attack, simple laser-dazzle devices have been added to combatants.

C. ANTISUBMARINE WEAPONS

Mk 10 Mortar (Limbo)

Triple-barreled mortar based on the Squid of World War II. Range: 400 to 1,000 m. Fires 177-kg time-fuzed shells, each with 94 kg of Minol explosive. Phased out of Royal Navy service in 1992, but still aboard British-built warships in other navies.

Mk 11 depth charge

Dropped from helicopters against shallow targets.

D. TORPEDOES

Spearfish Bldr: Marconi Underwater Systems, Ltd.

Heavyweight replacement for Tigerfish, began development in 1981. Has HAP (Hydrogen-Ammonium Perchlorate)-Otto fuel system and turbine engine, with pump-jet propulsor.

Length 8.50 m — Speed: 75 kts
Diameter: 533 mm — Range: 21 km
Weight: 1850 kg — Depth: 3,000 ft.
Warhead: 300 kg

By 1989, 100 pre-production models had been delivered, but reliability problems were experienced. Future production of 770–1,000 expected, with deliveries beginning mid-1990s, but planned procurement has been suspended.

Mk 24 Tigerfish (ex-ONGAR) Bldr: Marconi Underwater Systems, Ltd.

Wire-guided weapon for submarines; entered service 1980, with 2,000 on order by 1986. To improve reliability, the 600 Mod. 1 in service were updated by mid-1988. Mod. 2 entered service 1986 with 134-kg warhead. Licenses to build the weapon have been granted to Chile, Indonesia, and Turkey.

Length: 6.464 m — Speed: 35 kts
Diameter: 533 mm — Range: 16 km/35 kt; 22 km/24 kt
Weight: 1,551 kg — Warhead: 340 kg, magnetic & impact-fuzed

NST 75 11 Stingray Bldr: Marconi Underwater Systems, Ltd.

Lightweight antisubmarine torpedo replacement for Mk 44 and Mk 46 for use by surface ships and aircraft. Officially entered service in 1986, although was present during Falklands War in 1982. Electric-powered, with pump-jet propulsor.

Length: 2.60 m — Speed: 45 kts max.
Diameter: 325 mm — Range: 8 km at 45 kts
Weight: 267 kg — Warhead: 45 kg Torpex

STWS.2 triple ASW torpedo tube mount for Stingray or Mk 46 torpedoes Leo Van Ginderen, 10-91

Note: Still in inventory are large numbers of U.S. Mk 46 Mod. 5 ASW homing torpedoes.

E. MINES

Stonefish Bldr: Marconi Underwater Systems, Ltd.

Medium-depth modular magnetic/acoustic/pressure mine for launch by aircraft, surface ships, or submarines. Original version, described below, is being supplemented by a shorter, lighter Mk 2 version with 500-kg PBX explosive. There is also a training version. Has also been bought by Australia, Finland, and two unnamed countries.

Length: 2.4 m (1.9 exercise) — Warhead: 700 kg Torpex
Diameter: 533 mm — Life: up to 700 days in water
Weight: 990 kg (440 kg exercise) — Shelf-life: 20 yr.

Dragonfish Bldr: Marconi Underwater Systems, Ltd.

Lightweight, anti-invasion mine for use in waters down to 30 m. About 85 kg weight, it carries 80 kg of explosive and has a 200-day in-water lifetime.

Note: Also still in inventory are a number of older Mk 12, Mk 17, and Mk 28 mines (for details, see *The Naval Institute Guide to World Naval Systems, 1991–92,* by Dr. Norman Friedman), and the Vickers Versatile Exercise Mine System, a 2.71-m × 533-mm 560-kg device that can be laid and recovered, simulating virtually any known type mine for training.

G. SONARS

◆ **For surface ships:**

Type	Function	Freq. Band	Maker
184M/P	Hull, 360° scan	7.5 kHz	Graseby
185	Underwater telephone	8–9 kHz	Graseby
193,193M	Minehunting	100/300 kHz	Plessey
2008	Underwater telephone	High	Admiralty
2009	Underwater telephone/IFF	High	. . .
2016	Hull, 360° scan	5.5/6.5/7.5 kHz	Plessey/ Ferranti
2031, 2031(Z)	Towed passive	. . .	Plessey
2034	Sidescan	110 kHz	Waverly
2048	"Speedscan," fwd.-looking mine avoidance	High	Plessey
2050	Hull, 360° scan	5.5–7.5 kHz	Ferranti
2053	Sidescan mine locator	High	. . .
2057	Towed passive (2031(Z) replacement)	. . .	Ferranti
2059	Submersible tracking (Mounted with Type 193M towed-body)	High	. . .
2065	Thinline array for 2057	. . .	. . .
2068	Ray Path Predictor (SEPADS)	. . .	. . .
2070	Torpedo decoy system	. . .	. . .
2080	"Talisman" —joint U.K./French projected design project for surface ship suite	LF	. . .
2093	Minehunting	High	Plessey
2095	Minehunting	High	Plessey

◆ **For submarines:**

Type	Function	Freq. Band	Maker
2001	Active/Passive	2–16 kHz passive 5.5–5.7 active	Plessey
2007	Passive flank array	1–3 kHz	BAC
2019 (PARIS)	Intercept	2–14 kHz	MUSL
2020	Active/passive bow	2–16 kHz active/5.5–5.7 pass.	Plessey & Ferranti
(sub version of 2016, uses same array as 2001; 2020EX is an upgrad			
2023	Towed passive array (U.S. BQR-15)	. . .	Plessey
2024	Towed array (clip-on) (includes 2030 (U.S. BQR-22) and 2035 (U.S. BQR-23 16-channel processor)	. . .	. . .
2026	Towed array (Replaced by 2046)	VLF	Plessey/GE
2027	Passive-ranging (uses 2001 and 2020 arrays)	. . .	. . .
2032	Bow array beam-former for 2001, 2020	VLF	. . .
2040	Active/passive bow (*Upholder* class)	. . .	. . .
2043	Active/passive bow for SSBNs (part of 2054 suite)	. . .	Plessey
2045	Intercept (part of 2054 suite)	. . .	Plessey

.RS *(continued)*

Function	Freq. Band	Maker
Processor-display/ 50-m towed array (27 on order)	. . .	Ferranti
16-channel processor/freq. analyzer	. . .	. . .
"Triton" bow active/ passive array—backfit for *Oberon* class	. . .	Plessey
Towed array—clip on (interim system for SSNs)	. . .	. . .
Trident SSBN suite	. . .	Plessey
h 2043, 2044, 2045)		
Towed array, reelable	LF	. . .
Interim towed array for *Resolution*	LF	Dowty
Interim towed array for *Repulse*	LF	MUSL
Thinline towed array "wet end"	LF	McTaggart-Scott
Bandfish torpedo-countermeasure	. . .	Dowty
Noise augmentation decoy	. . .	. . .
Broadband linear passive flank array	. . .	. . .
Emergency Pinger	. . .	A.B. Precision
Bow active/passive replacement for 2001/2020; uses 2020 array	. . .	Plessey
Designation for entire suite for SSNs, includes 2074, 2077, and 2081—in design	. . .	MUSL and Ferranti-Thomson
Ice-navigation set for SSNs	HF	. . .
Environmental sonar/non-acoustic suite—in development	. . .	. . .
Sonar intercept to replace 2019	. . .	MUSL/ Ferranti-Thomson

The developmental Type 2075 suite for later *Upholder*-class submarines has anceled.

r helicopters:

.95M	Dipping	HF	Plessey
	Upgraded 195 M for Sea King	HF	Plessey
	195 successor (proposed)	HF	. . .

onobuoys:

se are the Australian SSQ-981 "Barra" (7,000 ordered 1986), the SSQ-904 and 06 "Jezebel," and SSQ-954 and 954B Miniature DIFAR. Also in use are SSQ-CAMBS (Command Active Multi-Beam Sonobuoy) by Dowty, with 50,000 de-d up to 1989. A new passive sonobuoy for the Merlin HAS.1 helicopter is to be ped.

ATA SYSTEMS

DA (Action Data Automation):

WS 7 Integrated AAW and ASW defense system. Fitted on the *ield-* and *Manchester*-class destroyers; updated ADAWS 4.
WS 8 On three Type 42 destroyers.
WS 10 Aerial and ASW defense. Fitted on the *Invincible*-class aircraft ers; update for ADAWS 5.
IS (Computer-Assisted Action Information System) *nazon-* and *Broadsword*-class frigates for tactical data handling; linked SA 4 fire-control system.
S 1 (Computer-Assisted Command System) In the *Cornwall*-class tes. Two Ferranti FM 1600E computers, 12 Argus M700 mini-ssors.
(Captain's Combat Aid) MUSL system in development for *Invincible* Type 42 classes.

SSCS (Surface Ship Command System) Successor to the abortive CACS 5 for the "Duke" class; ordered 10-89 from Dowty-Sema-Racal. Has parallel processing, modular software, and LINK 11 and 14 capability. To enter service mid-1990s.

A number of computerized command support and combat management systems are in development. The Pilot Flag Support System (PFSS) uses the U.S. JOTS I target position data bank software and acts as an intelligent data link terminal; it will be installed in Type 42 destroyers. The Fleet Ocean Surveillance Product (FOSP) will provide track correlation and dynamic updating of on-board data bases, in conjunction with the ship's Link 11 terminal. The CCA (Captain's Combat Aid), to be installed in carriers and Type 42 destroyers as part of the ADIMP (ADAWS Improvement Program) will process own ship's sensor data to assess the threat and recommend the best course of action. An Admiralty Research establishment data-fusion system is scheduled to undergo trials in the frigate *Marlborough*.

I. RADARS

♦ Navigational:

1006(1)—(9,650 MHz) in submarines; navalized Kelvin-Hughes 19/9A.
1006(2,3)—(9,445 MHz) in major surface units.
1006(4)—(9,425 MHz) in mine countermeasures ships.
1007—Kelvin-Hughes Series 1600 + Red Pac, I-band (3-cm) nav. radar with manual plot, to replace Type 1006.

Note: Auxiliaries use a number of different commercial navigational radars, primarily the Racal Decca 1226 and 1229 models.

♦ Combined air and surface search:

967/968—pulse-doppler, paired back-to-back antennas; 967 in L-band (1,260–1,360 MHz); 968 in S-band (2,950–3,040 MHz). Employed with GWS.25 Sea Wolf system in the *Broadsword* class. Type 967M with pulse-doppler to detect small targets in development, 1987. Rotates at 30 rpm. Incorporates Type 1010 interrogator for Mk XII IFF.
992Q (S-band)—stabilized medium range for low-altitude air-search, surface-search, and target designation. Most replaced by Type 996/2.
994—(S-band) Plessey AWS-4 using quarter-cheese antenna from the obsolete Type 993.
996—(S-band: 2,850–3,100 MHz) 3-D replacement for 992Q in older ships (996/2) and 996/1 version for Type 23-class frigates. Replaces canceled Type 1030 STIR program. Also for target designation. Has stabilized antenna. Plessey AWS-9 is commercial version.

Type 996 3-D radar—at top, above array for UAF-1 intercept equipment on *Norfolk* (F 230); spherical Sea Archer optronic director is on the platform at left — James W. Goss/NAVPIC, 4-90

♦ Air search, early warning:

965—(P-band) Long-range early-warning. Still found in foreign navies; AKE(2) antenna is a double-deck AKE(1). P-band. 965M has moving-target indicator feature.
966—Marconi P-band update to Type 965, with improved transmitter and receiver but same antenna. On one *Leander*-class frigate.
1022—(L-band) Dutch H.S.A. LW-08 radar with a Marconi antenna, on *Invincible* class, and *Manchester-* and *Sheffield*-class destroyers. Incorporates Cossor 850 IFF interrogator. Has approximate 225 n.m. range. Rotates at 6–8 rpm.
. . .—ASTRAL (Air Surveillance and Targeting Radar, L-band) with rotating planar array. In development by Thomson-CSF, Siemens-Plessey, and INISEL as a replacement for Type 1022. To have 400-km range.

RADARS *(continued)*

◆ Weapons control:

903 (I-band)—is used in Mk 6 and Mk 5, 114-mm gun directors (MRS.3) on *Leander* class.
904—MRS.3 and GWS.22 fire control for the Sea Cat.
909—Sea Dart system (also 114-mm Mk 8 gun in the *Sheffield*-class destroyers)
910—Tracking radar used with the Sea Wolf (GWS.25) system; also does vertical search in I-/J-band (8–15 GHz)
911—Marconi ST805 SW for Sea Wolf GWS.25 Mod. 3 system in *Cornwall* class; uses part of antenna array for the land-based "Blindfire" radar. Also used with GWS.26 (I/K-band). 911(2) version for vertical-launch Sea Wolf.
912—Used for Sea Cat (GWS.24) and 114-mm gun control in *Amazon*-class frigates. British designation for Selenia RTN-10X system.

◆ For aircraft:

Blue Fox—Multi-function, in Sea Harrier FRS.1.
Blue Kestral—Multi-function, for Merlin helicopter.
Blue Vixen—Multi-function for Sea Harrier FRS.2.
Sea Spray—For Lynx helicopters—surface-search and target designation.
Sea Searcher—(I-band) For Sea King Mk 5 ASW helicopters, for use in interrogating the LAPADS sonobuoy system.
Searchwater—(I-band) For surface search in Nimrod patrol aircraft and air and surface search in Sea King Mk 2 AEW helicopters. Frequency-agile.

J. COUNTERMEASURES

Note: The various active countermeasures systems are described as "outfits":

◆ Surface ship systems:

DEC—laser dazzling device to confuse or incapacitate aircraft pilots and IR-homing missiles.
DLA—6-tubed Sea Gnat multipurpose decoy rocket launcher.
DLB—Plessey Shield 6-tubed launcher, equipped to fire Corvus chaff or infrared decoy rockets.
DLC—Knebworth/Corvus 8-tubed launcher, often with 50-mm flare launcher atop.
DLD—U.S. Hycor Mk 137, 6-tubed launcher for U.S. Mk 36 SRBOC system; several different configurations.
DLE—Plessey Shield launcher for R.F.A. auxiliaries.
DLF—Irvin "Rubber Duck" floating corner reflectors.
DLF.2—Irvin "Replica" floating reflector.
DLH—proposed offboard active jammer; competing are Thorn-EMI/Thomson-CSF CARMEN and Marconi/Dassault Électronique SIREN.
UAA-1—"Abbeyhill," covers 1–18 GHz. Used on modern destroyer and frigate classes. Passive intercept. Associated with Type 670 jammer.
UAA-2—updated UAA-1, also covering 1–18 GHz. Associated with Type 675 jammer.
UA-8/9—older passive intercept system. (UA-8 covers 2.5–4.16 GHz, UA-9 7–11.5 GHz). UA-8 employs SARIE analyzer.
UA-10—G/H-band intercept, on *Penelope* only (to Ecuador, 1991).
UA-13—passive array covering A/C-bands.
UA-15—J-band intercept on towed-array *Leanders*; covers 12–18 GHz.
UAF-1—Racal Cutlass intercept suite for Type 23 "Duke" class. Associated with Type 675 or commercial Cygnus jammers.
UAG—E/J-band (to 40 GHz) intercept on *Fort Victoria* (Marconi Mentor)
UAR—Intercept suite for Royal Fleet Auxiliaries.
UAT—Thorn-EMI, for use on Type 23 frigates; covers 2–18, 18–40 GHz, with 360° sweep from −15° to +30°; 255 track capacity, 2,000-mode threat library. Based on Sceptre KL.
RCM-3—gate-stealing jammer by Decca—being added to large surface combatants.
668/669—jammers associated with UA-8 and UA-9.
670—Racal "Heather" jammer, used on UAA-1 ships.
675(2)—Thorn EMI Guardian low-cost point-defense jammer for UAA-2 ships (Type 42 and *Invincible* classes).

◆ Commercial equipment:

Type 242—Racal integrated intercept/jammer suite, with Cutlass, Scorpion, and Sadie processor.
Barricade—Wallop commercial design, used on Hunt-class minehunters.
Cutlass—Racal intercept 0.6–18 GHz, 5 MHz/5° accuracy.
Heather—Racal point-defense jammer (RN Type 670).
Matilda-E—Microwave Analysis Threat Indication and Launch Direction Apparatus; lightweight, low-cost intercept system by MEL. Six sets on mine countermeasures ships by 1989.
Mentor A/B/C—Marconi intercept sets, to 40 GHz.
Sabre—Racal intercept 0.6–40 GHz, 5 MHz/2° or 8° accuracy. For submarines.
Sarie—Thorn/EMI Selective Automatic Radar Identification Equipment; an add-on for existing EW suites.
Scorpion—Racal wide-beam jammer: can jam 5 to 8 targets, 50-kw output between 7.5 and 18 GHz.
Siren—Marconi *off*-board jammer.
Sceptre—Philips/MEL intercept suite: Sceptre 0 for small ships, Sceptre X for corvettes, Sceptre XL for large combatants.
Scimitar—Philips/MEL deception/jammer.

◆ Submarine systems:

UAB/UAC—Racal systems, mast-mounted antennas. UAB to be replaced by UAP. UAC-3 will be on Trident submarines.
UAH—EW suite on *Oberon* class, covers 2–18 GHz. Developed by MEL from Rapids. 2000 signal threat library.
UAJ—alternative EW suite on *Oberons*, by Racal; uses Cutlass display and processor; 2–18 GHz.
UAL—similar to UAH; on *Valiant/Churchill* classes. Same as commercial Manta system. Covers 2–18 GHz.
UAP—Racal EW suite, covers 0.6 to 40 GHz; also known as Sabre in com installations.

◆ Torpedo decoys:

Type 182, an obsolescent towed noisemaker, is aboard surface ships; a joint with the U.S. Navy seeks to develop a decoy and active countermeasures Russian-developed wake-homing torpedoes. Submarines employ 4-inch (102-r coy launchers: Mk 4 in the *Oberon* class, Mk 6 in the *Swiftsure* class, Mk 8 *Trafalgar* class, and Mk 10 in the *Vanguard* class.

K. COMMUNICATIONS

The Royal Navy employs the Skynet Super-High-Frequency (SHF) satellite c nications system in carriers, destroyers, and frigates, although since there sufficient sets, only units deploying or fully operational carry the twin SCOT (S Communications Terminal) radomes, which are 1–2 m in diameter and operat 500-MHz band. Royal Fleet auxiliaries, hydrographic ships, and corvettes of th tle" class carry the commercial INTELSAT SATCOMM system. Shipboard I HF/VHF systems are increasingly integrated and are among the best in the single-sideband is extensively employed. Eight frigates are equipped with the Alone Message Processing (SAMP) system, as used in the U.S. Navy's T-AGO ocean surveillance ships.

AIRCRAFT CARRIERS

Note: A replacement design for the *Invincible* class is reported to be in preli design. To displace 40,000 tons, it would operate conventional aircraft vice V fighters and would have two steam catapults and three aircraft elevators. Arr may include four vertical-launch Sea Wolf SAM groups (64 missiles).

◆ 3 Invincible class

	Bldr	Laid down	L	I
R 05 Invincible	Vickers, Barrow	20-7-73	3-5-77	1
R 06 Illustrious	Swan Hunter, Wallsend	7-10-76	14-12-78	2
R 07 Ark Royal	Swan Hunter, Wallsend	14-12-78	4-6-81	1

Invincible (R 05) Maritime Photographi

Invincible (R 05) Leo Van Gindere

Illustrious (R 06)—in reserve prior to modernization
Maritime Photographic

·RAFT CARRIERS *(continued)*

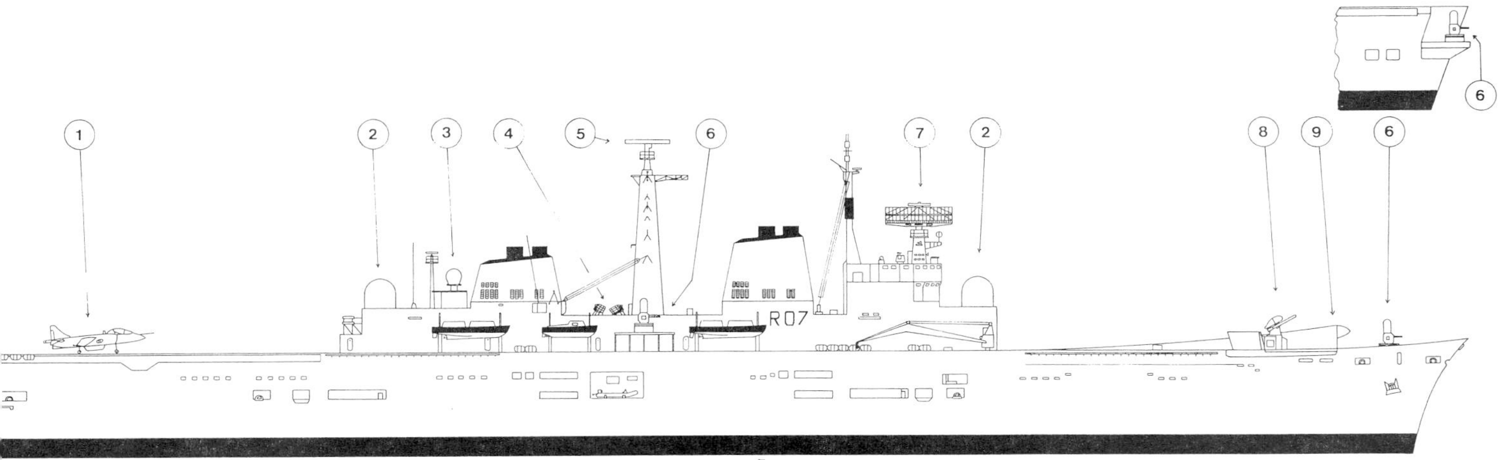

ɬoyal (R 07) 1. Sea Harrier FRS.1 2. Type 909 missile-control radars 3. SCOT SHF SATCOMM antennas 4. DLA decoy rocket launchers 5. Type radar 6. MK 15 Phalanx CIWS 7. Type 1022 early-warning radar 8. Sea Dart launcher 9. 12-degree "ski-jump" takeoff ramp Robert Dumas

ɬoyal (R 07)—with 5 Sea Harriers and 5 Sea Kings on deck French Navy, 11-90

ıcible (R 05) Peter Voss, 10-90

Ark Royal (R 07) Maritime Photographic, 6-91

AIRCRAFT CARRIERS *(continued)*

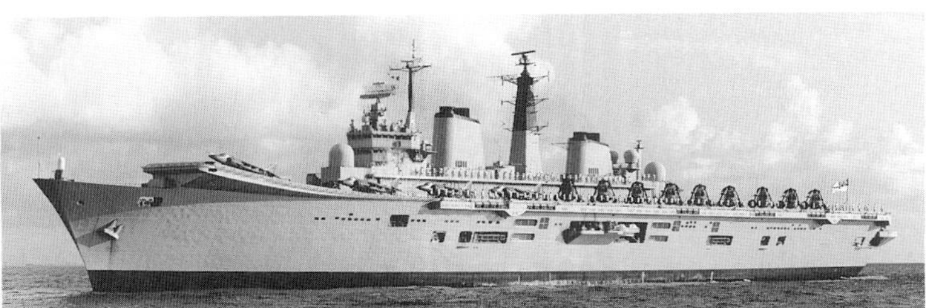

Ark Royal (R 07) Dr. Giorgio Arra, 9-91

Ark Royal (R 07) Dr. Giorgio Arra, 9-91

D: 16,860 tons (20,600 fl) **S:** 28 kts
Dim: 210.00 (R 06: 206.6) (all: 192.87 wl) × 36.0 (R 06: 31.89) (all: 27.50 wl) × 6.5 (8.8 over sonar dome)
Air Group:
R 05: 7 Sea Harrier FRS.1 V/STOL fighter-bombers, 8 Sea King HAS.5 ASW helicopters, 3 Sea King HAS.2 (AEW) helicopters
R 06: post-refit: 8 Sea Harrier, 9 Sea King HAS.6, 3 Sea King HAS.2 (AEW)
R 07: 8 Sea Harrier, 7 Sea King HAS.5, 3 Sea King HAS.2 (AEW)
A: 1/Sea Dart GWS.30 Mod. 2 SAM syst. (II × 1; 22 missiles)—R 05, R 06: 3/30-mm Goalkeeper CIWS (I × 3); R 07: 3/20-mm Mk 15 CIWS (I × 3)—all: 2/20-mm GAM-B01 AA (I × 2)
Electron Equipt:
Radar: 2/1006 nav., 1/992R (R 05, R 06: 996(2)) surf./air search, 1/1022 early warning, 2/909 missile f.c., 2 or 3 f.c. assoc. with CIWS
Sonar: 2016 hull-mounted, 1/762 echo-sounder, 1/185 underwater telephone
EW: UAA-1 intercept, 670 jammer (R 05: UAA-2/675(2)), R 05, 07: 4/DLA decoy RL (VI × 4), R 06: 2/DLC decoy RL (VIII × 2), 4/DLD decoy RL (VI × 4)
Combat System: ADAWS 10
M: 4 Rolls-Royce Olympus TM3B gas turbines; 2 props; 112,000 shp (94,000 sust.)
Electric: 14,000 kw **Range:** 7,000/18
Crew: 57 officers, 666 enlisted (plus air group: 80 officers, 286 enlisted)

Remarks: Redesignated "ASW aircraft carriers" in 1980, previously having been, for political reasons, considered to be a type of cruiser. Only two are operational at any one time. *Invincible* ordered 17-4-73, *Illustrious* on 14-5-76, and *Ark Royal* in 12-78. The ships can embark 960 Royal Marines for short periods. Some 75 women officers and enlisted joined the crew of R 05 in the fall of 1990.

Invincible and *Illustrious* originally had a 7-degree "ski jump" to assist Sea Harrier aircraft in making rolling takeoffs at full combat load. The ramp on *Ark Royal* was inclined 12 degrees and was 12 meters longer. The 183-meter-long by 13.5-m-wide flight deck is slightly angled to port to clear the Sea Dart launcher, which is awkwardly located on the ship's centerline and has been given an elaborate blast shield to protect the aircraft aboard. The single-level hangar has three separate bays, with the amidships bay narrower to permit passage of the gas-turbine exhausts. The two 9.7 by 16.7-m hydraulic scissors-lift aircraft elevators have given considerable trouble and are to be replaced by Strachan & Henshaw chain-type elevators during future refits. The electrical generating plant consists of eight General Electric 1,750-kw alternators driven by Paxman Valenta 16-RPM 200A diesels of 2,700 hp each.

Four planned MM 38 Exocet launchers were deleted from the design. *Ark Royal* was completed with three Mk 15 CIWS (Vulcan/Phalanx).

Invincible entered refit at Plymouth 17-3-86 for modernization, recommissioning 18-5-89. Received hangar modifications to permit stowing 9 Sea Harrier and 12 Sea King; magazine spaces enlarged by 50 percent to accommodate Sea Eagle missiles and Stingray ASW torpedoes; Type 2016 sonar in place of Type 184; Type 996 radar in place of 992R; the ADAWS 10 data system; the flight deck reconfigured to a 12-degree ramp; and three 30-mm Goalkeeper CIWS in place of the Mk 15 Phalanx—adding 600 tons to her displacement. Her crew was increased by 120, and she received the U.S. Masker acoustic bubbler system; aircraft fuel tankage was also increased. In 1991, *Invincible* received Enhance SCOT 1 satellite communications eqiuipment.

Illustrious began layup 3-5-89 at Portsmouth until beginning a two-year refit 1-7-91, after which she will replace *Ark Royal* as an active unit. Will be updated like *Invincible*. All are scheduled to receive further ADAWS data system updates, including the substitution of the Ferranti F2420 computer. Plans to install four lightweight Sea SAM launchers in all three were canceled 7-91.

Note: The helicopter transport/training ship *Argus* (A 135) is intended to be a carry up to 12 Sea Harriers and to operate 8 of them, although she is consi primarily to be a source of additional aircraft to act as spares for the carriers. A pla new "Aviation Support ship" has been redesignated an assault helicopter carrier (and is discussed in the section on amphibious warfare ships.

NAVAL AVIATION

The Flag Officer Naval Aviation (F.O.N.A.) is located at the principal nav facility, Yeovilton, and is chiefly responsible for training and maintenance. 7,500 personnel are involved in naval aviation activities. Land-based maritim veillance and strike aircraft belong to the R.A.F. and, since the reorganization latter, have constituted the Eighteenth, or Maritime, Group of Strike Command. the group is part of the R.A.F. as regards personnel and equipment, its employm determined by the Royal Navy's commander in chief.

The Fleet Air Arm consists of: First-line squadrons (designation characterize group of three figures beginning with an 8) whose missions are: attack, ASW helicopter assault. Second-line squadrons (designation characterized by a gr three figures beginning with a 7) that are used in schools, tests, and maintenan

Operational aircraft of the Royal Navy include (as of 4-92):

No.	Type	Function	Squadron
24	Sea Harrier FRS.1	attack/ interceptor	800, 801, 899
4	Sea Harrier T.4(N)/T.4	training	899
57	Sea King HAS.5/6	ASW, logistics	706, 771, 810, 81 819, 820, 826
29	Sea King HC.4	troop-carrying	707, 772, 845, 84
8	Sea King HAS.2A (AEW)	early warning	849
58	Sea Lynx HAS.3	ASW, attack	702, 815, 829
4	Lynx AH.2	transport	3 Brigade, Roya Marines
19	Gazelle HT.2	liaison, training	705
12	Gazelle AH.1	transport	3 Brigade, Roya Marines
17	Jetstream T.2	training	750
3	Jetstream T.3	liaison	H.M.S. *Heron* Comms. Flt.
13*	Hunter T.8C, GA.11	training	899 and contrac
16*	Falcon 20	training, transport	private contract
12	Chipmunk T.10	training	Flying Grading Unit, Roxboro
3	HS.125	VIP transport	RAF detachmen
1	Turbine Defender	ASW research	Dir. General Underwater Weapons

* Operated by FR Aviation, Ltd., for target and EW training: also contr operated are one Beech Baron and one Cessna Conquest II. The Falcon 20 aircraf the following functions: seven simulate threats using ALE-43 active emitters, chaff launchers, and other EW gear; three have ALQ-167(V) pods; three are equ for target towing, and three are "silent targets."

Note: Remaining Sea King HAS.5s are to convert to HAS.6; four new Mk 4 and Mk 6, ordered 1-88, began deliveries 11-89. AWS-504 and new EW gear will go c King HAS.6 conversions 1989 on. The first Sea Harrier FRS.2 flew 19-9-89, a c sion from an FRS.1. Series conversions are to start in 1991 and end in 1994, and te aircraft were ordered for delivery 1994 on. Three Sea Lynx were in trials late 1 prototypes for a "Mk 8" update: weight increased to 5,125 kg, Rolls-Royce Gen turboshafts fitted, composite rotor blades, chin radome for undetermined rada tactical data system; the first seven series conversions were ordered 2-92.

Royal Air Force Maritime Patrol Aircraft of No. 18 (Maritime) Group (as of included:

No.	Type	Function	Squadron
28	Nimrod MR.2	Maritime patrol	42, 120, 201, 206, 236(OCU)
24	Buccaneer S.2	Maritime strike	12, 208, 237(OCU)

Note: Also in use are three Nimrod R2 electronics aircraft. Six Nimrods have retired, and the R.A.F. is seeking a replacement for the entire force. The Buccane be retired soon and replaced with Tornado fighter-bombers.

Sea Lynx HAS.3—with Sea Skua missiles M.O.D., U.K.,

BAT AIRCRAFT

xed-wing

Harrier FRS.1 Manufacturer: British Aerospace

Harrier FRS.1 Mike Louagie, 7-88

ngspan: 7.60 m **Length:** 14.50 m **Height:** 3.71 m
ight: 10,500 kg **Speed:** Mach 0.96 (Mach 1.2 in dive)
pulsion: 1 Rolls-Royce Pegasus 104 vectored-thrust turbojet; 9,750-kg thrust
x. ceiling: 50,000+ ft. **Range:** VTOL: 50 n.m.; STOL: 200 n.m.
apons: 2,270 kg total: 4 AIM-9L Sidewinder, 2/30-mm Aden cannon, 454-kg bombs

rks: 29 existing FRS.1 are to be updated to FRS.2, and 10 new FRS.2 were d 6-3-90. FRS.1 has Blue Fox radar. FRS.2 has Blue Vixen multi-mode radar, on to carry up to six U.S. AIM-120 AMRAAM air-to-air missiles, and the s 105 engine. The five two-seat T.4-series trainers are to be rehabilitated.

licopters

n HAS.1 Manufacturer: Agusta-Westland

n HAS.1—prototype M.O.D., U.K., 1991

or diameter: 18.59 m **Length:** 22.70 m (15.85 folded)
ght: 6.50 m **Weight:** 6,917 kg empty (13,000 max.)
ed: 167 kts (150 cruise) **Max. ceiling:** 15,000 ft
nge/endurance: 5 hr. on-station (100 n.m. op. radius); 1,150 n.m. ferry range
pulsion: 3 Rolls-Royce/Turboméca/Piaggio RTM.322 turboshafts (2,100 shp each)
apons: Four Stingray torpedoes or 30 troops over 200 n.m. radius; 6,000 kg underslung to 550 n.m. range

rks: On 2-9-91, 44 production variants ordered from IBM-Westland consortium. nter service 1998 aboard frigates and carriers. Will carry Thomson-Sintra H (Type . . .) dipping sonar, Orange Reaper EW suite, and Kestrel I-band multi-n radar. Requires only one pilot and one systems operator in ASW rôle. Nine oduction prototypes delivered 1984–1990. Also being procured by British Army, a, and Italy. A mine countermeasures variant to tow the U.S. EDO Mk 106 rmeasures sled is being studied.

ynx HAS.3 Manufacturer: Westland

tor Diameter: 12.80 m **Length:** 15.16 m **Height:** 3.60 m
ight: 4,716 kg **Speed:** 145 kts **Max. ceiling:** 12,000 ft
pulsion: 2 Rolls-Royce Gem 4 turboshafts (1,120 shp each)
nge: 1 hr. 30 min. (half in transit, half hovering); 340 n.m. max.
apons: 2 Mk 46 or Stingray torpedoes, 2–4 Sea Skua ASM

Sea Lynx HAS.8 aerodynamic prototype Henry H. Hill, 3-91

Remarks: Shipboard antisubmarine attack and ship attack helicopter. Some equipped with U.S. ALQ-167(V) "Yellow Veil" ECM; most have MIR.2 "Orange Crop" EW. Have Sea Spray radar but no dipping sonar. All HAS.2 have now been brought up to HAS.3 standard. First seven series HAS.8 modernizations ordered 1992 to extend life to 2010. HAS.8 receives Sea Owl infrared search and tracking equipment, CAE-made boom-mounted MAD gear. Aircraft participating in the Persian Gulf War received 12.7-mm machine guns and scored notable success with Sea Skua missiles against Iraqi warships and small craft.

Sea King HC.4, HAS.5/6, HAS.2A Manufacturer: Westland

Sea King HC.4—transport Maritime Photographic, 6-92

Rotor diameter: 18.90 m
Length: 22.15 m (17.03 fuselage; 14.40 folded)
Weight: 9,750 kg max. t.o. **Speed:** 126 kts cruise
Max. ceiling: 10,000 ft.
Propulsion: 2 Rolls-Royce Gnome H.1400-1 turboshafts (1,535 shp each) driving a 5-bladed rotor and a tail rotor
Range/Endurance: 3 hr. 15 min. normal mission
Weapons: up to 4 Mk 46 or Stingray torpedoes or 4 Mk 11 depth charges; 1 or 2/7.62-mm mg (HC.4: 2,727 kg stores or 22 troops)

Remarks: All surviving HAS.2 updated to HAS.5 except for 10 converted as HAS.2A (AEW) air early-warning aircraft with Searchwater air/surface-search radar (with antenna in inflating radome on pivoting arm to starboard). HAS.5 has Sea Searcher radar (initially: ARI 5955), LAPADS sonobuoy system, Type 195M dipping sonar. HAS.6 conversions and new aircraft have ASQ-504(V) MAD gear, Type 2069 dipping sonar, AQS-9026 sonobuoy processor. Most HAS.5/6 have "Orange Crop" EW suite.

Gazelle AH.1, HT.2 Manufacturer: Aérospatiale-Westland

Gazelle AH.1—assigned to Royal Marines M.O.D., U.K., 1982

Rotor diameter: 10.80 m **Length:** 9.52 m **Height:** 2.74 m
Weight: 908 kg empty/1,700 kg max. **Speed:** 164 kts (140 cruise)
Propulsion: 1 Turboméca Astazou IIIA turboshaft (562 shp)
Max. ceiling: 16,730 ft. **Range/endurance:** 190 n.m.

Remarks: AH.1 employed by Royal Marines for reconnaissance, HT.2 used for training and liaison. Five seats. Have "fenestron"-type shrouded tail rotor, three-bladed main rotor.

Sea Harrier FRS.2—conversion prototype BAe, 1989

Sea King HAS.5 Bernard Prézelin, 9-91

Sea King HAS.2A AEW—with Searchwater radar deployed R.N.A.S. Culdrose

Jetstream T.2 trainer Mike Louagie, 7-88

Nimrod MR.2—with Sidewinder AAM M.O.D., U.K.

BALLISTIC-MISSILE SUBMARINES

Note: Royal Navy submarines do not wear their pendant numbers. The a numbers are included here for reference only.

♦ 0 (+4) Vanguard class Bldr: VSEL (Vickers Shipbldg. & Eng., L Barrow-in-Furness

	Ordered	Laid down	L	In
S . . . Vanguard	30-4-86	3-9-86	5-3-92	1994 (trials 1
S . . . Victorious	6-10-87	12-4-88	. . .	1995
S . . . Vigilant	13-11-90	16-2-91	3-94	1996
S . . . Venerable	7-7-92	. . .	. . .	1997

Vanguard—at launch VSE

D: 15,850 tons (submerged) **S:** 25 kts (sub.)
Dim: 149.30 × 12.80 × 10.10
A: 16/Trident D5 ballistic missiles—4/553-mm TT (. . . UGM-84 Block 2 Sub-Harpoon, Spearfish and Tigerfish torpedoes)
Electron Equipt:
Radar: 1/1007—EW: UAC-3 intercept suite
Sonar: Type 2054 suite: Type 2043 active/passive, Type 2046 to array; Type 2019 or 2082 intercept, Type 183 underwate telephone
M: 1 Vickers/Rolls-Royce PWR.2 pressurized-water reactor, W.H Allen steam generators, GEC-Alsthom steam turbines; 1 pum prop; 27,500 shp
Crew: 135 tot. (two crews per submarine)

Remarks: Program to replace the *Resolution* class began with announcement of the selection of the Trident D5 missile with eight multiple, independent r vehicle (MIRV) warheads, necessitating use of U.S. *Ohio*-class midsection (a the submarine will be shorter than the U.S. submarine, as eight fewer missiles carried). Will require refit and recoring only every eight–nine years. Have a hull coating. The U.S. Rockwell SINS Mk 2 inertial navigation system is instal Dowty-SEMA SMCS Submarine Command System was not expected to be full tional by the time of the first sea trials for *Vanguard*. For emergency propuls have diesel generators and 480-cell battery group. Program has experienced de cost overruns, including a lengthy work stoppage beginning 8-88. Third unit to have been named *Vengeance*. *Vanguard* was formally christened on 30-4-9 be based at Faslane, on the River Clyde.

♦ 3 Resolution class

	Bldr	Laid down	L	I
S 22 Resolution	Vickers-Armstrong, Barrow-in-Furness	26-2-64	15-9-66	2
S 23 Repulse	Vickers-Armstrong, Barrow-in-Furness	12-3-65	4-11-67	2
S 26 Renown	Cammell Laird, Birkenhead	25-6-64	25-2-67	15

.ISTIC-MISSILE SUBMARINES *(continued)*

',600 tons (surf.)/8,500 (sub.) **S:** 20 kts (surf.)/25+ kts (sub.)
: 129.54 × 10.06 × 9.15
16/Polaris A3TK ballistic missiles—6/533-mm bow TT (. . . Mk 24 Mod. 2 Tigerfish torpedoes)
:tron Equipt:
adar: 1/Type 1006(1) surf. search—EW: UAB/UAC intercept suite
onar: Type 2001 bow-mounted, Type 2007 LF flank array, Type 2047 towed passive array, Type 2019 PARIS intercept, Type 2032 beam-former
1 Rolls-Royce PWR.1 pressurized-water reactor; 1 set GEC-Alsthom turbines; 1 prop; 15,000 shp
w: 13 officers, 130 enlisted (2 crews)

se (S 23) Leo Van Ginderen, 10-76

wn (S 26) Leo Van Ginderen, 6-90

ks: All ordered 5-63. Plans to construct a fifth unit canceled 15-2-65. Charac-s are very similar to those of the U.S. *Lafayette* class, including the launching idance systems and the inertial navigation system. First patrol began 22-6-67 22; the 200th British Polaris patrol was carried out by *Repulse* in 1990. Form the ıbmarine Squadron. There are six crews for the four submarines. Reported 1991 ey have experienced the same reactor difficulties that forced the retirement of a r of attack submarines, but the force will be kept available until 1994, when the *ard* class will begin to phase in. Sister *Revenge* (S 27) completed last patrol 2 and paid off 25-6-92.

ɔriginal A3TK missiles were furnished by the U.S., but the six Chevaline MRV y vehicles with warheads of 150 kilotons each are of British conception and ction; introduced 1982 on S 26; S 22 (in refit 8-82 to 10-84) in 1984, and S 23 0-84 to 4-87) in 1986. S 26 began refit in 1988 at Rosyth, not completing until 92 for possible retention into the late 1990s. The long refit for S 22 has been d, and she will pay off at end-1993. Main ship's service turboalternator produces kw. Have diesel generator–driven electric emergency drive. Carry Gresham-CB and Gresham-CAP DCG combat data systems.

.EAR-PROPELLED ATTACK SUBMARINES

+ 4–6) "Trafalgar-II" class Bldr: VSEL, Barrow-in-Furness

	Laid down	L	In serv.
. . . .	. . .	. . .	2003

approx. 4,700 tons (surf.)/5,200 tons (sub.) **S:** 30+ kts (sub.)
ı: approx. 85.4 × 9.83 × 8.25
5/533-mm TT fwd (30 total weapons: Sub. Harpoon Block 2, Spearfish and Tigerfish torpedoes, mines)
ctron Equipt:
adar: Type 1007 surf. search—EW: UAC-3 intercept suite
onar: Type 2078 integrated suite (with Type 2074 active/passive bow array, Type 2077 HF under-ice navigational active, Type . . . towed passive array)
1 modified PWR.2 pressurized-water reactor, GEC-Alsthom geared turbine drive; 1/pump-jet prop; 15,000 shp—diesel-electric emergency propulsion system
w: 12 officers, 97 enlisted

rks: Initially, the *Trafalgar* class was to be followed by the "SSN-20" class with ımes and the new PWR.2 reactor developed for the *Vanguard* class. Will now the PWR.1 steam generator system with the reactor and controls for the PWR.2 eapons and electronics systems already in development to produce "95 percent of -class performance at 75 percent of the cost." Will probably employ non-ating optronic optical sensors. Requests for bids to build first unit may be issued y as 1993.

Trafalgar class Bldr: VSEL (Vickers), Barrow-in-Furness

	Ordered	Laid down	L	In serv.
Trafalgar	7-4-77	25-4-79	1-7-81	27-5-83
Turbulent	28-7-78	8-5-80	1-12-82	28-4-84
Tireless	5-7-79	1981	13-7-84	5-10-85
Torbay	26-6-81	12-82	8-3-85	7-2-87
Trenchant	22-3-83	28-10-85	4-11-86	14-1-89
Talent	10-9-84	1986	15-4-88	28-5-90
Triumph	3-1-86	1987	16-2-91	12-10-91

Talent (S 92) Dr. Giorgio Arra, 9-91

Torbay (S 118) Dr. Giorgio Arra, 8-91

Turbulent (S 110)—with hump aft over towed-array housing
Maritime Photographic, 7-90

Trafalgar (S 107) Ben Sullivan, 7-91

D: 4,700 tons (surf.)/5,208 (sub.) **S:** 30 kts (sub.)
Dim: 85.38 × 9.83 × 8.25
A: 5/533-mm TT fwd (30 total weapons: Sub. Harpoon Block 2, Spearfish and Tigerfish torpedoes, mines)
Electron Equipt:
Radar: Type 1007 surf. search—EW: UAB or UAP intercept suite
Sonar: Type 2020 MODEX bow active/passive array, Type 2007 passive flank arrays, Type 2019 PARIS sonar intercept array, S 107–S 91: Type 2026 towed passive array (S 92, 93: Type 2046), Type 2027 passive ranging, Type 2071 noise generator, Type 2077 active ice-navigation, Type 183 underwater telephone, Type 197 echo-sounder, Type 728 and Type 780 upward-looking echo-sounders
M: 1 pressurized-water PWR.1 reactor, GEC-Alsthom geared turbine drive; 1/pump-jet prop; 15,000 shp—diesel-electric emergency propulsion system: Paxman 400-kw diesel generator)
Endurance: 85 days **Crew:** 12 officers, 97 enlisted

Remarks: An improved version of the Swiftsure class. Have rubber anechoic coating tiles to reduce noise signature. S 107 has a standard seven-bladed propeller, while the others have pump-jet propellers. Diving depth: 300 m operating, 590 m maximum. Hull built of NQ-1 (HY-80) steel. Three internal decks, four watertight compartments. Carry Barr and Stroud CH 34 (1 to 5X) and CK 84 (6X) periscopes, the former also carrying the antennas for the UAB/UAP EW intercept suite and the latter also equipped with television and infrared intercept equipment. S 110 conducted trials with a reelable towed array (causing the hump to her casing abaft the sail); the others employ "clip-on" arrays. In 4-88, construction of S 93 was delayed when it was discovered that one pressure-hull section had been welded in upside down.

S 91 has been backfitted with the Type DCB tactical data system, which employs the Ferranti F2420 computer; the others have the FM1600 computer; all will standardize on the Dowty-Sema SMCS tactical data system. S 117 surfaced at the North Pole, 5-91. All are based at Devonport. Mid-life refits will update the sonar suite to the Type 2074 integrated array, retaining the 2020 transducer array and including Types 2074, 2077, and 2081 sonars. All are equipped with 102-mm tubes to launch the Dowty Bandfish (Type 2066) torpedo countermeasures device.

NUCLEAR-PROPELLED ATTACK SUBMARINES *(continued)*

♦ 5 Swiftsure class   Bldr: Vickers (VSEL), Barrow-in-Furness

	Ordered	Laid down	L	In serv.
S 104 Sceptre	1-11-71	25-10-73	20-11-76	14-2-78
S 108 Sovereign	16-5-69	18-9-70	22-2-73	22-7-74
S 109 Superb	20-5-70	16-3-72	30-11-74	13-11-76
S 111 Spartan	7-2-73	26-3-76	7-4-78	22-9-79
S 112 Splendid (ex-*Severn*)	26-5-76	23-11-77	5-10-79	21-3-81

Sovereign (S 108) Ben Sullivan, 5-91

Sceptre (S 104) Dr. Giorgio Arra, 3-89

Superb (S 109) Leo Van Ginderen, 8-91

D: 4,000 tons light/4,200 tons surf./4,500 tons sub.
S: 20 kts (surf.)/28 kts (sub.) **Dim:** 82.90 × 9.83 × 8.25
A: 5/533-mm bow TT (20 Mk 24 Mod. 2 Tigerfish torpedoes and UGM-84B2 Sub-Harpoon missiles)
Electron Equipt:
Radar: 1/1006(1) surf. search—EW: UAC intercept array
Sonar: Type 2001 (S 111, 112: Type 2020) bow active/passive array, Type 2007 passive flank array, Type 2019 PARIS sonar intercept; S 104, S 109, S 112: Type 2024 clip-on towed passive array, Type 2035 or 2047 narrowband processor/wideband frequency analyzer, Type 183 underwater telephone, Type 197 echo-sounder
M: 1 PWR.1 pressurized-water reactor; 2 GEC-Alsthom turbines; 1 prop or pump-jet; 15,000 shp (1 Paxman 400-shp auxiliary propulsion diesel, electric drive)
Crew: 12 officers, 85 enlisted (berthing)—but up to 120 total normally aboard

Remarks: High-performance, very quiet submarines with excellent passive sonars. Have 112-cell battery. The forward diving planes are below the surfaced waterline and retract within the outer hull. DCB weapons-control system, with two Ferranti 1600B computers. Have anechoic hull and sail coatings, new sonar processors, and Sub-Harpoon capability, beginning with S 109 in refit ending 28-9-85. S 108 refitted 1983 to 24-11-84. S 104 refit 1986–87, S 111 13-10-86 to 15-10-88, both with 2020, new 12-year reactor cores, 2024 towed array, new decoy system; S 109 completed similar refit 9-91. Sister *Swiftsure* (S 126) began "30-month" refit 5-10-88, but reactor problems were discovered, and she has been stored, minus sail, pending disposal, having been formally retired in 5-92. The survivors became the 3rd Submarine Squadron, based at Faslane, in 8-91 (they had previously been the 2nd Squadron at Devonport). Are to receive the Type 2076 integrated sonar suite and Dowty-Sema SMCS command/combat data system. They will be replaced by the "Trafalgar-II" class.

Note: All five ships of the *Valiant* class have been discarded: *Churchill* (S 46) in 12-90, *Conqueror* (S 48) in 8-90, *Courageous* (S 50) and *Valiant* (S 102) in 1991, and *Warspite* (S 103) in 12-90. Have all been placed in safe storage, stripped of their sails, pending a means of disposing of them.

DIESEL-POWERED ATTACK SUBMARINES

♦ 3 (+1) Upholder class

	Bldr	Laid down	L	In
S 40 Upholder	VSEL, Barrow-in-Furness	2-86	2-12-86	7-
S 41 Unseen	Cammell Laird, Birkenhead	12-8-87	14-11-89	2(
S 42 Ursula	Cammell Laird, Birkenhead	10-1-89	28-2-91	8
S 43 Unicorn	Cammell Laird, Birkenhead	13-3-90	16-4-92	

Upholder (S 40) Maritime Photographic

Unseen (S 41) Maritime Photographic

Upholder (S 40)—showing anechoic tile pattern, bare areas over fla hydrophone arrays R.J.L. Fry

Unseen (S 41) Maritime Photographi

D: 1,870 tons standard/2,185 tons surfaced/2,400 tons submerged
S: 12 kts (surf.)/20 kts (sub.)
Dim: 70.26 (47.5 pressure hull) × 7.60 × 5.50
A: 6/533-mm TT fwd (18 tot. Mk 24 and/or Spearfish torpedoes a UGM-84B2 Sub-Harpoon missiles, mines)

L-POWERED ATTACK SUBMARINES *(continued)*

:ron Equipt:
lar: Type 1007 surf. search—EW: UAC (Decca Porpoise) intercept
ar: Type 2040 bow active/passive, Type 2041 Micropuffs passive flank array, Type 2046 (S 40: Type 2026) towed array, Type 2019 (PARIS) intercept
Paxman Valenta 16 RPA 200SZ 16-cyl. diesel generators, ,035 bhp each, 2 G.E.C.-Alsthom 2,500-kw alternators; 1/7-bladed rop; 5,400 shp
rance: 50 days
e: 8,000/8 (snorkel); 54/20 (sub.); 270/3 (sub.)
: 200 tons **Crew:** 7 officers, 37 enlisted

:s: Design based on the Vickers commercial Type 2400 design and for financial were intended to provide successors to the *Oberon* class. The first unit was 28-11-83, the next three on 3-1-86. Plans to construct additional units canceled. rubber anechoic hull coating. Class intended to operate 15,000 hrs. (7 years) overhauls. Have 11 percent reserve buoyancy when surfaced. Two 240-cell batteries, 6,080 amp/hr. at one-hour rate, 8,800 amp/hr. at five-hour rate. Stroud CK 35 search periscope with Decca EW array; CH 85 attack scope with capability. Able to snorkel at 19 kts. 250+ m diving depth. DCC weapons with two Ferranti FM 1600E computers, Thorn E.M.T. 1553B data system. navigation system. Type 2040 sonar is a version of the Thomson-Sintra Arystem. The 2040's cylindrical array is at the bow, with intercept hydrophones l along the sides. The sail has a glass-reinforced plastic skin.
ry of S 40 delayed three years by propulsion and torpedo discharge system s; accepted and commissioned 7-12-90 but sent immediately into a ten-month orrect problems. Unit cost is between £ 150–200 million. S 41 began sea trials All four will be based at Devonport.

beron class

	Bldr	Laid down	L	In serv.
ACLE	Cammell Laird, Birkenhead	26-4-60	26-9-61	14-2-63
OSSUM	Cammell Laird, Birkenhead	21-12-61	23-5-63	5-6-64
PORTUNE	Scotts SB, Greenock	26-10-62	14-2-64	29-12-64

(S 13)—since retired — Ben Sullivan, 7-91

tune (S 20) — Ben Sullivan, 5-91

,650 tons std./2,080 tons surf./2,450 tons sub.
.5 kts (surf.)/15 kts (sub.)
89.92 (87.45 pp) × 8.07 × 5.48
/533-mm TT fwd (14 Mk 24 Mod. 2 Tigerfish torpedoes, mines)
tron Equipt:
dar: 1/1006(1) surf. search—EW: UAH and UAL intercept suite
nar: Type 2051 (Triton) bow active/passive array, Type 2007 passive flank array, Type 2046 "clip-on" towed passive array
/1,840-hp Admiralty Standard Range 16VVS-AS21 diesels, lectric drive; 2 props; 6,000 shp
urance: 56 days **Range:** 9,000/12 (surf.); 11,000/8 (snorkel)
: 298 m³ (446 m³ emergency) **Crew:** 6 officers, 62 enlisted

ks: Conventional propulsion and hull form. Streamlined sail. Maximum depth: ers. Air-conditioned. Batteries with 448 total cells provide 5,300 amp/hr. at e; 7,420 amp/hr. at 5-hr. rate. Pressure hull 73.45 m long by 5.41-m diameter. after torpedo tubes, intended for Mk 23 short ASW torpedoes, are no longer ne first *Onyx* transferred to Canada (1-64) and was renamed the *Ojibwa; Onyx* was built. Canada ordered three ships of this class, Australia six, Chile l Brazil three.
our remaining units have been modernized with new sonar suites and the i-Gresham Lion Dual Guidance System (to permit firing two Mk 24 torpedoes ; S 20 was the last to complete, recommissioning 22-6-90.
Olympus (S 12) sold as a static dockside trainer to Canada, 27-7-89. *Oberon* (S ken 10-12-86 and sold 2-87 to Seaforth Group for foreign sale but was scrapped *Orpheus* (S 11) stricken 6-87. *Sealion* (S 07) stricken 12-87; *Odin* (S 10) paid off and stricken 12-90; *Onslaught* paid off 6-90, stricken 12-90, and towed to for scrap 5-10-91; *Otter* (S 15) stricken 31-7-91; *Ocelot* (S 17) stricken 6-9-91; *Otus* (S 18) paid off 5-4-91; *Onyx* (S 21) stricken 14-12-90 and towed 14-11-91 to Birkenhead as a museum exhibit; and *Osiris* (S 13) stricken 31-5-92. The surviving three will be stricken during 1993.

GUIDED-MISSILE DESTROYERS

◆ 0 (+ 12) Type 84

Note: The first pair of a new class intended to replace the Type 42 class is to be ordered in 1995 for delivery in 1999; the names will reportedly be *Emerald* and *Eclipse*. Two ships per year would be ordered thereafter, for a total of twelve. Characteristics have yet to be determined, and an attempt is being made in cooperation with France to design a ship acceptable to both navies, in a venture announced 12-3-91. France, however, needs only four new antiaircraft ships and desires to keep them at under 3,500 tons, while the Royal Navy sees a larger vessel of 7,200 tons or more as being best suited to its needs. The weapons suite contemplated would include two 48-cell groupings of the French Aster 30 medium-range SAM, two 24-cell groupings of the vertical-launch Sea Wolf SAM, a medium-caliber gun, Goalkeeper CIWS, and helicopters. The sonar suite would include the Type 2080 integrated suite being developed with France.

◆ 4 Manchester class (Type 42C)

	Bldr	Laid down	L	In serv.
D 95 MANCHESTER	Vickers (SB) Ltd., Barrow-in-Furness	19-5-79	24-11-80	16-12-82
D 96 GLOUCESTER	Vosper Thornycroft, Southampton	26-10-79	2-11-82	11-9-85
D 97 EDINBURGH	Cammell Laird, Birkenhead	8-9-80	14-4-83	18-12-85
D 98 YORK	Swan Hunter, Wallsend-on-Tyne	18-1-80	21-6-82	9-8-85

D: 3,880 tons (4,775 fl) **S:** 29.5 kts (18 cruising)
Dim: 141.12 (132.3 wl) × 14.90 × 5.80 (4.20 hull)
A: 1/Sea Dart GWS.30 SAM syst. (II × 1, 22 missiles)—1/114-mm 55-cal. Mk 8 DP—D: 97 only: 4/30-mm BMARC GCM-A02AA (II × 2)—2/20-mm (D 97: 1) Mk 15 gatling CIWS (I × 1 or 2)—2/20-mm GAM-B01 AA (I × 2)—2/20-mm Oerlikon Mk 7A AA(I × 2)—6/324-mm STWS.1 or 3 ASW TT (III × 2)—1/Sea Lynx helicopter (with Sea Skua missiles, Mk 46 or Stingray torpedoes)
Electron Equipt:
Radar: 1/Type 1006 nav., 1/Type 992Q (D 95: Type 996) surf./air search, 1/Type 1022 early warning, 2/Type 909 f.c. (D 95: Type 909(1))
Sonar: Type 2016 (D 95: Type 2050) hull-mounted, Type 162M bottomed-target classification, Type 185 underwater telephone
EW: UAA-2 (D 98: UAA-1) intercept, 2/Type 670 (D 97: 675) jammer, 4/DLA decoy RL (VI × 4), 2/DEC laser-dazzler, Type 182 towed torpedo decoy
M: COGOG: 2 Rolls-Royce Olympus TM3B gas turbines of 27,200 shp each for boost, 2 Rolls-Royce Tyne RM1C of 5,340 shp each for cruise; 2/5-bladed CP props; 54,400/10,680 shp
Electron Equipt: 4,000 kw (4/1,000-kw diesel sets)
Range: 4,750/18 **Fuel:** 610 tons
Crew: 26 officers, 81 senior petty officers, 194 other enlisted

Edinburgh (D 97)—with Mk 15 CIWS forward — Dr. Giorgio Arra, 9-91

Gloucester (D 96) — Maritime Photographic, 6-92

GUIDED-MISSILE DESTROYERS *(continued)*

York (D 98) Maritime Photographi

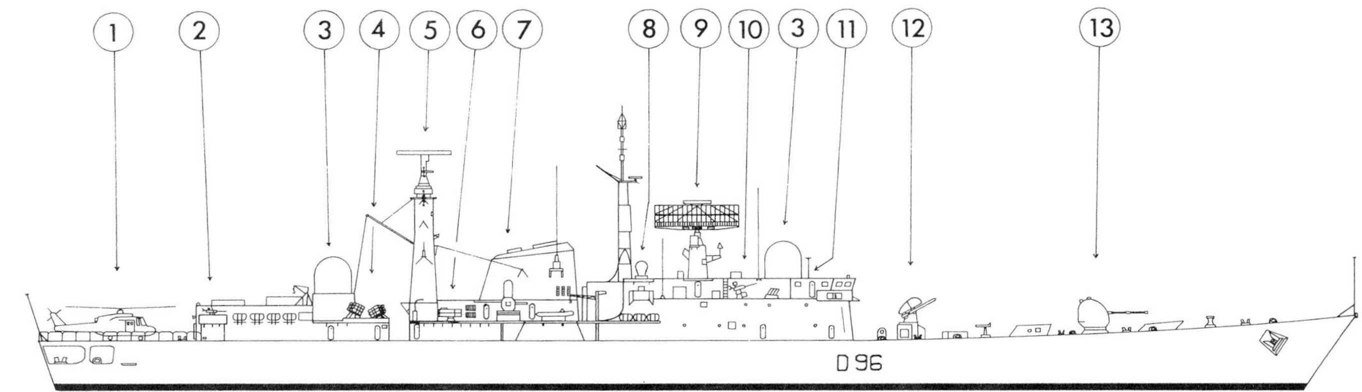

Gloucester (D 96) 1. Sea Lynx HAS.3 helicopter 2. 20-mm AA Mk 7A 3. Type 909 radar directors 4. decoy RL 5. Type 992Q radar 6. STWS.2 triple ASW TT 7. Mk 15 Phalanx CIWS 8. SCOT SATCOMM antenna radomes 9. Type 1022 early-warning radar 10. 20-mm GAM-B01 AA 11. Mk 137 decoy RL 12. Sea Dart SAM launcher 13. 114-mm Mk 8 DP Robert Dumas

Remarks: A lengthened version of the *Sheffield* class intended to provide better seaworthiness, endurance, and habitability, but having no change in armament despite the additional 16-m overall length. D 95 ordered 10-11-78, D 96 on 27-3-79, and D 97 and D 104 on 25-4-79. Completion of D 97 delayed by strike at yard. D 96 delivered 16-5-85. D 96 shot down an Iraqi-launched Silkworm antiship missile with a Sea Dart on 25-2-91 in the northern Persian Gulf.

Received hull-strengthening strakes amidships due to weight growth and cracking. There are two pair of fin stabilizers. The ADAWS 7 combat data system carried is being upgraded to ADAWS 8. Have LINK 11 data-link system. Several 7.62-mm mg are carried, including one on each bridge wing. Active EW jammers flank the Type 1022 radar's pylon. D 96 and later have a larger command center. All to receive the CCA ("Captain's Combat Aid") computerized decision-making system.

All will receive three long refits during planned 22-year service. All are to have Type 992Q radar replaced by Type 996, Type 2016 or Type 184 sonar replaced by Type 2050, and STWS.2 torpedo tubes replaced by STWS.3 to accommodate Stingray torpedoes; D 95 began one-year modernization/refit 11-91, and D 96 will follow.

Plans to reconfigure close-defense AA suite to include two lightweight Sea Wolf SAM launchers, with one Type 911 tracker (GWS.26 Mod. 2) plus one Mk 15 CIWS, have been canceled; D 97 received partial installation in 10-90, with single 20-mm Mk 15 CIWS forward and bulwarks added at bow, leaving the weapons platforms abreast the stack for the planned Sea Wolf installation (they are occupied by the twin 30-mm mounts); she will be restored to class standard.

♦ 8 Sheffield class (Type 42A/B)

Type 42A:

	Bldr	Laid down	L	In serv.
D 86 Birmingham	Cammell Laird, Birkenhead	28-3-72	30-7-73	3-12-76
D 87 Newcastle	Swan Hunter, Wallsend-on-Tyne	21-2-73	24-4-75	23-3-78
D 88 Glasgow	Swan Hunter, Wallsend-on-Tyne	7-3-74	14-4-76	24-5-79
D 108 Cardiff	Vickers (SB), Ltd., Barrow-in-Furness	3-11-72	22-2-74	24-9-79
Type 42B:				
D 89 Exeter	Swan Hunter, Wallsend-on-Tyne	22-7-76	25-4-78	19-9-80
D 90 Southampton	Vosper Thornycroft, Southampton	21-10-76	29-1-79	
D 91 Nottingham	Vosper Thornycroft, Southampton	6-2-78	12-2-80	
D 92 Liverpool	Cammell Laird, Birkenhead	5-7-78	25-9-80	

Southamptom (D 90)—after repair and modernization Maritime Photographi

Newcastle (D 87)—with radomes temporarily removed from Type radar directors Leo Van Gindere

UIDED-MISSILE DESTROYERS *(continued)*

eter (D 89) Leo Van Ginderen, 5-92

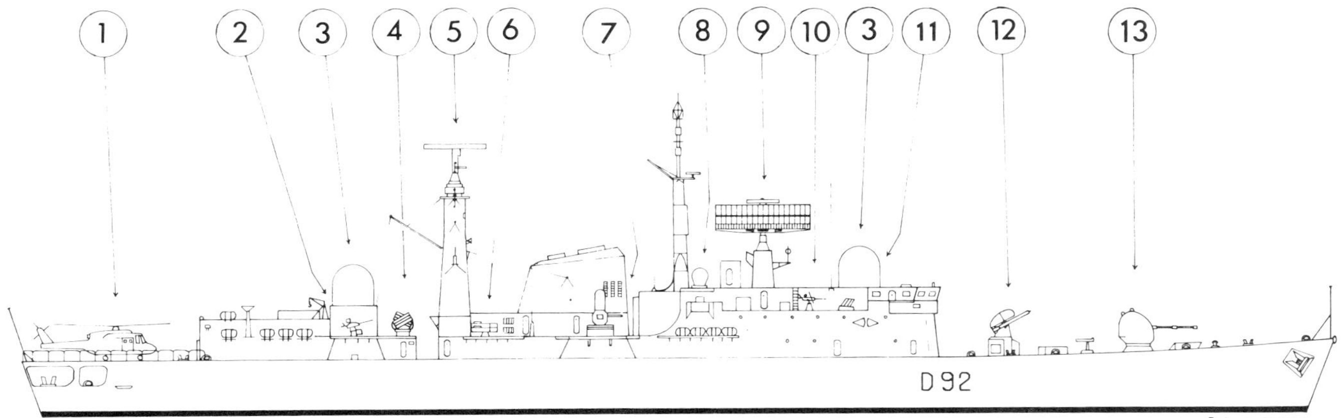

Liverpool (D 92) 1. Sea Lynx HAS.3 helicopter 2. 20-mm GAM-B01 AA 3. Type 909 radar director 4. DLC Corvus decoy RL 5. Type 996 3-D radar 6. STWS.2 triple ASW TT 7. Mk 15 Phalanx CIWS 8. SCOT SATCOMM system radome 9. Type 1022 early-warning radar 10. 20-mm Mk 7A AA 11. DLD decoy RL 12. Sea Dart SAM launcher 13. 114-mm Mk 8 DP gun Robert Dumas

diff (D 108)—with radomes temporarily removed from Type 909 ar directors Maritime Photographic, 11-91

ingham (D 86) Leo Van Ginderen, 9-91

3,560 tons (4,250 fl, after refits) **S:** 28 kts (18 cruising)
m: 125.0 (119.5 pp) × 14.34 × 5.9 (4.3 hull)
1/Sea Dart GWS.30 Mod. 2 SAM syst. (II × 1, 22 missiles)—1/114-mm 55-cal. Mk 8 DP—2/20-mm Mk 15 CIWS—2 (D 86, D 91: 4)/20-mm BMARC GAM-B01 AA (I × 2 or 4)—2 (D 86, D 91: none)/20-mm Oerlikon Mk 7A AA (I × 2)—6/324-mm STWS.2 or 3 ASW TT (III × 2, Mk 44 or Stingray torpedoes)—1/Sea Lynx helicopter (Sea Skua missiles and Mk 46 or Stingray torpedoes)

Electron Equipt:
Radar: 1/Type 1006 nav., 1/Type 996 3-D surf./air search (D 86: Type 992Q 2-D vice 996), 1/Type 1022 early warning, 2/Type 909(1) f.c.
Sonar: Type 2016 (D89–92: Type 2050) hull-mounted, Type 162M bottomed-target classification, Type 185 underwater telephone
EW: UAA-2 intercept, 2/Type 670 or 675 jammer, 2/DLC Corvus decoy RL (VIII × 2), 2/DLD decoy RL (VI × 2), 2/DEC laser-dazzlers, Type 182 towed torpedo decoy

M: COGOG; 2 Rolls-Royce Olympus TM3B gas turbines, 27,200 shp each for high speed; 2 Rolls-Royce Tyne RM1A gas turbines, 4,100 shp each for cruising; 2/5-bladed CP props (D 89 and later: Tyne RM1C, 5,340 shp each)
Electric: 4,000 kw (4/1,000-kw diesel sets) **Range:** 650/30; 4,500/18
Crew: 26 officers, 273 enlisted maximum (normal 250–280 tot.)

Remarks: *Cardiff,* delayed by labor problems, was completed by Swan Hunter. Completion of *Glasgow* delayed by fire 9-76. All can carry SCOT radomes for Skynet SHF satellite communications system. Very cramped ships. Helicopter used for surveillance and attack (Sea Skua missiles) as well as ASW. Have "Agouti" bubble ejector system for propellers (which rotate inwardly) to reduce cavitation noise. Two pair fin stabilizers fitted. Type 965M was replaced by 1022 in four early ships, beginning with D 108 and D 87 in 1984. Those same ships are updated with the ADAWS 7 data system and stack water-spray equipment to reduce IR signature. In 1987 it was announced that this class would be given three lifetime refits, guaranteeing 22-year retention; the Sea Dart system is to be improved. Have NATO Link 10, 11 , and 14 data-links.

Class prototype, *Sheffield* (D 80), foundered 10-5-82, having been hit by an Argentine AM 39 Exocet missile on 4-5-82. *Coventry* (D 118) was lost to bombs on 25-5-82. This class was found to be deficient in damage-control during the Falklands War and also to be limited in sensor capability and self-defense, although the Sea Dart system functioned effectively.

By 1989, all had received U.S. Mk 15 CIWS amidships on the platforms used earlier for BMARC twin 30-mm GCM-AO2 mounts. During refits, Type 996 radar is replacing Type 992Q, UAA-2 intercept equipment is replacing UAA-1, Type 675 jammers are replacing Type 670, U.S. Hycor Mk 137 decoy launchers (DLD) are replacing Corvus launchers (DLC), and a second fire-control station is being added to the Sea Dart system. The modernizations increase draft by .3 m and displacement by perhaps 100 tons. D 86 completed 78-week refit in 9-87; D 88 completed long refit 4-89, D 89 began 78-week refit in 10-88; D 92 completed long refit in 9-88; and D 108 was in refit during

GUIDED-MISSILE DESTROYERS *(continued)*

1989. Updates to their ADAWS 7 combat data systems receive Ferranti F2420 computers. All to receive the CCA ("Captain's Combat Aid") computerized decision-making system.

D 89–92 are receiving Type 2050 hull-mounted sonars during refits; the earlier D 86–88 and D 108 have had Type 2016 installed in place of their original Type 184P sets.

D 90 was hit by merchant vessel Tor Bay in the Persian Gulf on 4-9-88 and severely damaged; returned to the U.K. on dockship Mighty Servant I in 12-88, the destroyer was repaired and modernized at Swan Hunter, Wallsend, from 9-89 to 15-5-92. A new magazine and Sea Dart launcher were installed.

Note: The single Type 82 guided-missile destroyer *Bristol* (D 23) was stricken 27-6-91 after only 18 years' service; it had been hoped to convert her as a static training platform and accommodations ship to replace *Kent* (D 12), but that has not occurred.

FRIGATES

◆ **4 (+ 14) "Duke" (Type 23)-class general-purpose** Bldr: Yarrow (Shipbuilders), Ltd., Glasgow (except F 233, F 237–239: Swan Hunter Ltd., Wallsend-on-Tyne)

	Laid down	L	In serv.
F 230 NORFOLK	14-12-85	10-7-87	1-6-90
F 231 ARGYLL	20-3-87	8-4-89	30-5-91
F 229 LANCASTER	18-12-87	24-5-90	1-5-92
F 233 MARLBOROUGH	22-10-87	21-1-89	14-6-91
F 234 IRON DUKE	12-12-88	28-3-91	3-93
F 235 MONMOUTH	1-6-89	13-11-91	4-94
F 236 MONTROSE	1-11-89	1992	1994
F 237 WESTMINSTER	18-1-91	4-2-92	1994
F 238 NORTHUMBERLAND	4-4-91	4-4-92	1995
F 239 RICHMOND	11-2-92	1993	1995
F 240 SOMERSET	. . .	. . .	. . .
F 241 GRAFTON	. . .	. . .	. . .
F 242 SUTHERLAND	. . .	. . .	. . .
F 243	. . .	. . .	. . .
F 244	. . .	. . .	. . .
F 245	. . .	. . .	. . .
F 246	. . .	. . .	. . .
F 247	. . .	. . .	. . .

Marlborough (F 233) Leo Van Ginderen, 3-92

Argyll (F 231)—showing towed array bullnose at stern Maritime Photographic, 5

Norfolk (F 230) Maritime Photographic, (

D: 3,500 tons (4,200 fl) **S:** 28 kts (15 kts electric drive)
Dim: 133.0 (123.0 pp) × 16.1 (15.0 wl) × 4.3 (5.5 max. navigational)
A: 8/Harpoon SSM (IV × 2)—1/Sea Wolf GWS.26 vertical-launch group (32 missiles)—1/114-mm 55-cal. Vickers Mk 8 DP—2/30-m DS-30B AA (I × 2)—4/324-mm TT (II × 2, fixed)—1/Sea Lynx helicopter (Sea Skua missiles, Mk 46 or Stingray ASW torpedoes)
Electron Equipt:
Radar: 1/Type 1007 nav., 1/Type 996(1) 3-D surf./air search, 2/Ty 911 f.c.
Sonar: Type 2050NE bow-mounted, Type 2031(Z) towed linear passive array
EW: UAF-1 (Racal Cutlass) intercept, 2/Type 675 jammers, 4/DL Sea Gnat chaff RL (VI × 4), 2/DEC laser-dazzler, Type 182 towed torpedo decoy
M: CODLAG (Combined Diesel-Electric and Gas turbine): F 229–2 2 Rolls-Royce SM1A Spey gas turbines (18,770 shp each; 17,000 sust.), F 237 and later: 2 Rolls Royce SM1C Spey (26,150 shp each); all: 4 Paxman Valenta 12 RPA 200CZ diesel generator sets (5,200 kw total); 2/2,000-shp electric cruise moto 2 props; F 229–236: 41,540 shp max.; F 237–on: 52,300 shp max
Range: 7,800/17 **Fuel:** 800 tons
Electric: 1,890 kw—*see* Remarks
Crew: 12 officers, 157 enlisted (accommodations for 16 officers, 169 enlisted)

Remarks: Intended as lineal replacements for the remaining *Leander*-class fri Prototype design assigned to Yarrow. First unit ordered 29-10-84; letter of inte second signed 28-1-85, but second through fourth ordered 15-7-86. F 234–236 or 11-7-88; F 237–239 ordered 19-12-89; F 240 through F 242 orderd 23-1-92. Plan to three more early in 1993 and two in 1994 to complete class. *Norfolk* was origina

Lancaster (F 229) Maritime Photographic

RIGATES *(continued)*

.ve been named *Daring*. F 229 originally given pendant F 232; changed because a .orm 232" is used to report a collision or grounding! Aside from minor equipment .provements, all 18 ships are to be similarly equipped; the more powerful engines in 237 onward will probably provide 1–2 knots additional speed.

Flush-decked hull, with large helicopter hangar, helo in-haul system, fin stabilizers. .sign grew considerably as a result of Falklands "Lessons-Learned." Have first bow-.unted sonars in the Royal Navy. Have Marconi ICS4 integrated communications .stem, with U.S. URC-109 components. There is a GSA-8/GPEOD Sea Archer .tronic/IR director mounted on the mast for the 114-mm gun.

The propulsion system permits running the shaft-concentric electric propulsion mo-.s with the power from any combination of the four 1,300-kw ship's service genera-.s; power from both the gas turbines and the electric motors can be obtained; ship's-.vice power is derived from two 945-kw converter sets, and there is also a 250-kw .sel emergency generator powered by a Perkins CV 250GTCA diesel. Fixed-pitch .ps, with astern power available only by electric drive. Numerous improvements in .mage control, as a result of Falklands War lessons. The sterns have had to be .engthened to permit towing the Type 2031(Z) array; Type 2057 will replace Type 31(Z) when available.

The planned Ferranti CACS 4 combat data/control system for these ships was .celed in 7-87; its replacement, the Dowty-Sema-Racal SSCS (Surface Ship Control .stem), with parallel processing, modular software, and LINK 11 and 14 compatibil-., was not ordered until 10-8-89. In consequence, it may not be until the eighth unit .t a ship is delivered with an installed combat control system—severely handicap-.g the earlier ships for combat until they can be back-fitted. There is no provision for IWS. F 237 and later will have UAT vice UAF-1 EW equipment. The Merlin HAS.1 .icopter will replace HAS.3 Sea Lynx during the later 1990s.

. 233 ran trials 1992 with the Data-Fusion Technology Demonstrator (TDS), em-.ying five Microvax 3800 and five Sigmax 6264 computers.

4 Cornwall-class (Type 22 Batch 3) general-purpose

	Bldr	Laid down	L	In serv.
.9 CORNWALL	Yarrow (Shipbuilders), Scotstoun, Glasgow	12-9-83	14-10-85	23-4-88
.5 CUMBERLAND	Yarrow (Shipbuilders) Scotstoun, Glasgow	12-10-84	21-6-86	10-6-89
6 CAMPBELTOWN	Cammell Laird, Birkenhead	4-12-85	7-10-87	27-5-89
7 CHATHAM	Swan Hunter, Wallsend-on-Tyne	12-5-86	20-1-88	4-5-90

: 4,280 tons (4,850 fl) **S:** 30 kts (18 kts on Tyne gas turbines)
im: 148.10 (135.65 pp) × 14.75 × 5.35 hull (6.00 max.)
: 8/Harpoon SSM (IV × 2)—2/Sea Wolf GWS.25 Mod. 3 SAM systems (VI × 2)—1/114-mm 55-cal. Vickers Mk 8 DP—1/30-mm Goalkeeper CIWS—2/30-mm DS-30B AA (I × 2)—6/324-mm STWS.2 ASW TT (III × 2)—2/Sea Lynx helicopters (Sea Skua ASM, Stingray ASW torpedoes), or 1/Sea King helicopter
ectron Equipt:
Radar: 1/1006 nav., 1/967M-968 surf./air search, 2/911 f.c., 1/Goalkeeper f.c.
Sonar: Type 2050 (F 99: 2016) hull-mounted, Type 2031(Z) towed linear passive array
EW: UAA-2 intercept, 2/675(2) jammer, 4/DLA Sea Gnat decoy RL (VI × 4), 2/DEC laser-dazzler, Type 182 towed torpedo decoy
: COGAG: 2 Rolls-Royce Spey SM.1A DR gas turbines (18,770 shp each) *and* 2 Rolls-Royce Tyne RM.1C gas turbines (5,340 shp each); 2 Stone Manganese CP props; 48,220 shp max.
ectric: 4,000 kw (4/Paxman Valenta 12PA 200CZ diesel sets)
nge: 7,000/18 (on Tyne gas turbines); 12,000/14 (one shaft)
.**el:** 700 tons, plus 80 tons aviation fuel
ew: 13 officers, 62 petty officers, 157 other enlisted (as flagships: 21 officers, 65 petty officers, 159 other enlisted)

Cumberland (F 85) Maritime Photographic, 7-91

Chatham (F 87) Ben Sullivan, 5-91

Cornwall (F 99) Bernard Prézelin, 5-90

Remarks: Third series in the Type 22/*Broadsword*-class design, with same basic hull as Batch 2/*Boxer* class, but with a 114-mm gun on the forecastle, the antiship missile launchers moved abaft the pilothouse and oriented athwartships. The first pair were ordered 14-12-82 and the third and fourth on 28-1-85. Launch of F 99 delayed from 3-6-85 by strikes. The quartet forms the 8th Frigate Squadron.

Have two EASAMS Sea Archer GSA-8/GPEOD (Gun System Automation 8/General-Purpose Electro-Optical Director)t.v./IR/laser back-up directors for the 114-mm gun. The Goalkeeper gatling AA gun mount has its own integral I-band search/tracker and I/K-band tracking radars. Maximum generator output is 5,200 kw. All have the CACS-5 Computer-Assisted Command System, with LINK 11 and 14 compatibility. Equipped with ICS(3) communications suite.

◆ 6 Boxer-class (Type 22 Batch 2) ASW frigates

Bldrs: F 92–95: Yarrow (Shipbuilders) Ltd., Scotstoun, Glasgow; F 96,97: Swan Hunter (Shipbuilders) Ltd., Wallsend-on-Tyne

	Ordered	Laid down	L	In serv.
F 92 BOXER	25-4-79	5-11-79	17-6-81	14-1-84
F 93 BEAVER	25-4-79	20-6-80	8-5-82	13-12-84
F 94 BRAVE	27-8-81	24-5-82	19-11-83	4-7-86
F 95 LONDON	23-2-82	7-2-83	27-10-84	5-6-87
F 96 SHEFFIELD	14-12-82	29-3-84	26-3-86	26-7-88
F 98 COVENTRY	14-12-82	29-3-84	8-4-86	24-10-88

.pbeltown (F 86) Leo Van Ginderen, 7-91

FRIGATES *(continued)*

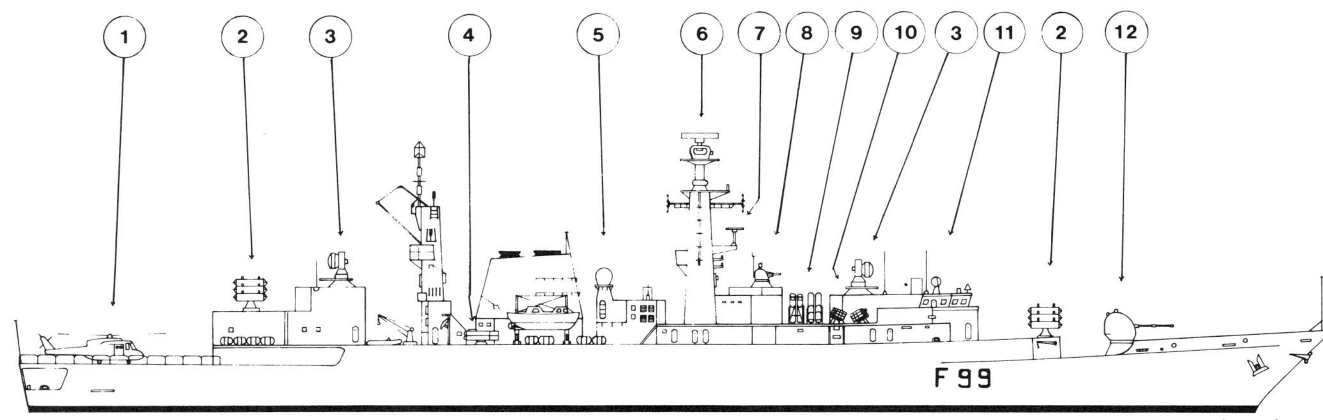

Cornwall (F 99)—Type 22 Batch 3 1. Sea Lynx HAS.3 helicopter 2. Sea Wolf SAM launchers 3. Type 911 radar directors 4. STWS.2 triple ASW TT 5. SCOT SATCOMM system radomes 6. Type 967/968 radar antennas 7. Type 1006 radar 8. Goalkeeper 30-mm CIWS 9. Harpoon SSM 10. DLA decoy RL 11. 114-mm Vickers Mk 8 DP gun Robert Dumas

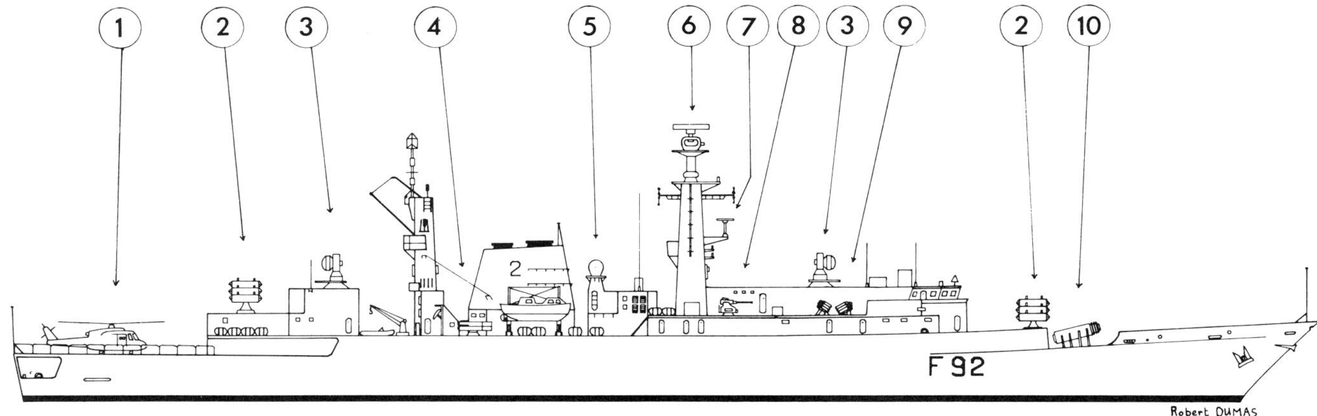

Boxer (F 92)—Type 22 Batch 2 1. Sea Lynx HAS.3 2. Sea Wolf SAM launchers 3. Type 910 radar directors 4. STWS.2 triple ASW TT 5. SCOT SATCOMM system radomes 6. Type 967/968 radar antennas 7. Type 1006 navigational radar 8. 30-mm DS-30B AA 9. decoy RL 10. MM 38 Exocet SSM

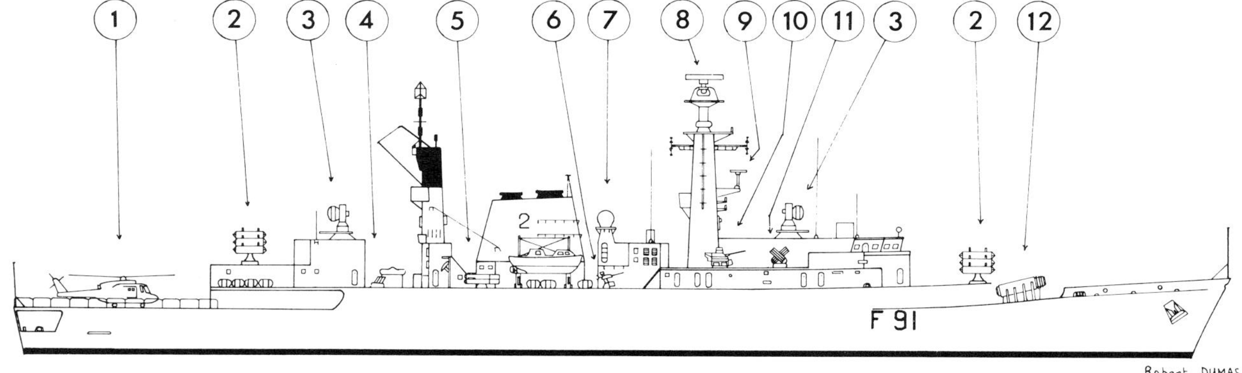

Brazen (F 91)—Type 22 Batch 1 1. Sea Lynx HAS.1 2. Sea Wolf SAM launchers 3. Type 910 radar directors 4. Mk 137 decoy RL 5. STWS.1 triple ASW TT 6. 20-mm AA (now removed) 7. SCOT SHF SATCOMM system radome 8. Type 967/968 radar 9. Type 1006 navigational radar 10. twin 30-mm GCM-AO2 AA 11. decoy RL 12. MM 38 Exocet SSM Robert Dumas

Sheffield (F 96) Ben Sullivan, 7-91

London (F 95) Dr. Giorgio Arr

ATES *(continued)*

e (F 94) James W. Goss/NAVPIC, 9-90

ntry (F 98)—with Type 911 radar directors Leo Van Ginderen, 6-90

er (F 93)—with Type 910 radar directors Leo Van Ginderen, 6-90

don (F 95) Leo Van Ginderen, 6-91

4,250 tons (4,850 fl) **S:** 30 kts (F 94: 28 kts)—18 kts on cruise engines

m: 145.00 (F 94–97: 148.10) (140.0 pp) × 14.75 × 4.3 hull (6.0 max.)

4/MM 38 Exocet SSM (I × 4)—2/Sea Wolf GWS.25 Mod. 0 SAM syst. (F 94–97: Mod. 3) (VI × 2)—4/30-mm BMARC GCM-A01 AA (II × 2)—6/324-mm STWS.1 ASW TT (III × 2)—2/Sea Lynx helicopters (Sea Skua ASM, Stingray torpedoes) (F 94, 95: 1/Sea King HAS.5 helicopter)—*see* Remarks

ectron Equipt:

Radar: 1/Type1006 nav., 1/Type 967M-968 surf./air search, 2/Type 910 (F 94–97: 2/911) f.c.

Sonar: Type 2016(F 92: Type 2050) hull-mounted, Type 2031(Z) towed linear passive array

EW: UAA-2 intercept, 2/675 jammers, 4/DLA decoy RL (VI × 4), 2/DEC laser-dazzler, Type 182 towed torpedo countermeasure

M: F 92, F 93: COGOG: 2 Rolls-Royce Olympus TM.3B gas turbines (27,300 shp each), *or* 2 Rolls-Royce Tyne RM.1C gas turbines (5,340 shp each); 2 Stone Manganese CP props; 54,600 shp max. F 95–F 97: COGAG: 2 Rolls-Royce Spey SM.1A gas turbines (18,770 shp each), *or* 2 Rolls-Royce Tyne RM.1C max. gas turbines (5,340 shp each); 2 CP props; 48,220 shp max. (F 94 same plant, but COGOG: 37,540 shp max.)

Electric: 4,000 kw (4 Paxman Valenta 12PA 200CZ diesel-driven sets)

Range: 7,000/18; 12,000/14 (one shaft)

Fuel: 700 tons, +80 tons aviation fuel

Crew: 19 officers, 246 enlisted (accommodations for 320 total)

Remarks: "Batch 2" employs a lengthened hull over the *Broadsword* class to improve seaworthiness, endurance, and habitability and to provide space for handling the Type 2031 towed linear passive hydrophone array. Names *Bloodhound, Boadicea,* and *Bruiser* originally selected for the final three; last two were ordered as replacements for Type 42 destroyers lost during the Falklands War. Constitute the 1st Frigate Squadron.

All having Type 2016 hull-mounted sonar replaced by Type 2050 during first major refits. Two 30-mm DS-30B AA will replace the twin GCM-A02 AA, where installed.

Have CACS 1 data system, with 26 operators and 16 displays. F 94 is first with lightweight Marconi 805-SW (Type 911) missile directors, but the CACS 1 action data system, which has been plagued with developmental delays, was not installed at time of commissioning. F 94's hull has greater flare at the stern to permit a larger helicopter deck for the Merlin helicopter, producing an overall length of 146.5 m; the hangar is also higher. F 94–98 have the higher hangar, but only F 94 and F 95 carry Sea Kings vice Sea Lynx. Water-displacement fuel tanks are used, and the ships are said to have twice the range of the "Batch 1" *Broadsword* class. During 1990, F 96 had a temporary deckhouse mounted just abaft the forward Type 911 radar director.

Two auxiliary boilers and two 50-ton/day flash evaporators are installed. F 94 received improved Spey SM1C engines during a 1989 refit, increasing available power, but remains unique in not being able to gear all four main engines to the shafts. All planned to receive three major refits during 22-year lifetimes.

♦ 4 Broadsword (Type 22)-class ASW frigates

Bldr: Yarrow (Shipbuilders) Ltd., Scotstoun, Glasgow

	Ordered	Laid down	L	In serv.
F 88 Broadsword	8-2-74	7-2-75	12-5-76	3-5-79
F 89 Battleaxe	4-9-75	4-2-76	18-5-77	28-3-80
F 90 Brilliant	7-9-76	24-3-77	15-12-78	10-4-81
F 91 Brazen (ex-*Boxer*)	21-10-77	19-8-78	4-3-80	2-7-82

Brazen (F 91) Maritime Photographic, 10-91

Battleaxe (F 89)—note lack of towed array fittings Ben Sullivan, 4-91

FRIGATES *(continued)*

Broadsword (F 88) Dr. Giorgio Arra, 3-91

Brilliant (F 90) Leo Van Ginderen, 1990

D: 3,900 tons (4,400 fl) **S:** 29 kts (18 cruise)
Dim: 131.2 (125.0 wl) × 14.8 × 4.3 (6.0 sonar)
A: 4/MM 38 Exocet SSM—2/Sea Wolf GWS. 25 SAM syst. (VI × 2)—4/30-mm BMARC GCM-A02 AA (II × 2)—6/324-mm STWS.1 ASW TT (III × 2)—1 or 2/Sea Lynx helicopters (Sea Skua SSM, Mk 46 or Stingray torpedoes)
Electron Equipt:
Radar: 1/Type 1006 nav., 1/Type 967-968 surf./air search, 2/Type 911 f.c.
Sonar: Type 2016 (F 88, 90: Type 2050) hull-mounted, Type 185 underwater telephone
EW: UAA-1 intercept, 2/Type 670 jammer, 2 DLC decoy RL (VIII × 2), 2/DEC laser-dazzler, Type 182 towed torpedo decoy
M: COGOG: 2 Olympus TM3B gas turbines, 27,300 shp each for high speed; 2 Tyne RM1A, 4,100 shp each for cruising; 2 CP props; 54,600 shp max.
Electric: 4,000 kw (4 Paxman Ventura 12PA 200CZ diesel sets)
Range: 4,500/18 (on Tyne); 1,200/29 (on Olympus)
Crew: 17 officers, 222 enlisted

Remarks: Originally to have been a class of 26. These ships are too small to accommodate the towed passive sonar arrays deemed necessary to perform an ASW rôle adequately; at one point consideration was given to selling them during 1992–93, but they instead have been altered as "Initial Sea Training Ships" to replace the stricken destroyer *Bristol*, operating in support of the Dartmouth training establishment. Berthing and training facilities for 65 officer trainees per ship had been added in all but F 89 by 4-92, with F 89 to complete conversion later in 1992. All can still be employed as combatants, if needed. Constitute the 2nd Frigate Squadron.

Two Sea Lynx helicopters were to have been carried, but only one is normally aboard. CAAIS combat data system. The 967-968 radar is a back-to-back array with track-while-scan features. Original Type 910 Sea Wolf SAM directors replaced with Sea Wolf GWS.25 Mod. 3 system (Type 911 trackers) beginning in 1988 with F 88, got Type 2050 sonar in place of 2016. First two had higher, more elaborate stacks, now altered. F 90 ended long refit 6-9-88; F 89 began 42-week refit 10-10-88. F 89 has 4/Mk 137 chaff RL (Outfit DLD) in addition to standard Outfit DLC. The original two single 40-mm 60-cal. Mk 9 AA mounts have been replaced by twin 30-mm mounts in all four.

◆ **6 Amazon-class (Type 21) general-purpose**
F 169, 171: Vosper Thornycroft, Woolston; others: Yarrow (Shipbuilders) Ltd., Scotstoun, Glasgow, Scotland

	Laid down	L	In serv.
F 169 Amazon	6-11-69	26-4-71	11-5-74
F 171 Active	23-7-71	23-11-72	17-6-77
F 172 Ambuscade	1-9-71	18-1-73	5-9-75
F 173 Arrow	28-9-72	5-2-74	29-7-76
F 174 Alacrity	5-3-73	18-9-74	2-4-77
F 185 Avenger	30-10-74	20-11-75	15-4-78

D: 2,860 tons (3,360 fl) **S:** 32 kts
Dim: 117.04 (109.70 pp) × 12.7 × 4.6 (6.2 over sonar)
A: 4/MM 38 Exocet SSM—1/Sea Cat GWS.24 SAM syst. (IV × 1)—1/114-mm 55-cal. Vickers Mk 8 DP—4/20-mm Mk 7A AA (I × 4)—F 171, 174, 184 only: 6/324-mm STWS.1 ASW TT (III × 2)—1/Sea Lynx helicopter (Sea Skua missiles, Mk 46 or Stingray torpedoes)

Electron Equipt:
Radar: 1/Type 1006 nav., 1/Type 992Q surf./air search, 2/Type 9 (RTN-10X Orion) f.c.
Sonar: Type 184P hull-mounted, Type 162M bottomed-target classification, Type 185 underwater telephone
EW: UAA-1 intercept, FH-12 HF/DF; F 173, 185 only: 2/670 jammer, 2/DLC decoy RL (VIII × 2), Type 182 towed torped decoy
M: COGOG; 2 Olympus TM.3B gas turbines, 25,000 shp each; 2 Ty RM.1A gas turbines, 4,250 shp each; 2 CP props; 50,000 shp ma
Electric: 3,000 kw **Range:** 4,500/18; 1,200/30
Endurance: 60 days **Crew:** 13 officers, 164 enlisted

Amazon (F 169)—without torpedo tubes Peter Voss

Active (F 171)—with ASW TT Maritime Photographic

Alacrity (F 174)—with ASW TT Dr. Giorgio Arra,

Arrow (F 173)—without ASW TT Maritime Photographic

ATES (continued)

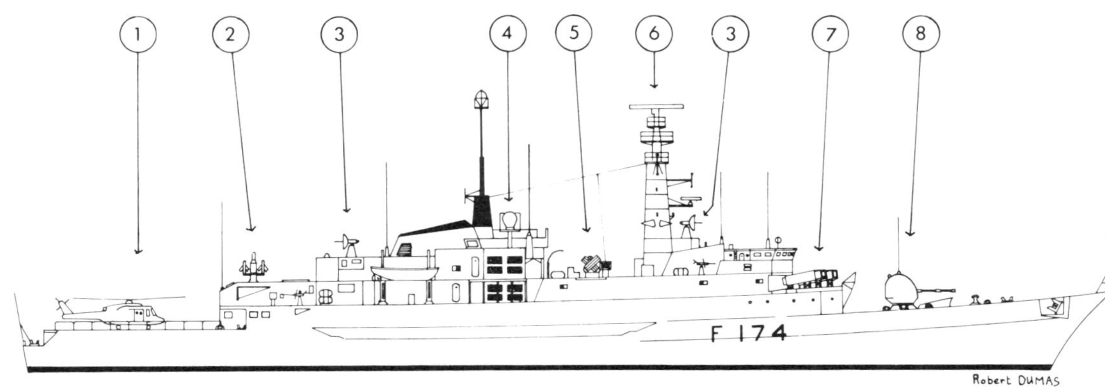

Alacrity (F 174) 1. Sea Lynx HAS.1 helo 2. Sea Cat SAM launcher 3. Type 912 (RTN-10X) radar director 4. SCOT SHF SATCOMM system antenna radome 5. DLC Corvus decoy RL 6. Type 992Q radar 7. MM 38 Exocet SSM launchers 8. 114-mm Vickers Mk 8 gun Robert Dumas

rks: Designed jointly by Vosper Thornycroft and Yarrow under 27-2-68 con- The ships have been criticized for fragility, vulnerability, and for being over- and top-heavy; permanent ballast had to be added, but none can carry the full ally intended weapon and sensor suite. Hulls strengthened due to cracking the Falklands War; doubler plates added amidships, beginning with F 173, ted 6-83; modifications added 100+ tons to displacement. Constitute the 4th e Squadron, based at Devonport, with F 171 as flagship.

ote control of engine room from the bridge. Ferranti WSA.4 digital system used control, employing two Selenia RTN-10X radar directors (Type 912) for both Sea d the 114-mm gun; there is also a backup optical director for each. The CAAIS combat data system is a separate entity whose data are automatically transmit- WSA.4; both use a single FM-1600B computer. F 169, 172 did not receive Exocet 984–85. The Exocet launchers are paired, toed-in, and forward of the bridge. can carry two SCOT radomes for the Skynet SHF communications satellite . Four 750-kw diesel generator sets supply the 450-volt, 3-phase, 60-Hz electri- rent. A separate Cossor Type 1010 IFF interrogator is mounted below the Type Type 670 jammers being added, and by 1989, all finally had UAA-1 intercept The 20-mm mounts are now mounted amidships and at the forward end of the pter deck on most, except that ships equipped to mount torpedo tubes have the air of guns at the forward end of the helicopter flight deck.

ent (F 184) of this class was lost to multiple bomb and rocket hits 21-5-82, and *pe* (F 170) sank 24-5-82 after an unexploded bomb detonated, causing uncon- fires and eventual magazine explosions. F 185 employed 1988 in trials with ulically actuated movable stern trim tab to increase speed/endurance.

Leander class

nvenience in describing the numerous appearances and functional variations in ass, they have been divided into separate listings, in general order of construc- nd conversion. The training ship *Juno* (F 52) of this class is listed with the aries. The design is an improvement on the *Rothesay* class, of which four were ally to have been members. Have twin rudders and one pair of fin stabilizers, set ft of amidships. The "Broad-beamed Leanders" incorporated engineering plant vements and were the first to be fitted with Sea Cat missiles on completion, ships having had 2/40-mm AA (I × 2). All were intended to carry Type 199 le-depth sonars, but these were installed in only a few of the class.

Sea Wolf antiaircraft missile conversions:

	Bldr	Laid down	L	In serv.
ANDROMEDA	HM Dockyard, Portsmouth	25-5-66	24-5-67	2-12-68
SCYLLA	HM Dockyard, Devonport	17-5-67	8-8-68	12-2-70

2,680 tons (3,140 fl) **S:** 25 kts
n: 113.38 (109.73) × 13.12 × 4.60 (5.60 props)
4/MM 38 Exocet SSM (I × 4)—1/Sea Wolf GWS.25 SAM syst. (VI × 1; 20 missiles)—2/20-mm BMARC GAM-B01 AA (I × 2)—2/20-mm Oerlikon Mk 7A AA (I × 2)—6/324-mm STWS.1 ASW TT (III × 2)—1/Sea Lynx helicopter (Sea Skua ASM, Mk 46 and Stingray torpedoes)
ctron Equipt:
Radar: 1/Type 1006 nav., 1/Type 967-968 surf./air search, 1/Type 910 f.c.
Sonar: Type 2016 (F 71: Type 2050) hull-mounted, Type 162M bottomed-target classification, Type 185 underwater telephone
EW: UAA-1 intercept, 2/Type 670 jammer, 2/DLC decoy RL (VIII × 2), 2/DLF decoy buoy dispensers (VIII × 2), Type 182 towed torpedo decoy
2 sets White–English Electric geared steam turbines, 2/5-bladed props; 30,000 shp
ilers: 2 Babcock & Wilcox 3-drum; 38.7 kg/cm², 450° C
ectric: 2,500 kw **Range:** approx. 4,500/12 **Fuel:** 500 tons
ew: 19 officers, 241 enlisted

Scylla (F 71 Leo Van Ginderen, 11-91

Andromeda (F 57) Maritime Photographic, 7-92

Remarks: Conversions from "Broad-beam Leanders" to improve warfare capabilities in all areas. Conversions completed 4-81, 21-10-83, and 7-12-84, respectively. Sisters *Charybdis* (F 75) stricken 10-91, *Jupiter* (F 60) on 30-4-92, and *Hermione* (F 58) on 30-6-92, after less than ten years' service in their new guise. The surviving *Leander*-series frigates form the 7th Frigate Squadron, along with the training ship *Juno*.

Speeds reduced 2 kts by weight growth. A Sea Wolf manually loaded launcher, and four Exocet replaced twin 114-mm gun mount; hangar enlarged to take Lynx, Type 184-series sonar replaced by Type 2016. Limbo mortar and Type 965 radar deleted, Type 967-968 radar stepped atop new foremast, and Type 910 Sea Wolf director placed atop bridge. Have CAAIS DBA-5 combat data/control system. *Jupiter* began trials with Type 2050 hull-mounted sonar in 10-86, and it has since replaced Type 2016 in F 71 also.

Have received RASS radar reflectivity reduction treatment and also have two Wallops Barricade chaff RL atop hangar in addition to other EW gear listed.

♦ **2 "Exocet Leander" Batch 2TA conversions with towed arrays**

	Bldr	Laid down	L	In serv.
F 40 SIRIUS	HMDY, Portsmouth	9-8-63	22-9-64	15-6-66
F 56 ARGONAUT	Hawthorne Leslie, Hebburn-on-Tyne	27-11-64	8-2-66	17-8-67

D: 2,750 tons (3,300 fl) **S:** 28 kts
Dim: 113.38 (109.73 pp) × 12.50 × 5.00 (6.40 props)—*see* Remarks
A: 4/MM 38 Exocet SSM (I × 4)—2 Sea Cat GWS.22 SAM syst. (IV × 2)—2/20-mm Oerlikon Mk 7A AA (I × 2)—6/324-mm STWS.1 ASW TT (III × 2)—1/Sea Lynx helicopter (Sea Skua ASM, Mk 46 and Stingray torpedoes)
Electron Equipt:
Radar: 1/Type 1006 nav., 1/Type 994 surf./air search, 1/Type 904 f.c.

FRIGATES *(continued)*

Sonar: Type 184P hull-mounted, Type 162M bottomed-target classification, Type 2031(1) towed passive linear array (F 56: 2031(Z)), Type 185 underwater telephone
EW: UA-8/9 and UA-15 (I-band) intercept, Type 667/668 jammer, 2/DLC decoy RL (VIII × 2), F 56 also: FH-12 HF D/F, Type 182 towed torpedo decoy

M: 2 sets White–English Electric geared steam turbines; 2/5-bladed props; 30,000 shp
Boilers: 2 Babcock & Wilcox 3-drum; 38.7 kg/cm², 450° C
Electric: 1,900 kw **Range:** approx. 4,000/12 **Fuel:** 460 tons
Crew: 18 officers, 248 enlisted

Sirius (F 40) Maritime Photographic, 10-91

Argonaut (F 56) Dr. Giorgio Arra, 3-91

Remarks: These ships have been further modified from "Exocet Leander" configuration by the deletion of the forward Sea Cat launcher and director, the lowering of the Exocet installation to the main-deck level, the substitution of 20-mm Mk 4 AA for the 40-mm AA, removal of the Type 965 early-warning radar (replaced by a Cossor Type 1010 IFF interrogator), and the addition of the Type 2031(1) towed passive linear hydrophone array on the starboard quarter. F 56 was damaged in the Falklands War, replaced *Minerva* (F 45) in the towed array conversion program, recommissioning 1984. The Type 2031(1) reel/winch is on a sponson projecting to starboard and astern, adding about 1 meter to the overall length. F 56, refitted 28-3-88 to 7-89, has the later 2031(Z) towed array.

Sister *Cleopatra* (F 28) paid off 28-1-92, and *Phoebe* (F 42) paid off 23-1-92. The surviving *Leander*-series frigates form the 7th Frigate Squadron, along with the training ship *Juno*.

Note: Since the last edition, the two remaining unmodified "Broad-beamed Leander"-class frigates have been stricken: *Achilles* (F 12) in 3-90, transferring to Chile on 27-11-90, and *Ariadne* (F 72) transferred to Chile in 6-92. Of the three "Exocet Leander" Batch 2B conversions, *Danae* (F 47) paid off in 6-91 and was transferred to Ecuador in 7-91, *Penelope* (F 127) paid off on 31-3-91 and was transferred to Ecuador on 25-5-91, and *Minerva* (F 45) paid off on 12-3-92. "Ikara Leander" *Naiad* (F 39), paid off 29-4-87 and used in structural damage trials as *Hultec,* was sunk 24-9-90.

PATROL SHIPS

♦ 3 Peacock class Bldr: Hall Russell, Aberdeen

	Laid down	L	In serv.
P 239 Peacock	29-1-82	1-12-82	12-10-83
P 240 Plover	13-5-82	12-4-83	20-7-84
P 241 Starling	9-9-82	7-9-83	10-8-84

D: 664 tons (712 fl) **S:** over 28 kts (25 kts sustained)
Dim: 62.60 (60.00 pp) × 10.00 × 2.72
A: 1/76-mm 62-cal. OTO Melara Compact DP—4/7.62-mm mg (I × 4)
Electron Equipt: Radar: 1/Type 1006 nav.
M: 2 APE-Crossley SEMT-Pielstick 18PA6V280 diesels; 2/3-bladed props; 14,188 bhp—1/Schottel S103 LSVEST drop-down, shrouded loiter prop; 181 shp
Range: 2,500/17 **Fuel:** 44 tons **Electric:** 755 kw
Crew: 7 officers, 29 enlisted

Peacock (P 239) LSPH Eric Pitman, R.A.N.,

Plover (P 240) Dr. Giorgio Arra,

Remarks: Replaced the five "Ton"-class former minesweepers used for patrol du Hong Kong, whose government paid 75 percent of the construction costs. Carr Avon Sea Raider 5.4-m, 30-kt, 10-man semi-rigid rubber inspection dinghies small "fast patrol craft." Some 450 rds 76-mm ammunition can be carried, with th controlled by a GSA7 Sea Archer Mk 1 electro-optical director, to which a G.E.C. thermal imager was added in 1987. The auxiliary drive employs a Schottel retrac steerable shrouded thruster. Accommodations for 44 total. Have 2/50-mm rocke projectors. Two rudders. Reported to be bad rollers, with deeper bilge keels havin to be fitted. Propulsion problems occurred with P 239. Sisters *Swallow* (P 242) and (P 243) returned to U.K. 3-9-88 and were paid off and sold to Ireland 8-10-88.

Note: British naval forces in Hong Kong also maintain the three 250-seat pers ferries *Jenny, Snore,* and *Ahmoy,* three 75-seat launches, and four 25-seat launc

♦ 2 "Castle"-class offshore patrol vessels

Bldr: Hall Russell, Aberdeen

	Laid down	L	In serv.
P 258 Leeds Castle	18-10-79	22-10-80	27-10-81
P 265 Dumbarton Castle	25-6-80	3-6-81	12-3-82

Leeds Castle (P 258) Maritime Photographic,

Dumbarton Castle (P 265) Maritime Photographic,

OL SHIPS *(continued)*

,350 tons (1,550 fl) **S:** 20 kts **Dim:** 81.0 (75.0 pp) × 11.5 × 3.42
/30-mm DS-30B AA—2/7.62-mm mg (I × 2)—helicopter platform
tron Equipt:
dar: 1/Type 1006 nav., 1/Plessey Type 994 surf./air search
V: MR-2 Orange Crop intercept; 2/Shield decoy RL, 8/DLF decoys
2 Ruston 12 RK 320DM diesels; 2 CP props; 5,640 bhp (4,380 sust.)
tric: 890 kw **Range:** 10,000/12 **Fuel:** 380 tons
w: 7 officers, 43 enlisted (plus 25 Marine detachment as required)

ks: Ordered 8-8-80, *after* both had been laid down. P 265 operated at over 2,000 splacement during the Falklands War. Can carry acoustic and mechanical veeping gear as well as being able to lay mines. The helicopter deck is large to accommodate either a Sea Lynx or Sea King helicopter. Carry two 50-mm flare launchers. Can carry 19.5 tons helicopter fuel and 30 tons of oil-spill ant detergent. Have Decca CANE-2 (Computer-Assisted Navigation Equipt.) T and Omega systems. Two Avon "Sea Raider" rubber rescue/inspection din- arried. Have one fire monitor and two oil-dispersing spray booms. Intended for patrols. P 258, equipped with MARISAT, conducted minelaying trials in mid- he Type 994 radars employ the Plessey commercial AWS-4 antenna in these Orange Crop" intercept equipment was developed for helicopter use and covers 8.0 GHz.

Island"-class offshore patrol vessels
: Hall Russell, Aberdeen

	L	In serv.
ANGLESEY	18-10-78	1-6-79
ALDERNEY	27-2-79	6-10-79
JERSEY	18-3-76	15-10-76
GUERNSEY	17-2-77	28-10-77
SHETLAND	22-11-76	14-7-77
ORKNEY	29-6-76	25-2-77
LINDISFARNE	1-6-77	26-1-78

sfarne (P 300) Maritime Photographic, 11-91

and (P 298) James W. Goss/NAVPIC, 3-91

998 tons (1,280 fl) **S:** 16.5 kts
n: 61.10 (51.97 pp) × 11.00 × 4.27
1/40-mm Bofors Mk 3 AA (P 297, 300: 1/30-mm 75-cal. DS-30B)—2/7.62-mm mg (I × 2)
ctron Equipt:
Radar: 1/Type 1006 nav.—Sonar: Simrad SU "Sidescan"
W: MR-2 Orange Crop intercept
2 Ruston 12 RK 3 CM diesels (750 rpm); 1/CP prop; 4,380 bhp
ctric: 536 kw **Range:** 11,000/12 **Fuel:** 310 tons
ew: 5 officers, 29 men (plus Marine detachment)

rks: Near duplicates of the Scottish Department of Fisheries ships *Jura* and a. *Jura* (as P 296) was loaned to the Royal Navy from 1975 to 1-77 for use in ling offshore oil rigs and the 200-nautical-mile economic zone, the purpose for the "Island" class was built. First five ordered 11-2-75, other pair 21-10-77. P 277 278 had fin stabilizers on completion, back-fitted in the others. Can maintain kts in a Force 8 gale. Have Decca CANES-2 Navaid. Avon Sea Raider semi-rigid ies are replacing the original Geminis for inspection purposes. Carry 28.6 tons detergent (a 6-hr. supply) for oil-spill cleanup. 30-mm DS-30 guns are replacing the hand-worked 40-mm guns during refits.

Note: Submarine escort ship *Sentinel* (P 246) was placed up for sale during 10-91, then recalled; see addenda for details and photo.

PATROL BOATS

◆ **3 Kingfisher class**
Bldr: Richard Dunston, Hessle (P 259: Fairmile Const., Berwick-on-Tweed)

	Laid down	L	In serv.
P 259 REDPOLE (ex-R.A.F. *Sea Otter*)	. . .	. . .	4-8-67
P 260 KINGFISHER	7-73	20-9-74	8-10-75
P 261 CYGNET	10-73	26-10-75	8-7-76

Redpole (P 259) James W. Goss/NAVPIC, 6-91

D: 167 tons (187 fl) **S:** 25 kts **Dim:** 36.60 (33.80 pp) × 7.16 × 2.00
A: 2/7.62-mm mg (I × 2)—*see* Remarks
Electron Equipt: Radar: 1/Type 1006(4) nav.
M: 2 Paxman 16 YCJM diesels (1,500 rpm); 2 props; 4,000 bhp
Range: 2,000/14 **Crew:** 4 officers, 10 enlisted

Remarks: Unsuccessful design based on R.A.F. *Seal*-class air-sea-rescue craft. P 259 was transferred to the R.N. 30-10-84 and towed to Brooke Marine, Lowestoft, 2-2-85 for refit, arming, and conversion to naval standard. A large number of additional planned sisters were canceled. Have fin stabilizers, but evidently still have stability problems. Only P 260 has hull portholes. 40-mm gun replaced by Zodiac boat and crane, exhaust stacks raised in 1985 refit to P 260, which, with P 259, operates in Northern Irish waters. Sisters *Peterel* (P 262) and *Sandpiper* (P 263), which had operated as naval officer training craft at Dartmouth, were stricken 14-12-90 and 17-12-90, respectively, and were sold to a Dutch civil operator in 4-91.

PATROL CRAFT

◆ **14 P.2000-class**
Bldr: Watercraft, Shoreham-by-Sea (last nine completed by Vosper Thornycroft)

2 patrol and search-and-rescue craft at Gibraltar:

	In serv.		In serv.
P 293 RANGER	3-8-88	P 294 TRUMPETER	8-11-88

8 Royal Naval Reserve training:

	In serv.	RNR Div.
P 264 ARCHER	1-3-86	Tay
P 270 BITER	5-11-85	Liverpool
P 272 SMITER	7-2-86	Clyde
P 273 PURSUER	19-2-88	Sussex
P 279 BLAZER	15-3-88	Forth
P 280 DASHER	6-5-88	Bristol
P 291 PUNCHER	13-7-88	London
P 292 CHARGER	8-7-88	Severn

Blazer (P 279) Maritime Photographic, 9-91

4 Royal Naval Auxiliary Service (R.N.X.S.) training:

	In serv.		In serv.
A 153 EXAMPLE	18-10-85	A 163 EXPRESS	26-5-88
A 154 EXPLORER	16-1-86	A 167 EXPLOIT	17-8-88

PATROL CRAFT *(continued)*

Explorer (A 154)—R.N.X.S. training craft
Maritime Photographic, 11-91

D: 44 tons (49 fl) **S:** 22.5 kts **Dim:** 20.80 (18.00 pp) × 5.80 × 1.80
A: P 293, 294: 1/20-mm AA, 2/7.62-mm mg (I × 2)
Electron Equipt: Radar: 1/Decca AC 1216 nav.
M: Perkins CV M800T diesels; 2 props; 1,590 bhp (1,380 sust.)
Electric: 62 kVA **Range:** 330/20; 500/15 **Crew:** 11 tot.

Remarks: Glass-reinforced plastic craft ordered 7-84, primarily for peacetime training: six for Royal Navy Reserve training, four for the Universities of Glasgow, Liverpool, Southampton, and Aberdeen, and four with "A" pendants for the Royal Naval Auxiliary Service. Now assigned as per the table above. Nine were incomplete (P 273 ready for trials) when Watercraft closed. Appear to have exceeded designed displacement by about six tons. P 293 and P 294 replaced *Cormorant* (P 256) and *Hart* (P 257) at Gibraltar in 1-91.

Note: The two ex-R.A.F. *Spitfire*-class patrol craft *Cormorant* (P 256, ex-*Sunderland*, 4000) and *Hart* (P 257, ex-*Stirling*, 4001) were placed up for sale at Gibraltar in 1-91. Of the one Tracker Mk 1 and four Tracker Mk 2 patrol/training craft, *Attacker* (P 281), *Chaser* (P 282), and *Fencer* (P 283) were offered for sale in 11-91 and paid off on 9-3-92, while *Hunter* (P 284) and *Striker* (P 285), which had been at Cyprus since 10-90, were placed up for sale there in 1-91, withdrawn, and again offered for sale in 6-91; the five had only been completed in 1983.

The following units are operated for the Ministry of Defence Police by the Royal Maritime Auxiliary Service (RMAS) and are not part of the Royal Navy proper:

◆ **6 Spear Mk 2 Class** Bldr: Fairey Marine, Cowes (In serv. 1978)

	Home Port		Home Port		Home Port
7871	Portsmouth	7873	Devonport	7875	Faslane
7872	Portland	7874	Faslane	7876	Rosyth

Spear class 7871 Maritime Photographic, 8-91

D: 10 tons (fl) **S:** 30 kts (26 cruise) **Dim:** 9.10 × 2.75 × 0.84
A: small arms **Electron Equipt:** Radar: 1/Decca . . . nav.
M: 2 Perkins T6-354 diesels; 2 props; 580 bhp
Range: 200/26 **Crew:** 3 tot.

Remarks: GRP, deep-vee hull.

◆ **2 Mk 4 & 5 Fast Motor Launches** Bldr: . . . (In serv. 1967)

6760 6785

Remarks: No data available; both based at Portsmouth.

◆ **4 Mk 9 Fast Motor Launches** (In serv. 1973)

	Home Port		Home Port
7301	Faslane	7303	Devonport
7302	Devonport	7304	Portland

Mk 9 Fast Motor Launch Maritime Photographic

Remarks: 10.2 m o.a.; no other data available. In addition to the craft listed a 16.40-meter patrol craft was completed at the Rosyth Dockyard in 8-90, a 11.0-meter patrol craft for the M.O.D. Police were delivered 5-90 by the Dev Dockyard.

MINE COUNTERMEASURES SHIPS

◆ **4 (+ 1) Sandown-class "Single-Role Minehunters" (SRMH)**
Bldr: Vosper Thornycroft, Woolston (Southampton), and Portsmouth

	Laid down	L	In serv.
M 101 Sandown	2-2-87	18-4-88	9-6-89
M 102 Inverness	11-5-89	27-2-90	5-3-91
M 103 Cromer	. . .	3-10-90	14-11-91
M 104 Walney	5-90	25-11-91	8-92
M 105 Bridport	1-6-91	30-7-92	6-93

Sandown (M 101) Paxman Diesels

Inverness (M 102) Leo Van Ginderen

Cromer (M 103) Maritime Photographic

MINE COUNTERMEASURES SHIPS *(continued)*

D: 378 tons light (465 fl) **S:** 15 kts (7.0 max. hunting)
Dim: 52.50 (50.00 pp) × 10.50 (9.00 waterline) × 2.30
A: 1/30-mm 75-cal. BMARC DS-30B AA
Electron Equipt:
Radar: 1/Type 1007 nav.
Sonar: Type 2093 variable-depth minehunting
M: 2 Paxman Valenta 6RPA 200-EM 1500 diesels; 2 Voith-Schneider vertical cycloidal props; 2,024 bhp—2/200-hp electric motors (7.0 kts)—2 Schottel bow-thrusters
Electric: 750 kw (3 diesel sets) **Range:** 2,600/11
Crew: 7 officers, 27 enlisted (40 accommodations)

Remarks: Pure minehunters, with no minesweeping capability. First unit ordered -8-85 for a design contracted to Vosper on 1-1-84. M 102 through M 105 ordered -7-87 (but not funded until 1988–89). Original plan called for construction of as many as 20. Requests for bids for seven more issued 22-10-90, but in 2-91, process was suspended, and there are no current plans to order more. All named for race courses. Planned to be operational for 6,000 hours between overhauls. Nine units have been ordered by Saudi Arabia, and Spain hopes to build 12 under license.

Glass-reinforced plastic construction. Use electric drive for low-speed, quiet operation. Plessey's Type 2093 sonar uses a variable-depth vertical lozenge-shaped towed body lowered beneath the hull; it has search, depth-finder, classification, and route survey modes. The ships will carry two Remote-Controlled Mine Disposal System Mk 2 (improved PAP 104 Mk 5) submersibles with up to 2,000 m of control cable and a depth capability of 300 m for mine identification and disposal. They also carry a mine-clearance diver team.

Have NAUTIS-M navigational C system. Capable of dealing with mines to 200-m depths. Have three Mawdsley generators, powered by Perkins V8-250G, 335-bhp diesels. Navigational equipment includes Racal Hyperfix, QM-14, and Navigator Mk 21 radio navaids (the latter to be replaced by Navigator Mk 53). Two Wallops "Barricade" decoy rocket launchers can be added for deployments to high-threat areas, but there is no electronic intercept equipment. There have reportedly been difficulties with the reliability of the sonar system.

12 "River"-class "Extra Deep Armed Team Sweeps" (MSM/EDATS)

Bldr: Richards (Shipbuilders) Ltd.; Lowestoft (L) or Great Yarmouth (G)

	Yard	Laid down	L	In serv.	Assigned
2003 Waveney (ex-*Amethyst*)	L	21-2-83	8-9-83	29-9-84	S. Wales
2004 Carron	G	21-2-83	23-9-83	29-9-84	Severn
2005 Dovey	G	3-3-83	1-12-83	30-3-85	Clyde
2006 Helford	G	12-10-83	16-5-84	7-6-85	Ulster
2007 Humber	G	21-10-83	17-5-84	7-6-85	(In reserve)
2008 Blackwater	G	16-1-84	29-8-84	20-6-85	R.N.*
2009 Itchen	L	26-3-84	16-11-84	12-10-85	Solent
2010 Helmsdale	L	21-5-84	11-1-85	6-6-85	(In reserve)
2011 Orwell	G	4-6-84	7-2-85	27-3-85	Tyne
2012 Ribble	G	17-9-84	7-5-85	28-6-86	Mersey
2013 Spey	L	12-11-84	22-5-85	19-7-86	Forth
2014 Arun	L	4-2-85	20-8-85	29-8-86	Sussex

* Fisheries Protection Squadron

Arun (M 2014) Maritime Photographic, 11-91

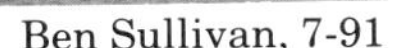

Helford (M 2006) Ben Sullivan, 7-91

Orwell (M 2011) Piet Sinke, 4-90

D: 630 tons (770 fl) **S:** 14 kts (15 on trials; 12 sust.)
Dim: 47.60 (42.00 pp) × 10.50 × 3.10 (3.75 max.)
A: 1/40-mm 60-cal. Bofors Mk 3 AA—2/7.62-mm mg (I × 2)
Electron Equipt: Radar: 2/Decca TM 1226 nav.—Sonar: none
M: 2 Ruston 6 RKCM diesels; 2 4-bladed CP props; 3,040 bhp
Electric: 460 kw **Range:** 4,500/10 **Fuel:** 88 tons
Crew: 7 officers, 7 petty officers, 16 other enlisted

Remarks: 638 grt. First four ordered 27-9-82, next six in 5-83, and last two on 25-2-84, to form the 10 Mine Countermeasures Squadron. Although announced 1985 that 12 more might be built (later reduced to 4), no further orders resulted. All manned by Royal Naval Reserve personnel, except M 2008, used by R.N. for Fisheries Protection Squadron. M 2007 and M 2010, which were to have been transferred to the Fisheries Protection Squadron, were instead placed in reserve late in 1991.

Built to commercial standards, following the design of a North Sea oilfield supply vessel. Single-compartment damage standard. There have been upper-deck corrosion problems. Intended to work in pairs, operating the BAJ-Vickers Wire Sweep Mk 9 Team Sweep System, essentially a wire catenary stretched between the ships. Can also sweep independently. Navigation gear includes two Kelvin-Hughes MS 48 echo-sounders. Have Decca QM 14(1), Decca Hifix Mk 6, and a satellite navigation receiver. Have the Racal System 880 Integrated Minehunting System (QX3/1). The 40-mm gun is hand-operated and is of limited utility.

◆ 13 "Hunt"-class minehunters

Bldr: Vosper Thornycroft, Woolston (except M 32, M 34: Yarrow (Shipbuilders), Scotstoun, Glasgow

	Laid down	L	In serv.
M 29 Brecon	15-9-75	21-6-78	21-3-80
M 30 Ledbury	5-10-77	5-12-79	11-6-81
M 31 Cattistock	20-6-79	22-1-81	16-6-82
M 32 Cottesmore	27-9-79	9-2-82	24-6-83
M 33 Brocklesby	8-5-80	12-1-82	3-2-83
M 34 Middleton	1-7-80	27-4-83	15-8-84
M 35 Dulverton	1-6-81	3-11-82	4-11-83
M 36 Bicester	2-1-85	4-6-85	14-2-86
M 37 Chiddingfold	. . .	6-10-83	26-10-84
M 38 Atherstone	9-1-84	1-3-86	30-1-87
M 39 Hurworth	1-83	25-9-84	19-7-85
M 40 Berkeley	9-9-85	3-12-86	14-1-88
M 41 Quorn	2-6-86	23-1-88	21-4-89

Berkeley (M 40)—with 20-mm AA mounts Maritime Photographic, 8-91

Cottesmore (M 32)—20-mm AA platforms removed Leo Van Ginderen, 10-91

MINE COUNTERMEASURES SHIPS *(continued)*

Chiddingfold (M 37)—with 20-mm AA flanking stack
Leo Van Ginderen, 1-92

Quorn (M 41) Pradignac & Léo, 6-90

D: 625 tons (725 fl) **S:** 17 kts (15 kts sust.; 8 kts on hydraulic drive)
Dim: 60.00 (56.60 pp) × 9.85 × 2.20
A: 1/30-mm 75-cal. BMARC DS-30B AA—2/7.62-mm mg (I × 2)—provision for 2/20-mm BMARC/Oerlikon GAM-B01 AA (*see* Remarks)
Electron Equipt:
Radar: 1/Type 1006(4) nav.
Sonar: Type 193M Mod. 1 variable-depth minehunting (100/300 kHz), with Type 2059 submersible-tracking set incorporated
M: 2 Ruston-Paxman Deltic 9-59K diesels (1,600 rpm); 2 props; 1,900 bhp (1,770 sust.); slow-speed hydraulic drive for hunting (8 kts)—bow-thruster
Electric: 1,140 kw (3 Foden FD 12 Mk 7 diesel alternators of 200 kw each for ship's service plus one 525-kw Deltic 9-55B diesel alternator for magnetic minesweeping and one 60-kw emergency set)
Range: 1,500/12 **Crew:** 6 officers, 39 enlisted

Remarks: Equipped for both hunting and sweeping mines. M 33 laid down *prior* to ordering on 19-6-80. M 40 and M 41 ordered 4-6-85. M 31, 34, 37, and 40 are in the 1st Mine Countermeasures Squadron; M 29, 31, 32, 38, and 39 are in the 2nd Mine Countermeasures Squadron; and M 30, 33, 35, and 36 are in the 4th Mine Countermeasures Squadron. M 29 went aground 10-89 in the Clyde but was salved and completed repairs 13-7-90. M 38 conducted trials with the COMTASS towed passive surface-target detection sonar in 1991.

All served at one time with UN Coalition forces in the Persian Gulf during Desert Shield/Desert Storm except M 29, 32, 33, 36, and 41, accounting for over 200 mines. When deployed in high-threat areas, can be equipped with single 20-mm AA mounts on platforms abreast the stack, decoy rocket launchers, DLF-2 "Rubber Duck" floating decoys, 2 Wallops "Barricade" decoy rocket launchers, Matilda-E radar intercept gear, and additional communications equipment, including commercial SATCOMM systems. In 1991–92, M 34, M 37, M 39, M40, and M 41 carried the 20-mm mounts.The orginal 40-mm 60-cal. Mk 9 AA mounts have been replaced by stabilized DS-30B 30-mm AA mounts.

Hull constructed of glass-reinforced plastic. Carry six or seven divers and two French PAP 104 Mk 5 remote-controlled mine location submersibles. Have Sperry "Osborn" TA 6 acoustic, M.M. Mk 11 magnetic loop and M. Mk 3 Mod. 2 Orepesa wire sweeping gear as well. Equipped with CAAIS DBA-4 (64 contact-tracking) data system and Decca Mk 21 "Hi-Fix" navigation system.

One Deltic 9-59B diesel (645 bhp) drives the 525-kw sweep current alternator *or* four Dowty hydraulic pumps used to power the props during minehunting; the engine also provides power for the bow-thruster and the sweep winch. All are receiving the Ferranti-Thomson VIMOS (Vibration Monitoring System), which is expected to cut radiated noise by 3–10 dB.

♦ 1 prototype glass-reinforced plastic minehunter
Bldr: Vosper Thornycroft, Woolston

	Ordered	L	In serv.
M 1116 Wilton	11-2-70	18-2-72	25-4-73

Wilton (M 1116)—with deckhouse in place of sweep winch
Ben Sullivan 6-

D: 450 tons (fl) **S:** 15 kts **Dim:** 46.33 × 8.76 × 2.6
A: 1/40-mm 60-cal. Bofors Mk 7A AA
Electron Equipt:
Radar: 1/Type 1006(4) nav.
Sonar: Type 193 variable-depth minehunting
M: 2 Paxman Deltic 18A-7A diesels; 2 props; 3,000 bhp
Electric: 240 kw (4/60-kw sets) **Range:** 1,900/13; 2,500/8
Fuel: 36 tons **Crew:** 5 officers, 32 enlisted

Remarks: First large warship with an all-glass-reinforced plastic hull. Machin and fittings are from *Derriton,* scrapped in 1970. Two six-tubed chaff launchers ad 1984. Completed major refit 21-11-88. Assigned to the Dartmouth Training Squad in early 1991; a classroom for officer cadets has replaced the winch and sweep gear but the minehunting equipment has been retained.

♦ 4 "Ton"-class minehunters

	Bldr	Laid down	L	In se
M 1113 Brereton*	Richards Ironworks	25-9-51	14-5-53	9-7-
M 1114 Brinton†	Cook, Welton & Gemmell	30-5-51	8-8-52	4-3-
M 1166 Nurton	Harland & Wolff, Belfast	31-8-55	22-10-56	21-8-
M 1181 Sheraton†	White's SY, Southampton	23-2-54	20-7-55	24-8-

* In reserve † Fisheries Protection Squadron

Nurton (M 1166) Maritime Photographic,

Iveston (M 1151)—since stricken Maritime Photographic,

IINE COUNTERMEASURES SHIPS *(continued)*

heraton (M 1181) Leo Van Ginderen, 3-90

D: 370 tons (425 fl) **S:** 15 kts (cruising)
Dim: 46.33 (42.68 pp) × 8.76 × 2.50
A: 1/40-mm 60-cal. Bofors Mk 7A AA—2/7.62-mm mg (I × 2)
Electron Equipt:
Radar: 1/Type 1006(4) nav.
Sonar: Type 193 variable-depth minehunting
M: 2 Paxman Deltic 18A-7A diesels; 2 props; 3,000 bhp
Electric: 240 kw (4/60-kw sets) **Range:** 1,900/13; 2,500/8
Fuel: 36 tons **Crew:** 5 officers, 32 enlisted

marks: Survivors of a class of 118 completed 1952–58. All are equipped with active ıders for low-speed operations, have a Type 193 sonar, and carry mine-clearance ers. The minehunter conversions were completed 1964–69 and have the Racal tem 880 (QX3/3) minehunting data system to permit route surveys of 80-km length, h up to 60 contacts per km. All have wooden hulls, sheathed with nylon below the terline. Fin stabilizers are fitted.
I 1113 was paid off for disposal 29-4-91 but reinstated on the list of ships to be ained during 2-92. *Iveston* (M 1115) and *Kellington* (M 1154) paid off for disposal 7-92 and 24-9-92, respectively. Of the three unconverted minesweeper sisters listed he previous edition, *Cuxton* (M 1125) paid off 22-3-91, *Upton* (M 1187) paid off for ıp 22-10-91, and *Soberton* (M 1200), which had operated throughout her 35-year eer in the Fisheries Protection Squadron, was paid off 27-2-92 to become Sea Cadet ıdquarters Ship at Erith, Kent, replacing sister *Wootton* (M 1195).

IPHIBIOUS WARFARE SHIPS
SAULT SHIPS

ıe: Landing ships and craft subordinated to the Royal Corps of Transport are ered in the British Army entry at the conclusion of the United Kingdom section, on e 779. *Invincible*-class carriers can also carry troops.

0 (+ 1) assault helicopter carrier (LPH)

	Bldr	Laid down	L	In serv.
. . . .	. . .	. . .	. . .	. . .

: approx. 14,000 tons (fl) **S:** . . . kts **Dim:** . . . × . . . × . . .
ir Group: 12/Sea King HC.4 troop helicopters, 6/Sea Lynx HAS.8 attack helicopters
: . . .
I: . . .
rew: . . . tot. + 700-man Royal Marine Commando

marks: Originally referred to as the ASS (Aviation Support Ship) and intended to ace the vertical assault capability lost with the disposal of the carriers *Hermes* and *vark*. To be ordered during the 3rd quarter of 1993 and may displace as much as 00 tons full load. Some thought was given to acquiring U.S. AH-64 Apache helicop- to perform the ground support rôle.

) (+ 2) assault landing ships (LPD)

	Bldr	Laid down	L	In serv.
. . . .	. . .	1995	. . .	1998
. . . .	. . .	1997	. . .	2000

: . . . tons (fl) **S:** 18 kts **Dim:** . . . × . . . × . . .
: . . ./30-mm Goalkeeper CIWS—. . . AA—4/Sea King HC.4 troop-carrying helicopters
lectron Equipt:
Radar: . . .
EW: . . . . . . intercept, . . . decoy RL
: . . .
ange: . . ./. . . **Crew:** 350 tot + 250–300 troops

arks: Long-awaited replacements for *Intrepid* and *Fearless* that had originally expected to be ordered in 1988. Announced 1992 that they will be orderd in 3-94 3-96. Competing designs offered by Y-ARD teamed with VSEL (Vickers), Swan er. Will have two flight-deck spots for Merlin-sized helicopters, four landing craft odable well-deck, and four more landing craft in davits.

Possible appearance of new LPD VSEL, 1989

♦ **2 Fearless class** (*in reserve)

	Bldr	Laid down	L	In serv.
L 10 FEARLESS	Harland & Wolff, Belfast	25-7-62	19-12-63	25-11-65
L 11 INTREPID*	John Brown, Clydebank	11-12-62	5-6-64	11-3-67

D: 11,582 tons (12,642 fl) (16,950 tons, draft 9.15, with well deck flooded)
S: 21 kts **Dim:** 158.5 (152.4 pp) × 24.38 × 6.2
Air Group: up to 4/Sea King HC.4 or Merlin helicopters
A: L 10: 2/Sea Cat GWS.20 SAM syst. (IV × 2)—2/20-mm Mk 15 CIWS (I × 2)—2/20-mm GAM-B01 AA (I × 2); L 11: 2/Sea Cat SAM syst. (IV × 2)—2/40-mm 60-cal. Bofors Mk 7A AA (I × 2)—4/30-mm 75-cal. Oerlikon GCM-A02 AA (II × 2)—2/20-mm Oerlikon GAM-B01 AA (I × 2)
Electron Equipt:
Radar: 1/Type 1006 nav., 1/Type 994 surf./air search
EW: L 10: Marconi Mentor-A intercept, 4/DLA Sea Gnat decoy RL (VI × 4); L 11: 2/DLC Corvus decoy RL (VIII × 2)
M: 2 sets English-Electric geared steam turbines; 2 props; 22,000 shp
Boilers: 2 Babcock & Wilcox, 38.66 kg/cm^2, 454° C superheat
Electric: 4,000 kw tot. **Range:** 5,000/20
Crew: 50 officers, 50 enlisted + air group: 3 officers, 19 enlisted + Royal Marine detachment: 3 officers, 85 enlisted + 380–700 troops

Fearless (L 10)—as modernized Maritime Photographic, 7-92

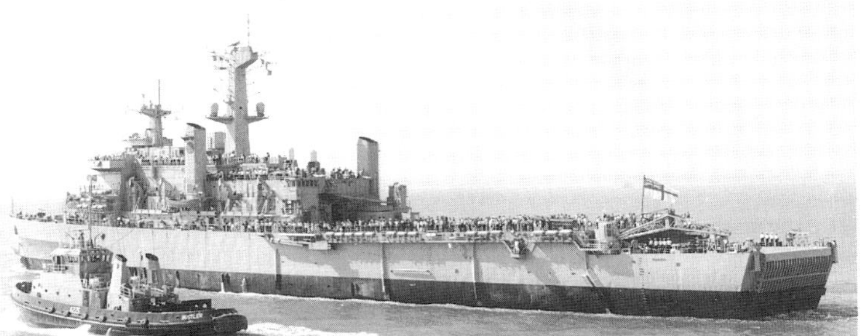

Fearless (L 10)—with tug *Bustler* (A 225) Leo Van Ginderen, 8-91

ASSAULT SHIPS *(continued)*

Intrepid (L 11)—now in reserve Leo Van Ginderen, 6-90

Remarks: Both intended to act as command ships for amphibious assaults as well as to carry troops and equipment. In emergencies, can carry up to 1,000 troops. Both are long overdue for replacement, which will now have to wait until 1998–2000.

Fearless, in reserve at Portsmouth 1985, was in reactivation refit 6-88 to 9-11-90, receiving 2/20-mm Mk 15 Phalanx CIWS in place of the after Sea Cat launchers; the Plessey NAUTIS-L navigation/action data system with seven display consoles; additional aviation fuel capacity and the capability to operate Sea King or Merlin helicopters. The mainmast was heightened by about 3.7 m, and new communications equipment, new EW equipment, and a major rehabilitation of machinery and piping were added. Her completion was delayed 21 weeks by corrosion, etc.

In L 11, two twin 30-mm AA replaced the after two Sea Cat launchers in 1985, and two 20-mm AA were added forward; the ship was placed in reserve at the end of 1990 and will probably not be reactivated again, barring national emergency. L 11 has the CAAIS combat data system.

Carried in davits are four LCVP Mk 4 landing craft, which can transport 35 men or a 5.5-ton vehicle. The well deck accommodates four LCM(9) landing craft carrying two Chieftain tanks or four vehicles or 100 tons of supplies each; four additional tanks can be carried on the tank deck. The vehicles are divided between the tank deck, a lower deck, and a half-deck reserved for jeeps.

TANK LANDING SHIPS

♦ 1 Sir Galahad class
Bldr: Swan Hunter Shipbuilders, Wallsend-on-Tyne

	Laid down	L	In serv.
L 3005 Sir Galahad	12-7-85	13-12-86	7-12-87

Sir Galahad (L 3005) Maritime Photographic, 11-91

D: 7,400 tons light (8,541 fl) **S:** 18 kts
Dim: 140.47 (126.02 pp) × 20.02 (19.50 hull) × 4.57 (3.97 light)
A: provision for: 2/20-mm GAM-B01 AA (I × 2)—2/20-mm Oerlikon Mk 7A AA (I × 2)
Electron Equipt:
Radar: 1/Type 1007 nav., 1/. . . X-band nav., 1/. . . S-band nav.
EW: . . . intercept, 4 DLB RL (VI × 4), Type 182 towed torpedo decoy
M: 2 Mirrlees-Blackstone KMR9 Mk 3 Major diesels; 2 CP props; 13,310 bhp
Range: 13,000/15 **Fuel:** 1,260 tons
Electric: 2,460 kw (4 × 540 kw, 1 × 300 kw sets)
Crew: 17 officers, 32 unlicensed, plus 340 troops—*see* Remarks.

Remarks: 8,861 grt/3,077 dwt. Ordered 6-9-84 as replacement for ship of the sam name lost in the Falklands War. Has Decca-Racal CANE navigational system, or 25-ton crane forward of the bridge, and two 8.6-ton cranes forward. There are bow an stern ramps, a visor-type bow door, a 20-ton scissor lift amidships to forward vehicl helicopter deck, and a 20-ton traveling crane on upper of two vehicle decks with 8.57-m moulded-depth hull. Can accommodate an additional 133 troops in publ spaces, plus another 64 without berths, for a maximum of 537. Completed tria 10-7-87.

♦ 4 Sir Bedivere class
Bldr: Hawthorn Leslie, Hebburn-on-Tyne (L 3027: Alex Stephen, Glasgow, Scotland)

	Laid down	L	In serv.
L 3004 Sir Bedivere	10-65	20-7-66	18-5-67
L 3027 Sir Geraint	6-65	26-1-67	12-7-67
L 3036 Sir Percivale	4-66	4-10-67	23-3-68
L 3505 Sir Tristram	2-66	12-12-66	14-9-67

Sir Geraint (L 3027) Leo Van Ginderen, 6-

Sir Percivale (L 3036)—note stern ramp Maritime Photographic, 10

Sir Tristram (L 3505)—lengthened, king posts supporting electronics arrays Mike Louagie,

D: 3,362 tons (5,766 fl) (L 3505: 5,800 fl) **S:** 17.25 kts
Dim: L 3505: 134.85 (120.43 pp) × 17.94 (17.70 wl) × 3.98
L 3027: 126.02 (111.64 pp) × 17.94 (17.70 wl) × 3.98
A: provision for: 2/20-mm GAM-B01 AA (I × 2)—2/20-mm Oerliko Mk 7A AA (I × 2)
Electron Equipt:
Radar: 1/Type 1007 nav., 1/. . . X-band nav., 1/. . . S-band nav.
EW: . . . intercept; 2/DLC chaff RL (VIII × 2)
M: 2 Mirrlees 10-ALSSDM 10-cyl. diesels; 2 props; 9,400 bhp
Electric: 1,600 kw tot. (L 3505: 2,000 kw tot.)
Range: 8,000/15
Fuel: 811 tons (L 3505: 850)
Crew: 21 officers, 44 enlisted (L 3505: 18 officers, 32 enlisted)

Remarks: 4473 grt (L 3505: 4,775 grt)/2,443 dwt. In 1963 the Ministry of Trans tion ordered the first of six specially designed LST-type ships for the army, charte peacetime to various private maritime firms. In 1970 the ships came under the c of the Royal Fleet Auxiliary Service. L 3505 badly damaged 8-6-83, but was c home in 6-83 and repaired by Tyne Shiprepair, South Shields, 7-84 to 7-85; 120-ton, 8.915-m midsection was added, along with rehabilitated accommoda increased generator capacity, a larger helicopter deck, a bow-thruster, and inc engineering automation. The rebuilding was not entirely successful, as the ship down by the stern and can no longer load tanks in the after portion of the main v

K LANDING SHIPS *(continued)*

The other three are to receive a similar modernization and lengthening to extend ıseful lives another 15 years, beginning in 1993 with L 3004.
ching cargo capacity is 340 tons. There are bow and stern ramps for vehicles, and ır ramps connect the two decks. Quarters for 402 men. Helicopter platform and cranes (two 8.5-ton capacity, one 20-ton). All have MARISAT SATCOMM gear.
ered overall length for L 3027 is 125.58 m. All can carry 2,077 tons water ballast.
armed, no longer carry 40-mm AA guns.
er *Sir Galahad* (L 3005) was fatally damaged on 8-6-82 and was scuttled 24-6-82.
ister *Sir Lancelot* (L 3029) for sale 31-3-89, sold commercial 1-6-89 as *Lowland* r.

DING CRAFT

M(9) class (In serv. 1963–66; L 713–715: 1986)

8 (Bldr: Vosper)
–L 702 (Bldr: Brooke Marine, Lowestoft)
–L 709 (Bldr: Richard Dunston, Thorne)
, L 711 (Bldr: J. Bolson, Poole)
–L 715 (Bldr: McTay Marine, Liverpool)

Mk 9 assigned to Intrepid—note built-up sides amidships, tank-cover segments stacked in front of pilothouse Maritime ographic, 8-90

3—with tank-deck covers partly installed Ben Sullivan, 5-91

75 tons light (176 fl) **S:** 10 kts (9 loaded) **Dim:** 25.7 × 6.5 × 1.7
ectron Equipt: Radar: 1/Decca 101 nav.
2 Paxman YHXAM diesels; Kort-nozzle props; 624 bhp
ew: 6 tot.

arks: Can carry two Centurion tanks or 70 tons of cargo. Most are naval-manned, wo (including L 713) are assigned to 539 Assault Squadron, Royal Marines. *ess* (L 10) and *Intrepid* (L 11) can each carry four of this class. L 703 (F4—*Fearless*) lost to bomb 8-6-82. L 713–L 715 have Dorman 8 JTM diesels, 540 bhp, and reinforced bow ramps. Hull sides on all have been built up amidships, and seg-ed covers to the tank deck are carried.

7 LCVP Mk 4 Class Bldrs: 8301: Fairey Allday Marine, Hamble; 401–8418: W.A. Souter, Cowes

	In serv.		In serv.		In serv.
	1982	8407	18-7-85	8414	1986
	5-3-85	8408	12-8-85	8415	1986
	29-3-85	8410	11-10-85	8416	1986
	1-5-85	8411	3-12-85	8417	1986
	30-5-85	8412	15-1-86	8418	1987
	10-7-85	8413	1986		

nouflaged LCVP Mk 4—with portable cargo-deck cover oyed Leo Van Ginderen, 1991

LCVP Mk 4—with cargo-deck cover stowed Ben Sullivan, 1991

D: 10 tons (fl) **S:** 20 kts (16 loaded)
Dim: 13.00 (11.90 pp) × 3.20 × 0.80 **A:** 2/7.62-mm mg (I × 2)
M: 2 Perkins 76-3544 diesels; 2 props; 440 bhp (8416–18: 2 Dorman diesels; 2 CP props; . . . bhp)
Range: 200/12 (8416–18: 300/12) **Crew:** 3 tot. + 20–35 troops

Remarks: Prototype 8301, ordered 6-2-80, is 13.50 long by 3.50 beam. Series units ordered 21-8-84. Have cargo well 8.80 × 2.13 and a cargo capacity of 5.5 tons. Aluminum construction. Cargo well can be fitted with windowed, segmented cover. 8416–8418 can reach 22 kts. Four others serve the army's Royal Corps of Transport: LCVP 8402, 8409, 8419, and 8420.

♦ **. . . SeaRide 6-class assault boats** Bldr: RTK Marine

D: 1.37 tons (fl) **S:** 30 kts **Dim:** 7.58 × 2.75 × . . .
M: 2 outboard motors

♦ **. . . TF.700-class assault boats** Bldr: Task Force Marine

D: . . . tons (fl) **S:** 42 kts max. **Dim:** 7.00 × 2.30 × . . .
M: 2 Suzuki outboards; 280 bhp **Crew:** 10 commandos

Remarks: 35 kts with 1,690-kg maximum payload; 42 kts with 300 kg. GRP construction.

♦ **3 Ferryman 18-class assault boats** Bldr: Freezer Aluminum Boats, Hayling Island (In serv. 1 on 13-8-84, 2 on 16-8-84)

LCR 5506–5508

D: 2.5 tons **S:** 30 kts **Dim:** 5.48 × 2.21 × 0.40
M: 1 OMC or Suzuki gasoline outboard; 140 shp
Crew: 1 coxwain, 8 troops

Remarks: Raider boats for Royal Marines; ordered 16-5-84. Can carry .9 tons cargo. GRP, deep-vee hull.

♦ **. . . Arctic 22 Rigid Inflatables** Bldr: Osborne, U.K.

D: 1.4 tons light **S:** 40+ kts **Dim:** 7.2 × . . . × . . .
M: 2 OMC or Suzuki outboards; 280 shp
Range: 30/40 **Cargo:** 15 troops or 1.12 tons stores

Two sizes of rigid inflatable assault boat Mike Louagie, 4-89

♦ **. . . Pacific 22 Rigid Inflatables** Bldr: Osborne, U.K.

D: 1.75 tons light **S:** 26 kts **Dim:** 6.8 × . . . × . . .
M: 1 Ford Mermaid diesel; 140 bhp
Range: 85/26 **Cargo:** 15 troops or 1.12 tons stores

♦ **. . . inflatable raiding craft** Bldr: . . .

D: 0.13 tons **S:** 18 kts (light) **Dim:** 4.7 × . . . × . . .
M: 1 OMC outboard motor; 35 or 40 shp
Range: 25/. . . (loaded) **Cargo:** 7 troops + coxswain

Remarks: The above three classes are employed by the Royal Marines.

♦ **35 or more "Mexiflote" self-propelled pontoons**

AUXILIARY SHIPS

Note: Major auxiliary and supply vessels are responsible to the Royal Fleet Auxiliary (R.F.A.), an organization peculiar to the Royal Navy and manned by uniformed civil servants. Built to the specifications of Lloyds of London (compartmentation, security, habitability), they also meet the standards of the Shipping Naval Acts of 1911 and of the Ministry of Transportation. In 1985, it was decided to reclassify all R.F.A. ships as "Government-Owned Vessels"; this was modified on 30-11-89 to place the vessels under the Director General of Supplies and Transport (Navy), Ministry of Defence (Navy). They fly the blue ensign of the reserve, rather than the white ensign. In addition, about 40 tugs, salvage vessels, cable layers, research vessels, etc., are assigned to the Royal Maritime Auxiliary Service (R.M.A.S.), whose personnel are also civil servants. The former Port Auxiliary Service (P.A.S.) was absorbed by the R.M.A.S. on 1-10-76. An additional group of service craft are operated by the Royal Naval Auxiliary Service (R.N.X.S.). Ships not listed below as either R.F.A., R.N.X.S., or R.M.A.S. are manned by the Royal Navy. R.M.A.S. ships have black hulls and buff upperworks, while R.N.X.S. units have black hulls and gray upperworks. When pendant numbers are not actually borne, the numbers assigned are given in parentheses.

HYDROGRAPHIC SHIPS

Note: All Royal Navy survey ships on survey duties are painted white, with buff-colored stacks and masts. See addenda for additional ship.

◆ **1 improved Hecla class** Bldr: Robb Caledon, Leith, Scotland

	Laid down	L	In serv.
(A 138) Herald	9-11-72	4-10-73	31-10-74

Herald (A 138)—in the Persian Gulf Leo Van Ginderen, 1991

D: 2,125 tons light, 2,510 std. (2,945 fl) **S:** 14 kts
Dim: 79.3 × 14.9 × 4.7
Electron Equipt:
Radar: 1/Type1006 nav., 1/. . . nav. Sonar: Type 2034 sidescan
M: 3 Paxman Ventura 12YJCZ diesels (1,280 bhp each), 3 generator sets, electric drive: 2 motors; 2 props; 2,000 shp—bow-thruster
Range: 12,000/11 **Crew:** 12 officers, 116 enlisted

Remarks: Improved version of the *Hecla* class. On ice-patrol duties 6-83 to 2-84, gray-painted, and with 2/20-mm Oerlikon Mk 7A AA. Flight deck extended to accommodate Lynx helicopter during refit ending 1-88; at same time a 10-man decompression chamber was installed on the bow. Survey equipment includes Hydroplot NAVSAT system, gravimetric, magnetometer, oceanographic equipment. Has passive tank stabilization, satellite communications equipment.

Employed mid-1988 to 3-89 as mine countermeasures support ship in Persian Gulf. During the 1990–91 Persian Gulf War, again operated as a mine countermeasures ship support vessel and was again armed; was equipped with "Minescan" high-frequency sonar (also fitted to one of the hydrographic launches) and the QUILLS precision navigation system. Has Qubit TRAC-V integrated navigational/data-logging system. Normally carries two 10.67-m hydrographic launches.

◆ **1 Hecla class** Bldr: Yarrow & Co., Blythwood, Scotland

	Laid down	L	In serv.
(A 133) Hecla	6-5-64	21-12-64	9-9-65

Hecla (A 133)—returning from Persian Gulf Ben Sullivan, 9-91

D: 1,915 tons (2,733 fl) **S:** 14 kts
Dim: 79.25 (71.63 pp) × 14.94 × 4.0
Electron Equipt:
Radar: 1/Type1006 nav., 1/. . . nav.—Sonar: Type 2034 sidescar
M: diesel-electric propulsion: 3 Paxman Ventura 12YJCZ diesels (1,280 bhp each), 2 electric motors; 1 prop; 2,000 shp—bow-thru
Range: 20,000/9; 12,000/11 **Fuel:** 450 tons
Crew: 13 officers, 102 enlisted

Remarks: Based on the oceanographic research vessel *Discovery*. Air-condit hull, reinforced against ice; bow-thruster for navigation in narrow waters. Hanga platform for one helicopter; carried Wasp but cannot accommodate Lynx. Exc scientific laboratories; usually carry six civilian hydrographers in addition to Carries two 10.7-m survey launches.

Sister *Hydra* (A 144) stricken 18-4-86 and sold to Indonesia. The surviving two to be paid off in late 1987 (*Hecla*) and early 1988 (*Hecate*), but striking delayed d search for a commercial charter successor; both given 25-week refits ending *Hecate* (A 137) was paid off and stricken 6-3-91. A 133 operated in the Persian during 1990–91 as a mine countermeasures support vessel; the flight deck wa larged to accommodate a Lynx helicopter, two 20-mm Oerlikon Mk 7A AA were a and the communications suite was enhanced.

◆ **1 Roebuck-class coastal survey ship**
Bldr: Brooke Marine, Lowestoft

	Laid down	L	In serv.
(A 130) Roebuck	. . .	14-11-85	30-10-86

Roebuck (A 130) Leo Van Ginderen,

D: 1,059 tons light (1,431 fl) **S:** 15 kts
Dim: 63.89 (57.00 pp) × 13.00 × 3.65
Electron Equipt:
Radar: 2/. . . nav.
Sonar: Marconi 2034BC Hydrosearch, Waverley Type 2033BB Sidescan
M: 4 Mirrlees ES-8 Mk 1 diesels; 2 CP props; 3,040 bhp
Range: 4,000/10 **Crew:** 8 officers, 11 senior P.O., 35 ratings

Remarks: Ordered 21-5-84 as first of a planned quartet; other three no l planned. Has Qubit SIPS (Survey Information Processing System). Survey equip includes Types 780AA and 778AG echo-sounders and Racal Hyperfix radio navig aid. Has three generator sets. Hydrosearch sonar provides high-definition imag 600-m depths. Has A-frame at stern to tow magnetometer and Waverley Sid sonar. Carries two survey launches, *Batchellor Delight* and *Jolly Prize*, des below.

◆ **2 Bulldog-class coastal survey ships**
Bldr: Brooke Marine, Lowestoft

	L	In serv.
(A 317) Bulldog	12-7-67	21-3-68
(A 319) Beagle (ex-*Barracuda*)	7-9-67	9-5-68

Bulldog (A 317) Ben Sullivan

IYDROGRAPHIC SHIPS *(continued)*

Beagle (A 319) Leo Van Ginderen, 11-90

D: 800 tons (1,088 fl) **S:** 15 kts
Dim: 60.95 (57.80 pp) × 11.43 × 3.6
Electron Equipt:
Radar: 1/Type 1007 nav.
Sonar: Type 2034 mapping (A 317: Marconi Hydrosearch)
M: 4 Lister-Blackstone ERS-8-M diesels; 2 KaMeWa CP props; 2,640 bhp
Electric: 720 kw **Range:** 4,600/12 **Crew:** 5 officers, 34 enlisted

emarks: Hulls built to commercial specifications and reinforced against ice damage. arry one 8.7-meter survey launch. Passive tank stabilization. Decca "Hi-Fix" preision plot. Can be equipped with two single 20-mm AA on bridge wings. Have Qubit PS-II (Survey Information and Processing System). *Bulldog* refitted 1985 with proype Marconi Hydrosearch and a new radar. Sister *Fox* (A 320) stricken 31-1-89, aced up for sale 8-3-89. *Fawn* (A 335) offered for sale 7-91 and paid off for disposal -9-91.

1 inshore survey craft Bldr: Emsworth SY, Emsworth

	L	In serv.
86) Gleaner	18-10-83	5-12-84

eaner (A 86) Mike Louagie, 9-89

D: 20 tons (22 fl) **S:** 14 kts **Dim:** 14.81 × 4.55 × 1.30
Electron Equipt: Radar: 1/Decca 110 nav.—Sonar: . . .
M: 2 Rolls-Royce CG M-310 diesels; 2 props; 524 bhp; 1 Perkins 4.236 M cruise diesel on centerline; 1 prop; 72 bhp
Range: 450/10 **Crew:** 1 officer, 4 enlisted

marks: Smallest commissioned "ship" in the R.N., intended for survey work in the ent-Portsmouth area and in the Channel Islands. Glass-reinforced plastic hull by matic. Speed on cruise engine: 3 to 7 kts. Referred to as "HMSML" (Her Majesty's vey Motor Launch) *Gleaner*.

3 survey boats Bldr: Halmatic, Havant (In serv. 1986)

tchellor Delight Jolly Prize . . . . . .

D: 8.75 tons (fl) **S:** 13 kts **Dim:** 8.94 (8.10 wl) × 3.60 × 0.99
M: 2 Perkins 6.3544 diesels; 2 props; 230 bhp
Range: 200/13 **Crew:** 4 tot.

narks: GRP construction; builder's "Serviceman" class. Ordered 12-84. First two ied by *Roebuck;* third (with wood-sheathed hull for ice protection) was carried by former ice-patrol ship *Endurance*.

e: Small motor vessel *Proud Seahorse* has been on charter since 1985 for coastal ey work, with owner's crew plus a Royal Navy survey team. On charter until 1993 e motor vessel *British Enterprise 4,* which carries a naval survey party.

EXPERIMENTAL AND TRIALS VESSELS

◆ **1 sonar-trials ship** Bldr: Appledore Furguson Shipbuilding

	Laid down	L	In serv.
A 285 Auricula	16-2-79	22-11-79	6-11-80

Auricula (A 285) Leo Van Ginderen, 1-92

D: 1,200 tons (fl) **S:** 12 kts **Dim:** 60.0 (52.0 pp) × 11.0 × 3.6
Electron Equipt: Radar: 1/Type 1006 nav.
M: 2 Mirrlees-Blackstone ESL-6-MGR diesels; 2 props; 1,300 bhp
Crew: 7 officers, 15 enlisted, 10 technicians

Remarks: Operated by R.M.A.S. Ordered 5-1-78. "Trials and Experimental Tender" to Admiralty Underwater Weapons Establishment, Portland; replaced *Steady*. Has a bow-thruster. Name means "Ear."

◆ **1 sonar-research ship** Bldr: Scott-Lithgow, Greenock

	Laid down	L	In serv.
A 367 Newton	19-12-73	26-6-75	17-6-76

Newton (A 367) Leo Van Ginderen, 1990

D: 3,940 tons (fl) **S:** 14 kts **Dim:** 98.6 (88.7 pp) × 16.15 × 4.7
Electron Equipt:
Radar: 1/Type 1006 nav.
Sonar: Type 185 underwater telephone, Type 2010, Type 2013
M: 3 Mirrlees-Blackstone EWSL-12 MA 1,450-hp diesels, electric drive; 1 Kort-nozzle prop; 2,680 shp—300-shp electric low-speed motor
Electric: 2,150 kw **Range:** 5,000/9 **Fuel:** 244 tons
Crew: 61 total (including 12 technicians)

Remarks: Intended for sonar-propagation trials and also fitted to lay cable over the bows. Equipped with 350-hp retractable bow-thruster and passive tank stabilization system. Propulsion plant extremely quiet, with a 300-hp electric motor for low speeds. Has four laboratories and seven special winches. Can carry and lay 400 tons of undersea cable and 361 tons cable repeaters. Navigation equipment includes SINS, communications and navigational satellite receivers, two optical rangefinders, Decca Mk 21, and considerable other equipment. R.M.A.S.–operated. Optical rangefinder atop pilothouse. Refitted 1986 to 3-87 to test new equipment, and again beginning 1-89.

Note: Torpedo research vessel *Whitehead* (A 364) was given a short refit in 1-90 and then placed in reserve; the ship was stricken during 1991. Sonar research barge *Crystal* (RDV 01) was offered for sale by the Defence Research Agency during 1991. Privately owned (BAe Dynamics) guided-missile trials and demonstration craft *Verifier* was offered for sale during 11-90.

REPAIR SHIP

◆ **1 former oilfield support tender**
Bldr: Øresundsvarvet AB, Landskrona, Sweden

	L	In serv. (R.N.)
A 132 Diligence	1981	12-3-84

D: 10,765 tons (fl) **S:** 15.5 kts
Dim: 111.47 (101.30 pp) × 20.97 × 6.70
A: 4/20-mm 85-cal. Oerlikon GAM-B01 AA (I × 4)

REPAIR SHIP *(continued)*

Electron Equipt:
Radar: 3/. . . nav.—EW: 4 DLB decoy RL (VI × 4)
M: 5 Nohab Polar F216V-D 16-cyl. diesels (3,600 bhp each), electric drive; 1 CP prop; 6,000 shp—2/ 1,500-shp side-thrusters forward, 2/1,500-shp rotatable thrusters aft
Electric: 4,400 kw from main engines + 2/208-kw emergency generators
Range: 5,000/12 **Fuel:** 837 tons
Crew: R.F.A.: 15 officers, 24 non-rated; 90 total naval repair party (total accommodations: 147 + 55 temporary)

Diligence (A 132) Walter Sartori, 1-90

Diligence (A 132) Carlo Martinelli, 4-89

Remarks: 6,544 grt/4,941 dwt. Built as a North Sea oilfield support ship and chartered during the Falklands War for emergency repair work in the open sea. Purchased outright 31-10-83 from Stena (U.K.) and accepted for Royal Fleet Auxiliary service 12-3-84 after conversion to add additional repair features. Major refit completed 26-10-89, during which she was relieved in the Falkland Islands by commercial near-sister *Stena Seaspread.* Employed in the Persian Gulf area during the 1990–91 crisis.

Has an ice-strengthened hull with a centerline "moonpool" for use by divers. Flight deck atop pilothouse can accept helicopters up to Chinook-size. Has four 20- to 40-ton, one 20-ton, one 15-ton, and one 5-ton cranes. Capable of being used for fire fighting, towing, and salvage. Very maneuverable and can make 6 kts sideways. A Köngsberg Albatross dynamic positioning system and four 5-ton anchors for a 4-point moor are provided. During conversion for naval use, a large hull and machinery repair workshop was added in the well deck aft; accommodations were increased; a saturation diving facility; armament; magazines; fuel, water, and electrical power overside transfer facilities; increased communications equipment, and additional cranes were added. Carries 2,313 tons cargo fuel.

Note: When *Diligence* is unavailable, commercial near-sister *Stena Seaspread* is normally chartered:

Stena Seaspread
Bldr: Øresundvarvet AB, Landskrona, Sweden (In serv. 1980)

D: . . . tons **S:** 18 kts **Dim:** 112.02 (101.33 pp) × 20.99 × 6.84
M: 5 Nohab Polar F216V-D 16-cyl. diesels (3,600 bhp each), electric drive; 1 CP prop; 6,000 shp—2/1,500-shp side-thrusters forward, 2/1,500-shp rotatable thrusters aft
Fuel: 837 tons (+ 2,000 tons cargo fuel)

Remarks: 6,061 grt/4,835 dwt. Ice-strengthened hull. Has "moonpool" amidships, four 20- to 40-ton cranes, one 20-ton, two 15-ton cranes. Helicopter platform atop pilothouse. Generally resembles *Diligence.*

ACCOMMODATIONS SHIP

♦ 1 "County"-class former guided-missile destroyer
Bldr: Harland & Wolff, Belfast

	Laid down	L	In serv.
D 12 Kent	1-3-60	27-9-61	15-8-63

D: approx. 5,400 tons (fl) **S:** . . . kts
Dim: 158.55 (153.90 pp) × 16.46 × . . .
A: 4/114-mm 45-cal. Vickers Mk 6 DP (II × 2; inactivated)
Electron Equipt (all inactivated):
Radar: 1/Type 978 nav., 1/Type 992Q surf./air search, 1/Type 965 early warning, 1/Type 277 height-finder, 1/Type 901 missile control, 1/Type 903 f.c.
Sonar: Type 184M hull-mounted, Type 162M bottomed-target classification
M (inactivated): COSAG: 2 sets A.E.I. geared steam turbines (15,000 shp each), 4 Type G6 gas turbines (7,500 shp each); 2 props; 60,000 shp
Boilers: 2 Babcock & Wilcox; 49.21 kg/cm^2, 510° C
Electric: 4,750 kw tot. **Range:** 3,500/28 **Fuel:** 600 tons

Kent (D 12) Jasper Van Raemdonck, 8-9

Remarks: Decommissioned and relegated to harbor training 16-5-83. Converted 3-10-84 to 6-8-85 to act as accommodations hulk for cadets; has 400 berths. Completed six-week refit on 10-3-88. During 1991, it was planned to replace her with the decommissioned *Bristol* (D 23), with *Kent* to be sold to Chile for use as spares, but the pl came to naught.

Note: The 100-m-long commercial oilfield accommodations barge *Bibby Progress* w leased during 1990 from Bibby Maritime, Inc.; refit to accommodate 300 troops w completed in Gdańsk, Poland, on 10-11-90. A 60-meter accommodations barge built Singapore was converted to military use at Devonport Dockyard during 1990.

FLEET REPLENISHMENT SHIPS

♦ 2 Fort Grange-class ammunition, food, and stores ships
Bldr: Scott-Lithgow, Greenock, Scotland

	Laid down	L	In serv.
A 385 Fort Grange	9-11-73	9-12-76	6-4-78
A 386 Fort Austin	9-12-75	9-3-78	11-5-79

Fort Grange (A 385) Ben Sullivan, 7

Fort Austin (A 386)—with tug *Basset* (A 250) R. J. L. Fry, 9

D: 22,749 tons (fl) **S:** 20 kts
Dim: 183.78 (170.00 pp) × 24.06 × 9.03
A: 2/20-mm 85-cal Oerlikon GAM-B01 AA (I × 2)—1 or 2/Sea King helicopters
Electron Equipt:
Radar: 1/Type 1006 nav., 1/Kelvin-Hughes 21/16P nav., 1/Kelvin Hughes 14/12 nav.
EW: 2/DLC decoy RL (VIII × 2), Type 182 towed torpedo decoy
M: 1 Sulzer 8 RND 90 diesel; 1 prop; 23,200 bhp—2/515-kw thrusters fwd
Electric: 4,120 kw tot. (8 × 515-kw diesel sets) **Range:** 10,000/2
Crew: 127 tot. R.F.A. + 45 R.N. + 36 civilian supply staff

Remarks: *Fort Grange:* 16,046 grt/8,300 dwt; *Fort Austin:* 16,054 grt/8,165 Ordered 11-71 and 7-72, respectively. In addition to the flight deck at the stern

T REPLENISHMENT SHIPS *(continued)*

roof can be used to operate helicopters. One Sea King is normally carried, gh up to four can be accommodated (A 386 acted as helicopter training ship while was operating in support of U.N. forces in the Mideast during 1991), and can ically be operated as auxiliary ASW helicopter support ships.

holds total 12,200 m³ to carry guided weapons and ammunition and general including 2,300 m³ of refrigerated provisions. Have three sliding-stay, constant-, alongside-replenishment stations on each side. There are two 10-ton and four lectric stores cranes. Platforms to accept the antennas for two SCOT SHF e communications system radomes were built atop the superstructure, but carry rcial MARISAT equipment instead. Have two auxiliary boilers. Two additional AA can be installed aft.

egent-class ammunition, food, and stores ships

	Bldr	Laid down	L	In serv.
Resource	Scotts SB, Greenock	6-64	11-2-66	18-5-67
Regent	Harland & Wolff, Belfast	9-64	9-3-66	6-6-67

urce (A 480) — Dr. Giorgio Arra, 11-89

nt (A 486) — Leo Van Ginderen, 6-90

22,890 tons (fl) **S:** 17 kts
n: 195.08 (182.68 pp) × 23.55 × 8.69
ctron Equipt:
adar: 1/Type 1006 nav., 1/Kelvin-Hughes 21/16P nav., 1/Kelvin-Hughes 14/12 nav.
W: 2/DLC decoy RL (VIII × 2), Type 182 towed torpedo decoy
2 sets A.E.I. geared steam turbines; 1 prop; 20,000 shp
lers: 2 Foster-Wheeler; 50.3 kg/cm², 454.5° C **Range:** 12,000/18
ctric: 5,000 kw tot. (4 × 1,250-kw turboalternator sets)
ew: 134 Royal Fleet Auxiliary, 37 civilian supply staff, plus naval air group

rks: 18,029 grt. R.F.A.–operated. Can be fitted with 2/20-mm GAM-B01 AA. sliding-stay, constant-tension, alongside-replenishment stations per side. Have holds. Can carry one Sea King helicopter. A 486 laid up at Rosyth 6-89 with half in "preservation by operation." A 480 given short refit 5-89 to 7-89.

ET OILERS

All Royal Fleet Auxiliary liquid-replenishment vessels employ 6-inch (152-mm) and pump at 100 p.s.i., transferring about 500 tons per hour per station. *Invinci-* quires only about two hrs to refuel and frigates about 40 min.

(+2) Fort Victoria-class replenishment ships

	Bldr	Laid down	L	In serv.
7 Fort Victoria	Harland & Wolff, Belfast	15-9-88	12-6-90	. . .
8 Fort George	Swan Hunter, Wallsend	9-3-89	1-3-91	3-93

32,550 (fl) **S:** 20 kts **Dim:** 203.50 (195.00 wl) × 28.50 × 9.75
provision for Sea Wolf GWS.26 vertical-launch SAM syst. (32 missiles)—4/30-mm DS-30B AA (I × 4)—3/Sea King helicopters
ectron Equipt:
Radar: 1/Type 1007 nav., 1/. . . nav., 1/Type 996 surf./air search, 2/911 f.c.
EW: UAG intercept; 4/DLB RL (VI × 4), Type 182 towed torpedo decoy
M: 2 Crossley-Pielstick 16 PC2.6 V400 medium-speed diesels; 2 props; 23,680 bhp
Electric: 3,900 kw (6 × 650-kw Cummins KTA 386I diesel sets)
Range: . . .
Crew: 102 RFA, 154 naval (including 122 aviation), 24 civilian supply staff

Fort George (A 388)—fitting out — James W. Goss/NAVPIC, 3-91

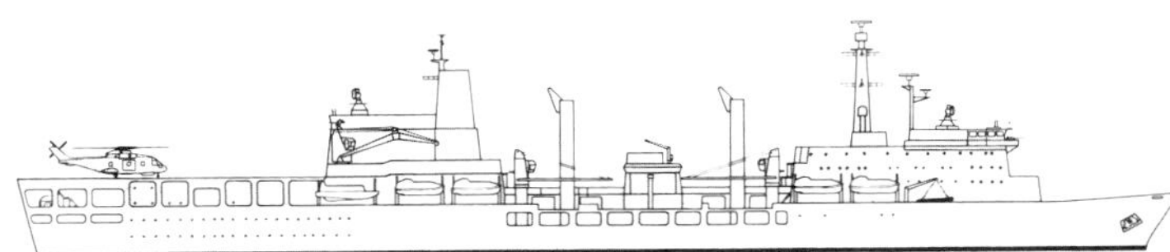

Fort Victoria (A 387) — M.O.D., U.K., 1990

Remarks: Intended to carry about 70,000 barrels (12,505 m³) liquid cargo and 6,234 m³ of munitions, dry stores, and refrigerated cargo. Were to have been a class of six to replace present generation of replenishment ships. The first was ordered 8-5-86; the second was ordered 18-12-87. Racal received the combat systems contract 10-8-89. Completion of A 387 delayed by terrorist explosion 6-9-90; the ship was said to be 32 months behind schedule and £ 63 M over the original price when she arrived at Cammell Laird, Birkenhead, on 2-7-92 to complete fitting out after a serious propulsion failure during sea trials. Because the combat data system is not ready, and to save money, these ships are being completed without the intended armament. Two more, without missile systems, may be ordered later; a planned second series of six simplified variants to replace the "Leaf"-series transport oilers now seems unlikely to be built.

Two dual-purpose liquid/solid replenishment stations per side, plus vertical replenishment and astern refueling capability. Have two pair of fin stabilizers. The ships carry ASW ordnance for their helicopters. Will have SCOT antennas for the SHF SATCOMM Skynet IV system. One 25-ton, two 10-ton, and two 5-ton electric cranes will be fitted, with one 10-ton crane capable of supporting an additional underway-refueling rig. Large helicopter flight deck with two landing spots can also land Sea Harrier fighter-bombers. Twin hangar with extensive helicopter repair facilities. Were originally to have had six 1,600-kw generators powered by Ruston 8RKCs diesels; now carry six 650-kw MB404E alternators powered by Cummins KTA386I diesels.

◆ 3 Olwen class

Bldr: Hawthorn Leslie, Hebburn-on-Tyne (A 124: Swan Hunter, Wallsend-on-Tyne)

	L	In serv.
A 122 Olwen (ex-*Olynthus*)	10-7-64	21-6-65
A 123 Olna	28-7-65	1-4-66
A 124 Olmeda (ex-*Oleander*)	19-11-64	18-10-65

Olna (A 123) — Dr. Giorgio Arra, 9-91

FLEET OILERS *(continued)*

Olwen (A 122) Leo Van Ginderen, 4-92

D: 10,890 tons light (36,000 fl) **S:** 20 kts
Dim: 197.51 (185.92 pp) × 25.6 × 10.5
A: 3/20-mm Oerlikon Mk 7A AA (I × 3)—2/7.62-mm mg (I × 2)
Electron Equipt:
Radar: 1/Type 1006 nav., 1/Kelvin-Hughes 14/12 nav., 1/Kelvin-Hughes 14/16 nav.
EW: 2/DLC decoy RL (VIII × 2), Type 182 towed torpedo decoy
M: 1 set Pamatrada geared steam turbines; 1 prop; 26,500 shp
Boilers: 2 Babcock & Wilcox, 60 kg/cm^2, 510° C
Electric: 6,500 kw tot. (4 × 1,500-kw turboalternators, 1 × 500-kw diesel set)
Range: . . ./. . . **Fuel:** 3,684 tons + 170.5 tons diesel
Crew: 95 RFA + 40 naval air group

Remarks: A 122: 18,604 grt/25,537 dwt; A 123: 18,582 grt/22,353 dwt; A 124: 18,536 grt/22,627 dwt. R.F.A.–operated. Hull reinforced for ice navigation, living space air-conditioned, advanced automation, excellent facilities for replenishment at sea. Helicopter platform; hangar to port enlarged to hold two Sea King helicopters, but normally only one is carried. Can carry 18,400 tons fuel oil, 1,720 tons diesel, 3,730 tons aircraft fuel, and 130 tons lube oil. Have INTELSAT commercial communications satellite system. A 124 completed long refit 1989, A 123 began one 31-7-89, experiencing a serious fire while in the yard, 9-1-90. A 123 has a bow-thruster and improved underway-replenishment equipment.

Note: "Later Tide"-class replenishment oiler *Tidespring* (A 75) was paid off on 13-12-91 and towed to India for scrapping 20-3-92.

SMALL FLEET OILERS

◆ **4 Rover class** Bldr: Swan Hunter, Hebburn-on-Tyne

	L	In serv.
A 269 GREY ROVER	17-4-69	10-4-70
A 270 BLUE ROVER	11-11-69	15-7-70
A 271 GOLD ROVER	7-3-73	22-3-74
A 273 BLACK ROVER	30-10-73	23-8-74

D: 4,700 tons light (11,522 fl) **S:** 19.25 kts
Dim: 140.62 (131.07 pp) × 19.26 × 7.14
A: 2/20-mm Oerlikon Mk 7A AA (I × 2)
Electron Equipt:
Radar: 1/Type 1006 nav., 1/Decca TM 1226 nav., 1/Decca 1229 nav.
EW: 2/DLC decoy RL (VIII × 2), Type 182 towed torpedo decoy
M: 2 Crossley-Pielstick 16PA 4 (A 271, 273: SEMT-Pielstick 16PC 2 2V400) diesels; 1 CP prop; 15,360 bhp—bow-thruster
Electric: 2,720 kw tot. (8 × 340-kw diesel sets) **Range:** 15,000/15
Fuel: 965 tons heavy oil + 123 tons diesel
Crew: 16 officers, 31 unlicensed

Black Rover (A 273) Ben Sullivan, 7-91

Blue Rover (A 270) Leo Van Ginderen

Blue Rover (A 270) Gilbert Gyssels,

Remarks: A 269: 7,513 grt/6,931 dwt; A 270: 7,513 grt/7,042 dwt; A 271 and 7,574 grt/6,799 dwt. R.F.A.–operated. Carry 6,600 tons of fuel plus water, dry and provisions. Have 13 cargo tanks totaling 8,128 m^3, one dry cargo hold. He deck but no hangar. A 271 is used in supporting the training squadron at Po First two re-engined 1973–74. Stern shapes vary, early units having two stern a and later units one. A 269 employed 1988 in trials of an over-the-horizon radar employing her HF radio antennas. A 269, 270, 273 have gun platforms o forecastles. Sister *Green Rover* (A 268) placed in reserve on 30-day notice 27-5- sold to Indonesia in 1-92.

TRANSPORT OILERS

◆ **1 ex-Norwegian tanker** Bldr: Uddevallavarvet, Uddevalla, Swede

	L	In serv.
A 111 OAKLEAF (ex-*Oktania*)	1981	14-8-86 (in RFA)

D: 49,310 tons (fl) **S:** 15.75 kts (14.5 sust.)
Dim: 173.69 (168.00 wl) × 32.26 × 10.22
A: 2/20-mm Oerlikon Mk 7A AA (I × 2)—2/7.62-mm mg (I × 2)
Electron Equipt:
Radar: 1/Decca TM1226 nav., 1/Decca 1229 nav.
EW: DLB decoy RL (VI × 2)
M: 2 Uddevalla-Burmeister & Wain 4L80GFCA 4-cyl., 2-stroke diesels; 1 CP prop; 12,250 bhp—bow and stern tunnel-thruster
Electric: 2,472 kw (3 × 800-kw diesel sets, 1 × 72-kw diesel set)
Range: . . ./. . . **Crew:** 36 tot.

Oakleaf (A 111) Dr. Giorgio Arra,

Oakleaf (A 111) Leo Van Ginderen

RANSPORT OILERS *(continued)*

emarks: 24,608 grt/34,800 dwt. Leased 7-85 to replace *Plumleaf* (A 78). Cargo: ,020 m³ in 16 tanks; no dry cargo. Can carry up to 15,430 tons water ballast. onverted for naval support service by Falmouth Ship Repairers, 17-2-86 to 14-8-86. eceived two alongside fueling stations (one per side) with raised working deck, astern fueling capability; two additional generator sets, additional communications, NAV-AT equipment, and INTELSAT SATCOMM. Has three 13.7 kg/cm² auxiliary boilers. etained sauna. Non-manned engine spaces when under way. Hull reinforced for ice avigation.

3 Appleleaf class Bldr: Cammell Laird, Birkenhead

	L	In serv.
81 Brambleleaf (ex-*Hudson Deep*)	22-1-76	3-80
109 Bayleaf	27-10-81	26-3-82
110 Orangeleaf (ex-*Balder London*, ex-*Hudson Progress*)	. . .	2-5-84 (RN)

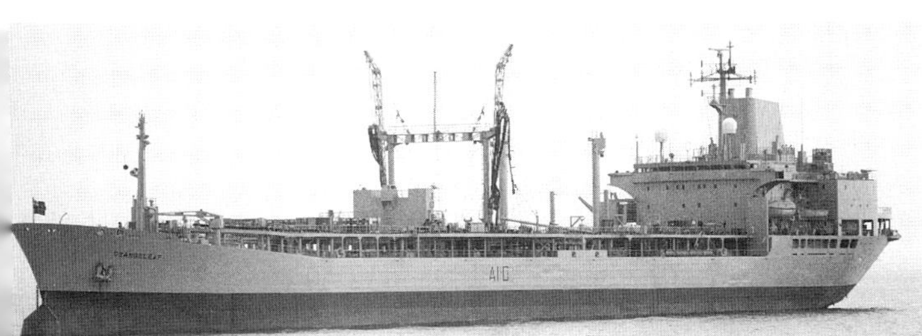
angeleaf (A 110) Maritime Photographic, 9-91

ambleleaf (A 81) Maritime Photographic, 8-90

D: 37,747 tons (fl) **S:** 16.5 kts
Dim: 170.69 (163.51 pp) × 25.94 × 11.56
A: 2/20-mm Oerlikon Mk 7A AA (I × 2)—2/7.62-mm mg (I × 2)
Electron Equipt:
Radar: 1/Decca TM1226 nav., 1/Decca 1229 nav.
EW: 2/DLC (VIII × 2) or DLB (VI × 2) decoy RL
M: 2 Crossley-Pielstick 14PC2V-400 diesels; 1 CP prop; 14,000 bhp
Electric: 6,660 kw tot. (2 × 2,704-kw diesel sets, 2 × 626-kw diesel sets)
Fuel: 2,498 tons **Crew:** 65 tot.

marks: A 81: 20,440 grt/33,257 dwt; A 109: 20,086 grt/29,999 dwt; A 110: 84 grt/33,751 dwt. R.F.A.–operated. A 81 acquired 1979 and refitted for naval ice by Cammell Laird 1979–80; stack raised 3.5 m, dry-cargo hold added forward, enishment-at-sea working deck added amidships, and superstructure enlarged aft. 9, on which work had been suspended while still on the ways, was chartered 3-4-81 Lombard Leasing Services and similarly altered. A 110, completed 1979 and on ter since 4-82 from Lloyds' Industrial Leasing, was rechartered 26-3-84 and ini-y operated without replenishment equipment, receiving a similar conversion to of her sisters in 1985 to 2-5-86. Sister *Appleleaf* (A 79) leased to Australia for five s (with purchase option) on 26-9-89.
quid-cargo capacity is 32,309 m³ (A 110: 41,881 m³) in 24 tanks; there is no cargo capacity. All now have one refueling station per side, over-the-stern fueling, MARISAT satellite communication equipment. Have three auxiliary boilers.

CELLANEOUS AUXILIARY SHIPS

Antarctic patrol ship
ldr: B. H. Ulstein SY, Hatlo, Norway (In serv. 1990)

1 Endurance (ex-*Polar Circle*, ex-A 176)

6,500 tons (fl) **S:** 12 kts **Dim:** 91.00 (82.50 pp) × 17.90 × 6.50
none (*see* Remarks)
ectron Equipt: Radar: . . .
: 2 Ulstein-Bergen BRM-8 diesels; 1 4-bladed Kort-nozzle prop; 8,152 bhp—1,000 shp bow-thruster, 775-shp stern side-thruster
ectric: 5,170 kw tot. (2 × Leroy Somer 1,980-kw shaft generators, 2 × 605-kw Mitsubishi diesel sets)
nge: 4–5,000/12 **Fuel:** 600 tons **Endurance:** 120 days
ew: 16 officers, 100 enlisted

Endurance (A 171)—as *Polar Circle* (A 176) Maritime Photographic, 10-91

Endurance (A 171)—as *Polar Circle* (A 176) Maritime Photographic, 10-91

Remarks: 5,129 grt/2,200 dwt. Chartered 14-10-91 for one year with option to purchase from Rieber Shipping, Norway, as a replacement for *Endurance* (A 171, ex-*Anita Dan*), which had failed a hull survey during 9-91. Purchased outright 24-1-92. The ship serves as Antarctic Territories patrol ship to guarantee the continuation of British sovereignty over the Falkland, South Georgia, and South Shetland islands in the Antarctic Atlantic. Original name retained through first deployment to South Atlantic, ending 5-92; officially renamed and renumbered 9-92.

The ship was built as a combination arctic exploration and research vessel, icebreaker, and supply vessel. Able to break 3-ft. ice at 3 kts. The double-skinned hull is equipped with ice fins forward of the propeller, and the rudder foundation has ice knives fitted. There is an elevator-equipped helicopter hangar below the flight deck. Scientific equipment includes a radiosonde balloon-launch facility, dry and wet labs, 174.4 m of scientific equipment storage, the capability to accept portable research vans, and a 20-ton A-frame crane at the stern to handle towed equipment. There are a 27-ton crane and a 5-ton electrohydraulic crane to handle cargo in a forward hold. Carries 78 m³ aviation fuel and 250 m³ potable water.

Navigation equipment provides fixes to 5-meter accuracy and includes two gyrocompasses, electromagnetic log, several echo-sounders, Furuno object-avoidance sonar, Robertson autopilot, and a homing beacon for the helicopter. Has INMARAT satellite communications equipment. Crew accommodations include a sauna, infirmary, and exercise room.

Note: The former South Atlantic patrol vessel, *Endurance* (A 171) was stricken 21-11-91 and offered for sale as an operating vessel. The "Seabed Operations Tender" *Challenger* (K 07) was paid off 22-11-90 after only six years' service and offered for sale to oilfield contractors; no offers had been made by 5-92.

◆ **1 aviation support ship** Bldr: CNR Breda, Venice, Italy

	L	In serv.
A 135 Argus (ex-*Contender Bezant*)	1981	1-6-88

D: 22,256 tons light (28,480 fl) **S:** 22 max. (19 sust.)
Dim: 173.01 (163.63 pp) × 30.64 × 8.20
Air Group: 6/Sea King helicopters—12/Sea Harrier V/STOL fighters (8 operational)
A: 2/30-mm BMARC DS-30B AA (I × 2)—2/20-mm Oerlikon GAM-B01 AA (I × 2)
Electron Equipt:
Radar: 1/Type 1006 nav., 1/Type 1007 nav., 1/Type 994 surf./air search
EW: Thorn Guardian intercept, 4/DLB decoy RL (VI × 4), Type 182 towed torpedo decoy
M: electric drive: 2 Lindholmen-Pielstick 18PC2.5 V400 diesel, 2 Lindholmen propulsion motors; 2 props; 23,400 shp
Range: 20,000/19
Fuel: 5,617 tons heavy oil, 3,251 tons aviation fuel
Electric: 3,850 kw (3 × 1,200-kw diesel sets, 1 × 250-kw diesel set)
Crew: 23 officers, 56 unlicensed RFA; 3 officers, 25 enlisted RN; 42 officers, 95 enlisted RN in training detachment (up to 750 troops in emergency)

MISCELLANEOUS AUXILIARY SHIPS *(continued)*

Argus (A 135)—returning from Persian Gulf Maritime Photographic, 4

Argus (A 135) Maritime Photographic, 6-92

Argus (A 135) James W. Goss/NAVPIC, 4-91

Remarks: 26,421 grt/12,221 dwt. Former roll-on/roll-off vehicle and container cargo ship. (A 135 purchased 2-3-84, having been on charter since 5-82, when she was used as an aircraft transport to the Falklands. Conversion at Harland and Wolff, Belfast, was to complete 1986, with vehicle cargo decks converted to a hangar and elevators added. Initially accepted 28-10-87, "accepted" 3-3-88, and "dedicated" 1-6-88, but continued in a trials status until commencing a 17-7-89 to 3-10-89 refit. Intended to replace *Engadine* (K 08) as helicopter training ship or to act as a transport for Harrier/Sea Harrier aircraft. Plans to purchase sister *Contender Argent* dropped late 1984.

Has space for eight Sea Harriers and three helicopters on the hangar deck and three helicopters on deck, aft. There are two aircraft elevators. Hangar segregates into four sections. The flight deck (created by upending the former hatch covers, filling these with concrete, and then laying over with steel, some 1.9 m *thick* for ballast and stability purposes) measures 113.52 × 28 but is encumbered by stack and superstructure to starboard. Has two flight deck aircraft elevators.

Racal supplied the sensors, data system, communications, and weapons control package, which includes the CANE action data system. Type 994 radar uses Plessey antenna, vice standard R.N. unit. Passive tank stabilization added, watertight compartmentation improved. Can carry 5,405 tons water ballast. Despite "auxiliary" status, may be employed in a combat role—although lack of ski jump inhibits V/ST operations. Can also transfer fuel to ships in company.

Deployed twice to the Persian Gulf during the 1990–91 crisis: on 16-10-90 equip with a 100-bed emergency hospital and carrying 4 Sea King helicopters, and du 4-91 with 11 Sea King HC.4 and several Lynx and Gazelle helicopters. Has devel hull cracking and is generally considered not to be a successful ship.

◆ **1 unmodified "Leander"-class cadet training ship, ex-frigate**

	Bldr	Laid down	L	In serv.
F 52 Juno	John I. Thornycroft, Woolston	16-7-74	24-11-65	18-7-67

Juno (F 52) Maritime Photographic,

D: 2,400 tons (2,800 fl) **S:** 28 kts
Dim: 113.38 (109.73 pp) × 12.50 × 4.40 (5.4 props)
A: 2/20-mm Oerlikon Mk 7A AA (I × 2)
Electron Equipt:
Radar: 1/Type . . . nav., 1/Type 994 surf./air search
Sonar: Type 184M hull-mounted, Type 162M bottomed-target classification
EW: 2/DLC decoy RL (VIII × 2), Type 182 towed torpedo decoy
M: 2 sets White–English Electric geared steam turbines; 2 props, 30,000 shp
Boilers: 2 Babcock & Wilcox 3-drum; 38.7 kg/cm², 450° C
Electric: 1,600 kw **Range:** approx. 4,500/12 **Fuel:** 460 tons
Crew: 17 officers, 245 enlisted

Remarks: *Juno* was the last unmodified early "Leander." She entered refit 9 Rosyth for conversion as a navigational training ship to replace *Torquay* in Economics forced delay of the plan, and the ship was given a regular overhaul enc 10-82 and placed in ready reserve. In 1984–85 the work was completed: th 114-mm gun mount, Limbo mortar, and Sea Cat SAM systems removed, Ty

LLANEOUS AUXILIARY SHIPS *(continued)*

d most EW equipment deleted; ASW TT, new navigational gear, and Type Interrogation added. Fin stabilizers removed 1986. The helicopter hangar is workshop. The torpedo tubes had been removed by 10-90. Although still listed gate" by the British M.O.D., has little combat potential. Is administratively to the 7th Frigate Squadron and operates for HMS *Dryad* Navigational School, Portsmouth. To be paid off and stricken 12-92.

artered navigational training ship, ex-trawler
Clelands SB, Wallsend

ELLA (In serv. 7-73; chartered 10-83)

ella James W. Goss/NAVPIC, 6-90

pprox. 2,300 tons (fl) **S:** 16.5 kts
70.20 (65.20 pp) × 12.70 × 4.90
tron Equipt: Radar: 3/. . . nav. **Electric:** 1,060 kw
Mirrlees-Blackstone KMR-7 diesel; 1 CP prop; 3,246 bhp

ks: 1,238 grt. Chartered during Falklands War as an auxiliary minesweeper. ed again 10-83 while lying idle, initially for submarine target and security t Faslane and since 1985 as a navigational training ship for HMS *Dryad* ional Training School, Portsmouth. Charter extended for four years in 4-90. ll, white superstructure, buff masting. Semi-rigid inflatable boats stowed ps are handled by a crane to starboard. Owned by J. Marr, Hull.

viation trials support ship
: Hall Russell, Aberdeen, Scotland (In serv. 1966)

EL TEMPLAR (ex-*Criscilla*)

el Templar Ben Sullivan, 5-89

pprox. 1,500 tons (fl) **S:** . . . **Dim:** 56.55 × 11.0 × 4.29
tron Equipt: Radar: 2/. . . nav.
1 Mirrlees National 7-cyl. diesel; 1 CP prop, 1,680 bhp
tric: 930 kw (2 × 260-kw, 2 × 180-kw, 1 × 50-kw)

ks: 892 grt/268 nrt. Former stern-haul trawler purchased 1980 by Royal Air- stablishment, Farnborough. Transferred to R.M.A.S. operational control (re- g as R.A.E. property) on 1-10-88. Refitted 1988–89 and was in R.M.A.S. Standby on reserve at Portsmouth at end 1989. Capsized during fire while under refit at 1-91; righted and refloated 8-2-91 and transferred to Portsmouth 30-4-91 for further service; to be operational again during 1992.

oyal yacht Bldr: John Brown & Co., Clydebank

	Laid down	L	In serv.
BRITANNIA	7-52	16-4-53	14-1-54

3,990 tons, 4,053 std. (4,961 fl) **S:** 21 kts
: 125.9 (115.82 pp) × 16.76 × 4.86
ctron Equipt: Radar: 2/Type 1006 nav.
2 sets geared steam turbines; 2 props; 12,000 shp **Boilers:** 2
ge: 2,800/20; 3,200/18; 3,675/14 **Fuel:** 510 tons
w: 21 officers, 256 enlisted

Britannia Dr. Giorgio Arra, 5-91

Remarks: 5,769 grt. Naval-manned. In wartime, would become a hospital ship (200 beds and 60 medical personnel) and have a helicopter platform. Gyrofin stabilizers. Reboilered during 1980 refit; equipped to burn distillate fuel 1984. Equipped with INTELSAT satellite communication equipment in 1982. Refitted 1986 to 12-10-87 to extend service 10–15 years, wooden decking deleted. In 1991, consideration was given to disposing of the ship, due to her operating expense.

MOORING, SALVAGE, AND NET TENDERS

♦ 3 "Sal" class Bldr: Hall Russell, Ltd., Aberdeen, Scotland

	Laid down	L	In serv.
A 185 SALMOOR	19-4-84	8-5-85	12-11-85
A 186 SALMASTER	17-9-84	12-11-85	12-5-86
A 187 SALMAID	29-6-84	22-5-86	28-10-86

Salmaid (A 187) James W. Goss/NAVPIC, 8-88

Salmoor (A 185) Maritime Photographic, 6-91

D: 1,700 tons (fl) **S:** 15 kts **Dim:** 77.10 (65.80 pp) × 14.80 × 3.80
Electron Equipt: Radar: 1/Decca . . . nav.
M: 2 Ruston-Paxman 8RKCM diesels; 1 CP prop; 4,000 bhp
Range: . . . **Crew:** 4 officers, 17 enlisted, 27 spare berths

MOORING, SALVAGE, AND NET TENDERS *(continued)*

Remarks: 1,967 grt. Ordered 29-1-84 as replacements for "Kin" class. R.M.A.S.–manned. Capable of mooring, buoy tending, salvage, diving support, and fire fighting. Have 400-ton tidal lift/200-ton deadlift capacity. Can carry 14-man salvage party. Based in the Clyde, at Rosyth, and at Portsmouth, respectively. A 187 conducted trials 1987 with 20-ton submersible LR 5. A 187 received reinforced bows, larger diameter bow roller during refit completed 23-3-89.

◆ **2 Pochard class** (1 in reserve)

	Bldr	L	In serv.
A 164 Goosander (ex-P 196)	Robb Caledon Ltd.	12-4-73	10-9-73
A 165 Pochard (ex-P 197)	Robb Caledon Ltd.	21-6-73	11-12-73

Pochard (A 165) James W. Goss/NAVPIC, 6-89

D: 750 tons (1,200 fl) **S:** 10 kts **Dim:** 55.4 (48.8 pp) × 12.2 × 5.5
Electron Equipt: Radar: 1/. . . nav.
M: 2 Paxman RPHXM 16-cyl. diesels; 550 bhp
Range: 3,250/9.5 **Crew:** 26 tot.

Remarks: R.M.A.S.–operated. All moorings, salvage, and boom vessels are multipurpose and are capable of transporting and servicing moorings, performing salvage duties, and, in wartime, handling harbor-defense nets. Can dead-lift 200 tons over bow horns. *Pochard* (A 165) to reserve at Portsmouth 1991.

Note: The "Insect"-class fleet tender *Scarab* is also equipped as a moorings tender (10-ton lift). The surviving "Kin"-class mooring tender, *Kinbrace* (A 281), was deactivated in 1989; sister *Kinloss* (A 482), in reserve since 1986, was towed to Rosyth 9-12-88 for use as a shock-trials barge through 4-90. The three "Wild Duck"-class moorings tenders have been stricken also: *Mandarin* (P 192) early in 1992 (sold for scrap 4-92), *Garganey* (P 194) in 1991, and *Goldeneye* (P 195) sold commercial in Scotland, 1991.

SEAGOING TUGS

◆ **3 Roysterer class** Bldr: C.D. Holmes, Beverley, Humberside

	L	In serv.
A 361 Roysterer	20-5-70	25-4-72
A 366 Robust	7-10-71	6-4-74
A 502 Rollicker	29-1-71	6-3-73

Robust (A 366) Leo Van Ginderen, 8-91

Rollicker (A 502) James W. Goss/NAVPIC, 3-90

D: 1,630 tons (fl) **S:** 15 kts **Dim:** 54.8 (49.4 pp) × 11.6 × 5.5
Electron Equipt: Radar: 2/Decca . . . nav.
M: 2 Mirrlees KMR6 diesels; 2 CP props; 4,500 bhp
Range: 13,000/12
Crew: 10 officers, 21 unlicensed (plus 10-man R.N. salvage party needed)

Remarks: R.M.A.S.–operated; 50-ton bollard pull. Although designed f distance towing, have been used primarily in port service, A 361 at Greenock, Portsmouth, A 366 at Devonport. Have heavy tripod mast, with after legs co engine exhausts.

AMMUNITION TRANSPORTS

◆ **2 Throsk class** Bldr: Appledore Furguson SB, Appledore

	Laid down	L	In serv
A 382 Arrochar (ex-*St. George*)	9-11-80	3-81	7-81
A 378 Kinterbury	1980	8-11-80	20-1-81

Kinterbury (A 378) Maritime Photographi

D: 2,193 tons (fl) **S:** 14 kts **Dim:** 70.57 (64.31 pp) × 11.9 × 4.
Electron Equipt: Radar: 1/Type 1006 nav.
M: 2 Mirrlees-Blackstone diesels; 1 prop; 3,000 bhp
Range: 1,500/14; 5,000/10 **Crew:** 10 officers, 22 unlicensed

Remarks: R.M.A.S.–operated. Two holds, two 5-ton cranes; 1,150 dwt. Tw holds: 750 m total. Can transport 760 tons in holds plus 25 tons of cargo on dec was operated by the army's Royal Corps of Transport until transferred to Roy time Auxiliary Service on 7-11-88; renamed 1-4-89, and began refit 20-10-89 to accommodations. Sister *Throsk* (A 379) was put up for sale in 7-91 and sold to in 1-92. A 382 in reserve 1992.

SERVICE CRAFT

Note: Most service craft are operated by the Royal Maritime Auxiliary (R.M.A.S.), a civilian organization, with some operated by the reservists of th Naval Auxiliary Service (R.N.X.S.). Increasingly, pendant numbers are be played; in the listings below, where the numbers are not borne, they are parentheses.

DEGAUSSING TENDER

◆ **1 Magnet class** Bldr: Cleland SB Co., Wallsend

	Laid down	L	In serv.
A 115 Lodestone	22-12-78	15-11-79	4-80

D: approx. 1,100 tons (fl) **S:** 12 kts
Dim: 54.8 (50.0 pp) × 11.4 × 3.0
Electron Equipt: Radar: 1/Type 1006 nav.
M: 2 Mirrlees-Blackstone ESL-6-MGR diesels, electric drive; 2 pr 1,650 shp
Electric: 245 kw **Range:** 1,750/12 **Fuel:** 40 tons
Crew: 15 tot.

Magnet (A 114)—since stricken James W. Goss/NAVPI

AUSSING TENDERS *(continued)*

ks: Built to commercial standards. R.M.A.S.–operated. Uses two 800-cell, battery banks and two variable-resistance capacitors to provide 4,000 amps d.c. econds. Can deperm a 60,000-ton ship. Completed a refit 21-12-84; normally in , she was activated 6-86 to 12-2-87, when another refit began. Sister *Magnet* (A aced in reserve in 1989, was reactivated 4-90 as support and berthing vessel for ictural trials ship *Hulval* (ex-frigate *Naiad*) and was stricken in 1991.

EDO RETRIEVERS

ornado class Bldr: Hall Russell, Aberdeen

	Laid down	L	In serv.	Based
Tornado	2-11-78	24-5-79	15-11-79	Clyde
Torch	5-12-78	7-8-79	12-2-80	Portland
Tormentor	19-3-79	6-11-79	29-4-80	Plymouth
Toreador	14-6-79	14-2-80	1-7-80	Clyde

entor (A 142) Ben Sullivan, 5-91

60 tons (698 fl) **S:** 14 kts **Dim:** 47.47 (40.0 pp) × 8.53 × 3.0
ctron Equipt: Radar: 1/Type 1006 nav.
2 Lister-Blackstone ESL-8-MGR diesels; 2 props; 2,200 bhp
ge: 3,000/. . . **Fuel:** 110 tons **Crew:** 14 tot.

ks: R.M.A.S.–operated. Stern ramp for weapon recovery. A 140 used in trials th Qubit TRAC IV B track recording system and Bathymetrics Bathyscan 300 n side-looking sonar/echo sounder. Are being fitted to accept the Fleet Exercise ying System, of which two sets are being procured; will be able to lay and 20 exercise mines or 16 Versatile Exercise Mines. The system employs three rails mounted on the fantail and adds 30 tons to the displacement when in-

orrent class

	Bldr	L	In serv.
Torrent	Cleland SB, Wallsend	29-3-71	10-9-71

nt (A 127) James W. Goss/NAVPIC, 6-80

468 tons (685 fl) **S:** 11.5 kts
: 49.55 (44.2 pp) × 9.72 × 3.05
ctron Equipt: Radar: 1/Type 1006 nav.
Paxman 16 RPHM diesel; 1 prop; 700 bhp **Electric:** 300 kw
ge: 1,500/11 **Fuel:** 49 tons **Crew:** 19 tot.

ks: Can stow 32 torpedoes in hold and 10 on deck and perform post-firing nance. Stern ramp for recovery. R.M.A.S.–operated; based on the Clyde. Sister (A 128) placed in reserve at Greenock in 1989 and offered for sale 1991.

orpedo-recovery launches Bldr: R. Dunston, Thorne (In serv. 1979)

7869 7870

15 tons **S:** 9 kts **Dim:** 13.8 × 2.98 × 0.76
1 Perkins 6-354 diesel; 1 prop; 104 bhp **Crew:** 4 tot.

ks: All based at Greenock.

◆ **1 ex-R.A.F. 1300 series former air/sea rescue launch**

L 72 (ex-R.A.F. . . .) (In serv. 1955–56)

D: 28.3 tons (fl) **S:** 13 kts **Dim:** 19.2 × 4.7 × 1.5
M: 2 Rolls-Royce C8 diesels; 2 props; 190 bhp

Note: Small torpedo retriever *Endeavour* (A 213) stricken 1990.

DIVING TENDERS

◆ **5 modified Cartmel class** Bldr: Gregson, Blyth

A 308 Ilchester
A 309 Instow
A 310 Invergordon
A 311 Ironbridge (ex-*Invergordon*)
A 318 Ixworth

Instow (A 309) James W. Goss/NAVPIC, 8-87

D: 150 tons (fl) **S:** 10.5 kts **Dim:** 24.38 (22.86 fl) × 6.40 × 2.10
Electron Equipt: Radar: 1/. . . nav.
M: 1 Lister-Blackstone ERS-4-MGR diesel; 1 prop; 330 bhp
Electric: 106 kw **Range:** 700/10 **Crew:** 6 tot. + . . . divers

Remarks: R.M.A.S.–operated, except A 308 and A 309, by Navy. All in service 1974, except A 310, ordered 7-80. Have a decompression chamber on deck forward, beneath a stowage platform for a Gemini dinghy. Can be used for harbor mine clearance. The similar Cartmel-class tenders *Dornoch* and *Fotherby* have also been used as diving tenders.

◆ **1 Datchet class** Bldr: Vosper Pty, Singapore (In serv. 1968)

A 357 Datchet

Datchet (A 357) Leo Van Ginderen, 4-90

D: 70 tons (fl) **S:** 12 kts **Dim:** 22.86 × 5.79 × 1.22
Electron Equipt: Radar: 1/Type 1006
M: 2 Gray Marine diesels; 2 props; 500 bhp **Range:** 500/12

Remarks: Was R.M.A.S., but now R.N.–manned; based at Plymouth. Refitted 8-91.

◆ **4 diver support craft** Bldr: Tough, Teddington (In serv. 1981–82)

D: 10 tons (fl) **S:** 8.5 kts **Dim:** 11.7 × 4.3 × 1.4
M: 1 Perkins 6-354.4 diesel; 120 bhp **Crew:** 2 crew, 12 divers

Remarks: Glass-reinforced plastic construction. One unit, unofficially named *Reclaim,* is attached to HMS *Vernon.*

LOCAL TRAINING SHIPS AND CRAFT

Note: In addition to the units listed below, the following ships are used for training: *Juno* (F 52), nine of the "River"-class minesweepers, and tenders *Glencoe* (A 392), *Clovelly* (A 389), *Cromarty* (A 488), *Froxfield* (A 354), *Hever* (A 1767), *Headcorn* (A 1776), *Aberdovey* (Y 10), *Alnmouth* (Y 13), and *Sultan Venturer* (A 103).

LOCAL TRAINING SHIPS AND CRAFT *(continued)*

◆ **1 modified "Loyal" class** Bldr: Richard Dunston, Thorne

	Laid down	L	In serv.
A 107 MESSINA	7-4-81	5-3-82	1-9-82

Manly (A 92)—since stricken Maritime Photographic, 5-90

D: 135 tons (157.4 fl) **S:** 11.5 kts **Dim:** 24.00 × 6.40 × 2.33
Electron Equipt: Radar: 1/Type 1006 nav.
M: 1 Lister-Blackstone ES4MGR diesel; 1 cycloidal prop; 330 bhp
Range: 700/10 **Fuel:** 4.5 tons **Crew:** 6 tot. (plus trainees)

Remarks: Employed for Royal Marine training. Sisters *Manly* (A 92), *Mentor* (A 94), and *Milbrook* (A 97), formerly used at the HMS *Raleigh* training facility, were paid off 11-91 and sold to Pounds Shipbreakers 4-2-92 for commercial use; A 92 was later purchased for use as a yacht.

◆ **3 target craft, ex-side-haul trawlers**
Bldr: Goole SB & Repair, Goole (In serv. 1961)

BULLSEYE (ex-*Tokio*) MAGPIE (ex-*Honda*) TARGE (ex-*Erimo*)

Targe Maritime Photographic, 12-91

D: 600 tons (fl) **S:** 12 kts **Dim:** 35.85 × 7.73 × 3.70
M: 1 Mirrlees 6-cyl. diesel; 1 prop; 700 bhp **Fuel:** 57 tons
Crew: *Magpie:* 1 officer, 12 enlisted; others: 2 enlisted (when not under radio control)

Remarks: 273 grt/91 nrt. First two acquired 6-82 and third in 6-84 for use as radio-controlled targets at Portland. Royal Navy–manned. "T.V." on hull before name means "Target Vessel." Radar corner reflectors mounted forward, and television camera placed on stub mast forward of stack. *Magpie* is the controller unit and has a large radome atop the pilothouse.

◆ **3 training tenders** (In serv. 1944–46) (* in reserve)

OLIVER TWIST SMIKE* URIAH HEEP

D: . . . **S:** 8 kts **Dim:** 15.2 × . . . × . . . **M:** 1 diesel; . . . bhp

Remarks: 20 grt. Wooden-hulled fishing-boat-type craft transferred from the Royal Corps of Transport in 1974–81 for use as Royal Naval Reserve training tenders. Sister *Martin* used in civil youth programs. *Oliver Twist* is based at HMS *President,* London; *Uriah Heep* at HMS *Wessex,* Southampton; *Smike* is in reserve.

Note: Attached to the Flag Officers Sea Training Staff at Portland are the 16-m personnel tenders *Penguin* (HL 7019), *Opal* (HL . . .), *Emu* (HL 7020), and *Kiwi* (HL . . .), and the 40-ton, 13.90-m *Metro* (HSL 8093). Two seamanship training barges are used at HMS *Raleigh,* Dartmouth: *Ajax* (ex-RNAL . . .) and *Hindustan* (ex-RNAL 54), which began conversion for the purpose on 10-1-90.

Uriah Heep Leo Van Ginderen

Penguin (HL 7019) Leo Van Ginderen

Ajax Ben Sulliva

SALVAGE CRAFT

◆ **3 self-propelled lifting lighters** Bldr: McTay Marine, Brombrou Dock, Wirral (A 72: Richard Dunston, Hessle)

	L	In serv.
Y 32 MOORHEN	10-2-89	26-4-89
Y 33 MOORFOWL	21-4-89	30-6-89
A 72 CAMERON	13-3-91	31-5-91

Moorhen (Y 32) Maritime Photographi

AGE CRAFT *(continued)*

pprox. 600 tons (fl) **S:** 8 kts
: 32.25 (30.00 pp) × 11.50 × 2.00
tron Equipt: Radar: 1/Decca . . . nav.
: Cummins NT19M diesels; 2 Aquamaster azimuth props;
'30 bhp—bow-thruster
tric: 528 kw (2 Cummins NTA 853 diesels)
ge: . . ./. . . **Crew:** 2 officers, 8 unlicensed, plus 5 divers

ks: 530 grt. First two ordered 25-4-88. Y 32 replaced dumb barge-lifting craft ortsmouth; Y 33 is at Devonport. Pontoon barge hulls with powerful winches on open deck to bow spanned by pilothouse/accommodations superstructure. A 32 2-90 for use as underwater trials and experimental vessel for the Defence h Agency at Rosyth.

LIGHTERS

il class (* in reserve) Bldr: Appledore SB (All in serv. 1979)

	L		L
OILPRESS*	10-6-68	(Y 25) OILBIRD	21-11-68
OILSTONE	11-7-68	(Y 26) OILMAN	18-2-69
OILWELL	20-1-69		

l (Y 23) James W. Goss/NAVPIC, 6-90

50 tons (535 fl) **S:** 10 kts **Dim:** 42.26 (39.62 pp) × 7.47 × 2.51
tron Equipt: Radar: 1/. . . nav.
. Lister-Blackstone ES-6-MGR diesel; 405 bhp
tric: 225 kw **Range:** 1,500/10 **Fuel:** 12 tons
v: 4 officers, 7 unlicensed

ks: 362 grt. Ordered 10-5-67. First three originally configured to carry diesel displaced 247 tons (527 fl), but Y 21 converted to handle heavy oil like Y 24–26. apacity: 250 tons. R.M.A.S.–operated. Y 21 to reserve 9-5-87. Y 22 at Devon-23 at Portsmouth, and Y 26 at Rosyth. Sister *Oilfield* (Y 24), in reserve since stricken 1991.

R LIGHTERS

'ater class
: Drypool, Hull, except A 146: Richard Dunston, Hessle

	In serv.		In serv.
'ATERSHED	1967	Y 31 WATERFOWL	25-5-74
'ATERSPOUT	1967	A 146 WATERMAN	6-78
'ATERCOURSE	1974		

shed (Y 18) James W. Goss/NAVPIC, 7-91

fowl (Y 31)—with deckhouse over after part of well deck
Ben Sullivan, 5-91

D: 344 tons (fl) **S:** 11 kts **Dim:** 40.02 (37.5 pp) × 7.5 × 2.44
Electron Equipt: Radar: 1/. . . nav.
M: 1 Lister-Blackstone ERS-8-MGR diesel; 600 bhp
Electric: 155 kw **Range:** 1,500/11 **Crew:** 11 tot.

Remarks: R.M.A.S.–operated. Built 1966–73. Carry 150 tons water cargo. Resemble "Oil" class. Y 30, Y 31, and A 146 have deckhouse over after cargo tanks, others do not. Sister *Waterfall* (Y 17) stricken 1988, sunk at Rosyth as a divers' training device. *Waterside* (Y 20) sold to Ecuador 11-91. Y 18 at Portsmouth, Y 19 and Y 20 at Greenock, Y 30 at Rosyth, Y 31 at Devonport, and A 146 at Portland.

GENERAL-PURPOSE TENDERS

◆ **7 100-foot "Insect" class**
Bldr: C.D. Holmes, Beverley (In serv. 1970–73)

A 216 BEE — A 229 CRICKET — A 230 COCKCHAFER — A 239 GNAT — A 253 LADYBIRD — A 263 CICADA — A 272 SCARAB

Bee (A 216) Leo Van Ginderen, 1991

D: 213 tons (450 fl) **S:** 10.5 kts **Dim:** 34.06 (30.48 pp) × 8.53 × 3.2
Electron Equipt: Radar: 1/Type 1006 nav.
M: 1 Lister-Blackstone ERS-8-HGR diesel; 660 bhp **Crew:** 10 tot.

Remarks: R.M.A.S.–operated; 200 tons cargo, one 3-ton crane. *Scarab,* with 5-ton winch and bow horn, is used as a moorings tender; *Bee, Gnat,* and *Ladybird* transport ammunition.

◆ **10 "Loyal" class** Bldr: Richard Dunston, Thorne

	In serv.
A 157 LOYAL HELPER	1978
A 158 SUPPORTER (ex-*Loyal Supporter*)	1977
A 159 LOYAL WATCHER	1977
A 160 LOYAL VOLUNTEER	1977
A 161 LOYAL MEDIATOR	1978
A 220 LOYAL MODERATOR	1973
A 251 LYDFORD (ex-*Alert,* P 252; ex-*Loyal Governor,* A 510)	1975
A 254 MEAVY (ex-*Vigilant,* P 254; ex-*Loyal Factor,* A 382)	1974
A 1770 LOYAL CHANCELLOR	1972
A 1771 LOYAL PROCTOR	1973

Loyal Helper (A 157) Gilbert Gyssels, 7-90

Remarks: Details as for *Cartmel* class, but equipped to carry up to 200 personnel for short distances (except *Loyal Moderator:* training craft, 12 extra berths instead). A 157, 160, 161, and 1771 are R.N.X.S.–operated: remainder by R.M.A.S.; A 251 and A 254 were recommissioned and renamed 16-9-86 and 25-10-86, respectively, after service as Royal Navy patrol boats off Ulster. A 158 operates as a stores carrier from Belfast. Four very similar craft built as training tenders; see above.

GENERAL-PURPOSE TENDERS *(continued)*

◆ **30 Cartmel class** Bldrs: (A): Isaac Pimblott & Sons, Northwich; (B): C.D. Holmes, Beverley; (C): John Lewis, Aberdeen; (D): R. Dunston, Thorne; (E): J. Cook, Wivenhoe

	Bldr	In serv.		Bldr	In serv.
A 83 Melton	D	21-8-81	A 381 Cricklade	B	1970
A 84 Menai	D	4-11-81	A 389 Clovelly	A	1971
A 87 Meon	D	9-11-82	A 391 Criccieth	A	1971
A 91 Milford	D	11-1-83	A 392 Glencoe	A	1971
A 207 Landovery	D	1973	A 393 Dunster	D	1970
A 208 Lamlash	D	1973	A 394 Fintry	C	1970
A 211 Lechlade	D	1973	A 402 Grasmere	C	1970
A 274 Ettrick	E	1970	A 488 Cromarty	C	1970
A 277 Elsing	E	1970	A 490 Dornoch	C	1970
A 341 Fotherby	D	1970	A 1767 Hever	D	1972
A 348 Felsted	D	1970	A 1768 Harlech	D	1972
A 353 Elkstone	E	1969	A 1769 Hambledon	D	1972
A 354 Froxfield	D	1970	A 1772 Holmwood	D	1973
A 355 Epworth	E	1970	A 1773 Horning	D	1973
A 365 Fulbeck	B	1969	A 1776 Headcorn	D	1972

Hambledon (A 1769) Maritime Photographic, 11-91

Felsted (A 348)—with deckhouse over cargo hold, two rigid inflatable boats stowed atop Ben Sullivan, 8-91

Meon (A 87) Leo Van Ginderen, 6-90

D: 143 tons (fl) **S:** 10.5 kts **Dims:** 24.38 (22.86 pp) × 6.40 × 1.98
Electron Equipt: Radar: 1/Type 1006 nav.
M: 1 Lister-Blackstone ERS-4-MGR diesel; 330 bhp
Electric: 106 kw **Range:** 700/10 **Crew:** 6 tot.

Remarks: R.M.A.S.–operated, except *Ettrick* and *Elsing,* R.N.–manned and patrol at Gibraltar, and *Glencoe,* transferred to Bristol Royal Naval Reserve I in 1991 for training; A 363, to R.N.X.S. on 22-3-89; A 392, which replaced *Portis* 2781) as R.N.X.S. training ship 15-9-87; and A 392, to R.N.X.S. as training 1987. Improved version of *Aberdovey* class. A 389 and A 391 have 5.49-mete Carry stores, personnel, food: 25 tons maximum. Can tow. *Clovelly, Hever,* an *corn* are attached to the Culdrose helicopter base, and *Dornoch* and *Fotherby* ha used as diving tenders. The last four were ordered 25-2-80. Sister *Cawsand* (A sale 10-85; *Cartmel* (A 350) stricken 1989; *Denmead* (A 363) stricken 1991.

◆ **4 Aberdovey class**
Bldr: Isaac Pimblott & Sons, Northwich (A 103: J. S. Doig, Grimsby)

	In serv.
Y 11 Abinger	1963
Y 13 Alnmouth	1968
A 383 Appleby (ex-Y 14)	1967
A 103 Sultan Venturer (ex-*Bibury*)	1969

Sultan Venturer (A 103) Maritime Photograph

D: 117.5 tons (fl) **S:** 10.5 kts **Dim:** 24.16 (22.86 pp) × 5.79 ×
Electron Equipt: Radar: 1/Decca 150
M: 1 Lister-Blackstone ER-4-MGR diesel; 225 bhp
Range: 700/10 **Crew:** 6 tot.

Remarks: Survivors of a group of twelve. R.M.A.S.–operated. Carry 25 ton *Abinger* (Y 11) attached to Aberdeen University for officer candidate training. A 383 have a deckhouse added amidships, extending forward from the pilotho deckhouse on Y 11 has few windows, while that on A 383 has numerous windows. A 103 renamed 1986 as tender to HMS *Sultan,* Portsmouth. Sisters A 12), *Ashcott* (Y 16), and *Brodick* (A 105) for sale 10-85. *Beddgelert* (A 100) strick and transferred to Sea Cadets. *Appleby* was transferred to the Sea Cadets on lo in 1986. *Beaulieu* (A 99) and *Blakeney* (A 104) to Falkland Islands Depen 1986–87, stricken 1989–90, and sold to Chile. *Bembridge* (A 101) stricken 1 sold to a private Dutch owner in 1991.

◆ **1 weapons range moorings tender** Bldr: Richards SB, Lowest

	Laid down	L	In serv.
A 368 Warden	16-8-88	29-5-89	20-11-89

Warden (A 368) Leo Van Gindere

D: 621 tons light (approx. 900 fl) **S:** 15 kts
Dim: 48.63 (42.00 pp) × 10.50 × 3.50
Electron Equipt: Radar: 1/Decca RM 1250 nav.—Sonar: Type
M: 2 Ruston 8 RKCM diesels; 2 CP props; 3,800 bhp
Range: . . . **Crew:** 4 officers, 11 unlicensed

Remarks: Ordered 25-4-88 as replacement for *Dolwen* (A 362) for use Aberporth Range, Milford Haven. Has two Gardner diesel alternators, tw driven alternators. Large quadrantial A-frame gantry at stern for handling marker buoys. Collided with mooring tender *Gargenay* 29-1-90; repaired by 4

◆ **2 trials craft, former harbor tugs**

A 126 Cairn (In serv. 1962) A 328 Collie (In serv. 1972)

D: 206 tons (248 fl) **S:** 12 kts **Dim:** 28.65 (25.91 pp) × 7.72 ×
Electron Equipt: Radar: 1/Decca . . . nav.
M: 2 Lister-Blackstone ERS-86-MGR diesels; 1 prop; 1,320 bhp
Electric: 80 kw **Crew:** 8 tot.

RAL-PURPOSE TENDERS *(continued)*

(A 126) and Collie (A 328)—at Kyle of Lochalsh
Ben Sullivan, 8-91

ks: Converted 1987 to serve as trials tenders at Kyle of Lochalsh. Towing gear d.

motor fishing vessel tenders

es carriers: MFV.7 (1943), MFV.15 (1942), MFV.96 (1944), V.256 (1944), MFV.740 (1945), MFV.911 (1945)
eral-purpose: MFV.175 (1945), MFV.609 Apollo, MFV.622 BIA, MFV.809 (ex-R.A.F. 1389), MFV.816 (1945),
ng tenders: MFV.642 Hannibal (1945), MFV.775 Merchant TURER (1945), MFV.1077 (1944)

hant Venturer (MFV.775) Maritime Photographic, 7-91

rks: Operated by the R.M.A.S. Wooden-hulled fishing boats of varying charac- cs. Most have "double-ended" hulls, engines and pilothouse aft. MFV.1502 (ex- uth Navigator) was transferred to the Sea Scouts youth organization on 1-4-90. (and possible two others) was apparently transferred from the former R.A.F. e Section prior to when it became part of the R.M.A.S. in 2-91; the craft displaces 8 tons (fl) and is 19.2-m overall.

GE HARBOR TUGS

+2) large water tractors Bldr: Richard Dunston, Thorne

.) Impetuous (In serv. 1993) (A . . .) Impulsive (In serv. 1993)

. . . **S:** 12.5 kts **Dim:** . . . (30.00 pp) × . . . × . . .
2 diesels; 2 cycloidal props; . . . bhp
nge: 3,000/10 **Crew:** . . .

rks: Originally to have been ordered 1989, but bid process canceled. Ordered 2 for use at Faslane, Scotland, to move ballistic-missile submarines on and off the pair facility ship-lift. To have 36-ton bollard pull.

Adept-class "Twin-Unit Tractors" Bldr: Richard Dunston, Hessle

	Laid down	L	In serv.	Based
Forceful	30-3-84	. . .	29-3-85	Devonport
Nimble	27-4-84	21-3-85	25-6-85	Rosyth
Powerful	21-6-84	3-6-85	3-10-85	Portsmouth
A 224 Adept	22-7-79	27-8-80	28-10-80	Portland
A 225 Bustler	28-11-79	20-2-80	15-4-81	Portsmouth
A 226 Capable	5-9-80	2-7-81	11-9-81	Gibraltar
A 227 Careful	15-1-81	12-1-82	12-3-82	Plymouth
A 228 Faithful	30-11-84	. . .	13-12-85	Plymouth
A 231 Dexterous	18-4-85	25-2-86	24-4-86	Rosyth

Powerful (A 223) Maritime Photographic, 9-91

Bustler (A 226) Maritime Photographic, 11-91

D: 450 tons **S:** 12.5 kts
Dim: 38.82 (37.00 pp) × 9.10 × 4.20 (3.40 mean)
Electron Equipt: Radar: 1/Decca . . .
M: 2 Ruston 6 RKCM diesels; 2 Voith-Schneider vertical-cycloidal props; 2,640 bhp
Electric: 294 kw tot. **Fuel:** 49 tons **Crew:** 10 tot.

Remarks: R.M.A.S.–operated. First four ordered 22-2-79. The five later units were ordered 8-2-84 to replace the *Confiance*-class seagoing tugs. Referred to as "Twin Unit Tractor Tugs (TUTT)." 28-ton bollard pull. Also used for coastal towing.

♦ **16 "Dog" class** Bldr: Various (In serv. 1962–72)

(A 106) Alsatian	(A 162) Elkhound	(A 188) Pointer
(A 327) Basset (ex-*Beagle*)	(A 326) Foxhound (ex-*Boxer*)	(A 182) Saluki
		(A 187) Sealyham
(A 330) Corgi	(A 169) Husky	(A 189) Setter
(A 129) Dalmatian	(A 168) Labrador	(A 250) Sheepdog
(A 155) Deerhound	(A 180) Mastiff	(A 201) Spaniel

D: 206 tons (248 fl) **S:** 12 kts **Dim:** 28.65 (25.91 pp) × 7.72 × 3.51
Electron Equipt: Radar: 1/Decca . . . nav.
M: 2 Lister-Blackstone ERS-86-MGR diesels; 1 prop; 1,320 bhp
Electric: 80 kw tot. **Range:** 2,236/10 **Crew:** 8 tot.

Saluki (A 182)—taller pilothouse with skylights Ben Sullivan, 5-91

LARGE HARBOR TUGS *(continued)*

Corgi (A 330)—flat, rounded pilothouse face Ben Sullivan, 5-91

Foxhound (A 326)—rounded windscreen above pilothouse Maritime Photographic, 6-91

Remarks: R.M.A.S.–operated. 18.7-ton bollard pull. *Foxhound* renamed 22-10-77. Appearances vary, some having streamlined upper pilothouse structures, others higher pilothouses. Sister *Airedale* (A 102) sold commercially at Gibraltar, 12-84. *Cairn* (A 126) and *Collie* (A 328) converted 1987 as trials craft for use at Kyle of Lochalsh; towing gear deleted.

MEDIUM HARBOR TUGS

◆ **8 Felicity-class water tractors** Bldrs: Richard Dunston, Thorne (A 148, A 152, A 196, A 198: Hancock, Pembroke)

	In serv.		In serv.
(A 112) Felicity	1969	(A 150) Genevieve	29-10-80
(A 147) Frances	5-80	(A 152) Georgina	1973
(A 148) Fiona	1973	(A 196) Gwendoline	1974
(A 149) Florence	8-8-80	(A 198) Helen	1974

Fiona (A 148) James W. Goss/NAVPIC, 12-90

D: 220 tons (fl) **S:** 10.2 kts
Dim: 22.25 (20.73 pp) × 6.40 × 2.97 (2.10 hull)
M: 1 Lister-Blackstone ERS-8-MGR diesel; 1 cycloidal prop; 615 bh
Range: 1,800/8 **Fuel:** 12 tons **Crew:** 6 tot.

Remarks: R.M.A.S.–operated, 138 grt. 5.9 to 6.1-ton bollard pull. Final three or 13-12-78. Do not have radars.

◆ **2 modified "Girl" class** Bldr: Richard Dunston, Thorne (In serv. 19

(A 156) Daphne (A 178) Edith

Edith (A 178) Maritime Photographic

D: 100 tons (fl) **S:** 10.5 kts **Dim:** 20.57 × 6.25 × 2.9
M: 1 Lister-Blackstone ERS-8-MGR diesel; 495 bhp
Range: 900/10 **Crew:** 4 tot.

Remarks: 50 grt; 6.5-ton bollard pull. R.M.A.S.–operated. *Edith* operates fr braltar. *Celia* (A 206) sold commercially, 1971. Strikings: *Clare* (A 218) in 12-85 (A 252) on 1-4-89, *Christine* (A 217) on 1-6-89, and *Charlotte* (A 210), *Daisy* (A 1 29-12-89, and *Dorothy* (A 173) during 5-91.

SMALL HARBOR TUGS

◆ **12 Triton-class water tractors**
Bldr: Richard Dunston, Thorne (In serv. 1972–73)

(A 181) Irene	(A 166) Kathleen	(A 175) Mary
(A 183) Isabel	(A 170) Kitty	(A 199) Myrtle
(A 190) Joan	(A 172) Lesley	(A 202) Nancy
(A 193) Joyce	(A 174) Lilah	(A 205) Norah

Kitty (A 170) Leo Van Ginderen,

D: 107.5 tons (fl) **S:** 7.75 kts **Dim:** 17.65 (16.76 pp) × 5.26 × 2.
M: 1 Lister-Blackstone ERS-4-M diesel; cycloidal prop; 330 bhp
Crew: 4 tot.

Remarks: R.M.A.S.–operated; 50 grt; 3-ton bollard pull. Voith vertical cycloida to provide instant mobility and full power in any direction. Do not have radars. A reserve 1989.

LONG-RANGE RECOVERY AND SUPPORT CRAFT (LRRSC)

Note: Former Royal Air Force craft with black hulls, gray upperworks, R.A.F. r on hull sides and top of pilothouse. The Royal Air Force Marine Branch, estab

;-RANGE RECOVERY AND SUPPORT CRAFT (LRRSC)
ɴued)

ɪ8, was disbanded 31-3-86, with afloat assets operated for the R.A.F. by James , Ltd., with civilian crews. Based at Plymouth, Invergordon, Holyhead, and Yarmouth. Fly Blue Ensign with gold eagle holding anchor. The aviation trials t ship *Colonel Templar*, property of the Royal Aircraft Establishment via the , was transferred to the R.M.A.S. for operations on 1-10-88. On 1-2-91, all former support craft were transferred to the control of the R.M.A.S., which will operate vhen the long-term contract to James Fisher, Ltd., has expired.

ʒeal class

	Bldr	In serv.
ʒEAL	Brooke Marine, Lowestoft	8-67
ʒEAGULL	Fairmile Const., Berwick-on-Tweed	1970

(5000) Leo Van Ginderen, 6-83

159 tons (fl) **S:** 21 kts **Dim:** 36.6 (33.8 pp) × 7.0 × 2.0
ctron Equipt: Radar: 1/Decca . . . nav.
2 Paxman 16 YJCM diesels; 2 props; 4,000 bhp
ctric: 110 kw **Range:** 2,200/12 **Fuel:** 31 tons
w: 9 tot.

rks: Design similar to Royal Navy's *Kingfisher*-class patrol boats. Used for and rescue, target towing, and recovering guided missiles and other air-dropped ıce. Sister *Sea Otter* (5002) transferred to Royal Navy 30-10-84 and renamed *le.* Both based at Invergordon.

;UE AND TARGET-TOWING LAUNCHES AND RANGE ;TY CRAFT

Spitfire (RTTL Mk 3) class Bldr: James & Stone, Brightlingsea

cue and Target Towing Launches (RTTL):

	In serv.		In serv.
SPITFIRE	1972	4005 HURRICANE	1980
HALIFAX	1977	4006 LANCASTER	1981
HAMPDEN	1980	4007 WELLINGTON	25-5-81

ıge Safety Craft:

FALCONET (ex-*Michael Murphy, V.C.*)	10-3-83
PETARD (ex-*Alfred Herring, V.C.*)	1978

fax (4003) Ben Sullivan, 7-89

Spitfire (4000) Ben Sullivan, 3-89

D: 48 tons (60 fl) **S:** 22 kts **Dim:** 23.70 (22.15 wl) × 5.50 × 1.50
Electron Equipt: Radar: 1/Decca . . .
M: 2 Paxman 8YJCM4 diesels; 2 props; 2,000 bhp
Electric: 30 kVA **Range:** 500/21; 1,000/15 **Fuel:** 10 tons
Crew: 6 tot.

Remarks: *Spitfire* is 20.6 m overall and has two side-by-side stacks; the series-construction units discharge exhaust through ports in the stern. YO 1 and YO 2 were transferred to the R.M.A.S. from the British Army on 1-10-88; YO 1 operates from Pembroke Dock, South Wales, and YO 2 from the Outer Hebrides Artillery Range. Sisters *Sunderland* (4001) and *Stirling* (4002), to Royal Navy 8-85 as *Hart* (P 257) and *Cormorant* (P 256), were stricken 1-91 after serving as patrol boats at Gibraltar.

Note: Of the five 1300-series R.A.F. rescue pinnacles listed in the previous edition, 1389 has been redesignated as Motor Fisheries Vessel 809, and the fate of the others is uncertain.

◆ **15 Samuel Morley, V.C.-class range safety craft** Bldrs: 7713: Fairey, Hamble; 7820, 21, 22: A.R.P., Whitstable; others: Halmatic, Havant

	In serv.	Based at
7713 (ex-*Samuel Morley, V.C.*)	1980	Whitehaven
7820 (ex-*Richard Masters, V.C.*)	1981	Weymouth
7821 (ex-*Joseph Hughes, G.C.*)	1981	Weymouth
7822 (ex-*James Dalton, V.C.*)	1981	Hebrides
8124 (ex-*Sir John Potter*)	24-8-82	Portsmouth
8125 (ex-*Sir Paul Travers*)	20-10-82	Pembroke
8126 (ex-*Sir Cecil Smith*)	6-7-82	Portsmouth
8128 (ex-*Sir Reginald Kerr*)	17-3-83	Dover
8129 (ex-*Sir Humphrey Gale*)	8-4-83	Dover
8487 (ex-*Geoffrey Rackham*, G.C.)	19-12-85	Weymouth
8488 (ex-*Walter Cleal, G.C.*)	1986	Pembroke
8489 (ex-*Sir Evan Gibb*)	8-86	Pembroke
LZ1	1-91	. . .
LZ2	1-91	. . .
LZ3	1-91	. . .

RSC 7820 Maritime Photographic, 6-91

D: 20.6 tons (23.6 fl) **S:** 20–22 kts **Dim:** 14.94 × 4.65 × 1.30
Electron Equipt: Radar: 1/. . . nav. **Crew:** 3 tot.
M: 7713–7821, 8487–8489: 2 Rolls-Royce C8M410 diesels; 2 props: 820 bhp; others: 2 Fiat 828SM diesels; 2 props; 880 bhp

Remarks: Transferred from British Army to R.M.A.S. on 1-10-88. All hulls built by Halmatic, Havant; GRP construction. Design based on "Talisman 49" hull form. Sister *Sir William Roe* remains in army service. 8124 and several others are used as pilot boats. The last three were ordered during 1991 for delivery 1-91 for use as pilot boats and have a slightly different superstructure.

RESCUE AND TARGET-TOWING LAUNCHES AND RANGE SAFETY CRAFT *(continued)*

1991-completion pilot boat LZ3—at Portsmouth Maritime Photographic, 7-91

FLOATING DRY DOCKS

◆ **2 miscellaneous:**

AFD 60 Bldr: Portsmouth Dockyard (In serv. 1966)

AFD 26—with tug *Foxhound* (A 326) Leo Van Ginderen, 9-84

Capacity: 13,500 tons
Dim: 149.7 × 28 (17.7 wide × 10.7 depth interior)

AFD 26 Bldr: Bombay Dockyard (In serv. 1944)

Capacity: 7,750 tons
Dim: 115.8 × 28.0 (15.2 wide by 5.6 depth interior)

Note: "AFD" means Admiralty Floating Dock. AFD 26 is at Rosyth and AFD 60 at the Gareloch. Most Royal Navy dockings are performed at permanent, fixed dry docks at Royal Dockyards and, recently, at private repair facilities. AFD 58 and AFD 59 were sold to a Netherlands operator in 5-91.

HARBOR SERVICE CRAFT

Note: The Royal Maritime Auxiliary Service (R.M.A.S.) operates a large number of harbor and coastal service launches and service barges at the Royal Navy's principal bases at Portsmouth, Devonport, Rosyth, Faslane, and Greenock, and at other, smaller facilities. Most craft have four-digit hull numbers, with the first two digits indicating the year of their authorization. Most non-self-propelled craft have numbers ending with a letter or letters in parentheses indicating their functions. (Many craft at Portsmouth have local pendants, and a few craft have names.)

◆ **3 hydrophone array tenders** Bldr: McTay Marine, Bromsborough

TRV 8611 . . . . . . (In serv. 3-86) TRV 8612 OHM'S LAW (In serv. 1986)
TRV 8613 . . . . . . (In serv. . . .)

Ohm's Law (TRV 8612) Ben Sullivan, 7-91

D: . . . **S:** 12.5 kts **Dim:** 20.10 (19.88 wl) × 6.00 × . . .
Electron Equipt: Radar: 1/Decca 150 nav. **Crew:** 8 tot.
M: 2 Perkins 6/3544 diesels; 2 Kort-nozzle props; 400 bhp

Remarks: Aluminum hulls built by Hall's Aluminium Shipbuilders, Portc Intended to service "clip-on" linear hydrophone arrays for submarines. *Tar* Portsmouth; *Ohm's Law* is at Plymouth. Not initially accepted; could not make speed. Basic design under evaluation 1986 for use as personnel launches.

◆ **2 (+2) generator test barges** Bldr: Richard Dunston, Hessle

	Laid down	L	In serv.
MAC. 1020	24-4-86	22-7-86	5-2-87
MAC. 1021	2-5-86	17-11-86	1987

Remarks: Ordered 19-12-85; two more planned. 260 tons (fl).

◆ **0 (+1) catamaran personnel launch**
Bldr: FBM Marine Holdings, Cowes (In serv. 1992)

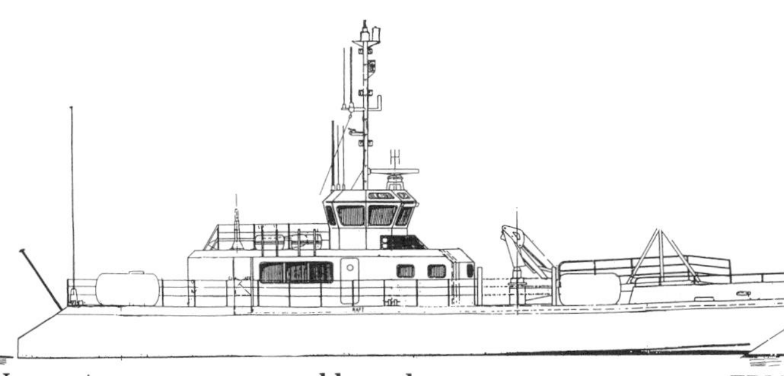

New catamaran personnel launch FBM,

D: . . . tons **S:** 23 kts **Dim:** 30.80 (27.50) × 7.80 × 1.10
M: 2 diesels; 2 waterjets; . . . bhp **Range:** 300/. . .
Crew: . . .

Remarks: Intended to serve ballistic-missile submarine crews based at Fasl the Firth of Clyde. To carry 40 personnel plus 1 ton of stores.

◆ **1 (+ . . .) prototype harbor launch** Bldr: FBM Marine, Cowes

D8837 (In serv. 1989)

D 37 (D8837) Maritime Photographic

D: 20.5 tons **S:** 13 kts (10 loaded)
Dim: 15.80 (13.80 wl) × 5.50 × 1.50
Electron Equipt: Radar: 1/Racal-Decca . . . nav.
M: Ford Mermaid Turbo-4 diesels; 2 props; 280 bhp
Range: 400/10 **Crew:** 2 crew + 30 to 60 passengers

Remarks: Prototype for a new series to replace the large number of outdated personnel launches. Can also carry 2 tons stores with 30 passengers. Also offe 20-kt, waterjet-driven version. Catamaran hull. Normally known as "D 37."

Note: In addition to the units listed below, four 10.77-m launches were ordere from Devonport Management, four 10.77-m launches were ordered from Richar ston, Thorne (three on 18-7-88, fourth on 22-9-88), and two 8.50-m workboat ordered from R. Dunston, Thorne, on 22-9-88. Two 11-meter harbor patrol launc the Ministry of Defence Police were delivered 4-5-90 by Devonport Dockyar 6.40-meter fast harbor launches were delivered by FBM Marine Holdings, (during 1990. The third of six 11-meter workboats, 8840, was delivered 9-1-90 by Yard, Polruan. A 36.6-m "support barge," ex-commercial *Kingscliff,* was con during 1990.

◆ **35 16-m harbor launches** (In serv. 1939–1970)

Portsmouth: 5438 (D 26), 56140 (D 49), 56142 (D 50), 56143 (D 58), 56149 (D 11), 6424 (D 17), 6505 (D 21), 6510 (D 15), 651 19), 6514 (D 24), 7015, 7016 (D 10)
Devonport: 56144, 56154, 6420, 6421, 6473, 6506, 6508, 6512, 6517,
Rosyth: 56141, 56147, 6425 (at Invergordon), 6515, 7021
Portland: 56137, 6516, 6808, 7017 *Kiwi,* 7018 *Opal,* 7019 *Penguin,* 7(*Emu.*
Greenock: 39461 *Loch Goil*

BOR SERVICE CRAFT *(continued)*

·ks: Local identifying pendants in parentheses. 7017–7021 are "New Zealand

5-meter harbor launches
8304—Both at Portsmouth

.3.90-meter harbor launches
r: R. Dunston, Hessle (In serv. 1981)
8093, 8095, 8096

(8095)—one of five built 1981 by Richard Dunston, Hessle: 40 tons .9 kts on one Dorman 8JTM diesel (270 bhp); 13.90 × 4.50 × 1.21; 3
Leo Van Ginderen, 8-90

rks: 8093, at Portland, named *Metro*; 8092, 8095 at Portsmouth (one named *w*—see caption), 8091 at Devonport, 8096 at Greenock.

1-meter harbor launches (In serv. 1979–80)
7996, 7997, 7998, 8000, 8001

rks: 7996, 8001 at Portsmouth; 7998 at Devonport; 7992, 8000 at Portland; 7997 enock.

45-ft Motor Launches (In serv. 1944–45)
44553

rks: 45989 at Portsmouth as mooring boat, 44553 used in oil-pollution control at port.

36-ft pinnaces (In serv. 1956)
5678, 5679—all at Portsmouth

13.6-meter range safety launch (In serv. 1974)
—at Faslane

12.9-meter stores boats (In serv. 1956, 1961)
., 6558—both at Portsmouth

Commander-in-Chief's Barge
—at Portsmouth

Hospital Launch:
(D 57)—at Portsmouth

9.75-meter Fast Motor Launch Mk 1
—at Portsmouth

Survey Motor Launches
(at Portsmouth) 6758 (at Rosyth) 6763 (at Faslane)

Fast Motor Launches Mk 4 or 5
, 6760, 6785, 6749, 6752, 6753, 6762, 6802, 6803

rks: 6757 at Portsmouth, 6760, 6785 and 6802 for M.O.D. Police. 6749–6762 Mk evonport, 6803 Mk 5 at Devonport.

2 8.53-meter General Service Launches

rks: Most are attached to mooring buoy tenders.

"MSMB": 7231—at Portsmouth

Fast Motor Launch Mk 9 (10.2-meter)—all M.O.D. Police
–7304

11-meter diving boats
7647

rks: At Portsmouth and Portland.

◆ **5 Fast Motor Launch Mk 8**
7701, 7702, 7705, 7706, 7144

Remarks: 7706 for M.O.D. Police, Faslane; 7702 assists training at Portland.

◆ **1 "Survey Boat"**
7721—at Portsmouth

◆ **2 Fast Motor Launch Mk 3**
6547, 6761—M.O.D. Police, Faslane

◆ **6 Fairey Spear Mk 2** (In serv. 1978)
7871–7876—all M.O.D. Police (see entry under patrol craft for data)

◆ **1 8.2-meter Motor Cutter**
5696—at Devonport

◆ **2 8.5-meter Surface Dredgers**
6989 (at Devonport) 7027 (at Rosyth)

◆ **3 Torpedo Recovery Launches**
7868–7870 (see entry under torpedo retrievers)

◆ **8 miscellaneous:**
1 9.44-meter Port Survey Boat: 69102—at Devonport
1 11-meter Harbor Diving Launch: 7028—at Devonport
1 9-meter Range Safety Boat: 7442—pilot boat at Rosyth
1 7.44-meter Motor Boat: with *Auricula* (A 285).
1 7.6-meter Motor Cutter: 475—at Loch Goil, Greenock
1 4.9-meter Small Motor Boat: 43288—at Fairlie
1 18.2-meter Range Safety Craft: 7001—at Greenock

LIQUID LIGHTERS

◆ **7 Water Lighters:**
2 27-meter, 250-ton capacity: 1516(W)—at Rosyth; 1517(W)—at Portsmouth
4 26.8-meter, 250-ton capacity: 1510(W), 1518(W), 1520(W)—at Devonport; 1511(W)—Portland
1 26.5-meter, 140-ton capacity: 1106(W)—at Rosyth

◆ **4 1600-series fuel-oil barges** (In serv. 1964–69)

	Tonnage	Dimensions	Cargo	Base
1601(F)	277.2 grt	40.16 × 9.14	500 tons	Portsmouth
1602(F)	277.2 grt	40.16 × 9.14	500 tons	Devonport
1603(F)	369.1 grt	44.8 × 10.2	500 tons	. . .
1604(F)	233 grt	36.6 × 8.5	. . . tons	Rosyth

◆ **12 1500-series fuel oil barges** (In serv. 1965–1976)

	Base		Base
1501(F)	Portsmouth	1507(F)	Portland
1502(F)	Faslane	1508(F)	Devonport
1503(F)	Portsmouth	1509(F)	Gibraltar
1504(F)	Devonport	1512(F)	Devonport
1505(F)	Portland	1513(F)	Portsmouth
1506(F)	Devonport	1514(F)	Portsmouth

D: . . . **Dim:** 27.12 × 7.85 × . . . **Cargo:** 250 tons

Remarks: 1501(F) is 32.61 × 7.65, same cargo capacity. Can carry diesel, oil, or aviation fuel.

◆ **6 Tank Cleaning Barges**
1901(TC)—1906(TC)

Remarks: Based: 1901(TC) and 1905(TC) at Portsmouth, 1906(TC) and 1907(TC) at Devonport, others at Rosyth.

◆ **24 Sullage Lighters**

Remarks: Numbers end with "(U)." Range from 31.4 m overall/120-ton capacity to 18.7 m overall/38-ton capacity radioactive effluent collection/storage barge at Faslane.

DRY CARGO BARGES

◆ **66 Ammunition Lighters**
17 × 21.3-m, 100-ton capacity ; 35 × 26.8-m, 200-ton capacity (11 with cranes); 4 × 28-m, 200-ton capacity; 3 × 24.4-m, 150-ton capacity; 3 × 21.8-m, 100-ton capacity; 3 × 31.9-m, 325-ton capacity; 1 × 23.9-m, 100-ton capacity

Remarks: Pendant numbers end with "(A)." Two 24.4-m ammunition barges, *Brussels III* and *Bagdad II*, were delivered 19-1-89 and 14-2-89 by Richard Dunston, Hessle.

DRY CARGO BARGES *(continued)*

88-foot Ammunition Lighter 1229 (A)—200-ton capacity
Ben Sullivan, 8-90

104.5-foot Ammunition Lighter 248A—325-ton capacity
Ben Sullivan, 8-90

♦ **36 Stores Lighters**

15 × 21.3-m, 150-ton capacity; 10 × 26.5-m, 200-ton capacity; 1 × 13.7-m, 40-ton capacity; 4 × 22-m, 150-ton capacity; 1 × 21.9-m, 100-ton capacity; 1 × 19.8-m, 100-ton capacity; 1 × 21.3-m, 95-ton capacity; 1 × 25.9-m, 150-ton capacity; 1 × 26.3-m, 180-ton capacity.

MISCELLANEOUS

♦ **7 "Named Fender Lighters"**

India 7 Ireland King Minna Muirhead
Herbert Strickland Pauline Elizabeth

Remarks: First five at Portsmouth, other two at Devonport.

♦ **3 Berthing Pontoons** (all based at Greenock)

Cardwell Bay Port Albert Port Edgar

♦ **1 Instrument Lighter** (based at Greenock)

Maytime

♦ **3 RNAL-series self-propelled lighters**

RNAL 50 RNAL 51 RNAL 52

RNAL 50 Leo Van Ginderen, 8-91

Remarks: RNAL= Royal Naval Air Lighter. RNAL 50 is used as a helicopter transport at Devonport, RNAL 51 as an accommodations lighter at Devonport, and RNAL 52 as a dumb barge at Rosyth. Sister RNAL 54, self-propelled, was converted to the training lighter *Hindustan* in 1990.

Hospital Launch 5857 (D 57)—at Portsmouth
Maritime Photographic

52.5-foot Harbor Launch 56140 (D 49)—at Portsmouth
Maritime Photographic

52-foot service launch Penguin—at Portland Leo Van Ginderen

12.9-meter Stores Transport NST 6558 Ben Sullivan

Tank Cleaning Lighter TCL 1902 Leo Van Ginderen

MISCELLANEOUS *(continued)*

◆ **4 Fenders**

247(A), 811 (MIS) (at Devonport) LC 10, LC 11 (at Greenock)

◆ **2 Fairlie Landing Pontoons** (at Faslane)

FLP 01 FLP 02

◆ **6 14.80-m pontoons**

Remarks: Ordered 9-12-88 from Richard Dunston, Hessle.

BRITISH ARMY ROYAL CORPS OF TRANSPORT

MEDIUM LANDING SHIPS

◆ **2 Ardennes-class logistic landing craft**
Bldr: Brooke Marine, Lowestoft

	Laid down	L	In serv.
L 4001 Ardennes	27-8-75	29-7-76	1977
L 4003 Arakan	16-2-76	23-5-77	9-6-78

Ardennes (L 4001) Bram Risseeuw, 8-90

D: 870 tons (1,663 fl) **S:** 10.0 kts
Dim: 72.16 (69.95 pp) × 15.03 × 2.01
M: 2 Mirrlees-Blackstone GWSL 8-MGR 2 diesels; 2 props; 2,000 bhp
Range: 2,500/10 **Fuel:** 150 tons
Crew: 4 officers, 31 enlisted

Remarks: Replacements for the LCT(8) class. Cargo: 355 tons: 5 70-ton tanks or 24 standard 20-foot containers as well as 6 officers and 28 troops. No armament. Normally used in freighting service between the U.K. and Europe.

LANDING CRAFT

◆ **9 Arromanches class**

	Bldr	L	In serv.
L 105 Arromanches	Brooke Marine, Lowestoft	6-1-81	31-7-81
L 106 Antwerp	Brooke Marine, Lowestoft	9-3-81	14-8-81
L 107 Åndalsnes	James & Stone, Brightlingsea	16-3-84	22-5-84
L 108 Abbeville	James & Stone, Brightlingsea	28-8-84	9-11-84
L 109 Akyab	James & Stone, Brightlingsea	20-11-84	21-12-84
L 110 Aachen	James & Stone, Brightlingsea	25-6-86	26-1-87
L 111 Arezzo	James & Stone, Brightlingsea	18-11-86	2-3-87
L 112 Agheila	James & Stone, Brightlingsea	27-4-87	12-6-87
L 113 Audemer	James & Stone, Brightlingsea	24-6-87	8-87

Aachen (L 110)—with "Portakabin" on tank deck Maritime Photographic, 4-91

Åndalsnes (L 107) Dr. Giorgio Arra, 1-87

D: 290 tons (fl) **S:** 9.25 kts
Dim: 33.26 (30.00 pp) × 8.30 × 1.45 loaded
Electron Equipt: Radar: 1/Decca 110 nav.
M: 2 Doorman 8 JTCWM diesels; 2 props; 660 bhp
Range: 900/9 **Fuel:** 17 tons **Crew:** 6 tot.

Remarks: First two ordered 18-3-80 to begin replacement of *Avon* class. Next three ordered 31-3-83, and four more in 3-85. Cargo: 96 tons. L 105 and L 106 displace 282 tons (fl) and can make 10 kts at light load; they operated in the Falklands 1982–83 and are now based at Cyprus. L 107, L 108, L 109 are based at Hong Kong.

◆ **3 Avon class** Bldr: Saunders-Roe, Isle of Wight (In serv. 1961–67)

RPL 05 Eden RPL 06 Forth RPL 12 Medway

Eden (RPL 05) Leo Van Ginderen, 3-87

D: 61 tons (100 fl) **S:** 8 kts **Dim:** 22.0 × 6.1 × 1.7
M: 2 diesels; 2 props; 870 bhp **Crew:** 6 tot.

Remarks: RPL—Ramped Powered Lighter: Rotate on duty at Belize, with two normally present. Sisters *Clyde* (RPL 03), *Dart* (RPL 04), *Itchen* (RPL 09), *Kennet* (RPL 10), and *Lodden* (RPL 11) stricken 1987.

◆ **4 LCVP 4-class landing craft** Bldr: W. A. Souters & Sons, Cowes

LCVP 8402 (In serv. 15-3-85) LCVP 8619 (In serv. 1987)
LCVP 8409 (In serv. 18-9-85) LCVP 8620 (In serv. 1987)

D: 10 tons (fl) **S:** 20 kts (16 loaded)
Dim: 13.00 (11.90 pp) × 3.20 × 0.80
A: 2/7.62-mm mg (I × 2; provision for)
M: 2 Perkins 76-3544 diesels; 2 props; 440 bhp
Range: 200/12 **Crew:** 3 crew + 35 troops

Remarks: Cargo well 8.80 × 2.13, with 5.5-ton capacity. Aluminum construction. Seventeen sisters in R.N. service. Two serve in Falklands, one in Belize, one in U.K.

SERVICE CRAFT

◆ **1 Samuel Morley, V.C.-class range safety craft**
Bldr: Halmatic, Havant

Sir William Roe (In serv. 1983)

D: 20.6 tons (23.6 fl) **S:** 22 kts **Dim:** 14.94 × 4.65 × 1.30
Electron Equipt: Radar: 1/Decca 110 nav.
M: 2 Fiat 828SM diesels; 2 props; 880 bhp
Range: 320/17 (300/18, last three) **Crew:** 3 tot.

Remarks: Based at Cyprus. Glass-reinforced plastic hull. Design based on "Talisman 49" hull. Twelve sisters transferred to R.M.A.S. on 1-10-88.

◆ **1 general-purpose workboat** Bldr: James & Stone, Brightlingsea

	Laid down	L	In serv.
WB 08 Mill Reef	17-3-86	17-11-86	16-2-87

SERVICE CRAFT *(continued)*

Mill Reef (WB 08) Leo Van Ginderen, 6-87

D: 25 tons (fl) **S:** . . . **Dim:** 14.75 × . . . × . . .
Electron Equipt: Radar: 1/Decca . . .
M: 2 diesels; 2 props; . . . bhp

Remarks: Prototype of design to replace class below. Ordered 6-12-85. Three more planned sisters were not ordered.

♦ **3 general-purpose workboats, Mk II** (In serv. 1966–71)

WB 03 Bream WB 05 Roach WB 06 Perch

D: 19 tons (fl) **S:** 8 kts **Dim:** 14.3 × . . . × . . .

Perch (WB 06) Leo Van Ginderen, 3-87

Remarks: Sisters *Barbel* (WB 04) stricken 1987, *Pike* (WB 07) in 1990.

♦ **8 workboats** Bldr: Anderson, Rigden & Perkins, Whitstable

HL 1 through HL 7 (In serv. 2-3-81) HL 8 (In serv. 2-6-81)

D: 8 tons (fl) **S:** 11 kts **Dim:** 11.2 × 3.5 × . . .
M: 1 Perkins T6-354 M diesel; 129 bhp **Crew:** 2 tot.

Remarks: Glass-reinforced plastic construction. Five also built for R.N.

♦ **1 general-service launch**

Jackson

Remarks: 15.2 m overall, 20 tons. Stationed at Hong Kong.

♦ **2 air-cushion vehicles** Bldr: Air Vehicles, Cowes
SH 01 (In serv. 11-5-82) SH 02 (In serv. 15-7-82)

D: 1 ton (fl) **S:** 34 kts **Dim:** 8.45 × 4.57 × 2.18 (high)
M: 1 diesel; 1 air screw; 1 lift-fan; 200 bhp
Crew: 1, plus 11 passengers

Note: The British Army also operates a large number of Fairey/FBM River Crossing Boats.

DEPARTMENT OF AGRICULTURE AND FISHERIES FOR SCOTLAND

Aviation: In late 1984, a Cessna Titan with Racal ASR 360 radar and aerial cameras was purchased for surveillance, to replace a Turbine Islander chartered in 1982. Three Dornier 228–200, one with Bendix RDR 1500 color radar, were acquired 1986, and a Fokker F-27 was leased during 1989.

British Army River Crossing Boat Maritime Photographic, 11-

FISHERIES PROTECTION SHIPS

♦ **3 Sulisker class**

	Bldr	Laid down	L	In ser
Sulisker	Ferguson Bros., Port Glasgow	. . .	8-80	19
Vigilant	Ferguson Ailsa, Port Glasgow	. . .	26-3-82	28-9-
Norna	Richards, Lowestoft	5-1-87	10-9-87	28-1-

Vigilant Gilbert Gyssels,

Sulisker Leo Van Ginderen,

D: 1,580 tons (fl) **S:** 18 kts **Dim:** 71.33 (64.00 pp) × 11.60 × 4.6
Electron Equipt:
Radar: 1/Sperry Mk 3012X-59 nav., 1/Sperry Mk 3012S-312 nav.
M: First two: 2 Ruston 12RK3CM diesels; 2 CP props; 5,640 bhp; *Norna:* 2 Ruston 6AT350M diesels; 2 CP props; 6,000 bhp
Electric: 638 kw **Range:** 7,000/14 **Fuel:** 198 tons
Crew: 7 officers, 14–18 crew, 6 passengers

Remarks: 1,177 grt/337 dwt. Equipped with 450-hp bow-thruster, Denny-Bro stabilizers. Equipped for rescue, fire fighting, and oil-spill cleanup. Elaborate n tional equipment, particularly in *Vigilant*. Third unit, ordered 11-6-86, has an A- mainmast. All have bow-thruster, Omega receiver, SATCOMM gear, EW int equipment. Endurance: 21 days. Sister *Corystes* is operated by the British Mini Agriculture and Fisheries, London.

ERIES PROTECTION SHIPS (continued)

ura class Bldr: Hall Russell & Co., Aberdeen (L: 6-8-74)

A

78 tons (1,285 fl) **S:** 16.5 kts **Dim:** 59.6 × 10.7 × 4.4
2 British Polar SP112VS-F diesels; 1 CP prop; 4,200 bhp
w: 28 tot.

ks: 885 grt. Design (with different engines) employed for Royal Navy's "Isles"-fshore patrol vessels. Operates on west coast of Scotland to the Orkneys and ds. Endurance: 16–18 days. Sister *Jura* sold commercial to J. Marr in 1-88 and erates on charter to Mauretania.

sheries patrol boats Bldr: Cheverton, Cowes (In serv. 31-1-83)

EN MOIDART

art Leo Van Ginderen, 1-84

37 tons (44 fl) **S:** 24 kts **Dim:** 19.8 (17.9 pp) × 5.77 × 1.63
3 G.M. 8V92 TI diesels; 3 props; 1,530 bhp **Electric:** 75 kw
lurance: 7 days **Crew:** 2 officers, 3 enlisted

ks: Glass-reinforced plastic construction. Use Murray, Cormack "North Cape ls, built at Cheverton, Newport, and fitted out at Cowes. Carry Avon Sea-Raider gid inflatable inspection dinghy. *Moidart* is home-ported at Leith.

igid inflatable fisheries patrol boats
r: Osbourne, Littlehampton (In serv. 4-84)

Y SKUA

6.25 tons **S:** 28 kts **Dim:** 10.06 × 3.05 × 1.12
2 Rolls-Royce Sabre 212 diesels; 2 props; 424 bhp
ge: 200/. . . **Crew:** 3 tot.

ks: Combines rigid hull with inflatable flotation/fender collar, which increases sions to 11.20 × 3.73 when inflated.

Operated by J. Marr, Ltd. for the Scottish Department of Agriculture and ies are the research trawlers *Scotia* and *Culpea*. For the British Ministry of lture, J. Marr operates the stern-haul trawler *Southella* as a fisheries patrol

a Leo Van Ginderen, 5-82

hella—near-sister to R.N.-chartered *Northella*, since 1990 on er to the British Ministry of Agriculture as a substitute for naval sweepers formerly used in the rôle Ben Sullivan, 8-90

H.M. CUSTOMS AND EXCISE MARINE DIVISION
Headquartered at HMS Vernon, Portsmouth

PATROL BOATS AND CRAFT

♦ **3 Protector-class patrol boats**
Bldr: FBM Marine, Cowes (In serv. 1989)

VIGILANT (L: 6-12-88) VALIANT VENTUROUS

Valiant Leo Van Ginderen, 6-89

D: 100 tons (fl) **S:** 25 kts **Dim:** 25.7 (22.8 wl) × 6.2 × 1.70
Electron Equipt: Radar: 2/Decca . . . nav.
M: 2 Paxman 12-SET-CWM diesels; 2 props; 2,880 bhp—1 Perkins T6. 3544 diesel-driven Hamilton waterjet; 212 hp (for speeds to 7 kts)
Range: . . . **Fuel:** 8.5 tons **Crew:** 8 tot. **Endurance:** 5 days

Remarks: Ordered 23-4-87, to begin replacement of Tracker-series. Smaller than Bahamian units of class, and with different propulsion plant; waterjet adds 1 kt to maximum speed. Sisters built in Chile for Chilean Coast Guard as pilot boats.

♦ **2 33-m-class patrol boats**
Bldr: Brooke Marine, Lowestoft (In serv. 1979)

SEARCHER SEEKER

Seeker Maritime Photographic, 1-92

D: 140 tons (160 fl) **S:** 21 kts **Dim:** 36.6 (33.8 pp) × 7.0 × 2.0
Electron Equipt: Radar: 1/Decca 1226 nav.
M: 2 Paxman 16YJCM diesels; 2 props; 4,000 bhp
Electric: 110 kw **Range:** 2,600/12 **Fuel:** 31 tons **Crew:** 10 tot.

Remarks: Generally similar to R.A.F.'s *Seal* class and Royal Navy's *Kingfisher* class, but have more extensive superstructures. Fin stabilizers. Used in Scottish waters.

♦ **3 Tracker-class patrol craft**
Bldr: Fairey Marine, Hamble (In serv. 1978)

ALERT SAFEGUARD SWIFT

Swift Maritime Photographic, 1-92

UNITED KINGDOM *(continued)*
PATROL BOATS AND CRAFT *(continued)*

D: 32 tons (34.54 fl) **S:** 21 kts **Dim:** 20.00 (19.30) × 5.18 × 1.50
Electron Equipt: Radar: 1/Decca 150 nav.
M: 2 G.M. 12V71 TI diesels; 2 props; 1,300 bhp **Electric:** 30 kw
Range: 650/20 **Crew:** 9 tot.

Remarks: *Alert* is a Tracker Mk I with pilothouse farther forward; the others are Tracker Mk IIs. Sisters *Active, Challenge,* and *Champion* sold to Maldive Islands; left U.K. 19-7-89.

◆ **3 service launches** Bldr: Fairey Cheverton, Cowes (In serv. 8-84 to 1986)

ANTELOPE AVOCET BITTERN

D: 3.75 tons (fl) **S:** 15 kts **Dim:** 8.23 × 2.74 × 0.81
M: 2 Perkins 4.236 diesels; 2 props; 140 bhp
Range: 100/13 **Crew:** 2 tot.

◆ **40 smaller craft, including Avon Surfrider semi-rigid inflatables**

Four 5.5-m and one 6.5-m TF 550-series craft were delivered 1985–86 by Task Force Boats; capable of 25 kts on their 110-hp Turbo Merlin diesel-powered P 90 waterjets.

U.S.A.

United States of America

Personnel (9-92): Authorized active strength at end Fiscal Year 1992: Active Navy: 577,687 (71,826 officers, 501,592 enlisted, 4,269 midshipmen); Naval Reserve: 141,715 total (27,354 officers, 114,361 enlisted); active Marine Corps: 194,040 total (19,753 officers, 174,287 enlisted); Marine Corps Reserve: 95,334 total (8,159 officers, 87,175 enlisted); navy civilians: 295,287; Marine Corps civilians: 16,372. About 54,600 women serve in the navy (5,000 on ships), and there are about 9,300 women in the Marine Corps.

At the end of Fiscal Year 1993, the authorized totals are to drop to 535,800 navy, 181,900 Marine Corps, and 283,206 civilians (267,671 navy/15,535 Marine Corps).

NAVAL PROGRAM

The table lists new-construction programs for fiscal years 1990 through 1997. The annual five-year program has fluctuated drastically for many years and, because of changing political pressures, cannot be relied on as an accurate projection of what will actually be proposed, let alone authorized and appropriated by Congress. It is nc less given here as the best available forecast; it will probably be reduced. In partial two-year authorization began, but funding remains annual.

SHIPBUILDING PROGRAM 1990–97*

	Authorized		Proposed				
New Construction:	FY 90	FY 91	FY 92	FY 93	FY 94	FY 95	FY 96
SSBN, *Ohio*	1	1	—	—	—	—	—
SSN, *Seawolf*	—	1	1	—	—	—	—
CVN, *T. Roosevelt*	—	—	—	—	—	1	—
DDG, *A. Burke*	5	4	5	3	3	4	4
LX	—	—	—	—	—	1	—
LHD, *Wasp*	—	1	—	—	—	—	1
LSD, *Harpers Ferry*	1	1	—	—	—	—	—
MCM, *Avenger*	3	—	—	—	—	—	—
MHC, *Osprey*	2	2	3	2	—	—	—
T-AGOS-23	1	—	1	—	1	2	—
AOE, *Supply*	1	—	1	—	—	—	—
AGOR, *Thompson*	—	1	—	—	1	—	—
T-AGS, *Pathfinder*	2	—	2	—	2	—	—
T-AGS, *Waters*	1	—	—	—	—	—	—
AR	—	—	—	—	—	1	—
LCAC	12	12	24	—	—	—	—
Conversions:							
CV SLEP	1	—	—	—	—	—	—
CVN Refuel	1	—	—	—	1	—	—
CGN Refuel	—	—	—	—	1	—	1
AO 177	1	—	—	—	—	—	—
AGOR	—	—	—	1	2	2	—

Note: The plan sent to Congress included one MHC(V) in FY 95 and two in FY were not included in the Mine Warfare Plan later submitted and that will requested under current planning. The administration declined to allocate the for the FY 91 and FY 92 *Seawolf*-class submarines; the FY 93 defense approp bill required the completion of *one* of the two. The AGOR conversion fundi instead be used for new construction. The program did not show any of the sealift ships tentatively planned.

MARINE CORPS

Created in 1775, the Marine Corps has three missions:

—to seize and/or defend advanced bases as needed for the operations of the fle
—to furnish security detachments on board ships and at land bases
—to carry out any other operations that the president of the United States may

The third mission permits the corps to be used in operations that are not purel (e.g., Belleau Wood in 1918 and Vietnam in the 1960s and 1970s).

Its total active strength of about 194,000 men and women forms three Expeditionary Force (MEF) divisions (one stationed in Okinawa/Japan, two United States), each of 32,600 men, and three air wings, organized under tw Marine Forces (FMF). These last also maintain heavy support elements for t sions. A fourth division-wing team constitutes a reserve cadre.

Anzio (CG 68)—Baseline 4 ship Ingalls S

NE CORPS *(continued)*

Marine Corps has approximately 400 fighter and attack aircraft (A-6, AV-8C,), 600 assault and utility helicopters, more than 500 tanks, and some 450 bious landing vehicles.
najor operational unit is the Marine Expeditionary Force (MEF), which consists livision, one air wing, and Fleet Marine Forces augmentation, for a total of about marines.
hibious ships currently in service do not permit the rapid overseas deployment 's, but only of two Marine Expeditionary Brigades (MEB). An MEB consists of gimental Landing Team, a strong unit with two or more battalion landing teams t 822 men each; one mixed air group of 110 fighter/attack fixed-wing aircraft) helicopters, 15 tanks and 30 artillery batteries, and some augmentation from et Marine Force, for a total of about 15,500 men. The smallest assault unit is the Expeditionary Unit (MEU), with a landing team, air squadrons, and support nel totaling 2,500, and has 5 tanks, 6 aircraft, 30 helicopters, and 5 artillery es.

SPECIAL FORCES

isting of 2,700 men, all capable of aerial or seaborne insertion, in 1991: 6 SEAL 2 Swimmer Delivery Vehicle Teams, 3 Special Boat Squadrons, and 4 reserve s.

THE NAVAL RESERVE FORCE

l Reserve Force ships have cadre crews of regular naval personnel, with reserve ntation personnel constituting up to two-thirds of the total crew assigned. During cal Year 1992, the Force included some 40 ships (scheduled to reduce to 37 in FY e two Naval Reserve Force Air Wings consisted of some 575 aircraft (to reduce to FY 93). Also incorporated in the Naval Reserve program are about 3,053 other upporting 35 programs to augment Regular Navy staffs in wartime.

THE MILITARY SEALIFT COMMAND

Military Sealift Command (MSC) operates or charters ships in support of the States Navy and the other armed services. Headed by an active-duty U.S. Navy cer, its ships are manned primarily by civilians, either civil service or contract ees. The ships of the MSC are listed in a separate section, after naval units.

WARSHIPS IN ACTIVE SERVICE, UNDER CONSTRUCTION, OR APPROPRIATED AS OF 1 JANUARY 1992

(Numbers authorized or under construction in parentheses)

	L	Std. tons	Main armament
(+3) attack carriers			
THEODORE)SEVELT (CVN)	1984–. . .	82,000	88–90 aircraft, 3/Sea Sparrow
ITZ (CVN)	1972–80	81,600	88–90 aircraft, 3/Sea Sparrow
'ERPRISE (CVN)	1960	75,700	88–90 aircraft, 2/Sea Sparrow
N F. KENNEDY (CV)	1967	61,000	88–90 aircraft, 3/Sea Sparrow
TY HAWK (CV)	1960–64	60,100	88 aircraft, 2–3/Sea Sparrow
RESTAL (CV)	1954–58	59,600	88 aircraft, 2/Sea Sparrow
WAY (CV)	1945–46	56,000	65 aircraft, 2/Sea Sparrow
(+4) amphibious assault helicopter carriers			
) WASP (LHD)	1987–. . .	28,000	up to 42 a/c, 2/Sea Sparrow
RAWA (LHA)	1972–78	28,000	19–30 helicopters, 2/127-mm DP, 2/Sea Sparrow
) JIMA (LPH)	1960–69	17,000	up to 28 helicopters, 4/76.2-mm, 2/Sea Sparrow
(+6) nuclear-powered ballistic-missile submarines		(surfaced)	
3) OHIO (SSBN)	1979–. . .	15,750	24/Trident, 4/TT
FAYETTE (SSBN)*	1962–66	7,250	16 Trident, 4/TT

. with Poseidon missiles deactivated as SSBN 1-10-91

	L	Std. tons	Main armament
(+23) nuclear-powered attack submarines			
) SEAWOLF	1995–.		8/TT
15) LOS ANGELES	1973–. . .	6,000	4/TT
33 STURGEON	1966–74	3,640	4/TT
1 NARWHAL	1967	4,550	4/TT
3 PERMIT	1964–66	3,526	4/TT
♦ **4 battleships**			
(In reserve)	1944	46,100	32 Tomahawk, 16 Harpoon, 9/406-mm, 12/127-mm DP
♦ **47 (+12) cruisers**			
9 nuclear-powered:			
4 VIRGINIA (CGN)	1974–78	10,400	2 SAM launchers, 8/Tomahawk, 8/Harpoon, 2/127-mm DP
2 CALIFORNIA (CGN)	1971–72	10,400	2 SAM launchers, 8/Harpoon, 2/127-mm DP, ASROC
1 TRUXTUN (CGN)	1964	8,600	1 SAM launcher, 8/Harpoon, 1/127-mm DP
1 BAINBRIDGE (CGN)	1961	8,600	2 SAM launchers, 8/Harpoon, ASROC
1 LONG BEACH (CGN)	1959	15,500	2 SAM launchers, 8/Tomahawk, 8/Harpoon, ASROC
38 (+12) conventional:			
20 (+7) TICONDEROGA	1981–92	7,400	2 SAM launchers, 8/Harpoon, 2/127-mm DP
9 BELKNAP (CG)	1963–65	6,570	1 SAM, 8/Harpoon, 1/127-mm DP
9 LEAHY (CG)	1961–63	6,070	2 SAM launchers, 8/Harpoon, ASROC
♦ **42 (+23) destroyers**			
1 (+23) ARLEIGH BURKE	1989–. . .	6,600	2/VLS missile groups, 8/Harpoon, 1/127-mm DP,
4 KIDD	1979–80	8,140	2 SAM launchers, 2/127-mm DP
31 SPRUANCE	1973–81	5,830	1/Sea Sparrow, 8/Harpoon, 2/127-mm DP, ASROC
3 CHARLES F. ADAMS	1961–63	3,370	1 SAM launcher, Harpoon, 2/127-mm DP, ASROC
3 COONTZ	1959–60	4,700	1 SAM launcher, 8/Harpoon, 1/127-mm DP, ASROC
♦ **80 frigates**			
51 OLIVER HAZARD PERRY	1976–88	2,997	1 SAM launcher, Harpoon, 1/76-mm DP
29 KNOX	1966–73	3,011	0 or 1/Sea Sparrow, Harpoon, 1/127-mm DP, ASROC

♦ **6 guided-missile patrol hydrofoils**

♦ **18 (+17) mine countermeasures ships**

♦ **49 (+5) amphibious warfare ships (plus helicopter carriers above)**

WEAPONS AND SYSTEMS

Note: Far more detailed and comprehensive descriptions of the weapons and other systems described below can be found in *The Naval Institute Guide to World Naval Weapons Systems 1991/92*, by Dr. Norman Friedman.

A. MISSILES

♦ **fleet ballistic missiles**

Trident-1 C-4 (UGM-96A)—Lockheed

Operational in 1978. Designed for the *Ohio*-class SSBNs, which carry 24, and for 12 *Lafayette* and *Benjamin Franklin* SSBNs, which carry 16. The first eight *Ohio*-class

MISSILES *(continued)*

SSBNs were to convert to the later D-5 but now will retain C4. Seventy-two procured FY 83, 52 approved FY 84, the final year of production requests.

Length: 10.4 m
Weight: 31.75 tons at launch
Propulsion: solid propellant, three stages
Guidance: inertial
Range: 4,350 nautical miles
Warhead: 8 Mk 4 MIRV with 100 kiloton W 76 warheads

Trident-2 D (UGM-133A)—Lockheed

In development, for deployment in the late 1980s in the Pacific Fleet and in 1992 in the Atlantic. First ship to carry one was SSBN 734. First 21 authorized under FY 87, 66 under FY 88 and FY 89, 41 under FY 90, 52 under FY 91, 28 under FY 92; 21 requested under FY 93. A total of 779 Trident D5 missiles has been funded, with 275 delivered by 30-9-92. Officially entered operational service 29-3-90. All were to get the new W 88 warhead, but a shortage of nuclear weapons production facilities forced retention of the W 76 warhead in the missiles supplied to the fifth and later *Ohio*-class SSBNs.

Length: 13.9 m Weight: 57.15 tons at launch
Propulsion: solid propellant, three stages
Range: 6,000 nautical miles with 122-m circular error probable (CEP)
Warhead: Mk 12A re-entry vehicles with 100-kiloton W 76 or 475-kiloton W87 warheads

♦ surface-to-surface missiles

LRCSW—McDonnell Douglas

Project to succeed Tomahawk: Long-Range Conventional Standoff Weapon. For air, surface, and submarine launch. Design contract 5-10-89.

Tomahawk (BGM-109)—General Dynamics and McDonnell Douglas

Two versions are in service, strategic and tactical. Planned procurement is for 3,830 total missiles, with 2,600 potential launchers: submarines (using torpedo tubes or special vertical launch tubes), surface ships (using 4-missile armored box launchers or vertical launch cells), and aircraft. Fifty-one procured FY 83, 124 approved FY 84, 180 in FY 85, 249 in FY 86, 324 in FY 87, 475 in FY 88, 510 in FY 89, 400 in FY 90, 678 in FY 91, and 176 in FY 92; 200 requested under FY 93, and plan to request 282 in FY 94 and FY 95. A total of 284 (264 T/LAM-C, 27 T-LAM-D) launched during Operation Desert Storm in 1991. The nuclear strategic attack version is being retired under a presidential order of 27-9-91.

Length: 6.17 m Diameter: 0.52 m Warhead weight: 450 kg
Weight: 1,542 kg at launch (1.816 kg encapsulated for submarine launch)
Propulsion: solid booster, F-107 turbojet sustainer

Strategic version: 1,400 nautical mile range, operating at an altitude between 15 and 100 meters, at a speed of Mach 0.7. For launching from submarines, the weapon is launched from torpedo tubes in a special container that is jettisoned on leaving the water. Guidance: TAINS (Tercom-Aided Inertial Navigation System) using preprogrammed data plus TERCOM (Terrain Contour Matching).
Tactical version: 250 nautical mile range, thus requiring an external means of target designation. Warhead weight up to 454 kg, conventional. Guidance: inertial, with active radar and anti-radiation homing.

Variations in service or planned include: RGM-109A land-attack, nuclear warhead (retired 10-91); RGM-109B antiship; RGM-109C conventional warhead land-attack planned to acquire 1,486 Block IIA with Bullpup warheads and 1,157 Block IIB with bomblet payloads; RGM-109D land-attack (with 166 BLU-97/B bomblets); RGM-109E antiship; RGM-109F land-attack, anti-airfield.

During 1993, the first Block II missiles, with better fuzing, 320-kg warhead, 50 percent more fuel, F107-WR-402 turbojets with 19 percent more thrust, Mk 111 booster, global positioning system, and faster missile mission planning will enter service.

Harpoon (RGM-84A/D)—McDonnell Douglas

An all-weather cruise missile that can be launched by aircraft, surface ships, or submarines. 5,700 had been delivered to the U.S. Navy and foreign customers by 10-91. For USN use, under FY 82, 240 were procured, with 221 approved under FY 83, 315 in FY 84, 354 in FY 85, 395 in FY 86, 96 in FY 87, 109 in FY 88, 119 in FY 89, 190 in FY 90, and 167 in FY 91 (the last year of procurement).

Length: 4.628 m ship-launched/3.848 m air-launched
Diameter: 0.343 m—Wingspan: 0.914 m
Weight: 681 kg from canister, 680 kg from SAM launcher or 653 kg from ASROC launcher (with booster)
Propulsion: CAE-JA02 turbojet, with a rocket booster added to the ship- and submarine-launched versions
Speed: Mach 0.85
Guidance: inertial, then active homing on J band in the final trajectory
Range: "over 67" nautical miles
Warhead: 227 kg

AGM-84 is the 526-kg, air-dropped version, which does not require a solid rocket booster, and **UGM-84** is the submarine version. The submarine version is shrouded and is launched from the torpedo tubes while submerged. In order to reach the maximum range, it is necessary to use targeting systems external to the launching unit. The AGM-84 can be carried by A-6E, P-3C, S-3A/B and Air Force B-52 (up to 12 each) aircraft. The U.S. Air Force acquired 85 undelivered Iranian AGM-84 in 8-84. Beginning with FY 88 procurement, have "Dash-4" seeker and improved guidance.

Block 1D missiles (first launch 4-9-91) have a 0.6-meter-longer fuselage to provide double the range and also have a re-attack feature if the missile misses on the first pass.

♦ surface-to-air missiles (*Note:* Standard and Sea Sparrow can also be used against surface ships)

Standard SM-1 MR (RIM-66B)—General Dynamics/Hughes, Rayth

Single-stage missile, replaced Tartar.

Length: 4.47 m
Diameter: 0.34 m
Weight: 625 kg
Guidance: semi-active homing
Range: 25 nautical miles, 150–60,000 ft

System comprises Mk 11 twin launcher or Mk 13 single launcher with a v ready-service magazine containing 40 missiles (on the FFG 1 class: Mk 22 w missiles), a computer, an air-search radar, a three-dimensional SPS-48 or S radar, and SPG-51 guidance radars. Acceptance trials with the Block 6 variant (computer, monopulse radar) were carried out 3-83. 650 approved under FY 83 procurement ended.

Standard SM-2 MR (RIM-66C)—General Dynamics, Raytheon

Single-stage missile. Initial procurement of 30 in FY 80. 150 approved under 846 in FY 86, 844 in FY 87, 1,310 in FY 88, 1,310 in FY 89, 1,200 in FY 90, 405 1991, and 330 in FY 92; 330 Block IIA and Block IIIB requested under FY 93. I 1991, 263 Block III were ordered from Raytheon and 142 from General Dynan these, about two-thirds were vertical-launch and the others configured for launc trainable launchers. Block IIIB will have a dual-mode radar/infrared seeker.

Length: 7.98 m
Weight: 1,306 kg
Range: 30–40 nautical miles
Diameter: 0.34 m (booster diameter: 0.46 m)
Guidance: semi-active homing

Standard SM-2 ER (RIM-67B)—General Dynamics, Raytheon

Two-stage missile employed in ships with Mk 10 or Mk 26 launch systems, and 48 vertical launchers. Initial procurement of 55 in FY 80. 470 authorized under 350 in FY 87, none in FY 88, 89. All Block I missiles are being retired with the D class destroyers. The 200-nautical-mile–ranged, 95,000 ft. altitude SM-2ER Blo for use in AEGIS cruiser vertical launchers, is now scheduled to enter serv 1993–94 and may be adapted as a defense against ballistic missiles attackin phibious landing forces.

Length: 7.98 m Diameter: 0.34 m (booster diameter: 0.46 m)
Weight: 1,442 kg Range: 75–90 nautical miles
Guidance: semi-active homing, with mid-course guidance capability, inertial reference, and improved ECCM

Sea Sparrow (RIM-7)—Raytheon

Known at first as BPDMS (Basic Point Defense Missile System). The 50 installations employed RIM-7E-5 fixed-fin missiles launched from the eight-cell 25 launcher and controlled by the Mk 115 radar-equipped fire-control system. were mostly replaced by the Mk 15 Vulcan/Phalanx 20-mm gatling gun s beginning in 1982. A lightweight launcher, Mk 29, employing eight RIM-7F fold missiles and the Mk 91 radar fire-control system, is now in use. In Europe thi system, IPDMS (Independent Point Defense Missile System), is also known as Sea Sparrow and was first tested in the *Downes* (FF 1070). The RIM-7M versic being procured uses a blast-fragmentation warhead vice the earlier RIM-7H's e ing rod variety and has a monopulse radar; 1,593 were ordered in FY 82–8 RIM-7M authorized under FY 85. Subsequent totals have been combined wi launched AIM-7F/M, page 786. Trials with Mk 48 vertical launcher conduct NATO users 1988 on *Briscoe* (DD 977). The RIM-7R missile, with dual-mode IR seeker, is in development. Present plans call for the continued development generations of Sea Sparrow for the foreseeable future.

Length: 3.657 m Weight: 204 kg
Diameter: 0.20 m Range: 8 nautical miles

RAM (Rolling Airframe Missile) (RIM-116A)—General Dynamics

A point-defense system becoming operational in 1992, over ten years behind ule. Uses a 127-mm-diameter missile that employs slow spinning for stability the name). Guidance is by dual-mode anti-radiation and/or infrared proportiona gation homing, and a Mk 49, 21-missile launcher that uses a modified Phalanx r ing. Plans to employ modified Mk 29 Sea Sparrow–type launchers with five miss each of two cells of the eight-celled launcher have been shelved. The missile ho active radiation from the target until it picks up an infrared target signatu employs the current Stinger seeker in conjunction with Sidewinder fuzes, war and rocket motors. The 21-missile launch installation weighs 4,977 kg above 800 kg below. Target designation will be by the Mk 23 TAS system in U.S. Navy Developed under a 7-76 agreement by the U.S., Denmark, and West Germany. F built under FY 85. The U.S. Navy plans to acquire 4,600 total. The 21-cell launcher will be installed on two LCC and five LHA, and selected units of the D class. Low-rate production began 3-89, and 500 were ordered 6-89 for delivery

Under FY 86, 117 initial production missiles were authorized for the U.S. Navy another 130–150 to be built for West Germany, with missiles produced by the System GmbH consortium (Messerschmidt, AEG-Telefunken, RTG). 240 auth 1988, 260 in FY 89, 580 in FY 90; 540 under FY 91; 500 under FY 92. Plan acquire 800 per year under FY 92 and 93, but the FY 92 request was canceled. A t 30 Mk 49 launchers is planned for the U.S. Navy.

Length: 2.819 m Weight: 73.5 kg Range: 9.6 km
Diameter: 127 mm Speed: Mach 2+

Stinger (FIM-92)—General Dynamics and Raytheon

The marines employ the shoulder-launched infrared-homing with troops, a navy uses it for shipboard defense. The navy acquired 585 for shipboard use. FI entered service 1981; over 16,000 delivered. FIM-92B "Stinger POST": 559 deli FIM-92C RMP (Reprogrammed Microprocessor) is the current production v Under FY 84, 1,205 Stingers were authorized for procurement, with 2,360 auth in FY 85, 3,439 in FY 86, and 536 for the navy in FY 87. The navy authorized 4 marines 3,067 in FY 88. 2,225 for marines, 0 for navy in FY 89.

Length: 1.52 m Warhead: 3 kg (proximity fuze)
Diameter: 0.07 m Speed: Mach 2.0 Weight: 15.1 kg

:LES *(continued)*

: (MIM-23B)—Raytheon

adily deployable point-defense SAM used by the Marine Corps in its latest ed Hawk ("I-Hawk") version for airfield and strong-point defense. 525 I-Hawks uthorized under FY 88, 467 in FY 89.

tisubmarine warfare missiles

C (RUR-5A)—Alliant

id-fuel rocket used with a parachute-retarded Mk 46 torpedo. Range is regu- y the combustion time of the rocket motor. Rocket-torpedo separation is timed. 112 launcher carries eight rockets that can be trained together and elevated in 'ire control is made up of a computer linked with an SQS-23, SQS-26, or SQS-53

: 4.42 m Range: 9,200 m
:er: 0.324 m Warhead: Mk 46 torpedo
:: 454 kg

nox-class frigates, the ASROC launcher was modified to permit the launching of rd SSM missiles (later, Harpoon) in place of two ASW weapons. On older ations, loading is slow because the rockets have to be manually transferred from gazines. However, on later *Brooke*- and *Garcia*-class and all *Knox*-class frigates, transfers the rocket from a magazine below the bridge for semiautomatic ;, while in *Spruance*-class destroyers still fitted with the system, the missiles are d vertically. Some 12,000 ASROC rounds were procured between 1960 and when production ceased. All nuclear rounds retired by end FY 89. ASROC is ed from the Mk 10 missile launchers in the CG 26 and CGN 35 classes and from 26 launchers in the CGN 38 class and early units of the CG 47 class.
rtical-launch ASROC was under development for use with Mk 41 launchers in and later *Ticonderoga*-class cruisers and in DDG 51-class destroyers. With attached, the weapon will be 5.08 m long, 0.358 m in diameter, and will weigh 50 kg. Originally to be built by Goodyear and Martin Marietta, vertical-launch ⊃ has suffered numerous program delays and was expected to enter service late 9, but Congress authorized no procurement under FY 88. For FY 89, Congress ed the navy to procure 300.
program was canceled in FY 90 but revived under FY 91 with the cancellation of a Lance program. The Loral Corporation was to conduct launchings of 30 l-launch ASROC missiles during July through September 1992. Plans now call ited procurement of vertical-launch ASROC to equip DDG 51 through DDG 73. missiles were ordered 9-91.

(Sea Lance)—Boeing

placement for SUBROC, designated the ASW SOW (Stand-Off Weapon), was ed in 1981 in favor of an abortive program to produce a *single* weapon to replace UBROC and ASROC. That having predictably proven impracticable, the pro- were again separated in 1982. The new SOW will be launched from SSN ass submarines operating at down to 80 percent of their test depths. Plans call for ition of 3,500 weapons, with either nuclear or conventional warheads. Program ctured in FY 90 as a surface (VLS) and submarine-launched weapon to replace SROC and SUBROC. Delayed to at least 1996, leaving many surface ships with)-launched ASW weapon. Sea Lance *canceled* under FY 91 request, with vertical- ASROC to be reinstated for surface ships only, then reinstated at a low rate of g under FY 92. Initially planned to have a range of up to 106 nautical miles.

1: 6.25 m Range: 15 nautical miles
ter: 0.533 m Guidance: inertial in flight Weight: 1,406 kg

r-to-surface missiles

M (AGM-137)—Northrop

Service Stand-off Attack Missile, in development since 1986. Low-observable air und-launched missile to enter service mid-1990s on A-6E and F/A-18. Plan to e 8,650 for Navy, Air Force, and Army.

n: . . . Range: 100 + n.m.
t: approx. 1,000 kg Propulsion: . . .
subsonic Warhead: unitary or submunitions
nce: autonomous, fire-and-forget

S (AGM-. . .)—Texas Instruments-LTV

t Navy-Air Force developmental program for an unpowered 7- to 15-n.m. "fire- rget" ground-attack weapon to replace Skipper, Walleye, Paveway, and Laser rick and enter service in 1998. Program decision point is 1992. May weigh up to kg, with either a 444- or 888-kg explosive or cluster bomb payload. Television, ed, and fiber-optic guidance all being considered. As many as 6,300 are planned th services. Air Force version will dispense six sensor-fuzed anti-tank sub- tions; Navy version will dispense bomblets.

M (AGM-84D SLAM)—McDonnell Douglas

SLAM (Stand-off Land Attack Missile) is under development. Only 290 total originally planned, but another 200 may be procured under FY 92. Using the on missile propulsion section and warhead, it has the infrared Maverick missile r, incorporates the Global Positioning System, and uses the Walleye missile's ink. Trials began 1987, with the initial 19 trials missiles requested under FY 87. could be carried by either A-6E or F/A-18 aircraft. First test launch 24-6-89. A n with an upgraded, 340-kg I-800 warhead is planned.

:h: 4.49 m Weight: 628 kg Diameter: 0.343 m
lsion: CAE-JA02 turbojet Speed: Mach 0.85 Warhead: 227 kg

Penguin Mk 2 Mod. 7 (AGM-119B)—Norsk Forsvarsteknologie/ Grumman

Initially tested for the U.S. Navy in 1982–83 as a surfaced-launched weapon, Penguin is being procured for firing by SH-60B LAMPS-III helicopters. Range extended, wings made foldable, and the infrared homing seeker improved. Only 200 were planned for procurement, to be carried aboard 39 FFG 7 frigates; total procurement reduced to only 106, vastly increasing the unit cost. Only 28 helicopters will be modified to carry the missile. The first 24 ordered under FY 90, 40 under FY 91, and 42 under FY 92.

Length: 3.00 m Weight: 385 kg
Span: 1.40 m (0.56 folded) Range: 30+ km
Diameter: 0.28 m Warhead: Bullpup Mk 19 (50 kg)

Skipper (AGM-123A)—Aerojet General, Emerson Electric, and Texas Instruments

Skipper is essentially a Mk 83 Mod. 5, 1,000-lb bomb, equipped with a Paveway II infrared seeker and guidance head and a Shrike (AGM-45) solid rocket motor. Developed by the Naval Weapons Station, China Lake, Cal., it offers a very low unit price ($20,000/weapon) and reasonable accuracy. A fiber-optic-guided (FOG-5) version and a laser training round are to be developed with FY 90 R & D funds. Some 2,500 were acquired during FY 84. 1,520 each year have been authorized through FY 87, with 1,274 under FY 88, and none thereafter.

Length: 4.33 m Span: 0.914 m Range: . . .
Diameter: 0.356 m Weight: 581.8 kg

Maverick (AGM-65E and AGM-65F)—Hughes

Developed from the air force AGM-65D, the AGM-65E is a laser-designated, air-launched missile for the marines, while the AGM-65F version for the navy uses infrared homing. Both have the same 136-kg penetrator, with 56.8-kg blast-fragment warhead. For use by F/A-18 aircraft and, later, the A-6E. Rapid escalation of price initially forced scaling back of procurement; 90 were procured under FY 83 and 165 were bought under FY 84. In FY 85, 600 were authorized, while under FY 86, 1,500 AGM-65E and 195 AGM-65F were authorized. In FY 87 0 laser and 248 IR variants were purchased. In FY 88 1,300 laser/425 IR, and for FY 89 0 laser and 731 of the IR variant. In FY 90, the last year of procurement, 560 were authorized.

Length: 2.49 m Propulsion: solid-fuel rocket
Diameter: 0.305 m Range: 50 nautical miles
Weight: E: 208.8 kg; F: 307 kg Span: 0.72 m

Walleye I and II (AGM-62)—Martin-Marietta/Hughes

Glide bomb guided by television. Uses Mk 82 or Paveway II bomb. No longer produced, and is being phased out of service.

Length: I: 3.5 m; II: 4.0 m Diameter: 0.325 m
Wingspan: 1.16 m Weight: I: 511 kg; II: 1,090 kg
Range: I: 16 nautical miles: II: 35 nautical miles
Warhead: conventional—I: 373 kg; II: 908 kg

Harpoon (AGM-84)

See under surface-to-surface missiles.

HARM (AGM-88A/B/C)—Texas Instruments and Ford Instrument

HARM (High-Speed Anti-Radiation Missile) will be employed by A-7E, A-6E, F/A-18, and U.S. Air Force F-4E Wild Weasel aircraft to suppress or destroy ground defenses. Replaced the Shrike. Ford Instrument developed a "low-cost seeker" variant, with the first six delivered 1987 for evaluation. The 4,000th was delivered 13-4-88. Production of 5,000 was scheduled to start in 1982, with 160 authorized in FY 83, 381 in FY 84, 813 in FY 85, 904 in FY 86, 988 in FY 87, 766 in FY 88, 1,307 in FY 89, 1,262 in FY 90; (800 FY 89 and 1,200 FY 90 are AGM-88B with "low-cost" seekers), 2,261 under FY 91, 749 under FY 92. None requested under FY 93.

Length: 4.17 m Span: 1.13 m
Diameter: 0.253 m Weight: 360 kg
Propulsion: solid-propellant, low-smoke rocket Range: . . .
Guidance: homes on electromagnetic radiation Speed: Mach 2.0+

Note: The Northrop AGM-136A Tacit Rainbow long-endurance, loitering anti-radiation missile program was canceled because of developmental problems and escalating costs; an Israeli missile that accomplishes the same purpose is being studied.

Sidearm (AGM-122A)—Motorola

A low-cost radiation-seeking conversion of early AIM-9C missiles for use by U.S. Marine Corps helicopters. Data generally as for AIM-9 series. Conversion of 885 authorized in FY 86, 256 in FY 87, 276 in FY 88, 0 in FY 89 and thereafter.

TOW-2 (MGM-71)—Hughes

Wire-guided, helicopter- or ground-launched anti-tank weapon that uses optical sight and tube launcher. TOW = Tube-launched, Optically tracked, Wire-guided. 400,000 TOW built since 1970 for all customers. TOW-2A detonates reactive armor, then penetrates; 16,000 in service by 4-88. 2,200 approved under FY 84, 4,782 ITOW-2 under FY 86, 2,575 under FY 87, 3,354 in FY 88, 2,566 in FY 89, 839 in FY 90, 1,098 in FY 91, and 170 under FY 92. Under FY 93, the first 938 of a new air-launched AAWS-M (Advanced Anti-tank Weapon System-Medium) version were requested.

Length: 1.174 m Span: 1.14 m
Weight: 18.9 kg (ITOW (Improved TOW) weighs 19.1 kg, ITOW-2 weighs 21.5 kg) Propulsion: solid-propellant rocket
Warhead: 3.6-kg hollow, shaped-charge
Range: 2.3 nautical miles at Mach 1.0
Diameter: 0.152 m

Hellfire (AGM-114A)—Rockwell, Martin-Marietta

A lightweight anti-tank missile replacing the M82 LAW. Hellfire has three variants: Laser-designated (1.625 m, 45.7 kg), RF/IR (Radio-Frequency Infrared), and IRIS (Imaging Infrared). During 1989, Hellfire was under evaluation for use on patrol boats

MISSILES *(continued)*

and in coast defense, using Swedish-version warheads. First 219 authorized under FY 84, 438 in FY 85, 1,304 in FY 86, none in FY 87, 1,393 in FY 88, 1,000 in FY 89, 1,098 in FY 90, 1,198 in FY 91, and none in FY 92. Under FY 93, 1,000 of an upgraded variant were requested.

Length: 1.727 m or 1.778 m (imaging IR version)
Diameter: 0.1778 m (span: 0.3262 m)
Weight: 45.7 to 47.88 kg (71 kg in container)
Range: 5 km+ Speed: Mach 1.0+

Dragon (AGM-. . .)—McDonnell Douglas

Small anti-tank weapon. 4,259 ordered under FY 88, 14,599 under FY 89 for marines; none requested under FY 90 or FY 91.

Note: Also for air-launched use, some 4,000 ADM-141 TALD (Tactical Air-Launched Decoy) glide-missiles in three variants have been acquired: RF for defense saturation, chaff for force-masking, and IR for IR missile training. ITALD (Improved TALD), with turbojet propulsion, is in development.

♦ air-to-air missiles

Note: The AIM-132A ASRAAM Sidewinder-replacement program has been terminated.

Sparrow-III (AIM-7F/M)—Raytheon

The AIM-7F entered service in 1976 with a continuous-rod warhead. AIM-7M, the current version, entered service in 1983 with a blast/fragmentation warhead, active fuze, and improved seeker. In FY 85, 936 were authorized for procurement; 1,948 in both air and surface launch were authorized under FY 86, 1,716 in FY 87, 600 in FY 88, 450 in FY 89, but none thereafter.

Length: 3.65 m — Diameter: 0.203 m
Weight: 232 kg — Guidance: semi-active homing
Range: 26,000 m — Speed: Mach 2.5
Propulsion: solid-fuel rocket — Warhead: 27 kg, proximity fuze

Sidewinder (AIM-9H/L/M)—Raytheon and Ford Instrument

Over 110,000 Sidewinder missiles have been built. The AIM-9L version uses an active optical fuze and has a guidance system permitting all-angle attacks. The AIM-9M version supplanted the -9L in production in 1981 and has improved capabilities against countermeasures and against targets seen against warm backgrounds. Only 500 AIM-9 L/M were authorized under FY 83, 350 under FY 84, none in FY 85, 1,850 (for all services) under FY 86, 391 in FY 87, 288 in FY 88, 0 in FY 89 and thereafter. Some 8,000 AIM-9M were in inventory as of 1991. An AIM-9R is in development, improvements to counter-countermeasures are being introduced to existing AIM-9M missiles, and an AIM-9X is projected for deployment post-2001.

Length: 2.90 m — Diameter: 0.127 m
Wingspan: 0.61 m — Weight: 84.4 kg
Propulsion: solid-fueled rocket — Speed: Mach 2.5
Range: 12 nautical miles — Guidance: infrared homing
Warhead: 9.45-kg fragmentation

Phoenix (AIM-54A/C)—Hughes

AIM-54A ceased production in 1980 after only 2,500 AIM-54A had been built for the U.S. and, unfortunately, Iran. The first 30 pilot-production AIM-54C were delivered 10-81, with 60 more to follow. By 10-88, 1,000 AIM-54C had been delivered. Only 90 procured under FY 83, rising to 265 under FY 84; in FY 85 only 265 were authorized, with 265 again in FY 86, 205 in FY 87, 350 in FY 88, 450 in FY 89, and 420 in FY 90, when procurement ended.

Length: 3.96 m — Weight: 453 kg
Diameter: 0.380 m — Propulsion: solid-fueled rocket
Wingspan: 0.914 m — Range: about 120 km
Warhead: 60.3 kg (continuous rod)

AMRAAM (AIM-120A)—Hughes and Raytheon

AMRAAM (Advanced Medium-Range Air-to-Air Missile) is intended to replace the AIM-7F Sparrow. First firings in 1985. The AIM-120B will have infrared homing added, and the AIM-120C will have improved aerodynamic performance. 90 developmental missiles requested under FY 86 for navy and air force use. Navy goal is 7,249 total, out of 24,320 planned grand total. For FY 89, only 26 were approved. 150 authorized under FY 90, 300 under FY 91, and 191 under FY 92. 140 requested under FY 93.

Length: 3.65 m — Diameter: 0.178 m
Weight: 151.5 kg — Warhead: 22.7 kg
Range: over 74 km — Guidance: inertial mid-course, active terminal homing

B. GUNS

406-mm, Model 1936

Fitted in 1,700-ton triple turrets in *Iowa*-class battleships. Requires a crew of 77 men per mount, plus 30–36 men in the magazine. In 1981, 15,500 high-capacity, 3,200 armor-piercing, and 2,300 B, L, & P rounds were available, with 12,500 full-service and 12,600 reduced-charge sets remaining. Armor-piercing rounds can penetrate 9 m of reinforced concrete. Reworked powder has produced very high accuracy. A new round with doubled range was to enter service in 1992, had the battleships not been decommissioned.

Length: 50 calibers
Muzzle velocity: armor-piercing: 739 m/sec.; high-cap: 902 m/sec.
Rate of fire: 2 rounds/minute/barrel
Maximum range: armor-piercing shell: 36,700 m; high-capacity shell: 38,000 m
Weight of projectile: armor-piercing shell: 1,226 kg; high-capacity shell: 863 kg
Cartridge bags: 6 per charge, 50-kg or 24-kg reduced-charge
Fire control: Mk 38 director with Mk 13 radar or SPQ-9 radar director

Note: With the striking of the last two *Des Moines*-class cruisers in 1991, the 20 Mk 16 Mod. 0 gun has been retired.

127-mm, twin barrel, Mk 12 Mod. 1

Semiautomatic, dual-purpose gun fitted in the Mk 32 series mounts of the *Iowa* battleships. 720,000 rounds of 127-mm ammunition for these and the single "5 38" mounts below remained available in 1981.

Length: 38 calibers
Muzzle velocity: 792 m/sec
Elevation: −15° to +85°
Rate of fire: 18 rds/minute/barrel with a well-trained crew
Maximum range on a surface target: 16,500 m
Maximum effective range on a ship target: 12,000 to 13,000 m
Maximum range in antiaircraft fire: 11,400 m
Maximum effective range in antiaircraft fire: 8,000 m
Weight of projectile: 25 kg Fire control: Mk 37 director with Mk 25 radar

127-mm, Mk 30

Single mounting, weighing 20.4 tons, enclosed Mk 30 series mountings on FFG 1040, and CGN 9 classes. Other data as for twin mounting.

127-mm, Mk 42—Northern Ordnance/FMC

Single-barrel, dual-purpose gun fitted on ships built in the 1950s and 1960s. Lo is entirely automatic from two ammunition drums in the handling room up loading tray by means of a rotating hoist. Each drum contains twenty rounds. Th of fire can be maintained for only one minute, inasmuch as it is necessary to relo drums. Firing rate reduced from original 40 rds/min for safety. Most mounts conv to Mk 42 Mod. 10 configuration. An SAL (Semi-Active Laser-guided projectile) r Deadeye was being developed for these and the Mk 45 gun in the early 1980s round is 1.548 m long, weighs 47.17 kg. Procurement of 15,100 was planne program again canceled FY 89; Congress, however, required 150 to be procured FY 89—from three different makers (the rounds were, however, never ordered).

Length: 54 calibers
Muzzle velocity: 810 m/second
Mount weight: 65.8 tons (Mod. 10: 63.9 tons)
Arc of elevation: −5° to +80°
Rate of train: 50°/second
Rate of elevation: 80°/second
Rate of fire: 20 rds/minute
Weight of projectile: 32 kg
Range: 23,700 m horizontal/14,840 vertical
Fire control: Mk 68 system with SPG-53 radar in most ships
Personnel: 13 men, with 2 in mount

127-mm Mk 45—Northern Ordnance/FMC

Single-barrel mount fitted on *Ticonderoga-* , *California-* , and *Virginia* cruisers, *Spruance-* , *Kidd-* , and *Arleigh Burke*-class destroyers, and *Tarawa* amphibious assault ships. The Mod. 1 version permits rapid switching from one t ammunition to another and has an electronic vice mechanical fuze-setter. A guided projectile development has been canceled; see above.

Length: 54 calibers
Muzzle velocity: 810 m/second
Mount weight: 21.7 tons
Arc of elevation: −5° to +65°
Rate of fire: 16 to 20 rds/minute
Range: 23,700 m horizontal/14,840 vertical
Fire control: Mk 86 GFCS with SPQ-9 search radar: SPG-60 tracking radar
Personnel: none on mount; 6 in handling room to reload ammunition drums

76.2-mm, Mk 21

Obsolescent. Single-fire, dual-purpose gun on some Coast Guard ships. Mk 26 m

Length: 50 calibers — Mount weight: 4.2 tons
Weight of projectile: 3.2 kg — Rate of fire: 20 rds/minu
Maximum range: 12,840 horizontal/8,950 vertical — Fire control: ring sight o

76-mm, Mk 75—Northern Ordnance/FMC and OTO Melara

Single-barrel, license-built version of OTO Melara Compact, tested in the fı *Talbot* and used in PHM and FFG 7 classes and Coast Guard *Bear*-class cu backfitted in some Coast Guard ships. 1985 order to OTO Melara vice U.S. lice Northern Ordnance.

Length: 62 calibers
Mount weight: 6.2 tons
Weight of projectile: 6.4 kg
Rate of fire: 85 rds/minute
Maximum rate: 19,200 m horizontal/11,900 m vertical
Fire control: Mk 92 radar system
Personnel: 4 below decks

40-mm, Mk 19 Mod. 3—Socko Corp.

Strictly speaking not a gun, but rather a lightweight rapid-fire grenade launch portable tripod-legged mountings. Found aboard small combatants, auxiliaries Coast Guard ships. Range: 2,195 m; rate of fire: 300 rds/min. During late 1980s being procured at 25 per year for navy. Marines authorized 350 under FY 89, 123 FY 90, 321 under FY 91, and 568 under FY 92; none requested under FY 93.

Note: One Italian Breda 30-mm AA gun was acquired 1988 for trials at Dah Proving Ground. The General Electric 20-mm and 25-mm Sea Vulcan gatling have been sold abroad but have not yet been acquired for the USN; Sea Vulcan 2

(continued)

.U-12/U gun (900 or 2,000 rpm) with 500 rds on mount. A 25-mm "breechless" being developed under a 2-89 contract to Tround, Inc.

n Mk 88 (M 242 Bushmaster)—Hughes Helicopter

nain gun," using linked Oerlikon M790 ammunition. For use on Cyclone-class boats, Mk-III patrol boats, and later LSD 42-class landing ships and also issued s deployed to the Mideast during the 1990–91 crisis. In FY 86, 29 were au- d; 25 in FY 87, 22 in FY 88, 57 in FY 89, 22 in FY 90, 55 under FY 91, and 55 FY 92, the last year of procurement. A stabilized mounting that will also nodate small missiles is under development to replace the cumbersome, low- Mk 88 mounting.

: 2.74 m overall	Rate of fire: single-shot, 100, or 200 rds/min
: 109 kg (gun)	Fire control: ring sight

n, Mk 16 Mod. 5

le-barrel Mk 67 or Mk 68 mounting in small combatants, amphibious ships, and aries.

: 80 calibers	Maximum range: 3,000 m horizontal
weight: . . .	Fire control: ring sights on mount
f fire: 800 rds/min	Weight of projectile: 0.34 kg

n, Mk 15 Mod. 0 Block 0 and 1 CIWS (Close-In Weapon m)—General Dynamics (with G. E. gun), and General Electric

an/Phalanx "Close-in" system designed to destroy missiles. It consists of a arrel, M61A1 20-mm gun with a very high rate of fire, which is co-mounted with dars, one of which follows the target and the other the projectile stream, using 90 integrated fire-control system. A computer furnishes necessary corrections in and elevation so that the two radar targets coincide, bringing heavy fire to the target. 676 units programmed to be fitted to U.S. ships. Only 989 rds in 0 magazine. The first production unit completed 9-8-79 and was installed, with hers, in *America* (CV 66) on 17-4-80. An improved "Block 1" version with more s on mount and a higher rate of fire entered service in late 1988—five years late. 0 mounts upgrading to Block 1, 45 in FY 88, 59 in FY 89. Originally used Mk 149 s with depleted uranium sub-caliber penetrators; now uses heavier tungsten s. Later versions may use a 4-barreled GAU-10, 30-mm gatling gun or a 5- or eled 25-mm gatling gun. Five Mk 15 Mod. 1 authorized under FY 88 and FY 89, ler FY 90, and 11 under FY 91, the final year of procurement. By 1995, some 64 version are to be aboard carriers. Mounts aboard ships being decommissioned be recycled to ships that had not yet had the Mk 15 CIWS installed.

weight: 5.4 tons	Maximum range: 1,486 m horizontal
f fire: 3,000 rds/minute (Block 1: 3,000 or 4,500/min.)	

)RPEDOES

0 ALWT—Alliant Telesystems (formerly Honeywell) and inghouse

ALWT (Advanced Lightweight Torpedo) is being procured as a replacement for k 46 series and is being supplied in surface-launched and air-droppable configu- s. It is of roughly the same weight as the Mk 46 and of the same dimensions, but is -diving (over 600 m), faster (over 40 knots), employs lithium fuel, has digital nce and control systems, and has better homing and counter-countermeasures ilities. Due to continuing program delays, did not enter service until 1991. t: 362 kg; length: 2.93 m. Under FY 87, 39 were authorized; 16 under FY 88, 140 89, 200 in FY 90, 265 in FY 91, and 218 in FY 92; under FY 93, 212 were sted. FY 92 and later procurements single-sourced to Westinghouse.

8 ADCAP—Westinghouse and Hughes Helicopter

gram began 1978 to provide a weapon with significant performance improve- s over the earlier Mk 48. Technical evaluation began 8-86, suffered initial set- . Westinghouse bought Mk 48 rights from Gould, 1-88. ADCAP was to enter e in 1989, with the first 30 having been authorized under FY 85 and 123 au- ed under FY 86, 50 in FY 87, 100 in FY 88, 320 in FY 89, 240 under FY 90 and FY d 108 under FY 92; again in FY 93, 108 were requested, with procurement to from a single source.

18 Mod. 1, Mod. 3–5—Westinghouse and Hughes Helicopter

ered service 1972. Can be launched from a submarine against a surface target or marine. No surface ships are currently equipped to launch Mk 48, although that ility was originally intended. Can be launched with its own active-passive or tic homing system or with a wire-guidance system. High speed (40 knots) and un duration (50,000 m). An improvement program was instituted, with the first y-two conversion kits requested under FY 80. The first "Near-Term Update" Mk d. 4 torpedo was delivered 12-80. A total of 3,059 Mk 48s were procured through plus 56 for Australia and 92 for the Netherlands; 144 additional for the U.S. Navy appropriated under FY 80 and again in FY 81 through FY 84. FY 85 was the last of production, with 108 authorized.

h: 5.84 m	Speed: 55 kts
eter: 0.533 m	Weight: 633 kg
: up to 760 m	Propulsion: 500-hp Otto-cycle swashplate engine

16 Mod. 0, 1, 2, 5, and 6—Alliant Telesystems (formerly Honeywell)

W torpedo using liquid fuel (Otto fuel), and twin, counter-rotating props. Entered e 1963 and expected to remain in service until 2017. Active-passive guidance. ched from Mk 32 ASW torpedo tubes or as payload for the ASROC ASW missile m. The Mk 46 Mod. 0 air-launched version is similar to the surface-launched on, but is equipped with a retarding parachute, solid vice liquid propellant, and not have a straight run-out before commencing helical search. e Mk 46 Mod. 1 and Mod. 2 are being upgraded to Mod. 6 NEARTIP (Near-Term Improvement Program) status with improved acoustic homing system and countermeasures resistance. Mod. 5 torpedoes are being upgraded to Mod. 5A, with improved sonar. Under FY 80, 576 conversion kits were requested, and 1,128 more were requested under FY 82; ultimately, some 2,700 torpedoes will be updated. The Mk 46 Mod. 4 is the payload for the Captor mine. 570 *new* Mk 46 Mod. 5 torpedoes were ordered from Honeywell in 1980, 440 under FY 83, and 1,200 under FY 84, 1,565 authorized FY 85, and 500 in FY 86. A Mod. 7 upgrade program is in development.

Length: 2.60 m (4.50 with ASROC booster)	Weight: 232.4 kg
Diameter: 0.324 m	Warhead:45.4 kg HE

NT-37E—Alliant Telesystems (formerly Honeywell)

Remanufactured and greatly improved Mk 37 homing torpedoes available for export, but not used by U.S. Navy. Propelled by a 90-hp Otto-fuel motor. The last U.S. Navy Mk 37 torpedo was retired 30-9-86. A further improvement, the NT-37F, was ordered by Egypt in 7-91; employing further improvements in guidance and controls, it has a 148-kg HBX warhead.

Length: 3.467 m	Speed: 35 kts
Diameter: 0.483 m	Range: 18,000 m
Weight: . . .	Warhead: 148 kg HE

D. MINES

Mk 52 Mod. 1, 2, 3, 5, 6

Air-dropped. All 2.75 m long by 338-mm diameter (830 mm over fins). All carry 270-kg HBX explosive. Mod. 1 is an acoustic mine, weight: 542.5 kg. Mod. 2 is a magnetic influence version, weight: 568 kg. Mod. 3 is a dual-pressure/magnetic influence version, weight: 572.5 kg. Mod. 5 is an acoustic/magnetic influence version, weight: 570.7 kg. Mod. 6 is a pressure/acoustic/magnetic influence version, weight: 546 kg. All are bottom mines for depths of up to 47 m (Mod. 2: 183 m) and can be carried by U.S.A.F. B-52D and H bombers as well as navy aircraft.

Mk 53

A 225-kg mine-sweep rig obstruction weapon used to protect minefields from mine countermeasures efforts.

Mk 55 Mod. 2, 3, 5, 6, 7

Air-dropped bottom mines. All 2.89 kg long by .592-m diameter (1.03 m over fins) and carry 577-kg HBX-1 explosive. Versions: Mod. 2: magnetic influence, weight: 989 kg; Mod. 3: pressure/magnetic influence, weight: 994 kg; Mod. 5: acoustic/magnetic influence, weight: 994 kg; Mod. 6: pressure/acoustic/magnetic, weight: 997 kg; Mod. 7: dual-channel magnetic influence, weight: 996 kg. All can be laid in 46-m-deep water, except Mod. 2, 7: 183 m. Can also be laid by surface ships using portable rails.

Mk 56 Mod. 0

Aircraft-dropped moored mine. 996 kg. 3.51 m long by 592-mm diameter (1.06 over fins). Total-field magnetic influence exploder. Carries 577-kg HBX-3 explosive. Depth: 350 m.

Mk 57 Mod. 0

Submarine-laid version of Mk 56 moored mine. 1,012 kg, 3.07 long by 510-mm diameter. Carries 935-kg HBX-3 explosive. Depth: 250 m.

Mk 60 CAPTOR (enCAPsulated TORpedo)

Submarine-laid or aircraft-dropped. Uses Mk 46 Mod. 4 acoustic-homing torpedo payload. Primarily ASW in function. 908 kg, 3.66 m long by 324-mm diameter. 44.5-kg warhead. Development began 1961. 260 requested under FY 80 in first major operational buy, with 500 approved under FY 83, 300 under FY 84, 300 under FY 85, and 150 (unrequested) under FY 86. Mod. 1 conversion kit gives improved target detection: 3.35 m long, 932 kg. All have 300-m mooring capability.

Mk 62 DST-36 Quickstrike series (Mods. 0–5)

Aircraft-dropped bottom mine. Converted from 500-lb (227-kg) Mk 82 standard aircraft bomb. Magnetic. 87-kg H-6 explosive charge. Over 4,000 procured.

Mk 63 DST-40 Quickstrike series (Mods. 0–5)

Aircraft-dropped bottom mine. Converted from 1,000-lb (454-kg) Mk 83 standard aircraft bomb. Magnetic-influence sensor.

Mk 64 DST-41 Quickstrike series (Mods. 0–5)

Aircraft-dropped bottom mine. Converted from 2,000-lb (908-kg) Mk 84 bomb. Magnetic or magnetic/seismic influence. 3.83 m long.

Mk 65 Quickstrike

Submarine-launched, 3.25 m long. 1,000 on order 1985.

Mk 66

A practice version of CAPTOR.

Mk 67 SLMM (Submarine-Launched Mobile Mine)

Converted Mk 37 Mod. 0 torpedo. 754 kg, 4.09 m long by 483-mm diameter. Bottom mine. Production version not yet in service.

GATOR—Aerojet

An air-dropped *land* mine using CBU-78/B mines; 227 kg.

Note: The U.S.-U.K. New Generation Mine was canceled due to U.K. withdrawal; no replacement program has been announced. The U.S. bought 15 U.K. Vickers Versatile Exercise Mines in 3-88. Although $7 million in R&D funds was authorized under FY 90 for a new "Substrike" mine, the money went unspent.

Minelaying: no surface ships are permanently equipped for minelaying except LCU 1641; portable rails have been developed and tested on a number of ship types. Naval

MINES *(continued)*

aircraft of the S-3, P-3, and A-6 types are capable of laying mines, as are some 80 operational air force B-52D bombers. Theoretically, any U.S. Navy submarine can lay mines from its torpedo tubes, except early units of the SSN 688 class.

E. RADARS

♦ surface-search and navigation

BPS-14: X-band. Raytheon. Submarine search, navigational, and fire-control radar. Mounted on telescoping masts.

BPS-15, 15A: X-band. Made by Sperry. Submarine search, navigational, and fire-control radar. Mounted on telescoping masts.

BPS-16: X-band. Made by Sperry. Successor to BPS-15. First of 35 delivered 1990.

SPS-10: C-band, Mods. B through F in service. Made by Raytheon. Primary surface-search set before the introduction of SPS-55. Being replaced by SPS-67.

SPS-53: X-band. Made by Sperry. Navigational set for large ships and for MSOs, auxiliaries, and USCG ships. Most replaced by later radars.

SPS-55: X-band, slotted waveguide antenna. Made by Cardion. On *Spruance*-class destroyers and FFG 7 frigates, etc.

SPS-59: X-band. Official designation for the Canadian Marconi LN-66 navigational radar. Being replaced by SPS-69 and other later equipments.

SPS-64: X-band. Made by Raytheon. Used by USCG in several versions and being introduced into the USN for auxiliaries and minesweepers, etc., in the SPS-64(V)9 version. Range: about 48 n.m.; can automatically track 20 targets.

SPS-66: X-band. Raytheon 1900 "Pathfinder" navigational set.

SPS-67: C-band. Made by Norden. A solid-state replacement for the SPS-10, using similar antenna. Also has an ultra-short pulse mode for navigation. First used on refitted *Long Beach* (CGN 9) in 1982.

SPS-69: X-band. Raytheon raster-scan, solid-state replacement for SPS-66, with four different antennas: R20X and R40X in radomes and R21X and R41X slotted-waveguide. 4 kw max. power. For use by USN and USCG.

Note: Also in use are the small navigational radar sets SPS-51, SPS-57, SPS-59, SPS-60, and SPS-66, all X-band and most using slotted-waveguide antennas. The UPS-3 TDAR (Tactical Defense Alert Radar), a land-based portable set, is available for use aboard amphibious warfare ships. Japanese Furuno 8050D and 904 X-band navigational radars are widely employed on U.S. Navy service craft.

♦ two-dimensional air-search

SPS-40-series: B-band (400–450 MHz). Made by Lockheed (SPS-40) and Sperry (SPS-40A), Norden (SPS-40B), and Westinghouse (SPS-40E). Range against medium bombers: 150–180 miles. Earlier "A" models modernized to SPS-40C and SPS-40B to SPS-40D, all with improved low-flyer detection, higher peak-power, ECCM improvements. SPS-40E has a solid-state transmitter with very low failure rate; conversions began under FY 87.

SPS-49: L-band (851–942 MHz). Made by Raytheon. (V)1 aboard FFG 7-class frigates; (V)2 for New Threat Upgrade (NTU) cruisers; (V)3 for Canadian Halifax-class frigates; (V)5 current version with digital pulse-doppler processing; and (V)7 for Aegis ships.

♦ three-dimensional air-search

SPS-48C/D/E: S-band (2900–3100.5 MHz). Made by ITT-Gilfillan. Electronic frequency scanning in elevation, improved SPS-48A. E version has doubled power, armored antenna, reduced side-lobe level, adaptive energy beam management, solid-state transmitter, and three transmitter power modes. D-model on *Mahan* (DDG 42) was the developmental model. As of 11-88, 49 SPS-48E had been ordered, of which 28 had been delivered by 9-90.

SPS-52C: S-band improvement on SPS-39. Made by Hughes. Electronic frequency scanning in elevation. Entered service 1978. Uses UYK-20 computer to provide stabilization and beam-control, target processing, and interface with the SYS-1 combat data system. Few remain in USN service. Older SPS-52B variant remains in use by some foreign fleets.

SPY-1A: S-band. Aegis system. Made by General Electric. Obtaining a directional effect by dipole radiation to secure an electronic sweep, it has four fixed phased-array antennas that provide instant 360-degree coverage. There are 4,096 transmitting and 4,352 receiving elements to the antenna array. Long-range air-search, target-tracking, and missile-guidance. SPY-1B, with reduced side lobes, entered service 1988; SPY-1C developed for possible use on carriers; lighter-weight SPY-1D for DDG 51 program. SPY-1E, with greater effectiveness against sea-skimming missiles, will be introduced in DDG 82.

♦ fire-control

Mk 13: 3-cm wavelength. Ranging set for Mk 38 director on *Iowa*-class battleships; replaced by SPQ-9 on several ships.

Mk 25: X-band. Made by Western Electric. Mounted on Mk 37 GFCS directors on battleships and still widely employed on ships transferred to foreign navies. Dish antenna.

Mk 35: 3-cm wavelength. Made by General Electric. Used with Mk 56 GFCS for 127-mm and 76.2-mm gun control. On decommissioned FFGs and FFs. Removed from auxiliaries. Dish antenna.

Mk 86: SPG-60 and SPQ-9A radars combined into a single system. Made by Lockheed. Versions currently in use include Mod. 3 with Mk 152 computer in DD 963 and CGN 37 classes; Mod. 5 with UYK-7 computer in CGN 38 and DDG 993 classes; Mod. 8, with UYK-7 computer in German and three USN DDG 2 class; Mod. 9, without the SPG-60 radar, in Aegis cruisers; and Mod. 10, an upgrade to Mod. 3 substituting the UYK-7 computer; Mod. 11, an upgraded Mod. 3 for the LHA 1 class, and Mod. 12, and up Mod. 5.

Mk 91: Technically, the fire-control *system* for the Sea Sparrow SAM system with the Mk 29 lightweight launcher. Either one (Mod. 0) or two (Mod. 1) directors per launcher. Uses the Mk 95 radar, which has separate transmit receiver antennas mounted on the same pedestal.

Mk 92: X-band. Made by Sperry. U.S. Navy adaptation of Dutch H.S.A. (Ho Signaal Apparaaten) WM-20 series track-while-scan gun/missile fire-control s itself designated the Mk 94. Used in FFG 7, PHM 1, and by the USCG. Sear fire-control antennas dual-mounted in egg-shaped radome. Combined with STI ified SPG-60) antenna in FFG 7 class. Improvement program in FFG 7 ended Ph 1984. Phase II CORT (COherent Receive/Transmit) was intended to further upd system; six sets were authorized under FY 88 (one as a trainer) and first insta FFG 61 and FFG 36. Further CORT upgrades have been canceled.

Mk 92 Mod. 1 is in *Pegasus*-class hydrofoils and U.S. Coast Guard ships; M version designed for use with STIR second-channel director in the FFG 7-class; was the version for use on the Saudi Arabian PCG and PCC classes; and Mod. CORT upgrade program version.

Mk 115: X-band. Technically the fire-control *system* for Sea Sparrow when la from the Mk 25 heavy launcher. Older than Mk 91 and being phased out. Uses transmitter antenna and Mk 19 receiver antenna, co-mounted on modified Mk director pedestal, with operator manning the director.

SPQ-9: X-band. Made by Lockheed. Track-while-scan special surface sear weapons control for use with Mk 86 GFCS. Antenna mounted in spherical r Range: 36 km. Received moving target indicator and "low noise front end" kits in

SPG-51B/C/D: Standard MR illuminator-tracker; used with Mk 74 missil control system.

SPG-53: Mounted on Mk 68 GFCS director on CG, DDG, and DD with 127-mm guns.

SPG-55A/B: Standard ER illuminator-tracker; used with Mk 76 missile fire- system.

SPG-60: X-band. Made by Lockheed. Standard MR missile, 4-horn monopulse, doppler illuminator-tracker with Mk 74 missile fire-control system in later classes; also illuminates for guns in conjunction with Mk 86 GFCS. STIR v used on FFG 7 class, is modified for use with Mk 92 Mod. 2 missile/gun control s STIR = Separate Tracking & Illumination Radar. Can track Mach 3.0 tar 183 km. Has a co-mounted t.v. tracker.

SPG-62: X-band. Made by Raytheon. Standard SM-2 illuminator; used with system in CG 47 class. Slaved to SPY-1 radar.

TAS/Mk 23: L-band. Hughes Ground Systems Group. Technically a Target sition System, employing a rapidly rotating, stabilized linear-array antenna i junction with a UYK-20 computer to counter high- and low-angle aircraft and c missile attacks. Range 20 n.m. on small missiles to 90 n.m. on aircraft. Mod *Downes* (FF 1070) in 1975, Mod. 1 being added to *Spruance* (DD 963) class, Mod. 2 UYA-4 console) on *Sacramento* class, beginning with AOE 3 in 4-80. Can tr targets simultaneously. Plan to procure 15 sets FY 88 through FY 91. A 3-D ve TAS(I), was in development as an upgrade to the standard TAS in 1992; if ad would double the field of view of TAS.

♦ air-control radars

SPN-35: X-band. Made by ITT-Gilfillan. Blind-approach radar, with antenna in spherical radome. Ship-based version of the TPN-8.

SPN-42: Ka-band ACLS (Automated Carrier Landing System) radar with X beacon receiver for CCA (Carrier-Controlled Approach). Associated with the S marshaling radar.

SPN-43A: S-band (3590–3700 MHz). Made by ITT-Gilfillan. The marshaling ponent of a landing system that also employs the SPN-42 or SPN-46 controlling Can also be used as a back-up air-search radar. Range is about 50 n.m. Has re most SPN-35 installations.

SPN-46: Ka-band (33.0-33.4 gHz) and X-band. Made by Bell-Textron. probability-of-intercept air traffic-control replacement for SPN-42, using the AS-1347 antenna. Installed in pairs.

F. COUNTERMEASURES SYSTEMS

Note: This section lists alphabetically systems classified as "countermeasures" U.S. Navy, including active and passive electronic and mechanical systems and countermeasures systems.

ADC Mk 1–5, 7–10: Various expendable, submarine-launched decoys, most propelled.

APR-39: Helicopter radar-warning set used on *Cyclone*-class patrol boats.

BLR-1–10, 13–15: Radar warning systems for submarines; BLR-14 also direc launching of countermeasures.

BLR-14: BSAWS (Basic Submarine Acoustic Warfare System). Made by Sperry. to detect, evade, and counter torpedoes employing the WLR-9A/12 detection sy and the WLR-14 processor.

CSA Mk 2: Countermeasures launching system for submarines, employing th 151 launcher. Employed in ballistic-missile and SSN 637- and SSN 688-class marines.

Mk 30: Submarine target simulator. Torpedo-sized.

Mk 33/34 RBOC: Rapid-Blooming Off-board Chaff launcher; largely replaced b 36. Mk 33 employed four Hycor Mk 135 launchers and was used by frigate-sized and larger; Mk 34 employed only two launchers.

Mk 36 SRBOC: "Super-RBOC"—Mod. 1 with two 6-tubed mortars for ships 140 m; Mod. 2 with four 6-tubed mortars for ships over 140 m. All use M

TERMEASURES SYSTEMS *(continued)*

spensing cartridges, which climb to 244 m. Primarily employed with the NATO t Mk 216 rocket. Employs the Hycor Mk 137 sextuple launcher with tubes fixed nd 60° elevation. Several different decoys are in development for launching e SRBOC system, including the HIRAM (Hycor Infrared Anti-Missile) decoy, floating infrared decoy, CAD radar simulator, and Hycor ALEX chaff or IR

IOSS: MObile Submarine Simulator—small torpedo-like device for launch by ass SSBNs.

: Passive D/F and EW receiver used in conjunction with ULQ-6, and SLQ-22/ ixed and trainable antenna arrays.

: Trainable tracker array for ULQ-6.

S: Shipboard Lightweight Electronic Warfare System, in development for non- -series-equipped ships. Under examination for the rôle were the Tadiran 9000, 42, MEL Sceptre, Argo AR-700, and Sperry Guardian systems, but the program celed in 1-92.

: Jammer array for carriers; creates false target. Unsatisfactory; being d by SLQ-32(V)4. Hughes Aircraft.

Nixie: Towed noisemaker, made by Aerojet. Employs two winches, each with ed body, one acting as a spare. Being updated.

): The combined WLR-1H/WLR-8/WLR-11/SLQ-17 package.

(V)1: Radar warning (H-, I-, J-bands) for auxiliaries and amphibious ships; be upgraded to (V)2.

(V)2: Radar warning (B–J bands) for newer destroyers and frigates; replaces where fitted. "Sidekick" jammer adjunct, authorized FY 89, being added to FFG others.

(V)3: Radar warning (B–J bands) *and* jamming/spoofing (H–J bands) for s, DDG 37 class, and major amphibious ships.

(V)4: Replacement for SLQ-17 on carriers.

(V)5: SLQ-32(V)2 with "sidekick" active jammer adjunct.

3: A ship-towed acoustic deception device.

4: An intelligence collection system, with SRD-19 and SLR-16. Known as c Outboard." Carried in 28 ships. To be superseded by the "Combat D/F" system, will be carried by later units of the DDG 51 class.

6: Towed torpedo detection and spoofing; in development. Comprises improved rray, a magnetic countermeasure, a wake-homing torpedo countermeasure, and l torpedo detector.

7(V): Magnetic/acoustic minesweeping array with A Mk 4(V) and A Mk 6(B) sweeps.

8: Wire sweep to counter moored mechanical mines.

9: Chaff-dispensing buoy.

1-47: Active expendable EW buoys.

8: Mine countermeasures system, using Alliant (formerly Honeywell) remote- led tethered MNS submersible.

9: Air- or surface-launched inflatable decoy, "Rubber Duck." U.S. version of LF. Some 1,650 were procured from Irvin Industries.

0: The Battle-Group Passive Horizon-Extension System (BGPHES), by E- s. Employs airborne passive intercept detector and shipboard processing system sing three UYQ-23 terminals.

3: Single-ship deep-sweep mine countermeasures system; in development.

4: Replacement program for SLQ-32 series; in development by Raytheon.

50: Small ship EW system using SLQ-640 intercept and SLQ-630 jammer.

6: HF SIGINT receiver set using SRD-19 antenna arrays; part of the SSQ-72 c Outboard" system.

1: Intercept set for PHM 1 class. Made by EM Systems. Covers 2–18 gHz and a DF system. Used in the *Pegasus*-class hydrofoils.

2: Cover and deception system for aircraft carriers developed in mid-1980s; uncertain.

3: Intercept D/F, J-band; works with WLR-1 and SLQ-32.

4: On-board torpedo detection processor, using towed torpedo detection array.

00: EW intercept system for small ships (2–20 gHz).

10: Another small-ship EW intercept system (6.5–22 gHz).

40: Improved SLR-610.

, 8: Communications jammers.

9: "Classic Outboard" LF/MF/VHF shipboard SIGINT exploitation system 24 small deck-edge antennas, whip antennas, and a masthead Adcock-type VHF ray; used in conjunction with SLR-16 as part of the SSQ-72 system.

: "Combat DF." Less elaborate version of SSQ-72/108 "Classic Outboard" for ip missile targeting. Made by Sanders. Has experienced cost increases and m delays.

2: "Classic Outboard" combat D/F Suite, with SRD-19 and SLR-16 antennas ter SSQ-74 is on DD 974). SSQ-108 is a more elaborate version, of which more cquired.

S: Surface Ship Torpedo Decoy System, an umbrella program encompassing towed and hull-mounted sensors to detect torpedoes and, for highly valuable ships such as aircraft carriers, launchers for modified Mk 46 ASW torpedoes to counter Russian Type 65-80 wake-homing torpedoes; the first 172 production active countermeasures are to be procured under the FY 93 Budget. Joint U.S.-U.K. program. Phase-I, introduced in 1987, employed the SLQ-25A Nixie. Deliveries of Phase-II, with the SLR-24 detector, were to begin in 1992.

T-Mk 6 Fanfare: Mechanical towed anti-torpedo noisemaker—obsolescent.

URD-9(V): Radar D/F (225–400 MHz).

URD-27: Broadcast frequency D/F device for SIGINT (250 MHz–18 gHz).

ULQ-6: Deception repeater/jammer in cruisers, destroyers—largely replaced by SLQ-32(V)3 in high-value ships, but still in use on many ships transferred abroad.

WLQ-4E: *Sturgeon*-class submarine "Sea Nymph" ESM system developed by GTE-Sylvania. WLQ-4(V)1 will be used by the *Seawolf* class.

WLR-1: Radar warning array in older ships, covering 50 MHz to 10.75 gHz. Being updated to WLR-1H (0.55–20 gHz). Employed with WLR-11.

WLR-3: Radar warning and signal collection—also in some submarines.

WLR-4: ESM receiver.

WLR-5: Acoustic intercept receiver.

WLR-6: Reconnaissance signal collection system; called "Waterboy" in submarines.

WLR-8(V)2: Radar warning system covering 0.5–18 gHz for the SSN 688 class; (V)5 version in *Ohio*-class SSBNs. Surface ship version canceled 1983, although one (V)3 set was installed in the carrier *Enterprise*. Made by GTE-Sylvania.

WLR-9: Sonar detection system.

WLR-10: Radar warning receiver for submarines; shares telescoping mast array with WLR-8(V)2/5.

WLR-11A: Radar warning/SIGINT system. 7–18 gHz. Uses WLR-1's antenna suite.

WRL-13: Infrared/electro-optical warning receiver.

WSQ-5: Portable ELINT collection system for SSN-688 class. Made by Watkins-Johnson.

G. SONARS

♦ on surface ships:

SQQ-14: High-frequency, minehunting, and classification set in retractable-transducer array on MSOs. Employs the U.K.–developed Type 193 sonar for classification. A towed version, SQQ-35, is in development. Search mode 80 kHz; 350 kHz classification.

SQQ-23A/B: PAIR (Performance and Integration Refit). Modified SQS-23 using two transducers: SQQ-23A with two sonar domes separated by 18 m in four DDG 2 and two DDG 37-class destroyers, and SQQ-23B with one dome in CGN 9, CGN 25, and CG 16 classes.

SQQ-25: High-definition 3-D set on *Pigeon*-class submarine rescue ships; 7 kHz.

SQQ-28: LAMPS-III helicopter data-link processing system; not a sonar, but employed in ASW.

SQQ-30: Minehunting sonar developed by General Electric for use on mine countermeasures ships. Essentially a digital, solid-state SSQ-14. Superseded by SQQ-32.

SQQ-32: Raytheon/Thomson-CSF sonar to replace SQQ-30 in later units of the MCM 1 class and for the MSH 1 class. Separate detection and classification transducers lowered through well and towed far below the hull. Uses two UYK-44 computers. First "pilot" version delivered early 1989. Performed extremely well during operations in the Persian Gulf in 1991.

SQQ-89: Suite integrating the SQR-19 towed array, SQS-53B hull-mounted sonar, Mk 116 Underwater Fire Control System, LAMPS-III helicopter, SQQ-28 processor, and UYQ-28 SIMAS (Sonar In-Situ Mode Assessment System) for CG 56 and later, for DDG 51, FFG 7 class. Trials in DD 980 late 1985. In FY 88, nine sets authorized, ten in FY 89, seven in FY 90, nine in FY 91. Acoustic Video Processor being added under FY 90. Its successor, SQQ-89I, has been redesignated SQY-1.

SQR-15: Developmental passive towed array, in six DD 963-class destroyers. Modular, deck-mounted system. Only six sets entered service.

SQR-17: Passive classification device for processing data transmitted to CG 26, DD 963, F 1040, 1052, and FFG 7-class ships via LAMPS-I helicopters from various sonobuoys. Uses SKR-4 link receiver, AKT-22 link, ARR-75 sonobuoy receiver, UYS-1 processor. 97 sets procured for shipboard use by 1989, plus 16 for Naval Reserve Mobile Inshore Undersea Warfare units. To develop for torpedo warning use.

SQR-18A: TACTAS (Tactical Towed Acoustic Sensor). Built by EDO; 47 sets delivered by 1989; 12 more SQR-18A ordered 6-88. For use on FF 1052 class equipped with SQS-35 VDS; array attaches to VDS towed body. Normal cable length is 1,706 m; towed at depths up to 366 m; array is 82.6-mm diameter, 222.5 m long. Latest version, SQR-18(V)1 with 730-m cable is aboard 35 FF 1052-class ships; uses 8 modular hydrophone sections. SQR-18A(V)2 uses SQR-19 towing rig for the non-VDS-equipped units of the FF 1052 class and has 1,524-m tow cable. R&D was to have begun FY 90 for SQR-18(V)3, an improved version.

SQR-19A/B: Improved TACTAS for use on CG 47, DD 963, and FFG 7 classes; to be deployed through port in stern. 1,707-m cable. Has 16 acoustic reception modules in array: eight VLF, four LF, two MF, two HF. UYQ-21 display. SQR-19A has UYH-3 data storage vice UYH-2. SQR-19B has four UYK-44 computers vice UYK-20; began deliveries 1-91.

SQS-23: Bow- or hull-mounted low-frequency (4.5, 5.0, and 5.5 kHz), active-passive. In CGN 25, some CG, older DDG, and DD 931 classes. Some 48 sets were upgraded with Raytheon DE 1191 solid-state transmitters. Versions through SQS-23H have been delivered. SQQ-23 PAIR is a version with two transducers (see above).

SONARS *(continued)*

SQS-26: Bow-mounted, low-frequency set, in AXR, BX, and CX versions. In older CGNs, CG 26, FFG 1, FF 1040, FF 1052, and FF 1098 classes. Transmits at around 3.5 kHz and receives between 1.5–4.0 kHz.

SQS-35: Independent, variable-depth, towed, active-passive in FF 1052 class. Operates at 13 kHz. Made by EDO. SQS-36 version used as hull in some foreign ships.

SQS-38: Hull-mounted SQS-35 for USCG *Hamilton*-class cutters; operates at 11.9, 13, and 14 kHz.

SQS-53: SQS-26 with digital computer interface, for use with Mk 116 UWFCS (Underwater Fire Control System) on DD 963, DDG 993, CG 47 classes. The digital SQS-53B (General Electric/Hughes) has multiple target tracking and classification aids, weapons checkout routines, UYK-44 imbedded computers, UYQ-21 display, UYS-1 signal processor, a 60-percent reduction in required manning, 2,000-hour mean time between failures, and a 30-minute mean time to repair. SQS-53C, with improved active performance, simultaneous active/passive modes, more power, greater bandwidth, UYH-1 mass memory, faster reaction time, etc., is in advanced development.

SQS-54: Shipboard sonobuoy data processor initially associated with the LAMPS-I helicopter.

SQS-56: U.S. Navy variant of the Raytheon 1160B commercial active-passive, hull-mounted, medium-frequency set; used on FFG 7 class. Operates at 5.6, 7.5, and 8.4 kHz.

SQS-58: Raytheon. Special set for private R&D trials ship *Sub Sig II;* solid-state MF set, offered for export sale as the DE 1167.

SQY-1: Successor system to SQQ-89, with first installations to be in later units of the DDG 51 class. Initially called SQQ-89I. In development.

UQQ-2 SURTASS: SURveillance Towed-Array Sonar System, for use in the *Stalwart* (T-AGOS 1) class. Trails 1,830-m passive hydrophone array at about 3 knots.

♦ on submarines

BQQ-5: Active-passive system on the SSN 688 class; being backfitted in SSN 594 and SSN 637 classes. Incorporates BQS-11, -12, or -13 spherical bow hydrophone array. BQQ-5C has expanded DIFAR reception. BQQ-5D, with TB-23 long-aperture, thin-line array, operational 1988. BQQ-5E, with TB-12X thin-line array, in development. BQQ-5E(V)4, with no active element, is the suite used by later units of the *Ohio*-class.

BQQ-6: Passive-only version of the BQQ-5 system, for earlier units of the SSBN 626 class; has 944 hydrophone transducers mounted on a sphere.

BQQ-9: Towed array signal-processing system for BQR-15; made by Rockwell. TASPE (Towed Array Signal Processing Equipment) for *Ohio* class.

BQR-15: Towed, passive array for SSN 608, SSBN 616 classes. Incorporates BQR-23 signal processor.

BQR-19: Active, short-range, navigational set for SSBNs. Raytheon.

BQR-21: DIMUS (Digital Multi-Beam Steering). Passive array for older SSBNs, SSNs.

BQR-23: STASS (Submarine Towed Array Sonar System). Used with BQR-25 in SSN 688, SSBN 726 classes. Current version: BQR-23A.

BQR-24: Raytheon; processor, used with BQR-21.

BQR-25: See BQR-23.

BQS-14, 20: Under-ice and mine-avoidance, high-frequency set, mostly on later SSNs. Part of the BQQ-2, -5, -6 systems.

BQS-13: Raytheon. Active component of the BQQ-5 system; low-frequency transmission (around 3.5 kHz).

BQS-14: Active sonar component of BQQ-2 and BQQ-5 suites on *Sturgeon*-class SSNs. Made by Hazeltine.

BQS-15: Under-ice active set tailored to the requirements of the SSN 688 class.

BQS-24: MIDAS (MIne Detection and Avoidance Sonar). Active set in development for the SSN 688 SSNs and *Ohio*-class SSBNs.

BSY-1 SUBACS: "Basic" BSY-1 version is suite for SSNs 651–773. Uses UYS-1 signal processor, USH-26 signal recorder, UYK-20A data processor. Passive arrays plus SADS (Submarine Active Detection Sonar, i.e. BQS-24) and towed passive array. IBM is prime contractor. Has experienced numerous delays, and the systems installed in earlier ships will not have all the planned capabilities. First suite delivered 7-87; SSN 756 on will have full capabilities.

BSY-2: In development for *Seawolf* class, will use distributed processing and will have 6 ship data displays and 11 consoles. Associated sensors include an external spherical bow array, an LF bow array inside the bow, and active hemispherical array in the lower part of the bow, an HF active array (BQS-24) in the sail, the BQG-5 wide-aperture flank array, the long TB-12X towed array, and a shorter TB-16D towed array. General Electric is prime contractor.

♦ on helicopters

ALFS: Airborne Low-Frequency Sonar. Replacement for the AQS-13 for SH-60F helicopters. Design competition won by Thomson-Sintra in 1992. To enter service around 1996 and also to be backfitted into SH-60B LAMPS-III helicopters.

AQS-13: Bendix-made dipping sonar used on SH-3 Sea King series.

AQS-14: Mine countermeasures set used by MH-53D helicopters.

AQS-20: Towed mine detection set for the MH-53E. Made by Westinghouse, with EDO and ARINC.

♦ Sonobuoys

A wide variety are in use, including those listed below, which are current production:

Production

		FY 87	FY 88	FY 89	F
SSQ-36	bathythermograph	31,600	28,231	30,173	
SSQ-53D	DIFAR	235,802	150,816	231,194	23
SSQ-57	Special-Purpose	11,935	11,947	68,329	
SSQ-62B	DICASS	20,900	12,229	15,026	1
SSQ-75	ERAPS	—	—	—	
SSQ-77A	VLAD	98,812	51,663	51,710	4
SSQ-86	DLC	—	—	—	
SSQ-95	Active EW	—	—	—	
SSQ-102	ADAR TSS	—	—	—	

Note: DICASS = DIrectional Command-Activated Sonobuoy System; VLAD = cal Line-Array DIFAR; ERAPS = Expendable Reliable Acoustic Path Sonobu scends to up to 16,000-ft. depths); ADAR TSS = Air-Deployed Active Receiver T Surveillance Sonar (a bistatic/multistatic sonobuoy that can work with a shi sonar acting as its illuminator) The SSQ-103 "Low Cost Sonobuoy" progra canceled (due to cost!). SSQ-71 and SSQ-86 are two-way, aircraft/submarine c nications buoys. Under FY 92 funding, 85,138 SSQ-77B VLAD buoys were o The SSQ-110 (XJ-1) sonobuoy is to enter production during 1992.

H. ELECTRO-OPTICAL SYSTEMS

The U.S. Navy greatly lags Europe and Russia in the development of electro- (television, low-light television, laser, infrared) devices for widespread use on s development are:

SAR-8: Joint U.S.–Canadian (General Electric, Spar) detection and tracking i system. Large, heavy antenna. Service entry much delayed, and may be suppla later, more effective and lighter-weight equipment under the SSDS (Ship Self-I System) program. None aboard ships as of 5-92, and the program has been c with only two developmental models delivered.

Seafire: The multi-mode fire-control system for the defunct "Deadeye" 127-mm projectile. Development halted several times because of rising costs.

I. PROCESSING OF TACTICAL DATA

The NTDS (Naval Tactical Data System) uses digital calculators (AN/UYK- AN/UYK-7) to give an overall picture of a tactical situation—air, surface, a derwater—and enables the commander to employ the means necessary to opp enemy. Excellent automatic data transmission systems (Link-11 and Link-14) the exchange of tactical information with similarly equipped ships and aircraf ing the ATDS (P-3C Orion and S-3A Viking) and amphibious landing forces ec with NTDS.

NTU (New Threat Upgrade)

Improved weapons control and command system to upgrade Standard SM-2 ships. Trials in DDG 42. Uses SPS-48E 3-D radar, SPS-49(V)2 2-D air sear SYS-2 IADT (Integrated Automatic Target Detection and Tracking) compu action information system, Mk 14 Weapons Direction System, and Standar ER/MR Block 2 missiles. To be installed in 31 or more ships.

Nearly all ships are equipped to receive SATCOMM (Satellite Communic messages, while most can send ultra-high-frequency messages via satellite, and send super-high-frequency messages. The Tactical Flag Command Center (T being backfitted into 13 CV/CVN, 2 LCC, and 5 CG. It employs USQ-81(V) con generated displays in an integrated 6.2-m × 6.2-m display space. T-AGOS surveillance ships use the AN/WSC-6 VHF SATCOMM system.

NUCLEAR-POWERED AIRCRAFT CARRIERS

Note: Although the Senate requested the navy to study employing a large, "floating airbase" concept under the FY 90 Budget, there is no likelihood of development of the concept.

♦ 3 (+2+1) Theodore Roosevelt class Bldr: Newport News SB &

(*Atlantic/† Pacific Fleet)

	Program	Laid down	L	In
CVN 71 Theodore Roosevelt*	FY 80	31-10-81	27-10-84	25-
CVN 72 Abraham Lincoln†	FY 83	3-11-84	13-2-88	11-
CVN 73 George Washington*	FY 83	25-8-86	21-7-90	4
CVN 74 John C. Stennis	FY 88	13-3-91	11-93	
CVN 75 United States	FY 88	8-92	3-96	
CVN 76	FY 95	1997	2000	

D: 73,973 tons light (96,300–96,836 fl) **S:** 30+ kts
Dim: 332.85 (317.0 pp) × 40.85 (flight deck: 78.33) × 11.71–11.88
Air Group:
CVN 71: 20 F-14A, 20 F/A-18, 20 A-6E, 4 EA-6B, 4 E-2C, 10 S-3 SH-3H
Others: 24 F-14A, 24 F/A-18, 10 A-6E, 4 KA-6D, 4 EA-6B, 4 E-2 10 S-3A, 6 SH-60F and/or HH-60H
A: 3/Mk 29 launchers (VIII × 3) for Sea Sparrow SAM—4/20-mm 15 CIWS gatling AA
Electron Equipt:
Radar: 1/Furuno 900 nav. (CVN 72: Sperry Raster), 1/SPS-64(V nav., 1/SPS-67(V) surface search, 1/SPS-48E 3-D air sea 1/SPS-49(V)5 2-D air search, 1/Mk 23 TAS target designation, 1/SPN-41 microwave landing aid, 1/SPN-4

EAR-POWERED AIRCRAFT CARRIERS *(continued)*

e Washington (CVN 73) John Bouvia, 6-92

air-control, 1/SPN-44 microwave landing aid, 2/SPN-42 or 46 CCA, 6/Mk 95 missile f.c., 4/Phalanx f.c.

V: SLQ-32(V)4 (CVN 71: SLQ-29 suite with WLR-8 and SLQ-17), Mk 36 SRBOC decoy RL (VI × 4), SLQ-25A Nixie towed torpedo decoy

CAN: URN-25

2 G.E. A4W/A1G pressurized-water reactors (42.3 kg/cm²), 4 sets geared steam turbines; 4 props; 280,000 shp

tric: 64,000-kw tot. from turboalternators + 8,000-kw emergency power from 4 diesel sets

w: average: 6,286 tot. (203 officers, 3,205 enlisted crew + 366 officers, 2,512 enlisted air wing)

ks: CVN 71 authorized under FY 80; had been repeatedly delayed in favor of tionally powered designs of inferior capabilities. Won out over both a Carter stration–sponsored 62,427-ton (fl) paper CVV design and a compromise 82,561-eat *John F. Kennedy* (CV 67) design. CVN 72 and 73 built in same graving dock, ng the latter to be made watertight during launch of CVN 72. CVN 74 and CVN red 30-6-88. CVN 72 is home-ported at Alameda, and CVN 73 will be home-at Norfolk.

Theodore Roosevelt (CVN 71)—note lack of bridle-catcher horns
Dr. Giorgio Arra, 10-90

Abraham Lincoln (CVN 72) Dr. Giorgio Arra, 2-90

dore Roosevelt (CVN 71) Dr. Giorgio Arra, 10-90

NUCLEAR-POWERED AIRCRAFT CARRIERS *(continued)*

Abraham Lincoln (CVN 72) Dr. Giorgio Arra, 2-90

Abraham Lincoln (CVN 72) Dr. Giorgio Arra, 2-90

Expected to operate for 15 years between refuelings (about 800,000 to 1,000,000 nautical miles' steaming). Maximum full-load displacement is 102,000 tons. The hangar has 7.6-m clear height. The angled deck is 237.7 m long and is equipped with four arrester wires (three on CVN 72 and later) and a Mk 7 Mod. 3 barrier, as well as four C 13 Mod. 1 catapults (92.1 m long), and four elevators (21.3 × 1.58 m, 47-ton capacity). An aviation payload of some 14,909 tons is carried, including 9,000 tons of aviation fuel and 1,954 tons of aviation ordnance. Kevlar armor 63.5 mm thick is fitted over vital spaces, and hull-protection arrangements have been improved. CVN 72 and later have new, lower-pressure catapults and SPN-46 landing aids. Other data under the *Nimitz* class generally apply.

The combat data systems include NTDS and ACDS, JDTS, POST, and CVIC (Carrier Intelligence Center). Data links include Links 4A, 11, and 14. Satellite communications equipment includes SSQ-82, SRR-1, WSC-3 (UHF), WSC-6 (SHF), and USC-38 (EHF). The Sea Sparrow systems are supported by three Mk 91 Mod. 1 control systems, each with two radar directors. CVN 71 will be backfitted with the SLQ-32(V)4 EW system, and all are to receive improved torpedo countermeasures systems.

♦ 3 Nimitz class (SCB 102 Type) Bldr: Newport News SB & DD

(*Atlantic Fleet/† Pacific Fleet)

	Program	Laid down	L	In serv.
CVN 68 Nimitz†	FY 67	22-6-68	13-5-72	3-5-75
CVN 69 Dwight D. Eisenhower*	FY 70	15-8-70	11-10-75	18-10-77
CVN 70 Carl Vinson*	FY 74	11-10-75	15-3-80	13-3-82

D: 72,798–72,916 tons light; 81,600 standard (93,300–93,900 fl)
S: 30+ kts
Dim: 327.0 (over catapult bridle retrieval horns: 332.8, pp: 317.0) × 40.85 (flight deck: 77.11, max.: 89.4) × 11.3

Nimitz (CVN 68) Dr. Giorgio Arra

Nimitz (CVN 68) David D. Broecker

Air Group: 24 F-14A, 24 F/A-18, 10 A-6E, 4 KA-6D, 4 EA-6B, 4 [illegible] 10 S-3A, 6 SH-3H or SH-60F
A: 3/Mk 29 launchers (VIII × 3) for Sea Sparrow—3 (CVN 70: 4)/20-mm Mk 15 CIWS
Electron Equipt:
Radar: 1/Furuno 900 nav., 1/SPS-64(V)9 nav., 1/SPS-67(V) surf search, 1/Mk 23 TAS target detection, 1/SPS-49(V)5 air search, 1/SPS-48E 3-D air search, 1/SPN-41 microwave landing aid, 1/SPN-43A marshaling, 1/SPN-44 microwa[ve] landing aid, 2/SPN-42 or 46 CCA, 6/Mk 95 missile f.c., 3/Phalanx f.c.
EW: SLQ-29 suite (WLR-1H, WLR-8, SLQ-17), Mk 36 SRBOC d[ecoy] RL (VI × 4), SLQ-25A Nixie towed torpedo decoy
TACAN: URN-25
M: 2 G.E. A4W/A1G pressurized-water reactors, 4 sets geared ste[am] turbines; 4 props; 280,000 shp
Electric: 64,000-kw + 8,000-kw emergency power from 4 diesel s[ets]
Crew: average: 6,286 tot. (569 officers, 3,091 enlisted, plus aviati[on] personnel: 304 officers, 2,322 enlisted)

Dwight D. Eisenhower (CVN 69) Dr. Giorgio Arr[a]

EAR-POWERED AIRCRAFT CARRIERS *(continued)*

ıt D. Eisenhower (CVN 69) Dr. Giorgio Arra, 4-91

ıt D. Eisenhower (CVN 69) Dr. Giorgio Arra, 1-90

ıt D. Eisenhower (CVN 69) Leo Van Ginderen, 6-90

ks: Carry 90% more aviation fuel and 50% more ammunition than the *Forres-*s. ASCAC (Anti-submarine Classification and Analysis Center) permits instant of target data between the carrier, its ASW aircraft, and escorting ships. refitted 6-83 to 9-84; *Eisenhower* refitted 28-10-85 to 13-4-87. Refueling of CVN yed to 1998.

tronics: SPS-49 replaced SPS-43A in CVN 68 and CVN 70 in 1983, and in CVN 1986. Carry OE-82 satellite communications antennas and have full NTDS ıtions. The Mk 23 TAS was added to improve defense against low fliers and missiles. CVN 68 has the SMQ-11 receiver for the TIROS-N ocean weather ting satellite.

ament: *Carl Vinson* completed with three Mk 29 launchers (VIII × 3) for Sea w, six directors for the missile (3 Mk 91 Mod. 1 FCS), and four Mk 15 CIWS n/Phalanx) gatling AA guns. The others have been similarly refitted, but have ree Vulcan/Phalanx. All Mk 15 CIWS now protected by "maintenance enclo- Have three Mk 95 Mod. 1 missile control systems with two radar directors each rol Sea Sparrow missiles.

or: Decks and hull are of extra-strong, high tensile steel to limit the impact of rmor-piercing bombs. Apart from the longitudinal bulkheads, there are twenty- watertight transverse bulkheads (more than 2,000 compartments) and ten fire- ılkheads. Foam devices for fire fighting are very well developed, and pumping ıent is excellent, a 15° list being correctable in 20 minutes. Thirty damage- teams are available at all times. *Nimitz*-class ships can withstand three times ere pounding survived by the *Essex*-class aircraft carriers in 1944–45, and they ce impacts and shock waves in the same proportion. They are being equipped 5-mm Kevlar armor over vital spaces during refits.

hinery: The cores of these ships are expected to last 13 years (CVN 70: 15) in usage, for a cruising distance of 800,000 to 1,000,000 miles. The evaporators oduce 1,520 tons of fresh water per day.

raft-handling installations: There are four side elevators: two forward, one he island to starboard, and one on the stern to port. There are also four C13 Mod. n catapults, 94.5 m long. CVN 69 and 70 have only the forward starboard bridle al horn, because most aircraft in service do not require the bridle for launching. ,134 m³ total aviation magazine spaces can hold 1,954 tons of aviation ordnance, e total aviation-associated payload is on the order of 15,000 tons. The hangar is ters high and can accommodate only 35–40% of the aircraft aboard. The angled the flight deck is 237.7 meters long and has four Mk 14 arrester wires and a r to halt aircraft (to be changed to 3 wires, 1 net). Sufficient aviation fuel for 16 operations is carried. CVN 69 has the prototype AVCARS (Augmented Visual r Aircraft Recovery System); the production version in service 1984.

◆ **1 Enterprise class (SCB 160 type)** Bldr: Newport News SB & DD (Atlantic Fleet)

	Program	Laid down	L	In serv.
CVN 65 Enterprise	FY 58	4-2-58	24-9-60	25-11-61

Enterprise (CVN 65) Dr. Giorgio Arra, 3-90

Enterprise (CVN 65)—at Norfolk, Va. awaiting overhaul Leo Van Ginderen, 6-90

Enterprise (CVN 65) Dr. Giorgio Arra, 3-90

D: 73,570 tons light (93,970 fl) **S:** 33 kts
Dim: 335.75 (over catapult bridle horn: 342.3, wl: 317.0) × 40.54 (flight deck: 78.4) × 11.9
Air Group: 24 F-14, 24 F/A-18, 10 A-6E, 4 KA-6D, 4 EA-6B, 4 E-2C, 10 S-3, 6 SH-60F
A: 3/Mk 29 launchers (VIII × 3) for Sea Sparrow—3/20-mm Mk 15 CIWS gatling AA (I × 3)
Electron Equipt:
Radar: 1/Furuno 900 nav., 1/SPS-64(V)9 nav., 1/SPS-67 surf. search, 1/Mk 23 TAS target acquisition, 1/SPS-48E 3-D air search, 1/SPS-49(V)5 air search, 1/SPN-41 microwave landing aid, 1/SPN-43A marshaling, 1/SPN-44 microwave landing aid, 2/SPN-46 CCA, 6/Mk 95 missile f.c., 3/Phalanx f.c.
EW: SLQ-32(V)4, Mk 36 SRBOC decoy RL (VI × 4), SLQ-25A Nixie towed torpedo decoy
TACAN: URN-25
M: 8 Westinghouse A2W reactors, supplying 32 Foster-Wheeler heat exchangers; 4 sets Westinghouse geared steam turbines; 4 props; 280,000 shp
Electric: 40,000 kw from turboalternators + 8,000 kw emergency
Crew: 5,695 tot. (171 officers, 3,044 + aviation personnel: 358 officers, 2,122 enlisted + flag staff: 25 officers, 45 enlisted)

Remarks: Began what was to have been a two-year overhaul at Puget Sound NSY 15-1-79, during which the radar and other electronics suites were extensively renovated; completed 3-82. The SPS-32 and SPS-33 "billboard" radar arrays were removed, as was the "beehive" dome atop the blockhouse superstructure. A new mast, resembling that on the *Nimitz*, was installed atop the superstructure. SPS-48C (now replaced by SPS-48E) and SPS-49 were mounted atop the island. Left Alameda, California, homeport 18-9-89 for 6-month deployment and transfer to the Atlantic Fleet. Being refitted and refueled at builder's 12-10-90 to 5-94.

Aviation facilities: There are four C13 Mod. 1 steam catapults and four elevators—one on the port side of the angled deck, three to starboard—two of which are forward of and one abaft the island. Elevators are steel and alloy and weigh 105 tons; 26 m long, 16 m wide, lift 45 tons. The hangar is 7.62 m high and the flight deck has more than 20,000 m² area. Carries half again as much aviation fuel as the *Forrestal* class (8,500 tons), which permits 12 days of intensive aerial operations without replenishment. Carries fuel oil to replenish other ships.

Electronics: Has NTDS, ASCAC (Antisubmarine Classification and Analysis Center) and TFCC (Tactical Flag Communications Center). Link 4A, 11, and 14 are fitted, and Link 16 will be installed during the refit. Satellite communications equipment

NUCLEAR-POWERED AIRCRAFT CARRIERS *(continued)*

includes SRR-1, WSC-3 (UHF), WSC-6 (SHF), and USC-38 (EHF), and a meteorological satellite receiver is fitted. There are three Mk 91 Mod.1 fire-control systems for the Sea Sparrow missiles, each with two radar directors. Electronic equipment listed above is what will be aboard at the completion of the 1990–94 refit.

CONVENTIONAL AIRCRAFT CARRIERS

♦ 1 John F. Kennedy class (SCB 127C type)

Bldr: Newport News SB & DD (Atlantic Fleet)

	Program	Laid down	L	In serv.
CV 67 JOHN F. KENNEDY	FY 63	22-10-64	27-5-67	7-9-68

John F. Kennedy (CV 67) Dr. Giorgio Arra, 7-90

John F. Kennedy (CV 67) Dr. Giorgio Arra, 3-91

John F. Kennedy (CV 67)—note angled stack Dr. Giorgio Arra, 3-91

D: 60,660 tons light (80,940 fl) **S:** 32 kts
Dim: 320.34 (301.8 wl) × 39.17 (flight deck: 81.38, max. 82.30) × 11.20
Air Group: 24 F-14, 24 F/A-18, 10 A-6E, 4 KA-6D, 4 EA-6B, 4 E-2C, 10 S-3A, 6 SH-3G or SH-60F
A: 3/Mk 29 launchers (VIII × 3) for Sea Sparrow—3/20-mm Mk 15 CIWS (I × 3)
Electron Equipt:
Radar: 1/Furuno 900 nav., 1/SPS-64(V)9 nav., 1/SPS-67 surf. search, 1/Mk 23 TAS target acquisition, 1/SPS-49(V)5 air search, 1/SPS-48C 3-D air search, 1/SPN-41 microwave landing aid, 1/SPN-43A marshaling, 1/SPN-44 microwave landing aid, 2/SPN-46 CCA, 6/Mk 95 missile f.c., 3/Phalanx f.c.
EW: SLQ-29 suite (WLR-1H, WLR-3, WLR-11, SLQ-17), Mk 36 SRBOC decoy RL (VI × 4), SLQ-25A Nixie towed torpedo decoy
TACAN: URN-25
M: 4 sets G.E. geared steam turbines; 4 props; 280,000 shp
Boilers: 8 Foster-Wheeler, 83.4 kg/cm^2, 520° C
Electric: 17,000 kw tot.
Crew: 5,279 tot. (155 officers, 2,775 enlisted + air group: 329 officers, 1,950 enlisted + flag staff: 25 officers, 45 enlisted

Remarks: Built with conventional steam propulsion as an economy measure. Distinguishing feature is the stack, which is angled outboard as on World War II–era Japanese carriers. Minor collision 29-8-88. Was to have received full SLEP mo tion 1993–95 but will now instead have only a 14-month "Complex Overhaul" under FY 93. Home port to change from Norfolk to Mayport, Florida, during

Aviation: Four side elevators, three to starboard (two forward of and one a island) and one on the port quarter. Completely automatic landing system, per all-weather operation. Four arrester wires and a barrier on the 227-m angle deck. Three 90-m C13 and one 94.5-m C13-1 catapults. The 11,808-m^3 a ordnance magazine can accommodate 1,250 tons of ammunition. Carries 5,91 aviation fuel.

Electronics: Equipped to carry SQS-23 sonar in bow dome, but it was not in SPS-49 replaced SPS-43A in 1979–80, and SPS-58 was deleted. Obsolescent chaff RL replaced with Mk 36 SRBOC (VI × 4) during 10-84 to 10-85 refit, w additional Mk 15 CIWS and the Mk 23 TAS radar were also added. To receive S radar during FY 93 refit, when EW suite will be replaced by SLQ-32(V)4.

♦ 3 Kitty Hawk class (SCB 127A and SCB 127B types)

(*Atlantic/† Pacific Fleet)

	Bldr	Laid down	L	I
CV 63 KITTY HAWK†	New York SB	27-12-56	21-5-60	2
CV 64 CONSTELLATION*	Brooklyn NSY	14-9-57	8-10-60	27
CV 66 AMERICA*	Newport News SB	9-1-61	1-2-64	2

Authorized: CV 63 in FY 56, CV 64 in FY 57, CV 66 in FY 61

Kitty Hawk (CV 63) George Nassiopoulo

America (CV 66) Dr. Giorgio Arr

America (CV 66)—in the Suez Canal PH3 Frank A. Marquart, USN

ENTIONAL AIRCRAFT CARRIERS *(continued)*

ca (CV 66) Maritime Photographic, 9-91

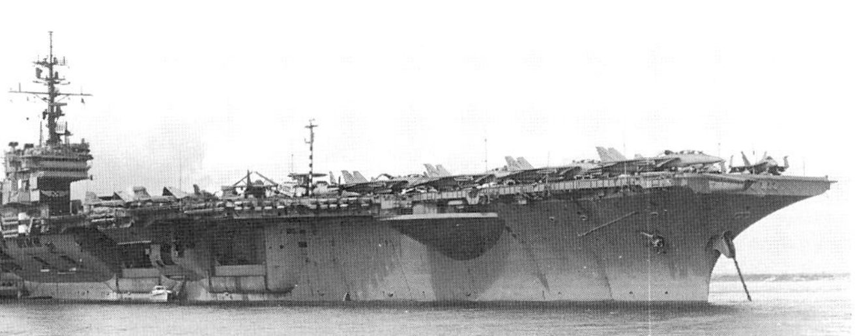
ca (CV 66) Leo Van Ginderen, 9-91

V 63: 60,100 tons light (81,123 fl); CV 64: 61,000 tons light 1,773 fl); CV 66: 60,300 tons light (79,724 fl)
kts
318.8 (CV 66: 319.25) (301.76 pp) × 39.62 (flight deck: 76.81) × 11.4 (CV 66: 11.3)
roup: 20 F-14A, 24 F/A-18, 10 A-6E, 4 KA-6D, 4 EA-6B, 4 E-2C, 10 S-3A, 6 SH-3H or SH-60F
/Mk 29 launchers (VIII × 3) for Sea Sparrow—3/20-mm Mk 15 IWS gatling AA (I × 3)
tron Equipt:
dar: 1/Furuno 900 nav., 1/SPS-64(V)9 nav., 1/SPS-67 surf. search, 1/Mk 23 TAS target acquisition, 1/SPS-49(V)5 air search, 1/SPS-48C 3-D air search, 1/SPN-41 microwave landing aid, 1/SPN-43A marshaling, 2/SPN-46 CCA, 6/Mk 95 missile f.c., 3/Phalanx f.c.
V: SLQ-29 suite (WLR-1H, WLR-8, WLR-11, SLQ-17), Mk 36 SRBOC decoy RL (VI × 4), SLQ-25A Nixie towed torpedo decoy
CAN: URN-25
sets Westinghouse geared steam turbines; 4 props; 280,000 shp
ers: 8 Foster-Wheeler, 83.4 kg/cm², 520° C
ge: 4,000/30; 8,000/20 **Fuel:** 7,800 tons
tric: 15,000 kw tot. (CV 66: 18,000 kw)
w: 5,480 tot. (155 officers, 2,775 enlisted + air group: 320 officers, 2,160 enlisted + flag staff; 25 officers, 45 enlisted)

ks: These ships are a great improvement over the *Forrestal* class, on which e based, and have one significant difference: three elevators on the starboard o forward of and one abaft the island, and one to port, abaft the angled flight ircraft can be landed and catapulted simultaneously, a difficult operation on the ships.
tion: Four C13 steam catapults, except on CV 66, on which one is of the longer ype. Carry 5,882 tons of aviation fuel.
ament: CV 66 was the first ship to receive the Mk 15 CIWS, in 4-80. CV 64 d two Mk 10 twin launchers for Terrier HT missiles and two SPQ-55B radar rs until 12-82 to 2-84 refit at Bremerton. Have three Mk 91 Mod. 1 missile-systems, each with two radar directors, for the Sea Sparrow SAM system.
tronics: CV 66 was the first to have a special integrated CIC and airborne ASW center (ASCAC). CV 66 had an SQS-23 bow sonar until 1981. SPS-48E has d the SPS-48C 3-D air-search radar.
ernizations: CV 63 entered SLEP (Service Life Extension Program) 28-1-88 to 2-8-91 with new catapult rotary engines, Mk 7 Mod. 3 arrester gear (3 wires), 3 landing-aid radar, SPS-48E and SPS-49(V) upgrade air-search radars, updated NTDS (Naval Tactical Data System), a torpedo decoy system, the WQN-1 "channel-finder" sonar, upgraded EW equipment, and the Mk 23 TAS low-altitude radar added; will also be able to handle ES-3A and SH-60F aircraft. The refit also included overhauling the propulsion plant and is expected to add 15 years to the ship's useful life. CV 64 in SLEP overhaul 2-7-90 to 5-92 at Philadelphia and will then return to San Diego home port. CV 66 is not scheduled for SLEP but received Mk 23 TAS during regular overhaul in the late 1980s; she will decommission during Fiscal Year 1996.

◆ **4 Forrestal class (CV 59: SCB 80 type; CV 60 to CV 62: SCB 80M type)** (*Atlantic/†Pacific Fleet)

	Bldr	Laid down	L	In serv.
AVT 59 FORRESTAL*	Newport News SB & DD	14-7-52	11-12-54	1-10-55
CV 60 SARATOGA*	Brooklyn NSY	16-12-52	8-10-55	14-4-56
CV 61 RANGER†	Newport News SB & DD	2-8-54	29-9-56	10-8-57
CV 62 INDEPENDENCE†	Brooklyn NSY	1-7-55	6-6-58	10-1-59

Authorized: CV 59 in FY 52, CV 60 in FY 53, CV 61 in FY 54, CV 62 in FY 55

Forrestal (AVT 59)—departing for Pensacola Dr. Giorgio Arra, 1-92

Forrestal (AVT 59)—during Mediterranean deployment as a CV Pradignac & Léo, 5-90

CONVENTIONAL AIRCRAFT CARRIERS *(continued)*

Saratoga (CV 60) Dr. Giorgio Arra, 8-91

Ranger (CV 61)—note forward gun sponsons retained
Dr. Giorgio Arra, 1991

Independence (CV 62) R.A.N

Independence (CV 62) Pieter Westdij

Independence (CV 62) R.A.N

ENTIONAL AIRCRAFT CARRIERS *(continued)*

VT 59: 59,060 tons light (79,250 fl); CV 60: 59,060 tons light
30,383 fl); CV 61: 60,000 tons light (81,163 fl); CV 62: 60,000 tons
ght (80,643 fl)
3 kts
: AVT 59: 331.0; CV 60: 324.0; CV 61: 326.4; CV 62: 326.1 (319.13 flight deck, 301.8 wl) × 39.63 (AVT 59, CV 60: 76.3; CV 61, 62: 82.3 max.) × 11.3
Group: 20 F-14A, 24 F/A-18, 10 A-6E, 4 KA-6D, 4 EA-6B, 4 E-2C, 10 S-3A, 6 SH-3H or SH-60F (AVT 59: none)
Mk 29 (CV 60, 62: 3) launchers (VIII × 2 or 3) for Sea Sparrow—/20-mm Mk 15 CIWS gatling AA (I × 3) (AVT 59: removed)
tron Equipt:
dar: 1/Furuno 900 nav., 1/SPS-64(V)9 nav., 1/SPS-67 surf. search, 1/Mk 23 TAS target acquisition, 1/SPS-49(V)5 air search, 1/SPS-48C 3-D air search, 1/SPN-41 microwave landing aid, 1/SPN-43A marshaling, 1/SPN-44 microwave landing aid, 2/SPN-42 or 46 CCA, 4 or 6/Mk 95 missile f.c., 3/Phalanx f.c.
V: AVT 59, CV 60: SLQ-32(V)4; others: SLQ-29 suite (WLR-1H, WLR-8, WLR-11, SLQ-17), Mk 36 SRBOC decoy RL (VI × 4), SLQ-25A Nixie towed torpedo decoy
CAN: URN-25
4 sets G.E. or Westinghouse geared steam turbines; 4 props; AVT 59: 260,000 shp, others: 280,000 shp
ers: 8 Babcock & Wilcox; AVT 59: 41.7 kg/cm^2, others: 83.4 kg/cm^2, 520°C
ge: 4,000/30; 8,000/20 **Fuel:** 7,800 tons
tric: 15,000 kw tot.
w: CV 60–62 typical: 5,249 tot. (154 officers, 2,746 enlisted + air group: 329 officers, 1,950 enlisted + flag staff: 25 officers, 45 enlisted)

ks: *Forrestal* redesignated training carrier (AVT) 4-2-91 to replace the *Lexington* (AVT 16) at Pensacola, Florida; will receive a "Complex Overhaul" adelphia Naval Shipyard 9-92 through 11-93 to enhance her training capabili- to remove weapons and sensor systems not needed for the training rôle. CV 60, carrier to undergo the SLEP modernization, will decommission during Fiscal 95. CV 61, which has not received SLEP, will decommission during FY 93. CV sferred to Pacific Fleet 8-10-88; home-ported at Yokosuka, Japan, from 11-9-91 of *Midway* and is due to decommission during Fiscal Year 1998.

systems: AVT 59 has three rudders and four propellers, the two outboard ve-bladed, the two inboard, four-bladed. Deck protection and internal com- ntation are extensive (1,200 watertight compartments). Two longitudinal ads are fitted from keel to waterline from stem to stern; there are transverse ads about every 10 meters.

tion: CV 62 air group: 22 F-14A, 22 F/A-18C, 15 A-6E, 5 EA-6B, 7 S-3B, 5 SH-3H. Hangar is 7.6 m high and 234–240 m long. Four side elevators (15.95 × eck angled at 8 degrees. Armored flight deck. Four-cable arresting gear. CV 59 60 have two Mk-C7 (75 m) and two Mk-C11 (65 m) steam catapults; the others ur Mk-C7. Carry 5,880 tons of aviation fuel.

ernization: CV 60 received first SLEP (Service Life Extension Program) mod- ion, beginning 1-10-80 at Philadelphia Navy Yard, completing 2-83 (but boiler kept her inoperative until 18-11-83). CV 59 SLEP from 21-3-83 to 20-5-85; CV -85 to 2-88. *Ranger* not scheduled for SLEP, but did get extensive overhaul at Sound NSY 5-84 to 6-85, when improved evaporators, Halon and aqueous film hting systems, Mk 23 TAS, and 3 Mk 15 CIWS were added. The SLEP ships have Kevlar armor, improved data systems, the Tactical Flag Command Center, and abitability.

ament: All originally carried eight 127-mm/54, Mk 42 guns. CV 61 relin- d her last two guns in 1977, later than her sisters did, and retains her forward onsons. There are three Mk 91 Mod. 1 fire-control systems, each with two radar rs, for the Sea Sparrow missile systems. All armament has been removed from 9.

Midway class Bldr: Newport News SB & DD (in reserve)

	Laid down	L	In serv.	To reserve
. Midway	27-10-43	20-3-45	10-9-45	11-4-92

way (CV 41) *Ships of the World,* 1991

Midway (CV 41) *Ships of the World,* 1991

D: 51,000 tons light (69,800 fl) **S:** 32 kts
Dim: 306.78 (274.32 wl) × 55.78 (42.98 wl) × 10.67
Air Group: none (*see* Remarks)
A: removed
Electron Equipt:
Radar: removed
EW: removed
TACAN: URN-25 (see Remarks)
M: 4 sets Westinghouse geared steam turbines; 4 props; 212,000 shp
Boilers: 12 Babcock & Wilcox; 41.7 kg/cm^2, 454°C
Electric: 11,700 kw tot. **Range:** 15,000/15
Crew: when active: 4,424 tot. (127 officers, 2,373 enlisted + air group: 225 officers, 1,629 enlisted + flag staff: 25 officers, 45 enlisted)

Remarks: CV 41 began stand-down 1-10-91 and decommissioned 11-4-92 for retention as possible mobilization asset, despite long service and cramped accommodations; had been home-ported at Yokosuka, Japan, since 10-73, departing for U.S. waters 10-8-91. Sister *Franklin D. Roosevelt* (CV 42) was stricken on 1-10-72. *Coral Sea* (CV 41) began layup in 10-89 for official decommissioning after stripping, on 30-4-90; she was stricken on 30-4-90 for scrap. Machinery and ship hull form originally very similar to that of the *Iowa*-class battleships.

Modernization: From 1954 to 1963, the ships underwent several overhauls: angled flight deck installed; flight deck lengthened; hydraulic catapults replaced with steam ones; side armor removed and "bulges" added. Reinforced arresting gear and barriers installed; centerline elevators replaced with side ones; aviation fuel capacity increased. In October 1967 CV 41 began another major overhaul and returned to service in 1-70. Her angled flight deck was extended to port; her three elevators were enlarged; her forward port elevator was moved aft; her catapults were replaced by more powerful ones; and all her electronic equipment was replaced. In 1979–80, during short overhauls at Yokosuka, CV 41's radar suite was updated and the Tactical Flag Command Center was added. Had 183-m-long by 3-m-wide bulges added during her 1-4-86 to 28-11-86 refit to reduce draft and hangar deck wetness. Unfortunately, the bulges caused the roll period to decrease to 9 seconds and increased flight deck wetness. Was to have had a "slot" cut into the bulges by Sumitomo Heavy Industries to restore her original waterline beam while retaining most of the added buoyancy during 1990, but decommissioned unaltered.

Aviation: Final air group was Carrier Air Wing 5, with 36 F/A-18, 18 A-6E, 4 EA-6B, 4 E-2C, and 6 SH-3H helicopters. Two side elevators to starboard, one forward of and one abaft the island; one side elevator to port abaft the angled flight deck. CV 41 has a considerably larger flight deck than did her sisters. Has two C13 steam catapults (both forward) and three arrester wires on the angled deck. The hangar is 211.1 m long by 25.9 m wide.

Deactivation: As part of the decommissioning process, all armament and all sensors except the antenna for the SPS-48C 3-D air search radar were removed. Final armament had been two Mk 25 Sea Sparrow SAM launchers and two Mk 15 CIWS.

Note: Of the four *Essex*- and *Hancock*-class carriers formerly in reserve at Bremerton, Washington, *Oriskany* (CV 34) was struck on 25-7-89, *Bennington* (CVS 20) and *Bon Homme Richard* (CVA 31) on 20-9-89, and *Hornet* (CVS 12) on 25-7-89. The training carrier *Lexington* (AVT 16, ex-CVT 16, ex-CVS 16) was stricken 30-11-91.

NAVAL AND MARINE CORPS AVIATION

Aviation is an integral part of the U.S. Navy and Marine Corps. In FY 92 there were about 5,100 aircraft (including 575 assigned to the Naval Reserve) assigned to naval aviation, of which a fourth were operated by the Marine Corps. In 1992, the principal combat aircraft included: F-14 Tomcat interceptors, F/A-18 Hornet fighter-bombers, AV-8B V/STOL fighter-bombers, A-6E Intruder attack bombers, KA-6D aerial refuelers, EA-6B Prowler electronics warfare, S-3A Viking ASW (shipboard), P-3B/C Orion maritime patrol and ASW (land-based), EP-3A/B/E Orion ELINT, SH-3-series Sea King ASW helo, SH-2F LAMPS-I Sea Sprite ASW helo, SH-60B/F Seahawk ASW helo, CH-53A and CH-53E heavy-lift helo, RH-53D and MH-53E minesweeping helos, and a CH-46 troop/utility helo. Carrier aircraft were organized into 12 active and 2 reserve wings, with the number of active wings to reduce to 11 by the end of 1993.

The U.S. Air Force had two 15-plane B-52G squadrons (one based on Guam and the other in California) equipped to launch up to 20 Harpoons each; by the end of 1991 they

NAVAL AND MARINE CORPS AVIATION *(continued)*

were being retired at the rate of two per month, but the Harpoon launch capability was being added to an equivalent number of B-52H bombers.

Air squadrons are designated alphanumerically, the letter prefixes for the principal squadron types being ("X" denotes various models in aircraft type listings):

Navy:

HC	Helicopter Combat Support (CH-46)
HCS	Helicopter Combat Support (HH-60H)
HM	Helicopter Mine Countermeasures (RH-53D, MH-53E)
HS	Helicopter Antisubmarine (SH-3)
HSL	Light Helicopter Antisubmarine (SH-2, SH-60B)
HT	Helicopter Training (TH-57X, UH-1E, TH-1L)
VA	Attack (A-6E, KA-6D)
VAQ	Tactical Electronic Warfare (EA-6B)
VAW	Carrier Airborne Early Warning (E-2C)
VC	Fleet Composite (utility aircraft)
VF	Fighter (F-14)
VFA	Fighter/Attack (F/A-18)
VP	Patrol (P-3)
VQ	Fleet Air Reconnaissance (EP-3, EA-3B), also Communications Support (E-6A)
VR	Fleet Logistics Support (C-9, C-130, C-131, etc.)
VRC	Fleet Logistics Support-COD (Carrier Onboard Delivery) (C-2A)
VS	Air Antisubmarine (S-3A)
VT	Training (TA-4J, T-2C, T-39D, T-44A)
VX	Air Test and Evaluation
VXE	Antarctic Development (LC-130F, UH-1)
VXN	Oceanographic Development (RP-3A/D)

Marine Corps:

HMA	Marine Attack Helicopter (AH-1)
HMH	Marine Heavy Helicopter (CH-53)
HML	Marine Light Helicopter (UH-1)
HMM	Marine Medium Helicopter (CH-46)
VMA	Marine Attack (A-4, A-6E, AV-8B)
VMAQ	Marine Electronic Warfare (EA-6B)
VMFA	Marine Fighter-Attack (F/A-18)
VMFP	Marine Photo Reconnaissance (RF-4B)
VMGR	Marine Refueler-Transport (KC-130F)
VMO	Marine Observation (OV-10)

♦ Marine Corps Aviation

The marines operate a considerable air force, with all aircraft procured and "owned" by the navy. U.S.M.C. aircraft are intended to operate principally from amphibious-warfare ships, but squadrons of attack, reconnaissance, and electronic warfare aircraft frequently operate from carriers as well.

Marine Corps combat aviation is organized into three active wings and one reserve wing, with each active wing nominally including: 48 F/A-18, 20 A-6E, 40 AV-8B, 9 TA-4 or OA-4, 8 F/A-18C/DR, 8 EA-6B, 12 KC-130 aerial refuelers, 48 CH-53, 60 CH-46, 24 AH-1T/W, 24 UH-1, and 12 OV-10. In addition, there are four Training Squadrons for fixed-wing aircraft, three for helicopters, and one Base and Command Support Squadron with about 36 fixed-wing aircraft and helicopters. The A-6E aircraft were being transferred to the navy and replaced by F/A-18C/D fighter-bombers during FY 92, and one KC-130 squadron was deactivated.

NEW NAVY AIRCRAFT PROCUREMENT PLAN

	FY 91	FY 92	FY 93	FY 94	FY 95	FY 96	FY 97
AV-8B Harrier	21	6	—	—	—	—	—
F-14D/DR Tomcat	12	—	—	—	—	—	—
F/A-18 Hornet	48	48	48	39	45	60	84
CH/MH-53E Super Stallion	—	16	20	20	—	—	—
AH-1W Sea Cobra	—	14	12	12	12	12	12
SH-60B Seahawk	6	13	12	12	12	12	12
SH-60F Seahawk	18	12	12	12	12	12	12
E-2C Hawkeye	6	6	—	—	—	—	—
T-45TS Goshawk	—	12	12	36	48	48	48
HH-60H	—	—	7	8	9	—	—
Total:	111	127	123	139	138	144	168

Note: The table does not include remanufacture of existing EA-6B Prowler electronics warfare aircraft: 1 in FY 91, none in FY 92, 3 in FY 93, 9 each in FY 94 and FY 95, and 12 each in FY 96 and FY 97. In addition, under FY 92, Congress added the following aircraft for use by Naval and Marine Corps Reserves: four MH-53 Super Stallion, six AH-1W Sea Cobra, and two KC-130T Hercules tankers. The planned level of acquisition of combat aircraft will ultimately not sustain even an 11-wing carrier aviation program.

♦ Beside the name given to an aircraft (Hornet, Tomcat, Orion, etc.), each basic aircraft type is alphanumerically designated as follows:

1. The letter immediately preceding the hyphen indicates the basic type:

A—attack
B—bomber
C—cargo/transport
E—airborne early warning
F—fighter
K—tanker, inflight refueling
O—observation
P—patrol
S—antisubmarine
T—training
U—utility
V—VTOL/STOL, vertical or s takeoff and landing
X—research

2. The figure that comes immediately after the hyphen is the design sequence nu When a letter follows this figure, its position in the alphabet indicates that the a is the first, second, third, etc., modification to the original design. Example: A-4 attack aircraft, the fourth attack plane design, the fifth modification. The sys occasionally abused, i.e., "R" in the F14-1DR would be a reconnaissance version Tomcat, while the suffix "B" has been used twice for the Tomcat (once for a up-engined prototype and now for re-engined and modernized F-14As that were typed the "F-14A+"), while for export versions of the P-3 Orion, the suffix lette for the country receiving the specific model ("J" for Japan, "P" for Pakistan, etc

3. When a basic aircraft is configured for a function that is not its original mis second letter precedes the letter of that mission (see para. 1 above):

A—attack
C—cargo/transport
D—direction or control of drones, aircraft, or missiles
E—special electronic installation
H—search and rescue
K—tanker, inflight refueling
L—cold weather; for arctic regions
M—missile carrier or mine countermeasures
Q—drone aircraft
R—reconnaissance
S—antisubmarine
T—trainer
U—utility, general service
V—staff
W—weather, meteorology

4. A third prefixed letter in front of an aircraft's designation (seldom seen) mea

G—permanently grounded
J—temporary special test
N—permanent special test
X—experimental
Y—prototype
Z—planning

CURRENT U.S. NAVY, MARINE CORPS AIRCRAFT DESIGNATIONS

♦ Attack

A-4 SKYHAWK:

A-4M	Single-seat attack
EA-4F	ECM version of TA-4F
TA-4F	Two-place training version
TA-4J	Advanced training version of TA-4F
OA-4M	TA-4F modified to TACA configuration

A-6 INTRUDER:

EA-6A	ECM mission equipment
EA-6B	ECM mission ("Prowler")
KA-6D	A-6A configured as tanker
A-6E	A-6A with improved systems

F/A-18 HORNET:

F/A-18A	First-line fighter/attack aircraft
TF/A-18A	Two-place trainer version
F/A-18C	Upgraded F/A-18A, AMRAAM-capable
F/A-18D	Two-seat attack, for USMC
F/A-18E	Proposed single-seat upgrade
F/A-18F	Proposed two-seat upgrade

AV-8 HARRIER:

TAV-8B	Two-seat trainer
AV-8B	Major redesign, improved capability
AV-8B+	Improved engine, APG-65 radar added

♦ Fighters

F-4 PHANTOM:

QF-4N/S/R	Target drone
YF-4S	One left; ejection-seat trials at Pt. Mugu

F-5 TIGER II:

F-5E	Adversary aircraft
F-5F	Two-place version

F-14 TOMCAT:

F-14A	Front-line fighter aircraft, TF-30
F-14B	Re-engined F-14A
F-14D	Improved systems, new engines

F-16 FIGHTING FALCON:

F-16N	Adversary aircraft

♦ Utility

OV-10 BRONCO:

OV-10A	COIN/LARA twin turboprop
OV-10D	Night gunship

♦ Patrol

P-3 ORION:

VP-3A	Personnel transport
P-3B	P-3A with T56-A-14 engines
EP-3B	Electronic reconnaissance ("Aries-I")
P-3C	Improved avionics systems
RP-3D	Configured for Project Magnet

:RCRAFT DESIGNATIONS *(continued)*

›-3E	Electronic reconnaissance ("Aries-II")
3G	Proposed update

Cargo Transport

2 GREYHOUND:

2A	Carrier logistics

SKYTRAIN II:

)B	Commercial DC-9; casualty evacuation and transport

12 SUPER KING AIR:

:-12B	Passenger logistics
-12M	Radar range surveillance and clearing

.30 HERCULES:

130F	Turboprop logistics transport (used by VR-22, VRC-50)
-130F	Tactical tanker/cargo transport (used by VMGR-352, -253)
-130F	Polar use, ski/wheel gear (used by VXE-6)
-130R	Improved tanker (used by VMGR-352, -253)
-130R	Improved polar version (used by VXE-6)
-130T	Improved avionics, tanker capabilities (used by VMGR-234, -432)
·130Q	Former EC-130G TACAMO communications, used by VR-22 at Rota, Spain

Antisubmarine Warfare

VIKING:

A	Carrier-based ASW aircraft
-3A	Carrier logistics version
B	Improved avionics
3A	EW conversion

Airborne Early Warning

HAWKEYE:

C	Improved system, several electronics configurations

Strategic Communications

MERCURY:

A	TACAMO (used by VQ-3 and VQ-4)

Trainers

BUCKEYE:

:	2-seat jet trainer, J85 engines

ACADEME:

4C	Bombardier/navigator trainer for A-6E; modified Gulfstream

MENTOR:

C	2-seat basic trainer, PT6A-25 turboprop engine

SABRELINER:

D	Pilot/NFO trainer, jet
39E	Rapid response airlift
39C	Modified CT-39E, lengthened fuselage

KING AIR:

A	Advanced multi-engine trainer

TS GOSHAWK:

A	Advanced jet trainer

Tilt-Wing Aircraft

OSPREY:

22A	Proposed Marine Corps Transport
2	Proposed ASW version

Helicopters

IROQUOIS/HUEY:

E	Single rotor, T 53-L-11 engine
L	Trainer, UH-1E armor/armament deleted, T53-L-13 engine
L	Utility, UH-1E, T53-L-13 engine
M	T53-L-13 engine
N	Special transport, twin-engine T400-CP-400

SEACOBRA:

T	Modified AH-1J, T400-WV-402 engine
W	Two T-700-GE-401 engines

SEASPRITE:

D	Oceanographic research support; utility
F	LAMPS MK 1 sea-based ASW
G	Re-engined SH-2F

SEA KING:

D	Executive transport
G	Improved SH-3A, sea-based ASW and logistics
H	SH-3G for sea-based ASW/ASMD, T58-GE-10 engines

H-46 SEA KNIGHT:

CH-46D	Improved T58-GE-10 engines
UH-46D	Utility version, T58-GE-10 engines
CH-46E	Improved T58-GE-16 engines
CH-46F	CH-46D with instrument panel changes

H-53 SEA STALLION:

CH-53A	Two-engine assault helicopter, T64-GE-6B engines
CH-53D	Improved T64-GE-413 engines
RH-53D	AMCM

H-53E SUPER STALLION:

CH-53E	Three engines
MH-53E	Mine countermeasures version of CH-53E, larger fuel tanks

H-57 SEA RANGER:

TH-57A	Trainer
TH-57C	Advanced Instrument Trainer

H-60 SEAHAWK:

HH-60H	Combat Support
SH-60B	Sea-based LAMPS MK III ASW
SH-60F	Carrier-based, dipping-sonar
VH-60A	VIP transport

PRINCIPAL COMBAT AIRCRAFT

◆ **560+ F/A-18A/B/C/D Hornet fighter-bombers** Manufacturer: McDonnell Aircraft Co. Div. of McDonnell Douglas Corp., St. Louis, Missouri

F/A-18D Hornet of VMFA (AW)-242 David D. Broecker, 7-91

F/A-18A Hornet of VFA-303 David D. Broecker, 7-91

F/A-18C Hornet of VFA-82 David D. Broecker, 5-90

Wingspan: 11.43 (12.3 with missiles) **Length:** 17.07
Height: 4.67 **Weight:** 10,620 kg empty/25,541 max.
Engines: 2 G.E. F404-GE-400 turbojets (6,800-kg thrust each)
Max. speed: Mach 1.8 **Ceiling:** 50,000+ ft.
Range: 2,303 n.m. ferry; 410 n.m. radius with 1,814-kg payload
Armament: 5,900 kg conventional or nuclear stores, including up to 4 Harpoon missiles: 2 Sidewinder, 4 Sparrow missiles, 1/20-mm M61A1 internal cannon
Avionics: APG-65 radar, AAS-38 FLIR-pod-capable, ALQ-165 ASPJ EW

Remarks: Multi-rôle fighter-bomber. Operational aircraft in 19 U.S. Navy and 13 U.S.M.C. 12-plane squadrons. B and D-models are two-seat versions. Carry 4,930 kg internal fuel/7,711 kg max. external fuel. Later F/A-18C/D have APG-73 radar. Uses a microprocessor to control the various weapons systems, depending on combat mode. First U.S.M.C. squadron operational 7-1-83; first U.S.N. during 10-83. F/A-18C/D have AMRAAM and IR Maverick missile capability. F/A-18D for U.S.M.C. have reconnaissance pod and are capable of all-weather attack. 130 F/A-18A retiring 1990–96. The F/A-18A is the mount of the "Blue Angels" flight demonstration team.

Planned F/A-18E/F will be 36 in. longer, have 3,000 lb. more fuel, and have the F412-GE-400 engine (9,800-kg thrust each). Aircraft would act as the interim replacement for the A-6E until the new AX becomes available in the next century.

PRINCIPAL COMBAT AIRCRAFT *(continued)*

♦ **528 F-14A/B/D Tomcat interceptors** Manufacturer: Grumman Corp. Aircraft Systems Div., Calverton, New York

F-14A Tomcat of VF-32 over the Red Sea LCDR Parsons, USN, 10-90

F-14D Tomcat of VF-124 David D. Broecker, 12-90

F-14A Tomcat of VF-41 David D. Broecker, 12-90

Wingspan: 19.53 m extended/11.63 m swept
Length: 18.85 m **Height:** 4.88 m
Weight: 18,186 kg empty/28,236 kg max. (F-14D: 32,865 kg max.)
Engines: 2 P&W TF30-P-414A turbojets (9,480-kg thrust each, with afterburner); F-14B,D: 2 G.E. F110-GE-4400 (12,698-kg thrust each)
Speed: Mach 2.34 max. (Mach 1.88 operational) **Ceiling:** 60,000 ft.
Range: 2,000 n.m. ferry; 500 n.m. combat radius (2.5–3 hours)
Armament: 6 Phoenix/Sparrow/Sidewinder AAM, 1/20-mm M61A1 cannon
Avionics: AWG-9 radar (F-14D: APG-71); TARPS recce pod on three in each squadron

Remarks: Operational aircraft in 28 12-plane squadrons. Last of 597 delivered 5-92. Barring losses, 404 F-14A, 69 F-14B (formerly F-14A+), and 55 F-14D in service at end FY 92. Thirty-eight F-14B were new-built, the remainder re-engined; F-14D has new engines plus APG-71 radar, ALR-67 and ALQ-165 EW equipment, and capability to launch HARM and Harpoon missiles. First three F-14D operational 16-11-90 to VF-124 at Miramar. Forty-nine F-14D are wired for TARPS photo-recce pod. Over 115 have been lost to accidents, none in combat. Plans to continue production and adapt the aircraft for ground attack have been canceled.

Note: The last U.S. Navy F-4-series Phantom fighter-bombers (except for one YF-4C trials aircraft and target drone conversions) was retired 2-90; Marine Corps VFMA-112 and 321 continued to fly the F-4S into 1991 before replacing with F/A-18. As successor to the F-14, the navy has been required to participate in the air force ATF (Advanced Tactical Fighter) program, the F-22, a modified version of which is also proposed for the AX strike bomber program.

♦ **0 (+575) AX strike bombers** Manufacturer: . . . . . .

Wingspan: . . . **Length:** . . . **Height:** . . .
Weight: . . . **Ceiling:** . . . **Engines:** . . . . . .
Speed: . . . . . . **Range:** 700 n.m. radius (high-low-low-high)
Armament: 5,442-kg. max. (4/1,000-lb. precision munitions + 2 AAM internal)
Avionics: . . . . . .

Remarks: To enter fleet service 2005, with 250 to be in squadron service by 2010. Design contracts 30-12-91 to McDonnell Douglas, General Dynamics, Rockwell, Grumman, and Lockheed. Expected to be between the size of an F-14 and an A-6. For initial phase of combat, would carry all ordnance internally to achieve stealth; external carriage would be added when air supremacy achieved. The air force will use sa airframe post-2010 as replacement for F-111, F-117, and F-15E. Unit cost to be $ million (FY 92 dollars). Program replaced the canceled A-12 (which may, however, modified as one of the design competitors). A reconnaissance capability is to be added 2010.

♦ **290 A-6E and ca. 60 KA-6D Intruder all-weather bombers**
Manufacturer: Grumman Corp. Aircraft Systems Div., Calverton, New York

A-6E Intruder of VA-145 David D. Broecker, 8

A-6E Intruder of VA-52 David D. Broecker,

Composite-structure re-winged A-6E B

Wingspan: 16.15 m **Length:** 16.67 m **Height:** 4.92 m
Weight: 11,627 kg empty/27,392 kg max.
Engines: 2 Pratt & Whitney J52-P8A/8B turbojets (4,218-kg thru each)
Speed: 594 kts max. **Ceiling:** 52,700 ft.
Range: 2,400 n.m. ferry; 320 n.m. radius at 460 kt with full comba load
Armament: 8,163 kg max. (typical: 46/250-lb bombs)—equipped t launch Harpoon, HARM, SLAM, Maverick, Walleye, Sidewinder
Avionics: APQ-156 radar, TRAM E/O sensor

Remarks: In operational service with 22 navy 10-plane squadrons; U.S.M.C. over to navy in 1991. KA-6D version, of which about 60 remain, carries 13,600 for transfer and is integrated into the A-6E squadrons. All A-6E now have (Target Recognition-Attack Multisensor). Last new A-6E delivered 3-2-92. rewing and re-engine all remaining A-6E and to give 260 SWIP (System Improvement Program) to add chaff dispensers, new head-up display, wing fill wing leading-edge slat, and towed missile decoy capability; first of 60 curre contract to deliver 6-95. In 1991, 50 re-winged A-6E were delivered and ano entered the program. A-6 will remain in service until 2015, having first flown early 1960s.

Note: The A-7 Corsair withdrawn from combat service 5-91. As of 10-91, 5 TA-7C, and EA-7C were left in subsidiary service; to be retired by end-1992. Skyhawk-series light fighter-bomber is no longer in first-line service, but o remain in training and subsidiary tasks.

ᐧCIPAL COMBAT AIRCRAFT *(continued)*

. 175 AV-8B Harrier V/STOL attack fighters Manufacturer: Donnell Aircraft Co., Div. of McDonnell Douglas Corp., St. Louis, Missouri

·B Harrier of HMH-362 aboard Saipan (LHA 2) PH2 Charles Stover, USN, 12-91

·B Harrier of HMH-362 PH2 Charles Stover, USN, 12-91

-8B Harrier two-seat trainer **McDonnell Douglas, 4-88**

ngspan: 9.22 m **Length:** 14.10 m **Height:** 3.53 m
ight: 8,720-kg max. takeoff in VTOL mode/13,492-kg max. STOL
gine: 1 Rolls-Royce Pegasus F402-RR-408 (9,751-kg thrust)
eed: 650 kts max.; 585 kts sea level **Ceiling:** 50,000 ft.
nge: 2,460 n.m. max. ferry; 100+ n.m. VTOL radius
mament: 1/25-mm GAU-12/U gatling gun; 2–4 Sidewinder AAM, up to 14/227-kg or 6/454-kg bombs, Maverick, Walleye

rks: 276 procured to date for Marine Corps, with additional through FY 92. een are two-seat TAV-8B trainers. First squadron operational 6-85. First night-le variant, with FLIR, flew 6-87. 167th-on have the more powerful F402-RR-408 e, which will replace the F402-RR-406 in surviving earlier units; the final 27 were e had the APG-65 radar added, but this now seems unlikely. By 11-90, 29 of the dered had been lost in accidents. Deploy aboard LHA 1- and LHD 1-class am-us warfare ships. A successor, the VLSF (Vertical-Landing Strike-Fighter), may eloped by 1998 for fleet introduction around 2010.

32 S-3A/B Viking shipboard ASW aircraft
anufacturer: Lockheed-California Co., Burbank, California

ngspan: 20.93 m **Length:** 16.26 m **Height:** 6.94 m
ight: 12,160 kg empty/23,853 kg max.
gines: 2 G.E. TF34-GE-400 turbofans (4,210-kg thrust each)
eed: 450 kts max.; 350 kts cruise; 210 kts patrol
iling: 40,000 ft.
nge: 3,000 n.m. ferry; 1,150 n.m. patrol radius (9-hr. endurance)
mament: 4 Mk 46 or Mk 50 torpedoes or 4 depth charges or 4 mines; 2 Harpoon on underwing stations
ionics: APS-116 radar, ASQ-81(V)1 MAD, 60 sonobuoys

S-3A Viking of VS-38 PH2 Grezdinski, USN, 3-89

S-3A Viking of VS-28 David D. Broecker, 5-90

Remarks: Operate in eleven 10-plane squadrons. 187 built. Conversions include six US-3A COD (Carrier On-board Delivery) aircraft for Indian Ocean deployment use, and one KS-3A aerial refueler. Beginning in 3-87, 132 updating to S-3B configuration, with APS-137(V)1 synthetic aperture radar, Harpoon ASM launch capability, new auxiliary power unit, ALE-40 countermeasures dispenser, and other updated avionics; last conversion to complete 1994, and the aircraft are expected to remain in service until 2015. Sixteen are being converted to ES-3A Battle Group Passive Horizon Extension System (BGPHES) ELINT aircraft to replace the retired EA-3B; weight increased to 13,520 kg empty, and 63 antennas fitted—two will be carried aboard each deployed aircraft carrier by the mid-1990s. During Operation Desert Storm in 1991, Vikings were used as conventional bombers against land targets and for aerial refueling.

♦ **117 E-2C Hawkeye airborne early-warning and air-control**
Bldr: Grumman Aerospace Corp., Bethpage, New York

E-2C Hawkeye of VAW-110 David D. Broecker, 3-91

E-2C Hawkeye David D. Broecker, 7-91

PRINCIPAL COMBAT AIRCRAFT *(continued)*

Wingspan: 24.58 m **Length:** 17.56 m **Height:** 5.59 m
Weight: 17,091 kg empty/23,810 kg max.
Engines: 2 Allison T56-A-425 turboprops (4,591 shp each)—*see* Remarks
Speed: 315 kts max.; 270 kts cruise **Ceiling:** 30,800 ft.
Range: 6-hour endurance **Armament:** none
Avionics: APS-138, APS-139, or APS-145 radar; ESM suite

Remarks: Radar, mounted in 7.32-m-diameter rotating radome, can track upwards of 600 air and surface targets within a 250-n.m. radius, while the aircraft controls up to 25 intercepts. Original APS-125 radar replaced by APS-138 TRAC-A (Total Radiation Aperture Control Antenna) to reduce side-lobes. 122nd and later aircraft got later APS-139 radar with improved ECCM, and the final 21 aircraft will have APS-145 radar with over-land capability, new IFF, Global Positioning System (GPS), and JTDS (Joint Tactical Information Distribution System); 54 earlier aircraft may be retrofitted to the same configuration, with deliveries beginning in 1995. Beginning with FY 86 aircraft, the uprated T56-A-427 engine (5,690 shp each) was installed. Crew of five.

◆ **ca. 120 EA-6B Prowler combat EW aircraft**
Bldr: Grumman Aerospace Corp., Calverton, New York

EA-6B Prowler of VAQ-130 over Saudi Arabia
CDR J. R. Leenhouts, USN, 8-90

EA-6B Prowler of VAQ-129 David D. Broecker, 8-91

EA-6A Prowler of VAQ-33 David D. Broecker, 4-90

Wingspan: 16.15 m **Length:** 18.11 m **Height:** 4.95 m
Weight: 12,185 kg empty/27,392-kg max.
Engines: 2 Pratt & Whitney J52-P-409 turbojets (5,442-kg thrust each)
Speed: 520 kts (410 kts cruise) **Ceiling:** 34,400 ft.
Range: 2,400 n.m. ferry; 710 n.m. combat radius
Armament: HARM missiles in recent aircraft
Avionics: ALQ-149, ALQ-99F jammers, APS-130 radar, etc.

Remarks: Operate in 13 squadrons of 4–6 aircraft. Crew of four. First EA-6B ADVCAP (Advanced Capability) delivered 10-89 with J52-P-409 engines, new slats, improved flaps, ALQ-149 communications intercept/jammer, etc. Earlier aircraft had 5,080-kg thrust J52-P-408 engines. HARM missile capability being added and can also carry two Sidewinder for self-defense. Last 9 new EA-6B procured under FY 89, but starting with 1 under FY 91, surviving earlier aircraft will be uprated to ADVCAP standard (3 under FY 93, 9 each under FY 94–95, and 12 per year thereafter). The last two-seat EA-6A electronics warfare aircraft were transferred to VAQ-33 at Key West in 1991 for use in aggressor training.

◆ **80 P-3B and 280 P-3C Orion maritime surveillance aircraft**
Manufacturer: Lockheed Aeronautical Systems Co., Burbank, California

P-3C Orion OS2 John Bouvia, USN

P-3C Orion—with 4 Harpoon and 2 Sidewinder missiles
M. Meyer, USN

Wingspan: 30.37 m (P-3B and P-3C Update IV: 31.13 m)
Length: 36.61 m **Height:** 10.28 m
Weight: 27,892 kg empty/62,994 kg max.
Engines: 4 Allison T65-A-14 turboprops (4,910 shp each)
Speed: 405 kts max.; 209 kts patrol cruise **Ceiling:** 34,000 ft.
Range: 4,500 n.m. (2,380 n.m. patrol radius/14.5 hrs. endurance)
Armament: 7,700-kg disposable ordnance, including 4 Mk 46 or M 50 torpedoes, 4 Harpoon ASM, 6/908-kg mines, etc.
Avionics: APS-115 radar, AQS-81(V)1 magnetic anomaly detecto ASQ-114 digital computer, AAS-36 FLIR on P-3C, 87 sonobuoys

Remarks: By FY 93 will be reduced to 18 active (all with P-3C as of 11-9-90 Naval Reserve squadrons, each with 8 aircraft. P-3B being retired, many abroad or converted to non-combat rôles; all P-3A retired by 9-90. Crew of up P-3C is fitted with an A-NEW central operations module built around the A computer and incorporating an Air Tactical Data System (ATDS). First fligh

CIPAL COMBAT AIRCRAFT *(continued)*

e-IV"-configured aircraft on 16-12-91, with APS-137 ISAR (Inverse Synthetic re Radar), ALR-66(V)5 EW gear, AAS-36 infrared detector, AQS-81 MAD, display/processor, UYS-2 acoustic processor; 109 total ASW-configured P-3C to ted to same standard, starting 1991. As of 11-91, 11 ISAR-equipped P-3C -IV were in service, one with "Outlaw Hunter" tactical data system for "Over-izon" missile targeting; "Outlaw Hunter" aircraft have Global Positioning (GPS), SATCOMM, and ISAR.
first of 12 P-3C converted to EP-3C "Aries-II" for Squadrons VQ-1 and VQ-2 ed to VQ-1 on 7-8-90 to replace the earlier EP-3B/E "Aries-I." Last RP-3A 11-7-91; VAX-8, at Patuxent River, Maryland, operates 3 UP-3B and 2 RP-3D arch.

The planned P-7A replacement for the P-3-series was canceled during 7-90 due overruns. Current plans call for re-introducing producion of a "P-3C+" (or P-3H) mid-1990s, although a rehabilitation program for earlier P-3Cs (new wings and s, Update-IV electronic configuration) is also a possibility.

OV-10D Bronco observation and light attack aircraft

nufacturer: North American Rockwell Corp., Columbus, Ohio

D Bronco — Rockwell, 1989

gspan: 12.19 m **Length:** 13.41 m **Height:** 4.57 m
ght: 3,261 kg empty/6,551 kg max.
ines: 2 Garrett T76-G-420/421 turboprops (1,040 shp each)
ed: 350 kts (260 kts cruise) **Ceiling:** 30,000 ft.
ge: 190-n.m. radius
nament: 1,632-kg disposable stores (5 positions), 4/7.62-mm mg
onics: ALQ-144 infrared flare launcher, AAS-37 FLIR

ks: First ordered 1966. Operated by three marine squadrons. Two-seat obser- aircraft that can operate from LPH, LHA, and LHD amphibious ships. Can carry ratroopers. Centerline store position can take a 20-mm gatling gun pod, and two nder AAM can be carried. Although 24 update kits to convert OV-10A to OV- d 16 kits to convert 16 "D"-model to OV-10D have been purchased, the survivng are to be discarded: 12 by the end of 1992, and the remaining 36 by 3-94. The V-10D+ had only been delivered 29-5-91.

E-6A Mercury strategic communications aircraft

nufacturer: Boeing Aerospace Div., The Boeing Co., Seattle, Wash.

gspan: 45.60 m **Length:** 46.61 m **Height:** 12.93 m
ght: 78,365 kg empty/155,100 kg max.
ines: 4 CFM Int'l. F108-CF-100 turbofans (9,977-kg thrust each)
ed: 530 kts (455 kts cruise) **Ceiling:** 40,000 ft.
ge: 7,300 n.m. ferry; 15.4 hr. without fueling/28.9 hr. with one fueling
onics: VLF communications suite, ESM

Mercury TACAMO — Boeing, 7-88

Remarks: Ordered 29-4-83 to replace EC-130Q TACAMO ("Take-Charge-and-Move-Out) strategic communications aircraft. Nickname changed from "Hermes" in 1992. Operated by VQ-3 from Barber's Point, Oahu, and VQ-4 from Patuxent River, Maryland. Have a 7,925-m trailing-wire main antenna and a 1,219-m trailing wire dipole. ECM pod on starboard wingtip. First flight 19-2-87; all delivered by end 1991. Ten crew, plus eight relief crew. Uses Boeing 707-320B transport airframe.

Note: The surviving EC-130Q aircraft reverted to transport configuration as TC-130Q or were retired in 1990.

♦ ca. 50 C-2A Greyhound carrier onboard-delivery aircraft

Manufacturer: Grumman Aerospace Corp., Bethpage, New York

C-2A Greyhound of VRC-30 — David D. Broecker, 3-91

Wingspan: 24.57 m **Length:** 17.27 m **Height:** 4.85 m
Weight: 14,175 kg empty/24,668 kg max.
Engines: 2 Allison T56-A-425 turboprops (4,910 shp each)
Speed: 343 kts (257 kts cruise) **Ceiling:** 33,800 ft.
Range: 1,490 n.m. at 260 kts

Remarks: Variant of the E-2 Hawkeye series with larger-diameter fuselage. Twelve of the original 17 ordered 1964 remained when a second batch of 39 with uprated engines was ordered in 1983; production ended 1989. Crew of three plus up to 32 passengers or 20 litter patients, rear loading ramp. Payload: 5,535 kg. Usage has been heavier than expected, and additional units or a similar aircraft may have to be acquired.

Note: The MV-22A Osprey assault troop-carrying tilt-wing transport, described in previous editions, now seems unlikely to go into production, due to cost.

♦ ca. 110 SH-3G/H Sea King shipboard ASW helicopters

Manufacturer: Sikorsky Aircraft Div., United Aircraft Corp., Stratford, Conn.

SH-3H Sea King of HS-14 — David D. Broecker, 12-90

Rotor diameter: 18.90 m **Length:** 22.16 (16.70 fuselage)
Height: 5.13 m **Weight:** 5,302 kg empty/9,300 kg max.
Engines: 2 G.E. T58-GE-10 turboshafts (1,400 shp each)
Speed: 144 kts max. (118 kts cruise) **Ceiling:** 10,800 ft.
Range: 624 n.m. ferry; 4.5-hr. mission endurance
Armament: two Mk 46 torpedoes, 25 sonobuoys
Avionics: AQS-13 dipping sonar, AQS-81(V)2 MAD, APS-124 radar

Remarks: First flew 11-3-59. Being replaced as standard aircraft carrier ASW/SAR helicopter by the SH-60F. Can also be accommodated on *Spruance*-class destroyers, etc. Crew of four. Most "G" models have been updated to "H" configuration. Eleven additional VH-3D serve the Presidential Flight and as VIP transports for senior navy and marine officials; also in service are several UH-3A utility models.

♦ ca. 110 SH-2F/G Seasprite LAMPS-I shipboard ASW helicopters

Manufacturer: Kaman Aircraft Corp., Bloomfield, Connecticut

Rotor diameter: 13.42 m **Length:** 16.04 m (11.69 fuselage)
Height: 4.73 m **Weight:** 3,925 kg empty/6,123 kg max.
Engines: F: 2 G.E. T58-GE-10 turboshafts (1,350 shp each); G: 2 G.E. T700-GE-401 turboshafts (1,723 shp each)
Speed: F: 143 kts sea level (120 kts cruise); G: 146 kts max.
Ceiling: 22,500 ft. **Range:** F: 440 n.m.; G: 560 n.m. (F: 2.5 hr; G: 5.7 hr.)
Armament: 2 Mk 46 torpedoes; 15 DIFAR and DISCASS sonobuoys
Avionics: LN-66 radar, ASQ-81(V)2 MAD, ALR-66A ESM, ARR-75 sonobuoy dispenser

PRINCIPAL COMBAT AIRCRAFT *(continued)*

SH-2F Seasprite aboard Independence (CV 60)
OS2 John Bouvia, USN, 1990

Remarks: First ordered 11-57 as a single-engined utility helicopter. Through 1983, all SH-2F LAMPS-I ASW helicopters were conversions of UH-2 Seasprites. Reintroduced into production, with 42 new aircraft approved in FY 83 through FY 87 to serve on ASW ships not getting the SH-60B LAMPS-III system. First new SH-2F delivered 12-8-83. Six SH-2G conversions with new engines, LN-66HP radar, digital database, new UYS-503 acoustic processor, ALR-66A(V)1 ESM, AAQ-16 FLIR, ALQ-144 infrared jammer, AAR-97 missile warning ESM, tactical navigation system, data link, and 99-channel sonobuoy receiver, were ordered 6-87, the first delivering 8-90. Subsequently, 12 all-new SH-2G and 8 additional rebuilds have been ordered, all to be delivered by 1994. Older SH-2F are beginning to be retired as older frigates are decommissioned; one of three Naval Reserve squadrons was to deactivate at the end of FY 92. Also in use are one HH-2D for oceanography and one NHH-2D bailed to Kaman.

♦ ca. 136 (+ 91) SH-60B Seahawk (LAMPS-III) and 42 (+90) SH-60F Ocean Hawk ASW helicopters

Manufacturer: Sikorsky Aircraft Div., United Aircraft Corp., Stratford, Conn.

Rotor diameter: 16.36 m **Length:** 19.76 m (15.24 fuselage)
Height: 5.23 m
Weight: SH-60B: 6,190-kg empty/9,435 max. (F: 10,658-kg max.)
Engines: early SH-60B2 G.E. T700-GE-401 turboshafts (1,723 shp max./1,543 shp continuous each); late B and SH-60F: 2 T700-GE-401C (1,940 shp max./1,662 shp continuous each)
Speed: 150 kts (130 cruise) **Range:** 150 n.m. mission radius (4 hrs.)
Armament: 2/Mk 46 or Mk 50 torpedoes (or 1 Penguin ASM in some SH-60B)
Avionics: SH-60B: APS-124 radar, ASQ-81(V)2 MAD, UYS-1 Proteus sonobuoy processor, 25 A-size sonobuoys, ALQ-142 ESM, Link 11; SH-60 F: AQS-13F dipping sonar, no radar or sonobuoy facilities

SH-60B Seahawk LAMPS-III CWO Ed Bailey, USN, 1990

SH-60F Ocean Hawk Jürg Kürsener, 7-92

HH-60H combat support helicopter Sikorsky,

VH-60 VIP transport of HMX-1 Sikorsky,

Remarks: SH-60B intended for use aboard frigates and destroyers as part of ar
suite, with the helicopter linked to the ship by data-link for data processing; s
display on the ship. First flight 12-12-79. Force goal is 204. Block I update, av
12-89, adds Mk 50 torpedo capability, Penguin missile capability, 99-channel son
processor, Global Positioning System, a third weapons station, ability to des
targets for ship-launched Harpoon and SLAM missiles. Block II, to enter ser
1996, will add ALFS (Airborne Low Frequency Sonar) dipping sonar, substi
multi-mode radar, and improve countermeasures and data-link capabilities. S
serving in the Persian Gulf area are given ALQ-144 infrared countermeasures d
ALE-39 chaff dispensers, and a 7.62-mm machine gun. Most SH-60B now ha
more powerful T700-GE-401C engines.

The first production SH-60F first flew on 19-3-87 as a replacement for the c
based SH-3 Sea King and differs from the "B"-model in having most of the LAN
equipment deleted and replaced by a dipping sonar. ALFS will replace AQS-
aircraft delivered in 1995 and later.

Also in navy service are 18 HH-60H combat search and rescue helicopters (w
more to be ordered 1993–95 as troop carriers for the U.S. Marine Corps); plans
the navy HH-60H with 2.75-in. rocket pods, a forward-firing 12.7-mm mg, H
missiles, PAVE LOW FLIR, etc., have been canceled despite the need demonstra
such a capability during the 1990–91 Mideast crisis. Nine VH-60 VIP transport
delivered to the marines in 1988–89 as replacements for the VH-1N in the Presic
Flight. The Coast Guard operates the HH-60J.

♦ ca. 340 CH-46E/UH-46D Sea Knight transport helicopters

Manufacturer: The Boeing Co., Vertol Div., Morton, Pennsylvania

HH-46A Sea Knight of HC-5 OS2 John Bouvia, USN

Rotor Diameter: 15.56 m **Length:** 25.72 m (13.67 fuselage)
Height: 5.08 m **Weight:** 5,947 kg empty/10,438 kg. max.
Engines: 2 G.E. T58-GE-16 turboshafts (1,870 shp each)
Speed: 144 kts max. **Ceiling:** 14,000 ft.
Range: 744 n.m. ferry; 206 n.m. mission

Remarks: First flight 16-10-62, with 624 procured through 1970. CH-46E opera
13 U.S. Marine Corps squadrons. Included in above total are about two dozen U
vertical replenishment versions with T58-GE-10 engines operated by the n
replenishment ships. CH-46E can accommodate 17 assault troops or 15 stretcher
attendants, while the UH-46D can carry 1,360-kg internal cargo or 4,536 kg
beneath. Surviving aircraft have been updated with automatic navigation sy
armored seats, glass-reinforced plastic rotor blades, and infrared jamming devi

♦ 70 CH-53D and 10 RH-53D Sea Stallion transport/mine countermeasures helicopters

Manufacturer: Sikorsky Aircraft Div., United Aircraft Corp., Stratford, Co

CIPAL COMBAT AIRCRAFT *(continued)*

3D Sea Stallion mine countermeasures helo PH2 Hicks, USN, 8-87

or diameter: 22.04 m **Length:** 26.92 (20.48 fuselage)
ght: 7.59 m **Weight:** 10,718 kg empty/19,050 kg max.
ines: 2 G.E. T64-GE-413 turboshafts (2,925 shp each)
ed: 170 kts (150 cruise) **Ceiling:** 21,000 ft.
ge: 886 n.m. ferry; 540 n.m. mission (3.5-hr. endurance)

ks: First ordered 8-62 for the marines. Last of 139 CH-53A and 174 CH-53D ed 1-72. Can carry 55 combat-equipped troops or 24 stretchers and 4 attendants s cargo. The Naval Reserve–operated RH-53D mine countermeasures version 64-GE-415 engines of 4,380 shp each) is equipped to tow Mk 103 cutters, Mk 104 ic minesweeping sled, Mk 105 hydrofoil sled, Mk 106 acoustic sweep array, or J-1 shallow-water sweep rig and also carries an AQS-14 minehunting dipping the aircraft is armed with two 12.7-mm machine guns. Sixteen U.S.M.C. CH- e also equipped to tow sweep gear.

5 (+ 66) CH-53E Super Stallion transport and 32 (+ 24) MH- ea Dragon mine-countermeasures helicopters
acturer: Sikorsky Aircraft Div., United Aircraft Corp., Stratford, Conn.

3E Super Stallion Sikorsky, 1987

3E Sea Dragon mine countermeasures helo Jürg Kürsener, 7-92

tor diameter: 24.08 m
gth: 30.18 m (22.35 fuselage, 18.44 folded) **Height:** 8.64 m
ight: 15,071 kg empty (MH-53E: 16,482 kg)/33,339 kg max.
gines: 3 G.E. T64-GE-416 turboshafts (4,380 shp max. each/3,695 cont.)
ed: 170 kts (150 cruise) **Ceiling:** 18,500 ft.
nge: 1,000 n.m. unrefueled ferry; 230 n.m. with 8,630-kg cargo; 50 n.m. with 14,512-kg cargo (MH-53E: 4-hr. endurance)

rks: YCH-53E first flew 1-3-74, YMH-53E on 23-12-81, both as upgraded suc- s to the successful CH-53A/D and RH-53D programs. As of 1992, the force goals had been extended to 191 U.S.M.C. CH-53E and 56 Navy MH-53E, with a dozen of the latter to be operated by the Naval Reserve. CH-53E can carry 56 fully-equipped troops or up to 14,512-kg cargo. Crew of three. Seven-bladed main rotor. CH-53E can also be used to tow Mk 105 mine countermeasures sleds. MH-53E has enlarged side sponsons holding 4,478-kg fuel and has a cable winch exerting a 13.6-ton pull; it can also be used to carry 56 troops. Both versions aerial refuelable. ALQ-166 towed mine countermeasures sled has been canceled for the MH-53E. Of the 20 authorized for procurement under FY 93, 10 will be CH-53E and 10 MH-53E.

◆ **70 (+ 74) AH-1W SeaCobra ground attack helicopters**
Manufacturer: Bell Helicopter Textron, Inc., Ft. Worth, Texas

AH-1W SeaCobra of HML/A-167 PH2 M. Harner, USN, 6-88

Rotor diameter: 13.42 m **Length:** 17.47 m (12.93 fuselage)
Height: 4.17 m **Weight:** 4,626 kg empty/6,689 kg max.
Engines: 2 G.E. T700-GE-410 turboshafts (1,690 shp each)
Speed: 180 kts max. **Ceiling:** 10,500 ft. **Range:** 360 n.m. (2 hrs.)
Armament: 1/20-mm XM-197 gatling gun, 76/2.75-in. rockets or 2/20-mm miniguns in pods, TOW and Hellfire ASM and/ or Sidearm or Sidewinder AAM

Remarks: First 49 AH-1J gunships ordered for U.S.M.C. 5-68; all now retired. Improved AH-1T (with T400-CP-400 engines) flew 20-5-76, and 55 production versions were ordered, of which the 37 survivors were to be converted to AH-1W standard by 1990. Deliveries of new up-engined AH-1W began 27-3-87. Five transferred from U.S.M.C. stocks to Turkey in 1991. Production of another 74 is to be reinstated under FY 92–97 Budgets.

Note: To act as shipboard-deployed gunships during the Mideast crisis in 1990–91, 15 U.S. Army AH-58D Kiowa armed helicopters operated from navy warships. Plans to arm additional navy helicopters for such service have been canceled in favor of again borrowing army assets and/or operating SeaCobras from frigates and destroyers.

◆ **ca. 60 UH-1N Iroquois transport/utility helicopters**
Manufacturer: Bell Helicopter Textron, Inc., Ft. Worth, Texas

UH-1N Iroquois—with 12.7-mm mg and rocket pods
PH3 H. Cleveland, USN, 9-87

Rotor diameter: 14.70 m **Length:** 17.47 m (12.93 m fuselage)
Height: 4.39 m **Weight:** 2,517 kg empty/4,763 kg max.
Engines: 2 Pratt & Whitney T400-CP-400 turboshafts (1,250 shp max. each)
Speed: 110 kts **Ceiling:** 15,000 ft. **Range:** 250 n.m. (2 hrs.)
Armament: 2/7.62-mm mg, rocket pods

Remarks: Used by U.S.M.C. as assault helicopters with up to 16 troops aboard and by the navy, in the single-engined UH-1E and UH-1L versions, as utility helicopters. First UH-1N delivered in 1971.

Other Navy and Marine Corps aircraft in service:
- 22 F-16N and 4 TF-16N Fighting Falcon adversary training aircraft
- 25 F-5E/F Tiger-II adversary training aircraft (12 ex-U.S.A.F. transfered 6-89)
- 20 OA-4M Skyhawk adversary aircraft for "Top Gun" training
- 27 C-9B Skytrain-II transports for the Marines and the Naval Reserve
- C-130 transport, 6 LC-130F/R arctic operations, DC-130 drone control, and U.S.M.C. KC-130T aerial refueling Hercules 4-engined transports
- T-2C Buckeye jet trainers (to be replaced by the T-45A Goshawk)
- T-45A Goshawk jet trainers, of which 302 are planned for procurement
- T-34C Mentor initial trainers, of which 361 had been delivered by 6-89 (T-34B retired)
- T-38A Talon jet test-pilot trainers at Patuxent River Naval Air Station, Maryland

PRINCIPAL COMBAT AIRCRAFT *(continued)*

T-39D Saberliner flight-officer trainers (and several CT-39E/G transports)
TC-4C Academe bombardier-navigator trainers for the A-6E Intruder
T-44A Pegasus (Beech King Air) twin-engine trainers
TH-57A/B training helicopters
4 OA-6B Cayuse helicopters on loan from the U.S. Army for test-pilot training
1 EC-24A (Douglas DC-8) electronics training
1 NKC-135A electronics training

The last C-131-series twin-engined transport was retired during 8-90. All A-3 Skywarrior variants have been retired. The navy plans to acquire 347 JPATS basic trainers during the 1990s. There are a number of other utility and training aircraft types in service.

The Navy ordered its first modern-era lighter-than-air aircraft on 5-6-87 from Westinghouse Airship Industries but subsequently terminated development of a larger airship. The Sentinel 1000 prototype was nonetheless delivered 26-6-91 for evaluation by the Defense Advanced Research Programs Administration (DARPA); powered by two 1,650 bhp Isotta-Fraschini diesels and one G.E. CT-7 turboshaft engine, the 129-meter overall aircraft has a crew of up to 15, a ferry range of up to 3,500 n.m., endurance 47 hours at 50 kts or 55 hours at 40 kts), and carries the APS-139 search radar.

MV-22A Osprey prototype Bell-Boeing, 1991

TF-16N Fighting Falcon of the Navy Fighter Warfare School David D. Broecker, 12-90

F-16N Fighting Falcon of VF-43 David D. Broecker, 12-90

F-5E Tiger-II of VF-45 David D. Broecker, 4-90

TA-4J Skyhawk of VR-126 David D. Broecker,

A-4J Skyhawk of VFC-13 David D. Broecker

C-9B Skytrain-II David D. Broecker

C-130 Hercules support aircraft for the Blue Angels David D. Broecker

T-2C Buckeye of VF-126 David D. Broecker

CIPAL COMBAT AIRCRAFT *(continued)*

Goshawk McDonnell Douglas

: Mentor of VF-124 David D. Broecker, 7-91

E Saberliner of VRC-30 David D. Broecker, 7-91

Sentinel 1000 airship prototype Westinghouse, 1991

T-44A Pegasus Beech Aircraft

TC-4C Academe of VA-42 David D. Broecker, 6-91

.EAR-POWERED BALLISTIC-MISSILE SUBMARINES

(+5) Ohio class (SCB 304 design)

.r: General Dynamics, Groton, Conn. (*Atlantic/†Pacific Fleet)

	Program	Laid down	L	In serv.
726 Ohio†	FY 74	10-4-76	7-4-79	11-11-81
727 Michigan†	FY 75	4-4-77	26-4-80	11-9-82
728 Florida†	FY 75	9-6-77	14-11-81	8-6-83
729 Georgia†	FY 76	7-4-79	6-11-82	11-2-84
730 Henry M. kson† (ex-*Rhode nd*)	FY 77	19-1-81	15-10-83	6-10-84
731 Alabama†	FY 78	27-8-81	19-5-84	20-5-85
SSBN 732 Alaska†	FY 78	9-3-83	12-1-85	25-1-86
SSBN 733 Nevada†	FY 80	8-8-83	14-9-85	16-8-86
SSBN 734 Tennessee†	FY 81	9-6-86	13-12-86	17-12-88
SSBN 735 Pennsylvania†	FY 83	2-3-87	23-4-88	9-9-89
SSBN 736 West Virginia†	FY 84	18-12-87	14-10-89	20-10-90
SSBN 737 Kentucky*	FY 85	18-12-87	11-8-90	13-7-91
SSBN 738 Maryland*	FY 86	18-12-87	10-8-91	13-6-92
SSBN 739 Nebraska	FY 87	18-12-87	15-8-92	8-93
SSBN 740 Rhode Island	FY 88	. . .	7-93	8-94
SSBN 741 Maine	FY 89	. . .	7-94	8-95
SSBN 742 Wyoming	FY 90	. . .	. . .	8-96
SSBN 743	FY 91	. . .	. . .	8-97

igan (SSBN 727) OS2 John Bouvia, USN, 2-90

NUCLEAR-POWERED BALLISTIC-MISSILE SUBMARINES
(continued)

West Virginia (SSBN 736) Dr. Giorgio Arra, 10-91

Georgia (SSBN 729) OS2 John Bouvia, 3-88

West Virginia (SSBN 736) Dr. Giorgio Arra, 10-91

D: 12,500 tons light (16,764 tons surf./18,750 tons sub.)
S: 20+ kts (sub.) **Dim:** 170.69 × 12.80 × 11.13 (surf.)
A: 24/Trident C-4 (SSBN 734 on: D-5) missiles—4/533-mm Mk 68 TT (Mk 48 or Mk 48 ADCAP torpedoes, Mk 30 decoys, etc.)
Electron Equipt:
Radar: BPS-15A nav.
Sonar: BQQ-5E(V)4 or BQQ-6 passive suite, BQS-13 active, BQS-15 ice-avoidance, BQR-15 towed array , BQR-19 active nav., BQQ-9 TASPE
EW: WLR-8(V)5 suite, WLR-10 radar intercept, 8 Mk 2 countermeasures launchers
M: 1 G.E. S8G natural-circulation pressurized-water reactor; turboreduction drive; 1 prop; 60,000 shp
Endurance: 70 days **Crew:** 15 officers, 142 enlisted (2 crews)

Remarks: SSBN 726 ran first trials 17-6-81 and was delivered three years late. Program now on schedule. The availability of this class as a whole is to be 66 percent, using a planned schedule of 70-day patrols, followed by 25-day refit periods, and with a 12-month overhaul every nine years. Each ship has two crews. None ordered under FY 79 because of program delays and cost overruns. Ordering of SSBN 734 was deferred to 7-1-82 due to contract disputes between the navy and General Dynamics. SSBN 738 was ordered 7-3-86. SSBN 739 offered to Newport News as well as General Dyn awarded to the latter 5-1-88. Name of SSBN 730 changed 27-9-83. SSBN 740 o 5-1-88, SSBN 741 on 5-10-88, SSBN 742 on 18-10-89, SSBN 743 on 19-12-90. SS completed the U.S. Navy's 3,000th ballistic missile submarine patrol spring 19

Systems: Able to submerge to 300 meters. Carry CCS Mk 2 Mod. 3 comb system, two Mk 2 SINS (Ship's Inertial Navigational System), and have navig satellite receivers. Mk 98 digital computer missile-fire-control system and M torpedo-fire-control system are installed. All have 1 Kollmorgen Type 152 and 82 periscopes. The reactor plant reportedly does not generate the full rated hors in service. Four 152-mm CSA (Countermeasures Stores Acoustic) Mk 2 Mod.0/ zontal launch tubes per side are located in the casing below the sail. Announc 1987 that later units may receive improved BSY-1 or BSY-2 sonar suites. Nav systems to update under 24-10-88 Unisys contract.

Status: SSBN 726 made her first operational deployment 1-10-82 to 10-12-8 ing fired her first missile on 17-1-82; her first refit/refueling is to be funded un 93. The first eight are based at Bangor, Washington; later units are to base at Bay, Georgia. SSBN 732 began sea trials 18-9-85 and SSBN 733 on 28-5-86.

Missile system: SSBN 734 and later have Trident D-5 as built. Plans to bac earlier, C-4-equipped, units have been canceled. SSBN 734–737 have missiles w newer Mk 5/W88, 300 to 450-kiloton variable-yield, re-entry body/warhead; late will have the older, 100-kiloton Mk 4/W76 combination because of the shutdow Rocky Flats weapons factory.

◆ 11 James Madison and Benjamin Franklin classes (SCB 21 SCB 216A types) (all Atlantic Fleet)

	Bldr	Laid down	L	
SSBN 629 Daniel Boone	Mare Isl. NSY	6-2-62	22-6-63	2
SSBN 630 John C. Calhoun	Newport News	4-6-62	22-6-63	1
SSBN 632 Von Steuben	Newport News	4-9-62	18-10-63	3
SSBN 633 Casimir Pulaski	Gen. Dyn.	12-1-63	1-2-64	1
SSBN 634 Stonewall Jackson	Mare Isl. NSY	4-7-62	30-11-63	2
SSBN 640 Benjamin Franklin	Gen. Dyn.	25-5-63	5-12-64	22
SSBN 641 Simon Bolivar	Newport News	17-4-63	22-8-64	29
SSBN 643 George Bancroft	Gen. Dyn.	24-8-63	20-3-65	2
SSBN 655 Henry L. Stimson	Gen. Dyn.	4-4-64	13-11-65	2
SSBN 657 Francis Scott Key	Gen. Dyn.	5-12-64	23-4-66	3
SSBN 658 Mariano G. Vallejo	Mare Isl. NSY	7-7-64	23-10-65	16

Authorized: SSBN 629 to SSBN 634 in FY 62, SSBN 640 to SSBN 64 63, and SSBN 655 to SSBN 658 in FY 64.

John C. Calhoun (SSBN 630)—high-mounted sail planes
Dr. Giorgio Arr

Henry L. Stimson (SSBN 655)—low-mounted sail planes
Dr. Giorgio Arr

[NUCL]EAR-POWERED BALLISTIC-MISSILE SUBMARINES
[contin]ued)

[Von S]teuben (SSBN 632) Dr. Giorgio Arra, 7-91

[D:] 7,350 tons surf./8,250 tons sub. **S:** 15 kts surf./23 kts sub.
[Dim]: 129.54 × 10.05 × 9.0
[A: 1]6/Trident-1 C-4 missiles—4/533-mm TT fwd (Mk 48 and Mk 48 ADCAP torpedoes), Mk 30 decoys
[Elec]tron Equipt:
[R]adar: BPS-15 nav.
[So]nar: BQR-7 passive, BQR-15 towed array with BQR-23 signal processor, BQR-19 nav., BQR-21 DIMUS, BQS-4 active
[E]W: WLR-8 intercept, WLR-10 radar warning, 8 Mk 2 countermeasures launchers
[M:] 1 Westinghouse SW5 pressurized-water reactor, 2 sets geared steam turbines; 1/7-bladed prop; 15,000 shp
[End]urance: 68 days **Crew:** 13–14 officers, 129–133 enlisted

[Remar]ks: Conversion of both classes from Polaris A-3 to Poseidon missiles was com[pleted] between 1970 and 1977. The 11 surviving units had received Trident-1 missiles [by 19]82. All units of the similar *Lafayette* (SSBN 616) class have been retired. On [...], President Bush announced the deactivation of the Poseidon missile system, [wi]ll missiles to be removed by 30-6-92; some of the submarines that carried [the]m (see Disposal section) will not be officially retired until Fiscal Year 1993, and [two ha]ve been earmarked for conversion to carry Dry Deck Shelters in support of SEAL forces: *Kamehameha* (SSBN 642) and *James K. Polk* (SSBN 645).

[Syst]ems: SSBN 640 and following units have quieter propulsion machinery; their [mo]unted forward diving planes are mounted about 2 m lower. Have three Mk 2 [i]nertial navigation system installations. Also carry a portable, commercial navi[gation]al radar for surfaced operations. There is an electric-powered, drop-down [emerge]ncy-propulsion propeller, as on SSNs. Submersion depth for all is more than 300 [m]. Mk 88 missile-fire-control system and Mk 113 torpedo-fire-control system. [S]SBN 657 commenced the first Trident-1 operational patrol on 20-10-79. All are [homep]orted at King's Bay, Georgia. They operate on a schedule of 68-day patrols, [separate]d by 32-day refit periods; every 6 years a 16-month yard period is requested, [for] an overall force availability of 55 percent. Each ship has two crews. SSBN 641 [and tw]o others are now on a nine-year operational/overhaul cycle.

[Disp]osals: *Sam Rayburn* (SSBN 635) began deactivation of her missile system [...] to be converted to an immobile engineering training craft, the ARTB (Auxil[iary R]eactor Training Barge); later redesignated MTS 635 (Moored Training Sub[marine]), but was stricken 28-8-89 without converting. *Andrew Jackson* (SSBN 619) stricken 31-8-89 for a similar conversion, with propeller removed, cement in missile tubes. *John Adams* (SSBN 620) deactivated 14-9-88 and stricken 24-3-89. *James Monroe* (SSBN 622) deactivated 22-2-90, decommissioned 23-6-90, and was stricken 25-9-90. *Henry Clay* (SSBN 625) deactivated 12-3-90 and was stricken 5-11-90. *Nathan Hale* (SSBN 623) and *Nathanael Greene* (SSBN 636) were deactivated 5-86 as SALT II compensation when *Nevada* (SSBN 733) began sea trials; both stricken 31-1-87. SSBN 623 formally decommissioned 3-11-86 and SSBN 636 (substituted for SSBN 619, as a result of grounding damage 13-3-86) on 15-12-86; both to be scrapped. *Lafayette* (SSBN 616) deactivated 1-3-91 and was decommissioned 12-8-91 for later striking. *Daniel Webster* (SSBN 626) was inactivated on 27-4-90 and decommissioned 30-8-90. *James Madison* (SSBN 627), the first Trident-conversion SSBN to be deactivated, was deactivated 11-8-91 and decommissioned 17-2-92.

The Poseidon units ordered disarmed by President Bush included *Alexander Hamilton* (SSBN 617), *Woodrow Wilson* (SSBN 624), *Tecumseh* (SSBN 628), *Ulysses S. Grant* (SSBN 631, which began deactivation 14-2-92), *Kamehameha* (SSBN 642, to become SSN 642), *Lewis and Clark* (SSBN 644, which deactivated 1-10-91), *James K. Polk* (SSBN 645, to become SSN 645), *George C. Marshall* (SSBN 654, which deactivated 13-5-92), *George Washington Carver* (SSBN 656), and *Will Rogers* (SSBN 659). Two of these may become Moored Training Submarines, one of which was authorized under FY 90 and one of which was requested under FY 93.

James Madison (SSBN 627), the first Trident-conversion SSBN to be deactivated, was deactivated 11-8-91 and decommissioned 17-2-92. SSBN 632 and SSBN 655 are scheduled to deactivate during Fiscal Year 1993.

NUCLEAR-POWERED ATTACK SUBMARINES

♦ 0 (+ . . .) "Centurion" project

Remarks: Currently projected to enter service in 2003, the first of a new, less-expensive class of nuclear-powered attack submarines is to be requested under the Fiscal Year 1998 Budget. At present, there is no firm design, and it is possible that several different designs tailored to specific major missions may evolve, all sharing the same basic platform and propulsion plant. Proposals range from a design smaller than the SSN 688 and armed with 4 533-mm torpedo tubes (and 22 total weapons) to an 8,500-ton design with 6 to 8 torpedo tubes and up to 16 vertical missile launch tubes. The reactor is likely to be the same as that in the *Seawolf* class.

♦ 0 (+2) Seawolf ("SSN 21") class

	Bldr	Laid down	L	In serv.
SSN 21 Seawolf	Gen. Dynamics, Groton	. . .	1995	5-96
SSN	Gen. Dynamics, Groton	. . .	. . .	. . .

Authorized: SSN 21 in FY 89, SSN 22 in FY 91

D: 7,460 tons surf./9,150 tons sub. **S:** 35+ kts (sub.)
Dim: 99.37 × 12.19 × 10.94
A: 8/762-mm TT (about 50 Tomahawk and Sub-Harpoon missiles, Mk 48 ADCAP torpedoes, mines)
Electron Equipt:
Radar: BPS-16 nav.—EW: WLQ-4(V)1 suite
Sonar: G.E. BSY-2(V) suite: BQG-5D (WAA) wide-aperture passive array, BQS-24 nav./ice-avoidance, TB-12X towed array, TB-16D towed array
M: 1 G.E. S6W pressurized-water reactor, . . . drive; 1 pumpjet prop; 60,000 shp
Crew: 12 officers, 121 enlisted

Seawolf (SSN 21)—artist's rendering U.S. Navy, 1990

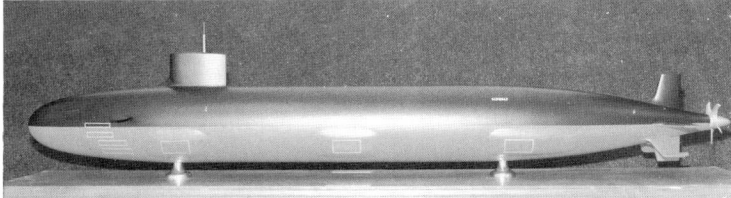

Seawolf (SSN 21)—official model; note that stern omits pumpjet shroud
PH2 Mark Therian, USN, 2-90

NUCLEAR-POWERED ATTACK SUBMARINES *(continued)*

Remarks: First unit requested under FY 89 and ordered 9-1-89. Second unit ordered 3-5-91 for $614,746,400 after intense competition between General Dynamics and Newport News SB & DD; the award was unsuccessfully contested in the courts, with General Dynamics winning on 17-3-92. The Bush administration had refused to proceed with the second unit and a third authorized under FY 92, but a compromise reached in 5-92 will allow one to be built, with the additional appropriated funds from FY 91/92 going toward possible additional construction of SSN 688I-class submarines (which is not likely to happen).

Construction of the first unit began on 25-10-89 but was interrupted in 1991 when weld cracks were discovered in the pressure hull, adding an estimated one year to the construction time and costing an additional $100 million for rework. Pressure hull constructed of HY100 steel.

Hull numbering sequence is peculiar, as U.S.N. hull numbers are by regulation to be sequential, yet SS 21 dates to 1912! Anomaly apparently came about when "SSN-21" was applied as the project title, indicating "Submarine for the 21st Century." Name *Seawolf* is *still* unofficial, but the non-traditional hull number is unfortunately to be retained. The second unit will reportedly be named for a city.

Systems: Will offer significant improvements in speed, quietness, weapons load, sonar processing, etc., over *Los Angeles* class, to continue U.S. lead over Russian submarine technology, being able to travel at up to 20 kts while silent. Designed for reliability and ease of maintenance, to operate for 15 years before first overhaul. Will be without question the world's finest nuclear submarines. To have Raytheon Mk 2 Combat Control System, Submarine Active Detection System (SADS), with bow-mounted medium-frequency active and high-frequency active sonar capability. The BQQ-5D passive sonar suite will include three flank arrays per side.

The submarine will have smaller length-to-beam ratio to improve maneuverability. Retractable bow planes and six stern fins will be carried. A small wedge at the base of the forward edge of the sail will improve hydrodynamic flow. Propeller will be of pumpjet design. Planned to carry 12 Tomahawk missiles.

A quarter-scale, 150-ton model of the SSN 21 design, named *Kokanee,* has been undergoing tests at the Naval Test Station, Bayview, Idaho, on Lake Pend Oreille.

◆ 49 (+13) Los Angeles class (SCB 303 type) (*Atlantic/†Pacific Fleet)

	Bldr	Laid down	L	In serv.
SSN 688 Los Angeles†	Newport News	8-1-72	6-4-74	13-11-76
SSN 689 Baton Rouge*	Newport News	18-11-72	18-4-75	25-6-77
SSN 690 Philadelphia*	Gen. Dynamics	12-8-72	19-10-74	25-6-77
SSN 691 Memphis*	Newport News	23-6-73	3-4-76	17-12-77
SSN 692 Omaha††	Gen. Dynamics	27-1-73	21-2-76	11-3-78
SSN 693 Cincinnati*	Newport News	6-4-74	19-2-76	10-6-78
SSN 694 Groton*	Gen. Dynamics	3-8-73	9-10-76	8-7-78
SSN 695 Birmingham*	Newport News	26-4-75	15-10-77	20-12-78
SSN 696 New York City†	Gen. Dynamics	15-12-73	18-6-77	10-3-79
SSN 697 Indianapolis†	Gen. Dynamics	19-10-74	30-7-77	5-1-80
SSN 698 Bremerton†	Gen. Dynamics	8-5-76	22-7-78	28-3-81
SSN 699 Jacksonville*	Gen. Dynamics	21-2-76	18-11-78	16-5-81
SSN 700 Dallas*	Gen. Dynamics	9-10-76	28-4-79	18-7-81
SSN 701 La Jolla†	Gen. Dynamics	16-10-76	11-8-79	24-10-81
SSN 702 Phoenix*	Gen. Dynamics	30-7-77	18-12-79	19-12-81
SSN 703 Boston*	Gen. Dynamics	11-8-78	19-4-80	30-1-82
SSN 704 Baltimore*	Gen. Dynamics	21-5-79	18-12-80	24-7-82
SSN 705 City of Corpus Christi*	Gen. Dynamics	4-9-79	25-4-81	8-1-83
SSN 706 Albuquerque*	Gen. Dynamics	27-12-79	13-3-82	21-5-83
SSN 707 Portsmouth*	Gen. Dynamics	8-5-80	18-9-82	1-10-83
SSN 708 Minneapolis-Saint Paul*	Gen. Dynamics	20-1-81	19-3-83	10-3-84
SSN 709 Hyman G. Rickover*	Gen. Dynamics	23-7-81	27-8-83	21-7-84
SSN 710 Augusta*	Gen. Dynamics	1-4-82	21-1-84	19-1-85
SSN 711 San Francisco†	Newport News	26-5-77	27-10-79	24-4-81
SSN 712 Atlanta*	Newport News	17-8-78	6-8-80	6-3-82
SSN 713 Houston†	Newport News	29-1-79	21-3-81	25-9-82
SSN 714 Norfolk*	Newport News	1-8-79	31-10-81	21-5-83
SSN 715 Buffalo†	Newport News	25-1-80	8-5-82	5-11-83
SSN 716 Salt Lake City*	Newport News	26-8-80	16-10-82	12-5-84
SSN 717 Olympia†	Newport News	31-3-81	30-4-83	17-11-84
SSN 718 Honolulu†	Newport News	10-11-81	24-9-83	6-7-85
SSN 719 Providence*	Gen. Dynamics	30-9-82	4-8-84	27-7-85
SSN 720 Pittsburgh*	Gen. Dynamics	15-4-83	8-12-84	23-11-85
SSN 721 Chicago†	Newport News	5-1-83	13-10-84	27-9-86
SSN 722 Key West*	Newport News	6-7-83	20-7-85	12-9-87
SSN 723 Oklahoma City*	Newport News	4-1-84	2-11-85	9-7-88
SSN 724 Louisville*	Gen. Dynamics	16-9-84	14-12-85	8-11-86
SSN 725 Helena†	Gen. Dynamics	28-3-85	28-6-86	11-7-87
SSN 750 Newport News*	Newport News	3-3-84	15-3-86	3-6-89
SSN 751 San Juan*	Gen. Dynamics	16-8-85	6-12-86	6-8-88
SSN 752 Pasadena†	Gen. Dynamics	20-5-86	12-9-87	11-2-89
SSN 753 Albany*	Newport News	22-4-85	13-6-87	7-4-90
SSN 754 Topeka*	Gen. Dynamics	13-5-86	23-1-88	21-10-88

	Bldr	Laid down	L	I
SSN 755 Miami*	Gen. Dynamics	24-10-86	12-11-88	
SSN 756 Scranton*	Newport News	29-8-86	3-7-89	2
SSN 757 Alexandria*	Gen. Dynamics	19-6-87	23-6-90	2
SSN 758 Asheville*	Newport News	9-1-87	28-10-89	2
SSN 759 Jefferson City†	Newport News	21-9-87	17-8-90	2
SSN 760 Annapolis*	Gen. Dynamics	15-6-88	19-5-91	1
SSN 761 Springfield	Gen. Dynamics	29-1-90	9-11-91	
SSN 762 Columbus	Gen. Dynamics	7-1-91	20-6-92	
SSN 763 Santa Fe	Gen. Dynamics	9-7-91	12-92	
SSN 764 Boise (ex-*Hartford*)	Newport News	25-8-88	23-3-91	
SSN 765 Montpelier	Newport News	19-5-89	23-8-91	
SSN 766 Charlotte	Newport News	1-90	7-92	
SSN 767 Hampton	Newport News	2-3-90	1992	
SSN 768 Hartford (ex-*Boise*)	Gen. Dynamics	2-92	. . .	
SSN 769 Toledo	Newport News	26-4-91	12-92	
SSN 770 Tucson	Newport News	20-9-91	. . .	
SSN 771 Columbia	Gen. Dynamics	8-92	. . .	
SSN 772 Greeneville	Newport News	1-92	. . .	
SSN 773 Cheyenne	Newport News	8-92	. . .	

Authorized: SSN 688 to SSN 690 in FY 70, SSN 691 to SSN 694 in F SSN 695 to SSN 700 in FY 72, SSN 701 to SSN 705 in FY 73, SSN 706 t 710 in FY 74, SSN 711 to SSN 713 in FY 75, SSN 714 to SSN 715 in F SSN 716 to SSN 718 in FY 77, SSN 719 in FY 78, SSN 720 in FY 79, SS to SSN 722 in FY 80, SSN 723 to SSN 724 in FY 81, SSN 725 and 750 82, SSN 751 to SSN 752 in FY 83, SSN 753 to SSN 755 in FY 84, SSN SSN 759 in FY 85, SSN 760 to SSN 763 in FY 86. Requested: SSN 764 t 767 in FY 87, SSN 768 to SSN 770 in FY 88, SSN 771 to SSN 772 in F SSN 773 in FY 90.

Alexandria (SSN 757) Dr. Giorgio Arra

Miami (SSN 755) Dr. Giorgio Arra

D: SSN 688–699: 6,080 tons surf./6,927 tons sub.; SSN 700–714: 6,1 tons surf./6,977 tons sub.; SSN 716–718: 6,165 tons surf./7,012 to sub.; SSN 719–750: 6,255 tons surf./7,102 tons sub.; SSN 751–77 6,300 tons surf./7,147 tons sub.; SSN 771–773: 6,330 tons surf./ 7,177 tons sub.

S: 30+ kts. (sub.) **Dim:** 109.73 × 10.06 × 9.75 (SSN 688–699)

A: SSN 719 and later: 12 Mk 36 vertical tubes for Tomahawk—all: 4/533-mm TT Mk 67 (amidships) for Tomahawk, Harpoon, Mk 4 torpedoes, etc. (22 reloads)—SSN 756 and later: mining capabilit

.EAR-POWERED ATTACK SUBMARINES *(continued)*

ville (SSN 758) Dr. Giorgio Arra, 11-91

nnati (SSN 693)—note anechoic tiles Leo Van Ginderen, 10-90

ctron Equipt:
adar: 1/BPS-15A or BPS-16 nav.
onar: 1/BQQ-5A(V)1 (SSN 616 on: BQQ-5D) suite, BQS-15 under-ice active, BQR-15 towed array with BQR-23 signal processor; SSN 710, 751 on: BSY-1 suite: same equipment plus BQG-5D WAA flank arrays
W: BRD-7 direction finder, WLR-8(V)2 intercept, WLR-10 intercept, WSQ-5 portable ELINT collection, CSA Mk 1 Mod. 2 acoustic decoy launchers
G.E. S6G pressurized-water reactor, 2 sets geared steam turbines; 1/7-bladed prop; 35,000 shp
ew: 12 officers, 115 to 127 enlisted (berths for 95 total)

rks: Were to have been four more (one in FY 90, two in FY 91, one in FY 92) but .ed due to defense cuts. Frequent proposals to continue construction in lieu of r *Seawolf*-class units or the proposed "Centurion" program are not likely to reach n, due to the lack of additional system growth possible in what is now a quarter-y-old basic design. Naval Sea Systems Command proposed spring 1992 that the ldest of the class be retired as their first refuellings come due and that new units ered at the rate of one per year until the "Centurion" class is ready for ordering under FY 98. Labor and other problems have greatly slowed program, particularly at General Dynamics Electric Boat Div., Groton; final unit may not deliver until 1996. SSN 724 and others launched Tomahawk missiles at Iraqi targets during 1-91. SSN 689 collided with a Russian Sierra-class SSN on 11-2-92; very minor damage.

Baton Rouge (SSN 689) Dr. Giorgio Arra, 9-91

Chicago (SSN 721) Vic Jeffery, R.A.N., 3-91

Newport News (SSN 750)—last unit with sail planes
Dr. Giorgio Arra, 9-91

NUCLEAR-POWERED ATTACK SUBMARINES *(continued)*

Norfolk (SSN 714) Leo Van Ginderen, 10-90

Systems: Maximum diving depth is 450 m. Described as the finest ASW platforms now afloat. Bow is of fiberglass as a streamlined cover over the spherical BQQ-5-A(V)1 sonar array. There are two SINS, to be replaced by the ESGN (Electrically Suspended Gyro Navigator). All have one Fairbanks-Morse 38D8Q diesel generator set and batteries for emergency propulsion. The BLD-1 electromagnetic interferometer was added, beginning 1985. The reactor core is expected to last 10–13 years between refuelings. SSN 694 traveled around the world submerged 4-4-80 to 8-10-80. SSN 701 was the first of the class to be equipped to launch Tomahawk missiles from the torpedo tubes, in 1983; SSN 712 first operational sub with Tomahawk, 30-11-83.

SSN 753 and 754 had partial HY100 steel pressure-hull sections to test fabrication procedures for the *Seawolf* class; the others have HY80 steel hulls.

SSN 719 and later have 12 vertical-launch tubes for Tomahawk cruise missiles, located between the forward end of the pressure hull and the spherical array for the BQQ-5 bow sonar. All carry a UYK-7 general-purpose computer and have WSC-3 satellite comms. gear. One Mk 2 optical and one Sperry Mk 18 multifunction periscope fitted.

SSN 751 and later are described as "Arctic-capable" and are referred to as the "688I" (for "Improved") class. SSN 751 and later have bow-mounted vice sail-mounted diving planes and have the first-generation BSY-1 (formerly SUBACS—Submarine Advanced Combat System) integrated sonar/weapons-control suite from I.B.M.; development problems have slowed delivery of SSN 751 on, and 751 through 755 are to be backfitted with their UYK-43 computers after completion. SSN 755 is the first unit with fully functional BSY-1. Mk 113 Mod. 10 torpedo-fire-control system originally installed in SSN 688 to SSN 699, Mk 117 in later units through SSN 750 and subsequently backfitted into SSN 688–699. Under FY 83, the Mk 117 f.c.s. was modified in many to permit launching SUBROC missiles, which were removed where carried in 1989. Harpoon began to be carried in 1978. SSN 688–718 carry 8 torpedo tube-launched Tomahawk cruise missiles, later units will have 20 (including the vertical launchers).

SSN 768 and later have improved sound quietening, additional stern fins (like *Seawolf*), and improved propulsion systems. SSN 691 redesignated as experimental submarine during 1989; one 762-mm torpedo tube to replace 2/533-mm tubes, and will test other systems for SSN 688 and SSN 21 classes (to revert to operational status in 1994 and will remain combat-capable). Will test composite hull structures, unmanned underwater vehicles, advanced sonars, hull friction reduction, etc. SSN 710 has served as trials boat for the BQG-5D(WAA) Wide Aperture Array passive sonar system since 7-87; WAA may be backfitted in other units.

♦ 1 Narwhal class (SCB 245 type)

Bldr: General Dynamics, Electric Boat Div., Groton, Connecticut (Atlantic Fleet)

	Laid down	L	In serv.
SSN 671 NARWHAL	17-1-66	9-9-67	12-7-69

D: 5,284 tons surf./5,830 tons sub. **S:** 20 kts surf./25 kts sub.
Dim: 96.0 × 11.5 × 7.9
A: 4/533-mm TT (amidships, for Mk 48 torp., Harpoon, up to 8 Tomahawk)
Electron Equipt:
Radar: BPS-15 nav.—EW: WLQ-4E "Sea Nymph" intercept suite
Sonar: BQQ-5D suite with BQS-11-series spherical hydrophone array, TB-23 towed array, BQS-14 active ice-avoidance
M: 1 G.E. S5G pressurized-water reactor, 2 sets geared steam turbines; 1 prop; 17,000 shp
Crew: 12 officers, 108 enlisted

Remarks: Authorized under Fiscal Year 1964 as prototype for a seagoing reactor designed to study the cooling of the S5G reactor by natural circulation, thus eliminating circulation pumps and their noise. In most other respects, essentially a lengthened *Sturgeon*. Original BQQ-2 sonar suite and Mk 113 Mod. 6 fire-control system replaced by Mk 117 f.c.s. and BQQ-5. Towed array housing is on starboard side of hull. Is equipped to launch acoustic decoys via Mk 1 Mod. 2 decoy launcher.

Note: The turboelectric-drive *Glenard P. Lipscomb* (SSN 685) was deactivated 22-2-90, decommissioned 10-7-90, and stricken 11-7-90.

Narwhal (SSN 671) Leo Van Ginderen, 3-87

♦ 32 Sturgeon class (SCB 188A and SCB 188M types)

(*Atlantic/† Pacific Fleet)

	Bldr	Laid down	L	In
SSN 637 STURGEON*	Gen. Dynamics	10-8-63	26-2-66	3
SSN 638 WHALE*	Gen. Dynamics	27-5-64	14-10-66	12-1
SSN 639 TAUTOG†	Ingalls SB	27-1-64	15-4-67	17
SSN 646 GRAYLING*	Portsmouth NSY	12-5-64	22-6-67	11-1
SSN 647 POGY†	New York SB	4-5-64	3-6-67	15
SSN 648 ASPRO†	Ingalls SB	23-11-64	29-11-67	20
SSN 649 SUNFISH*	Gen. Dynamics	15-1-65	14-10-66	15
SSN 650 PARGO*	Gen. Dynamics	3-6-64	17-9-66	1
SSN 652 PUFFER†	Ingalls SB	8-2-65	30-3-68	9
SSN 660 SANDLANCE*	Portsmouth NSY	15-1-65	11-11-69	25
SSN 662 GURNARD†	Mare Island NSY	22-12-64	20-5-67	6-1
SSN 663 HAMMERHEAD*	Newport News	29-11-65	14-4-67	28
SSN 666 HAWKBILL†	Mare Island NSY	12-9-66	12-4-69	4
SSN 667 BERGALL*	Gen. Dynamics	16-4-66	17-2-68	13
SSN 668 SPADEFISH*	Newport News	21-12-66	15-5-68	14
SSN 669 SEAHORSE*	Gen. Dynamics	13-8-66	15-6-68	19
SSN 670 FINBACK*	Newport News	26-6-67	7-12-68	4
SSN 672 PINTADO†	Mare Island NSY	27-10-67	16-8-69	11
SSN 673 FLYING FISH*	Gen. Dynamics	30-6-67	17-5-69	29
SSN 674 TREPANG*	Gen. Dynamics	28-10-67	27-9-69	14
SSN 675 BLUEFISH*	Gen. Dynamics	13-3-68	10-1-70	8
SSN 676 BILLFISH*	Gen. Dynamics	20-9-68	1-5-70	12
SSN 677 DRUM†	Mare Island NSY	20-8-68	23-5-70	15
SSN 678 ARCHERFISH*	Gen. Dynamics	19-6-69	16-1-71	24-
SSN 679 SILVERSIDES*	Gen. Dynamics	13-12-69	4-6-71	5
SSN 680 WILLIAM H. BATES (ex-*Redfish*)†	Ingalls SB	4-8-69	12-71	5
SSN 681 BATFISH*	Gen. Dynamics	9-2-70	9-10-71	1
SSN 682 TUNNY†	Ingalls SB	22-5-70	10-6-72	26
SSN 683 PARCHE†	Ingalls SB	10-12-70	13-1-73	17
SSN 684 CAVALLA†	Gen. Dynamics	4-6-70	19-2-72	9
SSN 686 MENDEL RIVERS*	Newport News	26-6-71	2-6-73	1
SSN 687 RICHARD B. RUSSELL†	Newport News	19-10-71	12-1-74	16

Authorized: SSN 637 to SSN 639 in FY 62, SSN 646 to SSN 653 in F SSN 660 to SSN 664 in FY 64, SSN 665 to SSN 670 in FY 65, SSN 672 t 677 in FY 66, SSN 678 to SSN 682 in FY 67, SSN 683 and SSN 684 in SSN 686 and SSN 687 in FY 69

D: 4,250 tons surf./4,780 tons sub.; SSN 678 on and 19 moderniz units: 4,460/4,960
S: 15 kts surf./30 kts sub.
Dim: 89.00 (SSN 678 on and 19 refitted units: 92.11) × 9.65 × 8.8
A: 4/533-mm TT (amidships for 19 Mk 48 torpedoes and 4/Harpoo up to 8 Tomahawk in lieu of other weapons)

Sturgeon (SSN 637) Maritime Photographi

Spadefish (SSN 668) Leo Van Ginderen

LEAR-POWERED ATTACK SUBMARINES *(continued)*

ard B. Russell (SSN 687)—with large sonar dome near stern, sail sion for "Bustle" comms buoy housing, and DSRV simulator on Dr. Giorgio Arra, 1989

rsides (SSN 679)—with Dry Deck Shelter door open Dr. Giorgio Arra, 3-92

ersides (SSN 679)—Dry Deck Shelter abaft sail Dr. Giorgio Arra, 3-92

ectron Equipt:
Radar: 1/BPS-14 or 15 nav.
Sonar: BQQ-5 with BQS-11-series spherical bow passive hydrophone array, BQS-14A active, BQR-15 towed array with BQR-23 signal processor
EW: WLQ-4E "Sea Nymph" suite, Mk 2 acoustic countermeasures launchers

: 1 Westinghouse S5W2 pressurized-water reactor, 2 sets G.E. or de Laval geared steam turbines; 1 prop; 20,000 shp

ew: 12 officers, 95 enlisted

Billfish (SSN 676)—showing towed array housing down starboard side Dr. Giorgio Arra, 11-91

Remarks: The construction contract of SSN 647 with New York Shipbuilding, Camden, N.J., was canceled in 4-6-67, and completion of the ship was given to Ingalls, Pascagoula, Miss., on 5-12-67. Class expected to serve 30 years each, but they are beginning to be retired early to save recoring expenses. SSN 668 collided with a French fishing trawler in the English Channel on 6-11-91.

Systems: The original Mk 113 torpedo-fire-control system has been replaced by Mk 117 to permit Harpoon launching. SSN 678 and later units (SCB 188M) were lengthened to permit installation of BQQ-5 sonar suite. Diving planes are each 3.5 m wide, and the sail is 6.25 m high. Maximum diving depth is about 400 m. The 70-megawatt S5W reactor plant operates at 160 kg/cm^2 and has two primary steam loops and two steam generators to supply steam to the two steam turbines. Original core life was 5,000 hours.

SSN 666, SSN 672, SSN 680, SSN 687, and others have been modified to carry a DSRV (salvage submarine), which can be launched and recovered while submerged; the after hatch is so constructed that personnel can be transferred between the two ships while submerged. Since 1978, SSN 679 and 687 have an aftward extension to the lower portion of the sail to accommodate a towed communications array.

SSN 665 conducted the initial Tomahawk missile trials. SSN 680 has a low, forward extension to the sail. Will be receiving ESGN (Electronically Suspended Gyro Navigator) in lieu of SINS. SSN 680 has the protruding sonar dome for BQR-26 at the upper, forward edge of the sail. SSN 684 modified 8-82 to 16-12-82 to accommodate Dry Deck Shelter to permit carrying 16 SEAL special forces personnel and their support equipment; by 1992, SSN 678, 679, 680, 682, and 686 had also received Dry Deck Shelter–carrying capability for combat swimmers, beginning with SSN 680, completed in 3-89.

SSN 687 conducted trials with the BQS-24 MIDAS/SADS active mine-avoidance sonar and other active sonar systems beginning in 1986. Three received anechoic hull coatings under FY 88; others to follow.

Disposals: *Queenfish* (SSN 651) deactivated 27-9-90 and decommissioned 8-11-91. *Lapon* (SSN 661) and *Guitarro* (SSN 665) deactivated 1-10-91. *Sea Devil* (SSN 664) deactivated 25-2-91. *Ray* (SSN 653) began deactivation 24-7-92.

♦ **3 Permit class** (*Atlantic/†Pacific Fleet)

	Bldr	Laid down	L	In serv.
SSN 614 Greenling*	Gen. Dynamics	15-8-61	4-4-64	3-11-67
SSN 615 Gato*	Gen. Dynamics	15-12-61	14-5-64	25-1-68
SSN 621 Haddock†	Ingalls SB	24-4-61	21-5-66	22-12-67

Authorized: SSN 614 and SSN 615 in FY 60, SSN 621 in FY 61

D: SSN 614, 615: 4,250 tons surf./4,770 tons sub.; SSN 621: 3,780 tons surf./ 4,465 tons sub.

S: 15 kts surf./30 kts sub.

Dim: SSN 614, 615: 89.10 × 9.65 × 8.80; SSN 621: 84.88 × 9.65 × 8.80

A: 4/533-mm Mk 53 TT (amidships; 4 Sub-Harpoon, . . . Mk 48-series torpedoes)

Electron Equipt:
Radar: BPS-15 nav.—EW: WLR-1 intercept
Sonar: BQQ-5 passive suite, BQS-14 active, BQR-15 towed array

Gato (SSN 615) Dr. Giorgio Arra, 1990

NUCLEAR-POWERED ATTACK SUBMARINES *(continued)*

M: 1 Westinghouse S5W reactor; 2 sets G.E. or de Laval geared steam turbines; 1 prop; 15,000 shp
Crew: 14 officers, 104–112 enlisted

Remarks: SSN 621 is the last example of the SCB 188 type, with slightly shorter hull and lower sail structure. SSN 614 and 615 are of the SCB 188M type and have longer hulls and larger sails (6.1 m long vice 4.2 or 4.6 in other ships), heavier machinery, and had safety features built in that were later backfitted in the others.

Systems: The BQQ-5 passive sonar system's spherical array is in the bow, necessitating placement of the tubes abreast the sail. These ships are fitted to carry Harpoon and received Mk 117 torpedo fire-control systems in place of Mk 113. All have received the BQQ-5 sonar suite during refits in place of their earlier BQQ-3 suites. SSN 621 ran trials in 7-79 for the Sperry PASRAN (passive-ranging) sonar system, which is similar to the exported "Micro Puffs" concept, but with an array of six larger hydrophones.

Disposals: Sister *Thresher* (SSN 593) was lost 10-4-63. *Dace* (SSN 607) deactivated 27-2-88 and stricken 30-3-89. *Pollack* (SSN 603) decommissioned 30-1-89 and stricken 1-3-89. *Plunger* (SSN 595) deactivated 10-2-89 and stricken 2-2-90. *Jack* (SSN 605), which retained her original unique contra-rotating turbines and propeller, deactivated 2-10-89 and stricken 11-7-90. *Barb* (SSN 596) deactivated and struck 20-12-89. *Permit* (SSN 594) decommissioned and struck 12-6-91. *Haddo* (SSN 604) deactivated 1-10-90. *Tinosa* (SSN 606) and *Guardfish* (SSN 612) deactivated 15-7-91. *Flasher* (SSN 613) deactivated 18-7-91.

◆ 0 (+ 2) Benjamin Franklin-class former ballistic-missile submarines

	Bldr	Laid down	L	In serv.
SSN 642 Kamehameha	Mare Isl. NSY	2-5-63	16-1-65	10-12-65
SSN 645 James K. Polk	Gen. Dynamics	23-11-63	22-5-65	16-4-66

Kamehameha (SSBN 642)—prior to conversion to SSN
Dr. Giorgio Arra, 6-90

D: 7,350 tons surf./8,250 tons sub. **S:** 15 kts surf./25 kts sub.
Dim: 129.54 × 10.05 × 9.0
A: 4/533-mm TT fwd (Mk 48 and Mk 48 ADCAP torpedoes)
Electron Equipt:
Radar: BPS-15 nav.
Sonar: BQR-7 passive, BQR-15 towed array with BQR-23 signal processor, BQR-19 nav., BQR-21 DIMUS, BQS-4 active
EW: WLR-8 intercept, WLR-10 radar warning, 8 Mk 2 countermeasures launchers
M: 1 Westinghouse SW5 pressurized-water reactor, 2 sets geared steam turbines; 1/7-bladed prop; 15,000 shp
Endurance: 68 days
Crew: 13–14 officers, 129–133 enlisted (as SSBN)

Remarks: Former Poseidon strategic ballistic-missile submarines allocated for conversion to carry two Dry Deck Shelters side by side amidships to replace the deactivated *Sam Houston* (SSN 609) and *John Marshall* (SSN 611). Will be able to carry up to 67 SEAL special forces personnel and their equipment. Each Dry Deck Shelter holds one swimmer-delivery vehicle, a decompression chamber, and an access section permitting entry while the submarine is submerged. Conversion completion dates not available.

Note: The two *Ethan Allen*-class former ballistic-missile submarines converted to carry Dry Deck Shelters in support of SEAL special forces teams have been deactivated for disposal: *Sam Houston* (SSN 609, ex-SSBN 609) deactivated 1-3-91, decommissioned 12-8-91, and was stricken 6-9-91; *John Marshall* (SSN 611, ex-SSBN 611) deactivated 14-2-92. The U.S. Navy's last diesel-powered attack submarine, *Barbel* (SS 581) was stricken 30-10-90. The *Darter*-class diesel attack submarine *Darter* (SS 576) was decommissioned 1-12-89, stricken 17-1-90, and sunk as a target 7-1-92. The research submarine *Dolphin* (AGSS 555) is described later, with auxiliary ships.

MIDGET SUBMARINES

Some 15 miniature Swimmer-Delivery Vehicle (SDV) submersibles are used by navy SEAL special forces. The smallest are modified Mk 37 torpedoes and the largest, which can be accommodated in the new Dry Deck Shelters carried by SSNs, can carry six swimmers, as well as mines and other weapons. Three EX-8 Mod. 1 SDVs were ordered 12-90 from Unisys. Ten new SDV are to be delivered 1998–2003 for use by eight-man SEAL squads.

A new type of Autonomous Underwater Vehicle (AUV) is being developed for submarine decoy, ASW, and mine-countermeasure purposes. Under the proposed program, 78 would be acquired as decoys for SSBNs, 204 for carriage by SSNs, and 97 for use by surface ships. A titanium-hulled Navy/DARPA prototype delivered in 1992 is 1[illegible] long by 1.12-m diameter and is controlled by fiber-optic cable.

BATTLESHIPS

◆ 4 Iowa class (In reserve)

Bldrs: BB 61, 63: New York Naval Shipya[rd], Brooklyn; BB 62, 64: Philadelphia Naval Shipyard

	Laid down	L	In serv.	Recomm.	Dec[omm.]
BB 61 *Iowa*	27-6-40	27-8-42	22-2-43	28-4-84	26-
BB 62 *New Jersey*	16-9-40	7-12-42	23-5-43	28-12-82	8
BB 63 *Missouri*	6-1-41	29-1-44	11-6-44	10-5-86	31
BB 64 *Wisconsin*	25-1-41	7-12-43	16-4-44	22-10-88	3C

Wisconsin (BB 64)—with drone control antenna radome atop after [mast], SPQ-9A radome on forward tower platform Dr. Giorgio Arra

Wisconsin (BB 64) Dr. Giorgio Arr[a]

Missouri (BB 63) Dr. Giorgio Arra,

D: 46,324 tons light (57,500 fl) **S:** 33+ kts (30.5 sust.)
Dim: 270.43 (262.13 pp) × 32.97 × 11.60
A: 32/Tomahawk SSM (IV × 8 Mk 143 launchers)—16 Harpoon S[SM] (IV × 4)—9/406-mm 50-cal. Model 1936 (III × 3)—12/127-mm Mk 12 Mod. 1 DP (II Mk 32 × 6)—4/20-mm Mk 15 Mod. 0 (BB [6?] Mod. 1) CIWS gatling AA (I × 4)—8/12.7-mm mg (I × 8)
Electron Equipt:
Radar: 1/SPS-64(V)9 nav., 1/SPS-67(V) surf. search, 1/SPS-49(V) air search, 1/SPQ-9A gun f.c., 2/Mk 13 gun f.c., 1/SPG-5[3] gun f.c., 3/Mk 25 gun f.c.
EW: SLQ-32(V)3 (BB 64: SLQ-32(V)4 with Sidekick jammer), M[k 36] SRBOC decoy RL (VI × 8), SLQ-25 towed torpedo decoy
TACAN: URN-25
M: 4 sets G.E. (BB 62, 64: Westinghouse) geared steam turbines; 4 props; 212,000 shp
Boilers: 8 Babcock & Wilcox; 44.6 kg/cm², 454°C
Electric: 10,500 kw **Range:** 5,000/30; 14,800/20 **Fuel:** 8,800 t
Crew: 65 officers, 1,453 enlisted + 2 marine officers, 42 enlisted

Remarks: BB 62, reactivated 6-4-68 for Vietnam service and decommissioned 17-12-69, was towed from the Bremerton, Washington, mothball facility on 2[illegible] arriving 8-8-81 at Long Beach Naval Shipyard. Congress voted $326 mil. under [illegible] to modernize the ship with new radars and gear, Tomahawk and Harpoon missiles, upgraded communications gear (including the WSC-3 SATCOMM sy[stem]), seven new 125-ton/hr. air-conditioning plants, provision for Link-11 data link ([illegible] NTDS), and conversion of the boilers to burn distillate fuel (which cut endura[nce] approx. 10 percent). Funds were authorized in FY 82 for work on BB 61 at Avond[ale]

'LESHIPS *(continued)*

rleans, and Ingalls, Pascagoula. BB 63, towed to Long Beach Naval SY, began ation 1-10-84. Funds to reactivate BB 64 were authorized under FY 86, with) take place 10-86 to 8-88 at Ingalls, Pascagoula. The reactivated ships were d to be the focal points of autonomous battle groups, augmenting carrier forces ying out independent assignments. An unexplained turret explosion killed 47 BB 61's No. 2 turret on 19-4-89; the turret was not repaired.

ships have been decommissioned to reserve because of the expense of operating leaving the U.S. Navy without a significant shore bombardment capability, the excellent work carried out by the ships in the Persian Gulf in 1991.

ems: The helicopter facilities include increased parking area to accommodate our helicopters, but there is no hangar; some maintenance facilities, a control l tankage, and a glide-path indicator were added. The Tomahawk missiles are t elevating armored box launchers, while the Harpoons are placed abreast the ack in the standard fixed four-missile canister arrangement. BB 62 successfully ed her first land-attack Tomahawk on 10-5-83.

The 406-mm guns are controlled by two Mk 38 radar (Mk 13) GFCS and one Mk 40 director, while four Mk 37 GFCS were retained for the 127-mm guns. BB 62's six Mk 56 AA GFCS were replaced by the Vulcan/Phalanx (Mk 15 CIWS) gatling guns and eight Super RBOC launchers. While in reserve, BB 61 retained six Mk 56 and two Mk 63 GFCS, and BB 63 had six Mk 57 and two Mk 63 GFCS; BB 64 had all light AA GFCS removed when decommissioned in 1958. SPQ-9 surface fire-control radars (normally a component of the Mk 86 GFCS) were added during 1989. Received SPG-53E fire-control radars atop their forward Mk 37 gun directors (in place of Mk 25) for use with 406-mm shell tracking. The ships use WRN-5A NAVSAT for positioning during bombardments, as part of the Mk 160 Mod. 5 Naval Surface Fire Support System.

BB 61 deployed 1-87 with five AAI/Mazlat Pioneer surveillance drones and a control system with antenna mounted in a radome atop the after stack; the drones were launched and recovered from the helo deck, using a net landing system. Although initially unsuccessful, drone control systems for artillery spotting were eventually fitted to all four and proved highly successful during 1991 Persian Gulf operations. Prior to decommissioning, BB 64 mounted the Sperry 25-kw, X-band RASCAR (Raster-Scan Collision Avoidance Radar) for trials. At least one of the ships was equipped with the McDonnell Douglas mast-mounted optronic surveillance system.

(BB 61) PH2 Michael Skeens, USN, 8-89

ouri (BB 63) Dr. Giorgio Arra, 10-91

BATTLESHIPS *(continued)*

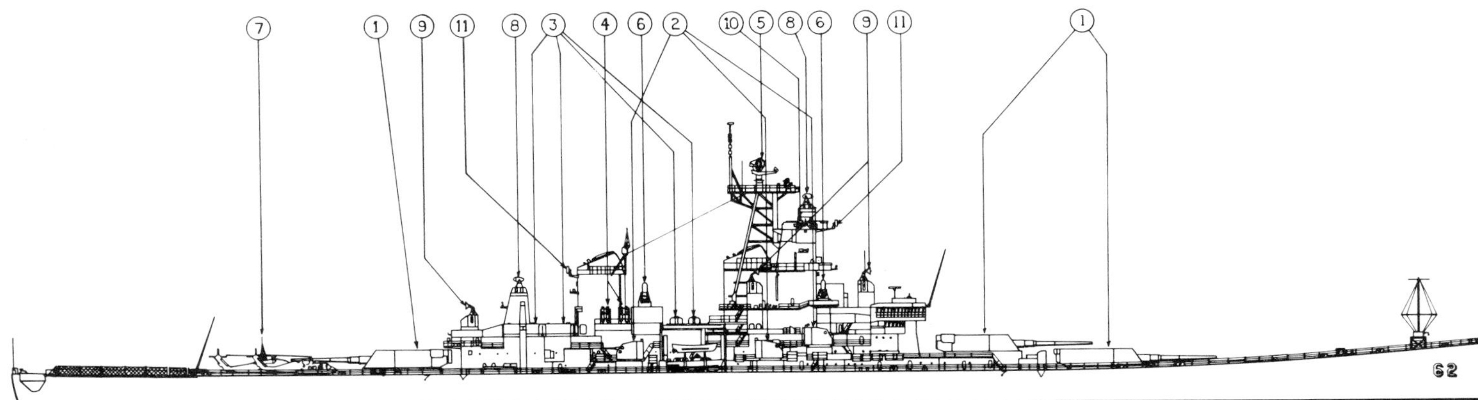

New Jersey (BB 62) 1. 405-mm triple turret 2. 127-mm twin DP 3. Tomahawk Mk 143 box-launcher 4. Harpoon canisters 5. SPS-4 radar 6. 20-mm Mk 15 CIWS 7. helicopter parking area, forward of helo platform 8. Mk 38 gunfire-control system director with Mk 8 radar 9. gunfire-control system, with Mk 25 radar (SPG-53 on forward director) 10. SLQ-32(V)3 EW antenna 11. OE-82 antenna for WSC-3 SATCOMM syst. 1 drawing omits drone-control antenna radome atop after stack and SPQ-9A fire-control radar radome above upper bridge on forward tower mast.) A. D. Ba

During Mideast service in 1991, BB 63 and 64 were each fitted with two 25-mm Mk 88 "Bushmaster" gun mounts and carried Stinger point-defense SAMs.
Armor: Belt: 307 mm, tapering to 41 mm (343 mm abreast prop shafts); main turrets: 432-mm face/184-mm top/305-mm back; barbettes: 295 mm max.; decks: 3 armored (152-mm second deck); conning tower: 440 mm (184-mm top).

Missouri (BB 63)—amidships detail Dr. Giorgio Arra, 10-91

NUCLEAR-POWERED GUIDED-MISSILE CRUISERS

◆ **4 Virginia class** Bldr: Newport News SB & DD (*Atlantic/†Pacific Fleet)

	Program	Laid down	L	In serv.
CGN 38 Virginia*	FY 70	19-8-72	14-12-74	11-9-76
CGN 39 Texas†	FY 71	18-8-73	9-8-75	10-9-77
CGN 40 Mississippi*	FY 72	22-2-75	31-7-76	5-8-78
CGN 41 Arkansas†	FY 75	17-1-77	21-10-78	18-10-80

D: 10,400 tons light (11,300 fl) **S:** 30+ kts
Dim: 177.3 × 19.2 × 9.6 sonar (7.4 hull)

Mississippi (CGN 40)—with SPS-49(V)5 radar Dr. Giorgio Arra, 3-91

Virginia (CGN 38)—note no helicopter landing area, box-launche Tomahawk just forward of VERTREP area at stern French Navy

Arkansas (CGN 41) LSPH S. Conolly, R.A.N.,

A: 8/Tomahawk SSM (IV × 2 Mk 143 launchers)—8/Harpoon SS (IV × 2)—2/Mk 26 twin launchers (II × 2; 68 total Standard S MR Block 2 SAM and ASROC ASW missiles)—2/127-mm 54-ca Mk 45 DP (I × 2)—2/20-mm Mk 15 CIWS gatling AA (I × 2)—4/12.7-mm mg (I × 4)—6/324-mm Mk 32 ASW TT (III × 2, Mk Mod. 5 torpedoes)

Electron Equipt:

Radar: 1/SPS-64(V)9 nav., 1/SPS-55 surf. search, 1/SPS-49(V)5 (CGN 38: SPS-40B) air search, 1/SPS-48C or E 3-D air search, 2/SPG-51D, 1/SPQ-9A gun f.c., 1/SPG-60D gun/missile f.c.

Sonar: SQS-53A bow-mounted LF—TACAN: URN-25

EW: SLQ-32(V)3, SSQ-108, Mk 36 SRBOC decoy RL (VI × 4), S 25 Nixie towed torpedo decoys

M: 2 G.E. D2G pressurized-water reactors, 2 sets geared turbines; props; 70,000 shp

Crew: 38–45 officers, 520–579 enlisted

Remarks: These ships are expected to operate for ten years on each nuclear f

.EAR-POWERED GUIDED-MISSILE CRUISERS *(continued)*

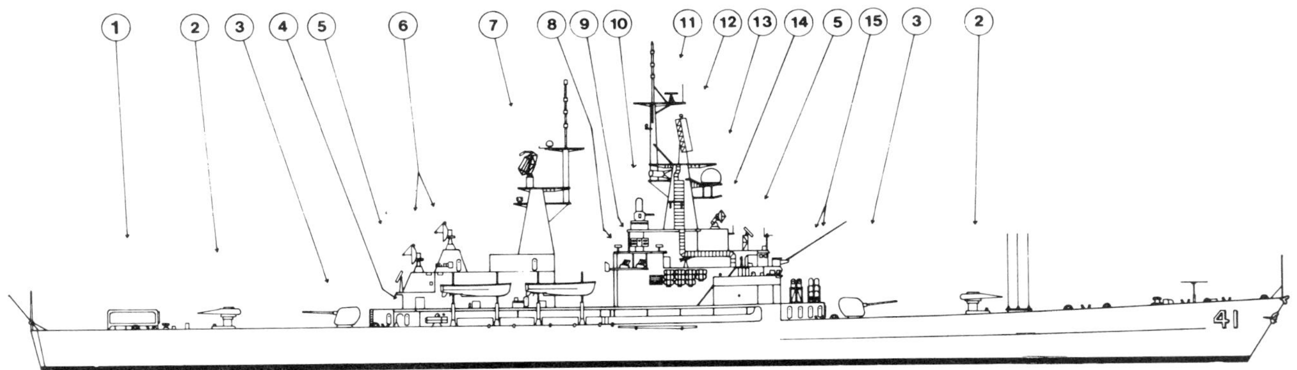

Arkansas (CGN 41) 1. Tomahawk Mk 143 quadruple armored box-launchers 2. Mk 26 twin missile launchers 3. 127-mm Mk 45 DP 4. Mk 32 triple ASW TT 5. OE-82 antenna for WSC-3 SATCOMM system 6. SPG-51D radar missile illuminators 7. SPS-40B radar (now replaced by SPS-49(V)5) 8. Mk 36 SRBOC decoy rocket-launch system (Mk 137 sextuple launchers) 9. SLQ-32(V)3 EW antennas 10. 20-mm Mk 15 CIWS 11. SPS-55 surface-search radar 12. SPS-48E 3-D air-search radar 13. SPQ-9A surface-gunfire radar director 14. SPG-60D missile/gun-control radar 15. Harpoon antiship missiles Robert Dumas

ssippi (CGN 40) Dr. Giorgio Arra, 3-91

) began refueling and electronics modernization 4-92, and CGN 38 will follow in ne Mk 74 SAM control system will be updated, the missile directors brought up -51D standard, and the SYS-2(V)2 Integrated Automatic Detection and Track will be incorporated. CGN 38 collided with a Greek fishing boat 23-1-91.

ems: The original Standard SM-1 MR antiaircraft missiles, stowed vertically, een replaced by SM-2 MR, and the ships have had the "New Threat Upgrade" system improvements installed. CGN 40 was the first to have the SPS-40B rch radar replaced by SPS-49(V)5, followed by CGN 41 and 39; it was still aboard 8 in 1991. SPS-48E is replacing the SPS-48A or C versions previously aboard; it anged on CGN 40 during her 20-5-91 to 8-92 overhaul.

arry eight Tomahawk cruise missiles in two armored box-launchers at the stern of the original helicopter facility (which had a below-decks hangar); helicopters longer land aboard. The Tomahawk missiles are launched by the SWG-2 ns Control System. Harpoon missile launch is controlled by the SWG-1 Weapons l System.

ave SRR-1, WSC-3, and USC-38 SATCOMM equipment and NTDS data system ata links LINK 4A, 11, and 14). ASW weapons control is Mk 116, and the GFCS 86 Mod. 5. Kevlar plastic armor was added over vital topside and magazine during sequential overhauls scheduled from FY 82 to FY 86. Mk 15 CIWS added 5-level platform, with the SLQ-32(V)3 arrays being moved down to the platform lly intended for the guns; this prevents electronic interference. During Mideast in 1991, CGN 41 carried two 25-mm Mk 88 "Bushmaster" gun mounts.

◆ **2 California class (SCB 241.65 type)** Bldr: Newport News SB & DD
(*Atlantic/†Pacific Fleet)

	Program	Laid down	L	In serv.
CGN 36 California†	FY 67	23-1-70	22-9-71	16-2-74
CGN 37 South Carolina*	FY 68	1-12-70	1-7-72	25-1-75

D: 9,676 tons light (10,530 fl) **S:** 30+ kts
Dim: 181.66 × 18.6 × 9.6 (sonar: 7.4 hull)
A: 8/Harpoon SSM (IV × 2)—2/Mk 13 single launchers (I × 2; 80 Standard SM-1 MR missiles)—2/127-mm 54-cal. Mk 45 DP (I × 2)—2/20-mm Mk 15 CIWS AA (I × 2)—4/12.7-mm mg (I × 4)— 1/Mk 16 Mod. 1 ASROC ASW RL (VIII × 1)— 4/324-mm Mk 32 ASW TT (II × 2, fixed)
Electron Equipt:
Radar: 1/SPS-64(V)9 nav., 1/SPS-67(V) surf. search, 1/SPS-40B air search, 1/SPS-48C 3-D air search, 4/SPG-51D missile f.c., 1/SPQ-9A gun f.c., 1/SPG-60 missile/gun f.c.
Sonar: SQS-26CX bow-mounted LF—TACAN: URN-25
EW: SLQ-32(V)3, SLQ-34, Mk 36 SRBOC decoy RL (VI × 4), T-Mk 6 Fanfare towed torpedo decoy

South Carolina (CGN 37) George Nassiopoulos, 5-91

.h Carolina (CGN 37) Dr. Giorgio Arra, 3-91

NUCLEAR-POWERED GUIDED-MISSILE CRUISERS *(continued)*

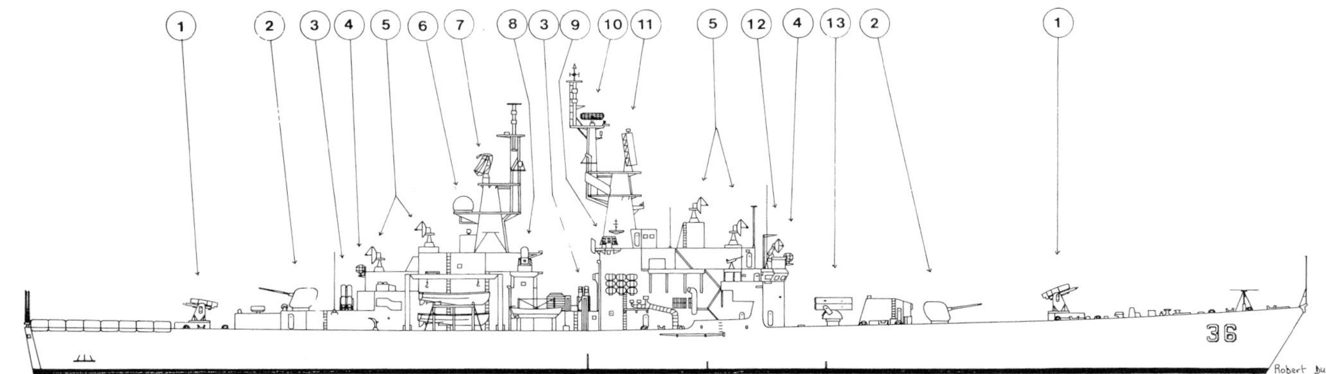

California (CGN 36) 1. Mk 13 single-arm launcher for Standard SM-1 MR SAM 2. 127-mm Mk 45 DP 3. Harpoon canister launchers 4. OE-82 antennas for WSC-3 UHF SATCOMM 5. SPG-51D radar director/illuminators 6. SPQ-9A surface-gunnery direction radar 7. SPS-40B air-search radar 8. 20-mm Mk 15 CIWS 9. SLQ-32(V)3 EW antennas 10. SPS-67(V) surface-search radar 11. SPS-48C 3-D search radar 12. SPG-60 missile/gun radar director/illuminator 13. Mk 16 Mod.1 octuple ASROC ASW missile launcher Robert Dumas

M: 2 G.E. D2G pressurized-water reactors, 2 sets geared turbines; 2 props; 70,000 shp
Crew: 44 officers, 559 enlisted

Remarks: Each Mk 13 launcher magazine holds 40 vertically stowed missiles, and the ASROC system includes automatic reloading from a magazine on deck, forward of the launcher. Helicopter platform but no hangar. Weapons are controlled by the Mk 11 Mod. 3 direction system, handling two Mk 74 Mod. 2 missile fire-control systems and Mk 86 Mod. 3 gunfire-control system. ASW fire is controlled by a Mk 114 system. Both have WSC-3 SATCOMM and NTDS data system. Kevlar plastic armor added over vital spaces. Both were to have received the NTU (New Threat Upgrade) modernization during FY 89 and FY 90, respectively, but this appears not to have been done; SPS-49(V) is to replace SPS-40B, SPS-48E the SPS-48C, and the weapons control system is to be modernized.

♦ **1 Truxtun class (SCB 222 type)** Bldr: New York SB, Camden, N.J. (Pacific Fleet)

	Program	Laid down	L	In serv.
CGN 35 Truxtun	FY 62	17-6-63	19-12-64	27-5-67

D: 8,322 tons light (9,127 fl) **S:** 30+ kts
Dim: 171.91 × 17.67 × 9.5 (sonar, 7.3 hull)
A: 8/Harpoon (IV × 2)—1/Mk 10 twin launcher (II × 1, for 40 Standard SM-2 ER Block 1 and 20 ASROC missiles)—1/127-mm 54-cal. Mk 42 DP—2/20-mm Mk 15 CIWS AA (I × 2)—4/12.7-mm mg (I × 4)—4/324-mm Mk 32 ASW TT (II × 2)—1/SH-2F LAMPS-I ASW helicopter
Electron Equipt:
Radar: 1/LN-66, 1/SPS-67(V) surf. search, 1/SPS-40D air search, 1/SPS-48C 3-D air search, 2/SPG-55C missile f.c., 1/SPG-gun/missile f.c.
Sonar: SQS-26AXR bow-mounted LF—TACAN: URN-25
EW: WLR-1H intercept, SLQ-32(V)3 active/passive, SSQ-72 intercept, Mk 36 SRBOC decoy RL (VI × 4), SLQ-25 towed torpedo decoy
M: 2 G.E. D2G pressurized-water reactors, 2 sets geared turbines; 2 props; 70,000 shp
Electric: 14,500 kw
Crew: 39 officers, 522 enlisted + flag staff: 6 officers, 12 enlisted

Remarks: During 4-10-82 to 4-84 overhaul, received two Vulcan/Phalanx M CIWS 20-mm AA, new TACAN, and EW suite. Eight Harpoon SSM (IV × 2) rep 2/76.2-mm DP in 1980. Two Mk 25 torpedo tubes at stern removed. The magazi 3/20-missile horizontal drums. Mk 76 Mod. 6 missile-control system. Mk 68 fire-c system for the 127-mm gun. Has Mk 14 weapon-direction system. WSC-3 SATC and NTDS data system. Mk 114 ASW fire-control system. The fixed Mk 32 ASW T mounted within the superstructure. Plans to decommission the ship during FY 9 money-saving measure were deferred.

Truxtun (CGN 35) G. Salmeri, R.A.N.

ˌEAR-POWERED GUIDED-MISSILE CRUISERS *(continued)*

ʒainbridge class

ɫr: Bethlehem Steel, Quincy, Mass. (Atlantic Fleet)

	Program	Laid down	L	In serv.
25 BAINBRIDGE	FY 59	15-5-59	15-4-61	6-10-62

ɓridge (CGN 25) James W. Goss/NAVPIC, 9-90

ɓridge (CGN 25) Leo Van Ginderen, 9-90

8,000 tons light (9,100 fl) **S:** 30+ kts
n: 172.21 (167.65 wl) × 17.57 × 9.5 (sonar, 7.7 hull)
8/Harpoon SSM (IV × 2)—2/Mk 10 twin launchers (II × 2; 80 Standard SM-2 ER missiles)—2/20-mm Mk 15 CIWS gatling AA (I × 2)—4/12.7-mm mg (I × 4)—1/Mk 16 Mod. 1 ASROC ASW RL (VIII × 1)—6/324-mm Mk 32 ASW TT (III × 2)
ectron Equipt:
ʀadar: 1/SPS-64(V)9 nav., 1/SPS-67(V) surf. search, 1/SPS-49(V)5 air search, 1/SPS-48C 3-D air search, , 4/SPG-55C missile f.c.
ʃonar: SQQ-23 PAIR bow-mounted—TACAN: URN-25
ɛW: SLQ-32(V)3 active/passive, Mk 36 SRBOC decoy RL (VI × 6), T.Mk 6 Fanfare towed torpedo decoy
2 G.E. D2G reactors, 2 sets geared turbines; 2 props; 70,000 shp
ectric: 14,500 kw
ew: 42 officers, 506 enlisted + flag staff: 6 officers, 12 enlisted

ırks: In refit-modernization at Puget Sound NSY from 30-6-74 to 24-9-76 to ɒve AAW; refit completed at San Diego in 4-77. Obsolete 76.2-mm DP removed, ɔrarily replaced by two 20-mm AA, 1978–79. Two quadruple Harpoon canister h groups replaced the 20-mm AA during 1979, those to port firing forward and to starboard firing aft. Large deckhouse added aft to house NTDS combat data m. Two Mk 15 Vulcan/Phalanx 20-mm AA added during 10-83 to 4-85 refit; ʒ7 replaced by SPS-49, SLQ-32(V)3 ECM/ESM and Mk 36 RBOC chaff-flare m added and missile system given the New Threat Upgrade to handle the Stan- SM-2 ER SAM. Helicopter platform but no hangar. Mk 111 ASW fire-control m, two Mk 76 missile fire-control systems. Mk 14 weapon-direction system. In ɪtic Fleet since 8-85. To decommission during FY 94 and be maintained in reserve.

Long Beach class (SCB 169 type)

ɫdr: Bethlehem Steel, Quincy, Mass. (Pacific Fleet)

	Program	Laid down	L	In serv.
9 LONG BEACH	FY 57	2-12-57	14-7-59	9-9-61

15,540 tons light (17,525 fl) **S:** 30.5 kts
m: 219.75 × 22.35 × 9.50 (over sonar)
8/Tomahawk SSM (IV × 2 Mk 143 launchers)—8/Harpoon SSM (IV × 2)—1/Mk 10 Mod. 0 and 1/Mk 10 Mod. 1 twin launchers (II × 2, 120 Standard SM-2 ER missiles)—2/127-mm 38-cal. Mk 30 Mod. 90 DP (I × 2)—1/Mk 16 Mod. 1 ASROC ASW RL (VIII × 1)—2/20-mm Mk 15 CIWS AA (I × 2)—6/324-mm ASW TT (III × 2)
ectron Equipt:
Radar: 1/LN-66 nav., 1/SPS-67(V) surf. search, 1/SPS-49(V)5 air search, 1/SPS-48C 3-D air search, 4/SPG-55D missile f.c., 2/Mk 35 gun f.c.
Sonar: SQQ-23 PAIR (single-dome) hull-mounted LF
TACAN: URN-25
EW: SLQ-32(V)3 active/passive, SSQ-108 "Outboard" intercept, Mk 36 SRBOC decoy RL (VI × 4), SLQ-25 Nixie towed torpedo decoy system
M: 2 Westinghouse C1W pressurized-water reactors, 8 Foster-Wheeler heat exchangers, 2 sets G.E. geared turbines; 2 props; 80,000 shp
Electric: 17,000 kw
Crew: 65 officers, 593 enlisted + flag staff: 10 officers, 58 enlisted + 1 marine officer, 47 enlisted

Long Beach (CGN 9) PH2 J. Elliot, USN, 11-87

Long Beach (CGN 9) Dr. Giorgio Arra, 1986

Remarks: The first U.S. surface ship to have nuclear propulsion. Original hull number was CLGN 160, then CGN 160. Originally intended to carry Regulus-II cruise missiles and eight Polaris ballistic missiles. Under FY 77, Congress appropriated long-lead funds to equip the ship with Aegis radar/fire-control system, since it was planned to operate the ship into the twenty-first century; the radical modernization plans were, however, canceled in 12-76. Planned to be decommissioned during FY 94 and will probably be scrapped.

Long Beach was modernized at Puget Sound NSY 6-10-80 to 26-3-83: the Mk 12 launch system aft for the Talos missile system (deactivated in 1978) was stripped out in 1979, and the pedestals on the after superstructure that formerly supported SPG-49B Talos missile-direction radars were used to carry the two Mk 15 CIWS (Vulcan/Phalanx) gatling AA guns. Harpoon canister clusters, arranged to fire athwartships, were situated abaft the superstructure, which is surmounted by a tall lattice mast to support the antenna for the SPS-49 air-search radar. The SPS-32 and SPS-33 "billboard" fixed-array antennas on the blockhouse-style forward superstructure were removed, and the forward superstructure received 44-mm aluminum armor. Radar foundations and waveguides also were armored. SPS-48C replaced SPS-12 on the foremast. The obsolescent Mk 30, 127-mm, dual-purpose guns (the last such mounts on an active U.S. Navy ship) and their two equally aged Mk 56 directors (with Mk 35 radars) were retained, as were the original ASW weapons and the forward missile-launching arrangements. No helicopter hangar was provided, only a pad on the stern.

NUCLEAR-POWERED GUIDED-MISSILE CRUISERS *(continued)*

Long Beach (CGN 9) Stefan Terzibaschitsch, 11-88

The Mk 10 Mod. 0 launcher for Standard missiles has two magazine drums, each holding 20 missiles; the Mk 10 Mod. 1 in the upper position has four magazine drums. Standard SM-2 ER has been substituted for SM-1 ER. Extensive satellite-communications facilities, including SRR-1, WSC-3, and USC-38, are provided. Armored box-launchers for Tomahawk SSM replaced the Harpoon SSMs on the stern in 1985; the Harpoon canister launchers were relocated atop the after superstructure. Has SWG-1 launch-control system for the Harpoon missiles and SWG-2 for the Tomahawks. SYS-1 Automated Data Tracking is provided, and the ship has LINK 4A, 11, and 14 data links.

GUIDED-MISSILE CRUISERS

◆ **23 (+ 4) Ticonderoga class** Bldrs: A: Ingalls SB, Pascagoula, Mississippi; B: Bath Iron Works, Bath, Maine (*Atlantic/†Pacific Fleet)

	Bldr	Laid down	L	In serv.
CG 47 Ticonderoga*	A	21-1-80	25-4-81	22-1-83
CG 48 Yorktown*	A	19-10-81	17-1-83	4-7-84
CG 49 Vincennes†	A	20-10-82	14-1-84	6-7-85
CG 50 Valley Forge*	A	14-4-83	23-6-84	11-1-86
CG 51 Thomas S. Gates†	B	31-8-84	14-12-85	22-8-87
CG 52 Bunker Hill†	A	11-1-84	11-3-85	20-9-86
CG 53 Mobile Bay	A	6-6-84	22-8-85	21-2-87
CG 54 Antietam†	A	15-11-84	14-2-86	6-6-87
CG 55 Leyte Gulf*	A	18-3-85	20-6-86	26-9-87
CG 56 San Jacinto*	A	22-7-85	14-11-86	23-1-88
CG 57 Lake Champlain†	A	3-3-86	3-4-87	12-8-88
CG 58 Philippine Sea*	B	8-5-86	25-4-87	18-3-89
CG 59 Princeton†	A	15-10-86	2-10-87	11-2-89
CG 60 Normandy*	B	7-4-87	19-3-88	9-12-89
CG 61 Monterey†	B	19-8-87	22-10-88	16-6-90
CG 62 Chancellorsville†	A	24-6-87	15-7-88	4-11-89
CG 63 Cowpens†	B	23-12-87	11-3-89	9-3-91
CG 64 Gettysburg*	B	17-8-88	22-7-89	22-6-91
CG 65 Chosin (ex-*Shiloh*)†	A	22-7-88	1-9-89	12-1-91
CG 66 Hue City (ex-*Chosin*)*	A	20-2-89	1-6-90	14-9-91
CG 67 Shiloh†	B	1-8-89	14-7-90	18-7-92
CG 68 Anzio*	A	21-8-89	2-11-90	2-5-92
CG 69 Vicksburg (ex-*Port Royal*)*	A	30-5-90	2-8-91	14-11-92
CG 70 Lake Erie†	B	14-3-90	13-7-91	3-93
CG 71 Cape St. George*	A	19-11-90	10-1-92	4-93
CG 72 Vella Gulf*	A	22-4-91	30-5-92	9-93
CG 73 Port Royal†	A	14-10-91	11-92	2-94

Authorized: CG 47 in FY 78, CG 48 in FY 80, CG 49, 50 in FY 81, CG 51–53 in FY 82, CG 54–56 in FY 83, CG 57–59 in FY 84, CG 60–62 in FY 85, CG 63–65 in FY 86; CG 66–68 in FY 87, CG 69–73 in FY 88

D: CG 47, 48: 7,019 tons light (9,589 fl); CG 49, 50: 7,014 light (9,407 fl); CG 52 and later: 8,910 tons std. (9,466 fl)
S: 30+ kts **Dim:** 172.46 (162.36 wl) × 16.76 × 6.55 (9.60 over sonar)
A: CG 47–51: 2/Mk 26 Mod. 1 twin launchers (II × 2; 68 Standard SM-2 MR and 20 ASROC)—8/Harpoon SSM (IV × 2)—2/127-mm 54-cal. Mk 45 Mod. 0 DP (I × 2)—2/20-mm Mk 15

Chancellorsville (CG 62)—Baseline 3 with vertical missile lau
Dr. Giorgio Arra

San Jacinto (CG 56)—Baseline 2 ship Dr. Giorgio Arra

Thomas S. Gates (CG 51)—Baseline 1 ship with Mk 26 launchers
Dr. Giorgio Arra

CIWS AA (I × 2)—4/12.7-mm mg (I × 4)—6/324-mm Mk ASW TT (III × 2)—1 or 2/SH-60B LAMPS-III ASW helico (CG 47, 48: SH-2F LAMPS-I)
CG 52–73: 2/Mk 41 Mod. 0 vertical launch groups (122 missile Standard SM-2 MR Block 2 or 3 or Tomahawk)—2/127-mm 54-cal. Mk 45 Mod. 1 DP (I × 2)—2/20-mm Mk 15 CIWS A (I × 2)—4/12.7-mm mg (I × IV)—6/324-mm Mk 32 Mod. 1 ASW TT (III × 2)—1 or 2/SH-60B LAMPS-III ASW helico

Electron Equipt:
Radar: 1/SPS-64(V)9 nav., 1/SPS-55 surf. search, 1/SPS-49(V)6 search, 1/SPY-1A (CG 59–73: SPY-1B) 3-D air search/f.c 4/SPG-62 illuminators, 1/SPQ-9A gun surface f.c.
Sonar: CG 47–53: SQS-53A bow-mounted LF; CG 54, 55: SQQ-89(V)3 suite (SQS-53A and SQR-19 towed array); CG 56– SQQ-89(V)3 suite (SQS-53B and SQR-19); CG 68–73: SQ 89(V). . . suite (SQS-53C and SQR-19)
EW: SLQ-32(V)3 active/passive, Mk 36 SRBOC decoy RL(VI × 6), SLQ-25 Nixie towed torpedo decoy system
TACAN: URN-25—IFF: UPX-29 interrogator

M: 4 G.E. LM-2500 gas turbines; 2/5-bladed CP props; 86,000 shp (80,000 normal)
Electric: 7,500 kw (3 × 2,500-kw gas turbine sets)
Range: 6,000/20 **Fuel:** 2,000 tons
Crew: 33 officers, 327 enlisted (CG 54: 37 officers, 372 enlisted; C 37 officers, 368 enlisted; CG 60: 30 officers, 344 enlisted)

)ED-MISSILE CRUISERS *(continued)*

ISEURS LANCE-MISSILES *(suite)*

Ticonderoga *(suite)*

ıderoga
G 47)

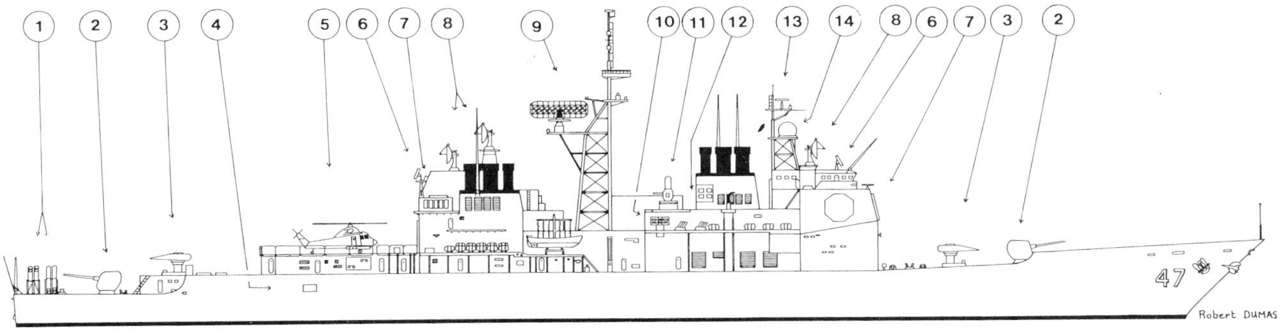

ennes
; 49)

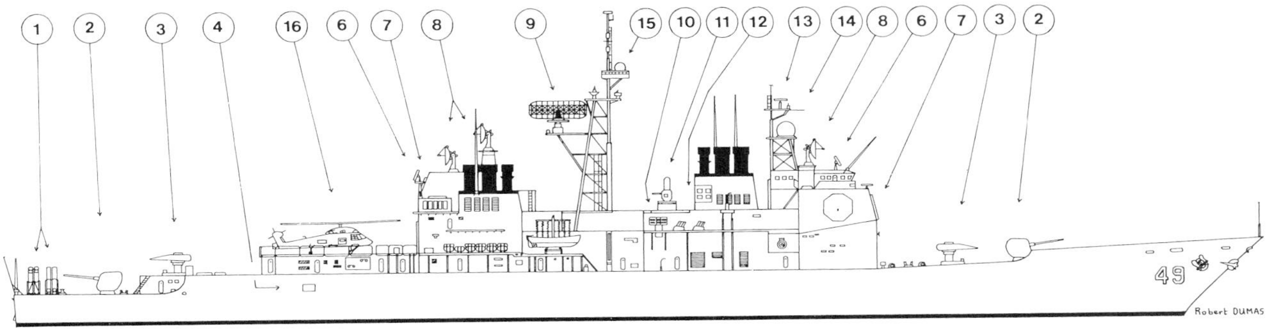

ker Hill
;G 52)

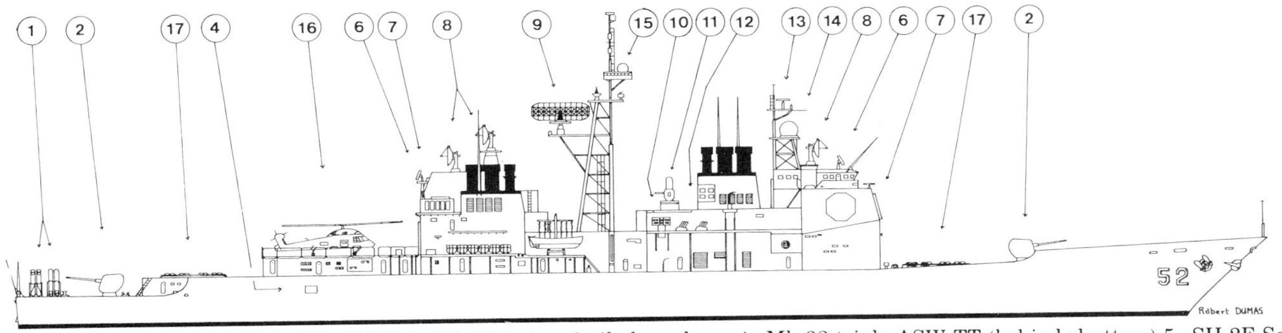

ırpoon quadruple canister launchers 2. 127-mm Mk 45 DP 3. Mk 26 twin missile launcher 4. Mk 32 triple ASW TT (behind shutters) 5. SH-2F Sea e LAMPS-I ASW helicopter 6. OE-82 antenna for WSC-3 UHF SATCOMM 7. SPY-1A radar fixed antenna arrays 8. SPG-62 radar ›inators 9. SPS-49(V)6 air-search radar 10. SLQ-32(V)3 EW antennas 11. 20-mm Mk 15 CIWS 12. Mk 36 SRBOC decoy RL(sextuple Mk 137 ›hers) 13. SPS-55 surface-search radar 14. SPQ-9A surface-gun control radar 15. SPS-64(V)9 navigational radar 16. SH-60B Seahawk LAMPS-III helicopter 17. Mk 41 vertical missile launcher groups

Robert Dumas

City (CG 66)—Baseline 4 ship with later computers

Ingalls SB, 9-91

Leyte Gulf (CG 55)—Baseline 2 ship

Dr. Giorgio Arra, 3-91

GUIDED-MISSILE CRUISERS *(continued)*

Normandy (CG 60)—Baseline 3 ship; note port for SQR-19 towed array just to starboard of centerline, twin ports for SLQ-25 Nixie towed acoustic torpedo decoys to starboard, two quadruple Harpoon launchers to port
Dr. Giorgio Arra, 6-91

Yorktown (CG 48)—Baseline 0 ship Dr. Giorgio Arra, 1990

Mobile Bay (CG 53)—Baseline 2 ship R.A.N.

Cowpens (CG 63)—Baseline 4 ship Bath Iron Works

Ticonderoga (CG 47)—Baseline 0 ship with heavy masting Pradignac & Léo

ED-MISSILE CRUISERS *(continued)*

ks: Greatly revised version of the *Spruance*-class destroyer, using same hull pulsion but incorporating the Aegis Mk 7 weapon system (SPY-1 series phased-adar, four missile illuminator radars, Mk 26 or Mk 41 missile-launch system, esignation changed from DDG to CG on 1-1-80. Named for battles and cam-except for CG 51, named for a former Secretary of Defense and of the Navy.
e have been a number of ill-informed criticisms of this class, which is nonethe-far *the* most capable AAW platform in any navy, as well as being among the fective ASW platforms and, with the addition of vertical-launch Tomahawk, a ic threat as well, as demonstrated during the 1991 Desert Storm operations.
ast five were to have been authorized two each in FY 88 and FY 89, and the last 0. Instead, Congress authorized a "buy-out" of this class under FY 88, denying a for three DDG 51-class destroyers. CG 60–62 ordered 26-11-84, CG 63 and 64 36, CG 65 on 8-1-86, CG 66–68 on 16-4-87, and CG 69–73 on 25-2-88.
2 is home-ported at Yokosuka. CG 69 renamed 8-12-89. CG 59 struck mine and was repaired at Dubai, conducting post-repair trials 23-4-91. CG 56 con-a Red Sea patrol in early 1991 armed only with Tomahawk missiles in her l launchers. CG 70 was laid down ahead of schedule in place of DDG 53. CG 57 ted trials launching the SLAM land-attack variant of Harpoon on 26-6-90, with ssile target designated by an SH-2F helicopter.
systems: Bow bulwarks were required to keep decks dry, as draft was in-l about one meter over that of the original *Spruance* design. No fin stabilization l. CG 49 and later have lighter tripod after masts. Kevlar armor is incorporated tal spaces. CG 48's keel was "laid" at Yorktown, Virginia, by President Reagan of the ceremonies commemorating the defeat of the British there in 1781; actual ral work commenced 12-81 at Pascagoula, Mississippi. The ships are not unsta-hough quite cramped, and have sufficient stability margin to operate at up to tons full load. CG 47 and 48 carry a small amount of lead ballast, but later units Carry two 4,081-kg anchors, with 180 fathoms of chain to the bow anchor and homs to the starboard anchor.
pons Systems: Each Mk 26 Mod. 1 missile-launcher magazine holds 44 mis-he forward magazine holding the 20 ASROC. The Mk 86 Mod. 9 fire-control for the 127-mm guns provides no AA capability in this class, as no SPG-60 radar ed. The R.C.A.–built Aegis Mk 7 Mod. 2 system, which uses 12 UYK-7 and 1 0 computers, uses the four fixed faces of the SPY-1A radar to detect and track up ral hundred targets simultaneously; the four illuminators are slaved to the and can, through time-share switching, serve more than a dozen missiles in the nce; the Mk 99 missile fire-control *system* uses 4 Mk 80 *illuminator-directors* PG-62 *radars.* The UPX-29 IFF circular antenna array is carried on the main-The Harpoon missiles, which are launched by the SWG-1 launch control system, n exposed position at the extreme stern. All have LINK 4A, 11, and 14 datalink ity, UQN-4 echo-sounders, and WRN-5 SATCOMM receivers.
fications to accept newly developed equipments were phased in, with the Ingalls tended to receive the building contract for the first ship of each new baseline:
line 0: CG 47, 48: Basic Aegis Mk 7 system, with SPY-1A, Weapons Control Mk 1, Standard SM-2 MR Block 1 missiles, the Mk 116 Mod. 4 ASW fire-control , and the SH-2F LAMPS-I ASW helicopter.
line 1: CG 49–51: The RAST haul-down and deck-maneuvering system and 8 helicopter data-link system are added for SH-60B LAMPS-III helicopters, rd SM-2 MR Block 2 missiles are carried, Aegis has improved data displays, and V suite is enhanced. Both masts tripods vice quadripods.
line 2: CG 52–58: The Mk 40 Mod. 0 vertical-launch system is substituted for 26 twin-armed launchers, vertical-launch Tomahawk capability with SWG-3 -control system is added, as is an improved LINK 11 data-link system. Congress ted the omission of SPS-49 radars and the SQQ-28 LAMPS-III data link in CG but gave permission in 5-84 to add the equipment. CG 54 and 55 have stand-SQR-19 linear towed passive sonar arrays and SQS-53A. CG 53 and later substi-7.32-m Rigid Inflatable Boat (RIB) for the 7.92-m (26-ft.) motor whaleboat. CG 56 ices the SQQ-89(V)3 integrated ASW suite, with SQQ-53B hull-mounted sonar, 9 towed array, and the Mk 116 Mod. 6 ASW fire-control system.
line 3: CG 59 and later: the lighter SPY-1B radar, with improved radiating teristics, is substituted for SPY-1A, and new computers (UYK-44) will be em-, along with improved displays.
line 4: CG 65–73 have UYK-43B and UYK-44 computers in place of UYK-7 and 20, as well as receiving the improved UYS-20 data display system. *All* ships of ss have the SQR-17 sonar data processor.
vertical-launch ASROC is no longer programmed to be installed in the Mk 41 l launchers in this class. All can carry up to 36 Mk 46 ASW torpedoes for their B helicopters. During overhauls, the ships are having the 127-mm guns up-l to Mk 45 Mod. 1, the Phalanx CIWS systems upgraded to Block 1, and the stle deck area strengthened to prevent cracking; *Leyte Gulf* completed such an ul in 5-92.

Belknap class (SCB 212 type) (*Atlantic/†Pacific Fleet)

	Bldr	Laid down	L	In serv.
3 BELKNAP*	Bath Iron Works	5-2-62	20-7-63	7-11-64
7 JOSEPHUS NIELS*	Bath Iron Works	23-4-62	2-12-63	8-5-65
3 WAINWRIGHT*	Bath Iron Works	2-7-62	25-4-64	8-1-66
9 JOUETT†	Puget Sound NSY	25-9-62	30-6-64	3-12-66
) HORNE†	San Francisco NSY	12-9-62	30-10-64	15-4-67
1 STERETT†	Puget Sound NSY	25-9-62	30-6-64	8-4-67
2 WILLIAM H. NDLEY†	Bath Iron Works	29-7-63	19-12-64	9-7-66
3 FOX†	Todd SY, San Pedro	15-1-63	21-11-64	28-5-66
4 BIDDLE*	Bath Iron Works	9-12-63	2-7-65	21-1-67

orized: CG 26–28 in FY 61 and CG 29–34 in FY 62

5,340 light/6,570 std. tons (8,065 fl; CG 26: 8,575)
33 kts **Dim:** 166.72 × 16.76 × 5.9 (8.8 over sonar)

A: 8/Harpoon SSM (IV × 2)—1/Mk 10 Mod. 7 twin launcher (II × 1, 40 Standard SM-2 ER and 20 ASROC missiles)—1/127-mm 54-cal. Mk 42 DP (aft)—2/20-mm Mk 15 CIWS AA (I × 2)—4/12.7-mm mg (I × 4)—6/324-mm Mk 32 ASW TT (III × 2; 18 Mk 46 Mod. 5 torpedoes)—1/SH-2F LAMPS-I helicopter (not in CG 26)

Electron Equipt:
Radar: 1/SPS-64(V)9 nav., 1/SPS-67(V) surf. search, 1/SPS-49(V)3 or (V)5 air search, 1/SPS-48C or SPS-48E 3-D air search, 2/SPG-55D missile f.c.,1/SPG-53A gun f.c.
Sonar: 1/SQS-26BX (CG 26: SQS-53A) bow-mounted LF
TACAN: URN-25
EW: SLQ-32(V)3, SLQ-34 (not in CG 26, 30, 31), Mk 36 SRBOC RL (VI × 4), SLQ-25 Nixie towed torpedo decoy

M: 2 sets G.E. (CG 29–31, 33: De Laval) geared steam turbines; 2/6-bladed props; 85,000 shp
Boilers: CG 24, CG 28, CG 32, CG 34: 4 Foster-Wheeler; others: 4 Combustion Engineering; 84 kg/cm^3, 520°C
Electric: 6,800 kw **Range:** 2,500/30; 8,000/14
Crew: 31 officers, 461 enlisted + flag group: 6 officers, 12 enlisted (CG 26: 30 officers, 81 enlisted in flag group)

Jouett (CG 29) Dr. Giorgio Arra, 10-91

William H. Standley (CG 32) David D. Broecker, 3-92

Fox (CG 33)—note fox silhouette below name
George R. Schneider, Jr., 4-91

GUIDED-MISSILE CRUISERS *(continued)*

Belknap (CG 26)—configured as 6th Fleet flagship French Navy,

Biddle (CG 34) Dr. Giorgio Arra, 3-91

Remarks: Formerly typed DLG; classified CG on 1-7-75. CG 26, severely damaged in collision with CV 67 in Mediterranean on 22-11-75, was out of commission for repairs at Philadelphia until 10-5-80. She had her 76.2-mm guns replaced by eight Harpoon SSM, received SPS-48C and SPS-49 radar, SM-2 ER missiles, the SLQ-25 Nixie towed torpedo decoy system, improved electronics (including NTDS Mod. 4) and communications gear, and SQS-53A sonar and is now officially considered to be a unit of a separate class. In a further refit, from 6-85 to 3-86, the ship was equipped as 6th Fleet flagship, with enhanced communications and staff accommodations at the expense of the helicopter hanger: included were the WSC-6 SHF SATCOMM antennas, a new two-level deckhouse before the bridge, and the conversion of the hangar to additional accommodations.

CG 31 was the first to lose her 76.2-mm guns, in 1976, to make way for eight Harpoon SSM (IV × 2), now also carried by the others (firing forward to port, aft to starboard). CG 28 was used as trials ship for the Standard SM-2 ER SAM, now carried by all units of the class. The 127-mm gun is controlled by a Mk 68 radar GFCS. Mk 114 (CG 26: Mk 116) ASW fire-control system, one Mk 11 (CG 26: Mk 14) weapon-direction system, and two Mk 76 Mod. 9 missile fire-control systems are fitted. These ships will not receive the SH-60B LAMPS-III ASW helicopter. CG 26, 28, 30, and 31 received the Tactical Flag Command Center in 1983–85.

All are having the SPS-48C updated to SPS-48E, SPS-49(V)3 updated to (V)5-configuration, and the weapons direction system Mk 14, missile tracking set SYR-1, and the SYS-2 weapon-control system added during New Threat Upgrade modernizations (NTU); CG 34 completed 7-87, CG 30 began during 9-88, CG 29 completed during 1989, CG 33 modernizing from 9-89 to 9-90, CG 31 from 8-7-91 to 8-92, CG 27 during 1991–92, and the others to complete by 9-93 (with CG 26 last). Several have enhanced electronics warfare suites, with additional equipment over the SLQ-32(V)3 fit.

♦ 9 Leahy class (SCB 172 type) (*Atlantic/†Pacific Fleet)

	Bldr	Laid down	L	In serv.
CG 16 Leahy†	Bath Iron Works	3-12-59	1-7-61	4-8-62
CG 17 Harry E. Yarnell*	Bath Iron Works	31-5-60	9-12-61	2-2-63
CG 18 Worden†	Bath Iron Works	19-9-60	2-6-62	3-8-63
CG 19 Dale*	New York SB Camden, N.J.	6-9-60	28-7-62	23-
CG 20 Richmond K. Turner*	New York SB Camden, N.J.	9-1-61	6-4-63	13
CG 21 Gridley†	Puget Sound Bridge & DD Co.	15-7-60	31-7-61	25
CG 22 England*	Todd SY, Los Angeles	4-10-60	6-3-62	7-
CG 23 Halsey†	San Francisco NSY	26-8-60	15-1-62	20
CG 24 Reeves†	Puget Sound NSY	1-7-60	12-5-62	15

Authorized: CG 16–18 in FY 58, CG 19–24 in FY 59

D: 6,070 tons (8,200 fl) **S:** 33 kts
Dim: 162.46 × 16.15 × 5.9 (7.9 over sonar)
A: 8/Harpoon SSM (IV × 2)—2/Mk 10 twin launchers (II × 2, 80 Standard SM-2 ER missiles)—2/20-mm Mk 15 CIWS AA (I × 2)—4/12.7-mm mg (I × 4)—1/Mk 16 Mod. 1 ASROC ASW (VIII × 1)—6/324-mm Mk 32 ASW TT (III × 2)
Electron Equipt:
Radar: 1/SPS-64(V)9 nav., 1/SPS-67 surf. search, 1/SPS-49(V)5 a search, 1/SPS-48E 3-D air search, 4/SPG-55D missile f.c.
Sonar: SQQ-23B PAIR (single-dome) bow-mounted LF
TACAN: URN-25
EW: SLQ-32(V)3, Mk 36 SRBOC decoy RL (VI × 4), SLQ-25 Nixie towed torpedo decoy
M: 2 sets G.E. (CG 20 to CG 22: De Laval; CG 23 and CG 24: Allis Chalmers) geared steam turbines; 2/5-bladed props; 85,000 shp
Boilers: CG 16 to CG 20: 4 Babcock & Wilcox; others: 4 Foster-Wheeler; 84 kg/cm³, 520°C
Electric: 6,800 kw **Range:** 2,500/30; 8,000/14 **Fuel:** 1,800 tons
Crew: 27–31 officers, 366–376 enlisted + flag group: 6 officers, 12 enlisted

Harry E. Yarnell (CG 17) Maritime Photographic,

■ED-MISSILE CRUISERS *(continued)*

▪y (CG 16) OS2 John Bouvia, USN, 1-90

▪en (CG 18) Dennis W. Moore, 6-91

▪ (CG 19) Dr. Giorgio Arra, 1-90

Halsey (CG 23) David D. Broecker, 7-91

Richmond K. Turner (CG 20) Dr. Giorgio Arra, 3-90

Remarks: These are former "frigates" (DLG), reclassified CG on 1-7-75. Like CGN 25, these ships are, unfortunately, completely devoid of larger gun armament. There are no reloads for the ASROC system. CG 24 accidentally bombed (1 × 500-lb.) 30-9-89 by USN aircraft in Indian Ocean; little damage. These ships will begin retiring toward the end of the 1990s.

Systems: During overhauls 1967–72, the *Leahy*-class ships received an advanced version of the Mk 76 missile fire-control system, permitting firing of Standard SM-1 ER missiles, returning to active service on 17-8-68. All had received SM-2 ER missile capability by 1985. The four 76.2-mm (II × 2) guns were removed from all, and their gun tubs are used as locations for Harpoon missile launchers, which have the SWG-1A launch control system.

CG 19 received SPS-49 in place of SPS-43 in 1976; the others were similarly re-equipped, and all now have the SLQ-32(V)3 EW system. SPS-49(V)3 updated to (V)5 configuration during NTU modernizations. The WLR-1H and WLR-3 intercept systems were retained by CG 21, 23, and 24 but have since been removed. All have the Mk 76 missile fire-control system, with four SPG-55C radar trackers/illuminators. Mk 114 ASW fire control, Mk 14 weapon-control system. All have NTDS data system and WCS-3 SATCOMM equipment. CG 16, 17, and 19 received NTU (New Threat Upgrade) modernization in FY 87–88, CG 18 in FY 88–89, CG 22 during refit 10-86 to 10-87, CG 20 during refit 6-88 to 7-89, CG 21 began 9-1-89, and CG 23 on 1-5-89. Not all yet have the SPS-64(N)9 navigational radar, retaining instead a mix of Marconi LN-66, Raytheon CRP-1900, etc., supplemented by Furuno 900 commercial sets.

Note: The all-gun cruisers *Des Moines* (CA 134) and *Salem* (CA 139) were stricken 9-7-91 and 12-7-91, respectively; their hulks, and that of their sister *Newport News* (CA 148, stricken 30-6-78), remain at the Philadelphia Naval Shipyard.

GUIDED-MISSILE DESTROYERS

◆ **1 (+21+19+. . .) Arleigh Burke class** (*Atlantic/†Pacific Fleet)

	Bldr	Laid down	L	In serv.
DDG 51 Arleigh Burke*	Bath Iron Works	6-12-88	16-9-89	4-7-91
DDG 52 Barry (ex-*John Barry*, ex-*Barry*, ex-*John Barry*)*	Ingalls, Pascagoula	29-2-90	10-5-91	11-92
DDG 53 John Paul Jones†	Bath Iron Works	8-8-90	26-10-91	7-93
DDG 54 Curtis Wilbur†	Bath Iron Works	12-3-91	16-5-92	10-93
DDG 55 Stout*	Ingalls, Pascagoula	12-8-91	9-92	1994
DDG 56 John S. McCain	Bath Iron Works	13-9-91	. . .	1994
DDG 57 Mitscher	Ingalls, Pascagoula	12-2-92	4-93	1994
DDG 58 Laboon	Bath Iron Works	3-92	2-93	1994
DDG 59 Russell	Ingalls, Pascagoula	13-7-92	9-93	1-95
DDG 60 Paul Hamilton	Bath Iron Works	8-92	7-93	1995
DDG 61 Ramage	Ingalls, Pascagoula	11-92	12-93	5-95
DDG 62 Fitzgerald	Bath Iron Works	2-93	12-93	1995
DDG 63 Stethem	Ingalls, Pascagoula	3-93	4-94	1995
DDG 64 Carney	Bath Iron Works	8-93	. . .	1995
DDG 65 Benfold	Ingalls, Pascagoula	8-93	. . .	1995
DDG 66 Gonzalez	Bath Iron Works	1-94	. . .	1996
DDG 67 Cole	Ingalls, Pascagoula	2-94	. . .	1996
DDG 68	Bath Iron Works	. . .	. . .	1997
DDG 69	Ingalls, Pascagoula	. . .	. . .	1997
DDG 70	Ingalls, Pascagoula	. . .	. . .	1997
DDG 71	Bath Iron Works	. . .	. . .	1997
DDG 72	Bath Iron Works	. . .	. . .	1998
DDG 73	. . . . . .	. . .	. . .	. . .
DDG 74	. . . . . .	. . .	. . .	. . .
DDG 75	. . . . . .	. . .	. . .	. . .
DDG 76	. . . . . .	. . .	. . .	. . .
DDG 77	. . . . . .	. . .	. . .	. . .
DDG 78	. . . . . .	. . .	. . .	. . .
DDG 79	. . . . . .	. . .	. . .	. . .
DDG 80	. . . . . .	. . .	. . .	. . .
DDG 81	. . . . . .	. . .	. . .	. . .
DDG 82	. . . . . .	. . .	. . .	. . .
DDG 83	. . . . . .	. . .	. . .	. . .

Authorized: DDG 51 in FY 85, DDG 52–54 in FY 87 (DDG 54 funded FY 89), DDG 55–58 in FY 89, DDG 59–63 in FY 90, DDG 64–67 in FY 91, DDG 68–72 in FY 92, DDG 73–75 in FY 93. Programmed: DDG 76–78 in FY 94, DDG 79–82 in FY 95, DDG 83–86 in FY 96, DDG 87–90 in FY 97.

Barry (DDG 52) Ingalls SB, 7-91

Arleigh Burke (DDG 51) Dr. Giorgio Arra

DDG 79 and later units—Baseline IIA, with twin helicopter hangar, no Harpoon SSM Allison/Gibbs & Cox

Arleigh Burke (DDG 51) Dr. Giorgio Arra

:D-MISSILE DESTROYERS *(continued)*

h Burke (DDG 51) Bath Iron Works, 5-91

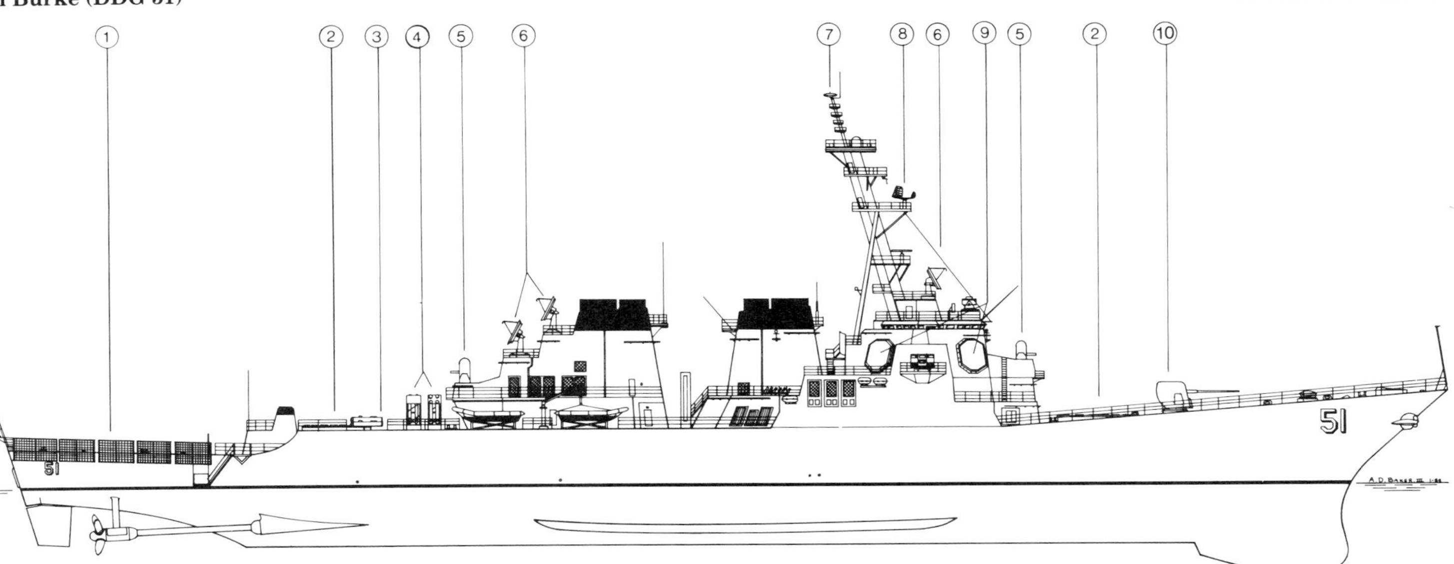

gh Burke (DDG 51) 1. helicopter deck 2. Mk 41 vertical-launch missile launcher 3. Mk 32 triple ASW TT 4. Harpoon SSM 5. 20-mm Mk 15 6. SPG-62 radars for Mk 99 missile target illuminator syst. 7. URN-20 TACAN 8. SPS-67(V)3 surface-search radar (SPS-64(V)9 just 9. SPY-1D radar fixed antenna arrays 10. 127-mm Mk 45 DP A. D. Baker III

gh Burke (DDG 51)—note SQR-19 and SLQ-25 ports in the transom Dr. Giorgio Arra, 8-91

D: DDG 51: 6,624 tons light (8,315 fl); DDG 52–78: 6,682 tons light (8,373 fl)

S: 30+ kts (32 kts on trials at 103,000 shp)

Dim: 153.77 (142.03 wl; 135.94 pp) × 20.27 (18.0 wl) × 6.31 (9.35 over sonar)

A: DDG 51–78: 2 Mk 41 Mod. 0 vertical-launch groups (1/64-cell, 1/32-cell; 90 Standard SM-2 MR Block 4 SAM, VLA ASROC and Tomahawk missiles)—8/Harpoon SSM (IV × 2)—1/127-mm 54-cal. Mk 45 Mod. 1 DP—2/20-mm Mk 15 Mod. 1 CIWS AA (I × 2)—6/324-mm Mk 32 ASW TT (III × 2)

DDG 78 on: 2 Mk 41 Mod. 0 vertical-launch groups (1/64-cell, 1/32-cell; 90 Standard SM-2 MR Block 4 SAM, VLA ASROC and Tomahawk missiles)—1/127-mm 54-cal. Mk 45 Mod. 1 DP—2/20-mm Mk 15 Mod. 1 CIWS AA (I × 2)—6/324-mm Mk 32 ASW TT (III × 2)—2/SH-60B/F Seahawk helicopters

GUIDED-MISSILE DESTROYERS *(continued)*

Electron Equipt:
Radar: 1/SPS-64(V)9 nav., 1/SPS-67(V)3 surf. search, 1/SPY-1D 3-D search/weapons control, 3/SPG-62 illuminators
Sonar: DDG 51–77: SQQ-89(V)4 suite: SQS-53C, SQR-19 towed array; DDG 78–on: SQS-53C only
EW: SLQ-32(V)2 intercept (DDG 59 on: SLQ-32(V)3 active/passive), Mk 36 Mod. 2 SRBOC RL (VI × 4), SLQ-25 Nixie towed torpedo decoy
TACAN: URN-25—IFF: UPX-29
M: 4 G.E. LM-2500-30 gas turbines; 2/5 bladed CP props; 100,000 shp (90,000 sust.)
Electric: 7,500 kw tot. (3 Allison 501-K34 gas turbines driving)
Range: 4,400/20 **Fuel:** . . . tons
Crew: 342 tot. accommodations (27 officers, 24 chief petty officers, 291 enlisted)

Remarks: This design is intended to provide a general-purpose destroyer capable of carrying out its assignments in the threat environment of the 1990s and beyond. DDG 54 was named in expectation of approval under FY 87, but Congress gave the navy only two ships. None approved FY 88 in favor of CG 47-class buy-out. Program well behind by late 1987, with launch of DDG 51 delayed one year, delivery by ten months. DDG 51 ordered 2-4-85, DDG 52 on 26-5-87, DDG 53 in 8-87. Congress required a third yard to participate in FY 89. Only three requested for FY 89 in 2-88, but Congress authorized and appropriated funds for three ($2,062,200,000) and authorized the use of unexpended prior-year funds for two more; all five were ordered 13-12-88. The name for DDG 52 was changed three times—twice in 1989! DDG 59–63 were ordered 22-2-90, DDG 64–67 were ordered 61-1-91, and DDG 68–72 were ordered 8-4-92.

Hull systems: The ships have steel superstructures, aluminum stacks, and the first comprehensive CBR protection system in a U.S. Navy ship. Over 130 tons of Kevlar or plastic armor will be used for vital spaces. The ships will have considerably reduced endurance as compared to other recent U.S.N. destroyers. The hull form is unusually broad in relation to length; fin stabilizers are not planned. The concept of the broad hull was borne out during sea trials for DDG 51, which was able to maintain 30 knots in 35-ft. seas and a 60-knot gale. Heels only slightly with full rudder at full speed. Have automated digital steering system, wherein course is entered and automatically maintained. Trials were conducted in DDG 51 during 1991 with a rudder roll-reduction system. Have WSN-5 inertial navigation system. Carry 2 7.32-m rigid inflatable boats and 15 25-person encapsulated liferafts. The original steel quadripod mast was changed before construction began to a lightweight structure employing composites to reduce radar signature.

Later incorporation of the RACER (RAnkine-Cycle Energy Recovery) propulsion concept has been abandoned, as has the use of electric propulsion, but future ships in the series may take advantage of a research effort contracted for with Westinghouse and Rolls-Royce in 1-92 to develop a 26,400-shp intercooled recuperated marine gas turbine propulsion system from the Rolls-Royce RB211 aircraft engine. The planned result is to be a plant with 30 percent less fuel consumption than the present LM-2500 engine.

Variations: In the Block I (DDG 51–77) series, no helicopter hangar is fitted. The flight deck will accept SH-60B or F Seahawk helicopters, and the SQQ-28 LAMPS-III data-link/control system is installed. DDG 52 and later have helicopter haul-down system, plus helicopter refueling/rearming facilities, which add 58 tons to the full-load displacement, delaying delivery of DDG 52 by 6 months. DDG 58 and later are to have improved fire control, Block 4, extended-range Standard missiles, NTDS Mod. 5, improved displays, and later communications.

In the Block IIA series (DDG 78 and later), a twin helicopter hangar will be incorporated, and the towed sonar array will probably be omitted. Plans to eliminate the two Mk 15 CIWS have been dropped, as the proposed alternative, an updated vertical-launch Sea Sparrow, would not be ready for them. The ships will also receive the Joint Tactical Data Information Distribution System (JTIDS) and an improved version of the SLQ-32(V) EW system incorporating "Combat D/F." The new variant will not be lengthened by 12.2 m as planned at one time, in order to save construction costs, which are in theory to be about $60 million less per ship than for the original series ships.

Systems: The Aegis SPY-1D radar has all four faces mounted on the forward superstructure; the system employs five UYK-43B computers, and the Combat Information Center is below the main deck. The 127-mm gun is controlled by the Mk 34 Mod. 0 Gun Weapon System with Mk 160 Mod. 4 Gun Computing System (which uses radar input data from the SPS-67(V)3 or SPY-1D); the planned Mk 121 Mod. 0 t.v./laser/infrared director was canceled but may yet be replaced by a less system, tentatively named the Passive Optical Sight EX46 Mod. 0. and intende added to the Mk 34 Mod. 0 Gun Weapon System. The gun has a secondary antia capability and is furnished with 600 rounds of ammunition. The Standard SM Block 2 missiles will be controlled by the Aegis system, using the three Mk 80 i nator systems' SPG-62 radars for terminal designation only.

The Mk 116 Mod. 7 ASW f.c.s. is carried, and the small number of vertical-l ASROC missiles to be procured will be reserved for DDG 51–78 of this class. satellite communications and Links 11 and 14 are fitted. The SQQ-89(V)4 ASW includes the SQS-53C bow-mounted sonar, SQR-19 towed passive sonar array, S helicopter data link, SIMAS, and the Mk 116 Mod. 7 weapon-control syster Rockwell USQ-82(V) data-bus is employed for internal data distribution. Th 32(V)2 passive-only EW suite in the initial units of the class will be upgra SLQ-32(V)4 through the addition of "Sidekick" jammers. Also carry SLQ-39 EW launcher system.

◆ 4 Kidd class
Bldr: Ingalls SB, Pascagoula, Miss. (*Atlantic/†Pacific)

	Laid down	L	In
DDG 993 Kidd (ex-*Kouroush*)*	26-6-78	11-8-79	27
DDG 994 Callaghan (ex-*Daryush*)†	23-10-78	1-12-79	29
DDG 995 Scott (ex-*Nader*)*	12-2-79	1-3-80	24-
DDG 996 Chandler (ex-*Andushirvan*)†	7-5-79	24-5-80	13

Authorized: FY 79 Supplemental

Kidd (DDG 993) Dr. Giorgio Arra

Callaghan (DDG 994) David D. Broecker

Chandler (DDG 996) George R. Schneider, Jr.

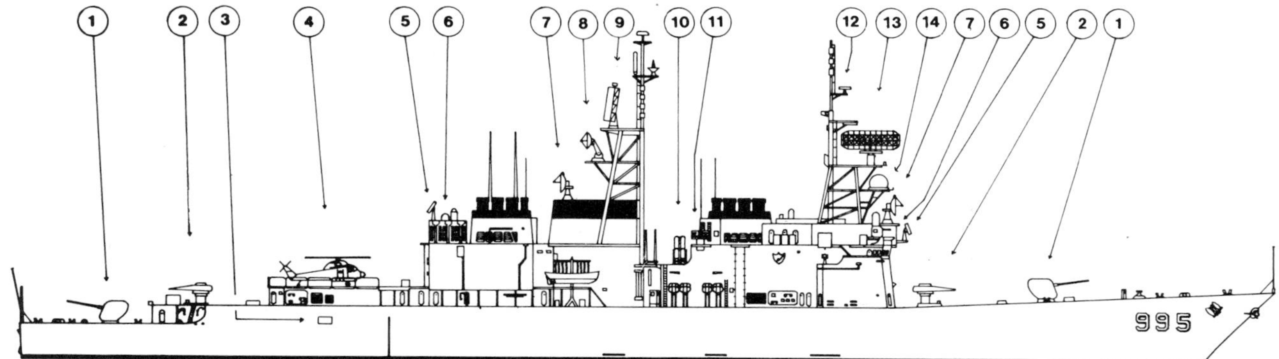

Kidd (DDG 993) 1. 127-mm Mk 45 DP 2. Mk 26 twin guided-missile launcher 3. Mk 32 triple ASW TT (behind shutters) 4. SH-2F Sea Sprite LAMPS-I ASW helicopter 5. OE-82 antenna for WSC-3 UHF SATCOMM 6. Mk 15 CIWS (to port of gas turbine air-intake structure) 7. SPG-51D missile radar illuminator 8. SPG-60 gun/missile-control radar 9. SPS-48E 3-D search radar 10. Harpoon antiship missiles 11. SLQ-32(V)5 EW antennas 12. SPG-55 surface-search radar 13. SPS-49(V)5 EW air-search radar 14. SPQ-9A gun surface-fire control radar Robert Dumas

[...]D-MISSILE DESTROYERS *(continued)*

DDG 995)—with SH-2F Sea Sprite on deck
Leo Van Ginderen, 2-92

,950 tons light (9,574 fl) **S:** 30+ kts
171.7 (161.23 wl) × 16.76 × 7.01 (10.06 over sonar)
/Mk 26 Mod. 3 and 1/Mk 26 Mod. 4 twin launchers (II × 2, 52 tandard SM-2 MR SAM and 16 ASROC missiles)—8/Harpoon SM (IV × 2)—2/127-mm 54-cal. Mk 45 DP (I × 2)—2/20-mm Mk 5 CIWS AA (I × 2)—4/12.7-mm mg (I × 4)—6/324-mm Mk 32 SW TT (III × 2; 24 torpedoes)—1/SH-2F LAMPS-I ASW elicopter
tron Equipt:
dar: 1/SPS-64(V)9 nav., 1/SPS-55 surf. search, 1/SPS-49(V)5 air search, 1/SPS-48E 3-D air search, 2/SPG-51D missile f.c., 1/SPG-60 missile/gun f.c., 1/SPQ-9A gun surf. f.c.
nar: SQS-53A bow-mounted LF—TACAN: URN-25—IFF: UPX-29
V: SLQ-32(V)5 passive with Sidekick jammer, Mk 36 SRBOC RL (VI × 4), SLQ-25 Nixie towed torpedo decoy
G.E. LM-2500 gas turbines; 2/5-bladed CP props; 86,000 shp
tric: 6,000 kw **Range:** 3,300/30; 6,000/20
v: 32 officers, 332 enlisted

ks: The original order for these superb ships, placed with the U.S. Navy by Iran was for six; two more were canceled 6-76 before the order to Ingalls Shipbuild- he remaining four was issued on 23-3-78. DDG 993 and DDG 994 were canceled ew Iranian government on 3-2-79, and the other pair on 31-3-79. Their com- for the U.S. Navy was authorized by the U.S. Congress under a Fiscal 1979 nentary Appropriation Act. Acquired 25-7-79, at approximately $510 million ey represented a considerable bargain. The hull numbers do not fit in U.S.N. mbering sequence for guided-missile destroyers.
systems: These ships were given larger-capacity air-intake filter systems than . *Spruance* class, in order to handle the dust and sand prevailing in Iranian ıg areas. They also have greater air-conditioning capacity. The Iranian Navy to type them as cruisers. Full-load displacement has grown by over 1,000 tons he original plan, partly as a result of additional Kevlar and aluminum-alloy eing added.
ons systems: During post-commissioning yard periods, URN-25 TACAN d URN-20, Harpoon was added amidships (with SWG-1A launch-control sys- d two Phalanx Mk 15 CIWS were installed. The NTDS system is supported by 4A, 11, and 14; they have the SRR-1, WSC-3, and USC-38 SATCOMM systems. Mk 74 missile fire-control systems (with SPG-55D radar tracker/illuminators) ied, as well as the Mk 86 Mod. 5 gunfire-control system, which uses the SPQ-9A r surface fire and the SPG-60 for AA (the latter can also be used as a missile ator). The ASROC missiles are carried in the larger Mk 26 Mod. 1 missile- system's magazine, which is *aft*; the Mk 116 underwater battery fire-control is carried. The ships were not intended to have the SQR-19A TACTASS towed sonar array, but it may be backfitted later, and SQS-53C is to replace the A bow-mounted sonar during future refits.
Threat Upgrade (NTU) modernizations add the SPS-49(V)5 2-D air-search substituted the SPS-48E for SPS-48C 3-D air-search radar, add the SYS-2 s data system and the Weapon Direction System Mk 14, and permit the use of d SM-2 MR Block 2 missiles. DDG 995 completed NTU conversion 3-88, DDG dified 8-88 to 9-89, DDG 994 during 8-89 to 7-90, and DDG 996 from 25-8-89 to .

Charles F. Adams class (SCB 155 type) (†Pacific Fleet)

	Bldr	Laid down	L	In serv.
e:				
20 DSBOROUGH†	Puget Sound SB & DD	3-1-61	15-12-61	9-11-63
serve for retention:				
BARNEY	New York SB	18-8-59	10-12-60	11-8-62
3 LYNDE CORMICK	Defoe SB	4-4-58	9-9-60	3-6-61
10 SAMPSON	Bath Iron Works	2-3-59	9-9-60	24-6-61
11 SELLERS	Bath Iron Works	3-8-59	9-9-60	28-10-61
12 ROBISON	Defoe SB	23-4-59	27-4-60	9-12-61
14 BUCHANAN	Todd, Seattle	23-4-59	11-5-60	7-2-62
19 TATTNALL	Avondale SY	14-11-60	26-8-61	13-4-63
21 COCHRANE	Puget Sound SB & DD	31-7-61	18-7-62	21-3-64
22 BENJAMIN DDERT	Puget Sound SB & DD	11-6-62	8-1-63	12-9-64

horized: 8 in FY 57, 5 in FY 58, 5 in FY 59, 3 in FY 60, and 2 in FY 61

Goldsborough (DDG 20)—last unit of class active in U.S. Navy
OS2 John Bouvia, USN, 6-91

Goldsborough (DDG 20) Dennis W. Moore, 6-91

Robison (DDG 12)—with twin Mk 11 SAM launcher
Vic Jeffery, R.A.N., 6-90

Sampson (DDG 10) Dr. Maurizio del Prete, 1991

GUIDED-MISSILE DESTROYERS *(continued)*

Benjamin Stoddert (DDG 22)—with Mk 86 gunfire-control system
Leo Van Ginderen, 1991

Buchanan (DDG 14)—with twin Mk 11 SAM launcher, ASROC reload magazine
Dennis W. Moore, 4-90

D: 3,570 tons light (4,825 fl) **S:** 31.5 kts
Dim: 133.19 (128.0 wl) × 14.32 × 6.1 (8.3 over sonar)
A: 1/Mk 11 twin missile launcher or, beginning with DDG 15, 1/Mk 13 single launcher (4–6 Harpoon and 34–36 Standard SM-1 MR)—2/127-mm 54-cal. Mk 42 DP (I × 2)—4/12.7 mm mg (I × 4)—1/Mk 16 Mod. 1 ASROC RL (VIII × 1; 8 or 12 missiles)—6/324-mm Mk 32 ASW TT (III × 2)
Electron Equipt:
Radar: 1/LN-66 nav., 1/SPS-10F surf. search, 1/SPS-40B/D air search, 1/SPS-52B 3-D air search, 2/SPG-51C missile f.c., 1/SPG-53A gun f.c.
(DDG 19, 20, 22: 1/LN-66 nav., 1/SPS-10D surf. search, 1/SPS-40D air search, 1/SPS-52C 3-D air search, 2/SPG-51D missile f.c., 1/SPG-60 missile/gun f.c., 1/SPQ-9A surf. gun f.c.)
Sonar: SQS-23A hull-mounted LF in DDG 2 to DDG 19; SQQ-23A bow- and hull-mounted in DDG 20 to DDG 24
EW: SLQ-32(V)2 passive, SLQ-20, Mk 36 SRBOC decoy RL (VI × 4)
TACAN: URN-25
M: 2 sets G.E. (DDG 14: Westinghouse) geared steam turbines; 2 props; 70,000 shp
Boilers: 4 Babcock & Wilcox (DDG 14: Foster-Wheeler); 84 kg/cm³, 520°C
Electric: 2,200 kw (DDG 19, 20, 22; 3,000 kw)
Range: 1,600/30; 6,000/14 **Fuel:** 900 tons
Crew: 24 officers, 330 enlisted

Remarks: Sisters DDG 25, DDG 26, and DDG 27, built at the Defoe Shipbuilding Company, Bay City, Michigan, were ordered by Australia; DDG 28, DDG 29, and DDG 30 were built at Bath Iron Works for the West German Navy. DDG 2–9 authorized as DD 952–959; reclassified as DDG on 26-6-57. Ships with bow-mounted sonars (DDG 20–24) have stem-mounted anchors. Many have been backfitted with an ASROC ASW missile reload magazine (with four missiles) beside the forward stack, to starboard.

Systems: It was planned to give these ships a badly needed modernization, beginning with DDG 3 under FY 80. Costs rose enormously, and the program was cut to ten, permitting them to operate for another fifteen to twenty years. Congressional reluctance to spend $221 million per ship (then equal to the cost of a new FFG 7-class forced cancellation of even the reduced program to only three ships: DDG 19, 22. DDG 19 underwent conversion 31-8-81 to 28-11-82 at Philadelphia; DDG 20 converted at Pearl Harbor 4-83 to 7-84 and 4-84 to 8-85. Changes included: repla of the Mk 68 GFCS with Mk 86 Mod. 8 (with 1/SPQ-9A and 1/SPG-60 radars 32(V)2, SLQ-20, and Mk 36 SRBOC replacing the original suite; the original f.c.s. replaced by Mk 74 Mod. 4, with the Weapons Direction System Mk 13 replacing the original Mk 4; the addition of the SYS-1 data system with UYA-4 upgrading the search radar suite to: 1/LN-66, 1/SPS-10D, 1/SPS-40D, and SF improving the communications suite; and increasing the output of the four ge sets to 750 kw each. The ships can direct three Standard missiles simultaneousl the SPG-60 and the two SPG-51D tracker/illuminators.

The non-conversion ships were less extensively upgraded during regular ove SPS-40 has replaced the SPS-37 originally fitted to the first 13 ships with DDC having SPS-37 as late as 10-88. SLQ-32(V)2 replaced the WLR-1F and ULQ-6I and Mk 36 SRBOC launchers have been added; URN-25 lightweight TACAN r SRN-6; the Mk 68 GFCS received a digital computer system in DDG 4–6, 8–12, and 21; SPS-39A radars have been replaced by SPS-52B, and other improvemen made to the communications suites. Only the last four ships had the SQQ-23 s

In ships with Mk 11 launchers, 4 Harpoons were carried; in Mk 13-equippe six were carried. DDG 9, 12, 15, and 21 had the Junior Participating Tactic System (JPTDS), as do DDG 19, 20, and 22; the system is in effect a simplified

Status: Of the inactive units listed above, DDG 6 decommissioned to rese 17-12-90, DDG 8 on 1-10-91, DDG 10 on 24-6-91, DDG 11 on 31-10-89, DDG DDG 14 on 1-10-91, DDG 19 on 18-1-91, and DDG 22 on 20-12-91. Of the other original 23 ships in the class, 5 were decommissioned and are retained only for or possible foreign transfer: *Charles F. Adams* (DDG 2) on 1-8-90, *John King* (on 30-3-90, *Claude V. Ricketts* (DDG 5, ex-*Biddle*) decommissioned 17-12-90, (DDG 6) on 17-12-90, and *Hoel* (DDG 13) on 1-10-90. Stricken altogether hav *Lawrence* (DDG 4) decommissioned on 30-3-90 and stricken 16-5-90, *Henry B.* (DDG 7) decommissioned 2-10-89 and stricken 26-1-91, *Towers* (DDG 10, dec sioned and stricken 1-10-90, and *Conyngham* (DDG 17), damaged by fire 8-5-90, missioned 29-10-90, and stricken 30-5-91. Transferred to Greece have been: *Strauss* (DDG 16), decommissioned 1-2-90 and transferred 1-10-92; *Berkeley* (D and *Waddell* (DDG 24) decommissioned and transferred 1-10-92; *Semmes* (DI decommissioned 12-4-91 and transferred 13-9-91, and *Richard E. Byrd* (DI decommissioned 23-1-90 and transferred for cannibalization and dockside train only during mid-1992. DDG 20 is to decommission during FY 93. Brazil and have indicated a desire to acquire units of this class.

◆ 7 Coontz class (SCB 142/149 type) (*Atlantic Fleet)

	Bldr	Laid down	L	In
2 active:				
DDG 39 MACDONOUGH* (ex-DLG 8)	Bethlehem Steel, Quincy	15-4-58	9-7-59	4-
DDG 42 MAHAN* (ex-DLG 11)	San Francisco NSY	31-7-57	7-10-59	2
5 in reserve:				
DDG 38 *LUCE* (ex-DLG 7)	Bethlehem Steel, Quincy	1-10-57	11-12-58	20
DDG 41 *KING* (ex-DLG 10)	Puget Sound NSY	1-3-57	6-12-58	17-
DDG 44 *WILLIAM V. PRATT* (ex-DLG 13)	Philadelphia NSY	1-3-58	16-3-60	4-
DDG 45 *DEWEY* (ex-DLG 14)	Bath Iron Works	10-8-57	30-11-58	7-
DDG 46 *PREBLE* (ex-DLG 15)	Bath Iron Works	16-12-57	23-5-59	9

Authorized: DDG 37 to 42 in FY 57, DDG 43 to 46 in FY 57

D: 4,700 tons (6,150 fl) **S:** 34 kts
Dim: 156.21 × 16.0 × 7.6 (max.)
A: 8/Harpoon SSM (IV × 2)—1/Mk 10 Mod. 0 twin launcher (II × 40 Standard SM-1 ER (DDG 42: SM-2 ER missiles)—1/127-mm cal. Mk 42 DP—4/12.7-mm mg (I × 4)—1/ASROC Mk 16 Mod. ASW RL (VIII × 1)—6/324-mm ASW TT (III × 2)
Electron Equipt:
Radar: 1/SPS-53 or Raytheon 2900 nav., 1/SPS-10B surf. search 1/SPS-49(V)2 (DDG 42: SPS-49(V)5 air search, 1/SPS-48 (DDG 42: SPS-48D) 3-D air search, 2/SPG-55B missile f. 1/SPG-53A gun f.c.
Sonar: SQQ-23A PAIR hull-mounted LF
TACAN: SRN-6 (DDG 37, 41, 42: URN-25)
EW: SLQ-32(V)3 active/passive, Mk 36 SRBOC decoy RL (VI × DDG 42 only: SLQ-25 Nixie towed torpedo decoy (others: T Mk 6 Fanfare)
M: DDG 37 to 39, DDG 46: 2 sets de Laval (others: Allis-Chalmers geared steam turbines; 2 props; 85,000 shp
Boilers: 4 Foster-Wheeler (DDG 40 to DDG 46: Babcock & Wilcox 84 kg/cm³, 520°C
Electric: 4,000 kw tot. **Range:** 1,500/30; 6,000/14 **Fuel:** 900
Crew: 21 officers, 356 enlisted + flag group: 7 officers, 12 enlisted

IDED-MISSILE DESTROYERS *(continued)*

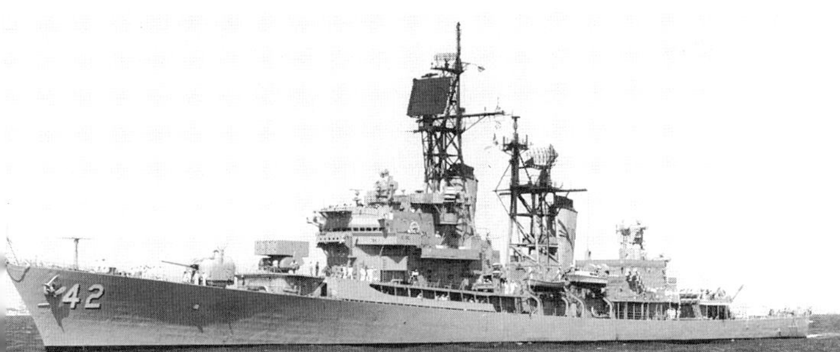

han (DDG 42)—NTU trials ship, with SPS-48D radar
Dr. Giorgio Arra, 2-90

han (DDG 42) Dr. Giorgio Arra, 2-90

e (DDG 38) Dr. Giorgio Arra, 1990

(DDG 41) Maritime Photographic, 10-90

(DDG 41) Gilbert Gyssels, 12-90

Remarks: These are the only U.S. Navy *destroyers* with Standard SM-1 ER. Reclassified DDG from DLG 6 to DLG 15 in 1975. All modernized between 1970 and 1977 with Standard SM-1 ER missiles, NTDS (fitted earlier in DDG 40, DDG 41), SPS-48 radar, etc.; four 76.2-mm DP (II × 2) removed and Harpoon launchers installed in their former locations (firing forward to port, aft to starboard). *Farragut* (DDG 37), the first to be modernized, received an ASROC reload magazine forward of the bridge and a taller after mast; to save weight and cost, the others were not similarly equipped.

Systems: Missile fire control is Mk 76. A Mk 68 fire-control system is carried for the 127-mm gun. The ships did not receive two Vulcan/Phalanx, due to their age, space, and weight problems. Mk 111 Mod. 8 ASW fire-control systems and satellite communications antenna systems in all units. The SQQ-23A PAIR sonar installed uses two separate domes. Helicopter landing pad on stern. The SPS-49 2-D air-search radar had replaced SPS-37, and the SLQ-32(V)3 EW system had replaced WLR-1, WLR-11, and ULQ-6B in all by 1982.

DDG 42 served as trials ship for the NTU (New Threat Upgrade) refit, with the SPS-48D 3-D radar (trials version of the SPS-48E), SPS-49(V)5 2-D radar, the SYS-2 IADT (Integrated Automatic Target Detection and Tracking) computerized action information system, Weapons Direction System Mk 14, and Standard SM-2 ER Block 2 missiles. The full suite was not backfitted to the others, but they did receive SM-2 Block 2 capability, with DDG 37 and 43 equipped by 1987.

Status: *Farragut* (DDG 37, ex-DLG 6) decommissioned 31-10-89 and was stricken for spare parts cannibalization; DDG 38 decommissioned 1-4-91; *Coontz* (DDG 40, ex-DLG 9) decommissioned 4-10-89 and was stricken 26-1-90 for spare parts; *Dahlgren* (DDG 43, ex-DLG 12) experienced a serious fire (two dead) on 22-2-92 and was decommissioned 31-7-92 without having been repaired, for eventual scrapping; DDG 44 was decommissioned 27-9-91; DDG 45 was decommissioned 31-8-90; and DDG 46 was decommissioned 15-11-91. The deactivated units are unlikely to see further service or to be transferred abroad. DDG 39 is to be decommissioned during Fiscal Year 1993, but DDG 42, because of her updated systems, will remain in service until the mid-1990s.

Note: Of the four *Decatur*-class guided-missile destroyers, *Parsons* (DDG 33, ex-DD 949), decommissioned 19-11-82, was stricken 15-5-84 and *John Paul Jones* (DDG 32, ex-DD 932) decommissioned 15-12-82, and had her name canceled 24-3-86. *Decatur* (DDG 31, ex-DD 936), decommissioned 30-6-83 and was stricken 16-3-88. *Somers* (DDG 34, ex-DD 947) decommissioned 19-11-82. DDG 32 and 34 remained on the Navy List in 1-90, awaiting striking and cannibalization. In 1992, *Decatur* was partially reactivated as trials platform for the Ship Self Defense System (SSDS) at Puget Sound Navy Yard; equipped with TAS Mk 23 target acquisition system, SLQ-32 EW equipment, a launcher for Sea Sparrow RIM-7P SAM, a launcher for RAM RIM-116A point-defense SAM, and Mk 15 Block 1 Phalanx CIWS, the ship will conduct trials at sea while moored next to a target barge under live missile attack.

DESTROYERS

◆ **31 Spruance class (SCN 275 type)** Bldr: Ingalls SB, Pascagoula, Miss. (Litton Industries) (*Atlantic/†Pacific Fleet)

	Laid down	L	In serv.
DD 963 SPRUANCE*	17-11-72	10-11-73	20-9-75
DD 964 PAUL F. FOSTER†	6-2-73	23-2-74	21-2-76
DD 965 KINKAID†	19-4-73	25-5-74	10-7-76
DD 966 HEWITT†	23-7-73	24-8-74	25-9-76
DD 967 ELLIOT†	15-10-73	19-12-74	22-1-76
DD 968 ARTHUR W. RADFORD*	14-1-74	1-3-75	16-4-77
DD 969 PETERSON*	29-4-74	21-6-75	9-7-77
DD 970 CARON*	1-7-74	24-6-75	1-10-77
DD 971 DAVID R. RAY†	23-9-74	23-8-75	19-11-77
DD 972 OLDENDORF†	27-12-74	21-10-75	4-3-78
DD 973 JOHN YOUNG†	17-2-75	7-2-76	20-5-78
DD 974 COMTE DE GRASSE*	4-4-75	26-3-76	5-8-78
DD 975 O'BRIEN†	9-5-75	8-7-76	3-12-77
DD 976 MERRILL†	16-6-75	1-9-76	11-3-78
DD 977 BRISCOE*	21-7-75	15-12-76	3-6-78
DD 978 STUMP*	25-8-75	29-1-77	19-8-78
DD 979 CONOLLY*	29-9-75	19-2-77	14-10-78
DD 980 MOOSBRUGGER*	3-11-75	23-7-77	16-12-78
DD 981 JOHN HANCOCK*	16-1-76	29-10-77	10-3-79
DD 982 NICHOLSON*	20-2-76	11-11-77	12-5-79
DD 983 JOHN RODGERS*	12-8-76	25-2-78	14-7-79
DD 984 LEFTWICH†	12-11-76	8-4-78	25-8-79
DD 985 CUSHING†	2-2-77	17-6-78	21-9-79
DD 986 HARRY W. HILL†	1-4-77	10-8-78	10-11-79
DD 987 O'BANNON*	24-6-77	25-9-78	1-12-79
DD 988 THORN*	29-8-77	22-11-78	12-1-80
DD 989 DEYO*	14-10-77	27-1-79	22-3-80
DD 990 INGERSOLL†	5-12-77	10-3-79	12-4-80
DD 991 FIFE†	6-3-78	1-5-79	31-5-80
DD 992 FLETCHER†	24-4-78	16-6-79	12-7-80
DD 997 HAYLER*	20-10-80	2-3-82	5-3-83

Authorized: D 963–965 in FY 70, DD 966–971 in FY 71, DD 972–978 in FY 72, DD 979–985 in FY 74, DD 986–992 in FY 75, DD 997 in FY 78

D: 5,916 tons light (8,040 fl; DD 997: 8,250 fl) **S:** 32.5 kts
Dim: 171.68 (o.a.) (161.25 pp) × 16.76 × 5.79 (8.84 over sonar)
A: DD 974, 976, 979, 983, 984, 989, 990: 8/Tomahawk SSM (IV × 2, in Mk 44 armored box-launchers)—DD 963, 964, 966, 967, 968, 969, 970, 971, 973, 975, 977, 978, 981, 985, 986, 990, 991, 992, 997 and ultimately all but box-launcher ships: 1/Mk 41 VLS group (61 Tomahawk)—1/Mk 29 launcher (VIII × 1, 24 Sea Sparrow SAM)—2/127-mm 54-cal. Mk 45 DP (I × 2)—2/20-mm Mk 15 CIWS (I × 2)—4/12.7-mm mg (I × 4)—non-VLS ships: 1/Mk 16

DESTROYERS *(continued)*

Conolly (DD 979)—Tomahawk armored box-launcher-equipped unit with aft Mk 15 CIWS raised one deck, SLQ-32(V)5 EW system
George Nassiopoulos, 5-91

Nicholson (DD 982)—still in near-original configuration, with ASROC launcher and without Tomahawk Leo Van Ginderen, 5-92

Deyo (DD 989)—with Tomahawk armored box-launchers flanking the ASROC launcher Pradignac & Léo, 6-91

Oldendorf (DD 972)—without Tomahawk or SQQ-89 ASW suite
LSPH K. Degener, R.A.N., 11-90

John Young (DD 973)—vertical launcher-equipped unit with raised M CIWS mount in maintenance enclosure atop hangar
George R. Schneider, Jr.,

Elliot (DD 967)—VLS unit with full SQQ-89 suite
Vic Jeffery, R.A.N.,

Hayler (DD 997)—prior to modernization; only unit with S radar Leo Van Ginderen,

Fletcher (DD 992)—with SQQ-89, but without Mk 23 TAS and stil ASROC launcher Leo Van Ginderen

Fife (DD 991)—Mk 41 VLS-equipped unit French Navy

Thorn (DD 988)—no Tomahawk missiles, SQQ-89, or Mk 23 TAS
Leo Van Ginderen

ROYERS *(continued)*

n (DD 975)—VLS-equipped unit with full SQQ-89 ASW suite Dr. Giorgio Arra, 10-91

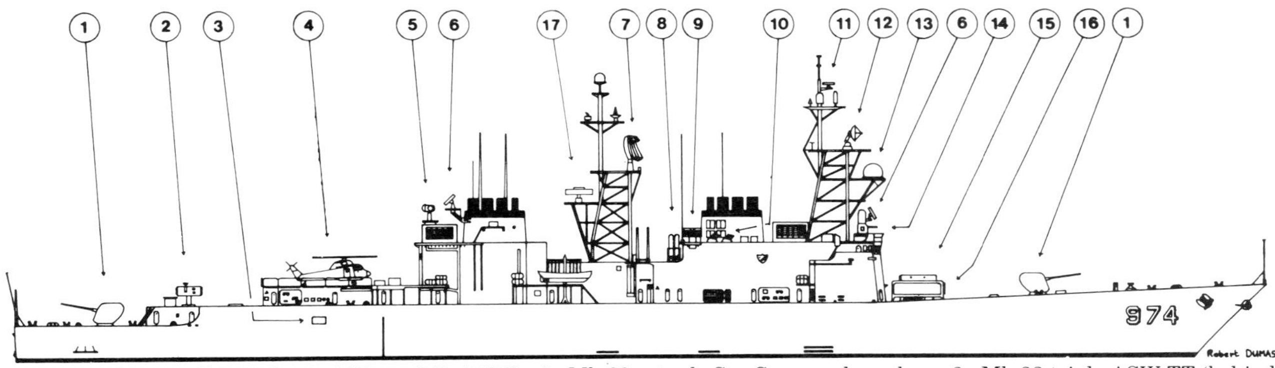

Comte de Grasse (DD 974) 1. 127-mm Mk 45 DP 2. Mk 29 octuple Sea Sparrow launcher 3. Mk 32 triple ASW TT (behind shutters) 4. SH-2F Sea Sprite LAMPS-I ASW helicopter 5. radar director for Mk 91 Mod. 0 Sea Sparrow control system 6. OE-82 antenna for WSC-3 UHF SATCOMM 7. SPS-40-series air-search radar 8. Harpoon antiship missiles 9. SLQ-32(V)2 EW antennas 10. Mk 137 launchers for Mk 36 SRBOC decoy system 11. SPS-55 surface-search radar 12. SPS-60 AAgun-control radar 13. SPQ-9A surface gun-control radar 14. 20-mm Mk 15 CIWS 15. Mk 16 Mod.1 octuple ASROC launcher 16. Tomahawk cruise missile armored box-launchers (flanking ASROC launcher) 17. Mk 23 TAS radar

Mod. 1 ASROC ASW RL (VIII × 1, 24 missiles)—all: 6/324-mm Mk 32 Mod. 5 ASW TT (III × 2, 18 Mk 46 torpedoes)—1/SH-2F LAMPS-I or SH-3G Sea King (DD 963–975, 979–982, 983, 985, 986, 991–997: SH-60B LAMPS-III) ASW helicopter

ctron Equipt:

adar: 1/SPS-64(V)9 or SPS-53 or LN-66 nav., 1/SPS-55 surf. search, 1/SPS-40B/C/D (DD 997: SPS-49(V)2) air search, 1/SPQ-9A surf. f.c., 1/SPG-60 gun f.c., 1/Mk 91 SAM f.c., 1 Mk 23 TAS Mod. 0, (not yet in DD 965, 976, 984, 988, 992)

onar: SQQ-89(V)1 (with SQS-53B or C hull sonar, SQR-19 TASS)—*see* Remarks

W: SLQ-32(V)2 passive or SLQ-32(V)5 with Sidekick active/passive, Mk 36 SRBOC decoy RL (VI × 4), most: SSQ-72 or SSQ-108 intercept, all: SLQ-25 Nixie towed torpedo decoy

ACAN: URN-25

4 G.E. LM-2500 gas turbines; 2 CP props; 86,000 shp (80,000 sust.)

ctric: 6,000 kw (3 × 2,000-kw Allison 501-K17 gas turbine-driven sets)

nge: 3,300/30; 6,000/20; 8,000/17 **Fuel:** 1,650 tons

w: 19–24 officers, 315–322 enlisted

Remarks: Largest post–World War II U.S. destroyer program, and the first non-SAM destroyers ordered since the 1950s. DD 997 intended by Congress to be of an "air-capable" design, with enlarged hangar for four ASW helicopters, but costs rose to the point that the ship was ordered 29-9-79 as a nearly standard version of the class. The basic *Spruance* hull and propulsion plant have also served as the basis for the *Kidd* (DDG 993) and *Ticonderoga* (CG 47, ex-DDG 47) designs. DD 981 carries her name across the stern in script, duplicating the signature of the first signer of the Declaration of Independence.

Hull systems: Displacements have risen considerably as equipment has been added; they were originally intended to displace under 7,000 tons full load. Limiting displacement is 8,800 tons. DD 997, with additional Kevlar armor as completed, displaces 8,250 tons full load. The hull form was designed to minimize rolling and pitching; there are no fin stabilizers. DD 985 conducted successful trials with a rudder roll reduction system during 1988. Habitability received particular attention, living spaces being divided by bulkheads and intended for no more than six men each, with a recreational area and good sanitary facilities. The crew is small for a ship the size of the *Spruance* class, because all the machinery and systems have advanced automation. Originally operated with 232 enlisted but now have up to 322. Hangars were widened to flush with starboard side during 1980s overhauls, and RAST helicopter haul-down and deck traversing equipment installed. The superstructure is aluminum, welded to the hull via bimetallic strips.

DESTROYERS *(continued)*

Machinery systems: The propulsion machinery is very quiet. Prairie-Masker bubbler systems are installed to enhance quietness. On each of the two shafts, two General Electric LM-2500 gas turbines are coupled to a reduction gear. Each shaft turns a controllable-pitch propeller (5.1 m in diameter, 168 rpm at 30 knots). Full speed can be reached from 12 knots in only 53 seconds. All propulsion machinery is under the control of a single operator in a central control station (CCS). 30 knots was considerably exceeded on trials. Endurance can be extended greatly by using one engine on one shaft for cruising. The plant has been very successful, except for the exhaust-gas auxiliary boilers. The mean time between overhauls for the LM-2500 gas turbines has been extended to 9,000 hours. DD 997 has the Litton automated engine-control system prototype for the DDG 51 class.

Weapons systems: ASW is handled by a Mk 116 fire-control system. The Mk 32 torpedo tubes are standard triple trainable mountings, fired through doors in the ships' sides. The Mk 91 Mod. 0 fire-control system for Sea Sparrow uses a single radar director; RAM missiles were to be installed, four each in two cells of the Mk 29 Sea Sparrow launcher, in the early 1990s, but the work has been canceled; some ships may later receive 21-cell Mk 49 trainable/elevatable RAM launchers. The Mk 86 Mod. 3 gun fire-control system for the 127-mm guns uses the SPG-60 radar for AA and the SPQ-9A for surface fire. Magazines hold 1,200 rounds 127-mm. In the ships still retaining the system, the ASROC reload missiles are stowed vertically, directly beneath the launcher. Kevlar plastic armor was added inside vital spaces, beginning with four ships under FY 81; the entire class was equipped by 1986. Seven ships (including DD 976 in FY 83, DD 979 and 983 in FY 84, DD 984, 985, 989 in FY 85, and DD 990 later) received eight Tomahawk cruise missiles (IV × 2); box-launcher firing trials were carried out on DD 976 in 1-81 and later, while first operational installation was in DD 974 in late 1984. Under FY 86 DD 963 and 990 received 61-cell Mk 41 Mod. 0 vertical-launch groups in place of the ASROC launcher; initially, it was planned to carry 45 Tomahawk cruise missiles and 16 vertical-launch ASROC ASW missiles, but the ASROC installation has been canceled for this class. During Operation Desert Storm in 1991, DD 991 launched 58 Tomahawks at Iraqi military targets. At some future date it may be possible to launch Standard SM-2 MR missiles from the vertical-launch cells as well, with the missiles to be controlled by an accompanying Aegis-equipped ship. DD 966, 967, and 968 received the vertical-launch group in 1986–87; the others (less the box-launcher ships) are receiving VLS during regular overhauls. DD 966 made first at-sea VLS ASROC launch during 12-87.

DD 977 has had the GFCS modified to Mk 86 Mod. 10 (with a UYK-7 computer in place of the Mk 152 computer, Mk 113 display consoles, new fuze-setters, etc.) to conduct trials with semi-active laser-guided projectiles. DD 977 tested Mk 38 VLS Sea Sparrow launcher for NATO, 1988–89. DD 976 was also used in 1981 for trials with the General Electric EX-83, 30-mm gatling gun system, which uses a GAU-8 heavy gun and was to carry out trials with an extended-range version of Sea Sparrow. Planned backfitting of the Mk 71, 203-mm gun in the forward position was canceled in 1978 when development of that excellent weapon was unfortunately canceled. DD 971 has carried a prototype Mk 49 (EX-41) RAM point-defense missile launcher on the starboard quarter and also has the prototype USC-38(V) EHF SATCOMM installation ("FLTSAT-7").

All ships of the class are scheduled to receive the Hughes Mk 23 TAS (Target Acquisition System), which uses a high-rpm radar mounted on an aft-projecting platform on the mainmast to detect low-flying, high-speed missiles and aircraft. The SPS-55 surface-search radar has been moved to a new, higher platform on the foremast in order to accommodate the radome housing the antenna for the SQQ-28 LAMPS III helicopter data link. DD 980 commenced trials fall 1985 with the integrated SQQ-89 sonar system, incorporating the SQS-53B (later: SQS-53C) active bow sonar and the SQR-19 TACTASS array. DD 965 conducted the unsuccessful operational evaluation of the SAR-8 infrared surveillance system in 1991, and the device will now not be fitted in this or other U.S.N. classes.

All will eventually have the SQQ-89(V)1 system, with SQS-53C sonar, SQR-19 towed array, SQQ-28 helicopter ASW data-link, Mk 116 Mod. 5 ASW f.c.s., and SIMAS processing. DD 966 carried the SQR-15 TASS on a WestPac tour during 1985, and the equipment is still normally mounted in two Atlantic Fleet and two Pacific Fleet ships on a rotational basis. All carry the SLQ-17 sonar signal processor. Early units were given the WLR-1 EW system as an interim installation until SLQ-32(V)2 was available; at least two ships (DD 971, 975) have carried *both.* In 1987, it was announced that the EW suite would be upgraded to SLQ-32(V)3 in all. DD 974 carries the prototype SSQ-74 ICADS (Integrated Cover and Deception System). RAST deck-haul systems were added (beginning with DD 989 in 4-85) to permit handling the SH-60B LAMPS-III ASW helicopter.

In the most recent overhaul/modernizations (see photos of DD 973 and DD 979), the Mk 15 CIWS mounts are being installed in "Maintenance Enclosures," and the aft mount has been raised atop a new deckhouse; in addition, the portside SLQ-32(V)3 antenna has been moved aft to beneath the CIWS mounting. During her 1991–92 refit at Bath Iron Works, DD 997 received the vertical launcher conversion, RAST equipment on the helicopter flight deck, the CIWS Maintenance Enclosure and Block 1 upgrade to hold more on-mount ammunition, the full SQQ-89 sonar/LAMPS III helicopter package, and her SLQ-32 EW system upgraded to SLQ-32(V)3.

Note: All units of the *Forrest Sherman* and *Hull*-class destroyers have now been stricken, having been placed in reserve during the early 1980s: *Morton* (DD 948) and *Richard S. Edwards* (DD 950) on 7-2-90; *Turner Joy* (DD 951) on 13-2-90 for use as an exhibit at Bremerton, Washington; *Manley* (DD 940), *Dupont* (DD 941), and *Bigelow* (DD 942) on 1-6-90; *Mullinix* (DD 944) on 26-7-90; and *Forrest Sherman* (DD 931), *Davis* (DD 937), and *Blandy* (DD 943) on 27-7-90. Four sisters had been stricken earlier: *Barry* (DD 933) on 31-1-83 for use as a memorial at Washington, D.C.; *Jonas Ingram* (DD 938) on 15-6-83; *Hull* (DD 945) on 15-10-83, and *Edson* (DD 946), the last to be active, on 15-8-88 for display in New York City.

GUIDED-MISSILE FRIGATES

♦ **51 Oliver Hazard Perry class (SCN 207/2081 type)** (*Atlantic/† Pacific Fleet; Naval Reserve Force ships: FFG 7, 9–13, 15, 20–23, 27)

	Bldr	Laid down	L	In[illegible]
FFG 7 Oliver Hazard Perry (ex-PF 109)*	Bath Iron Works	6-12-75	9-25-76	17-[illegible]
FFG 8 McInerney*	Bath Iron Works	16-1-78	4-11-78	15-[illegible]
FFG 9 Wadsworth†	Todd, San Pedro	13-7-77	29-7-78	2[illegible]
FFG 10 Duncan†	Todd, Seattle	29-4-77	1-3-78	2-[illegible]
FFG 11 Clark*	Bath Iron Works	17-7-78	24-3-79	[illegible]
FFG 12 George Philip†	Todd, San Pedro	14-12-77	16-12-78	15-[illegible]
FFG 13 Samuel Eliot Morison*	Bath Iron Works	4-12-78	14-7-79	10-[illegible]
FFG 14 Sides†	Todd, San Pedro	7-8-78	19-5-79	3[illegible]
FFG 15 Estocin*	Bath Iron Works	2-4-79	3-11-79	1[illegible]
FFG 16 Clifton Sprague*	Bath Iron Works	30-7-79	16-2-80	2[illegible]
FFG 19 John A. Moore†	Todd, San Pedro	19-12-78	20-10-79	14-[illegible]
FFG 20 Antrim*	Todd, Seattle	21-6-78	27-3-79	2[illegible]
FFG 21 Flatley*	Bath Iron Works	13-11-79	15-5-80	2[illegible]
FFG 22 Fahrion*	Todd, Seattle	1-12-78	24-8-79	1[illegible]
FFG 23 Lewis B. Puller†	Todd, San Pedro	23-5-79	15-3-80	1[illegible]
FFG 24 Jack Williams*	Bath Iron Works	25-2-80	30-8-80	1[illegible]
FFG 25 Copeland†	Todd, San Pedro	24-10-79	26-7-80	[illegible]
FFG 26 Gallery*	Bath Iron Works	17-5-80	20-12-80	5-[illegible]
FFG 27 Mahlon S. Tisdale†	Todd, San Pedro	19-3-80	7-2-81	13-[illegible]
FFG 28 Boone*	Todd, Seattle	27-3-79	16-1-80	1[illegible]
FFG 29 Stephen W. Groves*	Bath Iron Works	16-9-80	4-4-81	1[illegible]
FFG 30 Reid†	Todd, San Pedro	8-10-80	27-6-81	1[illegible]
FFG 31 Stark*	Todd, Seattle	24-8-79	30-5-80	23-[illegible]
FFG 32 John L. Hall*	Bath Iron Works	5-1-81	24-7-81	2[illegible]
FFG 33 Jarrett†	Todd, San Pedro	11-2-81	17-10-81	[illegible]
FFG 34 Aubrey Fitch*	Bath Iron Works	10-4-81	17-10-81	9-[illegible]
FFG 36 Underwood*	Bath Iron Works	3-8-81	6-2-82	2[illegible]
FFG 37 Crommelin†	Todd, Seattle	30-5-80	1-7-81	1[illegible]
FFG 38 Curts†	Todd, San Pedro	1-7-81	6-3-82	8-[illegible]
FFG 39 Doyle*	Bath Iron Works	16-11-81	22-5-82	2[illegible]
FFG 40 Halyburton*	Todd, Seattle	26-9-80	13-10-81	[illegible]
FFG 41 McCluskey†	Todd, San Pedro	21-10-81	18-9-82	10-[illegible]
FFG 42 Klakring*	Bath Iron Works	19-2-82	18-9-82	2[illegible]
FFG 43 Thach†	Todd, San Pedro	6-2-82	18-12-82	1[illegible]
FFG 45 De Wert*	Bath Iron Works	14-6-82	18-12-82	19-[illegible]
FFG 46 Rentz†	Todd, San Pedro	18-9-82	16-7-83	3[illegible]
FFG 47 Nicholas*	Bath Iron Works	27-9-82	23-4-83	1[illegible]
FFG 48 Vandegrift†	Todd, Seattle	13-10-81	15-10-82	24-[illegible]
FFG 49 Robert G. Bradley*	Bath Iron Works	28-12-82	13-8-83	1[illegible]
FFG 50 Taylor*	Bath Iron Works	5-5-83	5-11-83	1-[illegible]
FFG 51 Gary†	Todd, San Pedro	18-12-82	19-11-83	17-[illegible]
FFG 52 Carr*	Todd, Seattle	26-3-82	26-2-83	2[illegible]
FFG 53 Hawes*	Bath Iron Works	22-8-83	17-2-84	[illegible]
FFG 54 Ford†	Todd, San Pedro	16-7-83	23-6-84	2[illegible]
FFG 55 Elrod*	Bath Iron Works	14-11-83	12-5-84	[illegible]
FFG 56 Simpson*	Bath Iron Works	27-2-84	31-8-84	9-[illegible]
FFG 57 Reuben James†	Todd, San Pedro	10-9-83	8-2-85	2[illegible]
FFG 58 Samuel B. Roberts*	Bath Iron Works	21-5-84	8-12-84	1[illegible]
FFG 59 Kauffman*	Bath Iron Works	8-4-85	29-3-86	2[illegible]
FFG 60 Rodney M. Davis*	Todd, San Pedro	8-2-85	11-1-86	[illegible]
FFG 61 Ingraham†	Todd, San Pedro	30-3-87	26-6-88	[illegible]

Authorized: FFG 7 in FY 73, FFG 8–10 in FY 75, FFG 11–16 in F[illegible] FFG 19–26 in FY 77, FFG 27–34 in FY 78, FFG 36–43 in FY 79, FFG [illegible] in FY 80, FFG 50–55 in FY 81, FFG 56–58 in FY 82, FFG 59, 60 in [illegible] FFG 61 in FY 84

UIDED-MISSILE FRIGATES *(continued)*

hrion (FFG 22)—short-hulled Naval Reserve Force unit
Dr. Giorgio Arra, 2-91

rim (FFG 20)—short-hulled Naval Reserve Force unit
Dr. Giorgio Arra, 5-91

A. Moore (FFG 19)—short-hulled Naval Reserve Force unit
Dennis Moore, 7-90

in (FFG 15)—with steel fenders added for Great Lakes cruise
Victor M. Baca, 7-91

Reid (FFG 30)—short-hulled unit, with SLQ-32(V) 5 EW suite
Dr. Giorgio Arra, 10-91

Crommelin (FFG 37)—long-hulled unit, SH-60B LAMPS-III helo on deck
Leo Van Ginderen, 1992

John L. Hall (FFG 32)—with lengthened hull for LAMPS-III; note port for SQR-19 towed array to port on transom stern, twin slots for SLQ-25 Nixie torpedo decoy to starboard
Luciano Grazioli, 5-90

Underwood (FFG 36)—first unit built with long hull
Dr. Giorgio Arra, 3-91

GUIDED-MISSILE FRIGATES *(continued)*

Doyle (FFG 39) Peter C. Westdijk, 9-91

Nicholas (FFG 47) Dr. Giorgio Arra, 6-91

Stark (FFG 31) Bernard Prézelin, 5-90

Aubrey Fitch (FFG 34) Dr. Giorgio Arra, 3-91

D: Short hulls: 2,769 tons light (3,658 fl); long hulls: 3,010–3,210 tons light (3,900–4,100 fl)
S: 29 kts (30.6 trials)
Dim: 135.64; FFG 7, 8, 15, 28, 29, 32, 36–58: 138.80 (125.9 wl) × 13.72 × 5.8 (6.7 max.)
A: 1/Mk 13 Mod. 4 launcher (4 Harpoon and 36 Standard SM-1 MR missiles)—1/76-mm 62-cal. Mk 75 DP—1/20-mm Mk 15 CIWS—2/12.7-mm mg (I × 2)—6/324-mm Mk 32 Mod. 7 ASW TT (III × 2)— FFG 8, 15, 28, 29, 32, 36–61: 1 or 2/SH-60B Seahawk LAMPS-III (others: 1/SH-2F Seasprite LAMPS-I) ASW helicopters
Electron Equipt:
Radar: 1/SPS-55 surf. search., 1/SPS-49(V)2 (FFG 61: (V)5) air search, 1/Mk 92 Mod. 4 (FFG 50, 51, 53, 55, 56, 61: Mod. 6) missile/gun f.c., 1/STIR (SPG-60 Mod.) missile/gun f.c.
Sonar: SQQ-89(V)2 suite (SQS-56 hull-mounted LF, SQR-19 TACTASS towed array, SQQ-28 LAMPS-III datalink) except FFG 10, 24, 27, 31, 34, 51, 52, 54: SQS-56 only
EW: SLQ-32(V)2 passive or (V)5 with Sidekick jammer, Mk 36 SRBOC decoy RL syst. (VI × 2 Hycor Mk 137 launchers), SLQ-25 Nixie towed acoustic torpedo decoy
TACAN: URN-25
M: 2 G.E. LM-2500 gas turbines; 1 5.5-m-diameter CP, 5-bladed prop; 41,000 shp (40,000 sust.)—2 drop-down electric propulsors; 720 sh
Electric: 3,000 kw tot. **Range:** 4,200/20; 5,000/18
Fuel: 587 tons + 64 tons helicopter fuel
Crew: 17–20 officers, 15 chief petty officers, 183–190 enlisted (217 max. accomm.)

Remarks: These ships were originally conceived as low-cost convoy escorts (hence original "PF" hull number for the prototype). As older first-line destroyers and friga have been retired without replacement, however, the FFG 7 ships have been integra into the fleet, and numerous updates have been applied to permit them to cope w modern combat conditions. As a result, the fully equipped units displace nearly tons more than the designed displacement, and the size of crews has greatly increa The soundness of the design has permitted the expansion, and the ships have pro remarkably sturdy.

The navy had hoped to phase out construction of this class with the FY 83 ships, F 59 and 60, but Congress authorized (but did not fully fund) FFG 61 in FY 84; FF was initially mandated to have the unbuilt and untested Sperry Phase-III update to Mk 92 weapons-control system, adding four X-band fixed phased-array radar pa (two facing the after quadrants on a mast platform and two covering the forw quadrants atop the bridge).

Original complement was planned at 17 officers, 167 enlisted, which was found too many officers but far too few enlisted to run and maintain the ships. Therefore, 19 and up are fitted with 30 additional enlisted bunks, with the others backfit Naval Reserve Force ships have about 76 naval reservists in their complements.

FFG 17, 18, 35, and 44 of this class were built by Todd, Seattle, for Australia, w has built two more in-country. Spain has built four and has two more on order, Taiwan is to build at least eight. FFG 31 was hit 17-5-87 by two Exocet missiles (on not explode) and survived; repaired 1-11-87 to 31-8-88 at Ingalls, Pascagoula. FF hit a mine 14-4-88 and was repaired at Bath Iron Works 1-10-88 to 10-89.

Aviation systems: Although these ships were intended to operate the LAMP ASW helicopter, FFG 7–35 (less FFG 8), as completed, lacked the equipment neces to handle them. Beginning with the FY 79 ships (FFG 36 and later), helicopter su equipment was aboard on completion: fin stabilizers, RAST (Recovery Assist Securing, and Traversing system) not fitted as completed until FFG 50, and systems. The RAST system permits helicopter launch and recovery with the rolling through 28 degrees and pitching 5 degrees. The equipment was first install *McInerney* (FFG 8), which was reconstructed, completing 12-2-81 at Bath Iron W to act as LAMPS-III/SH-60B Seahawk helicopter trials ship; the stern was length by 3.16 m (the extension being slightly lower than the flight deck, to accomm mooring equipment) by changing the rake of the stern. The earlier ships are now lengthened: FFG 7, 15, 28, 29, and 32 lengthened or lengthening through FY 90. 39 conducted sea trials with the Canadair CL-227 drone surveillance helicopter d 1991.

Hull and propulsion systems: Displacements have steadily increased, to th riment of stability. FFG 59 was delivered at 4,100 tons full load, although the clas designed for 3,600 tons and a growth margin of only 39 tons! These ships are pa larly well protected against splinter and fragmentation damage, with 1 aluminum-alloy armor over magazine spaces, 16-mm steel over the main en

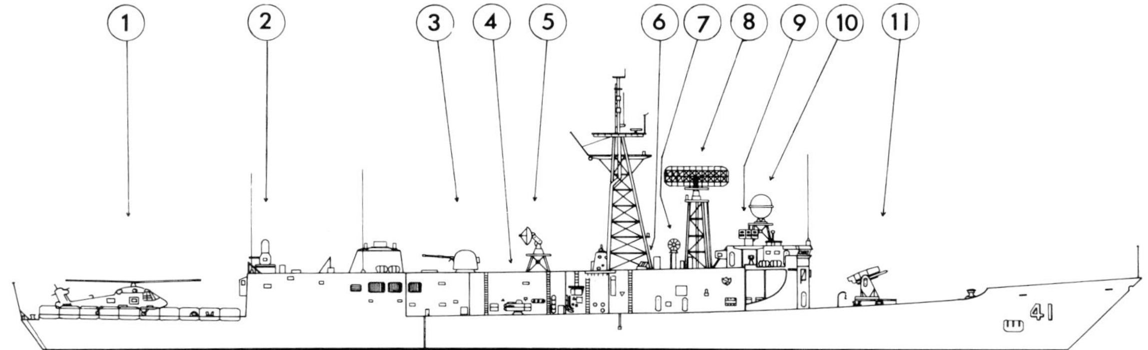

McCluskey (FFG 41) 1. SH-2F Seasprite LAMPS-I helicopter 2. 20-mm Mk 15 CIWS 3. 76-mm Mk 75 DP 4. triple Mk 32 ASW TT 5. STIR fire-control radar 6. Mk 137 rocket launchers for Mk 36 SRBOC decoy system 7. OE-82 antennas for WSC-3 UHF SATCOMM 8. SPS-49 air-search radar 9. SLQ-32(V)2 EW array 10. Mk 92 fire-control radar 11. Mk 13 missile launcher Drawing by Robert Dumas

:D-MISSILE FRIGATES *(continued)*

·oom, and 19-mm Kevlar plastic armor over vital electronics and command 3peed on one turbine is 25 knots; the auxiliary power system uses two retract-s located well forward and can drive the ships at up to 6 knots.

ons and sensor systems: The Mk 92 Mod. 4 fire-control system controls ınd 76-mm gunfire; it uses a STIR (modified SPG-60) antenna amidships and a ilt version of the Hollandse Signaal Apparaaten WM-28 radar forward, and k four separate targets. The Mk 92 system was programmed for three stages of ment; the first, given trials in FFG 29 in 1983, was to be backfitted to all by the "Near-Term Improvement," along with Standard SM-1 MR Block 6 mis-

two (Mk 92 CORT) began trials in FFG 15 in 5-86. The CORT (Coherent 'Transmit Transceiver) Phase-II upgrade to the Mk 92 weapons-control system s performance in jamming and clutter; the search radar was upgraded to V)5, and the SYS-2(V)2 integrated action data system was added. FFG 50, 51, ınd 56 received CORT under FY 88, and FFG 61 was completed with it. The ınd cost are considerable, and plans for further conversions were canceled. major weapons system improvement plans have been abandoned.

1k 75 gun is a license-built version of the OTO Melara Compact. A Mk 13 -direction system is fitted. Two Mk 24 optical missile and gun target designa-ınted in tubs atop the pilothouse) were not fitted to the ships as completed until and have been backfitted in the earlier ships. The only ship-launched ASW are the Mk 46 or Mk 50 torpedoes in the two triple torpedo tubes; a total of 24 s can be carried, but ships with magazines altered to accept the larger Mk 50 carry the Penguin antiship missile for helicopter use with the loss of one for each missile carried.

1k 15 CIWS (Close-In Weapon System) 20-mm Phalanx was backfitted into all 1988; the improved Mk 15 Block 1 will be backfitted in the 1990s. Harpoon are launched via the SWG-1 launch-control system.

1 incorporates all of the changes once planned for backfit to earlier ships and is ed the first "Baseline 8" unit; she has integrated radar sensors (with the ')2 Integrated Action Data System), Mk 92 Mod. 6 CORT weapons-control integrated EW suite, and integrated SPS-49(V)5 and SPS-55 radars. FFG ave the integrated EW suite, the SQQ-89 sonar suite, and Links 11 and 14. 35 had non-integrated SLQ-32(V)2 and Mk 92 Mod. 2 f.c.s. All are to be ed with the "Sidekick" active adjunct to the SLQ-32(V)2 EW system; FFG 29, nd several others had the antennas by mid-1992. A few ships have been given made navigational radars. All have SRR-1 and WSC-3 SATCOMM equipment.

nits with long hulls (FFG 7, 8, 15, 28, 29, 32, 36–61) were to have had the sonar graded to SQQ-89(V)2, with SQS-56 hull sonar retained, SQR-19 towed linear hydrophone array added, and SQQ-28 helicopter sonobuoy data-link system There were, however, significant delays in the development of the SQQ-89's r equipment, and many ships received the SQR-18 towed array with SQR-17 r as an interim fit. FFG 8 received the towed array during FY 87, along with -60; in FY 88, FFG 28, 29, 32, 36, and 39 were equipped; in FY 90, FFG 7 and 15 the system during overhauls (FFG 7 was lengthened, received fin stabilizers SQQ-89 suite, but was not equipped with RAST, leaving her unable to employ helicopters); in FY 91, FFG 9, 48–50, and 52 and in FY 92, FFG 20 and 51 were ııpped. As of 1992, it was not planned to install the SQQ-89 suite in FFG 10, 24, 4, 51, 52, and 54.

ersian Gulf service, FFG 22 and 47 were equipped with 25-mm "Bushmaster" le chain guns amidships on the main deck. FFG 47 received a "Kingfisher" oidance modification to her SQS-56 sonar. FFG 37 received the McDonnell Astronautics Mast-Mounted Sight (a modified helicopter electro-optical de-)p the pilothouse, with the display being in the CIC.

s: At one point, 15 ships of the class were assigned to the Naval Reserve Force, e have been returned to regular navy duty. Dates of assignment to the Naval Force were: FFG 10 on 13-1-84, FFG 7 on 31-5-84, FFG 16 on 31-8-84, FFG 9 on FFG 11 on 30-9-85, FFG 12 on 18-1-86, FFG 13 on 30-6-86, FFG 14 on 16-8-86, on 30-9-86, FFG 19 and FFG 20 on 30-1-87, FFG 23 on 1-6-87, FFG 27 on FFG 22 on 30-9-88, and FFG 25 on 30-9-89. On 1-11-90, FFG 14, 19, and 25 ıssigned to the regular navy; planned assignment of FFG 24 and 26 to the NRF celed during 7-90. FFG 41 and 43 have been home-ported in Yokosuka, Japan, 91.

rooke class (SCR 199B type) (In reserve)

	Bldr	Laid down	L	In serv.
Ramsey	Lockheed, Seattle	4-2-63	15-10-63	3-6-67
Schofield	Lockheed, Seattle	15-4-63	7-12-63	11-5-68

ıorized: FY 62

,643 tons (3,600 fl) **S:** 27.2 kts designed (29 kts in service)

: 126.33 (121.9 wl) × 13.47 × 7.9 (over sonar)

./Mk 22 launcher (I × 1, 16 Standard SM-1 MR missiles)—./127-mm 38-cal. Mk 30 DP—1/Mk 16 Mod. 4 ASROC ASW RL VIII × 1; no reloads)—6/324-mm Mk 32 ASW TT (III × 2)—1/SH-F LAMPS-I ASW helicopter

:tron Equipt:

ıdar: 1/LN-66 nav., 1/SPS-10F surf. search, 1/SPS-52B 3-D air search, 1/SPG-51C missile f.c., 1/Mk 35 gun f.c.

nar: 1/SQS-26BX hull-mounted LF—TACAN: SRN-15A

W: SLQ-32(V)2 intercept, Mk 36 SRBOC decoy RL (VI × 2, Hycor Mk 137 launchers), T. Mk 6 Fanfare towed acoustic torpedo decoy

1 set Westinghouse geared steam turbines; 1 prop; 35,000 shp

ers: 2 Foster-Wheeler; 84 kg/cm², 510°C **Electric:** 2,000 kw tot.

ge: 4,000/20 **Fuel:** 600 tons **Crew:** 16 officers, 250 enlisted

ks: Differed from the *Garcia* class in having their aft 127-mm gun replaced by le launcher. Excellent sea-keeping qualities. Anti-rolling stabilizers. The han-ııch was enlarged for the SH-2 LAMPS-I helicopter, is telescoping, as on the ass. A Mk 56 Mod. 43 radar gunfire-control system is carried, while the missile

Schofield (FFG 3) Dr. Giorgio Arra, 1984

system is Mk 74 Mod. 6; Mk 4 Mod. 2 weapons-direction system is fitted, as is the Mk 114 ASW control system. Have the SLQ-32(V)2 intercept array in place of the original WLR-1, WLR-3, and ULQ-6 suite.

Status: FFG 2 decommissioned 1-9-88 and FFG 3 on 8-9-88; both are stored at Bremerton and were to have been transferred to Turkey in 1989 but were rejected. Four sisters are on five-year lease to Pakistan: *Brooke* (FFG 1) decommissioned 16-9-88 and transferred 1-2-89; *Talbot* (FFG 4) decommissioned 30-9-88 and transferred 31-4-89; *Richard L. Page* (FFG 5) decommissioned 30-9-88 and transferred 31-3-89; and *Julius A. Furer* (FFG 6) decommissioned 10-11-88 and transferred 31-1-89.

FRIGATES

◆ 41 Knox class

Bldrs: A: Todd SY, Seattle, Washington; B: Todd SY, San Pedro, California; C: Lockheed SB & Construction, Seattle; D: Avondale SY, Avondale, Louisiana (*Atlantic/†Pacific Fleet)

8 Naval Reserve Force training ships:

	Bldr	Laid down	L	In serv.
FFT 1078 Joseph Hewes*	D	15-5-69	7-3-70	24-4-71
FFT 1079 Bowen*	D	11-7-69	2-5-70	22-5-71
FFT 1084 McCandless*	D	4-6-70	20-3-71	18-3-72
FFT 1085 Donald B. Beary†	D	24-7-70	22-5-71	22-7-72
FFT 1089 Jesse L. Brown*	D	8-4-71	18-3-72	17-2-73
FFT 1090 Ainsworth*	D	11-6-71	15-4-72	31-3-73
FFT 1095 Truett*	D	27-4-72	3-2-73	1-6-74
FFT 1097 Moinester*	D	25-8-72	12-7-73	2-11-74

8 active as of 30-9-92 (all for foreign transfer or reserve in FY 93):

	Bldr	Laid down	L	In serv.	Decomm.
FF 1063 Reasoner†	C	6-1-69	1-8-70	31-1-71	. . .
FF 1064 Lockwood†	A	3-11-67	5-9-68	5-12-70	. . .
FF 1076 Fanning†	B	7-12-68	24-1-70	23-7-71	. . .
FF 1077 Ouellet†	D	15-1-69	17-1-70	12-12-70	. . .
FF 1082 Elmer Montgomery*	D	23-1-70	21-11-70	30-10-71	. . .
FF 1087 Kirk†	D	4-12-70	25-9-71	9-9-72	. . .
FF 1092 Thomas C. Hart*	D	8-10-71	12-8-72	28-7-73	. . .
FF 1093 Capodanno*	D	12-10-71	21-10-72	17-11-73	. . .

25 in reserve as of 30-9-92:

	Bldr	Laid down	L	In serv.	Decomm.
FF 1052 *Knox*	A	5-10-65	19-11-66	12-4-69	14-2-92
FF 1053 *Roark*	A	2-2-66	24-4-67	22-11-69	14-12-91
FF 1054 *Gray*	A	19-11-66	3-10-67	4-4-70	29-6-91
FF 1055 *Hepburn*	B	1-6-66	25-3-67	3-7-69	20-12-91
FF 1057 *Rathburne*	C	8-1-68	2-5-69	16-5-70	14-2-92
FF 1058 *Meyerkord*	B	1-9-66	15-7-67	28-11-69	14-12-91
FF 1059 *W. S. Sims*	D	10-4-67	4-1-69	3-1-70	6-9-91
FF 1060 *Lang*	B	25-3-67	17-2-68	28-3-70	12-12-91
FF 1061 *Patterson*	D	12-10-67	3-5-69	14-3-70	30-9-91
FF 1062 *Whipple*	A	24-4-67	12-4-68	22-8-70	14-2-92
FF 1065 *Stein*	C	1-6-70	19-12-70	8-1-72	19-3-92
FF 1066 *Marvin Shields*	A	12-4-68	23-10-69	10-4-71	2-7-92
FF 1067 *Francis Hammond*	B	15-7-67	11-5-68	25-7-70	2-7-92
FF 1069 *Bagley*	A	22-9-70	24-4-71	6-5-72	26-9-91
FF 1070 *Downes*	A	5-9-68	13-12-69	28-8-71	5-6-92

FRIGATES *(continued)*

FF 1071 *Badger*	B	17-2-68	7-12-68	1-12-70	20-12-91
FF 1072 *Blakely*	D	3-6-68	23-8-69	18-7-70	15-11-91
FF 1074 *Harold E. Holt*	B	11-5-68	3-5-69	26-3-71	2-7-92
FF 1080 *Paul*	D	12-9-69	20-6-70	14-8-71	15-8-92
FF 1081 *Aylwin*	D	13-11-69	29-8-70	18-9-71	15-5-92
FF 1083 *Cook*	D	20-3-70	23-1-71	18-12-71	30-4-92
FF 1088 *Barbey*	D	5-2-71	4-12-71	11-11-72	19-3-92
FF 1091 *Miller*	D	6-8-71	3-6-72	30-6-73	15-10-91
FF 1094 *Pharris*	D	11-2-72	16-12-72	26-1-74	15-4-92
FF 1096 *Valdez*	D	30-6-72	24-3-73	27-7-74	15-12-91

Authorized: 10 in FY 64, 16 in FY 65, 10 in FY 66, 10 in FY 67

Barbey (FF 1088)—now in reserve Dr. Giorgio Arra, 10-91

Knox (FF 1052)—still with Mk 25 Sea Sparrow BPDMS
Leo Van Ginderen, 7-91

Donald B. Beary (FFT 1085)—still without bow bulwarks or spray strakes; Naval Reserve training unit George Nassiopoulos, 3-91

D: 3,130 tons light (4,260 fl) **S:** 27+ kts
Dim: 134.00 (126.49 wl) × 14.33 × 4.77 (7.83 over sonar)
A: 4/Harpoon SSM (using Mk 16 Mod. 8 ASROC launcher system)—1/127-mm 54-cal. Mk 42 DP—1/20-mm Mk 15 CIWS (FF 1052, 1065: 1/Mk 25 Sea Sparrow SAM launcher (VIII × 1) in lieu of CIWS)—1/Mk 16 Mod. 8 ASROC ASW RL (VIII × 1)—4/324-mm Mk 32 Mod. 9 fixed ASW TT (II × 2)—1/SH-2F Seasprite LAMPS-I ASW helicopter
Electron Equipt:
Radar: 1/LN-66, SPS-53, or SPS-64(V)9 nav., 1/SPS-10F or SPS-67 surf. search, 1/SPS-40D air search, 1/SPG-53F gun f.c. (Sea Sparrow ships: 1/Mk 115 f.c. also)

Ouellet (FF 1077)—active unit, Pacific Fleet
Percy C. Hunt via Malcolm Dipp

Miller (FF 1091)—with modified ASROC launcher
Dr. Giorgio Arr

Thomas C. Hart (FF 1092)—active unit, with SQS-35 VDS access transom stern; telescoping hangar extended Dr. Giorgio Arr

Sonar: 1/SQS-26CX bow-mounted LF, SQS-35(V) VDS (inactiv *see* Remarks; no VDS in FF 1053 to FF 1055, FF 1057 to 1062, FF 1072, FF 1077); SQR-18A(V)1 TACTASS on V ships, SQR-18A(V)2 towed passive linear hydrophone ar on others
EW: SLQ-32(V)2 intercept, Mk 36 SRBOC decoy 1 RL (VI × 2), T. Mk 6 Fanfare or SLQ-25 Nixie towed acoustic torpedo d
TACAN: SRN-15A
M: 1 set Westinghouse geared steam turbines; 1 prop; 35,000 shp
Boilers: 2 Babcock & Wilcox or Combustion Engineering D-Type 84 kg/cm^2, 510°C
Electric: 3,000 kw tot. (3 × 750-kw turbogenerators, 1 × 750-kw diesel set)
Fuel: 750 tons max. **Range:** 4,300/20
Crew: 17–20 officers, 255–267 enlisted

Remarks: An additional ten ships of the FY 68 program (FF 1098 to FF 110 canceled. During 1992 FFT 1079 had one woman officer and 11 enlisted wom 1084 was in collision with the Yugoslav merchant ship *Kalos* in the Red Sea on Plans to significantly upgrade the ships were greatly scaled back by 1990 a canceled altogether when it was deemed that there was a lessening need for th that the increasing cost of modernizing the aging vessels could not be justified

Status: Three transferred to Greece, *Vreeland* (FF 1068) on 25-7-92, *Tri* 1075) on 30-7-92, and *Connole* (FF 1056) on 30-8-92. Two have been transf Taiwan, *Brewton* (FF 1086) on 2-7-92 and *Robert E. Peary* (FF 1073, ex-*Con* 7-8-92; *Kirk* (FF 1087) is to transfer to Taiwan in 8-93, and three additional un follow. The eight units now officially typed as "FFT" were redesignated FF

RIGATES *(continued)*

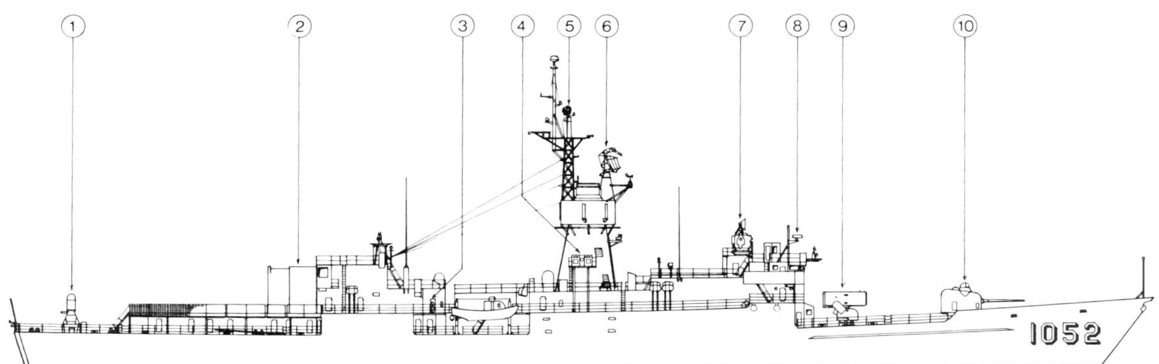

Knox (FF 1052) 1. 20-mm Mk 15 CIWS (note: on FF 1052 and FF 1065, Mk 25 Sea Sparrow BPDMS vice Mk 15 CIWS) 2. telescoping hangar for SH-2F Seasprite LAMPS-I helicopter 3. twin, fixed Mk 32 ASW TT 4. SLQ-32(V)2 EW array 5. SPS-10-series surface-search radar 6. SPS-40-series air-search radar 7. Mk 68 gun f.c. director 8. navigational radar 9. Mk 16 Mod. 8 ASROC launcher 10. 127-mm Mk 42 DP gun Drawing by A. D. Baker III

se L. Brown (FFT 1089) Dr. Giorgio Arra, 8-91

), 1085, and 1089 on 15-12-91 and FFT 1095, 1097, 1084, and 1090 on 31-12-91; are each intended to train sufficient crews to man the inactive units should they be tivated from 180-day reserve status. FF 1064 and FF 1076, which had been used as al Reserve Force ships, were returned to regular navy status at the end of FY 91. veen 1982 and 1991, 13 had been assigned to non-deploying Naval Reserve Force ice, with partial reservist crews.

ull systems: Except on FFT 1085 and FF 1093, bow bulwarks and a spray strake been added forward to reduce deck wetness, a problem in this class; the addition d 9.1 tons and extended the overall length from the original 133.59 m. The spray ke was longer in the earlier conversions. FF 1078 to FF 1097 have a TEAM (SM-5) outer system for the continual monitoring of the ship's electronic equipment. -rolling fin stabilizers fitted in all. Prairie-Masker bubbler system is fitted to hulls propellers to reduce radiated noise. FF 1088 had a controllable-pitch prop for trials, replaced by a standard screw.

eapons systems: The ASROC system has an automatic reloading magazine be- h the bridge; it is also used to stow the Harpoon missiles, which are launched from ort pair of eight launcher cells (FF 1091 first to receive Harpoon, 1976). FF 1091 ner ASROC launcher modified in 1988 in an effort to reduce launch flash and blast ts. FF 1084 to FF 1097 never received a Mk 25 BPDMS (Basic Point Defense ile System) launcher for Sea Sparrow. FF 1070 was used as NATO Sea Sparrow ship; she carried a Mk 29 NATO Sea Sparrow launcher and the two-director Mk od. 1 fire-control system, later reduced to one director (Mk 91 Mod. 0 system); FF also carried the Hughes Mk 23 Mod. 0 TAS (Target Acquisition System) in place of PS-40 radar; these systems were removed during her 1983 refit. The ASW torpedo are fixed in the forward end of the hangar superstructure, aimed outboard at an of 45 degrees. Except on FF 1052, 1061, and 1065, the Mk 25 BPDMS launcher for Sparrow was replaced by a 20-mm Mk 15 Phalanx CIWS gatling AA system, nning with FF 1087 in 1982. Ships with Sea Sparrow had a single Mk 115 missile ontrol system (Mk 71 director). All have Mk 114 ASW fire-control system. In some (see photo of FFT 1085), the optical rangefinder has been removed from the Mk 68 irector.

nsor systems: Beginning with 12 ships under FY 80, the SQS-35 towed VDS ducer body and hoist was modified to permit towing the SQR-18A TACTASS; the 35 sonars themselves were deactivated during 1991. Non-VDS ships received 18A(V)2 TACTASS; trials were conducted in FF 1077 during 1983. All carry a Mk nfire-control system with SPG-53D or F radar. SPS-67 radar has been replacing 0; a few earlier briefly had had their SPS-10 sets replaced by SPS-58. SLQ-32(V)1 upgraded to (V)2) replaced WLR-1C as the EW suite; some (FF 1064, 1067, 1070, etc.) had *both* for a while, but WLR-1C has now been removed from all. Most have X-band navigational radars, and all have two OE-82 antennas for the WSC-3 satellite-communications system. The ASW TDS (Tactical Data System) was led in all beginning FY 83, and they also have a form of "mini-NTDS" called S (Frigate Integrated Shipboard Tactical System) that employs off-the-shelf op computers. All have SQR-17 sonar data-link processors.

◆ **2 Garcia class (SCB 199A type)** (In reserve)

	Bldr	Laid down	L	In serv.
FF 1043 *Edward McDonnell*	Avondale SY	1-4-63	15-2-64	15-2-65
FF 1047 *Voge*	Defoe SB	21-11-63	4-2-65	25-11-66

Authorized: FF 1043 in FY 62, FF 1047 in FY 63

Voge (FF 1047) Pradignac & Léo, 11-88

D: 2,624 tons (3,400–3,560 fl) **S:** 27 kts (29 kts in service)
Dim: 126.33 (121.9 wl) × 13.47 × 7.90 (over sonar)
A: 2/127-mm 38-cal. DP (I × 2)—1/Mk 16 Mod. 4 ASROC ASW RL (VIII × 1; FF 1047 only: 8 reloads)—6/324-mm Mk 32 ASW TT (III × 2)—FF 1047 only: 1/SH-2F LAMPS-I ASW helicopter
Electron Equipt:
Radar: 1/LN-66 nav., 1/SPS-10F surf. search, 1/SPS-40 air search, 1/Mk 35 gun f.c.
Sonar: FF 1043: SQS-26BX hull-mounted LF; FF 1047: SQS-26AXR
EW: WLR-1H and WLR-3 intercept, ULQ-6 deception jammer, 2/Mk 33 RBOC (VI × 2), T. Mk 6 Fanfare towed torpedo decoy
TACAN: FF 1047 only: SRN-15
M: 1 set General Electric geared steam turbines; 1 prop; 35,000 shp
Boilers: 2 Foster-Wheeler; 83.4 kg/cm^2, 510°C
Range: 4,000/20 **Fuel:** 600 tons **Electric:** 2,000 kw
Crew: 18 officers, 250 enlisted

Remarks: Anti-rolling stabilizers fitted. FF 1047 has a special ASW NTDS. The boilers are vertical and have turbopressurized combustion. Hangar enlarged to 14.6 × 5.4 m for SH-2F LAMPS-I helicopter. Gunfire control is by a Mk 56 radar director, and the Mk 114 ASW fire-control system is installed. FF 1047 has an ASROC reload magazine beneath the bridge. Twin Mk 25 torpedo tubes at the stern were removed from the ships of the class that had them.

Status: FF 1043 to reserve 30-9-88, FF 1047 on 23-9-89; both were to have been leased to Turkey, which, however, declined them. Four sisters are on five-year lease to Pakistan: *Garcia* (FF 1040) decommissioned 10-11-88 and transferred 30-1-89; *Brumby* (FF 1044) decommissioned 31-3-89 and transferred same day; *Koelsch* (FF 1049) decommissioned 31-5-89 and transferred same day; and *O'Callahan* (FF 1051) decommissioned 20-12-88 and was transferred 8-2-89. Four have been leased to Brazil: *Bradley* (FF 1041) decommissioned 30-9-88 and transferred 25-9-89; *Davidson* (FF 1045) decommissioned 31-12-88 and transferred 25-7-89; *Sample* (FF 1048) decommissioned 23-9-88 and transferred 24-8-89; and *Albert David* (FF 1050) decommissioned 18-9-88 and transferred 18-9-89.

Note: Former experimental trials frigate *Glover* (FF 1098) was transferred to the Military Sealift Command on 15-6-90, disarmed, and re-typed T-AGFF 1; see later page for description. The *Bronstein*-class frigates *Bronstein* (FF 1037) and *McCloy* (FF 1038) were decommissioned 13-12-90 and 14-12-90, respectively, and both were stricken 4-10-91.

GUIDED-MISSILE PATROL BOATS

◆ **6 Pegasus class (SCB 602 type)** Bldr: Boeing Marine Systems, Seattle, Washington (all Atlantic Fleet)

	Laid down	L	In serv.
PHM 1 Pegasus (ex-*Delphinus*)	10-5-73	9-11-74	9-7-77
PHM 2 Hercules	12-9-80	13-4-82	12-3-83
PHM 3 Taurus	30-1-79	8-5-81	10-10-81
PHM 4 Aquila	10-7-89	16-9-81	26-6-82
PHM 5 Aries	7-1-80	5-11-81	11-9-82
PHM 6 Gemini	13-5-80	17-2-82	13-11-83

Authorized: PHM 1 and 2 in FY 73, PHM 3–6 in FY 75

Aquila (PHM 4)—under way on foils Dr. Giorgio Arra, 1991

Aries (PHM 5)—hullborne, with foils raised Dr. Giorgio Arra, 10-90

Pegasus (PHM 1)—hullborne, with foils extended Dr. Giorgio Arra, 5-91

D: 198 tons light (241 fl, except PHM 1: 235 fl)
S: 50 kts (12 on diesel)
Dim: 40.5 (44.7 with foils retracted; 36.00 wl) × 8.6 (14.5 over aft foils) × 7.1 (1.9 with foils retracted)/2.7 foilborne
A: 8/Harpoon SSM (IV × 2)—1/76-mm 62-cal. Mk 75 DP
Electron Equipt:
Radar: 1/SPS-64(V)1 nav., 1/Mk 92 Mod. 1 f.c.
EW: SLR-21 intercept, Mk 34 RBOC decoy RL syst. (VI × 2) (PHM 1: ALR-66 intercept, 2 Rospatch LADS RL (IX × 2); PHM 2: APS-137 intercept)
M: CODOG: 1 G.E. LM-2500 PB 102 gas turbine; 1 Aerojet AJW-18800-1 waterjet; 16,000–19,416 shp; 2 MTU 8V331 TC81, 815-bhp diesels; 2 Aerojet AJW-800-1 waterjets; 1,340 shp
Electric: 405 kVA **Range:** 600/40; 1,200+/11 **Fuel:** 50 tons
Crew: 4 officers, 17 enlisted

Remarks: PHM = Patrol Hydrofoil, Missile. PHM 2 originally authorized under F 73 using R & D funds and laid down on 30-5-74; her construction was suspended in 8- when 40.9 percent complete, but a new hull was laid down 12-9-80 with FY 76 fund Originally projected as a class of 30, also to be built by or for other NATO nations, b the additional cost over that of conventional missile craft with similar capabilities w prohibitive, and the U.S. Navy's interest in the type waned. PHM 1 began her pr tracted trials on 2-25-75. PHM 2 through PHM 6 were canceled on 4-6-77, then rei stated on 14-8-77 at the insistence of Congress, the contract going to Boeing on 20-1 77. PHM 4 hit a whale while traveling at 45 kts 16-4-91; two were injured a considerable damage caused to whale and ship. PHM 5 went aground 3-5-91 at Corp Christi, Texas; salved and repaired. These craft are extraordinarily steady weapo platforms and have proven most useful in anti-drug patrol work. They are based at K West, Florida, as PHM Squadron 2; they are supported by 7 officers and 181 enlist working from 73 mobile vans.

Systems: PHM 1's gas turbine develops 16,000 shp; on the others 19,416 shp possible, with the waterjet pumping some 341,000 liters/min. at full speed; 55 kts w achieved on trials. Two AIResearch ME 831-800 gas turbines power the two gene tors. The Mk 92 Mod. 1 fire-control system is an Americanized version of the Hollan Signaal Apparaaten WM-28 system. PHM 1 has the earlier Mk 94 Mod. 1 variant. T SPS-63, an Americanized version of the Italian SMA 3TM 20-H radar, was replaced Raytheon SPS-64(V)1 in 1985–86, when the radar antenna was moved onto a m platform. It was planned at one time to carry eight reload Harpoons, for a total sixteen. Magazine capacity 400 rds 76-mm. PHM 6 didn't receive her armament or 92 f.c.s. until 9-83. All have the SSQ-87(V) collision-avoidance and tracking syster

PATROL BOATS

◆ **0 (+13) Cyclone class** Bldr: Bollinger Machine Shop & SY, Lockport, La. (*Atlantic Fleet/†Pacific Fleet)

	Laid down	L	In serv.
PC 1 Cyclone*	22-6-91	15-2-92	12-92
PC 2 Tempest†	30-9-91	20-6-92	2-93
PC 3 Hurricane*	20-11-91	20-6-92	4-93
PC 4 Monsoon†	15-2-92	9-92	6-93
PC 5 Typhoon*	4-92	. . .	8-93
PC 6 Scirocco*	6-92	. . .	10-93
PC 7 Squall	8-92	. . .	12-93
PC 8 Zephyr	10-92	. . .	1-94
PC 9 Williwaw	. . .	. . .	3-94
PC 10 Chinook	. . .	. . .	4-94
PC 11 Torrent	. . .	. . .	6-94
PC 12 Lightning	. . .	. . .	8-94
PC 13 Thunderbolt	. . .	. . .	10-94

Cyclone (PC 1)—shortly after launch Bollinger,

D: 315 tons (fl) **S:** 35 kts (25 cruise) **Dim:** 52.00 × 7.60 × 2.40
A: . . ./Hellfire SSM—Stinger point-defense SAM station (6 missiles) 2/25-mm Mk 38 Bushmaster (I × 2)—2/12.7-mm mg (I × 2)—2/7.62-mm mg (I × 2)—4/40-mm Mk 19 grenade launchers (I ×
Electron Equipt:
Radar: 1/SPS-64(V) 9 nav., 1/Sperry RASCAR nav./surf. search
EW: APR-39 radar warning; 2/Mk 52 Mod. 0 decoy RL (VI × 2)
Sonar: Wesmar sidescanning hull-mounted HF
M: 4 Paxman Valenta RP-200 CM diesels; 4 props; 13,400 bhp
Electric: 310 kw tot. (2 Paxman 155 kw diesel sets)
Range: 2,000/12 **Fuel:** . . . tons **Endurance:** 10 days
Crew: 4 officers, 24 enlisted + 9 SEAL special forces or Coast Gua law-enforcement detachment

Remarks: PC = Coastal Patrol Boat. Originally to have been a class of 16 inten replace the 17 overaged PB Mk-III for use by SEAL Special Boat Squadrons program replaces the abortive PCM (canceled 12-87) and SWCM (work stopped efforts. The craft will be able to transport SEAL teams and their specialized d craft or Coast Guard boarding teams for counter-drug inspections. Were type (Patrol Boat, Coastal) until 6-91. The first eight were authorized under FY 90 ar ordered for \$91.3 million on 3-8-90 (along with an option for five more); the ne were authorized under FY 91, with the option picked up on 19-7-91 for \$48.7 n

ATROL BOATS *(continued)*

yclone-class—showing stern access for boat recovery U.S. Navy, 1991

clone class U.S. Navy, 1991

e remaining three will not be ordered, in part because it was belatedly discovered t they are too large for the inshore work for which they were intended. Under the ginal contract, the first was to have been delivered during 8-91, with the others to ver at eight week intervals. Hull numbers should have begun with PC 1651 per y custom and tradition.

ystems: Are about ten times the size of their predecessors but will carry about the e payload. Have Vosper fin-stabilization system, Kevlar armor on the command ce. The combat system will employ the navigational radars and a commercial puter to provide a modicum of gun control. At a later date it is hoped to provide a tweight fire-control system and more effective armament combining 25-mm guns 2.75-in. rocket launchers on a stabilized platform also equipped with a FLIR/t.v., r target designator and laser rangefinder; the Mk 38 mountings are an interim fit. re are four interchangeable mountings for 12.7-mm and 7.62-mm machine guns, or 19 40-mm grenade launchers. The radar intercept equipment was developed for use helicopters. Will carry two 16-ft SEAL CRRC and one 20-ft rigid inflatable nmer-delivery craft, and there is a recessed platform at the stern for swimmer arking and embarking.

TROL CRAFT

3 Sea Spectre PB Mk-IV class

Bldr: Atlantic Marine, Ft. George Island, Fla.

	Laid down	L	In serv.
'B851	24-12-84	23-9-85	2-1-86
'B852	25-3-85	11-11-85	2-1-86
'B853	17-6-85	31-12-85	15-2-86

3851—on trials, with 20-mm AA fore and aft U.S. Navy, 1-86

D: 42.25 tons (fl) **S:** 30 kts **Dim:** 20.85 × 5.50 × 1.07 (hull)
A: 1/25-mm Mk 38 "Bushmaster"—1/20-mm AA— 1/81-mm mortar/ 12.7-mm mg—2/40-mm Mk 19 grenade launchers
Electron Equipt: Radar: 1/. . . navigational
M: 3 G.M. 12V71 TI diesels; 3 props; 1,950 bhp
Range: . . ./. . . **Crew:** 5 tot.

Remarks: Approved FY 85 for Canal Zone service. Essentially a lengthened version of the PB Mk-III below. Aluminum construction. A 25-mm Bushmaster gun replaced one 20-mm gun in 1987.

♦ 14 Sea Spectre PB Mk-III class

Bldr: Peterson Bldrs., Sturgeon Bay, Wisconsin (In serv. 1975–79)

PB Mk-III class Dr. Giorgio Arra, 11-91

D: 28 tons (36.7 fl) **S:** 30 kts (now less)
Dim: 19.78 × 5.50 × 1.80 (props)
A: 1/40-mm 60-cal. Mk 3 Mod. 9 AA or 1–2/25-mm Mk 38 "Bushmaster" or 20-mm AA (I × 1 or 2)—2/12.7-mm mg (I × 2)—2/7.62-mm mg (I × 2)—1/81- or 60-mm mortar (*see* Remarks)
Electron Equipt: Radar: 1 or 2/. . . nav.
M: 3 G.M. 8V71 TI diesels; 3 props; 1,800 bhp **Endurance:** 3 days
Range: 450/26; 2,000/. . . **Crew:** 1 officer, 8 enlisted

Remarks: Survivors of eight built under FY 73, 10 under FY 75, and 3 under FY 77. Twelve that had operated with Special Boat Units were to be retired at the end of Fiscal Year 1992 (30-9-92), but some will be retained due to late deliveries of the *Cyclone* class. Two were transferred to Colombia in 1992. The 40-mm weapon is in a special stabilized mounting with a removable reload magazine. Armament is interchangeable. Additional personnel carried where full suite is installed. Have trouble making speed. Being replaced by the new *Cyclone* class.

RIVERINE WARFARE CRAFT

♦ 27 PBR (Patrol Boat, Riverine) Mk-II

Bldr: Uniflite, Bellingham, Wash. (In serv. 12-81 to 8-83)

PBR Mk-II class Dr. Giorgio Arra, 10-89

D: 8.9 tons (fl) **S:** 24 kts **Dim:** 9.73 × 3.53 × 0.81
A: 3/12.7-mm mg (II × 1, I × 1)—1/60-mm mortar
Electron Equipt: Radar: 1/Raytheon 1900 (SPS-66) nav.
M: 2 G.M. 6V53N diesels; 2 Jacuzzi waterjets; 430 bhp
Range: 150/23 **Crew:** 4 tot.

Remarks: Glass-reinforced plastic hull, plastic armor. Used for Naval Reserve training by Special Boat Units. Some recent export versions of this class have G.M. 6V53T engines, for 550 hp and speeds of 30 kts. Three delivered 1982 had G.M. 4-53N diesels. Some were used in Persian Gulf. Sisters 31RP6886, 7121, 7128, 7129, and 7130 were transferred to Colombia in 1990.

HARBOR PATROL CRAFT

◆ **75 Harbor Security Boats**
Bldr: Peterson Bldrs., Sturgeon Bay, Wisc. (In serv. 29-2-88 to 29-5-89)

24HS8701–24HS8750 24HS8801–24HS8825

24-ft. Harbor Security Boat George R. Schneider, Jr., 10-91

D: 2.5 tons (3.8 fl) **S:** 22.5 kts with 4 aboard
Dim: 7.32 × 2.31 × 1.57 (moulded depth)
A: 1/12.7-mm or 7.62-mm mg **Electron Equipt:** Radar: none
M: 2 Volvo Penta AGAD 41A diesels with Type 290 outdrives; 165 bhp
Range: . . ./. . . **Crew:** 4 tot.

Remarks: First 50 ordered 29-7-87; 10 more ordered 9-11-87, and final 15 in 3-88. Aluminum construction. No fixed armament, but have post-mountings fore and aft. For counter-terrorist patrol in sheltered waters. Have 12 V d.c., 50 amp. electrical power. Final 10 delivered 29-3-89.

◆ **4 Raider-class Harbor Security Boats** Bldr: NAPCO International, North Miami, Fla. (In serv. 1986)

D: 2.0 tons (2.95 fl) **S:** 40 kts **Dim:** 6.81 (6.40 pp) × 2.26 × 0.86
A: 2/12.7-mm M2 mg (I × 2)
Electron Equipt: Radar: none **Crew:** 3 tot.
M: 2 gasoline outboards; 280 hp **Range:** 167/40; 222/30

Remarks: GRP construction, using Boston Whaler hulls. Class also used by Coast Guard and has been widely exported. Acquired for counter-terrorist work.

Note: The navy has also purchased a number of SeaArk, Monticello, Arkansas–built 32-ft (9.80-m) "Protector" utility boats for range safety and patrol duties, including 33 UB 841 through 33 UB 846, delivered 14-10-86 to 6-87 for use at Point Mugu. They are powered by twin Volvo Penta AQAD outdrive diesels. Also from SeaArk, delivered 28-1-87, were two 30-ft (9.14-m) patrol craft.

SeaArk 32-ft Protector D. Merony/SeaArk, 1986

D: 6.8 tons (fl) **S:** . . . **Dim:** 9.80 × 3.40 × 0.60
M: 2 Volvo Penta diesel outdrives; . . . bhp
Crew: 4 tot. + 7 passengers

There are also a number of other range patrol craft, including several "cigarette boat and one Boghammar, Swedish-built 6.4-ton craft with a speed of 58 kts and dimensior 13.0 × 2.6 × 0.7.

U.S. Navy-operated Boghammar George R. Schneider, Jr., 2-

MINE WARFARE SHIPS

Note: In addition to the ships and craft listed below, there are also 10 RH-53D mi sweeping helicopters in service, and Marine Corps CH-53D helicopters that can be us to tow sweep gear; 56 MH-53E minesweeping helicopters are programmed, with 30 service by 1-92.

Under Fiscal Year 1994, it is planned to convert one Iwo Jima-class amphibi warfare helicopter carrier (PLH) to a mine countermeasures helicopter support s (MCS), with a second to convert under FY 96. By FY 1998, it is hoped to order built o purchase an existing float-on/float-off heavy-lift cargo ship to transport m countermeasures vessels to the scene of operations. The commercial oilfield support *Celina* was chartered for use as a tender to mine warfare ships in the Persian G during 1990–91.

◆ **0 (+12) Osprey-class coastal minehunters** (*Atlantic Fleet/†Paci Fleet)

	Bldr	Laid down	L	In se
MHC 51 Osprey*	Intermarine U.S.A., Savannah, Ga.	16-5-88	23-3-91	1
MHC 52 Heron†	Intermarine U.S.A., Savannah, Ga.	7-4-89	21-3-92	5
MHC 53 Pelican	Avondale, Gulfport, Miss.	6-5-91	5-92	11
MHC 54 Robin	Avondale, Gulfport, Miss.	2-92	11-92	3
MHC 55 Oriole	Intermarine U.S.A., Savannah, Ga.	8-5-91	. . .	7
MHC 56 Kingfisher	Avondale, Gulfport, Miss.	8-92	7-93	1
MHC 57 Cormorant	Avondale, Gulfport, Miss.	3-93	1-94	4
MHC 58	Intermarine U.S.A. Savannah, Ga.	. . .	. . .	
MHC 59	Intermarine U.S.A. Savannah, Ga.	. . .	. . .	
MHC 60	Intermarine U.S.A. Savannah, Ga.	. . .	. . .	
MHC 61	. . . .	. . .	. . .	
MHC 62	. . . .	. . .	. . .	

Authorized: MHC 51 under FY 86, MHC 52–53 under FY 89, MHC 5 under FY 90, MHC 56–57 under FY 91, MC 58–60 under FY 92, M 61–62 under FY 93

Osprey (MHC 51)—fitting out Intermarine

ıINE WARFARE SHIPS *(continued)*

eron (MHC 52)—at launch Intermarine, 3-92

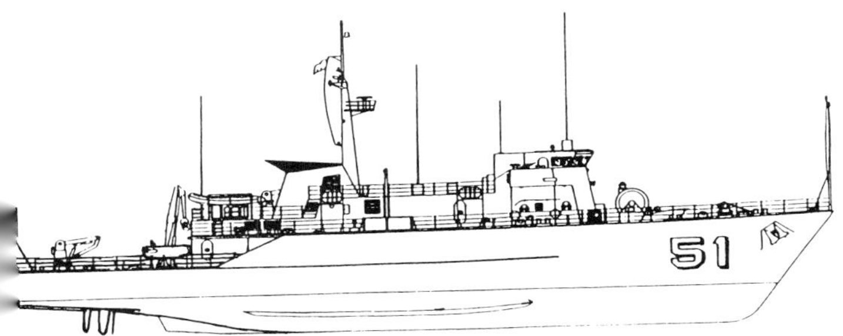

ıprey (MHC 51) U.S. Navy, 1990

D: 780 tons light (895 fl) **S:** 12 kts
Dim: 57.25 (53.10 pp) × 10.95 × 2.84
A: 2/12.7-mm M2 mg (I × 1 or 2)
Electron Equipt:
Radar: 1/SPS-64(V)9 nav.
Sonar: SQQ-32 variable-depth minehunting
M: 2 Isotta-Fraschini ID 36 SS 8V-AM diesels; 2 Voith-Schneider vertical cycloidal props; 1,160 bhp—2/180-shp hydraulic motors for quiet running—1/180-shp bow-thruster
Electric: 900 kw (3 × 300-kw Isotta-Fraschini 10 SS 8V-AM diesels driving)
Range: . . ./. . . **Endurance:** 5 days **Crew:** 5 officers, 46 enlisted

marks: MHC 51 ordered 20-2-87 as a replacement for the abortive *Cardinal* (MSH lass air-cushion-vehicle minehunter, using $5 million in remaining FY 84 funds ; FY 86 funds originally authorized for the MSH 1 program. The first unit is ding at leased former Sayler Marine boatyard at Savannah as a cooperative ven- e between Italy's Intermarine and the U.S. Hercules Powder Co., of Wilmington, aware; the latter was bought out by Intermarine in 1990. Second unit ordered 2-89, and third on 4-10-89 from congressionally mandated second-source yard. MHC ordered 1-4-91, after MHC 55 and 57, which were ordered 29-3-91. MHC 58–60 red 4-92. Because of delays in the program at the Avondale facility, its ships may ompleted by Intermarine U.S.A. After a one-year shakedown with regular navy vs, each ship will be passed to the Naval Reserve Force. Plans to construct a total of vere scaled back to 12 in the spring of 1992; although the later units will have more oard provisions stowage capacity, it is no longer planned to complete them to an rged "deployable" configuration.

ystems: Displacement has grown by 110 tons during final design phase. GRP truction, with the design based on the Italian Navy *Lerici*-class hull. In addition to ehunting capability (using the Alliant SLQ-48 Mine Neutralization System ote-controlled submersible), the ships will also carry mechanical minesweeping pment. Will have Paramax SYQ-13 tactical navigation/command and control pment. The Modular Influence Minesweeping System (MIMS), a towed influence p with its own gas-turbine sweep current generator, is under development to it the MHC 51 class to act as sweepers as well as hunters; when it is in use, the -48 would have to be removed. Also under development for these ships is the -53 Single-Ship Deep Sweep (SSDS), a surface ship-towed version of the helicopter rolled-Depth Moored Sweep. Have the SSQ-109 Ship/Machinery control system, 400-Hz motor-generator sets.

ȝ (+6) Avenger-class oceangoing minesweeper/ ninehunters (*Atlantic/†Pacific Fleet)

	Bldr	Laid down	L	In serv.
M 1 Avenger*	Peterson Bldrs.	3-6-83	15-6-85	12-9-87
M 2 Defender*	Marinette Marine	1-12-83	4-4-87	30-9-89
M 3 Sentry†	Peterson Bldrs.	8-10-84	20-9-86	2-9-89
M 4 Champion†	Marinette Marine	28-6-84	15-4-89	27-7-91
M 5 Guardian†	Peterson Bldrs.	8-5-85	20-6-87	16-12-89
M 6 Devastator*	Peterson Bldrs.	9-2-87	11-6-88	6-10-90
M 7 Patriot*	Marinette Marine	31-3-87	15-5-90	18-10-91
MCM 8 Scout*	Peterson Bldrs.	8-6-87	20-5-89	15-12-90
MCM 9 Pioneer*	Peterson Bldrs.	5-6-89	25-8-90	10-92
MCM 10 Warrior*	Peterson Bldrs.	25-9-89	8-12-90	1-93
MCM 11 Gladiator*	Peterson Bldrs.	7-5-90	29-6-91	7-93
MCM 12 Ardent	Peterson Bldrs.	22-10-90	16-11-91	10-93
MCM 13 Dexterous	Peterson Bldrs.	11-3-91	20-6-92	1-94
MCM 14 Chief	Peterson Bldrs.	19-8-91	10-92	10-94

Authorized: MCM 1 in FY 82, MCM 2 in FY 83, MCM 3–MCM 5 in FY 84, MCM 6–9 in FY 85, MCM 10–11 in FY 86, MCM 12–14 in FY 90

Scout (MCM 8) Dr. Giorgio Arra, 6-91

Guardian (MCM 5) Dr. Giorgio Arra, 3-91

Devastator (MCM 6) Dr. Giorgio Arra, 7-91

D: 1,195 tons light (1,312 fl—*see* Remarks) **S:** 13.5 kts
Dim: 68.37 (64.80 wl) × 11.86 × 3.42 (hull)
A: 2/12.7-mm M2 mg (I × 2)
Electron Equipt:
Radar: 1/Furuno . . . or SPS-66 nav., 1/SPS-55 surf. search
Sonar: SQQ-32 variable-depth minehunting (MCM 2–5: SQQ-30), WQN-1 channel finder

MINE WARFARE SHIPS *(continued)*

Scout (MCM 8) Dr. Giorgio Arra, 6-91

M: MCM 1 and 2: 4 Waukesha L-1616 diesels; 2 CP props; 2,280 bhp—MCM 3–14: 4 Isotta-Fraschini ID 36 SS 6V-AM diesels; 2 CP props; 2,600 bhp—all: 2/200-shp Hansome low-speed motors geared to props, 1/350-shp Omnithruster at bow
Electric: 1,125 kw (3 × 375-kw L-1616 or ID 36 SS 6V-AM diesel-driven sets)
Range: . . ./. . . **Crew:** 8 officers, 75 enlisted

Remarks: First unit was ordered 29-6-82.Wooden-hulled, with fiberglass superstructure. Able to sweep deep-moored mines to 180 m as well as magnetic and acoustic mines. The program has been fraught with major delays and cost increases. Contracts to build the FY 85 quartet had not been let by 3-86, and Congress cut the four requested for FY 86 authorization to two. Congress also stipulated that MCM 10 and later must have U.S.-made diesels. Three requested under FY 88 were denied because program was over a year behind schedule. The final three were reinstated in the FY 90 program and were ordered 14-12-89. Plans to turn the ships over to the Naval Reserve Force about a year after each was commissioned were placed in abeyance in 1991.

Hull systems: The wooden hull employs four glued layers of 127-mm planking over 254-mm by 457-mm frames spaced at 1.07-m intervals. All structural members are built up from thinner materials, using phenol/resorcinal glue. The hull had to be lengthened by about 1.8 m after construction had begun, due to stability problems. The first unit was also delayed by design problems and the discovery that the main engines rotated opposite to the gear boxes.

Weapons system: The Mk 116 Mod. 0 Mine Neutralization System (MNS) includes two Alliant (formerly Honeywell) SLQ-48 MNS, a remote-controlled minehunting and destruction device 3.8 m long by .9 m high, weighing 1,136 kg; powered by two 15-hp hydraulic motors for 6-kt speeds; it has 1,524 m of control cable. Also aboard are the SLQ-37(V)2 magnetic/acoustic sweep array (incorporating the A Mk 4(V) and A Mk 6(B) acoustic arrays), SLQ-38 (Type 0 Size 1) mechanical sweep gear, and two semi-rigid inflatable boats for mine-disposal divers. Carry the SSN-2(V) PINS (Precision-Integrated Navigation System) and the SYQ-13 navigational/command-and-control, which employs Racal-Decca Hyper-Fix radio-navaid, the Global Positioning System (GPS) NAVSAT receiver, LORAN, and a doppler sonar (WQN-1 channel-finder); MCM 9 and later will have a more versatile version of the same system ("Phase III"). MCM 2 used in trials 1989 with Marconi Nautis-M command-and-control system as a possible candidate for the planned SSN-2 Phase 3 system (SYQ-15). MCM 1 had her SQQ-30 sonar (a digital version of the SQQ-14) replaced with a developmental model of the SQQ-32 for trials in 1990 and performed admirably with it in the Persian Gulf during 1991; the remaining SQQ-30 ships were to have had it replaced by end-1992. The original 2,500 amp. magnetic-pulse sweep generators had to be replaced because the Siemens-made sets broke down after only 48 hours' use; the first new MagneTek solid-state replacements were fitted to MCM 9.

♦ 1 Acme-class oceangoing minesweeper

Bldr: Frank L. Sample, Jr., Boothbay Harbor, Maine (Atlantic Fleet, NRF)

	Laid down	L	In serv.
MSO 511 Affray	24-8-55	18-12-56	8-8-58

D: 682 tons light (818 fl) **S:** 14 kts
Dim: 52.73 × 10.97 × 4.3 **A:** 2/12.7-mm mg (I × 2)
Electron Equipt:
Radar: SPS-64(V)9 nav.
Sonar: SQQ-14 variable-depth minehunting
M: 4 Packard 1D-1700 diesels; 2 CP props; 2,280 bhp
Range: 3,000/10 **Fuel:** 47 tons
Crew: 8 officers, 37 enlisted + 4 officers, 33 enlisted Reserves

Remarks: Similar to the *Aggressive* class below, but slightly larger and originally equipped as Mine Division flagship. Not modernized. In Naval Reserve Force in Atlantic Fleet. Sister *Adroit* (MSO 509) decommissioned 12-12-91 for retention, but is unlikely to ever be reactivated. Has same mine countermeasures equipment as the *Aggressive* class below.

Affray (MSO 511) Dr. Giorgio Arra, 19

♦ 6 Aggressive-class oceangoing minesweepers

(*Atlantic/†Pacific Fleet)

	Bldr	Laid down	L	In se
MSO 440 Exploit*	Higgins, New Orleans	28-12-51	10-4-53	31-3-
MSO 441 Exultant*	Higgins, New Orleans	22-5-52	6-6-53	22-6
MSO 455 Implicit†	Wilmington Boat Wks.	29-10-51	1-8-53	10-3
MSO 488 Conquest†	J.M. Martinac, Tacoma	26-3-53	20-5-54	20-7
MSO 489 Gallant†	J.M. Martinac, Tacoma	21-5-53	4-6-54	14-9
MSO 492 Pledge†	J.M. Martinac, Tacoma	24-6-54	20-7-55	20-4

Enhance (MSO 437)—decommissioned 12-91 Victor M. Baca,

D: 716 tons light (853 fl) **S:** 14 kts **Dim:** 52.42 × 10.97 × 4.2
A: 2/12.7-mm M2 mg (I × 2)
Electron Equipt:
Radar: SPS-64(V)9 nav.
Sonar: SQQ-14 variable-depth minehunting
M: 4 Waukesha L-1616 diesels; 2 CP props; 2,400 bhp
Range: 3,300/10 **Fuel:** 48 tons
Crew: active fleet units: 6 officers, 75 enlisted; Naval Reserve Forc units: 5 officers, 52 enlisted + 25 reserves

Remarks: Wooden construction; nonmagnetic, stainless-steel machinery. MS transferred to the active fleet 31-7-89 and MSO 448 moved to NRF same date. N three of the MSO 421 to MSO 508 classes were built; many transferred abroad.

Status: Disposals of these old ships delayed by late delivery of MCM 1 class a MSH 1-class cancellation. Since the last edition, the following have been deco sioned to reserve or stricken: *Constant* (MSO 427) on 30-9-92, *Engage* (MSO 4 30-12-91, *Enhance* (MSO 437) on 13-12-91, *Esteem* (MSO 438) on 20-9-91 stricken), *Fearless* (MSO 442) on 28-10-90 (and stricken), *Fidelity* (MSO 443) on 1 (and stricken), *Fortify* (MSO 446) on 31-8-92 (and stricken), *Illusive* (MSO 4 1-6-90 (and stricken), *Impervious* (MSO 449) on 12-12-91, *Inflict* (MSO 456) on 2 (and stricken), *Pluck* (MSO 464) on 29-11-90 (and stricken), and *Leader* (MSC damaged by a mine 25-3-91 in the Persian Gulf but repaired, on 12-12-91. The re ing units will be decommissioned 1993–94.

IINE WARFARE SHIPS *(continued)*

eader (MSO 490)—decommissioned 12-91 Dr. Giorgio Arra, 2-90

Systems: Have the SLQ-37(V) magnetic sweep system, incorporating A Mk 4(V) d A Mk 6(B) acoustic arrays and the SLQ-38 wire sweep. Hoist machinery for the)Q-14 minehunting sonar occupies the position of the former 40-mm AA gun. *All* the rvivors were given very thorough rehabilitations during the early to mid-1970s, ceiving semi-enclosed bridges, enlarged superstructures abaft the bridge, SQQ-14 inehunting sonars, new communications gear, and upgraded accommodations. Eight nthos Super Sea ROVER tethered submersibles were acquired for use in these ships 1988: capable of 4 kts, weigh 72.5 kg, can dive to over 300 m. In 1975 MSO 440 was uipped with the prototype SSN-2 precise-navigation system for the new MCM class.

INESWEEPING BOATS

1 MSB 29 class Bldr: Trumpy, Annapolis (In serv. 1954)

ЗB 29 U.S. Navy, 1986

): 80 tons (fl) **S:** 12 kts **Dim:** 25.0 × 5.8 × 1.7
\: 1/12.7-mm M2 mg
:lectron Equipt:
Radar: 1/Raytheon 1900 nav.—Sonar: Mk 24 Mod. 0 Hydroscan
/I: 2 Packard 2D850 diesels; 2 props; 600 bhp
:rew: 2 officers, 9 enlisted

marks: Enlarged MSB 5; only one built. Based at Charleston, S. Carolina.

5 MSB 5 class

3 15, MSB 25, MSB 28, MSB 41, MSB 51

: 30 tons light (44 fl) **S:** 12 kts **Dim:** 17.45 × 4.83 × 1.2
: 1/12.7-mm M2 mg
lectron Equipt:
Radar: 1/Raytheon 1900 nav.—Sonar: Mk 24 Mod. 0 Hydroscan
: 2 Packard 2D850 diesels; 2 props; 600 bhp **Crew:** 6 tot.

arks: Survivors of a class of 47 built between 1952 and 1956. Wooden hulls, nagnetic machinery. Two Garrett diesel sweep generator sets, except MSB 25: two ng 502 gas-turbine sets. All based at Charleston. Former MSB 7, 13, 17, 35, and 50 rerated as training craft for the Surface Warfare Officers' School, San Diego, and ow used as utility boats in the Canal Zone. Four to Persian Gulf, 9-87. No plans to replace these very useful craft, which can be transported in LSD well-decks or ck cargo. MSB 51 damaged by Hurricane Hugo, 21-9-89. Sister MSB 16 for sale 1.

MSB 28 Leo Van Ginderen, 8-88

MSB 51 Dr. Giorgio Arra, 1984

NAVAL RESERVE FORCE ROUTE-SURVEY BOATS

Note: The navy, seeing no further need for the COOP program, has attempted to have it canceled, but Congress has reinstated it again for Fiscal Year 1992. The intent is to train crews for designated civilian fishing craft that would be pressed into service in wartime as mine-clearance craft for U.S. ports and harbors. During peacetime, the reservist crews were expected to train by doing route surveys in and out of ports.

♦ **2 protoype new-construction COOP (Craft of Opportunity) craft**
Bldr: Princess Yachts, Tacoma, Washington

CT-21 (In serv. 15-10-88) CT-23 (In serv. 5-11-88)

D: 20.4 tons light **S:** 12 kts **Dim:** 17.07 × 5.18 × 1.22
Electron Equipt:
Radar: 1/. . . 1220 nav.
Sonar: Dowty Type 3010 towed sidescan array
M: 2 G.M. 6-71 diesels; 2 props; 330 bhp **Electric:** 15 kw
Range: 750/12 **Crew:** 9 tot.

Remarks: Prototypes for a now-canceled program to build COOP training craft for the Naval Reserve Force. Glass-reinforced plastic construction. Resemble small, flush-decked fishing boats. Both operated on the Pacific Coast.

♦ **8 COOP (Craft of Opportunity Program) conversions from wooden-hulled training craft** Bldrs: Stephens Brothers, Stockton, Cal.; Elizabeth City SY, Elizabeth City, N. Carolina; Peterson Builders, Sturgeon Bay, Wisc. (In serv. 1959)

	Converted		Converted
CT-2 (ex-YP 668)	22-7-88	CT-9 (ex-YP 660)	1-10-85
CT-5 (ex-YP . . .)	7-4-88	CT-10 (ex-YP 664)	18-9-85
CT-6 (ex-YP . . .)	13-10-87	CT-11 (ex-YP 654)	1-8-88
CT-8 (ex-YP 661)	14-11-86	CT-15 (ex-YP 662)	14-11-86

NAVAL RESERVE FORCE ROUTE-SURVEY BOATS *(continued)*

CT-6 Dr. Giorgio Arra, 4-91

D: 60 tons (fl) **S:** 13.3 kts **Dim:** 24.51 × 5.72 × 1.60
Electron Equipt:
Radar: 1/Raytheon 1220 nav.
Sonar: Dowty Type 3010 towed side-scan array
M: 4 G.M. 6-71 diesels; 2 props; 590 bhp **Crew:** 9 tot.

Remarks: CT stands for "COOP Trainer." Conversions from YP 654–675 series wooden-hulled training craft built for the Naval Academy, Annapolis. Handling gear for a towed precision sidescan sonar was added at the stern. Have the SYQ-12 navigation/command-and-control system, which uses Hewlett-Packard DTC-1 or Sun DTC-2 desk-top computers. Each has four rotating, nine-man Naval Reserve Force crews, the idea being that three crews will take over previously designated civilian craft in wartime. All operate on the U.S. East and Gulf coasts. The program has experienced major delays because of low priorities, program indecision, and political difficulties over potential home-porting. Eleven others YPs scheduled for conversion have been eliminated from the program. The surviving units were reclassified as "boats" on 1-2-89.

♦ 4 COOP conversions from miscellaneous craft

	Converted	Home port
CT-18 (ex-*Simbad*)	15-3-85	Seattle, Washington
CT-19 (ex-*Cheyenne*)	16-8-85	Astoria, Oregon
CT-20 (ex-*Sirod*)	20-7-85	Seattle, Washington
CT-22 (ex-*Widgeon*)	. . .	Long Beach, California

CT-20 Victor M. Baca, 1988

Remarks: Conversion from commercial fishing craft. The nine-man crews conduct detailed bottom obstacle surveys using Mk 24 Mod. 0 Hydroscan or Dowty Type 3031 towed sidescan sonars, commercial ROVs, and net trawl gear. The COOP prototype, MSSB 1 (ex-*Robin Gail II*), has been discarded, as has CT-2 (ex-*Tiki*). CT-1 (ex-*Ida Green*) was returned to her owners 10-86.

MINE COUNTERMEASURES DRONES

Note: The U.S. Navy is seeking additional remote-controlled mine countermeasures drones and has reportedly investigated the German "Troika" class for possible purchase.

♦ 2 Swedish Uven-class Bldr: Karlskronavarvet

	In serv.		In serv.
Gerry (ex-SAM 03)	17-6-83	Peggy (ex-SAM 05)	26-5-83

D: 15 tons (20 fl) **S:** 8 kts
Dim: 18.0 × 6.10 × 0.70 (1.60 prop)
M: 1 Volvo Penta TAMD 70D diesel; 1 Schottel shrouded prop; 210 bhp **Range:** 330/7

Remarks: Acquired from the Swedish Navy for possible Persian Gulf service durin 1-91 and sent to Persian Gulf on 5-2-91. Are equipped with magnetic coils for magnet minesweeping, a towed noisemaker to counter acoustic mines, and a wire sweep. Th radio-controlled, catamaran-hulled craft also automatically lay eight swept-chann danbuoy markers. Are named informally for members of the U.S. Navy project ma ager's family.

MINELAYING CRAFT

♦ 1 LCU 1610-class exercise minelayer
Bldr: Marinette Marine, Marinette, Wisc.

LCU 1641 (In serv. 1967)

LCU 1641 Leo Van Ginderen, 8

D: 190 tons light **S:** 11 kts **Dim:** 41.07 × 9.07 × 2.08
A: 1 mine rail **Electron Equipt:** Radar: 1/LN-66 nav.
M: 4 G.M. 6–71 diesels; 2 Kort-nozzle props; 1,200 bhp
Range: 1,200/11 **Fuel:** 13 tons **Crew:** 6 tot.

Remarks: Standard utility landing craft fitted with one mine rail over stern, der to port, and raised, enclosed pilothouse. Based at Charleston, South Carolina.

AMPHIBIOUS WARFARE SHIPS

Note: Long-range planning calls for the introduction of an LVX design around 201 a modified version of the LHD design to replace the LHA class; the forward two-th will have a flight deck and hangar for up to 20 V/STOL fighters and 6 ASW helicop or a similar total number of assault helicopters, with superstructure across the s and a stern well deck for three LCAC; the ships would have a modular, remov vertical-launch SAM system.

The first of an LX design to replace the LPDs and *Newport*-class LSTs wi requested in the FY 95 Budget and the second in FY 97. At 23,000 tons full load, it be 185 m o.a., will have an LPD-4-class-sized well deck to accommodate two L air-cushion landing craft, two helicopter "spots," facilities for 700 troops, 2,322 r vehicle parking space, and 708 m² of palletized cargo space. Will resemble an enla LPD. The first ship is to complete in 2000, and at one time as many as 46 were plan

♦ 2 Blue Ridge-class amphibious command ships (SCN 400–65 type) (*Atlantic/†Pacific Fleet)

	Bldr	Laid down	L	In s
LCC 19 Blue Ridge†	Philadelphia NSY	27-2-67	4-1-69	14-1
LCC 20 Mount Whitney*	Newport News SB & DD	8-1-69	8-1-70	16-

Authorized: FY 65 and FY 66

D: 16,790 tons light (18,646 fl) **S:** 21.5 kts
Dim: 193.98 (176.8 wl) × 32.9 (25.0 wl) × 7.5 (8.8 max.)
A: 4/76.2-mm 50-cal. Mk 34 DP (II × 2)—2/Mk 25 BPDMS launche for Sea Sparrow SAM (VIII × 2)—2/20-mm Mk 15 CIWS (I × 2)

Mount Whitney (LCC 20) Leo Van Ginderen

HIBIOUS WARFARE SHIPS *(continued)*

Ridge (LCC 19) R.A.N., 4-90

nt Whitney (LCC 20) Leo Van Ginderen, 3-92

ctron Equipt:
Radar: 1/SPS-64(V)9 nav., 1/SPS-65(V)1 surf. search, 1/SPS-40C air search, 1/SPS-48C 3-D air search, 2/Mk 115 missile f.c.
W: SLQ-32(V)3 active/passive, Mk 36 SRBOC RL (VI × 4, Mk 137 launchers), SLQ-25 Nixie towed acoustic torpedo decoy
ACAN: URN-25
1 set G.E. geared steam turbines; 1 prop; 22,000 shp
el: 2,800 tons
ilers: 2 Foster-Wheeler; 42.3 kg/cm², 467°C **Range:** 13,000/16
ew: 43 officers, 778 enlisted + flag staff: 170–190 tot. + 700 troops

rks: LCC 19 is the flagship of the Seventh Fleet and is based at Yokosuka, ; LCC 20 is the flagship of the Second Fleet and is based at Norfolk. These ships have a good cruising speed (20 knots) and excellent satellite communications (including SSR-1, WSC-3 UHF, WSC-6 SHF, and USC-38 SHF) and analysis systems: ACIS (Amphibious Command Information System); NIPS (Naval Intelligence Processing System); NTDS (with LINK 4A, 11, and 14), and photographic laboratories and document-publication facilities. Have the SMQ-6 weather satellite receiver. Three LCP, two LCVP landing craft, and one 10-m personnel launch are carried in Welin davits. No helicopter hangar, but they do have a landing pad at the stern. Same machinery and basic hull form as the *Iwo Jima*-class LPH. Air-conditioned; fin stabilizers. Two Mk 56 fire-control systems for the 76.2-mm guns deleted in 1978; two Mk 115 fire-control systems for Sea Sparrow retained. Kevlar plastic armor has been added, Tactical Flag Command Center installed. LCC 19 received Mk 15 CIWS in 1985 and LCC 20 in 1987, with stern sponson and bow bulwarks lengthening the ships some 5 m overall. Satellite communications antennas on after masts differ. Planned armament modifications include deleting the Mk 25 Sea Sparrow launchers, relocating the Mk 15 CIWS mounts in their place, and installing Mk 49 launchers for the RAM point-defense missile fore and aft; also to be installed is the Mk 23 TAS target acquisition radar.

◆ 2 (+3+1) Wasp-class helicopter/dock landing ships

Bldr: Ingalls SB, Pascagoula, Mississippi (*Atlantic/†Pacific Fleet)

	Laid down	L	In serv.
LHD 1 WASP*	30-5-85	4-8-87	29-7-89
LHD 2 ESSEX†	20-3-89	4-1-91	30-6-92
LHD 3 KEARSARGE*	4-12-89	26-3-92	9-93
LHD 4 BOXER	8-1-91	1993	9-94
LDH 5 BATAAN	. . .	. . .	1997
LDH 6	. . .	. . .	. . .

Authorized: LHD 1 in FY 84, LHD 2 in FY 86, LHD 3 in FY 88, LHD 4 in FY 89, LHD 5 in FY 91; programmed: LHD 6 in FY 96

D: 28,233 tons light (40,532 fl) **S:** 24 kts
Dim: 257.30 (237.14 wl) × 42.67 (32.31 wl) × 8.13
Air group: Assault mode: 30–32/CH-46 (or fewer CH-53) helicopters and 6/AV-8B Harriers; carrier mode: 20/AV-8B Harriers and 4–6/SH-60B ASW helicopters (*see* Remarks)
A: 2/Mk 29 Sea Sparrow launchers (VIII × 2)—3/20-mm Mk 15 CIWS AA (I × 3)—8/12.7-mm M2 mg (I × 8)
Electron Equipt:
Radar: 1/SPS-64(V)9 nav., 1/SPS-67(V)3 surf. search, 1/SPS-49(V)5 air search, 1/SPS-52C (LHD 2 and later: SPS-48E) 3-D air search, 1/Mk 23 TAS target detection, 2/Mk 57 Mod. 2 (on Mk 91 f.c.s.), 1/SPN-35A marshaling, 1/SPN-43B CCA, SPN-47 precision CCA
EW: SLQ-32(V)3 active/passive, Mk 36 SRBOC decoy RL syst. (VI × 4 or 8), SLQ-25 Nixie towed acoustic torpedo decoy
TACAN: URN-25
M: 2 sets Westinghouse geared steam turbines: 2 props; 77,000 shp (70,000 sust.)
Boilers: 2 Combustion Engineering; 49.3 kg/cm², 482°C
Electric: 16,500 kw (5 × 2,000-kw turboalternators, 2 × 2,000-kw diesel sets)

x (LHD 2) Ingalls SB, 7-92

AMPHIBIOUS WARFARE SHIPS *(continued)*

Wasp (LHD 1)—with deck load of helicopters and Harriers
PH1 (SW) J. E. Westphal, USN, 1991

Wasp (LHD 1) U.S. Navy, 9-90

Kearsarge (LHD 3)—at launch Ingalls SB, 3-92

Range: 9,500/20
Fuel: 6,200 tons, plus 1,232 tons aircraft fuel
Crew: 98 officers, 61 chief petty officers, 921 enlisted, plus 1,873 troops (+ 200 additional emergency troops accom.)

Remarks: Design based on that of the LHA 1 class, but intended to be convertible from assault ships to ASW ships with Harrier V/STOL fighters for ground assault. Because of the desire to maximize the number of deck spots, no ski-jump V/STOL ramp is fitted. LHD 1 ordered 28-2-84, LHD 2 on 11-9-85, LHD 3 on 24-11-87, LHD 4 on

Wasp (LHD 1) Dr. Giorgio Arra,

3-10-88 as third unit in a three-ship option, and LHD 5 on 20-12-91. Efforts were made during the summer of 1992 to have LHD 6 moved forward to the FY 93 B from FY 96. At one point a total of 11 was planned.

Hull systems: Can take on up to 15,000 tons ballast to launch landing craft. 1,500 compartments. Differences from the LHA 1 include: use of an LSD/LPI lowering stern gate, vice the sectional, rising gate of the LHA; provision for LCAC in a single-bay, narrower docking well (which can alternatively hold up LCM(6)); use of larger 34-ton-capacity, 15.2 × 13.7 aircraft elevators, with the elevator relocated to starboard; internal stowage for ship's boats; a bulbous fore the bow; larger-area bilge-keels; a squared-off flight deck forward (made possible omission of the 127-mm guns and capable of spotting nine CH-53E helicopters at use of HY 100 steel to construct the stronger flight deck; additional cargo elevato 5.4-ton capacity, total: 7.6 × 3.6 m); a lower, narrower, and longer island; provis three hospitals, totaling 600 beds; a narrower vehicle ramp to the flight deck better ballistic protection. The hangar has 6.4-m vertical clearance and is 25.9 m it can accommodate 28 CH-46-equivalents. They have 2,127 m² of vehicle pa space and 3,087 m³ of dry cargo space. Some 1,232 tons of JP-5 aviation fuel and 50 tons of vehicle fuel can be carried. There are four 2,000-gallon/min. turbopum eight 1,000-gal./min. motor-driven pumps fitted. Plans to have later units propel LM-2500 gas turbines have been abandoned.

Weapons/sensor systems: Have the SYS-2(V)3 data system for defensive we control, Marconi ICS.3 (URC-109) integrated communications system, SM weather satellite receiving system, and USQ-82(V) data multiplexing system. D her first Mediterranean deployment commencing 20-6-91, *Wasp*'s Marine Com Helicopter Squadron comprised ten AV-8B Harriers, 12 CH-46 medium-lift a helicopters, 5 UH-1N light attack helicopters, and 4 CH-53E Sea Stallion hea assault helicopters and the 3 LCACs of Assault Craft Unit Four (ACU-4). Duri deployment, four more Harriers and two SH-3 Sea King ASW helicopters join complement, while several of the CH-46 and CH-53E helicopters left to make ro them.

◆ 5 Tarawa-class amphibious assault ships (SCB 410 type)

Bldr: Ingalls SB, Pascagoula, Miss. (*Atlantic/†Pacific Fleet)

	Laid down	L	In serv.
LHA 1 TARAWA†	15-11-71	1-12-73	29-5-76
LHA 2 SAIPAN*	21-7-72	18-7-74	15-10-77
LHA 3 BELLEAU WOOD†	5-3-73	11-4-77	23-9-78
LHA 4 NASSAU*	13-8-73	21-1-78	28-7-79
LHA 5 PELELIU (ex-*Da Nang*)†	12-11-76	25-11-78	3-5-80

Authorized: 1 in FY 69, 2 in FY 70, 2 in FY 71

D: 25,120 tons light (39,300 fl) **S:** 24 kts
Dim: 254.20 (237.14 pp) × 40.23 (32.31 wl) × 7.92
Air group: typical: 16/CH-46, 6/CH-53, and 4/UH-1 helicopters (maximum: 38 CH-46 equivalents)—*see* Remarks
A: 2/127-mm 54-cal. Mk 45 DP (I × 2)—2/20-mm Mk 15 CIWS (I × 2)—6/20-mm Mk 67 AA (I × 6)
Electron Equipt:
Radar: 1/SPS-64(V)9 nav., 1/SPS-67(V)3 surf. search, 1/SPS-40E search, 1/SPS-52B 3-D air search, 1/SPN-35A marshaling SPN-43B CCA, 1/SPG-60 AA gun f.c., 1/SPQ-9A surf. gu
EW: SLQ-32(V)3 active/passive, Mk 36 SRBOC decoy RL syst. (V 4, Hycor Mk 137 launchers), SLQ-25 Nixie towed acoustic torpedo decoy syst.
TACAN: URN-25

Tarawa (LHA 1) OS2 John Bouvia, USN,

IIBIOUS WARFARE SHIPS *(continued)*

u (LHA 4)—only unit with Mk 15 CIWS directly in front of bridge Leo Van Ginderen, 4-92

u (LHA 5) Leo Van Ginderen, 1991

n (LHA 2)—LCU 1656 alongside Pradignac & Léo, 4-90

au Wood (LHA 3) David D. Broecker, 3-92

: 2 sets Westinghouse geared steam turbines; 2 props; 77,000 shp (70,000 sust.)—900-hp bow-thruster
ilers: 2 Combustion Engineering Type V2M-VS; 49.3 kg/cm², 482°C
ectric: 14,600 kw (4 × 2,500-kw turboalternators, 2 × 2,000-kw diesel sets, 4 × 150-kw diesel sets)

Range: 10,000/20 **Fuel:** 5,900 tons
Crew: 56 officers, 874 enlisted + 1,924 troops

Remarks: The LHA is a multipurpose assault transport, a combination of LPH and LPD. Were originally to have been a class of nine, with four already on order canceled in 1971. LHA 5 renamed 15-2-78.

Hull systems: Have the general profile of an aircraft carrier, with superstructure to starboard, flight deck, helicopter elevators to port (folding) and aft, and an 80 × 23.4-m well deck for landing craft (up to four LCU 1610 class). Two LCM(6) and two LCP are stowed on deck. Vehicle stowage garage forward of docking well totals 3,134 m², and the palletized cargo holds total 3,311 m³. Carry approx. 1,200 tons JP-5 fuel for helicopters. The boilers are the largest ever installed in a U.S. Navy ship; the propulsion plant is highly automated. Very complete 300-bed hospital and mortuary facilities are fitted. All troops have bunks. Completely air-conditioned. Planned addition of bulbous bow canceled.

Systems: Communications systems include SRR-1, WSC-3 UHF, and USC-38 SHF SATCOMM receivers, SMQ-11 weather satellite receiver, and a large, long-range, high frequency, log-periodic array. LHA-1 carried 20 AV-8B Harrier V/STOL attack fighters during Operation Desert Storm in 1991. The 127-mm guns were included primarily to provide shore fire support, but can also be used for AA; they are controlled by a Mk 86 Mod. 4 fire-control system with SPQ-9A radar for surface fire, SPG-60 for AA, and two unmanned optronic backup directors. All have had original WLR-1 EW suite replaced by SLQ-32(V)3 and URN-20 TACAN replaced by URN-25. As completed, carried two Mk 25 BPDMS launchers for Sea Sparrow SAMs, controlled by two Mk 71 directors with Mk 115 radars, and three 127-mm DP. The Sea Sparrow launchers and the port aft 127-mm gun have been removed from all. All are to receive two Mk 49, 21-cell RAM point-defense missile launchers, starting with LHA 5 during an overhaul beginning in mid-1992.

AMPHIBIOUS ASSAULT HELICOPTER CARRIERS

◆ **7 Iwo Jima class (SCB 157, LPH 12: SCB 401–66)**
(*Atlantic/† Pacific Fleet)

	Bldr	Laid down	L	In serv.
LPH 2 Iwo Jima*	Puget Sound NSY	2-4-59	17-9-60	26-8-61
LPH 3 Okinawa†	Philadelphia NSY	1-4-60	14-8-61	14-4-62
LPH 7 Guadalcanal†	Philadelphia NSY	1-9-61	16-3-63	20-7-63
LPH 9 Guam*	Philadelphia NSY	15-11-62	22-8-64	16-1-65
LPH 10 Tripoli†	Ingalls, Pascagoula	15-6-64	31-7-65	6-8-66
LPH 11 New Orleans†	Philadelphia NSY	1-3-66	3-2-68	16-11-68
LPH 12 Inchon*	Ingalls, Pascagoula	8-4-68	24-5-69	20-6-70

Authorized: 1 each year in FY 58, 59, 60, 62, 63, 65, 66

D: 11,000 tons light (18,000–18,625 fl) **S:** 23 kts
Dim: 183.6 (169.5 wl) × 31.7 (25.5 wl) × 9.6 (max.)
Air group: 20–24/CH-46 helicopters—4/CH-53 heavy helicopters—4/UH-1E utility or AH-1W attack helicopters—*see* Remarks
A: 4/76.2-mm 50-cal. Mk 34 DP (II × 2)—2/Mk 25 Sea Sparrow launchers (VIII × 2); not in LPH 3—2/20-mm Mk 15 CIWS (I × 2)—4, 6, or 8/12.7-mm mg(I)
Electron Equipt:
Radar: 1/LN-66 (LPH 9: CRP-1900B) nav., 1/SPS-10 surf. search, 1/

AMPHIBIOUS ASSAULT HELICOPTER CARRIERS *(continued)*

Tripoli (LPH 10) Dr. Giorgio Arra, 10-91

Inchon (LPH 12)—note elevator stowed, LCVP on davits aft
Dr. Giorgio Arra, 3-91

Guam (LPH 9) Dr. Giorgio Arra, 1990

Iwo Jima (LPH 2) Dr. Giorgio Arra, 4-91

SPS-40-series air search, 1/SPN-35 marshaling, SPN-43 CCA, 2/Mk 115 (not in LPH 3)
EW: SLQ-32(V)3 active/passive, Mk 36 SRBOC decoy RL syst. (VI × 4, Mk 137 launchers)
TACAN: URN-25
M: 1 set Westinghouse (LPH 10: DeLaval, LPH 12: G.E.) geared steam turbines; 1 prop; 23,000 shp
Boilers: 2 Combustion Engineering (LPH 9: Babcock & Wilcox); 42.3 kg/cm², 467°C
Electric: 6,500 kw **Range:** . . ./. . .
Crew: 48 officers, 638 enlisted + 144 marine officers, 1,602 troops

Inchon (LPH 12) Pradignac & Léo

Guam (LPH 9) Dr. Giorgio Arra

Remarks: First ships designed exclusively to operate helicopters. In addition tc ing troop/transport helicopters, the ships can also carry RH-53/MH-53E minesw helicopters or AV-8B Harrier V/STOL fighter-bombers. LPH 12 may be conve act as a mine countermeasures support ship during FY 93 and would be redesi MCS 6; a second ship will be converted under FY 95, and the others are to be re by the *Wasp* class. LPH 10, while acting as a mine countermeasures helicopter c hit a mine 18-2-91 in the Persian Gulf but was repaired locally by 4-91.

Systems: One folding side elevator forward, to port; one to starboard, aft island, both of 22-ton capacity; 70-m hangar. Excellent medical facilities (30C LPH 9 has an ASCAC (Air-Surface Classification and Analysis Center). LPH 1 slightly different design, carries two LCVP in davits. Have 517 m² vehicle p space below decks. Carry 404,000 gallons aviation fuel (JP-5) and 30,000 vehicle and boat fuel. An 18-ton aircraft crane is mounted abaft the island, a 7-ton stores elevators serve the hangar and flight deck. The hangar can accom 19 CH-46 or 11 CH-53 helicopters.

Two Mk 15 CIWS gatling AA have been added to all; in LPH 3 only, they *repl* obsolescent Mk 25 BPDMS Sea Sparrow launchers, retained in the others. The n are controlled by two Mk 71 directors with Mk 115 radars. All now have SLQ- EW in place of the WLR-1 suite, and URN-25 has replaced SRN-6 TACAN.

AMPHIBIOUS TRANSPORTS, DOCK

◆ **11 Austin class (SCB 187B type)** (*Atlantic/†Pacific Fleet)

	Bldr	Laid down	L	In
LPD 4 Austin*	New York NSY	4-2-63	27-6-64	
LPD 5 Ogden†	New York NSY	4-2-63	27-6-64	1
LPD 6 Duluth†	New York NSY	18-12-63	14-8-65	18-
LPD 7 Cleveland†	Ingalls, Pascagoula	30-11-64	7-5-66	2
LPD 8 Dubuque†	Ingalls, Pascagoula	25-1-65	6-8-66	
LPD 9 Denver†	Lockheed SB, Seattle	7-2-64	23-1-65	26-
LPD 10 Juneau†	Lockheed SB, Seattle	23-1-65	12-2-66	1
LPD 12 Shreveport*	Lockheed SB, Seattle	27-12-65	25-10-66	1
LPD 13 Nashville*	Lockheed SB, Seattle	14-3-66	7-10-67	1-
LPD 14 Trenton*	Lockheed SB, Seattle	8-8-66	3-8-68	
LPD 15 Ponce*	Lockheed SB, Seattle	31-10-66	20-5-70	1

Authorized: 3 in FY 62, 4 in FY 63, 3 in FY 64, 2 in FY 65

HIBIOUS TRANSPORTS, DOCK *(continued)*

e (LPD 15)—hangar extended Pradignac & Léo, 4-90

eport (LPD 12)—with extra flag deck George Nassiopoulos, 7-91

au (LPD 10)—still without Mk 15 CIWS OS2 John Bouvia, USN, 6-91

ton (LSD 14) Dr. Giorgio Arra, 4-91

ville (LPD 13) George Nassiopoulos, 9-91

Denver (LPD 9)—flag variant, with Mk 15 CIWS David D. Broecker, 3-92

Duluth (LPD 6) George R. Schneider, Jr., 9-91

D: 11,050 tons (16,586–17,595 fl) **S:** 21 kts
Dim: 173.4 × 25.6 (hull) × 7.0–7.2
A: 4/76.2-mm 50-cal. Mk 33 DP (II × 2)—LPD 4, 9, 12–15 also: 2/20-mm Mk 15 CIWS (I × 2)
Electron Equipt:
Radar: 1/LN-66 nav., 1/SPS-10F or SPS-67 surf. search, 1/SPS-40B air search
EW: SLQ-32(V)1 intercept; Mk 36 SRBOC decoy RL syst. (VI × 4)
TACAN: URN-25
M: 2 sets de Laval geared steam turbines; 2 props; 24,000 shp
Boilers: 2 Foster-Wheeler (LPD 5, LPD 12: Babcock & Wilcox), 42.3 kg/cm^2, 467°C
Range: 7,700/20
M: 24 officers, 396 enlisted (+ 90 staff in LPD 7 to LPD 13) + 930 troops (840 in LPD 7 to LPD 13)

Remarks: Lengthened version of the *Raleigh* class. Combination LSD and assault transports. Sister *Coronado* (LPD 11) redesignated AGF 11, 1-10-80. During a Persian Gulf deployment 2- to 6-88, LPD 14 acted as tender to six minesweepers (MSO) and carried four AH-1T, two UH-1N, two CH-46E, and one SH-60B helicopters. All were programmed to receive a SLEP (Service Life Extension Program) modernization to extend their service lives by 10–15 years, but this was canceled by Congress in 1987. Will be reduced to reserve during the mid-1990s.

Systems: Either 1 LCU and 3 LCM(6) or 9 LCM(6) or 4 LCM(8) or 28 LVT can be carried in the 120 × 15.24 (687 m^2) well deck. One 30-ton and six 4-ton cranes, one 8.15-ton elevator, two forklifts. Up to six CH-46 helicopters can be carried for brief periods on the 1,394-m^2 flight deck, but the small, telescoping hangar can accommodate only one utility helicopter; no hangar in LPD 4. LPD 7 to LPD 13 are fitted for flagship duty and have one additional superstructure deck. All have 1,379-m^2 vehicle parking space, 1,540-m^3 ammunition stowage, 224,500 gallons aviation fuel, and 119,000 gallons vehicle fuel.

All have lost their one Mk 56 and two Mk 63 gun fire-control directors, leaving the 76.2-mm guns locally controlled. Two twin 76.2-mm DP removed 1977–78 (port fwd, stbd aft). Pacific Fleet ships lagged the Atlantic Fleet units in the installation of the Mk 15 CIWS, and the last will not be equipped until 1993. In LPD 4–6, 14, and 15, the SPS-40 antenna is set on a platform well below the apex of the tripod mast, while on the others it is on the masthead platform.

◆ **1 Raleigh class** (in Reserve)
Bldr: New York Naval Shipyard, Brooklyn

	Laid down	L	In serv.	Decomm.
LPD2 *Vancouver*	19-11-60	15-9-62	11-5-63	27-3-92

Authorized: FY 60

D: 8,491 tons light (14,865 fl) **S:** 21 kts
Dim: 159.0 (152.4 wl) × 25.60 (hull) × 6.7
A: 4/76.2-mm 50-cal. Mk 33 DP (II × 3)—2/20-mm Mk 15 CIWS (I × 2)

AMPHIBIOUS TRANSPORTS, DOCK *(continued)*

Vancouver (LPD 2) OS2 John Bouvia, USN, 6-91

Electron Equipt:
Radar: 1/LN-66 nav., 1/SPS-10F surf. search, 1/SPS-40B air search
EW: SLQ-32(V)1 intercept, Mk 36 SRBOC decoy RL syst. (VI × 4)
TACAN: URN-25
M: 2 sets de Laval geared steam turbines; 2 props; 24,000 shp
Boilers: 2 Babcock & Wilcox; 40.8 kg/cm^2, 467°C
Electric: 3,600 kw **Range:** 9,600/16; 16,500/10
Crew: 29 officers, 400 enlisted + 930 troops

Remarks: *Raleigh* (LPD 1) was decommissioned 13-12-91 and stricken during 1-92. Sister *La Salle* (LPD 3), modified as flagship for CoMideastFor in the Indian Ocean and reclassified AGF 3 on 1-7-72. LPD 2 being retained in reserve for possible recommissioning in an emergency. Docking well, 51.2 × 15.2 m, is shorter than on *Austin* class. The 1,386-m^2 flight deck, atop the 696-m^2 well deck, can handle up to six CH-46 helicopters; there is no hangar. The ship has 1,034 m^2 of vehicle parking space.

DOCK LANDING SHIPS

◆ 0 (+3) Harpers Ferry class Bldr: Avondale SY, New Orleans

	Laid down	L	In serv.
LSD 49 Harpers Ferry	15-4-91	10-92	12-93
LSD 50 Carter Hall	8-11-91	1993	1-95
LSD 51 Oak Hill	9-92	. . .	1995

Authorized: LSD 49 in FY 88, LSD 50 in FY 90, LSD 51 in FY 91

Harpers Ferry (LSD 49) U.S. Navy, 1989

D: 11,894 tons light (16,695 fl) **S:** 22 kts
Dim: 185.80 (176.80 wl) × 25.60 × 6.03
A: 2/20-mm Mk 15 CIWS AA (I × 2)—2/25-mm Mk 38 AA (I × 2)—8/12.7-mm mg (I × 8)
Electron Equipt:
Radar: 1/SPS-64(V)9 nav., 1/SPS-67(V) surf. search, 1/SPS-49(V) air search
EW: SLQ(V)2 intercept, Mk 36 SRBOC decoy RL syst. (VI × 6)
TACAN: URN-25
M: 4 Colt-Pielstick 16 PC2.5V400 diesels; 2 CP props; 41,600 bhp (33,600 sust.)
Electric: 9,200 kw (4 Fairbanks-Morse 12D38 ⅛ diesels driving)
Range: approx. 8,000/20 **Fuel:** 2,000 tons
Crew: approx. 410 crew + 504 troops

Remarks: Officially referred to as the "LSD 41 CV (Cargo Variant)" class. First unit originally requested FY 88, withdrawn because of late design changes (which may enlarge ship over figures given above) and then approved by Congress with navy concurrence. Were originally to have been a class of 12, but program terminated 1992 in favor of development of the LX class; LSD 52, approved under FY 92, will not be built. LSD 50 ordered 26-12-89, LSD 50 on 22-12-89, and LSD 51 on 27-3-91.

Systems: Modification of LSD 41 design with increased cargo capacity at the expense of a shorter well deck able to accommodate only 2 LCAC, leving space for 2 LCAC or 10 LCM (6). Cargo space: 1,208 m^2 vehicle parking, 1,133 m^3 cargo volume. Have greater air-conditioning capacity than the LSD 41 class and are equipped with only one crane.

◆ 8 Whidbey Island class (*Atlantic/†Pacific Fleet)

	Bldr	Laid down	L	In serv.
LSD 41 Whidbey Island*	Lockheed, Seattle	4-8-81	10-6-83	9-2-85
LSD 42 Germantown†	Lockheed, Seattle	5-8-82	29-6-84	
LSD 43 Fort McHenry†	Lockheed, Seattle	10-6-83	1-2-86	
LSD 44 Gunston Hall*	Avondale SY	26-5-86	27-6-87	24
LSD 45 Comstock†	Avondale SY	27-10-86	16-1-88	
LSD 46 Tortuga*	Avondale SY	23-3-87	15-9-88	17-
LSD 47 Rushmore†	Avondale SY	9-11-87	6-5-89	
LSD 48 Ashland*	Avondale SY	4-4-88	11-11-89	

Authorized: LSD 41 in FY 81, LSD 42 in FY 82, LSD 43 in FY 83, 44 in FY 84, LSD 45, 46 in FY 85, LSD 47, 48 in FY 86

Gunston Hall (LSD 44) Dr. Giorgio Arr

Comstock (LSD 45) Victor M. Bac

Germantown (LSD 42) Leo Van Ginderen

Tortuga (LSD 46) Dr. Giorgio Arr

OCK LANDING SHIPS *(continued)*

shmore (LSD 47)—Mk 15 CIWS in "Maintenance Enclosures" Dr. Giorgio Arra, 10-91

): 11,854 tons (15,165 fl) **S:** 22 kts
im: 185.80 (176.80 wl) × 25.60 × 5.97
: 2/20-mm Mk 15 CIWS AA (I × 2)—2/20-mm Mk 67 AA (LSD 47, 48: 25-mm Mk 38 Bushmaster) (I × 2)—6/12.7-mm M2 mg (I × 6)
lectron Equipt:
Radar: 1/SPS-64(V)9 nav., 1/SPS-67(V) surf. search, 1/SPS-49(V) air search
EW: SLQ-32(V)1 intercept, Mk 36 Mod. 6 SRBOC decoy RL syst. (VI × 4)
TACAN: URN-25
: 4 Colt-Pielstick 16 PC2.5V400 diesels; 2 5-bladed CP props; 41,600 bhp (33,600 sust.)
lectric: 9,200 kw (4 Fairbanks-Morse 12D 38⅛ diesels driving)
ange: 8,000/20 **Fuel:** 2,000 tons
rew: 23 officers, 391 enlisted + troops: 34 officers, 526 enlisted

arks: The design was originally to have been a near-repeat of the LSD 36 class ted for diesel propulsion, but with a requirement to be able to accommodate four C (Air-Cushion Landing Craft).
stems: The docking well measures 134.0 × 15.24 m clear and floods to 1.8 m 3.0 m aft. The helicopter deck is raised above the docking well (which can also hold CM(6) or 3 LCU or 64 LVTP) in order to provide all-around ventilation for the urbine-engined LCACs. There are two landing spots on the 64.6 × 25.3-m flight for up to CH-53-sized helicopters but no hangar facilities. Forward of the docking is 1,214 m² of vehicle parking space and space for 149 m³ of palletized cargo. Carry ns JP-5 fuel for helicopters. Carry one 15.24-m utility boat, two LCPL Mk-II, and CVP on deck, handled by one 20-ton and one 60-ton crane. LSD 44–48 have a tive BW/CW protection system. All have Inogen Leading Mark optical guidance m for LCAC entry to well deck. Two Mk 49, 21-cell launchers for the RAM missile be added; trials will be conducted during 1993 with one ship of the class, using ontrol inputs from the Mk 15 Phalanx CIWS radar.

Anchorage class (SCN 404-65 and -66 types)

ldr: LSD 36: Ingalls, Pascagoula; others: General Dynamics, Quincy, Mass.
Atlantic/†Pacific Fleet)

	Laid down	L	In serv.
36 ANCHORAGE†	13-3-67	5-5-68	15-3-69
37 PORTLAND*	21-9-67	20-12-69	3-10-70
38 PENSACOLA*	12-3-69	11-7-70	27-3-71
39 MOUNT VERNON†	29-1-70	17-4-71	13-5-72
40 FORT FISHER†	15-7-70	22-4-72	12-9-72

thorized: 1 in FY 65, 3 in FY 66, 1 in FY 67

D: 8,600 tons light (14,000 fl) **S:** 22 kts
Dim: 168.66 (162.8 wl) × 25.9 × 5.6 (6.1 max.)
A: 4/76.2-mm 50-cal. Mk 33 DP (II × 2)—2/20-mm Mk 15 CIWS (I × 2)
Electron Equipt:
Radar: 1/LN-66 nav., 1/SPS-10F surf. search, 1/SPS-40B air search
EW: SLQ-32(V)1 intercept, Mk 36 SRBOC decoy RL syst. (VI × 4)
M: 2 sets de Laval geared steam turbines; 2 props; 24,000 shp
Boilers: 2 Foster-Wheeler (LSD 36: Combustion Eng.); 42.3 kg/cm², 467°C
Range: . . ./. . . **Fuel:** 2,750 tons
Crew: 24 officers, 350 enlisted + troops: 18 officers, 348 enlisted

Pensacola (LSD 38) Leo Van Ginderen, 3-92

Anchorage (LSD 36) OS2 John Bouvia, USN, 6-91

DOCK LANDING SHIPS *(continued)*

Remarks: Can accommodate 3 LCU or 15 LCM(6) or 8 LCM(8) or 50 LVT in the 113.28 × 15.24 well deck. One or two LCM(6) can be stowed on deck, handled by the two 50-ton cranes. Have 1,115 m² of vehicle parking space forward of the docking well. The helicopter deck is removable. 90 tons JP-5 fuel carried for helicopters. Mk 56 and Mk 63 directors removed in 1977, and two additional twin 76.2-mm gun mounts by 1990.

Note: Of the eight *Thomaston*-class dock landing ships, *Thomaston* (LSD 28) was transferred to the Maritime Administration (MARAD) on 28-10-91, *Plymouth Rock* (LSD 29) was transferred to MARAD on 8-11-91, *Fort Snelling* (LSD 30) to MARAD on 7-9-89, *Point Defiance* (LSD 31) to MARAD on 12-8-91, *Spiegel Grove* (LSD 32) remains in navy custody in reserve, *Alamo* (LSD 33) was decommissioned and leased to Brazil for five years on 2-11-90, *Hermitage* (LSD 34) was decommissioned and leased to Brazil for five years on 2-10-89, and *Monticello* (LSD 35) was transferred to MARAD on 2-8-91. Ships transferred to MARAD are in the National Defense Reserve Fleet; in 2-92, they were declared surplus and available for foreign transfer.

TANK LANDING SHIPS

◆ 20 Newport class (SCN 405-66 type)

Bldrs: LST 1179: Philadelphia NSY; others: National Steel SB, San Diego (*Atlantic/†Pacific Fleet) (2 in Reserve)

	Laid down	L	In serv.	Decomm.
LST 1179 *Newport*	1-11-66	3-2-68	7-6-69	30-9-92
LST 1180 Manitowoc*	1-2-67	4-6-69	24-1-70	. . .
LST 1181 Sumter*	14-11-67	13-12-69	20-6-70	. . .
LST 1182 Fresno† (NRF)	16-12-67	28-9-68	22-11-69	. . .
LST 1183 Peoria†	22-2-68	23-11-68	21-2-70	. . .
LST 1184 Frederick†	13-4-68	8-3-69	11-4-70	. . .
LST 1185 Schenectady†	2-8-68	24-5-69	13-6-70	. . .
LST 1186 Cayuga†	28-9-68	12-7-69	8-8-70	. . .
LST 1187 Tuscaloosa†	23-11-68	6-9-69	24-10-70	. . .
LST 1188 Saginaw*	24-5-69	7-2-70	23-1-71	. . .
LST 1189 San Bernardino†	12-7-69	28-3-70	27-3-71	. . .
LST 1190 Boulder† (NRF)	6-9-69	22-5-70	4-6-71	. . .
LST 1191 Racine† (NRF)	13-12-69	15-8-70	9-7-71	. . .
LST 1192 Spartanburg County*	7-2-70	11-11-70	1-9-71	. . .
LST 1193 Fairfax County*	28-3-70	19-12-70	16-10-71	. . .
LST 1194 La Moure County*	22-5-70	13-2-71	18-12-71	. . .
LST 1195 *Barbour County*	15-8-70	15-5-71	12-2-72	31-3-92
LST 1196 Harlan County*	7-11-70	24-7-71	8-4-72	. . .
LST 1197 Barnstable County*	19-12-70	2-10-71	27-5-72	. . .
LST 1198 Bristol County†	13-2-71	4-12-71	5-8-72	. . .

Authorized: 1 in FY 65, 8 in FY 66, 11 in FY 67

Harlan County (LST 1196)—with 4 pontoon sections
PH2 Charles Stover, USN, 12-91

Manitowoc (LST 1180)—during exercise "Teamwork 92"
Jürg Kürsener, 3-92

Spartanburg County (LST 1192) Dr. Giorgio Arra, 4-

Tuscaloosa (LST 1187) Leo Van Ginderen, 7

D: 4,793 tons light (8,450 fl) **S:** 22 kts (20 sust.)
Dim: 159.2 (171.3 over horns) × 21.18 × 5.3 (aft) × 1.80 (fwd)
A: 4/76.2-mm 50-cal. Mk 33 DP (II × 2)—Atlantic Fleet units also: 1/20-mm Mk 15 CIWS—all: 2 or 4/12.7-mm mg (I × 2 or 4)
Electron Equipt:
Radar: 1/LN-66 nav., 1/SPS-10 surf. search
M: 6 Alco 16-251 (LST 1179 to LST 1181: G.M. 16-645-E5) diesels; 2 CP props; 16,500 bhp
Range: 2,500/14 **Fuel:** 1,750 tons
Crew: 13 officers, 174 enlisted + troops: 20 officers, 380 enlisted

Remarks: Seven more planned under FY 71 were canceled. LST 1190 transferr the Naval Reserve Force 1-12-80, LST 1191 on 15-1-81, and LST 1182 during 9-90. 1184 is home-ported at Sasebo, Japan. Are to be decommissioned to reserve durin mid-1990s.

Systems: Can transport 2,000 tons cargo, or, for beaching, 500 tons of carg 1,765 m² of deck space. A side-thruster propeller forward helps when marrying causeway. There is a 34-m-long, 75-ton-capacity mobile aluminum ramp forw which is linked to the tank deck by a second ramp from the upper deck. Aft is a 24 helicopter platform and a stern door for loading and unloading vehicles. Four pon causeway sections can be carried on the hull sides. The tank deck, which has a 75 capacity turntable at both ends, can carry 23 AAV-7A1 armored personnel carrie 29 M 48 tanks or 41 2.5-ton trucks, while the upper deck can accept 29 2.5-ton tr Normally carry three LCVP and one LCP in Welin davits. Have two 10-ton cr Carry 141,600 gallons vehicle fuel. Mk 63 radar gunfire-control systems rem 1977–78. SLQ-32(V)1 and decoy rocket launchers are *not* planned. Active Atl Fleet ships have one Mk 15 CIWS atop pilothouse, and Pacific Fleet units are begin to receive it; the 76.2-mm guns are being retained.

Note: The surviving *DeSoto County* tank landing ships, *Suffolk County* (LST 1 *Wood County* (LST 1178), and *Lorain County* (LST 1177), were stricken 16-2-89 the National Defense Reserve Fleet for possible overseas sale. Two *Terrebonne Pa* class tank landing ships, *Tioga County* (LST 1158) and *Wahkiakum County* (LST 1 remain in the Maritime Administration's National Defense Reserve Fleet, while sisters were leased to Peru on 7-8-84: *Traverse County* (LST 1160), *Waldo County* 1163), *Washoe County* (LST 1164), and *Walworth County* (LST 1165). The two N ships are subject to navy recall, but this is unlikely due to their age and conditic

AMPHIBIOUS CARGO SHIPS

◆ 5 Charleston class (SCB 403 Design)

Bldr: Newport News SB & DD) (*Atlantic/†Pacific Fleet) (1 in Reserve)

	Laid down	L	In serv.	Dec
LKA 113 *Charleston*	5-12-66	2-12-67	14-12-68	17
LKA 114 Durham†	10-7-67	29-3-68	24-5-69	.
LKA 115 Mobile†	15-1-68	19-10-68	29-9-69	.
LKA 116 St. Louis†	3-4-68	4-1-69	22-11-69	.
LKA 117 El Paso*	22-10-68	17-5-69	17-1-70	

Authorized: 4 in FY 65, 1 in FY 66

El Paso (LKA 117) Dr. Giorgio Arra

·IIBIOUS CARGO SHIPS *(continued)*

·so (LKA 117) Dr. Giorgio Arra, 3-91

·e (LKA 115)—Pacific Fleet unit without CIWS
OS2 John Bouvia, USN, 1991

.0,000 tons (18,600 fl) **S:** 20 kts
: 175.6 (167.6 wl) × 18.9 × 8.5 (max.)
·/76.2-mm 50-cal. Mk 33 DP (II × 2)—2/20-mm Mk 15 CIWS
I × 2)
·tron Equipt:
·adar: 1/LN-66 (LKA 113: CRP-2900) nav., 1/SPS-10F surf. search
·W: SLQ-32(V)1 intercept, Mk 36 SRBOC decoy RL syst. (VI × 2)
1 set Westinghouse geared steam turbines; 1 prop; 22,000 shp
(19,250 sust.)
·ers: 2 Combustion Engineering; 42.2 kg/cm², 443°C
·ge: . . ./. . . **Fuel:** 2,400 tons
·w: 22 officers, 334 enlisted + troops: 25 officers, 337 enlisted

·ks: All but LKA 116 had been transferred to the Naval Reserve Force: LKA 21-11-79, LKA 114 on 1-10-79, LKA 115 on 1-9-80, and LKA 117 on 1-3-81. ·ed to regular navy: LKA 113 on 18-2-83, LKA 114 on 1-10-82, LKA 115 on · and LKA 117 on 1-10-82. Will all be decommissioned during mid-1990s, LKA ·ing Fiscal Year 1993; to be transferred to the Ready Reserve Force and used as ·ent prepositioning ships.
·ems: Air-conditioned. Machinery control is automatic. Have a 565 m² helicop- ·form. Have 2,420 m³ of cargo capacity, including 4,371 m² of vehicle parking ·and 741 m³ of ammunition stowage. There are one 6-ton and five 2-ton stores ·rs. Fittings include two 70-ton heavy-lift booms, two 40-ton booms, and eight booms. Normally carry four LCM(8), five LCM(6), two LCVP, and two LCP · craft. Two Mk 56 radar gunfire-control systems and one twin 76.2-mm gun removed 1977–78, and a third later.

·ITY LANDING CRAFT

A new "LCX" design to replace the rapidly aging LCUs is in development. The ·construction contract, however, is not expected until 10-93, with two prototypes ·er 1995–96. The craft may either be conventional, a hybrid hydrofoil type, or an ·hion vehicle larger than the LCAC.

· LCU 1610 class (SCB 149, 149B, and 406 types)

·rs: *See* Remarks (In serv. 6-59 to 12-71, except LCU 1680: 11-10-87, and ·U 1681: 12-11-87)

·1616	LCU 1629 to 1635
1617	LCU 1643 to 1646
1619	LCU 1648 to 1666
·1624	LCU 1680 (135CU8501)
1627	LCU 1681 (135CU8502)

1663 Dr. Giorgio Arra, 4-91

LCU 1644 Dr. Giorgio Arra, 4-91

LCU 1680—Naval Reserve training unit Leo Van Ginderen, 1991

LCU 1647—tender to the AUTEC range, Bahamas
Dr. Giorgio Arra, 5-91

D: 190 tons (390 fl) (LCU 1680, 81: 404 tons fl) **S:** 11 kts
Dim: 41.07 × 9.07 × 2.08 **A:** 2/12.7-mm mg (I × 2)
Electron Equipt: Radar: 1/LN-66 or SPS-53 nav.
M: 4 G.M. 6-71 diesels; 2 Kort-nozzle props; 1,200 bhp (LCU 1680, 81: 2 G.M. 12V71 TI diesels; 2 Kort-nozzle props; 1,700 bhp)
Range: 1,200/11 **Fuel:** 13 tons
Crew: 6 enlisted + 8 troops (1680, 81: 2 officers, 12 enlisted)

Remarks: LCU 1616–1619, LCU 1623, LCU 1624 delivered 6-59 to 9-60 by Gunderson Bros., Portland, Oregon; LCU 1621, 1626, 1629, and 1630 delivered 6-60 to 1968 by Southern Shipbuilding, Slidell, La.; LCU 1627, 1628, 1631–1635 built by General Ship & Eng. Wks., East Boston, Mass.; LCU 1643–1645 delivered 8-67 to 1969 by Marinette Marine, Marinette, Wisc.; LCU 1646–1666 delivered 1969–70 by Defoe SB, Bay City, Wisc.; LCU 1667–1670 built by General Ship & Eng. Wks.; LCU 1680, 1681 ordered 10-85 from Moss Point Marine, Escatawpa, Miss., for delivery 9-86 to Naval Reserve Force units; both laid down 2-4-86, but not delivered until late 1987. Missing numbers have either been redesignated as yard craft (YFU—see later pages) or transferred to the U.S. Army (LCU 1667–1679). Twelve of these extremely useful craft are being rehabilitated, beginning with two under FY 87; the others will be discarded by the mid-1990s. At present, 17 each assigned to Assault Craft Units ACU 1 and ACU 2, and LCU 1665 is assigned to Fleet Activities, Sasebo. LCU 1650 aground Ft. Pierce, Florida, 16-4-91; salved. Four others serve as workboats: LCU 1613 (at Port Hueneme, Cal.), 1614 (at Naval Aviation Development Command, Key West), 1641 (as a minelayer; see page 846), and 1647 (at NUSC Detachment, Andros Island, the Bahamas); three others (LCU 1621, 1623, 1628) have been designated as ASDV (Auxiliary Swimmer Delivery Vehicle).
Systems: Cargo capacity is 143 tons; cargo space, 30.5 × 5.5 m. Usually unarmed. Minor differences as construction progressed.

MINOR LANDING CRAFT

♦ 48 (+36) LCAC class

Bldr: Textron, New Orleans (except LCAC 15–23, 34–36, 49–51, Avondale, Gulfport)

	In serv.		In serv.		In serv.
LCAC 1	24-12-84	LCAC 41	27-11-91	LCAC 81	. . .
LCAC 2	22-2-86	LCAC 42	12-12-91	LCAC 82	. . .
LCAC 3	9-6-86	LCAC 43	21-2-92	LCAC 83	. . .

MINOR LANDING CRAFT *(continued)*

	In serv.		In serv.		In serv.
LCAC 4	13-8-86	LCAC 44	28-2-92	LCAC 84	1996
LCAC 5	26-11-86	LCAC 45	26-3-92		
LCAC 6	1-12-86	LCAC 46	8-5-92		
LCAC 7	18-3-87	LCAC 47	24-6-92		
LCAC 8	3-6-87	LCAC 48	31-7-92		
LCAC 9	26-6-87	LCAC 49	10-92		
LCAC 10	4-9-87	LCAC 50	2-93		
LCAC 11	7-12-87	LCAC 51	6-93		
LCAC 12	23-12-87	LCAC 52	7-92		
LCAC 13	30-9-88	LCAC 53	8-92		
LCAC 14	3-11-88	LCAC 54	9-92		
LCAC 15	20-9-88	LCAC 55	11-92		
LCAC 16	4-11-88	LCAC 56	12-92		
LCAC 17	1989	LCAC 57	1-93		
LCAC 18	1989	LCAC 58	3-93		
LCAC 19	5-90-89	LCAC 59	4-93		
LCAC 20	1990	LCAC 60	5-93		
LCAC 21	1990	LCAC 61	7-93		
LCAC 22	11-90	LCAC 62	8-93		
LCAC 23	15-6-91	LCAC 63	9-93		
LCAC 24	1-3-90	LCAC 64	10-93		
LCAC 25	29-6-90	LCAC 65	11-93		
LCAC 26	7-90	LCAC 66	12-93		
LCAC 27	24-8-90	LCAC 67	1-94		
LCAC 28	12-10-90	LCAC 68	2-94		
LCAC 29	18-12-90	LCAC 69	3-94		
LCAC 30	19-12-90	LCAC 70	4-94		
LCAC 31	27-2-91	LCAC 71	5-94		
LCAC 32	1-5-91	LCAC 72	6-94		
LCAC 33	4-6-91	LCAC 73	. . .		
LCAC 34	31-5-92	LCAC 74	. . .		
LCAC 35	31-5-92	LCAC 75	. . .		
LCAC 36	1-5-92	LCAC 76	. . .		
LCAC 37	31-7-91	LCAC 77	. . .		
LCAC 38	6-9-91	LCAC 78	. . .		
LCAC 39	30-9-91	LCAC 79	. . .		
LCAC 40	6-11-91	LCAC 80	. . .		

Authorized: 3 in FY 82, 3 in FY 83, 6 in FY 84, 9 in FY 85, 12 in FY 86, 15 in FY 89, 12 in FY 90, 24 in FY 91, 12 FY 92.

LCAC 24—on builder's trials — Textron, 2-90

LCAC 7 — Dr. Giorgio Arra, 4-91

LCAC 4 — OS2 John Bouvia, USN, 11-90

D: 93 tons light (160 fl) **S:** 54 kts (40 when loaded)
Dim: 26.8 (24.7 hull) × 14.3 (13.4 hull) × 0.87 (at rest)
A: none **Electron Equipt:** Radar: 1/nav.
M: 4 Avco TF40B gas turbines (2 for lift); 2 shrouded airscrews/4 fans; 15,820 shp
Range: 223/48; 200/40 (loaded) **Fuel:** 6.2 tons
Crew: 5 crew + 25 troops

Remarks: Design derived from that of the JEFF-B prototype. Original progra for 108. Cargo capacity: 60 tons normal/75 overload. Carried by the LSD 41, and LHA 1 classes. Bow ramp is 8.8 m wide, stern ramp 4.6 m. The deck has parking area. First unit launched 2-5-84 and placed in service 24-12-84; secor launched 18-1-85 and delivered 19-7-85. First 12 by Bell-Halter, numbers ordered 10-85 from Lockheed, with orders for 7 other FY 85 units delayed; Av bought Lockheed facility and contracts 1-88. Experience has shown that the are damaged by spray and by gravel and dust when on land; spray-deflectors hav added and cargo deck covers may be fabricated. Are difficult to tow if broken Seventeen LCAC participated in the Mideast War in 2-91 and in post-typhoo efforts shortly thereafter, all with excellent results. To train LCAC crews, two Hovercraft AP-1-88/90 hovercraft are on lease from BHC, Cowes.

Status: LCAC 15, 17, 19, 20, 22–26 ordered 1-7-87; LCAC 27–33 ordered 7-87; 34–48 ordered 15-12-88; LCAC 49–60 on 22-12-89; LCAC 61–72 on 24-4-91; and 73–84 on 22-5-92; 12 other LCAC authorized in FY 92 will not be ordered. Co directed that one FY 88 LCAC be configured for Arctic duties; trials were con 6-88. LCAC 1–6 operate as ACU 5 from Camp Pendleton, Cal., LCAC 7–12 as from Little Creek, Va.

◆ **53 LCM(8) Mk 4 class** (In serv. 1967–79; 1985–88; 1991–92)

◆ **34 LCM(8) Mk 3 class** (In serv. 1953–55)

D: 34 tons light (121 fl) **S:** 12 kts **Dim:** 22.43 × 6.40 × 1.40 (a
M: 4 G.M. Detroit 6-71 diesels; 2 props; 590 bhp **Range:** 150/12

LCM(8) from El Paso (LKA 117) — Dr. Giorgio Arra

Remarks: Current Mk 4 version began building in 1967. Aluminum ver LCM(8) Mk 1. Cargo: 58 tons or 150 troops. Some have two G.M. 12V71 diese were to be built under FY 82 for use aboard the new T-AKX maritime preposi ships; canceled. Eight were ordered from Marine Power Co., Seattle, under FY authorized (some for T-AKX) under FY 84; three authorized under FY 85. Four 10-85 from Twin City shipyards. Ten ordered 2-3-90 from Swiftships, and ten 1991. Some 34 of the steel-hulled Mk 3 class are to be rehabilitated under FY 92 and 20 new aluminum-hulled versions are planned for FY 90/91. Totals above n be entirely accurate, as some were to be transferred to the Philippines in 1987

◆ **99 LCM(6) class**

D: 24 tons (56 fl) **S:** 10 kts **Dim:** 17.07 × 4.37 × 1.17 (aft)
M: 2 Gray Marine 64HN9 (G.M. V71 on Mk 3) diesels; 2 props; 330
Range: 130/10 **Crew:** 3 tot. + 80 troops

LCM(6)—attached to Naval Amphibious Base, Coronado — Willi Donko

Remarks: Designed during World War II and built between 1952 and 1980. used in utility roles. Cargo: 34 tons. Two new examples requested under FY delivery 1-86. Majority (67) in service are Mk 3, delivered 1977–80; another 36 2, delivered 1960–71.

◆ **136 LCVP Mk 7 class** (In serv. 1966–69)

D: 13 tons (fl) **S:** 9 kts **Dim:** 10.90 × 3.21 × 1.04 (aft)
M: 1 Gray Marine 64HN9 diesel; 225 bhp **Range:** 110/9

R LANDING CRAFT *(continued)*

stowed below an LCPL on LST 1197 Stefan Terzibaschitsch, 11-86

rks: Glass-reinforced plastic hulls. Can carry 36 troops or 3.5 tons cargo. Cargo 5.24 × 2.29 m, with 2.00-m-wide access through the bow ramp. Some 91 total are ly stowed aboard the various amphibious warfare ships.

4 LCPL Mk 12 and Mk 13 classes

Mk 12 class Dr. Giorgio Arra, 7-86

9.75 tons light (13 fl) **S:** 19 kts
: 10.98 (9.26 pp) × 3.97 × 1.13
ctron Equipt: Radar: 1/LN-66 nav.
1 G.M. 8V71 TI diesel; 350–425 bhp **Range:** 150/19
l: 630 liters **Crew:** 3 crew + 17 passengers

rks: Plastic construction. For use as control craft, but can carry two tons cargo. d aboard LHA, LPD, LSD, LST classes, etc. Total includes 75 LCP(L) Mk 12 d from Watercraft America, Edgewater, Fla., in 30-6-83, with 23 more on option; livered 8-84 and last by 9-85. Earlier Mk 12 delivered 9-81 to 4-84. In FY 85, 48 lanned for ordering, plus 50 in FY 86 and 16 in FY 87–88.
t LCPL Mk 13 class (36PL9001 through 9008) were ordered in 1989 from ger Boat, Lockport, Lousiana, and delivered 17-10-90 through 20-3-91.

new-construction side-loading warping tugs
dr: PACECO, Gulfport, Mississippi (In serv. 1989)

side-by-side self-propelled causeway sections—with portable ol booth, pushing 6 non-powered units Dr. Giorgio Arra, 1989

Remarks: No data available, but probably of similar dimensions, etc., to LWT 1 and 2 below. Original SLWT 1 through 5 stricken 1989. PACECO also built eight self-propelled causeway sections and eight non-self-propelled sections during 1989. Contracts to Wedtech for 37 powered and 51 unpowered causeway sections went unfilled with the company's collapse, but the navy has a number of earlier pontoon causeway sections that can be powered by what are essentially large diesel outboard engines.

◆ **2 amphibious warfare warping tugs** Bldr: Campbell Machine Wks., San Diego, Cal. (In serv. 4-70)

LWT 1 LWT 2

D: 61 tons light **S:** 9 kts **Dim:** 25.9 × 6.7 × 2.1
M: 2 G.M. 8V71 diesels; 2 steerable props; 420 bhp **Crew:** 6 tot.

Remarks: Aluminum construction, intended for handling causeway sections and ship-to-beach fuel lines. Series production not pursued.

SPECIAL WARFARE CRAFT

Note: The ill-fated SWCM—Special Warfare Craft, Medium—program was canceled by the Secretary of the Navy in 1987. The prototype, ordered 10-5-84, was never completed, and the navy placed the incomplete hull in storage 7-1-87, after work had ceased by the builder, R.M.I., Inc., in summer 1986. Congress had funded a new SWCM prototype under FY 87, to be powered by two MTU diesels and displace 132 tons full load, but no contracts were let. The SWCM (originally typed PBM—Patrol Boat, Medium), was to have been a rigid-sidewall air-cushion vehicle to deliver SEAL special forces and could accommodate two swimmer delivery submersibles in a floodable well aft. The 13 new *Cyclone*-class patrol boats (see earlier page) will be able to carry up to nine SEAL special force personnel. SEAL teams also operate four-man Mk-7, six-man Mk-8, and two-man Mk-9 swimmer-delivery submersibles.

◆ **7 (+8+100) "Stinger"-class riverine assault craft**
Bldr: First 7: SeaArk Marine, Monticello, Ark. (In serv.: 7 in 31-7-90, 7 in 1991); others: Swiftships, Inc.

"Stinger"-class riverine assault craft SeaArk, 1990

D: 7.48 tons (fl) **S:** 38 kts (34.6 sust.)
Dim: 10.64 × 2.82 × 0.66 (loaded)
A: 2/12.7-mm M2 mg (I × 2)—2/7.62-mm M60 mg (I × 2) (*see* Remarks)
Electron Equipt: Radar: 1/Raytheon 1900 Pathfinder nav.
M: 2 Cummins BTA5.9M2 diesels; 1 Hamilton 271 waterjet; 600 bhp
Range: . . ./. . . **Fuel:** 567 liters **Crew:** 4 tot. + 10 troops

Remarks: First seven ordered 5-5-90 as replacements for PBR-type riverine patrol craft for use by Special Boat Units. All are based at Camp Lejeune, North Carolina. Aluminum construction with 3/16-in. plating. Have weapons positions fore and aft that are convertible for twin or single 12.7-mm mg or single Mk 19 40-mm grenade launcher. Can be carried by a C-130 Hercules aircraft. Eight additional, slightly modified units ordered 1992, with an option for 100 more.

◆ **24 SWCL "Seafox" class** Bldr: Uniflite, Bellingham, Wash.

36PB801–807 (In serv. 1980–81) 36PB811 (In serv. 1981)
36PB821–836 (In serv. 1983–84)

"Seafox" Dr. Giorgio Arra, 1988

SPECIAL WARFARE CRAFT *(continued)*

D: 11.3 tons (fl) **S:** 30+ kts **Dim:** 11.0 × 3.0 × 0.84
A: 2/12.7-mm M2 mg (I × 2)—2/7.62-mm M60 mg (I × 2)
Electron Equipt: Radar: 1/LN-66 nav.
M: 2 G.M. 6V-92 TA diesels; 2 props; 930 bhp **Crew:** 3 tot.

Remarks: Glass-reinforced plastic construction. SWCL = Special Warfare Craft, Light. Intended for use by SEAL team commandos; can stow a rubber raft. Have secure voice communications gear, IFF, night-vision equipment, and an echo-sounder. Prototype delivered 11-77 and stricken 2-84. Seven built under FY 80, 1 under FY 81, and 16 under FY 82. Also built for foreign transfer. To be phased out by the beginning of 1993 and replaced by 9.14-m rigid-inflatable craft.

◆ **22 Mini-ATC class**
Bldr: Sewart Seacraft, Berwick, La. (In serv. 1972–73)

"Mini-ATC" Dr. Giorgio Arra, 10-88

D: 9.3 tons light (13 fl) **S:** 28.5 kts **Dim:** 10.97 × 3.89 × 0.30
A: up to 4/12.7-mm mg (I × 4)—1/40-mm Mk 19 grenade launcher—1/M60 mortar
M: 2 G.M. 8V53N diesels; 2 Jacuzzi 14YJ waterjets; 566 bhp
Range: 37/28 **Crew:** 2 tot. + 15 troops

Remarks: Aluminum construction. Rectangular planform; bow ramp. Seven weapon-mounting positions. Can carry an LN-66 radar. Very quiet in operation. All operated by Naval Reserve Force Special Boat Units.

◆ **122 Rigid Raider craft**
Bldr: Boston Whaler, Inc., Rockland, Mass. (In serv. 1988)

D: 1.2 tons (fl) **S:** 35 kts **Dim:** 6.81 × 2.26 × 0.46
A: 1/7.62-mm mg **Range:** 136/32 **Fuel:** 212 liters
M: 2 outboard motors; 140 bhp
Crew: 1 coxwain, 9–10 assault troops

Remarks: For U.S. Marine Expeditionary Unit (MEU) use. GRP construction, road transportable on special "combat trailer." Replace older Zodiac rigid inflatable craft. Each MEU will have 15.

◆ **3 Auxiliary Swimmer Delivery Vehicle carriers**
Bldr: Southern SB, Slidell, La. (In serv. 1960–68)

ASDV 1 (ex-LCU 1623) ASDV 2 (ex-LCU 1628)
ASDV 3 (ex-LCU 1621)

ASDV-2 Hartmut Ehlers, 11-90

D: approx. 210 tons (390 fl) **S:** 11 kts
Dim: 41.07 × 9.07 × 2.08 (max.)
Electron Equipt: 1/LN-66 or SPS-53 nav.
M: 4 G.M. 6-71 diesels; 2 Kort-nozzle (vertical cycloidal on ASDV 1) props; 1,200 bhp
Range: 1,200/11 **Fuel:** 13 tons **Crew:** 10–14 tot.

Remarks: Assigned to Special Boat Unit 12. Converted to train combat swimmers and to handle and service their equipment. Have a decompression chamber, large crane on port quarter.

Note: U.S. Marine Corps armored tracked vehicles available for amphibious in 1992 included: 853 AAV-7 and 294 AAV-7A1 personnel carriers, 77 AACV-7 AACV-7A command vehicles, and 54 AARV-7 and 10 AARV-7A recovery vehic LVTP/C/R-series vehicles were redesignated in 1985. The "7A-" series vehic built during 1983–85, while the earlier units were extensively overhauled a ernized during the 1980s. A 25,855-kg "Advanced Amphibious Assault Vehicle crew of 3 and a capacity of 15 troops is under development; it will be able 32 km/hr. in water and will be powered by a Cummins VTA 903T diesel on lar G.M. LM-120/T700/TC 7 gas turbine while waterborne.

AUXILIARY SHIPS

Note: This section includes only ships that are subordinate to the U.S. Navy Ships assigned to the civilian-manned Military Sealift Command are listed sep in a following section. Below, ships are listed alphabetically by their U.S. Na designation, i.e., AD, AF, AG, etc.

◆ **6 Samuel Gompers-class destroyer tenders (SCB 244 and 70 type)** Bldrs: AD 37 and AD 38, Puget Sound NSY; AD 41 to AD 44, National Steel, San Diego (*Atlantic/†Pacific Fleet)

	Laid down	L	In serv.
AD 37 Samuel Gompers†	9-7-64	14-5-66	1-7-67
AD 38 Puget Sound*	15-2-65	16-9-66	27-4-68
AD 41 Yellowstone*	27-6-77	27-1-79	28-6-80
AD 42 Acadia†	14-2-78	28-7-79	6-6-81
AD 43 Cape Cod†	27-1-79	2-8-80	17-4-82
AD 44 Shenandoah*	2-8-80	6-2-82	17-12-83

Authorized: 1 in FY 64, 1 in FY 65, 1 in FY 75, 1 in FY 76, 1 in FY 7 FY 79

D: AD 37, 38: 13,600 tons light (20,500 fl); AD 41–44: 13,318 tons light (20,224 fl)
S: 20 kts **Dim:** 196.29 × 25.91 × 6.86
A: AD 37, 38: 4/20-mm AA (I × 4); others: 2/20-mm Mk 67 AA (I 2)—all: 2/40-mm Mk 19 grenade launchers
Electron Equipt:
Radar: 1/LN-66 nav., 1/SPS-10 surf. search
TACAN: AD 38, 41: URN-25
M: 2 sets De Laval geared steam turbines; 1 prop; 20,000 shp
Boilers: 2 Combustion Engineering; 43.6 kg/cm², 462°C
Electric: 12,000 kw tot.
Crew: AD 37, 38: 43 officers, 1,233 enlisted; AD 41–44: 87 officer 1,508 enlisted

Remarks: Maintenance ships for guided-missile cruisers, destroyers, and f Similar in external appearance to *L. Y. Spear*-class submarine tenders; AD later considered a separate class (SCB 700 type) and have facilities to ca overhaul LM-2500 gas turbines, being tailored to support DD 963, DD 993, a 7-class ships. All have helo deck aft, no hangar (except AD 38). Two 30-ton cra 3.5-ton traveling cranes. Excellent workshops for electronic equipment and to-air missiles. Carry 60,000 different types of repair parts in 65 storerooms 1,795 m³. Originally planned to carry Sea Sparrow launchers in AD 41 and la 127-mm DP gun removed from AD 38 in 1979. AD 38 served as 6th Fleet flagsh 7-80 to 4-10-85, having received an extra mast to support a special SATCOMM (all have the standard WSC-3 SATCOMM installation, with two OE-82 drum antennas). Crews include numerous female officers and enlisted.

Shenandoah (AD 44) Dr. Giorgio Arr

Puget Sound (AD 38) Dr. Giorgio Arra,

LIARY SHIPS *(continued)*

Cod (AD 43) Dr. Giorgio Arra, 10-91

ixie-class destroyer tenders (*Atlantic/†Pacific Fleet)

	Bldr	Laid down	L	In serv.
Prairie†	New York SB	7-12-38	9-12-39	5-8-40
Sierra*	Tampa SB	31-12-41	23-2-43	20-3-44
Yosemite*	Tampa SB	19-1-42	16-5-43	25-3-44

mite (AD 19) Dr. Giorgio Arra, 3-91

mite (AD 19) Dr. Giorgio Arra, 3-91

D: 9,450 tons (17,190 fl) **S:** 18 kts **Dim:** 161.7 × 22.33 × 7.8
A: 4/20-mm Mk 67 AA (I × 4)
Electron Equipt: Radar: 1/LN-66 nav., 1/SPS-10 surf. search
M: 2 sets Allis-Chalmers (AD 15: Parsons) geared steam turbines; 2 props; 11,000 shp
Boilers: 4 Babcock & Wilcox; 28.4 kg/cm², 382°C **Electric:** 4,100 kw
Range: 12,200/12 **Fuel:** 3,680 tons **Crew:** 32 officers, 840 enlisted

Remarks: The design of these support ships dates to pre-1939 programs. Modernized under the FRAM program from 1959 to 1963 to serve as maintenance vessels for guided-missile ships, they have workshops, spare parts for missiles, and two 20-ton rotating cranes. Helicopter deck. 127-mm guns removed 1974–75. Sisters *Dixie* (AD 14) struck 15-6-82 for scrap, *Piedmont* (AD 17) decommissioned 30-9-82; leased to Turkey 18-10-82, and sold outright on 6-8-87.

Note: Plans to construct a new generation of ammunition ships, continually deferred since the middle 1980s, have now been indefinitely postponed.

♦ 7 Kilauea-class ammunition ships (SCB 703 type)

(*Atlantic/† Pacific Fleet)

	Bldr	Laid down	L	In serv.
AE 27 Butte*	Gen. Dynamics, Quincy	21-7-66	9-8-67	14-12-68
AE 28 Santa Barbara*	Bethlehem, Sparrows Pt.	20-12-66	23-1-68	11-7-70
AE 29 Mount Hood†	Bethlehem, Sparrows Pt.	8-5-67	17-7-68	1-5-71
AE 32 Flint†	Ingalls, Pascagoula	4-8-69	9-11-70	20-11-71
AE 33 Shasta†	Ingalls, Pascagoula	10-11-69	3-4-71	26-2-72
AE 34 Mount Baker*	Ingalls, Pascagoula	10-5-70	23-10-71	22-7-72
AE 35 Kiska†	Ingalls, Pascagoula	4-8-71	11-3-72	16-12-72

Authorized: 2 in FY 65, 2 in FY 66, 2 in FY 67, 2 in FY 68

Flint (AE 32) LSPH Scott Connolly, R.A.N., 3-91

AUXILIARY SHIPS *(continued)*

Shasta (AE 33) Dr. Giorgio Arra, 10-91

Santa Barbara (AE 28) French Navy, 3-90

Kiska (AE 35) Leo Van Ginderen, 3-91

D: 9,238 tons light (19,937 fl) **S:** 22 kts (21 sust.)
Dim: 171.90 (164.59 pp) × 24.69 × 8.5
A: 4/76.2-mm 50-cal. Mk 33 DP (II × 2)—AE 32–35: 2/20-mm Mk 15 CIWS (I × 2)—all: 2/UH-46E helicopters
Electron Equipt:
Radar: 1/LN-66 nav., 1/SPS-10F surf. search—TACAN: URN-25
EW: SLQ-32(V)1 intercept, Mk 36 SRBOC decoy RL syst. (VI × 2), SLQ-25 Nixie towed acoustic torpedo decoy
M: 3 sets G.E. geared turbines; 1 prop; 36,661 shp
Boilers: 3 Foster-Wheeler; 42.3 kg/cm^2, 467°C
Electric: 5,500 kw tot.
Range: 10,000/20; 18,000/11 **Crew:** 29 officers, 371 enlisted

Remarks: Sister *Kilauea* (AE 26) disarmed and transferred to Military Sealift Command 1-10-80. Sophisticated FAST rapid-replenishment system. Twin hangar and flight deck aft. Two twin 76.2-mm mounts and both Mk 56 directors removed. Mk 36 SRBOC chaff-flare launchers added to all. AE 32 and later have a larger bulbous forefoot to the bow. Carry cargo fuel for transfer, as well as ammunition. Several solid transfer rigs deactivated to reduce crew size. AE 27 to alter 6-90 to carry 60 female crewmembers.

◆ **3 Nitro-class ammunition ships (SCB 114A type)**
Bldr: Bethlehem Steel Corp., Sparrows Point, Md. (*Atlantic/†Pacific Fleet)

	Laid down	L	In serv.
AE 23 Nitro*	20-5-57	26-6-58	1-5-59
AE 24 Pyro†	21-10-57	5-11-58	24-7-59
AE 25 Haleakala†	10-3-58	17-2-59	3-11-59

D: 13,990 tons (17,450 fl) **S:** 20 kts **Dim:** 156.1 × 22.0 × 8.8
A: 4/76.2-mm DP (II × 2)—4/12.7-mm mg (I × 4)
Electron Equipt: Radar: 1/LN-66 nav., 1/SPS-10 surf. search
M: 2 sets Bethlehem geared steam turbines; 1 prop; 16,000 shp
Boilers: 2 Combustion Eng.; 43.9 kg/cm^2, 454°C
Range: 10,000/20; 12,000/15 **Crew:** 18–20 officers, 294 enlisted

Nitro (AE 23)—open gun mounts Leo Van Ginderen

Pyro (AE 24)—enclosed gun mounts Dr. Giorgio Arra,

Remarks: All had landing platforms for cargo helicopters added aft during the Mk 63 gun directors removed, 1977–78. SPS-6 air-search radar removed. AE 24 ferred to Naval Reserve Force 1-9-80 but returned to regular navy 1-1-82. AE 24 have enclosed gun houses. Planned to receive SLQ-32(V)1 and Mk 36 SRBC equipment, but had not by 1992. Will be retired without replacement, mid- t 1990s.

◆ **2 Suribachi-class ammunition ships (SCB 114 type)**
Bldr: Bethlehem Steel Corp., Sparrows Point, Md. (*Atlantic/†Pacific Fleet

	Laid down	L	In serv.
AE 21 Suribachi*	16-5-55	3-5-56	30-3-57
AE 22 Mauna Kea†	31-1-55	2-11-55	17-11-56

Suribachi (AE 21)—open gun mounts
PH3 Frank A. Marquart, USN

Mauna Kea (AE 22)—enclosed gun mounts Vic Jeffery

.IARY SHIPS *(continued)*

4,000 tons (17,000 fl) **S:** 21 kts **Dim:** 156.1 × 22.0 × 8.8
/76.2-mm 50-cal. Mk 33 DP (II × 2)
tron Equipt:
dar: 1/LN-66 nav., SPS-10 surf. search
/: AE 21: SLQ-32(V)1 intercept, Mk 36 SRBOC decoy RL syst. (VI × 2)
sets Bethlehem geared steam turbines; 1 prop; 16,000 shp
ers: 2 Combustion Eng.; 42.2 kg/cm^2, 440°C
tric: 12,550 kw tot. **Range:** 10,000/20; 12,000/15
v: 18–20 officers, 370 enlisted

ks: Gun mounts superfiring, whereas AE 23 to AE 25 have them side by side. unfire-control systems removed, 1977–78. SPS-6 air-search radar removed. AE ucted minelaying trials with Mk 55 aircraft mines laid from portable rails on er deck aft during 1983. AE 22 in Naval Reserve Force 1-10-79 to 1-1-82. AE v includes 4 officer and 31 enlisted females. Both ships to be retired by late ithout replacement.

lars-class combat stores ships (SCB 208 type)
: National Steel & SB Co., San Diego (*Atlantic/†Pacific Fleet)

	Laid down	L	In serv.
Mars†	5-5-62	15-6-63	21-12-63
Sylvania*	18-8-62	10-8-63	11-7-64
Niagara Falls†	22-5-65	25-3-66	29-4-67
White Plains†	2-10-65	23-7-66	23-11-68
Concord†	26-3-66	17-12-66	27-11-68
San Diego*	11-3-67	13-4-68	24-5-69
San Jose*	8-3-69	13-12-69	23-10-70

iorized: 1 in FY 61, 1 in FY 62, 1 in FY 64, 2 in FY 65, 1 in FY 66, 1 in

Plains (AFS 4) John Bouvia, 1991

nia (AFS 2) Victor M. Baca, 1991

9,200–9,400 tons light (16,070 fl) **S:** 20 kts
: 177.08 (161.54 pp) × 24.08 × 7.32
4/76.2-mm 50-cal. Mk 33 DP (II × 2)—AFS 2, 4: 2/20-mm Mk 15 CIWS (I × 2)—all: 2/UH-46E helicopters
ctron Equipt:
adar: 1/LN-66 nav., 1/SPS-10 surf. search—TACAN: URN-25
W: SLQ-32(V)1 intercept, Mk 36 SRBOC decoy RL syst. (VI × 2), SLQ-32 Nixie towed acoustic torpedo decoy
2 sets de Laval (AFS 6: Westinghouse) geared steam turbines; 1 prop; 22,000 shp
lers: 3 Babcock & Wilcox; 40.8 kg/cm^2, 440°C **Electric:** 4,800 kw
ige: 10,000/20; 18,000/11 **Crew:** 25 officers, 403 enlisted

rks: Four M-shaped cargo masts with constant-tension equipment; transfer

San Jose (AFS 7)—still without Mk 15 CIWS Leo Van Ginderen, 1991

from the supply ship to the receiving ship takes 90 seconds. The five holds (1 and 5 for spare parts, 3 and 4 for provisions, 2 for aviation parts) have only two hatches. Eleven hoists, which raise up to 5.5 tons, link the decks; several others feed into the helicopter area. Ten loading areas (five on each side) and palletized cargo help in the control of replenishment. There are four refrigerated compartments and three for the storage of dried provisions. Some 25,000 types of spare parts are divided between 40,000 bins and racks and are accounted for by five data-processing machines. 16,597 m^3 total stores volume. Quarters air-conditioned. Draw 2.7 m more aft than forward. One boiler always in reserve. SPS-40 radar, Mk 56 fire-control directors and two twin 76.2-mm mounts amidships removed. Remaining twin gun mounts on the forecastle are enclosed. Helicopter platform and hangar. AFS 1 will transfer to the Military Sealift Command in 1993.

Note: Three ex-Royal Fleet Auxiliaries of the "Ness" class are operated by the Military Sealift Command as T-AFS 8, 9, and 10 and are described on page 888.

◆ **1 heavy-lift salvage ship** (In reserve)
Bldr: Sun SB & Dry Dock, Chester, Pa.

	Laid down	L	In serv.
AG 193 (ex-*Hughes Glomar Explorer*)	. . .	14-11-72	7-73

AG 193 George R. Schneider, Jr., 3-80

D: 63,300 tons (fl) **S:** 10.8 kts **Dim:** 188.6 (169.8 pp) × 35.3 × 14.3
M: 5 Nordberg 16-cyl. diesels; 6 G.E. electric motors, 2 props; 13,200 shp—6 side-thrusters
Crew: 178 tot.

Remarks: 27,445 grt/37,705 dwt. Built for the Central Intelligence Agency for the sole purpose of recovering a sunken Soviet Golf-class ballistic-missile submarine; given the "cover" role as a deep-sea mining ship (for which she was also usable) by the titular owners, the Summa Corporation. Transferred to navy ownership 30-9-76 and laid up at Suisun Bay, California, under Maritime Administration control on 17-1-77; she was chartered in June 1978 for thirteen months by Global Marine Corporation for deep-water mineral exploration. In late 1979 it was announced that she would be placed at the disposal of the National Science Foundation and would embark on a ten-year research program as a deep-sea drilling ship for the Ocean Marine Drilling Program. When conversion was completed, the ship would have been able to drill to depths of 6,100 meters beneath the sea floor while operating in 4,000–5,500 meters of water. The project was unfortunately not funded, and AG 193 was returned to the navy 25-4-80 and transferred to the Maritime Administration for layup at Suisun Bay, California. The ship's associated support barge, HMB-1, was reacquired from the Environmental Protection Agency in 10-82 and laid up. Officially has no name, although is usually referred to as "Glomar Explorer." Very unlikely ever to be operational again.

◆ **1 Austin-class miscellaneous command ship, ex-amphibious transport, dock** (Pacific Fleet)

	Bldr	Laid down	L	In serv.
AGF 11 Coronado (ex-LPD 11)	Lockheed SB, Seattle	3-5-65	30-7-66	23-5-70

D: 11,050 tons (16,912 fl) **S:** 21 kts **Dim:** 173.4 × 25.6 (hull) × 7.2
A: 4/76.2-mm 50-cal. Mk 33 DP (II × 2)—2/20-mm Mk 15 CIWS (I × 2)—2/12.7-mm mg (I × 2)
Electron Equipt:
Radar: 1/LN-66 nav., 1/SPS-10F surf. search, 1/SPS-40E air search

AUXILIARY SHIPS *(continued)*

Coronado (AGF 11) Dr. Giorgio Arra, 1990

Coronado (AGF 11)—note sponson amidships U.S. Navy, 1990

EW: SLQ-32(V)2 intercept, WLR-1H intercept, Mk 36 SRBOC RL (VI × 2)
TACAN: URN-25
M: 2 sets De Laval geared steam turbines; 2 props; 24,000 shp
Boilers: 2 Foster-Wheeler; 42.3 kg/cm², 467°C **Range:** 7,700/20
Crew: 26 officers, 451 enlisted + staff: 120 officers, 47 enlisted

Remarks: Authorized Fiscal Year 1963. Redesignated AGF on 1-10-80, initially only as a temporary relief for *La Salle* (AGF 3), but now retained in a command ship role. Replaced *Puget Sound* (AD 38) as flagship, Sixth Fleet, 8-85 to 6-86. Transferred to Pacific Fleet and became Flagship, 3rd Fleet, on 26-11-86. Communications enhanced over that of rest of class, but otherwise not as extensively altered as AGF 3. Has WSC-6 SATCOMM system antenna on lattice mast to starboard (raised early 1987) and a one-deck-high sponson built out to port forward of the stack. Retains telescoping hangar (22.9 m extended by 6.3) and landing craft docking well.

◆ 1 Raleigh-class auxiliary command ship, ex-amphibious ship dock (Atlantic Fleet)

	Bldr	Laid down	L	In serv.
AGF 3 La Salle (ex-LPD 3)	New York NSY	2-4-62	3-8-63	22-2-64

La Salle (AGF 3)—white-painted *Ships of the World*, 4-88

La Salle (AGF 3)—note 25-mm gun on sponson below bridge wing PH2 Charles Stover

D: 8,040 tons light (14,650 fl) **S:** 21 kts
Dim: 158.4 (155.4 wl) × 25.6 × 6.4
A: 4/76.2-mm 50-cal. DP (II × 2)—2/25-mm Mk 38 Bushmaster (I × 2)—2/20-mm Mk 15 CIWS gatling AA (I × 2)
Electron Equipt:
Radar: 1/. . . nav., SPS-10D surf. search, 1/SPS-40E air search
EW: SLQ-32(V)2 intercept, WLR-1H intercept, Mk 36 SRBOC (VI × 4)
TACAN: URN-25
M: 2 sets De Laval geared steam turbines; 2 props; 24,000 shp
Boilers: 2 Babcock & Wilcox; 42.2 kg/cm², 467°C
Electric: 3,600 kw **Range:** 9,600/16; 16,500/10
Crew: 25 officers, 445 enlisted + flag staff: 12 officers, 47 enlisted

Remarks: Authorized Fiscal Year 1961 as an amphibious ship. Redesignat command ship 1-7-72 and since employed as flagship for Commander, Midd Force. Well deck used for ship's boats. Helicopter hangar (14.5 × 5.9 m) built o deck, to port, with shelter for ceremonial activities to starboard. One Mk 56 and 63 gunfire-control systems removed 1977–78; lost one gun mount but gai 20-mm Mk 15 CIWS during major overhaul commencing 27-1-81; resumed duty 13-3-83. A large parabolic dish SATCOMM antenna is mounted on the fi platform, and a radome for the WSC-6 SATCOMM system is mounted to port, of the hangar. Has all-white paint scheme. During Mideast War, briefly r *Tripoli* (LPH 10) as MH-53E mine countermeasures helicopter mother ship.

◆ 1 Dolphin-class (SCB 207 type) research submarine

	Bldr	Laid down	L	In
AGSS 555 Dolphin	Portsmouth NSY	9-11-62	8-6-68	17

Dolphin (AGSS 555) George R. Schneider, Jr

D: 860/950 tons **S:** 7.5/10 or 15 (*see* Remarks)
Dim: 50.29 × 5.92 × 4.9
Electron Equipt:
Sonar: BQS-15 active, BQR-2 bow passive array, towed array
M: diesel-electric: 2 G.M. Detroit 12V71 diesels; 1 prop; 1,650 shp
Endurance: 14 days (12 hours sub.)
Crew: 3 officers, 26 enlisted, 5 scientists

Remarks: Authorized under Fiscal Year 1961 budget. The pressure hull is a cylinder, 5.49 m in diameter, strongly braced and closed at the forward and aft

.IARY SHIPS *(continued)*

hemispheric bulkheads. Used for deep-diving tests as well as acoustic and raphic experiments. Single torpedo tube removed in 1970. Scientific payload of Using two 165-cell, 250-volt, lead-acid batteries, 10 knots can be reached when ged; when silver-zinc batteries are substituted, the speed is 15 knots. Very quiet ery. Has four mini-computers for scientific data processing. Several scientific, multihydrophone arrays are fitted at the bow, and acoustic arrays can be towed 4,000 feet behind the craft. Most support is shore-based. Home-ported at San Has a portable SPS-53 radar for surface navigation. Became last U.S. Navy ubmarine in 1990. To be overhauled during 1993.

imarron-class oilers (SCB 379 type)
r: Avondale SY, New Orleans (*Atlantic/†Pacific Fleet)

	Laid down	L	In serv.	Conversion
7 Cimarron†	18-5-78	28-4-79	10-1-81	25-6-90 to 1-4-92
8	15-8-78	4-8-79	5-9-81	29-1-90 to 11-5-91
ONGAHELA*				
9	16-7-79	17-5-80	14-11-81	6-3-89 to 22-4-91
RIMACK*				
0	4-8-80	18-7-81	18-12-82	30-10-89 to 8-7-91
.AMETTE†				
6 Platte*	2-2-81	30-1-82	16-4-83	26-11-90 to 9-92

mack (AO 179)—as lengthened Avondale SY, 3-91

ngahela (AO 178) Jürg Kürsener, 7-92

37,866 tons (fl) **S:** 19.4 kts
ı: 215.95 (203.30 pp) × 25.33 × 10.16 (11.35 prop)
2/20-mm Mk 15 CIWS (I × 2) **Electric:** 8,250 kw
ctron Equipt:
adar: 1/LN-66 nav., 1/SPS-55 (AO 180, 186: SPS-10E) surf. search
W: SLQ-32(V)1 intercept, Mk 36 SRBOC decoy RL syst. (VI × 4),
SLQ-25 Nixie towed acoustic torpedo decoy
1 set geared steam turbines; 1 prop; 24,000 shp

Boilers: 2 Combustion Engineering; 42.25 kg/cm², 454°C
Crew: 11 officers, 124 enlisted (225 tot. accommodations)

Remarks: Cargo capacity is 183,000 barrels fuel oil/JP-5, 401 m³ feedwater, 397 m³ potable water, 205 m³ dry stores, and 8 refrigerated stores containers. Can replenish ships while making 15 knots. There is a helicopter platform aft. Four constant-tension replenishment stations to port, three to starboard. Able to transfer 408,000 liters of fuel oil and 245,000 liters JP-5 per hour. No additional units planned; subsequent oilers are under Military Sealift Command control, and these ships may transfer to MSC also. Second woman to command a U.S. Navy warship took command of AO 177 on 23-11-91.

These ships were lengthened, AO 179 under FY 87 Budget, AO 180 under FY 1988, AO 177, 178 under FY 89, and AO 186 under FY 90—all by the builder. Congress required that all five be given an ammunition transport capability. Accommodations were increased to 235, a new-design propeller and rudder were fitted, and underway transfer capability was enhanced. AO 177, 178 did not have CIWS prior to conversion. All were originally 180.29 m overall (167.64 pp) and displaced 27,500 tons full load.

Note: Of the three *Ashtabula*-class fleet oilers listed in the previous edition, *Ashtabula* (AO 51), in reserve since 30-9-82, was stricken 6-9-91 for possible foreign transfer; *Caloosahatchee* (AO 98), in reserve since 28-2-90, was transferred to the Maritime Administration's National Defense Reserve Fleet on 28-2-91; and *Canisteo* (AO 99), in reserve since 2-10-89, was transferred to MARAD in 11-90.

◆ **0 (+0+16) AOE(V)-class fast combat support ships**

D: 48–50,000 tons (fl) **S:** 26 kts
Dim: 228.6 to 231.7 × 30.5 to 33.6 × 10.7 to 12.2
A: . . . **Electron Equipt:** Radar: . . .
M: 4 G.E. LM-2500 gas turbines; 2/6-bladed props; 100,000 shp
Range: . . . **Crew:** . . .

Remarks: Notional program to replace existing AE, AFS, AOR with uniform-design fuel and solid stores (food, ammunition, spares) carriers derived from *Supply* (AOE 6) design. First of 16 was originally to have been delivered in 1997 and the last in 2021, but the program has been deferred beyond the Fiscal Year 1997 construction program and may be canceled entirely.

◆ **0 (+4) new-construction fast combat support ships**
Bldr: National Steel, San Diego (*Atlantic Fleet/†Pacific Fleet)

	Laid down	L	In serv.
AOE 6 Supply*	24-2-89	6-10-90	4-93
AOE 7 Rainier (Ex-*Paul Hamilton*)	31-5-90	28-9-91	11-93
AOE 8 Arctic	2-12-91	3-93	6-94
AOE 9	. . .	. . .	. . .

Authorized: AOE 6 in FY 87, AOE 7 in FY 89, AOE 8 in FY 90, AOE 9 in FY 92

Supply (AOE 6)—artist's concept Tom Freeman/U.S. Navy, 1985

imack (AO 179)—as lengthened Avondale SY, 3-91

AUXILIARY SHIPS *(continued)*

Supply (AOE 6)—fitting out Leo Van Ginderen, 7-91

D: 19,700 tons light (48,800 fl) **S:** 26 kts
Dim: 230.10 × 32.61 × 11.89
A: 1/Mk 29 launcher (XVI × 1, Sea Sparrow missiles)—2/25-mm Mk 38 Bushmaster (I × 2)—2/20-mm Mk 15 CIWS (I × 2)—4/12.7-mm mg (I × 4)—3 UH-46E helicopters
Electron Equipt:
Radar: 1/SPS-64(V)9 nav., 1/SPS-67(V) surf. search, 1/Mk 23 TAS target detection, 2/Mk 91 SAM f.c.
EW: SLQ-32(V)3 active/passive, Mk 36 SRBOC decoy RL syst. (VI × 4), SLQ-25 Nixie towed passive torpedo decoy
TACAN: URN-25
M: 4 G.E. LM-2500 gas turbines; 2/6-bladed fixed-pitch props; 100,000 shp
Electric: 12,500 kw (5 Caterpillar 3608 diesel-driven sets)
Range: . . . **Crew:** 35 officers, 625 enlisted (accommodations)

Remarks: Modified versions of the AOE 1 class with better protective systems. AOE 6 ordered 23-1-87, with option to build AOE 7–9. AOE 7 ordered 3-11-88, AOE 8 on 6-12-89. Cargo: 156,000 bbl liquid, plus 2,450 tons dry stores (including 1,800 tons ammunition and 400 tons refrigerated provisions). Problems requiring the redesign of the Franco-Tosi-type clutch/gearbox caused the first unit to be launched with propulsion equipment installed, and yard's financial difficulties have further exacerbated the numerous delays. No additional units are planned.

♦ 4 Sacramento-class fast combat support ships (SCB 196 type)
(*Atlantic/†Pacific Fleet)

	Bldr	Laid down	L	In serv.
AOE 1 SACRAMENTO†	Puget Sound NSY	30-6-61	14-9-63	14-3-64
AOE 2 CAMDEN†	New York SB	17-2-64	29-5-65	1-4-67
AOE 3 SEATTLE*	Puget Sound NSY	1-10-65	2-3-68	5-4-69
AOE 4 DETROIT*	Puget Sound NSY	29-11-66	21-6-69	28-3-70

Authorized: 1 in FY 61, 1 in FY 63, 1 in FY 65, 1 in FY 66

Detroit (AOE 4)—alongside *Saratoga* (CV 60) U.S. Navy, 9-90

D: 18,700 tons light (53,600 fl) **S:** 26 kts
Dim: 241.4 (215.8 pp) × 32.9 × 11.6
A: 1/Mk 29 launcher for Sea Sparrow (VIII × 1)—2/20-mm Mk 15 CIWS (I × 2)—4/12.7-mm mg (I × 4)—2/UH-46E helicopters
Electron Equipt:
Radar: 1/SPS-64(V)9 nav., 1/SPS-10F surf. search, AOE 1 and 2 only: 1/SPS-40E air-search, AOE 3 only: Mk 23 TAS target detection, all: 1/Mk 91 Mod missile f.c. (2 directors)
EW: SLQ-32(V)3 active/passive, Mk 36 SRBOC decoy RL syst. (VI × 4), SLQ-25 towed acoustic torpedo decoys
TACAN: URN-25
M: 2 sets G.E. geared steam turbines; 2 props; 106,000 shp
Boilers: 4 Combustion Engineering, 42.2 kg/cm², 480°C
Range: 6,000/26; 10,000/17 **Crew:** 24 officers, 577 enlisted

Seattle (AOE 3)—with Mk 23 TAS on foremast David D. Broeck

Remarks: An authorized fifth unit was canceled. The steam turbines in AO AOE 2 are from the uncompleted battleship *Kentucky* (BB 66). Sea Sparrow l and Mk 91 Mod. 1 control system with two directors replaced two twin 76.2 forward; two Mk 56 GFCS removed. The two remaining 76.2-mm gun mounts replaced by two 20-mm Mk 15 CIWS. The SLQ-32(V)3 ECM replaced WLR-1 was the first to get the Mk 23 TAS Mod. 2 (Target Acquisition System), which ships is a stand-alone system employing the UYA-4 computer. Carry 177,00 fuel plus 2,150 tons ammunition, 750 tons provisions. Helicopter hangar a deck for 2–3 UH-46 Sea Knight vertical-replenishment helicopters. AOR 2 i the "standard Navy UNREP" suite, with new winches, rams, ram-tension control booths.

♦ 7 Wichita-class replenishment oilers (SCB 707 type)
Bldr: General Dynamics, Quincy, Mass. (*Atlantic/†Pacific Fleet)

	Laid down	L	In serv.
AOR 1 WICHITA†	18-6-66	18-3-68	7-6-69
AOR 2 MILWAUKEE*	29-11-66	17-1-69	1-11-69
AOR 3 KANSAS CITY†	20-4-68	28-6-69	6-6-70
AOR 4 SAVANNAH*	22-1-69	25-4-70	5-12-70
AOR 5 WABASH†	21-1-70	6-2-71	20-11-71
AOR 6 KALAMAZOO*	28-10-70	11-11-72	11-8-73
AOR 7 ROANOKE†	19-1-74	7-12-74	30-10-76

Authorized: 2 in FY 65, 2 in FY 66, 2 in FY 67, 1 in FY 72

Wichita (AOR 1)—unarmed John Bouvi

Kalamazoo (AOR 6)—with Mk 23 TAS George Nassiopoulc

D: 13,000 tons light (41,350 fl) **S:** 20 kts **Dim:** 200.9 × 29.3 ×
A: AOR 1: unarmed—AOR 2–7: 1/Mk 29 Sea Sparrow SAM laun (VIII × 1)—2/Mk 15 CIWS gatling AA (I × 2)—AOR 2 also: 2/20-mm Mk 67 AA (I × 2)
Electron Equipt:
Radar: 1/SPS-64(V)9 nav., 1/SPS-10F surf. search; Sea Sparrow ships: 1/Mk 91 Mod. 1 f.c. syst. (2 directors)—AOR 6 als Mk 23 TAS target acquisition
EW: SLQ-32(V)3 active/passive. Mk 36 SRBOC decoy RL syst. (×4), SLQ-25 towed acoustic torpedo decoy
TACAN: URN-25 (AOR 2, 3, 7: SRN-15)
M: 2 sets G.E. geared steam turbines; 2 props; 32,000 shp
Boilers: 3 Foster-Wheeler; 43.3 kg/cm², 454°C
Electric: 8,000 kw tot. **Range:** 6,500/20; 10,000/17
Crew: 20 officers, 434 enlisted

Remarks: Carry 175,000 barrels fuel (90,000 distillate fuel), 600 tons ammu 575 tons provisions. There are four stations for liquid transfer and two for solid t to port, three liquid and two solid to starboard; all have constant-tension devi except AOR 7 originally had no hangars flanking stack, and all but AOR 4/76.2-mm DP. Several carried interim armaments of two or four single 20-r

LIARY SHIPS *(continued)*

ash (AOR 5)—with hangar doors open Dennis W. Moore, 2-90

mazoo (AOR 6) Dr. Giorgio Arra, 6-91

hangars were added. As with AOE 1 class, they were all intended to receive the 3 Mod. 2 TAS (Target Acquisition System) radar with associated UYA-4 com-zed data system; AOR 6 had it by 7-86, but the others will apparently not now be The two Mk 76 radar directors for the Mk 91 Mod. 1 missile fire-control system ounted atop tall lattice towers just forward of the stack. AOR 2 used in minelay-als 1983, using Mk 55 mines and portable rails. Will be placed in reserve during id-1990s.

(+0+1+ . . .) new repair ship

rks: One new repair ship originally included in the FY 94 Budget has been d to Fiscal Year 1996. The ship is intended to replace AD 15, 18, and 19 and AR 5 no characteristics data available.

Vulcan-class repair ships (†Pacific Fleet; AR 5 in reserve)

	Bldr	Laid down	L	In serv.
VULCAN	New York SB, Camden	26-12-39	14-12-40	16-6-41
JASON†	Los Angeles SB & DD	9-3-42	3-4-43	19-6-44

9,325 tons (16,245 fl) **S:** 19.2 kts
m: 161.37 (158.5 pp) × 22.35 × 7.11
4/20-mm Mk 67 AA (I × 4)
ectron Equipt:
Radar: 1/CRP 1500 nav., 1/SPS-10-series surf. search
2 sets Allis-Chalmers geared steam turbines; 2 props; 11,535 shp
ilers: 4 Babcock & Wilcox; 28.2 kg/cm^2, 382°C
ectric: 4,500 kw **Range:** 18,000/12 **Fuel:** 3,800 tons
ew: 29 officers, 812 enlisted

rks: Very elaborately equipped repair facilities. Two 10-ton cranes fitted. Four m DP (I × 4) removed from all. *Jason*, typed ARH 1 (heavy hull-repair ship), was gnated as AR 8 in 1957. AR 8 badly damaged in collision with AO 186, 2-86, but ed by 6-86. Sister *Ajax* (AR 6), to reserve 31-12-86, was stricken 5-89; *Hector* (AR eserve 31-3-87, was transferred to Pakistan 20-4-89. AR 5 to reserve for retention 9-91.

Jason (AR 8) Stefan Terzibaschitsch, 10-88

Note: Small repair ship *Sphinx* (ARL 24) decommissioned and struck 19-6-89; sister *Indra* (ARL 37), stricken 1-12-77, remains in use as an accommodations barge at Norfolk Naval Shipyard.

◆ **4 ARS 50-class salvage ships**
Bldr: Peterson Bldrs., Sturgeon Bay, Wisc. (*Atlantic/†Pacific Fleet)

	Laid down	L	In serv.
ARS 50 SAFEGUARD†	8-11-82	12-11-83	17-8-85
ARS 51 GRASP*	30-3-83	21-4-84	14-12-85
ARS 52 SALVOR†	16-9-83	28-7-84	14-6-86
ARS 53 GRAPPLE*	25-4-84	8-12-84	15-11-86

Authorized: 1 in FY 81, 2 in FY 82, 1 in FY 83

Grapple (ARS 53) Dr. Giorgio Arra, 4-91

Grapple (ARS 53) Leo Van Ginderen, 5-91

D: 2,725 tons light (3,193 fl) **S:** 13.5 kts
Dim: 77.72 (73.15 wl) × 15.54 × 4.72 **A:** 2/12.7-mm mg (I × 2)
Electron Equipt:
Radar: 1/Raytheon 1900 nav., 1/SPS-64(V)9 nav.
M: 4 Caterpillar diesels, geared drive; 2 CP Kort-nozzle props; 4,800 bhp (4,200 sust)
Electric: 2,250 kw (3 Caterpillar diesel sets)
Range: 8,000/12 **Crew:** 6 officers, 85 enlisted

AUXILIARY SHIPS *(continued)*

Remarks: First unit ordered 1981, with option for four more from same shipyard; a fifth ship was deleted from program by Congress. One additional unit of this class was planned for request under FY 91 and then deferred to FY 94; in FY 91, it was planned to request *two* under FY 96, but by FY 93, the ships had disappeared from the building program. Design developed from ARS 38.

Systems: Have 54-ton open-ocean bollard pull and, using beach extraction gear, are able to exert 360-ton pull. Have 500-hp bow-thruster. 40-ton boom aft, 7.5-ton forward. Able to dead-lift 150 tons over bow or stern. Cargo hold 596 m. Two 914-m-long, 57-mm towing hawsers; able to tow a CVN at 5 kts. Have Mk 12 diving system; able to support hard-hat divers to 58 m and SCUBA divers; decompression chamber fitted. Up to 25 percent of crew may be women. Four foam fire-fighting monitors are carried.

Note: A new salvage tug class, the "ATR(X)," is currently under development for possible construction under Fiscal Year 1998 or later; the design is intended to replace the remaining ARS 8/38-class salvage tugs and ATS 1–3.

◆ **7 Diver- and Bolster-class salvage ships** Bldr: Basalt Rock Co., Napa, Calif. (Atlantic/†Pacific Fleet; NRF = Naval Reserve Force; ARS 8 in reserve)

	Laid down	L	In serv.
ARS 8 *Preserver*	26-10-42	1-4-43	11-1-44
ARS 38 Bolster† (NRF)	20-7-44	23-12-44	1-5-45
ARS 39 Conserver*	10-8-44	27-1-45	9-6-45
ARS 40 Hoist*	13-9-44	31-3-45	21-7-45
ARS 41 Opportune*	13-9-44	31-3-45	5-10-45
ARS 42 Reclaimer† (NRF)	11-11-44	25-6-45	20-12-45
ARS 43 Recovery*	6-1-45	4-8-45	15-5-46

Recovery (ARS 43) Dr. Giorgio Arra, 4-91

Hoist (ARS 40) George Nassiopoulos, 5-91

D: 1,530 tons (1,970 fl), ARS 38 to ARS 43: 2,045 (fl) **S:** 14.8 kts
Dim: 65.1 × 12.5 (ARS 38 to ARS 43: 13.4) × 4.0
A: 2/20-mm Mk 67 AA (I × 2)—2/12.7-mm M2 mg (I × 2)
Electron Equipt:
Radar: 1/SPS-53 nav., ARS 43 also: 1/Raytheon 3400, ARS 40, 41, 43 also: SPS-10 series surf. search
M: 4 Cooper-Bessemer GSB-8 or Caterpillar D399 diesels, electric drive; 2 props; 3,060 shp (2,440 sust.)
Electric: 460 kw tot. **Range:** 9,000/14; 20,000/7 **Fuel:** 300 tons
Crew: 6 officers, 97 enlisted

Remarks: Equipped for diver support, salvage, and towing. ARS 38, ARS 39, and ARS 42 re-engined with Caterpillar diesels. ARS 8 transferred to Naval Reserve Force 1-11-79, ARS 38 on 30-6-83. ARS 8 and 39 decommissioned 30-9-86 but were recommissioned 26-9-87 for salvage and patrol duties in the Caribbean area. ARS 8 to Naval Reserve Force 30-4-89, in exchange for ARS 40, which was returned to active navy duty 30-4-89. ARS 8 decommissioned to reserve 7-8-92. *Escape* (ARS 6) reactivated from Maritime Administration reserve and transferred to Coast Guard 4-12-80. *Clam* 33) stricken 1963 to MARAD reserve fleet; reacquired 1973, but not reactivat again stricken. *Curb* (ARS 21) and *Gear* (AR 34) stricken and sold 30-4-81. A received U.S. Navy's first woman commanding officer 27-12-90. All have SATC equipment, with two OE-82 antennas.

Note: A new submarine tender to replace AS 11 and designated the AS(X) is preliminary planning stage but will not be requested before Fiscal Year 199 number of submarine tenders is planned to be reduced overall, with the clos overseas strategic-missile submarine bases and the considerable decline in the n of U.S. Navy submarines in general.

◆ **5 L. Y. Spear-class submarine tenders (SCB 702 and 737 type** (Atlantic/†Pacific Fleet)

	Bldr	Laid down	L	In se
AS 36 L. Y. Spear*	Gen. Dynamics, Quincy	5-5-66	7-9-67	28-2
AS 37 Dixon†	Gen. Dynamics, Quincy	7-9-67	20-6-70	7-8
AS 39 Emory S. Land*	Lockheed SB, Seattle	2-3-76	4-5-77	7-7
AS 40 Frank Cable*	Lockheed SB, Seattle	2-3-76	14-1-78	5-2
AS 41 McKee†	Lockheed SB, Seattle	14-1-78	16-2-80	15-8

Authorized: 1 in FY 65, 1 in FY 66, 1 in FY 72, 1 in FY 73, 1 in FY

Frank Cable (AS 40) Dr. Giorgio Arra

L. Y. Spear (AS 36) Dr. Giorgio Arra

Emory S. Land (AS 39) Leo Van Ginderen

D: AS 36, 37: 12,770 tons light (23,493 fl); AS 39–41: 13,842 tons l (22,650 fl)
S: 20 kts (18 sust.) **Dim:** 196.29 × 25.91 × 7.77
A: 4/20-mm AA Mk 67 (I × 4)
Electron Equipt: Radar: 1/. . . nav., 1/SPS-10-series surf. search
M: 1 set De Laval geared steam turbines; 1 prop; 20,000 shp
Boilers: 2 Combustion Engineering; 43.6 kg/cm², 462°C
Electric: 11,000 kw
Crew: AS 36 and AS 37: 52 officers, 480 enlisted (accommodations 1,080 tot); AS 39 to AS 41: 53 officers, 567 enlisted + flag st 25 officers, 44 enlisted

Remarks: Provide support to up to 12 submarines with up to 4 alongside at on 39 to AS 41 having been specifically tailored to the needs of the *Los Angeles* clas 30-ton crane and two 5-ton traveling cranes. Have a total of 53 specialized repair Medical facilities include operating room, 23-bed ward, and dental clinic. AS later also carry 2/40-mm Mk 19 grenade launchers. Helicopter deck, but no hang 37 equipped to support Tomahawk cruise missiles. AS 36 and AS 37 have G

LIARY SHIPS *(continued)*

: turbines and Foster-Wheeler boilers. Originally planned to fit Mk 15 Phalanx r Sea Sparrow SAM in later ships. Two 127-mm DP (I × 2) removed from AS 36 37. AS 38 (in FY 69 Budget) canceled 27-3-69.

imon Lake-class submarine tenders (SCB 238 type)
tlantic Fleet)

	Bldr	Laid down	L	In serv.
SIMON	Puget Sound NSY	7-1-63	8-2-64	7-11-64
E*				
CANOPUS*	Ingalls, Pascagoula	2-3-64	12-2-65	4-11-65

horized: 1 in FY 63, 1 in FY 64

ı Lake (AS 33)—with deckhouse on helo platform
Leo Van Ginderen, 6-90

.2,000 tons (AS 33: 19,934 fl; AS 34: 21,089 fl) **S:** 18 kts
: 196.2 × 25.9 × 8.7 **A:** 4/20-mm Mk 67 AA (I × 4)
tron Equipt: Radar: 1/LN-66 nav., 1/SPS-10-series surf. search
1 set de Laval geared steam turbines; 1 prop; 20,000 shp
ers: 2 Combustion Engineering; 43.6 kg/cm², 462°C
tric: 11,000 kw **Range:** 7,600/18
w: AS 33: 58 officers, 857 enlisted; AS 34: 1,400 tot.

ks: Sister AS 35 canceled on 3-12-64. AS 32 was to have been converted to a er tender (AD 45) under Fiscal Year 1992 but instead relieved *Proteus* (AS 19) ral-purpose tender at Guam in 9-92; her crew includes 447 women.
ems: Specifically equipped to support nuclear-powered, ballistic-missile sub- s, with 16 missiles stowed vertically amidships. Converted to carry Poseidon s, 1969–71. Both further altered to serve Trident-equipped SSBNs; AS 33 ed under FY 78, and AS 34 converted 1984–85 and has been given new cranes. -ton cranes and four 5-ton traveling cranes. Helicopter deck aft, but no hangar; 3 there is a two-deck-high structure on the helicopter deck. Two twin 76.2-mm unts removed by 1990.

Iunley-class submarine tenders (SCB 194 type) (*Atlantic Fleet)

	Bldr	Laid down	L	In serv.
HUNLEY*	Newport News SB	28-11-60	28-9-61	16-6-62
HOLLAND*	Ingalls, Pascagoula	5-3-62	19-1-63	7-9-63

horized: AS 31 in FY 60, AS 32 in FY 62

nd (AS 32) Dr. Giorgio Arra, 11-89

11,000 tons light (19,819 fl) **S:** 19 kts **Dim:** 182.6 × 25.3 × 7.4
4/20-mm Mk 67 AA (I × 4)
ctron Equipt:
adar: 1/LN-66 nav., 1/SPS-10-series surf. search
10 Fairbanks-Morse 38D8⅛ diesels, electric drive; 1 prop; 15,000 shp
ctric: 12,000 kw tot. **Range:** 10,000/12
w: AS 31: 54 officers, 558 enlisted; AS 32: 55 officers, 604 enlisted (accommodations: 1,266 tot.)

rks: Intended to support SSBNs; converted to carry Poseidon missiles, 1973–75. employed as general-purpose submarine tenders. Air-conditioned. Helicopter m. Original 32.5-ton rotating hammerhead missile-handling gantry crane re- around 1970 and replaced by two 30-ton cranes.

Hunley (AS 31) Jürg Kürsener, 7-92

♦ **1 Fulton-class submarine tender** (*Atlantic Fleet)

	Bldr	Laid down	L	In serv.
AS 18 ORION*	Moore SB, Oakland, Cal.	31-7-41	14-10-42	30-9-43

Orion (AS 18)—with barge alongside, *Belknap* (CG 26) beyond
Leo Van Ginderen, 9-91

D: 9,734 tons (18,000 fl) **S:** 15.4 kts **Dim:** 161.4 × 22.3 × 7.8
A: 4/20-mm Mk 67 AA (I × 4)
Electron Equipt:
Radar: 1/LN-66 nav., 1/SPS-10-series surf. search
M: 8 G.M. 16-248 diesels, electric drive; 2 props; 11,200 shp
Electric: 2,300 kw **Range:** 32,000/15 **Fuel:** 3,760 tons
Crew: 53 officers, 522 enlisted (accommodations: 1,274 tot.)

Remarks: Received FRAM-II modernization and can support nuclear submarines. Foundry can cast pieces up to 250 kg. Two 20-ton rotating cranes are fitted. Of sisters, *Fulton* (AS 11) decommissioned and stricken 25-9-91; *Sperry* (AS 12) decommissioned and stricken 30-9-82; *Bushnell* (AS 15) stricken 15-11-80 and sunk 3-6-83 as a torpedo target; *Howard W. Gilmore* (AS 16) decommissioned 30-9-80 and struck 1-12-80; *Nereus* (AS 17), decommissioned and stricken 27-10-71, remains as a hulk at Bremerton (permission to scrap given 13-6-89). Lengthened former sister *Proteus* (AS 19) decommissioned 9-92 and stricken.

♦ **2 Pigeon-class submarine-rescue ships (SCB 721 type)**
Bldr: Alabama DD & SB, Mobile (*Atlantic)

	Laid down	L	In serv.
ASR 21 *PIGEON*	17-7-68	13-8-69	28-4-73
ASR 22 ORTOLAN*	22-8-68	10-9-69	14-7-73

Authorized: 1 in FY 67, 1 in FY 68

Pigeon (ASR 21) David D. Broecker, 3-91

D: 3,411 tons (4,570 fl) **S:** 15 kts **Dim:** 76.5 × 26.2 × 6.5
A: 2/20-mm Mk 67 AA (I × 2)
Electron Equipt: Radar: 1/SPS-53 nav., 1/. . . nav.
Sonar: SQQ-25 hull-mounted (7 kHz)
M: 4 Alco high-speed diesels; 2 props; 6,000 bhp **Range:** 8,500/13
Crew: 10 officers, 186 enlisted + DSRV crew: 4 officers, 20 men

Remarks: Not considered to be successful ships, being overly complex and difficult to maneuver. The catamaran hulls (7.92-m beam) are separated by 10.36 m. Diving bells

AUXILIARY SHIPS *(continued)*

Ortolan (ASR 22) Dr. Giorgio Arra, 6-90

and other salvage equipment are lowered between the two hulls by a moving crane. The ships can carry two small DSRV (Deep Submergence Rescue Vehicle) submarines, but the only two DSRV built are land-stored in fly-away status. Excellent lowering and handling equipment for up to 60 tons; divers to 260 m. Carry Mk 2 Mod. 1 saturation diving gear. Helicopter platform aft spans both hulls. ASR 21 has an LN-66 navigational radar, ASR 22 a Raytheon set. ASR 21 decommissioned 31-8-92.

◆ 2 Chanticleer-class submarine-rescue ships

Bldr: Savannah Machine & Foundry (*Atlantic Fleet)

	Laid down	L	In serv.
ASR 13 Kittiwake*	5-1-45	10-7-45	18-7-46
ASR 15 Sunbird*	2-4-45	3-4-46	28-1-47

D: 1,670 tons (2,015 fl) **S:** 14.9 kts **Dim:** 76.7 × 13.4 × 4.9
A: 2/20-mm Mk 67 AA (I × 2)
Electron Equipt: Radar: 1/SPS-53 nav., 1/LN-66 nav.
M: 4 G.M. 12-278A diesels, electric drive; 1 prop; 3,000 shp
Electric: 460 kw **Fuel:** 350 tons **Crew:** 7 officers, 96 enlisted

Kittiwake (ASR 13) Dr. Giorgio Arra, 3-91

Sunbird (ASR 15) Dr. Giorgio Arra, 3-92

Remarks: Carry a McCann rescue bell aft. All equipped for helium/oxygen d ASR 9 has Alco Model 539 diesels. All have sonar and underwater communica equipment. Sister *Greenlet* (ASR 10) transferred to Turkey on 12-7-70. Sister *Flo* (ASR 9) decommissioned 2-8-91 and stricken 3-9-91; *Petrel* (ASR 14) decommiss 30-9-91 and transferred to the Maritime Commission for storage in the Na Defense Reserve Fleet on 24-10-91.

Note: Of the five *Abnaki* and *Achomawi*-class fleet tugs listed in the previous ed *Paiute* (ATF 159) and *Papago* (ATF 160) were decommissioned and stricken 7-8-9 28-7-92, respectively; *Takelma* (ATF 113), in reserve since 30-9-83, was stricken 92 and offered to Argentina; and *Moctobi* (ATF 105) and *Quapaw* (ATF 110), in re since 1985, were stricken during 1-92. Two sisters survive in the Maritime Admin tion's National Defense Reserve Fleet: *Atakapa* (ATF 149) and *Mosopelea* (ATF both of the *Achomawi* class. *Seneca* (ATF 91), reacquired 21-11-85 from the ND an immobile engineering trials craft at Annapolis, Md., and *Tenino* (ATF 115) is as a salvage training hulk.

The four surviving units of the *Sotoyomo*-class auxiliary ocean tugs, *Tunica* 179), *Accokeek* (ATA 181), *Navigator* (ATA 203), and *Keywadin* (ATA 213), are u salvage training hulks.

◆ 3 Edenton-class salvage-and-rescue ships

Bldr: Brooke Marine, Lowestoft, U.K. (*Atlantic/†Pacific Fleet)

	Laid down	L	In serv.
ATS 1 Edenton*	1-4-67	15-5-68	23-1-71
ATS 2 Beaufort†	19-2-68	20-12-68	22-1-72
ATS 3 Brunswick†	5-6-68	14-11-69	19-12-72

Authorized: ATS 1 in FY 66; ATS 2 and 3 in FY 67

Edenton (ATS 1) Leo Van Ginderen,

Beaufort (ATS 2) Dr. Giorgio Arra,

D: 2,650 tons (3,200 fl) **S:** 16 kts **Dim:** 88.0 (80.5 pp) × 15.25 ×
A: 2/20-mm Mk 67 AA (I × 2)
Electron Equipt:
Radar: 1/SPS-53 nav., 1/SPS-64(V)9 nav.
M: 4 Paxman 12 YLCM (900 rpm) diesels; 2 Escher-Wyss CP props 6,000 bhp
Electric: 1,200 kw **Range:** 10,000/13
Crew: 7 officers, 123 enlisted

Remarks: ATS 4 (authorized FY 72) and ATS 5 (authorized FY 73) canceled in fa *Powhatan*-class T-ATF. Can tow ships up to AOE 1-class size. 272-ton dead lift ov bow. 20-ton crane aft; 10-ton boom forward. Can conduct dives to 260 m. Pov pumps and complete fire-fighting equipment. Equipped with bow-thruster.

Note: The training aircraft carrier *Lexington* (AVT 16, ex-CV 16) was deco sioned in formal ceremonies on 8-11-91 and stricken 30-11-91 for use as a pri maintained museum at Corpus Christi, Texas. The ship has been replaced i training role by *Forrestal* (AVT 59, ex-CV 59).

UNCLASSIFIED MISCELLANEOUS SHIPS (IX)

Note: The ships and craft in the "Unclassified Miscellaneous" below are lis descending order of IX-series hull number rather than by age.

◆ 1 Robert D. Conrad-class former oceanographic research sh

Bldr: Marinette SB, Marinette, Wisconsin

ASSIFIED MISCELLANEOUS SHIPS (IX) *(continued)*

	L	In serv.
PACIFIC ESCORT (ex-*Thomas G. mpson*, AGOR 9)	18-7-64	4-9-65

088 tons light (1,400 fl) **S:** 13.5 kts
63.7 (59.7 pp) × 11.4 × 4.9 mean
ron Equipt: Radar: . . .
Cummins diesels, electric drive; 1 prop; 1,000 shp
ric: 850 kw **Endurance:** 45 days
ge: 9,000/12; 8,500/9.5 **Fuel:** 211 tons **Crew:** . . .

s: Formerly assigned to University of Washington, Seattle; reclassified as IX -12-89 as replacement for the tug *Pacific Escort* (143WB8401) in support of sea ships overhauled at Mare Island Naval Shipyard, California. Large stack 620-hp gas-turbine generator set used to drive main shaft at speed of up to 6.5 xperiments requiring "quiet" conditions. Also has retractable electric bow-propulsor, which provides up to 4.5 kts. Modernized 1981–84 with new ocean-winches and cables to work to 4,000–5,000-m depths.

ident missile-firing-simulator barge
Sea Train SB Corp., Brooklyn, N.Y. (In serv. 1976)

(ex-barge *Matthew*, ex-*Christina F*)

. . **Dim:** 92.28 × 27.43 × 6.71

s: Former cargo barge converted to commercial tank barge in 1980. Acquired ed Barge Co. and converted by McDermott, Inc., Morgan City, La., as missile-imulation barge for service at the Trident SSBN facility, King's Bay, Ga. d 15-4-88.

I 110-class rigid sidewall surface effect trials craft

	Bldr	L	In serv.
(ex-SES-200, ex-*G Dorado*, WSES 1)	Bell-Halter, New Orleans	12-78	2-79

Textron Marine, 2-91

3 tons light (250 fl) **S:** 40+ kts (calm water)
48.77 × 12.50 × 2.83 at rest/1.68 on cushion
ron Equipt: Radar: 2/Decca navigational
MTU 16V396 TB94 diesels for propulsion; 2 KaMeWa 71S62/6-II waterjets; 6,960 bhp, 2 MTU 6V396 TB83 diesels for lift; 4/ .07-m dia. centrifugal fans; 1,980 hp
ric: 140 kw **Range:** 3,700/23; 2,950/30 **Fuel:** 59.6 tons
: 2 officers, 20 enlisted

s: Designed by Bell Aerospace-Textron and built by Halter Marine in a nanced effort. Leased 1-80 for one month by U.S. Coast Guard and then again ger trials period in 1981, commencing with a six-month joint USN/USCG nal evaluation from Key West. On 29-9-82 the ship came under U.S. Navy nd had accommodations for 14 additional personnel added. Placed in service Functions by trapping a fan-generated air bubble between the rigid sidewalls er seals at bow and stern. Assigned to David Taylor Research and Develop-nter. Conducted trials for U.S. Coast Guard late 1984. Two more lift-fans added nofficially named *Jaeger* for European tour 1985–86. Original G.M. 8V92 TI ngines replaced 1988. In spring 1987, conducted trials with G.E. EX-25, atling gun and in 3-89 with Rockwell Crossbow multi-use stabilized weapons/ latform. Redesignated IX 515 on 11-5-87, although still generally known as 0." Refitted 4-90 to 2-2-91 with waterjet propulsion by builder; original G.M. TI diesels (1,600 bhp each) replaced by MTU diesels.

FU 71-class helicopter training craft
Pacific Coast Eng. Co., Alameda, Cal. (In serv. 1968)

(ex-YFU 79)

20 tons (380 fl) **S:** 8 kts **Dim:** 38.1 × 10.97 × 2.30
tron Equipt: Radar: 1/Decca . . . navigational
G.M. 6-71 diesels; 2 props: 1,000 bhp **Crew:** . . .

ks: Redesignated 31-3-86 and completed conversion 28-4-86 to serve as heli-nding platform training craft at Pensacola, Fla. Bow ramp welded closed, new ucture with rudimentary flight-control station and flight deck added. Origi-sister to IX 506, below.

IX 514 David D. Broecker, 3-92

♦ **1 electric radiation trials barge**
Bldr: Eastern Marine, Panama City, Fla. (In serv. 6-88)

IX 513

IX 513 Leo Van Ginderen, 7-90

D: 2,200 tons (fl) **Dim:** 36.57 × 27.43 × 4.57
Electric: . . . kw (2 diesel sets)

Remarks: Design begun 10-8-82. Ordered 1986 in support of EMPRESS-II electric pulse protection trials. EMPRESS = ElectroMagnetic Pulse Radio-frequency Simulator for Ships. Has 45.7-m-high tower supporting 57.53-m-diameter ring pulse transmission antenna. Has 7-million-volt MARX pulse generator built by Maxwell Laboratory, San Diego. Associated with the barge are three 7.7-ton Data Acquisition and Processing System (DAAPS) receiver/analyzer trailers that are positioned on the test subject ship. Program stalled by bankruptcy of builder in 2-87 and environmental impact concerns by Congress and the state of Maryland. Began trials 7-6-88 off North Carolina coast, delivering 7-million-volt pulse; trials later moved to Gulf of Mexico. First trials with *Deyo* (DD 989) 7-90. Operated for Navy by E.G. & G., Inc.

♦ **1 Trident missile-firing-simulator barge**
Bldr: Gwater & Zimmerman (In serv. 1954)

IX 512 SUPLS II (ex-U.S. Army BD 6651)

IX 512 Dr. Giorgio Arra, 3-86

UNCLASSIFIED MISCELLANEOUS SHIPS (IX) *(continued)*

D: approx. 1,000 tons (fl) **Dim:** 43.28 × 17.68 × 1.55
A: 1/Trident D-5 launch tube

Remarks: Former U.S. Army design 413D floating crane. Acquired 1-9-83 and converted by Westinghouse Marine Division for San Clemente Island, Cal., test facility as SUPLS II (Simulated Underwater Partial Launch System) in support of the Trident-II D-5 SLBM program. Retains the original 52-ton crane and performs submerged launch and post-launch activities.

◆ **1 explosives damage-control barge**
Bldr: Norfolk NSY (In serv. 1942)

IX 509 Underwater Test Barge No. 1

IX 509 Wilhelm Donko, 7-88

D: 3,000 tons (fl) **Dim:** 56.1 × . . . × 3.7

Remarks: Operated for the Naval Ships Research and Development Center. Reclassified IX 509 on 1-12-79. Has a 60-ton crane.

◆ **1 satellite navigation systems trials craft**
Bldr: Gunderson Bros., Portland, Ore. (In serv. 1959)

IX 508 Orca (ex-LCU 1618)

Orca (IX 508) Dr. Giorgio Arra, 3-86

D: 190 tons (390 fl) **S:** 11 kts **Dim:** 41.07 × 9.07 (hull) × 2.08
M: 4 G.M. 6-71 diesels; 2 Kort-nozzle props; 1,200 bhp
Fuel: 13 tons **Range:** 1,200/11 **Crew:** . . .

Remarks: Adapted 1978 for Naval Ocean Systems Center, San Diego, to conduct trials with NAVSTAR global positioning system. Reclassified IX from LCU 1-12-79.

◆ **1 Admiral W.S. Benson-class barracks ship**
Bldr: Bethlehem Steel, Alameda, Cal. (In serv. 18-9-44)

IX 507 General Hugh J. Gaffey (ex T-AP 121, ex-*Admiral W.L. Capps*, AP 121)

D: 12,657 tons light (22,574 fl) **S:** 19 kts
Dim: 185.6 (174.65 pp) × 23.01 × 8.05
M: 2 sets G.E. geared steam turbines, electric drive; 2 props; 18,000 shp
Boilers: 4 Combustion Engineering "D," 42.3 kg/cm², 449°C
Electric: 2,875 kw **Fuel:** 4,037 tons
Crew: Berthing for 499 officers, 1,577 enlisted

Remarks: Former troop transport transferred to the army in 1946, reacquired by the navy on 1-3-50 for MSC (then MSTS). Stricken on 9-1-69 and transferred to Maritime Commission Reserve Fleet. Partially reactivated and redesignated IX 507 on 1-11-78 for service at Bremerton NSY, Washington, as berthing ship for crew of CVN 65, then undergoing overhaul; was towed to Yokosuka 11-85, but returned to Puget Sound NSY in 1987. Propulsion plant not reactivated. Sister IX 510 (ex-*General William O. Darby*, T-AP 127, ex-*Admiral W.S. Sims*, AP 127), reclassified as IX 510 in 10-81 and formerly used as berthing barge at the Norfolk Naval Shipyard, was transferred to the Maritime

IX 510—IX 507 very similar Wilhelm Donk

Commission on 23-4-91 for layup in the James River Division, National I Reserve Fleet for retention.

◆ **1 YFU 71-class trials tender**
Bldr: Pacific Coast Eng. Co., Alameda, Cal. (In serv. 10-68)

IX 506 (ex-YFU 82)

IX 506 Dr. Giorgio Arr

D: 220 tons (380 fl) **S:** 8 kts **Dim:** 38.1 × 10.97 × 2.29
Electric: 120 kw **A:** 3/324-mm Mk 32 ASW TT (III × 1)
Electron Equipt: Radar: 2/. . . nav.
M: 4 G.M. 6-71 diesels; 2 props; 1,000 bhp
Crew: 2 officers, 10 enlisted

Remarks: Ex–harbor utility craft. Reclassified on 1-4-78 for service with Ocean Systems Center, San Diego, to replace IX 505 (ex-YTM 759). Barge YFN used as a work platform with this unit. IX 506 has an extra generator set bene forecastle, atop which is mounted the ASW torpedo-tube mount.

◆ **3 Benewah-class barracks ships** Bldr: Boston Naval Shipyard

	Laid down	L	In serv.
IX 502 Mercer (ex-APB 39)	25-8-44	17-11-44	19-9-45
IX 503 Nueces (ex-APB 40)	2-1-45	6-5-45	30-11-45
IX 504 Echols (ex-APB 37)	6-45	30-7-45	1-1-47

Mercer (IX 502)—IX 503 similar Dr. Giorgio Arr

Echols (IX 504)—lower superstructure Chris Cavas

D: 2,189 tons light (3,640 fl) **S:** 10 kts **Dim:** 100.0 × 15.2 × 3.
M: 2 G.M. 12-267 ATL diesels; 2 props; 1,600 bhp
Electric: 500 kw
Man (when operational): 13 officers, 180 men + 26 officers, 1,200 troops

Remarks: IX 502 and IX 503 recommissioned 1968 for service in Vietnam back in reserve 1969–71; activated again on 1-11-75 as barracks ships on Wes IX 504, in reserve since completion in 1947, activated 1-2-76 as a barracks

ASSIFIED MISCELLANEOUS SHIPS (IX) *(continued)*

ass SSBN crews at General Dynamics, Groton. Propulsion plants inactivated.)-mm AA (IV × 2) removed. Names restored to all in 1986. IX 502, 503 at San X 504 at Groton, Connecticut.

arracks ship (ex-LSMR) Bldr: Brown SB, Houston, Texas

	Laid down	L	In serv.
Elk River (ex-LSMR 501)	24-3-45	21-4-45	27-5-45

iver (IX 501) Dr. Giorgio Arra, 1983

.,280 tons (fl) **S:** 11 kts **Dim:** 70.0 × 15.2 × 2.8
tron Equipt: Radar: 1/LN-66 nav.
2 G.M. 16-278A diesels; 2 props; 2,880 bhp
tric: 440 kw **Crew:** 25 tot.

ks: Former fire-support rocket ship converted 1967–68 at Avondale Shipyards, go, Louisiana, to act as support ship at the San Clemente Island Range for the ep-submergence diving program. 2.4-m bulges were added to her hull sides and well cut for lowering equipment through the hull. The well was straddled by a traveling gantry crane. Thrusters added to allow accurate dynamic mooring. ving procedures, equipment, and small diving vehicles. In 10-86, the crane was d, and IX 501 was relegated to serve as a barracks barge.

onar test barge

ks: Actually, two barges (built in 1917) moored in Lake Seneca, New York; nated to the Naval Underwater Sound Laboratory, Newport, Rhode Island. In 1-4-71.

J.S. Army FS 381-class torpedo-trials ship
eeler SB, Brooklyn, NY (In serv. 3-45)

New Bedford (ex-AKL 17, ex-FS 289)

526 tons light (940 fl) **S:** 13 kts
: 54.10 (50.29 wl) × 9.75 × 3.05
1/533-mm TT—3/324-mm Mk 32 ASW TT (III × 1)
2 G.M. 6-278A diesels; 2 props; 1,000 bhp **Electric:** 225 kw
ge: 3,200/11 **Fuel:** 67 tons **Crew:** 24 accomm.

ks: Operated by the coast guard for the army during World War II; transferred navy as a cargo ship on 1-3-50. Converted as a torpedo-trials ship in 1963. ed by the Naval Undersea Warfare Engineering Station, Keyport, Washington. s the CURV remote-controlled underwater recovery vehicle.

VICE CRAFT

Some 933 numbered service craft were on the Navy List at the end of Fiscal Year *The entries marked with an asterisk are non-self-propelled.*

ormer commercial floating dry dock*
dr: Sunship, Chester, Pa. (In serv. 1974)

3 9

n: 213.36 × 67.06 × 5.18 (empty) **Lift Capacity:** . . . tons

rks: Acquired 7-90.

inist (AFDB 8)—with *Knox* (FF 1052) aboard
PHC C. King, USN, 1987

◆ **1 former West German floating dry dock***
Bldr: Seebeckwerft AG, Bremerhaven (In serv. 1981)

AFDB 8 Machinist

Dim: 253.90 (253.00 on blocks) × 53.54 (44.50 between wingwalls) × 16.90 over blocks (flooded)
Lift Capacity: 39,300 tons (certified to 25,000 tons by U.S. Navy)

Remarks: Purchased from builder 5-8-85 and towed to the Philippines for service at Subic Bay, arriving 7-86. Has two 7.5-ton traveling cranes. Replaced *Artisan* (AFDB 1). Towed 28-3-92 to Pearl Harbor for refit and further use.

Note: The remaining sections of the large floating dry docks AFDB 2 and *Los Alamos* (AFDB 7) are now in reserve. AFDB 2 (sections D through F, H, and I) is at Pearl Harbor, and AFDB 7 (sections A through D) is in the Maritime Administration fleet at James River, Virginia, having been towed there on 10-2-92 from Holy Loch, Scotland, on the closure of the SSBN base; sections E and G have been in reserve since 1987, while Section F had been U.S. Army Corps of Engineers floating power barge *Andrew J. Weber* at Subic Bay, the Philippines, since 1968. AFDB 7 (Sections A–D) had two associated 82.3 × 45.7 pontoon barges, delivered 1989. *Artisan* (AFDB 1) was placed on sale in 1983. AFDB 3, long in reserve, was transferred to the state of Maine in 1982 for use by Bath Iron Works at Portland; AFDB 5 was transferred to the city of Port Arthur, Texas, in 1984 and leased to Todd Shipyards. AFDB 4 stricken 3-90.

◆ **3 AFDL small auxiliary floating docks***

	Bldr	In serv.	Capacity (tons)
AFDL 6 Dynamic	Chicago Bridge & Iron	3-44	1,000
AFDL 23 Adept	G. D. Auchter	12-44	1,900
AFDL 25 Undaunted	Doullut, Ewin	2-44	1,000

Dynamic (AFDL 6) Dr. Giorgio Arra, 8-86

Remarks: All one-piece docks. AFDL 6 and 25 are 61.0 m by 19.5 m; AFDL 23 is 87.8 × 19.5 m; AFDL 47 is 136.5 × 29.6 m. AFDL 6 has an assigned crew: 1 officer, 23 men. AFDL 23 towed from Subic Bay 22-2-92 to Guam, arriving 6-3-92 for probable further use. AFDL 25 reacquired 6-84 at end of commercial lease, refitted, and towed to Guantánamo Bay 9-84 to replace *Endeavor* (AFDL 1).

Diligence (AFDL 48), built of concrete, and the only postwar unit, was commercially leased 23-3-80. *Reliance* (AFDL 47) had been reacquired 18-1-81 from Maritime Commission reserve, but was returned 12-8-81; on 15-5-91, the craft was leased to Detyans Shipyard, Mount Pleasant, South Carolina. Two additional units (AFDL 21, 40) are leased to commercial shipbuilders and ship repairers; AFDL 37, 38, and 45, long on lease, were sold outright 1-10-81; AFDL 8 was stricken 1-12-81 and sunk as a fishing reef; AFDL 2 was stricken 15-11-81, AFDL 9 was stricken 15-7-82, AFDL 19 and 41 sold 4-83, *Endeavor* (AFDL 1) leased to the Dominican Republic in 1986 (renewed 10-3-91); AFDL 16, on commercial lease, returned and stricken 15-8-86; AFDL 14 stricken 1-10-83, AFDL 15 on 18-12-83, AFDL 22 (captured by Vietnam 30-4-75) stricken 30-7-85, AFDL 29 on 15-7-85. AFDL 21 was stricken 31-3-89 and transferred to another government agency. AFDL 40 was sold to the Philippines 30-6-90.

◆ **7 AFDM medium auxiliary floating dry docks*** Bldr: Everett Pacific (AFDM 2: Alabama Drydock; AFDM 8: Chicago Bridge & Iron; AFDM 14: Pollock-Stockton SB, Cal.)

	In serv.
AFDM 2 (ex-YFD 4)	10-42
AFDM 5 Resourceful (ex-YFD 21)	2-43
AFDM 6 Competent (ex-YFD 62)	6-44
AFDM 7 Sustain (ex-YFD 63)	1-45
AFDM 8 Richland (ex-YFD 64)	12-44
AFDM 10 Resolute (ex-YFD 67)	1945
AFDM 14 Steadfast (ex-YFD 71)	7-45

Resourceful (AFDM 5)—with *Spica* (T-AFS 9) aboard
John Bouvia, 1990

SERVICE CRAFT *(continued)*

Dim: 189.6 × 37.8 (28.3 clear width) × 1.9 (16.1 sub);
AFDM 14: 182.3 × 36.0 (26.5 clear width) × 1.1 (18.9 max.)
Crew: 4–6 officers, 139–157 enlisted

Remarks: All active and of 18,000-ton capacity except AFDM 2: 15,000 tons and AFDM 14: 14,000 tons. Built in three sections, with 26.5-m end sections bolted to mid-section. AFDM 5 was towed 17-4-92 from Subic Bay bound for Yokosuka, Japan, for overhaul and further use. AFDM 6 is at Pearl Harbor.

AFDM 14 reclassified 1-2-83. AFDM 3 is on commercial lease; AFDM 2 returned from lease and transferred to MARAD for lay-up 2-6-86 but was reacquired by navy 18-8-87 (still in reserve). AFDM 1 returned and stricken for scrap 1-9-86. AFDM 7 refitted 1987 to 2-88. AFDM 9 stricken 31-12-87 on return from commercial loan.

♦ 16 APL-series barracks craft*

APL 2, 4, 5, 15, 18, 19, 29, 31, 32, 34, 42, 43, 50, 54, 58, 60

APL 5 George R. Schneider, Jr., 6-91

APL 60 George R. Schneider, Jr., 1-92

Remarks: Built 1944–45 (except for APL 60, ex-British *Persuivant,* built 1977 by Dredge/Marine, Inc., and acquired by navy 25-9-89 for use at Philadelphia Naval Shipyard). All active. All are 2,600 tons (fl), 79.6 × 15.0 × 2.6, except APL 60, which is 91.4 m overall. World War II–built units can accommodate 6 officers and 680 enlisted and have 300-kw generator capacity. Sisters APL 47 and APL 53 are on lease to foreign navies. Sister APL 57 deactivated and transferred to Maritime Administration 19-8-91 for layup. Three (plus option for six more) 2,180-ton APL were to order 1-90, but the orders have not been placed. Five IX-designated hulks serve as accommodations barges (see earlier page), as does the stricken small repair ship *Indra* (ex-ARL 37). Also used for accommodations are the YRBM-series barges (see below).

♦ 2 ARD 4- and 12-class auxiliary repair dry docks*

Bldr: Pacific Bridge, Alameda, Cal.

ARD 5 Waterford (In serv. 6-42) ARD 30 San Onofre (In serv. 8-44)

San Onofre (ARD 30)—*Arco* (ARDM 5) in background
Florian Jentsch, 8-88

Dim: ARD 5: 148.1 × 21.6 (14.9 clear width) × 1.6 (9.9 sub.)
ARD 30: 149.9 × 24.7 (18.0 clear width) × 1.7 (10.0 sub.)
Crew: ARD 5: 6 officers, 125 enlisted; ARD 30: 5 officers, 105 enlisted

Remarks: 3,500-ton capacity. Sister *West Milton* (ARD 7) to Maritime Commission for lay-up 16-7-81 and stricken 23-8-90. Three sisters remain in use as ARDMs as well; see below.

♦ 2 Shippingport-class submarine support docks*

	Bldr	In serv.
ARDM 4 Shippingport	Bethlehem Steel, Sparrows Pt., Md.	27-1-79
ARDM 5 Arco	Todd Pacific, Seattle	27-2-86

Arco (ARDM 5) Stefan Terzibaschitsch, 10-88

Capacity: 7,800 tons (8,400 emergency)
Dim: 150.0 × 29.3 (29.3 clear width) × 16.6 (max.)
Crew: 5–6 officers, 125 enlisted

Remarks: ARDM = Medium Support Dock. Intended to support *Los Angel* submarines; 8,000-ton capacity. First floating dry docks built for U.S. Nav World War II. Length of blocks: 118 m × 20.7 m clear height inside. Requi support. Have 2/25-ton cranes. ARDM 5 ordered 13-10-82, laid down 25-7-83, la 14-12-84. Have accommodations for 12. ARDM 4 at New London, ARDM 5 Diego.

♦ 3 ARD 12-class submarine support docks*

Bldr: Pacific Bridge, Alameda, Cal.

	In serv.
ARDM 1 Oak Ridge (ex-ARD 19)	3-44
ARDM 2 Alamagordo (ex-ARD 26)	6-44
ARDM 3 Endurance (ex-ARD 18)	2-44

Oak Ridge (ARDM 1)—with APL 31 to port and YDND 36 to star
PH1 H. Dement, US

Alamagordo (ARDM 2) JO1 J. Cabot, US

Dim: 156.25 (ARDM 1, 2: 163.4) × 24.7 (13.0 clear width) × 2.2 (13.1 sub.)
Crew: 5 officers, 174 enlisted **Capacity:** 8,000 tons

Remarks: Lengthened and capacity increased from 3,500 tons to serve as sub repair docks. One end is closed, to permit towing. ARDM 1 at Kings Bay, Ga., A and 3 at Charleston, S.C.

Note: Other navy-owned floating dry docks include YFD 54 and YFD 69- commercial lease, and YFD 83, on loan to the U.S. Coast Guard since 1-47. YFD stricken 15-1-89 for sale.

♦ 1 YAG miscellaneous auxiliary yard craft

Bldr: Halter Marine, New Orleans, La.

YAG 62 Deer Island

Deer Island (YAG 62) Dr. Giorgio Arr

:CE CRAFT *(continued)*

pprox. 400 tons (fl) **S:** 10.5 kts **Dim:** 36.58 × 8.53 × 2.13
tron Equipt: Radar: 2/. . . nav.
diesels; 2 props; . . . bhp
ge: 6,200/10.5 **Crew:** 20 tot., including technicians

ks: 172 grt/117 nrt, former oilfield supply tug placed on Navy List 15-3-83 and for the Naval Ship Research and Development Center from Port Everglades, MAR Inc. in support of sound-quieting trials. Was to have been deactivated Y 88 but continues to operate.

AG miscellaneous auxiliary yard craft
: Zenith Dredge Co., Duluth, Minn.

	Laid down	L	In serv.
1 MONOB ONE (ex-IX 309, W 87)	1-12-42	3-4-43	11-11-43

ɔ **One (YAG 61)**—yellow hull & masts, white superstructure
Dr. Giorgio Arra, 7-89

,390 tons (fl) **S:** 11 kts **Dim:** 58.5 × 10.1 × 4.8
Caterpillar D 398 diesel; 1 Harbormaster swiveling prop; 850 bhp
ge: 2,500/9 **Crew:** . . .

ks: Redesignated from IX 309 on 1-7-70. Former water lighter modified in 1959 ɹrt the ballistic-missile submarine silencing program. Based at Port Canaveral, d operated for the Naval Ships Research and Development Center, Carderock, oustic Trials Detachment by MAR, Inc. Has four laboratories, totaling 279 m². xtended to house new engine. To be replaced in late 1992 by *Hayes* (T-AG 195, ƷOR 16).

YC open lighters* (22 in reserve) (In serv. 1915–1991)
YC 306–1645

0 David D. Broecker, 3-92

596—typical modern-construction YC Moss Point Marine, 3-87

ks: YC 1517 to YC 1522 built 1976–77, YC 1523–1527 built 1978–79, YC 551 built 1979–83. Three authorized under FY 82 Budget. Current design is YC ass, of which six were authorized FY 83, 14 authorized FY 84, 11 in FY 85, 2 in and 13 in FY 88. Moss Point Marine, Escatawpa, Miss., delivered YC 1572–1602 7-2-85 to 23-4-87: 250 tons light (660 fl), 33.53 × 9.75 × 1.98 (max.). YC 629 ordered 1-89 to same design, from Orange SB Corp., Orange, Texas, and r 15 (YC 1631 to YC 1645) were ordered 15-12-89 (YC 1630 was acquired in 1986 nother source).
1583 and 1586 converted 4-86 as cable-reel support barges for the T-AGOS m. YC 1572 and 1573 to MARAD 27-2-85 for lay-up but reacquired 21-5-85. YC ıs loaned to the Maritime Administration in 1-7-80; loan renewed 3-10-91. strikes: YC 769 on 17-5-90, YC 781 on 17-5-90, YC 1447 on 26-11-91, and YC nd YC 1427 in 1-92.

♦ **1 YCF car float***
YCF 16 (In serv. 25-1-42)

Remarks: 45.72 × 10.21; used to transport railroad cars. Active.

♦ **9 YCV aircraft transportation lighters***

YCV 8 (In serv. 4-3-44)	YCV 20 (In serv. 9-89)
YCV 10 (In serv. 21-8-44)	YCV 21 (In serv 10-89)
YCV 11 (In serv. 6-10-44)	YCV 22 (In serv. 1-4-91)
YCV 16 (In serv. 29-8-45)	YCV 23 (In serv. 2-2-91)
YCV 19 (In serv. 7-89)	

Remarks: All active. YCV 19–21 approved FY 88 and YCV 22 and 23 in FY 90 to replace earlier units; built by Alabama Shipyard, Mobile, they displace 2,480 tons and are 60.96 × 19.81 × 4.26. Earlier units are of similar dimensions and also displace 2,480 tons. YCV 15 is on loan to another government agency.

♦ **66 (+6) YD floating cranes*** (some are self-propelled)
Series YD 26–253

YD 247—completed 4-91 Jürg Kürsener, 7-92

YD 171—the navy's largest floating crane, at Long Beach, Cal.
George R. Schneider, Jr., 8-91

SERVICE CRAFT *(continued)*

YD 26—built in 1913 Leo Van Ginderen, 7-89

YD 236—at San Diego Wilhelm Donko, 7-88

YD 225—typical ex-U.S. Army floating crane Dr. Giorgio Arra, 1989

Remarks: Built 1913–90s. All active except YD 241. YD 171, ex-German, has capacity: 350 tons; refitted 1984–85, built 1941 by Demag, Bremerhaven (62.5 × 114.0 high, uses 3,560-m wire rope).

Most U.S. Navy YD are rectangular barges. Some 28 (YD 150, 159, 162, 16 188, 189, 192, 193, 197, 210, 213, 214, 217, 218, 222, 232–237, 239, 241–2 ex-U.S. Army: 1,630 tons (fl), 42.67 × 21.34 × 1.91, 90–100 tons capacity. (ex-army BD 6643) stricken 26-11-91.

One new YD authorized FY 82, three in FY 83, five in FY 84, three under FY in FY 86, and three in FY 87: 1,650 tons (fl); 54.4 × 24.4 × 2.0. Program sta builder's bankruptcy, 2-87. YD 249–253 ordered 1988 from Westmont Industr Angeles, and delivered during 1991: 2,134 tons (fl), 53.49 × 22.41 × 1.53, crev with 100-ton crane, 150-bhp Caterpillar 3304 diesel maneuvering propulsi 246–248 ordered 1988 from Halter Marine, Lockport, and Equitable Boat div Trinity Marine and delivered 11-2-91, 4-4-91, and 25-6-91, respectively. YD 254 same design ordered 25-7-91 from Alabama SY, Mobile.

♦ 3 YDT diving tenders

	Bldr	In serv.
YDT 14 PHOEBUS (ex-YF 294)	Erie Concrete & Steel	10-12-42
YDT 15 SUITLAND (ex-YF 336)	Erie Concrete & Steel	16-6-43

D: 600 tons (fl) **S:** . . . kts **Dim:** 40.4 × 9.1
M: 1 Union diesel; 600 hp

	Bldr	In
YDT 16 TOM O'MALLEY (ex-YFNB 43)	American Bridge, Ambridge, Pa.	

D: 2,000 tons (fl) **Dim:** 79.6 × 14.6 (non-self-propelled)

♦ 1 YF covered lighter, YF 852 class (in reserve)

	Bldr	L	In serv.
YF 885 KEYPORT	Defoe SB	19-5-45	4-8-45

D: 300 tons light (505 fl) **S:** 10 kts **Dim:** 40.5 × 9.1 × 2.7
A: 3/324-mm Mk 32 ASW TT (III × 1) **Electric:** 120 kw
M: 2 G.M. diesels; 2 props; 1,000 bhp **Fuel:** 40 tons

Remarks: YF 885 in reserve since 8-90 at Undersea Warfare Engineering S Keyport, Washington, with 3/324-mm Mk 32 ASW TT; has "Omnithruster thruster. Sister YF 862 stricken from reserve 15-2-85; *Kodiak* (YF 866) stricke YF 885 will probably soon follow.

♦ 6 YFB ferryboats

YFB 83 WA'A HELE HONUA
Bldr: John H. Mathis Co., Camden, N.J. (In serv. 4-49)

D: 500 tons (fl) **S:** 8.5 kts **Dim:** 49.4 × 17.7
M: 2 diesels **Cargo:** 500 passengers, 38 vehicles

YFB 87 MOKU HOLO HELE Bldr: Western Boat (In serv. 5-70)

Moku Holo Hele (YFB 87) Leo Van Ginderen

D: 773 tons (fl) **Dim:** 54.9 × 18 **Crew:** 2 G.M. diesels

YFB 88 (ex-LCU 1636) YFB 89 (ex-LCU 1638)
YFB 90 (ex-LCU 1639) YFB 91 (ex-LCU 1640)

YFB 91 Leo Van Ginderen

D: 390 tons (fl) **S:** 10 kts **Dim:** 41.0 × 9.0
M: 4 G.M. diesels; 2 props; 1,200 bhp **Crew:** 6 tot.

Remarks: YFB 88–91 built 1965–69 as landing craft and modified 1969–70 as All active. YFB 83 name means "A canoe that travels on land"; YFB 87 name "Ship that goes back and forth"; both at Pearl Harbor.

ICE CRAFT *(continued)*

(+22) **YFN covered lighters** (5 in reserve)

YFN 262–1283

.266 George R. Schneider, Jr., 1-91

·ks: Built 1940–88. Majority are 685 tons (fl), 33.5 × 9.8. Large rectangular .ıse. Nine YFN 1254 class authorized under FY 81 (11 actually built). 6 (3) under FY 85, 2 under FY 86: 260 tons light (660 fl); 33.53 × 9.75 × 2.23 m; small deckhouse; YFN 1265–1276 built by Eastern Marine, YFN 1265 de-1-87, YFN 1266–1271 in 8-87, YFN 1272–74 in service 18-4-88; YFN 1275–76 -88. YFN reclassified from YFRN 1235 in 1985. Under FY 90, 12 more 685-ton ith option for 22 additional (YFN 1289–1310) that were authorized under Fiscal 991 were to be ordered, but no contracts announced as of 7-92. Recent strikes : YFN 641 on 1-10-89. YFN 685 is named *Suwanee.*

YFNB large covered lighters* (1 in reserve)

5, 8, 30, 31, 32, 34, 36, 37, 39, 41, 42, 47 (ex-YRR 9)

30 George R. Schneider, Jr., 9-90

·ks: All active except YFNB 39. All 831 tons light (2,780 fl), 79.2 × 14.6 × 2.9, YFNB 47: 770 tons (fl), 46.6 × 18.7 × 1.8. YFNB 47 reclassified 11-83. YFNB 31 ed 4-92 from Holy Loch, Scotland, to Norfolk Naval Base.

FND dry-dock companion craft*

) 5 (ex-YFN 268; in serv. 3-2-41)

) 29 (ex-YFN 974; in serv. 28-8-45)

rks: 590 tons (fl), 33.53 × 9.75, converted YFN.

YFNX special-purpose lighters* (1 in reserve)

	In serv.		In serv.
4	1942	YFNX 25 (ex-YFN 1224)	1965
7	1942	YFNX 26 (ex-YFN 1225)	1965
15 (ex-YNG 22)	1942	YFNX 30 SEA TURTLE (ex-YFN 1186)	1952
20	1952		
22	1941	YFNX 31 (ex-YFN 1249)	1970
23 (ex-YFN 289)	1941	YFNX 32 (ex-YRBM 7)	1961
24 (ex-YFN 1215)	1965		

X 24—divers' berthing barge George R. Schneider, Jr., 8-83

Sea Turtle (YFNX 30)—submersible support craft Dr. Giorgio Arra, 8-86

Remarks: All active except YFNX 7. Most converted YFN. YFNX 30 (200 tons light; 34.0 × 10.0 × 1.7 m) at Naval Ocean Systems Center, San Diego, supports the remote-controlled submersible CURV II. YFNX 4–24 are 33.5 × 10.0 × 1.7 m; YFNX 25, 26 are 38.4 × 10.0. YFNX 24 is a berthing barge for divers. Several have maneuvering propulsion systems, including YFNX 30. YFNX 15 is a former "gate craft" (non-self-propelled net tender). YFNX 33 (ex-YFN 1192) redesignated as salvage lift craft in 6-86.

◆ **3 (+1) YFP floating power barges***

YFP 3 (ex-YC 1114) YFP 11 (ex-YFN 1207) YFP 12 (ex-YFN 1216)
YFP 15

Remarks: First three: 33.5 × 9.7 m; completed: YFP 3 in 4-45, YFP 11, 12 in 1965. YFP 15, completed in 11-91 by Alabama Shipyard, Mobile, is 44.5 × 18.3. *Inductance* (YFP 14, ex-army BD 6235) was stricken 29-5-91.

Note: All four YFRN refrigerated lighters listed in the previous edition have been stricken: YFRN 385, 412, and 997 on 16-5-90, and YFRN 1235 prior to 1-92.

◆ **3 YFRT covered lighter range tenders**

	Bldr	Laid down	L	In serv.
YFRT 287	Norfolk NSY	2-41	5-41	7-41
YFRT 451 SPIRIT	Basalt Rock Co., Napa, Cal.	2-44	7-44	10-44
YFRT 520 POTENTIAL	Erie Concrete & Steel, Erie, Pa.	10-42	3-43	8-43

Spirit (YFRT 451) Victor M. Baca, 1988

D: 300 tons light (650 fl) **S:** 9.5 kts **Dim:** 40.5 × 9.1 × 2.7
A: 3/324-mm Mk 32 ASW TT
Electron Equipt: Radar: 1/. . . nav.
M: 2 Caterpillar D 379 diesels; 2 props; 1,000 bhp **Electric:** 180 kw

Remarks: Torpedo trials craft. YFRT 287 built as such, rest converted from YFR. Sister YFRT 418 stricken 2-84, and YFRT 523 on 3-4-86. YFRT 287 is attached to the Naval Underwater Systems Center, Newport, R.I.; the others are assigned to the Naval Undersea Warfare Engineering Station, Keyport, Washington, and should soon be stricken, having been replaced by the four new torpedo trials craft of the YTT 9 class.

◆ **3 YFU harbor utility craft:**

1 LCU 1608 class Bldr: Defoe SB, Bay City, Mich. (In serv. 1957)

YFU 91 (ex-LCU 1608)

SERVICE CRAFT *(continued)*

YFU 91 — Dr. Giorgio Arra, 7-91

D: 351 tons (fl) **S:** 8 kts **Dim:** 35.11 × 10.36 × 1.52 (aft)
M: 3 Gray Marine 64 HN12 diesels; 3 Kort-nozzle props; 675 bhp (495 bhp sust.)
Range: 1,200/6 **Fuel:** 11.7 tons **Crew:** . . .

Remarks: Converted landing craft. Cargo: 183 tons. Supports Naval Underwater Systems Center Detachment, Andros Ranges, Bahamas.

♦ **1 YFU 71 class**
Bldr: Pacific Coast Eng. Co., Alameda, Cal. (In serv. 1968)

YFU 81

D: 220 tons (380 tons fl) **S:** 8 kts **Dim:** 38.10 × 10.97 × 2.29
M: 4 G.M. 6-71 diesels; 2 Kort-nozzle props; 1,000 bhp
Electric: 120 kw **Range:** . . . **Crew:** . . .

Remarks: In reserve. Built as a YFU, last of 12 sisters intended for Vietnam service. Engines and superstructure centerline aft. Bow ramp. Sister to IX 506 (ex-YFU 82) and IX 514 (ex-YFU 79). Sisters YFU 74 and 75 transferred to MARAD for lay-up 18-12-84, reacquired 3-6-86, and then stricken 30-9-86. YFU 71, 72, 76, and 77 to Department of the Interior 1-12-84; YFU 76 and 77 were further transferred to the Marshall Islands in 1987.

♦ **1 LCU 1610 class** Bldr: Defoe SB, Bay City, Mich. (In serv. 4-71)

YFU 83

D: 190 tons (390 fl) **S:** 11 kts **Dim:** 41.07 × 9.07 × 2.08
M: 4 G.M. 6-71 diesels; 2 Kort-nozzle props; 1,200 bhp
Range: 1,200/11 **Fuel:** 13 tons **Crew:** 6 tot.

Remarks: YFU 83 built as utility craft, but to standard LCU configuration. Cargo capacity: 143 tons in 30.5 × 5.5-m cargo deck. Retains bow ramp. Assigned to Atlantic Fleet Weapons Training Facility, Roosevelt Roads, Puerto Rico. Sisters YFU 100 (ex-LCU 1610) and YFU 102 (ex-YFU 1642) transferred to Maritime Administration 18-6-91 for disposal. Workboat 119WB8501, stationed at Guantánamo Bay, Cuba, is ex-YFU 50, ex-LCU 1486, and has similar characteristics.

♦ **3 YGN garbage lighters***
Bldr: Zidell, Portland, Ore. (In serv. 1970–71)

YGN 80 YGN 81 YGN 83

Remarks: All active. 309 tons light (855 fl), 37.8 × 10.7 rectangular barges. Have hopper-type bottoms to permit dumping at sea. Ex-YGN 70 and 82, redesignated as "floating equipment" 1-84, remain available also.

♦ **1 YLC salvage lift craft***

YLC 1 (ex-YFNX 33, ex-YFN 1192)

Remarks: Built 1952 as a covered lighter, became YFNX in 12-74; redesignated a salvage lift craft in 6-86 and is attached to Mobile Diving & Salvage Unit 2, Atlantic Fleet. Standard navy 685-ton, 33.5 × 9.8 barge hull.

Note: Ex-German heavy salvage lift craft *Crilley* (YHLC 1) and *Crandall* (YHLC 2), in reserve since 9-76, were transferred to the Maritime Administration 5-8-91 for disposal.

♦ **3 YM dredge** (1 in reserve)

YM 17 (In serv. 1934) YM 33 (In serv. 1970) YM 35 (In serv. 1970)

Remarks: Characteristics vary. YM 33 in reserve. YM 17 displaces 500 tons. YM 33, 35 are only 13.1 m and 21.3 m overall, respectively. YM 32 stricken 17-1-90.

♦ **1 non-self-propelled dredge**
Bldr: Ellicott Machine Corp., Baltimore, Md.

YMN 1 (In serv. 2-92)

Remarks: Authorized FY 88. No data available.

♦ **2 YNG gate craft***

YNG 11 (In serv. 7-41) YNG 17 (In serv. 6-41)

Remarks: Built to tend harbor-defense nets. 225 tons (fl); 33.5 × 10.5.

♦ **1 YO 46-class fuel-oil lighter** (in reserve)
Bldr: Lake Superior SB, Superior, Wisc.

	L	In serv.
YO 47 Casinghead	25-4-42	12-11-42

Casinghead (YO 47)—in reserve at Long Beach, Cal. — George R. Schneider, J

D: 950 tons (2,660 fl) **S:** 10 kts **Dim:** 71.6 × 11.3 × 4.6
M: 2 Enterprise diesels; 820 bhp **Electric:** 280 kw **Crew:** 34

Remarks: Cargo: 1,350 tons. In reserve at Long Beach, California.

♦ **8 YO 65 class** Bldr: Jeffersonville Boat & Machine Co., Jeffersonvi Ind. (except: YO 129: Smith SY, Pensacola, Fla.; YO 203: Manitowoc SB, Manitowoc, Wisc.; YO 130: Western Pipe Steel, Los Angeles)

	In serv.		In serv.		In serv.
YO 129	4-44	YO 220	8-45	YO 225	10-45
YO 130	1943	YO 223	9-45	YO 230	12-45
YO 203	8-45	YO 224	10-45		

YO 203—at light load — David D. Broeck

YO 220—at light load — Gilbert Gysse

D: 440 tons light (1,390 fl) **S:** 9 kts
Dim: 53.04 × 9.75 × 3.96
M: 1 G.M. (*see* Remarks) diesel; 1 prop, 640 bhp **Electric:** 80 kv

Remarks: Cargo 900 tons/6,570 bbl. YO 129 has a Union diesel, 560 bhp. Sam design as 53.04-m YOG and YW. Sister YO 228, long in reserve at Philadelph made available for foreign transfer in 1992.

Note: YO 153-class yard oiler YO 153, long in reserve at Philadelphia, was s for possible transfer in 1992. Two new YO were requested under the Fiscal Ye Budget to begin the long-overdue replacement of the surviving units above.

♦ **5 gasoline lighters** (2 in reserve) Bldrs: RTC SB, Camden, N.J. (except: YOG 78, 79: Puget Sound NSY; YOG 68: George Lawley & Sons, Neponset, Mass.) (In serv. 1945–46)

YOG 58 YOG 78 YOG 88 YOG 93 YOG 196 (ex-YO 196)

YOG 88—at light load — Dr. Giorgio Arra

VICE CRAFT *(continued)*

440 tons light (1,390 fl) **Dim:** 53.04 × 9.75 × 3.96
1 G.M. diesel; 1 prop; 640 bhp **Electric:** 80 kw

rks: YOG 58, 93 in reserve. Carry about 950 tons aviation fuel. YOG 58 has a diesel.

(+5) YOGN gasoline barges*

N 8, 9, 10, 26, 110, 111, 113, 114, 115, 123, 124, 125

N 110 Leo Van Ginderen, 10-74

arks: Built 1943–71. All active. Carry aviation fuel. All 1,270–1,360 tons (fl), x. 50 × 10.7 m. YOGN 126–131 were authorized under Fiscal Year 1991 Budget, ave not yet been ordered; 1,642 tons (fl).

2 (+2) YON fuel-oil barges*

s YON 2–313

91—with commercial tug George R. Schneider, Jr., 5-87

arks: Most built 1942–76. All active. Typical unit: 1,445 tons (fl); 50.3 × 12.0 . YON 305, 306 built under FY 80. YON 255–295 (30 units) were built 1964–76. are ex-U.S. Army, including YON 2, transferred 10-71, YON 255 and 256 trans- in 9-64, and YON 305, 306 transferred 7-79. YON 235 is ex-YWN 73. Can carry a y of fuels. YON 307–309 approved under FY 87: 1,600 tons (fl); 56.0 × 10.7 × 3.0; ed 29-7-88 from Alabama Shipyard, Mobile, and delivered 1-90, 12-89, and 1-90, ctively. Two more were requested under the Fiscal Year 1992 Budget.

4 YOS oil-storage barges*

8, 10, 12, 15–17, 20, 21, 24, 28 (ex-YC 707), 33 (ex-YSR 46), 34, 6

arks: YOS 8–33 built 1944–65. All active. Ten: 100 tons light; 24.4 × 10.4; s: 140 tons light; 33.5 × 10.4. YOS 34 (ex-army OB61-2) acquired 1-9-79. YOS 35, quested under FY 87: 725 tons (fl); ordered 29-7-88 from Alabama Maritime Corp., e, and delivered 6-90.

7 YP 676-class patrol craft/training tenders Bldrs: YP 676–682: eterson Bldrs., Sturgeon Bay, Wisc.; others: Marinette SB, Marinette, Wisc.

	Laid down	L	In serv.
76	7-4-83	9-4-84	14-11-84
77	10-10-83	23-6-84	5-12-84
78	15-12-83	3-11-84	13-5-85
79	18-4-84	11-12-84	6-6-85
80	2-7-84	23-3-85	8-8-85
81	29-10-84	1-6-85	30-9-85
82	7-1-85	3-8-85	18-11-85
83	23-7-85	19-6-86	13-10-86
84	29-8-85	14-8-86	10-12-86
85	8-10-85	25-9-86	23-11-86
86	23-1-86	25-10-86	12-86
87	27-2-86	3-87	7-3-87
88	7-4-86	4-87	15-3-87
89	15-7-86	5-87	10-6-87
90	18-8-86	4-87	10-6-87
91	28-10-86	5-87	7-87
92	10-12-86	18-6-87	27-7-87
93	26-1-87	14-8-87	22-9-87
94	25-2-87	21-9-87	27-10-87
95	24-3-87	26-10-87	1-12-87
96	23-4-87	. . .	10-5-88
97	26-5-87	1-2-88	26-5-88
98	22-6-87	29-3-88	16-6-88
99	17-8-87	11-4-88	30-6-88
700	22-9-87	12-5-88	21-7-88
701	28-10-87	14-6-88	9-8-88
702	10-12-87	19-7-88	2-9-88

YP 680—Peterson-built unit with twin ladders forward Dr. Giorgio Arra, 6-90

YP 691—Marinette-built unit with single ladder forward William E. Brooks III, 1991

D: 167–172.4 tons (fl) **S:** 13.25 kts
Dim: 32.92 (30.99 pp) × 7.39 × 1.83
Electric Equipt: Radar: 1/SPS-64(V)9 nav.
M: 2 G.M. 12V71N diesels; 2 props; 874 bhp **Electric:** 100 kw
Range: 1500/12
Crew: 2 officers, 4 enlisted, 24 midshipmen (30 berths)

Remarks: Wooden construction boats to replace YP 654 class. Aluminum superstructure. YP 676 ordered 15-10-82; YP 677–682 ordered 25-5-83; YP 683–695 ordered 12-6-84; YP 696–702 on 13-9-85. Made up to 13.3 kts on trials. Have NAVSAT and Loran C receivers. All to Naval Academy, except YP 677, 679, 696 through 702, to Officer Candidate School, Newport, R.I. YP 686 equipped for oceanographic research. Under FY 88, Congress directed that YP 702 be completed as a prototype inshore minehunter, a conversion neither required nor desired by the navy, which did not comply; Congress then demanded trials under FY 89. Marinette-built units can be distinguished by their having a single ladder forward to the bridge deck, whereas the Peterson-built craft have two.

◆ 6 YP 655-class patrol/training craft Bldr: Stephens Bros., Stockton, Cal. (YP 665: Elizabeth City SY, Elizabeth City, N.C.)

	L	In serv.		L	In serv.
YP 655	8-57	3-58	YP 658	11-57	6-58
YP 656	8-57	4-58	YP 665	8-60	11-60
YP 657	8-57	6-58	YP 667	4-66	1-67

YP 656 George R. Schneider, Jr., 6-89

SERVICE CRAFT *(continued)*

D: 57–60 tons (68–71 fl) **S:** 12.6–13.3 kts
Dim: 24.51 × 5.72 × 1.6
Electron Equipt: Radar: Raytheon 1220 nav.
M: 2 G.M. 6-71 diesels; 2 props; 590 bhp **Range:** 400/12
Electric: 20–30 kw **Crew:** 2 officers, 8 enlisted, 24 midshipmen

Remarks: Wooden construction. Employed at the Surface Warfare Officers School, San Diego. YP 658 is named *Perseverance,* and the others may also have unofficial names. Sisters YP 659 and YP 660 were transferred to the COOP minehunting program in 9-85 and 11-85. Fifteen others (YP 654, 661, 662, 664, 666, 668–675) were to have become COOP craft under FY 86–88, but not all were converted; they were redesignated as "floating property" on 1-2-89.

♦ 4 YPD floating pile drivers*

YPD 37 YPD 41 YPD 45 (ex-YC 1498) YPD 46 (ex-YFNB 35)

YPD 45 George R. Schneider, Jr., 11-86

Remarks: Built 1943–69. All active. Most built on standard 24.4 × 10.4 barge hulls, except YPD 46: 79.6 × 14.6; 2,700 tons (fl).

♦ 27 YR floating workshops* (1 in reserve)

YR 25–27, 29, 36, 44, 46, 50, 60, 63, 64, 67, 68, 70, 73, 76–78, 83 (ex-YRL 5), 84 (ex-army FMS 6), 85 QUALITY (ex-army FMS 87), 86 (ex-Army FMS 811), 87, 88 (ex-YRR 8), 89 (ex-YRR 4), 90 (ex-YRR 7), 91

YR 76—standard navy design Leo Van Ginderen, 1990

YR 85—ex-army repair barge, with YC 1085 alongside
Leo Van Ginderen, 10-87

Remarks: Built 1941–45, except YR 85, 86: 1954. YR 25 in reserve. Most 520 tons light (770 fl); 46.6 × 10.7 × 1.8. Differ in equipment. YR 89 reclassified from YRR 4 (ex-YFN 685) 15-8-86. Ex-army units are 1,525 tons (fl), 64.14 × 12.19 × 2.36, have crews of 30, and carry 140 tons fuel for their four 100-kw generators. YR 91 ordered 8-11-91; 825 tons (fl).

♦ 5 YRB repair and berthing barges*

YRB 1 (ex-YFN 258) YRB 2 (ex-YFN 310) YRB 22 (ex-YC 1079)
YRB 25 (ex-YFN 298) YRB 29 (ex-YRST 5)

YRB 22 George R. Schneider, Jr.

Remarks: All 33.5 × 9.1. Built 1940–45. Support submarines. All active.

♦ 38 YRBM repair, berthing, and messing barges*

YRBM 1–6, 8, 9, 11–15, 20, 23–46

YRBM 26—at San Diego George R. Schneider, Jr.

YRBM 38—Marinette-built unit, at San Diego
George R. Schneider, Jr.

YRBM 15—smaller unit on standard USN barge hull
Wilhelm Donko

’ICE CRAFT *(continued)*

·ks: Built 1955–83. All active; support submarines and ships in overhaul. ·tte SB constructed YRBM 31 to YRBM 46 during 1979–83: 688 tons; 44.5 × 1.3; accommodations for 26 officers, 231 enlisted. Have office, workshop, eating, creation spaces, 96-seat training theater, galley, etc. YRBM 23–30, also by ·tte (in serv. 8-70 to 6-71), of similar dimensions, but 585 tons (fl). YRBM 20 is ons, 79.6 × 14.6; remainder are approx. 310 tons (fl), 33.5 × 10.4.

ʼRDH floating dry-dock workshops, hull* (2 in reserve)

I 1 (ex-YR 55) YRDH 2 (ex-YR 56) YRDH 6 YRDH 7

·ks: Completed 1943–44. YRDH 2 and 6 are active. 770 tons (fl), 46.6 × 10.7

ʼRDM floating dry-dock workshops, machinery*

Л 1 (ex-YR 52) YRDM 2 (ex-YR 53) YRDM 5

M 5 — George R. Schneider, Jr., 8-85

·ks: Completed 1943–44. All active. 770 tons (fl), 46.6 × 10.7 × 1.8. Sister 7 converted at Portsmouth Naval Shipyard and redesignated YR 90 on 1-8-91.

YRR radiological repair barges*

1 (ex-YR 49)	YRR 5 (ex-YRDM 8)	YRR 11 (ex-YRDH 3)
2 (ex-YR 74)	YRR 6 (ex-YR 39)	YRR 12 (ex-YRDH 4)
3 (ex-YFN 333)	YRR 7 (ex-YR 31)	YRR 13 (ex-YRDM 3)
10 (ex-YR 79)	YRR 14 (ex-YRDM 4)	

·rks: In serv. 1937–45; all active in support of submarines. All converted from ·arge-hulled functions: 770 tons (fl), 46.6 × 10.7 × 1.8. Sister YRR 9 reclassified 47 in 11-83; YRR 4 became YR 89 on 15-8-86.

YRST salvage-craft tenders*

’ 1 (ex-YDT 11) YRST 2 (ex-YDT 12) YRST 6 (ex-YFNX 10)

·rks: Completed 1945; all active. YRST 3 and YRST 5 stricken 15-4-84. YRST 1, ,700 tons (fl), 79.6 × 14.6; YRST 6 is 670 tons (fl), 33.5 × 10.7. All are rectangular

YSD 39 and YSD 53, the last of the once-numerous “Mary Ann” self-propelled ne wrecking derricks, were stricken 8-10-91 and 29-5-91, respectively.

YSR sludge-removal barges*

6, 7, 11, 17, 20, 23, 25–33, 37–40, 45 (ex-army BC 6090)

6 — George R. Schneider, Jr., 5-84

·rks: Completed 1942–52. Seventeen active. Most either 24.4 × 9.8 or 33.5 4. YR 6 named *The Big W*. YSR 18 stricken 9-6-87, YSR 19 in 4-92.

) YTB large harbor tugs (SCB 147/147A type) (2 in reserve)

·drs: YTB 752: Christy Corp., Sturgeon Bay, Wisc.; YTB 756–759, 763–766, ·9–802: Southern SB Corp., Slidell, La.; YTB 760–761: Jakobson SY, Oyster ·y, New York; 762: Commercial Iron Wks., Portland, Ore.; YTB 767–771: ·obile Ship Repair, Mobile, Ala.; YTB 774–798, 816–836: Marinette Marine ·rp., Marinette, Wisc.; 803–815: Peterson Bldrs, Sturgeon Bay, Wisc.

752 Edenshaw
756 Pontiac
757 Oshkosh
YTB 758 Paducah
YTB 759 Bogalusa
YTB 760 Natick
YTB 761 Ottumwa
YTB 762 Tuscumbia
YTB 763 Muskegon
YTB 764 Mishawaka
YTB 765 Okmulgee
YTB 766 Wapakoneta
YTB 767 Apalachicola
YTB 768 Arcata
YTB 769 Chesaning
YTB 770 Dahlonega
YTB 771 Keokuk
YTB 774 Nashua
YTB 775 Wauwatosa
YTB 776 Weehawken
YTB 777 Nogales
YTB 778 Apopka
YTB 779 Manhattan
YTB 780 Saugus
YTB 781 Niantic
YTB 782 Manistee
YTB 783 Redwing
YTB 784 Kalispell
YTB 785 Winnemucca
YTB 786 Tonkawa
YTB 787 Kittanning
YTB 788 Wapato
YTB 789 Tomahawk
YTB 790 Menominee
YTB 791 Marinette
YTB 792 Antigo
YTB 793 Piqua
YTB 794 Mandan
YTB 795 Ketchikan
YTB 796 Saco
YTB 797 Tamaqua
YTB 798 Opelika
YTB 799 Natchitoches
YTB 800 Eufaula
YTB 801 Palatka
YTB 802 Cheraw
YTB 803 Nanticoke
YTB 804 Ahoskie
YTB 805 Ocala
YTB 806 Tuskegee
YTB 807 Massapequa
YTB 808 Wenatchee
YTB 809 Agawam
YTB 810 Anoka
YTB 811 Houma
YTB 812 Accomac
YTB 813 Poughkeepsie
YTB 814 Waxahatchie
YTB 815 Neodesha
YTB 816 Campti
YTB 817 Hyannis
YTB 818 Mecosta
YTB 819 Iuka
YTB 820 Wanamassa
YTB 821 Tontogany
YTB 822 Pawhuska
YTB 823 Canonchet
YTB 824 Santaquin
YTB 825 Wathena
YTB 826 Washtuena
YTB 827 Chetek
YTB 828 Catahecassa
YTB 829 Metacom
YTB 830 Pushmataha
YTB 831 Dekanawida
YTB 832 Petalesharo
YTB 833 Shabonee
YTB 834 Newagen
YTB 835 Skenandoa
YTB 836 Pokagon

Petalesharo (YTB 832) — Dr. Giorgio Arra, 8-91

Oshkosh (YTB 757) — Dr. Giorgio Arra, 4-91

D: 286 tons (356 fl) **S:** 12.5 kts **Dim:** 33.05 × 9.3 × 4.14
Electron Equipt: Radar: 1/LN-66 or CRP-1900 nav.
M: 1 Fairbanks-Morse 38D8Q × 12 diesel; 1 prop; 2,000 bhp
Electric: 120 kw **Range:** 2,000/12 **Crew:** 12 tot.

Remarks: Built 1959–70. YTB 752 to YTB 759 have a less-streamlined superstructure, and are considered a separate class (SCB 147 type); YTB 752 has Alco diesels. All active. Minor differences in displacement between units by different builders. All have a small commercial navigational radar. Three also built for Saudi Arabia. Sister *Marin* (YTB 753) stricken 21-5-91. YTB 780 and 793 returned from Holy Loch, Scotland, in 4-91 and were placed in reserve. YTB 788 aground 16-4-91 at Fort Pierce, Florida, but was salvaged without significant damage.

Note: Planned procurement of 28 YTB 839 tugs of 3,000–4,000 hp was canceled 1984 in favor of contracting for tug services from private industry to achieve lower overall costs and a diminished requirement for military personnel. Nearly all surviving active YTL- and YTM-type tugs were stricken during 1985–87 as a result of the same decision.

◆ 1 YTL 422-class small harbor tug Bldr: Robert Jacob, City Isl., N.Y.

YTL 602 (In serv. 10-45)

D: 70 tons (80 fl) **S:** 8 kts **Dim:** 20.1 × 5.5 × 2.4
M: 1 diesel; 375 bhp **Crew:** 4 tot.

SERVICE CRAFT *(continued)*

Remarks: Active at the Portsmouth Naval Shipyard, Portsmouth, New Hampshire, YTL 602 is the survivor of several hundred YTL 422 class; many still in foreign navies. A few others remain in U.S. Navy use, retyped as "floating equipment."

Note: A number of LCM(6) landing craft have been converted for use as push-tugs for local use, in place of YTLs; they are listed as "floating equipment."

LCM(6)—in use as a push-tug at Yokosuka — Wilhelm Donko, 11-89

♦ 4 torpedo trials ships
Bldrs: McDermott, Morgan City, La.

	Laid down	L	In serv.
YTT 9 Cape Flattery	29-7-88	5-5-89	30-5-91
YTT 10 Battle Point	5-10-88	17-8-89	30-11-91
YTT 11 Discovery Bay	3-4-89	22-2-90	30-5-92
YTT 12 Agate Pass	18-9-89	6-9-90	30-10-92

Battle Point [YTT 10)—prior to fitting torpedo gear — McDermott, 10-90

Cape Flattery (YTT 9)—with Mk 32 ASW TT swung out — U.S. Navy, 6-91

D: 1,000 tons light (1,168 fl) **S:** 11 kts sust.
Dim: 56.85 (53.83 pp) × 12.19 × 3.23
A: 2/533-mm Mk 59 TT (submerged)—3/324-mm Mk 32 Mod. 5 ASW TT
Electron Equipt: Radar: 1/. . . nav.
M: 1 Cummins KTA-50M diesel; 1 prop; 1,280 bhp—2 electric Z-drive thrusters, 350 shp each
Range: 1,800/11 **Fuel:** 70 tons **Endurance:** 12 days
Electric: 1,185 kw (3 × 395-kw, Cummins VTA-28 GS/G.C. sets)
Crew: 31 tot. crew + 9 civilian technicians

Remarks: All assigned to the Naval Underwater Warfare Engineering Station, Keyport, Washington. Names are unofficial; that of YTT 9 duplicates a cargo ship in the Ready Reserve Force. First two ordered 8-87, YTT 11 on 31-3-88, YTT 12 on 7-12-88. Have crane to recover torpedoes and to handle sensor arrays and recovery equipment. Will have batteries to permit quiet operations. Perform tests with Mk 48 ADCAP, Mk 46, and Mk 50 ASW torpedoes.

♦ 1 YW water lighter

	Bldr	L	In serv.
YW 127	Leatham D. Smith, Sturgeon Bay, Wisc.	5-45	7-45

D: 1,282 tons (fl) **S:** 8 kts **Dim:** 53.0 × 9.7 × 4.6 **Crew:** 22 tot
M: 1 G.M. 8-2784 (YW 86: Fairbanks-Morse) diesel: 1 prop; 560 bh

Remarks: Cargo: 930 tons water. Stationed at the Philadelphia Naval Shi Same basic design as YO and YOG classes. Sister YW 98, long in reserve, was ferred to the Maritime Administration for disposal on 10-9-91.

♦ 7 YWN water barges* (1 in reserve)

YWN 70 YWN 71 YWN 78 YWN 79 YWN 82 YWN 147
YWN 156

Remarks: Built 1942–52. All but YWN 79 active. All 220 tons light (1,270 fl) × 10.7 × 2.4, except YWN 156 (ex-U.S. Army BG 6089): 70 tons light (250 fl); 3 10.1 × 2.44.

MISCELLANEOUS UNNUMBERED AUXILIARIES

♦ 1 ex-German Tarantul-I guided-missile patrol boat
Bldr: Volodarskiy Zavod, Rybinsk, Russia (In serv. 2-4-85)

185NS9201 Hiddensee (ex-P6166, ex-*Rudolf Egelhofer*, 572)

Hiddensee (185NS9201) — U.S. Navy,

D: 385 tons light (455 fl) **S:** 43 kts
Dim: 56.10 (49.50 pp) × 10.20 (9.40 wl) × 2.14 hull (4.0 props)
A: 4/SS-N-2C SSM (II × 2)—1/76.2-mm 59-cal. AK-176 DP—1/SA-8 SAM syst. (IV × 1, 12 Gremlin missiles)—2/30-mm AK-630 gatling AA (I × 2)
Electron Equipt:
Radar: 1/Furuno . . . nav., 1/Plank Shave (Harpun-E) targeting/surf. search, 1/Bass Tilt (Koral-E/MR 123) gun f.c.
EW: no intercept, 2/RK-16 decoy RL (XVI × 2)
IFF: 1/High Pole transponder, 1/Square Head interrogator
M: M-15E COGAG plant: 2 DMR-76 cruise gas turbines (4,000 shp each), 2 PR-77 boost gas turbines (12,000 shp each); 2 props; 32,000 shp
Electric: 500-kw tot. (2 × 200-kw, 1 × 100-kw diesel sets)
Range: 760/43; 1,400/13 **Fuel:** 122,634 liters
Endurance: 10 days **Crew:** 12 contract crew

Remarks: Taken over from former East Germany on 1-10-90, and was the only c five *Volksmarine* sisters to be commissioned into the *Bundesmarine*. Decommissi 7-91 and transferred to U.S. Navy in 12-91 for use in comparative performance t for the Naval Sea Systems Command. Based at Solomons Island, Maryland, operated by a General Dynamics contractor crew trained by former East Ge personnel. Original military crew was 7 officers, 32 enlisted.

Can carry 252 ready-service rounds and another 150 in reserve. Has a 76.2-mm which has a three-man crew and local optical and low-light t.v. backup co Stainless-steel alloy, seven watertight compartment hull with aluminum alloy s structure, decks, and internal bulkheads. Very strongly constructed and rugged. difficulty maneuvering below 10 kts. Weapons system employs analog computer has many backup features. Propulsion system extremely smooth-running; c connected so that any engine can drive either fixed-pitch prop. Very thorough visions for BW/CW defense.

♦ 1 former air force space-booster recovery ship
Bldr: Halter Marine, Moss Point, Mississippi (L: 27-2-85)

Independence

D: 1,798 tons (fl) **S:** 13 kts **Dim:** 60.96 (55.47 wl) × 12.19 × 4.1
Electron Equipt: Radar: 1/KAE 8500 nav., 1/KAE 5500 nav.

ELLANEOUS UNNUMBERED AUXILIARIES *(continued)*

2 Cummins KTA 3067-M 16-cyl. diesels; 2 props; 2,500 bhp—2 azimuth thrusters; 1,000 shp
ctric: 550 kw total (2 × 275-kw sets, Cummins KT 1150-GC diesels)
ige: 7,800/13; 8,500/11 **Fuel:** 99,419 gallons
lurance: 30 days **Crew:** 13 tot. + 14 scientists/technicians

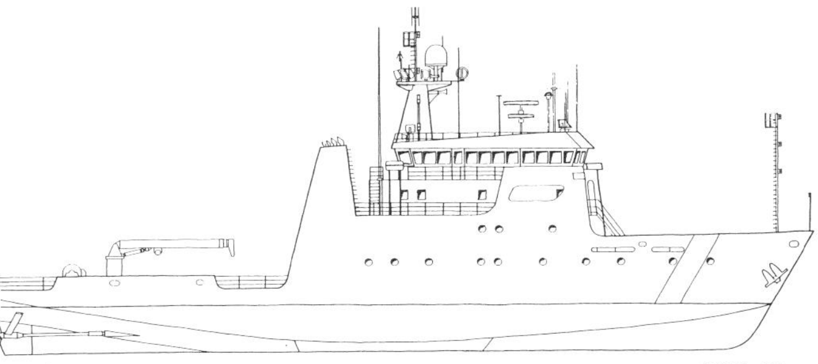

endence U.S. Navy

ks: Originally built to recover solid-fuel boosters launched from Vandenberg on the California coast; transferred to the U.S. Navy 1988 and operated for the Civil Engineering Laboratory, Port Hueneme, California, by Western Instru-orporation. Elaborate navigational equipment, including Magnavox MX 4400 Global Positioning System) receiver, Magnavox 11072 NAVSAT receiver, on dynamic positioning system, several echo-sounders. Has Flume passive-abilization system. Can carry 388 tons deck cargo, including modular laborato-as a hyperbaric chamber capable of accommodating seven divers and also a aboratory. Equipped with a 22-ton crane that telescopes to 19.8-m reach. Avail-other government agencies for charter.

pace-vehicle-booster recovery ship

r: Bishop Marine Service (In serv. 1966)

i762 RSB 1 (ex-*A.B. Wood II*)

. **(157NS762)** Dr. Giorgio Arra, 8-91

291 tons (fl) **S:** 13 kts **Dim:** 47.85 × 10.97 × 3.35
2 diesels; 2 props; 1,530 bhp **Crew:** 5 (civilians)

rks: Acquired 1976. Operated by civilian contractor for Naval Surface Warfare , Fort Lauderdale, Fla. Used to recover space-vehicle boosters. Has a bow-er and a 35-ton telescoping crane. Numbered as "floating property."

ropulsion trials craft

ER II

rks: Jupiter II is a 19.8-m workboat operated since 1976 by the Naval Ships ch and Development Center, Annapolis, Md. On 23-9-80 the gas-turbine-d craft began trials with a 300-kw superconducting electric propulsion motor, ing 6–7 kt speeds. A 2,250-kw, 3,000-hp superconducting motor was substituted . In 1988, a John Deere rotary diesel was substituted for propulsion trials.

er II U.S. Navy, 9-80

♦ 3 Asheville-class engineering-trials ships

Bldr: Tacoma Boat

	In serv.
165NS761 ATHENA (ex-*Chehalis*, PG 94)	11-8-69
165NS762 ATHENA II (ex-*Grand Rapids*, PG 98)	9-5-70
165NS763 LAUREN (ex-*Douglas*, PG 100)	6-2-71

Athena—at Panama City, Fla. Victor M. Baca, 1991

Athena II Dr. Giorgio Arra, 6-91

Lauren—note gun mount retained Dr. Giorgio Arra, 11-91

D: 225 tons (250 fl) **S:** 40 kts **Dim:** 50.14 × 7.28 × 2.9
A: *Lauren* only: 1/76.2-mm 50-cal. Mk 34 DP
Electron equipt: Radar: 2/. . . nav.
M: CODOG: 1 G.E. 7LM-1500-PE 102 LM-1500 gas turbine (12,500 shp), 2 Cummins VT12-875M diesels (1,400 bhp); 2 CP props
Electric: 200 kw **Range:** 325/37; 2,400/14 **Fuel:** 50 tons

Remarks: These craft are regarded as equipment, and therefore do not have USN hull numbers. Operate from Panama City, Florida, by MAR Inc. for the Naval Ships Research and Development Center, Carderock, Md. Have civilian crews and are disarmed. *Athena I* reclassified as "floating equipment" on 21-8-75, *Athena II* on 1-10-77. Have a 10-ton instrumentation payload. Both can carry a 14.9-m, portable, glass-reinforced plastic laboratory on the stern, and *Athena I* has a permanent 18.6-m lab added forward. *Douglas* (PG 100) was to have been converted to *Athena III* in FY 83; lack of funds canceled project and ship discarded 12-84, with *Deer Island* (YAG 62) acquired in her place. Ex-*Douglas*, however, was activated in 1990 for trials with the Integrated Warship System Demonstration Program and appears to be involved in signature-reduction trials; the name "*Lauren*" is unofficial. Sisters *Gallup* (PG 85) and *Canon* (PG 90) are being retained in storage as possible additions to the Naval Ships Research and Development Center fleet.

♦ 1 oceanographic research support craft

Bldr: Equitable Equipment Co., New Orleans, La. (In serv. 1965)

105UB821 ERLINE (ex-M/V *Orrin*)

D: 96 tons (120 fl) **S:** . . . **Dim:** 32.00 × 6.31 × 1.80
M: 2 diesels; 2 props; . . . bhp **Range:** 1,200/10

Remarks: Former offshore crew boat acquired 1967 and currently operated by the Naval Underwater Systems Center at Tudor Hill, Bermuda. At the same facility is the chartered oilfield supply tug *Seacor Ranger*.

MISCELLANEOUS UNNUMBERED AUXILIARIES *(continued)*

◆ **1 sonobuoy trials craft**
Bldr: Halter Marine, Moss Point, Miss. (In serv. 1981)

180WB8701 NADC 38 Acoustic Pioneer (ex-*September Morn*)

Acoustic Pioneer (NADC 38—185WB8701) Dr. Giorgio Arra, 6-91

D: approx. 1,500 tons (fl) **S:** . . .
Dim: 54.86 × 12.19 × 4.27
M: 2 G.M. EM Div. diesels; 2 props; . . . bhp

Remarks: Former 282-grt oilfield supply boat acquired 1987 and formerly employed with *Acoustic Explorer* at the Naval Avionics Development Center, St. Croix, Virgin Islands, for sonobuoy testing; now operates in Alaskan waters.

◆ **1 sonobuoy trials craft** Bldr: . . .

111NS8801 Acoustic Explorer (ex-. . .)

Remarks: No data available. Acquired 1988. Operates from St. Croix in the Virgin Islands.

◆ **1 oceanographic research barge**
Bldr: Gunderson Bros., Portland, Oregon (In serv. 6-8-62)

Flip

D: 700 tons (fl) **S:** 2–3 kts **Dim:** 109.73 × 8.53 × 3.81
M: 1/60-hp thruster **Crew:** . . .

Remarks: Operated for and by the Scripps Institute of Oceanography of California, although navy-owned. Designed to be towed into position and then "flipped" (hence name) upright to provide vertical enclosed column for water-property research; essentially a long cylinder with a ship-type bow at one end for towing.

Note: Navy-owned 19.8-m research craft *Edgerton* is on loan to the Massachusetts Institute of Technology. An 18.3 × 5.5-m research craft was delivered to the Naval Ships Research and Development Center in 7-91 by Gladding-Hearn SB, Somerset, Mass. The twin-hulled SWATH research ship *Kaimalino* (SSP 1) was transferred to the National Oceanic and Atmospheric Administration (NOAA) in 1991.

◆ **1 ocean construction platform** Bldr: Missouri Valley Br. & Iron, Ind.

	Laid down	L	In serv.
Seacon (ex-YFNB 33)	16-1-45	22-3-45	25-10-45

Seacon Alvin Grobmeier, 10-87

D: 2,780 tons (fl) **S:** 7 kts **Dim:** 79.25 × 14.63 × 2.9
M: 1 G.M. 12-71 diesel, 2 G.M. 6-71 diesels; 3 Voith-Schneider 14E/87 vertical cycloidal props; 1,020 bhp
Electric: 575 kw **Crew:** 50 tot.

Remarks: A large covered barge belonging to the navy and formerly used by NASA for transporting rockets, the *Seacon* was converted 1974–76 by Norfolk SB & Dry Dock Co. to serve as a seagoing work ship for the Navy Ocean Engineering and Construction Project Office. Intended to be towed at up to 11 knots to work locations and then to use own propulsion for precision maneuvering. Can be used to lay cable, can moor in 200-m water, and has open work deck 40 × 14 aft with 25-ton gantry A-frame crane. Also has a traveling 22-ton crane and can winch 100 tons over her stern roller. Unique in having no ship or yard-craft number.

◆ **1 sail frigate relic** Bldr: Hartt's SY, Boston, Mass. (L: 21-10-1797)

Constitution (ex-IX 21)

Constitution—on turn-around day U.S. Navy

D: 2,200 tons **S:** 13 kts (sail)
Dim: 62.18 (53.34 hull) × 13.26 × 6.86
A: 32/24-pdr—26/32-pdr carronade—2/24-pdr bow-chasers
Crew: 2 officers, 47 enlisted (orig.: 450 tot., incl. 55 marines and 3 "boys")

Remarks: Remains in commission. Wooden construction. First went to sea 22- Three masts: 28.7, 31.7, and 24.7 m high. Sail area: 3,968 m. Remains docked at Boston Navy Yard except for once-yearly "turnaround" to prevent warpage. nated IX 21 from 8-12-41 to 1-9-75, and bore name *Old Constitution* from 1917 t

CHARTERED RESEARCH AND TRIALS SUPPORT VESSEL

◆ **1 chartered tethered submersible tender**
Bldr: Halter Marine, Moss Point, Mississippi (In serv. 1981)

Marsea Fifteen

Marsea Fifteen—at San Diego at NOSC George R. Schneider, Jr

D: approx. 1,250 tons (fl) **S:** 12 kts
Dim: 54.87 (50.60 pp) × 12.20 × 3.60
Electron Equipt: Radar: . . .
M: 2 Caterpillar D399-PCTA-SCAC 16-cyl. diesels; 2 props; 2,250
Range: 2,880/12 **Fuel:** 241 tons **Electric:** 270-kw tot.
Crew: 16 tot.

Remarks: 283 grt/192 dwt. Former oilfield supply tug converted to support water research in 1988 at Escatawpa, Mississippi, and chartered by Naval Systems Command, San Diego, as tender to the ATV tethered submersible a AUSS autonomous submersible. Sister *Lake Guardian* (ex-*Marsea Fourteen*) op for the Environmental Protection Agency.

TERED RESEARCH AND TRIALS SUPPORT VESSELS
ued)

ubmersible tender
r: North American SB, Inc., Larose, Louisiana

CHOUEST (In serv. 1985)

Chouest—red hull, cream upperworks
George R. Schneider, Jr., 9-91

pprox. 2,600 tons (fl) **S:** 16 kts
: 71.33 (64.85 pp) × 15.24 × 4.33
tron Equipt: Radar: . . .
3 G.M. EMD 16-645-E7B diesels; 3 props; 9,210 bhp—3 side-thrusters
tric: 900 kw (3 × 300 kw) **Fuel:** 326 tons **Crew:** . . .

ks: 497 grt/1,200 dwt former oilfield support tug chartered 10-88 from her r, Edison Chouest Offshore, Inc., to act as tender to submersibles DSV 3 and at San Diego. Ice-strengthened hull. Lease renewed 9-91 and Caley Hydraulics e crane and a new hangar for submersibles added, in addition to a long-baseline c tracking system and a SeaBeam seafloor bathymetric mapping sonar. Em-summer 1992 for survey of World War II naval shipwrecks in Southwest Pacific

escue submersible tender
r: North American SB Co., Galliano, Louisiana (In serv. 1978)

ES CHOUEST

es Chouest
George R. Schneider, Jr., 9-90

approx. 1,600 tons (fl) **S:** 13 kts
: . . . (54.87 pp) × 12.20 × 3.64
ctron Equipt: Radar: . . .
2 Caterpillar D399-SCAC diesels; 2 CP props; 2,250 bhp
l: 148.5 tons **Crew:** . . .

rks: 199-grt former oilfield supply tug on charter to support the rescue sub-le *Mystic* (DSRV 1) and based at Naval Air Station, North Island, San Diego, nia.

ubmersible trials support tenders
r: Ulstein Hatlo A/S, Ulsteinvik, Norway (In serv. 1974)

CHOUEST (ex-*Far Comet*, ex-*Tender Comet*)
CHOUEST (ex-*Far Clipper*, ex-*Tender Clipper*)

approx. 3,900 tons (fl) **S:** 13.75 kts
: 80.78 (76.21 pp) × 18.04 × 4.32
ctron Equipt: Radar: . . .
2 Atlas-MaK 6M453AK diesels; 2 CP props; 4,000 bhp
ctric: *Amy Chouest:* 2,666-kw tot. (2 × 808 kw, 2 × 400 kw, 1 × 250 kw)
Cory Chouest: 2,350-kw tot. (2 × 800 kw, 3 × 250 kw)
nge: *Amy Chouest:* . . ./. . .; *Cory Chouest:* 5,940/13.75
el: *Amy Chouest:* 1,268 tons; *Cory Chouest:* 265 tons
ew: *Amy Chouest:* 16 tot. + 30 spare accommodations

rks: *Amy Chouest,* a 1,597-grt/1,800-dwt former oilfield deck cargo/pipe carrier ted into a diving support, fire-fighting, and pollution-control vessel, was char-9-90 for 17 months (with two 12-month extension options) from Alpha Marine es, Galliano, Louisiana, for acoustic research trials work; the ship has one , one 15-ton, and one 5-ton cranes. The very similar *Cory Chouest* was chartered 91 from the same owner and on similar conditions.

◆ **1 chartered torpedo and sonobuoy trials craft** Bldr: . . .

SEACOR RANGER (ex-.NUSC *Ranger,* ex-. . .)

Seacor Ranger Dr. Giorgio Arra, 11-88

D: . . . **S:** 12 kts **Dim:** 58.52 × . . . × 4.27
M: 2 diesels; 2 props; . . . bhp **Range:** 8,600/12

Remarks: Chartered from, and operated by, Seacor/MSO, Inc., for the Naval Undersea Systems Center, Tudor Hill, Bermuda. Replaced IX 306 (ex-U.S. Army FS 221) as a torpedo trials craft.

DEEP-SUBMERGENCE RESEARCH CRAFT

◆ **1 nuclear-powered research submarine for deep diving**

	Bldr	Laid down	L	In serv.
NR-1	General Dynamics, Groton, Conn.	10-6-67	25-1-69	27-10-69

NR-1 U.S. Navy

D: 372 tons surfaced/700 submerged **S:** 4.6/3.6 kts
Dim: 41.78 × 3.81 × 4.57
M: 1 pressurized-water reactor, turboelectric drive; 2 props
Crew: 2 officers, 3 enlisted, 2 scientists

Remarks: Project approved 18-4-65, and the ship funded under Fiscal Year 1966. Fitted for all oceanographic missions, military and civilian, and for bottom salvage. Thick cylindrical hull. Wheels for moving on ocean bottom. A very successful vehicle, but cost three times the original estimate. No periscope, uses television cameras. Four ducted maneuvering thrusters. Can dive to over 800 m. Now operates from New London, Connecticut.

◆ **2 DSRV-class rescue submersibles**
Bldr: Lockheed Missile & Space Co., Sunnyvale, Calif.

	In serv.	Accepted
DSRV 1 MYSTIC	6-8-71	4-11-77
DSRV 2 AVALON	28-7-72	1-1-78

Avalon (DSRV 2)—aboard *William H. Bates* (SSN 680)
Dr. Giorgio Arra, 1985

D: 30.5 tons (37 sub.) **S:** 4.5 kts **Dim:** 15.0 × 2.5 × 3.28 (high)
M: 1 electric motor; 1 shrouded pivoting prop; 15 shp
Crew: 4 tot. + 24 rescued personnel

Remarks: The DSRVs are intended to: operate at a maximum depth of 1,500 m; stand pressure equal to 2,750 m; dive and rise at 30 m a minute; make a maximum speed of 5 knots while submerged; remain submerged for 30 hours at 3 knots; maintain station in a 1-knot current; and operate all machinery even while submerged at a 45-degree angle. Motor, powered by a silver-zinc battery, turns a regular propulsion propeller and two thrusters, one forward and one aft, which can be positioned to permit a close approach to a sunken object. Their size and weight were determined by the possible

DEEP-SUBMERGENCE RESEARCH CRAFT *(continued)*

need to airlift them in an air force Lockheed C-141 Starlifter cargo plane. Additional equipment, especially a truck transport for the DSRV, would be carried in a second Starlifter. In addition, SSNs have received the equipment necessary to fasten a DSRV to their decks and carry it at 15 knots. The SSN then serves as a base for the DSRV while it awaits the arrival of a *Pigeon*-class rescue ship (ASR). Hull consists of two HY-140 steel spheres surrounded by a fiberglass outer hull. One received a potassium superoxide (KO) breathing system in 1982, providing 480 man hours submerged endurance. A cost overrun of nearly 1,500 percent prevented the procurement of any more DSRVs. Twelve were originally planned. Names were assigned in 1977. DSRV 1 is based at North Island, San Diego, California, assisted by the chartered tender *Dolores Chouest*; DSRV 2 is kept on the U.S. East Coast.

♦ 2 Turtle-class research submersibles

Bldr: General Dynamics, Groton, Conn.

DSV 3 Turtle (ex-*Autec-II*) DSV 4 Sea Cliff (ex-*Autec-I*)

Turtle (DSV 3) George R. Schneider, Jr., 4-91

D: 21 tons (*Sea Cliff:* 29) **S:** 2 kts
Dim: 7.9 (*Sea Cliff:* 9.4) × 2.4 (3.7 over thrusters)
M: 1 electric motor; 1 prop; 2 thrusters
Crew: 2 men + 1 scientist **Endurance:** 16 hrs.

Remarks: Launched on 11-12-68. Could originally descend to 1,980 m. Spherical pressure hull of HY-100 steel. The *Turtle* was modified in 1979 to descend to 3,660 meters, and the *Sea Cliff* received a titanium pressure sphere in 1981–84, permitting 6,100-m descents. Air transportable. Fitted with external manipulator arms. Eight hours' endurance at 1 knot. Operated by Submarine Development Group 1, San Diego. *Sea Cliff* dove to 6,096 m on 10-3-85, supported by *Point Loma* (AGDS 2). *Turtle* had a serious fire 17-8-84 and was still in repair at end-1985. The 77-meter support craft *Laney Chouest* was chartered 1987 as tender to DSV 3 and 4 (see earlier page for characteristics). DSV 3 became entangled in cable 8-11-89 but escaped; on 6-12-91, the craft was used to recover the remotely controlled submersible CURV III, which had sunk in 7,200 ft. of water off Los Angeles on 1-7-91 (CURV III was delivered in 1990 by Eastport International, Upper Marlboro, Maryland).

♦ 1 Alvin-class research submersible

Bldr: General Mills, Minneapolis, Minn. (In serv. 1965)

DSV 2 Alvin

D: 16 tons **S:** 2 kts **Dim:** 6.9 × 2.4 × . . .
M: electric motors; 1 prop; 2 thrusters **Crew:** 1 + 2 scientists

Remarks: Operated by civilian Woods Hole Oceanographic Institute on contract to the navy. Sank on 16-10-68, but raised, repaired, and returned to service in 11-72. Single titanium pressure sphere permits descents to 4,000 m. Supported by the Woods Hole Institute research ship *Atlantis II*. Made 2,000th dive 22-3-88. *Trieste II* (DSV 1) was stricken 1-4-85. *Nemo* (DSV 5) is a remote-controlled vehicle, now on display at the Naval Ocean Systems Center, San Diego.

SMALLCRAFT

In addition to the above yard and service craft, there are over 3,000 craft carried as "floating equipment." These range in size from the Naval Academy's rowing shells through the 2,780-ton *Seacon* described earlier and include all ships' boats and independent landing craft. Most of the more significant units are identified by a numbering system that begins with digits signifying the craft's length to the nearest foot, followed by an alphabetical designator indicating the craft's type, two digits indicating the fiscal year in which the craft was authorized, and subsequent digits indicating *which* craft of that year, i.e., "65PB778" is the eighth 65-ft patrol boat built under FY 77. *Unofficial* names and hull numbers are in widespread use.

Below are described some of the more significant and/or recent independent craft operated by the U.S. Navy.

♦ 2 torpedo retriever conversions

180NS9201 Hunter (ex-*Crystal Pelham*)
180NS9202 Hugo (ex-*Nola Pelham*)

Remarks: 298-grt, 54.9-meter former oilfield supply tugs converted by Leevac Shipyard as replacements for TWR 824 and TWR 831. Delivered 3-7-91. No data available.

♦ 8 TWR 821-class torpedo retrievers

	Laid down	L	In serv.
TWR 821 (120 TR 821)	. . .	17-10-84	4-11-85
TWR 822 (120 TR 822)	7-4-84	18-10-84	20-11-85
TWR 823 (120 TR 823)	22-8-84	4-5-85	6-12-85
TWR 825 (120 TR 825)	18-2-85	8-8-85	6-12-85
TWR 832 (120 TR 832)	10-5-85	22-3-86	3-7-86
TWR 833 (120 TR 833)	28-5-85	4-4-86	3-7-86
TWR 841 (120 TR 841)	2-8-85	15-8-86	18-10-86
TWR 842 (120 TR 842)	23-8-85	22-9-86	24-12-86

Swamp Fox (TWR 821) Dr. Giorgio Arr

D: 174 tons (213 fl) **S:** 16 kts **Dim:** 36.58 × 7.62 × 3.65
Electron Equipt: Radar: 1/LN-66 nav.
M: 2 Caterpillar D 3512 diesels; 2 props; 2,350 bhp
Electric: 128 kw **Range:** 1,700/16 **Fuel:** 28 tons
Endurance: 7 days **Crew:** 1 officer, 14 enlisted

Remarks: First five ordered 8-7-83 for delivery 15-12-84 to 15-3-85; three n dered 10-83, all for delivery 7-85; two ordered 2-85 for delivery 6-86. However, p was behind schedule, and first not accepted until 11-85; four more accepted 12-8 ramp and electro-hydraulic crane aft. Can carry 14 Mk 48 torpedoes. Have 4 permanent ballast! Congress halted further procurement, 1985. TWR 824 an 831 were irreparably destroyed during Hurricane Hugo at Roosevelt Roads, Rico. The survivors operate on West Coast, except for two (painted white) AUTEC range in the Bahamas. TWR 821 is named *Swamp Fox*.

♦ 7 modified patrol-boat-design torpedo retrievers

Bldr: Pet Bldrs., Sturgeon Bay, Wisc. (In serv. 1969–70)

TWR 1 Diamond	TWR 6 Ferret	TWR 681 Labrador
TWR 2	TWR 771 Phoenix	TWR 682 Crayfish
TWR 3 Condor		

Diamond (TWR 1) Dr. Giorgio Arra

D: 110 tons light (162 fl) **S:** 17 kts **Dim:** 31.09 × 6.40 × 2.36
Electron Equipt: Radar: 1/LN-66 nav.
M: 4 G.M. 12V149 diesels; 2 props; 2,000 bhp
Electric: 60 kw (2 × 30 kw) **Range:** 1,920/10 **Fuel:** 27 tons
Crew: 1 officer, 13 enlisted

Remarks: Design based on PGM 59-class patrol boat. Ramp at stern. Stowag tons of recovered ordnance. Maximum displacement without torpedoes is 149 t 771 (100TR771) serves the AUTEC range in the Bahamas.

♦ 2 85-ft torpedo retrievers

Bldr: Tacoma Boat, Tacoma, Wash. (In serv. 1975–76)

TWR 7 Chaparral TWR 8 Iliwai

.LLCRAFT *(continued)*

.i (TWR 8) OS2 John Bouvia, USN, 1990

. . . **S:** 18 kts **Dim:** 25.9 × . . . × . . .
.ctron Equipt: Radar: 1/LN-66 nav.
4 G.M. diesels; 2 props; . . . bhp **Crew:** . . .

.rks: Aluminum construction. TWR 7 is at San Diego.

65-ft torpedo retrievers Bldr: . . . (In serv. 10-67 to 7-68)

671	65TR674 . . . .
672	65TR675 HARRIER (TR 5)
.673	65TR676 PEREGRINE (TR 6)

.ier (TR 5) Dr. Giorgio Arra, 1989

34.8 tons (35.2 fl) **S:** 18.7 kts **Dim:** 22.17 × 5.18 × 1.68
.ectron Equipt: Radar: 1/. . .
2 G.M. 12V71 diesels; 2 props; 1,008 bhp (800 sust.)
.nge: 280/18 **Electric:** 10 kw **Crew:** 6 tot.

.arks: Aluminum construction. Can recover up to 5 tons of weapons (3 torpedoes). .n use is near-sister 65AR 681, completed in 11-69 as a general utility craft.

.iever (3)—a 33.5 weapons recovery craft; no data available
Dr. Giorgio Arra, 4-91

Cove-class training craft, former minesweeper
.dr: Bethlehem SY, Bellingham, Washington

	Laid down	L	In serv.
C841 CAPE (ex-MSI 2)	1-5-57	5-4-58	27-2-59

203 tons (239 fl) **S:** 12.5 kts **Dim:** 34.06 × 7.14 × 2.4
.ectron Equipt: Radar: 1/. . . nav.
4 G.M. 6-71 diesels; 2 props; 960 bhp **Electric:** 120 kw
.nge: 1,000/9 **Fuel:** 20 tons **Crew:** 20 tot.

Remarks: Wooden-hulled inshore minesweeper relegated to Naval Reserve training 31-7-70 and now employed as a training craft at the Naval Submarine Base, Bangor, Washington. Sisters built for Iran and Turkey.

Cape (110TC841) Victor M. Baca, 1988

◆ **3 95-ft. utility boats** Bldr: U.S. Coast Guard Yard, Curtis Bay, Md.

	In serv. (U.S.C.G.)
95NS8601 HM 20 (ex-*Cape Jellison,* WPB 95317)	7-9-55
95NS8801 VENTURE (ex-*Cape Wash,* WPB 95310)	15-12-53
95NS8901 (ex-*Cape Romain,* WPB 95319)	11-10-55

D: 87 tons (106 fl) **S:** 18 kts **Dim:** 28.96 × 6.1 × 1.55
Electron Equipt: Radar: 1/SPS-64(V)1 nav.
M: 4 Cummins VT-12-M-700 diesels; 2 props; 2,324 bhp
Electric: 40 kw **Range:** 570/20; 1,300/9 **Crew:** 6–8 tot.

Remarks: Former U.S. Coast Guard "Cape"-class cutters. HM 20 stricken 12-12-86 and transferred to Navy Pacific Missile Test Center, Port Hueneme, Cal., as a range safety craft. *Venture* stricken 1-6-87 and transferred to the U.S. Navy for use at the Naval Submarine Base, Bangor, Washington. 95NS8901 stricken 11-8-89 and transferred to navy for use as a pilot boat at San Diego. Sister *Vanguard* (ex-*Cape Hedge,* WPB 95311) returned to coast guard for transfer to Mexico, 1-90.

Note: Former maneuvering training craft *Knowledge* (UB 761), *Confidence* (UB 762), *Diligence* (UB 763), *Perseverance* (UB 764), and the unnamed UB 765, all formerly employed at the Surface Warfare Officers School, Coronado, were transferred to the Naval Station, Panama Canal, as patrol and utility boats in late 1987 as YP 654-class training boats began arriving to replace them; UB 761–765 were formerly MSB 7, 13, 17, 35, and 50.

◆ **2 pilot boats, former patrol boats**
Bldr: Sewart Seacraft, Berwick, La. (In serv. 1973)

65PB721 65PB722

722—at Charleston, South Carolina Dr. Giorgio Arra, 2-89

D: 27 tons (36.3 fl) **S:** 20 kts **Dim:** 19.78 × 5.25 × 1.37
A: provision for 2/12.7-mm mg (II × 1)
Electron Equipt: Radar: 2/. . . nav.
M: 2 G.M. 12V71 diesels; 2 props; 1,200 bhp

Remarks: Former patrol boats, Mk 1. Originally carried 2/20-mm AA (I × 2), 4/12.7-mm mg (II × 1, I × 2). 65PB722 is pilot boat at Charleston, South Carolina.

◆ **1 or more 64-ft Distribution Box (L Type) Boats**

D: 72.3 tons (fl) **S:** 9.5 kts **Dim:** 19.58 × 5.72 × 1.83
Electron Equipt: Radar: 1/. . . nav.
M: 1 G.M. Detroit 64HN11 diesel; 1 prop; 165 bhp
Range: 110/9.5

SMALLCRAFT *(continued)*

C-6977—at Norfolk, Va. George R. Schneider, Jr., 8-89

Remarks: Originally built to set and recover mine distribution boxes for controlled minefields. Have 2.5-ton crane forward.

◆ **8 Navy-44-class sail-training cutters** Bldr: Tillotson-Pearson, Inc., Warren, R.I. (In serv. 1987–89)

NA-1 AUDACIOUS NA-4 VALIANT NA-7 DAUNTLESS
NA-2 COURAGEOUS NA-5 ACTIVE NA-8 FEARLESS
NA-3 INVINCIBLE NA-6 ALERT

Dauntless (NA 7) William E. Brooks III, 1991

D: 12.65 tons (fl) **S:** . . . **Dim:** 13.41 (10.52 wl) × 3.78 × 2.21
M: 1 auxiliary diesel; 33 bhp **Crew:** 10 midshipmen

Remarks: First 8 ordered 3-87, with options for 20 more, not taken up. NA-1 delivered 21-5-87 for extensive trials; NA-2–8 delivered spring 1988. GRP construction; 88 m^2 sail area. Intended to replace Naval Academy's 12 Luders yawls and 18 miscellaneous donated craft used for midshipman training; the older boats in good condition are to be sent to universities with Naval Reserve Officer Training Centers. Designed by McCurdy and Rhodes, Inc. Naval Academy 18.3-m sailing craft *American Promise* sank 21-4-91 in Chesapeake Bay.

◆ **20 Mk II Dive Boats**
Bldr: Peterson Bldrs, Sturgeon Bay, Wisc. (In serv. 1986–90)

50DW8601–50DW8612 50DW8901–50DW 8908

D: 37.6 tons (fl) **S:** 9 kts **Dim:** 15.24 × 4.50 × 0.84
M: 1 diesel; . . . bhp **Crew:** 5 crew + . . . divers

Remarks: First 12 delivered 1986, 8 more ordered 1989.Carry a 5.0 × 3.7 × 2 11-ton diving module with compressors and decompression chamber. Can s divers to 58 m with Mk 12 diving gear.

◆ **119 50-ft workboats** Bldr: 52 by Marinette, Marinette, Wisc. (In se 1984 to 16-12-85) and 67 by Oregon Iron Works, Clackamas, Or. (In serv. 1987–89)

50WB841–8428 50WB851–8524
50WB861–8650 50WB871–8217

50-foot workboat Wilhelm Donko

D: . . . **S:** . . . **Dim:** 15.24 × 4.37 × 1.07
M: 2 G.M. 8V71 diesels; 2 props; . . . bhp

Remarks: Used for general-purpose workboats and as push-tugs. Steel constr First 28 ordered 2-84, 24 more in 11-84 from Marinette; 50 ordered 12-9-86 from (Iron Works, with 17 more ordered 11-88 (and an option for 64 more, which w taken up).

Note: As a measure of the number and variety of small craft in U.S. Navy servi following were to be acquired under FY 90 (not including craft listed elsewhere volume): 13 5.49-m GRP target boats, 15 7.32-m GRP boom-handling boats, 13 GRP Personnel Boats Mk 7, 16 10.06-m GRP Personnel Boats Mk 6, 3 10.67-r workboats, 1 12.19-m GRP utility boat, 2 12.50-m aluminum patrol boats, 2 1: aluminum personnel rescue boats, 8 (plus option for 5 more) 15.24-m GRP utility 8 17.10-m GRP target boats, 2 19.81-m aluminum Explosives Disposal Boats, 10 option for 200) Combat Rubber Raiding Craft, Large (CRRC(L)), 12 (plus option submersible recoverable craft (SRC), 4 (plus option for 3) High Speed Boats. Un 88, some 280 craft were approved, and 101 were requested under FY 89. The num such craft being ordered have declined markedly in the 1990s, however. A few many "floating equipment" service craft are illustrated below.

A contract was let with Hood Military Vessel Group, Rhode Island, in 19 10 26-ft. GRP-hulled motor whaleboats with a new hull design, with an option more; in 1992, there were over 1,200 26-ft. motor whaleboats in service aboard Other recent smallcraft acquisitions include a number of Boeing Aircraft Bar 7.30 × 2.74-m target boats, powered by a 300-hp diesel for 36-kt maximum sp 30 kts for 6 hours; two 10-m GRP-construction catamaran oilspill containmer toons for the Naval Facilities Engineering Command, Port Hueneme, Cal., from City Industries, Moss Point, Mississippi; and 6 18.28 × 9.75 Mexecell diving pla for use by underwater construction teams, from FBM Marine, Cowes, U.K.

Septar radio-controlled targets John Bouvia,

35NS831, a 35-ft (10.7-m) "cigarette boat" used as a chase boat at Lauderdale, Fla.; similar craft can be found at other USN ties Dr. Giorgio Arra,

.LCRAFT *(continued)*

utility boat 65UB841 Dr. Giorgio Arra, 8-89

an LCM(8) converted to serve as tender to the Naval Surface Warfare r detachment at Ft. Lauderdale, Fla.
Dr. Giorgio Arra, 1990

bearing her amphibious warfare hull number LCU 1614, this serves as tender to the Naval Air Development Center in Flor- See data under LCU 1610 class Dr. Giorgio Arra, 7-89

B 4—one of a large number of human waste holding-tank disposal es Peter C. Westdijk, 7-91

Ivan Ducky (652)—a self-propelled catamaran target that, when the rubber superstructure is inflated, resembles an Osa-class guided-missile patrol boat. George R. Schneider, Jr., 10-91

Mexecell divers' support pontoon barge FBM Marine

22UB8505 and 22UB8807—Boston Whaler "Outrage"-class 22-ft outboard launches George R. Schneider, Jr., 9-91

MILITARY SEALIFT COMMAND

The Military Sealift Command was founded 1-10-49 as the Military Sea Transportation Service and was given its current name on 1-8-70. It is headed by a flag officer of the U.S. Navy. Since 1-10-87, the MSC has been a component of the U.S. Transportation Command, which is headquartered at Scott Air Force Base in Illinois. Its ships are considered to be noncommissioned, and are manned by civilians (either government civil servants or contract personnel), although replenishment vessels and some research ships may have some navy personnel aboard. The prefix "T" is appended to the hull numbers of MSC ships.

The Military Sealift Command is also responsible for chartering ships for U.S. military support and for arranging for the shipping of military cargoes that travel by sea. During Operation Desrt Shield/Desert Storm, as many as 127 U.S.-flag and 293 foreign-flag merchant vessesl were on charter at one time.

In the following pages the government-owned units are listed and described in alphabetical order by ship type. Then MSC-chartered ships are described, in particular the ships of the Forward Deployment Logistics Force, the Near-Term Prepositioning Force, and, finally, the other ships on charter for cargo, tanker, scientific support, and fleet services duties.

MSC ships are now normally painted gray and have blue and gold-yellow stack bands; scientific ships are normally painted white, but more are appearing in gray paint schemes. Fleet support ships operated by MSC began to carry their hull numbers during late 1979; other MSC ships do *not* display hull numbers.

AMMUNITION SHIP (T-AE)

◆ **1 Kilauea class**

	Bldr	Laid down	L	In serv.
T-AE 26 Kilauea	Gen. Dynamics, Quincy	10-3-66	9-8-67	10-8-68

Kilauea (T-AE 26) John Bouvia, 1990

D: 17,937 tons (fl) **S:** 21 kts
Dim: 171.90 (164.59 pp) × 24.69 × 8.50 **A:** 2/12.7-mm mg
Electron Equipt:
Radar: 1/. . . nav., 1/SPS-10-series surf. search—TACAN: URN-25
M: 3 sets G.E. geared steam turbines; 1 prop; 36,661 shp
Boilers: 3 Foster-Wheeler; 42.3 kg/cm², 467°C
Electric: 3,000 kw tot. **Fuel:** 2,612 tons **Crew:** 121 MSC, 67 navy

Remarks: 18,257/8,593 dwt. Transferred to MSC 1-10-80; six sisters remain in regular navy. Can carry about 6,500 tons of munitions and has a hangar and flight deck for two UH-46E replenishment helicopters. Has seven underway replenishment stations, four to port and three to starboard. Can also refuel ships, using forward, starboard station. Navy personnel perform ammunition handling and operate the communications and helicopter. Superstructure filled in on starboard side to increase accommodations space. Unusual for MSC ship in being armed; operates in the Pacific. Other ships of the class may be transferred to the MSC during the mid-1990s.

STORES SHIP (T-AF)

◆ **1 Rigel class** (In reserve)

	Bldr	L	In serv.
T-AF 58 *Rigel*	Ingalls SB, Pascagoula, Miss.	15-3-55	2-9-55

Rigel (T-AF 58) George Nassiopoulos, 9-91

D: 9,696 tons light (15,540 fl) **S:** 20 kts
Dim: 152.70 (144.78 pp) × 21.95 × 8.80
Electron Equipt:
Radar: 1/Raytheon 1650/CX nav., 1/SPS-10 surf. search
M: 2 sets de Laval geared steam turbines; 1 prop; 16,000 shp
Boilers: 2 Combustion Engineering; 42.2 kg/cm², 440°C
Electric: 2,250 kw tot. (3 × 750 kw) **Range:** 10,000/21; 15,000/15
Crew: 16 officers, 97 unlicensed MSC, + 67 navy

Remarks: 10,781 grt/8,112 dwt. Six holds with 5.9 × 5.9 hatches, twelve 3-ton booms. Cargo: 5,975 m³ dry, 5,400 m³ refrigerated. Has helicopter platform aft, no hangar. Transferred to MSC 23-6-75 and disarmed. Provides fleet support. Satellite communications equipment carried. Operated in Atlantic area 14-9-92.

COMBAT STORES SHIPS (T-AFS)

◆ **3 British Lyness-class combat stores ships** Bldrs: Swan Hunter & Wigham Richardson, Wallsend-on-Tyne, U.K.

	Laid down	L	In serv.
T-AFS 8 Sirius (ex-*Lyness*)	4-65	7-4-66	22-12-66
T-AFS 9 Spica (ex-*Tarbatness*)	4-66	22-2-67	10-8-67
T-AFS 10 Saturn (ex-*Stromness*)	10-65	16-9-66	21-3-67

D: 9,010 tons light (16,792 fl) **S:** 19 kts
Dim: 159.52 (149.35 pp) × 22.0 × 7.77
Electron Equipt: Radar: 2/. . . nav.—TACAN: URN-25
M: 1 Sulzer 8RD76 diesel; 1 prop; 12,700 bhp
Electric: 3,575 kw tot. **Range:** 11,000/19; 27,500/12
Fuel: 1,310 tons heavy oil, 264 tons diesel
Crew: 110–125 MSC, 40–45 navy, + 27 navy helo detachment

Remarks: 12,358 grt/4,744 nrt. T-AFS 8 was leased from Great Britain on 17-1-81 for one year for use in the Mediterranean and was to be purchased outright 1-3-82; T-AFS 9, which had been in reserve at Gibraltar, was leased 30-9-81 and was purchased

Sirius (T-AFS 8) George Nassiopoulos

Saturn (T-AFS 10) Leo Van Ginderen

30-9-82. An agreement to purchase T-AFS 10 was made on 27-1-83, and th arrived at Bayonne, New Jersey, 4-83 awaiting purchase under the FY 84 b 13-12-83; T-AFS 10 was modernized under FY 85 with improved helicopter faci improved communications, five STREAM transfer stations, an automated data fa and conversion to use U.S. Navy fuel. T-AFS 8 completed a similar upgrading 1 and T-AFS 9 by 1986; all three can accommodate 2 UH-46E helicopters. Heli deck aft 33.5 × 18.3. Have four holds, with 15 levels, 8 stores elevators. Total volume: 12,234 m (8,313 m dry stores, 3,921 m refrigerated/frozen). Cranes: 1/2 2/12.5-ton, 1/12-ton, and 2/5-ton. Carry 40,000 different repair parts and can s 15,000 people at sea for one month. Accommodations for 193 total; in 1-90, T- carried 25 licensed and 100 unlicensed MSC mariners, plus 5 navy officers a enlisted. Very successful, comfortable ships—a useful bargain.

Note: *Mars*-class naval supply ships will begin to be resubordinated to the M Sealift Command during the mid-1990s.

MISCELLANEOUS RESEARCH SHIPS (T-AG)

◆ **1 sound trials ship (SCB 726 type)** Bldr: Todd SY, Seattle

	Laid down	L	In serv.
T-AG 195 Hayes (ex-T-AGOR 16)	12-11-69	2-7-70	21-7-71

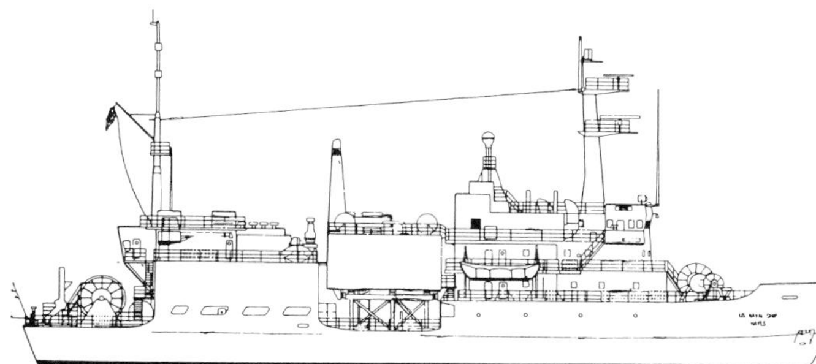

Hayes (T-AG 195)—as converted U.S. Navy

D: 4,037 tons (fl) **S:** 12 kts **Dim:** 75.10 (67.06 pp) × 22.86 × 6.7
Electron Equipt:
Radar: 1/Raytheon TM 1650/6X nav., 1/Raytheon TM 1660/12S
Sonar: TUMS towed sound-measurement array
M: diesel-electric drive: 3 Caterpillar 3516 diesels (1,410 bhp each) Kato 1,100-kw alternators, 2 Westinghouse motors; 2 props; 2,400 shp—2-165 shp low-speed motors
Electric: 640 kw (2 × Caterpillar 3412 diesels driving)
Range: 6,000/12 **Endurance:** 30 days
Crew: 10 officers, 26 unlicensed MSC crew + 29 technicians

Remarks: Catamaran, with each hull of 7.3 m. Was not a success as an oceanog research platform, suffering from excessive pitching. Had been laid up since 1 Bayonne, N.J., and was transferred from the Oceanographer of the Navy to the Ships Research and Development Center in 1983 awaiting conversion. Was converted 8-7-87 to 12-90 by Tacoma Boat, Tacoma, Wash., as sound trials vessel FY 86 Budget to replace *Monob One* (YAG 61). Bankruptcy of the conversion y 11-90 caused the ship to be towed to the Puget Sound Naval Shipyard, Brem where a new conversion contract was placed on 25-3-91 and the work comple 19-6-92.

Transports, deploys, and retrieves acoustic arrays in support of the Submarine Reduction Program. Has 371.6 m² laboratory space. Re-engined, with origin high-speed diesels driving controllable-pitch props being replaced by a diesel-e

ELLANEOUS RESEARCH SHIPS (T-AG) *(continued)*

with fixed-pitch props that are cavitation-free to 10 kts. New propulsion plant is ded in a vibration-damping compartment above deck, along with two Caar 3412 diesel generator sets.

Vanguard class Bldr: Marine Ship Corp., Sausalito, Cal.

	L	In serv.
194 VANGUARD (ex-T-AGM 19, ex-*Muscle als*, ex-*Mission San Fernando*, T-AO 122)	23-11-43	21-10-47

uard (T-AG 194) Dr. Giorgio Arra, 4-91

21,478 tons (fl) **S:** 16 kts **Dim:** 181.4 × 22.9 × 7.6
ctron Equipt:
adar: 1/Raytheon 1650/9X nav., 1/Raytheon 1660/12S nav.
2 sets G.E. geared steam turbines, electric drive; 1 prop; 8,700 shp
lers: 2 Babcock & Wilcox "D"; 42.3 kg/cm², 440°C
nge: 27,000/16 **Fuel:** 3,995 tons
w: 86 MSC, 34 navy, 40 contract technicians

rks: 16,060 grt/16,255 dwt.; *Vanguard* was converted 1964–66 from a T2-SE-e tanker to a tracking and communications ship to support NASA manned space . Reclassified 30-9-80 as T-AG 194 while under conversion to replace *Compass* (AG 153) as ballistic-missile submarine navigational system trials ship for the Strategic Systems Project Office. Conversion commenced 1-4-80 at Todd Ship-San Pedro, Cal. Appearance similar to *Redstone* (T-AGM 20) but without track-dars. Has a MARISAT satellite communications facility. Trials with a ring-laser or navigation began 4-85.

P SUBMERGENCE SUPPORT SHIP (T-AGDS)

auxiliary deep-submergence support ship
dr: Maryland SB & DD, Baltimore, Maryland

	L	In serv.
DS 2 POINT LOMA (ex-*Point Barrow*, T-AKD 1)	25-5-57	28-2-58

t Loma (T-AGDS 2) Leo Van Ginderen, 7-90

8,000 tons light (12,430 fl) **S:** 12 kts
n: 150.0 (144.8 pp) × 22.6 × 5.8
ctron Equipt: Radar: 1/SPS-53 nav., 1/SPS-10 surf. search
2 sets Westinghouse geared steam turbines; 2 props; 6,000 shp—2/WP1700 Omnithrusters; 6,000 hp
ilers: 2 Foster-Wheeler; 32 kg/cm², 400°C **Range:** 8,800/10
ew: 12 officers, 15 unlicensed MSC + 6 officers, 12 enlisted navy + 29 contract technicians

arks: Maritime Commission S2-ST-23A design. Built for Arctic supply and cond like a landing ship, dock (LSD). Served in MSC until 28-9-72, when placed in ve. Transferred to the navy on 28-2-74, renamed, renumbered, and reactivated as der for deep-submergence vehicles, recommissioning 30-4-75. Operates from San . Four "Golf Ball" geodesic radomes on deckhouses on bow. Can carry 275 tons of ine as flotation liquid for submersibles. Two cranes. Second stack added for -generator exhausts. Transferred to MSC 1-10-86. Now operates primarily in rt of the Pacific Missile Test Center Trident strategic-missile launch program.

FRIGATE RESEARCH SHIP (AGFF)

◆ **1 former experimental escort ship (SCB 198 type)**

	Bldr	Laid down	L	In serv.
AGFF 1 GLOVER (ex-FF 1098, ex-AGFF 1, ex-AGDE 1, ex-AG 163)	Bath Iron Works	29-7-63	17-4-65	13-11-65

Glover (AGFF 1) Dr. Giorgio Arra, 2-91

D: 2,700 tons (3,630 fl) **S:** 27 kts
Dim: 126.33 (121.9 wl) × 13.47 × 7.9 (over sonar) **A:** removed
Electron Equipt:
Radar: 1/LN-66 nav., 1/SPS-10F surf. search, 1/SPS-40B air search
Sonar: LFA hull-mounted, UBQ-5 wide-aperture hull array, Martin-Marietta RMES towed array
EW: WLR-1H intercept, ULQ-6 jammer
M: 1 set Westinghouse geared steam turbines; 1 prop; 35,000 shp
Boilers: 2 Foster-Wheeler; 83.4 kg/cm, 510°C
Electric: 2,000 kw tot. **Range:** 4,000/20 **Fuel:** 600 tons
Crew: 79 tot. MSC civilian mariners, 22 navy detachment

Remarks: Authorized FY 61. Redesignated from AGFF 1 to FF 1098 on 1-10-79 because she was being employed on operational cruises. "FF 1098" was previously used for a later-canceled *Knox*-class frigate. Transferred to Military Sealift Command on 15-6-90 and disarmed for further use as a sonar system trials ship. Refitted beginning 4-91. To be laid up at end of Fiscal Year 1992 (30-9-92).

Basically a *Garcia*-class ship with identical hull form, but with a pump-jet propeller and the after 127-mm gun omitted to provide laboratories and accommodations for civilian technicians. Extreme stern raised during installation of SQS-35 VDS, which has now been replaced by the Martin-Marietta Reconfigurable Multiline Evaluation System volumetric multi-array towed linear hydrophone array. All armament has been removed; the forward gunhouse has been retained as partial weight compensation.

RANGE INSTRUMENTATION SHIPS (T-AGM)

◆ **1 Mariner class**

	Bldr	L	In serv.
T-AGM 23 OBSERVATION ISLAND (ex-AG 154, ex-YAG 53, ex-*Empire State Mariner*)	New York SB, Camden, N.J.	15-8-53	5-12-53

Observation Island (T-AGM 23) John Bouvia, 1990

D: 16,076 tons (fl) **S:** 20 kts
Dim: 171.81 (161.09 pp) × 23.16 × 8.34
Electron Equipt:
Radar: 1/Raytheon 1650/9X nav., 1/Raytheon 1660/12S nav., 1/SPQ-11 tracking, 1/. . . tracking
TACAN: URN-25
M: 2 sets G.E. geared steam turbines; 1 prop; 19,251 shp—2/WP 1700 Omnithrusters; 6,000 hp
Boilers: 2 Combustion Engineering, 42.3 kg/cm², 467°C
Range: 17,000/13 **Fuel:** 2,652 tons
Crew: 78 MSC + 60–65 technicians

Remarks: 14,029 grt/6,322 nrt. Begun as a seven-hold cargo ship. Acquired by the navy on 10-9-56; used for Polaris and Poseidon missile trials until placed in reserve on 29-9-72. Reclassified T-AGM 23 on 1-5-79. Converted between 7-79 and 4-81 to carry Cobra Judy (SPQ-11) missile-tracking, trainable phased-array radar aft. Two large parabolic collection antennas in geodesic radomes atop bridge. Operated for the U.S.

RANGE INSTRUMENTATION SHIPS (T-AGM) *(continued)*

Air Force in the Pacific. Painted white. Refitted 10-84 to 3-85 by Northwest Marine, Portland, Ore., with a new foremast, heightened stacks, three new turbogenerator sets, new deckhouses, two new evaporators, and upgraded electronics (including an added X-band tracking radar abaft the stack).

◆ **1 converted Haskell-class attack transport** Bldr: Permanente Metals, Richmond, Cal.

	L	In serv.
T-AGM 22 RANGE SENTINEL (ex-*Sherburne*, APA 205)	10-7-44	20-9-44

Range Sentinel (T-AGM 22) Dr. Giorgio Arra, 11-89

D: 11,860 tons (fl) **S:** 15.5 kts **Dim:** 138.7 × 18.9 × 8.8
Electron Equipt:
Radar: 1/Raytheon TM 1650/9X nav., 1/Raytheon TM 1660/12S nav., 1/SPQ-7 tracking, 3/other tracking
M: 2 sets Westinghouse geared steam turbines; 1 prop; 8,500 shp
Boilers: 2 Combustion Engineering, 37 kg/cm^2, 399°C
Range: 10,000/15.5 **Fuel:** 1,197 tons
Crew: 14 officers, 54 unlicensed, 27 technicians

Remarks: 8,306 grt/5,301 dwt. Converted between 10-69 and 14-10-71 as support ship for the Poseidon (and later, Trident) program. Reclassified T-AGM 22 on 14-10-71. VC2-S-AP 5 Victory-type cargo-ship hull and propulsion. Operates from Port Canaveral, Florida, for the Atlantic Test Range.

◆ **1 Vanguard class** Bldr: Marine Ship, Sausalito, Cal.

	In serv.
T-AGM 20 REDSTONE (ex-*Johnstown*, ex-*Mission de Pala*, AO 114)	22-4-44

Redstone (T-AGM 20) Leo Van Ginderen, 5-90

D: 16,800 tons light (24,700 fl) **S:** 16 kts **Dim:** 181.4 × 22.9 × 7.6
Electron Equipt:
Radar: 1/Raytheon 1650/9X nav., 1/Raytheon 1660/12S nav.
M: 2 sets G.E. geared steam turbines, electric drive; 1 prop; 8,700 shp—bow-thruster
Boilers: 2 Babcock & Wilcox "D," 42.3 kg/cm^2, 440°C
Range: 27,000/16 **Fuel:** 3,995 tons
Crew: 19 officers, 71 unlicensed, 108 technicians

Remarks: 16,060 grt/16,255 dwt. Former T2-SE-A2-type tanker converted 1964–66 to serve as tracking and communications ship for NASA-manned space flights; 22 meters added amidships. Sister *Mercury* (T-AGM 21) stricken in 1969 after very little use, and sister *Vanguard* (T-AGM 19) redesignated T-AG in 1980. Two tracking radars, two large communications dish antennas, now all mounted in geodesic plastic radomes. Refitted under FY 87 Budget with new generators, bow-thruster, a retractable sonar, and a radiosonde balloon facility at the stern. Operates from Port Canaveral for the U.S. Air Force Eastern Space Missile Center, Patrick Air Force Base.

Note: *General H. H. Arnold* (T-AGM 9) was stricken and placed in the Maritime Commission National Defense Reserve Fleet on 23-2-82 and sold for scrap 25-10-82. Sister *General Hoyt S. Vandenberg* (T-AGM 10) was transferred to the MARAD NDRF on 8-2-83 and remains in storage in the James River in Virginia.

OCEANOGRAPHIC RESEARCH SHIPS (T-AGOR)

Note: *All* naval-owned oceanographic research ships are listed here, for conver sake; those without "T" before their hull numbers are operated by private orga tions, generally on naval-related research programs. Planned two 5,365-ton SW (Small Waterplane, Twin-Hull) oceanographic ships canceled after first was rejec Congress under FY 89; were to have been AGOR 24, 25. In future, all navy-ope ocean research ships are to be typed AGS, while university-operated ships will be AGOR—regardless of actual function. Five AGOR *conversions* listed for authoriz in FY 93–95 may instead become new-construction.

◆ **1 (+1+1) Thomas G. Thompson class**
Bldr: Trinity Marine Halter SY, Moss Point, Mississippi

	Laid down	L	In serv.
AGOR 23 THOMAS G. THOMPSON	29-3-89	27-7-90	8-7-91
AGOR 24 ROGER REVELLE	. . .	. . .	1994
AGOR 25	. . .	. . .	1997

Authorized: AGOR 23 in FY 88, AGOR 24 in FY 92; planned: AGOR FY 94

Thomas G. Thompson (AGOR 23) Trinity Marine

D: 2,100 tons light (3,250 fl) **S:** 15 kts **Dim:** 83.52 × 16.00 × 5.
Electron Equipt:
Radar: 2/. . . nav.—Sonar: Krupp-Atlas mapping, . . .
M: 6 Caterpillar diesels, electric drive; 2 Azimuth props; 6,000 shp 1,140-shp bow-thruster
Range: 12,000/12 **Endurance:** 60 days
Crew: 20 crew + 25 scientists (+10 in accommodations vans)

Remarks: First ship ordered 10-6-88, to replace AGOR 3, *Thomas G. Thomps* part of the UNOLS (University-National Laboratory System); bailed to the Univ of Washington on completion and is entirely civilian-operated. The second shi replace *Thomas Washington* (AGOR 10) for the Scripps Institute of Oceanograp Jolla, Cal. Third ship, if approved, will go to the Woods Hole Institute in Mass setts.

Has Dynamic Positioning System, accurate to 300 ft. in a 27-kt wind and 11-ft Has 372 m^2 laboratory space and space for four lab/accommodations vans on 325 m^2 working space on deck, stern A-frame and starboard oceanographic ga Markey DESH-9-11 double-drum waterfall winch. Capable of all-purpose o graphic research.

◆ **2 Gyre class (SCB 734 type)** Bldr: Halter Marine, New Orleans

	Laid down	L	In serv.
AGOR 21 GYRE	9-10-72	25-5-73	14-11-73
AGOR 22 MOANA WAVE	9-10-72	18-6-73	16-1-74

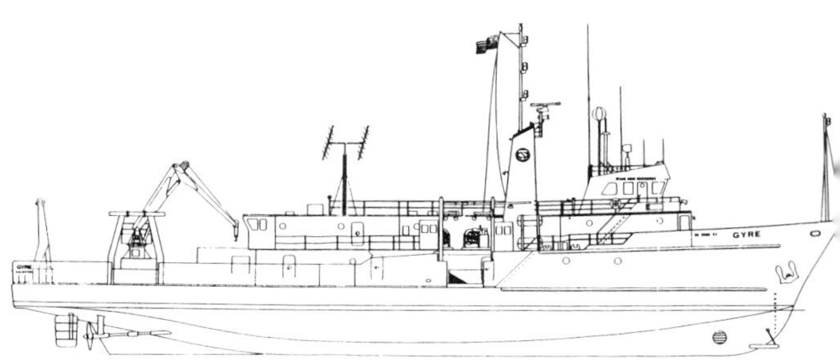

Gyre (AGOR 21) U.S.

D: AGOR 21: 946 tons light (1,190 fl); AGOR 22: . . . tons light (1,853 fl)
S: 11.8 (AGOR 22: 11.5) kts
Dim: 53.14 (AGOR 22: 64.92) × 11.05 × 3.05 (AGOR 22: 4.57 max.
Electron Equipt: Radar: 1/. . . nav.
Endurance: 40 days (AGOR 22: 50)
M: 2 Caterpillar diesels; 2 CP props; 1,700 bhp—170-hp bow-thrus
Range: 8,000/9.5 (AGOR 22: 12,000/10)
Fuel: 290 tons (AGOR 22: 418 tons)
Crew: 5 officers, 5 unlicensed, 19 scientists (AGOR 22: 4 officers, 9 unlicensed, 19 scientists)

Remarks: 294–298 grt. On completion, assigned to Texas A&M University an versity of Hawaii, respectively. Modified oil-field supply ships using modular

ANOGRAPHIC RESEARCH SHIPS (T-AGOR) *(continued)*

a Wave (AGOR 22) Leo Van Ginderen, 1991

ans on long, open fantail. AGOR 22 conducted trials 1979–84 with the satellite unications and towed passive sonar equipment for the T-AGOS program, under ct to the Naval Space Warfare Systems Command (SPAWAR); the SATCOMM a was mounted on a platform between the ship's paired stacks. In 1984–85, the as lengthened by Halter Marine at New Orleans and given a lengthened perma- eckhouse laboratory aft, plus facilities for two portable lab modules. AGOR 21 HY 600A computer, AGOR 22 a Nova 1220.

Melville class (SCB 710 type) Bldr: Defoe SB, Bay City, Mich.

	Laid down	L	In serv.	Modified
R 14 Melville	12-7-67	10-7-68	27-8-69	7-89 to 6-90
R 15 Knorr	9-8-67	21-8-68	14-1-70	11-88 to . . .

ille (AGOR 14)—prior to conversion Dr. Giorgio Arra, 5-89

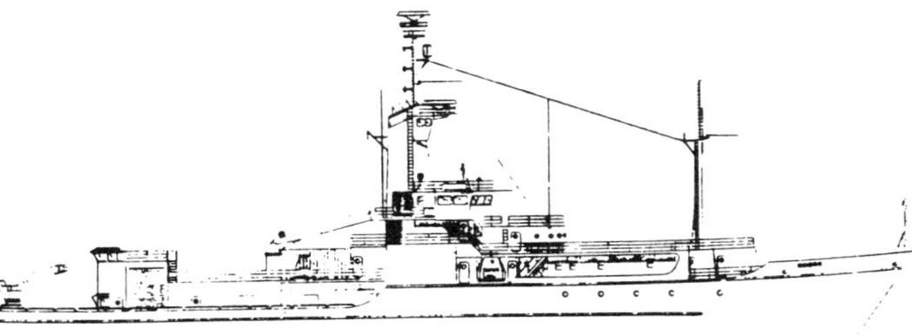

ille and Knorr—post-conversion U.S. Navy, 1989

2,670 tons fl **S:** 14 kts **Dim:** 85.0 × 14.1 × 4.57
4 diesel generator sets, electric drive; 3 Z-drive props (1 retractable forward); 3,000 shp
nge: 12,000/12 **Fuel:** 342 tons **Endurance:** 35–40 days
ew: 24 crew, 34 scientists

rks: 2,100 grt. Operated for the Office of Naval Research, AGOR 14 by Scripps ute, AGOR 15 by Woods Hole Oceanographic Institution. Contracts renewed 91 and 4-8-91, respectively. One vertical cycloidal propeller forward, larger unit ntended for precise maneuvering but, because mechanical rather than electric was used, proved troublesome. AGOR 19 and AGOR 20 of this class were there- anceled. AGOR 15 located the wreck of RMS *Titanic* on 1-9-85, using a new e-controlled submersible. AGOR 14 has 2 VAX-730 computers. Both were over- d and originally displaced only 1,915 tons (fl). New 10.36-m midbody added and have been re-engined, with troublesome cycloidal props replaced. Have 341.9-m^2 pace and 349.7-m^2 deck working space; accommodations were enlarged and the tific equipment updated.

◆ **3 Robert D. Conrad class (SCB 185 and 710* types)** Bldr: Northwest Marine, Portland, Ore. (AGOR 10: Marinette SB, Marinette, Wisc.)

	L	In serv.
AGOR 10 Thomas Washington	1-8-64	17-9-65
T-AGOR 12 De Steiguer*	3-6-66	28-2-69
T-AGOR 13 Bartlett*	24-3-66	15-4-69

Bartlett (T-AGOR 13)—in gray paint scheme Dr. Giorgio Arra, 12-91

De Steiguer (T-AGOR 12)—in white paint scheme David D. Broecker, 3-92

D: 1,088 tons light (1,643 fl) **S:** 13.5 kts
Dim: 63.7 (59.7 pp) × 11.4 × 4.9 (6.3 m max.) over sonar domes
Electron Equipt:
Radar: MSC units: 1/Raytheon 1650/SX nav., 1/Raytheon 1660/12S nav.
M: 2 Cummins diesels, electric drive; 1 prop; 1,000 shp—T-AGOR 12, 13 also: JT700 Omnithruster, 350 shp
Electric: 850 kw **Range:** varies: 9,000/12; 8,500/9.5 typical
Fuel: 211 tons **Endurance:** 45 days
Crew: MSC ships: 9 officers, 17 unlicensed, 15 scientists/technicians

Remarks: Navy units operated by MAR, Inc., Rockville, Md., under contract to MSC. AGOR 10 is assigned to the Scripps Institute of Oceanography, La Jolla, Cal. Displacements vary: AGOR 7: 1,643 fl; AGOR 9: 1,400 tons fl; AGOR 12 and 13: 1,643 tons fl. AGOR 10 has much longer forecastle than the others and has a blue-painted hull. Large stack contains 620-hp gas-turbine generator set used to drive main shaft at speed of up to 6.5 kts for experiments requiring "quiet" conditions. Also have retractable electric bow-thruster/propulsor, which provides up to 4.5 kts. AGOR 10 carries the Sea Beam bottom-contour mapping system. AGOR 10 was modernized 1981–84 with new oceanographic winches and cables to work to 4,000–5,000-m depths.

Near-sister *S.P. Lee* (ex-T-AG 192, ex-T-AGS 31) has been on loan to the Pacific Branch, U.S. Geological Survey since 27-2-74; near-sister *Keller* (T-AGS 25) transferred to Portugal 21-7-72. *Sands* (T-AGOR 6) on loan to Brazil since 1-7-74; *Charles H. Davis* (T-AGOR 5) on loan to New Zealand since 28-7-70; *James M. Gillis* (AGOR 4) loaned to Mexico 15-6-83. *Robert D. Conrad* (AGOR 3) was returned 6-89 for disposal by Lamont-Doherty Physical Observatory, Columbia University, and was replaced by the privately funded *Bernier*. *Thomas G. Thompson* (AGOR 9) was redesignated IX 517 on 11-12-89 and replaced by AGOR 23 (same name) in 1991. Lynch (T-AGOR 7) was transferred to the Maritime Administration for disposal 6-11-91. AGOR 10 will be replaced by the new AGOR 24 in 1994.

OCEAN SURVEILLANCE SHIPS (T-AGOS)

◆ **0 (+2+4) Impeccable-class SWATH ocean surveillance ships** Bldr: Tampa Shipyard Div., American SB Co., Tampa, Florida

	Laid down	L	In serv.
T-AGOS 23 Impeccable	. . .	. . .	1994
T-AGOS 24	. . .	. . .	. . .
T-AGOS 25	. . .	. . .	. . .
T-AGOS 26	. . .	. . .	. . .
T-AGOS 27	. . .	. . .	. . .
T-AGOS 28	. . .	. . .	. . .

Authorized: T-AGOS 23 in FY 90, T-AGOS 24 in FY 92; planned T-AGOS 25 in FY 94, T-AGOS 26, 27 in FY 95, T-AGOS 28 in FY 97

OCEAN SURVEILLANCE SHIPS (T-AGOS) *(continued)*

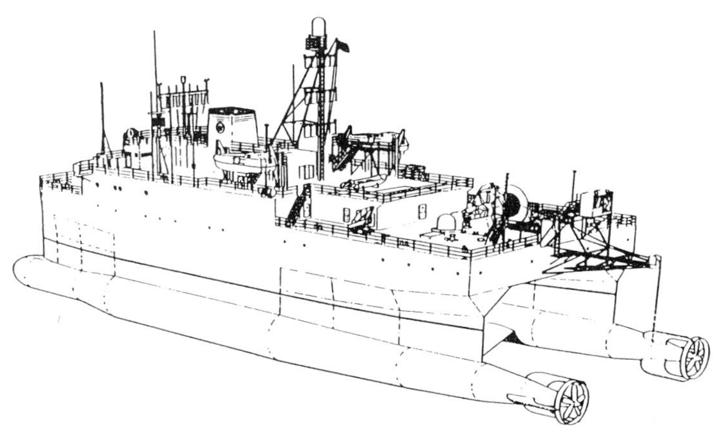

Impeccable (T-AGOS 23)—showing SWATH hull form
U.S. Navy, 1991

Impeccable (T-AGOS 23) U.S. Navy, 1991

D: 5,270 tons (fl) **S:** 15 kts **Dim:** 85.80 × 29.79 × . . .
Electron Equipt:
Radar: . . .
Sonar: UQQ-2 SURTASS, ATAS—*see* Remarks
M: 4 diesel generator sets, electric drive; 2 props; . . . shp—2 JT 1110 Omnithrusters; 1,800 shp
Range: 8,000/15 **Endurance:** 50–60 days **Crew:** . . .

Remarks: Enlarged version of T-AGOS 19 SWATH design. First unit ordered 28-3-91 under FY 90, with option for the two more, but no keel had been laid as of 7-92, and work is apparently progressing slowly. The Active Towed Array Sonar (ATAS) will have ten separate active, low-frequency sonar transducers. The design incorporates measures to improve seakeeping. Commencement of construction delayed by builder's financial problems.

♦ 3 (+1) Victorious-class SWATH ocean surveillance ships

Bldr: McDermott, Inc., Morgan City, La. (*Atlantic Fleet/†Pacific Fleet)

	Laid down	L	In serv.
T-AGOS 19 Victorious†	12-4-88	3-5-90	13-8-91
T-AGOS 20 Able*	23-5-89	16-2-91	24-3-92
T-AGOS 21 Effective†	15-2-91	26-9-91	28-8-92
T-AGOS 22 Loyal*	7-10-91	19-9-92	1993

Authorized: T-AGOS 19 in FY 87, T-AGOS 20–22 in FY 89

Able (T-AGOS 20)—showing SWATH hull form McDermott, 2-91

Victorious (T-AGOS 19) McDermott,

Victorious (T-AGOS 19)—note SURTASS boom protruding from ste
McDermott,

D: 2,486 tons light (3,370 fl)
S: 16 kts (9.6 sustained with SURTASS)
Dim: 70.71 (58.14 pp) × 28.96 × 7.54
Electron Equipt:
Radar: 2/Raytheon . . . nav.—Sonar: UQQ-2 SURTASS
M: 4 Caterpillar-Kato 3512-TA 835-kw diesel generator sets (600 V 60 Hz; 2 for ship's service); 2 G.E. 750 v.d.c. inductance motors (185 rpm max.); 2 props; 3,200 shp—2 600-hp Omnithrusters
Electric: 1,970 kw (2 × 835-kw main generators, 1 × 300-kw emergency)
Range: 3,000/9.6 plus . . ./3 **Fuel:** 778 tons
Endurance: 90 days
Crew: 8 officers, 13 unlicensed, 12 technicians

Remarks: First ship ordered 31-10-86, three more on 7-10-88. Carry same s payload as *Stalwart* class, including WSC-6(V)1 satellite communications data Able to maintain heading in Sea State 6 and be survivable in Sea State 9. SW (Small Waterplane Twin-Hull) hull form, with two submerged pontoons for buoy Horizontal fins between hulls control pitching. Should be remarkably stable ships to operate in higher latitudes in winter than *Stalwart* class. The SURTASS ar 2,614 m long and is towed at depths between 152 and 457 meters.

♦ 17 Stalwart class ocean surveillance ships (2 in reserve) Bl

T-AGOS 1–12: Tacoma Boat, Tacoma, Wash.; 13–18: Halter Marine, Moss Point, Miss. (*Atlantic Fleet/†Pacific Fleet)

	Laid down	L	In se
T-AGOS 1 *Stalwart*	3-11-82	11-7-83	9-4
T-AGOS 2 Contender†	1-10-82	20-12-83	29-7
T-AGOS 3 Vindicator*	14-4-83	1-6-84	21-11
T-AGOS 4 Triumph†	3-1-84	7-9-84	19-2
T-AGOS 5 Assurance†	31-5-84	12-1-85	1-
T-AGOS 6 Persistent*	22-10-84	6-4-85	14-
T-AGOS 7 Indomitable†	26-1-85	16-7-85	1-1
T-AGOS 8 Prevail*	13-3-85	7-12-85	5-
T-AGOS 9 Assertive†	30-7-85	20-6-86	12-
T-AGOS 10 Invincible*	8-11-85	1-11-86	30-

[...]I SURVEILLANCE SHIPS (T-AGOS) *(continued)*

	Laid down	L	In serv.
[...]11 AUDACIOUS (ex-[...]less)†	29-2-88	28-1-89	12-6-89
[...]12 BOLD (ex-*Vigorous*)*	13-6-88	22-5-89	20-10-89
[...]14 WORTHY*	3-4-86	6-2-88	7-4-89
[...]15 TITAN†	30-10-86	18-6-88	8-3-89
[...]16 *CAPABLE*	17-10-87	28-10-88	9-6-89
[...]17 TENACIOUS (ex-*Intrepid*)*	26-2-88	17-2-89	29-9-89
[...]18 RELENTLESS*	22-4-88	12-5-89	12-1-90

[...]rized: T-AGOS 1 and 2 in FY 79, T-AGOS 3 in FY 80, T-AGOS 4–8 [...], T-AGOS 9–12 in FY 82, T-AGOS 13, 14 in FY 85, T-AGOS 15, 16 [...]5, T-AGOS 17, 18 in FY 87.

[...] (T-AGOS 14) Dr. Giorgio Arra, 2-92

[...] (T-AGOS 8) Dr. Giorgio Arra, 1990

[...]less (T-AGOS 18) Dr. Giorgio Arra, 10-90

[...]600 tons light (2,285 fl) **S:** 11 kts
[...] 68.28 (62.10 wl) × 13.10 × 4.57
[...]**ron Equipt:** Radar: 2/. . . nav.—Sonar: UQQ-2 SURTASS
[...] Caterpillar-Kato D-398B 800-bhp diesels, G.E. electric drive; [...]/4-bladed props; 2,200 shp (1,600 hp sust.)—550-hp bow-thruster
[...]**tric:** 1,500 kVA from main generators, plus 265-kw emergency set
[...]**ge:** 3,000/11 plus 6,480/3 **Fuel:** 834 tons
[...]**rance:** 98 days
[...]**:** 8 officers, 11 unlicensed contract crew, 11 technicians (T-AGOS 16–18: 9 officers, 11 unlicensed, 10 technicians)

[...]**s:** 1,472–1,486 grt/786 dwt. The first three T-AGOS were contracted for [...] T-AGOS 13, 14 ordered 4-6-85, with option to build through T-AGOS 18; T-AGOS 15–18 ordered 30-6-86. Tacoma Boat's bankruptcy caused halt on work on T-AGOS 11, 12; rebid 1987, with new delivery dates. Halter-built units delivered on or ahead of schedule. First 12 operated under 1-2-85 contract with Sea Mobility Div., Falcon Contractors; contract duration four years, eight months, with six each based at Pearl Harbor and Little Creek, Va. Technicians supplied by RCA on contract. Ships repainted gray from original white during 1989 (after delivery, for new units), and hull numbers painted on. T-AGOS 2 completed the 100th T-AGOS patrol in mid-1988. T-AGOS 17 name changed 7-1-89 in response to complaints from former carrier *Intrepid* (CVS 12) crewmen that the ship was not grand enough to commemorate their ship!

Status: Because the mission to provide surveillance of Soviet submarines has largely disappeared, the ships of this class are being deactivated. The eight units built by Halter Marine are being transferred during 1992–93 to the National Oceanic and Atmospheric Administration (NOAA) of the Department of Commerce. Four (two on each coast) of the remainder may be retained active for training. *Adventurous* (T-AGOS 13) was deactivated 1-6-92 and transferred to NOAA. *Tenacious* (T-AGOS 17) was to have been deactivated 1-4-92 but was instead assigned to SPAWAR for electronics research. *Capable* (T-AGOS 16) was deactivated on 31-7-92, and by 7-92, *Stalwart* was out of service.

Hull systems: T-AGOS 13 and later have three more berths and more space for the crew, are 2,248 tons (fl), and carry 904 tons fuel. Flat-chine hull form without bilge keels; have passive tank roll stabilization. Intended to conduct 60–90-day patrols and to be at sea 292 days per year.

Electronics systems: The AN/UQQ-2 SURTASS (SURveillance Towed Array Sensor) is an 1,829-m linear hydrophone array deployed over the ship's stern in a flexible, neutrally buoyant cable; the output from the SURTASS is instantaneously relayed to shore monitoring stations via WSC-6 satellite communications, and the on-board technicians are primarily for maintenance and backup. Main-engine motor/generator sets also supply ship's-service power.

SURVEYING SHIPS (T-AGS)

♦ 0 (+0 + 1) SWATH ocean survey ship Bldr: . . .

	Laid down	L	In serv.
T-AGS	. . .	. . .	. . .

Programmed: 1 in FY 94

Remarks: Successor to SWATH (Small Waterplane, Twin-Hull) survey ship originally programmed for FY 89. Will apparently employ same hull and propulsion as new *Impeccable* (T-AGOS 23)-class SWATH.

♦ 0 (+1) ice-capable ocean survey ship Bldr: . . .

	Laid down	L	In serv.
T-AGS	. . .	. . .	11-94

Authorized: 1 in FY 92

D: . . . **S:** . . . **Dim:** . . . × . . . × . . .
Electron Equipt: Radar: . . . **M:** . . .

Remarks: No details available. Will fulfill long-standing need for an Arctic-capable survey and oceanographic ship. Funds to construct the ship were rescinded by the Bush Administration but were reinstated under FY 93 by Congress.

♦ 0 (+3) Pathfinder class

Bldr: Halter Marine, Inc., Moss Point, Mississippi

	Laid down	L	In serv.
T-AGS 60 PATHFINDER	1992	2-93	1-94
T-AGS 61 SUMNER	1992	6-93	8-94
T-AGS 62	. . .	. . .	1-95

Authorized: 2 in FY 90, 1 in FY 91

Pathfinder (T-AGS 60) Trinity Marine, 1992

D: 3,019 tons light (4,700 fl) **S:** . . .
Dim: 100.13 (94.49 pp) × 17.68 × 5.79 (hull)
Electron Equipt: Radar: . . .—Sonar: . . .
M: 4 . . . diesel generator sets producing 8,520 kw total for propulsion and ship's services, electric drive: 2 motors; 2 azimuth props; 8,000 shp—1,500 shp retractable bow-thruster
Range: 12,000/12 + 29 days on station at 3 kts **Fuel:** 1,221 tons
Endurance: 70 days **Crew:** 65 total, including scientific party

Remarks: Design essentially an enlarged AGOR 23, with increased space to meet Military Sealift Command accommodations standards. First two ordered 30-1-91 to replace *Lynch* (T-AGOR 7) and *De Steiguer* (T-AGOR 12); third ship to replace *Bartlett* (T-AGOR 13) ordered 6-92.

Will conduct physical, chemical, and biological oceanography; multi-discipline envi-

SURVEYING SHIPS (T-AGS) *(continued)*

ronmental investigations; ocean engineering and marine acoustics research; coastal hydrographic surveys; marine geology and geophysics research; and bathymetric, gravity, and magnetic surveys in deep ocean and coastal areas. Laboratory spaces will include a 232 m^2 main laboratory, a 16.8 m^2 wet lab, a 32.5 m^2 staging bay contiguous to the 325-m^2 working deck and the wet lab, a 28.2-m^2 dry and biochemical lab, a 5.9-m^2 darkroom, a 7.4-m^2 climate-controlled chamber/salinometer lab, a 7.4-m^2 survey freezer, an 18.6-m^2 electricians' shop, a 22.3-m^2 drafting room, 217.2 m^2 of survey equipment storage, and a 32.5-m^2 library/conference room. Anti-rolling tanks, precision navigation equipment, and on-board data-processing equipment are fitted. Will be able to launch, operate, and recover remotely operated vehicles. Will carry 962 tons ballast water, 32 tons potable water, and 24 tons lube oil.

◆ **0 (+1) Waters class** Bldr: Avondale SY, New Orleans

	Laid down	L	In serv.
T-AGS 45 WATERS	21-5-91	30-5-92	4-93

Waters (T-AGS 45) Calvert/U.S. Navy, 1991

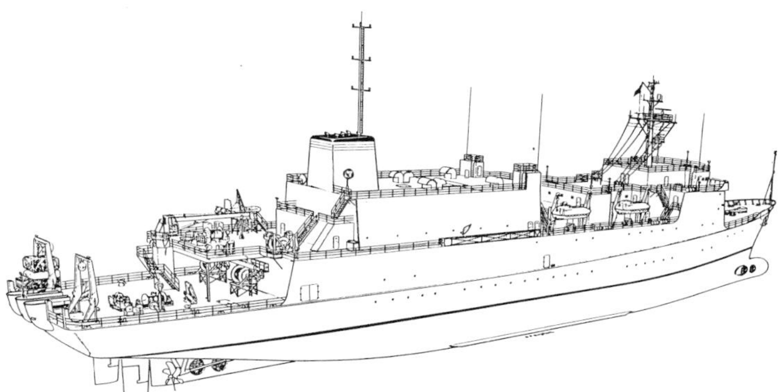

Waters (T-AGS 45) U.S. Navy, 1991

D: 7,312 tons light (12,200 fl) **S:** 12 kts (sust.)
Dim: 138.7 (130.6 wl) × 21.0 × 6.4
Electron Equipt:
Radar: 1/Raytheon X-band ARPA nav., 1/Raytheon S-band ARPA nav.
Sonar: G.E. Seabeam 853E mapping
M: Electric drive: 5 G.M. EMD 16-cyl. diesels, 5 2,500-kw generators, 2 Westinghouse motors; 2 props; 7,400 shp (6,800 sust.)—4/1,200-shp electric tunnel-thrusters
Electric: ship's service from propulsion generators + 1/365-kw emergency diesel set
Range: 6,500/12 + 30 days on station **Fuel:** 2,000 tons
Crew: 37 officers, 52 unlicensed MSC tot. + 6 spare berths

Remarks: Authorized under Fiscal Year 1990 Budget. Ordered 4-4-90. Intended as a replacement for the stricken *Mizar* (T-AGOR 11) to conduct hydrographic and oceanographic surveys in support of the Integrated Undersea Surveillance System. Will be capable of general oceanographic, bathymetric, and hydrographic survey work. Equipped with centerline "moonpool" for the launch and recovery of a remotely operated vehicle (ROV).

◆ **2 coastal survey ships** Bldr: Halter Marine, Moss Point, Mississippi

	Laid down	L	In serv.
T-AGS 51 JOHN MCDONNELL	3-8-89	13-12-90	15-11-91
T-AGS 52 LITTLEHALES	25-10-89	14-2-92	10-1-92

D: 1,245 tons light (2,054 fl) **S:** 14 kts (12 sust.)
Dim: 63.40 × 13.72 × 4.27
Electron Equipt:
Radar: 1/. . . . . . 3-cm nav., 1/. . . . . . 10-cm nav.

John McDonnell (T-AGS 51) Trinity Marir

Littlehales (T-AGS 52)—outboard *John McDonnell* (T-AGS 51) Trinity Marin

Sonar: 1/Simrad Multibeam (95 kHz), 1/towed sidescan (105 k 2/12-kHz deep-water echo-sounders, 2/24-kHz shallow-w echo-sounders, 2/200-kHz shallow-water echo-sounders
M: "father-son" diesel plant: 1 G.M. EMD12-645F7B turbocharge 900 rpm/1 Detroit Diesel 6V92N diesel; 1 prop; 2,550/230 bhp
Electric: 1,200 kw (3 × 350, G.M. 8V92TAB diesel-driven ship's service; 1 × 150-kw G.M. 6V92N-driven emergency set
Range: 12,000/12 **Crew:** 22 crew + 11 survey party

Remarks: Ships added to FY 87 Budget by Congress with non-binding sug that they should be converted from existing tuna clippers. Delay in order to 1 occasioned by need to define characteristics for the unexpected gifts. First replace *Silas Bent* (T-AGS 26) and *Kane* (T-AGS 27). To be operated for the Oceanography Command. Second pair to replace T-AGS 33 and 34 were to ha included in the FY 94 Budget. Hull numbers are the rationalization of an a administrative error: AGS 40–49 were never assigned, while AGS 50 was b *Rehoboth* (ex-AVP 50) from 9-48 to striking on 15-4-70, the "50" having been r as the result of an earlier error!

Intended to collect hydrographic data in waters from 10 to 4,000 m deep. The "son," diesel propels the ships at speeds from 4 to 6 kts. Have roll-stabilizatic Navigation equipment includes GPS and LORAN-C receivers, collision av system, dual-axis doppler speed log and HYSTAR II computerized data cc system. Laboratory space: 700 sq. ft., deck working space: 1,500 sq. ft.; and s storage space: 2,300 sq. ft. Two telescopic, 7-ton max. cranes fitted.

Carry two 10.36 × 2.82 × 0.91-m, 7.4-ton survey launches, equipped with 225-bhp diesel for 16 kts. The launches carry a towing winch for a 105-kHz s sonar (range of 600 m, towing speed 12.7 kts) and have two 24-kHz and two echo-sounders fitted; the craft have Global Positioning System, a microfix radio tion system, and can interface with the mother ship's HYSTAR II computerized data storage system. There is also a 5.33-m semi-rigid inflatable workboat.

◆ **2 Maury class** Builder: Bethlehem SY, Sparrows Pt., Maryland

	Laid down	L	In serv.
T-AGS 39 MAURY	29-7-86	4-9-87	31-3-89
T-AGS 40 TANNER	22-10-86	28-2-89	31-9-90

D: 8,810 tons light (15,821 fl) **S:** 21 kts (20 sust.)
Dim: 152.35 (142.04 pp; 145.09 wl) × 21.95 × 9.33
Electron Equipt: Radar: 2/. . . nav.—Sonar: SQN-17
M: 2 IMO De Laval DMRV-16-4 Enterprise diesels; 1 CP prop; 24,998 bhp
Range: 17,800/20 **Fuel:** 3,200 tons
Endurance: 34 days **Electric:** 2,700 kw (3 × 900-kw diesel set
Crew: 56 MSC crew; 3 naval officers, 29 enlisted, 20 scientists

Remarks: 12,517 grt/3,755 nrt. Ordered 28-6-85 under FY 85 funding. A th was planned for FY 91 to replace T-AGS-38 but has been deferred inde Replaced a program to convert two C3-S-33a cargo ships (*Lake* and *Scan*) f Navy/MARAD Ready Reserve Force. Intended as replacements for *Bowditch* 21) and *Dutton* (T-AGS 22) in support of SSBN operations through sea-floor and gravimetric mapping. Hull volume largely voids except for engineering Will carry up to 7,339 tons of water ballast. Ships delayed in launch by well ove due to engine installation problems. SQN-17 BOTOSS (BOttom TOpography System) maps to depths of 7,300 m. Also have two BQN-3 narrow-beam r sonars, doppler sonar, expendable bathythermograph, velocimeter, "MiniSIN

YING SHIPS (T-AGS) *(continued)*

(T-AGS 39) U.S. Navy, 1989

r (T-AGS 40) Victor M. Baca, 2-92

igation, Mk 29 gyro. Equipment on both removed from T-AGS 21 and 22. Have working deck space, helicopter platform atop after superstructure. T-AGS 39 s in the Pacific, T-AGS 40 in the Atlantic.

Survey ship *H.H. Hess* (T-AGS 38) was deactivated 24-2-92 and transferred to itime Administration for layup in the National Defense Reserve Fleet.

hauvenet class (SCB 723 type)
r: Upper Clyde SB, Glasgow, Scotland

	Laid down	L	In serv.
29 Chauvenet	24-5-67	13-5-68	13-11-70
32 Harkness	30-6-67	12-6-68	29-1-71

ness (T-AGS 32) Hartmut Ehlers, 1-89

,540 tons (4,830 fl) **S:** 15 kts
: 119.8 (101.8 pp) × 16.5 × 5.1
tron Equipt:
dar: 1/Raytheon TM 1650/6X nav., 1/Raytheon TM 1660/12S nav.
CAN: URN-25

M: 2 Alco diesels, electric drive: Westinghouse motor; 1 CP prop; 3,600 shp
Electric: 1,500 kw **Endurance:** 90 days
Fuel: 824 tons **Range:** 9,300/14; 15,000/12
Crew: contractor crew: up to 13 officers, 56 unlicensed + navy: 6 officers, 49 enlisted + 12 civilian scientists

Remarks: 2,890 grt/1,030 dwt. Very complete navigation and communications systems. Can carry four small survey launches; hangar (13.9 × 3.7 m) and flight deck for two HH-2D Seasprite helicopters. Operated for the Oceanographer of the Navy by MAR, Inc., 1989–91 (with two one-year extension options). Both in Pacific.

◆ **4 Silas Bent class (SCB 226, 725, and 728 types)** (*Atlantic Fleet/†Pacific Fleet)

	Bldr	L	In serv.
T-AGS 26 Silas Bent†	American SB, Lorain	16-5-64	23-7-65
T-AGS 27 Kane*	Christy Corp., Sturgeon Bay	20-11-65	19-5-67
T-AGS 33 Wilkes*	Defoe SB, Bay City, Mich.	31-7-69	28-6-71
T-AGS 34 Wyman*	Defoe SB, Bay City, Mich.	30-10-69	3-11-71

Wyman (T-AGS 34) Dr. Giorgio Arra, 3-91

Wilkes (T-AGS 33) Dr. Giorgio Arra, 1-90

D: 1,900 to 2,166 tons (2,550 to 2,827 fl) **S:** 15 kts
Dim: 86.9 (80.8 pp) × 14.6 × 4.6 (T-AGS 27: 6.1 max.)
Electron Equipt:
Radar: 1/Raytheon RM 1650/9X nav., 1/Raytheon TM 1660/12S nav.
M: 2 Alco diesels, electric drive: Westinghouse or G.E. motor; 1 CP prop; 3,600 shp (plus 350-hp bow-thruster)
Electric: 960 kw **Range:** 5,800–6,300/14.5; 8,000/13
Fuel: 461 tons
Crew: 7–9 officers, 26 unlicensed contractor crew + 26–30 scientists

Remarks: Operated for Oceanographer of the Navy. T-AGS 34, used in support of the strategic-missile programs, is equipped with the Sperry SQN-17 BOTOSS (BOttom TOpography Survey System) for mapping depths to 7,300 m; the system consists of two planar transducer arrays and an HP-2100 computer, which averages the results of four separate passes through an area. Have MARISAT satellite communications equipment. Full-load displacements vary: T-AGS 26: 2,743 tons; T-AGS 27: 2,827; T-AGS 33: 2,565; T-AGS 34: 2,550 tons. All operated by MAR, Inc., under contract to MSC, 1989–91 (with two one-year options). T-AGS 26 and 27 to be replaced by T-AGS 51, 52; others by T-AGS 53 and 54, if built.

SURVEYING SHIPS (T-AGS) *(continued)*

Silas Bent (T-AGS 26) Dr. Giorgio Arra, 10-91

HOSPITAL SHIPS (T-AH)

◆ **2 converted San Clemente-class merchant tankers**
Bldr: National Steel, San Diego, Cal.

	L	Conv. start	In serv.
T-AH 19 MERCY (ex-*Worth*)	1976	20-7-84	28-2-87
T-AH 20 COMFORT (ex-*Rose City*)	1976	2-4-85	1-12-87

Comfort (T-AH 20) French Navy, 1991

Comfort (T-AH 20)—in the Persian Gulf Leo Van Ginderen, 1991

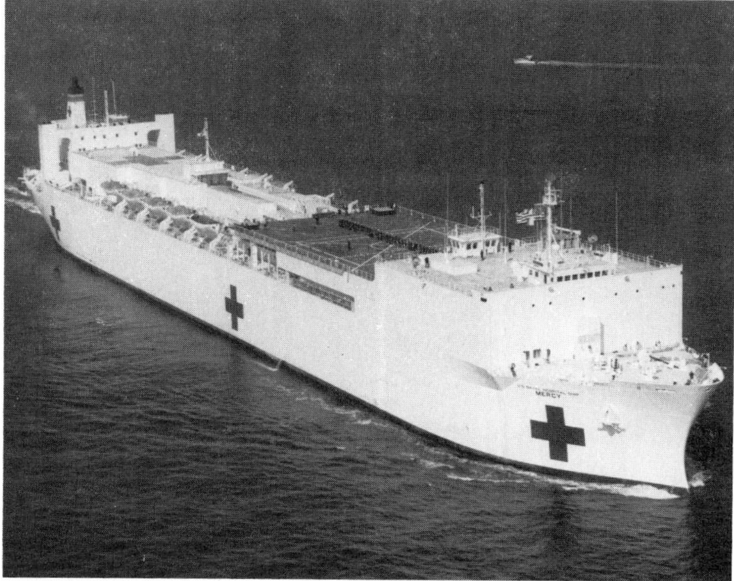
Mercy (T-AH 19) Dr. Giorgio Arra, 10-89

D: 24,752 tons light (69,360 fl) **S:** 17.5 kts (16.5 sust.)
Dim: 272.49 (260.61 pp) × 32.23 × 9.98
Electron Equipt:
Radar: 1/. . . nav., 1/SPS-67 surf. search—TACAN: URN-25
M: 2 sets G.E. geared steam turbines; 1 prop; 24,500 shp
Boilers: 2/. . . **Range:** 13,420/17.5 **Fuel:** 5,445 tons
Electric: 9,250 kw tot. (3 × 2,000-kw diesel, 1 × 1,500-kw diesel, 1 × 1,000-kw turbogenerator, 1 × 750-kw emergency d
Crew: 14 officers, 154 enlisted MSC, 1,207 navy staff + 1,000 pa

Remarks: 54,367 grt/45,480 dwt. Builder contracted 29-6-83 to conve Marine's tanker *Worth* to a hospital ship with FY 83 funds; T-AH 20's sion ordered from same yard 16-12-83 with FY 84 funds. Were originally 44 91,849 dwt.

The entire midships area has been altered to provide a large helicopter deck modations, and boat stowage. Have 12 operating rooms, 4 X-ray rooms, a intensive-care unit, a burn-care facility, a 50-bed reception/triage area, and 1,(beds. Of the 1,508 accommodations for naval personnel, there are 259 for office chief petty officers, and 530 for enlisted, augmented in emergencies by 37 medical support personnel; also aboard will be 14 communications specialist kept on each U.S. coast, on five-days' steaming notice, and they will be used abo days per year on exercises. In port, they are maintained by the MSC crew and civilian contract crew, totaling 68 per ship. Freshwater tankage for 1,525 carried, plus two 278-ton/day distilling plants. Much of the displacement is se ballast. There are two 7,000 ton/hour ballast pumps. Both were activated be 10-8-90 to participate in Operation Desert Shield/Desert Storm.

CARGO SHIPS (T-AK)

◆ **1 Northern Light class (C3-S-33a type)**
Bldr: Sun SB & DD Co., Chester, Pa.

	In serv.	In USN
T-AK 286 VEGA (ex-*Bay*, ex-*Mormacbay*)	14-10-60	15-10-81

Vega (T-AK 286) Leo Van Ginder

D: 16,363 tons (fl) **S:** 19 kts
Dim: 148.15 (139.59 pp) × 20.72 × 8.68
Electron Equipt:
Radar: 1/Raytheon TM 1650/6X nav., 1/Raytheon TM 1660/12
M: 2 sets G.E. geared steam turbines; 1 prop; 11,000 shp (15,700 emergency)
Boilers: 2 Combustion Engineering; 43.3 kg/cm², 457°C
Electric: 1,275 kw **Range:** 14,000/18 **Fuel:** 3,056 tons
Crew: 68 MSC + 7 navy communications group

Remarks: T-AK 286 (originally to have been renamed *King's Bay*) acquired and placed on the Navy List on 15-10-81, reactivated 18-3-83 after being conv transport 16 Trident ballistic missiles in vertical cells in place of No. 3 hold. 9,260-grt/12,500-dwt cargo ship acquired from Maritime Administration's I Defense Reserve Fleet. Last Holy Loch supply voyage completed 5-92; now between King's Bay, Georgia, and Charleston, South Carolina.

Sisters *Northern Light* (T-AK 284, ex-*Cove*, ex-*Mormaccove*) and *Souther* (T-AK 285, ex-*Trade*, ex-*Mormactrade*) were deactivated 26-4-84 and 13-9-84 tively, and transferred to the Maritime Administration–administered Ready Force, although remaining as navy property. Both were configured as gener ships. Funds were requested in FY 85 to convert sister *Cape* as a ballistic transport (T-AK 295) but were denied by Congress; *Cape* and sisters *Lake* a (which were to have been converted as survey ships T-AGS 39 and 40) are als Ready Reserve Force (*Cape* as *Cape Catawba*).

◆ **1 Norwalk class** Bldr: Permanente, Richmond, Calif.

	L	Conv.
T-AK 282 MARSHFIELD (ex-*Marshfield Victory*)	15-5-44	28-5-70

D: 6,700 tons light (11,150 fl) **S:** 16.5 kts
Dim: 138.76 (133.05 pp) × 18.90 × 7.32
Electron Equipt:
Radar: 1/Raytheon TM 1650/6X nav., 1/Raytheon 1660/12S na
M: 2 sets G.E. geared turbines; 1 prop; 9.349 shp
Boilers: 2 Combustion Engineering 37 kg/cm², 399°C
Electric: 600 kw tot. **Range:** 20,000/16.5 **Fuel:** 2,824 tons
Crew: 14 officers, 57 unlicensed MSC + 7 navy comms continge

GO SHIPS (T-AK) *(continued)*

hfield (T-AK 282) Dr. Giorgio Arra, 1984

ks: 7,608 grt/10,669 dwt. Hold No. 3 (of five) accommodates 16 vertically SLBMs to support SSBN activities. Has MARISAT SATCOMM system. Carries es, submarine spares, etc.; also carries 18,000 barrels cargo fuel (7,566 bbl 0,434 bbl fuel oil). Has 40-ton cargo booms. Refitted 1-9-88 to 14-12-89. Operthe Atlantic.

r Furman (T-AK 280), originally converted like T-AK 282, was to have been n 20-9-81, but was instead reserved for conversion to a cable transporter for the Electronics Command. Contracted to Atlantic Drydock Co., Jacksonville, Fla., 1-82, the ship had all winches and cargo booms removed, as well as the refrigeruipment deleted; completed 20-4-83, she was laid up 10-86 in the Maritime istration's National Defense Reserve Fleet at Beaumont, Texas.

The Arctic-capable cargo ship *Mirfak* (T-AK 271), deactivated 11-12-79, was n 2-92.

CLE CARGO SHIPS (T-AKR)

+ 11) large medium-speed roll-on sealift ships

Bldrs: . . .

	Laid down	L	In serv.
R	. . .	. . .	. . .
R	. . .	. . .	. . .
R	. . .	. . .	. . .
R	. . .	. . .	. . .
R	. . .	. . .	. . .
R	. . .	. . .	. . .
R	. . .	. . .	. . .
R	. . .	. . .	. . .
R	. . .	. . .	. . .
R	. . .	. . .	. . .
R	. . .	. . .	1997

horized: FY 90

53,000 tons (fl) **S:** 24 kts
n: 289.56 (271.28) × 32.16 × 12.19 max.
ctron Equipt: Radar: . . .
4 Colt-Pielstick 14PC4.2V diesels; 2 props; 33,500 bhp
ctric: 5,000 kw (2 × 2,500-kw diesel sets)
nge: 12,000/24 **Crew:** . . . + 300 troops

rks: *Added* by Congress to FY 90 shipbuilding request due to concerns that the nd its allies lack sufficient sealift assets, military or commercial. Design conet spring 1992, with intention to order all 11 by 12-92 and all to be completed by Had originally planned for a 36-kt-capable ship, but costs would have been itive and the advantages minimal. Program may be replaced by converted rcial cargo vessels.

iminary design characteristics above may be altered considerably in final ver-Required to have three 50-ton capacity twin pedestal cranes, two side vehicle orts, and a slewing stern ramp. To be able to carry 13,260 tons military cargo. In y cargo configuration, would have 35,300 m² of military vehicle parking space.

Nine 27,870 m² vehicle parking capacity, 213 m-long versions of the above are to be procured for pre-positioning military equipment, to augment the t fleet of MSC-chartered vessels engaged in that task; see later page.

SL-7-class container cargo ships

	Bldr	In serv.	In Navy	AKR conv.
R 287 ALGOL (ex-*-Land Exchange*)	Rotterdamse DDM, Rotterdam	7-5-73	13-10-81	22-6-84
R 288 BELLATRIX *-Sea-Land Trade*)	Rheinstahl Nordseewerke, Emden	6-4-73	13-10-81	10-9-84
R 289 DENEBOLA *-Sea-Land ource*)	Rotterdamse DDM, Rotterdam	4-12-73	27-10-81	10-10-85
R 290 POLLUX *-Sea-Land rket*)	A. G. Weser, Bremen	20-9-73	16-11-81	27-3-86
R 291 ALTAIR *-Sea-Land ance*)	Rheinstahl Nordseewerke, Emden	17-9-73	5-1-82	13-11-85
T-AKR 292 REGULUS (ex-*Sea-Land Commerce*)	A. G. Weser, Bremen	30-3-73	27-10-81	28-8-85
T-AKR 293 CAPELLA (ex-*Sea-Land McLean*)	Rotterdamse DDM, Rotterdam	4-10-72	16-4-82	30-6-84
T-AKR 294 ANTARES (ex-*Sea-Land Galloway*)	A. G. Weser, Bremen	27-9-72	16-4-82	12-7-84

Capella (T-AKR 293) Leo Van Ginderen, 7-91

Algol (T-AKR 287) Leo Van Ginderen, 11-91

Antares (T-AKR 294) Peter C. Westdijk, 10-91

Bellatrix (T-AKR 288) Leo Van Ginderen, 10-91

D: 29,692 tons light (43,000 tons normal/55,355 to 55,372 fl)
S: 33 kts (30.1 loaded) **Dim:** 288.38 (268.37 pp) × 32.16 × 11.18
M: 2 sets G.E. MST-19 geared steam turbines; 2 props; 120,000 shp
Boilers: 2 Foster-Wheeler; 61.6 kg/cm², 507°C
Electric: 8,000 kw **Range:** 14,000/33 light, 12,200/27 loaded
Fuel: 8,500 tons **Crew:** 57 max. (42 normal crew; 12 layup crew)

Remarks: 48,525 grt/24,270 dwt (varies). Six acquired under FY 81 and two under FY 82, with the original intent of extensively converting them to serve as T-AKR, "Roll-on/Roll-off" vehicle cargo ships for the Rapid Deployment Force. Instead, under FY 82 Congress mandated that four be given a "partial" Ro/Ro conversion and the other four be given only a "mini-modification." This was later changed to give all the same modification, T-AKR 287, 288, 293, and 294 under FY 82 and the others under FY 84. The conversions were performed by: T-AKR 287, 288, 292: National Steel, San Diego; T-AKR 289 and 293: Pennsylvania SB, Chester, Pa.; and the others by Avondale SY, Westwego, La.; the latter ships have an additional hinged internal ramp. The ships

VEHICLE CARGO SHIPS (T-AKR) *(continued)*

were given T-AK hull numbers when purchased; these were changed to T-AKR without changing the actual numbers assigned, AKR 287 on 19-6-84, AKR 288 on 10-9-84, AKR 293 and 294 on 30-6-84, rest on 1-11-83. Operated on contract by Bay Ship Management Co., Englewood Cliffs, N.J., since 5-90. Maintained in ready-to-steam status: T-AKR 287 and T-AKR 288 at Galveston, Texas; T-AKR 289 and T-AKR 291 at Norfolk, Va.; T-AKR 290 and T-AKR 292 at New Orleans; and T-AKR 291 and T-AKR 294 at Jacksonville, Florida. During Operation Desert Shield/Desert Storm in 1990–91, steamed at an average of 27 kts and performed the work of an estimated 116 World War II–era break-bulk ships; seven of the ships carried 11 percent of all the cargo transported to the Mideast. T-AKR 294, however, broke down on her initial voyage, requiring extensive machinery repairs.

Systems: The ships were originally tailored to transport up to 1,086 nonstandard *35-ft.* containers (standard cargo containers are either 20 or 40 feet in length); 4,000 containers were purchased along with the first six ships. These ships proved expensive to operate for the former merchant owner, and their sophisticated propulsion plants have not been overly reliable. Made 35 kts on trials in light condition, 33 kts at 32,600 tons. Fuel tankage includes 5,384 tons fuel oil, 3,116 tons diesel. Also carry 569 tons potable water and 4,893 tons permanent ballast water. Have 2 × 3,000-kw, 1 × 1,500-kw, and 1 × 500-kw diesel generators. Up to 9,484 tons of saltwater ballast can be carried.

Conversion entailed filling in the amidships portion to produce a multi-deck vehicle cargo area and helicopter hangar totaling 12,170 m^2 on five decks (can accommodate up to 120 UH-1 helicopters or 183 M-1 tanks). This is topped by a flight deck of 3,252 m^2, with a twin 35-ton crane plumbing two hatches interrupting the forward half. The stern provides 1,719 m^2 of vehicle parking, as well as cargo space for 8 "Sea Shed" containerized vehicle stowage or 44 or 46/20-ft. containers; it is served by a twin 50-ton crane. There are vehicle access ramps amidships, port and starboard.

◆ **1 Maine (C7-S-95a-type) class** Bldr: Bath Iron Wks., Maine.

	L	In serv.
T-AKR 10 Mercury (ex-*Illinois*)	7-76	1977

Mercury (T-AKR 10) Leo Van Ginderen, 12-90

D: 14,222 tons light (33,765 fl) **S:** 23 kts (sust.)
Dim: 208.71 (195.07 pp) × 31.09 × 9.78
Electron Equipt:
Radar: 1/Raytheon TM 1650/6X nav., 1/Raytheon TM 1660/12S nav.
M: 2 sets G.E. geared steam turbines; 2 props; 37,000 shp
Boilers: 2 Babcock & Wilcox; 77.5 kg/cm^2
Electric: 4,000 kw **Range:** 10,000/23 **Fuel:** 3,394 tons
Crew: 41 tot. MSC

Remarks: 13,156 grt/19,172 dwt. T-AKR 10 long-term chartered from Lykes Brothers 14-4-80; later sold to Wilmington Trust Co. Now operates in cargo service in Far East with MSC Civil Service crew. Capable of carrying container, as well as vehicle, cargo and can land helicopters amidships on upper deck; can also transport 728 tons liquid cargo. Two 15-ton cranes (paired) forward. A 7.3-m-wide by 24.4-m stern ramp is fitted, and there are two side-loading doors also. Total bale cargo volume is 56,640 m^3; vehicle cargo deck space is 16,258 m^2. Plans to acquire two more ships of this class and to enlarge and modify T-AKR 10 were abandoned. Sister *Jupiter* (T-AKR 11) (ex-*Lipscomb Lykes*, ex-*Arizona*), chartered 7-5-80, went to the Maritime Administration on 24-4-86 and became part of Ready Reserve Force on 2-5-86. Sister *Cape Isabel* (ex-*Charles Lykes*, ex-*Nevada*) became part of the RRF on 23-5-86.

REPLENISHMENT OILERS

◆ **10 (+8) Henry J. Kaiser class** Bldr: Avondale SY, Westwego, La. (T-AB 191, 192: hulls by PennShip, Chester, Pa.; completed by Tampa SY, Florida) (*Atlantic/†Pacific Fleet)

	Laid down	L	In serv.
T-AO 187 Henry J. Kaiser*	22-8-84	5-10-85	19-12-86
T-AO 188 Joshua Humphreys*	17-12-84	22-2-86	3-4-87
T-AO 189 John Lenthall*	15-7-85	9-8-86	25-6-87
T-AO 190 Andrew J. Higgins†	21-11-85	17-1-87	22-10-87
T-AO 191 Benjamin Isherwood†	12-7-86	15-8-88	11-92
T-AO 192 Henry Eckford*	22-1-87	14-8-89	12-92
T-AO 193 Walter S. Diehl†	7-8-86	2-10-87	13-9-88
T-AO 194 John Ericsson†	15-3-89	21-4-90	19-3-91
T-AO 195 Leroy Grumman*	6-7-87	3-12-88	2-8-89
T-AO 196 Kanawha*	13-7-89	22-9-90	6-12-91
T-AO 197 Pecos	17-2-88	23-9-89	6-7-90
T-AO 198 Big Horn*	9-10-89	2-2-91	7-7-92
T-AO 199 Tippecanoe†	19-11-90	16-5-92	4-93
T-AO 200 Guadalupe†	9-7-90	5-10-91	11-92
T-AO 201 Patuxent*	16-10-91	3-93	6-94
T-AO 202 Yukon†	13-5-91	10-92	12-93
T-AO 203 Laramie*	11-92	. . .	6-95
T-AO 204 Rappahannock†	3-92	. . .	1-95

Authorized: T-AO 187 in FY 82, T-AO 188 in FY 83, T-AO 189–19[illegible] 84, T-AO 191–193 in FY 85, T-AO 194–195 in FY 86, T-AO 196–19[illegible] 87, T-AO 198–199 in FY 88, and T-AO 200–204 in FY 89

John Lenthall (T-AO 189) George Nassiopoul[illegible]

Pecos (T-AO 197) Victor M. Bac[illegible]

Henry J. Kaiser (T-AO 187) Pradignac & Lé[illegible]

Andrew J. Higgins (T-AO 190) PH1 Scott Allen, US[illegible]

D: 9,500 tons light (40,700–42,000 fl) **S:** 20 kts (sust.)
Dim: 206.51 (198.13 pp) × 29.75 × 10.97
A: provision for 2/20-mm Mk 15 CIWS (I × 2)
Electron Equipt:
Radar: 2/. . .nav.—EW: SLQ-25 towed torpedo decoys
M: 2 Colt-Pielstick 10 PC4.2V 570 diesels; 2 CP props; 32,540 bh[illegible]
Electric: 12,000 kw (2 × 3,500-kw, 2 × 2,500-kw diesel sets)
Range: 6,000/20 **Fuel:** 1,629 tons heavy oil, 165 tons diesel
Crew: 20 officers, 75 unlicensed MSC crew, plus 21 navy (137 berths tot.)

Remarks: 20,706 grt/28,407 dwt. Design contract to George Sharp, Inc., Intended to replace all earlier MSC-manned replenishment oilers. Deliverie[illegible] delayed by the bankruptcy of the second-source builder, PennShip, but Avonda[illegible] well behind schedule. T-AO 191, 192 originally ordered 6-5-85 for delivery [illegible] 7-90, respectively, but all work ceased by spring 1989; contract relet to Ta[illegible]

:NISHMENT OILERS *(continued)*

Florida, on 16-11-89. T-AO 191 left builders 18-10-89 and T-AO 192 on 30-10- mporary layup. Towed to completion yard, but T-AO 191 aground off Kitty Jorth Carolina, 24-12-89, repaired at Norfolk. T-AO 194 and 196 originally 7-86 from PennShip, but canceled at yard's request and reordered 16-6-88 from e. T-AO 198, 200, 202, 204 ordered 6-10-88, with T-AO 199, 201, 203 to have an alternate yard; instead, Avondale bid lowest and won contract 28-3-89, ng for out-of-sequence construction schedule. Navy had requested only one for lanned two each year in FY 90, 91; instead, Congress "bought out" remainder ogram. Time from authorization to completion for later units roughly equals to build an aircraft carrier! Have proven very successful in service, however: 8 provided 25 million gallons fuel, 4,000 pallets of food and spares, and carried sengers during 1-11-90 to 24-5-91 deployment to Mideast. T-AO 190 went off Omani coast 2-1-90, was repaired locally.

ms: Equipped for underway replenishment of liquids and solids. Helicopter no hangar. Cargo: 32 tanks totaling 21,161 m^3 : 180,000 bbl liquid (86,400 bbl 54,000 bbl JP-5; 39,600 convertible; plus 327 tons feedwater, 390 tons potable lus 534 pallets dry cargo and eight 20-ft provisions containers. Five alongside tations (three to port), one solid transfer station per side. There are eight cargo vith a combined capacity of 5,448 tons/hr. The engines for the first two were Alsthom in France. Have a CGEE-Alsthom integrated auxiliary electric drive or low speeds, driving either or both props. Last three to have double-bottom tion, per contract modification announced 8-92; will increase cost by $125

eosho class (SCB 82 type) (5 in reserve) Bldr: New York SB, den, N.J. (T-AO 143: Bethlehem, Quincy, Mass.) (†Pacific Fleet)

	L	In serv.	To MSC	In reserve
43 *Neosho**	10-11-53	24-9-54	25-5-78	10-8-92
44 *ISSINEWA*	12-6-54	18-1-55	15-11-76	30-7-91
45 *AYAMPA*	12-9-54	19-4-55	17-8-78	14-11-91
46 *SHIWI*	11-12-54	6-7-55	1-10-79	31-7-92
47 *Truckee*	10-3-55	23-11-55	30-1-80	12-12-91
48 :HATOULA†	9-7-55	12-1-56	5-9-80	. . .

iiwi (T-AO 146)—no helo deck John Bouvia, 6-91

ee (T-AO 147)—refueling *Nicholson* (DD 982) French Navy, 3-90

sinewa (T-AO 144)—extra bridge deck George Nassiopoulos, 5-91

9,533 tons light (36,840 fl) **S:** 20 kts
: 199.65 (195.07 wl) × 26.21 × 10.67
tron Equipt:
dar: 1/Raytheon TM 1650/6X or 12X nav., 1/SPS-10 surf. search
: sets G.E. geared steam turbines; 2 props; 28,000 shp
ers: 2 Babcock & Wilcox; 42.2 kg/cm^2, 357°C
tric: 1,500 kw **Fuel:** 5,000 tons
v: 19 officers, 88 unlicensed MSC + 21 navy

ks: Active pair: 19,255 grt/37,431 dwt. Carry 180,000 bbl liquid cargo (approx. ons). Helicopter platform aft in T-AO 143, 144, 147 only. Operated by MSC as ay-replenishment ships for navy. Transferred to MSC as a cost-saving measure (navy crew was 360 total). Masting and superstructures differ in detail. Have 29 cargo tanks, 9 cargo pumps with combined output of 4,556 tons/hr. T-AO 148 in collision with *Chancellorsville* (CG 62) 7-8-91 in the South China Sea; repaired.

Status: Five have been transferred to the Maritime Administration for layup in the National Defense Reserve Fleet on the dates listed in the table; they are being retained for possible reactivation in an emergency. T-AO 148 will probably follow during Fiscal Year 1993. One may be transferred to Argentina.

Note: Of the five *Mispillion*-class oilers listed in the previous edition, all have been transferred to the Maritime Administration's National Defense Reserve Fleet, most for disposal: *Mispillion* (T-AO 105) on 8-2-90; *Navasota* (T-AO 106) on 2-10-91 (permission to scrap given 1-92); *Passumpsic* (T-AO 107) on 30-9-91 for scrap (UNREP gear had been ruined by Mount Pinatubo eruption); *Pawcatuck* (T-AO 108) on 21-9-91 for scrap; and *Waccamaw* (T-AO 109) to reserve on 11-10-89 and to MARAD 22-10-89 as spare parts source. Of the two *Cimarron*-class oilers listed in the previous edition, *Marias* (T-AO 57), in reserve since 2-10-73, remains in the National Defense Reserve Fleet, while permission to scrap *Taluga* (T-AO 62), which had been in reserve since 4-5-72, was given during 2-92.

TRANSPORT OILERS (T-AOT)

Note: Congress authorized (but did not fund) two sealift tankers under FY 90 to begin replacement of the *Sealift* class, in part out of concern for the rapid decline in U.S. sealift resources and shipyards. To date, no funding has been provided.

◆ **9 Sealift class** Bldrs: First four: Todd Shipyards, Los Angeles; others: Bath Iron Works, Bath, Me.

	L	In serv.
T-AOT 168 Sealift Pacific	13-10-73	14-8-74
T-AOT 169 Sealift Arabian Sea	26-1-74	6-5-75
T-AOT 170 Sealift China Sea	20-4-74	9-5-75
T-AOT 171 Sealift Indian Ocean	27-7-74	29-8-74
T-AOT 172 Sealift Atlantic	26-1-74	26-8-74
T-AOT 173 Sealift Mediterranean	9-3-74	6-11-74
T-AOT 174 Sealift Caribbean	8-6-74	10-2-75
T-AOT 175 Sealift Arctic	31-8-74	22-5-75
T-AOT 176 Sealift Antarctic	26-10-74	1-8-75

Sealift Mediterranean (T-AOT 173) Dr. Giorgio Arra, 1-92

Sealift China Sea (T-AOT 70) Dr. Giorgio Arra, 1-91

D: 33,000 tons (fl) **S:** 16 kts
Dim: 178.92 (170.80 pp) × 25.61 × 10.50
Electron Equipt:
Radar: 1/Raytheon TM 1650/6X nav., 1/Raytheon TM 1645 nav.
M: 2 Colt-Pielstick, 14PC-2V400 14-cyl., 520-rpm diesels; 1 CP prop; 14,000 bhp
Electric: 2,600 kw **Range:** 12,000/16 **Fuel:** 3,440 tons
Crew: 9 officers, 17 unlicensed, 2 cadets (contract crew)

Remarks: 17,157 grt/27,217 dwt (vary slightly). All now used in freighting service. Cargo: 225,154 barrels fuel oil, diesel, etc. Equipped with bow-thruster. MSC chartered these ships for twenty years and has a commercial contractor operating them; current owner is the Irving Trust Co., New York. All redesignated T-AOT on 30-9-78. A five-year operating contract for these ships was signed with International Maritime Carriers, Inc., Mineola, New York, on 9-3-90. All were engaged in ocean transport of fuels in 1992.

Note: Of the two *Maumee*-class transport oilers listed in the last edition, *Maumee* (T-AOT 149) and ex-*Yukon* (T-AO 152), both were made available for foreign transfer on 20-2-92, with Argentina being offered a choice. Mission-class transport oiler *Mission*

TRANSPORT OILERS (T-AOT) *(continued)*

Santa Ynez (T-AO 134) was listed for disposal from the NDRF on 1-11-90, while *Suamico*-class transport oiler *Saugatuck* (T-AO 75) remained in the NDRF through mid-1992.

Permission to scrap the three Admiral-class transports listed in the previous edition, *General Alexander M. Patch* (AP 122), *General Simon B. Buckner* (AP 123), and General *Maurice Rose* (AP 126), was given 20-8-90, and the ships were transferred to Maritime Administration control for disposal.

CABLE SHIPS (T-ARC)

◆ **1 Zeus class** Bldr: National Steel SB, San Diego, Cal.

	Laid down	L	In serv.
T-ARC 7 Zeus	1-6-81	9-10-82	19-3-84

Zeus (T-ARC 7) Dr. Giorgio Arra, 4-91

Zeus (T-ARC 7) Leo Van Ginderen, 2-91

D: 8,297 tons light (14,225 fl) **S:** 15.8 kts
Dim: 153.2 (138.4 pp) × 22.3 × 7.3
Electron Equipt: Radar: 2/. . . nav.
M: 5 G.M. EMD 20-cyl., 3,600-bhp diesels, electric drive; 2 CP props; 12,500 shp
Range: 10,000/15 **Fuel:** 1,816 tons **Electric:** 3,500 kw
Crew: 88 MSC crew, 8 navy, 32 civilian technicians, 38 spare berths

Remarks: 3,750 dwt. Authorized under Fiscal Year 1979 Budget and ordered 17-8-79 to replace T-ARC 3. Plans to request a second were canceled. Has passive tank roll stabilization, two 1,200-hp funnel bow-thrusters forward and two aft. Cable capacity is 1,170 m³ coiled (about 590 n.m.) plus 1,004 m³ spare capacity (506 n.m.), and up to 3,117 tons of cable repeaters can be stowed. Able to conduct acoustic, hydrographic, and bathymetric surveys. The five main engines also provide for the ship's-service generators; there is also a 500-kw emergency generator. Painted white. Operates primarily in the Atlantic.

◆ **1 Neptune class (S3-S2-BP1 type)**
Bldr: Pusey & Jones, Wilmington, Del.

	L	In Navy
T-ARC 6 Albert J. Meyer	1945	13-5-63

Neptune (T-ARC 2)—T-ARC 6 is similar Walter Sartori, 2-89

D: 5,818 tons light (8,510 fl) **S:** 12.5 kts
Dim: 112.8 (98.15 pp) × 14.35 × 7.60
Electron Equipt:
Radar: 1/Raytheon TM 1650/6X nav., 1/Raytheon TM 1660/12S nav.
M: 3 G.E. 12-cyl. diesels, electric drive; 2 props; 4,100 shp
Electric: 4,250 kw tot. (2 × 2,000-kw , 1 × 250-kw diesel sets)
Range: 10,000/13 **Fuel:** 1,129 tons
Crew: 16 officers, 58 unlicensed + MSC 18 technicians

Remarks: 4,012 grt/4,332 dwt. Transferred from army on 18-9-63. Extensivel ernized 3-78 to 5-80, including the replacement of the original Skinner Uniflow r cating steam plants with diesel-electric machinery. Has a 1,000-hp tunnel-th forward. Cable capacity is nominally 1,240 m³ (about 625 nautical miles), and t can carry 2,020 tons of cable repeaters. Sister *Neptune* (T-ARC 2, ex-U.S. *Wm. H.G. Bullard)* was transferred to the Maritime Administration 24-9-91 for tion in the National Defense Reserve Fleet.

FLEET TUGS

◆ **7 Powhatan class** Bldr: Marinette Marine, Marinette, Wisc.
(*Atlantic/†Pacific Fleet)

	Laid down	L	In serv.
T-ATF 166 Powhatan*	30-9-76	24-6-78	15-6-79
T-ATF 167 Narragansett†	5-5-77	28-11-78	9-1-79
T-ATF 168 Catawba†	14-12-77	12-5-79	28-5-80
T-ATF 169 Navajo†	14-12-77	20-12-79	13-6-80
T-ATF 170 Mohawk*	22-3-79	5-4-80	16-10-80
T-ATF 171 Sioux†	22-3-79	30-10-80	12-5-81
T-ATF 172 Apache*	22-3-79	20-12-80	30-7-81

Authorized: 1 in FY 75, 3 in FY 76, 3 in FY 78

Powhatan (T-ATF 166)—with salvage equipment Dr. Giorgio Arra

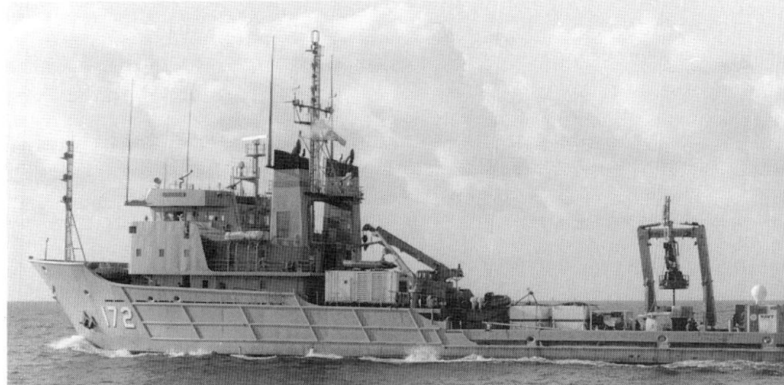

Apache (T-ATF 172)—with diving equipment modules Dr. Giorgio Arr

Mohawk (T-ATF 170)—in standard configuration Leo Van Gindere

D: 2,000 tons (2,260 fl) **S:** 15 kts
Dim: 73.20 (68.88 pp) × 12.80 × 4.74
Electron Equipt:
Radar: 1/Raytheon TM 1660/12S nav., 1/SPS-53 nav.
M: 2 G.M. EMD 20-645X7 20-cyl. diesels, electric drive; 2 Kort-n CP props; 4,500 shp (3,600 sust.)

LEET TUGS *(continued)*

Electric: 1,200 kw (3 × 400-kw diesel sets)
Range: 10,000/13 **Fuel:** 600 tons
Crew: 6 officers, 14 unlicensed + 6 Navy communications team

emarks: 902 grt/613 nrt. Modified oilfield-supply-boat design built to merchant arine specifications. If required, could mount two 20-mm AA (I × 2) and two 12.7-mm achine guns (I × 2). Five were requested under FY 78, three approved. Have a 300-hp w-thruster and one 10-ton electrohydraulic crane. Can carry the Mk 1 Mod. 1, 90-ton ep-diving support module on the stern and can support a 20-man Navy salvage team. ave a 60-ton bollard-pull capacity. Foam fire-fighting equipment. Hull has unusual uble-chine configuration.

IRCRAFT MAINTENANCE SHIPS

2 converted Maritime Administration C5-S-78a, "Seabridge" type Bldr: Ingalls SB, Pascagoula, Miss.

	In serv.	Converted
AVB 3 WRIGHT (ex-*Young America*, ex-*Mormacsun*)	1970	14-12-84 to 14-5-86
AVB 4 CURTISS (ex-*Great Republic*, ex-*Mormacsky*)	1969	17-12-85 to 18-8-87

ight (T-AVB 3)—in layberth at Philadelphia
George R. Schneider, Jr., 5-89

tiss (T-AVB 4) U.S. Navy, 8-87

: 12,409 tons light (27,580 fl) **S:** 23.6 kts
im: 183.49 (170.69 pp) × 27.43 × 10.36
ectron Equipt: 2/. . . nav.
: 2 sets G.E. geared steam turbines; 1 prop; 30,000 shp
ilers: 2 Combustion Engineering
ectric: 3,000 kw (2 × 1,500 kw)
ange: 9,000/23 **Fuel:** 2,781 tons + 839 tons diesel
ew: 11 off., 22 unlicensed + 300 marines

arks: 23,255 grt/13,651 dwt. Roll-on/Roll-off vehicle cargo and container carriers rted by Todd SY, Galveston, Texas, to transport the men and equipment vans of a ne Intermediate Maintenance Activity in support of aircraft deployed ashore. ional accommodations built on aft and helicopter deck added over former forward Still able to carry 664 standard 20-ft containers and 14,000 bbl liquid cargo. ded to revert to cargo-carrying role after delivering the aviation support person- nd equipment. Maintained in reduced operating status (not part of the Ready ve Force), being broken out for exercises. T-AVB 3 at Philadelphia, T-AVB 4 at Iueneme, California. Cargo capacity: 34,903 m³ grain/31,824 m³ bale, including ³ refrigerated cargo. Can carry 332 40-ft containers or 654 20-ft containers, 352 es. Have stern ramp and two side doors aft for vehicles. Ten 30-ton, one 70-ton derricks. Six holds, but forward two can only be unloaded by off-ship cranes. Both activated for Operation Desert Shield/Desert Storm in 8-90.

MILITARY SEALIFT COMMAND CHARTERED FLEET

following section describes those MSC-controlled ships on long-term charter, ing with the units intended for the Afloat Prepositioning Force (formerly the Deployment Logistics Force). Ships listed are those that were on long-term r to the Military Sealift Command in 7-92; MSC also charters ships for single- deliveries as well as managing the shipment of all military cargo by sea by of contract with established U.S.-flag shippers.

MARITIME PREPOSITIONING SHIPS

♦ 0 (+ 9) large roll-on/roll-off prepositioning ships Bldrs: . . .

	Laid down	L	In serv.
. . . .	. . .	. . .	. . .
. . . .	. . .	. . .	. . .
. . . .	. . .	. . .	. . .
. . . .	. . .	. . .	. . .
. . . .	. . .	. . .	. . .
. . . .	. . .	. . .	. . .
. . . .	. . .	. . .	. . .
. . . .	. . .	. . .	. . .
. . . .	. . .	. . .	. . .

D: 38,000 tons (fl) **S:** . . . kts
Dim: 213.36 (195.00 pp) × 32.16 × 12.19 max.
Electron Equipt: Radar: . . .
M: 4 Colt-Pielstick 14PC4.2V diesels; 2 props; 33,500 bhp
Electric: 5,000 kw (2 × 2,500-kw diesel sets)
Range: 12,000/24 **Crew:** . . .

Remarks: *Added* by Congress to FY 90 shipbuilding request due to concerns that the U.S. and its allies lack sufficient sealift assets, military or commercial. Design contracts let spring 1992, with intention to order nine by 12-92 and all to be completed by 1997. Preliminary design characteristics above may be altered considerably in final version. Required to have three 50-ton-capacity twin pedestal cranes, two side vehicle cargo ports, and a slewing stern ramp. Will have 27,870 m² of military vehicle parking space. Construction may all or in part be replaced by converted commercial vessels.

♦ 5 2nd Lt John P. Bobo class Bldr: General Dynamics, Quincy, Mass.

	Laid down	L	In serv.
2ND LT JOHN P. BOBO	1-7-83	19-1-85	14-2-85
PFC DEWAYNE F. WILLIAMS	1-9-83	18-5-85	6-6-85
1ST LT BALDOMERO LOPEZ	23-3-84	26-10-85	21-11-85
1ST LT JACK LUMMUS	22-6-84	22-2-86	6-3-86
SGT WILLIAM R. BUTTON	22-8-84	17-5-86	22-5-86

1st Lt Baldomero Lopez Peter Voss, 2-91

1st Lt Jack Lummus Dr. Giorgio Arra, 9-91

D: 22,700 tons light (40,846 fl)
S: 18.8 kts (trials); 17.7 kts sustained
Dim: 205.18 (187.32 pp/199.00 wl) × 32.16 × 8.99
Electron Equipt: Radar: 2/. . . nav.
M: 2 Stork Werkspoor 18TM410V diesels; 1 prop; 26,400 bhp—1,000-shp bow-thruster
Electric: 7,850 kw **Range:** 11,107/17.7 **Fuel:** 3,080 tons
Crew: 30 contractor crew, 7 MSC crew, 7 navy, 25 maintenance crew

Remarks: 44,543 grt/26,523 dwt (22,454 cargo dwt)/14,461 nrt. Maritime Administration C8-M-MA134j design. First two contracted for on 17-8-82, others on 14-1-83. Intended to transport material needed for one quarter of one Marine Assault Brigade. In addition to listed personnel, have 102 temporary berths for vehicle crews. Cargo capacity includes up to 522 standard 20-ft. vans (350 for ammunition, 110 general stores, 30 with fuel drums, and 32 refrigerated), plus 14,000 m of roll-on/roll-off vehicle capacity to carry up to 1,400 vehicles. A Navire stern slewing ramp provides access to the six vehicle decks and can either discharge 60-ton vehicles to a pier or amphibious

MARITIME PREPOSITIONING SHIPS *(continued)*

vehicles of up to 23 tons directly into the water; the stern door is 11 × 4.55 m. The upper deck can stow 2 LCM(8) landing craft, 6 unpowered causeway sections, 4 powered causeway sections, a warping tug, 4 pipe trailers, and 16 hose reels. The ships carry 5,764.6 m^3 (1,523,000 gallons) of transferable bulk fuel, plus 2,039 55-gallon fuel drums. They can also transport 307 m^3 of potable water. Five 39-ton pedestal cranes are fitted, with two sets being paired, and there is a large helicopter deck at the stern. Unloading rates: all vehicles and one-sixth cargo at a pier in 12 hrs; all cargo at a pier in three days; all cargo while moored out in five days; there is a four-point mooring system.

Are actually owned by a variety of holding corporations and were operated on an expected 25-year charter by American Overseas Marine, a subsidiary of General Dynamics; operating rights sold 6-92 to Maersk Lines, Madison, New Jersey, a subsidiary of A.P. Møller, Denmark. *Bobo* is in MPS Squadron One in the Atlantic; rest formed MPS Squadron 3 in 10-86, operating near Guam, carrying equipment for the 1st Marine Expeditionary Brigade, Kaneohe Bay, Oahu. *Button* spent 230 days in the Persian Gulf from 29-8-90 to 7-5-91 providing contingency support to U.S. Marine forces.

♦ 5 Cpl Louis J. Hauge, Jr., class

Bldr: Odense Staalskibsvaerft A/S, Lindo, Denmark

	In serv.	Acq.	Conv. by	In serv.
Cpl Louis J. Hauge, Jr. (ex-*Estelle Maersk*)	10-79	3-1-84	Bethlehem SY, Sparrows Pt., Md.	7-9-84
Pfc William B. Baugh (ex-*Eleo Maersk*)	4-79	17-1-83	Bethlehem SY, Beaumont, Tx.	30-10-84
Pfc James Anderson, Jr. (ex-*Emma Maersk*)	7-79	31-10-83	Bethlehem SY, Sparrows Pt., Md.	26-3-85
1st Lt Alex Bonnyman (ex-*Emelie Maersk*)	1-80	30-1-84	Bethlehem SY, Beaumont, Tx.	26-9-85
Pvt Harry Fisher (ex-*Evelyn Maersk*)	4-80	2-4-83	Bethlehem SY, Sparrows Pt., Md.	12-9-85

Cpl Louis J. Hauge, Jr. Peter Voss, 11-90

Pfc James Anderson, Jr. Peter C. Westdijk, 12-90

Pfc William B. Baugh Leo Van Ginderen, 7-90

D: 28,249 tons light (46,484 fl) **S:** 18.5 kts (17.2 sust.)
Dim: 230.25 (215.00 pp) × 27.48 × 10.02
Electron Equipt: Radar: 2/. . . nav.
M: 1 Sulzer 7RND 76M, 7-cyl. diesel; 1 prop; 16,800 bhp
Electric: 4,250 kw **Range:** 10,800/17.2 **Fuel:** 3,228 tons
Crew: 20 contractor and 7 MSC crew, 30 maintenance crew + 80 troops

Remarks: Operated by owner, Maersk Lines, on long-term charter. Carry one-fifth o the vehicles, equipment, and supplies to outfit a Marine Assault Brigade. Transport u to 413 containers (280 ammunition, 86 general cargo, 23 drummed fuel, 24 refriger ated), plus providing 11,369 m^2 vehicle cargo space. There are 4/30-ton and 2/36-to pedestal cranes, side-loading vehicle ports amidships, and a Navire slewing ramp ha been added aft, beneath a helicopter deck. There are eight cargo hatches, and thre vehicle parking decks. Liquid cargo includes 4,920 m^3 transferable vehicle fuel, 504 m potable water, and 2,252 m^3 of lube oil. There is a bow-thruster. First three ordere 17-8-82, others on 14-1-83.

All five are part of Maritime Prepositioning Ship Squadron 2, operating in the India Ocean, with *Bonnyman,* as flagship, carrying eight-man navy communications tea and equipment for the 7th Marine Expeditionary Brigade, Twenty-Nine Palms, Ca fornia. *Bonnyman* originally to be named *1st Lt Alexander Bonnyman, Jr.;* change 4-3-86. Name of *Pvt. Harry Fisher* was to have been changed to *Pvt Franklin S. Philli* under a Secretary of the Navy directive signed 27-6-89, but the order was not carrie out; "Harry Fisher" was a pseudonym in use by Phillips when he won the Medal Honor.

♦ 3 Sgt Matej Kocak class

Bldr: Sun Shpbldg., Chester, Pa. (Converted by National Steel Shipbuilding, San Diego, Cal.)

	In serv.	In serv.
Sgt Matej Kocak (ex-*John D. Waterman*)	14-3-81	5-10-84
Pfc Eugene A. Obregon (ex-*Thomas Heywood*)	1-11-82	15-1-85
Maj Stephen W. Pless (ex-*Charles Carroll*)	14-3-83	1-5-85

Sgt Matej Kocak—note traveling container crane
Leo Van Ginderen, 9

Maj Stephen W. Pless Peter C. Westdijk,

D: . . . tons light (51,612 fl) **S:** 20.9 kts
Dim: 250.24 (234.85 pp) × 32.16 × 10.06
Electron Equipt: Radar: 2/. . . nav.
M: 2 sets G.E. geared steam turbines; 1/6-bladed prop; 32,000 shp
Boilers: 2; Combustion Engineering
Range: 13,000/20.9 **Fuel:** 3,450 tons (+300 tons diesel)
Crew: 85 crew, 7 MSC crew, 8 navy, 25 maintenance crew

Remarks: 25,426 grt/22,910 dwt. First two contracted for on 17-8-82, third on 14 all with Waterman Steamship Co. as operator. Intended to transport one-fourth vehicles, fuel, supplies, and provisions to support a Marine Assault Battalion. 213 ammunition containers, 150 "Lo/Lo" containers, 10 general cargo containe drummed fuel containers, and 32 refrigerated containers, plus a large num vehicles and cargo fuel and water. Lengthened 39.8 m during conversion, and he ter deck and ramp added. Have paired 50-ton and paired 35-ton portal crane retain a traveling container gantry forward. Owned by various investment cons

All operated by Waterman Steamship Corp. from U.S. East Coast in MPS Sq 1, carrying equipment for the 6th Marine Expeditionary Brigade, Camp Le North Carolina.

ERAL CARGO SHIPS

nobile hospital prepositioning ship
lr: Kaldnes M/V A/S, Tønsberg, Norway (In serv. 1977)

E STAR (ex-*Concordia Star*, ex-*Hoegh Star*, ex-*Concordia Star*, ex-
ta Atlantica, ex-*Concordia Star*)

e Star M.S.C., 1990

24,000 tons (fl) **S:** 17.5 kts
n: 171.41 (163.02) × 25.43 × 10.55
1 Nylands/Burmeister & Wain 7-cyl. diesel; 1 prop; 13,100 bhp
ıge: . . ./. . . **Fuel:** 2,935 tons heavy oil; 465 tons diesel
ctric: 2,040 kw (3 × 680 kw) **Crew:** 21 total

rks: 10,472 grt/15,922 dwt. Chartered 31-12-88 from Sealift Tankships, Inc. ed to Diego Garcia 11-89 as part of Afloat Prepositioning Force for two years 00-bed deployable hospital contained in 330 standard containers. The hospital es 1,000 medical staff to operate fully and covers 30 acres when set up; it has a self-support capability. The ship has five holds, nine hatches, a 570 TEU ner capacity, one 150-ton heavy lift, six 10-ton, four 16-ton, and one 5-ton cranes. 7-month charter with two 17-month extension options. The hospital was de- during Operation Desert Shield/Desert Storm in 1990–91.

afloat ammunition prepositioning ship
dr: Nippon Kokan, Tsurumi (In serv. 7-77)

NTAGE (ex-*Tacna II*, ex-*Thermopylae*, ex-*Confidence*, ex-*Barber*
ermopylae, ex-*Thermopylae*)

27,750 tons (fl) **S:** 17.5 kts
n: 171.02 (165.41 pp) × 26.37 × 9.99
1 Mitsubishi-Sulzer 7-cyl. diesel; 1 prop; 14,000 bhp
ctric: 2,220 kw (3 × 740-kw diesel sets) **Range:** . . ./. . .
el: 1,886 tons heavy oil; 161 tons diesel **Crew:** 22 tot.

rks: 11,675 grt/22,180 dwt. Chartered from Red River Shipping 5-88, with r beginning 10-88 for 17 months with two 17-month options. Originally owned by can Automar, on hire charter to Red River, with an option to buy that was taken 1992 by the first minority-owned shipping line in the United States; operated by Gulf Marine. Employed as air force munitions prepositioning ship in the Medi- ean. Has five holds, 762 TEU container capacity (20 refrigerated), four 16-ton, 0-ton, and ten 10-ton cranes.

combination cargo carriers Bldr: Howaldtswerke, Kiel, Germany

	In serv.
N RIDGE (ex-*Woerman Mercur*, ex-*Carol Mercur*, ex-*man Mercur*)	1979
N WAVE (ex-*Woerman Mira*, ex-*Sloman Mira*)	1-80

n Wave—showing surface-piercing bow bulb
Peter C. Westdijk, 10-91

18,178 tons (fl) **S:** 17 kts
n: 154.57 (146.06 pp) × 21.26 × 7.46
2 Krupp-MaK diesels; 1 prop; 10,000 bhp
nge: 11,000/17 **Fuel:** 1,052 tons heavy oil; 168 tons diesel
ctric: 410 kw **Crew:** 9 officers, 12 unlicensed

Remarks: *Green Ridge:* 5,805 grt/9,549 dwt; *Green Wave:* 9,521 grt/12,487 dwt—but are generally similar sisters. Both chartered from Central Gulf Lines: *Green Wave* in 8-84 (renewed 30-11-88 for 17 months, plus two 17-month extension options) for Greenland and Antarctic supply, *Green Ridge* in 1-10-88 (for 17 months, plus two 17-month extension options) for general cargo transportation. Both charters since extended. Have ice-strengthened hulls, four long hatches/four holds, 543 TEU container capacity, six 25-ton cranes (four of which can be ganged to lift 80 tons from hold No. 4).

◆ **1 combination cargo carrier** Bldr: Odense Staalskibsvaerft A/S, Lindo, Denmark (In serv. 1980)

MAERSK CONSTELLATION (ex-*Elizabeth Maersk*)

D: 34,069 tons (fl) **S:** 18.6 kts **Dim:** 168.21 pp × 27.44 × . . .
M: 2 Sulzer 7-cyl. diesels; 1 prop; 15,960 bhp
Range: . . . **Fuel:** 2,708 tons heavy oil; 160 tons diesel
Electric: 2,550 kw (3 × 850 kw) **Crew:** . . .

Remarks: 29,750 tons dwt. Chartered 30-11-88 for 17 months (with two 17-month extension options) from Maersk Lines, which operates her for Pacific area service. Has a starboard quarter stern door/ramp for vehicle cargo. Sister to *Cpl Louis J. Hauge*-class maritime prepositioning ships; similar appearance.

◆ **1 C5-78 type combination cargo ship** Bldr: Ingalls SB, Pascagoula

	In serv.	Chartered
ROVER (ex-*American Rover*, ex-*Defiance*, ex-*Mormacsea*)	4-69	6-3-82

Rover Leo Van Ginderen, 9-91

D: 27,980 tons (fl) **S:** 23.6 kts
Dim: 183.33 (170.69 pp) × 27.43 × 10.39
Electron Equipt: Radar: 2/. . . nav.
M: 2 sets G.E. geared steam turbines; 1 prop; 30,000 shp
Boilers: 2 Combustion Eng.; 74 kg/cm^2 **Electric:** 3,000 kw
Range: 12,000/23.6 **Fuel:** 2,790 tons
Crew: 11 off., 23 unlicensed

Remarks: 11,757 grt/15,694 dwt. Chartered from Central Gulf Lines for general cargo carrying. Charter renewed 30-11-88 for 18 months, with two 17-month extension options. Cargo: 70 standard containers, plus 33,814 m^3 dry cargo volume. Stern door for vehicle cargo, seven hatches. Carries ammunition from Sunny Point, N. Carolina, to Nordenham, West Germany. Sister *Rapid* off-charter 12-85, to RRF 9-12-87 as *Cape Nome*.

◆ **1 Maritime Administration C4-S-1u-type general cargo ship**
Bldr: Newport News SB & Dry Dock (In serv. 1969)

CLEVELAND (ex-*President Cleveland*, ex-*American Mail*)

D: 31,995 tons (fl) **S:** 21 kts
Dim: 184.41 (177.55 pp) × 25.05 × 10.68
M: 2 sets G.E. geared steam turbines; 1 prop; 24,000 shp
Boilers: 2 Babcock & Wilcox
Electric: 2,500 kw (2 × 1,250-kw turboalternators)
Range: 14,000/20.8 **Fuel:** 3,701 tons **Crew:** 47 tot.

Remarks: 15,949 grt/22,536 dwt (11,559 grt/18,260 dwt at 9.53 max. draft in container service) general cargo vessel on charter from Sealift Inc. to transport cargo to and from Diego Garcia. Has six holds and seven hatches and can transport up to 409 standard 20-ft. cargo containers. Cranes include 1 × 70-ton heavy-lift, 20 × 20-ton, and 4 × 15-ton. Can carry 12 passengers and has refrigerated cargo facilities. Sisters *Cape Gibson* and *Cape Girardeau* are in the Maritime Administration's Ready Reserve Force.

◆ **1 Maritime Administration C4-S-66a-type general cargo ship**
Bldr: Avondale SY, Avondale, Louisiana (In serv. 1966)

TAMPA BAY (ex-*Stella Lykes*)

D: 21,840 tons (fl) **S:** 19 kts
Dim: 164.60 (156.95 pp) × 23.22 × 9.96 max.
M: 2 sets Westinghouse geared steam turbines; 1 prop; 15,500 shp
Boilers: 2 Foster-Wheeler; 49 kg/cm^2
Electric: 1,500 kw (2 × 750-kw turboalternators)
Range: 12,000/19 **Fuel:** 2,724 tons
Crew: 12 officers, 26 unlicensed

Remarks: 10,723 grt/14,897 dwt (7,189 grt/10,996 dwt in container service at 9.12 m max. draft) general cargo/container ship chartered from Afram Lines for service between the U.S. East Coast and Northern Europe. Has four holds, six hatches, and two wing hatches. Equipped with bow-thruster. Can carry 62 standard 20-ft. cargo containers. Cargo capacity: 21,240 m^3 bale plus 4,000 bbl liquid. Cranes include 1 × 80-ton and 20 × 15 tons. Five sisters serve in the Maritime Administration's Ready Reserve Force.

GENERAL CARGO SHIPS *(continued)*

◆ 1 general cargo ship
Bldr: Bethlehem Steel SY, Sparrows Point, Md. (In serv. 1962)

LESLIE LYKES

D: approx. 20,000 tons (fl) **S:** 18 kts
Dim: 180.60 (172.98 pp) × 21.04 × 9.17 max.
M: 2 sets G.E. geared steam turbines; 1 prop; 9,000 shp
Boilers: 2 **Electric:** 1,200 kw (2 × 600-kw turboalternators)
Fuel: 2,937 tons **Crew:** . . .

Remarks: 11,891 grt/14,759 dwt (8,762 grt/11,774 dwt in container service at 8.20 m draft) general cargo/container vessel chartered from Lykes Brothers, Jacksonville, Florida, for Mediterranean and Mideast support and was also employed in Operation Desert Sortie to return materials from the Mideast in 1991–92. Has three holds, eight hatches. Can transport 204 standard 20-ft. cargo containers. Has a bow-thruster and can carry 12 passengers. Cranes include 1 × 60-ton, 4 × 35-ton, 12 × 16-ton, and 4 × 10-ton capacity.

◆ 1 "Down-range support ship"
Bldr: Moss Point Marine, Escatawpa, Miss.

	L	In serv.
SEACOR CLIPPER (ex-*Nicor Clipper*)	20-4-82	5-83

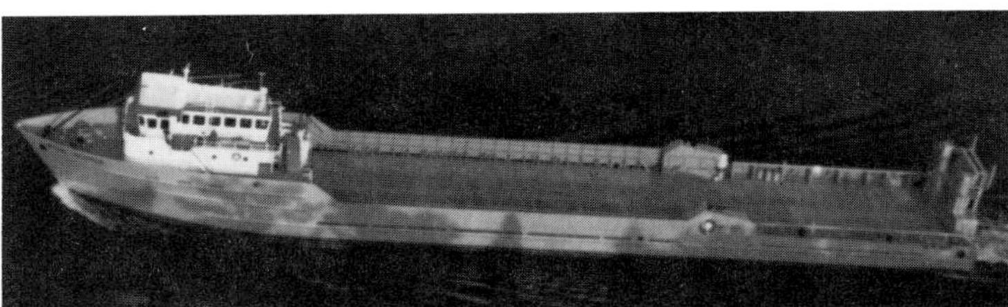

Seacor Clipper (as Nicor Clipper) Moss Point, 1983

D: . . . **S:** 10 kts **Dim:** 77.42 × 13.42 × 3.98
M: 2 G.M. EMD 12-567C diesels; 2 props; 2,700 bhp—bow-thruster
Range: . . ./. . . **Electric:** 300 kw **Crew:** . . .

Remarks: 424 grt/1,200 dwt. Chartered 6-5-87 from Nicor Supply Ships for 17 months, with two 17-mo. extension options, for transportation of cargo to Andros Island and other Caribbean-area experimental facilities. Now owned by Seacor, with charter extended. Former oilfield tug–supply vessel. Has stern ramp for vehicle cargo.

◆ 1 "Down-range support ship"
Bldr: Ira S. Bushey & Sons, Inc., New York, N.Y.

OCEAN PRINCE

D: approx. 550 tons (fl) **S:** . . . **Dim:** 30.79 (29.11) × 8.28 × 3.41
M: 1 Fairbanks Morse 38D8⅛ × 10 diesel; 1 prop; 1,800 bhp

Remarks: 198-grt oilfield supply tug chartered from Forester Towing for use in supplying U.S. Navy facilities at Andros Island in the Bahamas and elsewhere in the Caribbean area.

FLOAT-ON/FLOAT-OFF CARGO SHIP

◆ 1 converted tanker
Bldr: Eriksbergs Mek. Verkstads, Gothenburg, Sweden (In serv. 17-9-75)

AMERICAN CORMORANT (ex-*Ferncarrier*, ex-*Kollbris*)

American Cormorant—with Army equipment Leo Van Ginderen, 8-89

D: 69,555 tons (fl) **S:** 15 kts
Dim: 225.06 (213.90 pp) × 41.15 × 10.49 (19.81 flooded)
M: 1 Eriksberg/Burmeister & Wain 10K84EF 10-cyl., 114-rpm diesel; 1 prop; 25,000 bhp (19,900 under owner's restrictions)—1,500-hp thrusters fore and aft
Electric: 3,360 kw **Range:** 23,700/13 **Fuel:** 3,464 tons
Endurance: 76 days **Crew:** 19 tot.

Remarks: 10,195 grt/47,230 dwt. Former 135,900-dwt tanker converted to a heavy-lift float-on/float-off cargo ship in 1982. Capacity: 45,000 tons on the 120-m × 42-m, 4,870-m² midbody cargo deck created by removing the upper portions of the cargo tanks and reducing original length by 55 m. Can also be used to transport 10,000 bbl liquid cargo. Stationed primarily at Diego Garcia since 1985 with 7,000 tons of U.S. Army floating equipment: two BD-series floating cranes, four LCU 1466 and ten LCM(8) landing craft, four 32.6-m tugs, and two LASH barges; stowed atop these are four cranes, nine fork-lifts, and various cargo-handling gear. The equipment was al ported to Saudi Arabia during Operation Desert Shield in 8-90. Can also stow containers (15 refrigerated) on fantail. Takes four hours to ballast/deballast Owned by American Automar and operated by Pacific Gulf Marine. Used to tr ex-East German Tarantul-I missile boat *Hiddensee* to United States, 12-91.

VEHICLE CARGO SHIPS

◆ 1 Dock Express class
Bldr: Arnhemsche Schipswerf Maats., Arnhem, the Netherlands (In serv.

STRONG TEXAN (ex-*Dock Express Texas*, ex-*Happy Runner*)

D: approx. 4,200 tons (fl) **S:** 12 kts
Dim: 81.82 (74.40 pp) × 15.70 × 5.55
M: 2 Stork-Kromhout 9F-CHD240 diesels; 2 props; 2,500 bhp
Electric: 720 kw (3 × 240-kw diesel sets)
Fuel: 421 tons **Crew:** . . .

Remarks: 1,382 grt/2,776 dwt roll-on/roll-off and heavy-lift cargo ship w 160-ton-capacity derricks and a stern door/ramp leading to the single cargo de hold/one hatch: 62.1 × 11.9. Chartered from Dock Express for U.S. West Coas East transportation.

◆ 2 Finneagle class
Bldr: Kockums AB, Mälmo, Sweden

	In serv.	Chartered	To
AMERICAN EAGLE (ex-*Zenit Eagle*, ex-*Finneagle*)	20-2-81	22-8-83	. . .
AMERICAN CONDOR	1981	. . .	. . .

American Eagle Peter C. Westdij

D: approx. 30,000 tons (fl) **S:** 19.5 kts
Dim: 194.00 (180.80 pp) × 28.02 × 9.22
M: 2 Cegielski-Sulzer 6RND68M diesels; 1 prop; 21,500 bhp
Electric: 4,200 kw (3 × 1,400 kw) **Range:** 16,000/19
Fuel: 2,823 tons **Crew:** 8 officers, 12 unlicensed

Remarks: *American Eagle:* 15,632 grt/20,404 dwt, chartered from America mar and operated by Pacific Gulf Marine, Inc. for U.S. to Europe service. *A Condor:* 15,636 grt/20,731 dwt, chartered from Crowley Maritime and oper American Transport Lines, Inc. Versatile design capable of transporting up standard 20-ft cargo vans or vehicles, with 10,500 m² parking space for the latte two side-by-side 26.8-m-long by 8-m-wide slewing stern ramps, two bow-thrust carry up to 8,500 tons saltwater ballast. There are five holds and six hatches. include 1 × 25-ton and 1 × 5-ton.

CARGO BARGE CARRIERS

◆ 3 Maritime Administration C9-S-81d Type
Bldr: Avondale SY, Westwego, La.

	In serv.
AMERICAN KESTREL (ex-*Lash Pacifica*)	1974
GREEN ISLAND (ex-*George Wythe*, ex-*Green Island*)	2-75
GREEN VALLEY (ex-*Button Gwinett*, ex-*Green Valley*)	1974

Green Island—with container cargo Leo Van Gindere

D: 62,314 tons (fl) **S:** 22 kts
Dim: 272.29 (243.03 pp) × 30.48 × 12.44
M: 2 sets de Laval geared steam turbines; 1 prop; 32,000 shp
Boilers: 2 Combustion Eng.; 75.7 kg/cm² **Electric:** 4,000 kw
Range: 15,000/22 **Fuel:** 5,800 tons **Crew:** 27 tot

Remarks: 32,278 grt/46,152 dwt. *Green Island* and *Green Valley* charter Central Gulf Lines, *American Kestrel* from Kestrel Shipholding Corp. (oper Pacific Gulf Marine); all used as prepositioning ships at Diego Garcia. Unlik LASH ships, do not have a separate, self-loading container-handling capabilit *Island* and *American Kestrel* can carry 89 standard LASH barges, loaded and u by a 455-ton-capacity traveling crane. Carry a small tug to move the barges *Valley* has a 510-ton traveling barge/container crane and can carry 6,016 tons

O BARGE CARRIERS *(continued)*

Iaritime Administration C8-S-81b-type lighter carriers
r: Avondale SY, Westwego, La.

	In serv.	Chartered
AL RAINBOW (ex-*China Bear*)	1-73	12-4-84
HARBOUR (ex-*William Hooper*, ex-*Green bour*)	5-72	27-10-81

al Rainbow Leo Van Ginderen, 3-86

4,606 tons (fl) **S:** 22.5 kts
: 249.94 (220.68 pp) × 30.48 × 12.43
2 sets de Laval geared steam turbines; 1 prop; 32,000 shp
ers: 2 Babcock & Wilcox **Electric:** 4,500 kw
ge: 13,000/22.5 **Fuel:** 5,500 tons (10,427 max.)
w: 12 officers, 21 unlicensed

ks: 26,456 grt/29,820 dwt. Converted from cargo-barge-only carriers to con-)r barge carriers by owners, prior to lease. Both now owned and operated by Gulf Lines. Prior to Operation Desert Shield/Desert Storm, both were ed at Diego Garcia carrying palletized munitions, the largest such explosive ver carried by individual ships; their cargoes have since been re-established, h are once again stationed at Diego Garcia.

carry up to 71 cargo barges or 840 (*Green Harbour:* 1,004) standard cargo ers, handled by a 30-ton traveling crane. The traveling barge crane can lift 446 lso have two 5-ton cranes. Have one 2,500- and one 2,000-kw diesel generator

KERS

Paul Buck (T-5) class Bldr: American SB, Tampa, Fla.

	Laid down	L	In serv.
BUCK (ex-*Ocean Champion*)	28-10-84	1-6-85	11-9-85
J. DARNELL (ex-*Ocean Freedom*)	25-11-84	10-8-85	11-9-85
EL L. COBB (ex-*Ocean Triumph*)	17-4-85	2-11-85	15-11-85
RD G. MATTHIESON (ex-*Ocean it*)	13-8-85	15-2-86	18-2-86
ENCE H. GIANELLA (ex-*Ocean* ·)	2-12-85	19-4-86	22-4-86

el L. Cobb George R. Schneider, Jr., 4-90

W. Darnell Bernard Prézelin, 12-90

9,000 tons light (39,624 fl) **S:** 16 kts
n: 187.45 (179.07 pp) × 27.43 × 10.36
ctron Equipt: Radar: 1/. . . nav.
1 Mitsubishi or Ishikawajima-Sulzer 5RTA-76 diesel; 1 prop; 15,300 bhp
ctric: 3,400 kw **Range:** 12,000/16 **Fuel:** 1,675 tons
w: 9 officers, 15 unlicensed

rks: 19,037 grt/30,150 dwt. First two contracted for on 30-9-82, and other three d 24-4-83. Some sections of the ships built at Nashville, Tenn., for later joining to the main body, and the forebodies were subcontracted to Avondale SY. Chartered for five years; renewed. Operated by Ocean Ships for investor-owners: *Paul Buck* owned by Bell Atlantic Leasing, *Samuel L. Cobb* by Baltimore Capital Reserves, Inc., *Gus W. Darnell* by Pocatine Hills Leasing, Inc., and other two by Ford Motor Credit Co. In mid-1992, *Lawrence Gianella* was acting as a strategic prepositioning ship at Diego Garcia while the others were on freighting duties.

Ice-strengthened hulls. Engines in first two built by Mitsubishi; others by Ishikawajima-Harima Heavy Industries. Cargo: 238,400 bbl (last two: 239,500 bbl). The last two were completed with the capability to add rapidly an underway-replenishment station on each beam, as well as an astern refueling capability. All have three Caterpillar 3/50 diesel generator sets, plus a Nishishiba shaft generator and a G.M. emergency diesel generator. Can make 16 kts at 75 percent full power. Can carry up to 14,675 bbl liquid ballast.

Note: Tankers *Falcon Leader* and *Falcon Champion*, specially designed for MSC Service, went off charter 8-88 and 1-89, respectively; on 22-8-91 and 17-8-91, respectively, they were turned in to the Maritime Administration on Title XI loan default and were laid up in the National Defense Reserve Fleet at Beaumont, Texas.

◆ **3 Maritime Administration T6-M-982 type**
Bldr: Todd SY, San Pedro, Cal.

	In serv.
COURIER (ex-*Zapata Courier*)	1-77
PATRIOT (ex-*Zapata Patriot*)	1976
RANGER (ex-*Zapata Ranger*)	1-76

Rover—now off charter Leo Van Ginderen, 10-83

D: 44,150 tons (fl) **S:** 16 kts **Dim:** 216.7 × 25.6 × 11.3
M: 2 Fairbanks-Morse diesels; 1 prop; 14,000 bhp
Range: 12,000/16 **Fuel:** 3,416 tons **Crew:** . . .

Remarks: 21,572 grt/35,100 dwt. Cargo: 308,000 bbl. All now owned by OMI and operated by Vulcan Carriers. Charter contract extended 10-90 for one year with three one-year extension options. *Patriot* employed as prepositioning ship at Diego Garcia, the others in ocean transportation. Sister *Rover* off-charter by 1992.

◆ **1 coastal tanker**
Bldr: Fosen Mek. Verksteder, Fevag, Norway (In serv. 1-77)

BRAVADO

D: 5,995 tons (fl) **S:** 12.5 kts **Dim:** 92.7 × 14.6 × 6.7
M: 1 MaK diesel; 1 prop; 2,800 bhp **Electric:** 399 kw (3 × 133 kw)
Range: 6,000/12 **Fuel:** 250 tons **Crew:** 7 officers, 4 unlicensed

Remarks: 2,110 grt/4,330 dwt. Cargo: 28,000 bbl. Chartered from Sealift, Inc., and operated by Ocean Carriers in the western Pacific in place of three MSC-owned T-AOG since 1984.

◆ **1 coastal tanker**
Bldr: Kleven Mek. Verksted A/S, Ulsteinvik, Norway (In serv. 1973)

VALIANT (ex-*Seta*, ex-*Chimborazo*, ex-*Thomona*)

D: approx. 10,600 tons (fl) **S:** 13.5 kts
Dim: . . . (120.76 pp) × 16.03 × 6.90
M: 2 MaK 6M453AK diesels; 1 CP prop; 4,200 bhp
Electric: 862 kw tot. (1 × 350-kw, 2 × 256-kw diesel sets)
Fuel: 406.5 tons heavy oil, 101.5 tons diesel **Crew:** . . .

Remarks: 4,375 grt/7,634 dwt. Chartered from and operated by Sealift, Inc. Former chemical tanker employed in fuel freighting service in the western Pacific area. Ice-strengthened hull. Cargo: 8,788 m^3 in 19 tanks.

◆ **1 coastal tanker** Bldr: Niewe Noord Nederlandse Scheepswerven N.V., Groningen (In serv. 1972)

PACIFIC TRADER

D: approx. 2,500 tons (fl) **S:** 10.5 kts
Dim: 70.11 (64.80 pp) × 11.71 × 4.17
M: 1 Klöckner-Humboldt-Deutz 8-cyl. diesel; 1 prop; 1,320 bhp
Electric: 158 kw (2 × 56-kw, 1 × 36-kw diesel sets) **Fuel:** 148 tons

Remarks: 970 grt/1,644 dwt. Chartered from Dilmum Navigation, Pty., Suva, Fiji, for local transportation of fuels in the western Pacific area. Cargo: 2,175 m^3 in ten tanks.

◆ **1 tug-and-fuel barge combination** Bldr: *Malanae:* Albina Eng. & Mechanical Works, Portland Oregon (In serv. 1970)

MALANAE + PUNA HELE

D: approx. 900 tons (fl) **S:** 15 kts
Dim: . . . (32.57 pp) × 9.91 × 4.19
M: 2 Fairbanks-Morse 38D8⅛ × 12 diesels; 2 props; 2,670 bhp
Electric: 120 kw (2 × 60 kw) **Fuel:** 255 tons **Crew:** . . .

TANKERS *(continued)*

Remarks: 285-grt pull-tug on charter from Hawaiian Tug & Barge Corp., Honolulu, with associated fuel barge *Puna Hele* for fuel transportation in the mid-Pacific area. No data available for the barge.

◆ **1 tug-and-fuel barge combination**
Bldr: *Seneca:* J. M. Martinac, Washington (In serv. 1970)

Seneca + Barge 255

D: approx. 750 tons (fl) **S:** 12.5 kts
Dim: 31.86 × 10.37 × 3.71
M: 2 G.M. EMD 8-cyl. diesels; 2 props; 2,900 bhp
Electric: 230 kw (2 × 115 kw) **Fuel:** 196 tons **Crew:** . . .

Remarks: 193-grt articulated push-tug linked to 2,971-grt *Barge 255.* On charter from Crowley/Puget Sound Tug & Barge for fuel transportation in the western Pacific area.

READY RESERVE FORCE

The Ready Reserve Force (RRF), created in 1976, is intended to compensate for the decline of the U.S.-flag merchant marine as a wartime strategic sealift asset. The RRF is maintained within the National Defense Reserve Fleet (NDRF) by the Maritime Administration (MARAD) in 5-, 10-, or 20-day readiness status. RRF ships are activated by a navy (Military Sealift Command) request to MARAD. Selected ships are exercised periodically.

Through FY 89, acquisition and maintenance of the RRF ships was funded by the navy, which retains ownership of former naval units included in the fleet. As of FY 90, the Maritime Administration became responsible for all funding for the RRF, except for some sealift-capability enhancements. Responsibility for acquisition of new ships was returned to the navy under FY 91.

As of 1-7-92, there were 95 ships in the RRF, a number that had not grown significantly in several years, despite a stated goal of 142 by FY 99 (stretched out from FY 94 in 1991). The majority of the ships are quite elderly and are powered by steam plants that are increasingly difficult to maintain. None were added during FY 91 due to inadequate funding and the sharp rise in the price of suitable used ships on the world market—caused in part by the need demonstrated by the United States for vehicle cargo ships during the Mideast War in 1990–91. Under Fiscal Year 1992, it was intended to purchase four general cargo ships, one vehicle cargo ship, and three tankers for the RRF; as of 7-91, no contracts had been announced.

Over 60 of the RRF ships were activated for service during Operation Desert Shield/Desert Storm, and as of 5-92, 15 of them were still operating, most involved in returning materials from the Middle East or in support of U.S. troops there. Although some ships took longer to activate for the emergency than had been planned (due largely to maintenance funding having been inadequate), and a small number broke down, the vast majority performed admirably, as did the U.S. merchant mariners who manned them.

Administrative responsibility for the RRF ships is maintained at NDRF anchorages at Beaumont, Texas, Suisun Bay, California, and in the James River, Virginia, but most of the vessels are kept in layberth in various ports around the United States, in proximity to the shipyards that are under contract to maintain and activate them. In addition to these ships, there are a few older ex-naval or merchant marine units in the NDRF that could be activated given longer notice.

Before inclusion in the Ready Reserve Fleet, ships are upgraded as to their navigation, safety, and communications systems (including provision of a MARISAT SATCOMM facility) and repainted gray, with red, white, and blue stack striping. Certain sealift enhancement features, as specified by the Military Sealift Command, are added during the overhauls or during later maintenance overhauls; these include such items as provision to carry "Seashed" or "Flatrack" large-capacity containers, helicopter decks, refueling-at-sea gear, and extra tie-downs.

TROOPSHIPS

◆ **1 Maritime Administration S5-S-MA49C type**

	Bldr	Laid down	L	In serv.	In RRF
Patriot State (ex-*Santa Mercedes*)	Bethlehem SY, Sparrows Pt., Md.	29-10-62	30-7-63	7-4-64	4-3-86

Patriot State Mass. Maritime Academy, 1989

D: approx. 20,500 tons (fl) **S:** 20 kts
Dim: 166.12 (155.00 pp) × 24.13 × 8.87
Electron Equipt: Radar: 2/Raytheon. . . nav.
M: 2 sets G.E. geared steam turbines; 2 props; 19,800 shp
Boilers: 2/Babcock & Wilcox **Range:** 7,000/20
Fuel: 2,120 tons **Electric:** 2,250 (3 × 750-kw turbogenerators)
Crew: 11 officers, 22 unlicensed

Remarks: 11,188 grt/9,376 dwt. Former passenger/cargo liner now employed by Massachusetts Maritime Academy as training ship. *Patriot State* is fully active and, when not on training cruises, is at her home port of Buzzard's Bay. Can carry 175 containers and up to 598 passengers (normally 121 cadets). Has 5 holds, 13 ha 4 × 20-ton, 2 × 6-ton, and 2 × 5-ton cargo derricks. Did not participate in Storm/Desert Shield. Administratively assigned to James River Fleet.

◆ **1 Maritime Administration C4-S-1u type**
Bldr: Newport News SB & DD

	Laid down	L	In serv.	In RRF
Empire State VI (ex-*Cape Junction,* ex-*Mormactide,* ex-*Oregon*)	1-3-61	16-9-61	19-4-62	20-11-89

Empire State VI—en route school ship conversion Leo Van Ginderen

D: 22,629 tons (fl) **S:** 20 kts **Dim:** 172.22 (161.09) × 23.22 × 9.
M: 2 sets G.E. geared steam turbines; 1 prop; 17,500 shp
Boilers: 2 Foster-Wheeler **Fuel:** 3,538 tons
Range: . . ./. . . **Electric:** 1,500 kw **Crew:** . . .

Remarks: Tonnage before conversion: 9,298 grt/12,691 dwt. Acquired 14-10-8 National Defense Reserve Fleet for conversion as New York State Maritime Ac training ship in place of *Empire State V* (ex-*Barrett,* AP 196). Converted b Shipbuilding, Wisconsin. Sisters *Cape Johnson* and *Cape Juby* are in the RRF as ships. Originally had six holds, one 60-ton, ten 20-ton, two 10-ton, and ten derricks, but some facilities have converted for berthing and classrooms. Fully tional. Designation as "transport" is nominal, as only a couple of hundred troops be accommodated. Did not participate in Desert Shield/Desert Storm. Admi tively assigned to the James River fleet.

ROLL-ON/ROLL-OFF CARGO SHIPS

◆ **3 former Barber Line Ro/Ro vehicle cargo ships**

	Bldr	In serv.	In R
Cape Henry (ex-*Barber Priam*)	Mitsubishi, Nagasaki	1979	1
Cape Horn (ex-*Barber Tønsberg*)	Kaldnes Mek. Verksted A/S, Tønsberg	1979	10-1
Cape Hudson (ex-*Barber Tiaf*)	Tangen Vaerft, Kragerø	1979	30-1

Cape Henry Jürg Kürsener

Cape Horn—with ramp deployed Leo Van Ginderen

L-ON/ROLL-OFF CARGO SHIPS *(continued)*

approx. 47,200 tons (fl) **S:** 21 kts
m: 228.50 (211.50 pp) × 32.26 × 10.80
1 Mitsubishi-Sulzer diesel; 1 prop; 30,150 bhp
nge: 25,000/21 **Fuel:** 4,154 tons
ew: 9 officers, 18 unlicensed

rks: Vary slightly in design: *Cape Henry* is 21,747 grt, *Cape Horn* 22,090, and *Hudson* is 21,976 grt. All purchased 1-6-86 and overhauled at Norfolk SB & DD entering RRF. Data above are for *Cape Henry;* others have one Burmeister & diesel; 30,700 bhp. All have one 40-ton crane. Can also carry 1,607 to 1,629 20-ft iners. *Cape Horn,* assigned to the Suisun Bay Fleet, is at San Francisco, other two rmally maintained in the James River Fleet. All activated for Desert Shield/ t Storm; *Cape Hudson* remained active through 5-92.

Maritime Administration C7-S-95a type Bldr: Bath Iron Works, ath, Me.

	L	In serv.	In RRF
INSCRIPTION (ex-*Tyson Lykes,* ex-*ine)*	24-5-75	27-5-76	2-9-87
ISABEL (ex-*Charles Lykes,* ex-*Nevada)*	15-5-76	1977	23-5-86
TER (ex-T-AKR 11, ex-*Lipscomb Lykes,* *Arizona)*	1-11-75	14-5-76	2-5-86

e Inscription Peter Voss, 11-90

iter Peter C. Westdijk, 8-91

14,222 tons light (33,765 fl) **S:** 23 kts
m: 208.71 (195.07 pp) × 31.09 × 9.78
: 2 sets G.E. geared steam turbines; 2 props; 37,000 shp
ilers: 2 Babcock & Wilcox; 77.5 kg/cm **Electric:** 4,000 kw
nge: 10,000/23 **Fuel:** 3,394 tons
ew: 12 officers, 24 unlicensed

arks: 13,156 grt/19,172 dwt. Can carry containers as well as vehicles and 728 liquid. Cargo capacity is 56,640 m³ bale, with 16,258 m² vehicle cargo space. Two doors, plus 7.3-m-wide by 24.4-m-long stern ramp. Sister *Mercury* (T-AKR 10) ins active in MSC service. All three activated for Desert Shield/Desert Storm; by all were inactive again, assigned to the Gulf RRF Fleet, Beaumont, Texas.

former Barber Line Ro-Ro vehicle cargo ships

	Bldr	In serv.	In RRF
E DECISION x-*Tombarra)*	Eriksberg M/V, Lindholmen, Sweden	30-8-73	15-10-85
E DIAMOND x-*Tricolor)*	Ch. de France, Dunkerque	22-9-72	15-10-85
E DOMINGO x-*Tarago)*	Ch. de France, Dunkerque	11-1-73	30-10-85
E DOUGLAS x-*Lalandia)*	Eriksberg M/V, Lindholmen, Sweden	22-2-73	15-11-85
E DUCATO (ex-*rranduna)*	Eriksberg M/V, Lindholmen, Sweden	11-9-72	5-12-85

: 35,173 tons (fl) **S:** 22 kts
im: 207.40 (193.24 pp) × 29.57 × 9.59
lectron Equipt: 2/Raytheon . . . nav.
: French-built: 3 Ch. d'Atlantique-Pielstick diesels; 1 CP prop; 28,890 bhp; Swedish-built: 3 Lindholmen-Pielstick 18 PC2V diesels; 1 CP prop; 27,000 bhp (22,860 sust.)—1,500-hp bow-thruster, 1,000-hp stern-thruster in all
lectric: 6,384 kw (2 × 2,200-kw, 2 × 992-kw diesel sets)
ange: 26,000/20.6 **Fuel:** 3,529–3,658 tons heavy oil, 240 diesel
ew: 9 officers, 18 unlicensed

Cape Douglas Peter Voss, 11-90

Cape Diamond Peter C. Westdijk, 8-91

Remarks: Tonnages vary: 23,972–24,437 grt/21,299–21,398 dwt. Five-deck vehicle cargo ships purchased 1-85 and "reflagged" (safety features brought into line with U.S. Coast Guard standards) by Bethlehem SY, Sparrows Point, Maryland. Have 65-ton-capacity stern ramp. Can carry 1,327 20-ft containers and have 52,863 m³ bale capacity internal, including 1,784 m³ refrigerated. All activated for Desert Shield/Desert Storm; *Cape Decision* remained active through 5-92. Are all administratively assigned to James River Fleet, where they are laid up.

◆ **2 former Great Lakes newsprint/vehicle carriers**
Bldr: Port Weller Dry Dock, St. Catharines, Ontario

	In serv.	In RRF
CAPE LAMBERT (ex-*Federal Lakes,* ex-*Avon Forest)*	1973	23-10-87
CAPE LOBOS (ex-*Federal Seaway,* ex-*Laurentian Forest,* ex-*Grand Encounter,* ex-*Laurentian Forest)*	1972	31-3-88

D: 30,375 tons (fl) **S:** 19 kts
Dim: 207.88 (189.44 pp) × 22.92 × 9.30
M: 2 Crossley-Pielstick 18-cyl. diesels; 2 props; 18,000 bhp
Electric: 2,700 kw (3 × 900-kw diesel sets)
Range: 6,000/17.5 **Fuel:** 1,207 tons heavy oil, 217 tons diesel
Crew: 10 officers, 17 unlicensed

Cape Lambert—at Mobile, Alabama Victor M. Baca, 2-92

Cape Lobos—note surface-piercing bow bulb Leo Van Ginderen, 6-89

ROLL-ON/ROLL-OFF CARGO SHIPS *(continued)*

Remarks: 15,005 grt/16,382 dwt. Ice-strengthened hull with side doors and two vehicle ramps. Cargo capacity 35,428 m^3 bale, 17,094 m^2 vehicle parking. Purchased 5-6-87 for $14.5 million each from Fed Nav (U.S.A.), but permission to retain *Cape Lobos* in commercial service into 1988 later granted. Under FY 89 plan, both were to be converted to range instrumentation support ships for live and simulated firing exercises, testing tactics, simulating aggressor forces during exercises, and providing limited services as research-and-development platforms; design work in progress, FY 90, but funding for the conversion was never approved. Both activated for Desert Shield/Desert Storm; in 1982, were laid up, assigned to the Gulf RRF Fleet, Beaumont, Texas.

◆ **1 commercial roll-on/roll-off vehicle cargo ship**
Bldr: Eriksberg M/V, Lindholmen, Sweden

	In serv.	In RRF
Cape Edmont (ex-*Parralla*)	1972	10-4-87

Cape Edmont Peter Voss, 11-90

D: approx. 32,000 tons (fl) **S:** 19 kts
Dim: 199.00 (183.70 pp) × 28.65 × 9.40
M: 3 diesels; 1 prop; 25,920 bhp **Range:** 17,000/19
Fuel: 3,369 tons **Crew:** 32 tot.

Remarks: 13,355 grt/20,224 dwt. Has one stern ramp, container capacity: 309 TEU above decks, 903 below; 10,649 m^2 vehicle space. Activated from layberth at Portland, Oregon, for Desert Shield/Desert Storm; by 1992 was inactive again, assigned to the James River Fleet.

◆ **1 Admiral Wm. M. Callaghan class**
Bldr: Sun SB & DD Co., Chester, Pa.

	L	In serv.	In RRF
Admiral Wm. M. Callaghan	17-10-67	12-67	31-5-87

Adm Wm. M. Callaghan—in dry dock at Palermo
Luciano Grazioli, 3-91

D: 26,573 tons (fl) **S:** 26 kts
Dim: 211.61 (193.12 pp) × 28.00 × 8.86
Electron Equipt: Radar: 1/. . . nav.
M: 2 G.E. LM-2500 gas turbines; 2 props; 40,000 shp
Electric: 1,500 kw **Fuel:** 4,421 tons **Range:** 6,000/25
Crew: 10 officers, 18 unlicensed

Remarks: 24,471 grt/13,500 dwt. Built for U.S. Navy service, as the earliest example of the current "Build-and-Charter" concept. Original Pratt & Whitney FT-4 gas turbines replaced 12-77 by LM-2500 engines; used as trials ship for LM-2500 engine life extension and fuel economy improvements. Has stern ramp and four side-loading ports for up to 750 vehicles, on 15,607 m^2 of parking area. Unusual for a "Ro/Ro" in having full set of cargo booms: 2 of 120 tons capacity and 12 of 5–10 tons; flush hatches permit access to 38,515 m^3 of cargo space. To Ready Reserve Force 31-5-87, at expiration of nearly 20 years on navy charter. Activated from James River Fleet for Desert Shield/Desert Storm; ran aground early 1991 in the Red Sea, tearing out much of bottom and bending propeller shaft; repaired in Greece. By 1992 was back in storage at James River Fleet.

◆ **1 Meteor class (C4-ST-67a type)** Bldr: Puget Sound Bridge & D

	Laid down	L	In serv.	I
Meteor (T-AKR 9, ex-*Sea Lift*, ex-LSV 9)	19-5-64	18-4-64	25-5-67	31-

Meteor Leo Van Ginderen

D: 9,154 tons light (21,480 fl) **S:** 22 kts **Dim:** 164.7 × 25.5 × 8
Electron Equipt:
Radar: 1/Raytheon TM 1650/6X nav., 1/Raytheon TM 1660/12S
M: 2 sets geared steam turbines; 2 props; 19,400 shp
Boilers: 2; 52.8 kg/cm^2, 471°C **Range:** 10,000/20 **Crew:** . . .

Remarks: 16,467 grt/12,326 dwt. Cargo: 10,200 tons: 26,819 m^3 vehicle p volume (7,896 m^2 deck space). Stern and four side ramps for Ro/Ro loading/unlc Can carry 12 passengers. Authorized as T-AK 278, completed as T-LSV 9, r T-AKR 14-8-69. Renamed 12-9-75. Assigned to Rapid Deployment Force 4-80 Placed in Ready Reserve Force 30-10-85, at San Pedro, Cal. Activated for Shield/Desert Storm.

◆ **1 Maritime Administration C3-ST-14A type**
Bldr: Sun SB & DD, Chester, Pa.

	Laid down	L	In serv.
Comet (T-AKR 7)	15-5-56	31-7-57	27-1-58

Comet Leo Van Ginderer

D: 8,175 tons light (18,286 fl) **S:** 18 kts
Dim: 152.1 (141.73 pp) × 23.77 × 8.90
Electron Equipt:
Radar: 1/Raytheon TM 1650/6X nav., 1/Raytheon TM 1660/12S
M: 2 sets G.E. geared steam turbines; 2 props; 13,200 shp
Boilers: 2 Babcock & Wilcox; 43.3 kg/cm^2, 454°C
Electric: 1,200 kw (2 × 600-kw turboalternators)
Range: 12,000/18
Fuel: 2,423 tons **Crew:** 11 officers, 33 unlicensed

Remarks: 13,792 grt/10,111 dwt. Cargo: 7,350 tons: more than 700 military v in holds totaling 19,370-m volume (7,525-m deck space). Side and stern ramps. Brown fin stabilizers. Authorized as T-AK 269, changed to T-LSV 7 on 1-6-63, T-AKR 7 on 1-1-69. Remains navy property; placed in the Maritime Adminis RRF on 15-3-85, having been out of service since 22-4-84. Was activated for Shield/Desert Storm. Stored at Portland, Oregon.

AUXILIARY CRANE SHIPS (T-ACS)

Note: Two more planned T-ACS crane ship conversions, with T-ACS 11 to hav the former cargo ship *American Banker,* have been canceled.

◆ **1 converted Maritime Administration C6-S-60b type**
Bldr: Ingalls SB, Pascagoula, Miss.

	Laid down	L	In serv.	In
T-ACS 9 Green Mountain State (ex-*American Altair*, ex-*Mormacaltair*)	2-12-63	20-8-64	23-6-65	31

D: 16,600 tons light (26,119 fl) **S:** 21 kts
Dim: 202.98 (193.55 pp) × 22.96 × 9.63
M: 2 sets G.E. geared steam turbines; 1 prop; 19,000 shp
Boilers: 2 Combustion Engineering
Electric: 4,780 kw (2 × 1,640 kw-turboalternators, 2 × 750-kw di sets)
Range: 17,000/20 **Fuel:** 4,083 tons **Crew:** 64 + 35 spare bert

LIARY CRANE SHIPS (T-ACS) *(continued)*

n Mountain State—completing conversion
Don S. Montgomery, USN, 8-90

·ks: 14,001-grt/12,763-dwt containership prior to conversion; could carry 649 ontainers. Has three pair 30-ton capacity, 36.9-m-reach electrohydraulic cranes ed to starboard. Conversion authorized FY 88; conversion contract let 27-1-89. sion began 28-2-89 at Norshipco, Norfolk, Va., but was slowed by lack of fund- nversion of sister *American Draco* (ex-*Mormacdraco*) to be *Beaver State* (T-ACS s begun 26-3-89, also by Norshipco, but was canceled 12-1-90. T-ACS 9 is ed to the Suisun Bay reserve fleet.

onverted Maritime Administration C6-S-1qc type

lr: Todd SY, San Pedro, Cal.

	Laid down	L	In serv.	In RRF
S 7 DIAMOND STATE (ex-*sident Truman*, ex-*Japan il*)	22-11-60	8-8-61	14-4-62	22-2-89
S 8 EQUALITY STATE (ex-*erican Builder*, ex-*lippine Mail*, ex-*Santa a*, ex-*President Roosevelt*, *Washington Mail*)	12-5-61	6-1-62	25-7-62	24-5-89

ond State — Leo Van Ginderen, 8-91

15,138 tons (fl) **S:** 20 kts
n: 203.61 (192.95 pp) × 23.22 × 10.13
ctron Equipt: Radar: 2/. . . nav.
2 sets G.E. geared steam turbines; 1 prop; 22,000 shp
ilers: 2 Combustion Engineering **Range:** 14,000/20
el: 3,124 tons **Electric:** 2,275 kw **Crew:** . . .

rks: 16,518 grt/19,871 dwt prior to conversion under FY 86, which was con- d with Tampa SB, Tampa, Florida, 14-9-87. Resemble *Keystone State*, with three 0-ton, 36.9-m-reach electrohydraulic cranes mounted to starboard. Were con- ships with 625 20-ft. container capacity prior to conversion. Both attached to the nont, Texas, RRF facility; activated for Desert Shield/Desert Storm in 8-90, they ned operational through 5-92.

converted Maritime Administration C5-S-73b type

dr: Bath Iron Works, Bath, Maine

	In serv.	Converted
S 4 GOPHER STATE (ex-*Export nder*)	1969	21-10-86 to 22-10-87
S 5 FLICKERTAIL STATE (ex-*htning*)	1970	18-12-86 to 8-2-88
S 6 CORNHUSKER STATE (ex-*ghound*)	20-6-69	3-87 to 12-4-88

15,060 tons light (25,000 fl) **S:** 20 kts (sust.)
m: 185.93 (177.35) × 27.77 × 9.14
ectron Equipt: Radar: 2/. . . nav.
2 sets geared steam turbines; 1 prop; 17,500 shp
ilers: 2 Babcock & Wilcox **Range:** 9,340/20 **Fuel:** 3,450 tons
ew: 11 officers, 41 unlicensed

Cornhusker State — Don S. Montgomery, USN, 7-88

Gopher State — Peter Voss, 9-90

Remarks: 17,902 grt as built. T-ACS 3 had been used in ARAPAHO portable helicopter facility trials 20-9-82 to 27-10-82. All three acquired 11-8-86 from Maritime Administration for conversion. Two pair 30-ton-capacity/36.9-m-reach electrohydraulic cranes mounted on starboard side. Equipped to stow sea shed and standard cargo containers. Can carry three LCM(8) landing craft and two side-loading warping tugs (self-propelled pontoons) and pontoon sections on deck. Bow-thruster added. Converted by Norshipco, Norfolk. Two 1,200-kw diesel generators added in after hold during conversion. Have 5,800 tons fixed and portable ballast, 32 lighter mooring fittings added to hull sides. All three activated for Desert Shield/Desert Storm in 8-90; T-ACS 4 and 5 remained active through 5-92. All three are assigned to the James River Fleet.

◆ **3 Maritime Administration C6-S-1qd class**

Bldr: National Steel, San Diego, Cal.

	L	In serv.	Conversion to T-ACS
T-ACS 1 KEYSTONE STATE (ex-*President Harrison*)	2-10-65	1-66	21-3-83 to 7-5-84
T-ACS 2 GEM STATE (ex-*President Monroe*)	22-5-65	1965	26-9-84 to 31-10-85
T-ACS 3 GRAND CANYON STATE (ex-*President Polk*)	23-1-65	1966	28-10-85 to 27-10-87

Keystone State — M.S.C., 6-84

D: 28,660 tons (fl) **S:** 20 kts
Dim: 203.82 (192.95 pp) × 23.22 × 10.06
Electron Equipt: Radar: 2/. . . nav.
M: 2 sets G.E. geared steam turbines; 1 prop; 19,250 shp

AUXILIARY CRANE SHIPS (T-ACS) *(continued)*

Boilers: 2 Foster-Wheeler **Electric:** 4,780 kw tot.
Range: 13,000/20 **Fuel:** 3,450 tons
Crew: 14 officers, 50 unlicensed

Remarks: 17,128 grt/13,600 dwt. Cargo: 303 20-ft. containers. "T-ACS" is an authorization number and not an official U.S. Navy hull number designation. Conversion of T-ACS 1 by Bay SB, Sturgeon Bay, Wisc., took place under FY 83 funding; ordered 18-3-83. T-ACS 2 (FY 84) converted by Continental Marine, San Francisco. T-ACS 3 under FY 85 converted by Dillingham, San Francisco. All three activated during Desert Shield/Desert Storm; subsequently returned to layberths: T-ACS 1 in James River, T-ACS 2 at Tacoma, Wash., and T-ACS 3 at Portland, Oregon.

The original cargo-handling gear was replaced by three sets of twin 30-ton cranes mounted on the starboard side. The T-ACS is expected to unload its own container cargo and then unload containers from non-self-sustaining container carriers at the rate of about 300 containers per day; the cranes have a 33-m reach. Additional generator capacity (3,280 kw) was added.

CARGO BARGE CARRIERS

♦ 3 "Sea Bee"-type, Maritime Administration C8-S-82 type
Bldr: General Dynamics, Quincy, Mass.

	In serv.	In RRF
CAPE MAY (ex-*Almeria Lykes*)	1972	21-7-86
CAPE MENDOCINO (ex-*Doctor Lykes*)	1972	15-10-86
CAPE MOHICAN (ex-*Tillie Lykes*)	1973	22-8-86

Cape Mohican Leo Van Ginderen, 1-91

Cape May—note barge elevator in raised position Leo Van Ginderen, 1-91

D: 18,880 tons light (57,290 fl) **S:** 20 kts
Dim: 266.39 (219.92 pp) × 32.31 × 11.93
Electron Equipt: Radar: 2/. . . nav.
M: 2 sets G.E. geared steam turbines; 1 prop; 36,000 shp
Boilers: 2 Babcock & Wilcox **Range:** 16,000/20
Electric: 4,000 kw (2 × 2,000-kw turbogenerators)
Fuel: 6,346–6,448 tons **Crew:** 12 officers, 26 unlicensed

Remarks: 21,667 grt/38,410 dwt. All purchased 1-86. "Sea-Bee" design intended to carry 38 cargo barges totaling 41,476-m^3 bale capacity and placed in the water via a 2,000-ton-capacity elevator at the stern. Can also accommodate 4,000 bbl (*Cape Mohican:* 11,000 bbl) liquid cargo and 797 tons water. Have 797-ton-capacity passive antirolling tanks. Each has 24 Sea Bee barges stored aboard. All activated for Desert Shield/Desert Storm, then returned to layberth; all three now assigned to James River storage facility.

♦ 2 Maritime Administration C9-S-81d type
Bldr: Avondale SY, Westwego, La.

	In serv.	In RRF
CAPE FAREWELL (ex-*Delta Mar*)	1973	2-4-87
CAPE FLATTERY (ex-*Delta Norte*)	1973	5-6-87

Cape Farewell—with load of LASH barges aft Peter Voss, 11-90

Cape Farewell Leo Van Ginderen

D: 63,314 tons (fl) **S:** 22 kts
Dim: 272.30 (243.03) × 30.56 × 12.44
Electron Equipt: Radar: 2/. . . nav.
M: 2 sets de Laval geared steam turbines; 1 prop; 32,000 shp
Boilers: 2 Combustion Engineering; 75.7 kg/cm^2
Electric: 4,000 kw (2 × 2,000-kw turbogenerators)
Range: 15,000/22 **Fuel:** 6,016 tons
Crew: 12 officers, 20 unlicensed

Remarks: 29,508 grt/41,363 dwt. First two purchased 1-86, along with *Del* which was to have become *Cape Fear* but suffered severe machinery damage RRF overhaul and will probably be scrapped. Have 510-ton traveling crane to 85 cargo lighters and 72 20-ft. containers, 74 lighters, and 288 20-ft. contai 1,728 20-ft. containers alone. Also have one 30-ton crane and one 5-ton crane. *Edward Rutledge* and *Benjamin Harrison* acquired by MARAD 1987 for later ing for RRF but are currently in the National Defense Reserve Fleet at Be Texas. Activated for Desert Shield/Desert Storm, both are again stored at Mob

♦ 2 Maritime Administration C8-S-81b-type lighter carriers
Bldr: Avondale SY, Westwego, La.

	In serv.	I
AUSTRAL LIGHTNING (ex-*Lash España*)	4-71	3
CAPE FLORIDA (ex-*Delta Caribe,* ex-*Lash Turkey*)	1971	1

Cape Florida—with load of containers Peter Vos

D: 44,606 tons (fl) **S:** 22.5 kts
Dim: 249.94 (220.68 pp) × 30.48 × 10.70
M: 1 set de Laval geared steam turbines; 1 prop; 32,000 shp
Boilers: 2 Babcock & Wilcox **Electric:** 4,500 kw tot.
Range: 13,000/22.5 **Fuel:** 5,500 tons (10,427 max.)
Crew: 12 officers, 20 unlicensed

Remarks: *Austral Lightning:* 26,456 grt/29,820 dwt. *Cape Florida:* 26,4 29,820 dwt. LASH-ships, converted from cargo-barge-only carriers to conta barge carriers. Can carry up to 71 cargo barges or 840 standard cargo con handled by a 30-ton traveling crane. The traveling barge crane can lift 446 to have two 5-ton cranes. *Austral Lightning* formerly chartered for the Near-Te positioning Force, until 1-4-85. Both activated for Desert Shield/Desert Storr *Florida* is again stored at Mobile, Ala., *Austral Lightning* at San Francisco.

GENERAL CARGO SHIPS

♦ 1 Maritime Administration C5-78 combination cargo ship
Bldr: Ingalls SY, Pascagoula, Miss.

	In serv.	I
CAPE NOME (ex-*Rapid,* ex-*American Rapid,* ex-*Red Jacket,* ex-*Mormacstar*)	9-69	9

Cape Nome—with load of containers Leo Van Gindere

RAL CARGO SHIPS *(continued)*

7,980 tons (fl) **S:** 23.6 kts
: 183.33 (170.69 pp) × 27.43 × 10.39
tron Equipt: Radar: 2/. . .
2 sets G.E. geared steam turbines; 1 prop; 30,000 shp
ers: 2 Combustion Engineering; 74 kg/cm^2
tric: 3,000 kw **Range:** 12,000/23.6 **Fuel:** 2,790 tons
v: 11 officers, 23 unlicensed

ks: 11,757 grt/15,964 dwt. Cargo: 70 20-ft. containers, plus 33,814-m dry cargo Stern door for vehicle cargo, seven cargo holds. Off charter to MSC from Gulf Lines 12-85; to MARAD 6-87. Attached to James River RRF facility. rcial sister *Rover* is on charter to MSC.

Iaritime Administration C5-S-75a type
: Newport News SB & DD (In serv. 1968)

	In RRF
GIBSON (ex-*President Jackson*, ex-*Indian Mail*)	1-4-88
GIRARDEAU (ex-*President Adams*, ex-*Alaskan Mail*)	12-4-88

Gibson — Peter Voss, 11-90

Girardeau — Leo Van Ginderen, 8-91

1,995 tons (fl) **S:** 21 kts
: 184.41 (177.55 pp) × 25.05 × 9.50 (10.68 max.)
tron Equipt: Radar: 2/. . . nav.
2 sets G.E. geared steam turbines; 1 prop; 24,000 shp—bow-thruster
ers: 2 Babcock & Wilcox **Electric:** 2,500 kw (2 × 1,250 kw)
ge: 14,000/20.8 **Fuel:** 3,702 tons **Crew:** 47 tot.

ks: 15,949 grt/22,208 (*Cape Gibson:* 22,216; *Cape Girardeau:* 22,273) dwt. taining container/break-bulk ships with six holds, seven hatches. Cargo: 409 ntainers/28,830 m^3 bale dry cargo (623 m^3 refrigerated), 17,000 bbl liquid, and engers. Have 1 70-ton, 20 20-ton, and 4 15-ton-capacity cargo derricks. Pur- from American President Lines 5-6-87 for $5M each. Attached to Suisun Bay cility. Sister *President Taylor* (ex-*Korean Mail*) was acquired at the same time s to have become *Cape Grieg*, but she remains in the National Defense Reserve Sister *Cleveland* was on charter to MSC during 1992.

Iaritime Administration C4-S-1u type Bldrs: *Cape nson:* National Steel, San Diego; *Cape Juby:* Newport News SB & DD

	Laid down	L	In serv.	In RRF
JOHNSON *Mormacsaga, I.M. Dant)*	17-8-61	5-5-62	26-11-62	25-2-88
JUBY (ex-*macsea*, ex-*vaii)*	31-7-61	9-2-62	16-8-62	29-2-88

Juby — Leo Van Ginderen, 10-91

D: 22,629 tons (fl) **S:** 20 kts
Dim: 172.22 (161.09 pp) × 23.22 × 9.63
M: 2 sets G.E. geared steam turbines; 1 prop; 17,500 shp
Boilers: 2 Foster-Wheeler **Electric:** 1,500 kw tot.
Range: . . . **Fuel:** 3,538 tons **Crew:** 14 off., 30 unlicensed

Remarks: 9,298 grt/12,691 dwt. Selected 1986 from ships turned in to the Maritime Administration and stored in the NDRF. Six holds. Can carry up to 200 20-ft. containers. Have one 60-ton, ten 20-ton, two 10-ton, and ten 5-ton cargo derricks. Refitted for RRF service under FY 87 for storage in the James River. Sister *Mormactide* (ex-*Oregon*) was to have become *Cape Junction* but has instead been converted as the New York State Maritime Academy training ship *Empire State VI* and is assigned to the RRF as a "transport." Both were activated for Desert Shield/Desert Storm and remained active through 5-92.

◆ **3 Maritime Administration C3-S-76a type**
Bldr: Ingalls SB, Pascagoula, Miss. (In serv. 1968)

DEL MONTE (ex-*Delta Brazil*) DEL VALLE (ex-*Delta Uruguay*)
DEL VIENTO (ex-*Delta Mexico*)

Del Monte — Leo Van Ginderen, 10-91

D: 19,285 tons (fl) **S:** 18.6 kts **Dim:** 159.1 × 21.3 × 9.4
M: 2 sets G.E. GT; 1 prop; 11,700 shp
Boilers: 2 Babcock & Wilcox **Range:** 15,000/18.6
Fuel: 2,175 tons **Crew:** 9 officers, 18 unlicensed

Remarks: 10,396 grt/13,039 dwt. Cargo: 17,077 m^3 bale dry cargo, 1,246 m^3 refrigerated cargo, 11,000 bbl liquid. Six holds. One 75-ton boom, several smaller. All laid up at Beaumont, Texas.

◆ **5 Maritime Administration C4-S-66a type**
Bldr: Avondale SY, Westwego, La.

	L	In serv.	In RRF
CAPE BLANCO (ex-*Mason Lykes*)	10-7-65	9-66	9-7-85
CAPE BON (ex-*Velma Lykes*)	16-7-65	1-67	26-6-85
CAPE BORDA (ex-*Howell Lykes*)	16-4-66	1-67	25-4-85
CAPE BOVER (ex-*Frederick Lykes*)	12-2-66	1-67	1-4-85
CAPE BRETON (ex-*Dolly Turman*)	4-6-66	5-67	11-10-85

Cape Bover — Dr. Giorgio Arra, 10-91

Cape Bon — Peter Voss, 7-91

GENERAL CARGO SHIPS *(continued)*

D: 21,840 tons (fl) **S:** 20 kts
Dim: 164.59 (156.94 pp) × 23.16 × 9.96
Electron Equipt: Radar: 1/nav.
M: 2 sets de Laval or Westinghouse geared steam turbines; 1 prop; 15,500 shp
Boilers: 2 Foster-Wheeler; 49 kg/cm^2 **Electric:** 1,500 kw
Range: 12,000/20 **Fuel:** 2,753 tons
Crew: 12 officers, 26 unlicensed

Remarks: 10,723 grt/14,662 dwt. Break-bulk ships purchased from Lykes Brothers Lines for $21,250,000 in 1-85. Cargo: 21,240 m^3 bale plus 4,000 bbl liquid. Four holds, six hatches; 1 80-ton heavy-lift boom, 20 15-ton. All assigned to Suisun Bay Fleet; *Cape Blanco* remained in operational service through 5-92.

♦ **5 Maritime Administration C3-S-37d type**
Bldr: Avondale SY, Westwego, La.

	L		L
GULF BANKER	5-10-63	GULF SHIPPER	15-2-64
GULF FARMER	3-8-63	GULF TRADER	28-12-63
GULF MERCHANT	16-5-64		

Gulf Trader Dr. Giorgio Arra, 8-90

D: 17,210 tons (fl) **S:** 18 kts
Dim: 150.78 (143.26 pp) × 21.09 × 9.17
Electron Equipt: Radar: 2/. . . nav.
M: 2 sets Westinghouse (*Banker, Farmer:* G.E.) geared steam turbines; 1 prop; 11,000 shp
Boilers: 2 Combustion Engineering
Electric: 1,200 kw (2 × 600-kw turbogenerators)
Range: 15,000/18 **Fuel:** 1,978 tons
Crew: 13 officers, 32 unlicensed

Remarks: First two: 8,970 grt/11,367 dwt; others: 8,988 grt/11,368 dwt. Can carry 41 20-ft. containers in addition to dry cargo. Have five holds. One 66-ton, two 15-ton, two 10-ton, and ten 5-ton cargo derricks. Can carry 12 passengers and 6,000 bbl liquid cargo. Were activated for Desert Shield/Desert Storm, *Gulf Shipper* breaking down and being returned to the Maritime Administration by MSC for repairs. *Gulf Banker* and *Gulf Trader* remained active through 5-92; all are assigned to the Beaumont, Texas, reserve fleet.

♦ **5 Maritime Administration C4-S-58a class**
Bldr: Ingalls SY, Pascagoula, Miss.

	L
CAPE ANN (ex-*Mercury,* ex-*African Mercury*)	12-5-62
CAPE ALEXANDER (ex-*Meteor,* ex-*African Meteor*)	7-7-62
CAPE ARCHWAY (ex-*Neptune,* ex-*African Neptune*)	15-9-62
CAPE ALAVA (ex-*Comet,* ex-*African Comet*)	24-3-62
CAPE AVINOFF (ex-*Sun,* ex-*African Sun*)	8-12-62

D: 18,560 tons (fl) **S:** 20 kts
Dim: 174.35 (164.90 pp) × 22.92 × 9.40
M: 2 sets G.E. geared steam turbines; 1 prop; 18,150 shp
Boilers: 2 . . . **Electric:** 1,800 kw (3 × 600 kw)
Range: 17,000/20 **Fuel:** 3,407 tons
Crew: 11 officers, 28 unlicensed

Cape Alexander Leo Van Ginderen, 8-91

Cape Ann—with flying deck added above aft cargo deck
Leo Van Ginderen,

Remarks: 11,309 grt/12,932 dwt. Cargo: 19,385 m^3 grain/19,022 m^3 bale in holds. Booms: 1/60-ton, 6/10-ton, 14/5-ton. *Cape Avinoff* and *Cape Ann* receive copter decks and other sealift-enhancement features during overhauls ending and 13-7-88, respectively. *Cape Alexander* received the first of 11 planned sets Modular Cargo Delivery System in an overhaul ending 2-89: two solid-tr STREAM systems were added on the port side. Two more MCDS systems installe on *Cape Alava* and *Cape Archway.* Assigned to Quonset Point, Rhode Island, Ja ville, Fla., Baltimore, Md., James River, and Quonset Point, respectively, for st

♦ **8 Maritime Administration C3-S-37c type** Bldr: Avondale SY, Westwego, La.

	L
CAPE CANAVERAL (ex-*Allison Lykes*)	11-5-63
CAPE CANSO (ex-*Aimee Lykes*)	13-10-62
CAPE CARTHAGE (ex-*Margaret Lykes*)	9-3-63
CAPE CATOCHE (ex-*Christopher Lykes*)	22-12-62
CAPE CHALMERS (ex-*Adabelle Lykes*)	6-12-62
CAPE CHARLES (ex-*Charlotte Lykes*)	16-5-63
CAPE CLEAR (ex-*Mayo Lykes*)	14-8-63
CAPE COD (ex-*Sheldon Lykes*)	11-7-62

Cape Clear Peter Voss

D: 18,560 tons (fl) **S:** 18.0 kts **Dim:** 150.8 × 21.0 × 9.75
Electron Equipt: Radar: 1/. . . nav.
M: 2 sets G.E. geared steam turbines; 1 prop; 11,000 shp
Boilers: 2/Combustion Engineering (last four: Foster-Wheeler)
Range: 17,000/18 **Fuel:** 2,827 tons
Crew: 11 officers, 23–29 unlicensed

Remarks: 9,296 grt/12,684 dwt. Cargo: 16,000 m dry bale, plus 8,000 bbl liquid cargo holds; 1/60-ton boom, 20 others. Normally stored at Portland, Me., Norfol Melville, R.I., Providence, R.I., and, last four, Beaumont, Texas, respectively *Carthage* remained operational in 1992.

♦ **3 Maritime Administration C4-S-57a type**
Bldr: Bethlehem SY, Quincy, Mass.

	L
PIONEER COMMANDER (ex-*American Commander*)	20-12-62
PIONEER CONTRACTOR (ex-*American Contractor*)	22-3-63
PIONEER CRUSADER (ex-*American Crusader*)	30-7-63

D: 21,053 tons (fl) **S:** 21.0 kts **Dim:** 171.0 × 22.9 × 9.8
M: 2 sets Bethlehem GT; 1 prop; 19,500 shp
Boilers: 2 Foster-Wheeler **Range:** 12,000/21
Fuel: 2,538 tons **Crew:** 13 officers, 30 unlicensed

Remarks: 11,164 grt/13,535 dwt (varies slightly). Cargo: 18,210 m^3 bale dry 1,246 m^3 refrigerated, 8,000 bbl liquid. Six holds. One 70-ton derrick, 14 smal assigned to Beaumont, Texas.

RAL CARGO SHIPS *(continued)*

er Contractor—activated for exercise — Peter Voss, 2-87

Maritime Administration C4-S-1u type
dr: National Steel SB, San Diego (L: 18-8-62)

A ANA (ex-*C.E. Dant*)

Ana — Leo Van Ginderen, 10-91

22,629 tons (fl) **S:** 20.0 kts **Dim:** 172.2 × 23.2 × 9.8
2 sets G.E. geared steam turbines; 1 prop; 19,200 shp
lers: 2 Foster-Wheeler **Range:** 14,000/20
el: 3,266 tons **Crew:** 14 officers, 27 unlicensed

rks: 12,724 grt/14,376 dwt. Cargo: 19,059 m^3 bale dry cargo, 1,104 m^3 refriger- 7,000 bbl liquid; can also carry 12 passengers. Has six holds; one 60-ton derrick, 1 smaller. Stored at Beaumont, Texas.

Maritime Administration C4-S-1u type
dr: Newport News SB & DD (L: 28-7-61)

ORNIA (ex-*Santa Rita*, ex-*California*)

fornia — Peter C. Westdijk, 3-91

22,629 tons (fl) **S:** 20.0 kts **Dim:** 172.2 × 23.2 × 9.8
2 sets geared steam turbines; 1 prop; 19,200 shp
ilers: 2 Foster-Wheeler **Range:** 14,000/20
el: 3,266 tons **Crew:** 12 officers, 31 unlicensed

arks: 12,693 grt/14,349 dwt. Cargo: 19,059 m bale dry cargo; 1,104 m refriger- cargo; 17,000 bbl liquid; 12 passengers. Six holds; one 60-ton boom; several er. Assigned to the Suisun Bay RRF and stored at Naval Supply Center, Oakland, Engines built by builder.

Maritime Administration C3-S-46a type

	Bldr	L	To RRF
NER (ex-*Export nner*)	National Steel, San Diego	17-12-60	1985
ER (ex-*Export Buyer*)	National Steel, San Diego	1960	29-2-88
RIER (ex-*Export urier*)	Sun Ship, Chester, Pa.	5-4-62	1985

Banner — Don S. Montgomery, USN, 6-87

D: 19,400 tons (fl) **S:** 18.5 kts
Dim: 150.26 (143.26 pp) × 22.25 × 9.32
Electron Equipt: Radar: 2/. . . nav.
M: 2 sets G.E. geared steam turbines; 1 prop; 13,750 shp
Boilers: 2 Babcock & Wilcox; 53 kg/cm^2 **Electric:** 1,400 kw
Range: 13,000/18.5 (*Courier:* 9,000)
Fuel: 3,280 tons (*Courier:* 1,333 tons)
Crew: 12 officers, 27 unlicensed

Remarks: *Banner:* 10,659 grt/12,629 dwt; *Courier:* 11,000 grt/12,705 dwt; *Buyer:* 10,659 grt/12,529 dwt. Cargo: *Banner:* 18,776 m^3 bale dry cargo, 708 m^3 refrigerated, 12,000 bbl liquid; *Courier:* 20,277 m^3 bale dry cargo, 12,000 bbl liquid. Six holds; 1 60-ton boom, 18 smaller, plus 2 cranes. *Courier* altered to carry containers. *Banner* and *Courier* are assigned to James River, Virginia, with non-RRF sisters *Builder* and *Commerce*. *Buyer,* assigned to Beaumont, Texas, joined RRF 1987; activated for Desert Shield/Desert Storm, the ship remained operational through 5-92.

◆ **6 Maritime Administration C3-S-33a type**
Bldr: Sun SB & DD Co., Chester, Pa., and Todd SY, San Pedro, Cal.

	L	In serv.	In RRF
CAPE CATAWBA (ex-*Cape*, ex-*Mormaccape*)	. . .	1961	15-2-87
LAKE (ex-*Mormaclake*)	5-1-61	1961	1985
NORTHERN LIGHT (T-AK 285, ex-*Cove*, ex-*Mormaccove*)	14-10-60	29-6-61	22-7-85
PRIDE (ex-*Mormacpride*)	1-2-60	1960	1985
SCAN (ex-*Mormacscan*)	21-3-61	1961	1985
SOUTHERN CROSS (T-AK 286, ex-*Trade*, ex-*Mormactrade*)	23-1-62	1962	30-9-85

Lake — Leo Van Ginderen, 10-91

D: 18,365 tons (fl) **S:** 19 kts
Dim: 148.15 (139.59 pp) × 20.72 × 8.68
Electron Equipt:
Radar: ex-T-AK: 1/Raytheon TM 1650/6X nav., 1/Raytheon TM 1650/12S nav.; others: 1/. . . nav.
M: 1 set G.E. geared steam turbines; 1 prop; 12,100 shp (15,700 emergency/11,000 normal)
Boilers: 2 Combustion Engineering; 43.3 kg/cm^2, 457°C
Electric: 1,275 kw **Range:** 14,000/18
Fuel: 2,556 (ex-T-AK: 3,064; *C. Catawba:* 5,461) tons
Crew: 11 officers, 30 unlicensed + 12 passengers

Remarks: 9,260 grt/12,500 dwt. Cargo: 16,992 m^3 bale dry cargo and 1,333 m^3 refrigerated cargo, 20,000 bbl liquid cargo. Have five holds, plus ten deep tanks for liquids. One 75-ton, eight 10-ton, and ten 5-ton cargo booms. Accommodations for 12 passengers. *Lake* and *Scan* (which remained active through 5-92), normally stored at Philadelphia Naval Shipyard with *Pride* and *Southern Cross,* were to have been converted into survey ships T-AGS 39 and 40; *Northern Light* was acquired for the U.S. Navy Military Sealift Command 22-4-80 and laid up 22-10-84, while *Southern Cross,* acquired 30-4-80 for MSC and placed out of service on 13-9-84, refitted for the RRF beginning 2-85. *Cape Catawba,* renamed 1987 on joining RRF, is assigned to Beaumont, Texas, and remained active through 5-92; *Northern Light* is at Portland, Ore.

◆ **4 Maritime Administration C3-S-38a type**
Bldr: National Steel, San Diego (*Adventurer:* New York Ship, Camden, N.J.)

	L
ADVENTURER (ex-*Export Adventurer*)	9-7-60
AGENT (ex-*Export Agent*)	30-1-60
AIDE (ex-*Export Aide*)	4-6-60
AMBASSADOR (ex-*Export Ambassador*)	23-4-60

GENERAL CARGO SHIPS *(continued)*

Adventurer Dr. Giorgio Arra, 4-86

Agent Leo Van Ginderen, 6-90

D: 17,570 tons (fl) **S:** 18.5 kts **Dim:** 150.27 × 22.25 × 8.53
M: 1 set G.E. geared steam turbines; 1 prop; 13,000 shp
Boilers: 2 Babcock & Wilcox **Range:** 13,000/18.5
Fuel: 2,230 tons **Crew:** 10 officers, 23 unlicensed

Remarks: 7,848 grt/10,986–11,089 dwt. Cargo: 16,284 m³ bale dry plus 9,000 bbl liquid. Can carry 12 passengers. Have five holds. All activated for Desert Shield/Desert Storm, returned to reserve 4-91, assigned to Suisun Bay Fleet: *Adventurer* is stored at Hunters Point SY, San Francisco, California.

Note: Former Seatrain railcar carriers *Maine* and *Washington,* which had been activated for Desert Shield/Desert Storm, were deleted from the Ready Reserve Force and returned to the National Defense Reserve Fleet on 12-6-91.

TANKERS

Note: For transportation aboard RRF tankers, a total of six additional Offshore Petroleum Discharge Systems (OPDS) are planned. The prototype is aboard *Potomac,* while *American Osprey* had the first production set, consisting of a skid launching system for a 45.7 × 16.5-m barge, 4-point mooring system, and hydraulic-powered reels for 6,400 m of 152-mm fuel piping to act as an offshore fuel transfer point to serve beachheads. The fifth and sixth sets, funded under FY 91 and FY 92, were for delivery 6-91 and 10-92 by Orange Shipbuilding, Orange, Texas. *American Osprey,* however, while only completed in 7-88, has been deleted from the RRF and returned to the National Defense Reserve Fleet.

◆ **1 Falcon-class commercial tanker**
Bldr: Ingalls SY, Pascagoula, Miss.

	L	In serv.	In RRF
MISSION CAPISTRANO (ex-*Falcon Lady,* ex-*Columbia,* T-AOT 182, ex-*Falcon Lady*)	12-9-70	11-3-71	29-2-88

Mission Capistrano—as *Columbia* (T-AOT 182) Bernard Prézelin, 1982

D: 45,877 tons (fl) **S:** 16.5 kts
Dim: 204.93 (194.47 pp) × 27.18 × 11.04
M: 2 Crossley-Pielstick 16 PC-2V400 diesels; 1 prop; 16,000 bhp
Electric: 1,000 kw (2 × 500-kw diesel sets)
Range: 16,000/16.5 **Fuel:** 2,272 tons heavy oil
Crew: 9 officers, 14 unlicensed

Remarks: 20,751 grt/37,874 dwt. Cargo: 303,000 bbl (49,213 m³) in 18 tanks. Served on charter to U.S. Navy from 1974 to 1985. Purchased 5-6-87 from Falcon Carriers for $10.9M.

◆ **2 former commercial tankers**
Bldr: Bethlehem SY, Sparrows Point, Md.

	In serv.	In R
CHESAPEAKE (ex-*Hess Voyager*)	1964	20-
PETERSBURG (ex-*Sinclair Texas,* ex-*Charles Kurz,* ex-*Keystone*)	1963	1-

D: approx. 65,000 tons (fl) **S:** 15 to 15.5 kts
Dim: 224.44 (214.89 pp) × 31.22 × 12.13
M: 2 sets Bethlehem geared steam turbines; 1 prop; 15,000 shp
Boilers: 2 . . . **Electric:** 1,200 kw (*Chesapeake:* 1,800 kw)
Range: . . ./. . . **Fuel:** 1,420 tons fuel oil/80 diesel **Crew:** . . .

Remarks: *Chesapeake:* 27,015 grt/50,826 dwt; *Petersburg:* 27,469 grt/50,072 *Chesapeake* has 21 tanks. 56,146 m³ cargo volume: *Petersburg:* 25 tanks/61,73 *Petersburg* acquired 11-1-88. Upgrading to RRF delayed by funding and enginee problems. *Chesapeake* acquired 1989 for conversion as third ship with the Pro Transfer System (see entry for *Potomac,* below). *Chesapeake* is assigned to the Su Bay Fleet, *Petersburg* to Beaumont, Texas.

◆ **2 former commercial tankers** Bldr: Bethlehem SY, Quincy, Mass

	In serv.	In RRF
MOUNT VERNON	1963	31-3-90
MOUNT WASHINGTON	1963	30-9-89

Mount Washington MARAD,

D: approx. 65,800 tons (fl) **S:** 17.5 kts
Dim: 224.44 (215.50 pp) × 31.17 × 12.26
M: 2 sets Bethlehem geared steam turbines; 1 prop; 21,500 shp
Boilers: 2 Foster-Wheeler **Electric:** 1,500 kw (2 × 750 kw)
Range: . . ./. . . **Fuel:** 4,356 tons **Crew:** . . .

Remarks: 27,412 grt/47,751 dwt. Purchased 30-9-89. Have 31 cargo tanks, 59,4 total cargo capacity. *Mount Vernon* has two 600-kw generators. Assigned to Beaum Texas, RRF facility.

◆ **1 former commercial tanker**
Bldr: Bethlehem SY, Sparrows Point, Md. (In serv. 1968)

MISSION BUENAVENTURA (ex-*Spirit of Liberty*)

D: 46,243 tons (fl) **S:** 16.5 kts
Dim: 201.23 (192.03) × 27.49 × 11.67
M: 2 sets G.E. geared steam turbines; 1 prop; 15,000 shp
Boilers: 2 Foster-Wheeler **Electric:** 2,000 kw
Range: 12,000/16.5 **Fuel:** 2,869 tons
Crew: 9 officers, 17 unlicensed

Remarks: 20,947 grt/38,851 dwt. Cargo: 326,000 bbl (53,186 m³) in 16 tanks. chased 5-6-87 from Keystone Shipping for $9.0M and delivered to RRF 9-10-87 signed to the Beaumont, Texas, RRF facility.

◆ **1 Potomac class** Bldr: Ingalls SB, Pascagoula, Miss.

	Laid down	In s
POTOMAC (T-AOT 181, ex-*Shenandoah,*ex-*Potomac,* T-AO 150)	9-6-55	1-57/14-1

D: 34,800 tons (fl) **S:** 18.5 kts
Dim: 188.98 (180.22 pp) × 25.51 × 10.24
Electron Equipt:
Radar: 1/Raytheon RM 1650/6X nav., 1/Raytheon 1660/12S nav.
M: 1 set Westinghouse geared steam turbines; 1 prop; 20,460 shp
Boilers: 2 Combustion Engineering **Electric:** 1,000 kw (2 × 500 k
Range: 18,000/18 **Fuel:** 4,321 tons
Crew: 11 officers, 19 unlicensed

Potomac—prior to RRF alterations John Jedrlinic, 1

KERS *(continued)*

rks: 15,739 grt/27,908 dwt. Carries 200,000 bbl fuel in 22 tanks totaling 5 m^3, plus 878 m^3 dry cargo. Originally belonging to the *Maumee* class, she was y damaged in 1961; only her stern was salvaged. Rebuilt by Sun SB & DD, er, Pa., and operated on charter to MSC as the *Shenandoah* from 1964 until ased on 12-1-76. Reclassified T-AOT on 30-9-78. Placed in RRF at Suisun Bay on . Used for trials with the prototype "Product Transfer System," a four-mile ng offshore pipeline for bringing fuels to a beachhead, from 5-4-85 to 29-4-86. ated for Desert Shield/Desert Storm, the ship remained active through 5-92, ted for the Military Sealift Command under contract by American Foreign ing.

American Explorer class (T5-S-RM2A type)
dr: Ingalls SB, Pascagoula, Miss.

	Laid down	L	In serv.	To RRF
RICAN EXPLORER (T-AOT 165)	9-7-57	11-5-58	27-10-59	6-84

rican Explorer — Bernard Prézelin, 8-83

8,400 tons light (32,628 fl) **S:** 20 kts
m: 187.5 (181.36 pp) × 24.39 × 10.99
ectron Equipt:
Radar: 1/Raytheon TM 1650/6X nav., 1/Raytheon TM 1660/12S nav.
2 sets de Laval geared steam turbines ; 1 prop; 22,000 shp
ilers: 2 Babcock & Wilcox **Electric:** 1,200 kw (2 × 600 kw)
nge: 14,000/20 **Fuel:** 3,482 tons
ew: 11 officers, 21 unlicensed

arks: 14,984 grt/24,615 dwt. Cargo: 174,000 bbl (27,835 m^3) fuel oil, diesel, etc., 878 m^3 dry cargo. Has four cargo pumps with 3,760 tons/hr. combined output. ed T-AO on 30-9-78. Deactivated to RRF 6-84 at Beaumont, Texas.

Maumee class (Maritime Administration T5-S-12a type)
ldr: Sun SB, Chester, Pa.

	Laid down	L	In serv.	In RRF
SHONE (T-AOT 151)	15-8-85	17-7-57	15-4-57	6-84

34,757 tons (fl) **S:** 18 kts
m: 188.98 (180.82 pp) × 25.46 × 10.25
ectron Equipt:
Radar: 1/Raytheon TM 1650/6X nav., 1/Raytheon TM 1660/12S nav.
: 1 set Westinghouse geared steam turbines; 1 prop; 20,460 shp
oilers: 2 Combustion Engineering **Electric:** 1,000 kw (2 × 500 kw)
ange: 18,000/18 **Fuel:** 4,321 tons
rew: 11 officers, 19 unlicensed

arks: 15,626 grt/27,395 dwt. Cargo: 187,000 bbl (29,733 m^3) fuel oil, diesel, etc. in nks, plus 878 m^3 dry cargo. Four cargo pumps have a combined output of 3,740 hr. Has ice-reinforced bow. Sister *Potomac* (T-AO 150, now T-AOT 181) rebuilt to rent design. Attached to the Near-Term Rapid Deployment Force on 30-9-83, but tivated to the RRF at Suisun Bay 6-84. Sisters *Maumee* (T-AOT 149) and *Yukon* OT 152) were added to the RRF on 15-10-85 and 20-10-85, respectively, but both "demoted" to the National Defense Reserve Fleet on 2-4-87, still under Navy ership; in 2-92 they were authorized for disposal.

Alatna class (T1-MET-24a type)
Bldr: Bethlehem Steel, Staten Island, N.Y.

	L	In serv.	In RRF
ATNA (T-AOG 81)	6-9-56	7-57	1985
ATTAHOOCHEE (T-AOG 82)	4-12-56	22-10-57	1985

: 5,720 tons (fl) **S:** 12 kts **Dim:** 92.0 × 18.6 × 7.0
: 4 Alco diesels, Westinghouse electric motors; 2 props; 4,000 shp
ange: 5,760/10 **Fuel:** 535 tons **Crew:** 9 officers, 15 unlicensed

arks: 3,459 grt/4,933 dwt. Icebreaker-type hulls; originally intended as Arctic/ arctic aviation support ships. Cargo: 30,000 bbls light petroleum products. Both ed in the Maritime Administration's reserve fleet on 8-8-72; reacquired 10-5-79 and -79, respectively; reactivation began 28-11-79 at National Steel, San Diego. Re- ed to service to replace T-AOG 77 and T-AOG 79, T-AOG 81 on 3-2-82 and T-AOG n 11-1-82. Received new diesel engines. Laid up 22-1-85 in Japan as part of the RRF n replaced by chartered tug/barge combinations. Not reactivated for Desert Shield/ ert Storm.

Chattahoochee — Leo Van Ginderen, 12-83

◆ **1 Tonti class (T1-M-BT2 type)**
Bldr: Todd-Houston SY, Houston, Texas

	Laid down	L	In serv.
NODAWAY (T-AOG 78, ex-*Belridge*, ex-*Tarcoola*)	19-2-42	15-5-45	11-9-50

Nodaway — Leo Van Ginderen, 1982

D: 2,060 tons light (5,984 fl) **S:** 10 kts
Dim: 99.10 (94.18 pp) × 14.69 × 5.90
Electron Equipt:
Radar: 1/Raytheon 1600 nav., 1/R.C.A. CRM-N1C-75 nav.
M: 2 Nordberg diesels; 1 prop; 1,400 bhp **Electric:** 515 kw
Range: 5,500/10 **Fuel:** 154 tons **Crew:** 9 officers, 15 unlicensed

Remarks: 3,160 grt/3,933 dwt. Cargo: 31,284 bbl light fuels (diesel, JP-5, gasoline). Laid up 22-7-84 at Pearl Harbor, transferred to RRF on 30-9-85. Not reactivated for Desert Shield/Desert Storm.

UNITED STATES COAST GUARD

Personnel (1-92): 37,527 total (5,522 officers, 1,501 warrant officers, 29,583 enlisted, and 921 cadets), plus 11,857 reserves (1,623 officers), and about 40,000 Coast Guard Auxiliary. There were 2,800 women in the Coast Guard in 6-91.

GENERAL

The Revenue Marine, which was created in 1790, became the Coast Guard on 28 January 1915 by act of Congress. Until 1 April 1967 the Coast Guard was part of the Department of the Treasury; at that time it was transferred to the Department of Transportation. The act that created the service calls for it to operate in time of crisis under the control of the U.S. Navy. The principal responsibilities of the Coast Guard are:

—preparation and training for combat in cooperation with the navy;
—enforcement of the laws of the sea and the policing of navigation;
—control of territorial waters, suppression of smuggling, and policing and assisting the fishing industry;
—surveillance of the coasts and protection of access to ports and bases;

GENERAL *(continued)*

—search and rescue at sea, including transocean air routes;
—manning and maintaining aids to navigation: lighthouses, beacons, buoys, and Omega and Loran stations (47,000 in all, plus 44,000 privately maintained);
—control of piloting and the investigation of accidents at sea;
—control of the safety and seaworthiness aspects of shipbuilding;
—international ice patrols (keeping track of drifting icebergs);
—protection of offshore oil installations;
—pollution control and protection of the environment;
—meteorologic, oceanographic, and hydrographic surveying.

ORGANIZATION

The Coast Guard is divided into two main areas, one for the Pacific and one for the Atlantic. The Coast Guard is further divided into ten Coast Guard Districts in order to fulfill its responsibilities along the U.S. coastline (more than 10,000 nautical miles, not including Hawaii).

A four-star admiral heads the Coast Guard. He is appointed for four years and is assisted by a general staff. The commandant reports to the Secretary of Transportation and not the Joint Chiefs of Staff.

Coast Guard patrol ships have their names preceded by USCGC (United States Coast Guard Cutter). Cutters and patrol craft are white, icebreakers have red hulls, buoy tenders, black. All ships and craft carry diagonal international orange (with thin white and blue) stripes and the USCG shield on the hull.

PRINCIPAL U.S. COAST GUARD AIRCRAFT

◆ **31 HC-130H/H-7 Hercules SAR/cargo/personnel transports**
Manufacturer: Lockheed-Georgia Co., Marietta, Georgia

U.S.C.G. HC-130H-7 Hercules Lockheed, 1983

Wingspan: 40.42 m **Length:** 29.80 m **Height:** 11.66 m
Weight: 33,397 kg empty; 49,780 loaded; 70,300 max.
Engines: 4 Allison T56-A-15 turboprops; 4,508 shp (4,061 sust.) each
Speed: 302 kts max.; 287 cruise **Ceiling:** 25,000 ft.
Range: 3,734 n.m. ferry; 2,517 n.m. with max. payload at 5,000 ft.

Remarks: The C-130Hs are receiving APS-125 radars; two have side-looking radars for ice-patrol duties; and one was converted to EC-130V with a 7.3-m-diameter rotodome as a radar surveillance prototype under Project Delphi in 1991. About 20 were in regular service during 1992.

◆ **25 HU-25A search and rescue, 7 HU-25B oil-spill detection, and 9 HU-25C drug intercept Guardian** Manufacturer: Avions Marcel Dassault-Bréguet Aviation, Merignac, Bordeaux, France

HU-25A Guardian—with prototype "Air Eye" surveillance system Aerojet General, 1983

Wingspan: 16.30 m **Length:** 17.15 m **Height:** 5.32 m
Weight: 8,618 kg empty; 9,476 kg loaded; 14,515 kg
Engines: 2 Garrett AiResearch ATF3-6-2C turbofans; 2,512 kg thrust each
Speed: 461 kts max.; 150 kts search-speed **Ceiling:** 40,000 ft.
Range: 2,250 n.m. in SAR mode

Remarks: Were initially unsuccessful, not meeting performance specifications. HU-25A and HU-25C have APS-127 radar; APG-65 is carried by the drug-hunting HU-25B. Conversion of nine to HU-25C began 1-4-87; they have SLAR (Side-Looking Airborne Radar), an IR/ultraviolet line-scanner, KS-87B aerial camera, and active-gated television camera and are used for detection of oilspills, mapping, and on the International Ice Patrol. Crew of five, including two pilots, surveillance systems operator, and two search crew; can also carry four stretchers.

◆ **19 (+13+12) HH-60J Jayhawk search-and-rescue helicopter**
Manufacturer: Sikorsky Aircraft Div., United Technologies Corp., Stratford, Connecticut

HH-60J Jayhawk U.S.C.G.

Rotor diameter: 16.36 m **Length:** 19.76 m (15.24 fuselage)
Height: 5.23 m **Weight:** 9,435 kg max.
Engines: 2 G.E. T700-GE-401 turboshafts; 1,723 max. shp each (1,543 sust.)
Speed: 150 kts max.; 140 kts cruise
Range: 700 n.m. (3.5 hrs; 300 n.m. radius with 45 min. on station

Remarks: First flight 8-8-89. Some 32 have been ordered, and the Coast Commandant has indicated a need for a dozen more equipped for anti-drug work first six, three each operate from Elizabeth City, North Carolina, and Mobile, Al others operate from Traverse City, Michigan, San Francisco, Cape Cod, Kodi Sitka, Alaska, and Clearwater, Florida. Have the Bendix RDR-1300C search ra can carry six rescuees plus the crew of four.

◆ **95 HH-65A Dolphin search-and-rescue helicopters**
Manufacturer: Aérospatiale SNI, Helicopter Div., Marigname, France

HH-65A Dolphin—in all-red paint scheme Victor M. Baca

Rotor diameter: 11.94 m **Length:** 11.43 m
Height: 3.99 m
Weight: 2,717 kg empty/4,049 kg max.
Engines: 2 Avco-Lycoming LTS 101-750A-1 or LTS 101-750A-3 turboshafts; 680 shp each (646 sust.)
Speed: 165 kts max.; 145 kts cruise; 128 kts search mode
Ceiling: 7,150 ft. **Range:** 400 n.m. max. (3.8 hr. mission)

Remarks: Selected 1978 to replace the HH-52A Sea Guardian, but due to engi other problems, the aircraft did not enter service until 19-11-84. Last unit de 24-4-89. Carry a crew of two pilots, aircrew/hoist-operator, and up to six pass Operated from 20 shore bases and from Coast Guard cutters. Were assembled in One lost 1-89.

◆ **20 HH-3F Pelican search-and-rescue helicopters**
Manufacturer: Sikorsky Aircraft Division, United Technologies Corp., Stra Connecticut

HH-3F Pelican U.S

CIPAL U.S. COAST GUARD AIRCRAFT *(continued)*

or diameter: 18.90 m **Length:** 22.25 m
ght: 5.51 m **Weight:** 10,000 kg max.
ines: 2 G.E. T58-GE-5 turboshafts; 1,500 shp each
ed: 141 kts max.; 109 kts cruise **Ceiling:** 11,400 ft.
ge: 400 n.m.

ks: Variant of the U.S. Air Force CH-3C (Sikorsky model S-61). Watertight e to permit landings at sea. Forty were built, and the remainder are to be retired , replaced by the HH-60J. Have APN-215 radar.

Other aircraft in service include three ex-U.S. Air Force CH-3E Sea King ed for SAR with an APN-215 radar and auxiliary fuel tanks; three more ex-U.S. re held in reserve), one Grumman VC-1A Gulfstream turboprop VIP transport, mman VC-11A Gulfstream jet VIP transport, and two RG-8A Condor-powered ance gliders. Of four E-2C Hawkeye radar surveillance aircraft acquired 1989– from the Navy, two from the Customs Service), one was lost 8-90, and the others turned to the Navy in 2-92. A Spanish CASA 212-300 in maritime surveillance ration was given a one-year trial at Opa Locka, Florida, in 1990–91, but the not being procured.

-ENDURANCE CUTTERS

Hamilton class (378-ft. class) Bldr: Avondale SY, Westwego, La.

	Laid down	L	In serv.	Modernized
715 HAMILTON	23-11-65	18-12-65	20-2-67	10-85 to 15-11-88
716 DALLAS	7-2-66	1-10-66	1-10-67	11-86 to 12-89
717 MELLON	25-7-66	11-2-67	22-12-67	10-85 to 3-6-89
718 CHASE	15-10-66	20-5-67	1-3-68	7-89 to 5-3-91
719 TWELL	12-12-66	17-6-67	14-6-68	3-3-89 to 4-91
720 SHERMAN	13-2-67	23-9-67	23-8-68	14-5-86 to 2-90
721 GALLATIN	17-4-67	18-11-67	20-12-68	3-90 to 26-1-92
722 RGENTHAU	17-7-67	10-2-68	14-2-69	11-11-89 to 12-91
723 RUSH	23-10-67	16-11-68	3-7-69	7-89 to 9-91
724 MUNRO	18-2-70	5-12-70	10-9-71	12-86 to 11-11-89
725 JARVIS	9-9-70	24-4-71	30-12-71	3-91 to 3-93
726 MIDGETT	5-4-71	4-9-71	17-3-72	9-90 to 31-3-92

2,716 tons (3,050 fl) **S:** 29 kts (28.4 post-modernization)
: 115.37 (106.68 pp) × 13.06 × 4.27 (6.2 over sonar)
8/RGM-84A Harpoon SSM (IV × 2)—1/76-mm 62-cal. Mk 75 DP—1/20-mm Mk 15 CIWS—4/12.7-mm mg (I × 4)—2/40-mm Mk 64 grenade launchers (I × 2)—6/324-mm Mk 32 Mod. 7 ASW TT (III × 2)—1/HH-65A Dolphin helicopter

Electron Equipt:
Radar: 2/SPS-64(V)6 nav., 1/SPS-40B air search, 1/Mk 92 Mod. 1 f.c.
Sonar: SQS-38 hull-mounted MF—TACAN: URN-25
EW: WLR-1C intercept, WLR-3 intercept, 2/Mk 36 SRBOC decoy RL (VI × 2)

M: CODOG: 2 Fairbanks-Morse 38TD8⅛, 12-cyl. diesels, 3,500 bhp each; 2 Pratt & Whitney FT4-A6 gas turbines, 18,000 shp each; 2 CP props; 36,000 shp—350-shp retractable bow propeller
Electric: 1,500 kw **Endurance:** 45 days
Range: 2,400/29; 9,600/19 (gas turbines); 14,000/11 (diesel)
Fuel: 800 tons **Crew:** 19 officers, 156 enlisted

Dallas (WHEC 716)—telescoping hangar extended
Dr. Giorgio Arra, 5-91

Dallas (WHEC 716) Dr. Giorgio Arra, 5-91

twell (WHEC 719)—without Harpoon or CIWS Dr. Giorgio Arra, 10-91

HIGH-ENDURANCE CUTTERS *(continued)*

Hamilton (WHEC 715)—with Harpoon SSM and Mk 15 CIWS
Dr. Giorgio Arra, 1-91

Remarks: Helicopter platform, 26.82 × 12.2. Living spaces air-conditioned. Laboratories for weather and oceanographic research. Welded hull; aluminum superstructure. Named after early Secretaries of the Treasury and Coast Guard heroes. Thirty-six planned, only 12 built. All but WHEC 721 now operate from West Coast ports.

Systems: Mk 309 ASW fire-control system installed. SQS-38 is a hull-mounted version of the navy's SQS-35 variable-depth sonar. WHEC 716–723 have synchronizing clutches; the final three have synchro-self-shifting (SSS) clutches. WHEC 717, 722, and 725 have rudder roll-stabilization systems. All are to receive Fairey Hydraulics "Talon" helicopter landing systems.

Modernization: Funded FY 85 through FY 88, modernizations were to have included: replacing the 127-mm gun and Mk 56 gunfire-control system with a 76-mm Mk 75 (OTO Melara Compact) gun and Mk 92 Mod. 1 radar gunfire-control system, replacing the SPS-29D radar with SPS-40B, replacing the WLR-1 EW system with SLQ-32 and the Mk 36 SRBOC system, and adding satellite communications gear; provision was made to carry the LAMPS-I ASW helicopter and one 20-mm Mk 15 CIWS gatling AA gun. Other modifications were to have included: Mk 32 Mod. 7 ASW TT, SQR-17A(V)1 sonobuoy signal analyzer, URN-25 TACAN, RAYCAS (Raytheon Collision-Avoidance System), an HP-9020 computer, SLQ-25 Nixie acoustic torpedo decoys, new secure communications gear, and telescoping hangars. The SLQ-32 EW system was later deleted from the program, as was SLQ-25, but all are being given the capability to carry up to eight Harpoon missiles (WHEC 717 conducted first USCG missile launch 16-1-90). When the missiles are not carried, two single 20-mm AA can be installed. The grenade launchers have replaced the 81-mm mortars formerly carried. Eight modified by Todd SY, Seattle, and WHEC 715, 716, 718, and 721 by Bath Iron Works, Maine. The helicopter hangars had been blanked off but are now operational.

MEDIUM-ENDURANCE CUTTERS

◆ **13 Bear class (270-ft. class)** Bldrs: WMEC 901–904: Tacoma Boatbuilding, Tacoma, Wash.; WMEC 905–913: Robert E. Derecktor, Middletown, R.I.

	Laid down	L	In serv.
WMEC 901 Bear	23-8-79	25-9-80	4-2-83
WMEC 902 Tampa	2-4-80	19-3-81	16-3-84
WMEC 903 Harriet Lane	15-10-80	6-2-82	20-9-84
WMEC 904 Northland	9-4-81	7-5-82	17-12-84
WMEC 905 Spencer (ex-*Seneca*)	26-6-82	16-6-84	28-6-86
WMEC 906 Seneca (ex-*Pickering*)	16-9-82	16-6-84	4-5-87
WMEC 907 Escanaba	1-4-83	24-8-85	27-8-87
WMEC 908 Tahoma (ex-*Legare*)	28-6-83	24-8-85	6-4-88
WMEC 909 Campbell (ex-*Argus*)	10-8-84	30-8-86	19-8-88
WMEC 910 Thetis (ex-*Tahoma*)	24-8-84	30-8-86	30-6-89
WMEC 911 Forward (ex-*Erie*)	11-7-86	18-8-87	4-8-90
WMEC 912 Legare (ex-*McCulloch*)	11-7-86	18-8-87	4-8-90
WMEC 913 Mohawk (ex-*Ewing*)	18-6-87	18-5-88	1991

Authorized: 2 in FY 77, 2 in FY 78, 2 in FY 79, 3 in FY 80, 1 in FY 81, 3 in FY 82.

Seneca (WMEC 906) Dr. Giorgio Arra, 6-91

Bear (WMEC 901) Dr. Giorgio Arr

Harriet Lane (WMEC 903) Dr. Giorgio Ar

Forward (WMEC 911)—with HH-65A Dolphin on deck
Dr. Giorgio Arr

D: 1,200 tons light (1,780 fl) **S:** 19.5 kts
Dim: 82.3 (77.7 wl) × 11.58 × 4.11
A: 1/76-mm 62-cal. Mk 75 DP—2/12.7-mm mg (I × 2)—2/40-mm 19 grenade launchers (I × 2)—1/HH-65A helicopter
Electron Equipt:
Radar: 1/SPS-64(V)1 nav., 1/SPS-64(V)6 nav., 1/Mk 92 Mod. 1
Sonar: Provision for SQR-19A TASS—TACAN: URN-25
EW: SLQ-32(V)1 intercept, Mk 36 SRBOC RL (VI × 2)
M: 2 Alco Model 18V-251E, 18-cyl. diesels; 2 Escher-Wyss CP pro 7,200 bhp
Electric: 1,350 kw (3 × 475-kw Kato sets, Caterpillar D398 diese driving)
Range: 3,850/19.5; 6,370/15; 10,250/12 **Endurance:** 14 days
Crew: 11 officers, 89 enlisted

Remarks: Program suffered numerous delays; first ship was to have complete 80; WMEC 913 entered active service over three years late. WMEC 905–913 or ordered from Tacoma in 8-80, but lawsuit caused reassignment to R. E. De 17-1-81. Originally intended to be able to act as ASW escorts in wartime. The

ЈM-ENDURANCE CUTTERS *(continued)*

ɔmputerized control system on this class has given considerable difficulty. ılly overloaded and very uncomfortable ships in a seaway; 76-mm gun raised reduce damage. Have accommodations for up to 17 officers, 123 enlisted. All d on the U.S. East Coast.

ms: No hull-mounted sonar or on-board ASW weapons. Can carry van- towed passive sonar array on fantail; equipment was procured but has never talled. Space and weight reserved for Mk 15 CIWS 20-mm gatling AA gun and druple Harpoon missile-launch canisters, but are very unlikely ever to have stalled. WSC-3 UHF satellite-communications system is carried. Telescoping provision for later installation of fin stabilization. Have six light weapons gs capable of accepting 12.7-mm mg or 40-mm Mk 19 grenade launchers. ess provided $20M in FY 88 to equip one ship for ASW, with SQR-18A TASS, A sonobuoy analyzer, APR-78 sonobuoy receiver, SKR-4 helicopter data-link ; this would have made the ship compatible with the U.S. Navy's LAMPS-III WMEC 907 conducted trials with navy SH-60B LAMPS-III helicopter during

Reliance class (210-ft. A* and 210-ft. B class) Bldrs: 1: Todd yards; 2: Christy Corp., Sturgeon Bay, Wisconsin; 3: Coast Guard SY, is Bay, Maryland; 4: American SB, Lorain, Ohio.

	Bldr	L	In serv.	Modernization
615 Reliance*	1	25-5-63	20-6-24	6-4-87 to 1-89
616 Diligence*	1	20-7-63	26-8-64	7-90 to 12-91
617 Vigilant*	1	24-12-63	3-10-64	2-89 to 6-90
618 Active*	2	31-7-65	17-9-66	10-84 to 12-2-87
619 Confidence*	3	8-5-65	19-2-66	18-10-86 to 6-88
620 Resolute	3	30-4-66	8-12-66	6-94 to 11-95
621 Valiant	4	14-1-67	28-10-67	12-91 to 5-93
622 Courageous	4	18-5-67	10-4-68	3-87 to 1-90
623 Steadfast	4	24-6-67	25-9-68	6-92 to 11-93
624 Dauntless	4	21-10-67	10-6-68	6-93 to 11-94
625 Venturous	4	11-11-67	16-8-68	12-93 to 5-95
626 Dependable	4	16-3-68	27-11-68	12-94 to 5-96
627 Vigorous	4	4-5-68	2-5-69	6-91 to 11-92
628 Durable	3	29-4-67	8-12-67	10-86 to 10-88
629 Decisive	3	14-12-67	23-8-68	6-95 to 11-96
630 Alert	3	19-10-68	4-8-69	12-92 to 5-94

59 tons (930 fl) **S:** 18 kts **Dim:** 64.16 (60.96 pp) × 10.36 × 3.2
/76.2-mm 50-cal. Mk 22 DP—2 or 4/12.7-mm M2 mg (I × 2
r 4)—2/40-mm Mk 64 grenade launchers (I × 2)—1/HH-65A
elicopter
tron Equipt: Radar: 2/SPS-64(V)1 nav.
: Alco 16V-251B diesels; 2 CP props; 5,000 bhp
tric: 500 kw **Range:** 2,700/18; 6,100/14 (*2,200/18; 5,000/15)
urance: 21 days (modernized ships: 30 days)
v: 8 officers, 54 enlisted (accommodations: 12 officers, 70 enlisted)

nt (WMEC 617)—post-modernization Dr. Giorgio Arra, 3-91

nt (WMEC 621)—unmodified; note diesel exhausts at stern Dr. Giorgio Arra, 11-91

Courageous (WMEC 622)—modernized unit Dr. Giorgio Arra, 4-91

Valiant (WMEC 621)—unmodified Dr. Giorgio Arra, 4-91

Remarks: No hangar. Designed to operate up to 500 miles off the coast. High superstructure permits 360-degree visibility. Can tow a 10,000-ton ship. Air-conditioned. Operate from U.S. East Coast ports except WMEC 618 from Port Angeles, Washington, and WMEC 623 and 630 from Astoria, Oregon.

Systems: WMEC 615–WMEC 619 originally had CODAG propulsion, with two 1,500-bhp Cooper-Bessemer FVBM12-T diesels and two Solar Saturn T-100s gas turbines providing an additional 2,000 shp; the turbines have been removed. These five ships have now been re-engined and otherwise updated by the U.S. Coast Guard Yard, Curtis Bay, with Alco 251B engines like their sisters. The remaining ships are being refitted by Colonna's SY, Norfolk, beginning with WMEC 628 in 10-86 (see schedule in ship listing); the ships received a new stack, enlarged superstructure, greater fire-fighting capability, but the helo deck is reduced in size, and topweight is reduced. During the modernization, the crews are enlarged to 86 total, provisions capacities are enlarged, and engine exhausts are rearranged; displacements rise to over 1,300 tons on completion. The projected completion date for the program has slipped *six years* since the 1988–89 edition, and funds may not be available to perform the work on all the units listed.

◆ **3 Diver class (213-ft. class) former U.S. Navy salvage ships**
Bldr: Basalt Rock Co., Napa, California

	Laid down	L	In serv.
WMEC 6 Escape (ex-ARS 6)	24-8-42	22-11-42	20-11-43
WMEC 167 Acushnet (ex-WAGO 167, ex-WAT 167, ex-*Shackle*, ARS 9)	26-10-42	1-4-43	5-2-44
WMEC 168 Yocona (ex-WAT 168, ex-*Seize*, ARS 26)	28-9-43	8-4-44	3-11-44

D: 1,246 tons (1,746 fl) **S:** 15.5 kts
Dim: 65.08 (63.09 wl) × 12.5 × 4.57
A: none **Electron Equipt:** Radar: 2/SPS-64(V)1 nav.
M: 4 Cooper-Bessemer GSB-8 diesels, electric drive; 2 props; 3,030 shp
Electric: 460 kw **Range:** 10,000/14.5; 13,700/10.3
Fuel: 300 tons **Crew:** 7 officers, 65 enlisted

Acushnet (WMEC 167)—single mast Dr. Giorgio Arra, 4-90

MEDIUM-ENDURANCE CUTTERS *(continued)*

Escape (WMEC 6)—two masts Dr. Giorgio Arra, 1990

Remarks: WMEC 167, 168 taken over from the navy in 1946. WMEC 167 served as WAGO 167 from 1968 to 1978, then retyped WMEC. WMEC 6, reactivated from reserve and transferred on loan from U.S. Navy 4-12-80, has a mainmast. Maximum sustained speed is 13 kts. Plan to strike 1990 deferred to at least 1995, due to lack of replacements. WMEC 6 and WMEC 167 operate in the Atlantic, WMEC 168 in the Pacific.

♦ 1 Storis class (230-ft. class) Bldr: Toledo SB, Toledo, Ohio

	Laid down	L	In serv.
WMEC 38 Storis (ex-Eskimo)	14-7-41	4-4-42	30-9-42

Storis (WMEC 38) 1971

D: 1,296 tons light (1,916 fl) **S:** 14 kts **Dim:** 70.1 × 13.1 × 4.6
A: 1/76.2-mm 50-cal. Mk 22 DP—4/12.7-mm M2 mg (I × 4)
Electron Equipt: Radar: 2/SPS-64 nav.
M: 3 Fairbanks-Morse $38D8\frac{1}{8}$ diesels, electric drive; 1 prop; 1,800 shp
Range: 12,000/14; 22,000/8 **Fuel:** 330 tons
Crew: 10 officers, 96 enlisted

Remarks: Rated as WAG until 1966, and WAGB until 1-7-72, when she was retyped WMEC. Resembles a *Balsam*-class buoy tender, but is larger. Has an icebreaker hull, but is no longer considered capable of acting as such. Based at Kodiak, Alaska. Will be retained through at least 1995.

♦ 1 Cherokee (205-ft.) class ex-U.S. Navy fleet tug
Bldr: Commercial Iron Works, Portland, Oregon

	Laid down	L	In serv.
WMEC 166 Tamaroa (ex-*Zuni,* ATF 95)	8-3-43	13-7-43	9-10-43

D: 1,217 tons (1,641 fl) **S:** 16.5 kts
Dim: 62.48 (59.44 pp) × 11.73 × 5.18
A: removed **Electron Equipt:** Radar: 2/SPS-64 nav.
M: 4 G.M. 12-278 diesels, electric drive; 1 prop; 3,000 shp
Electric: 260 kw **Range:** 4,055/16.5; 13,097/10.1
Fuel: 315 tons **Crew:** 6 officers, 65 enlisted

Cherokee (WMEC 165)—since stricken, *Tamaroa* (WMEC 166) similar
Dr. Giorgio Arra, 6-90

Remarks: Last of a once numerous group. Loaned to the Coast Guard in 19 transferred outright on 1-6-69. The 76.2-mm gun has been removed. Operates Atlantic.

Sisters *Ute* (WMEC 76, ex-ATF 76) and *Lipan* (WMEC 85, ex-ATF 85), transfe the navy 30-9-80, were returned for disposal on 26-5-88 and deactivated 3 respectively; WMEC 85 was subsequently transferred to the Military Sealift Cor for transfer to MARAD on 9-6-88. Sisters *Chilula* (WMEC 153, ex-ATF 15 *Cherokee* (WMEC 165, ex-ATF 66) were stricken 27-6-91 and 28-2-91, respective transferred to the U.S. Navy for use as targets at the Naval Air Training Com Patuxent River, Maryland.

Note: Of the three *Balsam*-class former buoy tenders used as medium-end cutters, *Clover* (WMEC 292, ex- WLB 292) was stricken 20-6-90 and transferre navy for use as a target; *Evergreen* (WMEC 295, ex-WAGO 295, ex-WLB 29 stricken 29-8-90 and transferred to the navy for use as a target; and *Citrus* (WM ex-WLB 300) was stricken during 1990 as well.

Of the five chartered aerostat balloon radar tenders listed in the previous edit were transferred from Coast Guard control during 1991 and have since been in providing considerable comfort to drug-runners in the Caribbean route.

ICEBREAKERS

♦ 0 (+1) new-construction polar icebreakers Bldr: . . .

	Laid down	L	In serv.
WAGB 20 Healy	. . .	. . .	. . .

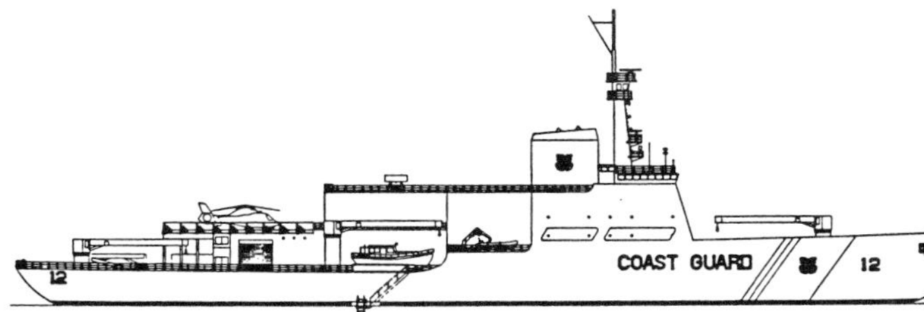

Healy (WAGB 20) U.S.C.G.

D: 17,710 tons (fl) **S:** 12.5 kts (cruise)
Dim: 140.06 (122.32 pp) × 28.80 (26.85 wl) × 9.75
A: 2/12.7-mm M2 mg (I × 2)—1 or 2/. . . helicopters
Electron Equipt:
Radar: . . .—Sonar: hydrographic mapping set
M: diesel-electric: 4 Colt-Pielstick 10,000-bhp medium-speed dies 10,000 kVA, 4,160-volt main generators; 2 fixed-pitch, 4.88-m- props; 30,000 shp—bow-thruster, 2,000 shp
Range: 34,500/12.5; 37,000/9.25 **Endurance:** 80 days
Fuel: 4,595 tons, plus 120 tons aviation fuel **Electric:** 1,500 kw
Crew: 19 officers, 114 enlisted, 49 spare

Remarks: Long required to replace the "Wind" class and *Glacier*. Some $274.8 authorized and appropriated for under the Fiscal Year 1990 Navy Budget to pa new Coast Guard icebreaker; another $62M was added by Congress under FY 9 requested 13-3-91, but the bidding was canceled 16-3-92 after no yard bid with available funds. Current status of the program is in doubt; a planned second u omitted from the FY 92 Budget. *Healy* was to have been completed 8-96.

To be capable of breaking 1.4-m ice at 3 kts continuous or 2.4-m ice by backi ramming. Conventional icebreaker hull not incorporating modern icebreakin nologies. To have five laboratories totaling 377 m², four cranes, LCVP landing port.

♦ 2 Polar Star class (399-ft. class) Bldr: Lockheed SB, Seattle

	Laid down	L	In serv.
WAGB 10 Polar Star	15-5-72	17-11-73	19-1-76
WAGB 11 Polar Sea	27-11-73	24-6-75	23-2-78

D: 10,863 tons (13,623 fl) **S:** 18 kts
Dim: 121.91 (102.78 pp) × 25.45 × 1.14
Electron Equipt: Radar: 2/SPS-64 nav.—TACAN: SRN-15
M: CODAG: 6 Alco 16V251 diesels, 3,000 bhp each; 3 Pratt & Wh FT-4A12 gas turbines, 25,000 shp each, down-rated; electric dr 3 CP props; 66,000 shp
Range: 16,000/18; 28,275/13 **Fuel:** 3,555 tons
Crew: 13 officers, 125 enlisted + 10 scientists, 14 helicopter detachment

Polar Star (WAGB 10) Malcolm Dippy

REAKERS *(continued)*

Sea (WAGB 11) Peter Voss, 9-90

rks: Carry two HH-65A helicopters, painted red. Can break 2-meter ice at 3 6.4-meter ice maximum. Propulsion plant completely cross-connected and auto- Two 15-ton cranes. Four 20-mm AA (I × 4), and two 40-mm Mk 64 grenade ıers (I × 2) can be installed. Scientific facilities upgraded in WAGB 10 in 1990– l in WAGB 11 during 1992–93 refit. Both home-ported at Seattle.

Mackinaw class (290-ft. class) Bldr: Toledo SB, Toledo, Ohio

	Laid down	L	In serv.
B 83 Mackinaw (ex-*Manitowoc*)	20-3-43	4-3-44	20-12-44

kinaw (WAGB 83) U.S.C.G., 1985

3,049 tons (5,252 fl) **S:** 18.7 kts **Dim:** 88.39 × 22.66 × 5.79
ctron Equipt: Radar: 2/SPS-64
4 Fairbanks-Morse 38D8⅛ × 12 diesels, electric drive; 3 props (2 aft, 1 fwd); 10,000 shp
ctric: 1,260 kw **Range:** 10,000/18.7; 41,000/9
ew: 10 officers, 97 enlisted

rks: Built for use on the Great Lakes. Helicopter platform. Fitted with two cranes. Can break 0.76-m ice continuously, 3.3-m ice by backing and ramming. auled 1982 at Bay SB, Sturgeon Bay, Wisc.; cranes aft removed and some fuel ge converted to ballast tanks. Placed in caretaker status in the spring of 1988, but vated 1989. Received extensive refit during 1991. Based at Cheboygan, Mi- 1.

ROL BOATS

The 96-unit "Heritage"-class patrol boat program was canceled 25-11-91, al- n the prototype, *Leopold* (WPB 1400), had been laid down 27-8-90 and was ng launch. The steep decline in the number of Coast Guard patrol boats, coupled n increase in the drug trade, has put a strain on the remaining assets. A new, r design is now in development; to be about 23–26 m overall, it will provide replacements for the 82-ft. "Point" class.

) "Island" (110-ft. class) Bldr: Bollinger Machine Shop & SY, ckport, Louisiana

	Laid down	L	In serv.
1301 Farallon	. . .	27-8-85	21-2-86
1302 Manitou	. . .	9-10-85	28-2-86
1303 Matagorda	. . .	15-12-85	25-4-86
1304 Maui	. . .	13-1-86	9-5-86
1305 Monhegan	. . .	15-2-86	16-6-86
1306 Nunivak	. . .	15-3-86	4-7-86
1307 Ocracoke	. . .	12-4-86	4-8-86
1308 Vashon	. . .	10-5-86	15-8-86
1309 Aquidneck	. . .	14-6-86	26-9-86
1310 Mustang	. . .	11-7-86	29-8-86
1311 Naushon	. . .	22-8-86	3-10-86
1312 Sanibel	. . .	3-10-86	14-11-86
1313 Edisto	. . .	21-11-86	7-1-87
1314 Sapelo	. . .	8-1-87	24-2-87
WPB 1315 Matinicus	. . .	26-2-87	16-4-87
WPB 1316 Nantucket	. . .	17-4-87	4-6-87
WPB 1317 Attu	4-5-87	4-12-87	9-5-88
WPB 1318 Baranof	8-6-87	15-1-88	20-5-88
WPB 1319 Chandeleur	13-7-87	19-2-88	8-6-88
WPB 1320 Chincoteague	17-8-87	25-3-88	8-8-88
WPB 1321 Cushing	21-9-87	29-4-88	8-8-88
WPB 1322 Cuttyhunk	26-10-87	3-6-88	15-10-88
WPB 1323 Drummond	23-11-87	8-7-88	19-10-88
WPB 1324 Key Largo (ex-*Largo*)	1-1-88	12-8-88	24-12-88
WPB 1325 Metomkin	1-2-88	16-9-88	12-1-89
WPB 1326 Monomoy	21-3-88	21-10-88	16-12-88
WPB 1327 Orcas	25-4-88	25-11-88	14-4-89
WPB 1328 Padre	30-3-88	6-1-89	24-2-89
WPB 1329 Sitkinak	4-7-88	10-2-89	31-3-89
WPB 1330 Tybee	8-8-88	17-3-89	9-5-89
WPB 1331 Washington	12-9-88	21-4-89	1989
WPB 1332 Wrangell	17-10-88	26-5-89	24-6-89
WPB 1333 Adak	25-11-88	30-6-89	17-11-89
WPB 1334 Liberty	26-12-88	4-8-89	22-9-89
WPB 1335 Anacapa	30-1-89	8-9-89	13-1-90
WPB 1336 Kiska	6-3-89	13-10-89	1-12-89*
WPB 1337 Assateague	10-4-89	17-11-89	1-1-90*
WPB 1338 Grand Isle	18-6-90	. . .	14-12-90*
WPB 1339 Key Biscayne	16-7-90	. . .	27-4-91
WPB 1340 Jefferson Island	20-8-90	. . .	17-4-91
WPB 1341 Kodiak Island	24-9-90	8-2-91	21-6-91
WPB 1342 Long Island	29-10-90	19-3-91	27-8-91
WPB 1343 Bainbridge Island	3-12-90	19-4-91	14-6-91*
WPB 1344 Block Island	14-1-91	. . .	19-7-91*
WPB 1345 Staten Island	18-2-91	. . .	23-8-91*
WPB 1346 Roanoke Island	25-3-91	. . .	27-9-91*
WPB 1347 Pea Island	29-4-91	. . .	1-11-91*
WPB 1348 Knight Island	3-10-91	. . .	6-12-91*
WPB 1349 Galveston Island	8-7-91	15-11-91	17-1-92*

*Delivery date vice commissioning date

D: WPB 1301–1317: 117 tons light (165 fl); WPB 1318–1349: 107 tons (155 fl)
S: 29.7 kts (WPB 1338–1349: 28 kts) **Dim:** 33.53 × 6.40 × 2.23
A: 1/20-mm AA (WPB 1338 on: 1/25-mm Mk 38 Bushmaster low-angle)—2/40-mm Mk 19 grenade launchers—2/12.7-mm M2 mg (I × 2)
Electron Equipt: Radar: 1/SPS-64(V)1 nav.

Adak (WPB 1333) Dr. Giorgio Arra, 6-91

Baranof (WPB 1318) Dr. Giorgio Arra, 2-92

PATROL BOATS *(continued)*

Maui (WPB 1304) Dr. Giorgio Arra, 1990

M: WPB 1301–1337: 2 Alco-Paxman Valenta 16 RP200-1 CM diesels; 2 props; 5,820 bhp (5,760 sust.); WPB 1338–1349: 2 Caterpillar 8516 diesels; 2 props; 5,460 bhp
Electric: 198 kw tot. **Endurance:** 5 days
Range: 1,853 n.m. (26 kts × 24 hrs + 13.1 kts × 96 hrs); 3,380/8
Crew: 2 officers, 2 CPO, 12 enlisted

Remarks: Fifteen ordered 8-84; 16th ordered 3-5-85 in place of earlier winner Marine Power & Equipment, Seattle, Washington, whose contract was successfully contested by Bollinger. Modified Vosper Thornycroft design, with increased top-hamper. Steel hull, aluminum deck and superstructure. Fin stabilizers fitted. Carry Loran-C and Omega receivers, IFF transponder, and SQN-18 echo-sounder. Engines governor-limited to 2,880 bhp each from nominal max. 4,000 bhp. First delivered 23-8-85 for trials; others were to follow at 45-day intervals. Minimum speed is about 8 kts, making them difficult to employ in SAR and small-boat towing. Cost about $6.5M each.

Sixteen more ordered 11-2-87 under Congressional Coast Defense Augmentation; five more ordered 24-2-87 under Drug Omnibus Act of 1987. These 21 later units were to be delivered at 35-day intervals and have minor improvements, including heavier bow plating, a better anchor, 10 tons lighter weight, 300 gallon/day water generator added, and C.O.'s cabin relocated. Dates given for "in service" are for commissionings, which often followed delivery by several months. Have 3-ton payload margin. Expected to last only 15 years.

Twelve more, ordered 26-12-89 under FY 90 with navy funds, have different main engines and are armed with 1/25-mm Bushmaster (+ space for second aft), 4/12.7-mm mg; WPB 1309 trials with 25-mm gun 1990.

◆ 3 Bell 110 surface-effect patrol boats
Bldr: Bell-Halter, Inc., New Orleans

WSES 2 Sea Hawk (In serv. 17-11-82)
WSES 3 Shearwater (In serv. 17-11-82)
WSES 4 Petrel (In serv. 8-7-83)

D: 110 tons (160 fl) **S:** 35 kts (designed; now make about 30 kts max.)
Dim: 33.53 × 11.89 × 2.36 at rest/1.37 on cushion
A: 2/12.7-mm mg (I × 2)
Electron Equipt: Radar: 2/Decca 914 nav.
M: 2 G.M. 16V149 TI diesels for propulsion; 2 CP props; 3,600 bhp; 2 G.M. 8V92 TI diesels for lift; 2 centrifugal lift-fans; 990 bhp
Electric: 60 kw **Range:** 1,100/25; 1,500/23 on cushion
Crew: 2 officers, 16 enlisted

Sea Hawk (WSES 2) Dr. Giorgio Arra, 4-90

Shearwater (WSES 3) Leo Van Ginderen, 6-90

Remarks: Ordered 6-82 after the very successful trials with *Dorado* (WSES 1 is now in U.S. Navy service as IX 515 (SES 200). Rigid sidewall design, with rub bags fore and aft. Aluminum construction. Extra equipment had greatly performance to 18 kts max., vibration problems caused redesign of skirt ve speed has now been largely restored. Based at Key West on anti-drug pat intercept duties.

PATROL CRAFT

Note: All "Cape" (95-ft.)-class patrol boats have been stricken. The four liste last edition were retired: *Cape Hattaras* (WPB 95305) on 3-9-89 and transf Mexico 18-3-91; *Cape George* (WPB 95306) on 2-3-90; *Cape Cross* (WPB 95 30-3-90 and transferred to Micronesia; and *Cape Corwin* (WPB 95326) on 6-4 transferred to Micronesia. Three others were transferred to the Navy and are service craft.

◆ 41 83-ft. Point class
Bldr: Coast Guard Yard, Curtis Bay, Md. (ex WPB 82346 to WPB 83249: J. Martinac SB, Tacoma, Wash.)

	In serv.
A-series:	
WPB 82312 Point Swift	22-3-61
B-series:	
WPB 82333 Point Highland	27-6-62
WPB 82334 Point Ledge	18-7-62
WPB 82335 Point Countess	8-8-62
WPB 82336 Point Glass	29-8-62
WPB 82337 Point Divide	19-9-62
WPB 82338 Point Bridge	10-10-62
WPB 82339 Point Chico	29-10-62
WPB 82340 Point Batan	21-11-62
WPB 82341 Point Lookout	12-12-62
WPB 82343 Point Wells	20-11-63
WPB 82344 Point Estero	11-12-66
WPB 82346 Point Arena	26-8-66
WPB 82347 Point Bonita	12-9-66
WPB 82349 Point Spencer	25-10-66
WPB 82350 Point Franklin	14-11-66
WPB 82351 Point Bennett	19-12-66
WPB 82352 Point Sal	5-12-66
WPB 82354 Point Evans	10-1-67
WPB 82355 Point Hannon	23-1-67
WPB 82356 Point Francis	3-2-67
WPB 82357 Point Huron	
WPB 82358 Point Stuart	
WPB 82359 Point Steele	
WPB 82360 Point Winslow	
WPB 82363 Point Nowell	
WPB 82364 Point Whitehorn	
WPB 82365 Point Turner	
WPB 82366 Point Lobos	
WPB 82368 Point Warde	
WPB 82369 Point Heyer	
WPB 82370 Point Richmond	
D-series:	
WPB 82371 Point Barnes	
WPB 82372 Point Brower	
WPB 82373 Point Camden	
WPB 82374 Point Carrew	
WPB 82375 Point Doran	
WPB 82376 Point Harris	
WPB 82377 Point Hobart	
WPB 82378 Point Jackson	
WPB 82379 Point Martin	

Point Highland (WPB 82333) Victor M. Baca

Point Barnes (WPB 82371) Dr. Giorgio Arra

L CRAFT *(continued)*

Class (WPB 82336) Dr. Giorgio Arra, 10-91

Franklin (WPB 82350) Leo Van Ginderen, 6-90

4 tons (66–69 fl) **S:** 23.7 kts (*see* Remarks)
25.3 × 5.23 × 1.95
/12.7-mm M2 mg (I × 2)—2/40-mm Mk 64 grenade launchers
× 2)
tron Equipt: Radar: 1/SPS-64(V)1 nav.
Cummins VT-12-M diesels; 2 props; 1,600 bhp
ge: 490/23.7; 1,500/8 **Fuel:** 5.7 tons
v: 1 officer, 7 enlisted

ks: Hull in mild steel. High-speed diesels controlled from the bridge. The WPB 82371 and later make 22.6 knots, and have a range of 320/22.6; 1,200/8. uipped for salvage and towing. Beginning in 6-65, 26 others were sent to ı; they were transferred to the Vietnamese government in 1969–70. "Group A": 1. WPB 82371–82379 (less WPB 82374) have a range of 320/22.6 or 1,200/8 and 69 tons (fl). Were to strike 1992–98, but in late 1989 it was announced that 41 be re-engined with 750-bhp (at 1,800 rpm) Caterpillar 3412 V-12 diesels (23 kts eed) and refitted for further service.
ed since the last edition have been: *Point Hope* (WPB 82302) to Costa Rica *Point Verde* (WPB 82311) stricken 12-6-91 and transferred to Mexico 19-7-91; *hatcher* (WPB 82314) stricken 13-3-92 for fire-fighting training; *Point Herron* 2318) stricken and transferred to Mexico 26-7-91; *Point Roberts* (WPB 82332) 1991; *Point Baker* (WPB 82342) stricken 1991; *Point Judith* (WPB 82345) 15-1-92 and transferred to Venezuela; *Point Barrow* (WPB 82348) stricken and red to Panama 7-6-91; *Point Monroe* (WPB 82353) stricken 13-3-92; *Point* (WPB 82361) stricken 13-12-91 and transferred to Texas A&M University for ; *Point Brown* (WPB 82362) stricken 30-9-91 and transferred to Kingsborough nity College, Brooklyn, New York, for training; *and Point Knoll* (WPB 82367) 11-9-91 and transferred to Venezuela 20-12-91.

NING CUTTER

Horst Wessel class Bldr: Blohm + Voss, Hamburg, Germany

	L	In U.S.C.G.
27 Eagle (ex-*Horst Wessel*)	13-6-36	15-5-46

1,519 tons light (1,816 fl) **S:** 17 kts (10 under power)
: 89.92 (70.41 wl) × 11.92 × 5.18
ctron Equipt: Radar: 1/SPS-64(V)1 nav.
M: 1 Caterpillar D-399, V-16 diesel; 1 prop; 1,000 bhp (10 kts); 1,983 m² sail area
Electric: 450 kw **Range:** 5,450/7.5 (diesel) **Fuel:** 79 tons
Crew: 19 officers, 46 enlisted, 175 cadets and instructors

Eagle (WIX 327) Dr. Giorgio Arra, 1990

Remarks: Training ship at the Coast Guard Academy, New London. Sisters operate in the Portuguese Navy and Russian merchant marine. Re-engined and extensively overhauled at the U.S. Coast Guard Yard, Curtis Bay. Has 344 tons fixed ballast.

Note: Four small training tenders, T1 through T4, are used at the Coast Guard Academy for navigational and maneuvering training.

BUOY TENDERS, SEAGOING

Note: A new class of 28 buoy tenders to replace the elderly and hard-worked *Balsam* class is being planned, with detailed plans to be completed by 3-91. Some 28 ships would be built. The design proposed by Bollinger Machine Shop and Shipyard, Lockport, Louisiana, in conjunction with Wärtsilä-Kvaerner of Finland includes:

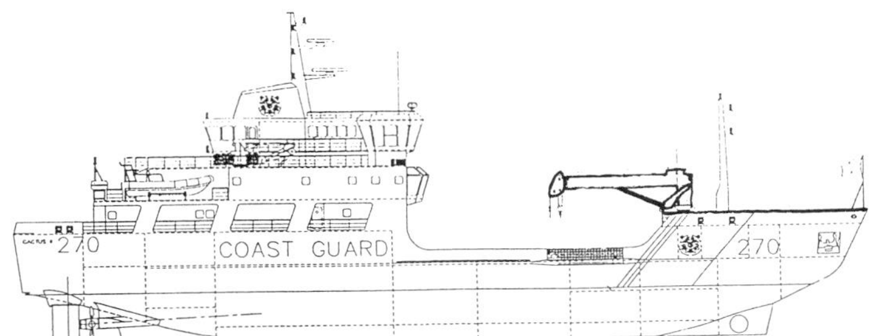

Possible appearance of new WLB class Kvaerner-Wärtsilä, 1991

D: . . . tons **S:** 15 kts **Dim:** 68.89 (62.79 pp) × 13.41 × . . .
M: 2 diesels, electric drive: 2 props; 6,700 shp
Range: 6,000/15 **Endurance:** 21 days **Crew:** 40 tot.

The other competitors for the lead-ship contract to be let late-summer 1992 are Marinette Marine, Marinette, Wisconsin, and Trinity Marine. Subsequent ships to be ordered 1995-on. Three yards are expected to be involved in the construction program, with deliveries coming over a period of ten years. Will have a 15-ton (30,000 lb.) crane, 2,500 ft.² working deck, and the ability to handle buoys in 8-ft. seas.

◆ **27 Balsam class** Bldrs: WLB 297: U.S. Coast Guard Yard, Curtis Bay, Md.; others: A: Marine Iron SB Co.; B: Duluth Iron & SB Co.

	Bldr	Laid down	L	In Serv.	SLEP
WLB 277 Cowslip†	A	16-9-41	11-4-42	17-10-42	1-83 to 7-84
WLB 290 Gentian*	B	3-10-41	23-5-42	3-11-43	11-79 to 8-83
WLB 291 Laurel*	B	17-4-42	4-8-42	24-11-42	7-86 to 2-90
WLB 296 Sorrel*	B	26-5-42	28-9-42	15-4-43	10-79 to 1-83
WLB 297 Ironwood‡		2-11-42	16-3-43	4-8-43	
WLB 301 Conifer*	A	6-7-42	3-11-42	1-7-43	8-83 to 1-86
WLB 302 Madrona*	B	6-7-42	11-11-42	30-5-43	4-84 to 14-9-89
WLB 306 Buttonwood*	A	5-10-42	30-11-42	24-9-43	3-91 to 1-93
WLB 307 Planetree*	A	4-12-42	20-3-43	4-11-43	3-93 to 3-94
WLB 308 Papaw*	A	16-11-42	19-2-43	12-10-43	14-9-89 to 11-90
WLB 309 Sweetgum*	A	21-2-43	15-4-43	20-11-43	2-90 to 12-91
WLB 388 Basswood†	A	21-3-43	20-5-43	12-1-44	
WLB 389 Bittersweet‡	B	16-9-43	11-11-43	11-5-44	
WLB 390 Blackhaw*	A	16-4-43	18-6-43	17-2-44	10-92 to 10-93
WLB 392 Bramble‡	B	2-8-43	23-10-43	22-4-44	

BUOY TENDERS, SEAGOING *(continued)*

	Bldr	Laid down	L	In Serv.	SLEP
WLB 393 Firebrush	B	12-11-43	3-2-44	20-7-44	
WLB 394 Hornbeam‡	A	19-6-43	14-8-43	14-4-44	
WLB 395 Iris†	B	10-12-43	18-5-43	11-8-44	
WLB 396 Mallow*	B	10-10-43	9-12-43	6-6-44	10-93 to 10-94
WLB 397 Mariposa‡	B	25-10-43	14-1-44	1-7-44	
WLB 401 Sassafras†	A	16-8-43	5-10-43	23-5-44	
WLB 402 Sedge‡	A	6-10-43	27-11-43	5-7-44	
WLB 403 Spar‡	A	13-9-43	2-11-43	12-6-44	
WLB 404 Sundew‡	A	29-11-43	8-2-44	24-8-44	
WLB 405 Sweetbrier‡	A	3-11-43	30-12-43	26-7-44	
WLB 406 Acacia (ex-*Thistle*)‡	B	16-1-44	7-4-44	1-9-44	
WLB 407 Woodrush‡	B	4-2-44	28-4-44	22-9-44	

*Service Life Extension overhaul program
†has received austere renovation
‡has received major renovation

Bramble (WLB 392) Leo Van Ginderen, 1991

Acacia (WLB 406) Leo Van Ginderen, 4-92

Laurel (WLB 291) Dr. Giorgio Arra, 8-91

Conifer (WLB 301) Victor M. Bac

D: 697 tons light (1,038 fl) **S:** 12.8–13 kts
Dim: 54.9 (51.8 pp) × 11.3 × 4.0
A: WLB 297, 389, 401, 402, 405: 2/20-mm AA (I × 2); others (not 392, 397, 404): 2/12.7-mm M2 mg (I × 2)
Electron Equipt: Radar: 1/SPS-64(V)1 nav.
M: 2 diesels, electric drive; 1 prop; WLB 277 to WLB 302: 1,070 s WLB 297, WLB 306 to WLB 407: 1,200 shp. WLB 404: 1,800 s (*see* Remarks)
Range: most: 4,600/12–18: 14,000/7.4; WLB 297, WLB 306 to W 308, WLB 388, WLB 390, WLB 396, WLB 401: 8,000/12; 23,500/7.5; WLB 392, WLB 406, WLB 407: 10,500/13; 31,000/7.5
Fuel: varies **Electric:** 400 kw **Crew:** 6 officers, 47 enlisted

Remarks: *Evergreen* (WLB 295) converted to oceanographic research ship a used as a patrol ship. WLB 296, WLB 390, WLB 392, WLB 402, WLB 403, and W have strengthened hulls for icebreaking, but all have icebreaker hull form. A 20-ton derrick. Ships in SLEP (Service Life Extension Program) have rebu EMD 8-645E6A engines and propulsion motors, improved habitability, h cargo-handling gear, bow-thrusters, and new generator sets (including 3 G diesels, one 8V-71 diesel), while endurance is increased to 5,500/10; 14 were to SLEP (see table), but the total may reduce, due to fiscal constraints. *Blackthor* 391) rammed and sunk 28-1-80, replaced by *Cowslip* (WLB 277), which was pre stricken 23-3-73, sold 1976, repurchased 19-1-81, and recommissioned 9-11-81 (WLB 292) redesignated WMEC in 2-80, *Citrus* (WLB 300) redesignated W 6-79. WLB 404 has a maximum speed of 15 knots. WLB 297, 307, 396, 402, 405, have long-range communications suites. WLB 397, 404, and 406 operate on th Lakes. Sister *Sagebrush* (WLB 399) stricken 26-4-88, and *Mesquite* (WLB 30 aground 5-12-89 in the Great Lakes and was declared a total loss. WLB 401 re- 1990. Sister *Salvia* (WLB 400), which was to have been given a major modern was stricken 12-4-91; Service Life Extension modernization of WLB 306 was tuted.

BUOY TENDERS, COASTAL

◆ **5 Red class (157-ft. class)** Bldr: Coast Guard Yard, Curtis Bay, M

	Laid down	L	In serv.
WLM 685 Red Wood	1-7-63	4-4-64	4-8-64
WLM 686 Red Beech	14-10-63	6-6-64	20-11-64
WLM 687 Red Birch	6-7-64	19-2-65	7-6-65
WLM 688 Red Cedar	1-7-69	1-8-70	18-12-70
WLM 689 Red Oak	26-10-70	19-6-71	10-12-71

Red Cedar (WLM 688) Leo Van Gindere

D: 371 tons light (525 fl) **S:** 12 kts (14 trials)
Dim: 47.85 (45.72 pp) × 10.10 (9.60 wl) × 1.90
M: 2 Caterpillar diesels; 2 CP props; 1,800 bhp
Range: 2,248/12.8; 3,055/11.6 **Crew:** 4 officers, 28 enlisted

Remarks: Can break light ice. Have 10-ton derrick and a bow-thruster. All ope U.S. East Coast. Range also reported as 2,570/10.

◆ **6 White class (133-ft. class)** Bldrs: Erie Concrete & Steel Supply Erie, Pa. (WLB 540: Niagara SB, Buffalo, New York; WLB 543: Basalt Roc Co., Napa, Cal.)

TENDERS, COASTAL *(continued)*

	Laid down	L	In serv.	In U.S.C.G.
540 White Sumac	31-8-42	14-6-43	6-11-43	19-9-47
543 White Holly	3-8-43	8-4-44	6-6-44	1-12-47
544 White Sage	28-3-43	9-6-43	29-5-44	9-8-47
545 White Heath	4-6-43	21-7-43	9-8-44	9-8-47
546 White Lupine	28-4-43	28-7-43	31-5-44	3-9-47
547 White Pine	12-6-43	28-8-43	11-7-44	3-8-48

Sumac (WLM 540) Dr. Giorgio Arra, 1-92

Heath (WLM 545) Victor M. Baca, 1991

435 tons (600 fl) **S:** 9.8 kts **Dim:** 40.49 × 9.14 × 2.67
2 diesels; 2 props; 600 bhp **Electric:** 90 kw
ge: 2,100/9.8; 4,500/5.1 **Fuel:** 40 tons
w: 1 officer, 23 enlisted

ks: Former U.S. Navy self-propelled covered lighters YF 416, 341, 444, 445, d 448, respectively. One 10-ton boom. Sister *White Bush* (WLM 542, ex-YF 339) n 16-9-85. All operate on U.S. East Coast.

Hollyhock-class coastal buoy tender *Fir* (WLM 212) was stricken 1-10-91.

TENDERS, INLAND

uckthorn class Bldr: Mobile Ship Repair, Mobile, Alabama

	Laid down	L	In serv.
42 Buckthorn	1962	. . .	17-7-64

thorn (WLI 642) Victor M. Baca, 1991

D: 188 tons (196 fl) **S:** 11.9 kts
Dim: 30.48 (29.26 pp) × 7.32 × 1.42
M: 2 Caterpillar diesels; 2 props; 600 bhp
Range: 1,300/11.9; 2,000/7.3 **Crew:** 1 officer, 13 enlisted

Remarks: Bow rectangular at main deck. Has one 5-ton boom. Based on the Great Lakes.

◆ **2 Bayberry class (65-ft. class)**
Bldr: Reliable Welding Works, Olympia, Washington

	In serv.
WLI 65400 Bayberry	28-6-54
WLI 65401 Elderberry	28-6-54

Bayberry (WLI 65400) Victor M. Baca, 3-90

D: 68 tons (71 fl) **S:** 11.3 kts **Dim:** 19.91 × 5.18 × 1.32
M: 2 G.M. 6-71 diesels; 2 props; 400 bhp
Range: 800/11.3; 1,700/6 **Crew:** 5 tot.

Remarks: Both launched 2-6-54. Based at Seattle, Wash., and Petersburg, Alaska, respectively.

◆ **2 Blackberry class (65300 class)**
Bldr: Dubuque Boat & Boiler Co., Dubuque, Iowa

	In serv.
WLI 65303 Blackberry	24-8-46
WLI 65304 Chokeberry	30-8-46

Chokeberry (WLI 65304) Victor M. Baca, 1991

D: 68 tons (fl) **S:** 9 kts **Dim:** 19.81 (19.20 pp) × 5.18 × 1.07
M: 1 G.M. diesel; 1 prop; 220 bhp **Range:** 700/9; 1,500/5
Crew: 5 tot.

Remarks: Based at Southport, North Carolina, and Crisfield, Maryland, respectively.

◆ **1 Cosmos class (100-ft. class)**
Bldr: Birchfield Boiler Co., Tacoma, Washington

	Laid down	L	In serv.
WLI 313 Bluebell	20-3-44	28-9-44	24-3-45

D: 153 tons light (178 fl) **S:** 10.5 kts
Dim: 30.48 (29.26 pp) × 7.49 × 1.62
M: 2 Waukesha diesels; 2 props; 600 bhp
Range: 1,400/10.5; 2,700/7 **Crew:** 1 officer, 14 enlisted

Remarks: Four sisters retyped WLIC on 1-10-79. WLI 313 based at Portland, Ore.

BUOY TENDERS, RIVER

◆ **2 Kankakee (75-ft. (F)) class** Bldr: Avondale Ind., New Orleans

	L	In serv.
WLR 75500 Kankakee	8-7-89	1-90
WLR 75501 Greenbrier	. . .	12-4-90

Kankakee (WLR 75500)—at launch Avondale, 7-89

D: 136 tons (175 fl) **S:** 12 kts
Dim: 22.86 (22.25 wl) × 7.32 × 1.53
Electron Equipt: Radar: 1/. . . nav.
M: 2 Caterpillar 3412-DIT diesels; 2 props; 1,024 bhp
Range: 600/11 **Fuel:** 11 tons **Crew:** 13 tot.

Remarks: Approved under FY 86 Budget, to act as push-tug for aids-to-navigation barge on Arkansas River; two ordered 3-88 to replace *Lantana* (WLR 80310) and *Dogwood* (WLR 259). Three more are planned. Have *six* rudders.

◆ **9 Gasconade class (75-ft. class)** Bldrs: WLR 75401: St. Louis SB & DD, St. Louis, Missouri; WLR 75402–75405: Maxon Construction Co., Tell City, Indiana; others: Halter Marine, New Orleans

	In serv.		In serv.
WLR 75401 Gasconade	15-1-64	WLR 75406 Kickapoo	20-5-69
WLR 75402 Muskingum	25-3-65	WLR 75407 Kanawha	22-9-69
WLR 75403 Wyaconda	30-5-65	WLR 75408 Patoka	9-2-70
WLR 75404 Chippewa	5-10-65	WLR 75409 Chena	27-5-70
WLR 75405 Cheyenne	3-10-66		

Gasconade (WLR 75401)—with CGB 90008, a 27.4-m buoy barge U.S.C.G., 6-83

D: 127 tons light (141 fl) **S:** 7.6–8.7 kts
Dim: 22.86 (22.25 pp) x 6.73 × 1.37
M: 2 Caterpillar diesels; 2 props; 600 bhp
Range: 1,600/7.6; 3,100/6.5 **Crew:** 12 tot.

Remarks: Flat-ended, barge-like hulls. WLR 75405 has an associated buoy push-barge and a slightly larger crew. One 1-ton crane. All operate on the Mississippi River and its tributaries. Four new 39.62 × 9.14 construction barges were ordered for this class 1985 from Thrift SB & Repair, Sulphur, La.; when yard went bankrupt, were completed at U.S. Coast Guard Yd., Curtis Bay, Md.: CG 72 delivered 4-88 for use with WLR 75408 at Greenville, Miss.; CG 73 for use with WLR 75407 at Memphis, Tenn.; other pair were to deliver in 1989, and eight more new barges will be built.

◆ **6 Ouachita class (65-ft. class)** Bldrs: WLR 65501, 65502: Platzer SY, Houston, Texas; others: Gibbs Corp., Jacksonville, Florida

	In serv.		In serv.
WLR 65501 Ouachita	22-7-60	WLR 65504 Scioto	27-3-62
WLR 65502 Cimarron	30-9-60	WLR 65505 Osage	15-5-62
WLR 65503 Obion	5-1-62	WLR 65506 Sangamon	16-6-62

Ouachita (WLR 65501)—with CGB 90009, a 27.4-m buoy barge U.S.C.G.,

D: 130 tons light (145 fl) **S:** 10 kts **Dim:** 20.02 × 6.40 × 1.52
M: 2 Caterpillar diesels; 2 props; 600 bhp
Range: 1,700/10.5; 3,500/6 **Crew:** 10 tot.

Remarks: WLR 65504 has an associated push-type buoy barge with a 3-ton cran a larger crew. All have a 3-ton crane aboard. Operate on the Mississippi River a tributaries.

◆ **1 Sumac class (115-ft. class)**
Bldr: Peterson & Haecker, Blair, Nebraska (In serv. 11-11-44)

WLR 311 Sumac

Sumac (WLR 311)—with work barge U.S.C.G.

D: 404 tons (478 fl) **S:** 10.6 kts **Dim:** 34.90 × 9.29 × 1.80
M: 3 G.M. diesels; 3 props; 2,250 bhp
Range: 5,000/10.6; 11,600/5 **Crew:** 1 officer, 22 enlisted

Remarks: Based at St. Louis, Missouri. To retire 1993.

CONSTRUCTION TENDERS, INLAND

◆ **4 Pamlico class (160-ft. class)**
Bldr: Coast Guard Yard, Curtis Bay, Md.

	Laid down	L	In serv.
WLIC 800 Pamlico	1-6-74	13-12-75	11-8-76
WLIC 801 Hudson	6-6-75	29-5-76	14-10-76
WLIC 803 Kennebec	9-1-76	11-12-76	6-4-77
WLIC 804 Saginaw	5-7-76	11-6-77	22-9-77

Hudson (WLIC 801) Dr. Giorgio Arra,

TRUCTION TENDERS, INLAND *(continued)*

13 tons (459 fl) **S:** 11.5 kts **Dim:** 30.48 × 9.14 × 1.17
tron Equipt: Radar: 1/Raytheon 1900 nav.
2 Cummins D379, 8-cyl. diesels; 2 props; 1,000 bhp
ge: 1,400/11; 2,200/6.5 **Crew:** 1 officer, 13 enlisted

ks: Design combines capabilities of the *Anvil* class and their associated equip-
rges. One 9-ton crane. All operate on Atlantic Coast inland waterways.

nvil class (75-ft. class) Bldrs: WLIC 75301, 75302: Gibbs SY,
ksonville, Florida; WLIC 75303–75305: McDermott Fabricators, Morgan
, Louisiana; WLIC 75306, 75307: Sturgeon Bay SB & DD, Sturgeon Bay,
c.; others: Dorchester SB, Dorchester, New Jersey

	In serv.		In serv.
75301 Anvil	14-5-62	WLIC 75306 Clamp	24-11-64
75302 Hammer	20-11-62	WLIC 75307 Wedge	10-12-64
75303 Sledge	5-12-62	WLIC 75309 Hatchet	23-6-66
75304 Mallet	1-2-63	WLIC 75310 Axe	17-10-66
75305 Vise	14-3-63		

WLIC 75305)—with spud-equipped work barge
Florian Jentsch, 1-91

129 tons light (145 fl) **S:** 9.1 kts
: 23.19 (22.26 pp) × 6.83 × 1.37
2 diesels; 2 props; 600 bhp **Range:** 1,000/10
w: 0 or 1 officer, 9 enlisted

ks: All except *Anvil* and *Mallet* have an associated push-type barge with a
rane. WLIC 75306 to WLIC 75310 are 23.2 m overall and can make 9.4 knots.
Spike (WLIC 75308) and associated barge stricken 30-5-86. Ranges vary: WLIC
and 75302: 1,300/9; 2,400/5; WLIC 75303–75305: 1,000/9; 2,200/5; others:
; 2,500/5. All on Atlantic and Gulf Coast inland waterways.

Cosmos class (100-ft. class)
r: Dubuque Boat & Boiler, Dubuque, Iowa

	Laid down	L	In serv.
298 Rambler	7-12-42	6-5-43	26-5-43
315 Smilax	26-11-43	18-8-44	1-11-44
316 Primrose	26-11-43	18-8-44	23-10-44

rose (WLIC 316) Leo Van Ginderen, 7-90

178 tons (fl) **S:** 10.5 kts **Dim:** 30.48 (29.26 pp) × 7.49 × 1.62
ctron Equipt: Radar: 1/Raytheon 1900 nav.
2 Waukesha diesels; 2 props; 600 bhp
nge: 1,400/10.5; 2,700/7 **Crew:** 1 officer, 14 enlisted

rks: Reclassified from WLI on 1-10-79. Sister *Bluebell* remains typed WLI (WLI
VLIC 298 has an associated construction barge, while WLIC 316 has a pile driver
bow. All have a 5-ton crane. Sister *Cosmos* (WLIC 293) stricken 1985.

BREAKING TUGS

Katmai Bay class (140-ft. class) Bldrs: Tacoma Boatbuilding,
acoma, Wash., except WTGB 107, 109: Bay City Marine, Tacoma, Wash.

	Laid down	L	In serv.
B 101 Katmai Bay	7-11-77	8-4-78	8-1-79
WTGB 102 Bristol Bay	13-2-78	22-7-78	5-4-79
WTGB 103 Mobile Bay	13-2-78	11-11-78	6-5-79
WTGB 104 Biscayne Bay	29-8-78	3-2-79	8-12-79
WTGB 105 Neah Bay	6-8-79	2-2-80	18-8-80
WTGB 106 Morro Bay	6-8-79	11-7-81	25-1-80
WTGB 107 Penobscot Bay	1-7-83	27-7-84	2-1-85
WTGB 108 Thunder Bay	20-7-84	15-8-85	4-11-85
WTGB 109 Sturgeon Bay	9-7-86	12-9-87	20-8-88

Sturgeon Bay (WTGB 109) Dr. Giorgio Arra, 6-90

Morro Bay (WTGB 106)—white-painted as training ship
Victor M. Baca, 1991

D: 662 tons (fl) **S:** 14.7 kts **Dim:** 42.67 (39.62 pp) × 11.43 × 3.66
Electron Equipt: Radar: 1/SPS-64(V)1 nav.
M: 2 Fairbanks-Morse 38D8⅛ diesels, Westinghouse electric drive; 1 prop; 2,500 shp
Electric: 250 kw (2 × 125 kw) **Range:** 1,800/14.7; 4,000/12
Fuel: 71 tons **Crew:** 3 officers, 14 enlisted

Remarks: Displace 673 tons in fresh water. Reclassified from WYTM on 5-2-79. WTGB 101–105 operate on the Great Lakes, the others on the U.S. East Coast. WTGB 106 acts as enlisted training ship in the summer, at Yorktown, Va.

Can break .51-m ice continuously, or 1.8-m ice by backing and ramming. Have portable bubble-generator system housed in a removable deckhouse on the fantail. Two fire-fighting monitors atop the pilothouse, which provides near 360-degree viewing. One 2-ton crane handles a 4.9-m plastic workboat. Initially intended to replace the older WYTMs in service. WTGB 109 ordered 11-2-86, using navy funds; at least one more was planned, to be named *Curtis Bay*, but funds will not be available.

WTGB 102 operates with a 45.72 × 18.29 × 3.05 former jack-up barge converted 11-84 by Bay SB, Sturgeon Bay, Wisc., for a two-year experimental program on the Great Lakes. A 300-hp Schottel vertical cycloidal bow-thruster prop, powered by a G.M. 8V92 diesel, was added to the barge, as was a 10-ton 21.3-m extendable boom, to permit the craft to act as an aids-to-navigation tender. As a follow-on, WTGB 102 and 103 received new 45.72 × 18.29-m aids-to-navigation barges in 7-91 and 4-92, respectively; built by Marinette Marine, Marinette, Wisconsin, and equipped with 20-ton crane, machine shop, paint locker, bridge/pilothouse, bow-thruster, and indented sterns for pushing; seven crew.

HARBOR TUGS, SMALL

◆ **14 65-ft. class** Bldrs: WYTL 65601–65606: Gibbs Corp., Jacksonville, Florida; WYTL 65607–65612: Barbour Boat Works, New Bern, North Carolina; others: Western Boatbldg., Tacoma, Washington

	In serv.		In serv.
WYTL 65601 Capstan	19-7-61	WYTL 65608 Pendant	8-63
WYTL 65602 Chock	12-9-62	WYTL 65609 Shackle	7-5-63
WYTL 65603 Swivel	27-10-61	WYTL 65610 Hawser	17-1-63
WYTL 65604 Tackle	1962	WYTL 65611 Line	21-2-63
WYTL 65605 Towline	27-3-62	WYTL 65612 Wire	19-3-63
WYTL 65606 Catenary	4-62	WYTL 65614 Bollard	10-4-67
WYTL 65607 Bridle	3-4-63	WYTL 65615 Cleat	10-5-67

HARBOR TUGS, SMALL *(continued)*

Wire (WYTL 65612) Leo Van Ginderen, 2-92

Bollard (WYTL 65614)—note shorter superstructure
Dr. Giorgio Arra, 1990

D: 62 tons light (72 fl) **S:** 9.8 (first 6: 10.5) kts
Dim: 19.79 (19.08 pp) × 5.82 × 2.74
Electron Equipt: Radar: 1/Raytheon 1900 or SPS-66A nav.
M: 1 diesel; 1 prop; 400 bhp **Crew:** 10 tot.
Range: 850/9.8; 2,700/5.8 (WYTL 65601 to WYTL 65606: 3,600/6.8, 8,900/10.5)

Remarks: Sister *Bitt* (WYTL 65613) stricken 10-4-82. Can break ice up to 152-mm thick. All serve on U.S. East Coast.

◆ **1 former U.S. Army harbor tug**
Bldr: Equitable Equipment, New Orleans (In serv. 5-9-45)

85009 Messenger (ex-ST-710)

Messenger (85009) Victor M. Baca, 1991

D: . . . tons **S:** 9 kts **Dim:** 26.21 × 7.01 × 3.05
M: 1 diesel; 1 prop; 650 bhp **Crew:** . . .

Remarks: Acquired mid-1950s from U.S. Army. Attached to the Coast Guar Curtis bay, Maryland. Sister *Research* (85010) stricken 23-5-73.

FERRIES

Note: The following four ships are not commissioned cutters of the U.S. Coas but are under Coast Guard control. Their status is "in service" and they are manned. They operate from Governors Island in New York Harbor.

◆ **2 ex-U.S. Army ferries**
Bldr: John H. Mathis, Camden, N.J. (In serv. 1956)

Lt Samuel S. Coursen   Pvt Nicholas Minue

Lt Samuel S. Coursen Leo Van Ginder

D: 869 tons **S:** 12 kts **Dim:** 54.9 × 18.9 × 3.0
M: diesel-electric drive; 2 props; 1,000 shp

Remarks: Former U.S. Army ferries FB 812 and FB 813. *Coursen* refitted 1

◆ **1 former Puget Sound ferry**
Bldr: Moore DD, Oakland, Cal. (In serv. 1952)

Governor (ex-*Kulshan*, ex-*Crown City*)

Governor Dr. Giorgio Ar

D: 1,600 tons (fl) **S:** 12 kts **Dim:** 73.97 × 19.96 × 4.27
M: 2 diesels, electric drive; 2 props; . . . shp

Remarks: Originally built for use at San Diego, then sold to Washingto Acquired 1982 and refitted at U.S.C.G. Yard, Curtis Bay, into early 1985 fo Governors Island. Can carry 55 automobiles and 150 passengers.

◆ **1 former New York City ferry** Bldr: . . . (In serv. 1946)

The Tides

The Tides Dr. Giorgio Arr

D: 774 tons (fl) **S:** 12 kts **Dim:** 56.4 × 16.8 × 2.7
M: diesel-electric drive; 2 props; 1,350 shp

FLOATING DRY DOCK

◆ **1 U.S. Navy dock, on loan** Bldr: Foundation Co. (In serv. 12-43

YFD 83 (ex-AFDL 31)

Lift capacity: 1,000 tons **Dim:** 60.96 × 19.51 × 1.04 (light)

'ING DRY DOCK *(continued)*

:s: Steel dock used at U.S.C.G. Yard, Curtis Bay, Md., since completion and loaned 1-47. Length over blocks is 56.4 m, clear width is 13.7 m, maximum r blocks is 4.4 m, and maximum draft flooded is 8.2 m.

L CRAFT

.S. Coast Guard operates some 2,000 small craft, including over 1,000 under ng classified as UTL (Utility Boat, Light). Sizes range from 3.35-m light skiffs m aids-to-navigation tenders. No central registry of their numbers is main- heir administration being the responsibility of the stations to which they are . All carry five-digit serial numbers, the first two digits of which denote the ngth in feet.

)L CRAFT/UTILITY BOATS

st coastal interceptors

Tempest Marine, North Miami Beach, Florida

In serv. 1-4-87) 43503 (In serv. 7-87) 43505 (In serv. 1988)
In serv. 6-87) 43504 (In serv. 11-8-87)

Dr. Giorgio Arra, 1-90

tons (fl) **S:** 39 kts **Dim:** 13.26 × 2.90 × 0.99
nall arms **Electron Equipt:** Radar: 1/Raytheon 1900 nav.
Caterpillar 3208 TA diesels; 2 props; 750 bhp
ge: . . . **Fuel:** 1,287 liters **Crew:** 4 to 6 tot.

:s: Adaptation of commercial "Riviera"-class "cigarette boat" with diesel vice soline engines. Operate from Miami in drug-interdiction duties. GRP construc- with 25-deg. V-bottom hull. An unspecified number of seized and donated craft eneral type are also used by the U.S.C.G. in the "drug war."

-ft. search-and-rescue boat

: Munson Mfg., Edmonds, Washington (In serv. 6-92)

. . **S:** . . . **Dim:** 14.94 × 4.57 × . . .
G.M. 8V92 TI diesels; 2 props; . . . bhp

ks: Prototype for a new class of fast rescue craft.

41-ft. utility boats

: U.S.C.G. Yard, Curtis Bay, Md. (In serv. 1973–83)

41300-41448

—41-ft. class Victor M. Baca, 1990

3–14 tons (fl) **S:** 22–26 kts **Dim:** 12.40 × 4.11 × 1.22
tron Equipt: Radar: 1/Raytheon 1900 nav.
2 Cummins V903M or VT903M diesels; 2 props; 560 or 636 bhp
ge: 300/18 **Fuel:** 1.54 tons **Crew:** 3 tot.

41352—41-ft. class Dr. Giorgio Arra, 7-91

Remarks: Prototype delivered 1971; between 1973–1982 some 206 more followed. Aluminum construction. Hull numbers start with 41300. 43400 has special vanes on the propeller shafts, adding 2.5 kts speed; will be backfitted to others. Designed weight 12.97 tons, but displacements have increased to almost 14 tons. Have a 250-gal./min. firepump.

◆ **2 38-ft.-class utility boats**

Bldr: Munson Mfg., Edmonds, Washington (In serv. 5-91)

380502—380501 in background Dr. Giorgio Arra, 6-91

D: . . . tons **S:** . . . **Dim:** 11.58 × 3.96 × . . .
M: 2 Caterpillar 3208TA diesels; 2 props; . . . bhp **Crew:** 4 tot.

Remarks: Built to test the concept of providing crew accommodations and services aboard utility craft, with the crew "living off the economy" rather than being tied to a Coast Guard shore station.

◆ **365 32-ft. ports and waterways boats**

32318—32-ft. class Dr. Giorgio Arra, 1990

PATROL CRAFT/UTILITY BOATS *(continued)*

D: 7.5 tons light (8.6 fl) **S:** 20.4 kts **Dim:** 10.16 × 3.58 × 0.86
Electron Equipt: Radar: 1/Raytheon 1900 nav.
M: 2 Caterpillar 3208 diesels; 2 props; 406 bhp
Range: 190/16.5 **Fuel:** 0.65 tons **Crew:** 3 tot.

Remarks: GRP construction; built late 1970s to replace 30-ft. Mk-III class. Have a 90-bhp G.M. 3-53 diesel to drive a 500 gallon/min. fire pump.

◆ **28 31-ft. port security boats** Bldr: 31001–31004: Bertram Boat, Miami; others U.S.C.G. Yard, Curtis Bay, Md. (In serv. 14-3-64-. . .)

31001–31028

31012—31-ft. class Dr. Giorgio Arra, 1989

D: 7.38 tons (fl) **S:** 14 kts **Dim:** 9.27 × 3.51 × 1.19
Electron Equipt: Radar: 1/Raytheon 1900 nav.
M: 1 G.M. diesel; 1 prop; 197 bhp **Range:** 165/12.5 **Crew:** 3 tot.

Remarks: GRP construction. Originally built for navigational training.

◆ **. . . 30-ft. utility boats** Bldr: U.S. Coast Guard Yard (In serv. 1954–83)

series 30376–30598

D: 5.9 tons (fl) **S:** 20 kts **Dim:** 9.14 × 2.66 × 1.07
M: 1 diesel; 1 prop; . . . bhp **Range:** 120/22 **Crew:** 3 tot.

Remarks: Survivors of a once-large group. Final Mk-III version with GRP hull remains in use in small numbers; early wood and steel variants have been retired.

◆ **1 Lake Champlain patrol craft**
Bldr: SeaArk Boat, Monticello, Arkansas (In serv. 1987)

Lake Champlain patrol craft SeaArk, 1987

D: . . . **S:** 38 kts **Dim:** 8.69 × 3.56 × 0.56
Electron Equipt: Radar: 1/Furuno . . . nav. **Crew:** 2–3 tot.
M: 2 Volvo AQAD 41/290 outdrive diesels; 2 props; 400 bhp

Remarks: Aluminum construction. Based at Burlington, Vermont. Used for SAR.

◆ **4 21-ft. search-and-rescue boats**
Bldr: SeaArk, Monticello, Arkansas (In serv. 2 in 8-91, 2 in 9-91)

D: . . . **S:** . . . **Dim:** 6.40 × 2.44 × . . .
M: 2 Volvo Penta TAMD outdrives

◆ **24 Raider patrol craft** Bldr: NAPCO International, Hopkins, Minnesota (In serv.: 1st 3 in 1987, others: 10-88 to 6-89)

233510–233524

Raider patrol craft NAPCO

D: 1.5 tons light (2 tons fl) **S:** 40 kts **Dim:** 6.81 × 2.26 × . . .
A: 2/12.7-mm mg or small arms **Crew:** 3 tot.
M: 2 outboard motors; 360 bhp **Range:** 167/40; 750/. . .

Remarks: GRP Boston Whaler hulls, outfitted by NAPCO. Series of 21 ordered.

◆ **6 or more Whaler patrol craft**
Bldr: Boston Whaler, Rockland, Mass. (In serv. late 1980s)

225502—a 22-ft. Boston Whaler Victor M. Baca

D: . . . **S:** 40 kts **Dim:** 6.81 × 2.26 × . . . **Crew:** 3 tot.
A: small arms **M:** 2 gasoline outboards: 360 bhp

Remarks: Same hull as craft above, but are in utility configuration.

252511—a 25-ft. GRP-hulled craft powered by two gasoline outboards
Dr. Giorgio Arra

GATIONAL AIDS CRAFT

able repair craft, former LCM(6)

)

0 U.S.C.G., 6-86

50 tons (fl) **S:** 10 kts **Dim:** 17.07 × 4.37 × 1.17
tron Equipt: 1/. . . nav. **Range:** 130/10
2 G.M. 6-71 diesels; 2 props; 330 bhp

ks: Conversion from U.S. Navy landing craft completed 6-86 at U.S.C.G. Yard, Bay, Md., for service at South Portland, Maine, as a telephone and power cable New pilothouse added, bow altered.

55-ft.-class aids-to-navigation boats
r: Robert E. Derecktor, Mamaroneck, New York (In serv. 1976–77)

–55125

Dr. Giorgio Arra, 7-91

28.8 tons (31.25 fl) **S:** 22 kts **Dim:** 17.68 × 5.18 × 1.52
ctron Equipt: Radar: 1/Raytheon 1900 nav.
2 G.M. 12 V71 TI diesels; 2 props; 1,080 bhp
ge: 350/18 **Fuel:** 3,995 liters **Crew:** 4 tot.

ks: Aluminum construction. Can carry 4,000 lbs (2 tons) cargo and have a b. crane.

6-ft. stern-loading buoy boats Bldrs: 46301–46306: Hunt pyard; others: U.S. Coast Guard Yard, Curtis Bay, Md. (In serv. 1966–69)

–46309

Dr. Giorgio Arra, 6-91

D: 19.9 tons light (27 fl) **S:** 9 kts **Dim:** 14.12 × 4.93 × 1.73
Electronic Equipt: Radar: 1/Raytheon 1900 nav.
M: 1 G.M. 6-71 diesel; 1 Schottel prop; 180 bhp
Range: 440/9 (46301–46306: 320/9) **Crew:** 4 tot.

Remarks: Pilothouse configurations vary. Have a 4,000-lb crane aft.

◆ **32 45-ft.-class aids-to-navigation boats**
Bldr: U.S. Coast Guard Yard, Curtis Bay, Md. (In serv. 1957–. . .)

45302 series

45306—with Raytheon 1900 radar Victor M. Baca, 1991

D: 21.5 tons light (31.2 fl) **S:** 8.5 kts **Dim:** 13.8 × 4.6 × 0.91
Electron Equipt: Radar: 1/Raytheon 1900 nav.
M: 1 G.M. 6-71 diesel; 1 prop; 150 bhp (45313–45316: 180 bhp)
Range: 550/8.5 **Fuel:** 2.2 tons **Crew:** 4 tot.

Remarks: Can carry up to 10 tons cargo and have a quadrantial buoy crane forward. It is hoped to replace these craft with a new class of 24 boats, the first 7 of which it had been hoped to order in 1991.

◆ **50 21-ft. aids-to-navigation boats**
Bldr: MonArk, Monticello, Ark. (In serv. 1981–. . .)

21-ft. aids-to-navigation boat MonArk, 1985

D: 1.59 tons light (3.17 fl) **S:** 28 kts **Dim:** 6.56 × 2.24 × 0.36 (hull)
M: 1 gasoline engine; 1 prop; 228-bhp or Mercruiser 165-bhp outboard
Range: 100/20 **Crew:** . . . tot.

Remarks: Aluminum construction, design based on builder's 21-V, deep-Vee hull design. Can be mounted on a trailer for land transport.

◆ **1 46-ft. oil-spill clearance boat**
Bldr: U.S.C.G. Yard, Curtis Bay, Md. (In serv. 1982)

Zero Relative Velocity Skimmer U.S.C.G., 1982

Remarks: Catamaran hull with rotary belt/wringer oil-spill cleanup system. Prototype. Aluminum construction.

NAVIGATIONAL AIDS CRAFT *(continued)*

172585—GRP-hulled, SeaArk-built navigational aids tender
Dr. Giorgio Arra, 7-88

LIFEBOATS

♦ **1 (+5+100) 47-ft. lifeboats**
Bldr: Textron Marine, New Orleans, La. (In serv. 25-6-90 to . . .)

47200–series

47200—in bare aluminum finish Victor M. Baca, 1992

D: 17.9 tons (fl) **S:** 25 kts (20 sust.) **Dim:** 14.33 × 4.27 × 1.22
Electron Equipt: Radar: 1/. . . nav.
M: 2 G.M. 6V92 TA diesels; 2 props; 850 bhp
Range: 200/25; 208/10 **Crew:** 4 tot. plus 5 survivors

Remarks: Intended to replace the 44-ft. class and to provide significantly greater speed of reaction. Prototype and option for five more ordered 5-4-88; the five option boats were ordered 9-12-91. First unit laid down 1-8-89 and launched 18-5-90. Aluminum construction, with deep-vee hull form. Trials in heavy seas were highly successful. Can tow craft displacing up to 150 tons.

♦ **105 44-ft. motor lifeboat class**
Bldr: U.S.C.G. Yard, Curtis Bay, Md. (In serv. 31-3-61 to 8-5-73)

44300–44409

44-ft. Motor Lifeboat Dr. Giorgio Arra, 1989

D: 14.9 tons light (17.7 fl) **S:** 13 kts (11.8 sust.)
Dim: 13.44 × 3.87 × 1.19 **Electron Equipt:** Radar: 1/SPS-57 n
Crew: 4 tot. **M:** 2 G.M. 6V53 diesels; 2 props; 372 bhp
Range: 185/11.8; 200/11 **Fuel:** 1.2 tons **Crew:** 4 tot.

Remarks: "Unsinkable" design. Four were also built for foreign countries. Can up to 21 rescued personnel. 44300 is used for training at Motor Lifeboat School, with 44301, 44304, 44369, and 44381. The rest are on independent detachment has been discarded; the others are to be disposed of by 1998.

♦ **4 52-ft. motor lifeboats** Bldr: U.S.C.G. Yard, Curtis Bay, Md.

52312 Victory (In serv. 29-11-56)
52313 Invincible (In serv. 11-10-60)
52314 Triumph II (In serv. 1-4-61)
52315 Intrepid (In serv. 11-10-61)

D: 31.7 tons (35 fl) **S:** 11 kts **Dim:** 15.85 × 4.43 × 1.91
M: 2 G.M. 6-71 diesels; 2 props; 340 bhp
Range: 495/11 **Crew:** 5 + up to 35 rescued personnel

Remarks: Designed for service under extremely heavy sea conditions. All in s on Pacific Northwest coast. Have a 250-gal./min. fire-fighting and salvage pum

♦ **19 30-ft. surf rescue boats**
Bldr: U.S.C.G. Yard, Curtis Bay, Md. (In serv. 1979–83)

30201 series

30615—30-ft. surf rescue boat Victor M. Baca,

D: 4.5 tons (5.2 fl) **S:** 28 kts **Dim:** 9.25 × 2.84 × 1.09
Crew: 2 tot.
M: 1 G.M. 6V92T diesel; 1 prop; 375 bhp **Range:** 150/25

Remarks: Self-bailing/self-righting design; GRP construction. Can operate in surf and can carry up to six rescued personnel. Can tow boats up to 12-m lengt

♦ **206 25-ft. 8-in. surf boats**
Bldr: U.S.C.G. Yard, Curtis Bay, Md. (In serv. 1969–83)

253301–253507

253308—a 25-ft. motor surfboat, with 30-ft. surf rescue boat 30618
Victor M. Baca

D: 2.3 tons (3.4 fl) **S:** 11 kts **Dim:** 7.82 × 2.16 × 0.64
M: 1 G.M. 3-53 diesel; 1 prop; 80 bhp **Range:** 60/11 **Crew:** 3 t

Remarks: Can carry up to 13 survivors. GRP construction. Design essentially s

:BOATS *(continued)*

U.S. Navy 26-ft. motor whaleboat, and a number are carried aboard U.S. Coast cutters. Most are assigned to shore stations around the United States.

)—a "Hurricane" rigid inflatable boat with a Johnson outboard motor, for SAR duties Zodiac, 1990

U.S. ARMY TRANSPORTATION CORPS

U.S. Army's fleet is divided into units (primarily survey craft, dredges, and uction craft) operated by the Corps of Engineers, and landing craft and logistics rt craft operated by the Transportation Corps. At the end of 1991, the Transporta- orps had some 511 numbered ships and craft, including 122 in storage and 10 on o other agencies. Principal Transportation Corps units are listed below.

ie 1,065 6-ton, 8-m bridging boats for use by combat troops have been delivered or n order to a design by Fairey Marine, U.K.; most recent order was for 225 on 37 to American Development, Charleston, S.C.

. Army Transportation Corps ships and craft are classed by design number. They alphanumeric serials in the following categories:

Barge, dry cargo, non-self-propelled
Conversion kit, barge, deck enclosure
Crane, floating
Lighter, beach discharge
Barge, liquid cargo, non-self-propelled
Barge, dry cargo, non-self-propelled, knock-down
Pier, barge-type, self-elevating
Barge, refrigerated, non-self-propelled
Repair shop, floating, marine repair, non-self-propelled
Freight and supply vessel, over 140-ft. (42.67 m) o.a.
Refrigerated cargo vessel, self-propelled, all sizes
Work and inspection boat, under 50 ft. (15.24 m) o.a.
Lighter, amphibious, resupply, cargo
Landing Craft, Mechanized
Landing Craft, Utility
Landing Craft, Vehicle
Tug, large, 100 ft. (30.48 m) and over
Work and inspection boat, large, over 50 ft (15.24 m)
Tug, Small, under 100 ft. (30.48 m)
Freight and supply vessel, small, under 100 ft. (3.48 m)
Liquid cargo vessel, self-propelled, all sizes

ICLE LANDING SHIPS

Gen. Frank S. Besson-class vehicle landing ships
dr: Halter–Moss Point Marine, Escatawpa, Miss.

	L	In serv.	Based
01 Gen. Frank S. SSON, Jr.	30-6-87	20-1-88	Ft. Eustis, Va.
02 CW3 Harold C. .INGER	16-9-87	20-4-88	Ford Isl., Oahu
03 Gen. Brehon B. MERVELL	18-11-87	26-7-88	Tacoma, Wa.
04 Lt. Gen. William B. JNKER	11-1-88	1-9-88	Ft. Eustis, Va.
05 MGen. Charles P. ROSS	11-7-90	30-4-91	. . .

3 Harold C. Clinger (LSV 02) Leo Van Ginderen, 1990

MGen. Charles P. Gross (LSV 05) Trinity/John Sims, 1991

D: 1,612 tons light (4,199 tons fl) **S:** 12 kts trials (11.6 sust.)
Dim: 83.14 (78.03 pp) × 18.28 (18.16 wl) × 3.66 (max.) **A:** none
Electron Equipt: Radar: 1/SPS-64(V)2 nav., 1/SPS-64(V) . . . nav.
M: 2 G.M. EMD 16-645-E2 diesels; 2 props; 3,900 bhp—250-shp Schottel bow-thruster
Electric: 599 kw (2 × 250-kw Caterpillar 3406, 1 × 99-kw Caterpillar 3304 diesel sets)
Range: 8,358/11 **Fuel:** 524 tons **Endurance:** 38 days
Crew: 6 officers, 24 enlisted

Remarks: Ordered 19-9-86. Design based on Australian roll-on/roll-off, beachable cargo ship *Frances Bay*, designed by Burness, Corlett, Ltd. Built to commercial specifications. Intended to transport 816 to 1,815 metric tons of vehicles or containers on 975 m² cargo deck. Carry up to 122 tons potable water and 1,631 tons salt-water ballast. Bow and stern ramps of 8.23-m width. LSV 1 laid down 16-1-87. All use rebuilt engines. Fifth unit authorized FY 89, ordered 3-90. Two near-sisters ordered for the Philippines in 1992.

UTILITY LANDING CRAFT

♦ **35 2000 Design utility landing craft** Bldr: First three: Lockheed SB, Savannah Div., Savannah, Ga.; others: Trinity–Moss Point Marine, Escatawpa, Miss.—*see* Remarks

	Laid down	L	In serv.
LCU 2001 Runnymede	2-12-86	14-8-87	21-2-90
LCU 2002 Kenesaw Mountain	22-5-87	6-10-87	28-2-90
LCU 2003 Macon	1-10-87	1-2-88	23-3-90
LCU 2004 Aldie	11-4-88	4-89	23-2-90
LCU 2005 Brandy Station	11-9-88	5-89	7-3-90
LCU 2006 Bristoe Station	11-2-89	31-7-89	30-3-90
LCU 2007 Broad Run	11-3-89	28-8-89	4-5-90
LCU 2008 Buena Vista	11-4-89	10-9-89	18-4-90
LCU 2009 Springfield (ex-*Calabozo*)	22-11-89	9-2-90	13-7-90
LCU 2010 Cedar Run	27-12-89	12-3-90	17-8-90
LCU 2011 Chickahominy	31-1-90	16-4-90	21-9-90
LCU 2012 Chickasaw Bayou	7-3-90	26-5-90	26-10-90
LCU 2013 Churubusco	11-4-90	25-6-90	10-90
LCU 2014 Coamo	16-5-90	28-7-90	4-1-91
LCU 2015 Contreras	20-6-90	3-9-90	8-2-91
LCU 2016 Corinth	25-7-90	10-90	15-3-91
LCU 2017 El Caney	29-8-90	11-90	19-4-91
LCU 2018 Five Forks	3-10-90	17-12-90	24-5-91
LCU 2019 Fort Donelson	7-11-90	1-91	28-6-91
LCU 2020 Fort McHenry	12-12-90	2-91	2-8-91
LCU 2021 Great Bridge	16-1-91	1-4-91	6-9-91
LCU 2022 Harpers Ferry	2-91	5-91	11-10-91
LCU 2023 Hobkirk	27-3-91	6-91	15-11-91
LCU 2024 Hormigueros	1-5-91	15-7-91	20-12-91
LCU 2025 Malvern Hill	5-6-91	8-91	24-1-92
LCU 2026 Matamoros	10-7-91	9-91	28-2-92
LCU 2027 Mechanicsville	8-91	10-91	3-4-92
LCU 2028 Missionary Ridge	18-9-91	11-91	8-5-92
LCU 2029 Molino Del Rey	22-4-91	7-11-91	11-5-92
LCU 2030 Monterrey	27-5-91	5-12-91	15-5-92
LCU 2031 New Orleans	20-6-91	10-1-92	1-6-92
LCU 2032 Palo Alto	15-7-91	6-2-92	9-7-92
LCU 2033 Paulus Hook	15-8-91	5-3-92	18-9-92
LCU 2034 Perryville	15-9-91	2-4-92	4-8-92
LCU 2035 Port Hudson	15-10-91	30-4-92	1-9-92

D: 672 tons light (1,102 fl) **S:** 11.5 kts
Dim: 53.03 (47.55 pp) × 12.80 × 1.43 (2.60 max. loaded) **A:** none
Electron Equipt: Radar: 1/SPS-64(V)2 nav., 1/SPS-64(V) . . . nav.
M: 2 Cummins KTA-50M diesels, 2 Kort-nozzle props; 2,500 bhp—300 shp bow-thruster
Range: 4,500/11.5 (light) **Fuel:** 282 tons **Endurance:** 18 days
Electric: 540 kw (2 × 250 kw, 1 × 40 kw)
Crew: 2 officers, 10 enlisted

Remarks: First seven ordered 11-6-86, seven on 31-3-87, three on 22-9-87, five on

UTILITY LANDING CRAFT *(continued)*

Contreras (LCU 2015) George Nassiopoulos, 9-91

Bristoe Station (LCU 2006) Dr. Giorgio Arra, 7-90

26-2-88, one on 30-8-88, and remainder on 11-1-89. Two more, to have been named *Sackett's Harbor* and *Sayler's Creek,* were not ordered. Program, including uncompleted first three, transferred to Moss Point when Trinity Marine purchased Thunderbolt Marine from Lockheed.

Can carry up to 350 tons beaching cargo. Vehicle/container deck totals 237.8 m. Beaching draft forward is 1.22 m. There is a 50-ton kedging winch. Have a MacGregor-Navire 6.56-m-long by 4.48-m-wide bow ramp. Built to commercial, vice military, standards.

Note: The 13 U.S. Navy LCU 1646-class and 42 U.S. Navy 1466-class utility landing craft listed in the previous edition were retired 1990–92; some were transferred to foreign countries.

MECHANIZED LANDING CRAFT

◆ **123 U.S. Navy LCM(8)-class landing craft** (In serv. 1954–72)

U.S. Army LCM 8544 Jürg Kürsener, 7-92

D: 58.8 tons light (116 fl) **S:** 9.2 kts (loaded)
Dim: 22.40 × 6.42 × 1.40 (mean)
M: 2 G.M. 6-71 diesels; 2 props; 600 bhp
Range: 150/9.2 (loaded) **Fuel:** 2.4 tons **Crew:** 2–4 tot.

Remarks: Data apply to final 96 built, Mod. 1, delivered late 1960s–1972. Earlier army LCM(8) Mod. 0 were rated at 57.8 tons light/111.4 full load. Mod. 1 carries up to 57.4 tons cargo, Mod. 0: 53.5. As of 1991, located: 18 at Ft. Eustis, Va.; 15 at Ft. Clayton, Canal Zone; 15 at Alexandria, Va. (Army Reserve); 5 at Kwajalein; 8 in Puerto Rico (4 National Guard); 1 at Okinawa; 4 in the Azores; 2 in Japan; 1 in South Korea; 6 in Alaska (National Guard); 13 in Florida (Army Reserve); 18 at Tacoma, Wash. (National Guard); 3 in storage/repair at Charleston, S.C.; 4 prepositioned on LASH ships (LCM 8511, 8517, 8583, 8585), 10 at Diego Garcia. A rehabilitation program is under way for all, commencing with LCM 8545 at Tacoma.

AIR-CUSHION LANDING CRAFT

Note: The LAMP-H air-cushion vehicle landing craft project was canceled 18-.

◆ **26 LACV-30 class** (2 in reserve)
Bldr: Textron Marine, New Orleans (In serv. 1976–87)

LACV-01 to LACV-26 series

LACV-30 on cushion Dr. Giorgio Arra

LACV-30—with two standard cargo containers on deck, coming c beach Te

D: 52 tons (fl) **S:** 40 kts
Dim: 23.29 × 11.20 × 17.63 (high, on cushion)
M: 4 Pratt & Whitney ST6T gas turbines; 2/2.74-m-dia. airscrew propellers; 2/21.3-m-dia. centrifugal lift-fans; 7,200 shp (5,600 sust.)
Endurance: 2 hrs. with 30 tons cargo; 9.1 hrs. with 23.7 tons
Crew: . . .

Remarks: Cargo: 35 tons max., two 20-ft. containers at 35 kts. Cargo deck 1 9.75. Can be broken down into 15 sections for transport aboard trailers, ra aircraft, or ships. Intended for Logistics-Over-The-Shore (LOTS) support duti active units based at Ft. Story, Virginia. Under a contract let 10-8-91, Textro overhaul sequentially the entire class.

AMPHIBIOUS VEHICLES

◆ **30 LARC XV Design 8004** Bldr: . . .

D: 20.8 tons light (35.7 fl) **S:** 8.25 kts water/29.5 mph land
Dim: 13.72 × 4.42 × 4.75 (high) **M:** 2 diesels; 1 prop; 600 bhp
Range: 45/8.25 water; 300/29.5 mph land

Remarks: Four-wheeled vehicle with 15-ton payload, unloading ramp. As of 19 were in use at Ft. Story, Va., 8 were in use at Palatka, Florida, and 10 were in sto

◆ **19 LARC XV Design 2303** Bldr: . . .

D: 88 tons light (about 190 fl) **S:** 6.5 kts max./15.2 mph on land
Dim: 19.07 × 8.10 × 5.92 **M:** 4 diesels; 2 props; 660 bhp
Range: 75/6 (60-ton load) **Crew:** . . .

Remarks: Four-wheeled vehicle with 100-ton maximum/60-ton normal pa Cargo well 12.9 × 4.1, with full-width bow ramp. All are in California.

◆ **3 LARC V Design 8005** Bldr: . . .

D: 8.9 tons light (13.4 fl) **S:** 9 kts/29.5 mph on land
Dim: 10.67 × 3.05 × 3.10 **M:** 1 diesel; 1 prop; 300 bhp
Range: 40/8.7 loaded **Crew:** . . .

Remarks: Four-wheeled vehicle with 5-ton payload, bow unloading ramp.

·IARIES

·-commercial heavy-lift ship Bldr: Peterson Bldrs, Sturgeon , Wisc. (In serv. 7-79)

· JAMES MCHENRY (ex-*Paul Bunyan*)

·s McHenry (HLS-01) Dr. Giorgio Arra, 3-90

·,453 tons (fl) **S:** . . . kts **Dim:** 85.00 × 16.80 × 8.25
·tron Equipt: Radar: 1/. . . nav.
·2 G.M. EMD 16-645-E2 diesels; 2 props; 5,750 bhp
·tric: 1,000 kw (2 × 500 kw) **Crew:** . . .

·ks: 2,647 grt/2,626 dwt. Purchased 1988 to replace *Gen. William J. Sutton* as ·g ship at Ft. Eustis, Virginia. Has same propulsion engines as LSV 1 class based ·Maritime Administration C1-MT-123a Design, with two heavy-lift cargo der- ·las 150 tons permanent concrete ballast. Has bow door and vehicle ramp, stern ·nd passageway through superstructure for vehicles.

+ 6) LT 130 Design large tugs Bldr: Robert E. Derecktor, Inc., ·dletown, R.I. (*see* remarks)

	Laid down	L	In serv.
1 MG. NATHANIEL GREEN	25-3-88	4-7-89	8-91
2 MG. HENRY KNOX	. . .	10-89	11-91
3 MG. ANTHONY WAYNE	11-1-89	2-8-90	. . .
4 BG. ZEBULON PIKE	15-2-89	. . .	. . . .
5 MG. WINFIELD SCOTT	. . .	. . .	. . .
6 COL. SETH WARNER	. . .	. . .	. . .
7 SGM. JOHN CHAMPE	. . .	. . .	. . .
8 MG. JACOB BROWN	. . .	. . .	. . .

·Nathaniel Green class R. E. Derecktor, 2-89

. . . **S:** 12 kts **Dim:** 39.01 × . . . × . . .
provision for 4/12.7-mm mg (I × 4)
·ctron Equipt: Radar: 2/. . . nav.
2 G.M. EMD 12-645FMB diesels; 2 props; 5,000 bhp
·ctric: 550 kw (2 × 275 kw) **Range:** 5,000/12 **Crew:** . . .

Remarks: First two ordered 5-1-88 under FY 87 funding with option for eight more. Two were ordered 1988, fifth on 22-2-89, and two more in 9-89. Plan 13 total. The builder went bankrupt early in 1992, and the fate of the program is uncertain.

◆ **18 Design 3006 large harbor tugs** Bldr: . . . (In serv. mid-1950s)

LT-1937 SGT. WILLIAM W. SEAY
LT-1953 SALERNO
LT-1956 FREDERICKSBURG
LT-1959 MURFREESBORO
LT-1960 LUNDY'S LANE
LT-1970 OKINAWA
LT-1971 NORMANDY
LT-1972 GETTYSBURG
LT-1973 SHILOH
LT-1974 CHAMPAGNE-MARNE
LT-1977 ATTLEBORO
LT-2076 NEW GUINEA
LT-2081 SAN SAPOR
LT-2085 ANZIO
LT 2088 PETERSBURG
LT-2090 SP4 LARRY G. DAHL
LT-2092 NORTH AFRICA
LT-2096 VALLEY FORGE

North Africa (LT-2092) Leo Van Ginderen, 6-89

D: 295 tons light (390 fl) **S:** 12.75 kts
Dim: 32.61 × 8.08 × 3.71 (max.)
M: 1 Fairbanks-Morse diesel; 1 prop; 1,200 bhp **Electric:** 80 kw
Range: 3,323/12 light **Fuel:** 54 tons **Crew:** 16 tot.

Remarks: Bollard pull: 12 tons. Built in two series: LT-1936 through 1977 and LT-2202, and LT-2075 through LT-2096. LT-1960, -1973, and -1974 are in storage at Hythe, England, and LT-2081, -2085, -2090, and -2092 are prepositioned at Diego Garcia.

Note: Also used are leased commercial tugs LT-101 and LT-102 at Kwajalein and LT-100 at Port Neches, Texas—all of 1,500 bhp—and LT-981 and LT-982 at Lagos, in the Azores.

◆ **11 Design 3004 medium harbor tugs** Bldr: . . . (In serv. circa 1954)

ST-1988 BEMIS HEIGHTS
ST-1989 EUTAW
ST-1990 MOHAWK VALLEY
ST-1991 ORISKANY
ST-1993 COWPENS
ST-2104 MONMOUTH
ST-2116 KING'S MOUNTAIN
ST-2118 GUILFORD COURT HOUSE
ST-2119 BENNINGTON
ST-2126 STONY POINT
ST-2130 FORT MIFFLIN

Bemis Heights (ST-1988)—since stricken Jürg Kürsener, 7-92

D: 100 tons light (122 fl) **S:** 12 kts **Dim:** 21.31 × 5.94 × 2.50
M: 1 diesel; 1 prop; 600 bhp **Range:** 3,500/12 **Fuel:** 15 tons
Crew: 6 tot.

Remarks: Eight units formerly stored at Hythe, England, were cannibalized 1990–91, and two others have been discarded since the last edition. The survivors are all attached to facilities in the United States.

TUGS *(continued)*

◆ **2 Design 320 small tugs** (In serv. 1950s)

ST-2154 ST-3000

D: 25.2 tons light (29 fl) **S:** 10 kts **Dim:** 13.77 × 3.91 × 1.83
M: 1 diesel; 1 prop; 170 bhp **Electric:** 2 kw
Range: 700/10 **Crew:** 4 tot.

Remarks: Operate at Tacoma, Wash. (National Guard); and Sharpe Army Depot, respectively. Bollard pull: 2.5 tons initial. Sister *Santiago* (ST-2028) stricken 1990.

SERVICE CRAFT

◆ **2 catamaran ferries** Bldr: Nichols Bros., Whidbey Island, Wash.

FB-816 Jera (In serv. 2-88) FB-817 Jelang K (In serv. 1988)

Jelang K (FB-817) Nichols Bros., 1988

D: 63.7 tons (fl) **S:** 25 kts **Dim:** 23.00 × 8.68 × 1.80
Electron Equipt:
Radar: 1/Furuno FCR 1411/6 nav., 1/Furuno 8030D nav.
M: 2 G.M. 16V92 TA diesels; 1,920 bhp **Electric:** 100 kw

Remarks: Intended to carry 75 passengers at Kwajalein. "Wavepiercer" proprietary design from Australia.

◆ **11 Design 264B floating cranes** Bldr: . . . (In serv. 1950s)

BD-6069 Luzon
BD-6070 Qui Nhon
BD-6072 Algiers
BD-6073 Pine Ridge
BD-6074 Naples
BD-6658 Mindanao
BD-6659 Wilderness
BD-6660 Prairie Fire
BD-6661 Diamond Island
BD-6700 Big Switch
BD-6701 Big Bethel

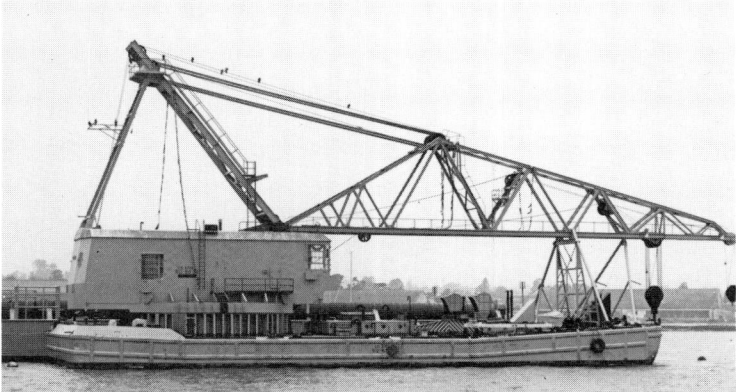

Pine Ridge (BD-6073)—in storage at Hythe Mike Louagie, 9-89

D: 1,630 tons (fl) **Dim:** 42.67 × 21.34 × 1.91
Electric: 250 kw **Fuel:** 40 tons

Remarks: Crane capacity is 89 tons at 24.4-m radius, 75 tons at 31.8-m radius; auxiliary hook can lift 15 tons at 37.3 m. BD-6659 refitted 1989 as protoype for a class-wide refurbishment program. BD-6073 is in storage at Hythe, England, and BD-6072 and -6074 are prepositioned at Diego Garcia; the others are all in active service. *Sicily* (BD-6071) stricken 1990. A number of sisters serve the U.S. Navy.

◆ **3 Design 413D floating cranes** Bldr: . . . (In serv. 1950s)

BD-6236 BD-6237 BD-6650

D: 1,000 tons (fl) **Dim:** 43.28 × 17.68 × 1.04 (1.55 max.)
Electric: 155 kw **Fuel:** 4 tons

Remarks: Crane capacity: 60 tons at 22.2-m radius; auxiliary hook can lift 1[illegible] 30.5 m. First two at Sharpe Army Depot, BD-6650 at Tacoma with Washing[illegible] tional Guard.

◆ **3 Design 7011 floating machine shops** Bldr: . . .

FMS 786 Athena FMS 788 Ares FMS 789 Vulcan

Athena (FMS 786)—in storage at Hythe Leo Van Ginder[illegible]

D: 1,160 tons light (1,525 fl) **Dim:** 64.14 × 12.19 × 2.36 (max.)
Electric: 400 kw (4 × 100 kw) **Fuel:** 140 tons **Crew:** 30 tot.

Remarks: Modified from Design 7016 refrigerated stores barges (which t[illegible] wardly resemble). Have 8.9-ton crane amidships. Workshops include: batter[illegible] smith, carpentry, electrical, engine, fuel injector, machine, paint, pipefitti[illegible] tronic, refrigeration, sheet metal, shipfitting, and welding. Three more serve YR 84–86. FMS 786 is at Hythe, U.K.; FMS 788 at Ft. Eustis, Va.; FMS 789 [illegible] National Guard at Tacoma, Wash.

◆ **2 Design 7016 refrigerated stores barges** Bldr: . . .

BRM-6232 BRM-6233

D: 1,100 tons light (2,250 fl) **Dim:** 64.14 × 12.19 × 2.62
Electric: 360 kw (3 × 100 kw, 1 × 60 kw)
Fuel: 129 tons **Crew:** 28 tot.

Remarks: Cargo capacity: 1,316 m^3 in seven refrigerated holds. Resemble 7011 repair barges, except for smaller 1-ton crane and no forward deckho[illegible] two-level storehouse. In storage at Charleston, S.C.; sister BRM-6668 discard[illegible]

◆ **5 J-boat Design 243B picket boats** (In serv.: 1950s)

J-3756 J-3761 J-3793 J-3795 J-7860

D: 6.7 tons (light) **S:** 15 kts **Dim:** 11.13 (10.06 wl) × 3.23 × [illegible]
M: 1 diesel; 1 prop; 200 bhp **Range:** 355/15

Remarks: Wooden construction. Resemble U.S. Navy LCVP but are decked [illegible] have cab forward. Located in the Azores; the U.S. Military Academy, West Po[illegible] York; in Japan; at Rio Vista, California; and at Morehead City, North [illegible] respectively.

◆ **10 high-speed patrol boats**

J-3830 J-3850 J-3852-7859

Remarks: No data available. Used as range safety boats at Aberdeen Grounds on Chesapeake Bay, Maryland.

◆ **3 T-boat Design 2001 inshore transports** (In serv. 1950s)

T-449 T-512 T-600

Mobjack—a "T-boat" employed by the U.S. Army Corps of Engine[illegible] R. Parkins[illegible]

/ICE CRAFT *(continued)*

66 tons (95 fl) **S:** 10.5 kts **Dim:** 19.98 × 5.38 × 1.98 (max.)
1 diesel; 1 prop; 300 bhp **Range:** 596/10.5 light; 397/7 loaded
ctric: 5 kw **Crew:** 4 tot., plus 24 passengers

rks: Steel construction. Used to transport passengers and cargo in harbors and waters. Can carry 24 tons cargo; have one hatch, one 1-ton derrick. Located at a, Wash. (National Guard), Baltimore, Maryland, and Kwajalein, respectively. ass is also used by the Army Corps of Engineers.

double-ended harbor ferry (In serv. . . .)

4

rks: No data available; used at U.S. Military Academy, West Point.

decked, enclosed conversion kit barges (In serv. 1950s)

K-6204 BCDK-6206 BCDK-6464

K-6462—with two BC-series open barges, in storage at Hythe
Mike Louagie, 8-88

175 tons (760 fl) **Dim:** 36.58 × 10.06 × 2.44

deck cargo barges, Design 218D/E (In serv. . . .)

415 BK-8469 BK-8472 BK-8477 BK-8479

185 tons (578 fl) **Dim:** 36.58 × 10.06 × 2.59 (loaded)

nesting deck cargo barges, Design 7001

327 BK-8336

51 tons (181 fl) **Dim:** 24.69 × 6.70 × 1.45

refrigerated barges, Design 7010

-6232 BRM-6233

225 tons (546 fl) **Dim:** 36.58 × 10.06 × 1.77
rgo: 395 m^3 refrigerated stores **Electric:** 120 kw

deck or liquid cargo barges, Design 231B/C (8 in reserve)

eries

185 tons light (763 fl) **Dim:** 36.58 × 10.06 × 2.59

3 miscellaneous BC-series Deck Cargo Barges, Harbor or cean Towing

155—of the 6th Transportation Corps Detachment, Marcus Hook, Pa.
George R. Schneider, Jr., 5-89

120 tons (690 fl) **Dim:** 33.53 × 9.75 × 2.34 **Cargo:** 570 tons

arks: Nine are on loan to Maritime Administration, 43 are in storage at Hythe, and.

Delong Type A mobile piers

-series

m: 91.44 × 24.38

arks: Have 22 jacking caissons, 15.24 m long to anchor to beachhead. Four stored the, U.K.; five stored in South Korea. A new generation of mobile piers is planned.

U.S. ARMY CORPS OF ENGINEERS

e U.S. Army Corps of Engineers operates hundreds of tugs, utility craft, and s in construction, local transportation, and survey service. Dredging, formerly a s of Engineers responsibility, is now performed by commercial operators under s supervision. There is no central registry of Corps of Engineers boats and craft.

U.S. AIR FORCE

The Air Force operates about 55 "Watercraft," all managed by the San Antonio Logistics Center, Kelly Air Force Base, Texas. In addition, there are about 350 smaller craft of under 6.7-m length.

MISSILE RETRIEVERS

◆ **5 120-ft. class** Bldr: Swiftships, Inc., Morgan City, La. (In serv. 1988–89)

MR-120-8801 through MR-120-8805

MR-120-8801—white hull, red superstructure, yellow decks
Swiftships, 1988

D: 91 tons light (113 tons operational, 133 fl) **S:** 30 kts (27 sust.)
Dim: 35.78 × 7.51 × 2.06 (max. aft)
Electron Equipt: Radar: 1/Furuno . . .
M: 4 G.M. Detroit Diesel 16V92 MTA diesels; 4 props; 5,600 bhp
Range: 600/27 **Fuel:** . . . tons
Electric: 50 kw (2 × 25 kw) **Crew:** 10 tot.

Remarks: Used for location and recovery of practice missiles and can transport 20 tons deck cargo. Aluminum construction. MR-120-8802 and 8803 were at Tyndall Air Force Base, Florida; others at Wallace Air Base, the Philippines, but have been relocated following the removal of U.S. bases.

◆ **3 85-ft. missile retrievers** (In serv. 1967–68)

MR-85-1602 MR-85-1603 MR-85-1604

Remarks: No data available. First at Key West, Fla.; second at Tyndall AFB; third was at Wallace Air Base, the Philippines.

◆ **3 65-ft. missile retrievers** (In serv. 1967–1970)

MR-65-2068 MR-65-2109 MR-65-2110

Remarks: No data available. MR-65-2068 was at Wallace Air Base, the Philippines; other two are at Eglin AFB, Florida.

◆ **1 31-ft. training/recovery boat** (In serv. 1969)

TR-31-2107

Remarks: No data available; at Homestead AFB, Fla.

PARASAIL TRAINING CRAFT

◆ **9 parasail training craft**
Bldr: SeaArk, Monticello, Ark. (In serv. 29-7-86 to 6-4-87)

PR-40-8601 through PR-40-8609

PR-40-8601 SeaArk, 7-86

D: . . . **S:** 29 kts **Dim:** 12.57 × . . . × . . .
M: 2 G.M. 8V71 TI diesels; 2 props; 870 bhp

Remarks: For use in parasail training by 3616th Combat Crew Training Squadron, Homestead AFB, Fla. Aluminum construction.

MISCELLANEOUS SERVICE CRAFT

◆ **6 miscellaneous personnel boats** (In serv. 1960–1988)

	Based		Based
P-21-7601	Moffett Field, Cal.	P-26-2198	Kulusuk, Greenland
P-21-2131	Eglin AFB, Fla.	P-26-2222	Wake Isl.
P-26-2195	Sondestrom, Greenland	P-50-2108	Carrabelle, Fla.

Remarks: No data. Lengths part of serial, i.e., are 21 ft., 26 ft., or 50 ft. o.a. (6.4, 7.9, or 15.2-m o.a.).

◆ **1 new-construction tug**
Bldr: Swiftships, Inc., Morgan City, La. (In serv. 1991)

TG-72-. . .

D: . . . tons **S:** 10 kts **Dim:** 21.94 × . . . × . . .
M: 2 G.M. 16V92 TI diesels; 1 Kort-nozzle prop; 1,800 bhp

Remarks: Intended to replace former U.S. Army Design 320 tugs TG-45-1919 and TG-45-2215 at Thule, Greenland.

◆ **8 LCM(8) Mod. 0-class landing craft**

	Based	In serv.
C-74-1866	Tuslog, Turkey	1954
C-74-2167	Sondestrom, Greenland	1966
C-74-2168	Sondestrom, Greenland	1966
C-74-2205	Wake Island	1984
C-74-2206	Wake Island	1984
C-74-8701	Wake Island	1987
C-74A-1938	Sondestrom, Greenland	1966
C-74A-2113	Homestead AFB	1954

D: 58.8 tons light (116 fl) **S:** 9.2 kts (loaded)
Dim: 22.40 × 6.42 × 1.40 (mean)
M: 2 G.M. 6-71 diesels; 2 props; 600 bhp
Range: 150/9.2 (loaded) **Fuel:** 2.4 tons **Crew:** 2–4 tot.

Remarks: Cargo: 57.4 tons.

◆ **1 50-ft. dredge** (In serv. 1984)

D-50-2202

Remarks: No data available. At Lajes, the Azores, with dredge tender DT-30-2203 (In serv. 1984).

◆ **1 65-ft. ferry** (In serv. 1969)

F-65A-2154

Remarks: No data available. At Homestead AFB, Florida.

◆ **1 U.S. Army LARC-V, Design 8005 amphibious craft** (In serv. 1964)

L-35-2212

D: 8.9 tons light (13.4 fl) **S:** 9 kts/29.5 mph on land
Dim: 10.67 × 3.05 × 3.10 **M:** 1 diesel; 1 prop; 300 bhp
Range: 40/8.7 loaded **Crew:** . . .

Remarks: Four-wheeled landing craft, at Osan, South Korea.

◆ **8 miscellaneous utility boats** (In serv. 1982–88)

	Based		Based
U-19-8201	Patrick AFB	U-22-8801	Westhampton, NY
U-20-8401	Moffett Naval Air Sta.	U-25-8801	Eglin AFB, Fla.
U-20-8402	Tyndall AFB	U-25-8802	Eglin AFB, Fla.
U-22-8701	Langley AFB, Va.	U-27-8701	Osan, S. Korea

◆ **7 miscellaneous barges**

	Army Design	Dim:	Based	In serv.
B-110-1944	BC-229	33.5 × 9.1 × 2.1	Sondestrom, Grld.	1944
B-142-1883	BD-413D	. . .	McClellan AFB	1953
B-35-8701	BK-218E	13.8 × 5.5 × 0.5	Kulusuk, Grld.	1987
B-35-8702	BK-218E	13.8 × 5.5 × 0.5	Kulusuk, Grld.	1987
B-81-1926	BK-7001	24.7 × 6.7 × 1.4	Ascension Island	1954
B-81-2033	BK-7001	24.7 × 6.7 × 1.4	Ascension Island	1954
B-81-2034	BK-7001	24.7 × 6.7 × 1.4	Ascension Island	1954

NATIONAL OCEANIC AND ATMOSPHERIC ADMINISTRATION U.S. DEPARTMENT OF COMMERCE

Personnel: 400 commissioned officers, approx. 12,250 civilians

The NOAA Corps operates a fleet of research ships divided into the two categories of Research and Survey. Headquartered in Rockville, Maryland, headed by a civilian, with a rear admiral deputy as director, NOAA Corps, it has its major maritime facilities at the Atlantic Marine Center in Norfolk, Virginia, and the Pacific Marine Center in Seattle, Washington; minor NOAA maritime facilities exist at Woods Hole, Massachusetts, Pascagoula, Mississippi, Miami, Florida, La Jolla, California, and Honolulu, Hawaii.

Hulls and superstructures are white, masts and stacks buff. Hull numbers app either side (preceded by "R" for research or "S" for Survey) above the letters "N The front digit in the three-digit hull number is the NOAA class (i.e., size) num the ship, determined from the gross tonnage and horsepower. The ships are de below in descending order size.

OCEANOGRAPHIC RESEARCH SHIPS

◆ **1 (+7) Stalwart-class former ocean surveillance ships**
Bldr: ex-T-AGOS 1–12: Tacoma Boat, Tacoma, Wash.; 13–18: Halter Mari Moss Point, Miss.

	Laid down	L	In serv.
Adventurous (ex-T-AGOS 13)	19-12-85	23-9-87	19-8-88

Adventurous—as T-AGOS 13 Don Montgomery, USN

D: 1,600 tons light (2,248 fl) **S:** 11 kts
Dim: 68.28 (62.1 wl) × 13.10 × 4.57
Electron Equipt: Radar: 2/. . . navigational
M: 4 Caterpillar-Kato D-398B 800-bhp diesels, G.E. electric drive; bladed props; 2,200 shp (1,600 hp sust.)—550-hp bow-thruster
Range: 3,000/11 plus 6,480/3 **Fuel:** 904 tons
Endurance: 98 days
Electric: 1,500 kVA from main generators, plus 265-kw emergenc
Crew: . . .

Remarks: 1,584 grt/786 dwt. *Adventurous* was transferred to NOAA on 1-6-92 is expected that seven additional units of the class will be transferred during late through 1993. All will be re-equipped to perform ocean survey and general c graphic research duties.

The first three T-AGOS were contracted for 26-9-80. Main-engine motor/ger sets also supply ship's-service power: flat chine hull form without bilge keel passive tank roll stabilization. T-AGOS 13, 14 ordered 4-6-85, with option t through T-AGOS 18; T-AGOS 15–18 ordered 30-6-86.

◆ **2 Oceanographer class** Bldr: Aerojet-General SY, Jacksonville, F

	L	In serv.	Base
R 101 Oceanographer	18-4-64	13-7-66	Seattle (inactive)
R 102 Discoverer	29-10-64	29-4-67	Seattle

Oceanographer (R 101) NOAA

D: 4,033 tons (fl) **S:** 15 kts (sust.) **Dim:** 92.4 × 15.8 × 6.0
M: 2 Westinghouse 1150 diesel generator sets, 2 Westinghouse mo 2/4-bladed props; 5,000 shp
Range: 12,250/15 **Fuel:** 937 tons **Electric:** 1,200 kw
Endurance: 34 days
Crew: R 102: 13 NOAA officers, 6 licensed officers, 60 crew, 24 scientists

Remarks: 3,701 grt/1,095 nrt. Maritime Administration S2-MET-MA62a d Both carry PDP 11/34 data-processing computers. R 101 has a large weather rad both have two navigational radars. Laboratories include chemistry, wet and dry ographic, meteorological, gravimetric, and photographic. A computerized data r

NOGRAPHIC RESEARCH SHIPS *(continued)*

'erer (R 102) NOAA, 1985

processing system is installed. There are several precision oceanographic . A 400-hp bow-thruster is fitted. R 102 received the Sea-beam, 12-kHz multi- thymetric mapping sonar, Inmarsat SATCOMM system for dataline transmis- d the TI-410 Global Position Indicator in 1985; she has an underwater observa- mber. In 1987, R 102 was employed by the U.S. Navy as a replacement for *h* (T-AGS 21); she was equipped with T-AGS 21's two BQN-3 narrow-beam g sonars, doppler sonar, and navigational equipment. R 101, in reserve in 7-81, ted 8-4-86 after refit with Alden weatherfax, Sperry Mk 37 gyro, a new Ray- -band Pathfinder radar, Inmarsat, MX1102 Global Positioning System, a new eter, a Shipboard Environmental Acquisition System (SEAS) with expendable ermograph gear, a new meteorological station, and a doppler current profiling R 101 back to inactive status, 1989.

esearcher class Bldr: American Shpbldg., Toledo, Ohio

	L	In serv.	Base
MALCOLM BALDRIGE (ex-*Researcher*)	5-10-68	8-10-70	Miami

lm Baldrige (R 103) NOAA, 1989

lm Baldrige (R 103) Leo Van Ginderen, 3-90

2,963 tons (fl) **S:** 12.5 kts (sust.) **Dim:** 84.8 × 15.5 × 5.6
2 Alco diesels; 2 CP props; 3,200 bhp **Electric:** 1,500 kw
ge: 10,800/12.5 **Fuel:** 568 tons **Endurance:** 36 days
w: 13 NOAA officers, 5 licensed officers, 50 crew, 14 scientists

ks: 2,802 grt/946 nrt. Maritime Administration S2-MT-MA7a design. Bow r sonars and echo-sounders, five laboratories, five oceanographic winches. PDP 11/34 computerized data system. Has a 450-hp Pleuger retractable bow-thruster. Received Inmarsat and Global Position Indicator, Sea-beam multi-beam mapping sonar in 1986. Carries seismic profile compressors. Helicopter deck aft removed, replaced by quadrantial gallows for towed equipment. Renamed 5-3-88.

◆ **1 Miller Freeman class** Bldr: American Shipbldg., Lorain, Ohio

	L	In serv.	Base
R 223 MILLER FREEMAN	1967	1974	Seattle

Miller Freeman (R 223) NOAA, 1992

D: 1,920 tons (fl) **S:** 14 kts (sust.) **Dim:** 66.0 × 12.5 × 6.1
M: 1 G.M. diesel; 1 CP prop; 2,200 bhp **Electric:** 700 kw
Range: 13,800/14 **Fuel:** 450 tons **Endurance:** 41 days
Crew: 7 NOAA officers, 4 licensed officers, 30 crew, 11 scientists

Remarks: 1,515 grt/680 nrt. Conducts fisheries and living marine resources research. Chemical, wet oceanographic, fish processing, utility labs. Fish-finder sonars, several echo-sounders. Lowerable stabilization centerboard increases draft to 9.3 m. Has a stern trawl ramp and net-handling gallows. 400-hp Schottel lowerable bow-thruster. To be replaced during 1990s.

◆ **1 Oregon II class** Bldr: Ingalls SB, Pascagoula, Miss.

	L	In serv.	Base
R 332 OREGON II	2-67	8-67	Pascagoula

Oregon II (R 332) NOAA, 1987

D: 952 tons **S:** 12 kts (sust.) **Dim:** 51.8 × 10.4 × 4.3
M: 2 Fairbanks-Morse diesels; 1 CP prop; 1,600 bhp
Range: 9,500/12 **Fuel:** 255 tons **Electric:** 400 kw
Endurance: 33 days **Crew:** 6 licensed officers, 10 crew, 6 scientists

Remarks: 703 grt/228 nrt. Conducts fisheries and living marine resource research in the Gulf of Mexico, Caribbean, South Atlantic, and southeast U.S. Atlantic Coast. Has two trawls, one hydrographic and one bathythermographic winches, five laboratories. Was to be deactivated 1990 for lack of operating funds but continues in service.

◆ **1 Albatross IV class** Bldr: Southern SB, Slidell, Louisiana

	L	In serv.	Base
R 342 ALBATROSS IV	4-62	5-63	Woods Hole, Mass.

Albatross IV (R 342) NOAA, 1987

OCEANOGRAPHIC RESEARCH SHIPS *(continued)*

D: 1,089 tons (fl) **S:** 12 kts (sust.) **Dim:** 57.0 × 10.0 × 4.9
M: 2 Caterpillar diesels; 1 Kort-nozzle CP prop; 1,130 bhp
Range: 4,300/12 **Fuel:** 150 tons **Electric:** 450 kw
Crew: 7 NOAA officers, 15 crew, 15 scientists
Endurance: 15 days

Remarks: 931 grt/300 nrt. Has conducted fisheries and living marine resources research off the U.S. northeastern Atlantic coast. Inactive since 1988. Has wet and dry oceanographic, photographic, biological, plankton, and electronics laboratories, four scientific winches, vertical fish-finding sonar, and deep- and shallow-water echo-sounders. There is a 125-hp bow-thruster. Reactivated under Fiscal Year 1992; to be replaced during the 1990s.

◆ 1 Townsend Cromwell class
Bldr: J. Ray McDermott Co., Morgan City, La.

	L	In serv.	Base
R 443 Townsend Cromwell	7-62	7-63	Honolulu

Townsend Cromwell (R 443) NOAA, 1985

D: 652 tons (fl) **S:** 11.5 kts (sust.) **Dim:** 49.7 × 10.0 × 3.9
M: 2 White-Superior diesels; 2 CP props; 800 bhp
Electric: 350 kw **Range:** 8,300/11.5 **Fuel:** 132 tons
Endurance: 30 days
Crew: 4 NOAA officers, 3 licensed officers, 10 crew, 9 scientists

Remarks: 564 grt/384 nrt. Conducts fisheries and living marine resources research off the Hawaiian Islands and in the central Pacific. Has a single oceanographic laboratory and an underwater bow observation chamber. Taken over by NOAA 6-75. To be replaced during 1990s.

◆ 1 David Starr Jordan class
Bldr: Christy Corp., Sturgeon Bay, Wisc.

	L	In serv.	Base
R 444 David Starr Jordan	12-64	1-66	San Diego, Cal.

David Starr Jordan (R 444) NOAA, 1987

D: 993 tons (fl) **S:** 11.5 kts (sust.)
Dim: 52.1 × 11.2 × 3.8 (4.8 over sonar)
M: 2 White-Superior diesels; 2 CP props; 1,086 bhp
Electric: 400 kw **Range:** 8,560/11.5 **Fuel:** 180 tons
Endurance: 31 days **Crew:** 6 licensed officers, 10 crew, 13 scientists

Remarks: 873 grt/262 nrt. Conducts fisheries and living marine resources research off U.S., Central, and South American Pacific coasts. Physical and biological [oceanog]raphy, chemical, and photographic labs. Has a retractable fish-finding sonar, a fish-finder, and several echo-sounders. Schottel retractable bow-thruster of 20[0 hp and] an underwater observation chamber at the bow.

◆ 1 Delaware II class
Bldr: South Portland Engineering Corp., South Portland, Maine

	L	In serv.	Base
R 445 Delaware II	12-67	10-68	Woods Hole, Mass.

Delaware II (R 445) Leo Van Ginder[en]

D: 758 tons (fl) **S:** 11.5 kts (sust.) **Dim:** 47.2 × 9.2 × 4.5
M: 1 G.M. diesel; 1 prop; 1,230 bhp **Electric:** 300 kw
Range: 6,600/11.5 **Fuel:** 132 tons
Crew: 6 licensed officers, 9 crew, 9 scientists

Remarks: 483 grt/231 nrt. Conducts fisheries and living marine resources [research] off U.S. Atlantic coast. Two oceanographic labs, fish-finding sonars, stern n[...]. Endurance: 24 days.

◆ 1 Chapman class
Bldr: Bender SB & Repair Co., Wash.

	L	In serv.	Base
R 446 Chapman	12-79	7-80	Pascagoula, Miss.

Chapman (R 446) NOA[A]

D: 520 tons (fl) **S:** 11 kts (sust.) **Dim:** 38.7 × 9.1 × 4.3
M: 1 Caterpillar D 399 diesel; 1 CP prop; 1,250 bhp
Electric: 420 kw **Range:** 6,000/11 **Fuel:** 126 tons
Crew: 3 NOAA officers, 1 licensed officer, 7 crew, 6 scientists

Remarks: 427 grt/290 nrt. Conducts fisheries and living marine resources res[earch in] the Gulf of Mexico. Has a fish-processing and a dry laboratory. Stern-haul traw[l ...] a 150-hp Omnithruster bow-mounted waterjet. Laid up 1984 to 1-86; refitte[d ...] 9-86.

◆ 1 ex-U.S. Army T-boat
Bldr: . . ., Leavenworth, Kansas (In serv[...]

R 693 Shenahon (ex-T-465)

D: 69 tons light (98 fl) **S:** 10 kts **Dim:** 19.96 × 5.38 × 2.00
M: 1 Caterpillar D375 diesel; 1 prop; 270 bhp **Electric:** 42 kw
Range: 700/10 **Fuel:** 3.7 tons **Crew:** 4–6 tot.

Remarks: Acquired 25-6-65 from army. Operates on Great Lakes from Mu[...] Michigan, for the Great Lakes Environmental Research Laboratory and for [the Na]tional Weather Service. Appearance similar to craft depicted in Army sectio[n ...] *Virginia Key* (ex-Army T-433), formerly used for training at the NOAA T[...] Center, Ft. Eustis, Virginia, has been discarded.

◆ 1 John N. Cobb class
Bldr: Western Boatbldg., Tacoma, Wash.

	L	In serv.	Base
R 552 John N. Cobb	1-50	2-50	Seattle (inactive)

OGRAPHIC RESEARCH SHIPS *(continued)*

. Cobb (R 552) NOAA

0 tons (fl) **S:** 9.3 kts (sust.) **Dim:** 28.3 × 7.9 × 3.3
Fairbanks-Morse diesel; 1 prop; 325 bhp **Electric:** 60 kw
e: 2,900/9.3 **Fuel:** 25 tons **Endurance:** 13 days
: 4 licensed officers, 4 crew, 4 scientists

s: 185 grt/78 nrt. Formerly conducted fisheries and living marine resources off southeastern Alaska and the U.S. Pacific Northwest. Has a single labora- urance: 13 days. Inactivated 1989; to be replaced during the 1990s.

-U.S. Army lighter Bldr: J. Martinolich SB, San Francisco, Cal.

	L	In serv.	Base
URRE II (ex-BSP-. . .)	1943	1944	Juneau, Alaska

5 tons (fl) **S:** 8 kts **Dim:** 39.92 (29.15 pp) × 9.37 × 2.44
Caterpillar diesels; 2 props; 330 bhp (270 sust.)
ric: 32 kw **Endurance:** 8 days
e: 1,500/8; 2,915/7.5 **Fuel:** 15 tons
: 2 licensed officers, 1 crew, 5 scientists

s: 189 grt/95 nrt. Has conducted fisheries research and cargo shipment duties eastern Alaskan waters. Wooden-hulled former army powered lighter. One and one biological laboratory. Has a 2-ton cargo boom for deck cargo. Requires ent.

EY SHIPS

rveyor class Bldr: National Steel & SB, San Diego, Cal.

	L	In serv.	Base
URVEYOR	25-4-59	30-4-60	Seattle

yor (R 132) Victor M. Baca, 1991

D: 3,440 tons (fl) **S:** 15 kts (sust.) **Dim:** 89.0 × 14.0 × 5.9
M: 2 sets de Laval GT; 1 prop; 3,200 shp **Electric:** 800 kw
Boilers: 2 Combustion Engineering; 32.7 kg/cm², 385°C
Range: 13,680/15 **Fuel:** 785 tons **Endurance:** 38 days
Crew: 12 NOAA officers, 6 licensed officers, 58 crew, 16 scientists

Remarks: 2,653 grt/682 nrt. Maritime Administration S2-S-RM 28a design. Has PDP 11/34 data-processing computer, seismic reflection profile compressors, wet and dry oceanography, gravimetric, and photographic laboratories, extensive navigational equipment, deep and shallow echo-sounders, stabilized mapping sonar system, Hydroplot data-processing system, seismic reflection profile compressors, and a small helicopter platform. Carries 3/11-m wooden survey launches, an ex-U.S. Navy LCVP, and 2/7.9-m motor whaleboats. Has a 200-hp electric auxiliary propulsion motor aft. Received Sea-beam 12-kHz, 9,000-m multibeam mapping sonar in 1985. To be replaced during 1990s.

◆ **3 Mt. Mitchell class** Bldr: Aerojet-General SY, Jacksonville, Fla.

	L	In serv.	Base
S 220 Fairweather	15-3-67	2-10-68	Seattle (inactive)
S 221 Rainier	15-3-67	2-10-68	Seattle
S 222 Mt. Mitchell	29-11-66	23-3-68	Norfolk

Rainier (S 221) NOAA, 1992

Mt. Mitchell (S 222) Victor M. Baca, 8-91

D: 1,800 tons (fl) **S:** 13 kts **Dim:** 70.4 × 12.8 × 4.2
M: 2 G.M. diesels; 2 CP props; 2,400 bhp **Electric:** 600 kw
Range: 7,000/13 **Fuel:** 353 tons **Endurance:** 22 days
Crew: 12 NOAA officers, 5 licensed officers, 52 crew, 4 scientists

Remarks: 1,591 grt/578 nrt. Maritime Administration S1-MT-72a design. Have an oceanographic laboratory, Hydroplot data-processing system (also carried in two of the three or four 8.8-m survey boats aboard), several echo-sounders, and an oceanographic winch. In addition to the survey launches, carry two motor whaleboats and three Boston Whaler utility boats. Have a 200-hp bow-thruster. S 220 inactivated during FY 89.

◆ **2 Peirce class** Bldr: Marietta Mfg. Co., Pt. Pleasant, West Va.

	L	In serv.	Base
S 328 Peirce	15-10-62	6-5-63	Norfolk
S 329 Whiting	20-11-62	8-7-63	Norfolk

D: 907 tons (fl) **S:** 12 kts (sust.) **Dim:** 49.7 × 10.1 × 3.4
M: 2 G.M. diesels; 2 CP props; 1,600 bhp **Electric:** 440 kw
Range: 5,700/12 **Fuel:** 138 tons **Endurance:** 20 days
Crew: 8 NOAA officers, 3 licensed officers, 30 crew, 2 scientists

Remarks: 696 grt/151 nrt. Maritime Administration S1-MT-59a design. Have the Hydroplot data system to record hydrographic data; also fitted to the two 8.8-m survey launches. Have deep, shallow, and hydrographic survey echo-sounders. S 329 works on the U.S. Atlantic coast, Gulf of Mexico, and in the U.S. Caribbean possessions; S 328 laid up 1987; reactivated 1991 for training cruises.

SURVEY SHIPS *(continued)*

Whiting (S 329) NOAA, 1992

♦ **2 McArthur class** Bldr: Norfolk SB & DD, Norfolk, Va.

	L	In serv.	Base
S 330 McArthur	15-11-65	15-12-66	Seattle
S 331 Davidson	7-5-66	10-3-67	Seattle (inactive)

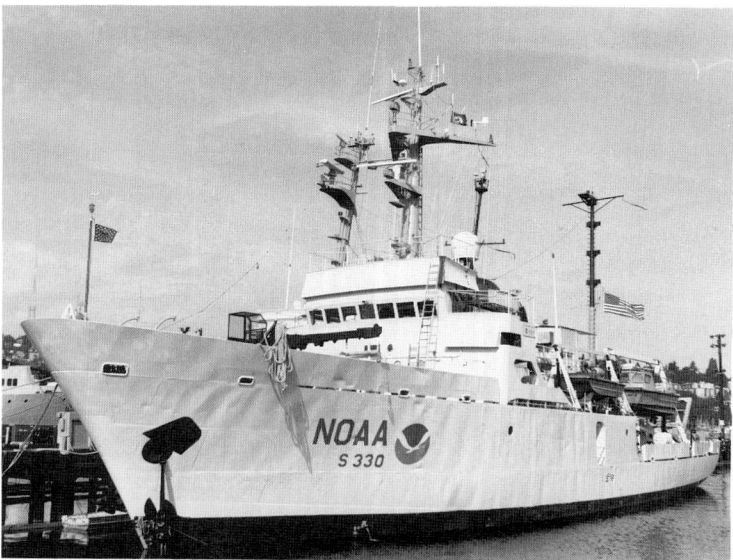

McArthur (S 330) Victor M. Baca, 1992

D: 995 tons (fl) **S:** 13 kts (sust.) **Dim:** 53.3 × 11.6 × 3.7
M: 2 G.M. diesels; 2 CP props; 1,600 bhp **Electric:** 440 kw
Range: 4,500/13; 6,000/12 **Fuel:** 186 tons
Endurance: 17 days
Crew: 8 NOAA officers, 3 licensed officers, 27 crew, 2 scientists

Remarks: 854 grt/207 nrt. Maritime Administration S1-MT-70a design. S 330 primarily performs seawater circulatory studies, while S 331 formerly performed hydrographic surveys, both off the U.S. Pacific coast and in Alaskan coastal waters. S 331 has the Hydroplot data-recording system, while S 330 uses the same system's PDP 11/34 computer to record current data. S 331 has the Bathymetric Swath Survey System, a stabilized, 22-beam, 600-m-deep mapping sonar. S 331 inactivated FY 89.

♦ **1 Ferrel class** Bldr: Zigler SY, Jennings, La.

	L	In serv.	Base
S 492 Ferrel	4-4-68	4-6-68	Norfolk

D: 360 tons (fl) **S:** 10 kts (sust.) **Dim:** 40.5 × 9.8 × 2.5
M: 2 Caterpillar diesels; 2 props; 750 bhp **Electric:** 300 kw
Range: 2,200/10 **Fuel:** 46 tons **Endurance:** 9 days
Crew: 5 NOAA officers, 2 licensed officers, 12 crew

Remarks: 349 grt/86 nrt. Maritime Administration S1-MT-MA83a design. Has a PDP 11/34 data-processing computer. Conducts coastal and estuarine seawater circulation studies off the U.S. East Coast and Gulf of Mexico. Has an electronics laboratory

Ferrel (S 492) NOAA

and a small oceanographic laboratory, and carries an 8.5-m workboat. Has a General Electric bow-thruster. Computerized data-recording system.

♦ **2 Rude class** Bldr: Jakobson SY, Oyster Bay, N.Y.

	L	In serv.	Base
S 590 Rude	17-8-66	3-67	Norfolk
S 591 Heck	1-11-66	3-67	Norfolk

Rude (S 590) NOAA

Heck (S 591) Leo Van Ginderen

D: 220 tons (fl) **S:** 10 kts (sust.) **Dim:** 27.4 × 6.7 × 2.2
M: 2 Cummins diesels; 2 Kort-nozzle props; 800 bhp
Electric: 120 kw **Range:** 800/10 **Fuel:** 12 tons
Endurance: 3 days
Crew: 3 NOAA officers, 1 licensed officer, 7 crew

Remarks: 150 grt/42 nrt. Were designed to work together in making wi

EY SHIPS *(continued)*

off U.S. Atlantic and Gulf coasts, but no longer do so. Have side scan sonars and rized data storage. Equipped with two 70-hp hydraulic auxiliary drives.

WATH (Small Waterplane Area, Twin-Hull) prototype
: U.S. Coast Guard, Curtis Bay, Md. (L: 7-3-73)

KAIMALINO

lino (SSP 1)—while working for U.S. Navy U.S. Navy

28 tons (fl) **S:** 22 kts **Dim:** 26.92 × 12.99 × 4.65
tron Equipt: Radar: 1/LN-66 (SPS-59) nav.
ODOG 2 G.E. T64-6B gas turbines, chain drive; 2 CP props;
,000 shp—or: 2 G.M. 6-71 diesels, 2 hydraulic motors; 160 bhp
tric: 78 kw **Range:** 450/17; 1,500/5 **Crew:** 15 max.

ks: SSP = Stable Semi-submerged Platform. Catamaran hull with cigar-flotation pontoons. Helicopter deck. Operated by the Naval Ocean Systems Hawaii Laboratory. The SWATH concept shows great promise as an economi--performance/high-endurance ASW ship, but has been hampered in its devel-by a lack of funding. *Kaimalino* has been used in torpedo-firing trials and as a -recovery craft. Planned stretch to 600 tons (fl) not carried out, due to costs, material was assembled 1982 for the conversion. The ship was leased to the l Oceanographic and Atmospherics Administration (NOAA) during 1991.

rmer oilfield crewboat Bldr: Equitable SY, New Orleans

(ex-. . .)

. . tons **S:** 18–20 kts **Dim:** 17.98 × . . . × 1.06
G.M. 12V71 diesels; 2 props; . . . bhp

ks: Operates from Solomon's Island, Maryland. Also in use are the former boat *Gloria Michelle,* on Narragansett Bay, several 30-ft. hydrographic s, and three 7.92 × 2.74 aluminum research boats (one powered by a Mer-7.4 inboard/outboard engine and the others by Volvo Penta outdrive diesels) vered 8-91 by SeaArk, Monticello, Arkansas.

J.S. Navy sludge-removal barge YSR 29 was transferred to NOAA 8-85 for use derwater habitat support barge. Completed 12-45, the craft displaces 160 tons 0 fl) and measures 24.4 × 9.8. It will be equipped with a centerline "moon pool." oilfield supply tugs *Point Hope, Petramar Dorado,* and *Petramar Explorer,* in e Administration custody, were earmarked for possible conversion as NOAA vessels in 1990, but the transfer of navy T-AGOS vessels will probably cancel version plans for the tugs.

ENVIRONMENTAL PROTECTION AGENCY

UTION RESEARCH AND PATROL SHIPS

reat Lakes pollution control vessel
: Halter Marine, Moss Point, Mississippi (In serv. 1981)

GUARDIAN (ex-*Marsea Fourteen*)

pprox. 1,250 tons (fl) **S:** 12 kts
: 54.87 (50.60 pp) × 12.20 × 3.60
2 Caterpillar D399 SCAC 16-cylinder diesels; 2 props; 2,250 bhp
ge: 2,880/12 **Fuel:** 241 tons **Crew:** 16 tot.

ks: Conversion completed 9-90 by builder as replacement for former U.S. Coast uoy tender *Roger R. Simons* (ex-*Maple,* WAGL 234) to serve in pollution survey nology studies. Based on Lake Erie at Cleveland, Ohio. Former 282-grt oilfield tug.

x-U.S. Navy Asheville-class gunboat
: Tacoma Boatbuilding, Tacoma, Wash.

	Laid down	L	In serv.
W. ANDERSON (ex-*Antelope,* PG 86)	1-6-65	18-6-66	4-11-67

Peter W. Anderson Dr. Giorgio Arra, 3-92

D: 225 tons (250 fl) **S:** 14 kts **Dim:** 50.14 × 7.28 × 3.20 max.
Electron Equipt: Radar: 2/. . . nav.
M: 2 Cummins VT12-875M diesels; 2 CP props; 1,400 bhp
Electric: 200 kw **Range:** 5,000/12 **Fuel:** 50 tons **Crew:** 30 tot.

Remarks: Acquired 1974 from navy and now based at Annapolis, Md. Operated for EPA by MAR, Inc. G.E. 7LM-1500-PE main propulsion gas turbine removed. Has "wet lab," microbiology lab, and computerized survey center. Sister *Rachel Carson* (ex-*Crockett,* PG 88) transferred to state of Illinois 1983 and then to Combined Great Lakes Navy Association as an exhibit.

DEPARTMENT OF THE INTERIOR
U.S. GEOLOGICAL SURVEY

RESEARCH SHIP

◆ **1 former U.S. Navy survey ship** Bldr: DeFoe SB, Bay City, Michigan

	Laid down	L	In serv.
S.P. LEE (ex-T-AG 192, ex-T-AG 31)	27-6-66	19-10-67	2-12-68

S. P. Lee—as built U.S. Navy, 10-68

D: 1,297 tons (fl) **S:** 13.5 kts
Dim: 63.50 (58.00 pp) × 11.90 × 4.32
M: 2 Caterpillar D378 diesels; electric drive; 1 prop; 1,000 shp
Fuel: 211 tons **Crew:** . . .

Remarks: On loan to the Pacific Branch, U.S. Geological Survey, since 27-2-74; prior to that performed survey work and acoustic research for the navy. Sister *Almeida Carvalho* (A 527, ex-*Kellar,* T-AGS 25) is on loan to the Portuguese Navy.

U.S. FISH AND WILDLIFE SERVICE

RESEARCH SHIP

◆ **1 sub-arctic-area research ship**
Bldr: Moss Point Marine, Escatawpa, Miss. (In serv. 1987)

EAGLE/TIGLAX

D: . . . **S:** 12 kts **Dim:** 37.0 × 10.1 × . . .
Electron Equipt: Radar: 1/Furuno . . .
M: 2 Caterpillar 3412 TA diesels; 2 props; . . . bhp
Range: 8,000/8 **Crew:** 18 tot.

Remarks: Serves the Alaska Maritime National Wildlife Refuge, covering 3,500 miles of Alaskan coastline; home-ported at Homer, Alaska. Used for animal and bird surveys, marine research, and transport. Has wet and dry laboratories, scuba-diver support capability, extensive navigational systems, weather satellite receiver. Has 1.5-ton crane forward, .5-ton crane aft, 12.5 × 9.1-m helipad.

U.S.A. *(continued)*
RESEARCH SHIP *(continued)*

Eagle/Tiglax Moss Pt., 1987

NATIONAL SCIENCE FOUNDATION

RESEARCH SHIP

♦ **1 Antarctic exploration icebreaker**
Bldr: North American Shipbuilding, Larose, Louisiana (In serv. 4-92)

NATHANIEL B. PALMER

Nathaniel B. Palmer—red hull, cream superstructure, green decks North American SB, 1992

D: 6,605 tons (fl) **S:** 16 kts
Dim: 93.89 (85.27 wl) × 18.29 × 6.63
Electron Equipt: Radar: . . .
M: 4 Caterpillar diesels; 2 CP, Kort-nozzle props; 12,720 bhp—1,500-shp bow-thruster—800-shp stern-thruster
Endurance: 265 days **Range:** . . ./. . .
Crew: 26 crew + 39 scientists

Remarks: Contracted for construction and ten-year lease in 2-90 with Atlantic Support Associates, with construction sub-contracted to Edison Couest Offshore, Inc., which built the ship at its yard listed above. Palmer is intended to operate 265 days consecutively at sea and in temperatures as low as –50°F. The ship was to be delivered at Punta Arenas, Chile.

Capable of breaking 3-ft. ice at 3 kts continuous and 6-ft. ice by ramming. Equipped with two 20-ton A-frame equipment cranes and three scientific winches. The 6,000 ft.^{2} of laboratory space includes wet, dry, biochemical, electronic, computer, darkroom, hydrology, and aquarium facilities, as well as two climate-controlled chambers and a special-specimen freezer. Has 3.5 and 12 kHz precision depth-sounders and is equipped to receive a multi-beam mapping sonar.

URUGUAY

Eastern Republic of Uruguay

Personnel (1992): 4,500 total, including 500 Fusileros Navales and 360 Air Arm

Naval Aviation: Fixed wing: 3 S-2G and 1 S-2A Tracker ASW patrol aircraft, 1 Beech 200T King Air maritime patrol aircraft, 2 Beech T-34C-1 and 2 Beech T-34B trainers, 1 Piper PA-18A light transport, and 3 Cessna 172 light liaison aircraft. Helicopters include: 3 Sikorsky CH-34C (2 bought 1991, all re-engined with turbines), and 1 Bell 47G-5 trainer. A Bell 222 helicopter formerly used by the Navy was sold during 1991, and the Air Force's sole CASA 212-AS28 SAR aircraft was sold to Sweden.

CH-34C Seabat Uruguayan Navy

Beech 200T King Air Uruguayan Navy

FRIGATES

♦ **3 French Commandant Rivière class** Bldr: DCAN, Lorient

	Laid down	L	In serv.
1 URUGUAY (ex-*Commandant Bourdais*)	4-59	15-4-61	10-3-63
2 GENERAL ARTIGAS (ex-*Victor Schoelcher*)	10-57	11-10-58	15-10-62
3 MONTEVIDEO (ex-*Amiral Charner*)	11-58	12-3-60	14-12-62

Uruguay (1) Hartmut Ehlers

General Artigas (2)—without Exocet SSM Uruguayan Navy

ATES *(continued)*

video (3) Uruguayan Navy, 1991

,750 tons (2,070 normal, 2,230 fl) **S:** 26 kts
: 102.70 (98.00 pp) × 11.80 × 4.35 (max.)
, 3: 4/MM 38 Exocet SSM (II × 2)—all: 2/100-mm 55-cal. Model
963 DP (I × 2)—2/40-mm 70-cal. AA (I × 2)—1/305-mm ASW
ortar (IV × 1)—6/550-mm ASW TT (III × 2, L-3 torpedoes)
tron Equipt:
dar: 1/DRBN 32 nav., 1/DRBV 22A air-search, 1/DRBC 32C f.c.
nar: 1/SQS-17 hull-mounted MF search, 1/DUBA 3 HF attack
V: ARBR 16 intercept
SEMT-Pielstick 12 PC 1V400 diesels; 2 props; 16,000 bhp
tric: 1,280 kw **Range:** 2,300/26; 7,500/16.5 **Fuel:** 210 tons
urance: 45 days **Crew:** 9 officers, 157 enlisted

ks: *General Artigas* transferred 19-12-88 and refitted through 9-1-89. Four Exocet missiles removed, but launch racks and box protective housings re- aboard. *Uruguay* transferred 20-8-90 after striking from French Navy 27-4-90, *ntevideo* transferred 28-1-91; both retained their Exocet missiles. The 305-mm can also be employed against shore targets. All three had two Dagaie decoy aunchers removed prior to transfer. Can also carry up to 80 troops.

The U.S. *Dealey*-class frigate *18 de Julio* (3, ex-*Dealey*, DE 1006) was stricken .S. *Cannon*-class frigate *Uruguay* (1, ex-*Baron*, DE 166) was stricken 2-5-90, sister *Artigas* (2, ex-*Bronstein*, DE 189) was stricken 1988.

OL BOATS

The French-built Vigilante-class patrol boats *15 De Noviembre* (5), *25 De Agosto* *Comodoro Coe* (7) were placed up for sale in mid-1992 after only 11 years of

x-U.S. Coast Guard 95-ft Cape class
: Coast Guard Yard, Curtis Bay, Maryland

	In serv.
ONIA (ex-*Cape Higgon*, WPB 95302)	14-10-53
NEGRO (ex-*Cape Horn*, WPB 95322)	3-9-58

egro (11) Uruguayan Navy, 1991

0 tons (106 fl) **S:** 20 kts **Dim:** 28.96 × 6.10 × 1.55
./12.7-mm M2 mg
tron Equipt: Radar: 1/SPS-64(V)1 nav.
2 G.M. Detroit Diesel 16V149 TI diesels; 2 props; 2,470 bhp
ge: 556/20; 1,900/11.5 **Endurance:** 5 days
tric: 60 kw **Crew:** 3 officers, 8 enlisted

ks: Both transferred 25-1-90 and left for Uruguay under own power. Were ned while in U.S.C.G. service, completing 13-2-81 and 21-1-83, respectively. QN-18 echo-sounder, LORAN-C, and SATNAV receivers. Unarmed at transfer; ried 2/12.7-mm mg (I × 2), 2/40-mm Mk 64 grenade launchers (I × 2). Despite rable age, are rugged craft and are being employed on search-and-rescue duties.

aysandu class Bldr: CNR, Ancona, Italy (L: 11-8-35)

TO (ex-GS 24)

Salto (14) Uruguayan Navy, 1991

D: 150 tons (180 fl) **S:** 17 kts **Dim:** 42.1 × 5.8 × 1.58
A: 1/40-mm 60-cal. Bofors, U.S. Mk 3 mount
M: 2 Krupp-Germania diesels; 2 props; 1,000 bhp
Range: 4,000/10 **Crew:** 26 tot.

Remarks: Survivor of a class of three. Since 1972, has been used for hydrographic survey and navigational aid tender duties, but is still considered to be a combatant. Has a small commercial navigational radar.

PATROL CRAFT

♦ **1 U.S. 85-ft Commercial Cruiser class**
Bldr: Sewart Seacraft, Morgan City, Lousiana (L: 11-68)

12 PAYSANDU

Paysandu (12) Uruguayan Navy, 1991

D: 43.5 tons (54 fl) **S:** 22 kts **Dim:** 25.91 × 5.69 × 2.1
A: 3/12.7-mm M2 mg (I × 3)
Electron Equipt: Radar: 1/Raytheon 1500B Pathfinder nav.
M: 2 G.M. 16V71N diesels; 2 props; 1,400 bhp **Electric:** 40 kw
Range: 800/21 **Crew:** 8 tot.

Remarks: Built under U.S. Military Assistance Program. Aluminum construction.

Note: The German FL-9-class patrol craft *Carmelo* (11) was stricken during 1990.

MINE COUNTERMEASURES SHIPS

♦ **3 ex-East German Kondor II-class patrol minesweepers**
Bldr: Peenewerft, Wolgast

	L	In serv.
31 TEMERARIO (ex-*Riesa*, 322)	2-10-72	3-7-73
32 VALIENTE (ex-*Eilenburg*, M 2674, ex-344)	31-8-72	22-12-72
33 FORTUNA (ex-*Bernau*, M 2673, ex-343)	3-8-72	1-12-72
34 AUDAZ (ex-*Eisleben*, M 2671, ex-312)	2-1-73	24-5-73

Valiente (32) Hartmut Ehlers, 4-92

MINE COUNTERMEASURES SHIPS *(continued)*

Audaz (34) Leo Van Ginderen, 11-91

D: 414 tons (482 fl) **S:** 18 kts **Dim:** 56.52 × 7.78 × 2.46
A: 1/40-mm 60-cal. Bofors AA (*see* Remarks)
Electron Equipt: Radar: TSR-333 nav. (32: Raytheon 1900)
M: 2 Type 40DM diesels; 2 CP Kort-nozzle props; 4,400 bhp
Electric: 625 kw (5 × 125 kw diesel sets)
Range: 2,000/15 **Endurance:** 10 days
Crew: 6 officers, 24 enlisted

Remarks: Former *Volksmarine* units; 32–34 had served in the *Bundesmarine* briefly after German unification. Transferred 8-11-91 with a five-year supply of spare parts. Left Germany 13-11-91 for Montevideo under their own power, arriving 23-12-91. A quadruple SA-5 Grail point-defense SAM launcher and three twin 25-mm Soviet 2M-8 AA were removed prior to transfer; a single 40-mm AA is to replace the forward 25-mm mount. Two minerails probably remain, but no mines were transferred. The high-frequency, hull-mounted sonar has probably been removed. Although most of the sweep gear was transferred with the ships, they will be employed primarily as patrol boats. On 32, the TSR-333 radar has been removed from the masthead and a Raytheon radar substituted atop the pilothouse.

Note: The U.S. *Adjutant*-class coastal minesweeper *Rio Negro* (13, ex-MS 32, ex-French *Marguerite,* ex-U.S. MSC 94) was stricken 1990.

AMPHIBIOUS WARFARE CRAFT

◆ **2 LD 43-class landing craft** Bldr: Dieque Nacional, Montevideo

42 (In serv. 26-7-78) 45 (In serv. 1981)

42—with high pilothouse Hartmut Ehlers, 4-92

45—with low pilothouse Hartmut Ehlers, 4-92

D: 15 tons (31.4 fl) **S:** 9 kts **Dim:** 14.1 × 3.50 × 0.80
M: 2 G.M. 6-71 diesels; 2 props; 272 bhp **Range:** 580/9

Remarks: Can carry 10 tons cargo. 42 has the pilothouse placed atop the poop deck, while in 45 (which has British Bedford diesels), the pilothouse is recessed into the poop. Previous listing of a third unit was apparently in error.

◆ **2 U.S. LCM(6)-class landing craft**

40 41

D: 24 tons (57 fl) **S:** 10 kts **Dim:** 17.07 × 4.37 × 1.17
M: 2 Gray Marine 64HN9 diesels; 2 props; 450 bhp
Range: 130/9

Remarks: Leased in 10-72; lease extended 1982. Cargo: 30 tons.

41 Hartmut Ehle

AUXILIARY SHIPS

◆ **1 U.S. Auk-class Antarctic support ship, former fleet minesweeper** Bldr: Defoe Boiler & Machine Works, Bay City, Mic

	Laid down	L	In
24 Comandante Pedro Campbell (ex-4, ex-MS 31, ex-*Chickadee,* MSF 59)	21-8-41	20-7-42	9-

Comandante Pedro Campbell (24) Uruguayan Nav

Comandante Pedro Campbell (24) Hartmut Ehle

D: 90 tons (1,250 fl) **S:** 18 kts
Dim: 67.41 (65.53 wl) × 9.78 × 3.28
A: none **Electron Equipt:** Radar: 2/. . . nav.
M: 4 Alco 539 diesels, electric drive; 2 props; 3,118 shp
Electric: 300 kw **Range:** 4,300/10 **Crew:** . . .

Remarks: Transferred 18-8-66 on loan and purchased outright on 18-8-76. A sweeping and ASW gear removed except for the sweep winch, which was towing. Typed as a corvette until late 1980s. Converted for service as General Base supply ship in 1990; left on first Antarctic mission on 15-1-91. Armament and former forecastle 76.2-mm gun position used to stow a refrigerated-pr container. Hull and stacks red, superstructure white.

Note: The 42,235-grt tanker *Presidente Rivera* (29) was placed up for sale in m

◆ **1 Polish Piast-class salvage ship**
Bldr: Stocznia Północna, Gdańsk (In serv. 29-12-76)

26 Vanguardia (ex-*Otto von Guericke,* A 441)

.IARY SHIPS *(continued)*

,560 tons (1,732 fl) **S:** 16.5 kts
: 72.6 (67.2 pp) × 12.0 × 4.0
one **Electron Equipt:** Radar: 2/TSR-333 nav.
Cegielski-Sulzer 6TD48 diesels; 2 CP props; 3,600 bhp
ge: 3,000/12 **Crew:** 16 officers, 44 enlisted

ks: Acquired from former East German *Volksmarine* by the newly unified y in 10-90. Purchased by Uruguay 10-91, refitted at Neptun-Warnow Werft, ; sailed for Montevideo in 1-92. Armament of two twin 30-mm AK-230 AA and two 25-mm 2M-8 AA mounts removed, as was the Drum Tilt radar director 30-mm AA. Variation of *Moma* design for salvage and rescue duties. Carries sible diver's decompression chamber to port. Can tow and has extensive pump -fighting facilities. Has two sisters in the Polish Navy. Took the name of the neous service tender *Vanguardia* (26), built in 1908 and stricken 1991.

x-U.S. Cohoes-class salvage ship
: Commercial Ironworks, Portland, Oregon

	Laid down	L	In serv.
RACÁN (ex-*Nahant*, AN 83, N 102)	31-3-45	30-6-45	24-8-45

án (25) Uruguayan Navy, 1991

50 tons (855 fl) **S:** 12.3 kts **Dim:** 51.36 (44.5 pp) × 10.31 × 3.3
/20-mm AA (I × 3) **Electron Equipt:** Radar: 1/. . . nav.
2 Busch-Sulzer BS539 diesels, electric drive; 1 prop; 1,200 bhp
w: 48 tot.

ks: Former netlayer. Transferred in 12-68. A decompression chamber for s carried. In marginal condition.

avigational buoy tender
: Dique Nacional, Montevideo (In serv. 1988)

US

(21)—outboard Uruguay (1) and Montevideo (3)
Hartmut Ehlers, 4-92

290 tons (fl) **S:** 11 kts **Dim:** 35.0 × 10.0 × 2.8
2 G.M. 12V71 TA diesels; 2 props; 860 bhp **Crew:** 15 tot.

ks: Built with assistance from Damen SY, Hardinxveld, the Netherlands. hydraulic articulated crane forward.

J.S. Sotoyomo-class auxiliary ocean tug
: Levingston SB, Orange, Texas

	Laid down	L	In serv.
N JOSÉ (ex-Chilean *Lautaro*, ex-A 122)	19-10-42	27-11-42	10-6-43

534 tons (835 fl) **S:** 13 kts
: 43.59 (41.00 pp) × 10.31 × 4.01
A: none (*see* Remarks) **Electron Equipt:** Radar: 1/. . . nav.
M: 2 G.M. 12-278A diesels, electric drive; 2 props; 1,500 shp
Electric: 120 kw **Range:** 16,500/18 **Fuel:** 171 tons **Crew:** 49 tot.

San José (22)—76.2-mm gun since removed Uruguayan Navy, 1991

Remarks: Purchased by Chile from the United States in 9-47 and donated to Uruguay 17-5-91. Employed on salvage and rescue duties. Retained one 76.2-mm 50-cal. U.S. Mk 26 single-fire gun mount at transfer, but by 4-92, it had been removed.

♦ **1 former East German-class coastal tug**
Bldr: Peenewerft, Wolgast (In serv. 14-7-59)

27 BANCO ORTIZ (ex-*Zingst*, Y 1695; ex-*Elbe*, A 443)

Banco Ortiz (27)—outboard Huracán (25) Hartmut Ehlers, 4-92

D: 261 tons (fl) **S:** 10 kts **Dim:** 30.50 × 8.00 (7.50 wl) × 2.50
Electron Equipt: Radar: 1/. . . nav.
M: 1 Buckau-Wolff R6DV 148 diesel; 1 prop; 550 bhp
Range: 1,400/10 **Crew:** 12 tot.

Remarks: Acquired by Germany at unification, 10-90, and used by *Bundesmarine* until transferred to Uraguay 10-91; sailed under own power for Montevideo 13-11-91. Nine-ton bollard pull at 10 kts. Had been refitted in 1983 and given new auxiliary machinery.

Note: A craft named *Oyarvide* is also in naval service, function and characteristics not available.

♦ **1 sail-training ship** Bldr: Soc. Española de Construcción Naval, Matagorda, Cádiz, Spain (In serv. 1930)

20 CAPITAN MIRANDA (ex-GS 20)

Capitan Miranda (20) Uruguayan Navy, 1991

URUGUAY *(continued)*
AUXILIARY SHIPS *(continued)*

D: 587 tons (715 fl) **S:** 11 kts (14 sail)
Dim: 54.60 (61.21 bowsprit/45.00 pp) × 8.4 × 3.60
Electron Equipt: Radar: 1/Decca TM 1226C nav.
M: 1 G.M. diesel; 1 prop; 600 hp **Fuel:** 45 tons **Crew:** 49 tot.

Remarks: Originally built as a hydrographic survey ship. Refitted, re-engined, and rigged as a three-masted schooner for cadet training, recommissioning 1978. Circumnavigated globe 2-8-87 to 24-7-88, covering 34,101 nautical miles. Sail area: 722 m^2.

COAST GUARD (PREFECTURA MARITIMA)

The Uruguayan Coast Guard has 100 officers and about 1,900 enlisted men. Primarily intended for a shore-based coast watch and port police function, it was to be integrated into the Uruguayan Navy by the end of 1992. In addition to the three craft listed below, it has four 4.9-meter outboard-motor-powered semi-rigid inflatable rubber boats.

◆ **3 23-meter tug/tenders** (In serv. . . .)

70 (ex-PS 1) 71 (ex-PS 2) 72 (ex-PS 3)

70 Hartmut Ehlers, 4-92

Remarks: No data available.

VANUATU

Republic of Vanuatu

Personnel: . . .

PATROL BOATS

◆ **1 Australian ASI 315 class**
Bldr: Australian SB Industries, South Coogie, Western Australia

	L	In serv.
TUKORO	20-5-87	13-6-87

Tukoro Leo Van Ginderen, 10-91

D: 165 tons (fl) **S:** 20 kts
Dim: 31.50 (28.60 wl) × 8.10 × 2.12 (1.80 hull)
A: none **Electron Equipt:** Radar: 1/Furuno 1011 nav.
M: 2 Caterpillar 3516 diesels; 2 props; 2,820 bhp (2,400 sust.)
Electric: 116 kw tot. **Range:** 2,500/12 **Fuel:** 27.9 tons
Endurance: 8–10 days **Crew:** 3 officers, 15 enlisted

Remarks: Provided by Australian Defence Cooperation Program. Ordered 13-9-85. Sisters built for other Southwest Pacific nations. A second unit is planned. Carries 5-m aluminum boarding boat. Extensive navigational suite, including Furuno FSN-7 NAVSAT receiver, 525 HF/DF, 120 MH/HF/DF, FE-881 echo-sounder and DS-7 doppler log.

◆ **1 patrol boat, former yacht** (In serv. . . .)

MALA

Mala Leo Van Ginderen, 5-

Remarks: No data available. May have been discarded.

VENEZUELA

Republic of Venezuela

Personnel (1992): approximately 20,000 total, including 8,500 Marines and 35 naval aviation.

Naval Aviation: For shipboard use, nine AQS-13 dipping sonar-equipped Agu Bell 212 helicopters (three delivered in 1990) are in use. The Maritime Patrol & A Squadron operates three CASA 212-S43 Aviocar maritime surveillance aircraft. Transport Squadron operates one de Havilland Dash-7 and 2 CASA 212-S200 Avi transports; the VIP Transport Squadron operates one Beech Super King Air B-200 Beech King Air C90, and one Aerocommander Turbo 980 transports; and the Trai Squadron has two Cessna Turbo 402, one Cessna Turbo 310, and one Cessna 210 aircraft. Venezuelan Air Force Mirage-V jet fighters are being equipped to launch AM-39 Exocet anti-ship missile.

de Havilland Dash-7—Venezuelan Navy Transport Squadron
Venezuelan Navy,

Organization: The fleet is divided into five Strategic Commands: Fleet, Ma Naval Aviation, Coast Guard, and Riverine Forces. There is also a Special Oper Unit with combat swimmers. All ship names are prefaced by A.R.V. (*Armada República de Venezuela*).

SUBMARINES

Note: Plans to acquire up to three additional submarines have been pla abeyance for lack of funds.

◆ **2 German Type 209/1300 class** Bldr: Howaldtswerke, Kiel

	Laid down	L	In serv.
S-31 SÁBALO	2-5-73	1-7-75	6-8-76
S-32 CARIBE	1-8-73	6-11-75	11-3-77

D: 1,100 tons light (1,265 surf./1,295 sub.) **S:** 11 kts surf./22 kts
Dim: 59.50 × 6.30 × 5.50
A: 8/533-mm bow TT (14 tot. U.S. Mk 37 and German SST-4 wire guided torpedoes)

ARINES *(continued)*

lo (S-31)—prior to modifications Venezuelan Navy, 1990

ɔe (S-32) Gilbert Gyssels, 1984

ctron Equipt:
adar: Thomson-CSF Calypso
W: Thomson-CSF DR-2000 intercept
onar: KAE CSU-3 series suite, Thomson-Sintra DUUX-2 passive ranging
diesel-electric: 4 MTU 12V492 Tb90, 600-bhp diesels; 4/405-kw generators; Siemens electric motor; 5,000 shp
nge: 11,200/4 snorkel; 25/20 sub.; 445/4 sub. **Fuel:** 108 tons
durance: 50 days **Crew:** 5 officers, 28 enlisted

rks: Ordered 1971; a planned second pair were not ordered. S-31 damaged by 1979 and overhauled at Kiel through 1981. S-32 refitted by builder 1984. ally had H.S.A. Mk 8 Mod. 24 fire-control system. Operating depth: 250 m. Have 20-cell batteries producing 11,500 amp./hr. and weighing 257 tons total.
began refit to West German Navy Type 206A standard by builder in 4-90 and t returned to Venezuela by mid-1992; S-32 is to be similarly refitted. The refit es a new casing and sail, substitution of the KAE ISUS integrated command, l, and sonar suite, substitution of an AS-40 attack periscope for the original AS he BS 19 search 'scope is retained), and re-engining. May be rearmed with n-manufactured Marconi Tigerfish wire-guided torpedoes during the 1990s.

The U.S. GUPPY-II-class submarine *Picua* (S-22, ex-*Grenadier*, SS 525) was n 10-12-91.

ATES

Italian Lupo class Bldr: CNR, Riva Trigoso and Ancona(*), Italy

	Laid down	L	In serv.
Mariscal Sucre	4-10-77	28-9-78	14-7-80
Almirante Brion	26-1-78	22-2-79	7-3-81
General Urdaneta*	23-1-78	23-3-79	8-8-81
General Soublette	26-8-78	4-1-80	4-12-81
General Salom*	7-11-78	13-1-80	3-4-82
Almirante José M. Garcia (-*General José Félix Ribas*)	21-8-79	4-10-80	30-7-82

ral Salom (F-25) Venezuelan Navy, 1991

Mariscal Sucre (F-21) Venezuelan Navy, 7-88

General Urdaneta (F-23)—USS *Hayler* (DD 997) in background
JO1 Gregg L. Snaza, USN, 1990

D: 2,213 tons (2,525 fl) **S:** 35 kts (20.5 on diesels)
Dim: 112.8 (106.0 pp) × 11.98 × 3.84 (hull)
A: 8/Otomat Mk II SSM (I × 8)—1/Albatros SAM system (VIII × 1, 8 Aspide missiles)—1/127-mm 54-cal. OTO Melara DP—4/40-mm Breda Dardo AA (II × 2)—6/324-mm Mk 32 ASW TT (III × 2, for A244S torpedoes)—1/AB-212 ASW helicopter
Electron Equipt:
Radar: 1/3RM-20 nav., 1/RAN-11/X air/surf.-search, 1/RAN-10S air search, 2/Orion RTN-10X f.c., 2/Orion RTN-20X f.c.
Sonar: Edo 610E hull-mounted MF—TACAN: SRN-15A
EW: Lambda-F D/F-intercept, 2/SCLAR chaff RL (XX × 2)
M: CODOG: 2 Fiat G.E. LM-2500 gas turbines (25,000 shp each), 2 GMT A230-2M diesels (3,900 bhp each); 2 CP props; 50,000 shp max.
Electric: 3,120 kw **Range:** 900/35; 1,050/31.7; 5,500/16
Crew: 185 tot.

Remarks: Ordered 24-10-75. Fin stabilizers fitted. Gun (127-mm) and missile fire control by two Elsag NA-10 Mod. 0 systems. The Albatros system uses Aspide missiles, a re-engineered version of NATO Sea Sparrow. Each twin 40-mm Dardo system anti-aircraft mount has an associated RTN-20X radar director. All weapons controlled by a Selenia IPN-10 computerized data system. Fixed, nontelescopic hangar. The helicopter performs over-the-horizon targetting for the Otomat missiles as well as ASW duties. Original Lambda-F EW system was to be replaced with U.S. Sperry Marine "Guardian Star" automatic D/F-intercept system during 1989–90, but the contract was never consummated. Near-sisters in the Italian and Peruvian navies.

Under a contract signed in 7-92, F-21 and F-22 are to be updated and refitted by Ingalls Shipbuilding, Pascagoula, Mississippi. The Otomat missiles are to be replaced by the U.S. Harpoon, the EW suite altered to the U.S. SLQ-32(V)3, and Mk 36 Super RBOC decoy launching system substituted for SCLAR. The Global Positioning System NAVSAT receiver is to be added, and new speed log and gyrocompass to be substituted. The work will begin in 9-92 with F-21, and it is hoped eventually to update the other four.

◆ **2 Almirante Clemente class** Bldr: Ansaldo, Livorno

	Laid down	L	In serv.
GC-11 Almirante Clemente (ex-F-11, ex-D-12)	5-5-54	12-12-54	1956
GC-12 General José Trinidad Moran (ex-F-12, ex-D-22)	5-5-54	12-12-54	1956

D: 1,300 tons (1,500 fl) **S:** 22 kts **Dim:** 97.6 × 10.84 × 2.6
A: 2/76-mm 62-cal. OTO Melara Compact DP (I × 2)—2/40-mm 70-cal. Breda AA (II × 1)—6/324-mm Whitehead ILAS-3 ASW TT (III × 2; 6 A 244S torpedoes)
Electron Equipt:
Radar: 1/Decca 1226 nav., 1/Plessey AWS-2 air/surf. search, 1/Orion RTN-10X f.c.
Sonar: Plessey MS-26 hull-mounted (10 kHz)
M: 2 G.M.T. 16-645E7CA diesels; 2 props; 6,000 bhp **Range:** . . .
Fuel: 350 tons **Crew:** 12 officers, 150 enlisted

Remarks: Survivors of a class of six: *General José de Austria* stricken 1976, *General*

FRIGATES *(continued)*

Almirante Clemente (GC-11) Venezuelan Navy, 7-88

General José Trinidad Moran (GC-12) Venezuelan Navy, 1991

José Garcia stricken 1977, and *General Juan José Flores* and *Almirante Brion* stricken 1978. Both were extensively refitted by Cammell Laird, Birkenhead, from 1968 to 1975–76 (much delay caused by financial and labor problems). New radars, sonar, and armament fitted, with OTO Melara Compact mounts replacing the original four 102-mm dual-purpose (II × 2) guns. Have Elsag NA-10 GFCS for the 76-mm guns and a lead-computing sight for the 40-mm AA mount. When new, could make 32 knots. Very lightly built, with much use of aluminum alloy. Denny-Brown fin stabilizers. Re-engined by C.N.R., Genoa, Italy, with diesels 10-84 to 24-7-85 and operated under the Coast Guard Command since 3-86.

PATROL BOATS

Note: To replace the *Constitución* class, Bender Marine, Mobile, Alabama, has offered to build six 800-ton or six to ten 41-meter patrol boats.

◆ **6 Constitución class** Bldr: Vosper Thornycroft, Portsmouth, U.K.

	Laid down	L	In serv.
PC-11 CONSTITUCIÓN	1-73	1-6-73	16-8-74
PC-12 FEDERACIÓN	8-73	26-2-74	25-3-75
PC-13 INDEPENDENCIA	2-73	24-7-73	20-9-74
PC-14 LIBERTAD	9-73	5-3-74	12-6-75
PC-15 PATRIA	3-73	27-9-73	9-1-75
PC-16 VICTORIA	3-73	3-9-74	22-9-75

D: 150 tons (170 fl) **S:** 31 kts **Dim:** 36.88 (33.53 wl) × 7.16 × 1.73
A: P-11, P-13, P-15: 1/76-mm 62-cal. OTO Melara Compact DP
P-12, P-14, P-16: 1/40-mm 70-cal. Bofors AA

Federación (PC-12)—40-mm gun version

Constitución (PC-11)—76-mm gun version (old number) Venezuelan Navy, 19..

Electron Equipt:
Radar: 1/SPQ-2D surf. search; P-11, P-13, P-15: 1/Orion RTN-10X also
M: 2 MTU MD 16V538 TB90 diesels; 1 prop; 7,080 max. bhp (5,900 sust.)
Electric: 250 kw **Range:** 1,350/16 **Crew:** 3 officers, 14 enlisted

Remarks: Ordered 4-72. All equipped with Vosper fin stabilizers. New hull numb.. assigned 1978. Maximum sustained speed is 27 knots. NA-10 Mod. 1 GFCS in 76-m.. gun-equipped boats. Eighteen Harpoon missiles were to have been purchased in 1.. for use on P-11, P-13, and P-15, along with Breda single 30-mm AA to replace 40-mm mounts in P-12, P-14, and P-16; the modernization program, however, has b.. deferred. The two Otomat Mk 1 missiles formerly carried by P-12, P-14, and P-.. having probably reached the end of their useful lives, were removed in 1991. All six assigned to the Coast Guard Command.

PATROL CRAFT

◆ **2 (+ 8) U.S. Coast Guard "Point" (82-ft.) class**
Bldr: U.S. Coast Guard Yard, Curtis Bay, Maryland (PG 32: J. Martinac SB, Tacoma, Washington)

	In Serv.	Transfer
PG-31 PETREL (ex-*Point Knoll,* WPB 82367)	26-6-67	18-10-..
PG-32 ALCATRAZ (ex-*Point Judith,* WPB 82345)	26-7-66	15-1-..

D: 64 tons (69 fl) **S:** 23.7 kts **Dim:** 25.30 × 5.23 × 1.95
A: 2/12.7-mm mg (I × 2)
Electron Equipt: Radar: 1/SPS-64(V)1 nav.
M: 2 Cummins VT-12-M diesels; 2 props; 1,600 bhp
Range: 490/23.7; 1,500/8 **Fuel:** 5.7 tons **Crew:** 8 tot.

Remarks: Donated for use by the Coast Guard Command in anti-drug work. P.. transferred at New London, Connecticut, and PG-32 at Santa Barbara, Califo.. Capable of towing and fire fighting. Assigned to the Coast Guard Command. Up to .. additional units may eventually be transferred.

◆ **3 (+ 17) GRP-hulled fast patrol craft** Bldr: . . . . .

	In serv.		In ser..
LRG-001 CONSTANCIA	12-91	LRG-003 HONESTIDAD	12-..
LRG-002 PERSEVERANCIA	12-91		

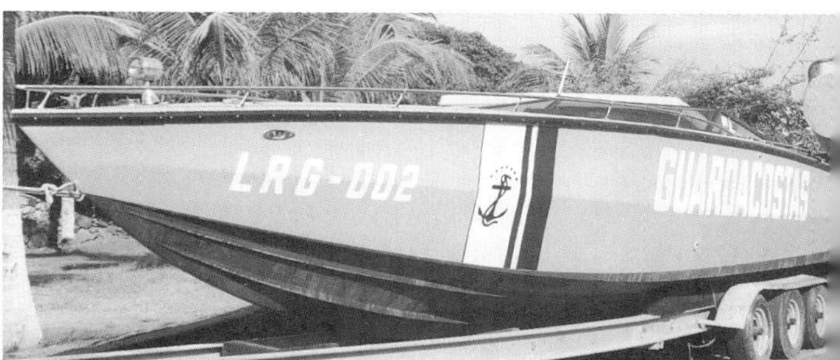

Perseverancia (LRG-002) Carlos Hernández Gonzalez

Remarks: Three prototypes of a planned group of twenty delivered 12-91 for .. the Coast Guard Command. Are about 7.3 to 10.0 m overall. Of "cigarette.. configuration.

◆ **7 UFPB-1/1000 class** Bldr: Cougar Marine, Ltd., U.K. (In serv. 19..

LG-21 POLARIS
LG-22 . . . . . .
LG-23 RIGEL
LG-24 ALDEBARAN
LG-25 ANTARES
LG-26 CANOPUS
LG-27 ALTAIR

ROL CRAFT *(continued)*

5 tons (fl) **S:** 50 kts **Dim:** 10.05 (7.92 wl) × 2.60 × 0.78
small arms **Electron Equipt:** Radar: 1/. . . nav.
2 diesel outdrives; 400 bhp **Range:** 150/50 **Crew:** 4 tot.

rks: GRP construction. Assigned to Coast Guard for coastal/harbor service.

ER PATROL CRAFT

following craft are all subordinated to the River Command. Letters in the hull ers stand for: BNMA—Machado Naval Base; ANFRI—Franz Rizquez Iribarren Post; PFCM—Clemente Maldonado River Post; PFJCQ—José Cipriano ero River Post; PNPA—Páez Naval Post; ANMU—Muñoz Naval Post.

18-ton

1 MANAURE PF-22 MARA

aure (PF-21) Venezuelan Navy, 1991

rks: Resemble a U.S. Navy "Swiftboat" but have narrower beam. A 12.7-mm mg unted above the pilothouse, and a small radar is carried.

13.6-ton

3 GUAICAIPURO PF-24 TAMANACO

3-ton, 9-meter Bldr: Mercruiser, Miami, Florida (In serv. 1983)

1 TEREPAIMA PF-33 YARACUI LA-01 EL AMPARO
2 TIUNA PF-34 SOROCAYMA

paima (PF-31) Venezuelan Navy, 7-88

5 Apure class—500 kg

IA-51 to 53 PFCM-51 to 54 PNPA-51, 52
RI-51 to 55 PFJCQ-51 to 54 ANMU-51 to 57

U.S. Cobia class—500 kg

IU-81 to 82 PFJCQ-81

Profine class—500 kg

RI-41, 42

Bolivar class—500 kg

IA-61 PFCM-61

Puerto Páez class—2.5 tons

IA-31

air-gliders (propeller-driven)—2.5 tons

IU-71 ANMU-72

ANMU-71 or 72 Venezuelan Navy, 1991

Note: Also in use by the River Command are: ANFRI-11 (10 tons), ANFRI-12 (4 tons), ANFRI-13 (1.5 tons), PFCM-11 (4 tons), PFCM-12 (1.5 tons), and PFCM-21 (1.2 tons).

AMPHIBIOUS WARFARE SHIPS

◆ **4 Capaña-class tank landing ships**
Bldr: Korea-Tacoma SY, Masan, S. Korea

	L	In serv.
T-61 CAPAÑA	25-3-83	21-6-84
T-62 ESEQUIBO	25-3-83	21-6-84
T-63 GOAJIRA	. . .	11-84
T-64 LOS LLANOS	. . .	11-84

Capaña (T-61) Venezuelan Navy, 7-88

D: 1,800 tons light (4,070 fl) **S:** 15 kts
Dim: 104.0 × 15.4 × 3.0 (4.2 max.)
A: 2/40-mm 70-cal. Breda Dardo AA (II × 1)
Electron Equipt: Radar: 1/. . . nav.
M: 2 SEMT-Pielstick 16 PA 6V diesels; 2 props; 6,400 bhp (5,600 sust.)
Electric: 750 kw tot. **Range:** 7,500/13
Crew: 13 officers, 104 enlisted + troops: 10 officers, 192 enlisted

Remarks: Ordered 8-82. Cargo: 1,800 tons maximum, 690 beaching load. Improved version of U.S. WW II–era LST. Have an elevator to the upper deck and a 50-ton tank turntable on the tank deck. Sisters in the Indonesian Navy. T-61, 62 arrived 10-84 in Venezuela, T-63 in 12-84, and T-64 early in 1985; all delivered without armament. Have a helicopter deck aft.

◆ **1 ex-U.S. Terrebonne Parish–class landing ship**
Bldr: Ingalls SB, Pascagoula, Mississippi

	Laid down	L	In serv.
T-51 AMAZONAS (ex-T-21, ex-*Vernon County,* LST 1161)	14-4-52	25-11-52	18-5-53

Amazonas (T-51) Leo Van Ginderen, 1990

AMPHIBIOUS WARFARE SHIPS *(continued)*

D: 2,590 tons (5,786 fl) **S:** 14.5 kts **Dim:** 117.35 × 16.76 × 5.18
A: 6/76.2-mm 50-cal. Mk 33 DP (II × 3)
Electron Equipt: 1/Decca . . . nav., 2/SPG-34 f.c.
M: 4 G.M. 16-278A diesels; 2 CP props; 6,000 bhp
Electric: 600 kw **Range:** 6,000/9 **Fuel:** 1,060 tons
Crew: 116 tot.

Remarks: Loaned 29-6-73, purchased outright 30-12-77. Cargo: 2,200 tons vehicles and stores, 395 troops. Two Mk 63 radar fire control systems for the 76.2-mm gunmounts. Normally carries two LCVPs. Went aground 6-8-80 at St. Lucia in a hurricane but was salvaged. Began repair/refit 1987 at DIANCA, Puerto Cabello.

◆ **2 utility landing craft** Bldr: Swiftships, Morgan City, Louisiana

T-71 MARGARITA (In serv. 20-1-84) T-72 LA ORCHILA (In serv. 11-5-84)

Margarita (T-71) Carlos Hernández Gonzalez, 11-90

D: 428 tons (fl) **S:** 13 kts **Dim:** 39.62 × 10.97 × 1.30
A: 2/12.7-mm M2 mg (I × 2)
Electron Equipt: Radar: 1/. . . nav.
M: 2 G.M. Detroit Diesel 16V149 N diesels; 2 props; 1,800 bhp
Range: 2,500/10 **Fuel:** 64 tons **Crew:** 4 officers, 17 enlisted

Remarks: Aluminum construction. Cargo: vehicles, supplies, up to 108 tons fuel and 149 tons water. Bow ramp, 15-ton crane on bow. Carry 156 tons ballast. Intended for coastal and riverine use. Both transferred to River Command in 1984.

◆ **12 U.S. LCVP-class landing craft**
Bldr: DIANCA, Puerto Cabello (In serv. 1976–77)

01 through 12

D: 12 tons (fl) **S:** 9 kts **Dim:** 10.9 × 3.2 × 1.0
M: 1 diesel; 1 prop; 225 bhp **Range:** 110/9

Remarks: Follow design of U.S.-built LCVP. Used as harbor support craft. Several other LCVP and LCPL transferred with U.S. Navy ships probably also survive.

Note: The Venezuelan Marine Corps has nine U.S.-supplied LVTP-7 amphibious armored personnel carriers, one LVTC-7 amphibious armored command vehicle, and one LVTR-7 amphibious armored recovery vehicle at its disposal.

A special warfare craft attached to the Venezuelan Marine Corps practicing swimmer pickup using a rubber boat lashed alongside
Venezuelan Navy, 1991

Venezuelan Marine Corps LVTP-7 Venezuelan Navy, 1991

HYDROGRAPHIC SURVEY VESSELS

◆ **1 multipurpose survey ship** Bldr: E.N. Bazán, San Fernando, Spain

	Laid down	L	In serv.
BO-11 PUNTA BRAVA	12-88	9-3-90	2-5-91

Punta Brava (BO-11) Carlos Hernández Gonzalez, 11-

D: 1,170 tons (1,250 fl) **S:** 14.6 kts
Dim: 61.70 (55.60 pp) × 11.90 × 3.46
A: none **Electron Equipt:** Radar: 2/. . . nav.
M: 2 Bazán-MAN 7L 20/27 diesels; 2 props; 2,500 bhp—bow-thruster
Range: 8,000/12.8 **Fuel:** 210 tons
Crew: 6 officers, 8 non-comm. officers, 20 enlisted + 12 scientists, 4 technicians

Remarks: Ordered 9-88 to replace U.S. *Cohoes*-class survey ship *Puerto Santo* (H- ex-*Marietta,* AN 82, ex-YN 101), stricken 1-6-89. Has biological, meteorological, g logical, electronic, and oceanographic laboratories in addition to cartographic fac ties. Equipped with Qubit hydrographic survey data-recording equipment, TRAC survey and navigation system, and CHART (M) data log. Two 8.5-m hydrograp survey launches are carried. Has two Raytheon 6000 echo-sounders. Initially assig to the Coast Guard, but will eventually be operated by the *Direccion de Geografi Navigacion de las Fuerzas Armadas.*

◆ **1 hydrographic survey launch**
Bldr: DIANCA, Puerto Cabello (In serv. 8-89)

F-001 MAQUITITARE

Remarks: No data available. Assigned to the *Dirreccion de Geografia y Cartografi las Fuerzas Armadas* for use in riverine charting.

◆ **2 Gabriela-class hydrographic survey craft**
Bldr: Abeking & Rasmussen, Lemwerder, Germany

	Laid down	L	In se
LH-11 ARAYA (ex-*Gabriela,* ex-LH-01)	10-3-73	29-11-73	5-2
LH-12 PARAGUANA (ex-*Lely,* ex-LH-02)	28-5-73	12-12-73	7-2

Araya (LH-11) Carlos Hernández Gonzalez

IYDROGRAPHIC SURVEY VESSELS *(continued)*

D: 90 tons (fl) **S:** 20 kts **Dim:** 27.0 × 5.6 × 1.5
M: 2 MTU diesels; 2 props; 2,300 bhp **Crew:** 1 officer, 9 enlisted

emarks: Transferred to Navy in 1986 from National Institute of Hydrography. H-11 serves River Command, LH-12 the Coast Guard.

UXILIARY SHIPS

ote: Plans to acquire an underway-replenishment ship have been deferred.

1 transport, former merchant ship Bldr: Drammen SY, Drammen, Norway (In serv. 1972)

-44 PUERTO CABELLO (ex-*Sierra Nevada*, ex-*Ragni Berg*, ex-*Golar Ragni*, ex-*Kongsfjell*)

uerto Cabello (T-44) Dr. Giorgio Arra, 5-91

D: 13,500 tons (fl) **S:** 22.5 kts
Dim: 140.62 (131.88 pp) × 18.04 × 9.04
A: none **Electron Equipt:** Radar: 2/. . . nav.
M: 1 Sulzer diesel; 1 prop; 13,200 bhp

marks: 6,682-grt/9,218-dwt former refrigerated cargo ship with 10,280 m³ refrig-ated cargo capacity in four holds. Acquired for Venezuelan Navy in mid-1985 from a vernment shipping agency and commissioned 22-5-86. Replaced transport *Las Aves* 11), stricken 1983.

te: The cargo ship *Porlamar* (T-43), described in the previous edition, had been carded in 1987.

1 ex-U.S. Achomawi-class fleet tug
Bldr: Charleston Shipbuilding and Dry Dock, Charleston, South Carolina

	Laid down	L	In serv.
-32 MIGUEL RODRIGUEZ (ex-R-23, ex-*Salinin*, ATF 161)	13-4-45	20-7-45	11-9-45

guel Rodriguez (RA-32)—old number Leo Van Ginderen, 5-81

: 1,235 tons (1,675 fl) **S:** 16.5 kts
im: 62.48 (59.44) × 11.74 × 4.67
: none **Electron Equipt:** Radar: 1/. . . nav.
: 4 G.M. 16-278A diesels, electric drive; 1 prop; 3,000 shp
ectric: 400 kw **Range:** 7,000/15 **Fuel:** 300 tons
ew: 85 tot.

arks: R-21 loaned 3-9-71; purchased outright 30-12-77. R-23 purchased 1-9-78. r *Antonio Picardi* (R-22, ex-*Nipmuc*, ATF 157) ran aground and was lost 12-4-82. 3 transferred to Coast Guard in 1983 along with sister *Felipe Larrazabel* (ex-R-21, *tina*, ATF 163), which was stricken 9-90.

◆ **1 sail-training ship** Bldr: Ast. Celeya, Bilbao, Spain

	Laid down	L	In serv.
BE-11 SIMÓN BOLÍVAR	5-6-79	21-9-79	14-8-80

Simón Bolívar (BE-11) Venezuelan Navy, 1991

D: 1,260 tons (fl) **S:** 10.5 kts **Dim:** 82.42 (58.5 pp) × 10.6 × 4.2
M: 1 G.M. 12V149 diesel; 1 prop; 750 bhp
Crew: 17 officers, 75 enlisted + 18 instructors, 84 cadets

Remarks: 934 grt. Ordered 7-78. Sister to Ecuadorian *Guayas*. Three-masted bark; sail area: 1,650 m². Does not have pendant number painted on.

SERVICE CRAFT

◆ **2 salvage, search-and-rescue ships** Bldr: . . . (In serv. . . .)

LG-11 LOS TAQUES (ex-LA-11, ex-IA-01)
LG-12 LOS CAYOS (ex-LA-12, ex-IA-02)

Los Cayos (LG-12) Carlos Hernández Gonzalez, 7-88

D: 300 tons (fl) **S:** . . . **Dim:** . . . × . . . × . . .
M: 1 diesel; 1 prop; . . . bhp

Remarks: Small former fishing trawlers assigned to Coast Guard Command for search and rescue and light salvage duties. Acquired and commissioned on 15-5-81 and in 1984, respectively.

◆ **1 river tug** Bldr: . . . (In serv. 1-86)

R-. . . CARDONES

Remarks: No data available.

◆ **1 ex-U.S. Cholocco-class medium harbor tug**
Bldr: Commercial Iron Works, Portland, Oregon

	Laid down	L	In serv.
RP-21 FERNANDO GÓMEZ (ex-R-11, ex-*General José Félix Ribas*, R-13, ex-*Oswegatchie*, YTM 778, ex-YTB 515)	13-8-45	24-10-45	14-12-45

D: 250 tons light (345 fl) **S:** 12 kts **Dim:** 30.48 × 7.92 × 2.92
A: 2/12.7-mm mg (I × 2) **Electron Equipt:** Radar: 1/. . . nav.
M: 2 Enterprise diesels; 1 prop; 1,270 bhp **Crew:** 14 tot.

Remarks: Transferred from United States 4-6-65; had been in reserve from 3-46 to 3-63. Transferred to Coast Guard Command in 1989. Incorrectly identified in previous editions.

SERVICE CRAFT *(continued)*

Fernando Gómez (RP-21) Carlos Hernández Gonzalez, 7-88

◆ **1 small VIP yacht**

LA ALMIRALANTANA

Remarks: Assigned to the Venezuelan Chief of Naval Operations and based at Puerto Cabello.

◆ **1 personnel launch**

ANTV-01

ANTV-01 George R. Schneider, Jr., 4-92

Remarks: Assigned to the Tomás Vega Naval Post, Turiamo; no data available.

◆ **5 service launches**

BANAR-01 through BANAR-05

Three Banar-01-class launches Carlos Hernández Gonzalez, 11-90

D: 50 tons (fl) **S:** 10 kts **Dim:** 17.0 × 4.37 × 1.17
M: 2 G.M. 6-71 diesels; 2 props; 330 bhp
Range: 130/10 **Crew:** 3 tot.

Remarks: Rebuilt U.S. LCM(6) landing craft assigned to the Agustin Armario Naval Base, Puerto Cabello.

◆ **1 or more ANGU-01-class launches** Bldr: Ast. del Lago Maracaibo

ANGU-01 (In serv. 5-80)

Remarks: Assigned to the Francisco Javier Gutierrez Naval Post, Puerto Hierro; there may be additional units available. No data available.

NATIONAL GUARD

PATROL CRAFT

◆ **12 Protector-class** Bldr: SeaArk Workboats, Monticello, Arkansas

	In serv.		In serv.
B-8421 RIO ARAUCA II	2-7-84	B-8423 RIO APURE II	1-8-84
B-8422 RIO CATATUMBO II	2-7-84	B-8424 RIO NEARO II	1-8-84
B-8425 RIO META II	30-8-84	B-8429 RIO CINARUCO	1-11-84
B-8426 RIO PORTUGUESA II	1984	B-8430 RIO ICABARA	1-11-84
B-8427 RIO SARARE	4-9-84	B-8431 RIO GUARICO II	1984
B-8428 RIO URIBANTE	4-9-84	B-8432 RIO YARACUY	1984

Rio Catatumbo II (B-8422) Sea Ark, 7-

Rio Yaracuy (B-8432) SeaArk, 7

D: 15 tons (fl) **S:** 28 kts **Dim:** 13.03 (12.55 pp) × 4.47 × 1.17
A: 3/12.7-mm mg **Electron Equipt:** Radar: 1/Furuno FR10 nav.
M: 2 G.M. Detroit Diesel 8V92 T diesels; 2 props; 1,100 bhp
Electric: 10.5 kw **Range:** 600/25 **Crew:** 4 tot.

Remarks: Aluminum construction. For river and lake patrol. Replace twelve Fre built craft delivered 1970–77. Four of the craft were transferred to the Navy's R Command in 1986.

◆ **10 21-ft design** Bldr: SeaArk Workboats, Monticello, Arkansas

A-6901 LAGO 1	A-7918 RIO CABRIALES	A-7921 RIO TUY
A-6902 LAGO 2	A-7919 RIO CHAMA	A-8223 RIO GOAIGOAZA
A-6903 LAGO 3	A-7920 RIO CARIBE	A-7929 RIO MANATI
A-6904 LAGO 4		

21-ft design—outboard motors not fitted SeaArk,

D: 1.25 tons (fl) **S:** 30 kts **Dim:** 6.02 × 2.36 × 0.33
A: 1/12.7-mm mg **Electron Equipt:** Radar: 1/Furuno FR 10 nav.
M: 2 Evinrude gasoline outboard motors; 230 bhp **Crew:** 4 tot.

Remarks: Aluminum construction. For river and lake patrol. Equipped with knees to act as pusher tugs. Completed 1985. The last four are used as yachts.

◆ **15 18-ft aluminum chase-boat design**

Bldr: SeaArk Workboats, Monticello, Arkansas (In serv. 11-1-85)

'ENEZUELA *(continued)*
'ATROL CRAFT *(continued)*

8-ft chase boat SeaArk, 1985

D: 0.5 tons (fl) **S:** 30 kts **Dim:** 5.48 × 2.08 × 0.15
A: 1/12.7-mm mg **Crew:** 4 tot.
M: 1 Evinrude gasoline outboard motor; 140 bhp

12 U.S. design Bldr: Robert E. Derecktor SY, Mamaroneck, N.Y.

.-8201 Punta Peret	A-8207 Punta Ballena
.-8202 Punta Mulato	A-8208 Punta Macuro
.-8203 Punta Barima	A-8209 Punta Mariusa
.-8204 Punta Mosquito	A-8210 Punta Moron
-8205 Punta Playa	A-8211 Punta Macoya
.-8206 Punta Mulatos	A-8212 Punta Cardon

'unta" class—ramped stern version F. Nakajima/Derecktor SY, 1984

D: approx. 50 tons (fl) **S:** 28.5 kts **Dim:** 23.44 × 4.88 × . . .
A: . . . **Electron Equipt:** Radar: 1/Furuno . . . nav.
M: 2 G.M. 12V92M TI diesels; 2 props; 1,950 bhp
Electric: 60 kw **Range:** 1,100/22 **Crew:** 10 tot.

·marks: First six ordered 1980, delivered 8-82; second six ordered 1982 and de-·ered by 10-84. Aluminum construction. Of the first increment, three have a small ·icopter platform aft, and three have ramps for landing small vehicles. Funds permit-·g, these craft are to be re-engined with MTU diesels.

15 28.3-m class Bldrs: *units: INMA, La Spezia, Italy; others: DIANCA, Puerto Cabello (In serv. 1974–78)

7414 Rio Orinoco*	A-7423 Rio Torres*
7416 Rio Ventuari*	A-7424 Rio Escalante*
7417 Rio Caparo*	A-7430 Rio Yuruan
7418 Rio Tucuyo*	A-7436 Rio Guaicaipuro
7419 Rio Venamo*	A-7437 Rio Tamanaco
7420 Rio Limon*	A-7438 Rio Manaure
7421 Rio San Juan*	A-7439 Rio Ara
7422 Rio Turbio*	

): 43 (*48) tons (fl) **S:** 30–31 kts **Dim:** 23.8 × 4.8 × 1.5
\: 1/12.7-mm mg **Range:** 500 to 1,000/. . . **Crew:** 8 to 12 tot.
Electron Equipt: Radar: 1/Furuno FR 711 or FR 24 nav.
/I: Italian-built: 2 MTU 12V493 TY diesels; 2 props; 2,200 bhp; Venezuelan-built: 2 G.M. 12V92 TI diesels; 2 props; 2,000 bhp

narks: Wooden construction. Eleven sisters have been discarded.

2 Venezuelan design Bldr: . . . (In serv. . . .)

'404 Rio Altagracia A-7405 Rio Manzanare

): . . . **S:** 12 kts **Dim:** 15.0 × 3.8 × 1.9
.: . . . **Electron Equipt:** Radar: 1/Furuno FR 10
I: 1 diesel; . . . bhp **Range:** 140/12 **Crew:** 6 tot.

17 U.S. Enforcer class Bldr: Bertram Yacht, Miami, Florida

narks: Four of the 11.6-m version delivered 1978, ten more in 1980. One 14.0-m ion and two 13.4-m version delivered 1980. All have outdrive motors and glass-forced-plastic hulls.

e: The National Guard has also acquired numbers of 11.6-m "Batalla del Lago" 8.5-m "General José Antonio Piez"-class glass-reinforced-plastic-hulled patrol : built in Venezuela by Yamaha Fibra, C.A. Numbers built and characteristics are vailable.

VIETNAM

Socialist Republic of Vietnam

Personnel (1992): Approx. 7,000 total

Note: The following listings include ships known to have been in North Vietnamese service in 1975, those units left behind in South Vietnam that did not escape the communist victory, and a number of ships known to have been turned over to Vietnam by the Soviet Union since 1975. The operability of much of the former U.S. equipment is questionable, but several of the larger units have been seen at sea.

New ship names are not known. The pendant number system works as follows: HQ plus two digits: major combatant; HQ 1XX: seagoing patrol boat; HQ 2XX: harbor patrol craft; HQ 3XX: Soviet-supplied Osa, Shershen, and Turya classes; HQ 4XX: landing craft; HQ 5XX: amphibious landing ships; HQ 6XX: cargo ships; HQ 7XX: fisheries protection craft; HQ 8XX: mine warfare units; and HQ 9XX: auxiliaries and service craft.

Naval Aviation: Three Soviet Beriev Be-12 Mail antisubmarine patrol amphibians were delivered in 1981 for coastal surveillance duties, and there may be up to ten Mi-4 helicopters.

FRIGATES

◆ **1 ex-U.S. Savage-class former radar picket**
Bldr: Consolidated Steel Corp., Orange, Texas

	Laid down	L	In serv.
HQ 03 Dai Ky (ex-*Tran Khan Du*, ex-*Forster*, DER 334)	31-8-43	13-11-43	25-1-44

D: 1,590 tons (1,850 fl) **S:** 20 kts
Dim: 93.3 (91.4 wl) × 11.2 × 4.3 (hull)
A: 2/76.2-mm 50-cal. Mk 34 DP (I × 2)—1/81-mm mortar—2/12.7-mm mg (I × 2)
Electron Equipt:
Radar: 1/SPS-10 surf. search, 1/SPS-29 air search, 1/SPG-34 f.c.
M: 4 Fairbanks-Morse 38D8⅛ × 10 diesels; 2 props; 6,080 bhp
Electric: 580 kw tot. **Range:** 10,000/15 **Fuel:** 310 tons
Crew: approx. 170 tot.

Remarks: Transferred to South Vietnam 25-9-71. Was in overhaul at Saigon in 1975 and was reactivated by the current government. Mk 63 radar GFCS forward, Mk 51 Mod. 2 optical GFCS aft. Additional AA guns probably added. Doubtful that any of the radars listed are still usable, and the SQS-29-series sonar has almost certainly been removed or inactivated. Reported to be used as a training ship. Sister *Brister* (DER 327) was also captured but was not put back into service.

◆ **1 ex-U.S. Barnegat class former seaplane tender**
Bldr: Lake Washington SY, Houghton, Washington

	Laid down	L	In serv.
HQ 01 . . . . (ex-*Tham Ngu Lao*, ex-U.S.C.G. *Absecon*, WHEC 374, ex-AVP 23)	23-7-41	8-3-42	28-1-43

D: 1,766 tons (2,800 fl) **S:** 18 kts **Dim:** 94.7 (91.4 wl) × 12.5 × 4.1
A: 2/SS-N-2A Styx SSM (I × 2)—1/127-mm 38-cal. Mk 30 DP—3/37-mm 63-cal. AA (I × 3)—4/25-mm 60-cal. 2M-8 AA (II × 2)—2/SA-N-5 Grail SAM launchers (IV × 2)—2/81-mm mortars (I × 2)
Electron Equipt:
Radar: 1/SPS-21 nav., 1/SPS-29 air-search, 1/Mk 26 f.c.
M: 4 Fairbanks-Morse 38D8⅛ x 10 diesels; 2 props; 6,080 bhp
Electric: 600 kw **Range:** 20,000/10 **Fuel:** 26 tons
Crew: approx. 200 tot.

Remarks: Transferred to South Vietnam in 1971, having served in the U.S. Coast Guard since 1948. Was equipped with 2 SS-N-2A Styx missiles removed from a stricken Komar-class missile boat during the late 1970s.

CORVETTES

◆ **5 ex-Soviet Petya-II (Project 159A) and -III (Project 159AE) class**

HQ 09 HQ 11 HQ 13 HQ 15 HQ 17

Petya-III of the Vietnamese Navy—on delivery voyage U.S. Navy, 1982

CORVETTES *(continued)*

D: 950 tons (1,150 fl) **S:** 30 kts **Dim:** 82.3 × 9.1 × 3.2
A: 4/76.2-mm 59-cal. AK-276 DP (II × 2)—3/533-mm or 5/400-mm TT (III or V × 1)—4/RBU-2500 or 2/RBU-6000 ASW RL (XVI × 4 or XII × 2)—2/d.c. racks—mines
Electron Equipt:
Radar: 1/Don-2 nav., 1/Strut Curve air-search, 1/Hawk Screech f.c.
Sonar: hull-mounted MF search/HF attack
EW: 2/Watch Dog intercept
M: CODAG: 2 gas turbines, 15,000 shp each; 1 Type 61-V3 diesel, 6,000 bhp; 3 props
Range: 4,000/10 (diesel); 500/30 (CODAG) **Crew:** 80–90 tot.

Remarks: HQ 09 and HQ 11 are Petya-III export models transferred 12-78. Other three are standard Petya-IIs with 2/RBU-6000 ASW RL and 5/400-mm ASW TT (V × 1): two transferred 1-83, one transferred 12-84.

♦ ex-U.S. Admirable-class former fleet minesweeper
Bldr: Gulf SB, Chickasaw, Louisiana

	Laid down	L	In serv.
HQ 07 . . . . . .(ex-*Ha Hoi*, ex-*Prowess*, IX 305, ex-MSF 280)	15-9-43	17-2-44	27-9-44

D: 650 tons (945 fl) **S:** 14.8 kts **Dim:** 56.2 (54.9 wl) × 10.1 × 3.0
A: 2/57-mm DP (II × 1)—2/37-mm 63-cal. AA (I × 2)—6/23-mm AA (II × 3)
Electron Equipt: Radar: 1/. . . nav.
M: 2 Cooper-Bessemer GSB-8 diesels; 1,710 bhp **Electric:** 280 kw
Range: . . ./. . . **Fuel:** 138 tons **Crew:** approx. 80 tot.

Remarks: Transferred to South Vietnam 6-70. All minesweeping gear removed before transfer, and antisubmarine warfare gear removed during overhauls in early 1970s. Rearmed with Soviet or Chinese weapons. Sister HQ 05 (ex-*Ky Hoa*, ex-*Sentry*, MSF 299) has been stricken.

GUIDED-MISSILE PATROL BOATS

♦ 8 Soviet Osa-II (Project 205M) class
HQ 384 HQ 385 HQ 386—5 others

D: 215 tons (245 fl) **S:** 35 kts **Dim:** 38.6 × 7.6 × 2.0
A: 4/SS-N-2B P-15 Styx SSM (I × 4)—4/30-mm 65-cal. AK-230 AA (II × 2)
Electron Equipt:
Radar: 1/Square Tie surf.-search/target designation, 1/Drum Tilt gun f.c.
IFF: 2/Square Head interrogators, 1/High Pole B transponder
M: 3 M504 diesels; 3 props; 15,000 bhp **Range:** 500/34; 750/25
Crew: 30 tot.

Remarks: Transferred: two in 10-79, two in 9-80, two in 11-80, and two in 2-81. Assuming that they are in operable status, these are the most formidable combatants in Vietnamese service.

TORPEDO BOATS

♦ 16 Soviet Shershen class
HQ 301 through HQ 316

Vietnamese Shershen—with torpedo tubes, under tow to Vietnam
U.S. Navy, 9-79

D: 145 tons (170 fl) **S:** 44 kts **Dim:** 36.0 × 7.8 × 1.6
A: 4/30-mm 65-cal. AK-230 AA (II × 2)—4/533-mm TT—2/d.c. racks (12 d.c.)
Electron Equipt:
Radar: 1/Pot Drum surf.-search, 1/Drum Tilt gun f.c.
IFF: 1–2/Square Head interrogators, 1/High Pole A transponder
M: 3 M503A diesels; 2 props; 12,000 bhp
Range: 460/42; 850/30 **Crew:** 22 tot.

Remarks: Transferred: two (without torpedo tubes) on 16-4-79, two on 12-9-79, two in 8-80, two in 10-80, two in 1981, and four in 6-83. Probably most now in marginal operating condition.

PATROL BOATS

♦ 5 Soviet Turya-class (Project 206) semi-hydrofoils
Bldr: Vladivostokskiy Sudostroitel'nyy Zavod (Ulis), Vladivostok

D: 210 tons (245 fl) **S:** 40 kts
Dim: 39.0 × 7.6 (12.5 over foils) × 2.0 (4.0 over foils)
A: 2/57-mm Ak-257 DP aft (II × 1)—2/25-mm 60-cal. 2M-8 AA fwd (II × 1)
Electron Equipt:
Radar: 1/Pot Drum surf. search, 1/Muff Cob gun f.c.
IFF: 1/Square Head interrogator, 1/High Pole B transponder
M: 3 M504 diesels; 3 props; 15,000 bhp
Range: 400/38; 650/25 **Crew:** 24 tot.

Remarks: One transferred 5-84, the second in 11-84, and two in 1986. Had no t[illegible] tubes nor the standard helicopter-type dipping sonar.

♦ 15 Soviet Zhuk class (Project 199)

D: 48 tons (60 fl) **S:** 34 kts **Dim:** 24.0 × 5.0 × 1.2
A: 4/14.5-mm AA (II × 2)
Electron Equipt: Radar: 1/Spin Trough nav.
M: 2 M50F diesels; 2 props; 2,400 bhp
Range: 700/28, 1,100/15 **Crew:** 12 tot.

Remarks: Transferred: three in 1978, three in 11-80, one in 11-81, one in 5-85 in 1986, two in 12-89, and two in 1990.

Note: All former U.S. PGM 59 and PGM 71-class patrol boats are believed t[illegible] been stricken by 1992 as have been the eight Chinese Shanghai-II-class gu[illegible] transferred 1966–68.

♦ 4 ex-Soviet S.O.-I class (Project 201) submarine chasers

D: 190 tons (215 fl) **S:** 28 kts **Dim:** 42.0 × 6.1 × 1.9
A: 4/25-mm 60-cal. 2M-8 AA (II × 2)—4/RBU-1200 ASW RL (V × 4)—2/d.c. racks (24 d.c.)—mines
Electron Equipt:
Radar: 1/Pot Head surf. search
Sonar: Tamir-11 HF searchlight-type
M: 3 Type 40D diesels; 3 props; 7,500 bhp
Range: 1,100/13 **Crew:** 30 tot.

Remarks: Survivors of eight transferred: two in 3-80, two in 9-80, two in 5-81, a[illegible] in 9-83. An earlier increment transferred in 1960–66 have all been discarded poor sea-boats and very noisy in operation. ASW capability minimal, due to hand-turned searchlight sonar and maximum sonar operating speed of 10 kts.

PATROL CRAFT

♦ 2 ex-Soviet PO 2 class

D: 50 tons (fl) **S:** 9 kts **Dim:** 21.0 × 4.5 × . . .
A: 1/12.7-mm mg
M: 1 6D12 diesel; 1 prop; 150 bhp

Remarks: Transferred 2-80. Utility craft also usable as a tug or, with appro[illegible] equipment, a diving tender. Two near-sister Nyryat 2-class diving tenders wer[illegible] transferred.

♦ 2 ex-East German Bremse class

D: 25 tons **S:** 14 kts **Dim:** 23.13 (20.97 pp) × 4.58 × 1.50
A: . . . **Electron Equipt:** Radar: 1/TSR-333 nav.
M: 1 Type 6VD 18/15 diesel; 1 prop; 496 bhp

Remarks: Transferred late 1970s. Intended for patrol in sheltered waters and [illegible] waterways.

Note: All remaining U.S. Swift Mk-I and Mk-II-class inshore patrol craft are be[illegible] to have been discarded by 1992. Some 107 had been captured in 1975.

RIVERINE WARFARE CRAFT

♦ . . . ex-U.S. PBR (Patrol Boat, Riverine) Mk-II class
Bldr: Uniflite, Bellingham, Washington (In serv. 1968–70)

D: 6.7 tons light (8 fl) **S:** 24 kts **Dim:** 9.73 × 3.53 × 0.6
A: 3/12.7-mm mg (II × 1, I × 1)—1/60-mm mortar
M: 2 G.M. 6V53N diesels; 2 Jacuzzi waterjets; 430 bhp
Range: 150/23 **Crew:** 4 tot.

Remarks: A few survivors of the over 290 captured in 1975 probably remain in u[illegible] inland waterways.

Note: Due to their age and the lack of spare parts, the up to nine ex-U.S. command boats, up to sixty ex-U.S. ASPB assault support patrol boats, up to fort[illegible] ex-U.S. Monitor Mk-V river monitors, up to twenty-two ex-U.S. converted L[illegible] river monitors, and up to sixty ex-U.S. ATC Armored Troop Carriers have been de[illegible] from this edition.

MINE WARFARE SHIPS AND CRAFT

♦ 2 ex-Soviet Yurka-class (Project 266) fleet minesweepers
HQ 851 HQ 885

D: 400 tons (460 fl) **S:** 16 kts **Dim:** 52.0 × 9.3 × 2.0
A: 4/30-mm 65-cal. AK-230 AA (II × 2)—20 mines

WARFARE SHIPS AND CRAFT *(continued)*

tron Equipt:
dar: 1/Don-2 nav., 1/Drum Tilt f.c.
F: 3/Square Head interrogators, 1/High Pole B transponder
2 diesels; 2 props; 4,000 bhp **Range:** 3,200/10 **Crew:** 45 tot.

ks: Both transferred 12-79. Aluminum alloy hulls.

onya-class (Project 1265) coastal minesweepers

350 tons (400 fl) **S:** 15 kts **Dim:** 48.5 × 7.3 × 1.9
2/30-mm 65-cal. AK-230 AA (II × 1)—2/25-mm 60-cal. 2M-8 AA
II × 1)
tron Equipt:
dar: 1/Spin Trough nav.–
F: 2/Square Head interrogators, 1/High Pole B transponder
2 diesels; 2 props; 2,400 bhp
ge: 1,600/14; 3,000/10 **Crew:** 40 tot.

ks: First delivered 16-2-87, second in 2-88, third in 7-89, and fourth in 3-90.

oviet Yevgenya-class (Project 1258) inshore minesweepers
r: Sudostroitel'noye Obyedineniye "Almaz" (Sredniy Neva), Kolpino

30 tons (90 fl) **S:** 11 kts **Dim:** 26.2 × 6.1 × 1.5
2/14.5-mm mg (II × 1)
tron Equipt: Radar: 1/Spin Trough nav.
2 diesels; 2 props; 660 bhp **Range:** 300/10 **Crew:** 10 tot.

ks: Delivered to Cam Ranh Bay 11-84. Glass-reinforced-plastic hull. Employ a on minehunting system that dispenses marker buoys to permit later disposal of ıes; useful to 30-m depths. Can carry and support two or three mine clearance

x-Soviet K-8-class (Project 361T) minesweeping boats

26 tons (fl) **S:** 12 kts **Dim:** 16.9 × 3.2 × 0.8
2/14.5-mm mg (II × 1) **M:** 2 3D6 diesels; 2 props; 300 bhp
ctric: 80 kw **Range:** 300/9 **Crew:** 6 tot.

ks: Transferred 10-80. Wooden construction; built in Poland in the late 1950s. ar.

HIBIOUS WARFARE SHIPS

x-Soviet Polnocny-B class (Project 771) medium landing ips Bldr: Stocznia Północna, Gdańsk, Poland

11 HQ 512 HQ 513

740 tons normal (800 fl) **S:** 18 kts
n: 74.0 × 8.9 × 1.2 fwd/2.4 aft
2/30-mm 65-cal. AK-230 AA (II × 1)—2/140-mm barrage RL (XVIII × 2)
ctron Equipt:
adar: 1/Spin Trough nav.
FF: 1/Square Head interrogator, 1/High Pole-B transponder
2 Type 40D diesels; 2 props; 5,000 bhp
nge: 900/18; 1,500/14 **Crew:** 404 tot. + 60 troops

rks: Transferred: one in 5-79, one in 11-79, and one in 2-80. Have a bow door Iull has a pronounced "beak" at bow to aid in beaching. Hatches to upper deck are ıtilation only. Can carry up to 180 tons of vehicles (five PT-76 light amphibious is a typical load).

ex-U.S. LST 1- and LST 542-class tank landing ships Bldrs: Q 502: Jeffersonville Building and Mach., Indiana; HQ 503: Chicago Bridge & n, Seneca, Illinois; HQ 506: Bethlehem SY, Hingham, Massachusetts

	Laid down	L	In serv.
02 Qui Nhon (ex-*Bullock County*, T 509)	7-10-43	23-11-43	8-1-44
03 Vung Tau (ex-*Coconino* ınty, LST 603)	10-12-43	15-4-44	15-5-44
06 ex-Da Nang (ex-*Maricopa* ınty, LST 938)	12-7-44	15-8-44	9-9-44

1,623 tons light (4,080 fl) **S:** 11.6 kts
n: 99.98 × 15.24 × 4.29 **A:** 4/37-mm 63-cal. AA (I × 4)
ctron Equipt: Radar: 1/. . . nav.
2 G.M. 12-567A (ex-HQ 501: G.M. 12-278A) diesels; 2 props; 1,700 bhp
ctric: 300 kw **Range:** 6,000/9 (loaded) **Fuel:** 590 tons
ew: approx. 100 tot.

rks: Transferred to South Vietnam 7-62, 7-69, and 4-70, respectively. All be- to be operational; have been rearmed with Soviet-supplied weapons.

p to 4 ex-U.S. LCU 1466-class utility landing craft

367 tons (fl) **S:** 8 kts **Dim:** 35.14 × 10.36 × 1.5
4/20-mm AA (II × 2)
3 Gray Marine 64YTL diesels; 3 props; 675 bhp
nge: 1,200/6 **Fuel:** 11 tons **Crew:** 14 tot.

rks: Transferred 1954–70 (ex-YFU 90 in 7-71). Cargo: 167 tons. About ten have stricken. Captured in 1975 were: LCU 1475, 1479, 1480, 1481, 1484, 1485, 1493, 1494, 1498, 1501, 1502, 1594, 1595, and YFU 90 (ex-LCU 1582). Cargo: 150 tons or 300 troops on 15.8 × 9.0-m deck, with a 4.3-m-wide bow ramp.

Note: Eighty-four U.S. LCM(6), thirty-eight LCM(8), forty LCVP, and several LCP-type landing craft were also abandoned to North Vietnam in 1975; some have probably been returned to service.

◆ **12 ex-Soviet T4-class landing craft**

D: 35 tons (93 fl) **S:** 10 kts **Dim:** 19.9 × 5.6 × 1.4
M: 2 3D6 diesels; 2 props; 600 bhp **Range:** 6,500/10

Remarks: Transferred 1979 and later.

AUXILIARIES AND SERVICE CRAFT

Note: Among the ships and craft listed below are all of the U.S. Navy service craft left behind in 1975; many of these may have been stricken or turned over to civilian agencies. Also in use may be a number of the small coastal cargo craft built during the Vietnam War for infiltration of military cargoes to Viet Cong forces in South Vietnam.

◆ **1 ex-Soviet Kamenka-class hydrographic survey ship/buoy tender** Bldr: Stocznia Północna, Gdańsk, Poland

D: 703 tons (fl) **S:** 13.7 kts **Dim:** 53.5 × 9.1 × 2.6
Electron Equipt: Radar: 1/Don-2 nav.
M: 2 diesels; 2 CP props; 1,765 bhp **Range:** 4,000/10 **Crew:** 40 tot.

Remarks: Transferred 12-79. One 5-ton buoy crane. Primary function is navigational aids tending; does not carry a hydrographic survey launch.

◆ **1 ex-Soviet Neptun-class mooring buoy tender**
Bldr: Neptunwerft, Rostock, Germany (In serv. 1957–60)

D: 700 tons light (1,240 fl) **S:** 12 kts
Dim: 57.3 (46.5 pp) × 11.4 × 3.4
M: 2 sets triple-expansion reciprocating steam; 2 props; 1,000 ihp
Boilers: 2, Scotch-type **Range:** 1,000/11 **Crew:** 41 tot.

Remarks: Transferred post-1975 to handle moorings at Haiphong. Has a fixed 80-ton lift crane at the bow to handle mooring buoys. May not be naval-subordinated.

◆ **2 ex-U.S. 174-foot-class gasoline tankers** Bldr: George Lawley & Sons, Neponset, Massachusetts (ex-YOG 56: R.T.C. SB, Camden, New Jersey)

	Laid down	L	In serv.
ex-HQ 472 (ex-YOG 67)	26-1-45	17-3-45	4-5-45
ex-HQ 475 (ex-YOG 56)	17-5-44	30-9-44	19-2-45

D: 440 tons light (1,390 fl) **S:** 11 kts
Dim: 53.04 (51.2 pp) × 9.75 × 3.94 **A:** 2/20-mm AA (I × 2)
M: 1 G.M. diesel (ex-YOG 56: Union diesel); 1 prop; 640 bhp (ex-YOG 56: 540 bhp)
Electric: 80 kw **Fuel:** 25 tons **Cargo:** 860 tons **Crew:** 23 tot.

Remarks: Transferred to South Vietnam in 7-67 and 6-72, respectively. Employed in transporting diesel fuel. Remain in service as coastal tankers. Sister ex-HQ 473 (ex-YOG 71) is believed to have been cannibalized to maintain the other two.

◆ **2 Soviet Poluchat-I-class torpedo retrievers**

D: 90 tons (fl) **S:** 18 kts **Dim:** 29.6 × 6.1 × 1.9
A: 2/14.5-mm AA (II × 1)
Electron Equipt: Radar: 1/Spin Trough nav.
M: 2 M50-F4 diesels; 2 props; 2,400 bhp
Range: 450/17; 900/10 **Crew:** 20 tot.

Remarks: Transferred 1-90. Can also be employed as patrol boats. Have ramp at stern and crane for recovering exercise torpedoes.

◆ **2 Russian Nyryat-2 class diving tenders**

D: 50 tons (fl) **S:** 9 kts **Dim:** 21.0 × 4.5 × . . .
Electron Equipt: Radar: 1/Spin Trough nav. or none
M: 1 Type 3D6 diesel; 1 prop; 150 bhp **Crew:** 10 tot. including divers

Remarks: Built during the 1950s. Transferred post-1975. Essentially similar to the PO 2 class patrol craft, except that the hull has bulwarks and there is a small derrick to handle the divers.

◆ **up to 3 ex-U.S. Cholocco-class medium harbor tugs**
Bldr: Commercial Iron Wks., Portland, Oregon

	In serv.
ex-HQ 9550 (ex-*Poknoket*, YTM 762, ex-YTB 517)	25-1-46
ex-HQ 9551 (ex-*Hombro*, YTM 769, ex-YTB 508)	7-7-45
ex-HQ 9552 (ex-*Nootka*, YTM 771, ex-YTB 506)	8-11-45

D: 260 tons (350 fl) **S:** 11 kts **Dim:** 30.8 × 8.5 × 3.7
M: 2 Enterprise diesels; 1 prop; 1,270 bhp **Crew:** 8 tot.

Remarks: Reclassified YTM from YTB in 1966; transferred to South Vietnam 1971.

◆ **up to 9 ex-U.S. YTL-type small harbor tugs**

ex-YTL 152	ex-YTL 245	ex-YTL 456
ex-YTL 200	ex-YTL 423	ex-YTL 457
ex-YTL 206	ex-YTL 452	ex-YTL 586

D: 70 tons (80 fl) **S:** 10 kts **Dim:** 20.16 × 5.18 × 2.44
M: 1 Hoover-Owens-Rentschler diesel; 1 prop; 300 bhp
Electric: 40 kw **Fuel:** 7 tons **Crew:** 4 tot.

Remarks: Built 1941–45. Four transferred to South Vietnam in 1955–56, two in

VIETNAM *(continued)*
AUXILIARIES AND SERVICE CRAFT *(continued)*

1969, and two in 1971. Quite possibly, any survivors have been turned over to civilian agencies.

◆ **up to 2 ex-U.S. Navy repair barges (non-self-propelled)**

ex-HQ 9601 (ex-YR 24)   ex-HQ 9611 (ex-YR 71)

D: 520 tons light (770 fl) **Dim:** 46.6 × 10.7 × 1.8

◆ **up to 4 ex-U.S. Navy repair, berthing, and messing barges (non-self-propelled)**

ex-HQ 9610 (ex-YRBM 17)   ex-HQ 9613 (ex-YRBM 21)
ex-HQ 9612 (ex-YRBM 16)   ex-HQ-. . . (ex-YRBM 18)

D: 236 tons (310 fl) **Dim:** 34.1 × 11.0 × 0.9

Remarks: Completed 1964–65. Ex-HQ 9613 is 498 tons (585 fl); 44.5 × 14.0 × 0.9 and was completed in 1970.

◆ **up to 2 ex-U.S. Navy barracks craft (non-self-propelled)**

ex-HQ 9050 (ex-APL 26)   ex-HQ 9051 (ex-APL 27)

D: 1,300 tons (2,580 fl) **Dim:** 79.6 × 15.0 × 2.6

Remarks: Completed 1944–45.

◆ **up to 2 ex-U.S. Navy large covered lighters**

ex-YFNB 18   ex-YFNB 28

D: 700 tons (2,700 fl) **Dim:** 79.6 × 14.6 × 4.0

Remarks: Ex-HQ numbers not available. Transferred 1971. Cargo: 2,000 tons.

◆ **up to 8 ex-U.S. Navy open lighters**

ex-YC 791, 797, 806, 807, 1108, 1320, 1414, 1415

Remarks: Ex-YC 791, 1108, and 1320 displace 190 tons light/690 fl, others are 130 tons light/630 fl (33.5 × 9.8 × 2.4). Transferred around 1971.

◆ **up to 2 ex-U.S. Navy floating cranes**

ex-HQ 9650 (ex-YD 230)   ex-HQ 9651 (ex-YD 195)

◆ **up to 2 ex-U.S. floating dry docks** (In serv. 1944)

ex-HQ 9600 (ex-AFDL 13)   ex-HQ 9604 (ex-AFDL 22)

Remarks: Ex-HQ 9600 has a capacity of 1,000 tons and is 61.0 × 19.5. Ex-HQ 9604 has a capacity of 1,900 tons and is 87.8 × 19.5. Both were left behind in 1975.

Note: Also available are two Russian floating drydocks transferred during the 1980s for commercial employment.

◆ **up to 1 ex-U.S. water barge (non-self-propelled)**

ex-HQ 9113 (ex-YWN 153)

D: 220 tons (1,270 fl) **Dim:** 36.6 × 10.1 × 2.4 **Cargo:** 1,050 tons

Note: In addition to the ships and craft listed above, the Vietnamese Navy undoubtedly employs many smaller craft ("junks") in patrol and logistics duties.

VIRGIN ISLANDS

British Virgin Islands

ROYAL VIRGIN ISLANDS POLICE FORCE

◆ **1 M 140-class patrol craft**   Bldr: Halmatic, Hamble, U.K.

URSULA (In serv. 4-7-88)

D: 17.3 tons (fl) **S:** 27+ knots
Dim: 15.40 (12.20 pp) × 3.86 × 1.15
A: 1/76.2-mm mg **Electron Equipt:** Radar: 1/Decca 370BT nav.
M: 2 G.M. 6V92 TA diesels; 2 props; 1,100 bhp (770 sust.)
Range: 300/20 **Fuel:** 2,700 liters **Crew:** 6 tot.

Remarks: Provided by U.K. government; sisters in several other Caribbean island countries. Glass-reinforced-plastic construction. Has davits aft for inflatable inspection boat.

Ursula   Halmatic, 19

◆ **2 Model SR5M "Sea Rider" dinghies**
Bldr: Avon, U.K. (In serv. 1986)

Remarks: Semi-rigid inflatables with 70-bhp Evinrude outboards; replaced two "S Eagle" craft delivered 1980.

WESTERN SAMOA

Independent State of Western Samoa

PATROL BOAT

◆ **1 Australian ASI 315 class**
Bldr: Australian SB Industries, South Coogie, Western Australia

	Laid down	L	In serv.
NAFANUA	20-5-87	18-2-88	19-3-88

Nafanua   Leo Van Ginderen,

D: 165 tons (fl) **S:** 20 kts **Dim:** 31.5 (28.6 wl) × 8.1 × 2.12
A: small arms **Electron Equipt:** Radar: 1/Furuno 1011 nav.
M: 2 Caterpillar 3516 diesels; 2 props; 2,820 bhp **Electric:** 116 k
Range: 2,500/12 **Fuel:** 29 tons **Crew:** 3 officers, 14 enlisted

Remarks: Provided under the Australian Defense Cooperation Program. O 3-10-85. Sisters built for other Southwest Pacific nations. A second unit is pla Extensive navigational suite, including Furuno FSN-70 NAVSAT receive HF/DF, 120 MH/HF/DF, FE-881 echo-sounder, and DS-70 doppler log.

◆ **1 utility landing craft**   Bldr: Yokohama Yacht, Japan (L: 28-7-88)

LADY SAMOA II

Remarks: No details available; government-owned craft for local cargo and per transport.

EMEN

Arab Republic

The formerly separate states of the People's Democratic Republic of Yemen Yemen) and the Yemen Arab Republic (North Yemen) united on 22-5-90 as the Arab Republic. Their defense forces have also been united. A large number of an naval units defected to Yemeni ports in the spring of 1991; their return to the of the new Ethiopian government was arranged during 6-92.

nel (1992): Approximately 2,000 total, plus 250 naval port police and 500 ıfantry.

ED MISSILE PATROL BOATS

'arantul-I class (Project 1241.1) Bldr: Volodarskiy SY, Rybinsk

ı serv. 7-12-90) 976 (In serv. 15-1-91)

en route Yemen U.S. Navy, 11-90

385 tons light (455 fl) **S:** 43 kts
: 56.10 (49.50 pp) × 10.20 (9.40 wl) × 2.14 hull (4.0 props)
4/SS-N-2C SSM (II × 2)—1/76.2-mm 59-cal. AK-176 DP—1/SA-N-3 SAM syst. (IV × 1, 12 Gremlin missiles)—2/30-mm AK-630 gatling AA (I × 2)
ctron Equipt:
adar: 1/Kivach-3 nav., 1/Plank Shave (Harpun-E) surf.-search/targeting, 1/Bass Tilt (Koral-E/MR 123) gun f.c.
W: 2/RK-16 decoy RL (XVI × 2)
'F: 1/High Pole transponder, 1/Square Head interrogator
M-15E COGAG plant: 2 DMR-76 cruise gas turbines (4,000 shp each), 2 PR-77 boost gas turbines (12,000 shp each); 2 props; 32,000 shp max.
ctric: 500 kw tot. (2 × 200 kw, 1 × 100 kw diesel sets)
ıge: 760/43; 1,400/13 **Fuel:** 122,634 liters
lurance: 10 days **Crew:** 7 officers, 32 enlisted

rks: Standard export versions; "in service" dates above are the dates of deliv-ainless-steel alloy, seven watertight compartment hull with aluminum alloy tructure, decks, and internal bulkheads. Very strongly-constructed and rugged. lifficulty maneuvering below 10 kts. Weapons system employs digital computers ıs many backup features. Normally carry two infrared-homing and two radar-g missiles. The 76.2-mm gun has a crew of three and a local control system with 'ht-level night sight. Carry 252 ready-service rounds and another 150 in reserve 76.2-mm gun.

ı to 6 Soviet Osa-II (Project 205M) class

117 118 119 120 121

eni Osa-II 122—lost 1-86 A. Zioko, 11-85

D: 215 tons (245 fl) **S:** 35 kts **Dim:** 38.6 × 7.6 × 2.0
A: 4/SS-N-2B P-15 Styx SSM (I × 4)—4/30-mm 65-cal. AK-230 AA (II × 2)
Electron Equipt:
Radar: 1/Square Tie surf.-search/target designation, 1/Drum Tilt gun f.c.
IFF: 2/Square Head interrogators, 1/High Pole B transponder
M: 3 M504 diesels; 3 props; 15,000 bhp
Range: 500/34; 750/25 **Crew:** 30 tot.

Remarks: Transferred: two in 2-79 to 4-79, three in 1-80, one in 12-80, one in 2-83, one in 9-83. Two (122, 123) were lost during the 1986 coup. Two Osa-IIs delivered to the former Yemen Arab Republic (North Yemen) on 20-5-82 were returned to the U.S.S.R. in 1986. The remaining units are in poor condition, and not all may be considered operational. Former People's Democratic Republic of Yemen assets.

PATROL BOATS

◆ 3 Broadsword class Bldr: Halter Marine, New Orleans, Louisiana (In serv. 1978)

141 25 SEPTEMBER 142 RAMADAN (ex-*13th June*) 143 SANA'A

Ramadan (142)—old number 1981

D: 90 tons (fl) **S:** 28 kts **Dim:** 32.0 × 6.3 × 1.9
A: 2/23-mm AA (II × 1)—2/14.5-mm mg (II × 1)—2/12.7 mm mg (I × 2)
Electron Equipt: Radar: 1/Decca 914 nav.
M: 3 G.M. 16V71 TI diesels; 3 props; 1,400 bhp **Electric:** 120 kw
Fuel: 16.3 tons **Crew:** 14 tot.

Remarks: Ordered 1977. Armament, added after delivery, is of Soviet origin. Former North Yemeni assets. In poor condition but are still operational.

PATROL CRAFT

◆ 5 Soviet Zhuk class (Project 199)

400 500 600 700 800

Yemeni Zhuk—former North Yemeni unit 1981

D: 48 tons (60 fl) **S:** 34 kts **Dim:** 24.6 × 5.2 × 1.2
A: 4/14.5-mm mg (II × 2) **Electron Equipt:** Radar: 1/Spin Trough
M: 2/M50F diesels; 2 props; 2,400 bhp
Range: 700/28; 1,100/15 **Crew:** 12 tot.

Remarks: Two transferred to former Yemen Arab Republic (North Yemen) in 12-84, and three in 1-87; two transferred to People's Democratic Republic of Yemen (South Yemen) in 2-75. The five survivors are believed to be the former North Yemeni boats

PATROL CRAFT *(continued)*

Unlike some other units of this class, have their twin machine guns in enclosed gun houses with hemispherical covers.

MINE COUNTERMEASURES SHIPS AND CRAFT

◆ 1 Natya-I-class (Project 266M) minesweeper

Bldr: Sudostroitel'noye Obyedineniye "Almaz" (Sredniy Neva), Kolpino

641

D: 780 tons (880 fl) **S:** 17 kts **Dim:** 61.0 (57.6 wl) × 10.2 × 3.3 hull
A: 2/30-mm AK-630 gatling AA (I × 2)—2/SA-N-8 SAM syst (IV × 2, 16 Gremlin missiles)—2/RBU-1200 ASW RL (V × 2)—mines
Electron Equipt:
Radar: 1-2/Don-2 nav.—Sonar: HF hull-mounted
IFF: 1/High Pole-B transponder, 2/Square Head interrogators
M: 2 diesels: 2 props; 5,000 bhp
Range: 1,800/16; 5,200/10 **Crew:** 8 officers, 70 enlisted

Remarks: Delivered 3-91; a sister, bearing pendant 634, was delivered to Ethiopia in 1991 and defected to Yemen shortly thereafter; the ship was to be returned to Ethiopia in 7-92. Both are units of a new variant with single 30-mm AK-630 gatling guns substituted for the twin 30-mm AK-230 mounts, but without 25-mm guns, Drum Tilt fire control radar, or net trawl facilities when completed; two others were transferred from the Baltic to the Russian Pacific Ocean Fleet in 1991.

Equipped also to serve as ASW escorts, with the RBU-1200 rocket launchers also used for detonating mines. Sweep gear includes SEMP-3 magnetic and MPT-3 mechanical arrays. Low magnetic signature, aluminum-steel alloy hull. Stem cut back sharply below waterline, as in T-43 and Yurka classes.

Note: An ex-Soviet Sonya-class coastal minesweeper delivered 1-91 to Ethiopia defected to Yemen in the spring of 1991 but was returned in mid-1992.

◆ 5 Soviet Yevgenya (Project 1258) class inshore minehunter/sweepers

Bldr: Sudostroitel'noye Obyedineniye "Almaz" (Sredniy Neva), Kolpino

11 12 15 + 2 others

D: 80 tons (90 fl) **S:** 11 kts **Dim:** 26.2 × 6.1 × 1.5
A: 2/14.5 or 25-mm 60-cal. 2M-8 AA (II × 1)
Electron Equipt: Radar: 1/Spin Trough nav.
M: 2 diesels; 2 props; 600 bhp **Range:** 300/10 **Crew:** 10 tot.

Remarks: First two delivered to North Yemen 5-82, third in 11-87. The People's Democratic Republic of Yemen (South Yemen) received two in 12-89. Glass-reinforced-plastic construction. Export Yevgenyas normally have a twin 25-mm AA mount; uncertain in this instance. Have television minehunting system that dispenses marker buoys for later mine disposal; useful to 30-m depth. Can also carry two to three mine clearance divers.

AMPHIBIOUS WARFARE SHIPS AND CRAFT

◆ 1 Ropucha-class (Project 775) tank landing ship

Bldr: Stocznia Północna, Gdańsk, Poland (In serv. 1979)

139

Yemeni Ropucha 139 8-81

D: 3,500 tons normal (4,080 fl) **S:** 17.8 kts
Dim: 112.70 × 15.00 × 4.00 (aft)
A: 4/57-mm 70-cal. AK-257 DP (II × 2)
Electron Equipt:
Radar: 2/Don-2 nav., 1/Strut Curve surf./air search, 1/Muff Cob gun f.c.
IFF: 1/High Pole-B or Salt Pot-B transponder, interrogation by radar
M: 2 diesels; 2 props; 10,000 bhp **Range:** 3,500/16
Crew: 7 officers, 64 enlisted + 190 troops

Remarks: Delivered new in 1979, refitted 1984–86 at Vladivostok. Bow and stern doors permit roll-on/roll-off loading. Cargo capacity: 450 tons; usable deck space: 600 m^2. The hull has a moulded depth of 8.60 m amidships and is equipped with a "beak" bow projection to aid in beaching. There are both bow and stern doors. No vehicle cargo is carried on the upper deck, the hatch serving for loading by crane and for ventilation when vehicle motors are running.

◆ 2 ex-Soviet Polnocny-B (Project 771)-class medium landing ships

Bldr: Stocznia Północna, Gadańsk, Poland

136 Al Wadi'a 137 Siri

Siri (137) Leo Van Gindere[n]

D: 740 tons normal (800 fl) **S:** 18 kts
Dim: 74.0 × 8.9 × 1.2 fwd/2.4 aft
A: 2/30-mm 65-cal. AK-230 AA (II × 1)—2/140-mm barrage RL (XVIII × 2)
Electron Equipt:
Radar: 1/Spin Trough nav.
IFF: 1/Square Head interrogator, 1/High Pole-B transponder
M: 2 Type 40D diesels; 2 props; 5,000 bhp
Range: 900/18; 1,500/14 **Crew:** 404 tot. + 60 troops

Remarks: Both delivered 8-73; a third (138) was delivered 7-77 and lost to fire [...] Previously reported fourth unit was in fact the Ropucha described above. Hav[e] [...] door. Hull has a pronounced "beak" at bow to aid in beaching. Hatches to upper d[eck] for ventilation only. Can carry up to 180 tons of vehicles.

◆ 2 Soviet Ondatra (Project 1176)-class landing craft

13 14

D: 90 tons (140 fl) **S:** 10 kts **Dim:** 24.2 × 6.0 × 1.5
A: none **M:** 2 diesels; 2 props; 600 bhp **Crew:** 4 tot.

Remarks: Transferred to North Yemen in 1-83. Cargo well 13.5 × 4.0 m; bow [...]

◆ 2 ex-Soviet T-4-class landing craft

134 135

D: 35 tons light (93 fl) **S:** 10 kts (light)
Dim: 19.9 × 5.6 × 1.4 max. aft
M: 2 Type 3D6 diesels; 2 props; 300 bhp
Range: 1,500/10 **Crew:** 3–4 tot.

Remarks: Transferred to People's Democratic Republic of Yemen in 1982; thre[e] transferred in 11-70 have been discarded, as had two sisters delivered to the Arab Republic around 1970.

SERVICE CRAFT

◆ 2 Toplivo-2 coastal tankers

135 140

D: 466 tons (1,180 tons fl) **S:** 10 kts
Dim: 54.26 (49.40 pp) × 7.40 × 3.10
Electron Equipt: Radar: 1/Spin Trough nav.
M: 1 Russkiy Dizel 6 DR30/50-5-2 diesel; 1 prop; 600 bhp
Electric: 250 kw **Fuel:** 19 tons **Range:** 1,500/10 **Crew:** 24

Remarks: 308 grt/508 dwt. Delivered early 1980s; may have been built in Eg[ypt] [...] U.S.S.R. Four cargo tanks, totaling 606 m^3. 135 reportedly is equipped as a [...] tanker and 140 as a fuel tanker. Fully seagoing if required.

◆ 1 Spear class C-in-C's yacht

Bldr: Fairey Marine, Cowes, U.K.

D: 4.5 tons (fl) **S:** 26 kts **Dim:** 9.1 × 2.8 × 0.8
A: 3/7.62-mm mg (I × 3)
Electron Equipt: Radar: 1/Decca . . . nav.
M: 2 Perkins diesels; 2 props; 290 bhp **Crew:** 4 tot.

Remarks: Delivered in 1978. Glass-reinforced-plastic construction. Two sister[s] [...] the Customs Service.

Note: Former Soviet Navy Oskol-class repair ship PM 28, which had arrived a[t] [...] in 1988, returned to Russia late in 1991 and was not part of the Yemeni navy.

CUSTOMS SERVICE

Note: The craft described below were attached to the People's Democratic Rep[ublic of] Yemen Ministry of the Interior Customs Service and based at Aden prior to unifi[cation.] Current subordination unknown.

◆ 1 Tracker-2-class patrol craft

Bldr: Fairey Marine, Cowes, U.K.

1034

D: 31 tons (fl) **S:** 29 kts **Dim:** 19.25 × 4.98 × 1.45

.EN *(continued)*
TOMS SERVICE *(continued)*

1/20-mm Oerlikon AA
ɛctron Equipt: Radar: 1/Decca . . . nav.
2 MTU 8V331 TC diesels; 2 props; 2,200 bhp
nge: 650/25 **Crew:** 11 tot.

ırks: Ordered 8-77; delivered 1977–78. Four sisters lost during 1-86 coup. Glass-ɾced-plastic construction.

Spear class Bldr: Fairey Marine, Cowes, U.K.

4.5 tons (fl) **S:** 26 kts **Dim:** 9.1 × 2.8 × 0.8
3/7.62-mm mg (I × 3)
ɛctron Equipt: Radar: 1/Decca . . . nav.
2 Perkins diesels; 2 props; 290 bhp **Crew:** 4 tot.

ırks: Three delivered 30-9-75; fourth delivered in 1978 serves the navy. One lost Glass-reinforced-plastic construction.

'UGOSLAVIA

ral Republic of Yugoslavia

With the breakup of Yugoslavia in 1991, three separate navies were established formerly constituent republics. That of Slovenia reportedly consists of only two patrol craft. The Croatian Navy (*Hrvatska Ratna Mornarica*) was created during , initially with several hundred former Yugoslav Navy personnel and a fleet bed as one gunboat, two missile boats, one torpedo boat, two patrol boats, one t boat, three cargo ships, three tugs, and seven miscellaneous craft. The Croatian is described in the addenda.

ile Yugoslavia retained most of the fleet's afloat assets and all of its aircraft, the uilding industry is concentrated largely in Croatia and Slovenia, boding ill for construction. The Yugoslav Federation consists of the republics of Serbia and ɘnegro, with only the latter having a seacoast.

ɔnnel (1992): 1,200 officers, 6,800 enlisted

l Aviation: Helicopters: One squadron of twelve Ka-25 Hormone ASW, five Helix-A ASW, six Mi-14 PL Haze-A ASW, up to twenty Mi-8 Hip utility. Fixed two DHC-2 Beaver utility, four CL-215 firefighting/SAR.

Yugoslav Air Force has a "Naval Cooperation Regiment" with fifteen to twenty Jastreb and RT-33 reconnaissance aircraft, eighteen to twenty-four MiG-21 rs, eighteen Jastreb and Orao B light attack aircraft, and several SA-341 tte-III helicopters.

t Defense: In 1-86 Swedish RBS-15 antiship missiles were ordered to begin cement of the existing SSC-3 Styx missiles.

MARINES (P = *Podmornica*)

: The reported *Lora*-class submarine program at Split did not produce an actual arine prior to the breakup of Yugoslavia.

Sava-class submarines Bldr: Brodosplit, Split, Croatia

	Laid down	L	In serv.
1 Sava	1975	1977	1978
2 Drava	1977	1982	1982

va (P 832) *Front*, 1-83

770 tons (surf.)/964 tons (sub.)
10 kts (surf.)/16 kts (sub.) **Dim:** 55.8 × 7.2 × 5.5
6/533-mm TT (10 total Soviet Type 53 or Swedish TP 61 wire-guided torpedoes or 20 mines)
ectron Equipt:
Radar: Soviet Snoop Plate—EW: Stop Light intercept
Sonar: Krupp-Atlas PRS-3 suite
: 2 Sulzer diesels (1,600 bhp each), 2 generators (1,000 kw each), 1 electric motor; 1 prop; 1,560 shp
ıdurance: 28 days **Crew:** 27 tot.

arks: Maximum diving depth: 300 meters. Resemble the *Heroj* class, but are ler. Carry a mixture of Soviet and Western European equipment. Attached to the Brigade.

◆ **3 Heroj class**
Bldr: Uljanik SY, Pula, Croatia (P 822: Brodosplit, Split, Croatia)

	Laid down	L	In serv.
P 821 Heroj	1964	1967	1968
P 822 Junak	1966	1968	1969
P 823 Uskok	1968	1-70	1970

Junak (P 822)—with Stop Light intercept array raised 1984

Uskok (P 823) 1984

D: 1,068 tons std. 1,170 tons (surf.)/1,350 tons (sub.)
S: 10 kts (surf.)/16 kts (sub.) **Dim:** 64.0 × 7.2 × 5.0
A: 6/533-mm TT fwd. (10 total Soviet Type 53 torpedoes or 20 mines)
Electron Equipt:
Radar: . . .—Sonar: Krupp-Atlas PRS-3 suite
EW: Stop Light intercept
M: 2 Sulzer diesels (1,600 bhp each), 2 generators (1,000 kw each), 1 electric motor; 1 prop; 1,560 shp
Range: 9,700/8 (surf.); 4,100/10 (snorkel) **Crew:** 36 tot.

Remarks: *Heroj* (821) reported stricken 1982 after an accident; cannot be confirmed; the ship, however, was operational in 1986. Designed and built with Soviet assistance. Attached to the 88th Brigade.

MIDGET SUBMARINES (*Diverzantska Podmornica*)

◆ **6 Una (M-100D) class** Bldr: Brodosplit, Split, Croatia

911 Tisa (In serv. 1981)
912 Una (In serv. 1983)
913 Zeta (In serv. 5-85)
914 Soca (In serv. 1986)
915 Kupa (In serv. 1988)
916 Vardar (In serv. 1989)

D: 76 tons (surf.)/88 tons (sub.) **S:** 8.0 kts (surf.)/11.0 kts (sub.)
Dim: 18.8 × 3.0 × 2.5

Una (912) Siegfried Breyer Collection

MIDGET SUBMARINES *(continued)*

A: 6 mines or 4 R1 swimmer-delivery vehicles, externally carried
M: electric only: two 18-kw motors; 1 5-bladed prop
Electronic Equipt:
Radar: none—Sonar: Krupp-Atlas PP-10 active, PSU 1-2 passive
Range: 250/. . . **Crew:** 4 crew + 6 swimmers

Remarks: Have no on-board generators; power is supplied by two shore-charged 128-cell, 1,450 amp./hr (5-hour rate) batteries, and maximum service depth is 100 m. Theoretically capable of remaining submerged for 96 hours. The R1 swimmer-delivery vehicles each weigh 145 kg, are 3.7 m long by 0.52 m diameter, and have a range of 12 n.m. at 3 kts.

◆ 4 or more Type R2, Mala-class swimmer-delivery vehicles
Bldr: Brodosplit, Split, Croatia

Mala (R2) class 1984

D: 1.4 tons **S:** 4.4 kts **Dim:** 4.90 × 1.22 × 1.32 (1.70 fins)
A: 2/50-kg mines **M:** 1 electric motor; 1 prop; 6 hp
Range: 18/4.4; 23/3.7 **Crew:** 2 tot.

Remarks: Diving depth: 60 m. Free-flooding personnel space enclosed within clear-plastic dome. Sweden has acquired one, and six were sold to Libya; the U.S.S.R. may also have received examples.

Note: Also available are a number of R1 "chariot"-type swimmer delivery vehicles with a length of 3.72 m, a beam of 1.05 m and a surfaced draft of 0.80 m; the craft have a range of 6 n.m. at 3 kts and can dive to 60 m. Three personnel can be carried astride the craft.

FRIGATES (VPB—*Veliki Patrolni Brod*—Large Patrol Ship)

◆ 2 Kotor class

	Bldr	Laid down	L	In ser
VPB 33 Kotor	Uljanic SY, Pula, Croatia	1981	29-5-84	1-8
VPB 34 Pula	Tito SY, Kraljevica, Croatia	. . .	1986	198

Kotor (VPB 33) Yugoslav Navy,

D: 1,850 tons (fl) **S:** 27 kts
Dim: 96.7 (92.0 wl) × 11.2 × 3.55 (5.80 over sonar)
A: 4/SS-N-2C Styx SSM (I × 4)—1/SA-N-4 SAM syst. (II × 1; 20 Gecko missiles)—2/76.2-mm 59-cal. AK-276 DP (II × 1)—4/30-mm 65-cal. AK-230 AA (II × 2)—2/RBU-6000 ASW RL (VII × 2)—6/324-mm ILAS-3 ASW TT (III × 2)
Electron Equipt:
Radar: 1/Palm Frond nav., 1/Strut Curve surf./air-search, 1/Pop Group SAM f.c., 1/BEAB 9LV200 for 76.2-mm guns, 1/Dr Tilt f.c. for 30-mm guns
Sonar: hull-mounted MF search and HF attack
EW: 2 intercept arrays, 2 Wallops Barricade decoy RL (XVIII ×
M: CODAG: 2 SEMT-Pielstick 12 PA6V280 diesels (4,800 bhp each Soviet gas turbine (19,000 shp); 3 props (CP outboard); 28,600 s
Electric: 1,350 kw **Crew:** approx. 90 tot.

Remarks: Design is Yugoslavian and is definitely *not* a modification of the some similar Koni class, which has a different hull form and layout. The main-propu diesels were ordered in 6-80 (two to be built under license in Yugoslavia), and th was delivered 31-3-81; the propulsion concept duplicates the arrangement in the class.

◆ 2 Soviet Koni (Project 1159) class
Bldr: Zelenodolsk SY, Russia

VPB 31 . . . (ex-*Split*) (In serv. 4-80)
VPB 32 Zagreb (ex-*Koper*) (In serv. 19-2-83)

D: 1,440 tons light (1,596 tons normal, approx. 1,900 fl) **S:** 30 kts
Dim: 96.40 × 12.55 × 3.48 (4.70 over sonar)
A: 4/SS-N-2C Styx SSM (I × 4)—1/SA-N-4 SAM syst. (II × 1, 20 Gecko missiles)—4/76.2-mm 59-cal. AK-276 DP (II × 2)—4/30-mm 65-cal. AK-230 AA (II × 2)—2/RBU-6000 ASW RL (XII × 2)—2/d.c. racks (24 d.c.)—20 mines

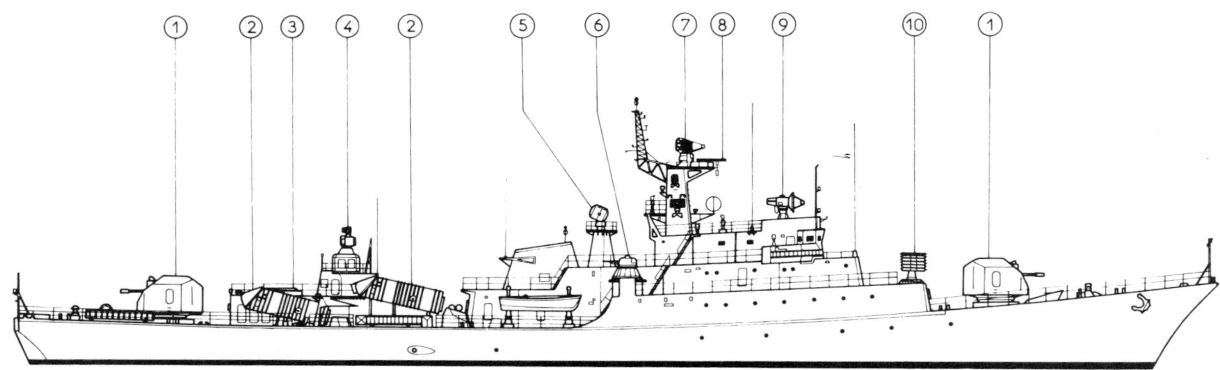

Yugoslav Navy Koni class 1. twin AK-276 76.2-mm DP 2. SS-N-2C Styx SSM launchers 3. launcher/magazine for SA-N-4 SAM system 4. Pop Group radar director for SA-N-4 system 5. Drum Tilt radar director for AK-230 AA guns 6. twin 30-mm AK-230 AA 7. Strut Curve air/surface-search radar 8. Don-2 navigational radar 9. Hawk Screech radar director for 76.2-mm guns 10. 2 RBU-6000 12-tubed ASW rocket launchers Drawing by Louis Gassier

ATES (continued)

plit (VPB 31) 1983

ctron Equipt:
adar: 1/Don-2 nav., 1/Strut Curve surf./air-search, 1/Pop Group SAM f.c., 1/Hawk Screech 76.2-mm gun f.c., 1/Drum Tilt 30-mm gun f.c.
onar: hull-mounted MF search, hull-mounted HF attack
W: 2/Watch Dog intercept, 2/RK-16 decoy RL (XVI × 2)
CODAG: 1 M8G gas turbine (19,000 shp), 2 Type 68B diesels (8,000 bhp each); 3 props (CP outboard); 35,000 hp max.
nge: 1,800/14 **Crew:** 110 tot.

rks: *Koper* arrived in Yugoslavia on 5-12-83. *Koper* received Styx missiles 1984–85; they were added to *Split* during 1982. Have fin stabilizers. The ails can only be used to carry mines when the depth-charge racks are unbolted moved. Sisters in the Algerian, Bulgarian, Cuban, and Libyan navies. VPB was ed by Croatian gunfire 15-11-91 but has been repaired. Both were renamed

ED-MISSILE PATROL BOATS (RT = *Raketna Topovnjača*)

The incorporation of Kraljevica in the new Croatian Republic brought the Type Kobra") missile boat program under Croatian control; the first unit, *King Petar nir IV*, was completed during 4-92.

Rade Končar (Type 240) class Bldr: Tito SY, Kraljevica, Croatia

	L	In serv.
01 Rade Končar	15-10-76	4-77
03 Ramiz Sadiku	1978	10-9-78
04 Hasan Zahirovič Lasa	1979	11-79
05 Jordan Nikolov-Orce	1979	8-79
06 Ante Banina	1979	11-80

e Končar (RT 401)—prior to re-arming 1977

242 tons (fl) **S:** 39 kts (37 sust.)
m: 45.00 × 8.00 × 1.80 (2.50 props)
2/SS-N-2B Styx SSM—2/57-mm 70-cal. Bofors SAK 57 Mk 1 DP (I × 2)— RT 401 only: 1/57-mm Bofors DP—1/30-mm AK-630 gatling AA
ectron Equipt:
Radar: 1/Decca 1226 nav.—1/9LV200 Mk II target detection/f.c. system
EW: 2/Wallops Barricade decoy RL (XVIII × 2)
IFF: 1/Square Head interrogator, 1/High Pole-B transponder
: CODAG: 2 Rolls-Royce Proteus gas turbines (4,500 shp each); 2 MTU 20V538 TB92 diesels (3,600 bhp each); 4 CP props; 16,200 hp max.
lectric: 300 kVA **Range:** 880/23; 1,650/15
ndurance: 7 days **Crew:** 5 officers, 10 petty officers, 15 enlisted

arks: Of Yugoslav design, using Swedish fire control and guns and Soviet mis- Styx missiles chosen over the Exocet originally planned for economic reasons.

Rade Končar (RT 401)—30-mm gun mount on extended deckhouse has replaced the after 57-mm gun 1977

Steel hull, aluminum superstructure. Have NBC warfare protection. In RT 401 and RT 402 (*Vlado Ćetović*, which is under Croatian control), the after 57-mm mount was removed and replaced with a Soviet-supplied 30-mm gatling gun to improve anti-missile defenses; the gatling gun, however, is controlled only by a Kolonka-II ringsight director mounted in a cupola just abaft the mast.

◆ **9 ex-Soviet Osa-I (Project 205) class** (RC = *Raketni Čamac*)

RČ 301 Mitar Acev
RČ 302 Vlado Bagat
RČ 303 Petar Drapšin
RČ 304 Steven Filipovič
RČ 305 Velimir Škorpik
RČ 306 Nikola Martinovič
RČ 307 Josip Mazar
RČ 308 Karlo Rojc
RČ 309 Franc Rozman-Stane

Mitar Acev (RČ 301)

D: 175 tons (209 fl) **S:** 35 kts **Dim:** 38.6 × 7.6 × 1.8
A: 4/SS-N-2 Styx SSM—4/30-mm 65-cal AK-230 AA (II × 2)
Electron Equipt:
Radar: 1/Square Tie target detection/surf. search, 1/Drum Tilt gun f.c.
IFF: 2/Square Head interrogators, 1/High Pole-B transponder
M: 3 M503A diesels; 3 props; 12,000 bhp
Range: 500/34; 750/25 **Crew:** 25 tot.

Remarks: Transferred 1965–69. Reported to be showing their age. Can be operated at 220 tons full load, with 11 tons extra fuel. Sister *Zikaca Jovanovič-Španac* (RČ 310) is under Croatian control.

TORPEDO BOATS (TC = *Torpedni Čamac*)

◆ **11 Soviet Shershen class** Bldrs: 4 in U.S.S.R.; others: Tito SY, Kraljevica, Croatia (In serv. 1966–71)

TČ 211 Pionir
TČ 212 Partizan
TČ 214 Topčider
TČ 215 Ivan
TČ 216 Jadran
TČ 217 Kornat
TČ 218 Biokovac
TČ 220 Crvena Zvijezda
TČ 221 Strilko
TČ 223 Napredak
TČ 224 Pionir III

D: 145 tons (170 fl) **S:** 44 kts **Dim:** 36.0 × 7.8 × 1.6 (hull)
A: 4/30-mm 65-cal. AK-230 AA (II × 2)—4/533-mm TT—mines

Strilko (TČ 221) 1980

TORPEDO BOATS *(continued)*

Electron Equipt:
Radar: 1/Pot Drum surf.-search, 1/Drum Tilt gun f.c.
IFF: 1/Square Head interrogator, 1/High Pole-B transponder
M: 3 M503A diesels; 3 props; 12,000 bhp
Range: 460/42; 850/30 **Crew:** 22 tot.

Remarks: Ten built in Yugoslavia under license, after four were transferred in 1965. Unlike Soviet units, have no depth-charge racks. Sister *Sloga* (TČ 219) stricken 1988, *Proleter* (TČ 213) in 1989. *Partizan-II* (TČ 222) is under Croatian control.

PATROL BOATS (PBR = *Patrolni Brod*; PC = *Patrolni Čamac*)

♦ **2 Mornar class** Bldr: Tito SY, Kraljevica, Croatia

	Laid down	L	In serv.
PBR 551 Mornar	1957	1958	10-9-59
PBR 552 Borac	1964	1965	1965

Mornar (PBR 551) Eric Grove, 10-90

D: 330 tons (430 fl) **S:** 20 kts **Dim:** 51.8 × 6.97 × 3.1 (2.0 hull)
A: 2/40-mm 70-cal. Bofors AA (I × 2)—2/20-mm Hispano-Suiza AA (I × 2)— 4/RBU-1200 ASW RL (V × 4)—2/Mk 6 d.c. projectors—2/Mk 9 d.c. racks
Electron Equipt:
Radar: 1/. . . nav.—EW: 2/Wallops Barricade decoy RL (XVIII × 2)
Sonar: 1/Tamir-11 hull-mounted HF searchlight
M: 4 SEMT-Pielstick PA1 175 diesels; 3 props; 3,240 bhp
Range: 2,000/15; 3,000/12 **Fuel:** 55 tons **Crew:** 60 tot.

Remarks: Modernized and re-engined 1970–73 at Sava Kovacevic Naval Yard, Tivat. Original two 76.2-mm DP guns, two older-model 40-mm AA, and Mousetrap ASW rocket launchers replaced by new Bofors guns and Soviet ASW rocket launchers. Original three 2,500 bhp diesels replaced by four French-built engines.

♦ **9 Mirna (Type 140) class**
Bldr: Tito SY, Kraljevica, Croatia (In serv. 1981–82)

PČ 171 Biokovo	PČ 174 Učka	PČ 177 Frusk-gora
PČ 172 Phorse	PČ 175 Crmec	PČ 178 Kosmaju
PČ 173 Koprivnik	PČ 176 Mukos	PČ 179 Kozul

Biokovo (PČ 171) Yugoslav Navy, 1987

D: 120 tons (. . . fl) **S:** 30 kts
Dim: 32.00 × 6.68 × 1.60 (2.30 max.)
A: 1/40-mm 70-cal. Bofors L70 AA—1/20-mm M71 AA—8/Type MDB-MT3 d.c.
Electron Equipt: Radar: 1/. . . nav.—Sonar: hull-mounted HF
M: 2 SEMT-Pielstick 12 PA4 200GDS diesels; 2 props; 6,000 bhp—electric motors for low speeds (6 kts)
Range: 400/20 **Crew:** 3 officers, 4 petty officers, 12 enlisted

Remarks: The first ten propulsion diesels were ordered in 1979 for license production in Yugoslavia. Endurance at 20 kts can be increased to 530 n.m. in emergencies. Peacetime endurance is four days; wartime: eight days. Have 4-rail chaff launcher amidships. There are four chaff or illumination rocket rails on the sides of the 40-mm AA. PC 176 was damaged by gunfire by Croatian forces on 15-11-91 but ha[s been] repaired. Sisters *Zelengora* (PČ 180) and *Cer* (PČ 181) are in Croatian hands.

Note: Although units of the Type 90 class (described as the Type 80 class [in the] previous edition) have been exported to a number of foreign countries, the desi[gn does] not appear to have entered Yugoslav service.

♦ **7 Type 131 coastal patrol craft** Bldr: Trogir SY (In serv. 1965–

PČ 132 Kalnik	PČ 135 Grudnik	PČ 137 Kamenar
PČ 133 Velebit	PČ 136 Romanija	PČ 140 Kozuf
PČ 134 Grandičar		

Grudnik (PČ 135)

D: 85 tons (120 fl) **S:** 22 kts **Dim:** 32.0 × 5.5 × 2.5
A: 6/20-mm Hispano Suiza HS831 AA (III × 2)
Electron Equipt: Radar: 1/Kelvin-Hughes 14/9 nav.
M: 2 MTU MB820 Db diesels; 2 props; 1,600 bhp

Remarks: Sisters *Cer* (PC 138) and *Durmitor* transferred to Malta 31-3-82. S[ome] others have been scrapped.

PATROL CRAFT

♦ **6 Type 20 coastal and riverine** (In serv. 1984–. . .)
PČ 211–PČ 216

PČ 215 Yugoslav Navy

D: 55 tons (fl) **S:** 16 kts **Dim:** 21.78 (20.06 wl) × 5.29 × 1.20
A: 2/20-mm M71 AA (I × 2)—mines
Electron Equipt: Radar: 1/Decca 110 nav.
M: 2 diesels; 2 props; 1,156 bhp **Range:** 200/15 **Crew:** 10 tot.

Remarks: Steel hull, glass-reinforced-plastic superstructure.

♦ **. . . Type 18 coastal and riverine** (In serv. 1984–. . .)

Type 18 patrol craft

:OL CRAFT *(continued)*

:9 tons (fl) **S:** 20 kts **Dim:** 18.70 × 3.60 × 0.90 mean
:/20-mm M71 AA (I × 2)—9/7.62-mm mg (I × 9)
·tron Equipt: Radar: 1/Decca 110
2 diesels; 2 props; 752 bhp **Range:** 480/17
·w: 9 crew + 40 troops

·ks: Intended for patrol, troop transport, and logistic support duties, with up to
of cargo.

'ype 16 riverine
1 PČ 302 PČ 303 PČ 304 PČ 306

16 (Botica class) patrol craft 1984

23 tons (fl) **S:** 15 kts **Dim:** 17.00 × 3.60 × 0.85 mean
1/20-mm M71 AA—7/7.62-mm light mg (I × 7)
ctron Equipt: Radar: 1/Decca 110 nav.
2 diesels; 2 props; 464 bhp **Range:** 340/15
w: 7 crew + 30 troops or combat swimmers

·ks: Intended for patrol, troop transport, and logistic support duties, with up to
of cargo. NATO class name is "Botica." PC 305 was transferred to Tanzania.

Type 15-class riverine and lake
-1 through PČ 15-12

5-5 and two sisters 1984

19.5 tons (fl) **S:** 16 kts **Dim:** 16.87 × 3.90 × 0.65 (0.70 props)
1/20-mm M71 AA—2/7.62-mm mg (I × 2)
ctron Equipt: Radar: 1/Decca 110 nav.
2 diesels; 2 props; 330 bhp **Range:** 160/12 **Crew:** 6 tot.

·ks: Steel hulls, glass-reinforced-plastic superstructures. Four sisters delivered
Sudan, 5-89.

MINE WARFARE SHIPS (M = *Minolovac*)

◆ **4 French Sirius-class coastal minesweepers/minehunters**
Bldrs: M 161: Mali Losinj SY, Yugoslavia; others: A. Normand, Le Havre, France

	In serv.
M 151 VUKOV KLANAC (ex-*Hrabri*, ex-MSC 229)	9-57
M 152 PODGORA (ex-*Smeli*, ex-MSC 230)	9-57
M 153 BLITVENICA (ex-*Slobodni*, ex-MSC 231)	9-57
M 161 GRADAC (ex-*Snazhi*)	1960

Vukov Klanac (M 151) Eric Grove, 10-90

D: 400 tons (440 fl) **S:** 15 kts (sweeping: 11.5)
Dim: 46.4 (42.7 pp) × 8.55 × 2.5 **A:** 2/20-mm Oerlikon AA (II × 2)
Electron Equipt:
Radar: 1/DRBN-30 nav.—Sonar: Plessey 193M—*see* Remarks
M: 2 SEMT-Pielstick 16 PA1-175 diesels; 2 props; 2,000 bhp
Electric: 375 kw **Range:** 3,000/10 **Fuel:** 48 tons **Crew:** 40 tot.

Remarks: First three built with U.S. Offshore Procurement funds. Wooden-planked hulls on metal framing. Equipped with Plessey 193M minehunting sonar, French PAP-104 remote-controlled minehunting/disposal submersibles, and Decca Hifix precision navigation systems, commencing 1981. Two sets Thomson-Sintra TSM 2022 minehunting sonars were delivered 1988 further to update two of these ships, M 151 and M 153. M 151 was extensively damaged during 11-91 and may not have been repaired.

◆ **4 British "Ham"-class inshore minesweepers**
Bldr: Yugoslavia (In serv. 1964–66)

M 141 MILSET (ex-MSI 98) — M 143 IŽ (ex-MSI 100)
M 142 BRSEC (ex-MSI 99) — M 144 OLIB (ex-MSI 101)

D: 123 tons (164 fl) **S:** 14 kts **Dim:** 32.43 × 6.45 × 1.7
A: 1/40-mm 60-cal. Bofors AA
Electron Equipt: Radar: 1/Decca 45 nav.
M: 2 Paxman YHAXM diesels; 2 props; 1,100 bhp
Range: 1,500/12; 2,000/9 **Fuel:** 15 tons **Crew:** 22 tot.

Remarks: Built under U.S. Offshore Procurement Program. Composite construction: wooden planking over a metal-framed hull.

◆ **7 Nestin-class (Type 50) river minesweepers**
Bldr: Brodotehnika, Belgrade (In serv. 1976–80)

	L		L
RML 331 NESTIN	20-12-75	RML 335 VUČEDOL	1979
RML 332 MOTAJICA	18-12-76	RML 336 DJERDAP	1980
RML 333 BELEGIS	1-77	RML 337 PANONSKO MORE	1980
RML 334 BOSUT	1978		

Nestin (RML 331) 1978

MINE WARFARE SHIPS *(continued)*

D: 68 tons (78 fl) **S:** 12 kts **Dim:** 27.00 × 6.50 × 1.05 (1.15 max.)
A: 5/20-mm AA (III × 1, I × 2)—24 small mines
Electron Equipt: Radar: 1/Decca 101 nav.
M: 2 Torpedo diesels; 2 props; 520 bhp
Range: 864/10.8 **Crew:** 17 tot.

Remarks: RML = *Recni Minolovac.* M 331 launched 20-12-75, M 332 launched 18-12-76, and M 333 launched 1-77. Hull of light metal alloy. Sweep gear includes type PEAM magnetic and acoustic sweep, Type AEL-1 explosive sweep, and Types MDL-1 and MDL-2 mechanical sweeps. Two illumination chaff rocket launchers are fitted. Used on the Danube. Three also built for Iraq and six for Hungary.

AMPHIBIOUS WARFARE SHIPS

Note: The Type PO, *Lubin*-class multipurpose transports can also be used as landing ships.

◆ **1 Silba class tank landing craft/minelayer**
Bldr: Brodosplit, Split, Croatia (In serv. 1990)

DBM 241 SILBA

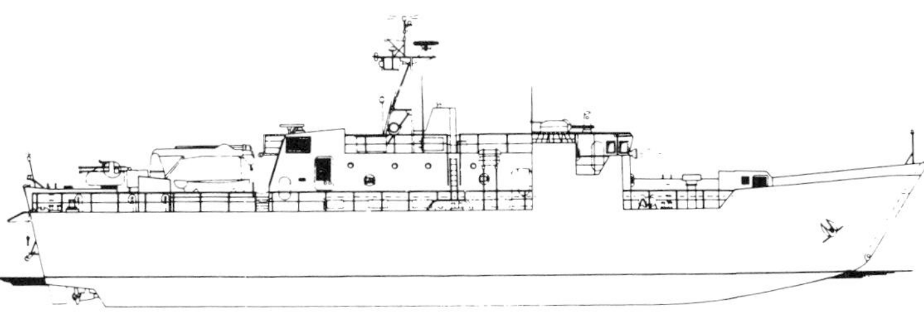

Silba class 1990

D: 880 tons (fl) **S:** 12 kts
Dim: 49.00 (43.90 pp) × 10.20 × 2.60 max.
A: 4/30-mm 65-cal. AK-230 AA (II × 2)—4/20-mm M75 AA (IV × 1)—1/SA-7 Strela SAM launcher (IV × 1)—94 mines
Electron Equipt: Radar: 1/Decca . . . nav.
M: 2 diesels; 2 CP props; 3,100 bhp
Range: 1,200/12 **Crew:** 3 officers, 30 enlisted + up to 300 troops

Remarks: Has bow and stern ramps, with continuous covered vehicle deck also used for portable minerails. Cargo capacity: 460 tons or four medium tanks or up to seven armored personnel carriers. Has two 128-mm rocket flare launchers. The 30-mm gunmounts are mounted port and starboard, just abaft the bridge, while the 20-mm mount is located near the stern. "Silba" is the NATO nickname. A second ship of the class was launched for Croatia on 18-7-92.

◆ **13 DTM 211-class landing craft/minelayers**
Bldr: Yugoslavia (In serv. 1950s)

DTK 213, 215, 219, 221, 223, 226, 228, 229, 232, 233, 234, 237, GOLOR

DTK 213 Leo Van Ginderen, 6-84

D: 240 tons (410 fl) **S:** 10.3 kts **Dim:** 49.8 × 8.6 × 1.6 (2.1 max.)
A: 3/20-mm Hispano-Suiza AA (III × 1)
M: 3 Gray Marine 64HN9 diesels; 3 props; 625 bhp
Range: 500/9.3 **Crew:** 27 tot.

Remarks: DTM= *Desantni Tenkonosac/Minopolagac.* Near-duplicates of the World War II German MFP-D class. Nearly all have been equipped with 1-m-wide hull sponsons, extending beam to 8.6 meters and providing space for two mine rails with a total capacity of up to 100 small mines. Bow ramp. Can carry 140 tons of vehicles or 200 troops. Ten additional units have been discarded. Unit now named *Golor* is probably considered an auxiliary. DTM 217, named *Jastreb,* is in Croatian hands.

◆ **4 RTK 401 class** (In serv. 1950s)

D: 227 tons (350 fl) **S:** 10.3 kts **Dim:** 46.5 × 6.5 × 1.3 (max.)
A: 5/20-mm AA (III × 1, I × 2)—2/mortars
M: 3 Gray Marine 64HN9 diesels; 3 props; 678 bhp **Range:** 500/9

Remarks: RTK = *Recni Tenkonosac* (River Tank Landing Craft). Similar to the DTM 211 class; used on the Danube River. No mine sponsons.

◆ **9 DJČ 623-class (Type 22) landing craft**
Bldr: Gleben SY, Vela Luka, Korcula (In serv. 1986–87)

DJČ 623 DJČ 625 to DJČ 632

DJČ 627—planing at speed Yugoslav Nav

D: 48 tons (fl) **S:** 35 kts **Dim:** 22.30 × 4.84 × 1.07 (1.58 props
A: 2/20-mm M71 AA (I × 2)
Electron Equipt: Radar: 1/Decca 101 nav.
M: 2 diesels; 2 waterjets; 1,740 bhp
Range: 320/22 **Crew:** 6 tot. + 40 troops

Remarks: DJČ = *Desantni Jurisni Čamac.* Additional power permits the plane, greatly increasing speed over the Type 21 design. Glass-reinforced-plas struction. Bow ramp. Can carry vehicles totalling 15 tons in 32-m² cargo area DJC 624 is in Croatian hands, and three others may be as well.

◆ **22 DJČ 601-class (Type 21) landing craft** Bldr: Gleben SY, V Luka, Korcula (In serv. 1976–77)

DJČ 601 to DJČ 622

D: 32 tons (fl) **S:** 23.5 kts **Dim:** 21.20 × 4.84 × 1.07 (1.58 prop
A: 1/20-mm M71 AA **Electron Equipt:** Radar: 1/Decca 101 n
M: 1 MTU 12V331 TC81 diesels; 1 prop; 1,450 bhp
Range: 320/22 **Crew:** 6 tot. + 40 troops

Remarks: DJČ = *Desantni Jurisni Čamac.* Glass-reinforced-plastic const Bow ramp. Can carry vehicles totaling 6 tons in 32-m² cargo area. Offered fo also.

◆ **15 Type 11 vehicle/personnel landing craft**

Type 11 landing craft

D: 5.5 tons light (11 fl) **S:** 23 kts **Dim:** 11.30 × 3.10 × 0.30
A: 1/7.62-mm mg **Electron Equipt:** Radar: 1/Decca 101 nav.
M: 2 diesels; 2 waterjets *or* 2 outdrives; . . . bhp
Range: 100/15 **Crew:** 2 tot.

Remarks: Glass-reinforced-plastic construction. Can carry two jeeps or a s troops for a total of 4.8 tons.

AUXILIARY SHIPS

Note: Moma-class hydrographic survey ship *Andrija Mohorovičić* (PH *Spasilac*-class salvage and rescue ship *Spasilac* (PS 12) are in Croatian ha 6,151-grt Yugoslav Navy–chartered cargo ship *Sol Phryne* was lost off Vis to a 6-12-91.

◆ **1 cadet-training ship** Bldr: Ansaldo, Genoa (L: 6-3-38)

M 11 GALEB (ex-*Kuchuk,* ex-*Rhamb III*)

Galeb (M 11) Alexandre Sheldon-Duplai

.IARY SHIPS *(continued)*

,182 tons (5,700 fl) **S:** 16 kts
: 121.2 (116.9 pp) × 15.2 × 5.6
/40-mm 60-cal. Bofors AA (I × 4)—8/20-mm M75 AA (IV × 2)
2 Burmeister & Wain diesels; 2 props; 7,200 bhp
ge: 20,000/16 **Crew:** . . .

ks: Begun as a commercial banana carrier; used as an auxiliary cruiser and 'er by the Italian Navy during World War II. Ceded to Yugoslavia after the war. n used as the presidential yacht, but is mostly used as a cadet-training ship and flagship. Formerly referred to as a *Minopolagac* (Minelayer), for which purpose still be usable.

issile-boat tender and command ship
: . . . , Yugoslavia (In serv. 1956)

Vis

10 tons (680 fl) **S:** 17 kts **Dim:** 57.0 × 8.5 × 3.5
/40-mm 60-cal. Bofors AA—2/20-mm Oerlikon AA (I × 2)
2 diesels; 2 props; 1,900 bhp

ks: PB = *Pomočni Brod* (Auxiliary Ship). Resembles a yacht; primarily an strative flagship for the Adriatic Fleet.

psail training schooner
: Blohm + Voss, Hamburg (In serv. 1932)

N

n Yugoslav Navy

720 tons (800 fl) **S:** 14.5 sail/9.5 diesel kts
: 60.0 × 8.8 × 4.2
12 Linke-Hoffman diesel; 375 bhp **Sail area:** 933 m^2

ks: Accommodations for 100 cadets and 20 instructors.

iverine command ship
r: Linzer Schiffswerft, Austria (In serv. 1940)

Kozara (ex-U.S. *Oregon*, ex-German *Brünhild*)

ra (PB 30) Yugoslav Navy, 1982

D: 535 tons (693 fl) **S:** 12.4 kts **Dim:** 67.0 × 9.5 × 1.4
A: 9/20-mm Hispano-Suiza AA (III × 3) **Fuel:** 44 tons
M: 2 Deutz RV6M545 diesels; 2 props; 800 bhp

Remarks: Taken over by U.S. in immediate postwar period, then turned over to Yugoslavia. Used as a floating hotel until 1960, when taken over by the navy. In 1962 recommissioned as flagship of the Danube River Flotilla. Painted blue and white and home-ported at Bosanka Gradiska. A sister, SSV 10, served as the Soviet Danube River Flotilla flagship.

♦ **3 Type PO multipurpose transports**
Bldr: Brodosplit, Split, Croatia (In serv. mid-1980s)

PO 91 Lubin PO 92 Ugor PO 93 Kit

Lubin (PO 91) Brodosplit, 1988

D: 600 tons (860 fl) **S:** 16 kts (sust.)
Dim: 58.20 × 11.00 × 2.75 (mean)
A: 1/40-mm 60-cal. Bofors AA—4/20-mm M75 AA (IV × 1)
Electron Equipt: Radar: 1/. . . nav. **Endurance:** 10 days
M: 2 diesels; 2 CP props; 3,480 bhp **Range:** 1,500/16
Crew: 43 crew + 150 fully equipped troops, 6 vehicle drivers

Remarks: PO = *Pomocni Oruzar* (Ammunition Auxiliary). Intended to supply combatants with missiles, torpedoes, mines, and other ordnance, using two slewing cranes on upper deck. Continuous cargo deck can accommodate up to six tanks; have a visor-type bow and extendable bow ramp, two electrohydraulic cranes. Has a 128-mm M66 illumination rocket launcher.

SERVICE CRAFT

♦ **2 inshore survey craft** (In serv. mid-1980s)

BH 1 BH 2

BH 2 Leo Van Ginderen, 1987

D: 46 tons (fl) **S:** 12 kts **Dim:** 20.50 × 4.50 × 1.42
Electron Equipt: Radar 1/Decca 101 nav.
M: 2 diesels; 2 props; 304 bhp **Range:** 400/12 **Crew:** 10–12 tot.

Remarks: Same basic design as PT 82-series transports.

♦ **1 M 117-class inshore survey craft, former minesweeper** (In serv. 1968)

PH 123 (ex-ML 123)

D: 115 tons (126 fl) **S:** 12 kts **Dim:** 30.0 × 5.5 × 1.4
M: 2 G.M. diesels; 2 props; 1,000 bhp **Crew:** 20 tot.

Remarks: Survivor of a class of six wooden-hulled inshore minesweepers. Sister *Lastovo* (ML 117) may also remain in service as a training craft. Other hydrographic survey craft reported in service include the 70-ton BH 11 and BH 12 and the 4.5-ton CH 1 and CH 2.

SERVICE CRAFT *(continued)*

PH 123 Leo Van Ginderen, 1991

◆ **1 or more diving tenders** (In serv. mid-1980s)

BM 70

BM 70 Eric Grove, 10-90

D: 46 tons (fl) **S:** 12 kts **Dim:** 20.50 × 4.50 × 1.42
A: 2/20-mm M71 AA (I × 2)
Electron Equipt: Radar 1/Decca 101 nav.
M: 2 diesels; 2 props; 304 bhp **Range:** 400/12
Crew: 6 crew + 4 divers

Remarks: Same basic design as PT 82–87-series transports and survey craft BH 2. Guns not always mounted. Has a decompression chamber and is capable of supporting two divers simultaneously. Carries a six-person launch, handled by a .5-ton crane.

◆ **1 riverine degaussing craft** Bldr: Bordotehnika, Belgrade

PB 36 Sabač (In serv. 1985)

Sabač (PB 36)—at launch *Front,* 1985

D: 110 tons (fl) **S:** 10 kts **Dim:** 32.2 × 7.1 × 1.2
A: 2/20-mm M71 AA (I × 2)
Electron Equipt: Radar: 1/Decca 110
M: 1 diesel; 1 prop; 528 bhp **Range:** 660/10 **Crew:** 20 tot.

Remarks: Patrol boat–type hull, with superstructure set well aft. Initially intended to be a command ship, but in fact acts as deperming tender for river craft.

◆ **2 PN 24-class fuel tankers**
Bldr: Split SY, Croatia (In serv. early 1950s)

PN 24 PN 25

D: 300 tons (430 fl) **S:** 7 kts **Dim:** 46.4 × 7.2 × 3.2
M: 1 Burmeister & Wain diesel; 1 prop; 300 bhp

Remarks: PN = *Pomoćni Nafta* (Oil Fuel Auxiliary)

◆ **2 PT 71-class cargo lighters** Bldr: Split SY, Croatia (In serv. 1

PT 71 Medusa PT 72 Jastoc

D: 310 tons (428 fl) **S:** 7 kts **Dim:** 43.1 × 7.2 × 4.85
M: 1 Burmeister & Wain diesel; 1 prop; 300 bhp

Remarks: PT = *Pomoćni Transporter.* Two others, PT 73 and PT 74, ha stricken.

Note: The 3 PT 61-class cargo lighters (PT 64–66) and 2 PO 52-class amm lighters (PO 55, 56) listed in the previous edition are believed to have been scra 1990.

◆ **4 utility transports** (In serv. 1987)

PT 82 PT 83 PT 86 PT 87

D: 43 tons (58 fl) **S:** 12 kts **Dim:** 20.50 × 4.50 × 1.42
A: 2/20-mm M71 AA (I × 2)
Electron Equipt: Radar 1/Decca 101 nav.
M: 2 diesels; 2 props; 304 bhp **Range:** 400/12
Crew: 6 tot. + 70 troops

Remarks: Have 55 m^3 for 15 tons cargo in lieu of the 70 troops. Armamen usually aboard. Generally resemble the survey craft BH 2 and diving tender above, except that there is a low deckhouse forward of the pilothouse. One m been lost to a mine on 25-9-91.

◆ **1 water tanker** Bldr: Split SY, Croatia (In serv. 1950s)

PV 17 Alga

Alga (PV 17) Eric Grove

D: 200 tons (600 fl) **S:** 7.5 kts **Dim:** 44.0 × 7.9 × 3.2
A: 1/40-mm 60-cal. Bofors AA—1/20-mm M71 AA
Electron Equipt: Radar: 1/. . . nav.
M: 1 diesel; 1 prop; 300 bhp **Range:** 1,500/7.5

Remarks: PV = *Pomoćni Vodonosac.* Cargo: 380 tons. Sister *Koral* (PV 16) s during the mid-1980s.

◆ **4 PR 37-class coastal tugs** Bldr: Split SY, Croatia (In serv. 1950

PR 36 Dupin PR 37 Zubatac PR 38 . . . PR 39 . . .

D: 550 tons (fl) **S:** 11 kts **Dim:** 32.0 × 8.0 × 5.0 **M:** diesels

Remarks: PR = *Pomorski Remorker* (Auxiliary Tug). Originally reciprocating propelled; re-engined with diesels. One may be in Croatian hands.

◆ **8 LR 67-class harbor tugs** Bldr: Split SY, Croatia (In serv. 1960

LR 67 LR 68 LR 69 LR 70 LR 71 LR 72 LR 73 LR 74

Remarks: LR = *Lučki Remorker* (Harbor Tug). Some may be civilian-crew several may be in Croatian hands.

AIRE

lic of Zaire

nel (1992): Approx. 900 total, plus 600 Marines

OL BOATS AND CRAFT

hinese Shanghai-II class

22.5 tons (134.8 fl) **S:** 28.5 kts
: 38.78 × 5.41 × 1.49 (1.554 max.)
/37-mm 63-cal. V-47M AA (II × 2)—4/25-mm 60-cal. 2M-8 AA
I × 2)
tron Equipt: Radar: 1/Pot Head nav.
2 M50F-4, 1,200-bhp diesels; 2 Type 1206, 910-bhp diesels; 4 props;
,220 bhp
tric: 39 kw **Range:** 750/16.5
urance: 7 days **Crew:** 36 tot.

ks: Two operable units delivered 2-87. Three others, inoperable, are probably repair; they, and a stricken fourth unit, were delivered 1976–78. Two that had ttomed at Banana and Boma were raised 9-90 but have not been repaired. d for coastal patrol duties at the mouth of the Congo River.

Twenty North Korean TB-11PA riverine patrol craft were ordered 1989 for by end-1990; they never arrived, however, due to Zairian insolvency. The craft have displaced 8 tons, been capable of 35 kts, and been 11.3-m overall; intended ations on the Congo river and on Lake Tanganyika, they were to have been with a single 7.62-mm machine gun.

orth Korean Sin Hung class

5 tons **S:** 40 kts **Dim:** 18.3 × 3.4 × 1.7 (max.)
/14.5-mm mg (II × 2)
2 M50-series diesels; 2 props; 2,400 bhp

ks: Designed to be torpedo boats, but tubes were removed prior to delivery in ay no longer be operable.

atrol craft
Bldr: . . . , the Netherlands (In serv. 1988)

IE

ks: On Lake Tanganyika; no data available.

rcoa class
Bldr: Arcoa SY, France (In serv. 1975–81)

2 tons (fl) **S:** 30 kts **Dim:** 7.68 × 3.04 × 0.80
2 Baudouin diesels; 2 props; 320 bhp

ks: Original twelve ordered in 7-74; fourteen more delivered by 11-80, another delivered 1981. By 1992, only eight survived. For use on lakes and rivers. GRP ction.

x-U.S. Swift Mk-II class
r: Swiftships, Morgan City, Louisiana (In serv. 1971)

IALA P 25 LUADIA P 51 KANITSHA P 62 MBOKO

19.2 tons (fl) **S:** 25 kts **Dim:** 15.64 × 4.14 × 1.07
/12.7-mm mg (II × 1, I × 4)
2 G.M. 12V71N diesels; 2 props; 860 bhp
ge: 400/24 **Crew:** 12 tot.

ks: Based at Kalemie, Lake Tanganyika. Aluminum construction. In poor on despite several attempts at refurbishing with U.S. aid; two others have been n.

Note: There are a number of additional small riverine patrol and logistics support craft.

AUXILIARIES

◆ 1 presidential yacht

KAMANYOLA

Remarks: No data available. Large, lightly armed vessel with helicopter deck aft large enough to accept an AS-332 Super Puma helicopter.

ZIMBABWE

DISTRICT DEVELOPMENT FUND FOR THE ADMINISTRATION AND DEVELOPMENT OF THE SOUTH BANK OF LAKE KARIBA

PATROL CRAFT

◆ 8 type B 79 lake patrol craft
Bldr: S.K.B. Yard, Antwerp, Belgium (In serv. 1986)

KF 590 CHIPO CHEBELGIUM
KF 591 MUDZIMUNDIRINGE
KF 592 CHIROVAMURA
KF 593 VAMASHAYAMOMBE
KF 594 CHAYAMURA VARWERE
KF 595 CHIFAMBISA NYORE
KF 596 CHIORORA MVURA
KF 597 CHIBATANIDZA MATUNHU

Chiorora Mvura (KF 596) Leo Van Ginderen, 6-86

D: . . . tons (fl) **S:** 22–25 kts **Dim:** 11.50 × 3.85 × 0.65
M: 2 Caterpillar 3208 diesels; 2 props; 400 bhp **Crew:** . . .

Remarks: Glass-reinforced-plastic police craft; shipped to Africa 6-86. First five based at Kariba on Lake Kariba, about 300 km west of Harare, others at Binga. Used for patrol, medical assistance, and supply duties.

INDEX OF SHIPS

All ships are indexed by their full names, e.g., Almirante Guillermo Brown.

NAME	Pages

NAME	Pages	NAME	Pages	NAME	Pages	NAME	Pages	NAME	Pages

T

NAME

DDENDA

BANIA

ıll naval tug *Kozmamushi* and Huchuan-class torpedo boat 902 defected to Italy and were not returned.

tor Huchuan-class torpedo boat 902 — Giuseppe Valentini, 5-91

IGOLA

t of the four new Spanish-built patrol boats was laid down during 12-91 by E. N. San Fernando, for delivery during 4-93; the other three will follow at 3-month ls:

04.5 tons (fl) **S:** 25 kts **Dim:** 29.13 × 5.93 × 2.00
/20-mm AA—2/12.7-mm mg
tron Equipt: Radar: 1/. . . nav.
2 Paxman Vega 12-SETCWN diesels; 2 props; 4,144 bhp 3,800 sust.)
tric: 190 kVA **Range:** 800/15 **Crew:** 11 tot.

RGENTINA

0-91, the navy was discussing the ordering of a Spanish *Mar del Norte*–class shment oiler from Bazán, el Ferrol; see under Spanish Navy for characteristics. ited States offered the choice of one or another of the long-decommissioned *Iaumee* (AOT 149) or ex-*Yukon* (AOT 152) early in 1992. Also in 10-91, it was ced that modernization/re-engining of the carrier *Veinticinco de Mayo* would ceed and that the carrier will eventually be sold for scrap; by 5-92, she had been d from the shipyard. Eight Kaman SH-2F helicopters are sought for operation rface combatants. Two SH-3 Sea King helicopters were lost with the sinking of arctic supply ship *Bahia Paraiso* (Q 6) in 1989.
91, the Prefectura Naval acquired the following ship to replace the *Recalada* as ation ship for the Rio Plata:

ilot station ship
r: Astilleros Argentinos Rio de la Plata, San Fernando

. . . . (ex-*Rio Limay*)

approx. 14,000 tons (fl) **S:** 18 kts
ı: 147.61 (138.00 pp) × 20.20 × 8.25
1 ASNE-GMT B750-7L reversing diesel; 1 prop; 10,500 bhp
ıge: 14,000/18 **Fuel:** 1,197 tons **Crew:** . . . tot.

rks: 9,059 grt. Acquired 9-91 to act as Rio Plata pilot station ship in place of the *da* (ex-*Lago Lacar*). Former general cargo ship.

ıing frigates Murature and King — Hartmut Ehlers, 4-92

MEKO 140-class frigate Robinson (F 45)—still fitting out — Hartmut Ehlers, 4-92

AUSTRALIA

The submarine *Oxley* (S 57) was retired 2-92. The number of active submarines will probably be reduced to two during 1994–96 due to a 6-month delay in the refitting of *Onslow* and the probable cancellation for the last refit of *Otama*, which is no longer dive-certified.

The MEKO 200 frigates are to be named *Anzac*, *Arrernte*, *Warumunga*, *Stuart*, *Toowoomba*, *Ballarat*, *Parramatta*, and *Perth*; the names of the second and third commemorate earlier ships named *Arunta* and *Warramunga* but employ the spellings preferred by contemporary Aborigine leaders. The frigate *Melbourne* (F 05) was commissioned 15-2-92 and *Newcastle* (FFG 06) was launched 21-2-92. During 1992, the frigate *Derwent* (DE 49) was placed in maintained layup in Western Australia, and one FFG was to be placed in 6-month rotating layup at Sydney.

Melbourne (F 05)—commissioned 15-2-92 — R.A.N., 5-92

The seven Sea King helicopters are being modified in 1992 to serve as utility and troop transports; the replenishment ship *Success* is having her hangar enlarged to accommodate a Sea King. Initial construction on the first ANZAC frigate began 2-92. Reserve training patrol boat *Adroit* (P 82) stricken for scrap 28-3-92. The support ship *Protector* (ASR 241) is to be based in Western Australia by the end of 1992.

As a replacement for the COOP ("Craft of Opportunity") minesweeper *Salvatore V*, the 27.5-m diving charter and underwater research craft *Flamingo Bay* was commissioned as H.M.A.S. *Gunundaal* on 11-5-92; the craft had been built as a prawn trawler in 1979.

AZERBAIJAN

A small naval force was established late in July 1992 using 16 former Soviet Caspian Sea Flotilla and KGB Maritime Border Guard craft based at Baku. Azerbaijan and Russia had agreed to split half of the available Caspian Sea assets between them, with the division of the other half to be decided later (and some of it to go to Turkmenistan). Although the composition of the force has not been announced, it is likely that Azerbaijan received one or more Stenka-class patrol craft.

BAHRAIN

Four Halmatic 20-meter patrol craft were delivered to the Coast Guard in late-1991 to early-1992; *Dera'a 2* replaced an earlier craft of the same name:

◆ **4 20-meter class** Bldr: Halmatic, Havant, U.K.

DERA'A 2 DERA'A 6 DERA'A 7 DERA'A 8

D: 31.5 tons (fl) **S:** 25 kts **Dim:** 20.1 × 5.3 × 1.5
A: 2/7.62-mm mg (I × 2) **Electron Equipt:** Radar: 1/Decca . . . nav.
M: 2 G. M. 12V71 TA diesels; 2 props; 820 bhp
Range: 500/20 **Crew:** 7 tot.

Remarks: Glass-reinforced-plastic construction.

BELGIUM

Adjutant-class minesweepers *Heist* (M 929) and *Rochefort* (M 930) were stricken 17-2-92. *Herstal*-class inshore minesweepers *Turnhout* (M 474) and *Dinant* (M 484, ex-MSI 96) were stricken 17-3-92. The navy is to be reduced to about 2,500 personnel from its

4,228 total in mid-1992; two of the four frigates are to be placed in reserve, only eleven mine countermeasures ships are to be maintained active, and the new minehunter class will probably be cancelled.

BRAZIL

The submarine *Tamoio* is scheduled to begin sea-trials during 1993. U.S. Guppy III-class submarine *Amazonas* (S 16, ex-*Greenfish*, SS 351) was to be decommissioned during 1992. The frigate *Inhauma* was accepted for service 1-2-92; with the settling of strikes at Verolme, work has continued on the second pair, and *Julio de Noronha* was launched 16-2-92. The first Vosper-design patrol boat, *Grauna* (P 40) was to commission in 4-92. The contract to modernize the *Niteroi*-class frigates may only affect two ships. One of the seven Lynx helicopters was lost at sea during 7-92. The three U.S. LCU 1610-class utility landing craft were decommissioned during 1991 but are being retained active as support craft for shore facilities. The six *Paraibaino*-class inshore survey craft were likewise officially decommissioned but are still retained in use in their original rôle.

Jaceguari (V 31) George R. Schneider, Jr., 2-92

BULGARIA

By mid-1992, only one Romeo-class submarine remained in service, with two others surviving as hulks.

Koni-class frigate Druzki (11)—with U.S.S. Yorktown (CG 48) in background U.S. Navy, 8-91

CANADA

Frigate *Halifax* was at last commissioned on 29-6-92, although at least a year of trials remained until the ship would be combat-ready. Sister *Fredericton* (FFH 337) was laid down 25-4-92. Current completion dates are projected as: *Vancouver* (FFH 331): 12-92; *Ville de Quebec* (FFH 332): 29-3-93; *Toronto* (FFH 333): 29-12-92; *Regina* (FFH 334): 29-12-93; *Calgary* (FFH 335): 29-9-94; *Montreal* (FFH 336): 29-9-93; *Fredericton* (FFH 337): 29-5-94; *Winnepeg* (FFH 338): 29-5-95; *Charlottetown* (FFH 339): 29-9-95, *St. Johns* (FFH 340): 29-3-96; and *Ottawa* (FFH 341): 29-3-96. Note that the order of the names has been changed from that given in the main text.

Ojibwa (SS 72) Dr. Giorgio Arra, 11-91

Winning "Coast Defence Vessel" design Fenco

CHILE

The U.S. *Brooklyn*-class gun cruiser *O'Higgins* (02, ex-*Brooklyn*, CL 40) was s during 1992 and was to be sold for scrap. The unmodified British *Leander*-class *Ariadne* (F 72) was purchased 3-6-92 and renamed *General Banquedano* (PF 0

General Banquedano (PF 09) Maritime Photographi

The Project Taitão patrol boats ordered during 1991 have the following cha istics:

◆ **0 (+ 4) Project Taitão class multi-rôle** Bldr: ASMAR, Talcahu

	Laid down	L	In serv.
P	. . .	. . .	. . .
P	. . .	. . .	. . .
P	. . .	. . .	. . .
P	. . .	. . .	. . .

D: 483 tons (fl) **S:** 15 kts **Dim:** 41.70 (36.30 pp) × 8.50 × 2.80
A: 1/40-mm 60-cal. Bofors Mk. 3 AA—2/20-mm Oerlikon AA (I ×
Electron Equipt: Radar: 2/. . . nav.
M: 2 . . . . . . diesels; 2 props; 2,500 bhp
Electric: 200 kw tot. **Range:** 3,800/12 **Endurance:** 30 days
Fuel: 59 m^3 **Crew:** 23 tot. + 30 passengers

Remarks: Designed with the assistance of NEVASABU, the Netherlands. Ir for offshore patrol duties and fisheries protection. May later be upgraded w provision of a sonar, bow-thruster, fin stabilizers, and minerails. Will have generator sets, electrohydraulic crane on fantail, and provision for stowing containers aft; have 90 m^3 stores capacity. First to deliver 1993. Four larger Zonomac patrol vessels with helicopter facilities are planned; no data availabl

CHINA

The Project EF5 destroyer class described on page 90 has been given the nic Luhu class. Two units of the new frigate design described on pages 90–91, hull n 539 and 540, have been completed and are referred to as the Jangwei class resemble a slightly enlarged version of the Jianghu III class as built for Thailan a raised helicopter deck aft and no after twin 100-mm gunmount, but the hull ha freeboard and a prominent spray knuckle forward. Armament includes on 100-mm DP gunmount forward, four twin enclosed AA gunmounts resembl Italian Breda Dardo mount, a sextuple possible SAM launcher on the forecast the 100-mm mount that has individual, very large-diameter tubes in two rows o and probable C-801 or C-802 anti-ship missiles. Pendant 991, a new variant Yukan-class landing ship (p. 96) with a raised helicopter platform aft, was fittin Shanghai in mid-1992, and a new naval supply vessel dubbed the Dayun clas *Yun* 952, was also completing at Shanghai in 1992.

COLOMBIA

A newly constituted Coast Guard was established under navy subordination i Initially employing the two *Asheville*-class patrol combatants, seven other small ıd the four LCU 1466-class landing craft described below, it was to begin ›ns in 7-92 and may grow to a 8–900-man personnel level.

x-U.S. Army LCU 1466-class landing craft (In serv. 1954)

)RROSQUILLO (ex-*Shenandoah*, LCU 1516)
RUBA (ex-*White Wing*, LCU 1550)
HIA HONDA (ex-*Carolina*, LCU 1543)
HIA POTRETE (ex-*Chattanooga*, LCU 1583)

80 tons light (347 fl) **S:** 8 kts
: 35.08 × 10.36 × 1.60 (aft) **A:** 2/12.7-mm mg (I × 2)
: Gray Marine 64 YTL diesels; 3 props; 675 bhp
tric: 40 kw **Range:** 1,200/6 (700/7 loaded) **Fuel:** 11 tons
v: 11 tot.

ks: Transferred from U.S. Army reserve stocks in 10-90 and made operational Cargo: 150 tons or 300 troops on 15.8 × 9.0 m deck with 4.3 m-wide bow ramp. ed as troop transports and mother ships for small "Boston Whaler"–type patrol the Coast Guard.

ROATIA

›atian Navy (*Hrvatska Ratna Mornarica*) was created during 10-91 and was said to be comprised of several hundred former Yugoslav Navy officers and enlisted el. Ships and craft were said to include: two guided-missile boats, one torpedo e gunboat, two patrol boats, one assault boat, three cargo ships, three tugs, and iscellaneous units. Subsequently, at the Tito Shipyard at Kraljevica, Croatia gun to complete warships begun for the Yugoslav Navy. What follows is as e a listing of ships and craft in the Croatian Navy as could be compiled from the le press sources.

ED MISSILE PATROL BOATS

+1 + . . .) King Petar Kresimir IV class
r: Tito SY, Kraljevica

	L	In serv.
PETAR KRESIMIR IV	21-3-92	1992
. . . . . .	. . .	. . .

350 tons (fl) **S:** 36 kts (32.5 sust.) **Dim:** 53.63 × 8.54 × 2.00
-8RB-15 SSM (I or II × 4)—1/57-mm 70-cal. Bofors SAK 57 Mk 1)P—1/30-mm AK-630 gatling AA (II × 1)—4–6/mines
tron Equipt:
adar: 1/Decca BT 502 nav., 1/BEAB 9LV 249 Mk 2 search/f.c. suite
W: 2/Wallops Barricade decoy RL (XVIII × 2)
3 Soviet M 5048 diesels; 3 props; 15,000 bhp
tric: 420 kVA tot. **Range:** 1,500/20 **Endurance:** 10 days
w: 5 officers, 12 non-commissioned officers, 16 enlisted

ks: Rather than being units of the larger Type 400, or "Kobra"-class missile iginally ordered and then cancelled by Libya, this design is a probable expan- the *Rade Koncar*, adapted for newer weapons systems. The class is being l for the Croatian Navy and will use missiles originally delivered for coastal use. The missile containers can be stacked two high to achieve the maximum t. The 57-mm gun may be one of those removed from units of the *Rade Koncar*–issile boats being rearmed. There is probably a Russian Kolonka-II ringsight r for the 30-mm gatling gun. Either four Type AIM-70 or six Type SAG-1 mines carried. The ships have a CBR protection system, Collins and Harris commu- ns gear, a Furuno LORAN-C receiver, and a Thomson-CSF doppler log.

Rade Koncar (Type 240) class Bldr: Tito SY, Kraljevica

	L	In serv.
K (ex-*Vlado Četovič*, RT 402)	28-8-77	3-78

242 tons (fl) **S:** 39 kts (37 sust.)
: 45.00 × 8.00 × 1.80 (2.50 props)
2/SS-N-2B Styx SSM—1/57-mm 70-cal. Bofors SAK 57 Mk 1 DP—/30-mm AK-630 gatling AA
ctron Equipt:
adar: 1/Decca 1226 nav.—1/9LV200 Mk II target detection/f.c. system
W: 2/Wallops Barricade decoy RL (XVIII × 2)
F: 1/Square Head interrogator, 1/High Pole-B transponder
CODAG: 2 Rolls-Royce Proteus gas turbines (4,500 shp each); 2 MTU 20V538 TB92 diesels (3,600 bhp each); 4 CP props; 16,200 hp max.
ctric: 300 kVA **Range:** 880/23; 1,650/15 **Endurance:** 7 days
w: 5 officers, 10 petty officers, 15 enlisted

rks: Of Yugoslav design, using Swedish fire control and guns and Soviet mis- Styx missiles chosen for economic reasons over the Exocet originally planned. ull, aluminum superstructure. Have NBC warfare protection. In *Sibenik*, the 7-mm mount was removed and replaced with a Soviet-supplied 30-mm gatling improve anti-missile defenses; the gatling gun, however, is controlled only by a ka-II ringsight director mounted in a cupola just abaft the mast.

x-Soviet Osa-I (Project 205) class

. . . . (ex-*Zikaca Jovanovic-Španac*, RC 310)

175 tons (209 fl) **S:** 35 kts **Dim:** 38.6 × 7.6 × 1.8
4/SS-N-2 Styx SSM—4/30-mm 65-cal. AK-230 AA (II × 2)

Electron Equipt:
Radar: 1/Square Tie target detection/surf. search, 1/Drum Tilt gun f.c.
IFF: 2/Square Head interrogators, 1/High Pole-B transponder
M: 3 M503A diesels; 3 props; 12,000 bhp
Range: 500/34; 750/25 **Crew:** 25 tot.

Remarks: Transferred 1965–69. Can be operated at 220 tons full load, with 11 tons extra fuel.

TORPEDO BOATS

◆ **1 Soviet Shershen class** Bldr: Tito SY, Kraljevica (In serv. 1971)

VUKOVAR (ex-*Partizan-II*, TC 222)

D: 145 tons (170 fl) **S:** 44 kts **Dim:** 36.0 × 7.8 × 1.6 (hull)
A: 4/30-mm 65-cal. AK-230 AA (II × 2)—4/533-mm TT—mines
Electron Equipt:
Radar: 1/Pot Drum surf.-search, 1/Drum Tilt gun f.c.
IFF: 1/Square Head interrogator, 1High Pole-B transponder
M: 3 M503A diesels; 3 props; 12,000 bhp
Range: 460/42; 850/30 **Crew:** 22 tot.

Remarks: Ten built in Yugoslavia under license after four were transferred in 1965. Unlike Soviet units, has no depth-charge racks.

PATROL BOATS

◆ **2 Mirna (Type 140) class** Bldr: Kraljevica SY (In serv. 1981–82)

. . . . (ex-*Zelengora*, PC 180) . . . . (ex-*Cer*, PC 181)

D: 120 tons (. . . fl) **S:** 30 kts
Dim: 32.00 × 6.68 × 1.60 (2.30 max.)
A: 1/40-mm 70-cal. Bofors L70 AA—1/20-mm M71 AA— 8/Type MDB-MT3 d.c.
Electron Equipt: Radar: 1/. . . nav.—Sonar: hull-mounted HF
M: 2 SEMT-Pielstick 12 PA4 200GDS diesels; 2 props; 6,000 bhp—electric motors for low speeds (6 kts)
Range: 400/20 **Crew:** 3 officers, 4 petty officers, 12 enlisted

Remarks: The first ten propulsion diesels were ordered in 1979 for license production in Yugoslavia. Endurance at 20 kts can be increased to 530 n.m. in emergencies. Peacetime endurance is four days; wartime: eight days. Have four-rail chaff launcher amidships. There are four chaff or illumination rocket rails on the sides of the 40-mm AA. PC 176 was damaged by gunfire by Croatian forces on 15-11-91 but has been repaired.

AMPHIBIOUS WARFARE CRAFT

◆ **0 (+ 1) Silba-class tank landing craft/minelayer**
Bldr: Brodosplit, Split (L: 18-7-92)

CETINA (ex-*Rab*)

D: 880 tons (fl) **S:** 12 kts
Dim: 49.00 (43.90 pp) × 10.20 × 2.60 max.
A: 4/30-mm 65-cal. AK-230 AA (II × 2)—4/20-mm M75 AA (IV × 1)—1/SA-7 Grail SAM launcher (IV × 1)—94 mines
Electron Equipt: Radar: 1/Decca . . . nav.
M: 2 diesels; 2 CP props; 3,100 bhp **Range:** 1,200/12
Crew: 3 officers, 30 enlisted + up to 300 troops

Remarks: Has bow and stern ramps, with continuous covered vehicle deck also used for portable mine rails. Cargo capacity: 460 tons or four medium tanks or up to seven armored personnel carriers. Has two 128-mm rocket flare launchers. The 30-mm gun-mounts are mounted port and starboard, just abaft the bridge, while the 20-mm mount is located near the stern. The first ship of the class was completed in 1990 and is in Yugoslav Navy hands.

◆ **1 DTM 211-class landing craft/minelayer**
Bldr: Yugoslavia (In serv. 1950s)

JASTREB (ex-DTM 217)

D: 240 tons (410 fl) **S:** 10.3 kts **Dim:** 49.8 × 8.6 × 1.6 (2.1 max.)
A: 3/20-mm Hispano-Suiza AA (III × 1)
M: 3 Gray Marine 64HN9 diesels; 3 props; 625 bhp
Range: 500/9.3 **Crew:** 27 tot.

Remarks: DTM= *Desantni Tenkonosac/Minopolagac*. Near-duplicate of the World War II German MFP-D class. Equipped with 1-m-wide hull sponsons, extending beam to 8.6 meters and providing space for two mine rails with a total capacity of up to 100 small mines. Bow ramp. Can carry 140 tons of vehicles or 200 troops.

◆ **1 to 4 DJČ 623-class (Type 22) landing craft**
Bldr: Gleben SY, Vela Luka, Korcula (In serv. 1986–87)

. . . . . . (ex-DJČ 624) possibly 3 others

D: 48 tons (fl) **S:** 35 kts **Dim:** 22.30 × 4.84 × 1.07 (1.58 props)
A: 2/20-mm M71 AA (I × 2)
Electron Equipt: Radar: 1/Decca 101 nav.
M: 2 diesels; 2 waterjets; 1,740 bhp
Range: 320/22 **Crew:** 6 tot. + 40 troops

Remarks: DJČ = *Desantni Jurisni Čamac*. Glass-reinforced-plastic construction. Bow ramp. Can carry vehicles totalling 15 tons in 32-m^2 cargo area.

AUXILIARIES

◆ **1 Soviet Moma-class hydrographic ship**
Bldr: Stocznia Północna, Gdańsk, Poland (In serv. 1971)

. . . . (ex-*Andrija Mohorovičić*, PH 33)

D: 1,260 tons (1,540 fl) **S:** 17 kts **Dim:** 73.3 × 10.8 × 3.8
Electron Equipt: Radar: 1/Don-2 nav.
M: 2 Zgoda-Sulzer 6TD48 diesels; 2 CP props; 3,600 bhp
Range: 8,700/11 **Crew:** 4 officers, 33 enlisted

Remarks: Transferred from Russia in 1972. Carries one survey launch. Five-ton crane for navigational buoy handling. Four laboratories totaling 35 m^2 deck space. Used for oceanographic research, hydrographic surveys, and buoy tending.

◆ **1 submarine rescue and salvage ship**
Bldr: Tito SY, Belgrade (In serv. 10-9-76)

. . . . (ex-*Spasilac*, PS 12)

D: 1,590 tons (fl) **S:** 13.4 kts
Dim: 55.50 × 12.00 × 3.84 (4.34 max.)
A: 10/20-mm AA (IV × 2 M75, I × 2 M71)
Electron Equipt: Radar: 1/. . . nav.—Sonar: . . .
M: 2 diesels; 2 Kort-nozzle props; 4,340 bhp
Electric: 540 kVA **Range:** 4,000/13.4 **Crew:** 53 tot. (72 accomm.)

Remarks: PS = *Pomočni Spasilecki Brod* (Seagoing Rescue Ship). Resembles an oilfield supply vessel; low freeboard aft. Sister *Aka* is in the Iraqi Navy and another has been sold to Libya (ex-*Zlatica*). Equipped for underwater cutting and welding, towing, carrying up to 250 tons deck cargo, transferring 490 tons cargo fuel, 48 tons cargo water, and 5 tons lube oil. Also capable of salvage lifting, fire fighting, and other salvage tasks. Can support divers to 300 m with a three-section decompression chamber. Also has capability to support a small rescue submersible. Has a bow-thruster and can lay a four-point moor.

NORTH CYPRUS

Two FPB-23-class patrol craft, one named *Sergey Krstanovic* and launched 15-8-91 by Brodotehnica, Belgrade, Yugoslavia, were delivered during 1991 to North Cyprus for use in economic exclusion zone patrol, search and rescue, and police duties:

D: 57 tons (fl) **S:** 42.7 kts **Dim:** 24.60 (23.00 pp) × 5.73 × 1.05
A: 1/20-mm M 71 AA—2/12.7-mm mg (I × 2)
M: 2 diesels; 2 waterjets; 2,035 bhp **Range:** 600/20 **Crew:** 9 tot.

DENMARK

During 4-92, both *Peder Skram*–class frigates, the remaining *Hvidbjørnen*-class fisheries patrol frigates, two previously stricken *Daphne*-class patrol boats, and the fisheries patrol boats *Maagen* (Y 384) and *Mallemukken* (Y 385) were auctioned for scrap. During the fall of 1991, *Hvidbjørnen*-class fisheries patrol frigate *Fylla* (F 351), stricken submarine *Spækhuggeren*, four *Daphne*-class patrol boats, and all five *Søløven*-class torpedo boats were sold; three of the *Daphnes* were purchased by a missionary organization, and the other units were sold for scrap.

Thetis-class fisheries protection frigate *Vædderen* (F 359) was commissioned on 9-6-92; sister *Hvidbjørnen* (F 360) will commission in 3-93, and *Triton* (F 358) commissioned 2-12-91.

Nils Juel (F 354)—after collision Leo Van Ginderen, 4-92

EGYPT

Work on modernizing the four Chinese-built Romeo-class submarines began only in 1992, due to contract problems. Soviet T-301-class inshore minesweepers *El Fayoud* and *El Manufieh* were stricken 1991, as were the last two SMB-1-class utility landing craft, 374 and 376, and one of the two Nyryat-1-class diving tenders. The U.S mine countermeasures route survey boats are named *Safaga* (610) and *Abu el G* (613). The U.S.-built inshore minesweepers will deliver in 1993.

ESTONIA

A small coastal patrol force was established on 22-4-92 when the first of fou 236-class 16.2-meter patrol craft donated by Sweden was delivered. Finland deliver three *Koskelo*-class coast guard patrol craft during 1992 also. Both a Navy Coast Guard are being established.

FINLAND

A new "Tarmo II"-class icebreaker was ordered 10-91 for delivery 3-93, from Finn (formerly named Hollming), Rauma, where it was laid down 3-92; a sister shi ordered mid-1992 for delivery in 1994. Characteristics include:

D: . . . **S:** 16 kts
Dim: 115.00 (96.00 pp) × 26.00 × 8.40 (7.00 as Baltic icebreaker)
M: diesel-electric: 2 Wärtsilä 16R32 (9,900 bhp each) and 2 Wärtsi 12R32 (6,650 bhp each) diesels, 4 ABB alternators, 2 ABB elect motors; 2 Kort-nozzle swivelling props; 28,500 shp
Range: . . ./. . . **Crew:** 82 tot.

Remarks: Intended for winter icebreaking in Finnish waters and charter to No Ugland Offshore in the summer in support of North Sea oil and gas operations. dwt. 200-ton bollard pull. Has 120-ton A-frame gantry at stern, 15-ton general-pu crane to starboard aft, helicopter hangar with elevator forward.

The third Helsinki-II-class guided-missile boat, *Porvoo* (72) was commissioned 92, and the fourth, *Naantali* (73) on 23-6-92. The 1,330-ton full load minelayer *eenmaa* (02) was commissioned 15-4-92; her sister will be completed late in 1 replace *Keihassalmi* (05). Coast Guard Koskelo-class patrol craft *Telkkä, Kuikk Tavi* were transferred to Estonia during 1992.

FRANCE

On 9-12-91, the British and French governments announced joint development of anti-air warfare frigate to displace around 5,500 tons full load. The French N planning to build four of the ships, which may be equipped with the NH-90 heli and the FAMS area-defense SAM system. Italy and Spain may join the proj mid-1993.

The third *Améthyste*-class nuclear-powered attack submarine, *Turquoise* (S was cancelled altogether during 6-92, and it is likely that only four *Le Triomp* class ballistic-missile submarines will be built. Completion of the carrier *Char Gaulle* will be delayed beyond the current 10-98 completion goal. *Acajou*-cla *Balsa* (Y 607) and fireboat *Geyser* (Y 646) were stricken 1991.

Frigate *La Fayette* launched 13-6-92. Destroyer *Duperré* retired 1-6-92. F *Protet* stricken 29-6-92 and trials ship, former frigate *Commandant Rivière*, r 15-7-92. First flight of modernized Crusader fighter 15-6-92; 16 other aircraft to soon.

GERMANY

Only four Type 212 submarines are to be requested under the 1993 defens curement plan; additional units will now not be requested before 2005. Only fo planned ten new large missile patrol boats will be ordered before 2005.

New Type 123 frigate *Brandenburg* (F 215) laid down 11-2-92 and launched 28 sisters to be numbered and built in order: *Mecklenburg-Vorpommern, Bayern Schleswig-Holstein.* Former East German Darss-class cargo ships *Darss* (A *Mönchgut* (A 1431), *Wittow* (A 1430). *Kühlung* (A 1434), *Werdau* (A 1435), and *G* (A 1433) were sold to a Norwegian commercial owner 9-91 and renamed *Eide Re* through *VI*; yard tugs *Peene, Oder* (Y 1659), and *Ernst Krenkel* were sold to the owner as *Eide Guard I–III*. Type 340/341 minesweeper *Pollux* (M 1054) str 25-5-92.

Type 520 landing craft *Barbe* (L 790), *Delphin* (L 791), and *Dorsch* (L 792) stricken 26-9-91, *Karpfen* (L 761) on 30-1-92, *Rochen* (L 764) on 7-2-92, *Stör* (L *Tümmler* (L 767), *Wels* (L 768), and *Zander* (L 769) in 9-92, *Butt* (L 786) on 4- *Brasse* (L 789) on 16-4-92, *Felchen* (L 793) and *Forelle* (L 794) on 1-11-91 (and t ferred to Greece), *Inger* (L 795) on 9-9-92, *Makrele* (L 796) on 8-11-91, and *M* (L 797) on 14-2-92.

Tender *Mosel* (A 67) sold 19-2-92 for scrap. Small former East German tugs *Dr* (Y 1658), *Wustrow* (Y 1656), *Koos* (Y 1651), and fuel lighter *Fleesensee* (Y 1657) ar scheduled to be retained until 31-12-98. Ammunition ship *Westerwald* (A 1435) t ferred to the Wilhelmshaven Naval Base 3-92 and manned by the crew of the d missioned oiler *Eifel* (A 1429). Stricken submarine U 1 will be employed by Th Nordseewerke for trials beginning late 1992 with a 250-kW closed-cycle diesel ge tor set developed with Cosworth Deep Sea Systems, U.K.

Names and builder data for the new Type 404 multi-purpose tenders are as fo

	Bldr	In serv.
A 511 Elbe	Bremer Vulkan	11-92
A 512 Mosel	Bremer Vulkan	2-93
A 513 Rhein	Flensburger Schiffbauwerke	10-93

	Bldr	In serv.
Werra	Flensburger Schiffbauwerke	12-93
Main	Flenderwerke/Krögerwerft	7-94
Donau	Flenderwerke/Krögerwerft	11-94

REECE

endant numbers, names, and dates of transfer for U.S. Navy ships leased or d to Greece during 1991–92 are as follows: D 218 *Kimon* (ex-*Semmes*, DDG 18) 9-91; D 219 *Nearchos* (ex-*Waddell*, DDG 24) on 1-10-92; D 220 *Formion* (ex- *Strauss*, DDG 16) on 1-10-92; D 221 *Themistocles* (ex-*Berkeley*, DDG 15) on 2; F 456 *Epirius* (ex-*Conolle*, FF 1056) on 30-8-92; F 457 *Thrace* (ex-*Trippe*, FF on 30-7-92; and F 458 *Makedonia* (ex-*Vreeland*, FF 1068) on 30-8-92. DDG 15, was transferred outright vice on loan, was a substitute for *Richard E. Byrd* (DDG hich, after purchase, was found to require too extensive an overhaul to warrant missioning; ex-DDG 23 was to be towed to Greece during 1992 to serve as a spares and pierside trainer.

former U.S. *Gearing* FRAM II DDR–class destroyer *Themistocles* (D 210, ex-*Knox*, DD 742) was stricken during 1992. Trials for the German-built MEKO ass frigate *Ydra* (F 452) began during June 1992. None of the tank landing ships construction in Greece had been completed as of 9-92. The four ex-U.S. *Cannon*-rigates have been stricken: *Aetos* (D 01, ex-*Ebert*, DE 768), *Hierax* (D 31, ex-DE 766), and *Leon* (D 54, ex-*Garfield Thomas*, DE 193)) in 1991, and *Panthir* (D -*Eldridge*, DE 173) in 1992; D 31 and D 54 are being retained as training hulks. craft *E. Panagopoulos I* (P 61) stricken 1991.

ner German replenishment ship *Coburg* has been named *Axios* (A 464); torpedo vers TF 6 and TF 4 have been renamed *Strymon* (A 462) and *Nestos* (A 464), tively; water tanker FW 6 has been renamed *Trichonsis* (A 466) and the *Lütje* class tugs have been renamed *Pilefs* (A 413), *Minos* (A 436), *Pelias* (A 437), and (A 438). German Type 520 utility landing craft *Felchen* (L 793) and *Forelle* (L ere transferred to Greece 31-1-92; new names and numbers not yet available.

(F 452)—on trials   Hartmut Ehlers, 6-92

on (D 218)—at Philadelphia Naval Shipyard prior to departing for ce   George R. Schneider, Jr., 1-92

ONDURAS

46-grt cargo vessel was acquired during 1991:

refrigerated cargo ship

dr: Mutzelfeldtwerft, Cuxhaven (In serv. 1959)

UMBLA II (ex-*Carib Freeze*, ex-*Armic*, ex-*Tsefat*)

. . . tons **S:** 11 kts **Dim:** 75.21 × 11.83 × 4.12
1 Deutz diesel; 1 prop; 1,470 bhp

ONG KONG

Sikorsky S-70A troop transport helicopters were ordered for the Royal Hong Kong iary Air Force in 4-92. In 1993, it is planned to turn the Royal Hong Auxiliary Air over to a civilian-manned Hong Kong government agency, in keeping with its military rôle.

(+4) ASI-315 "Pacific Forum"–class patrol boats

dr: Australian SB Industries (WA), Pty, Ltd., South Coogie

	Laid down	L	In serv.
PL	. . .	. . .	20-8-92
PL	. . .	. . .	20-8-92
PL	. . .	. . .	19-1-93
PL	. . .	. . .	19-1-93
PL	. . .	. . .	25-6-93
PL	. . .	. . .	25-6-93

D: 148 tons (fl) **S:** 26+ kts
Dim: 32.60 (31.50 hull, 28.60 wl) × 8.20 × 1.60 hull
A: 1/12.7-mm mg—2/7.62-mm mg (I × 2)
Electron Equipt: Radar: 1/. . . nav.
M: 2 Caterpillar 3516 Phase II diesels; 2 props; 2,820 bhp (2,400 sust.)—1 Caterpillar 3412 TA cruise diesel; 1 Hamilton 521 waterjet; 775 bhp
Range: 600/18 **Fuel:** 21,000 liters **Endurance:** 8–10 days
Electric: 186 kVA (2/Caterpillar 3306T diesel sets) **Crew:** 19 tot.

Remarks: Ordered 8-91. Modified standard Australian foreign aid patrol boat design, with less draft and fuel, third engine added centerline for cruising. Carry a 5-m rigid inflatable boarding boat.

HUNGARY

Szazhalombatta (AM 21)—with AN-1-class minesweeping boats 542-053, 542-011, and 542-003   Eric Grove, 1992

ICELAND

◆ **1 68-grt hydrographic survey and patrol craft**
Bldr: Velsmidje Seydisfjordar H/H, Seydisfjorda (In serv. 1991)

Baldur

D: . . . tons **S:** . . . kts **Dim:** 20.06 × 5.25 × 1.30
M: 1 Caterpillar diesel; . . . bhp

INDIA

Foxtrot-class submarine *Kursura* completed a ten-year overhaul at Vishakhaptanam Dockyard in 1-92. Also at the same yard in 1-92 were 25 other warships in various states of overhaul, including submarines *Karanj*, *Vagir*, *Sinduraj*, and *Sindhughosh*, Petya-class corvettes *Amini*, *Arnath*, and *Kadmath*, and an unidentified destroyer. Tarantul-class guided-missile patrol combatant *Vipul* was commissioned 16-3-92. The decline in real terms of the Indian Defense budget is likely to cause further delays in the Indian carrier program. U.K. *Leopard*-class training frigate *Betwa* (F 38) was stricken 31-12-91. Petya-II-class corvette *Kamorta* (P 77) was stricken 1991.

INDONESIA

On 24-7-92, it was announced that Germany was transferring thirty-nine former *Volksmarine* units to Indonesia: sixteen Parchim-I-class corvettes, twelve Frosch-I-class landing ships, nine Kondor-II-class patrol minesweepers, and two Frosch-II-class amphibious warfare support ships. The exact dates of transfer were still to be announced, as were the identities of the nine minesweepers.

◆ **16 Parchim-I-class (Type 133.1) corvettes**
Bldr: Peenewerft, Wolgast

		In serv.
. . . .	(ex-*Wismar*, P 6170, ex-241)	9-7-81
. . . .	(ex-*Parchim*, 242)	9-4-81
. . . .	(ex-*Perleberg*, 243)	19-9-81
. . . .	(ex-*Bützow*, 244)	30-12-81

		In serv.
. . . .	(ex-*Lübz*, P 6169, ex-221)	12-2-82
. . . .	(ex-*Bad Doberan*, 222)	30-6-90
. . . .	(ex-*Güstrow*, 223)	10-11-82
. . . .	(ex-*Waren*, 224)	23-11-82
. . . .	(ex-*Prenzlau*, 231)	11-5-83
. . . .	(ex-*Ludwigslust*, 232)	4-7-83
. . . .	(ex-*Ribnitz-Damgarten*, 233)	29-10-83
. . . .	(ex-*Teterow*, P 6168, ex-234)	27-1-84
. . . .	(ex-*Gädebusch*, P 6167, ex-211)	31-8-84
. . . .	(ex-*Grevesmuhlen*, 212)	21-9-84
. . . .	(ex-*Bergen*, 213)	1-2-85
. . . .	(ex-*Angermünde*, 214)	26-7-85

ex-Lübz in German service Hartmut Ehlers, 6-91

D: 792 tons light/873 normal tons (908 fl) **S:** 24.3 kts
Dim: 75.20 (69.00 pp) × 9.78 (8.95 wl) × 2.65 hull (4.40 sonar)
A: as built: 2/57-mm 70-cal. AK-257 DP (II × 1)—2/30-mm AK-230 AA (II × 1)—2/SA-N-5 FASTA SAM systems (IV × 2)—4/400-mm ASW TT (I × 4)—2/RBU-6000 ASW RL (XII × 2)—2/d.c. racks
Electron Equipt:
Radar: 1/TSR-333 nav., 1/Strut Curve air/surf. search, 1/Muff Cob f.c.
Sonar: medium freq. hull-mounted; high-freq. dipping sonar
EW: 2/Watch Dog intercept, 2/RK-16 decoy RL (XVI × 2)
M: 3 Type M504A-3, 56-cyl. diesels; 3 props; 14,250 bhp
Range: 1,200/20; 2,200/14 **Endurance:** 10 days
Crew: 9 officers, 71 enlisted (normally operated with 59 tot.)

Remarks: Four served briefly in the German Navy, hence the "P"-series former pendants. Reportedly suffer from too much topweight. Previously referred to by NATO as the "Bal-Com-4" and by the press as the "Koralle" class. Twelve near-sisters were built for the Soviet Navy.

A helicopter-type dipping sonar deploys through door on starboard side of main deck superstructure; next to it is another door with a second dipping device, possibly a bathythermograph. D.C. racks exit through doors in stern. The centerline propeller has controllable pitch; the others are fixed. Are to retain armament and sensor suites.

◆ **12 German Frosch-I-class (Type 108) landing ships**
Bldr: Peenewerft, Wolgast

		In serv.
. . . .	(ex-*Hoyerswerda*, 611)	2-11-76
. . . .	(ex-*Hagenow*, 632, ex-612)	1-12-76
. . . .	(ex-*Frankfurt/Oder*, 613)	2-2-77
. . . .	(ex-*Eberswalde/Finow*, 634, ex-614)	28-5-77
. . . .	(ex-*Lübben*, 632, ex-631)	15-3-78
. . . .	(ex-*Schwerin*, 612, ex-632)	19-10-77
. . . .	(ex-*Neubrandenburg*, 633)	28-12-77
. . . .	(ex-*Cottbus*, 614, ex-634)	26-5-78
. . . .	(ex-*Anklam*, 635)	14-7-78
. . . .	(ex-*Schwedt*, 636)	7-9-79
. . . .	(ex-*Eisenhüttenstadt*, 615)	4-1-79
. . . .	(ex-*Grimmen*, 616)	15-6-79

ex-Anklam in East German service Leo Van Ginderen, 1989

D: 1,744 tons normal (1,900 fl) **S:** 19 kts (18 sust.)
Dim: 90.70 × 11.12 × 2.80 mean (3.40 max.)
A: 4/57-mm 70-cal. AK-257 DP (II × 2)—4/30-mm AK-230 AA (II × 2)—most: 2/122-mm artillery RL (XL × 2; 360 tot. rocke 40 mines
Electron Equipt:
Radar: 1/TSR-333 nav., 1/Strut Curve surf./air-search, 1/Muff f.c.
M: 2 Type 61B 16-cyl. diesels; 2 CP props; 12,000 bhp
Range: 2,450/14 **Crew:** 42 tot.

Remarks: Cargo capacity 400 to 600 tons or twelve light tanks and a com troops. Complex bow door/ramp mechanism; no stern ramp. The vehicle dec 425 m² and is 4.2 m high. Two 40-tubed rocket launchers of the type carrie Soviet ship *Ivan Rogov* were mounted forward of the bridge on all except fi which do, however, each carry two RK-16 decoy rocket launchers. Armament prior to transfer.

◆ **2 Frosch-II-class (Type 109) amphibious warfare support s**
Bldr: Peenewerft, Wolgast

		L	In serv.
. . . .	(ex-*Nordperd*, E-171, ex-E-35)	30-8-78	3-10-79
. . . .	(ex-*Südperd*, E-172, ex-E-36)	30-10-78	26-2-80

ex-Nordperd in East German service J. Hilton, USI

D: 1,530 tons normal (fl) **S:** 16 kts
Dim: 90.70 × 11.12 × 3.40 max.
A: as built: 4/57-mm 70-cal. AK-257 DP (II × 2)—4/25-mm 2M-8 (II × 2)—36 mines
Electron Equipt:
Radar: 1/TSR-333 nav., 1/Strut Curve surf./air-search, 1/Muff Co
EW: 2/RK-16 decoy RL (XVI × 2)
M: 2 Type 61B 16-cyl. diesels; 2 CP props; 12,000 bhp **Crew:** 35

Remarks: Were typed as "High Seas Supply Ships" (*Hochseeversorger*) in *Vo rine* service and have a 650-ton deadweight cargo capacity. Differed from Fro having an 8-ton Type 2Hy SWK8 crane amidships and two cargo hatches, having 25-mm (mounted right forward to cover the beach) in place of 30-m Armament removed prior to transfer. Although they had an auxiliary-series p number, the bow ramp was retained to permit a beaching capability, and they p ably can be used as assault landing ships if needed. Chaff rocket launchers (X added 1986, just forward of bridge.

In 1-92, the Indonesian Navy purchased the British "Rover" class repleni oiler *Green Rover* (A 268):

	Bldr.	L	I
. . . Arum (ex-*Green Rover*)	Swan Hunter, Hebburn-on-Tyne	19-12-68	1

Arum—on delivery voyage to Indonesia Leo Van Gindere

D: 4,700 tons light (11,522 fl) **S:** 19.25 kts
Dim: 140.5 × 19.2 × 7.3
A: 2/20-mm AA (I × 2) **Electron Equipt:** Radar: 3/. . . nav.
M: 2 SEMT-Pielstick 16PA 4 diesels; 1 CP prop; 15,300 bhp
Electric: 2,720 kw **Range:** 15,000/15 **Fuel:** 965 tons
Crew: 16 officers, 31 enlisted

Remarks: 7,510 grt/6,822 dwt. Carries 6,600 tons of fuel plus water, dry stor provisions. Helicopter deck but no hangar. Re-engined 1973–74. Had been pla reserve on 30-days notice 27-5-88, with six-man crew.

AN

d 3-92 that Iran has ordered up to 12 "Hegu" (Hoku)-class guided-missile patrol om China to be armed with either Hai Ying-2 (Silkworm) or Ying Ji (C-801) p missiles; deliveries were to begin late in 1992 and end in 1993. The first two of ed three Kilo-class submarines were reported to be ready for delivery at a port ga, Estonia, on 29-4-92, but had not left the Baltic by the end of August; the nent officially confirmed the order for a total of three Kilos in June.

RAEL

est officially released data for the Dolphin (IKL Type 800) submarine design The two Israeli units are now expected to be operational in 1997.

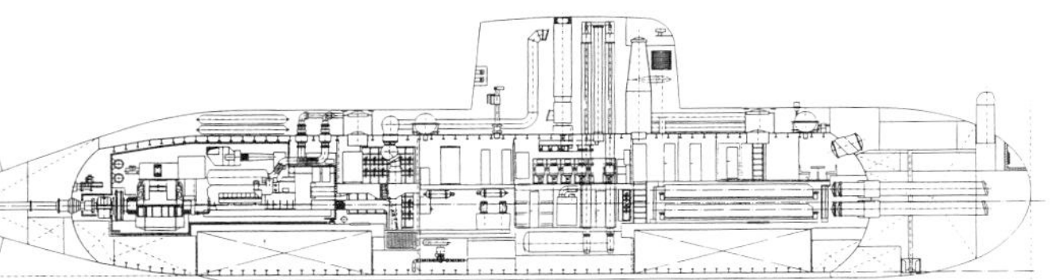

in class (IKL 800) — HDW, 1992

,750 tons (sub.) **S:** 11 kts (snorkel)/20 kts (sub.)
: 57.00 × 7.40 × . . . (13.90 high, masts retracted)
/533-mm swim-out TT fwd (14 weapons)
3 diesel generator sets (970 kw each), 1 motor; 17-bladed prop;
5,000 shp
ge: 14,000/4 snorkel; 8,000/8 snorkel; 420/. . . sub.; 25/20 sub.
urance: 60 days **Crew:** 6 officers, 24 enlisted

ks: Diving depth 350 m. To have 10 percent reserve buoyancy. Two 216-cell es.

ALY

rd *San Giorgio*-class landing ship is to be named *Cristoforo Colombo* (L 9984); wn 7-4-92.

0-6-92, the new guided-missile destroyers *Animoso* and *Ardimentoso* were re- *Luigi Durand de la Penne* (D 560) and *Francesco Mimbelli* (D 561), respectively. four ex-Iraqi *Lupo*-class frigates have been renamed *Aviere*, *Artigliere*, *Ber-*, and *Granatiere* and are equipped with the Atlas Electronik DSQS-21BZ (ASO tronically stabilized sonar vice the Raytheon set listed; the six missile corvettes r Iraq were equipped with the Atlas DSQS-21C (ASO 83) sonar vice Thomson- Diodon. In late 6-92, the Italian Parliament Defense Committee decided against the acquisition of the ships, again casting their fate into doubt. Corvette (F 555) commissioned 6-9-91 and sisters *Chimera* (F 556) and *Sibilla* (F 558) on 1.

narine *Primo Longobardo* (S 524) was laid down 19-12-91. Minehunter *Crotone* 8) was launched 11-4-92. Sea trials for guided-missile destroyer *Luigi Durand enne* (D 560) began 9-91, those for *Francesco Mimbelli* (D 561) were to begin r 1992. Minehunters *Chiggi* (M 5560) and *Rimini* (M 5561) were canceled 7-92, ork had already begun. Minehunter *Loto* (M 5538) was stricken 1992. Salvage *icudi* (A 5304, ex-U.S. AN 99) was stricken 20-2-92.

-92, aircraft acquisition plans included only sixteen EH.101 heavy helicopters n option for eight more later), but the number of AV-8B+ fighters had risen to -four.

MAICA

10.06-meter patrol boats built by Offshore Marine Performance, Inc., U.S.A., ommissioned on 20-4-92; they are powered by two 225-bhp outboard motors each.

PAN

ng submarine *Isoshio* (ATSS 8001, ex-SS 568) was stricken 25-3-92, as were veeping boats MSB 707 and MSB 708 and miscellaneous auxiliary, ex-frigate ASU 7015, ex-DE 211). Coastal minesweepers *Yokose* (MSC 642) and *Sakate* 543) were redesignated YAS 93 and YAS 94 on 12-3-92 for use as mine clearance tenders.

the Maritime Safety Agency, the first of a new series of small patrol craft were red early in 1992:

+ . . .) **Suzukaze (20-meter) class** Bldr: . . . . . .

. Suzukaze (In serv. 20-2-92) CL 13 Sugikaze (In serv. 28-2-92)
Asakaze (In serv. 9-3-92) CL 16 Hibikaze (In serv. 3-4-92)

D: 19 tons (23 fl) **S:** 30 kts **Dim:** 20.0 × 4.3 × . . .
M: 2 diesels; 2 props; 1,820 bhp **Range:** 160/. . . **Crew:** 5 tot.

Remarks: Replace Chiyokaze-class patrol craft *Suzukaze* (CL 50, stricken 3-2-92), *Urakaze* (CL 51, stricken 20-2-92), *Sugikaze* (CL 53, stricken 10-2-92), *Fujikaze* (CL 54), *Miyakaze* (CL 55), and *Satakaze* (CL 78); additional units are being constructed.

Three additional units of the *Hakuun*-class navigational aid tenders should be added: *Sekiun* (LM 203, in serv. 12-3-91), *Houn* (LM 204, in serv. 22-2-91), and *Reiun* (LM 205, in serv. 28-2-92); the earlier *Reiun* (LM 102) was stricken 15-2-92. The radiation monitoring craft *Kinagusa* (MS 01) has been replaced by an 18.0 × 9.0 catamaran-hulled craft with the same name and number, completed 31-1-92. 130-ton-class patrol boat *Takatsuki* (PS 108) was delivered 3-92 by Mitsubishi's Shimonoseki yard.

LATVIA

The first unit of a small Coast Guard intended to number eleven units and with around 1,000 personnel was commissioned during 4-92; a converted fisheries patrol craft, it is armed with one machine gun.

LITHUANIA

On 4-7-92, the first three patrol boats of what is planned to be a ten-ship naval force were commissioned; no data available. Eventually, Lithuania hopes to operate guided-missile patrol boats and mine countermeasures ships.

MALAYSIA

Up to four new offshore patrol vessels are to be ordered as the beginning of what is hoped will become an eighteen-unit economic exclusion zone patrol force by the year 2007. Preliminary characteristics for the OPVs are:

D: 800–1,200 tons (fl) **S:** 20+ kts **Dim:** circa 80.0 × 10.0 × 3.0
A: 1 medium-caliber DP gun—1/ light AA—1/helicopter
Electron Equipt: 1/. . . nav., 1/. . . search, 1/optronic director—ESM: . . .
M: 2 or 4 diesels; 2 props; . . . bhp **Range:** 6,000/12
Endurance: 21 days **Crew:** 7 officers, 43 enlisted

Remarks: Would be built in Malaysia. To be capable of operating in a State 5 sea. Would have telescoping helicopter hangar and automated landing/deck transit system.

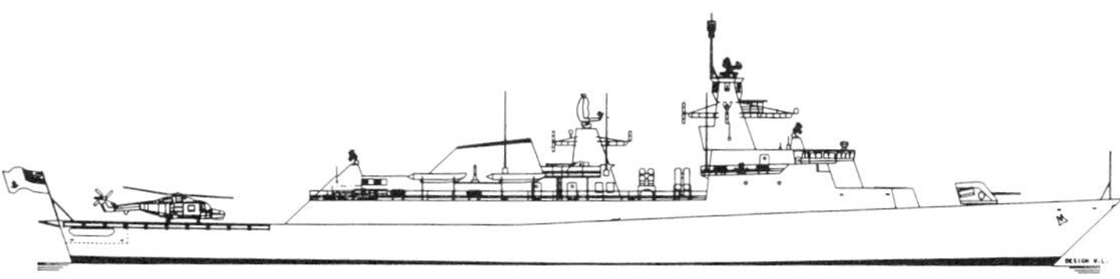

Malaysia's new Yarrow frigates — *Navint*, 3-92

MALTA

The former East German Tarantul-I-class guided-missile patrol boats listed in the text had not been transferred as of 7-92. Instead, however, two former *Volksmarine* Kondor-I-class patrol minesweepers have been acquired:

◆ **2 former East German Kondor-I class patrol boats**
Bldr: VEB Peenewerft, Wolgast

	L	In serv.
P 30 (ex-*Ueckermünde*, GS 01, ex-G 411)	27-2-69	1-7-69
P 31 (ex-*Pasewalk*, GS 05, ex-G 423)	18-6-69	18-10-69

D: 225 tons light (339 fl) **S:** 20 kts **Dim:** 52.00 × 7.12 × 2.40
A: . . . . . . **Electron Equipt:** Radar: 1/TSR-333 nav.
Range: 1,900/. . .
M: 2 Type 40DM diesels; 2 CP props; 4,000 bhp (sust.) **Crew:** . . .

Remarks: After the unification of Germany, had been incorporated in the Maritime Border Guard (*Bundesgrenzschutz-See*) but not used operationally. Transferred to Malta in 7-92 without armament, along the two Bremse-class (GB 23) patrol launches, which have been renumbered P 32 and P 33. Do not have names.

Also transferred to Malta during the summer of 1992 from the Italian Customs Service were three GL 313–class patrol craft and two Nardi-Hughes NH-500M light helicopters. Current aviation assets also include: five Cessna O-1E Bird Dog light observation aircraft (transferred from Italy on 4-2-92), and two AB-204B, one AB-206A, and three AB-47G-2 helicopters.

MARSHALL ISLANDS

Former U.S. Coast Guard Cape-class patrol boat *Ionmeto 2* (ex-*Cape Small*, WPB 95300) was sold during 3-92.

MEXICO

Aguila-class patrol ship *Blas de Lezo* (C 02, ex-*Mitla,* GA 02) was not commissioned until 22-3-92. Three ex-U.S. *Admirable*-class patrol ships are to be rehabilitated, re-engined, and equipped with helicopter decks.

NETHERLANDS

The first of the new replenishment oilers is to be named *Amsterdam* vice *Jan Van Ghent* and was laid down on 21-5-92 at Merwede Shipyard, Hardinxveld-Giessendam, as hull subcontractor for Royal Schelde, which will fit her out. Crew will be 180 total. *Karel Doorman*–class frigate *Van Nes* was launched 16-5-92. LCA Mk 1-class landing craft L 9520 and small tug Y 8028 were stricken during 1990. Diving tenders *Nautilus* (A 849) and *Hydra* (A 850) were stricken 1992 and their names passed to two new craft, A 853 and A 854.

NORWAY

Storm-class guided-missile patrol boats *Glimt* (P 962), *Arg* (P 968), *Brann* (P 970), *Tross* (P 971), *Traust* (P 973), *Brott* (P 974), *Odd* (P 975) and *Rokk* (P 978) were stricken 1991–92. *Kvalsund*-class landing craft *Kvalsund* (L 4500) and *Raftsund* (L 4501) were stricken in 1992. The *Sleipner*-class corvettes *Sleipner* (F 310) and *Ægir* (F 311) were to be stricken by end-1992.

OMAN

"Province"-class guided-missile boats built after *Dhofar* (B 10) have the Plessey AWS-6 surface/air-search radar vice AWS-4.

PERU

Cruiser *Aguirre* (CH 84), *Dos de Mayo*–class submarines *Dos de Mayo* (SS 41), *Abtao* (SS 42), and *Iquique* (SS 44), and *Daring*-class destroyers *Palacios* (DM 73) and *Ferré* (DM 74) were decommissioned 1992 to reserve because of a lack of personnel.

POLAND

Kaszub (240)—with AK-176 gun installed Maritime Photographic, 5-92

Rolnik (437) Leo Van Ginderen, 4-92

Kaper-I (SG-311)—blue hull with white superstructure, red and go stripes

PORTUGAL

São Roque–class patrol boats *Lagoa* (M 403) and *Rosario* (M 404) were stricke The pendant number for the new Rio Minho patrol craft *Rio Minho* is P 370.

QATAR

Four 56-meter guided-missile patrol boats were ordered from Vosper Thorny 4-6-92:

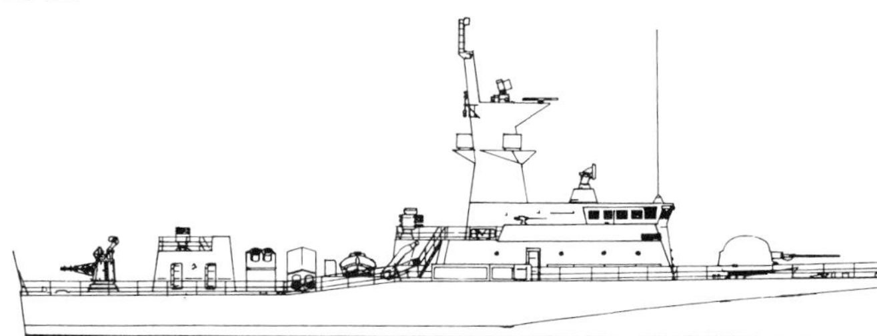

56-meter guided-missile patrol boat *Navir*

D: 530 tons (fl) **S:** 38 kts **Dim:** 56.50 (52.00 wl) × 9.00 × 2.25
A: 4/MM 40 Exocet SSM (II × 2)—1/76-mm 62-cal. OTO Melara Rapid DP—1/Sadral point-defense SAM syst. (VI × 1, Mistral missiles)—1/30-mm Goalkeeper CIWS—2/12.7-mm mg (I × 2
Electron Equipt:
Radar: 1/Decca 1226 nav., 1/Thomson-CSF MRR 3-D surf./air-search, 1/Thomson-CSF Castor II gun f.c., 1/Goalkeeper
EW: Dassault Salamandre intercept/jammer suite, 1/Dagaie decoy RL
M: 4 . . . . . . diesels; 4 props; . . . bhp **Range:** 2,500/15
Crew: . . .

Remarks: Design derived from Vosper Thornycroft's "Vita" and "Falcon" c Will reportedly have Thomson-CSF TACTICOS combat data system. Work late 1992.

ROMANIA

Tetal-class frigate 264 is named *Comtraamiral Eustatiu Sebastian.* Croitor-cl der 283 is named *Midia.*

Two Huchwan-class hydrofoil torpedo boats with Tetal-class f Vice Admiral Vasile Scodrea (261) in background

U.S. Navy

ian Osa-I 195 U.S. Navy, 1992

SSIA

somolets-names applied to Pacific Ocean Fleet units were ordered replaced by ditional names in 5-92; the "Cross of St. Andrew" ensign was hoisted in place of mer-and-sickle on 26-7-92. Black Sea Fleet assets are to be shared jointly by and Russia until 1995, when a final division will be made, according to a cision by Presidents Yeltsin and Kravchuk; a special ensign will be flown by

ev-class aircraft carrier *Novorossiysk* was officially relegated to "second-class in 8-92, along with sister Pacific Fleet unit *Minsk*, which was sold for scrap- ndia during 8-92.

l of the former KGB Maritime Border Guard passed from the C.I.S. to the Ministry of Security Frontier Guard Forces on 12-6-92; the fleet thus remains from the Russian Navy.

l of seven Pomornik-class air-cushion vehicle landing craft were in service in in the Baltic and three in the Black Sea. Construction of the class has ceased siya, but three more are to be completed at the Almaz Shipbuilding Consor- ekabristov Boatyard, St. Petersburg; a fourth was begun, but will not be d. Known as the Zubr-class in Russia, the craft are said to displace 350 tons, peed of 63 knots, and have an endurance of five days (one day when carrying ombat load is three battle tanks, ten armored personnel carriers, and a naval company.

are 24 SA-N-7 missiles per launcher in the *Sovremennyy* class, for a total of 48.

II-class corvette SKR-112 defected to Ukraine on 21 July 1992.

rst Dergach-class guided-missile surface effect ship is named *Bora* ("Wind") ch; *Sivuch* is the project nickname.

ar icebreaker Vaygach TASS, 1990

ntul-class guided-missile boat—modified with CADS-1 twin 30-mm aft (without missiles) and Cross Dome search radar forward
Leo Van Ginderen, 1992

Admiral Zozulya—on post-modernization trials 1992

Tomba-class generator ship ZNS-254 R.Neth.N., 1991

Admiral Panteleyev—the eleventh and last Udaloy-class destroyer
Jürg Kürsener, 7-92

SINGAPORE

Twelve inshore patrol craft were delivered to the navy in 1990–91 by Singapore Shipbuilding and Engineering Corporation; similar to but more streamlined in appearance than the Marine Police PT 12 class, they are based at Brani and have hull numbers in the FB series.

D: 20 tons (fl) **S:** 30 kts **Dim:** 14.5 × 4.1 × . . .
A: 1/7.62-mm mg **Electron Equipt:** Radar: 1/Decca . . . nav.
M: 2 MTU 12V183 TC 91 diesels; 2 props; 1,200 bhp **Crew:** 4 tot.

SPAIN

Atalaya (P 73) the last of four *Serviola*-class corvettes, was commissioned 29-6-92. Sail training ship *Juan Sebastian de Elcano* was damaged in a collision with a ferry in San Juan harbor, Puerto Rico during 7-92.

The fisheries protection ship *Childreu* (ex-*Pescalonso*) acquired on 30-3-92 has the following characteristics:

D: approx. 1,900 tons (fl) **S:** 15 kts
Dim: 67.80 (57.82 pp) × 11.02 × 4.66
M: 1 MaK 6M-453aK diesel; 1 prop; 2,460 bhp
Range: 15,000/. . . **Crew:** 25 tot.

Remarks: 1,316-grt former stern-haul trawler transferred from the Ministry of Fisheries, Food, and Agriculture. Built by Gijon Naval.

TUNISIA

The U.S. *Savage*-class frigate *Indakh* (E 7), badly damaged by fire in 1992, has been relegated to pierside service. Transferred from Germany to the Tunisian Navy in 7-92 for use by the National Guard (*Gendarmerie Nationale—Direction Maritime*) were:

♦ **4 former East German Kondor-I class patrol boats**
Bldr: Peenewerft, Wolgast

	In serv.
Ras El Blad (ex-*Demmin*, GS 02, ex-G 422)	16-8-69
Ras Mamoura (ex-*Altentreptow*, GS 04, ex-G 414)	5-9-69
Ras El Drek (ex-*Malchin*, GS 03, ex-G 441, ex-*Klütz*, G 13)	18-10-69
Ras Ajdir (ex-*Templin*, BG 31, ex-GS 06, ex-G 442)	20-12-69

D: 225 tons light (339 fl) **S:** 20 kts **Dim:** 52.00 × 7.12 × 2.40
A: . . . . . . **Electron Equipt:** Radar: 1/TSR-333 nav.
Range: 1,900/. . .
M: 2 Type 40DM diesels; 2 CP props; 4,000 bhp (sust.) **Crew:** 20 tot.

Remarks: After the unification of Germany, had been incorporated in the Maritime Border Guard (*Bundesgrenzschutz-See*) but not used operationally. Transferred to Tunisia in 7-92 without armament.

Also transferred from Germany in 7-92 for the National Guard use were five former East German Border Guard Bremse-class patrol craft completed in 1971–72:

D: 25 tons (fl) **S:** 14 kts **Dim:** 23.13 (20.97 pp) × 4.58 × 1.50
A: small arms **Electron Equipt:** Radar: 1/TSR-333 nav.
M: 1 Type 6VD 18/15 diesel; 1 prop; 496 bhp

UNITED KINGDOM

♦ **1 chartered ex-trawler**
Bldr: A. G. Weser Werk Seebeck, Bremen, Germany

Marine Explorer (ex-*Trinity Explorer*, ex-*Sir Tristan*, ex-*Sir Walter Raleigh*, ex-*Swanella*, ex-*British Viking*, ex-*Vickers Viking*, ex-*Dortmund*, ex-*Hamburg*)

D: approx. 3,300 tons (fl) **S:** 13 kts
Dim: 83.60 (72.40 pp) × 13.64 × 5.49
M: 1 Klockner-Humboldt-Deutz 12-cyl. diesel; 1 CP prop; 3,000 bhp—bow-thruster
Range: . . ./. . . **Crew:** . . .

Remarks: Chartered 6-92 from Eidesvik Shipping, Ltd., for use by Captain "H" (Hydrographic) as a survey vessel; painted with red hull, white superstructure and stack. Built as a stern-haul trawler and converted 1974 by Vickers as a submersible mother ship.

The former submarine escort ship *Sentinel* (P 246), placed on the Sales List during 10-91, will now be converted into a support vessel for the BUTEC underwater systems test range.

♦ **1 test range support vessel** Bldr: Husumer Werft, Husum, Germany

	In serv.	In R.N.
A . . . Sentinel (ex-P 246, ex-*Seaforth Warrior*, ex-*Edda Sun*)	27-6-75	14-1-84

D: 1,710 tons (fl) **S:** 14 kts **Dim:** 60.50 (52.80 pp) × 13.00 × 4.50
Electron Equipt: Radar: 2/KAE . . . nav.
M: 2 MaK 12M453 A4 diesels; 2 Kort-nozzle props; 7,760 bhp
Electric: 692 kVA tot. **Crew:** approx 32 tot.

Remarks: 934 grt/733 dwt former oilfield supply tug purchased 3-83 for s patrol vessel, supply vessel, and moorings tender for Falkland Islands service. 1986–87 as replacement for tug *Wakeful* (A 236) as submarine security Faslane. Two single 40-mm Mk 9 guns have been removed. Has two Becke rudders, 500 bhp bow-thruster, 150-ton towing winch, and 87-ton bollard pull

H.M. Customs and Excise has ordered two 34-meter patrol boats from Thornycroft for delivery in the fall of 1993. The craft will have a beam of 7.5 m be powered by two Paxman Valenta 12CM diesels for transit and one Perkin CV8M600TI diesel driving a Hamilton 422 waterjet for cruising. The design is that of the Vosper-designed "Island" class for the U.S. Coast Guard.

Sentinel (ex-P 246)—en route conversion Maritime Photograph

New 34-meter Customs patrol boat Vosper Thornycro

U.S.A.

As of 7-92, the National Science Foundation was seeking to acquire the "surplus" USN nuclear-powered submarine for research purposes.

In 7-92, the Military Sealift Command chartered the following commerc vessels for 17 months, with options for extensions: Japanese-built LASH barg *Atlantic Forest* (33,231 grt), French-owned Ro-Ro-vehicle carrier/container sh *Monet* (26,409 grt) and *CGM Utrillo* (26,419 grt), and heavy-lift ship *Strong V* the same month, the charters were extended for the Ro-Ro vehicle cargo ship *Constellation*, semi-submersible lift ship *American Cormorant*, and cargo ship *tage*, *Green Ridge*, *Green Wave*, and *Noble Star*.

Submarine rescue ship *Pigeon* (ASR 21) was stricken 31-8-92.

The **Naval Institute Press** is the book-publishing arm of the U.S. Naval Institute, a private, nonprofit society for sea service professionals and others who share an interest in naval and maritime affairs. Established in 1873 at the U.S. Naval Academy in Annapolis, Maryland, where its offices remain, today the Naval Institute has more than 100,000 members worldwide.

Members of the Naval Institute receive the influential monthly magazine *Proceedings* and discounts on fine nautical prints, ship and aircraft photos, and subscriptions to the quarterly Naval History magazine. They also have access to the transcripts of the Institute's Oral History Program and get discounted admission to any of the Institute-sponsored seminars offered around the country.

The Naval Institute's book-publishing program, begun in 1898 with basic guides to naval practices, has broadened its scope in recent years to include books of more general interest. Now the Naval Institute Press publishes more than sixty titles each year, ranging from how-to books on boating and navigation to battle histories, biographies, ship and aircraft guides, and novels. Institute members receive discounts on the Press's nearly 400 books in print.

Full-time students are eligible for special half-price membership rates. Life memberships are also available.

For a free catalog describing Naval Institute Press books currently available, and for further information about U.S. Naval Institute membership, please write to:

Membership & Communications Department
U.S. Naval Institute
118 Maryland Avenue
Annapolis, Maryland 21402-5035

Or call, toll-free, (800) 233-USNI.